Algebra 2

with CalcChat® and CalcView®

Ron Larson
Laurie Boswell

Big Ideas Learning™
Erie, Pennsylvania
BigIdeasLearning.com

Big Ideas Learning, LLC
1762 Norcross Road
Erie, PA 16510-3838
USA

For product information and customer support, contact Big Ideas Learning
at **1-877-552-7766** or visit us at ***BigIdeasLearning.com***.

Cover Image
Dmitriy Rybin/Shutterstock.com

Printed in the U.S.A.

ISBN 13: 978-1-64432-866-8

2 3 4 5 6 7 8 9 10—24 23 22 21

One Voice From Kindergarten through Algebra 2

Dr. Ron Larson and Dr. Laurie Boswell are a hands-on authorship team that began writing together in 1992. Since that time, they have authored over four dozen textbooks. This successful collaboration allows for one voice from Kindergarten through Algebra 2.

Ron Larson

Ron Larson, Ph.D., is well known as the lead author of a comprehensive program for mathematics that spans school mathematics and college courses. He holds the distinction of Professor Emeritus from Penn State Erie, The Behrend College, where he taught for nearly 40 years. He received his Ph.D. in mathematics from the University of Colorado. Dr. Larson's numerous professional activities keep him actively involved in the mathematics education community and allow him to fully understand the needs of students, teachers, supervisors, and administrators.

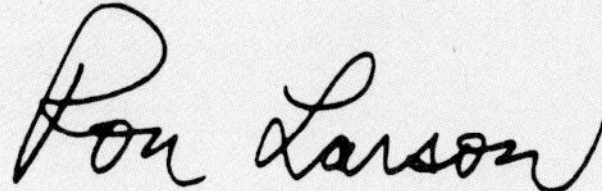

Laurie Boswell

Laurie Boswell, Ed.D., is the former Head of School at Riverside School in Lyndonville, Vermont. In addition to textbook authoring, she provides mathematics consulting and embedded coaching sessions. Dr. Boswell received her Ed.D. from the University of Vermont in 2010. She is a recipient of the Presidential Award for Excellence in Mathematics Teaching and is a Tandy Technology Scholar. Laurie has taught math to students at all levels, elementary through college. In addition, Laurie has served on the NCTM Board of Directors and as a Regional Director for NCSM. Along with Ron, Laurie has co-authored numerous math programs and has become a popular national speaker.

Contributors, Reviewers, and Research

Contributing Specialists and Reviewers

Big Ideas Learning would like to express our gratitude to the mathematics education and instruction experts who served as our advisory panel, contributing specialists, and reviewers during the writing of *Big Ideas Math Algebra 2*. Their input was an invaluable asset during the development of this program.

- **Sophie Murphy, Ph.D. Candidate**, Melbourne School of Education, Melbourne, Australia
Learning Targets and Success Criteria Specialist and Visible Learning Reviewer
- **Michael McDowell, Ed.D.**, Superintendent, Ross, CA
Project-Based Learning Specialist
- **Nancy Siddens**, Independent Language Teaching Consultant, Las Cruces, NM
English Language Learner Specialist and Teaching Education Contributor
- **Linda Hall**, Mathematics Educational Consultant, Edmond, OK
Content Reviewer
- **Beverly Stitzel**, Secondary Mathematics Teacher, Oxford, MI
Content Reviewer
- **Elizabeth Caccavella, Ed.D.**, Supervisor of Mathematics, Paterson, NJ
Content Reviewer
- **Matthew L. Beyranevand, Ed.D.**, K–12 Mathematics Coordinator, Chelmsford, MA
Content Reviewer
- **Jill Kalb**, Secondary Math Content Specialist, Arvada, CO
Content Reviewer
- **Jason Berkholz**, Mathematics Department Chair, Metropolitan School District of Washington Township, Indianapolis, IN
Content Reviewer
- **Larry Dorf**, Secondary Mathematics Teacher, Harrisburg, PA
Content Reviewer

Research

Ron Larson and Laurie Boswell developed this program using the latest in educational research, along with the body of knowledge collected from expert mathematics educators. This program follows the best practices outlined in the most prominent and widely accepted educational research, including:

- *Visible Learning*, John Hattie © 2009
- *Visible Learning for Teachers*, John Hattie © 2012
- *Visible Learning for Mathematics,* John Hattie © 2017
- *Principles to Actions: Ensuring Mathematical Success for All*, NCTM © 2014
- *Adding It Up: Helping Children Learn Mathematics,* National Research Council © 2001
- *Mathematical Mindsets: Unleashing Students' Potential through Creative Math, Inspiring Messages and Innovative Teaching,* Jo Boaler © 2015
- *Classroom Instruction That Works: Research-Based Strategies for Increasing Student Achievement,* Marzano, Pickering, and Pollock © 2001
- *What Works in Schools: Translating Research into Action,* Robert Marzano © 2003
- *Principles and Standards for School Mathematics,* NCTM © 2000
- *Universal Design for Learning Guidelines,* CAST © 2011
- *Rigorous PBL by Design: Three Shifts for Developing Confident and Competent Learners,* Michael McDowell © 2017
- Rigor/Relevance Framework® International Center for Leadership in Education
- *Understanding by Design*, Grant Wiggins and Jay McTighe © 2005
- Achieve, ACT, and The College Board
- *Evaluating the Quality of Learning: The SOLO Taxonomy,* John B. Biggs & Kevin F. Collis © 1982
- *Formative Assessment in the Secondary Classroom,* Shirley Clarke © 2005
- *Improving Student Achievement: A Practical Guide to Assessment for Learning,* Toni Glasson © 2009

Explore Every Chapter Through the Lens of STEM

National Geographic Explorers

Meet a National Geographic Explorer at the start of every chapter, and follow the context through the chapter to connect their research to your learning.

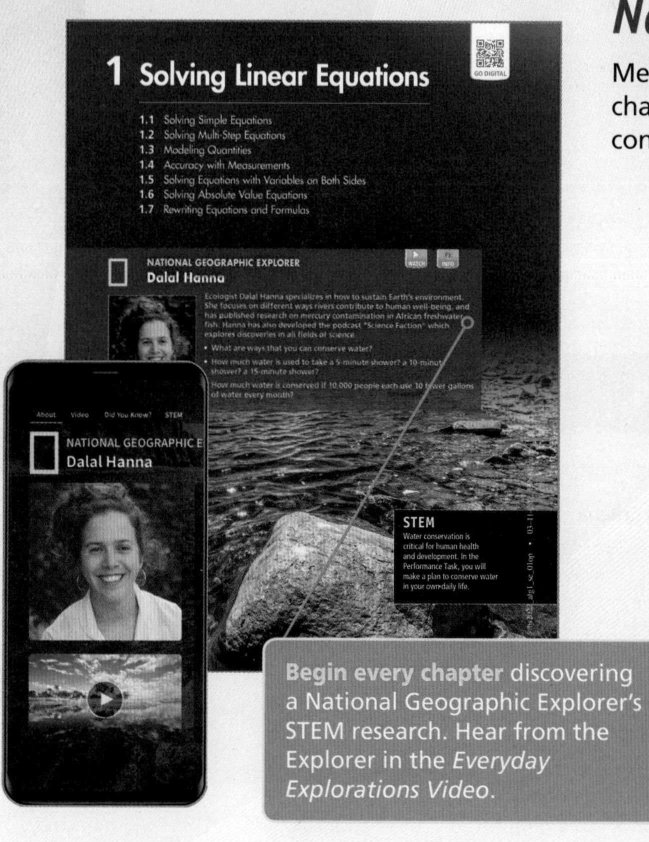

Begin every chapter discovering a National Geographic Explorer's STEM research. Hear from the Explorer in the *Everyday Explorations Video*.

Throughout the chapter, revisit the Explorer's field of study to apply the math you are learning.

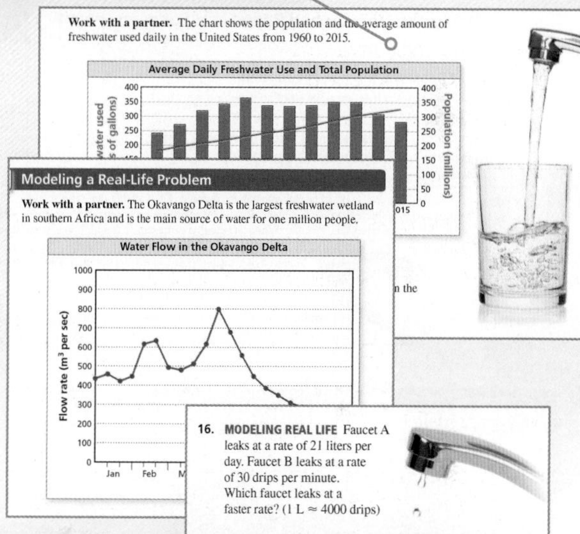

Conclude the chapter with a Performance Task related to the National Geographic Explorer's field of study. Explore the task digitally to experience additional insights.

Focus, Coherence, and Rigor

Instructional Design

A single authorship team from Kindergarten through Algebra 2 results in a seamless articulation of focused topics with meaningful coherence from course to course.

Every chapter and every lesson contain a rigorous balance of conceptual understanding, procedural fluency, and application.

FOCUS

A focused program emphasizes the major work of each course, the widely applicable prerequisites needed for you to be college and career ready.

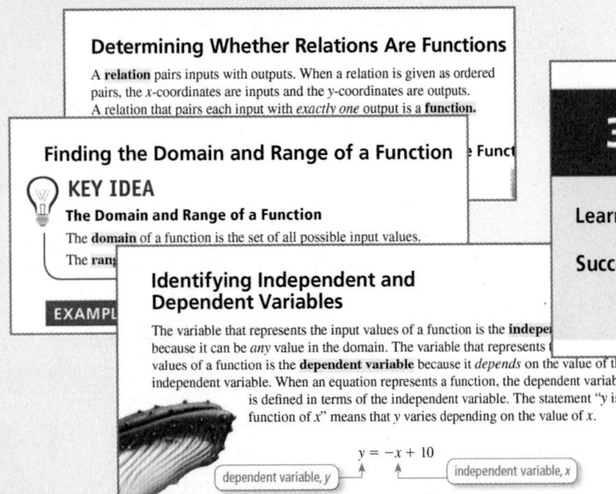

Determining Whether Relations Are Functions

A **relation** pairs inputs with outputs. When a relation is given as ordered pairs, the x-coordinates are inputs and the y-coordinates are outputs.
A relation that pairs each input with *exactly one* output is a **function.**

Finding the Domain and Range of a Function

KEY IDEA
The Domain and Range of a Function
The **domain** of a function is the set of all possible input values.
The **ran**

EXAMPL

Identifying Independent and Dependent Variables

The variable that represents the input values of a function is the **indepe** because it can be *any* value in the domain. The variable that represents values of a function is the **dependent variable** because it *depends* on the value of the independent variable. When an equation represents a function, the dependent variable is defined in terms of the independent variable. The statement "y is a function of x" means that y varies depending on the value of x.

$$y = -x + 10$$

3.1	Functions
Learning Target	Understand the concept of a function.
Success Criteria	• I can determine whether a relation is a function. • I can find the domain and range of a function. • I can distinguish between independent and dependent variables.

Learning targets, success criteria, and content headings through each section focus the learning into manageable chunks.

The authors gave careful thought to how the learning should progress from prior chapters and grades to future ones, as shown in the Teaching Edition progressions charts.

COHERENCE Through the Grades

Prior Learning	Current Learning	Future Learning
Middle School • Translate, reflect, and rotate figures in the coordinate plane. • Use similar triangles to explain why the slope is the same between any two distinct points on a nonvertical line. • Graph proportional relationships, interpreting the unit rate as the slope of	**Chapter 3** • Understand the definition of a function and use function notation. • Sketch a graph of a function from a verbal description. • Compare properties of two functions each represented in a different way. • Graph linear and absolute value … and show key features of	**Algebra 1** • Create equations of linear functions using points and slopes. • Graph piecewise, exponential, quadratic, square root, and cube root functions, and show key features of the graph. • Solve systems of linear equations by

You have used *linear regression* to find an equation of the line of best fit. Similarly, you can use *exponential regression* to find an exponential function that best fits a data set.

EXAMPLE 6 **Modeling Real Life**  

The table shows the temperatures y (in degrees Fahrenheit) of coffee x minutes after pouring a cup. Use technology to find a function that fits the data. Predict the temperature of the coffee 10 minutes after it is poured.

SOLUTION

Step 1 Enter the data from the table into a tech… of the data.

Throughout the course, you will build on prior learning as you learn new concepts.

COHERENCE

A coherent program has intentional progression of content between courses (building new understanding on foundations from prior years) and within the course (connecting concepts throughout).

from a Single Authorship Team

RIGOR

A rigorous program provides a balance of three important building blocks.

- **Conceptual Understanding** Discovering why
- **Procedural Fluency** Learning how
- **Application** Knowing when to apply

EXPLORE IT! Describing Relations

Work with a partner. You buy an item from the vending machine.

a. Describe two possible relations associated with the vending machine.

b. Think about each relation in part (a).
- What are the inputs?
- What are the outputs?
- Does each input pair with *exactly* one output? Explain.

In mathematics, a **function** is a relation that pairs each input with exactly one output.

c. How can you use a coordinate plane to represent a relation? What are the inputs? What are the outputs?

Math Practice
Contextualize Relationships
Can you think of any mathematical relations? Are any of these relations functions?

Conceptual Understanding
Explore, question, explain, and persevere as you discover foundational concepts central to the learning target of each section.

42. WRITING A quadratic function is increasing when $x < 2$ and decreasing when $x > 2$. Is the vertex the highest or lowest point on the parabola? Explain.

53. **MP NUMBER SENSE** Without evaluating, order $(7 \cdot 7)^5$, $(7 \cdot 7)^{-8}$, and $(7 \cdot 7)^0$ from least to greatest. Explain your reasoning.

Conceptual Understanding
Understand the ideas behind key concepts, see them from varied perspectives, and explain their meaning.

EXAMPLE 1 Graphing $f(x) = a(x - p)(x - q)$ 

Graph $f(x) = -(x + 1)(x - 5)$. Find the domain and range.

SOLUTION

Step 1 Identify the x-intercepts. Because the x-intercepts are $p = -1$ and $q = 5$, plot $(-1, 0)$ and $(5, 0)$.

Step 2 Find and graph the axis of symmetry.

$$x = \frac{p + q}{2} = \frac{-1 + 5}{2} = 2$$

Step 3 Find and plot the vertex. The x-coordinate of the vertex is 2. To find the y-coordinate of the vertex, substitute 2 for x and evaluate.

$$f(2) = -(2 + 1)(2 - 5) = 9$$

So, the vertex is $(2, 9)$.

Step 4 Draw a parabola through the vertex and the points where the x-intercepts occur.

▶ The domain is all real numbers. The range is $y \le 9$.

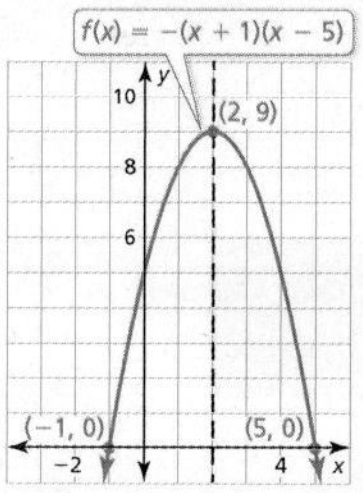

(Graph labels: $f(x) = -(x + 1)(x - 5)$; $(2, 9)$; $(-1, 0)$; $(5, 0)$; axes x, y; 10, 8, 6, −2, 4)

Procedural Fluency
Learn with clear, stepped-out teaching and examples, and become fluent through *Self-Assessment*, *Practice*, and *Review & Refresh*.

EXAMPLE 6 Modeling Real Life  

A jellyfish emits about 1.25×10^8 particles of light, or photons, in 6.25×10^{-4} second. How many photons does the jellyfish emit each second? Write your answer in scientific notation and in standard form.

SOLUTION

Divide to find the unit rate in photons per second.

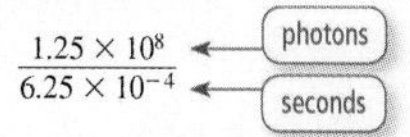

$\dfrac{1.25 \times 10^8}{6.25 \times 10^{-4}}$ ← photons / ← seconds — Divide the number of photons by the number of seconds.

$= \dfrac{1.25}{6.25} \times \dfrac{10^8}{10^{-4}}$ — Rewrite.

$= 0.2 \times 10^{12}$ — Simplify.

$= 2 \times 10^{11}$ — Write in scientific notation.

▶ The jellyfish emits 2×10^{11}, or 200,000,000,000 photons per second.

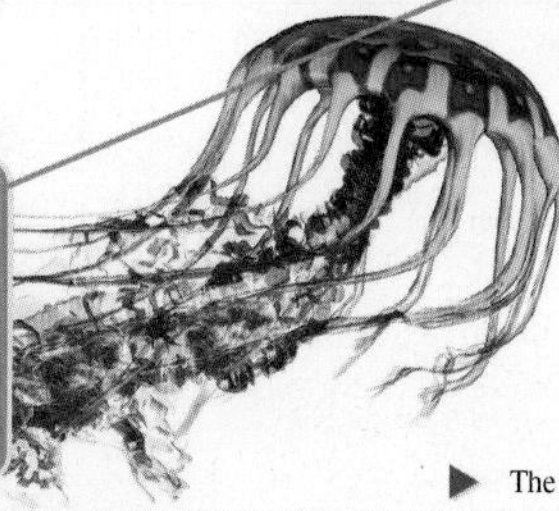

Application
Make meaning of mathematics in problem-solving contexts and real-life applications.

Visible Learning Through Learning Targets,

Making Learning Visible

Knowing the learning intention of a chapter or lesson helps you focus on the purpose of an activity, rather than simply completing it in isolation. This program supports visible learning through the consistent use of learning targets and success criteria to ensure positive outcomes for all students.

Every chapter and section show the learning target and related success criteria, so you know exactly what the learning should look like.

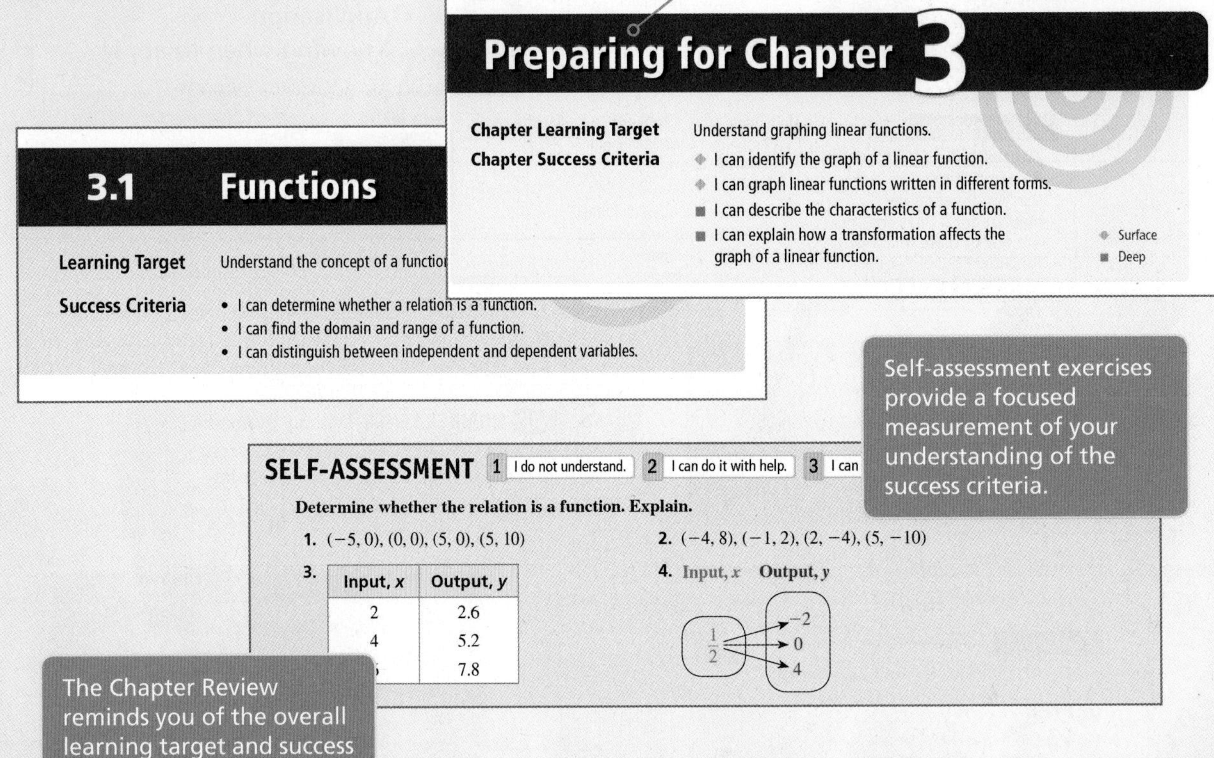

Preparing for Chapter 3

Chapter Learning Target Understand graphing linear functions.

Chapter Success Criteria
- ◆ I can identify the graph of a linear function.
- ◆ I can graph linear functions written in different forms.
- ■ I can describe the characteristics of a function.
- ■ I can explain how a transformation affects the graph of a linear function.

◆ Surface
■ Deep

3.1 Functions

Learning Target Understand the concept of a functio

Success Criteria
- I can determine whether a relation is a function.
- I can find the domain and range of a function.
- I can distinguish between independent and dependent variables.

SELF-ASSESSMENT 1 I do not understand. 2 I can do it with help. 3 I can

Self-assessment exercises provide a focused measurement of your understanding of the success criteria.

Determine whether the relation is a function. Explain.

1. $(-5, 0), (0, 0), (5, 0), (5, 10)$
2. $(-4, 8), (-1, 2), (2, -4), (5, -10)$
3.

Input, x	Output, y
2	2.6
4	5.2
[illegible]	7.8

4. Input, x Output, y

The Chapter Review reminds you of the overall learning target and success criteria for the chapter.

3 Chapter Review WITH CalcChat®

Chapter Learning Target Understand graphing linear functions.

Chapter Success Criteria
- ◆ I can identify the graph of a linear function.
- ◆ I can graph linear functions written in different forms.
- ■ I can describe the characteristics of a function.
- ■ I can explain how a transformation affects the graph of a linear function.

Review each section with a reminder of that section's learning target.

t understand. 2 I can do it with help. 3 I can do it on

3.1 Functions *(pp. 111–118)*

Learning Target: Understand the concept of a function.

QUESTIONS FOR LEARNERS

As you progress through a section, you should be able to answer the following questions.

1. What am I learning?
2. Why am I learning this?
3. Where am I in my learning?
4. How will I know when I have learned it?
5. Where am I going next?

Success Criteria, and Self-Assessment

SELF-ASSESSMENT 1 I do not understand. 2 I can do it with help. 3 I can do it on my own. 4 I can teach someone else.

Find the domain and range of the function represented by the graph.

14. **15.** 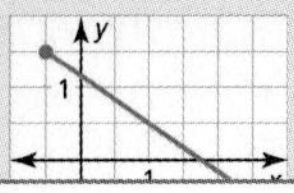 **16.**

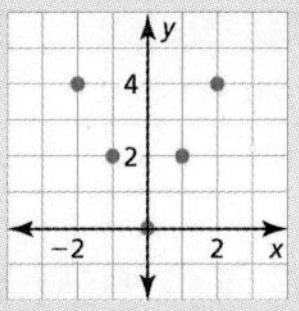

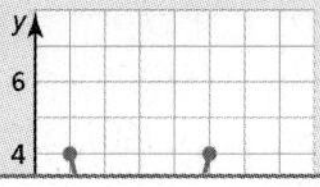

17. DIFFERENT WORDS, SAME

SELF-ASSESSMENT 1 I do not understand. 2 I can do it with help. 3 I can do it on my own.

3.1 **Functions** *(pp. 111–118)* WATCH

Learning Target: Understand the concept of a function.

Determine whether the relation is a function. Explain.

1. (0, 1), (5, 6), (7, 9), (8, 9)

2.

Input, x	Output, y
5	11
7	19
9	3

Self-Assessments are included throughout every section, and in the Chapter Review, for you to take ownership of your learning.

SELF-ASSESSMENT

1 I do not understand.

2 I can do it with help.

3 I can do it on my own.

4 I can teach someone else.

As you complete the Self-Assessment exercises, rate your understanding of each success criterion using the 4-point scale. Keep track of your learning on paper or online.

	Rating	Date
Chapter 3 Graphing Linear Functions		
Learning Target: Understand graphing linear functions.	1 2 3 4	
I can identify the graph of a linear function.	1 2 3 4	
I can graph linear functions written in different forms.	1 2 3 4	
I can describe the characteristics of a function.	1 2 3 4	
I can explain how a transformation affects the graph of a linear function.	1 2 3 4	

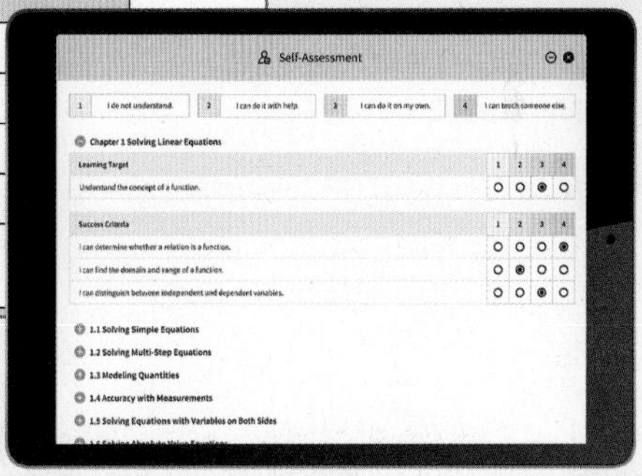

Self-Assessment

Chapter 1 Solving Linear Equations

1.1 Solving Simple Equations

1.2 Solving Multi-Step Equations

1.3 Modeling Quantities

1.4 Accuracy with Measurements

1.5 Solving Equations with Variables on Both Sides

Ensuring Positive Outcomes

John Hattie's *Visible Learning* research consistently shows that using learning targets and success criteria can result in two year's growth in one year, ensuring positive outcomes for student learning and achievement.

Sophie Murphy, M.Ed., wrote the chapter-level learning targets and success criteria for this program. Sophie is currently completing her Ph.D. at the University of Melbourne in Australia with Professor John Hattie as her leading supervisor. Sophie completed her Masters' thesis with Professor John Hattie in 2015. Sophie has over 20 years of experience as a teacher and school leader in private and public-school settings in Australia.

Embedded Mathematical Practices

Encouraging Mathematical Mindsets

Developing proficiency in the **Mathematical Practices** is about becoming a mathematical thinker: learning to ask why and being able to reason and communicate with others as you learn. Use this guide to help you understand more about each practice.

BUILDING TO FULL UNDERSTANDING

Throughout this course, you will have opportunities to demonstrate specific aspects of the mathematical practices. Labels throughout indicate gateways to those aspects. Collectively, these opportunities will lead you to a full understanding of each math practice. Developing these mindsets and habits will give meaning to the mathematics you learn.

1

One way to **Make Sense of Problems and Persevere in Solving Them** is to use the problem-solving plan. Take time to analyze the given information and what the problem is asking to help you to plan a solution pathway.

Look for these labels:

- Explain the Meaning
- Find Entry Points
- Analyze Givens
- Interpret a Solution
- Make a Plan
- Consider Similar Problems
- Check Progress
- Consider Simpler Forms
- PROBLEM SOLVING
- THOUGHT PROVOKING
- DIG DEEPER

EXAMPLE 3 **Modeling Real Life** WATCH

The function $E(d) = 0.25\sqrt{d}$ approximates the number of seconds it takes a dropped object to fall d feet on Earth. The function $M(d) = 1.6 \cdot E(d)$ approximates the number of seconds it takes a dropped object to fall d feet on Mars. How long does it take a dropped object to fall 64 feet on Mars?

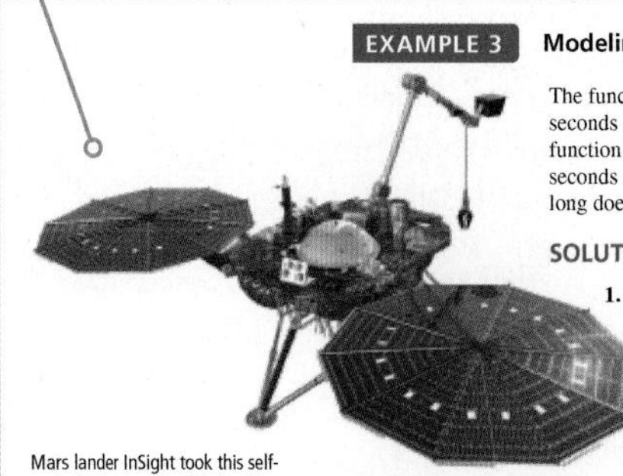

Mars lander InSight took this self-portrait of one of its 7-foot-wide solar panels in December 2018.

SOLUTION

1. **Understand the Problem** You are given functions that represent the number of seconds it takes a dropped object to fall d feet on Earth and on Mars. You are asked how long it takes a dropped object to fall a given distance on Mars.
2. **Make a Plan** Multiply $E(d)$ by 1.6 to write a rule for M. Then find $M(64)$.
3. **Solve and Check** $M(d) = 1.6 \cdot E(d)$

$= 1.6 \cdot 0.25\sqrt{d}$ Substitute $0.25\sqrt{d}$ for $E(d)$.

$= 0.4\sqrt{d}$ Simplify.

2

You **Reason Abstractly** when you explore a concrete example and represent it symbolically. Other times you **Reason Quantitatively** when you see relationships in numbers or symbols and draw conclusions about a concrete example.

EXPLORE IT! **Finding a Composition of Functions**

Work with a partner. The formulas below represent the temperature F (in degrees Fahrenheit) when the temperature is C degrees Celsius, and the temperature C when the temperature is K (Kelvin).

$F = \frac{9}{5}C + 32$ $C = K - 273$

a. Write an expression for F in terms of K.

b. Given that

$f(x) = \frac{9}{5}x + 32$

and

$g(x) = x - 273$

write an expression for $f(g(x))$. What does $f(g(x))$ represent in this situation?

Math Practice

Make Sense of Quantities

Does $g(f(x))$ make sense in this context? Explain.

11. **MP REASONING** Explain why a V-shaped graph does *not* represent a linear function.

12. **MP REASONING** How can you tell whether a graph shows a discrete domain or a continuous domain?

Look for these labels:

- Make Sense of Quantities
- Use Equations
- Use Expressions
- Understand Quantities
- Use Operations
- Contextualize Relationships
- Reason Abstractly
- REASONING
- NUMBER SENSE

3

When you **Construct Viable Arguments and Critique the Reasoning of Others,** you make and justify conclusions and decide whether others' arguments are correct or flawed.

25. MAKING AN ARGUMENT Your friend says that a line always represents a function. Is your friend correct? Explain.

Math Practice

Make Conjectures
Which type of reasoning helps you to make a conjecture? Which type helps you to justify a conjecture? How do you know when to use each type?

Look for these labels:

- Use Assumptions
- Use Definitions
- Use Prior Results
- Make Conjectures
- Build Arguments
- Analyze Conjectures
- Use Counterexamples
- Justify Conclusions
- Compare Arguments
- Construct Arguments
- Listen and Ask Questions
- Critique Reasoning
- MAKING AN ARGUMENT
- LOGIC
- ERROR ANALYSIS
- DIFFERENT WORDS, SAME QUESTION
- WHICH ONE DOESN'T BELONG?

Math Practice

Listen and Ask Questions
Ask a few classmates to read their answers to parts (b)–(d). Ask any questions you have about their answers.

4

To **Model with Mathematics,** you apply the math you have learned to a real-life problem, and you interpret mathematical results in the context of the situation.

Look for these labels:

- Apply Mathematics
- Simplify a Solution
- Use a Diagram
- Use a Table
- Use a Graph
- Use a Formula
- Analyze Relationships
- Interpret Results
- MODELING REAL LIFE
- PROBLEM SOLVING

45. MODELING REAL LIFE Flying fish use their pectoral fins like airplane wings to glide through the air.

a. Write an equation of the form $y = a(x - h)^2 + k$ with vertex (33, 5) that models the flight path, assuming the fish leaves the water at (0, 0).

b. What are the domain and range of the function? What do they represent in this situation?

c. Does the value of a change when the flight path has vertex (30, 4)? Justify your answer.

43. MP **PROBLEM SOLVING** An online ticket agency charges the amounts shown for basketball tickets. The total cost for an order is \$220.70. How many tickets are purchased?

Charge	Amount
Ticket price	\$32.50 per ticket
Convenience charge	\$3.30 per ticket
Processing charge	\$5.90 per order

Embedded Mathematical Practices (continued)

5

To **Use Appropriate Tools Strategically**, you need to know what tools are available and think about how each tool might help you solve a mathematical problem. You can use a tool for its advantages, while being aware of its limitations.

9. **MP CHOOSE TOOLS** For a large data set, would you use a stem-and-leaf plot or a histogram to show the distribution of the data? Explain.

EXPLORE IT! **Reflecting Figures in Lines**

Work with a partner. Use technology to draw any scalene triangle and label it $\triangle ABC$. Draw any line, $\overleftrightarrow{DE}$, and another line that is parallel to $\overleftrightarrow{DE}$.

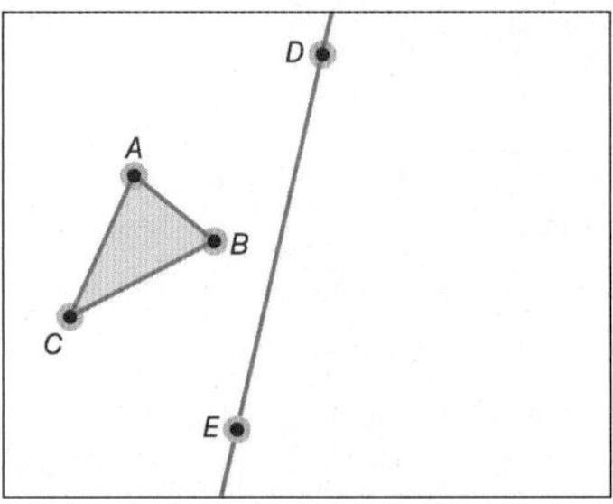

a. Reflect $\triangle ABC$ in $\overleftrightarrow{DE}$, followed by a reflection in the other line to form $\triangle A''B''C''$. What do you notice? Make several observations.

b. Is there a single transformation that maps $\triangle ABC$ to $\triangle A''B''C''$? Explain.

c. Repeat parts (a) and (b) with other figures. What do you notice?

d. Using the same triangle and line $\overleftrightarrow{DE}$, draw line $\overleftrightarrow{DF}$ that intersects $\overleftrightarrow{DE}$ at point D so that $\angle EDF$ is an acute or right angle. Then reflect $\triangle ABC$ in $\overleftrightarrow{DE}$, followed by a reflection in $\overleftrightarrow{DF}$ to form $\triangle A''B''C''$. What do you notice? Make several observations.

Look for these labels:

- Choose Tools
- Recognize Usefulness of Tools
- Use Other Resources
- Use Technology to Explore
- CHOOSE TOOLS
- USING TOOLS

MP PRECISION In Exercises 27–30, determine whether the statement uses the word *function* in a way that is mathematically correct. Explain your reasoning.

27. The selling price of an item is a function of the cost of making the item.

28. The sales tax on a purchased item in a given state is a function of the selling price.

29. A function pairs each student in your school with a homeroom teacher.

30. A function pairs each chaperone on a school trip with 10 students.

6

When you **Attend to Precision**, you are developing a habit of being careful how you talk about concepts, label your work, and write your answers.

Math Practice

Communicate Precisely

In part (b), for a function $y = f(x)$, explain the meaning of f, x, and $f(x)$.

Look for these labels:

- Communicate Precisely
- Use Clear Definitions
- State the Meaning of Symbols
- Specify Units
- Label Axes
- Calculate Accurately
- Understand Mathematical Terms
- PRECISION

Math Practice

Look for Structure
Why is it helpful to multiply each side by 6? How else could you begin to solve this equation?

b. $\frac{n}{6} = -\frac{n}{6} + \frac{1}{2}$ — Write the equation.

$6 \cdot \frac{n}{6} = 6 \cdot \left(-\frac{n}{6} + \frac{1}{2}\right)$ — Multiplication Property of Equality

$n = -n + 3$ — Simplify.

$+n \quad +n$ — Addition Property of Equality

$2n = 3$ — Simplify.

$\frac{2n}{2} = \frac{3}{2}$ — Division Property of Equality

$n = \frac{3}{2}$

Look for these labels:

- View as Components
- Look for Patterns
- Look for Structure
- STRUCTURE
- PATTERNS

56. **MP STRUCTURE** Use the Quadratic Formula and the numbers below to create a quadratic equation with the solutions $x = \frac{3 \pm \sqrt{89}}{10}$.

$\_\_x^2 + \_\_x + \_\_ = 0$

−5	−4	−3	−2	−1
1	2	3	4	5

7

You **Look For and Make Use of Structure** by looking closely to see structure within a mathematical statement, or stepping back for an overview to see how individual parts make one single object.

Math Practice

View as Components
Notice that the function consists of the product of the principal, 100, and a factor independent of the principal, $(1.005)^{12t}$.

SOLUTION

a. $m(t) = P\left(1 + \frac{r}{n}\right)^{nt}$ — Use the compound interest formula.

$= 100\left(1 + \frac{0.06}{12}\right)^{12t}$ — Substitute 100 for P, 0.06 for r, and 12 for n.

$= 100(1.005)^{12t}$ — Simplify.

Work with a partner. Use a p… Record your data in the table.

a. Measure the length of the r… Describe your measurement.

b. Make a knot in the rope, then measure the length of the rope again. Continue to make identical knots in the rope, measuring the length of the rope after each knot is tied.

Number of knots	Length of rope
0	
1	
2	
3	
4	
5	
6	
7	
8	

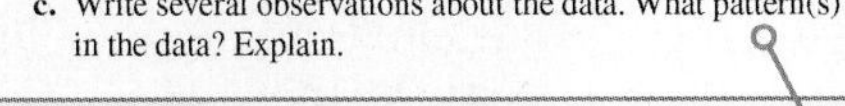

c. Write several observations about the data. What pattern(s) do you notice in the data? Explain.

20. **MP REPEATED REASONING** Use the diagram.

a. Find the perimeter and area of each square.

b. What happens to the area of a square when its perimeter increases by a factor of n?

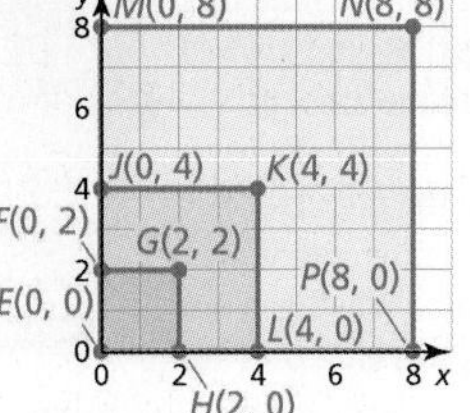

Look for these labels:

- Repeat Calculations
- Find General Methods
- Maintain Oversight
- Evaluate Results
- REPEATED REASONING

When you **Look For and Express Regularity in Repeated Reasoning**, you can notice patterns and make generalizations. Keeping in mind the goal of a problem helps you evaluate reasonableness of answers along the way.

8

The Modeling Process

Modeling Real Life

Learning how to apply the mathematics you learn to model real-life situations is an important part of this course. Here are some ways you may approach the modeling process.

THE PROBLEM-SOLVING PLAN

1. **Understand the Problem**
   Before planning a solution, you must identify what the problem is asking, analyze givens and goals, and think about entry points to a solution.
2. **Make a Plan**
   Plan your solution pathway before jumping in to solve. Identify any variables or relationships and decide on a problem-solving strategy.
   - Use a verbal model
   - Draw a diagram
   - Write an equation
   - Solve a simpler problem
   - Sketch a graph or number line
   - Make a table
   - Make a list
   - Break the problem into parts
3. **Solve and Check**
   As you solve the problem, be sure to monitor and evaluate your progress, and always check your answers. Throughout the problem-solving process, you must continually ask, "Does this make sense?" and be willing to change course if necessary.

66. PERFORMANCE TASK The black rhino is a critically endangered species with a current population of about 5500. In the late 1900s, the population decreased by 98% to about 2500. Create a plan to restore the black rhino population. Include the expected annual growth rate and the amount of time it will take to restore the population. Explain how you will determine whether your plan is working over time.

Creating a Model
In a *Performance Task*, you first identify the problem and the variables in a situation and decide what questions to ask or models to create. Any answers you obtain must always be interpreted in the context of the situation to determine whether they are viable.

73. MP PROBLEM SOLVING When X-rays of a fixed wavelength strike a material x centimeters thick, the intensity $I(x)$ of the X-rays transmitted through the material is given by $I(x) = I_0 e^{-\mu x}$, where I_0 is the initial intensity and μ is a value that depends on the type of material and the wavelength of the X-rays. The table shows the values of μ for various materials and X-rays of medium wavelength.

Material	Aluminum	Copper	Lead
Value of μ	0.43	3.2	43

You wear a lead apron to protect you from harmful radiation while your dentist takes X-rays of your teeth. Explain why lead is a better material to use than aluminum or copper.

Interpreting Parameters Within a Context
To be able to interpret the parameters of a situation, you must understand the significance of the variables. Knowing how they relate and affect one another will help you find an entry point and make a plan to solve.

Defining Quantities

In this problem, you know that the side length of the map doubles on each click, and you are given the lengths for the first few clicks. You need to know how many clicks will make the side length 640 miles.

Writing Functions

You know that the side length of the map is related to the number of clicks. Your plan should include writing a function to represent that relationship.

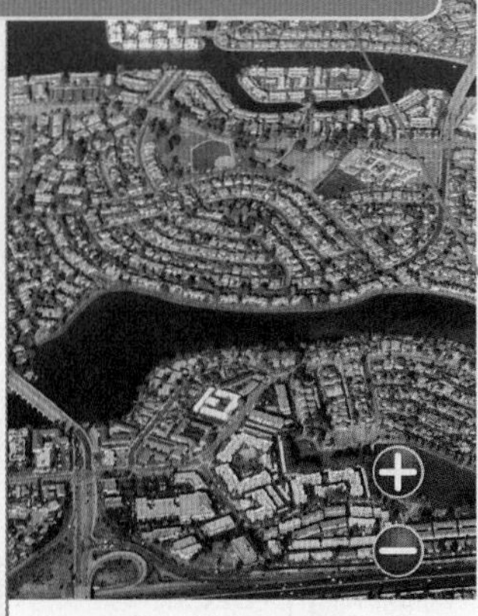

EXAMPLE 5 **Modeling Real Life** 

Clicking the *zoom-out* button on a mapping website doubles the side length of the square map. After how many clicks on the *zoom-out* button is the side length of the map 640 miles?

Zoom-out clicks	1	2	3
Map side length (miles)	5	10	20

SOLUTION

1. **Understand the Problem** You know that the side length of the square map doubles after each click on the *zoom-out* button. So, the side lengths of the map represent the terms of a geometric sequence. You need to find the number of clicks it takes for the side length of the map to be 640 miles.
2. **Make a Plan** Begin by writing a function f for the nth term of the geometric sequence. Then find the value of n for which $f(n) = 640$.
3. **Solve and Check** The first term is 5, and the common ratio is 2.

$f(n) = a_1r^{n-1}$ Function for a geometric sequence

$f(n) = 5(2)^{n-1}$ Substitute 5 for a_1 and 2 for r.

The function $f(n) = 5(2)^{n-1}$ represents the geometric sequence. Use this function to find the value of n for which $f(n) = 640$. So, use each side of the equation $640 = 5(2)^{n-1}$ to write a function.

$y = 5(2)^{n-1}$

$y = 640$

Then use technology to graph the functions and find the point of intersection. The point of intersection is (8, 640).

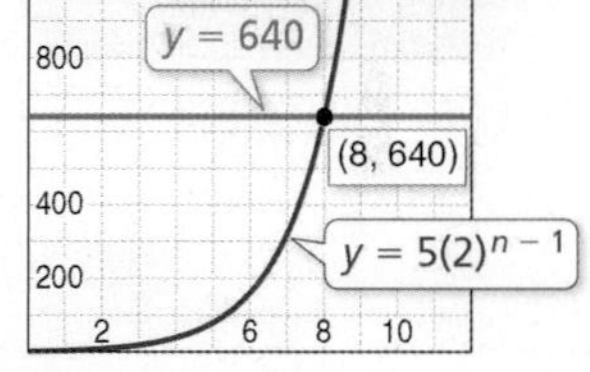

▶ So, after eight clicks, the side length of the map is 640 miles.

Analyze Functions Using Different Representations

Graphing your function and the line $y = 640$ allows you to approximate a solution.

Another Method Find the value of n for which $f(n) = 640$ algebraically.

$640 = 5(2)^{n-1}$ Write the equation.

$128 = (2)^{n-1}$ Divide each side by 5.

$2^7 = (2)^{n-1}$ Rewrite 128 as 2^7.

$7 = n - 1$ Equate the exponents.

$8 = n$ ✓ Add 1 to each side.

Solving an Equation to Solve a Problem

Step 3 of the problem-solving plan must always include checking your results. In this case, you can solve using another method to make sure you get the same answer.

MODELING STANDARDS

For a full list of opportunities to practice all the modeling standards of this course, visit *BigIdeasMath.com*.

How to Use This Program

Scan the QR code on any page to access digital content.

Designed for You

From start to finish, this program was designed with you, the learner, in mind. Let's take a quick tour of a chapter. Look for each **highlighted feature** mentioned below, in your book or online.

GET READY

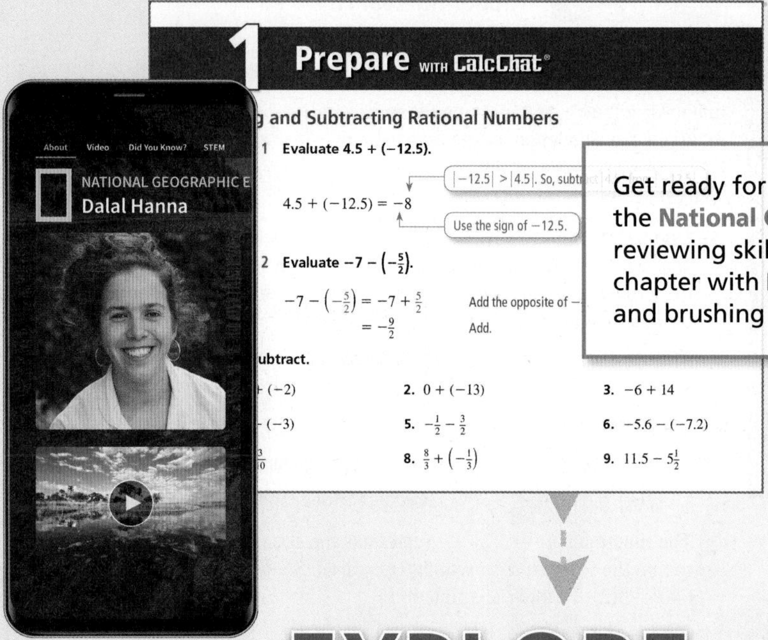

Get ready for the chapter by watching the **National Geographic Explorer** video, reviewing skills you will need for the chapter with **Prepare with CalcChat®**, and brushing up with the **Skills Trainer**.

EXPLORE

EXPLORE IT! Reflecting a Polygon

Work with a partner.

a. The diagram shows the *reflection* of $\triangle DEF$ to $\triangle D'E'F'$. How would you define a reflection?

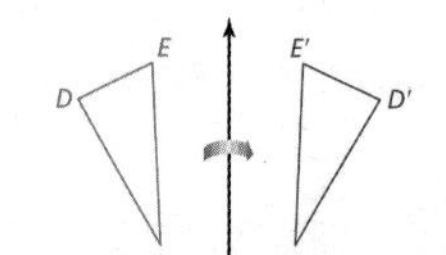

b. Use technology to draw any triangle and label it $\triangle ABC$.

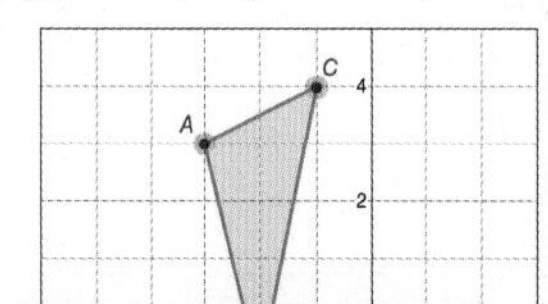

Math Practice

Choose Tools
What other tools can you use to perform reflections of figures?

Read the **Learning Target and Success Criteria** for each section. Work with a partner to complete the **Explore It!** and discuss the **Math Practice** with your partner.

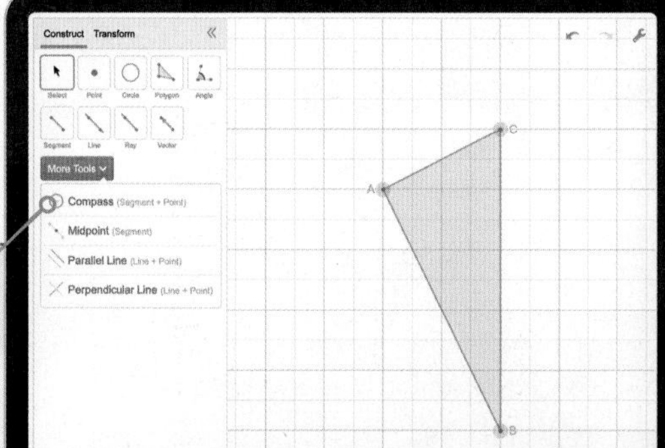

Interactive Explore Its
Explore concepts digitally using **Interactive Tools** in the **Dynamic Student Edition**.

LEARN

Example Support

See a **Digital Example** video of every example in the book, or watch a **Tutorial Video** for a tutor to walk you step-by-step through a similar example.

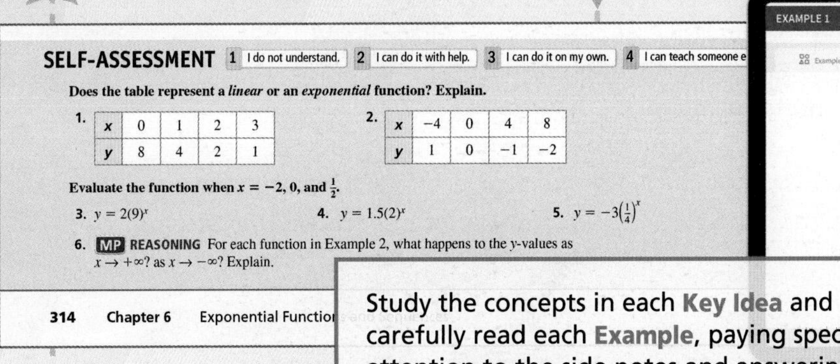

Study the concepts in each **Key Idea** and carefully read each **Example**, paying special attention to the side notes and answering the **Math Practice** questions to solidify concepts. Use the **Self-Assessment** to assess your understanding of the Learning Target and Success Criteria.

PRACTICE and APPLY

In every section, use the **Practice with CalcChat® and CalcView®** to practice and apply your learning and **Review & Refresh** to stay fluent in major topics throughout the course.

At the end of the chapter, use the **Chapter Review with CalcChat®**, take a **Practice Test with CalcChat®**, or complete the **Performance Task** using the concepts of the chapter. Practice questions from current and prior concepts with **College and Career Readiness with CalcChat®** to prepare for high-stakes tests.

How to Study Math

Preparing for College and Career

Math is a cumulative subject. What you learn tomorrow will build on what you learn today. So, to be successful, commit to these positive steps.

- Routinely study
- Practice every day
- Be patient and persevere
- Believe that you can learn

Committing to these habits and mindsets will help you succeed!

In Class

When you are in class, be "all there." Here are some ways to stay focused.

- Actively participate
- Think about what is being said
- Take good notes
- Ask questions

At Home

Practice is an important part of your learning process. Here is where you solidify and apply the concepts you learn.

- Find a quiet location, away from any potential distractions.
- Review your notes and what you learned in class. Talk through them if that helps you remember more.
- Don't be afraid to make mistakes! These are the times that your brain grows and learning happens.
- Lean into challenge. Instead of saying, "I'm not good at this," say, "I can train my brain to figure this out."

Taking Tests

It is completely normal to feel a little nervous about a test! Here are some tips for test-taking success.

Before the test

- Study a little bit each day
- Get a good night's sleep
- Eat breakfast

During the test

- Read the directions and questions carefully
- Answer easy questions first
- Check your work
- Answer every question
- Take your time—You don't have to finish first!
- Take a brain break
- Do your best!

Reinforce Your Studies with CalcChat® and CalcView®

As you complete the exercises throughout the chapter, CalcChat® and CalcView® give you access to solutions and tutor help.

CalcChat®

- View worked-out solutions for select exercises
  - *Prepare with CalcChat®*
  - *Practice with CalcChat® and CalcView®*
  - *Chapter Review with CalcChat®*
  - *Practice Test with CalcChat®*
  - *College and Career Readiness with CalcChat®*
- Chat with a live tutor about the solutions

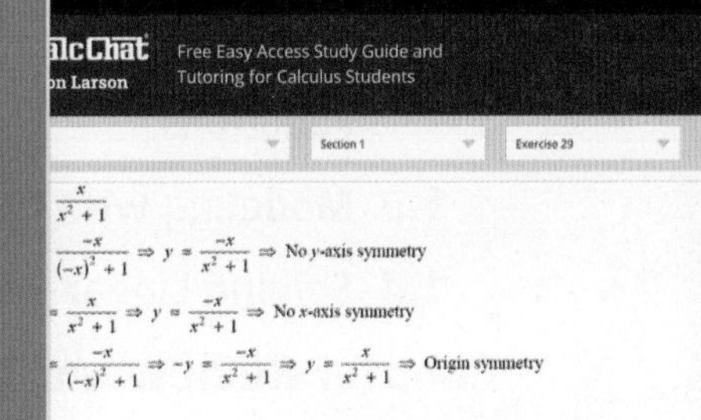

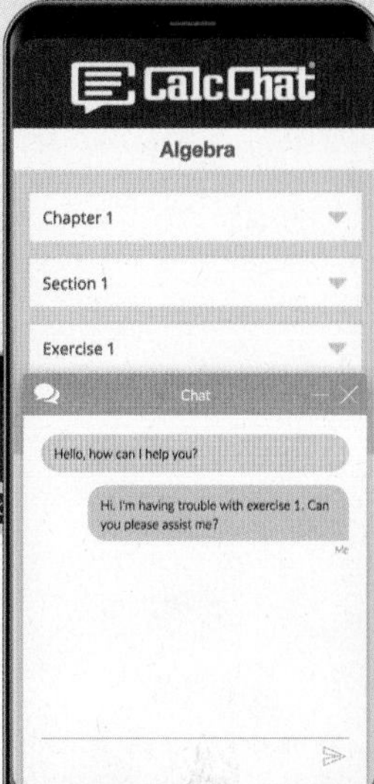

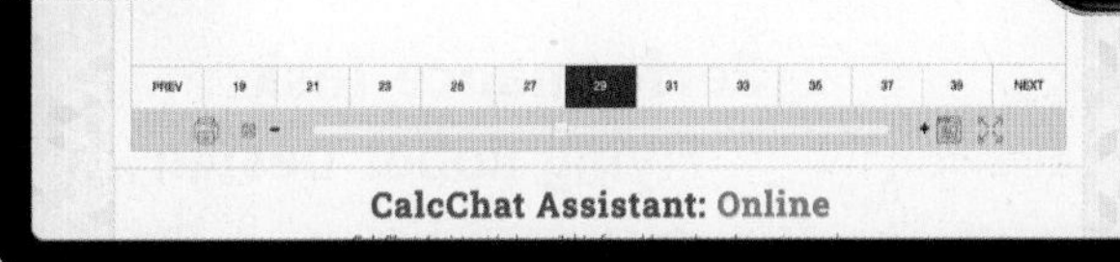

CalcView®

- Watch a video of a worked-out solution for any exercise with a blue exercise number.
- Hear a teacher explain step-by-step how to solve the problem

1.3 Practice WITH CalcChat® AND CalcView®

In Exercises 1–4, solve the proportion.

1. $\frac{x}{6} = \frac{10}{12}$
2. $\frac{36}{8} = \frac{9}{h}$
3. $\frac{13}{p} = \frac{5}{4}$
4. $\frac{4}{15} = \frac{w}{27}$

5. **USING RATIOS** A repairman needs to climb to the top of a building. He takes the measurements shown. The right triangles created by each object and its shadow are similar. Can he use a ladder that reaches heights of up to 28 feet? *Example 1*

In Exercises 13 and 14, complete the statement. Round to the nearest hundredth, if necessary.

13. $\frac{7 \text{ gal}}{\text{min}} \approx \frac{\square \text{ qt}}{\text{sec}}$

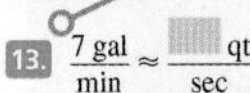

14. $\frac{8 \text{ km}}{\text{min}} \approx \frac{\square \text{ mi}}{\text{h}}$

15. **MODELING REAL LIFE** Roller coaster A can reach a top sp... reach... coast...

16. **MOD**... leaks... day. ... of 30... Whic... faste...

17. **ERRO**... the e...

1 Linear Functions

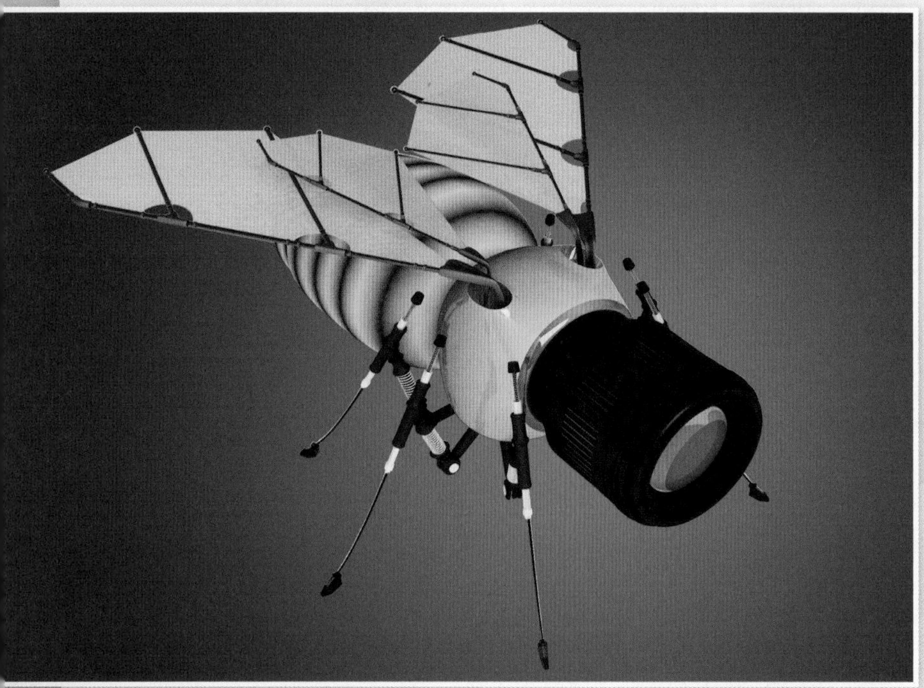

Robotics

Design a flying robot and determine how fast it needs to flap its wings to be able to take flight.

Quadratic Functions

2

Space Technology

Design a radio telescope and use a quadratic equation to describe its parabolic cross section.

3 Quadratic Equations and Complex Numbers

Nuclear Engineering

Investigate how the number of operable nuclear reactors has grown over time.

Polynomial Functions

Wildlife Conservation

Study the effects wolves have on the elk population in Yellowstone.

5 Rational Exponents and Radical Functions

Sound Art

Compare the sounds of notes in different octaves. Then explain properties of the sound waves that produce those notes.

Exponential and Logarithmic Functions

Andean Prehistory

Use carbon dating to approximate the age of an ancient manuscript made from a plant called papyrus.

7 Rational Functions

3-D and 4-D Printing
Analyze the costs and profits of creating and selling your own 3-D printed object.

Probability

8

Prehistoric Archaeology

Help a team of archaeologists choose between three potential excavation sites.

9 Data Analysis and Statistics

Volcanology

Use data to write a report about worldwide volcanic activity.

Trigonometric Ratios and Functions

10

Ethnographic Rescue

Learn how bearings are used in navigation.

11 Sequences and Series

Ocean Conservation
Analyze a plan to stabilize a fish population.

Matrices

12

Additional Resources

Conservation Photography
Analyze a food web to see how animals are interdependent.

1 Linear Functions

GO DIGITAL

NATIONAL GEOGRAPHIC EXPLORER

Robert Wood

Electrical engineer Robert Wood is an expert in tiny robots called microrobots. Microrobots are about the size of a bee. He leads a team that invents and develops entirely new classes of microrobots. For years, the team has focused on creating flying microrobots called RoboBees that can be sent on missions that are too dangerous for humans.

- A RoboBee has a 3-centimeter wingspan and a mass of 60 milligrams. Compare these measurements to the wingspan and mass of an actual honey bee.
- On what types of assignments might RoboBees be sent?

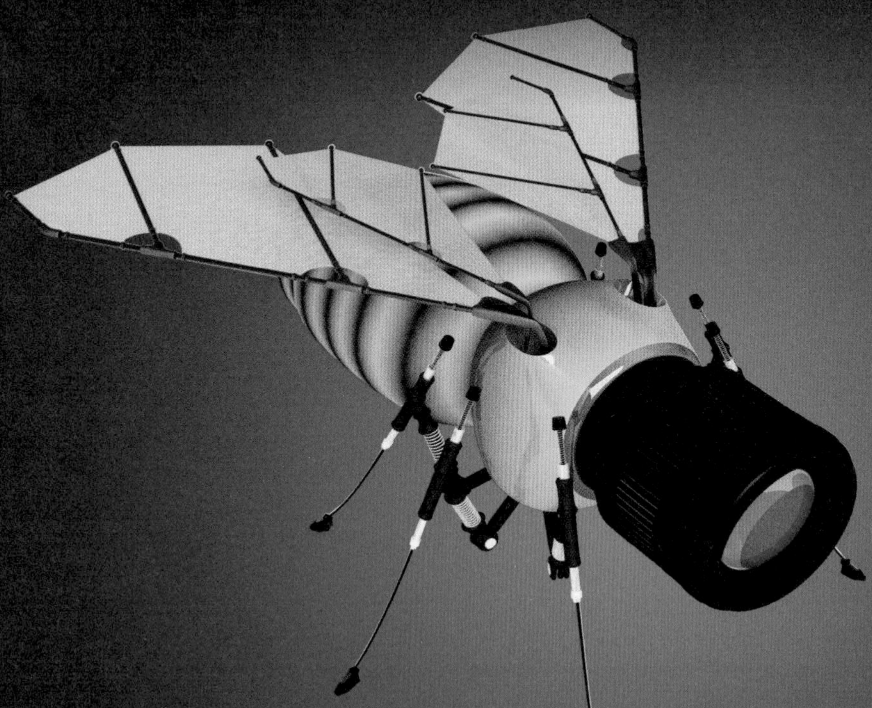

STEM

Robots can be used for a wide variety of applications. In the Performance Task, you will design a flying robot and determine how fast it needs to flap its wings to be able to take flight.

Robotics

Preparing for Chapter 1

Chapter Learning Target Understand linear functions.

Chapter Success Criteria
- ◆ I can identify parent functions and transformations.
- ◆ I can describe transformations of parent functions.
- ■ I can model with linear functions.
- ■ I can solve linear systems.

◆ Surface
■ Deep

Chapter Vocabulary

Work with a partner. Discuss each of the vocabulary terms.

parent function
transformation
translation
reflection
vertical stretch
vertical shrink
line of fit
line of best fit
correlation coefficient
linear equation in three variables
system of three linear equations
ordered triple

Mathematical Practices

Model with Mathematics

Mathematically proficient students apply what they know and are comfortable making assumptions and approximations to simplify a complicated situation.

Work with a partner. A company wants to use a robotic arm to help manufacture items. The arm costs about $250,000 to purchase and install. The graph shows the estimated savings over time.

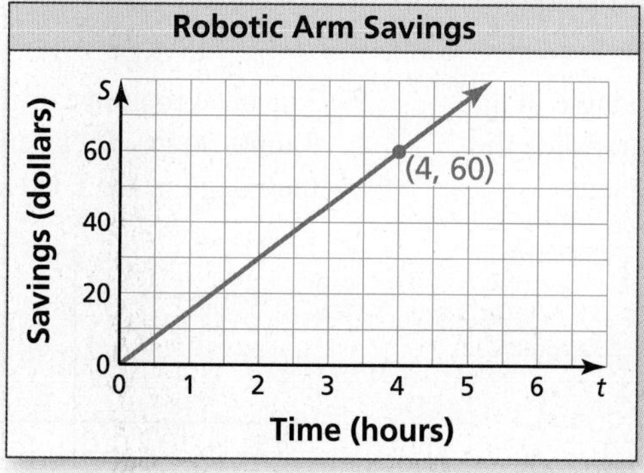

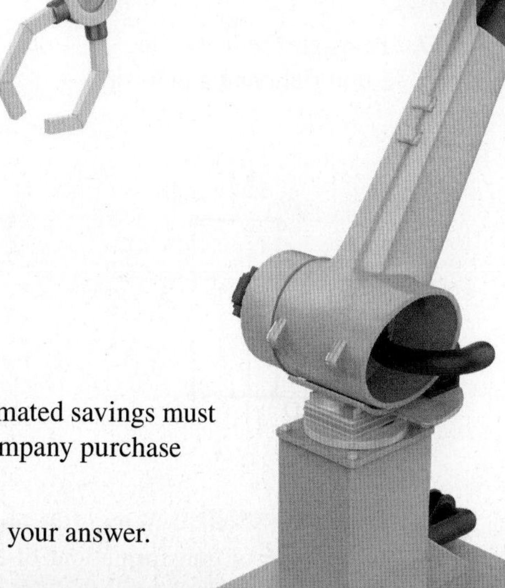

1. A manager decides that to purchase the robotic arm, the estimated savings must be greater than the cost in less than two years. Should the company purchase the robotic arm?
2. Explain the assumptions or approximations you made to find your answer.

1 Prepare WITH CalcChat®

Evaluating Expressions

Example 1 **Evaluate the expression $36 \div (3^2 \times 2) - 3$.**

$$36 \div (3^2 \times 2) - 3 = 36 \div (9 \times 2) - 3$$ Evaluate the power within parentheses.

$$= 36 \div 18 - 3$$ Multiply within parentheses.

$$= 2 - 3$$ Divide.

$$= -1$$ Subtract.

Evaluate.

1. $5 \cdot 2^3 + 7$

2. $4 - 2(3 + 2)^2$

3. $48 \div 4^2 + \frac{3}{5}$

4. $50 \div 5^2 \cdot 2$

5. $\frac{1}{2}(2^2 + 22)$

6. $\frac{1}{6}(6 + 18) - 2^2$

Transformations of Figures

Example 2 **Reflect the black rectangle in the *x*-axis. Then translate the new rectangle 5 units to the left and 1 unit down.**

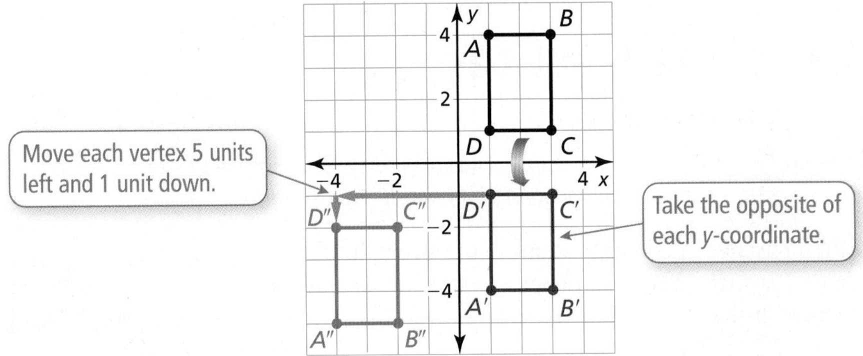

Graph the transformation of the figure.

7. Translate the rectangle 1 unit right and 4 units up.

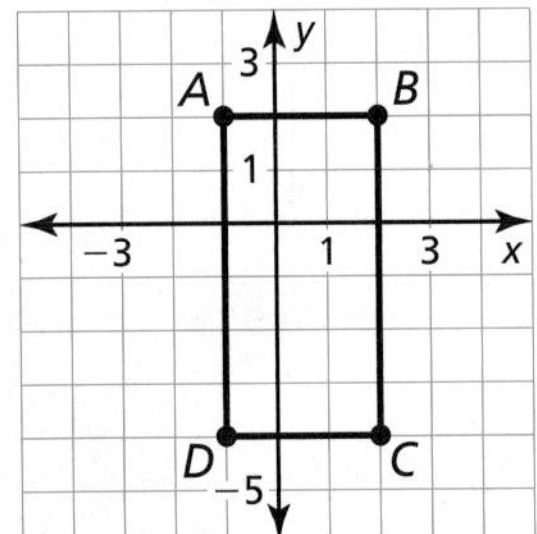

8. Reflect the triangle in the *y*-axis. Then translate the image 2 units left.

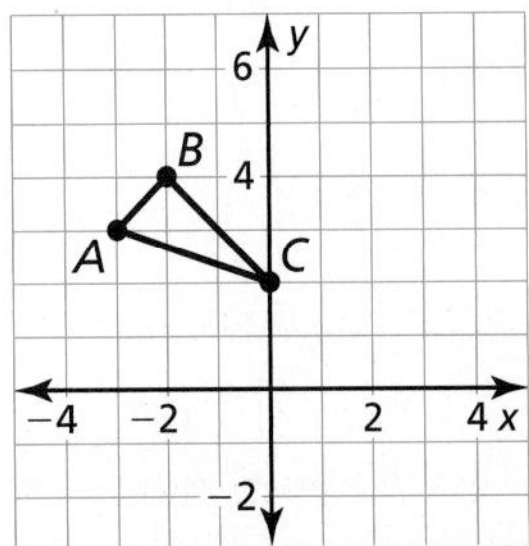

9. Translate the trapezoid 3 units down. Then reflect the image in the *x*-axis.

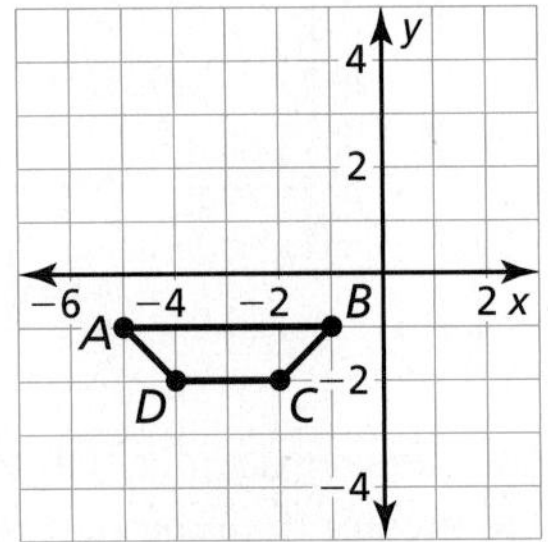

10. **MP** **REASONING** Why is the order of operations important when evaluating a numerical expression? Is the order of transformations of a figure also important? Justify your answers.

1.1 Parent Functions and Transformations

Learning Target Graph and describe transformations of functions.

Success Criteria

- I can identify the function family to which a function belongs.
- I can graph transformations of functions.
- I can explain how translations, reflections, stretches, and shrinks affect graphs of functions.

EXPLORE IT! Identifying Basic Parent Functions

Math Practice

Find Entry Points
Can considering the domain and range help you identify the graphs of any of the functions?

Work with a partner.

a. Graphs of six basic parent functions are shown below. Classify each function as *constant*, *linear*, *absolute value*, *quadratic*, *square root*, or *exponential*. Justify your reasoning.

i.

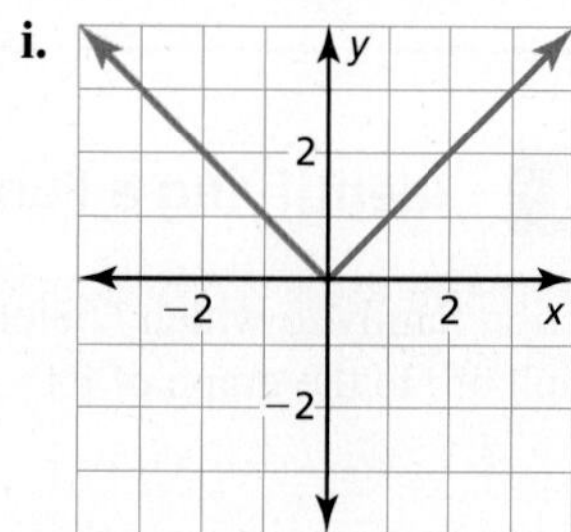

ii.

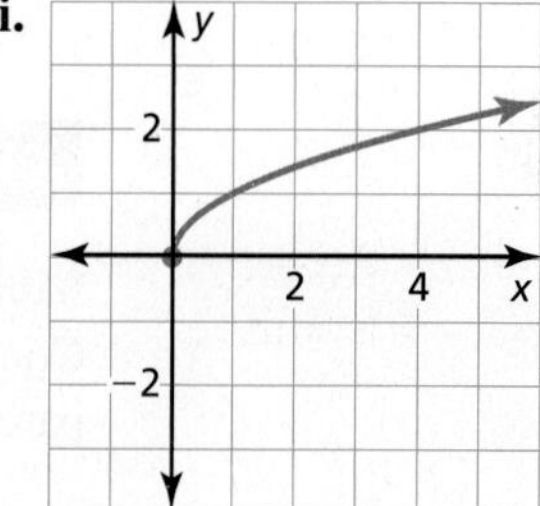

iii.

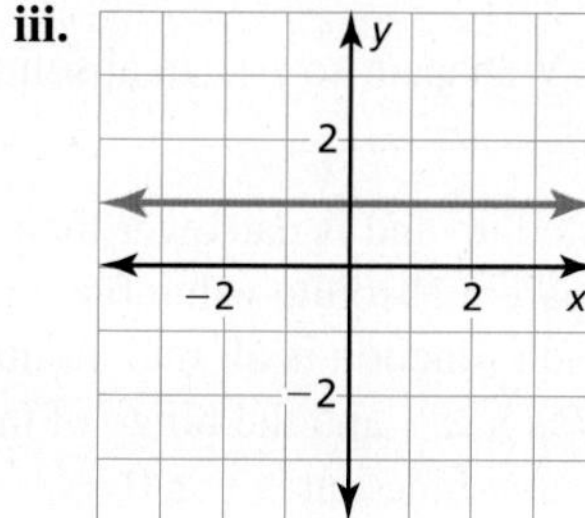

iv.

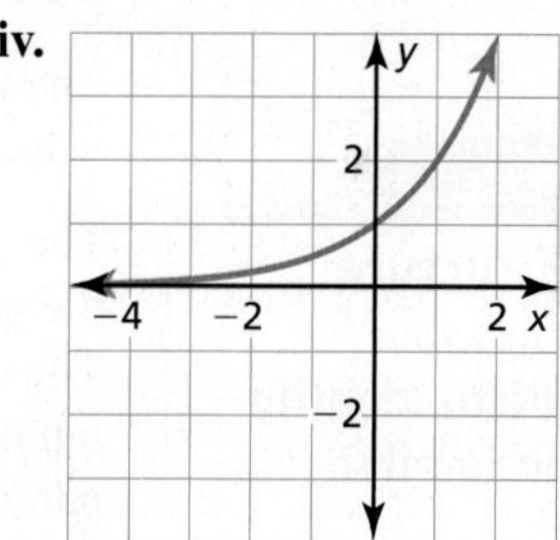

v.

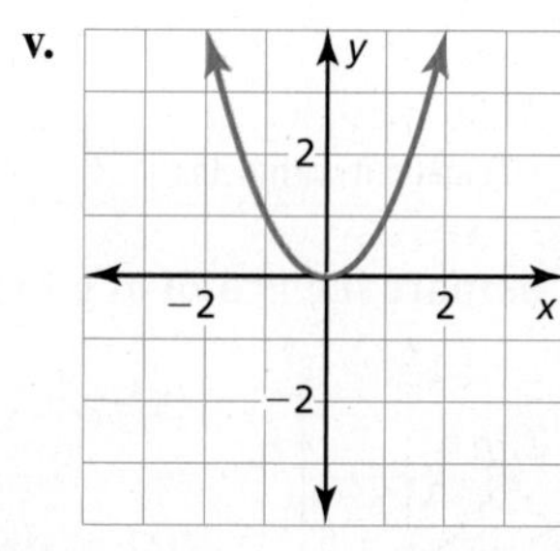

vi.

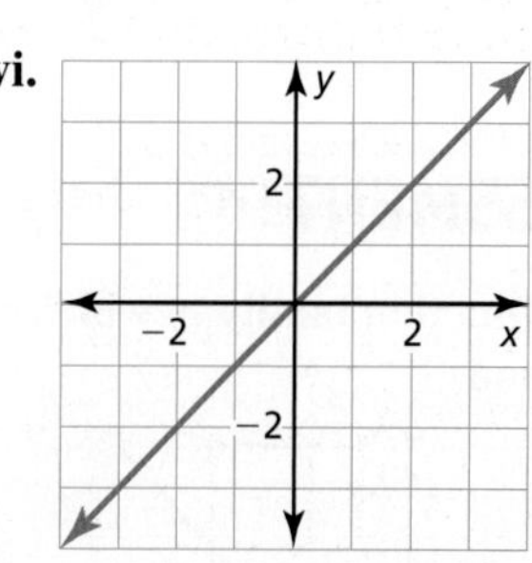

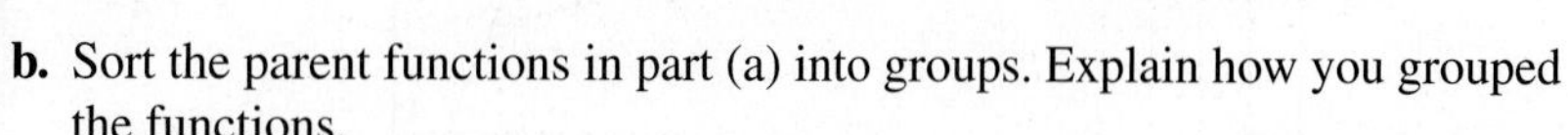

b. Sort the parent functions in part (a) into groups. Explain how you grouped the functions.

c. What are the characteristics of the graphs of some of the basic parent functions?

Identifying Function Families

Vocabulary

parent function, *p. 4*
transformation, *p. 5*
translation, *p. 5*
reflection, *p. 5*
vertical stretch, *p. 6*
vertical shrink, *p. 6*

Functions that belong to the same *family* share key characteristics. The **parent function** is the most basic function in a family. Functions in the same family are *transformations* of their parent function.

KEY IDEA

Parent Functions

Family	Constant	Linear	Absolute Value	Quadratic
Rule	$f(x) = 1$	$f(x) = x$	$f(x) = \|x\|$	$f(x) = x^2$
Graph	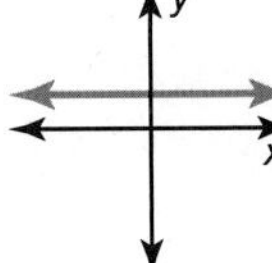	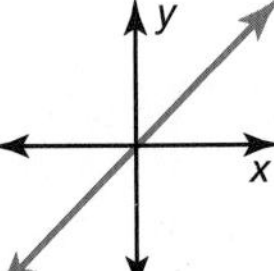	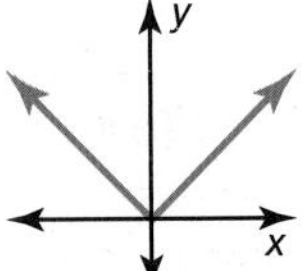	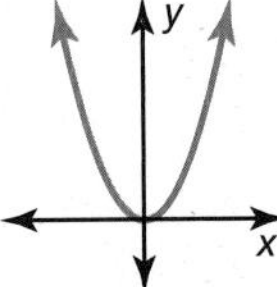
Domain	All real numbers	All real numbers	All real numbers	All real numbers
Range	$y = 1$	All real numbers	$y \geq 0$	$y \geq 0$

EXAMPLE 1 Identifying a Function Family

Identify the function family to which f belongs. Compare the graph of f to the graph of its parent function.

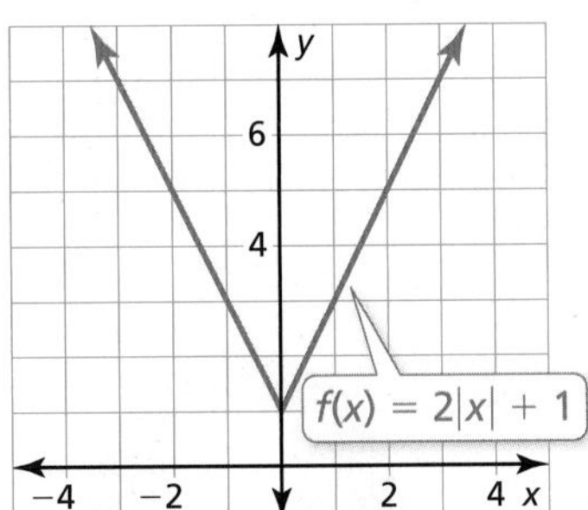

SOLUTION

The graph of f is V-shaped, so f is an absolute value function.

The graph is shifted up and is narrower than the graph of the parent absolute value function. The domain of each function is all real numbers, but the range of f is $y \geq 1$ and the range of the parent absolute value function is $y \geq 0$.

Math Practice

Look for Structure
How can you use a function rule to identify the function family?

SELF-ASSESSMENT

1 I do not understand. 2 I can do it with help. 3 I can do it on my own. 4 I can teach someone else.

Identify the function family to which g belongs. Compare the graph of g to the graph of its parent function.

1.

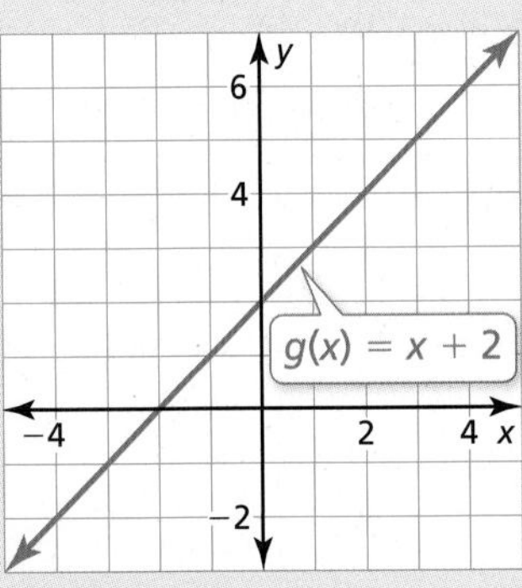

2.

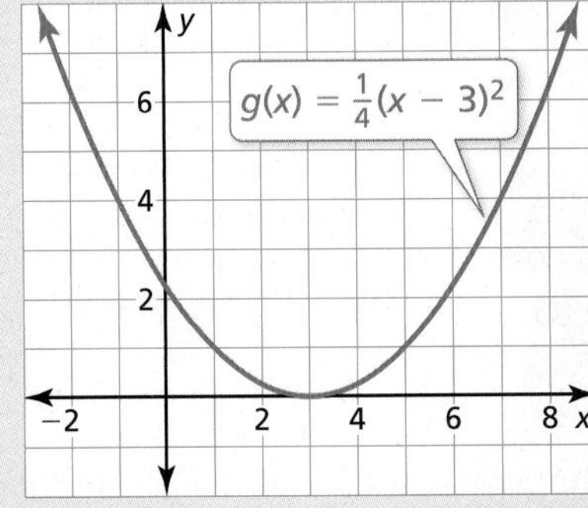

Describing Transformations

A **transformation** changes the size, shape, position, or orientation of a graph. A **translation** is a transformation that shifts a graph horizontally and/or vertically but does not change its size, shape, or orientation.

EXAMPLE 2 Graphing and Describing Translations

Graph $g(x) = x - 4$ and its parent function. Then describe the transformation.

SOLUTION

REMEMBER

The slope-intercept form of a linear equation is $y = mx + b$, where m is the slope and b is the y-intercept.

The function g is a linear function with a slope of 1 and a y-intercept of -4. So, draw a line through the point $(0, -4)$ with a slope of 1.

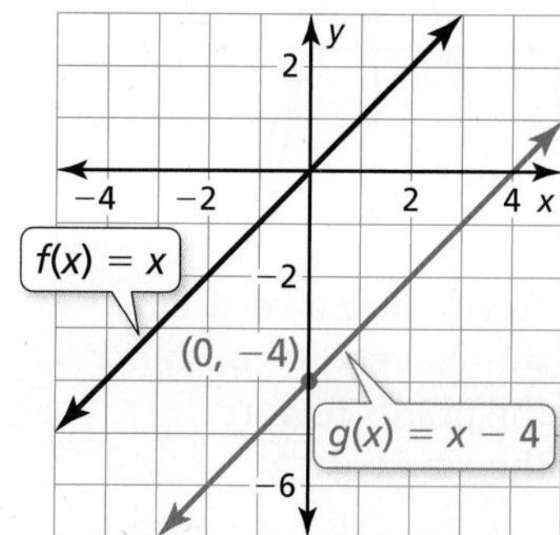

The graph of g is 4 units below the graph of the parent linear function f.

▶ So, the graph of $g(x) = x - 4$ is a vertical translation 4 units down of the graph of the parent linear function.

A **reflection** is a transformation that flips a graph over a line called the *line of reflection*. A reflected point is the same distance from the line of reflection as the original point but on the opposite side of the line.

EXAMPLE 3 Graphing and Describing Reflections

Graph $p(x) = -x^2$ and its parent function. Then describe the transformation.

SOLUTION

The function p is a quadratic function. Use a table of values to graph each function.

REMEMBER

The function $p(x) = -x^2$ is written in *function notation*, where $p(x)$ is another name for y.

x	$y = x^2$	$y = -x^2$
-2	4	-4
-1	1	-1
0	0	0
1	1	-1
2	4	-4

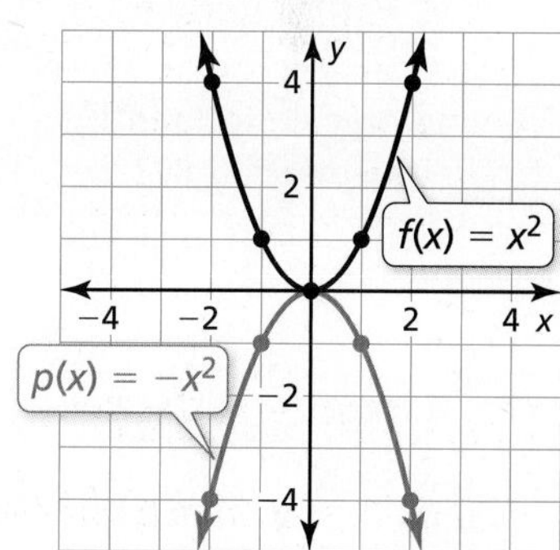

The graph of p is the graph of the parent function flipped over the x-axis.

▶ So, the graph of $p(x) = -x^2$ is a reflection in the x-axis of the graph of the parent quadratic function.

SELF-ASSESSMENT 1 I do not understand. 2 I can do it with help. 3 I can do it on my own. 4 I can teach someone else.

Graph the function and its parent function. Then describe the transformation.

3. $g(x) = x + 3$
4. $h(x) = (x - 2)^2$
5. $n(x) = -|x|$
6. MP **REASONING** Can you describe the transformation in Example 2 in a different way? Explain your reasoning.

Another way to transform the graph of a function is to multiply all of the y-coordinates by the same positive factor. When the factor is greater than 1, the transformation is a **vertical stretch**. When the factor is greater than 0 and less than 1, it is a **vertical shrink**.

STUDY TIP

To visualize a vertical stretch, imagine *pulling* the points away from the x-axis.

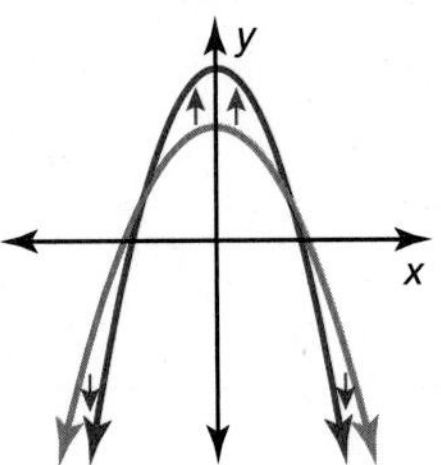

To visualize a vertical shrink, imagine *pushing* the points toward the x-axis.

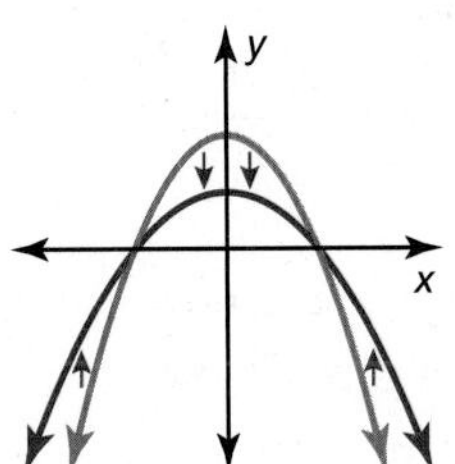

EXAMPLE 4 Graphing and Describing Stretches and Shrinks

Graph each function and its parent function. Then describe the transformation.

a. $g(x) = 2|x|$ **b.** $h(x) = \frac{1}{2}x^2$

SOLUTION

a. The function g is an absolute value function. Use a table of values to graph the functions.

x	$y = \lvert x \rvert$	$y = 2\lvert x \rvert$
−2	2	4
−1	1	2
0	0	0
1	1	2
2	2	4

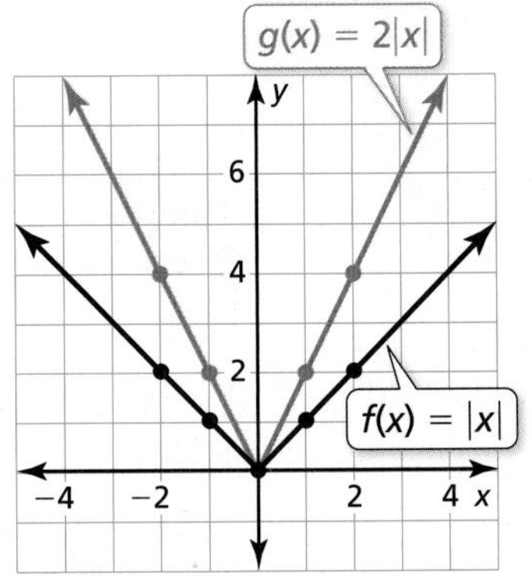

The y-coordinate of each point on g is two times the y-coordinate of the corresponding point on the parent function.

▶ So, the graph of $g(x) = 2|x|$ is a vertical stretch of the graph of the parent absolute value function by a factor of 2.

b. The function h is a quadratic function. Use a table of values to graph the functions.

x	$y = x^2$	$y = \frac{1}{2}x^2$
−2	4	2
−1	1	$\frac{1}{2}$
0	0	0
1	1	$\frac{1}{2}$
2	4	2

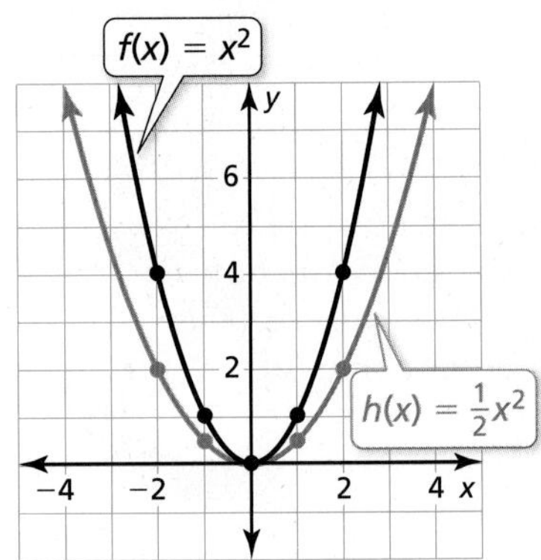

The y-coordinate of each point on h is one-half of the y-coordinate of the corresponding point on the parent function.

▶ So, the graph of $h(x) = \frac{1}{2}x^2$ is a vertical shrink of the graph of the parent quadratic function by a factor of $\frac{1}{2}$.

SELF-ASSESSMENT 1 I do not understand. 2 I can do it with help. 3 I can do it on my own. 4 I can teach someone else.

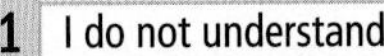

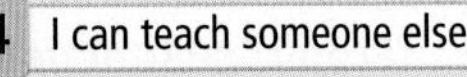

Graph the function and its parent function. Then describe the transformation.

7. $g(x) = 3x$ **8.** $h(x) = \frac{3}{2}x^2$ **9.** $c(x) = 0.2|x|$

GO DIGITAL

Combinations of Transformations

You can use more than one transformation to change the graph of a function.

EXAMPLE 5 Describing Combinations of Transformations

Use technology to graph $g(x) = -|x + 5| - 3$ and its parent function. Then describe the transformations.

SOLUTION

The function g is an absolute value function.

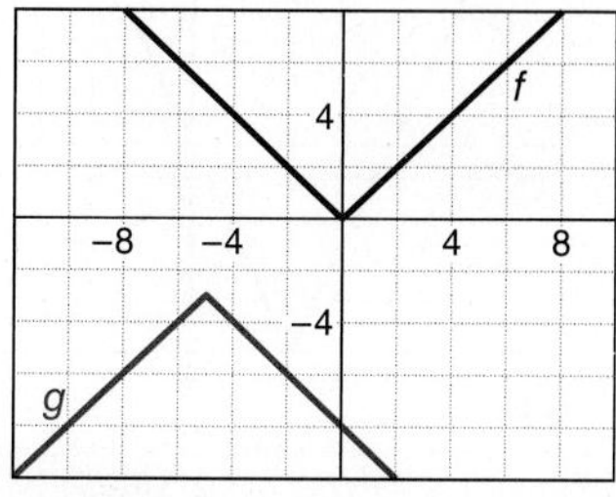

▶ The graph of $g(x) = -|x + 5| - 3$ is a reflection in the x-axis followed by a translation 5 units left and 3 units down of the graph of the parent absolute value function.

EXAMPLE 6 Modeling Real Life

Time (seconds), x	Height (feet), y
0	8
0.5	20
1	24
1.5	20
2	8

The table shows the height y of a dirt bike x seconds after jumping off a ramp. What type of function can you use to model the data? Estimate the height after 1.75 seconds.

SOLUTION

1. **Understand the Problem** You are asked to identify the type of function that can model the table of values and then to find the height at a specific time.
2. **Make a Plan** Create a scatter plot of the data. Then use the relationship shown in the scatter plot to estimate the height after 1.75 seconds.
3. **Solve and Check** Create a scatter plot.

   The data appear to lie on a curve that resembles a quadratic function. Sketch the curve.

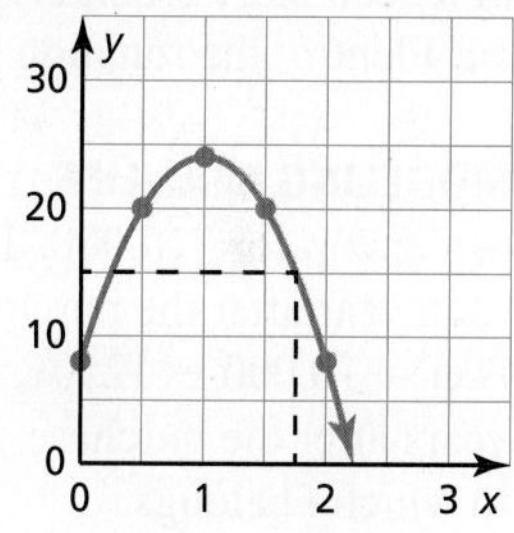

▶ So, you can model the data with a quadratic function. The graph shows that the height is about 15 feet after 1.75 seconds.

Check Reasonableness To check that your solution is reasonable, analyze the values in the table. Because 1.75 is between 1.5 and 2, the height is between 20 feet and 8 feet, and 8 ft < 15 ft < 20 ft. ✓

SELF-ASSESSMENT

1 I do not understand. 2 I can do it with help. 3 I can do it on my own. 4 I can teach someone else.

Use technology to graph the function and its parent function. Then describe the transformations.

10. $h(x) = -\frac{1}{4}x + 5$

11. $d(x) = 3(x - 5)^2 - 1$

12. $g(x) = |2x| - 3$

13. The table shows the amount of fuel in a chainsaw after x minutes. What type of function can you use to model the data? When will the tank be empty?

Time (minutes), x	0	10	20	30	40
Fuel remaining (fluid ounces), y	15	12	9	6	3

1.1 Practice WITH CalcChat® AND CalcView®

In Exercises 1–4, identify the function family to which *f* belongs. Compare the graph of *f* to the graph of its parent function. ▷ *Example 1*

1. 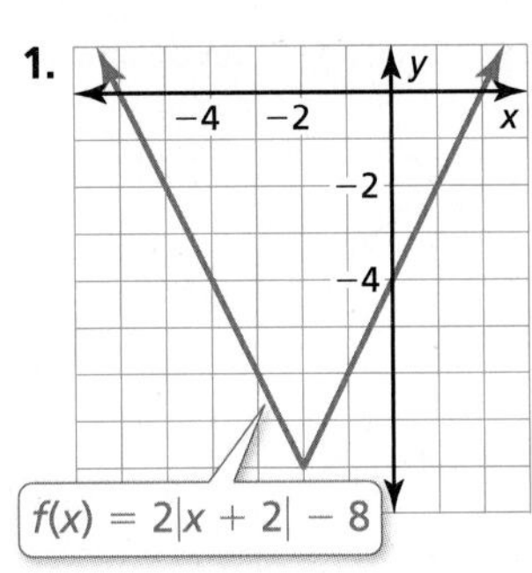

2. 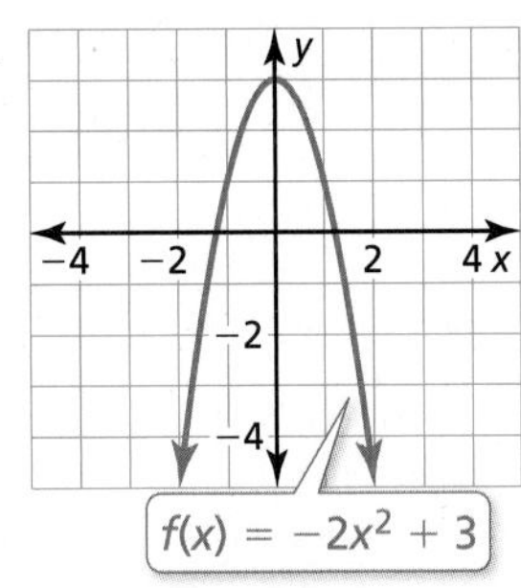

3. 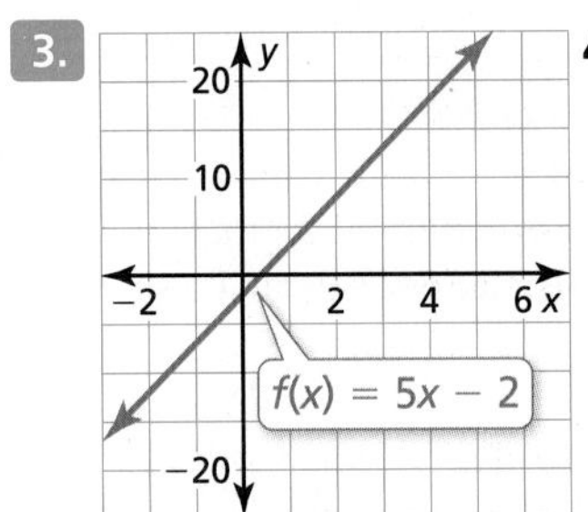

4. 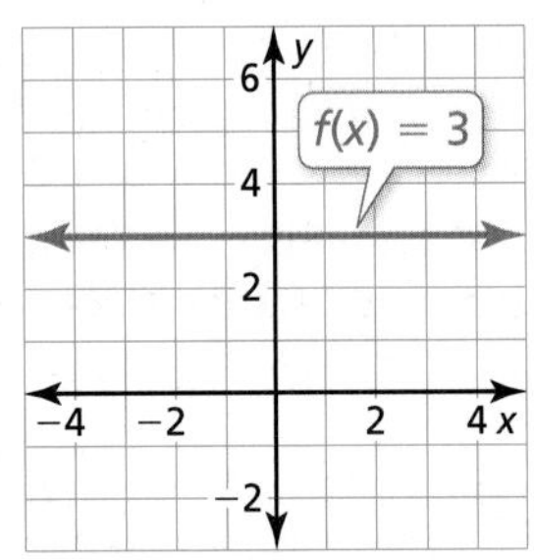

5. **MODELING REAL LIFE** The function $f(t) = -16t^2 + 22t + 4$ represents the height (in feet) of a bean bag t seconds after it is tossed up into the air. Identify the function family to which f belongs.

6. **MODELING REAL LIFE** You purchase a car from a dealership for \$10,000. The trade-in value of the car each year after the purchase is given by the function $f(x) = 10{,}000 - 1250x$, where x is the number of years after the purchase. Identify the function family to which f belongs.

In Exercises 7–16, graph the function and its parent function. Then describe the transformation. ▷ *Examples 2 and 3*

7. $g(x) = x + 4$
8. $f(x) = x - 6$
9. $f(x) = x^2 - 1$
10. $h(x) = (x + 4)^2$
11. $g(x) = |x - 5|$
12. $f(x) = 4 + |x|$
13. $g(x) = -x$
14. $h(x) = (-x)^2$
15. $f(x) = 3$
16. $f(x) = -2$

In Exercises 17–24, graph the function and its parent function. Then describe the transformation. ▷ *Example 4*

17. $f(x) = \frac{1}{3}x$
18. $g(x) = 4x$
19. $f(x) = 2x^2$
20. $h(x) = \frac{1}{3}x^2$
21. $h(x) = \frac{3}{4}x$
22. $g(x) = \frac{4}{3}x$
23. $h(x) = 3|x|$
24. $f(x) = \frac{1}{2}|x|$

In Exercises 25–32, use technology to graph the function and its parent function. Then describe the transformations. ▷ *Example 5*

25. $f(x) = 3x + 2$
26. $h(x) = -x + 5$
27. $h(x) = -3|x| - 1$
28. $f(x) = \frac{3}{4}|x| + 1$
29. $g(x) = \frac{1}{2}x^2 - 6$
30. $f(x) = 4x^2 - 3$
31. $f(x) = -(x + 3)^2 + \frac{1}{4}$
32. $g(x) = -|x - 1| - \frac{1}{2}$

33. **ERROR ANALYSIS** Describe and correct the error in graphing $g(x) = |x + 3|$ and its parent function.

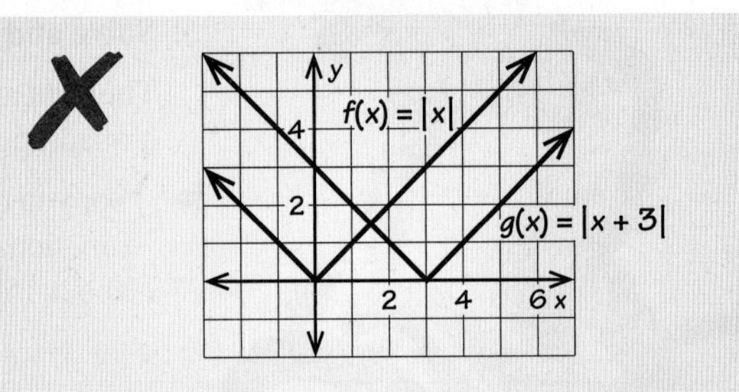

34. **ERROR ANALYSIS** Identify and correct the error in describing the transformation of the parent function.

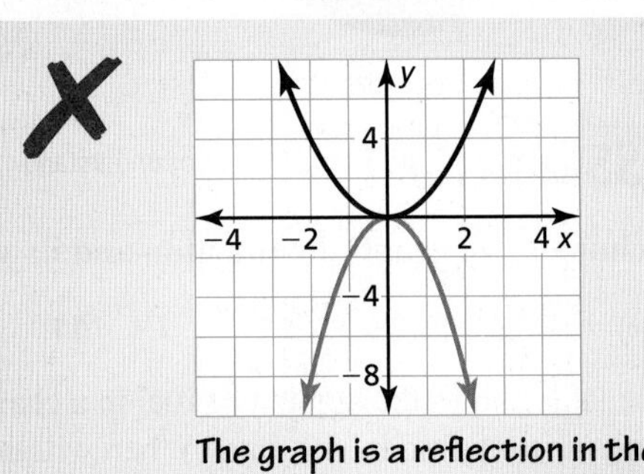

CONNECTING CONCEPTS In Exercises 35 and 36, find the coordinates of the figure after the transformation.

35. Translate 2 units down.

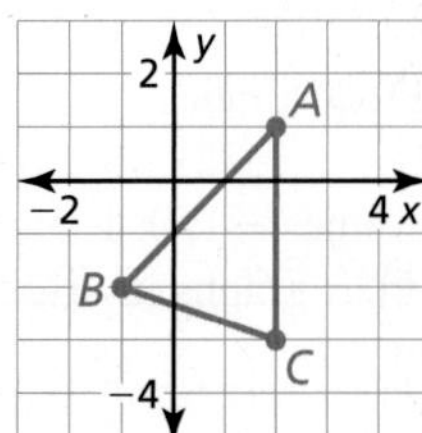

36. Reflect in the x-axis.

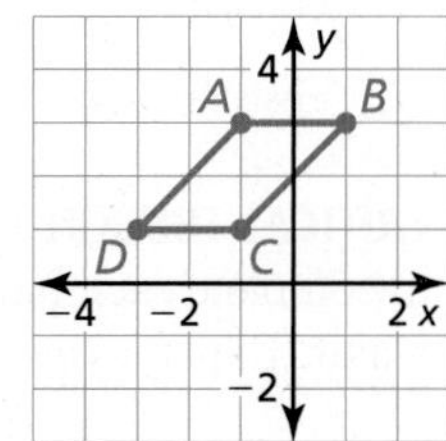

MP USING TOOLS In Exercises 37–42, identify the function family to which the function belongs. Then find the domain and range. Use technology to verify your answer.

37. $g(x) = |x + 2| - 1$

38. $h(x) = |x - 3| + 2$

39. $g(x) = 3x + 4$

40. $f(x) = -4x + 11$

41. $f(x) = 5x^2 - 2$

42. $f(x) = -2x^2 + 6$

43. MODELING REAL LIFE The table shows the speeds of a car as it travels through an intersection with a stop sign. What type of function can you use to model the data? Estimate the speed of the car when it is 20 yards past the intersection. *Example 6*

Displacement from sign (yards), x	Speed (miles per hour), y
−100	40
−50	20
−10	4
0	0
10	4
50	20
100	40

44. MODELING REAL LIFE The table shows the battery life of a robotic vacuum over time. What type of function can you use to model the data? Interpret the meaning of the x-intercept in this situation.

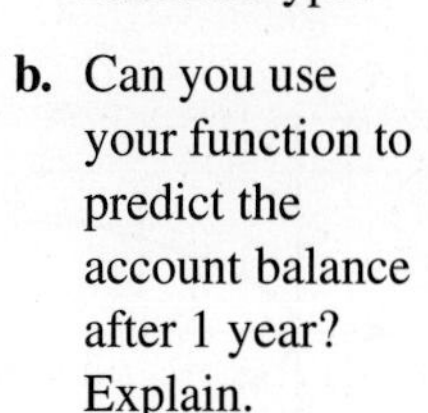

Time (minutes), x	Battery life remaining, y
30	75%
90	25%
120	0%
180	50%
240	100%

45. MP STRUCTURE Are the graphs of the functions $f(x) = |x - 4|$ and $g(x) = |x| - 4$ the same? Explain.

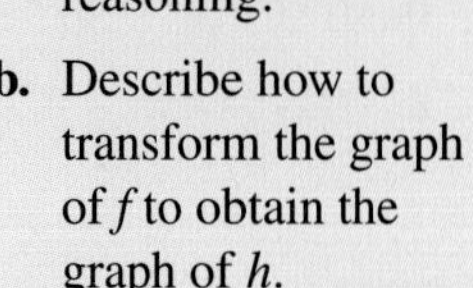

46. HOW DO YOU SEE IT?
Consider the graphs of f, g, and h.

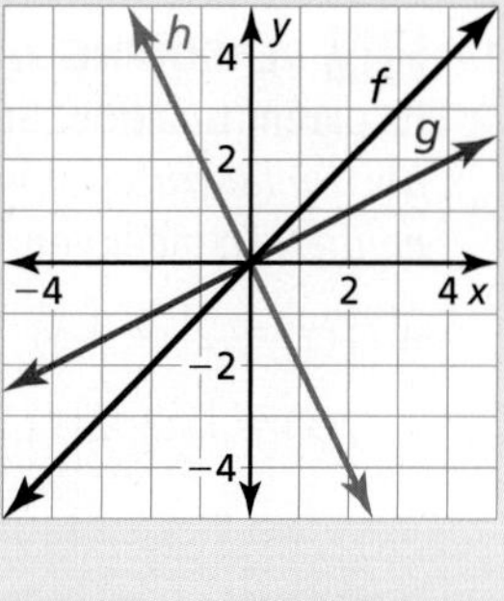

a. Does the graph of g represent a vertical stretch or a vertical shrink of the graph of f? Explain your reasoning.

b. Describe how to transform the graph of f to obtain the graph of h.

47. DRAWING CONCLUSIONS A person swims at a constant speed of 1 meter per second. What type of function can be used to model the distance the swimmer travels? If the person has a 10-meter head start, what type of transformation does this represent? Explain.

48. DRAWING CONCLUSIONS The graph shows the balance of a savings account over time.

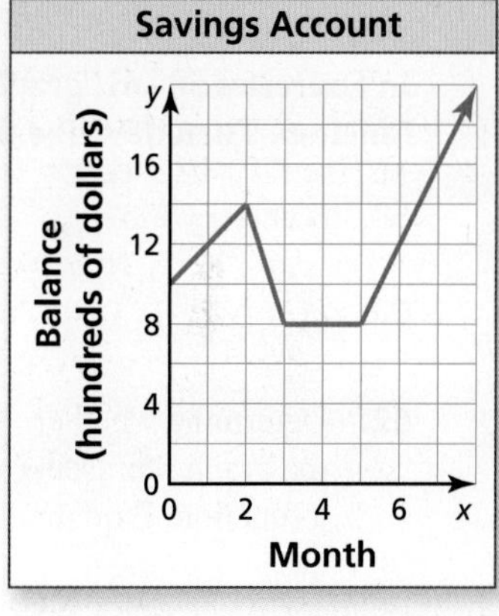

a. Write a function that represents the account balance for the domain shown. Identify the function type.

b. Can you use your function to predict the account balance after 1 year? Explain.

c. What is the initial balance? How would the graph change if the account had an initial balance of \$2000?

49. MP PROBLEM SOLVING You are playing basketball with your friends. The height (in feet) of the ball above the ground t seconds after you take a shot is modeled by the function $f(t) = -16t^2 + 26t + 6.5$.

a. Without graphing, identify the type of function that models the height of the basketball.

b. What is the value of t when the ball is released from your hand? Explain your reasoning.

c. How many feet above the ground is the ball when it is released from your hand? Explain.

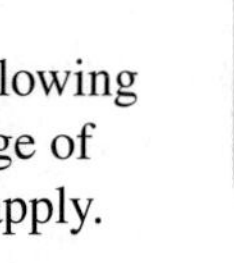

50. THOUGHT PROVOKING
The graph of $f(x) = mx + b$ is transformed to obtain the graph of $g(x) = mx + c$, where m is a rational number and b and c are integers. Describe the transformation from the graph of f to the graph of g in terms of b and c.

51. MP REASONING Compare each function with its parent function. State whether each represents a *horizontal translation*, *vertical translation*, *both*, or *neither*. Explain your reasoning.

a. $f(x) = 2|x| - 3$ **b.** $f(x) = (x - 8)^2$

c. $f(x) = |x + 2| + 4$ **d.** $f(x) = 4x^2$

52. COLLEGE PREP Which of the following function types *cannot* have a range of all real numbers? Select all that apply. Explain your reasoning.

Ⓐ constant Ⓑ linear

Ⓒ absolute value Ⓓ quadratic

53. CRITICAL THINKING Use the values −1, 0, 1, and 2 to complete each function so their graphs intersect the x-axis. Explain your reasoning.

a. $f(x) = 3x^{\square} + 1$ **b.** $f(x) = |2x - 6| - \square$

c. $f(x) = \square x^2 + 1$ **d.** $f(x) = \square$

REVIEW & REFRESH

54. Tell whether (5, 2) is a solution of $y \leq x - 3$.

In Exercises 55 and 56, find the x- and y-intercepts of the graph of the equation.

55. $y = x + 2$ **56.** $x - 2y = 8$

57. MP NUMBER SENSE The sum of three-halves a number and eight is seventeen. What is the number?

In Exercises 58–61, graph the function and its parent function. Then describe the transformation.

58. $f(x) = x^2 + 5$ **59.** $g(x) = |x - 2|$

60. $h(x) = \frac{3}{2}x$ **61.** $f(x) = 3x^2$

62. Determine whether the graph represents a function. Explain.

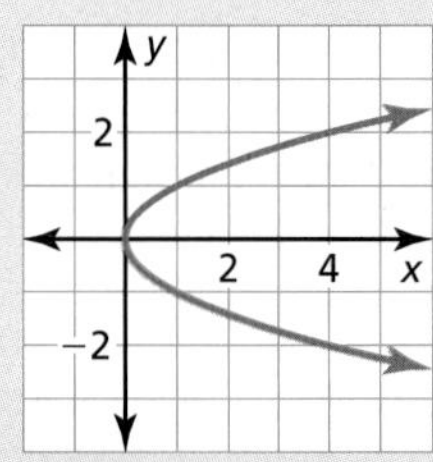

In Exercises 63–66, solve the equation.

63. $4\sqrt{x} - 5 = 7$ **64.** $\sqrt{3x - 2} = \sqrt{x + 6}$

65. $x^2 - 64 = 0$ **66.** $2x^2 - 5x = 9$

67. Tell whether the table of values represents a *linear*, an *exponential*, or a *quadratic* function.

x	−1	0	1	2	3
y	8	4	2	1	$\frac{1}{2}$

In Exercises 68 and 69, find the volume of the solid. Round your answer to the nearest tenth.

68.

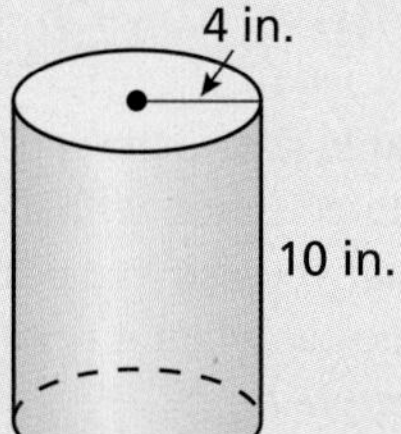

69.

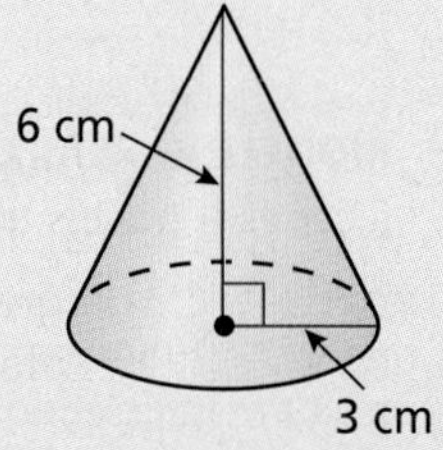

70. Determine which of the lines, if any, are parallel or perpendicular.

Line a: $2y + x = 12$
Line b: $y = 2x - 3$
Line c: $y + 2x = 1$

71. MODELING REAL LIFE The growth rate of a bacterial culture is 125% each hour. Initially, there are 5 bacteria. Find the number of bacteria in the culture after 6 hours.

72. The two-way table shows the results of a survey. Make a two-way table that shows the joint and marginal relative frequencies.

		Use Social Media	
		Yes	**No**
Own a Cell Phone	**Yes**	132	59
	No	87	46

In Exercises 73–76, factor the polynomial completely.

73. $x^2 - x - 30$ **74.** $3x^2 + 15x + 12$

75. $x^2 - 18x + 81$ **76.** $2x^3 - 2x$

1.2 Transformations of Linear and Absolute Value Functions

Learning Target Write functions that represent transformations of functions.

Success Criteria
- I can write functions that represent transformations of linear functions.
- I can write functions that represent transformations of absolute value functions.

EXPLORE IT! Transforming the Parent Absolute Value Function

Work with a partner. For parts (a)–(d), graph the function for several values of k, h, or a. Then describe how the value of k, h, or a affects the graph.

a. $y = |x| + k$

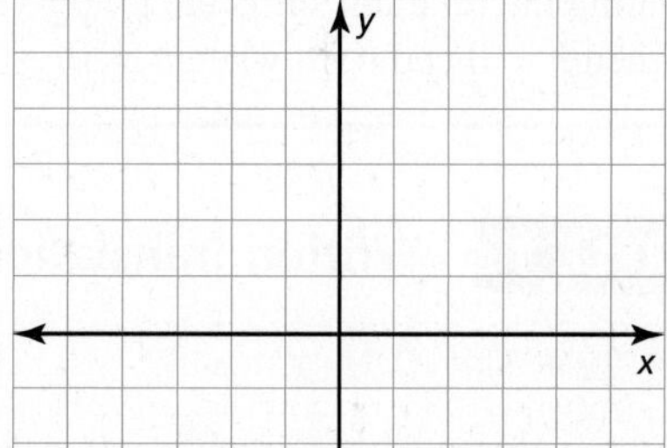
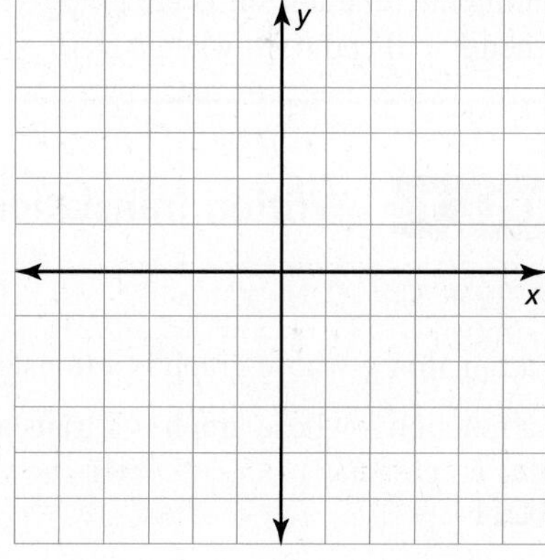

b. $y = |x - h|$

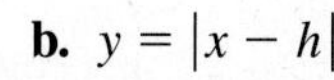
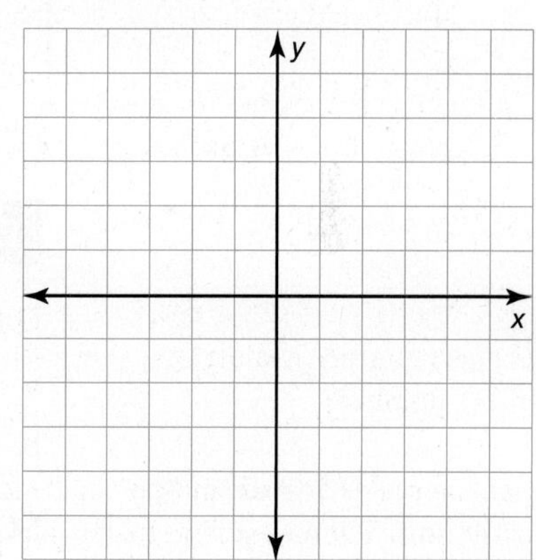

Math Practice

Construct Arguments
In parts (c) and (d), how does a affect the graph when $a = -1$? Explain why this occurs.

c. $y = a \cdot |x|$

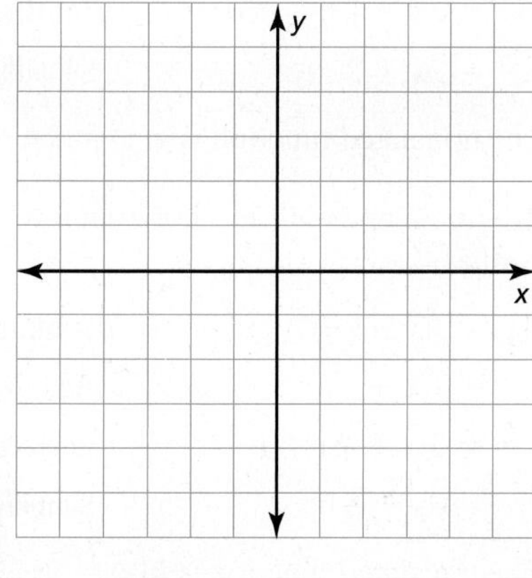

d. $y = |a \cdot x|$

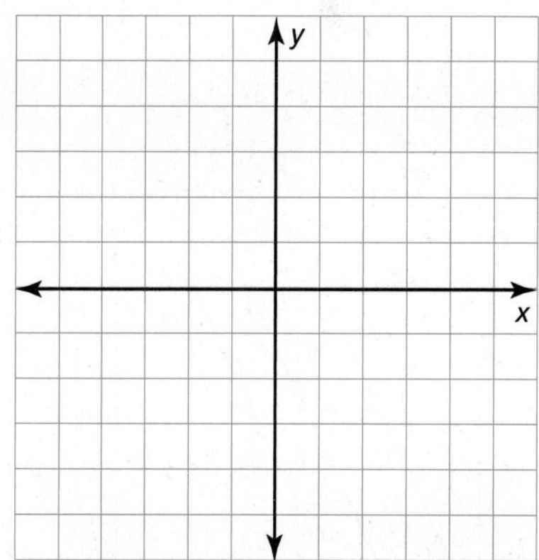

e. Let f be the parent absolute value function. How do the graphs compare to the graph of f?

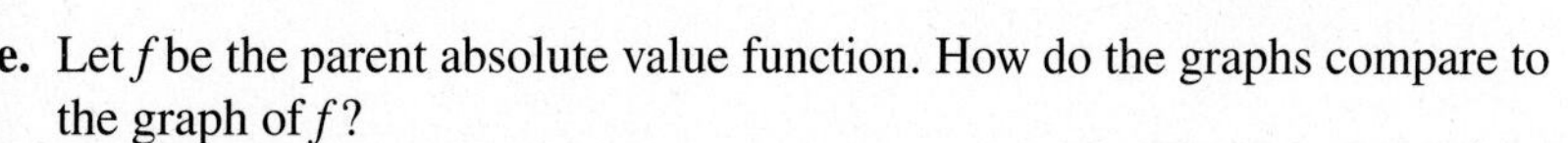

i. $y = f(x) + k$ **ii.** $y = f(x - h)$

iii. $y = a \cdot f(x)$ **iv.** $y = f(a \cdot x)$

Translations and Reflections

You can use function notation to represent transformations of graphs of functions.

KEY IDEAS

Horizontal Translations

The graph of $y = f(x - h)$ is a horizontal translation of the graph of $y = f(x)$, where $h \neq 0$.

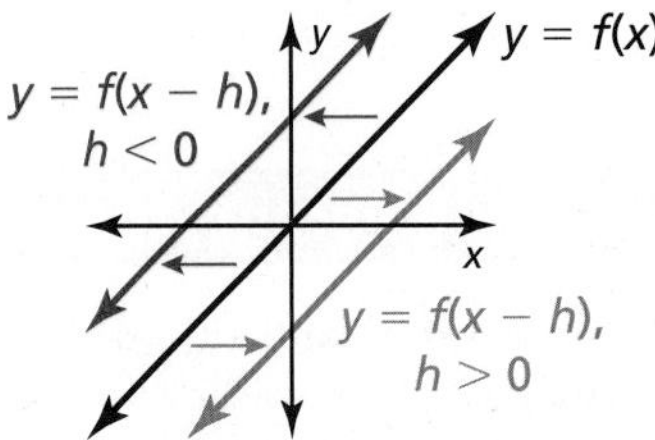

Subtracting h from the *inputs* before evaluating the function shifts the graph left when $h < 0$ and right when $h > 0$.

Vertical Translations

The graph of $y = f(x) + k$ is a vertical translation of the graph of $y = f(x)$, where $k \neq 0$.

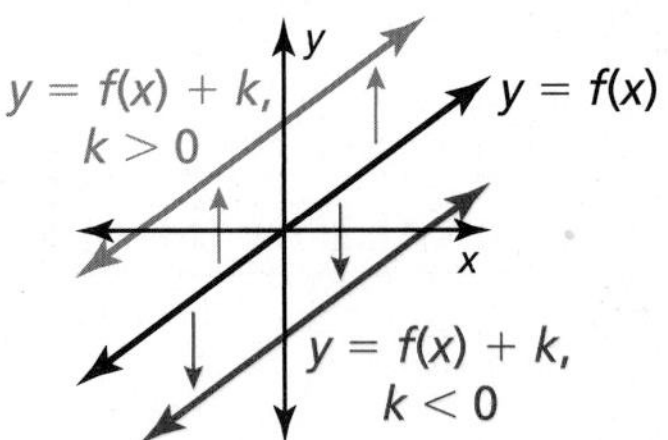

Adding k to the *outputs* shifts the graph down when $k < 0$ and up when $k > 0$.

EXAMPLE 1 Writing Translations of Functions

Let $f(x) = 2x + 1$.

a. Write a function g whose graph is a translation 3 units down of the graph of f.

b. Write a function h whose graph is a translation 2 units left of the graph of f.

SOLUTION

a. A translation 3 units down is a vertical translation that adds -3 to each output value.

$g(x) = f(x) + (-3)$	Add -3 to the output.
$= 2x + 1 + (-3)$	Substitute $2x + 1$ for $f(x)$.
$= 2x - 2$	Simplify.

▶ The translated function is $g(x) = 2x - 2$.

Check

b. A translation 2 units left is a horizontal translation that subtracts -2 from each input value.

$h(x) = f(x - (-2))$	Subtract -2 from the input.
$= f(x + 2)$	Add the opposite.
$= 2(x + 2) + 1$	Replace x with $x + 2$ in $f(x)$.
$= 2x + 5$	Simplify.

The translated function is $h(x) = 2x + 5$.

SELF-ASSESSMENT

1 I do not understand. 2 I can do it with help. 3 I can do it on my own. 4 I can teach someone else.

Write a function g whose graph represents the indicated transformation of the graph of f. Use technology to check your answer.

1. $f(x) = 3x$; translation 5 units up

2. $f(x) = |x| - 3$; translation 4 units right

KEY IDEAS

STUDY TIP

When you reflect a graph in a line, the graphs are symmetric about that line.

Reflections in the *x*-Axis

The graph of $y = -f(x)$ is a reflection in the *x*-axis of the graph of $y = f(x)$.

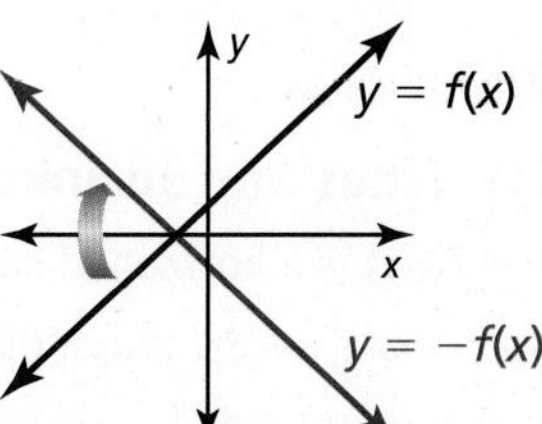

Multiplying the *outputs* by -1 changes their signs.

Reflections in the *y*-Axis

The graph of $y = f(-x)$ is a reflection in the *y*-axis of the graph of $y = f(x)$.

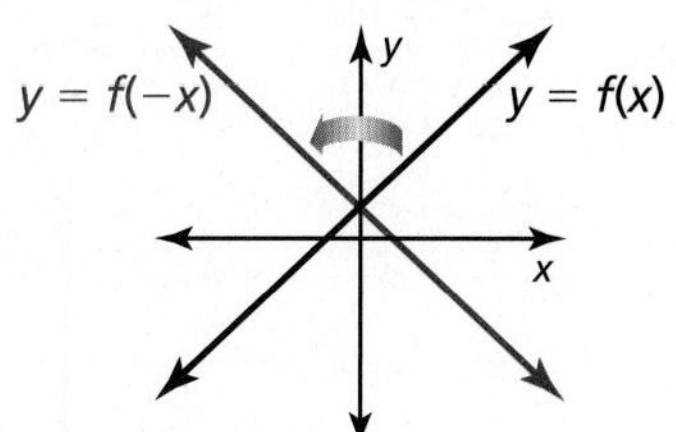

Multiplying the *inputs* by -1 changes their signs.

GO DIGITAL

EXAMPLE 2 Writing Reflections of Functions

Let $f(x) = |x + 3| + 1$.

a. Write a function g whose graph is a reflection in the *x*-axis of the graph of f.

b. Write a function h whose graph is a reflection in the *y*-axis of the graph of f.

SOLUTION

a. A reflection in the *x*-axis changes the sign of each output value.

$g(x) = -f(x)$	Multiply the output by -1.
$= -(|x + 3| + 1)$	Substitute $|x + 3| + 1$ for $f(x)$.
$= -|x + 3| - 1$	Distributive Property

▶ The reflected function is $g(x) = -|x + 3| - 1$.

b. A reflection in the *y*-axis changes the sign of each input value.

$h(x) = f(-x)$	Multiply the input by -1.
$= |-x + 3| + 1$	Replace x with $-x$ in $f(x)$.
$= |-(x - 3)| + 1$	Factor out -1.
$= |-1| \cdot |x - 3| + 1$	Product Property of Absolute Value
$= |x - 3| + 1$	Simplify.

▶ The reflected function is $h(x) = |x - 3| + 1$.

Check

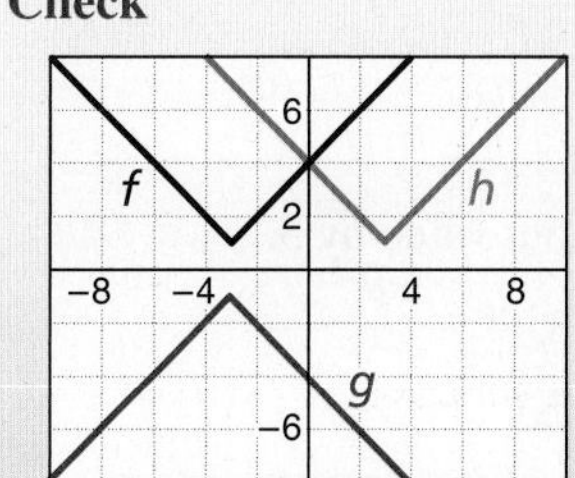

SELF-ASSESSMENT

1 I do not understand. 2 I can do it with help. 3 I can do it on my own. 4 I can teach someone else.

Write a function g whose graph represents the indicated transformation of the graph of f. Use technology to check your answer.

3. $f(x) = -|x + 2| - 1$; reflection in the *x*-axis

4. $f(x) = \frac{1}{2}x + 1$; reflection in the *y*-axis

5. WHICH ONE DOESN'T BELONG? Let $f(x) = x - 1$ and $g(x) = x + 1$. Which function does *not* belong with the other three? Explain your reasoning.

$h(x) = -f(x)$	$h(x) = f(-x)$	$h(x) = g(-x)$	$h(x) = 1 - x$

Stretches and Shrinks

In the previous section, you learned that vertical stretches and shrinks transform graphs. You can also use *horizontal* stretches and shrinks to transform graphs.

KEY IDEAS

Horizontal Stretches and Shrinks

The graph of $y = f(ax)$ is a horizontal stretch or shrink by a factor of $\frac{1}{a}$ of the graph of $y = f(x)$, where $a > 0$ and $a \neq 1$.

Multiplying the *inputs* by a before evaluating the function stretches the graph horizontally (away from the y-axis) when $0 < a < 1$, and shrinks the graph horizontally (toward the y-axis) when $a > 1$.

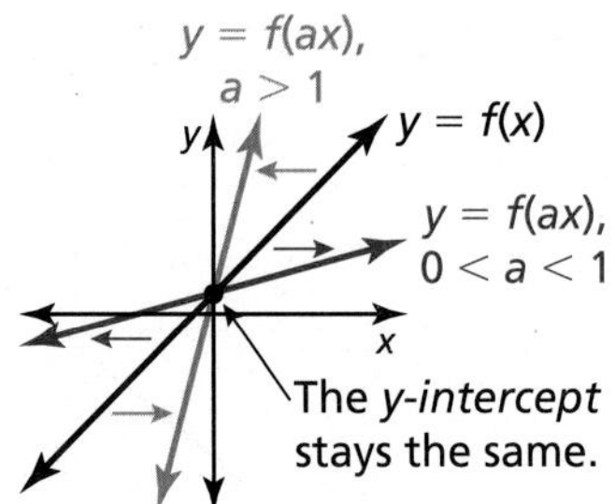

Vertical Stretches and Shrinks

The graph of $y = a \cdot f(x)$ is a vertical stretch or shrink by a factor of a of the graph of $y = f(x)$, where $a > 0$ and $a \neq 1$.

Multiplying the *outputs* by a stretches the graph vertically (away from the x-axis) when $a > 1$, and shrinks the graph vertically (toward the x-axis) when $0 < a < 1$.

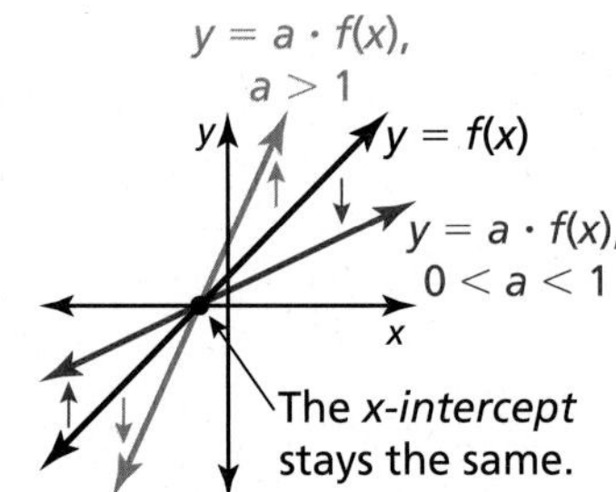

STUDY TIP

The graphs of $y = f(-ax)$ and $y = -a \cdot f(x)$ represent a stretch or shrink *and* a reflection in the x- or y-axis of the graph of $y = f(x)$.

EXAMPLE 3 Writing Stretches and Shrinks of Functions

Let $f(x) = |x - 3| - 5$. Write (a) a function g whose graph is a horizontal shrink of the graph of f by a factor of $\frac{1}{3}$, and (b) a function h whose graph is a vertical stretch of the graph of f by a factor of 2.

SOLUTION

a. A horizontal shrink by a factor of $\frac{1}{3}$ multiplies each input value by 3.

$g(x) = f(3x)$	Multiply the input by 3.
$= \lvert 3x - 3 \rvert - 5$	Replace x with $3x$ in $f(x)$.

▶ The transformed function is $g(x) = |3x - 3| - 5$.

b. A vertical stretch by a factor of 2 multiplies each output value by 2.

$h(x) = 2 \cdot f(x)$	Multiply the output by 2.
$= 2 \cdot (\lvert x - 3 \rvert - 5)$	Substitute $\lvert x - 3 \rvert - 5$ for $f(x)$.
$= 2\lvert x - 3 \rvert - 10$	Distributive Property

▶ The transformed function is $h(x) = 2|x - 3| - 10$.

Check

SELF-ASSESSMENT 1 I do not understand. 2 I can do it with help. 3 I can do it on my own. 4 I can teach someone else.

Write a function g whose graph represents the indicated transformation of the graph of f. Use technology to check your answer.

6. $f(x) = 4x + 2$; horizontal stretch by a factor of 2

7. $f(x) = |x| - 3$; vertical shrink by a factor of $\frac{1}{3}$

Combinations of Transformations

You can write a function that represents a series of transformations on the graph of another function by applying the transformations one at a time in the stated order.

EXAMPLE 4 Combining Transformations

Let the graph of g be a vertical shrink by a factor of 0.25 followed by a translation 3 units up of the graph of $f(x) = x$. Write a rule for g.

SOLUTION

Step 1 First write a function h that represents the vertical shrink of f.

$h(x) = 0.25 \cdot f(x)$ Multiply the output by 0.25.

$= 0.25x$ Substitute x for $f(x)$.

Step 2 Then write a function g that represents the translation of h.

$g(x) = h(x) + 3$ Add 3 to the output.

$= 0.25x + 3$ Substitute $0.25x$ for $h(x)$.

▶ The transformed function is $g(x) = 0.25x + 3$.

Check

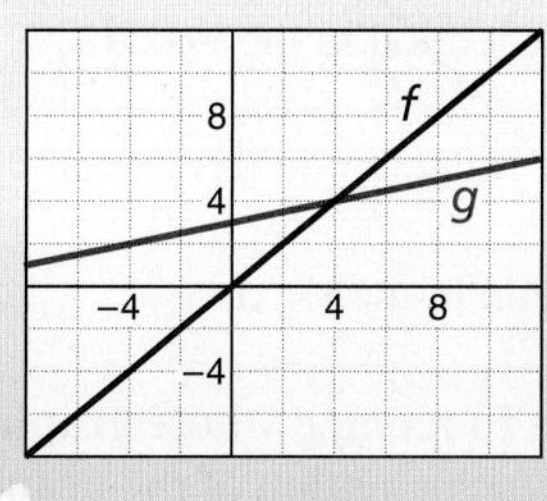

EXAMPLE 5 Modeling Real Life

You design a computer game. Your revenue (in dollars) for x downloads is given by $f(x) = 2x$ and your profit is \$50 less than 90% of the revenue. What is your profit for 100 downloads?

SOLUTION

1. **Understand the Problem** You are given a function that represents your revenue and a verbal statement that represents your profit. You are asked to find your profit for 100 downloads.
2. **Make a Plan** Write a function p that represents your profit. Then use this function to find the profit for 100 downloads.
3. **Solve and Check** profit = 90% • revenue − 50

$p(x) = 0.9 \cdot f(x) - 50$

Vertical shrink by a factor of 0.9 (0.9) — Translation 50 units down (− 50)

$= 0.9 \cdot 2x - 50$ Substitute $2x$ for $f(x)$.

$= 1.8x - 50$ Simplify.

To find the profit for 100 downloads, evaluate p when $x = 100$.

$p(100) = 1.8(100) - 50 = 130$

▶ Your profit is \$130 for 100 downloads.

Look Back The vertical shrink decreases the slope, and the translation shifts the graph 50 units down. So, the graph of p is below and not as steep as the graph of f.

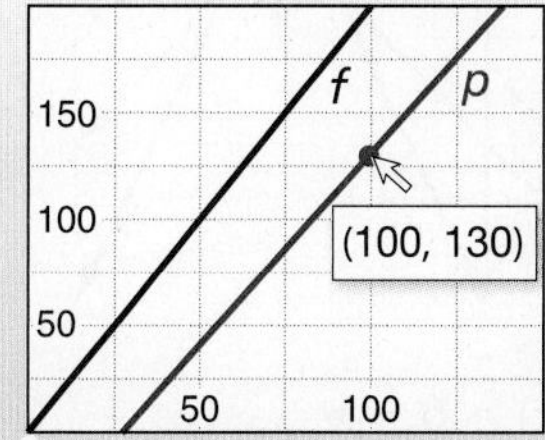

SELF-ASSESSMENT

1 I do not understand. 2 I can do it with help. 3 I can do it on my own. 4 I can teach someone else.

8. Let the graph of g be a translation 6 units down followed by a reflection in the x-axis of the graph of $f(x) = |x|$. Write a rule for g. Use technology to check your answer.

9. **WHAT IF?** In Example 5, your revenue function is $f(x) = 3x$. How does this affect your profit for 100 downloads?

1.2 Practice WITH CalcChat® AND CalcView®

In Exercises 1–6, write a function g whose graph represents the indicated transformation of the graph of f. Use technology to check your answer. *Example 1*

1. $f(x) = x - 5$; translation 4 units left

2. $f(x) = x + 2$; translation 2 units right

3. $f(x) = |4x + 3| + 2$; translation 2 units down

4. $f(x) = 2|x| - 9$; translation 6 units up

5. $f(x) = 4 - |x + 1|$

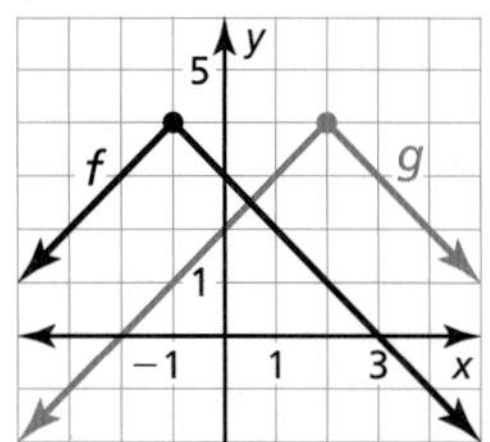

6. $f(x) = |4x| + 5$

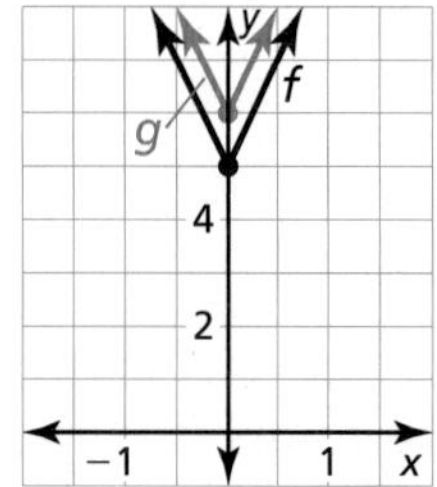

7. **WRITING** Describe the translation from the graph of f to the graph of g in two different ways.

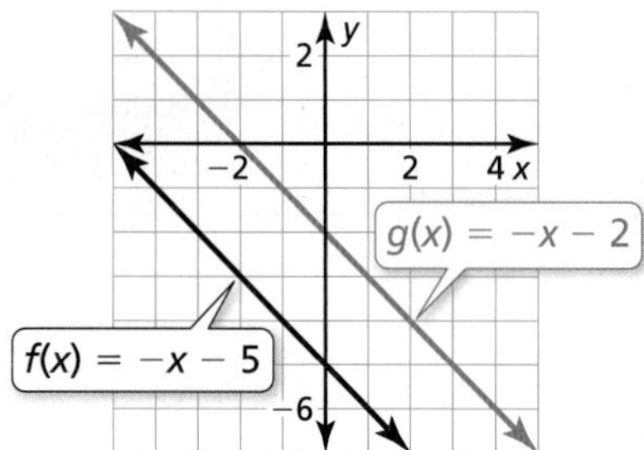

8. **MP PROBLEM SOLVING** You start a photography business. The function $f(x) = 4000x$ represents your expected total net income (in dollars) after x weeks. Before you start, you incur an expense of \$12,000. What transformation of f is necessary to model this situation? How many weeks will it take to pay off the extra expense?

In Exercises 9–14, write a function g whose graph represents the indicated transformation of the graph of f. Use technology to check your answer. *Example 2*

9. $f(x) = -5x + 2$; reflection in the x-axis

10. $f(x) = \frac{1}{2}x - 3$; reflection in the x-axis

11. $f(x) = |6x| - 2$; reflection in the y-axis

12. $f(x) = |2x - 1| + 3$; reflection in the y-axis

13. $f(x) = -3 + |x - 11|$; reflection in the y-axis

14. $f(x) = -x + 1$; reflection in the y-axis

In Exercises 15–22, write a function g whose graph represents the indicated transformation of the graph of f. Use technology to check your answer. *Example 3*

15. $f(x) = x + 2$; vertical stretch by a factor of 5

16. $f(x) = 2x + 6$; vertical shrink by a factor of $\frac{1}{2}$

17. $f(x) = |2x| + 4$; horizontal shrink by a factor of $\frac{1}{2}$

18. $f(x) = |x + 3|$; horizontal stretch by a factor of 4

19. $f(x) = x - 3$; horizontal stretch by a factor of 2

20. $f(x) = |x + 1| - 1$; vertical stretch by a factor of 3

21. $f(x) = -2|x - 4| + 2$

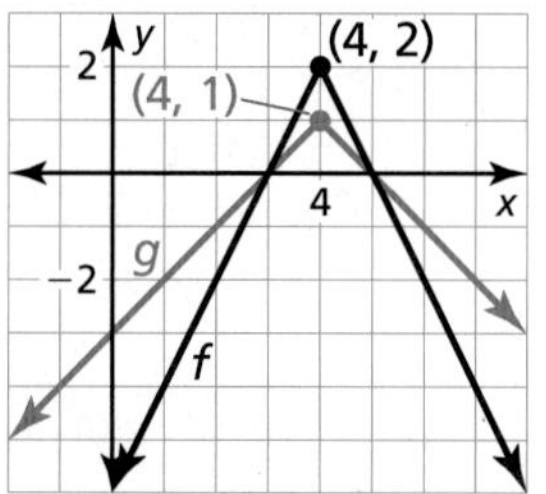

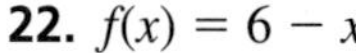

22. $f(x) = 6 - x$

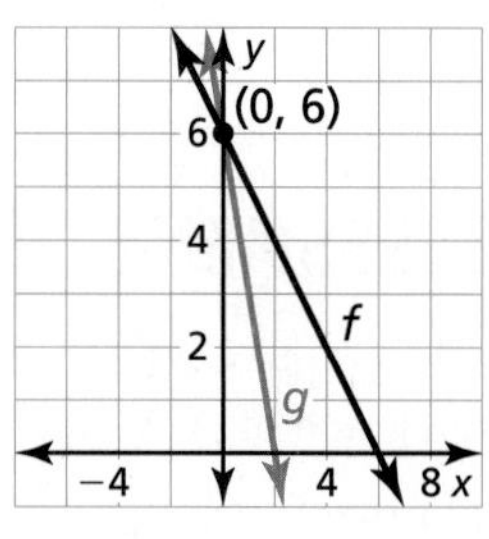

ANALYZING RELATIONSHIPS In Exercises 23–26, match the graph of the transformation of f with the correct equation shown. Explain your reasoning.

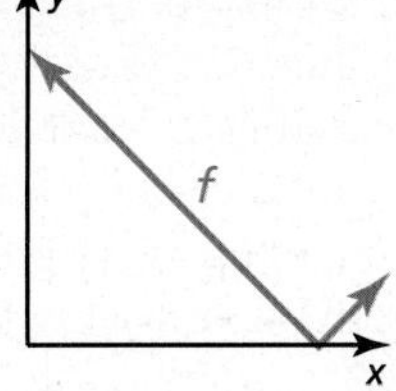

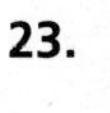

23.

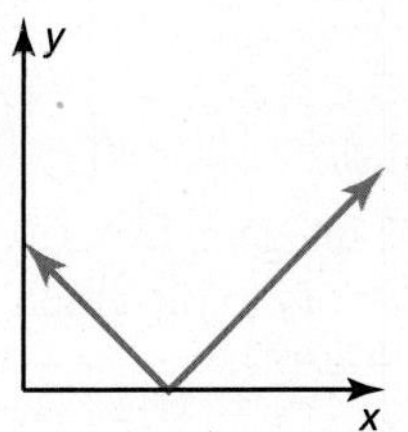

24.

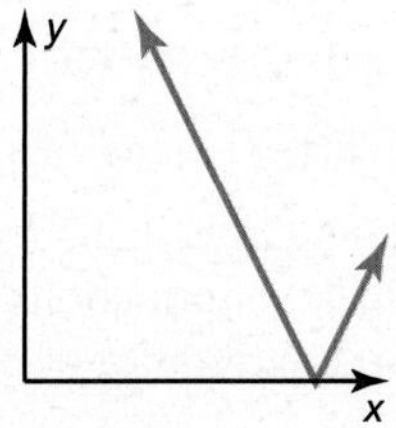

25.

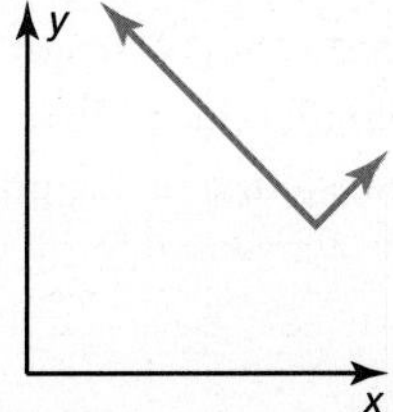

26.

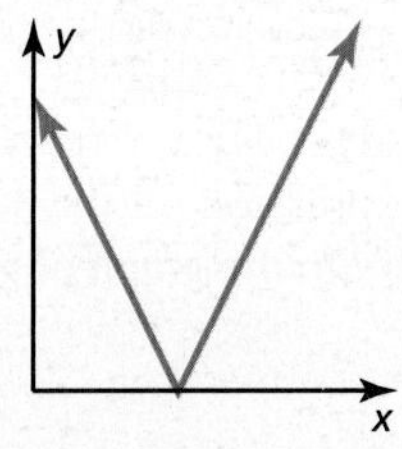

A. $y = 2f(x)$ **B.** $y = f(2x)$

C. $y = f(x + 2)$ **D.** $y = f(x) + 2$

In Exercises 27–32, write a function g whose graph represents the indicated transformations of the graph of f. *Example 4*

27. $f(x) = x$; vertical stretch by a factor of 2 followed by a translation 1 unit up

28. $f(x) = x$; translation 3 units down followed by a vertical shrink by a factor of $\frac{1}{3}$

29. $f(x) = |x|$; translation 2 units right followed by a horizontal stretch by a factor of 2

30. $f(x) = |x|$; reflection in the y-axis followed by a translation 3 units right

31. $f(x) = |x|$

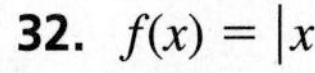

32. $f(x) = |x|$

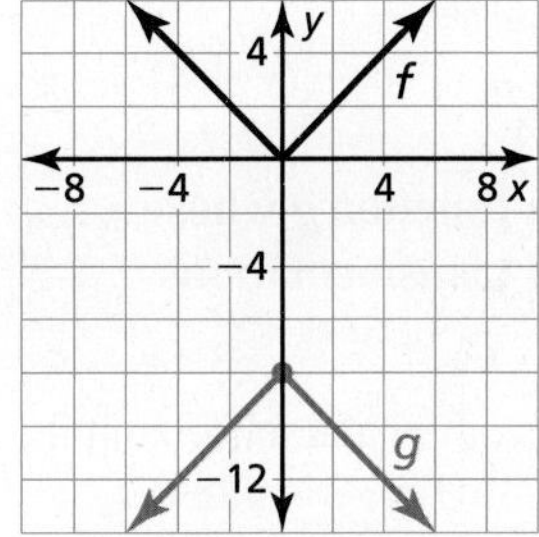

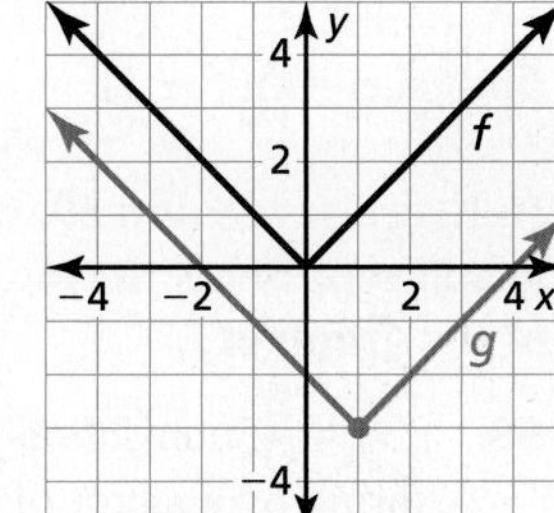

ERROR ANALYSIS In Exercises 33 and 34, identify and correct the error in writing the function g whose graph represents the indicated transformations of the graph of f.

33.

$f(x) = |x|$; translation 3 units right followed by a translation 2 units up

$g(x) = |x + 3| + 2$

34.

$f(x) = x$; translation 6 units down followed by a vertical stretch by a factor of 5

$g(x) = 5x - 6$

35. MODELING REAL LIFE The cost (in dollars) of a car ride from a ride sharing company during regular hours is modeled by $f(x) = 2.30x$, where x is the number of miles driven. The cost of a ride during high-demand hours, including a tip, is \$5 more than 120% the cost during regular hours. What is the cost of a 6-mile ride during high-demand hours? *Example 5*

36. MODELING REAL LIFE Recently, bookstore sales have been declining. The sales (in billions of dollars) can be modeled by the function $f(t) = -\frac{1}{4}t + 11.3$, where t is the number of years since 2014. Transform the graph of f to model sales that decrease at twice this rate. Explain how this affects bookstore sales in 2022.

CONNECTING CONCEPTS In Exercises 37 and 38, describe the transformation of the graph of f to the graph of g. Then find the area of the shaded triangle.

37. $f(x) = |x - 3|$

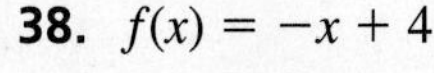

38. $f(x) = -x + 4$

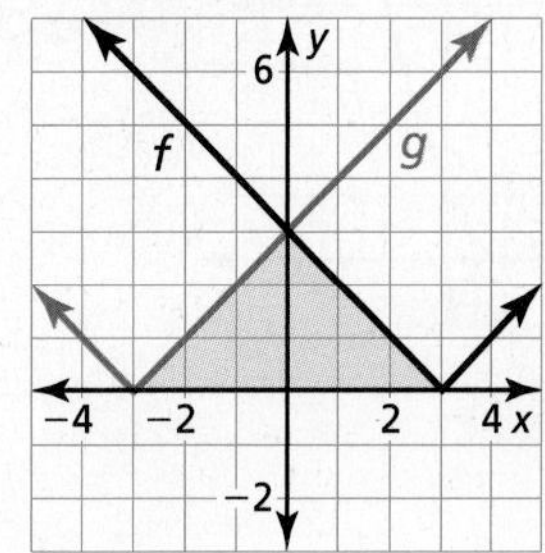

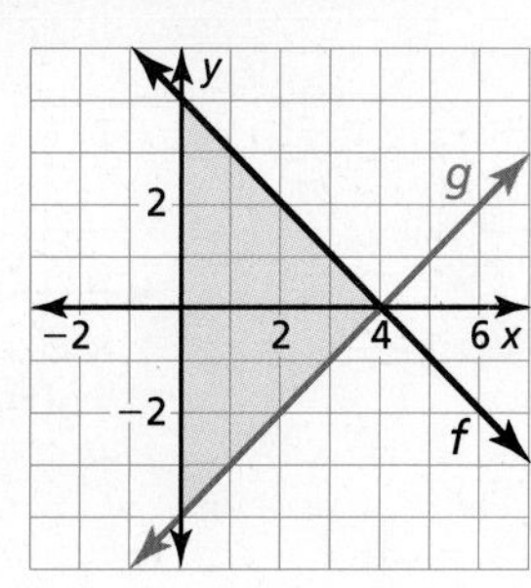

39. **MP REASONING** Describe the transformations of the graph of the parent absolute value function to obtain the graph of $g(x) = -4|x| + 2$. Explain your reasoning.

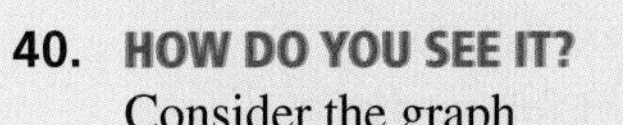

40. **HOW DO YOU SEE IT?** Consider the graph of $f(x) = mx + b$. Describe the effect each transformation has on the slope of the line and the intercepts of the graph.

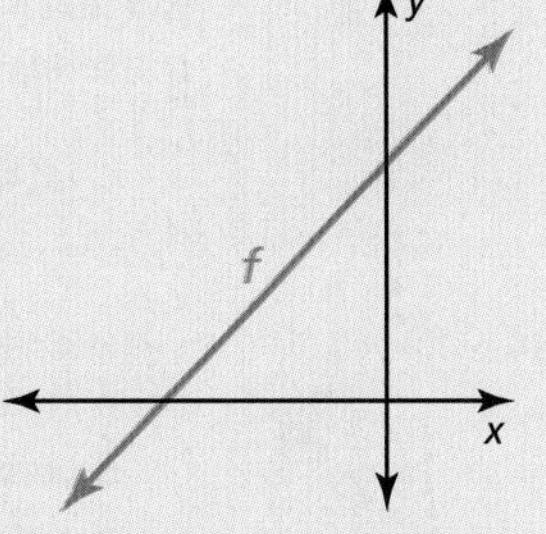

a. Reflect the graph of f in the y-axis.

b. Shrink the graph of f vertically by a factor of $\frac{1}{3}$.

c. Stretch the graph of f horizontally by a factor of 2.

41. **CRITICAL THINKING** Complete the function $g(x) = \square|x - \square| + \square$ so that g is a reflection in the x-axis followed by a translation one unit left and one unit up of the graph of $f(x) = 2|x - 2| + 1$. Explain your reasoning.

GO DIGITAL

42. **THOUGHT PROVOKING** Let $f(x) = a|x - h| + k$ and $g(x) = -|x - j| - \frac{k}{a}$, where a, h, j, and k are positive integers. Describe the transformations of the graph of f to the graph of g in terms of a, h, j, and k.

43. **DIG DEEPER** The functions $f(x) = mx + b$ and $g(x) = mx + c$ represent two parallel lines. Write an expression for the horizontal translation of the graph of f to the graph of g.

REVIEW & REFRESH

In Exercises 44 and 45, evaluate the function for the given value of x.

44. $f(x) = x + 4;\ x = 3$

45. $f(x) = -2x - 2;\ x = -1$

In Exercises 46 and 47, make a scatter plot of the data. Then describe the relationship between the data.

46.

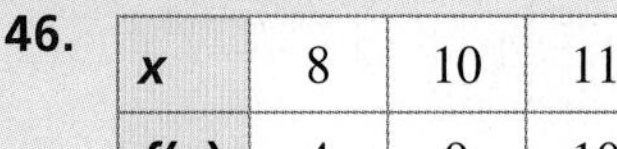

x	8	10	11	12	15
f(x)	4	9	10	12	12

47.

x	2	5	6	10	13
f(x)	22	13	15	12	6

48. Identify the function family to which g belongs. Compare the graph of the function to the graph of its parent function.

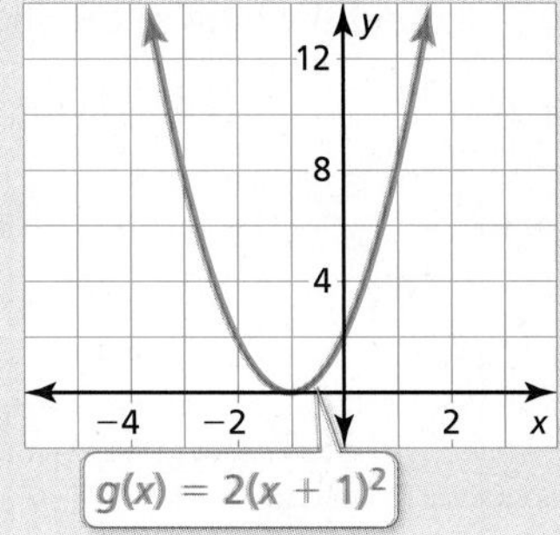

In Exercises 49–52, solve the system using any method. Explain your choice of method.

49. $3x - 2y = -15$
$4x + 2y = 8$

50. $y = \frac{2}{3}x - 4$
$y = \frac{4}{3}x + 2$

51. $x = -4y + 7$
$-2y + 3x = 9$

52. $2.5x - 2.5y = 10$
$-5x + 5y = -15$

53. **MODELING REAL LIFE** The function $f(x) = -1.5x + 50$ represents the amount (in pounds) of dog food in a bag after x days.

a. Graph the function and find its domain and range.

b. Interpret the slope and the intercepts of the graph.

In Exercises 54–57, graph the function. Compare the graph to the graph of $f(x) = x^2$.

54. $f(x) = \frac{3}{2}x^2$

55. $g(x) = -x^2 + 5$

56. $p(x) = 3(x - 1)^2$

57. $q(x) = -\frac{1}{2}(x + 4)^2 - 6$

In Exercises 58 and 59, write a function g whose graph represents the indicated transformations of the graph of f.

58. $f(x) = x$; translation 2 units down and a horizontal shrink by a factor of $\frac{2}{3}$

59. $f(x) = |x|$; reflection in the x-axis and a vertical stretch by a factor of 4 followed by a translation 7 units down and 1 unit right

1.3 Modeling with Linear Functions

Learning Target Use linear functions to model and analyze real-life situations.

Success Criteria
- I can write equations of linear functions.
- I can compare linear equations to solve real-life problems.
- I can determine a line of best fit.

EXPLORE IT! Modeling with Linear Functions

Work with a partner. A company purchases a demolition robot for $87,000. The spreadsheet shows how the robot depreciates over an 8-year period.

	A	B
1	Year, t	Value, V
2	0	$87,000
3	1	$79,750
4	2	$72,500
5	3	$65,250
6	4	$58,000
7	5	$50,750
8	6	$43,500
9	7	$36,250
10	8	$29,000
11		

a. Explain how you can write a linear function to represent the value V of the robot as a function of the number t of years.

b. Sketch a graph of the function. Explain why this type of depreciation is called *straight line depreciation*.

c. Interpret the slope and intercepts of the graph in the context of the problem.

d. MP **CHOOSE TOOLS** Use the Internet or another reference to find a real-life example of straight line depreciation. Then write a function that models the example you found and sketch its graph.

e. Describe a real-life situation that can be modeled by each graph below. Exchange situations with your partner and match each of your partner's situations with its corresponding graph. Explain your reasoning.

i.

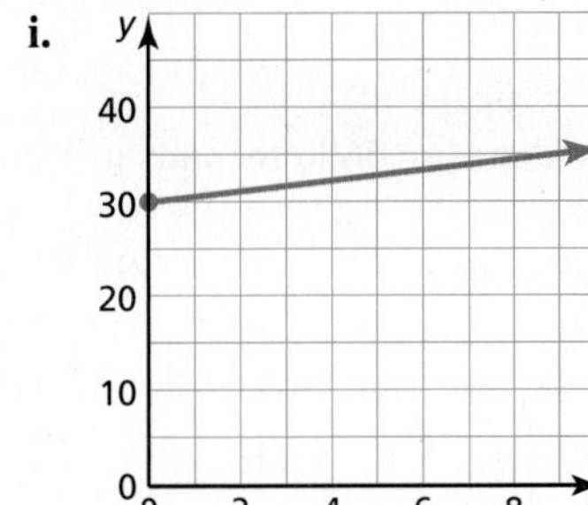

ii.

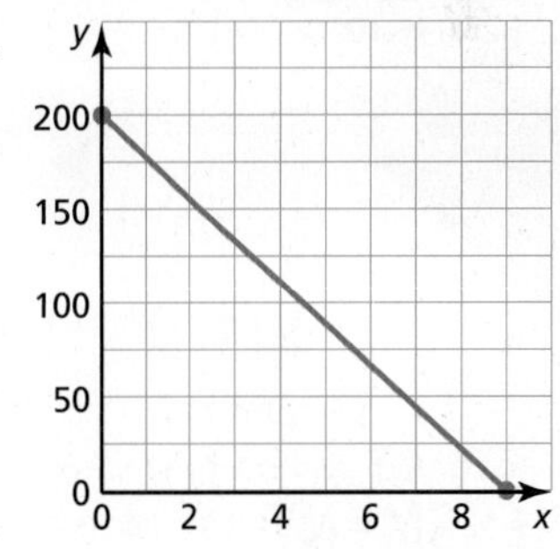

iii.

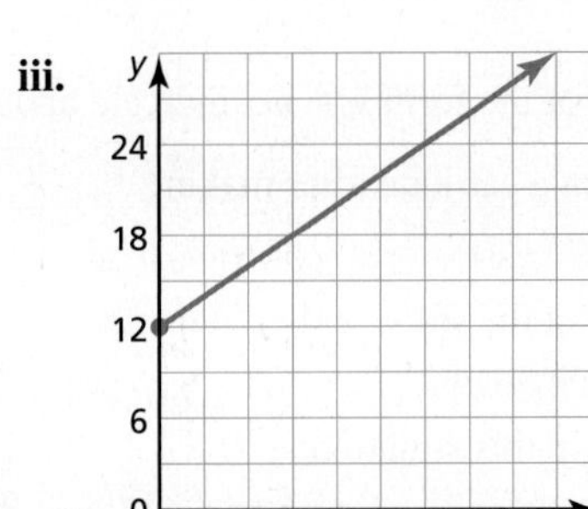

iv.

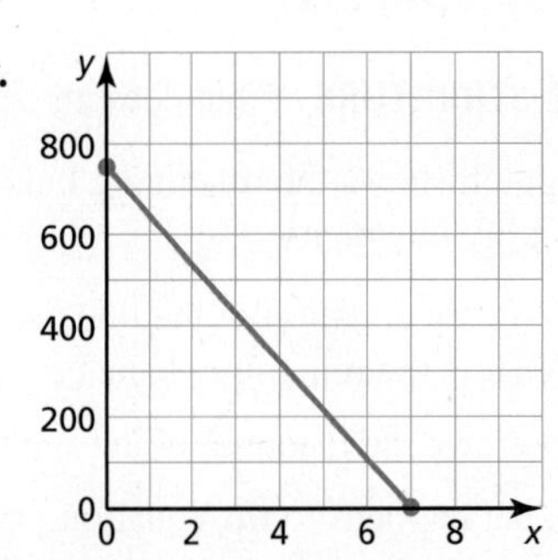

f. How can you use a linear function to model and analyze a real-life situation?

Math Practice

Label Axes

After matching a situation with its graph, label the axes to clarify their correspondence with the quantities in the situation.

Writing Linear Equations

Vocabulary 

line of fit, *p. 22*
line of best fit, *p. 23*
correlation coefficient, *p. 23*

KEY IDEA

Writing an Equation of a Line

Given slope m and y-intercept b	Use slope-intercept form: $y = mx + b$
Given slope m and a point (x_1, y_1)	Use point-slope form: $y - y_1 = m(x - x_1)$
Given points (x_1, y_1) and (x_2, y_2)	First use the slope formula to find m. Then use point-slope form with either given point.

Asteroid 2019 GC6 is about as large as a house. NASA and other international organizations are constantly scanning our skies for threats from space rocks.

EXAMPLE 1 Writing a Linear Equation from a Graph

The graph shows the distance Asteroid 2019 GC6 travels in x seconds. Write an equation of the line and interpret the slope. The asteroid came within 136,000 miles of Earth in April, 2019. About how long does it take the asteroid to travel that distance?

Asteroid 2019 GC6

Distance (miles); Time (seconds); (6, 21)

SOLUTION

From the graph, you can see the slope is $m = \frac{21}{6} = 3.5$ and the y-intercept is $b = 0$. Use slope-intercept form to write an equation of the line.

$y = mx + b$ Slope-intercept form

$= 3.5x + 0$ Substitute 3.5 for m and 0 for b.

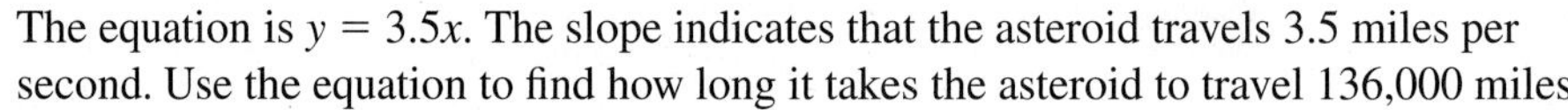

The equation is $y = 3.5x$. The slope indicates that the asteroid travels 3.5 miles per second. Use the equation to find how long it takes the asteroid to travel 136,000 miles.

$136{,}000 = 3.5x$ Substitute 136,000 for y.

$38{,}857 \approx x$ Divide each side by 3.5.

▶ Because there are 3600 seconds in 1 hour and

$$38{,}857 \text{ sec} \div \frac{3600 \text{ sec}}{1 \text{ h}} = 38{,}857 \cancel{\text{sec}} \times \frac{1 \text{ h}}{3600 \cancel{\text{sec}}} \approx 11 \text{ h},$$

it takes the asteroid about 11 hours to travel 136,000 miles.

SELF-ASSESSMENT

1 I do not understand. 2 I can do it with help. 3 I can do it on my own. 4 I can teach someone else.

1. **MP STRUCTURE** What does an equation of the form $y = mx$ indicate about x and y?

2. The graph shows the remaining balance y on a car loan after making x monthly payments.

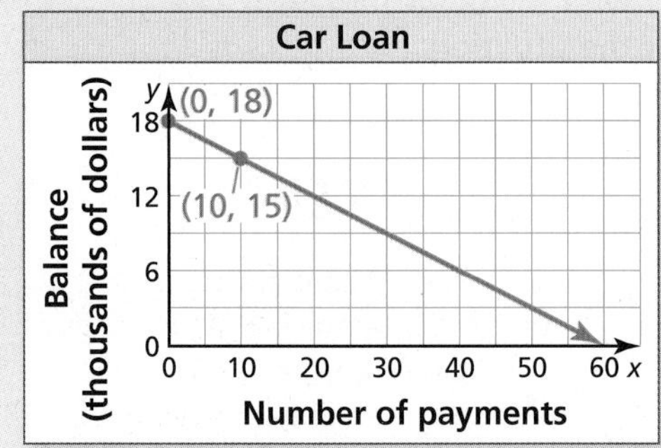

   a. Write an equation of the line and interpret the slope and y-intercept. What is the remaining balance after 36 payments?

   b. Interpret the meaning of the x-intercept in this situation.

   c. What happens to the equation you wrote in part (a) when the y-intercept remains the same and the x-intercept is changed to 72? What changed in the problem?

EXAMPLE 2 Comparing Linear Equations

Lakeside Inn	
Number of students, x	Total cost, y
100	\$1500
125	\$1800
150	\$2100
175	\$2400
200	\$2700

Two prom venues charge a rental fee plus a fee per student. The table shows the total costs (in dollars) for different numbers of students at Lakeside Inn. The total cost y (in dollars) for x students at Sunview Resort is represented by the equation

$y = 10x + 600.$ Sunview Resort

Which venue charges less per student? How many students must attend for the total costs to be the same?

SOLUTION

1. **Understand the Problem** You are given cost information for two venues. You need to compare the costs.
2. **Make a Plan** Compare the slopes to determine which venue charges less per student. Then write an equation that models the total cost at Lakeside Inn. Equate the cost expressions and solve to determine the number of students for which the total costs are equal.
3. **Solve and Check** The table shows a constant rate of change. Find the slope using any two points. Use $(x_1, y_1) = (100, 1500)$ and $(x_2, y_2) = (125, 1800)$.

$$m = \frac{y_2 - y_1}{x_2 - x_1} = \frac{1800 - 1500}{125 - 100} = \frac{300}{25} = 12$$

Comparing the slopes, Sunview Resort charges \$10 per student, which is less than the \$12 per student that Lakeside Inn charges.

Write an equation that represents the total cost at Lakeside Inn using the slope of 12 and a point from the table. Use $(x_1, y_1) = (100, 1500)$.

$y - y_1 = m(x - x_1)$ Point-slope form

$y - 1500 = 12(x - 100)$ Substitute for m, x_1, and y_1.

$y - 1500 = 12x - 1200$ Distributive Property

$y = 12x + 300$ Add 1500 to each side.

Equate the cost expressions and solve.

$10x + 600 = 12x + 300$ Set cost expressions equal.

$300 = 2x$ Combine like terms.

$150 = x$ Divide each side by 2.

▶ The total costs are the same when 150 students attend the prom.

Another Way
Another way to check your solution is to graph each cost equation and find the point of intersection. The x-value of the point of intersection is 150.

Check Notice that the table shows the total cost for 150 students at Lakeside Inn is \$2100. To check that your solution is correct, verify that the total cost at Sunview Resort is also \$2100 for 150 students.

$y = 10(150) + 600$ Substitute 150 for x.

$= 2100$ ✓ Simplify.

SELF-ASSESSMENT 1 I do not understand. 2 I can do it with help. 3 I can do it on my own. 4 I can teach someone else.

3. **WHAT IF?** Maple Ridge charges a rental fee plus a \$10 fee per student. The total cost is \$1900 for 140 students. Describe the number of students that must attend for the total cost at Maple Ridge to be less than the total costs at the other two venues. Use a graph to justify your answer.

Finding Lines of Fit and Lines of Best Fit

Data do not always show an *exact* linear relationship. When the data in a scatter plot show an approximately linear relationship, you can model the data with a **line of fit**.

KEY IDEA

Finding a Line of Fit

Step 1 Make a scatter plot of the data.

Step 2 Draw the line that most closely appears to follow the trend given by the data points. There should be about as many points above the line as below it.

Step 3 Choose two points on the line and estimate the coordinates of each point. These points do not have to be original data points.

Step 4 Write an equation of the line that passes through the two points from Step 3. This equation is a model for the data.

EXAMPLE 3 Finding a Line of Fit

Femur length (cm), x	Height (cm), y
40	170
45	183
32	151
50	195
37	162
41	174
30	141
34	151
47	185
45	182

The table shows the femur lengths (in centimeters) and heights (in centimeters) of several people. Do the data show a linear relationship? If so, write an equation of a line of fit and use it to estimate the height of a person whose femur is 35 centimeters long.

SOLUTION

Step 1 Make a scatter plot of the data. The data show a linear relationship.

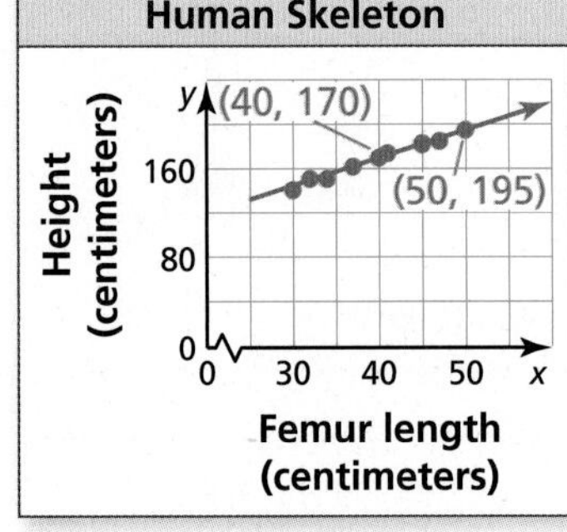

Step 2 Draw the line that most closely appears to fit the data. One possibility is shown.

Step 3 Choose two points on the line. For the line shown, you might choose (40, 170) and (50, 195).

Step 4 Write an equation of the line.

First, find the slope.

$$m = \frac{y_2 - y_1}{x_2 - x_1} = \frac{195 - 170}{50 - 40} = \frac{25}{10} = 2.5$$

Use point-slope form to write an equation. Use $(x_1, y_1) = (40, 170)$.

$y - y_1 = m(x - x_1)$	Point-slope form
$y - 170 = 2.5(x - 40)$	Substitute for m, x_1, and y_1.
$y - 170 = 2.5x - 100$	Distributive Property
$y = 2.5x + 70$	Add 170 to each side.

Use the equation to estimate the height of a person whose femur is 35 centimeters long.

$y = 2.5(35) + 70$	Substitute 35 for x.
$= 157.5$	Simplify.

▶ The approximate height of a person whose femur is 35 centimeters long is 157.5 centimeters.

The **line of best fit** is the line that best models a set of data and lies as close as possible to all of the data points. Many technology tools have a *linear regression* feature that you can use to find the line of best fit for a set of data.

The **correlation coefficient**, denoted by r, is a number that ranges from -1 to 1. When r is near 1, there is a strong positive correlation and the points lie close to a line with a positive slope. When r is near -1, there is a strong negative correlation and the points lie close to a line with a negative slope. As r gets closer to 0, the correlation becomes weaker.

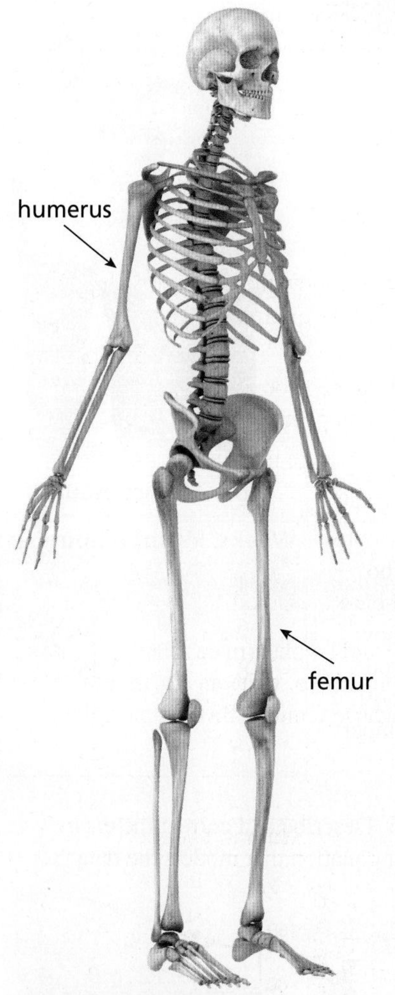

EXAMPLE 4 Finding a Line of Best Fit Using Technology

Use technology to find an equation of the line of best fit for the data in Example 3. Estimate the height of a person whose femur is 35 centimeters long. Compare this height to your estimate in Example 3.

SOLUTION

Step 1 Enter the data into two lists.

x	y
40	170
45	183
32	151
50	195
37	162
41	174
30	141

Step 2 Find an equation of the line of best fit. The values in the equation can be rounded to obtain $y = 2.6x + 65$.

$y = mx + b$

PARAMETERS

$m = 2.6036$ $b = 64.9968$

STATISTICS

$r^2 = 0.9891$

$r = 0.9945$

The value of r is close to 1.

Step 3 Graph the regression equation with the data.

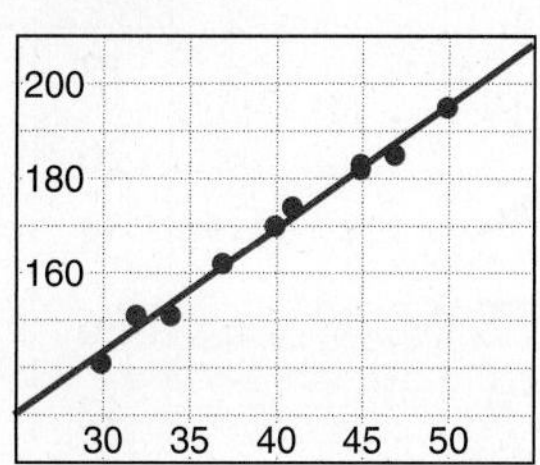

Step 4 Find the value of y when $x = 35$.

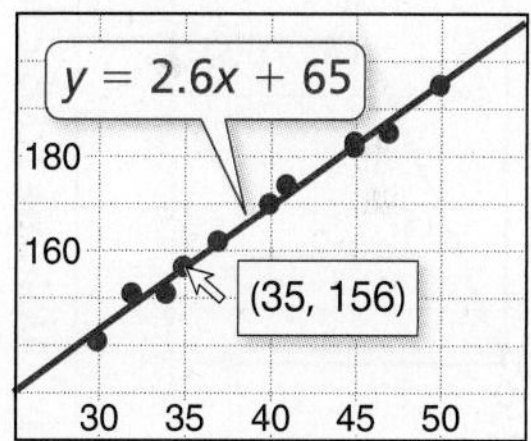

▶ The height of a person with a 35-centimeter femur is about 156 centimeters. This is less than the estimate of 157.5 centimeters found in Example 3.

Math Practice

Analyze Givens

How can you determine appropriate scales for your graph?

SELF-ASSESSMENT

1 I do not understand. 2 I can do it with help. 3 I can do it on my own. 4 I can teach someone else.

4. **VOCABULARY** A line of best fit has a correlation coefficient of -0.98. What can you conclude about the slope of the line?

5. The data pairs (x, y) represent the humerus lengths x (in centimeters) and heights y (in centimeters) of several females.

   (33, 166), (25, 142), (22, 130), (30, 154), (28, 152), (32, 159), (26, 141), (27, 145)

   a. Do the data show a linear relationship? If so, write an equation of a line of fit and use it to estimate the height of a female whose humerus is 40 centimeters long.

   b. Use technology to find an equation of the line of best fit for the data. Estimate the height of a female whose humerus is 40 centimeters long. Compare this height to your estimate in part (a).

1.3 Practice WITH CalcChat® AND CalcView®

In Exercises 1–6, use the graph to write an equation of the line and interpret the slope. *Example 1*

1.

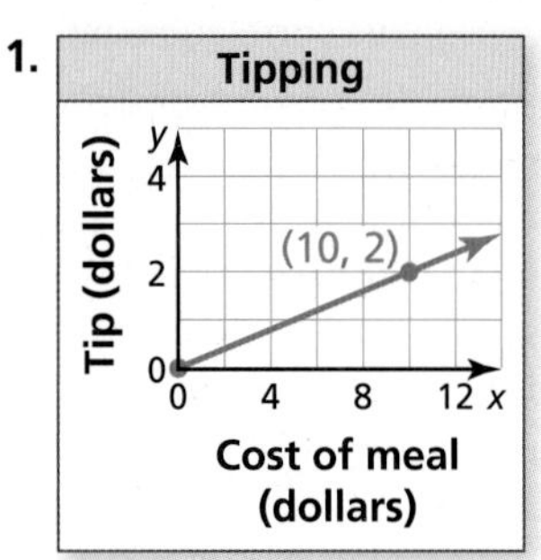

2.

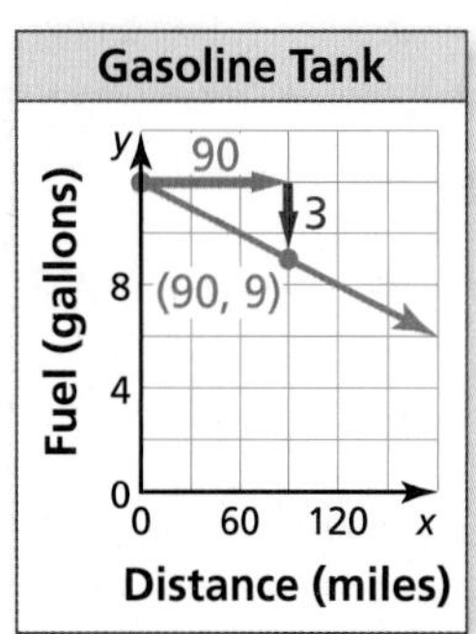

3.

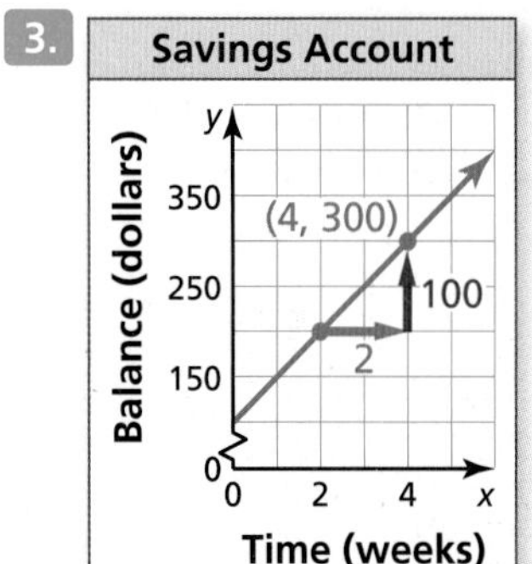

4.

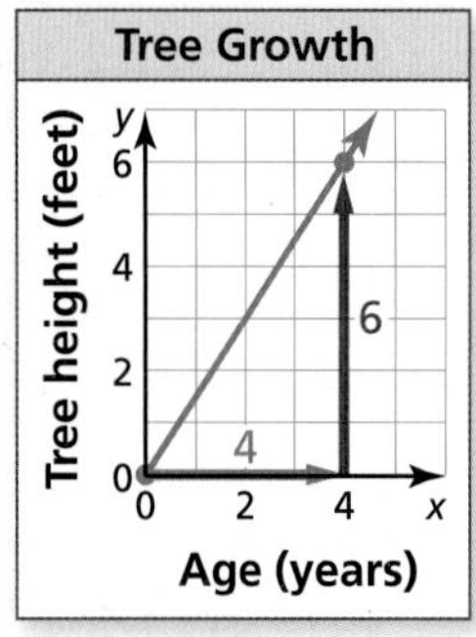

5.

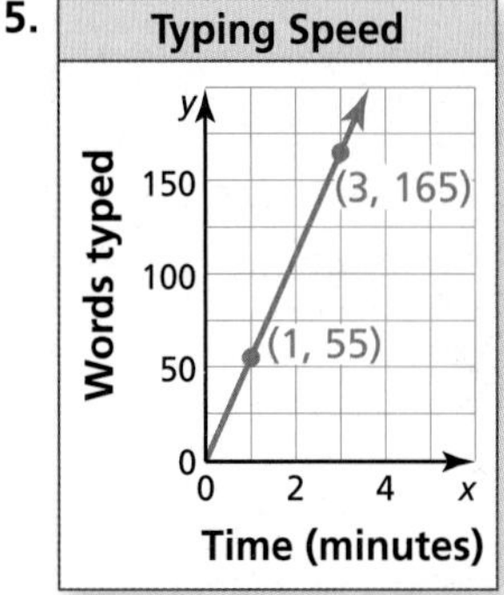

6.

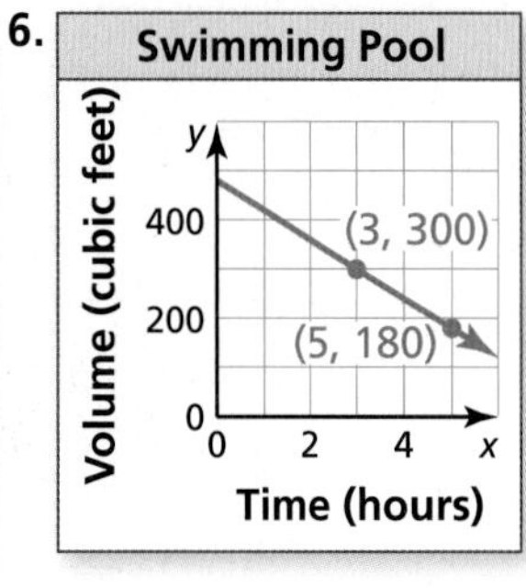

7. MODELING REAL LIFE You consider buying a phone from one of two cell phone carriers. The table shows the total costs (in dollars) of the phone and service for different numbers of months at Carrier A. The total cost y (in dollars) of the phone and x months of service at Carrier B is represented by the equation $y = 55x + 300$. Which carrier charges less per month? After how many months of service are the total costs the same? *Example 2*

Carrier A	
Months, x	**Total cost, y**
3	\$500
6	\$650
9	\$800
12	\$950
15	\$1100

8. MODELING REAL LIFE You and a friend sign up for a new volunteer project to increase your service hours. The table shows your total numbers of service hours after different numbers of weeks on the new project. Your friend initially has 8 service hours and spends 2 hours on the new project each week. Who initially has more service hours? Who volunteers more hours per week? After how many weeks do you and your friend have the same total number of service hours?

Your Service Hours	
Weeks, x	**Total hours, y**
4	15
6	20
8	25
10	30
12	35

9. ERROR ANALYSIS Describe and correct the error in writing a linear equation that models the data in the table.

x	y
12	17
20	23
28	29
36	35
42	41

✗

$$m = \frac{20-12}{23-17} = \frac{8}{6} = \frac{4}{3}$$

$$y - 17 = \frac{4}{3}(x - 12)$$

$$y - 17 = \frac{4}{3}x - 16$$

$$y = \frac{4}{3}x + 1$$

10. MP PROBLEM SOLVING You notice that temperatures in Canada are reported in degrees Celsius. You know there is a linear relationship between degrees Fahrenheit and degrees Celsius, but you forget the formula. From science class, you remember the freezing point of water is 0°C or 32°F, and its boiling point is 100°C or 212°F.

a. Write an equation that represents degrees Fahrenheit in terms of degrees Celsius.

b. A forecast for Toronto shows a high of 15°C. What is this temperature in degrees Fahrenheit?

c. Rewrite your equation in part (a) to represent degrees Celsius in terms of degrees Fahrenheit.

d. A forecast for your city shows a high of 68°F. What is this temperature in degrees Celsius?

In Exercises 11–14, determine whether the data show a linear relationship. If so, write an equation of a line of fit. Then estimate y when $x = 15$ and explain its meaning in the context of the situation. *Example 3*

11.

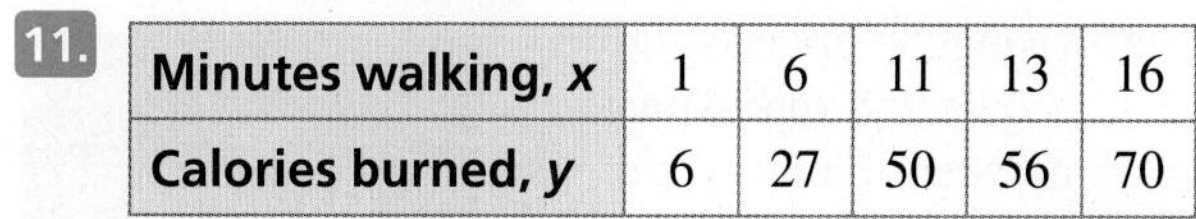

Minutes walking, x	1	6	11	13	16
Calories burned, y	6	27	50	56	70

12.

Months, x	9	13	18	22	23
Hair length (in.), y	3	5	7	10	11

13.

Hours, x	3	7	9	17	20
Battery life (%), y	86	61	50	26	0

14.

Shoe size, x	6	8	8.5	10	13
Heart rate (bpm), y	112	94	100	132	87

15. **MODELING REAL LIFE** The data pairs (x, y) represent the average annual tuition and fees y (in dollars) for private nonprofit colleges and universities in the United States x years after the 2012-2013 academic year. Use technology to find an equation of the line of best fit. Interpret the slope and y-intercept in this situation. Estimate the average annual tuition in the 2022-2023 academic year. *Example 4*

(0, 31,890), (1, 32,500), (2, 33,090), (3, 34,150)
(4, 35,080), (5, 35,720), (6, 35,830)

16. **MODELING REAL LIFE** The table shows the numbers y (in billions) of active users on a social media site x years after 2009. Use technology to find an equation of the line of best fit. Interpret the slope and y-intercept in this situation. Estimate the number of active users on the site in 2022.

Years after 2009, x	Active users, y
0	0.36
1	0.61
3	1.06
5	1.39
7	1.86
8	2.13
9	2.32

MP USING TOOLS In Exercises 17–20, use technology to find an equation of the line of best fit for the data. Identify and interpret the correlation coefficient.

17.

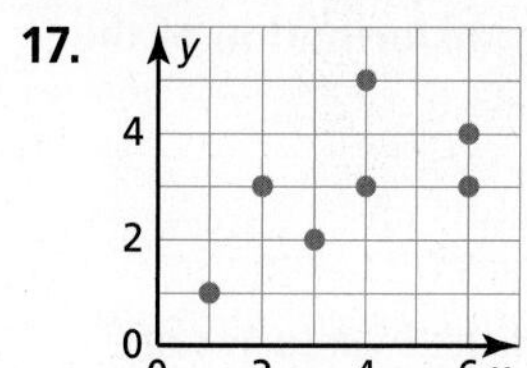

18.

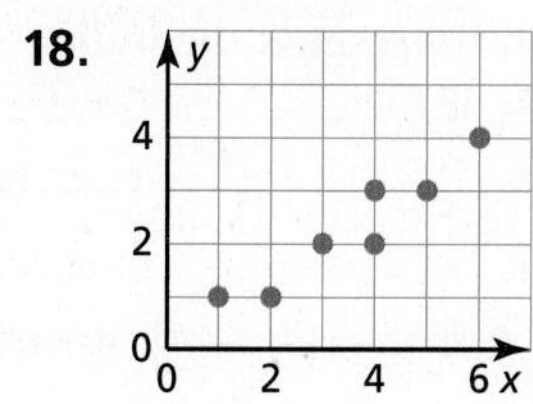

19.

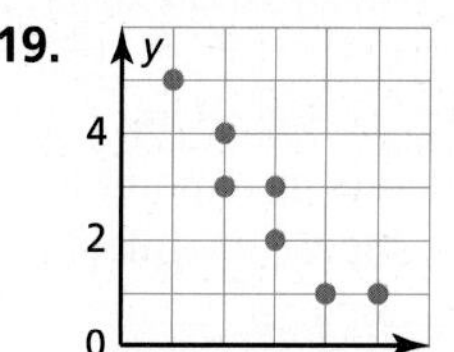

20.

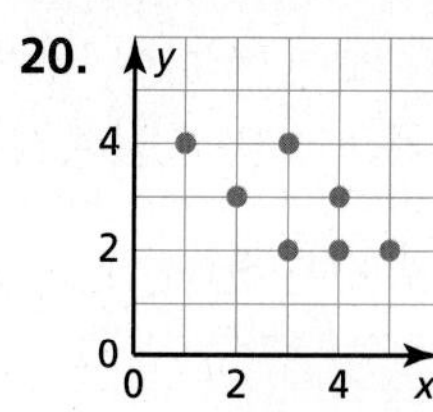

21. **MP REASONING** The table shows the numbers of tickets sold for a concert when different prices are charged. Write an equation of a line of fit for the data. Does it seem reasonable to use your model to predict the number of tickets sold when the ticket price is \$85? Explain.

Ticket price (dollars), x	17	20	22	26
Tickets sold, y	450	423	400	395

22. **HOW DO YOU SEE IT?**
You secure an interest-free loan to purchase a boat. You agree to make equal monthly payments for the next two years. The graph shows the amount of money you still owe.

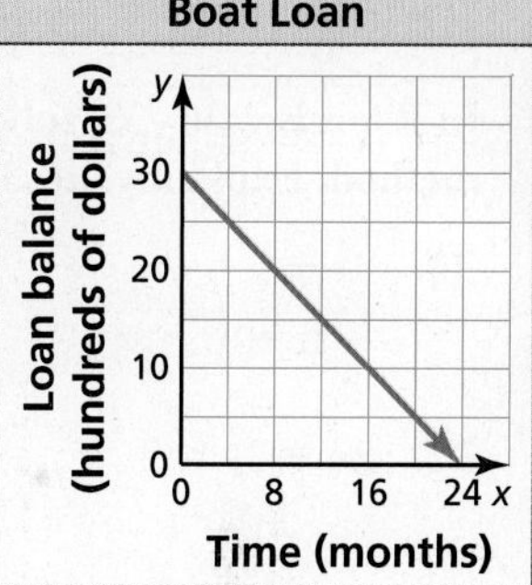

a. What is the slope of the line? What does the slope represent?

b. What is the domain and range of the function? What does each represent?

c. How much do you still owe after making payments for 12 months?

23. **OPEN-ENDED** Give two real-life quantities that have (a) a positive correlation, (b) a negative correlation, and (c) approximately no correlation. Explain.

24. **MAKING AN ARGUMENT** A set of data pairs has a correlation coefficient $r = 0.3$. Your friend says that because the correlation coefficient is positive, it is logical to use the line of best fit to make predictions. Is your friend correct? Explain your reasoning.

25. **COLLEGE PREP** Which equation has a graph that is a line passing through the point $(8, -5)$ and is perpendicular to the graph of $y = -4x + 1$?

Ⓐ $y = \frac{1}{4}x - 5$ Ⓑ $y = -4x + 27$

Ⓒ $y = -\frac{1}{4}x - 7$ Ⓓ $y = \frac{1}{4}x - 7$

26. THOUGHT PROVOKING
Points A and B lie on the line $y = -x + 4$. Point C is the same distance from point A as it is from point B but does not lie on the same line. Choose coordinates for points A, B, and C. Write equations for the lines connecting points A and C and points B and C.

27. ABSTRACT REASONING If x and y have a strong positive correlation, and y and z have a strong negative correlation, then what can you conclude about the correlation between x and z? Explain.

28. ANALYZING RELATIONSHIPS Data show a positive correlation between the attendance at a local beach and the attendance at a local amusement park.

a. Does a positive correlation make sense in this situation? Explain.

b. Is it reasonable to conclude that an increase in attendance at the beach will cause an increase in attendance at the amusement park? Explain.

29. PERFORMANCE TASK Your family wants to purchase a new vehicle that comes in either a gasoline model or an electric model.

a. Using the information shown, the approximate number of miles your family drives per year, and gas and electricity prices in your area, determine which vehicle is a better buy. Use linear equations to support your answer.

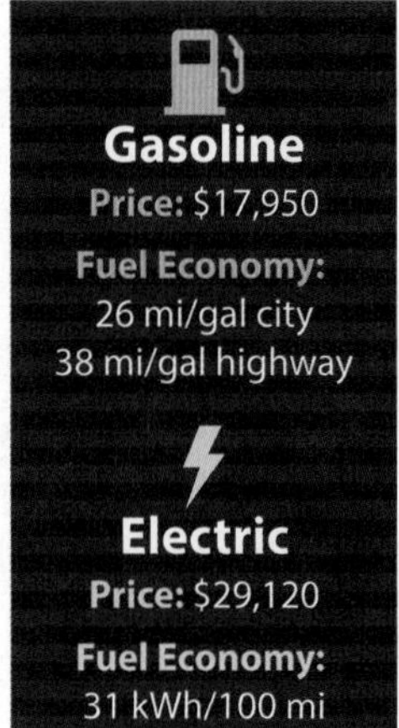

b. Research other factors that impact the cost of vehicle ownership. How might these factors support or change your answer?

REVIEW & REFRESH

WATCH

In Exercises 30–33, solve the system using any method. Explain your choice of method.

30. $3x + y = 7$
$-2x - y = 9$

31. $4x - 6y = 2$
$2x - 3y = 1$

32. $2x + 2y = 3$
$x = 4y - 1$

33. $y = x - 4$
$y = -4x + 6$

34. Write a system of inequalities represented by the graph.

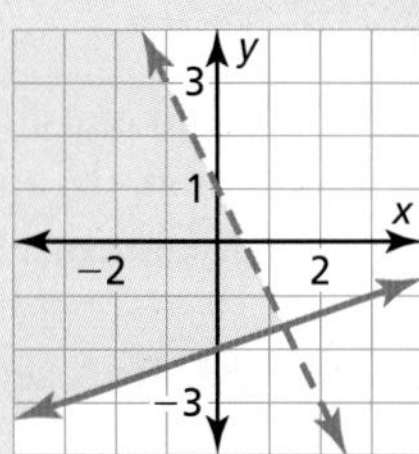

35. Solve the literal equation $z = 4y + 2x + 8$ for x.

36. What percent of 25 is 14?

In Exercises 37–40, graph the function and its parent function. Then describe the transformation.

37. $f(x) = \frac{3}{2}$

38. $f(x) = 3x$

39. $f(x) = 2(x - 1)^2$

40. $f(x) = -|x + 2| - 7$

In Exercises 41 and 42, find the sum or difference.

41. $(x^2 + 2x + 16) + (4x^2 - 7x - 18)$

42. $(-5n^3 + n^2 - 12n) - (6n^2 + 4n - 13)$

43. MODELING REAL LIFE Two internet service providers charge an installation fee plus a monthly service fee. The table shows the total costs (in dollars) for different numbers of months at Company A. The total cost y (in dollars) for x months of service at Company B is represented by $y = 45x + 50$. Which company charges less per month? After how many months of service are the total costs the same?

Company A	
Months, x	Total cost, y
2	\$180
3	\$220
4	\$260
5	\$300
6	\$340

44. What number is 34% of 50?

In Exercises 45 and 46, write a function g whose graph represents the indicated transformation of the graph of f.

45. $f(x) = 2x + 1$; translation 3 units up

46. $f(x) = -3|x - 4|$; vertical shrink by a factor of $\frac{1}{2}$

1.4 Solving Linear Systems

Learning Target Solve linear systems in three variables.

Success Criteria
- I can visualize solutions of linear systems in three variables.
- I can solve linear systems in three variables algebraically.
- I can solve real-life problems using systems of equations in three variables.

EXPLORE IT! Solving Three-Variable Systems

Work with a partner. Consider the system shown.

$$y = 4x \qquad \text{Equation 1}$$
$$x + 2y - z = 7 \qquad \text{Equation 2}$$
$$3x - 4y + 2z = -9 \qquad \text{Equation 3}$$

a. How is this linear system different from linear systems you have solved in previous courses?

b. Explain a method you can use to solve the system. Solve the system and show how you can represent the solution.

c. The graph of each equation in the system is a plane in three-dimensional space. A three-dimensional coordinate system is shown below. How can the solution of this system be represented in the graph?

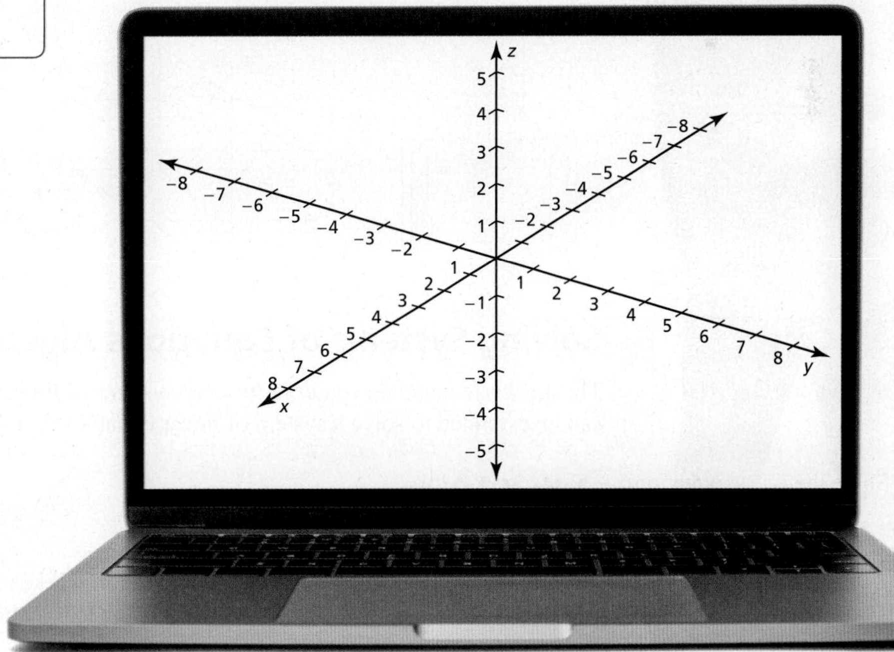

d. Can a linear system in three variables have no solution? infinitely many solutions? If so, sketch an example of what each type of solution might look like in three-dimensional space. Explain your reasoning.

Math Practice

Use Prior Results
How can you use previously established methods of solving linear systems to help you solve systems with three variables?

Visualizing Solutions of Systems

GO DIGITAL

A **linear equation in three variables** x, y, and z is an equation of the form $ax + by + cz = d$, where a, b, and c are not all zero.

Vocabulary

linear equation in three variables, *p. 28*
system of three linear equations, *p. 28*
solution of a system of three linear equations, *p. 28*
ordered triple, *p. 28*

Here is an example of a **system of three linear equations** in three variables.

$3x + 4y - 8z = -3$ Equation 1

$x + y + 5z = -12$ Equation 2

$4x - 2y + z = 10$ Equation 3

A **solution** of such a system is an **ordered triple** (x, y, z) whose coordinates make each equation true.

The graph of a linear equation in three variables is a plane in three-dimensional space. The graphs of three such equations that form a system are three planes whose intersection determines the number of solutions of the system.

Exactly One Solution

The planes intersect in a single point, which is the solution of the system.

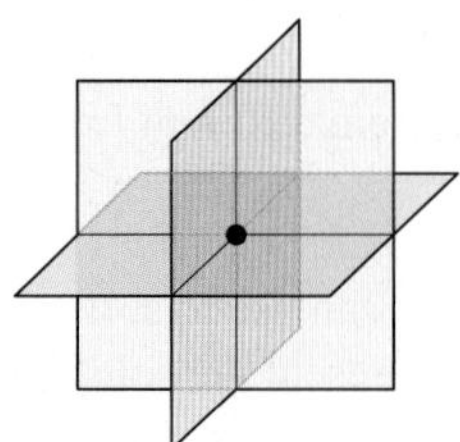

Infinitely Many Solutions

The planes intersect in a line. Every point on the line is a solution of the system.

The planes can also be the same plane. Every point in the plane is a solution of the system.

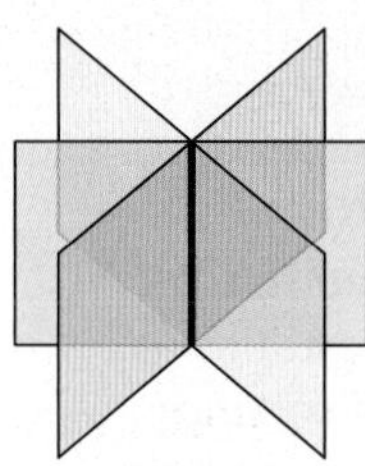

No Solution

There are no points in common with all three planes.

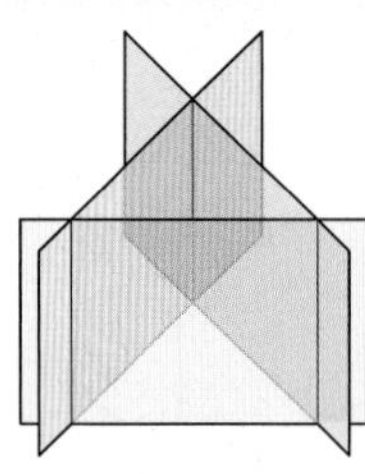

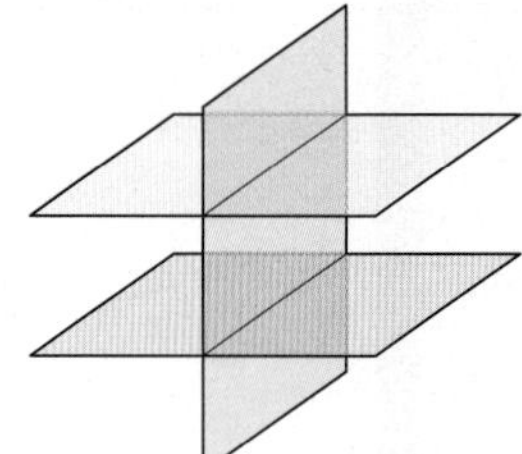

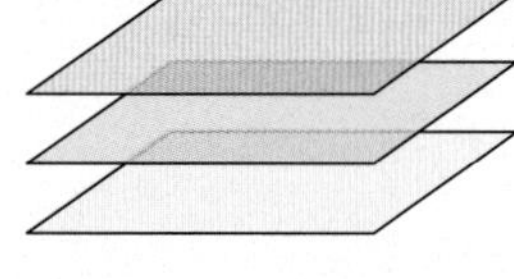

Solving Systems of Equations Algebraically

The algebraic methods you used to solve systems of linear equations in two variables can be extended to solve a system of linear equations in three variables.

KEY IDEA

Solving a Three-Variable System

Step 1 Rewrite the linear system in three variables as a linear system in two variables by using the substitution or elimination method.

Step 2 Solve the new linear system for both of its variables.

Step 3 Substitute the values found in Step 2 into one of the original equations and solve for the remaining variable.

When you obtain a false equation, such as $0 = 1$, in any of the steps, the system has *no solution*. When you do not obtain a false equation, but obtain an identity such as $0 = 0$, the system has *infinitely many solutions*.

EXAMPLE 1 Solving a Three-Variable System (One Solution)

WATCH

Math Practice

Look for Structure

Why is y a convenient variable to eliminate? Are any other variables convenient to eliminate? Explain.

Solve the system.

$4x + 2y + 3z = 12$ Equation 1

$2x - 3y + 5z = -7$ Equation 2

$6x - y + 4z = -3$ Equation 3

SOLUTION

Step 1 Rewrite the system as a linear system in *two* variables.

$$\begin{array}{rl} 4x + 2y + 3z = 12 & \\ \underline{12x - 2y + 8z = -6} & \text{Add 2 times Equation 3 to Equation 1 (to eliminate } y\text{).} \\ 16x + 11z = 6 & \text{New Equation 1} \end{array}$$

$$\begin{array}{rl} 2x - 3y + 5z = -7 & \\ \underline{-18x + 3y - 12z = 9} & \text{Add } -3 \text{ times Equation 3 to Equation 2 (to eliminate } y\text{).} \\ -16x - 7z = 2 & \text{New Equation 2} \end{array}$$

Step 2 Solve the new linear system for both of its variables.

$$\begin{array}{rl} 16x + 11z = 6 & \text{Add new Equation 1 and new Equation 2.} \\ \underline{-16x - 7z = 2} & \\ 4z = 8 & \\ z = 2 & \text{Solve for } z. \\ x = -1 & \text{Substitute into new Equation 1 or 2 to find } x. \end{array}$$

Step 3 Substitute $x = -1$ and $z = 2$ into an original equation and solve for y.

$$\begin{array}{rl} 6x - y + 4z = -3 & \text{Write original Equation 3.} \\ 6(-1) - y + 4(2) = -3 & \text{Substitute } -1 \text{ for } x \text{ and 2 for } z. \\ y = 5 & \text{Solve for } y. \end{array}$$

▶ The solution is $x = -1$, $y = 5$, and $z = 2$, or the ordered triple $(-1, 5, 2)$.

Check

Equation 1	Equation 2	Equation 3
$4x + 2y + 3z = 12$	$2x - 3y + 5z = -7$	$6x - y + 4z = -3$
$4(-1) + 2(5) + 3(2) \stackrel{?}{=} 12$	$2(-1) - 3(5) + 5(2) \stackrel{?}{=} -7$	$6(-1) - 5 + 4(2) \stackrel{?}{=} -3$
$12 = 12$ ✓	$-7 = -7$ ✓	$-3 = -3$ ✓

SELF-ASSESSMENT

1 I do not understand. 2 I can do it with help. 3 I can do it on my own. 4 I can teach someone else.

1. **VOCABULARY** Describe two different ways you can represent the solution of a system of three linear equations in three variables.

Solve the system. Check your solution.

2. $x - 2y + z = -11$
   $3x + 2y - z = 7$
   $-x + 2y + 4z = -9$

3. $5x - 3y + 2z = 18$
   $-2x + 4y - z = -11$
   $-3x - 2y + 3z = 14$

4. $5x + 2y - 4z = -6$
   $4x - 3y + 2z = 20$
   $-x + 4y + 6z = 8$

EXAMPLE 2 Solving a Three-Variable System (No Solution)

Solve the system.

$x + y + z = 2$ Equation 1
$5x + 5y + 5z = 3$ Equation 2
$4x + y - 3z = -6$ Equation 3

SOLUTION

Rewrite the system as a linear system in *two* variables.

$$\begin{array}{r} -5x - 5y - 5z = -10 \\ \underline{5x + 5y + 5z = 3} \\ 0 = -7 \end{array}$$

Add −5 times Equation 1 to Equation 2.

▶ Because you obtain a false equation, the original system has no solution.

EXAMPLE 3 Solving a Three-Variable System (Many Solutions)

Solve the system.

$x - y + z = -3$ Equation 1
$x - y - z = -3$ Equation 2
$5x - 5y + z = -15$ Equation 3

SOLUTION

ANOTHER WAY

Subtracting Equation 2 from Equation 1 gives $z = 0$. After substituting 0 for z in each equation, you can see that each is equivalent to $y = x + 3$.

Step 1 Rewrite the system as a linear system in *two* variables.

$$\begin{array}{r} x - y + z = -3 \\ \underline{x - y - z = -3} \\ 2x - 2y = -6 \end{array}$$

Add Equation 1 to Equation 2 (to eliminate z).

New Equation 2

$$\begin{array}{r} x - y - z = -3 \\ \underline{5x - 5y + z = -15} \\ 6x - 6y = -18 \end{array}$$

Add Equation 2 to Equation 3 (to eliminate z).

New Equation 3

Step 2 Solve the new linear system for both of its variables.

$$\begin{array}{r} -6x + 6y = 18 \\ \underline{6x - 6y = -18} \\ 0 = 0 \end{array}$$

Add −3 times new Equation 2 to new Equation 3.

Because you obtain the identity $0 = 0$, the system has infinitely many solutions.

Step 3 Describe the solutions of the system using an ordered triple. One way to do this is to solve new Equation 2 for y to obtain $y = x + 3$. Then substitute $x + 3$ for y in original Equation 1 to obtain $z = 0$.

▶ So, any ordered triple of the form $(x, x + 3, 0)$ is a solution of the system.

SELF-ASSESSMENT

1 I do not understand. 2 I can do it with help. 3 I can do it on my own. 4 I can teach someone else.

Solve the system. Check your solution, if possible.

5. $x + y - z = -1$
$4x + 4y - 4z = -2$
$3x + 2y + z = 0$

6. $-2x - 6y - 3z = 15$
$3x + 9y - 3z = 0$
$4x - 2y - 5z = 3$

7. $x + y + z = 8$
$x - y + z = 8$
$2x + y + 2z = 16$

8. Describe the solutions of the system in Example 3 using an ordered triple in terms of y.

Solving Real-Life Problems

EXAMPLE 4 Modeling Real Life

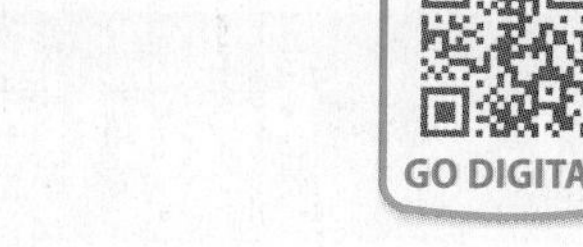

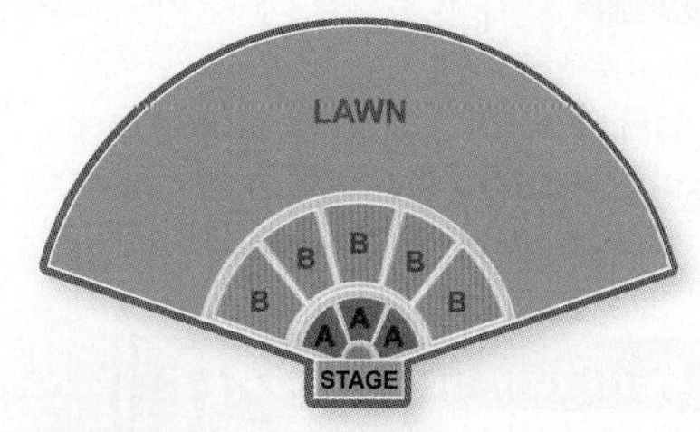

An amphitheater charges \$75 for each seat in Section A, \$55 for each seat in Section B, and \$30 for each lawn seat. There are three times as many seats in Section B as in Section A. The revenue from selling all 23,000 seats is \$870,000. How many seats are in each section of the amphitheater?

SOLUTION

Step 1 Write a verbal model for the situation.

Number of seats in B, y = 3 • Number of seats in A, x

Number of seats in A, x + Number of seats in B, y + Number of lawn seats, z = Total number of seats

75 • Number of seats in A, x + 55 • Number of seats in B, y + 30 • Number of lawn seats, z = Total revenue

Step 2 Write a system of equations.

$y = 3x$	Equation 1
$x + y + z = 23{,}000$	Equation 2
$75x + 55y + 30z = 870{,}000$	Equation 3

Step 3 Rewrite the system in Step 2 as a linear system in *two* variables by substituting $3x$ for y in Equations 2 and 3.

$x + y + z = 23{,}000$	Write Equation 2.
$x + 3x + z = 23{,}000$	Substitute $3x$ for y.
$4x + z = 23{,}000$	New Equation 2
$75x + 55y + 30z = 870{,}000$	Write Equation 3.
$75x + 55(3x) + 30z = 870{,}000$	Substitute $3x$ for y.
$240x + 30z = 870{,}000$	New Equation 3

Step 4 Solve the new linear system for both of its variables.

$$\begin{aligned} -120x - 30z &= -690{,}000 \\ 240x + 30z &= 870{,}000 \end{aligned}$$

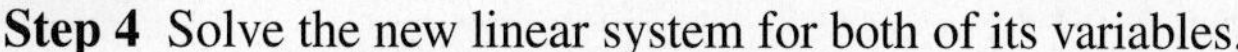

Add -30 times new Equation 2 to new Equation 3.

$$120x = 180{,}000$$

$x = 1500$	Solve for x.
$y = 4500$	Substitute into Equation 1 to find y.
$z = 17{,}000$	Substitute into Equation 2 to find z.

STUDY TIP

When substituting to find values of other variables, choose the equations that are easiest to use.

▶ The solution is $x = 1500$, $y = 4500$, and $z = 17{,}000$, or (1500, 4500, 17,000). So, there are 1500 seats in Section A, 4500 seats in Section B, and 17,000 lawn seats.

SELF-ASSESSMENT

1 I do not understand. 2 I can do it with help. 3 I can do it on my own. 4 I can teach someone else.

9. **MP REASONING** Another concert is held in the amphitheater. On the first day, 10,000 tickets are sold for \$356,000. On the second day, 7640 tickets are sold for \$284,300. How many seats remain in each section after the first two days of ticket sales when equal numbers of tickets for Sections A and B are sold on the first day, and twice as many tickets are sold for Section B as for Section A on the second day?

1.4 Practice WITH CalcChat® AND CalcView®

In Exercises 1–12, solve the system using the elimination method. *Examples 1, 2, and 3*

1. $x + y - 2z = 5$
$-x + 2y + z = 2$
$2x + 3y - z = 9$

2. $x + 4y - 6z = -1$
$2x - y + 2z = -7$
$-x + 2y - 4z = 5$

3. $3x - y + 2z = 4$
$6x - 2y + 4z = -8$
$2x - y + 3z = 10$

4. $5x + y - z = 6$
$x + y + z = 2$
$12x + 4y = 10$

5. $2x + y - z = 9$
$-x + 6y + 2z = -17$
$5x + 7y + z = 4$

6. $3x + 2y - z = 8$
$-3x + 4y + 5z = -14$
$x - 3y + 4z = -14$

7. $x + 3y - z = 2$
$x + y - z = 0$
$3x + 2y - 3z = -1$

8. $x + 2y - z = 3$
$-2x - y + z = -1$
$6x - 3y - z = -7$

9. $2x + 2y + 5z = 6$
$2x - y + z = 2$
$2x + 4y - 3z = 14$

10. $-2x - 3y + z = -6$
$x + y - z = 5$
$7x + 8y - 6z = 31$

11. $x + 2y + 3z = 4$
$-3x + 2y - z = 12$
$-2x - 2y - 4z = -14$

12. $3x + 2y - 3z = -2$
$7x - 2y + 5z = -14$
$2x + 4y + z = 6$

ERROR ANALYSIS In Exercises 13 and 14, describe and correct the error in the first step of solving the system of linear equations.

$4x - y + 2z = -18$
$-x + 2y + z = 11$
$3x + 3y - 4z = 44$

13.

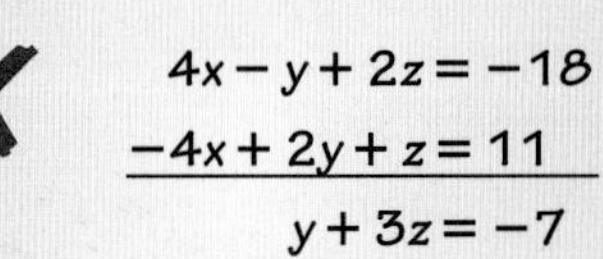

14.

✗
$12x - 3y + 6z = -18$
$3x + 3y - 4z = 44$
$15x + 2z = 26$

15. MODELING REAL LIFE Three orders are placed at a pizza shop. Two small pizzas, a liter of soda, and a salad cost \$14; one small pizza, a liter of soda, and three salads cost \$15; and three small pizzas, a liter of soda, and two salads cost \$22. How much does each item cost?

16. MODELING REAL LIFE Sam's Furniture Store places the following advertisement in the local newspaper. What is the price of each piece of furniture?

In Exercises 17–26, solve the system of linear equations using the substitution method. *Example 4*

17. $2x - 3y + z = 10$
$y + 2z = 13$
$z = 5$

18. $x = 4$
$x + y = -6$
$4x - 3y + 2z = 26$

19. $y = 2x - 6z + 1$
$3x + 2y + 5z = 16$
$7x + 3y - 4z = 11$

20. $-x + 5y + 3z = 2$
$x = 6y + 2z - 8$
$3x - 2y - 4z = 18$

21. $x + y + z = 4$
$5x + 5y + 5z = 12$
$x - 4y + z = 9$

22. $x + 2y = -1$
$-x + 3y + 2z = -4$
$-x + y - 4z = 10$

23. $x + y - z = 4$
$3x + 2y + 4z = 17$
$-x + 5y + z = 8$

24. $2x - y - z = 15$
$4x + 5y + 2z = 10$
$-x - 4y + 3z = -20$

25. $4x + y + 5z = 5$
$8x + 2y + 10z = 10$
$x - y - 2z = -2$

26. $x + 2y - z = 3$
$2x + 4y - 2z = 6$
$-x - 2y + z = -6$

27. MODELING REAL LIFE The results of a track meet are described in the article below. How many athletes from Lawrence High finished in each place?

Local News

Lawrence High prevailed in Saturday's track meet with the help of 20 individual-event placers earning a combined 68 points. A first-place finish earns 5 points, a second-place finish earns 3 points, and a third-place finish earns 1 point. Lawrence had a strong second-place showing, with as many second place finishers as first- and third-place finishers combined.

28. **MP PROBLEM SOLVING** The percent of left-handed people in the world is one-tenth the percent of right-handed people. The percent of right-handed people is nine times the percent of left-handed people and ambidextrous people combined. What percent of people are ambidextrous?

29. **WRITING** Explain when it might be more convenient to use the elimination method than the substitution method to solve a linear system. Give an example to support your claim.

30. **COLLEGE PREP** Which of the following systems has infinitely many solutions?

System A	System B
$3x + 2y - z = -5$	$x + 3y + 5z = 13$
$-2x + 5y + 3z = 12$	$-x - 6y + z = -4$
$-12x - 8y + 4z = -20$	$x + 5y + z = 7$

Ⓐ System A Ⓑ System B
Ⓒ both Ⓓ neither

CONNECTING CONCEPTS In Exercises 31 and 32, write and use a linear system to answer the question.

31. The triangle has a perimeter of 65 feet. What are the lengths of sides ℓ, m, and n?

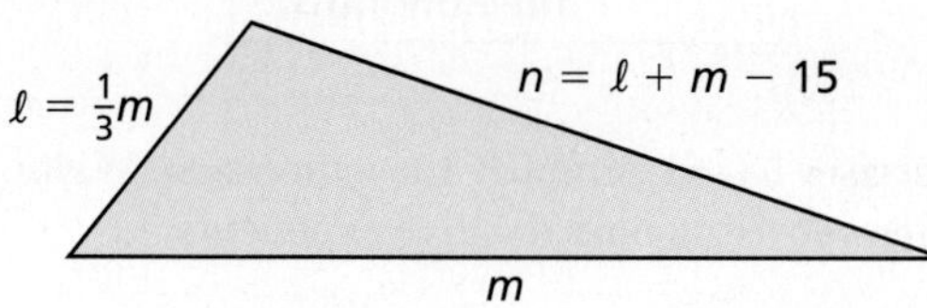

32. What are the measures of angles A, B, and C?

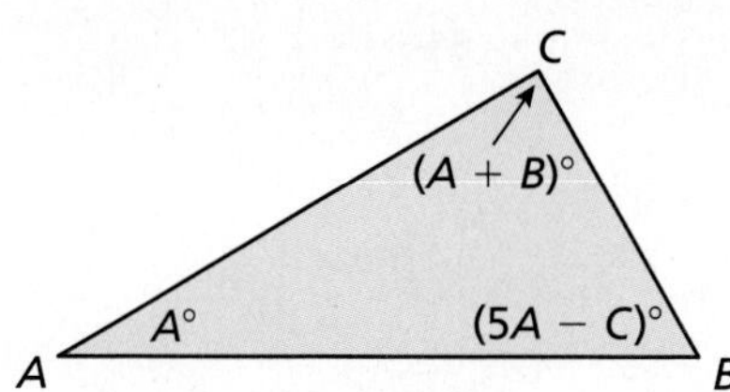

33. **MP REPEATED REASONING** Using what you know about solving linear systems in two and three variables, plan a strategy for how to solve a system that has *four* linear equations in *four* variables.

34. **CRITICAL THINKING** Find the values of a, b, and c so that the linear system shown has $(-1, 2, -3)$ as its only solution. Explain your reasoning.

$$x + 2y - 3z = a$$
$$-x - y + z = b$$
$$2x + 3y - 2z = c$$

35. **MAKING AN ARGUMENT** A linear system in three variables has no solution. Your friend concludes that it is not possible for two of the three equations to have any points in common. Is your friend correct? Explain your reasoning.

GO DIGITAL

36. **HOW DO YOU SEE IT?**
Determine whether the system of equations that represents the circles has *no solution*, *one solution*, or *infinitely many solutions*. Explain your reasoning.

a.
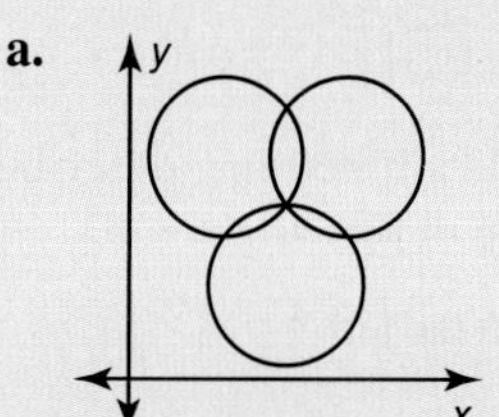

b.
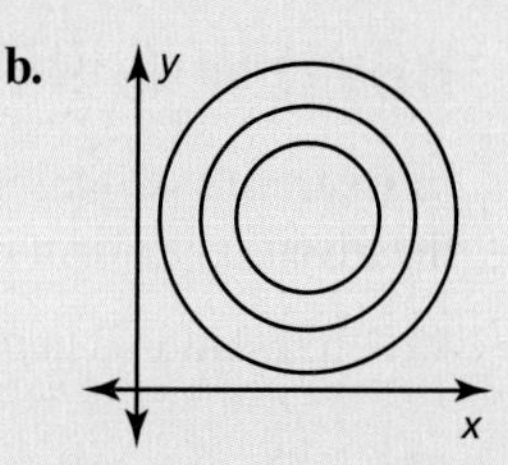

37. **OPEN-ENDED** Consider the system of linear equations below. Choose nonzero values for a, b, and c so the system satisfies each condition. Explain your reasoning.

$$x + y + z = 2$$
$$ax + by + cz = 10$$
$$x - 2y + z = 4$$

a. The system has no solution.

b. The system has exactly one solution.

c. The system has infinitely many solutions.

38. **MP PROBLEM SOLVING** A florist must make 5 identical bouquets. The budget is \$160, and each bouquet must have 12 flowers. Roses cost \$2.50 each, lilies cost \$4 each, and irises cost \$2 each. The florist wants twice as many roses as the other two types of flowers combined.

a. Assuming the florist plans to use the entire budget, how many of each type of flower should be in each bouquet?

b. Suppose there is no limitation on the total cost of the bouquets. Does the problem still have exactly one solution? If so, find the solution. If not, give three possible solutions.

39. **ANALYZING RELATIONSHIPS** Determine which arrangement(s) of the integers -5, 2, and 3 produce a linear system with a solution that consists of only integers. Justify your answer.

$$x - 3y + 6z = 21$$
$$\_\_x + \_\_y + \_\_z = -30$$
$$2x - 5y + 2z = -6$$

40. **THOUGHT PROVOKING** Solve the system.

$$-\frac{1}{x} - \frac{1}{y} + \frac{6}{z} = -3$$
$$\frac{6}{x} + \frac{5}{y} - \frac{12}{z} = 11$$
$$\frac{3}{x} + \frac{2}{y} - \frac{2}{z} = 4$$

41. **DIG DEEPER** The scales shown are used to compare the weights of apples, tangerines, grapefruits, and bananas. How many tangerines will balance one apple? Justify your answer using a linear system.

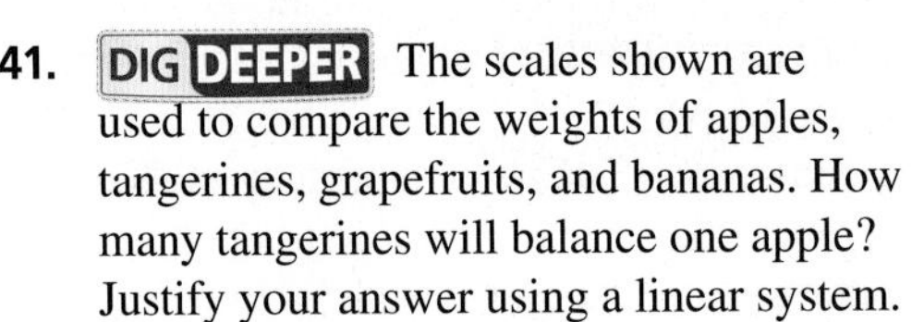

REVIEW & REFRESH

WATCH

In Exercises 42–45, write a function g described by the given transformation of $f(x) = |x| - 5$.

42. translation 2 units to the left

43. reflection in the x-axis

44. translation 4 units up

45. vertical stretch by a factor of 3

In Exercises 46 and 47, find the product.

46. $(x - 2)^2$

47. $(3m + 1)^2$

In Exercises 48–53, solve the inequality. Graph the solution.

48. $6 + w > -15$

49. $5y - 2 \leq 28$

50. $6.5 \geq -\frac{n}{3}$

51. $2(x - 4) > 6x - 16$

52. $|2h + 3| - 3 < -1$

53. $4t + 21 < -7$ *or* $-\frac{1}{2}t \leq 2$

54. **MODELING REAL LIFE** The table shows the total distance a new car travels each month after it is purchased. What type of function can you use to model the data? Estimate the mileage after 1 year.

Time (months), x	Distance (miles), y
0	0
2	2300
5	5750
6	6900
9	10,350

55. Solve $\frac{4}{x} = \frac{16}{10}$.

56. **OPEN-ENDED** Create a nonnumerical data set that has more than one mode.

57. Use the graph to write an equation of the line and interpret the slope.

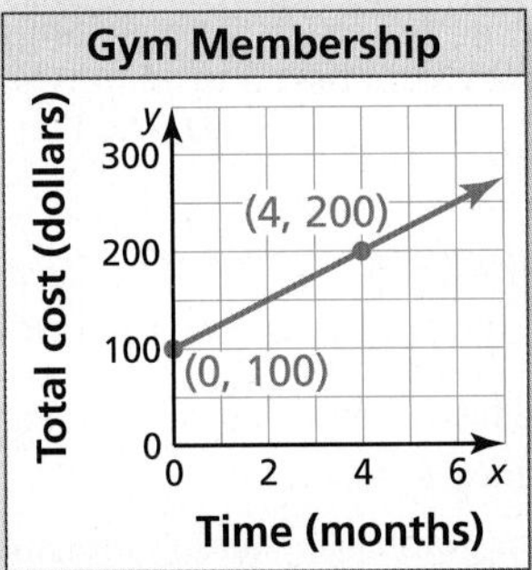

In Exercises 58–61, simplify the expression. Write your answer using only positive exponents.

58. $\frac{k^{10}}{k^2}$

59. $b^{-12} \cdot b^9$

60. $(2c)^6$

61. $\left(\frac{z^7}{3}\right)^{-4}$

62. Find the value of x.

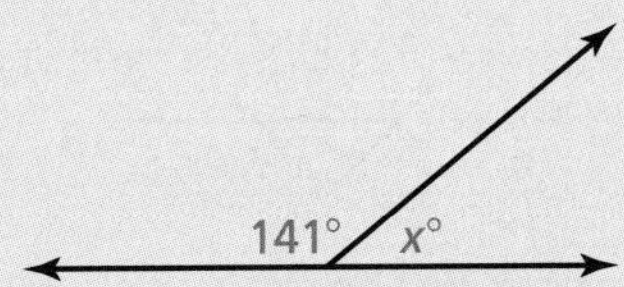

In Exercises 63 and 64, solve the system.

63. $-3x + y - 2z = 8$
$2x + 2y + 4z = 13$
$x = y - 5$

64. $4x + 3y - 5z = 7$
$x + 2y - z = 1$
$-2x - 4y + z = -4$

65. Explain how to determine the number of real solutions of $x^2 = 100$ without solving.

1 Chapter Review WITH CalcChat®

Chapter Learning Target Understand linear functions.

Chapter Success Criteria
- ◆ I can identify parent functions and transformations.
- ◆ I can describe transformations of parent functions.
- ■ I can model with linear functions.
- ■ I can solve linear systems.

◆ Surface
■ Deep

SELF-ASSESSMENT **1** I do not understand. **2** I can do it with help. **3** I can do it on my own. **4** I can teach someone else.

1.1 Parent Functions and Transformations *(pp. 3–10)*

Learning Target: Graph and describe transformations of functions.

Vocabulary

parent function
transformation
translation
reflection
vertical stretch
vertical shrink

Graph the function and its parent function. Then describe the transformation.

1. $h(x) = 4$
2. $f(x) = x + 3$
3. $g(x) = |x| - 1$
4. $h(x) = \frac{1}{2}x^2$
5. $g(x) = -3(x + 3)^2$
6. $f(x) = -|x| - 3$

7. The graphs of f and g are shown. Describe two different transformations from the graph of f to the graph of g.

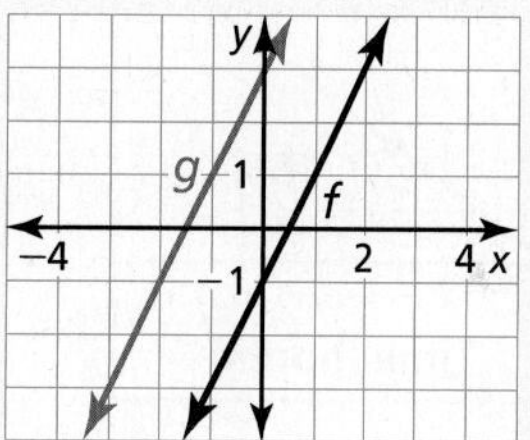

8. A function g is a translation 4 units right and 6 units down, followed by a reflection in the y-axis of the graph of $f(x) = -\frac{1}{2}(x + 1)^2$. Graph f and g.

Describe a transformation from the graph of f to the graph of g.

9.

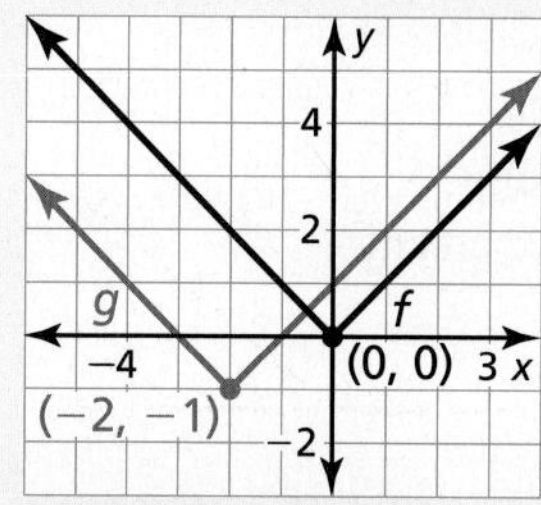

10.

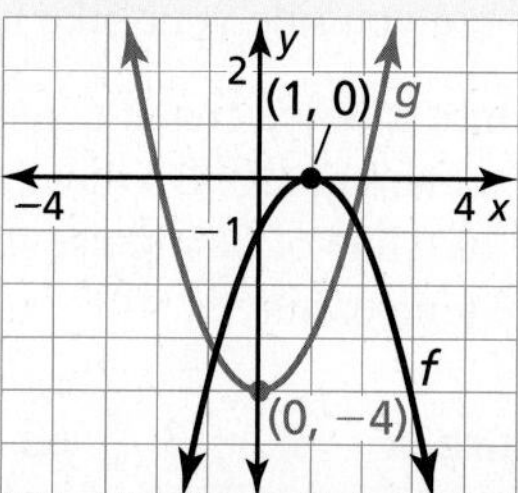

11. The table shows the total distance traveled by a space probe after x seconds. What type of function can you use to model the data? Estimate the distance traveled by the space probe after 1 minute.

Time (seconds), x	0	8	20	36	50
Distance (miles), y	0	76	190	342	475

1.2 Transformations of Linear and Absolute Value Functions (pp. 11–18)

Learning Target: Write functions that represent transformations of functions.

Write a function g whose graph represents the indicated transformations of the graph of f. Use technology to check your answer.

12. $f(x) = x$; horizontal shrink by a factor of $\frac{1}{3}$

13. $f(x) = |x|$; reflection in the x-axis followed by a translation 4 units left

14. $f(x) = -3x + 4$; translation 3 units down and a reflection in the y-axis

15. $f(x) = |x + 1| - 2$ vertical shrink by a factor of $\frac{1}{2}$ followed by a translation 2 units up

16. The total cost of an annual pass for admission to a national park plus camping for x days can be modeled by the function $f(x) = 20x + 80$. A senior citizen pays \$20 less than half of this price for x days. What is the total cost for a senior citizen to go camping for three days in the park?

1.3 Modeling with Linear Functions (pp. 19–26)

Learning Target: Use linear functions to model and analyze real-life situations.

Vocabulary

line of fit
line of best fit
correlation coefficient

Use the graph to write an equation of the line and interpret the slope.

17.

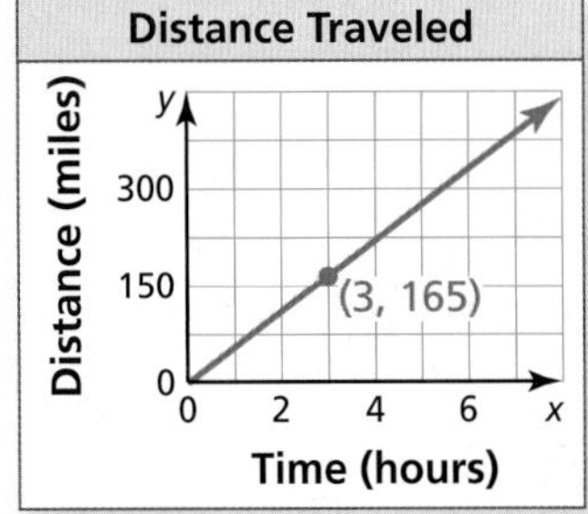

18.

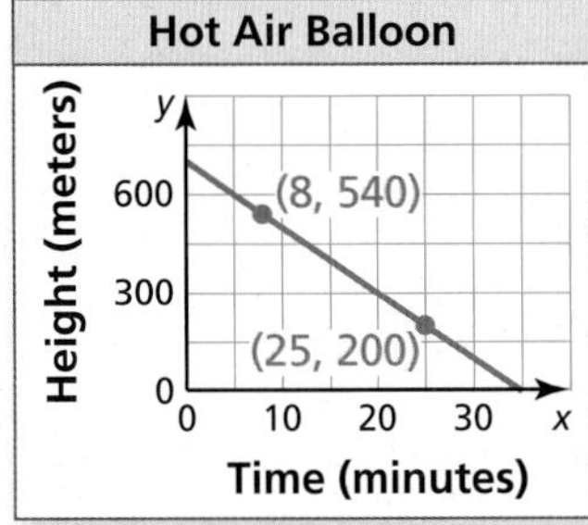

19. You ride your bike and measure how far you travel. After 10 minutes, you travel 3.5 miles. After 30 minutes, you travel 10.5 miles. Write an equation to model your distance. How far can you ride your bike in 45 minutes?

20. The table shows the numbers of ice cream cones sold for different outside temperatures (in degrees Fahrenheit). Do the data show a linear relationship? If so, write an equation of a line of fit and use it to estimate how many ice cream cones are sold when the temperature is 60°F.

Temperature, x	53	62	70	82	90
Number of cones, y	90	105	117	131	147

21. The table shows the total number y (in thousands) of tickets sold at a movie theater each year for x years. Use technology to find an equation of the line of best fit for the data. Then interpret the slope and y-intercept. Estimate the number of tickets sold in the 12th year.

Year, x	0	2	4	6	8	10
Tickets sold, y	224	226	239	247	1249	257

1.4 Solving Linear Systems (pp. 27–34)

Learning Target: Solve linear systems in three variables.

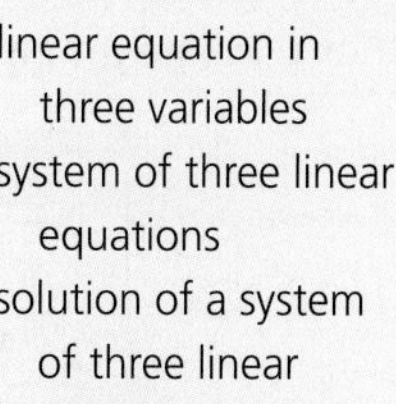

Solve the system. Check your solution, if possible.

22. $x + y + z = 3$
$-x + 3y + 2z = -8$
$x = 4z$

23. $2x - 5y - z = 17$
$x + y + 3z = 19$
$-4x + 6y + z = -20$

24. $x + y + z = 2$
$2x - 3y + z = 11$
$-3x + 2y - 2z = -13$

25. $x + 4y - 2z = 3$
$x + 3y + 7z = 1$
$2x + 9y - 13z = 2$

26. $x - y + 3z = 6$
$x - 2y = 5$
$2x - 2y + 5z = 9$

27. $x + 2z = 4$
$x + y + z = 6$
$3x + 3y + 4z = 28$

28. A school band performs a spring concert for a crowd of 600 people. The revenue for the concert is \$3150. There are 150 more adults at the concert than students. How many of each type of ticket are sold?

29. Complete the equations so that the system has infinitely many solutions. Then write an ordered triple that represents the solutions of the system.

$-2x + 2y - z = 4$
$\square x + \square y + \square z = -2$
$\square x + \square y + \square z = -8$

30. A total of 100 million people vote in a national election. The table shows the percent of the total votes for each candidate that were cast in two regions. Find the total number of votes cast for each candidate.

Region	Party A candidate (%)	Party B candidate (%)	Other candidates (%)	Total voters (millions)
Northeast	20	15	20	18
South	30	35	25	31.5

Mathematical Practices

Model with Mathematics

Mathematically proficient students apply what they know and are comfortable making assumptions and approximations to simplify a complicated situation.

1. The data in Chapter Review Exercise 30 are approximated. Explain why it is helpful to use the approximated data instead of exact data in this context.
2. Use a linear function to model the distance that you jog over time. How far can you jog in 20 minutes? What assumptions did you make to solve the problem?

1 Practice Test WITH CalcChat®

Write an equation of the line and interpret the slope and y-intercept.

1.

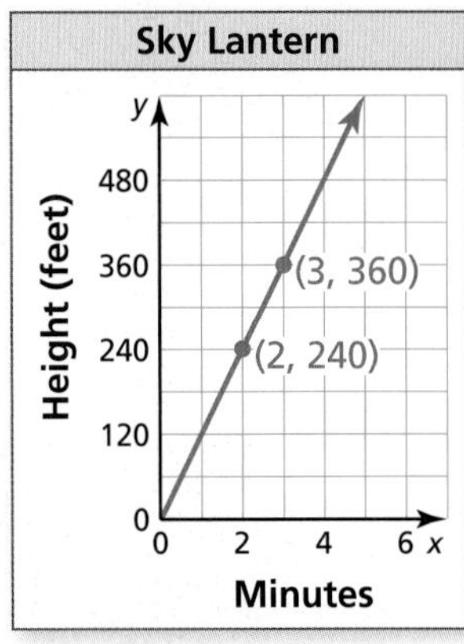

2.

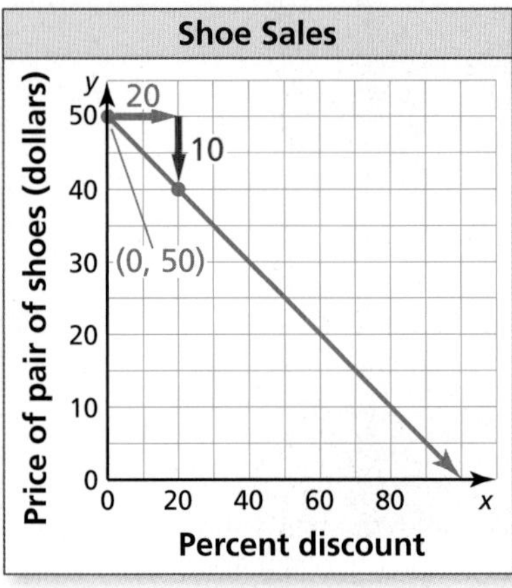

Solve the system. Check your solution, if possible.

3. $-2x + y + 4z = 5$

$x + 3y - z = 2$

$4x + y - 6z = 11$

4. $y = \frac{1}{2}z$

$x + 2y + 5z = 2$

$3x + 6y - 3z = 9$

5. $x - y + 5z = 3$

$2x + 3y - z = 2$

$-4x - y - 9z = -8$

Graph the function and its parent function. Then describe the transformation.

6. $f(x) = |x - 1|$

7. $f(x) = (3x)^2$

8. $f(x) = \frac{1}{4}x - 5$

Match the transformation of $f(x) = x$ with its graph. Then write a rule for g.

9. $g(x) = 2f(x) + 3$

10. $g(x) = 3f(x) - 2$

11. $g(x) = -2f(x) - 3$

A.

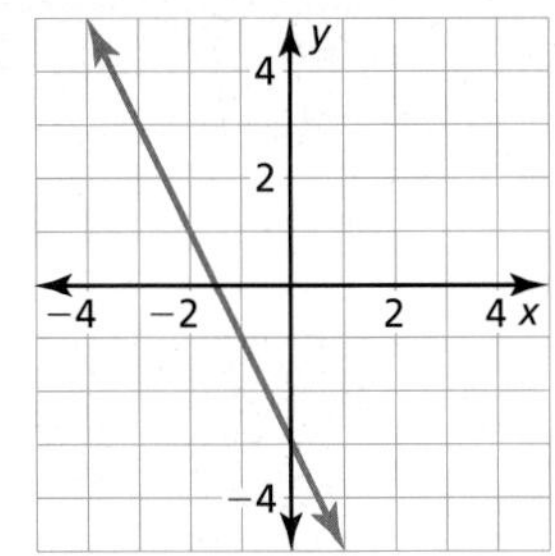

B.

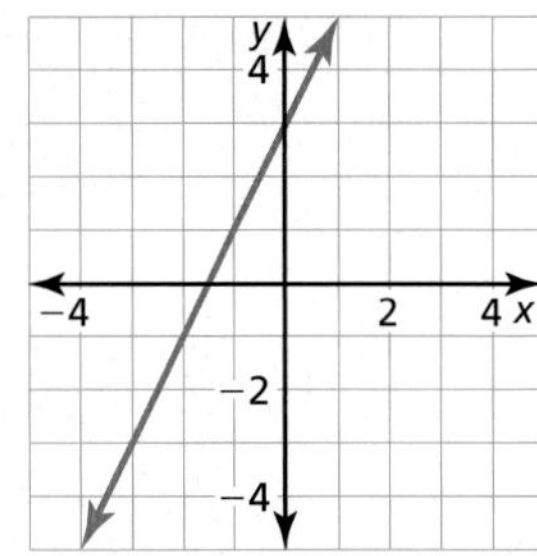

C.

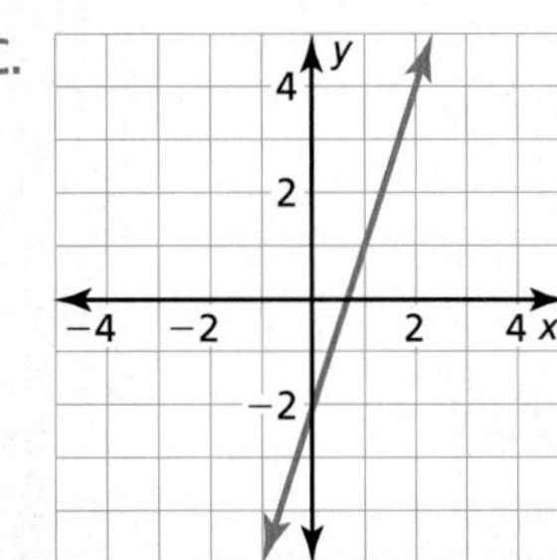

12. A bakery sells doughnuts, muffins, and bagels. The bakery makes three times as many doughnuts as bagels. The bakery earns a total of \$150 when all 130 baked items in stock are sold. How many of each item are in stock? Justify your answer.

13. A fountain with a depth of 5 feet is drained and then refilled. The water level (in feet) after t minutes can be modeled by $f(t) = \frac{1}{4}|t - 20|$. At the same time, a second fountain with the same depth is drained and filled twice as quickly as the first fountain. Describe how to transform the graph of f to model the water level in the second fountain after t minutes. When are the fountains at the same depth? Justify your answer.

1 Performance Task
Flying Robot Design

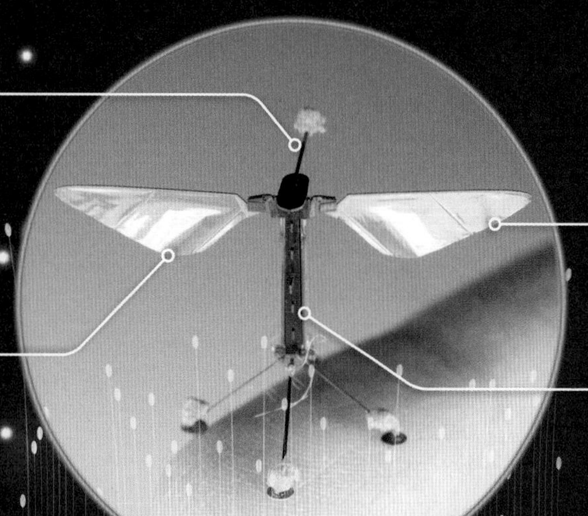

Optical-flow sensors could potentially be used for stability and to navigate surroundings.

Some of the smallest flying robots have masses as low as 175 milligrams and wing frequencies as high as 300 hertz.

For a robot to fly, its mass (in grams) must be less than the lift force (in gram-forces) of its wings.

The frame houses actuators to transfer power to the wings.

hertz (Hz): cycles per second

gram-force (gf): the amount of force exerted by gravity on 1 gram of matter

CREATE A FLYING ROBOT

INFO

You are a member of a team that is creating a prototype for a flying robot. For each wing design, your team measures lift forces for various flapping frequencies. The tables show the results. Choose a wing design and a frame style for your robot and find the minimum flapping frequency needed for your robot to take flight.

Hint: Using the general form of a quadratic equation, $y = ax^2 + bx + c$, substitute three different pairs of x- and y-values from the table of your chosen design. Then solve the resulting linear system in three variables.

Wing A

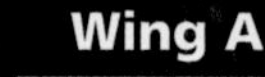

Frequency (Hz), x	10	13	16	19
Lift Force (gf), y	3.2	7.1	11.8	16.9

Wing B

Frequency (Hz), x	11	14	17	20
Lift Force (gf), y	3.3	6.1	9.4	13.1

Wing C

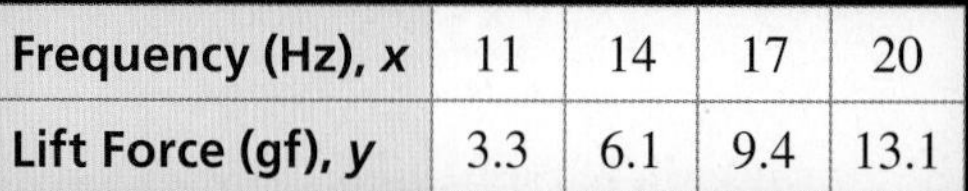

Frequency (Hz), x	12	15	18	21
Lift Force (gf), y	4.6	8.0	11.9	16.4

Frame A
22 grams

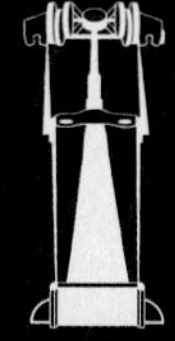

Frame B
20 grams

Frame C
12 grams

1 College and Career Readiness WITH CalcChat®

Tutorial videos are available for each exercise.

1. Which transformation of the graph of $f(x) = 2x - 4$ is represented by the graph of g?

Ⓐ a horizontal stretch by a factor of 2

Ⓑ a horizontal shrink by a factor of $\frac{1}{2}$

Ⓒ a vertical stretch by a factor of 2

Ⓓ a vertical shrink by a factor of $\frac{1}{2}$

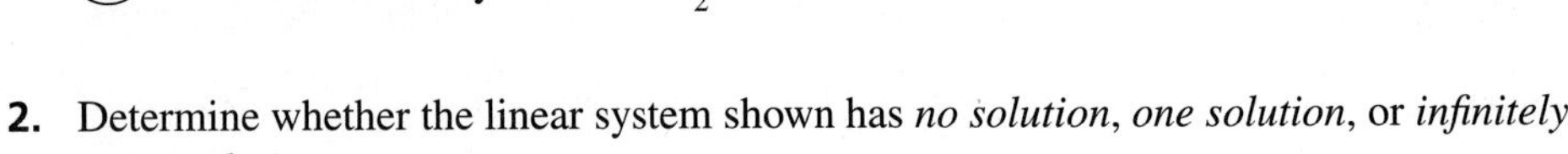

2. Determine whether the linear system shown has *no solution*, *one solution*, or *infinitely many solutions*.

$$-3x - 2y - z = 0$$
$$2x - 3y + 8z = -4$$
$$-x + 4y - 5z = 14$$

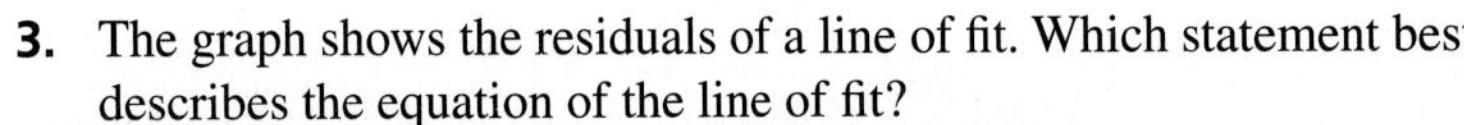

3. The graph shows the residuals of a line of fit. Which statement best describes the equation of the line of fit?

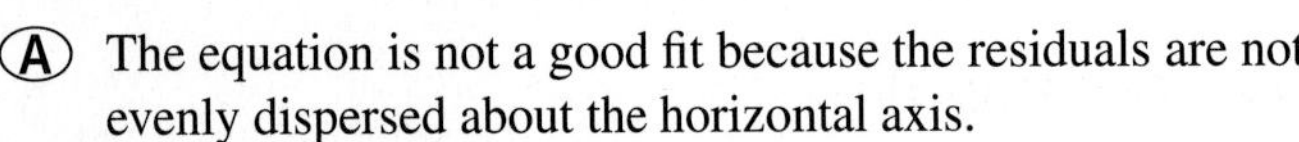

Ⓐ The equation is not a good fit because the residuals are not evenly dispersed about the horizontal axis.

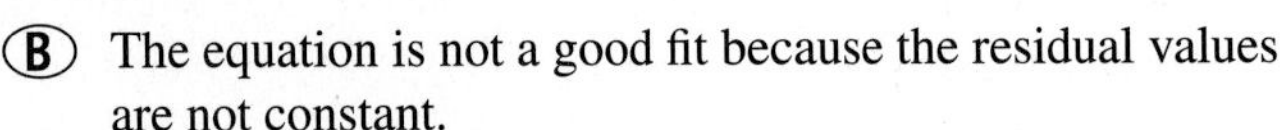

Ⓑ The equation is not a good fit because the residual values are not constant.

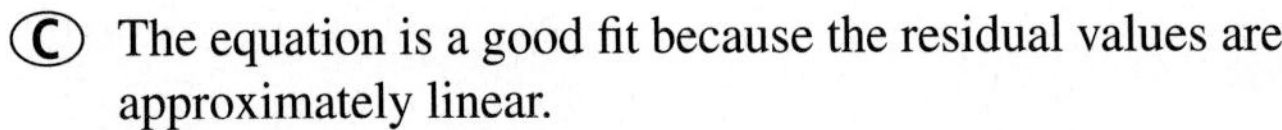

Ⓒ The equation is a good fit because the residual values are approximately linear.

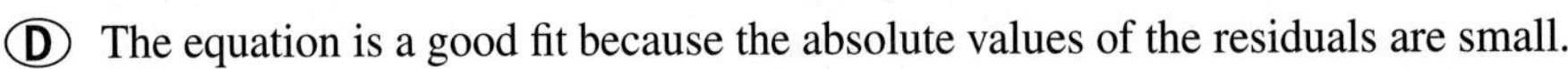

Ⓓ The equation is a good fit because the absolute values of the residuals are small.

4. Use <, =, or > to complete the statement comparing linear functions f and g. Explain your reasoning.

x	f(x)
−5	−23
−4	−20
−3	−17
−2	−14

x	g(x)
−2	−18
−1	−14
0	−10
1	−6

$f(22)$ ☐ $g(22)$

5. Which equation is equivalent to $\frac{2}{3}x - 3 = 4x + 2$?

Ⓐ $x - 3 = 6x + 3$

Ⓑ $\frac{1}{3}x - \frac{3}{2} = 2x + 1$

Ⓒ $\frac{2}{3}x - 1 = 4x$

Ⓓ $\frac{1}{6}x - \frac{3}{4} = x + 2$

6. The graph shows the height of a hang glider over time. Which equation models the situation?

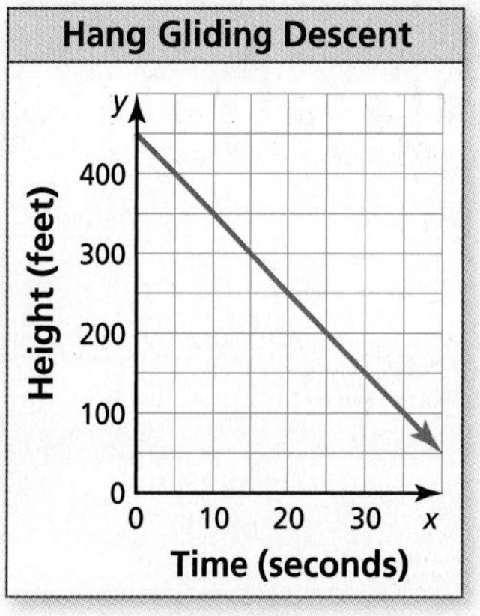

Ⓐ $y + 450 = 10x$

Ⓑ $y + 450 = -10x$

Ⓒ $-x + \frac{1}{10}y = 450$

Ⓓ $10x + y = 450$

7. Let $f(x) = -3x - 4$. The graph of g is a translation 2 units left, followed by a horizontal stretch by a factor of 3 of the graph of f. Which function represents g?

Ⓐ $g(x) = -x + 2$

Ⓑ $g(x) = -9x - 10$

Ⓒ $g(x) = -x - 10$

Ⓓ $g(x) = -x - 6$

8. The table shows the tuition costs for a private school x years after it opens.

Year, *x*	0	1	2	3
Tuition (dollars), *y*	36,208	37,620	39,088	40,594

a. Verify that the data show a linear relationship. Then write an equation of a line of fit.

b. Interpret the slope and y-intercept in this situation.

c. Predict the cost of tuition after 5 years.

9. The area A of a trapezoid is represented by the formula $A = \frac{1}{2}h(b_1 + b_2)$. Which equation represents the height h of a trapezoid?

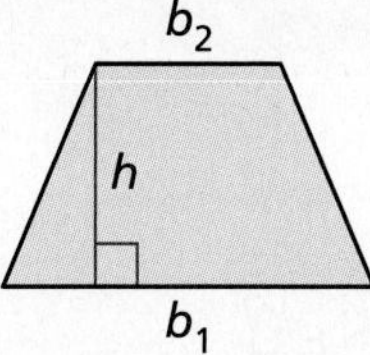

Ⓐ $h = \dfrac{A}{2(b_1 + b_2)}$

Ⓑ $h = \dfrac{2A}{b_1 + b_2}$

Ⓒ $h = 2A - (b_1 + b_2)$

Ⓓ $h = 2A(b_1 + b_2)$

10. In a trivia game, each correct answer is worth 10 points in the first round, 15 points in the second round, and 25 points in the third round. You score 370 points by answering 24 questions correctly. You score 55 more points in the third round than you do in the first round. How many questions do you answer correctly in each round?

2 Quadratic Functions

NATIONAL GEOGRAPHIC EXPLORER

Jennifer Lopez

Jennifer Lopez is a technologist and data scientist with a mission to use citizen science to help unravel secrets of the cosmos. She is a founding member of NASA's Datanaut Corps, which inspires future engineers, data scientists, and entrepreneurs to engage with NASA in solving data challenges.

- What is a technologist? What is a data scientist?
- What is in-space manufacturing?
- Why is in-space manufacturing crucial to the success of long-term exploration missions in space?

STEM

Radio telescopes can be used to study the compositions of stars, planets, and moons. In the Performance Task, you will design a radio telescope and use a quadratic equation to describe its parabolic cross section.

Space Technology

Preparing for Chapter 2

Chapter Learning Target Understand quadratic functions.

Chapter Success Criteria
- ◆ I can describe transformations of quadratic functions.
- ◆ I can identify characteristics of quadratic functions.
- ■ I can write equations of parabolas.
- ■ I can model with quadratic functions.

◆ Surface
■ Deep

Chapter Vocabulary

Work with a partner. Discuss each of the vocabulary terms.

quadratic function
parabola
vertex of a parabola
vertex form of a quadratic function
axis of symmetry
standard form of a quadratic function
minimum value
maximum value
intercept form of a quadratic function

Mathematical Practices

Make Sense of Problems and Persevere in Solving Them

Mathematically proficient students consider analogous problems.

Work with a partner. In Chapter 1, you compared the graphs of several different types of functions to the graphs of their parent functions. One type of function that you graphed was a *quadratic function*.

1. Compare the graph of each quadratic function to the graph of $y = x^2$.

a. $y = -x^2$ **b.** $y = x^2 + 3$

c. $y = (x + 1)^2$ **d.** $y = -(x - 2)^2 - 4$

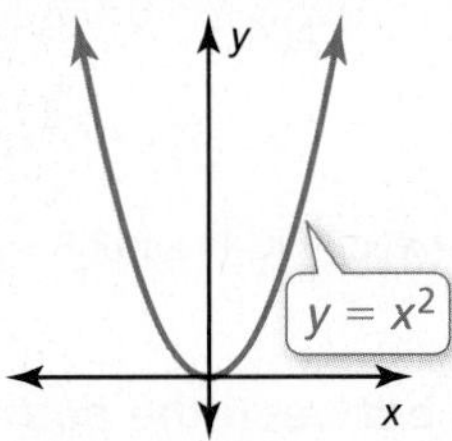

2. Without graphing, compare the graph of each equation below to the graph of $x = y^2$. Use technology to check your answers.

a. $x = -y^2$ **b.** $x = y^2 + 6$

c. $x = (y + 3)^2$ **d.** $x = -(y - 1)^2 - 5$

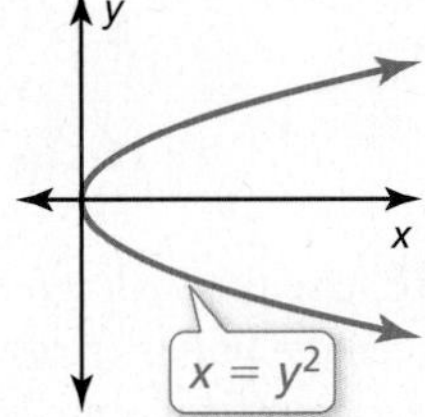

3. In Exercise 2, how did comparing the equations to the equations in Exercise 1 help you describe the graphs?

2 Prepare WITH CalcChat®

Finding *x*-Intercepts

Example 1 **Find the *x*-intercept of the graph of the linear equation $y = 3x - 12$.**

$y = 3x - 12$	Write the equation.
$0 = 3x - 12$	Substitute 0 for *y*.
$12 = 3x$	Add 12 to each side.
$4 = x$	Divide each side by 3.

▶ The *x*-intercept is 4.

Find the *x*-intercept of the graph of the linear equation.

1. $y = 2x + 7$ **2.** $y = -6x + 8$ **3.** $y = -10x - 36$

4. $y = 3(x - 5)$ **5.** $y = -4(x + 10)$ **6.** $3x + 6y = 24$

Finding Distances in a Coordinate Plane

Example 2 **Find the distance between (1, 4) and (−3, 6).**

Plot the points in a coordinate plane. Then draw a right triangle with a hypotenuse that represents the distance between the points.

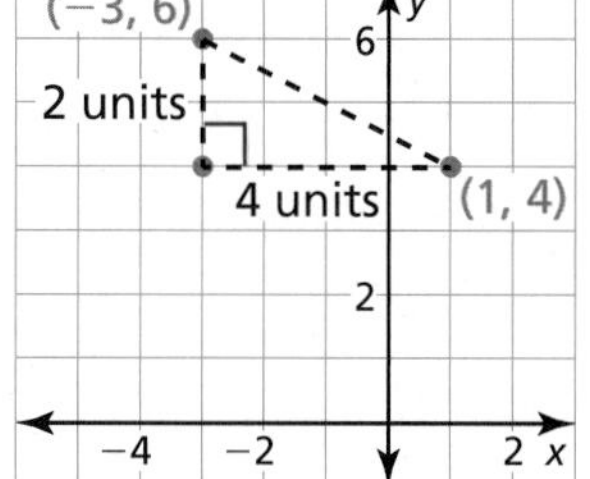

Use the Pythagorean Theorem to find the length of the hypotenuse.

$a^2 + b^2 = c^2$	Write the Pythagorean Theorem.
$2^2 + 4^2 = c^2$	Substitute 2 for *a* and 4 for *b*.
$4 + 16 = c^2$	Evaluate powers.
$20 = c^2$	Add.
$\sqrt{20} = c$	Take the positive square root of each side.

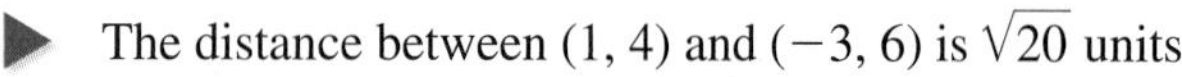

▶ The distance between (1, 4) and (−3, 6) is $\sqrt{20}$ units.

Find the distance between the points.

7. (2, 5), (−4, 7) **8.** (−1, 0), (−8, 4) **9.** (3, 10), (5, 9)

10. (7, −4), (−5, 0) **11.** (4, −8), (4, 2) **12.** (0, 9), (−3, −6)

13. **MP STRUCTURE** Use the Pythagorean Theorem to write an expression for the distance between the points (p, q) and (r, s). Is there an easier way to find the distance when the *x*-coordinates are equal? when the *y*-coordinates are equal? Explain your reasoning.

2.1 Transformations of Quadratic Functions

GO DIGITAL

Learning Target Describe and graph transformations of quadratic functions.

Success Criteria

- I can describe transformations of quadratic functions.
- I can graph transformations of quadratic functions.
- I can write functions that represent transformations of quadratic functions.

EXPLORE IT! Identifying Graphs of Quadratic Functions

Work with a partner. In parts (a)–(f), match each quadratic function with its graph. Explain your reasoning. Then use technology to check your answer.

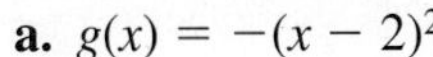

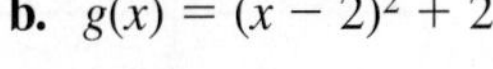

a. $g(x) = -(x - 2)^2$ **b.** $g(x) = (x - 2)^2 + 2$

c. $g(x) = -(x + 2)^2 - 2$ **d.** $g(x) = 0.5(x - 2)^2 - 2$

e. $g(x) = 2(x - 2)^2$ **f.** $g(x) = -(x + 2)^2 + 2$

Math Practice

Use Prior Results
How can your knowledge of transformations of absolute value functions help you match each function with its graph?

A.

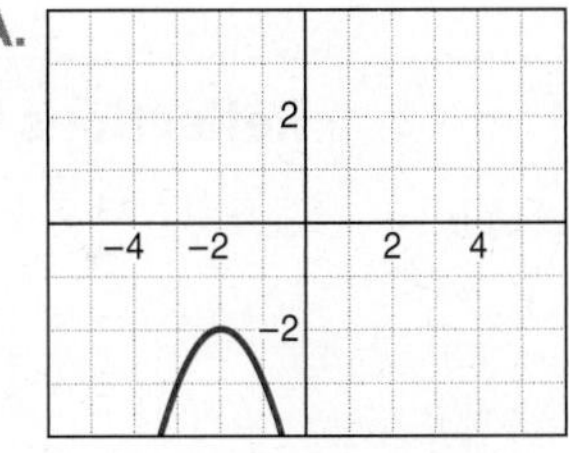

B.

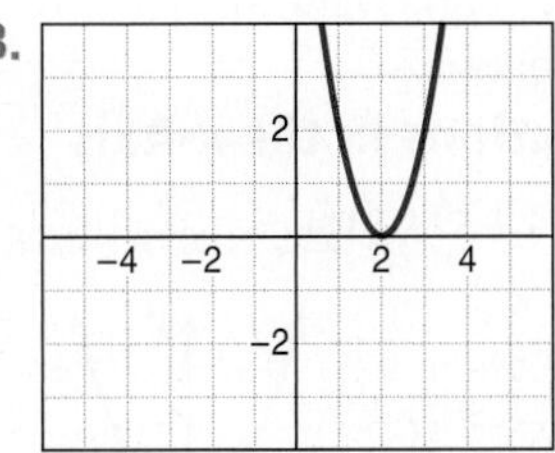

C.

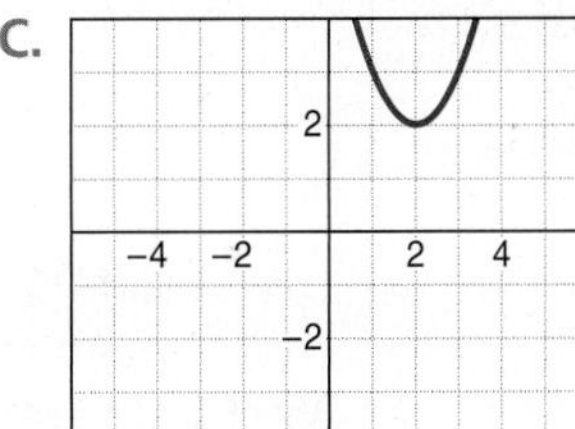

D.

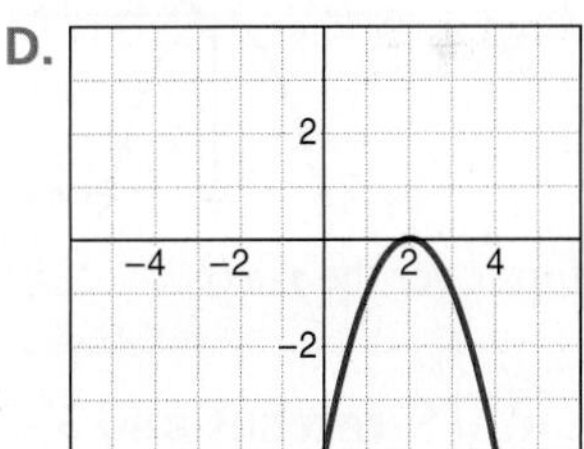

E.

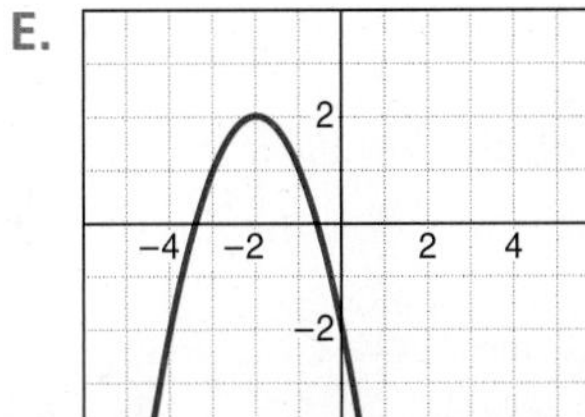

F.

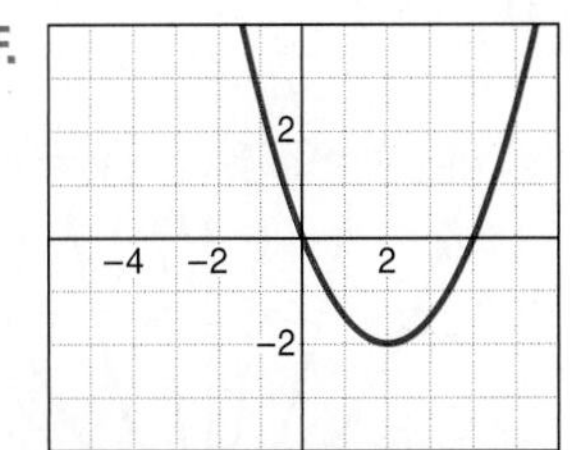

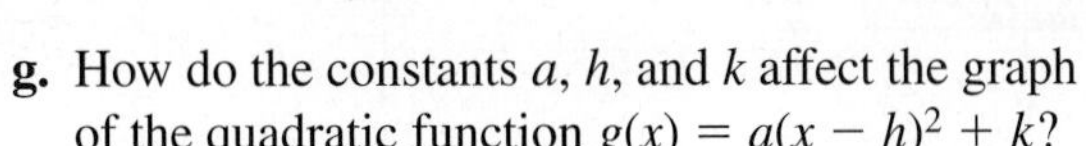

g. How do the constants a, h, and k affect the graph of the quadratic function $g(x) = a(x - h)^2 + k$?

h. Write the equation of the quadratic function whose graph is shown at the right. Explain your reasoning. Then use technology to check your answer.

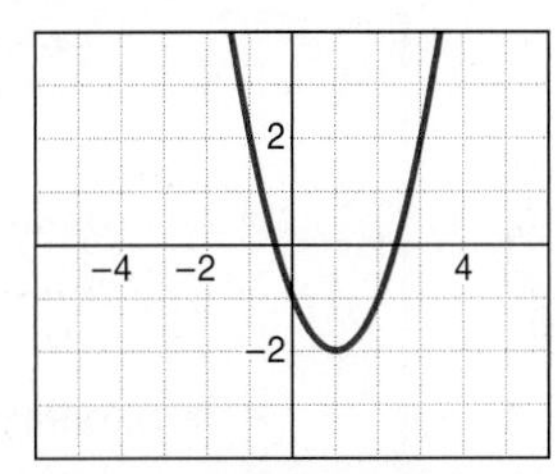

Describing Transformations of Quadratic Functions

Vocabulary

quadratic function, *p. 46*
parabola, *p. 46*
vertex of a parabola, *p. 48*
vertex form, *p. 48*

A **quadratic function** is a function that can be written in the form $f(x) = a(x - h)^2 + k$, where $a \neq 0$. The U-shaped graph of a quadratic function is called a **parabola**.

In Section 1.1, you graphed quadratic functions using tables of values. You can also graph quadratic functions by applying transformations to the graph of the parent function $f(x) = x^2$.

KEY IDEAS

Let $f(x) = x^2$.

Horizontal Translations

$f(x - h) = (x - h)^2$

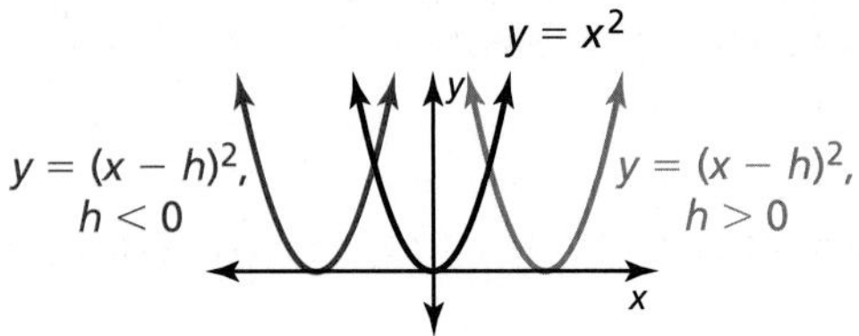

- shifts left when $h < 0$
- shifts right when $h > 0$

Vertical Translations

$f(x) + k = x^2 + k$

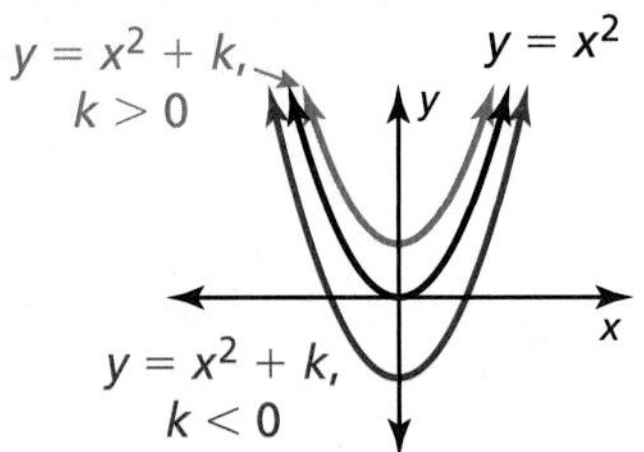

- shifts down when $k < 0$
- shifts up when $k > 0$

Reflections in the *x*-Axis

$-f(x) = -(x^2) = -x^2$

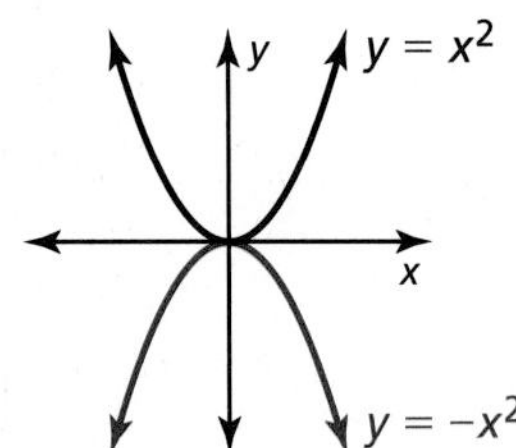

flips over the x-axis

Reflections in the *y*-Axis

$f(-x) = (-x)^2 = x^2$

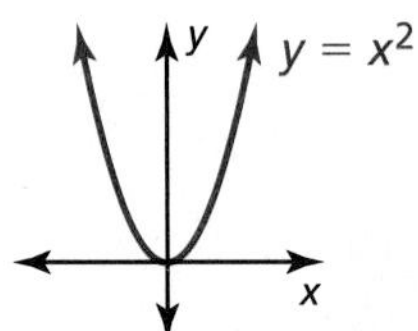

$y = x^2$ is its own reflection in the y-axis.

Horizontal Stretches and Shrinks

$f(ax) = (ax)^2$

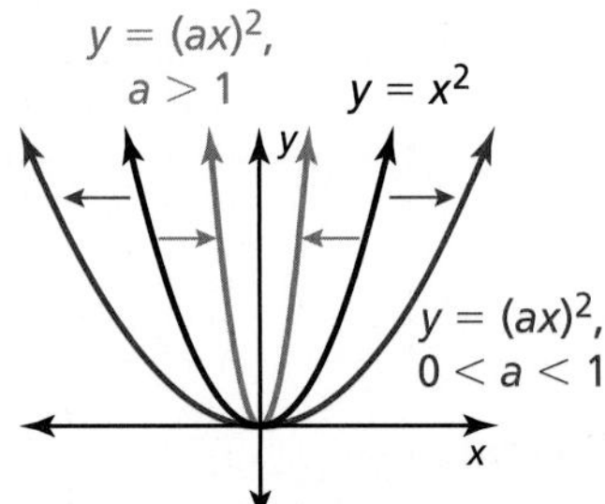

- horizontal stretch (away from y-axis) by a factor of $\frac{1}{a}$ when $0 < a < 1$
- horizontal shrink (toward y-axis) by a factor of $\frac{1}{a}$ when $a > 1$

Vertical Stretches and Shrinks

$a \cdot f(x) = ax^2$

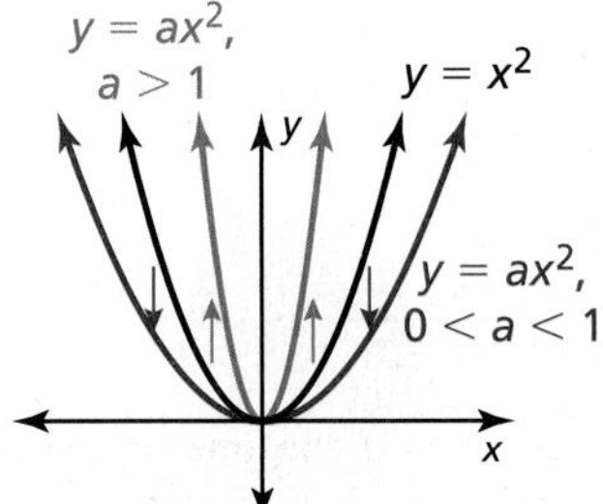

- vertical stretch (away from x-axis) by a factor of a when $a > 1$
- vertical shrink (toward x-axis) by a factor of a when $0 < a < 1$

EXAMPLE 1 Transformations of a Quadratic Function

Describe the transformation of $f(x) = x^2$ represented by $g(x) = (x + 4)^2 - 1$. Then graph each function.

SOLUTION

Notice that the function is of the form $g(x) = (x - h)^2 + k$. Rewrite the function to identify h and k.

$$g(x) = (x - (-4))^2 + (-1)$$

↑ h ↑ k

▶ Because $h = -4$ and $k = -1$, the graph of g is a translation 4 units left and 1 unit down of the graph of f.

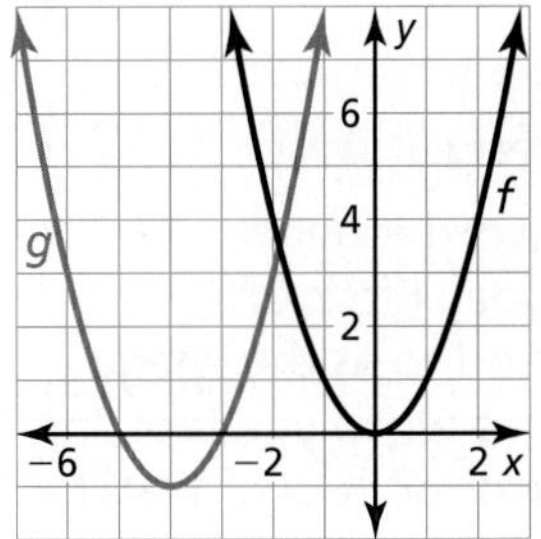

EXAMPLE 2 Transformations of Quadratic Functions

WATCH

Describe the transformation of $f(x) = x^2$ represented by g. Then graph each function.

a. $g(x) = -\frac{1}{2}x^2$

b. $g(x) = (2x)^2 + 1$

SOLUTION

a. Notice that the function is of the form $g(x) = -ax^2$, where $a = \frac{1}{2}$.

▶ So, the graph of g is a reflection in the x-axis and a vertical shrink by a factor of $\frac{1}{2}$ of the graph of f.

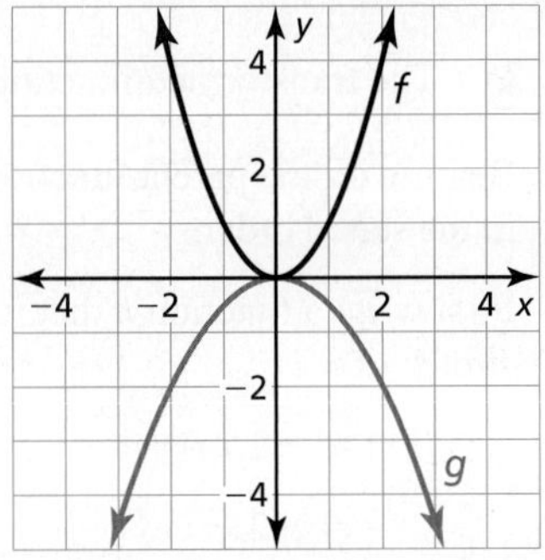

b. Notice that the function is of the form $g(x) = (ax)^2 + k$, where $a = 2$ and $k = 1$.

▶ So, the graph of g is a horizontal shrink by a factor of $\frac{1}{2}$, followed by a translation 1 unit up of the graph of f.

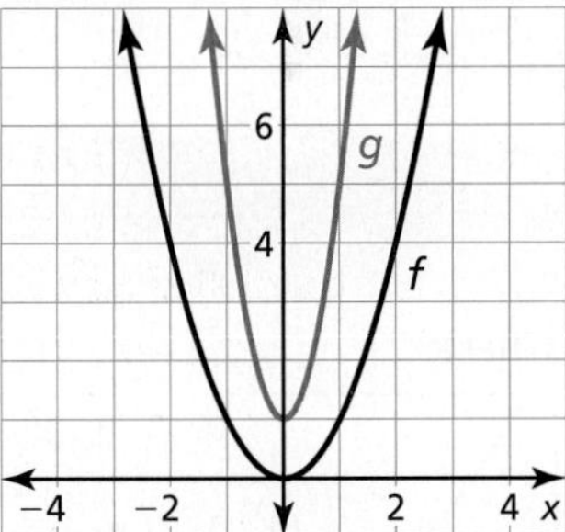

Math Practice

Look for Structure

In Example 2(b), how can you rewrite g to describe the transformation a different way?

SELF-ASSESSMENT

1 I do not understand. 2 I can do it with help. 3 I can do it on my own. 4 I can teach someone else.

Describe the transformation of $f(x) = x^2$ represented by g. Then graph each function.

1. $g(x) = (x - 3)^2$
2. $g(x) = (x - 2)^2 - 2$
3. $g(x) = (x + 5)^2 + 1$
4. $g(x) = \left(\frac{1}{3}x\right)^2$
5. $g(x) = 3(x - 1)^2$
6. $g(x) = -(x + 3)^2 + 2$
7. **MP STRUCTURE** The graph of $g(x) = 9x^2$ is a vertical stretch by a factor of 9 of the graph of $f(x) = x^2$. Describe the graph of g as a horizontal shrink of the graph of f. Explain your reasoning.

Writing Transformations of Quadratic Functions

The lowest point on a parabola that opens up or the highest point on a parabola that opens down is the **vertex**. The **vertex form** of a quadratic function is $f(x) = a(x - h)^2 + k$, where $a \neq 0$ and the vertex is (h, k).

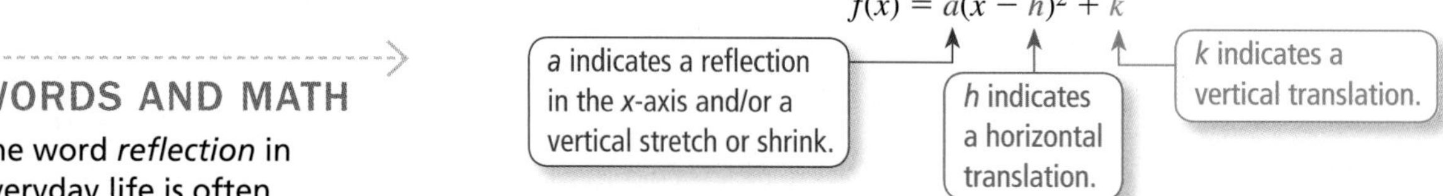

WORDS AND MATH

The word *reflection* in everyday life is often referred to as the image you see when you look in a mirror or pool of water. In math, a reflection is a transformation that flips a graph over a line known as the line of reflection.

EXAMPLE 3 Writing a Transformed Quadratic Function

Let the graph of g be a vertical stretch by a factor of 2 and a reflection in the x-axis, followed by a translation 3 units down of the graph of $f(x) = x^2$. Write a rule for g and identify the vertex.

SOLUTION

Method 1 Identify how the transformations affect the constants in the vertex form.

$$\left.\begin{array}{l}\text{reflection in } x\text{-axis}\\ \text{vertical stretch by 2}\end{array}\right\} a = -2$$

$$\text{translation 3 units down}\} \ k = -3$$

Write the transformed function.

$g(x) = a(x - h)^2 + k$	Vertex form of a quadratic function
$= -2(x - 0)^2 + (-3)$	Substitute -2 for a, 0 for h, and -3 for k.
$= -2x^2 - 3$	Simplify.

▶ The transformed function is $g(x) = -2x^2 - 3$. The vertex is $(0, -3)$.

STUDY TIP

Because there is no horizontal translation, $h = 0$.

Method 2 Begin with the parent function and apply the transformations one at a time in the stated order.

First write a function h that represents the reflection and vertical stretch of f.

$h(x) = -2 \bullet f(x)$	Multiply the output by -2.
$= -2x^2$	Substitute x^2 for $f(x)$.

Then write a function g that represents the translation of h.

$g(x) = h(x) - 3$	Subtract 3 from the output.
$= -2x^2 - 3$	Substitute $-2x^2$ for $h(x)$.

▶ The transformed function is $g(x) = -2x^2 - 3$. The vertex is $(0, -3)$.

Check

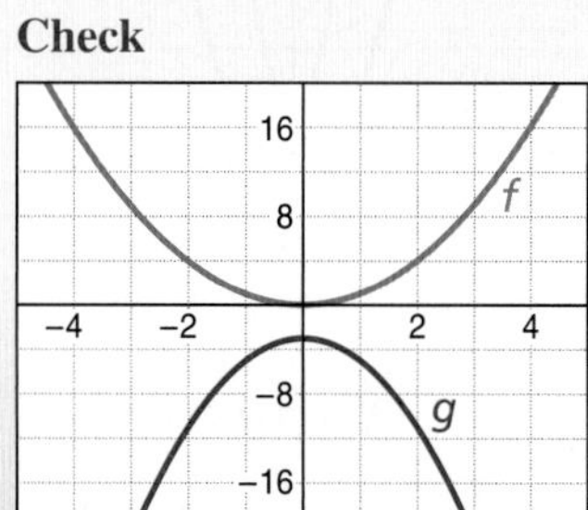

SELF-ASSESSMENT 1 I do not understand. 2 I can do it with help. 3 I can do it on my own. 4 I can teach someone else.

8. Let the graph of g be a vertical shrink by a factor of $\frac{1}{2}$, followed by a translation 2 units up of the graph of $f(x) = x^2$. Write a rule for g and identify the vertex.

Writing a Transformed Quadratic Function

Let the graph of g be a translation 3 units right and 2 units up, followed by a reflection in the y-axis of the graph of $f(x) = x^2 - 5x$. Write a rule for g.

REMEMBER

To multiply two binomials, use the FOIL Method.

$(x + 1)(x + 2) = x^2 + 2x + x + 2$

First Inner Outer Last

SOLUTION

Step 1 First write a function h that represents the translation of f.

$h(x) = f(x - 3) + 2$	Subtract 3 from the input. Add 2 to the output.
$= (x - 3)^2 - 5(x - 3) + 2$	Replace x with $x - 3$ in $f(x)$.
$= x^2 - 11x + 26$	Simplify.

Step 2 Then write a function g that represents the reflection of h.

$g(x) = h(-x)$	Multiply the input by -1.
$= (-x)^2 - 11(-x) + 26$	Replace x with $-x$ in $h(x)$.
$= x^2 + 11x + 26$	Simplify.

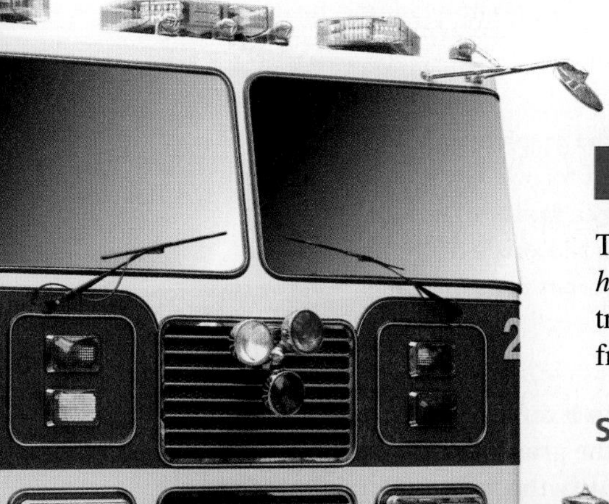

EXAMPLE 5 Modeling Real Life

The height (in feet) of water spraying from a fire hose can be modeled by $h(x) = -0.03x^2 + x + 25$, where x is the horizontal distance (in feet) from the fire truck. The crew raises the aerial ladder so that the water hits the ground 10 feet farther from the fire truck. Write a function that models the new path of the water.

SOLUTION

1. **Understand the Problem** You are given a function that represents the path of water spraying from a fire hose. You are asked to write a function that represents the path of the water after the crew raises the ladder.
2. **Make a Plan** Analyze the graph of the function to determine the translation of the ladder that causes water to travel 10 feet farther. Then write the function.
3. **Solve and Check** Use technology to graph the original function.

Because $h(50) = 0$, the water originally hits the ground 50 feet from the fire truck. After raising the ladder, $h(60) = 0$. So, by observing that $h(60) = -23$ before the crew raises the ladder, you can determine that a translation 23 feet up causes the water to travel 10 feet farther from the fire truck.

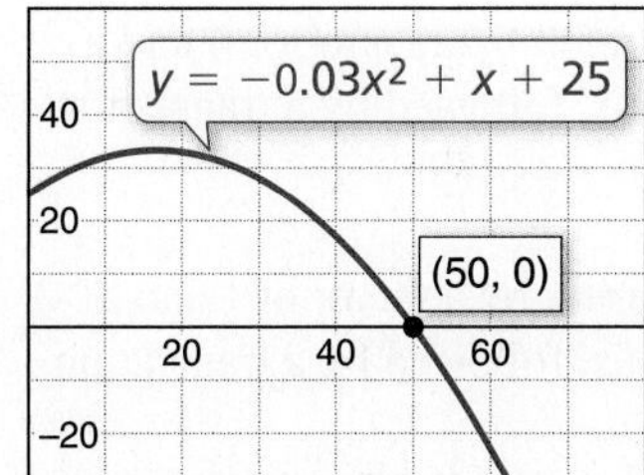

$g(x) = h(x) + 23$	Add 23 to the output.
$= -0.03x^2 + x + 48$	Substitute for $h(x)$ and simplify.

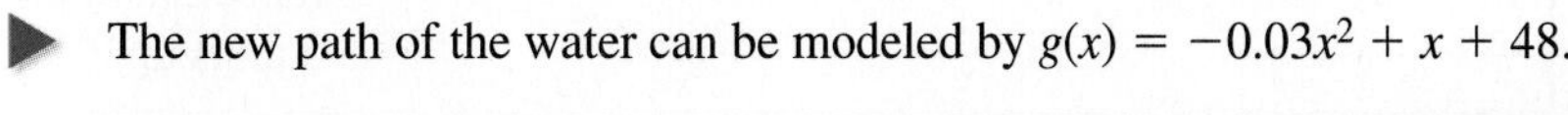

▶ The new path of the water can be modeled by $g(x) = -0.03x^2 + x + 48$.

Check Verify that $g(60) = 0$.

$$g(60) = -0.03(60)^2 + 60 + 48 = -108 + 60 + 48 = 0 \checkmark$$

SELF-ASSESSMENT

1 I do not understand. 2 I can do it with help. 3 I can do it on my own. 4 I can teach someone else.

9. Let the graph of g be a translation 4 units left, followed by a horizontal shrink by a factor of $\frac{1}{3}$ of the graph of $f(x) = x^2 + x$. Write a rule for g.
10. **WHAT IF?** In Example 5, the water hits the ground 10 feet closer to the fire truck after lowering the ladder. Write a function that models the new path of the water.

2.1 Practice WITH CalcChat® AND CalcView®

In Exercises 1–10, describe the transformation of $f(x) = x^2$ represented by g. Then graph each function. *Example 1*

1. $g(x) = x^2 - 3$
2. $g(x) = x^2 + 1$
3. $g(x) = (x + 2)^2$
4. $g(x) = (x - 4)^2$
5. $g(x) = (x - 1)^2$
6. $g(x) = (x + 3)^2$
7. $g(x) = (x + 6)^2 - 2$
8. $g(x) = (x - 9)^2 + 5$
9. $g(x) = (x - 7)^2 + 1$
10. $g(x) = (x + 10)^2 - 3$

ANALYZING RELATIONSHIPS **In Exercises 11–14, match the function with the correct transformation of the graph of f. Explain your reasoning.**

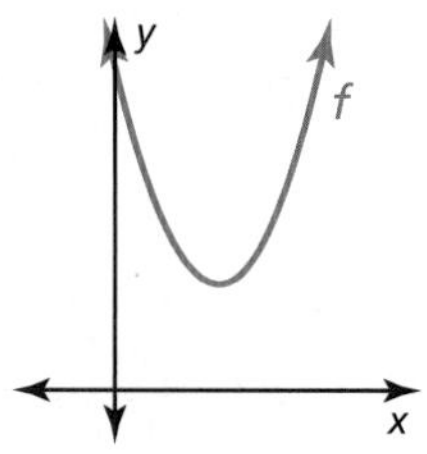

11. $y = f(x - 1)$
12. $y = f(x) + 1$
13. $y = f(x - 1) + 1$
14. $y = f(x + 1) - 1$

A. 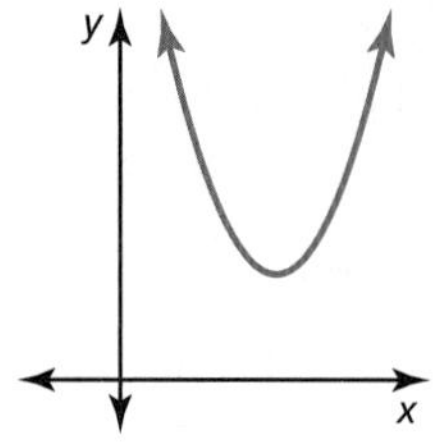

B. 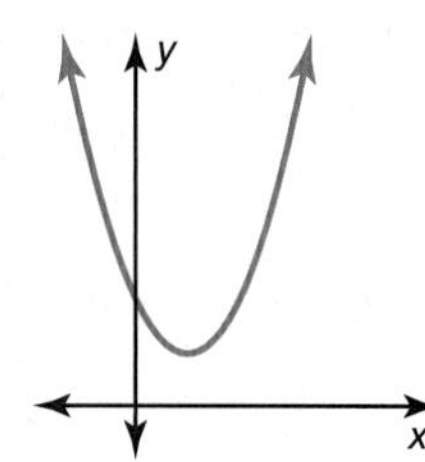

C. 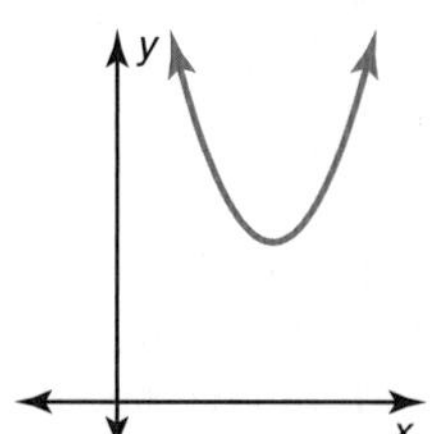

D. 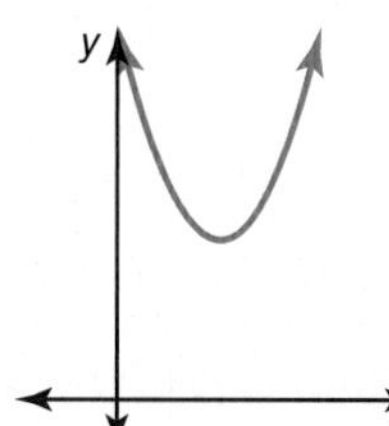

In Exercises 15–22, describe the transformation of $f(x) = x^2$ represented by g. Then graph each function. *Example 2*

15. $g(x) = -x^2$
16. $g(x) = (-x)^2$
17. $g(x) = 3x^2$
18. $g(x) = \frac{1}{3}x^2$
19. $g(x) = (2x)^2$
20. $g(x) = -(2x)^2$
21. $g(x) = \frac{1}{5}x^2 - 4$
22. $g(x) = \frac{1}{2}(x - 1)^2$

ERROR ANALYSIS **In Exercises 23 and 24, describe and correct the error in analyzing the graph of $f(x) = -6x^2 + 4$.**

23.

The graph is a reflection in the y-axis and a vertical stretch by a factor of 6, followed by a translation 4 units up of the graph of the parent quadratic function.

24.

The graph is a translation 4 units up, followed by a vertical stretch by a factor of 6 and a reflection in the x-axis of the graph of the parent quadratic function.

MP STRUCTURE **In Exercises 25–28, describe the transformation of the graph of the parent quadratic function. Then identify the vertex.**

25. $f(x) = 3(x + 2)^2 + 1$
26. $f(x) = -4(x + 1)^2 - 5$
27. $f(x) = -2x^2 + 5$
28. $f(x) = \frac{1}{2}(x - 1)^2$

In Exercises 29–32, write a rule for g described by the transformations of the graph of f. Then identify the vertex. *Examples 3 and 4*

29. $f(x) = x^2$; vertical stretch by a factor of 4 and a reflection in the x-axis, followed by a translation 2 units up
30. $f(x) = x^2$; vertical shrink by a factor of $\frac{1}{3}$ and a reflection in the y-axis, followed by a translation 3 units right
31. $f(x) = 8x^2 - 6$; horizontal stretch by a factor of 2 and a translation 2 units up, followed by a reflection in the y-axis
32. $f(x) = (x + 6)^2 + 3$; horizontal shrink by a factor of $\frac{1}{2}$ and a translation 1 unit down, followed by a reflection in the x-axis

MP STRUCTURE In Exercises 33–38, match the function with its graph. Explain your reasoning.

33. $g(x) = 2(x - 1)^2 - 2$

34. $g(x) = \frac{1}{2}(x + 1)^2 - 2$

35. $g(x) = -2(x - 1)^2 + 2$

36. $g(x) = 2(x + 1)^2 + 2$

37. $g(x) = -2(x + 1)^2 - 2$

38. $g(x) = 2(x - 1)^2 + 2$

A.

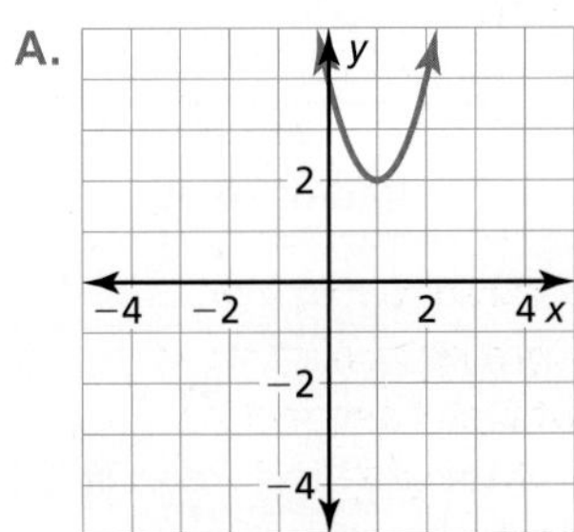

B.

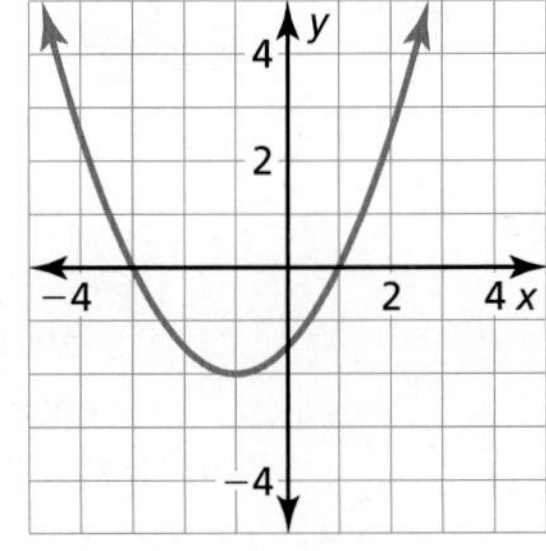

C.

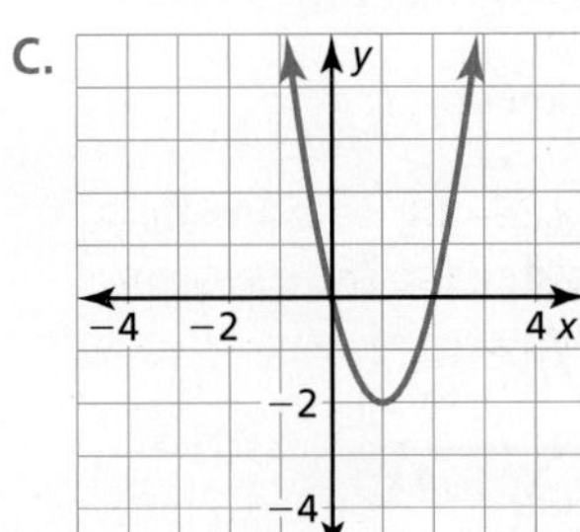

D.

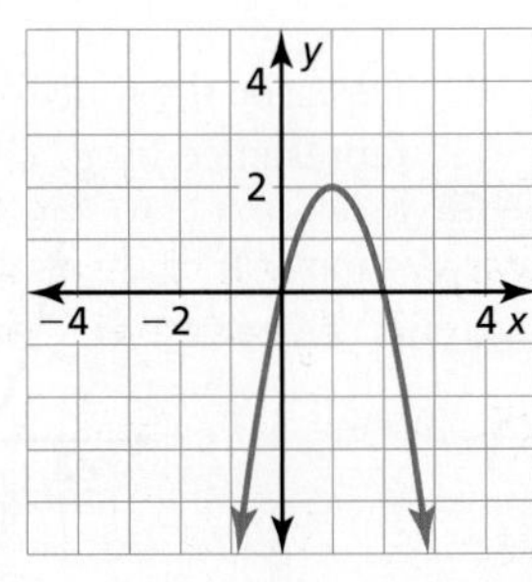

E.

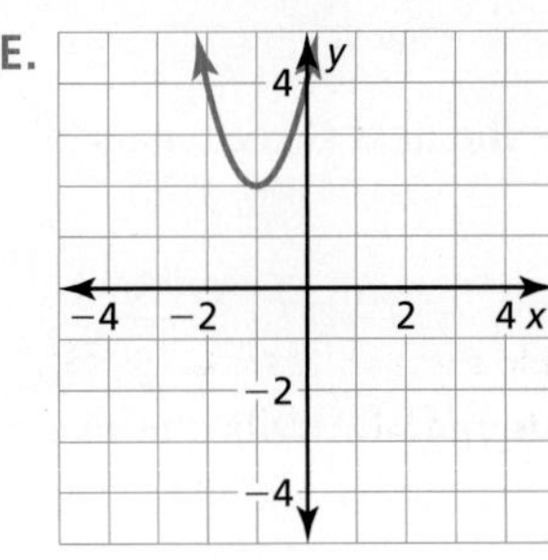

F.

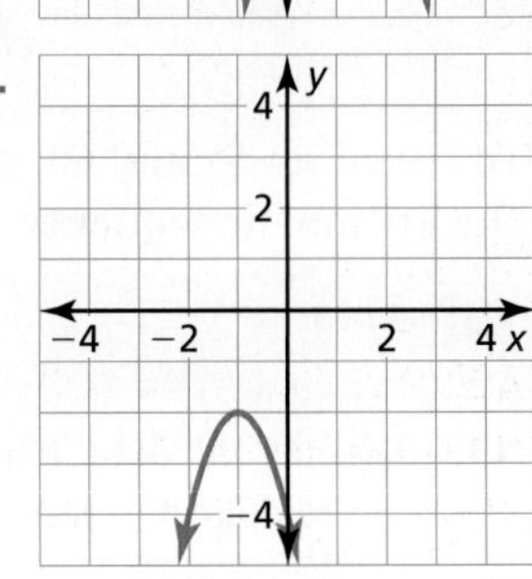

JUSTIFYING STEPS In Exercises 39 and 40, justify each step in writing a rule for g described by the transformations of $f(x) = 2x^2 + 6x$.

39. translation 6 units down, followed by a reflection in the x-axis

$h(x) = f(x) - 6$

$= 2x^2 + 6x - 6$

$g(x) = -h(x)$

$= -(2x^2 + 6x - 6)$

$= -2x^2 - 6x + 6$

40. reflection in the y-axis, followed by a translation 4 units right

$h(x) = f(-x)$

$= 2(-x)^2 + 6(-x)$

$= 2x^2 - 6x$

$g(x) = h(x - 4)$

$= 2(x - 4)^2 - 6(x - 4)$

$= 2x^2 - 22x + 56$

41. MODELING REAL LIFE A grasshopper can jump incredible distances, up to 20 times its length. The height (in inches) of a 1-inch-long grasshopper during a jump can be modeled by $h(x) = -\frac{1}{20}x^2 + x$, where x is the horizontal distance traveled (in inches). When the grasshopper jumps off a rock, it lands on the ground 2 inches farther away. Write a function that models the new path of the jump. *Example 5*

42. MODELING REAL LIFE The height (in feet) of a red kangaroo during a jump can be modeled by $h(x) = -0.03(x - 14)^2 + 6$, where x is the horizontal distance traveled (in feet). When the kangaroo jumps from a higher location, it lands on the ground 5 feet farther away. Write a function that models the new path of the jump.

43. MP PROBLEM SOLVING The function $f(t) = -16t^2 + 10$ models the height (in feet) of an object t seconds after it is dropped from a height of 10 feet on Earth. The same object dropped from the same height on the moon is modeled by $g(t) = -\frac{8}{3}t^2 + 10$. Describe the transformation of the graph of f to obtain g. From what height must the object be dropped on the moon so it hits the ground after the same number of seconds as on Earth?

44. HOW DO YOU SEE IT?
Describe the transformation of $f(x) = x^2$ represented by g.

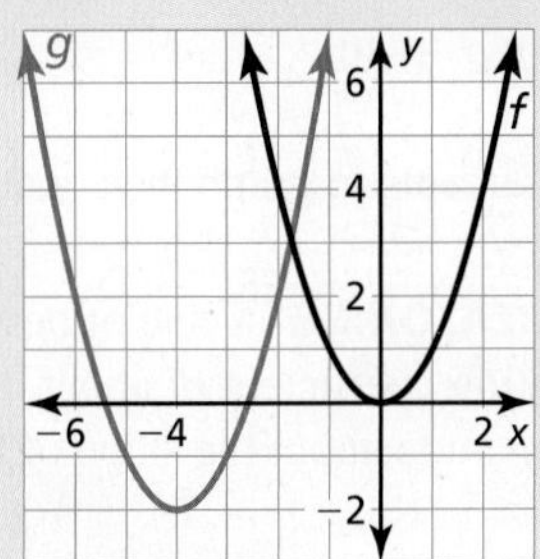

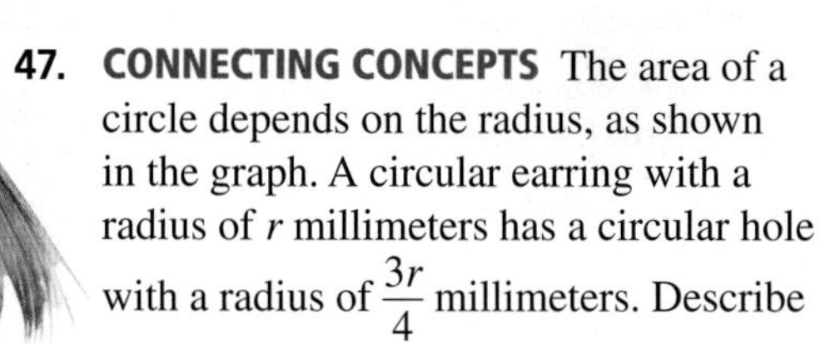

45. MODELING REAL LIFE Flying fish use their pectoral fins like airplane wings to glide through the air.

a. Write an equation of the form $y = a(x - h)^2 + k$ with vertex (33, 5) that models the flight path, assuming the fish leaves the water at (0, 0).

b. What are the domain and range of the function? What do they represent in this situation?

c. Does the value of a change when the flight path has vertex (30, 4)? Justify your answer.

46. THOUGHT PROVOKING
Let $f(x) = (x - 2)^2 + 3$. Describe a combination of different types of transformations of f that results in the original function.

47. CONNECTING CONCEPTS The area of a circle depends on the radius, as shown in the graph. A circular earring with a radius of r millimeters has a circular hole with a radius of $\frac{3r}{4}$ millimeters. Describe a transformation of the graph below that models the area of the black and white portion of the earring.

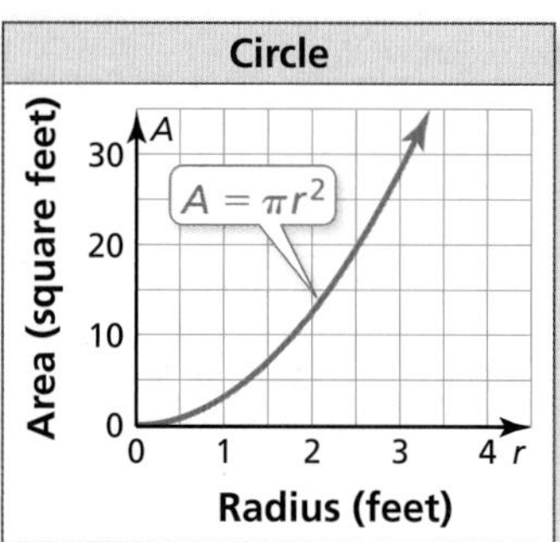

REVIEW & REFRESH

In Exercises 48–51, solve the system.

48. $2x - y - 2z = -5$
$-x + 4y + 5z = -7$
$3x + y - 4z = 5$

49. $x + y - 3z = -2$
$x - 2y + 6z = 10$
$-2x + y - 3z = -8$

50. $6x - 3y - z = 4$
$-3x + y + 3z = 9$
$z = -2y$

51. $2x - y + 3z = 1$
$3x + 3y - 6z = -12$
$-x - y + 2z = -4$

52. Let the graph of g be a translation 1 unit left and 6 units down, followed by a vertical shrink by a factor of $\frac{1}{2}$ of the graph of $f(x) = 3(x + 2)^2$. Write a rule for g and identify the vertex.

In Exercises 53 and 54, write an inequality that represents the graph.

53.

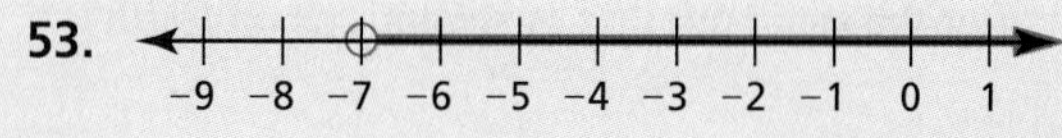

54.

0 1 2 3 4 5

55. Factor $8x^4 - 40x^3$.

56. Use intercepts to graph the equation $4x - 5y = 30$.

57. MP REASONING A line of best fit has a correlation coefficient of about 0.973. What can you conclude about the slope of the line?

58. Describe the transformation of $f(x) = x^2$ represented by g.

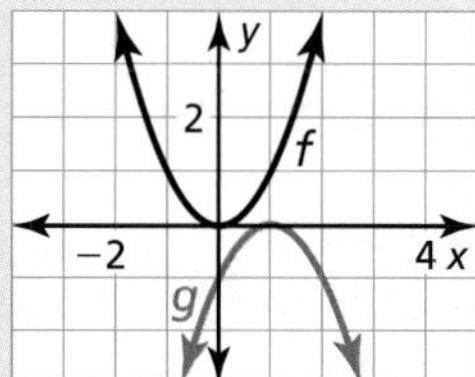

In Exercises 59 and 60, write the next three terms of the arithmetic sequence.

59. 21, 9, −3, −15, . . .

60. −10, −6, −2, 2, . . .

61. Display the data in a histogram. Describe the shape of the distribution.

Age	1–3	4–6	7–9	10–12	13–15
Frequency	8	12	5	3	2

62. MODELING REAL LIFE The cost (in dollars) of x pairs of jeans at a store's regular price is modeled by the function $f(x) = 40x$. The cost of x pairs of jeans during a sale is \$5 less than 85% of the cost at regular price. What is the cost of three pairs of jeans during the sale?

In Exercises 63 and 64, simplify the expression.

63. $\sqrt{48}$

64. $\frac{5}{\sqrt{7}}$

2.2 Characteristics of Quadratic Functions

Learning Target Graph and describe quadratic functions.

Success Criteria
- I can use properties of parabolas to graph quadratic functions.
- I can identify characteristics of quadratic functions and their graphs.
- I can use characteristics of quadratic functions to solve real-life problems.

EXPLORE IT! Parabolas and Symmetry

Work with a partner.

a. Sketch the graph of the function

$$f(x) = \frac{1}{2}x^2 - 2x - 2$$

on graph paper. Make sure you plot points on each side of the vertex.

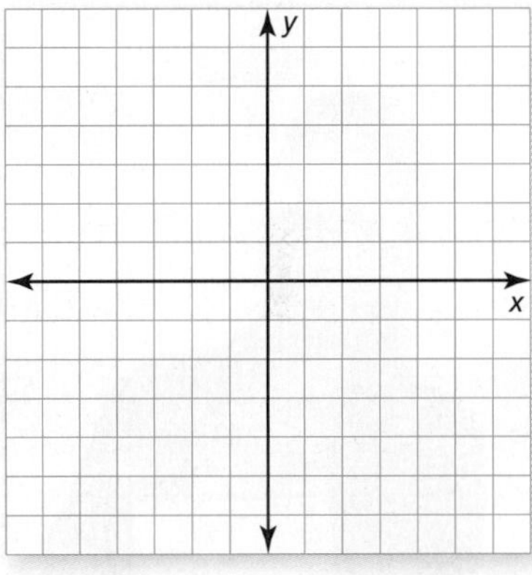

Math Practice

Look for Structure
What characteristics can you determine from the vertex form of a quadratic function?

b. Find a vertical line on your graph paper so that when you fold the paper, the left portion of the graph coincides with the right portion of the graph. What is the equation of this line? How does it relate to the vertex?

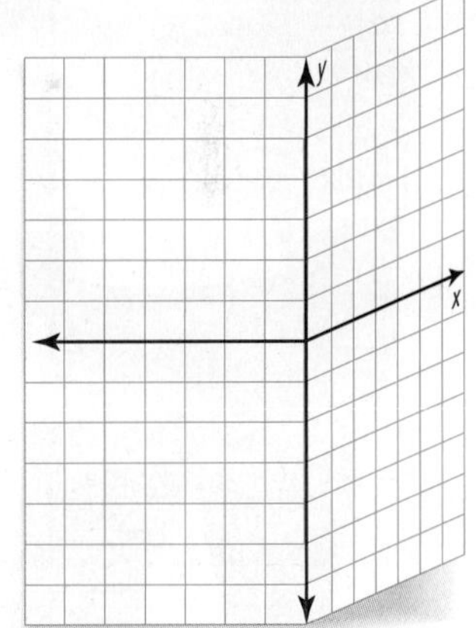

c. Show that the vertex form

$$f(x) = \frac{1}{2}(x - 2)^2 - 4$$

is equivalent to the function given in part (a).

d. Repeat parts (a)–(c) for the function given by

$$f(x) = -\frac{1}{3}x^2 + 2x + 3$$
$$= -\frac{1}{3}(x - 3)^2 + 6.$$

e. Consider the graph of $f(x) = a(x - h)^2 + k$.

- How can you describe the symmetry of the graph?
- How can you determine whether the graph opens up or down? Explain.
- What is the y-intercept?
- What is the least or greatest value of the function? Explain.

Exploring Properties of Parabolas

Vocabulary

axis of symmetry, *p. 54*
standard form, *p. 54*
minimum value, *p. 56*
maximum value, *p. 56*
intercept form, *p. 57*

An **axis of symmetry** is a line that divides a parabola into mirror images and passes through the vertex. Because the vertex of $f(x) = a(x - h)^2 + k$ is (h, k), the axis of symmetry is the vertical line $x = h$.

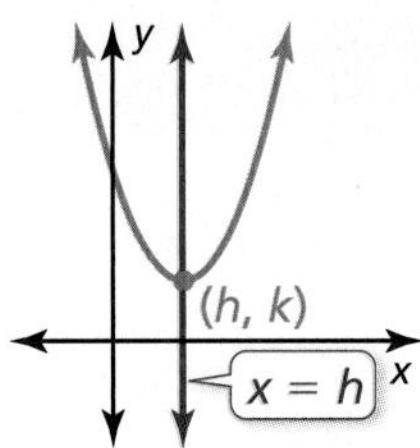

Previously, you used transformations to graph quadratic functions in vertex form. You can also use the axis of symmetry and the vertex to graph quadratic functions written in vertex form.

EXAMPLE 1 Using Symmetry to Graph a Quadratic Function

Graph $f(x) = -2(x + 3)^2 + 4$. Label the vertex and axis of symmetry.

SOLUTION

Step 1 Identify the constants $a = -2$, $h = -3$, and $k = 4$.

Step 2 Plot the vertex $(h, k) = (-3, 4)$ and draw the axis of symmetry $x = -3$.

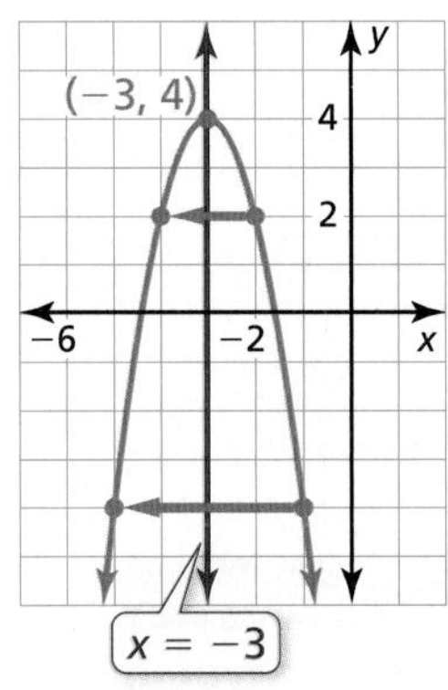

Step 3 Evaluate the function for two values of x, such as $x = -2$ and $x = -1$.

$$f(-2) = -2(-2 + 3)^2 + 4$$
$$= 2$$
$$f(-1) = -2(-1 + 3)^2 + 4$$
$$= -4$$

Plot the points $(-2, 2)$, $(-1, -4)$, and their reflections in the axis of symmetry.

Step 4 Draw a parabola through the plotted points.

Quadratic functions can also be written in **standard form**, $f(x) = ax^2 + bx + c$, where $a \neq 0$. You can derive the standard form by expanding the vertex form.

$f(x) = a(x - h)^2 + k$	Vertex form
$f(x) = a(x^2 - 2hx + h^2) + k$	Expand $(x - h)^2$.
$f(x) = ax^2 - 2ahx + ah^2 + k$	Distributive Property
$f(x) = ax^2 + (-2ah)x + (ah^2 + k)$	Group like terms.
$f(x) = ax^2 + bx + c$	Let $b = -2ah$ and let $c = ah^2 + k$.

This allows you to make the following observations.

$a = a$: So, a has the same meaning in vertex form and standard form.

$b = -2ah$: Solve for h to obtain $h = -\frac{b}{2a}$. So, the axis of symmetry is $x = -\frac{b}{2a}$.

$c = ah^2 + k$: In vertex form $f(x) = a(x - h)^2 + k$, notice that $f(0) = ah^2 + k$. So, c is the y-intercept.

KEY IDEA

Properties of the Graph of $f(x) = ax^2 + bx + c$

$y = ax^2 + bx + c, a > 0$ $\qquad$ $y = ax^2 + bx + c, a < 0$

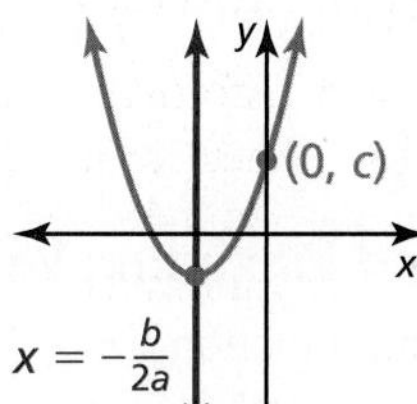

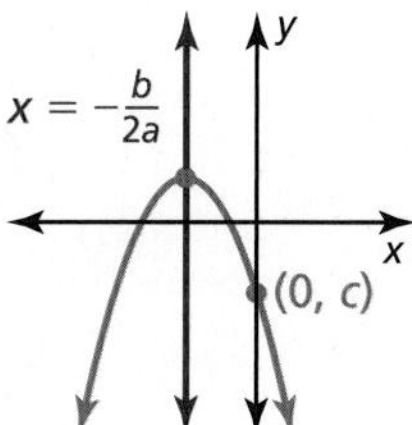

- The parabola opens up when $a > 0$ and opens down when $a < 0$.
- The graph is narrower than the graph of $f(x) = x^2$ when $|a| > 1$ and wider when $|a| < 1$.
- The axis of symmetry is $x = -\frac{b}{2a}$ and the vertex is $\left(-\frac{b}{2a}, f\left(-\frac{b}{2a}\right)\right)$.
- The y-intercept is c. So, the point $(0, c)$ is on the parabola.

EXAMPLE 2 Graphing a Quadratic Function in Standard Form

Graph $f(x) = 3x^2 - 6x + 1$. Label the vertex and axis of symmetry.

SOLUTION

Step 1 Identify the coefficients $a = 3$, $b = -6$, and $c = 1$. Because $a > 0$, the parabola opens up.

Step 2 Find the vertex. First calculate the x-coordinate.

$$x = -\frac{b}{2a} = -\frac{-6}{2(3)} = 1$$

Then find the y-coordinate of the vertex.

$$f(1) = 3(1)^2 - 6(1) + 1 = -2$$

So, the vertex is $(1, -2)$. Plot this point.

COMMON ERROR
Be sure to include the negative sign when writing the expression for the x-coordinate of the vertex.

Step 3 Draw the axis of symmetry $x = 1$.

Step 4 Identify the y-intercept c, which is 1. Plot the point $(0, 1)$ and its reflection in the axis of symmetry, $(2, 1)$.

Step 5 Evaluate the function for another value of x, such as $x = 3$.

$$f(3) = 3(3)^2 - 6(3) + 1 = 10$$

Plot the point $(3, 10)$ and its reflection in the axis of symmetry, $(-1, 10)$.

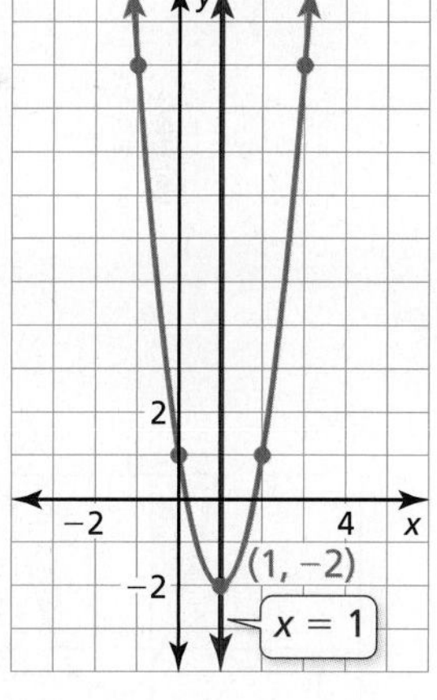

Step 6 Draw a parabola through the plotted points.

SELF-ASSESSMENT

1 I do not understand. 2 I can do it with help. 3 I can do it on my own. 4 I can teach someone else.

Graph the function. Label the vertex and axis of symmetry.

1. $g(x) = 2(x - 2)^2 + 5$
2. $h(x) = x^2 + 2x - 1$
3. $g(x) = -2x^2 - 8x + 1$
4. **MP REASONING** A parabola passes through the points $(-1, 4)$ and $(4, 4)$. Find the axis of symmetry.

Maximum and Minimum Values

Because the vertex is the highest or lowest point on a parabola, its y-coordinate is the *maximum value* or *minimum value* of the function. The vertex lies on the axis of symmetry, so the function is *increasing* on one side of the axis of symmetry and *decreasing* on the other side.

KEY IDEA

Minimum and Maximum Values

For the quadratic function $f(x) = ax^2 + bx + c$, the y-coordinate of the vertex is the **minimum value** of the function when $a > 0$ and the **maximum value** when $a < 0$. These values can be used to describe other properties of the function, as shown below.

$a > 0$

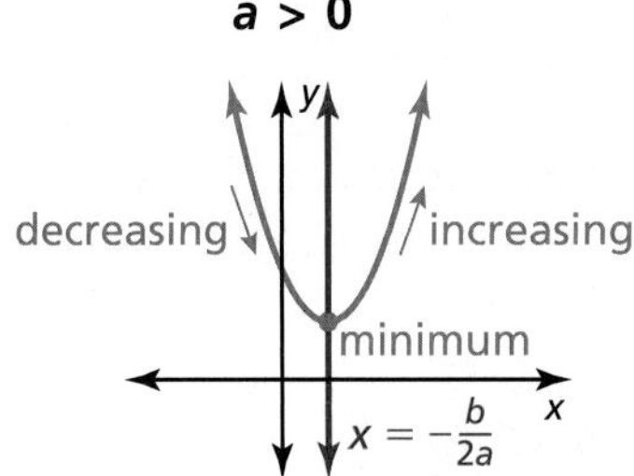

- Minimum value: $f\left(-\frac{b}{2a}\right)$
- Range: $y \geq f\left(-\frac{b}{2a}\right)$
- Decreasing when $x < -\frac{b}{2a}$
- Increasing when $x > -\frac{b}{2a}$

$a < 0$

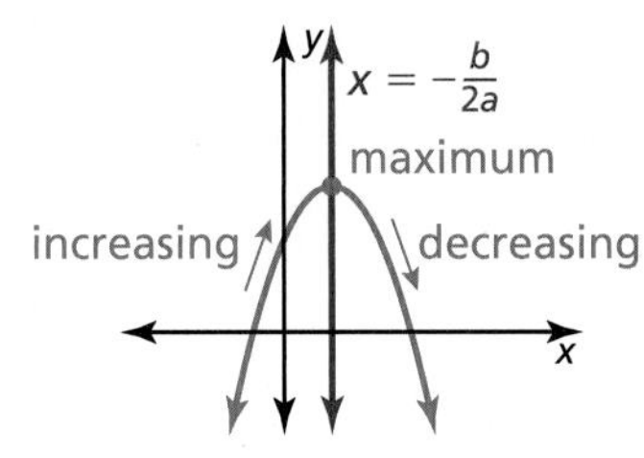

- Maximum value: $f\left(-\frac{b}{2a}\right)$
- Range: $y \leq f\left(-\frac{b}{2a}\right)$
- Increasing when $x < -\frac{b}{2a}$
- Decreasing when $x > -\frac{b}{2a}$

EXAMPLE 3 Finding a Minimum or a Maximum Value

Find the minimum value or maximum value of $f(x) = \frac{1}{2}x^2 - 2x - 1$. Find the domain and range of the function, and when the function is increasing and decreasing.

SOLUTION

Identify the coefficients $a = \frac{1}{2}$, $b = -2$, and $c = -1$. Because $a > 0$, the parabola opens up and the function has a minimum value. To find the minimum value, calculate the coordinates of the vertex.

$$x = -\frac{b}{2a} = -\frac{-2}{2\left(\frac{1}{2}\right)} = 2 \quad \Rightarrow \quad f(2) = \frac{1}{2}(2)^2 - 2(2) - 1 = -3$$

▶ The minimum value is -3. So, the domain is all real numbers and the range is $y \geq -3$. The function is decreasing when $x < 2$ and increasing when $x > 2$.

Check

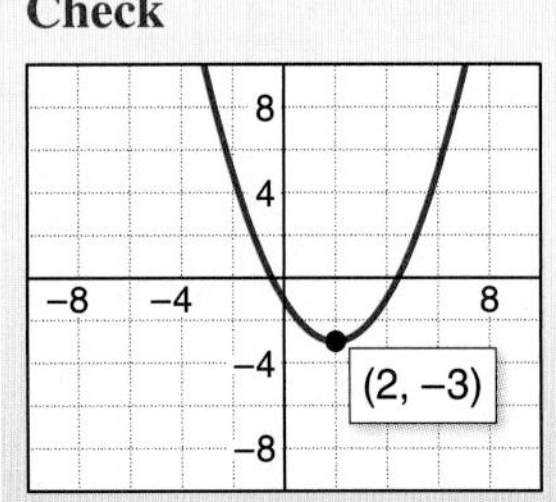

SELF-ASSESSMENT 1 I do not understand. 2 I can do it with help. 3 I can do it on my own. 4 I can teach someone else.

5. Find the minimum value or maximum value of (a) $f(x) = 4x^2 + 16x - 3$ and (b) $h(x) = -x^2 + 5x + 9$. Find the domain and range of each function, and when each function is increasing and decreasing.

Graphing Quadratic Functions Using x-Intercepts

REMEMBER
An x-intercept of a graph is the x-coordinate of a point where the graph intersects the x-axis. It occurs where $f(x) = 0$.

When the graph of a quadratic function has at least one x-intercept, the function can be written in **intercept form**, $f(x) = a(x - p)(x - q)$, where $a \neq 0$.

KEY IDEA

Properties of the Graph of $f(x) = a(x - p)(x - q)$

- Because $f(p) = 0$ and $f(q) = 0$, p and q are the x-intercepts of the graph of the function.
- The axis of symmetry is halfway between $(p, 0)$ and $(q, 0)$. So, the axis of symmetry is $x = \frac{p + q}{2}$.
- The parabola opens up when $a > 0$ and opens down when $a < 0$.

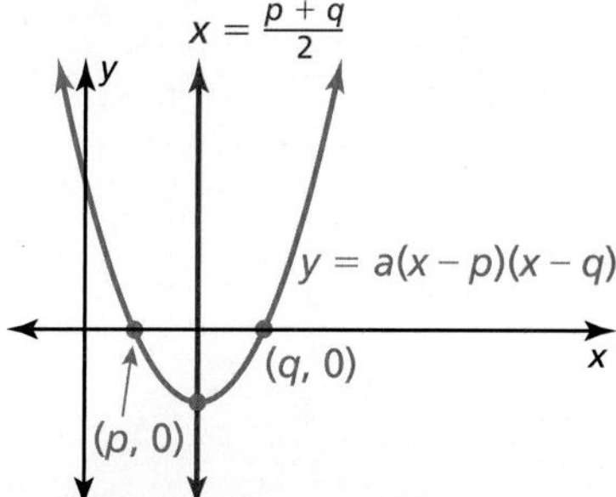

EXAMPLE 4 Graphing a Quadratic Function in Intercept Form

Graph $f(x) = -2(x + 3)(x - 1)$. Label the x-intercepts, vertex, and axis of symmetry.

SOLUTION

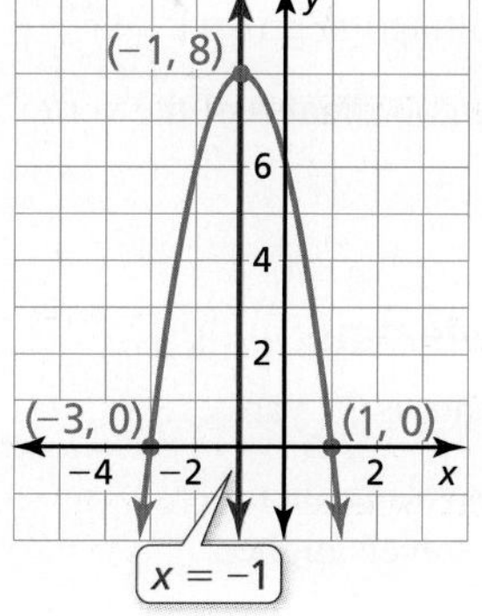

Step 1 Identify the x-intercepts. The x-intercepts are $p = -3$ and $q = 1$, so the parabola passes through the points $(-3, 0)$ and $(1, 0)$.

Step 2 Find the coordinates of the vertex.

$$x = \frac{p + q}{2} = \frac{-3 + 1}{2} = -1$$

$$f(-1) = -2(-1 + 3)(-1 - 1) = 8$$

So, the axis of symmetry is $x = -1$ and the vertex is $(-1, 8)$.

Step 3 Draw a parabola through the vertex and the points where the x-intercepts occur.

Check Use technology to generate a table of values for f.

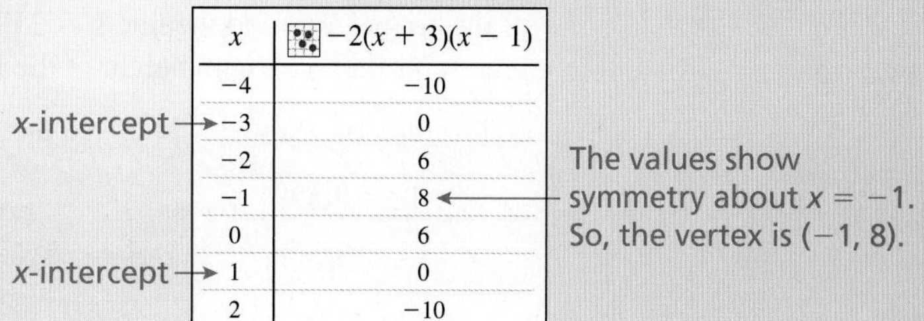

x	$-2(x + 3)(x - 1)$
−4	−10
−3	0
−2	6
−1	8
0	6
1	0
2	−10

SELF-ASSESSMENT 1 I do not understand. 2 I can do it with help. 3 I can do it on my own. 4 I can teach someone else.

Graph the function. Label the x-intercepts, vertex, and axis of symmetry.

6. $f(x) = -(x + 1)(x + 5)$

7. $g(x) = \frac{1}{4}(x - 6)(x - 2)$

Solving Real-Life Problems

EXAMPLE 5 **Modeling Real Life** 

The parabola shows the path of your first golf shot, where x is the horizontal distance (in yards) and y is the corresponding height (in yards). The path of your second shot is modeled by the function $f(x) = -0.02x(x - 80)$. Which shot travels farther before hitting the ground? Which travels higher?

y
(50, 25)
(0, 0)
(100, 0)
x

SOLUTION

1. **Understand the Problem** You are given a graph and a function that represent the paths of two golf shots. You are asked to determine which shot travels farther before hitting the ground and which shot travels higher.

2. **Make a Plan** Determine how far each shot travels by interpreting the x-intercepts. Determine how high each shot travels by finding the maximum value of each function. Then compare the values.

3. **Solve and Check**

First shot: The graph shows that the x-intercepts are 0 and 100. So, the ball travels 100 yards before hitting the ground.

Because the axis of symmetry is halfway between (0, 0) and (100, 0), the axis of symmetry is $x = \frac{0 + 100}{2} = 50$. So, the vertex is (50, 25) and the maximum height is 25 yards.

Second shot: By rewriting the function in intercept form as $f(x) = -0.02(x - 0)(x - 80)$, you can see that $p = 0$ and $q = 80$. So, the ball travels 80 yards before hitting the ground.

To find the maximum height, find the coordinates of the vertex.

$$x = \frac{p + q}{2} = \frac{0 + 80}{2} = 40$$

$$f(40) = -0.02(40)(40 - 80) = 32$$

The maximum height of the second shot is 32 yards.

▶ Because 100 yards > 80 yards, the first shot travels farther. Because 32 yards > 25 yards, the second shot travels higher.

Check To check that the second shot travels higher, graph the function representing the path of the second shot and the line $y = 25$, which represents the maximum height of the first shot.

The graph rises above $y = 25$, so the second shot travels higher. ✓

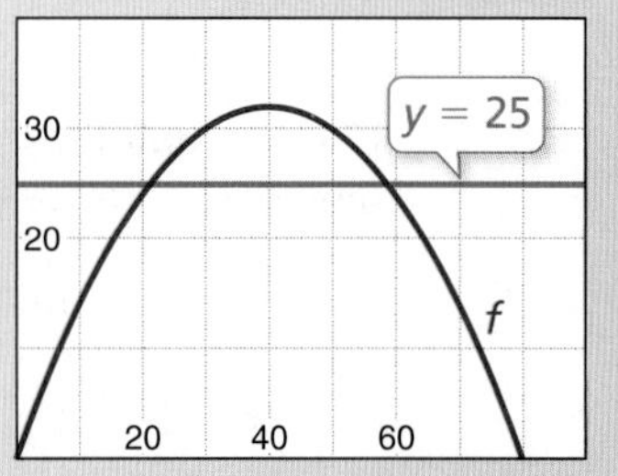

SELF-ASSESSMENT 1 I do not understand. 2 I can do it with help. 3 I can do it on my own. 4 I can teach someone else.

8. **WHAT IF?** The graph of your third shot is a parabola through the origin that reaches a maximum height of 28 yards when $x = 45$. Compare the distance it travels before it hits the ground with the distances of the first two shots.

2.2 Practice WITH CalcChat® AND CalcView®

In Exercises 1–12, graph the function. Label the vertex and axis of symmetry. ▶ *Example 1*

1. $f(x) = (x - 3)^2$
2. $h(x) = (x + 4)^2$
3. $g(x) = (x + 3)^2 + 5$
4. $y = (x - 7)^2 - 1$
5. $y = -4(x - 2)^2 + 4$
6. $g(x) = 2(x + 1)^2 - 3$
7. $h(x) = 4(x + 4)^2 + 6$
8. $f(x) = -2(x - 1)^2 - 5$
9. $y = -\frac{1}{4}(x + 2)^2 + 1$
10. $y = \frac{1}{2}(x - 3)^2 + 2$
11. $f(x) = 0.4(x - 1)^2$
12. $g(x) = 0.75x^2 - 5$

ANALYZING RELATIONSHIPS In Exercises 13–16, use the axis of symmetry to match the equation with its graph.

13. $y = 2(x - 3)^2 + 1$
14. $y = (x + 4)^2 - 2$
15. $y = \frac{1}{2}(x + 1)^2 + 3$
16. $y = (x - 2)^2 - 1$

A. 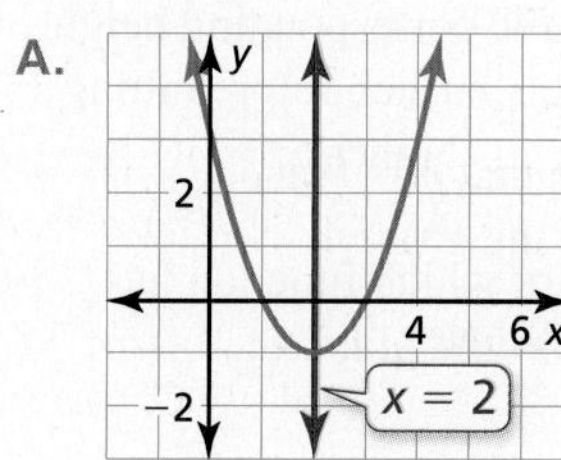

B. 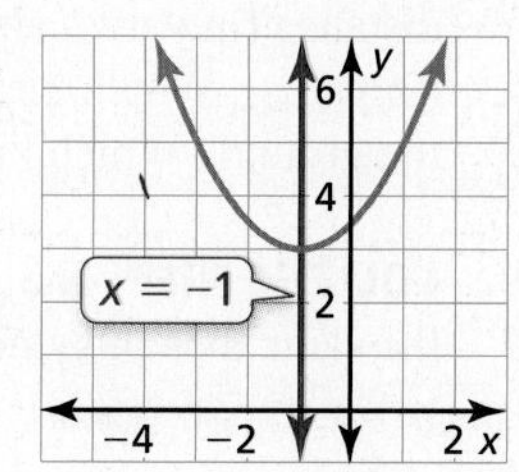

C. 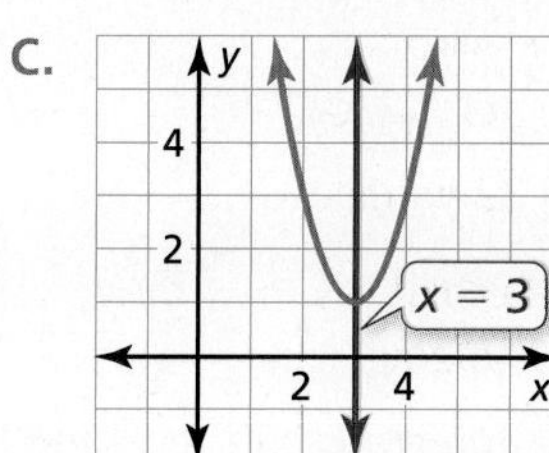

D. 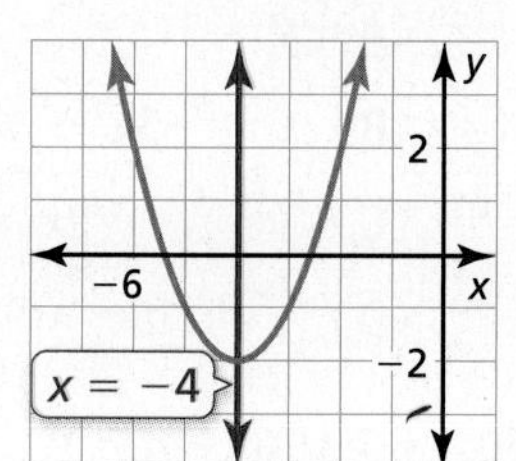

In Exercises 17–26, graph the function. Label the vertex and axis of symmetry. ▶ *Example 2*

17. $y = x^2 + 2x + 1$
18. $y = 3x^2 - 6x + 4$
19. $y = -4x^2 + 8x + 2$
20. $f(x) = -x^2 - 6x + 3$
21. $g(x) = -x^2 - 1$
22. $f(x) = 6x^2 - 5$
23. $g(x) = -1.5x^2 + 3x + 2$
24. $f(x) = 0.5x^2 + x - 3$
25. $y = \frac{3}{2}x^2 - 3x + 6$
26. $y = -\frac{5}{2}x^2 - 4x - 1$

ERROR ANALYSIS In Exercises 27 and 28, describe and correct the error in analyzing the graph of $y = 4x^2 + 24x - 7$.

27. 

The x-coordinate of the vertex is

$$x = \frac{b}{2a} = \frac{24}{2(4)} = 3.$$

28. 

The y-intercept of the graph is the value of c, which is 7.

MODELING REAL LIFE In Exercises 29 and 30, x is the horizontal distance (in feet) and y is the height (in feet). Find and interpret the coordinates of the vertex.

29. The path of a basketball thrown at an angle of 45° can be modeled by $y = -0.02x^2 + x + 6$.

30. The path of a shot put released at an angle of 35° can be modeled by $y = -0.01x^2 + 0.7x + 6$.

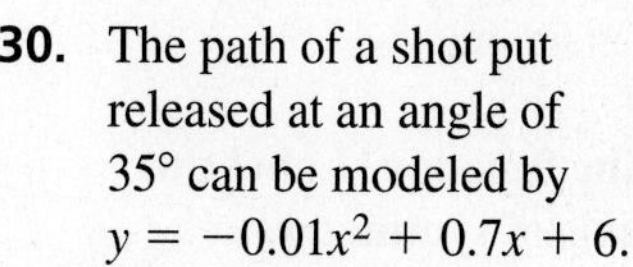

In Exercises 31–40, find the minimum value or maximum value of the function. Find the domain and range of the function, and when the function is increasing and decreasing. ▶ *Example 3*

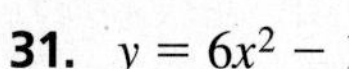

31. $y = 6x^2 - 1$
32. $y = 9x^2 + 7$
33. $y = -x^2 - 4x - 2$
34. $g(x) = -3x^2 - 6x + 5$
35. $f(x) = -2x^2 + 8x + 7$
36. $g(x) = 3x^2 + 18x - 5$
37. $h(x) = 2x^2 - 12x$
38. $h(x) = x^2 - 4x$
39. $y = \frac{1}{4}x^2 - 3x + 2$
40. $f(x) = \frac{3}{2}x^2 + 6x + 4$
41. **WRITING** Two quadratic functions have graphs with vertices (2, 4) and (2, −3). Explain why you cannot use the axes of symmetry to distinguish between the two functions.

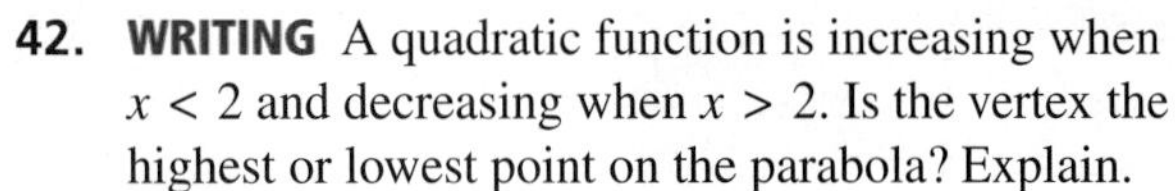

42. **WRITING** A quadratic function is increasing when $x < 2$ and decreasing when $x > 2$. Is the vertex the highest or lowest point on the parabola? Explain.

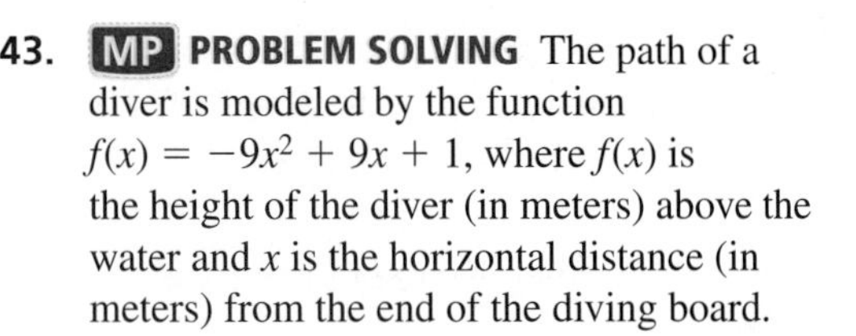

43. **MP PROBLEM SOLVING** The path of a diver is modeled by the function $f(x) = -9x^2 + 9x + 1$, where $f(x)$ is the height of the diver (in meters) above the water and x is the horizontal distance (in meters) from the end of the diving board.

   a. What is the height of the diving board?

   b. What is the maximum height of the diver?

   c. Determine when the diver is ascending and when the diver is descending.

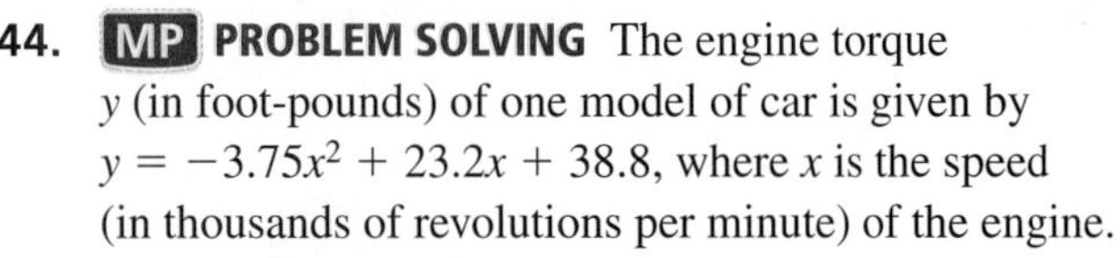

44. **MP PROBLEM SOLVING** The engine torque y (in foot-pounds) of one model of car is given by $y = -3.75x^2 + 23.2x + 38.8$, where x is the speed (in thousands of revolutions per minute) of the engine.

   a. Find the engine speed that maximizes torque. What is the maximum torque?

   b. Explain what happens to the engine torque as the speed of the engine increases.

In Exercises 45–52, graph the function. Label the x-intercept(s), vertex, and axis of symmetry.
Example 4

45. $y = (x + 3)(x - 3)$

46. $y = (x + 1)(x - 3)$

47. $y = 3(x + 2)(x + 6)$

48. $f(x) = 2(x - 5)(x - 1)$

49. $g(x) = -x(x + 6)$

50. $y = -4x(x + 7)$

51. $f(x) = -2(x - 3)^2$

52. $y = 4(x - 7)^2$

MP USING TOOLS In Exercises 53–56, identify the x-intercepts of the graph of the function and find when the function is increasing and decreasing. Use technology to verify your answers.

53. $f(x) = \frac{1}{2}(x - 2)(x + 6)$

54. $y = \frac{3}{4}(x + 1)(x - 3)$

55. $g(x) = -4(x - 4)(x - 2)$

56. $h(x) = -5(x + 5)(x + 1)$

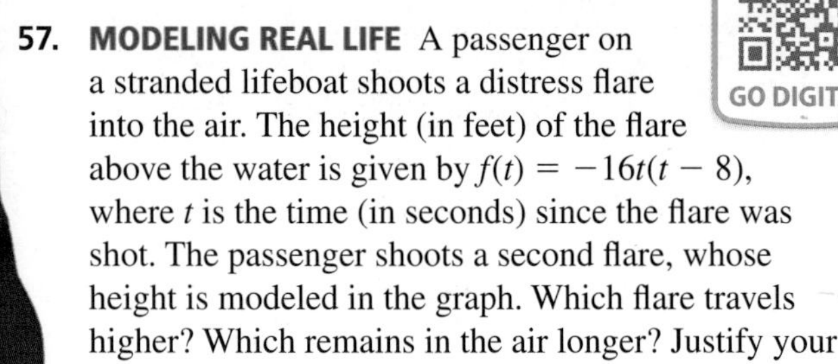

57. **MODELING REAL LIFE** A passenger on a stranded lifeboat shoots a distress flare into the air. The height (in feet) of the flare above the water is given by $f(t) = -16t(t - 8)$, where t is the time (in seconds) since the flare was shot. The passenger shoots a second flare, whose height is modeled in the graph. Which flare travels higher? Which remains in the air longer? Justify your answers. *Example 5*

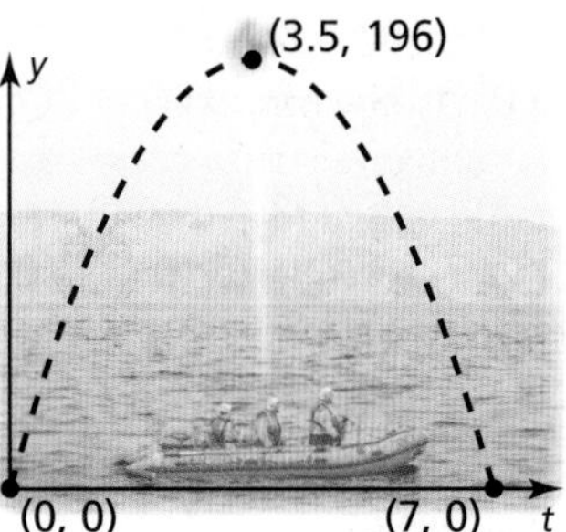

58. **MODELING REAL LIFE** A soccer player kicks a ball downfield. The height of the ball increases until it reaches a maximum height of 8 yards, 20 yards away from the player. A second kick is modeled by $y = x(0.4 - 0.008x)$, where x is the horizontal distance (in yards) and y is the corresponding height (in yards). Which kick travels farther before hitting the ground? Which kick travels higher?

59. **COLLEGE PREP** The graph of which function has the same axis of symmetry as the graph of $y = x^2 + 2x + 2$?

   Ⓐ $y = 2x^2 + 2x + 2$

   Ⓑ $y = -3x^2 - 6x + 2$

   Ⓒ $y = x^2 - 2x + 2$

   Ⓓ $y = -5x^2 + 10x + 2$

60. **COLLEGE PREP** Which function represents the widest parabola? Explain your reasoning.

   Ⓐ $y = 2(x + 3)^2$

   Ⓑ $y = x^2 - 5$

   Ⓒ $y = 0.5(x - 1)^2 + 1$

   Ⓓ $y = -x^2 + 6$

CONNECTING CONCEPTS In Exercises 61 and 62, write an equation for the area of the figure. Then determine the maximum possible area of the figure.

61.

62.

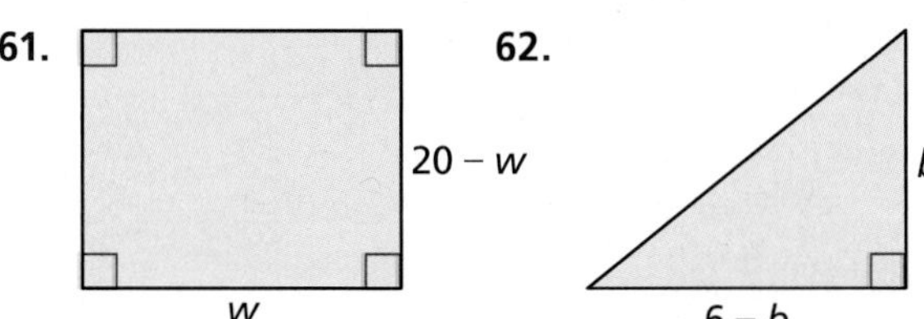

63. **MP REASONING** The points (2, 3) and $(-4, 2)$ lie on the graph of a quadratic function. Determine whether you can use these points to find the axis of symmetry. If so, write the equation of the axis of symmetry. If not, explain.

64. **OPEN-ENDED** Write two different quadratic functions in intercept form whose graphs have the axis of symmetry $x = 3$.

65. **MODELING REAL LIFE** Although a football field appears to be flat, some have parabola-shaped cross sections so that rain runs off to both sides. The cross section of a field can be modeled by $y = -0.000234x(x - 160)$, where x and y are measured in feet. What is the width of the field? What is the maximum height of the surface of the field?

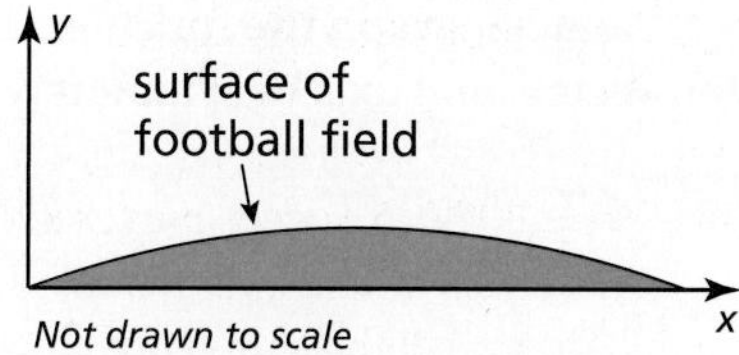

Not drawn to scale

66. **MP PROBLEM SOLVING** An online music store sells about 4000 songs each day when it charges $1 per song. For each $0.05 increase in price, about 80 fewer songs per day are sold. Use the verbal model and quadratic function to determine how much the store should charge per song to maximize daily revenue.

Revenue (dollars)	=	Price (dollars/song)	•	Sales (songs)
$R(x)$	=	$(1 + 0.05x)$	•	$(4000 - 80x)$

67. **DRAWING CONCLUSIONS** Compare the graphs of the three quadratic functions. What do you notice? Justify your answer.

$$f(x) = (x + 3)(x + 1)$$
$$g(x) = (x + 2)^2 - 1$$
$$h(x) = x^2 + 4x + 3$$

68. **MP PROBLEM SOLVING** A woodland jumping mouse hops along a parabolic path given by $y = -0.2x^2 + 1.3x$, where x is the mouse's horizontal distance traveled (in feet) and y is the corresponding height (in feet). Can the mouse jump over a fence that is 3 feet high? Justify your answer.

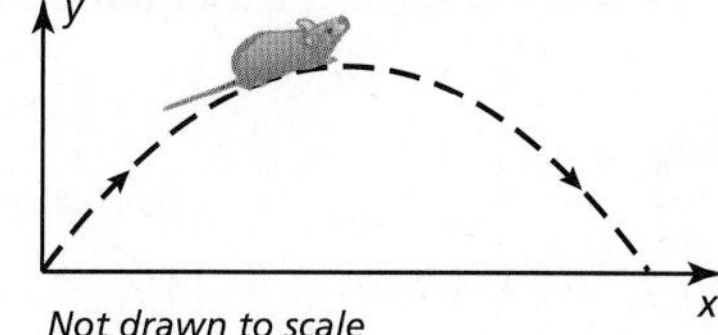

Not drawn to scale

69. **MP PRECISION** The Gateshead Millennium Bridge in England spans the River Tyne. The arch of the bridge can be modeled by a parabola. The arch reaches a maximum height of 50 meters at a point roughly 63 meters across the river. Graph the curve of the arch. How did you label the axes? What are the domain and range? What do they represent in this situation?

70. **HOW DO YOU SEE IT?**
Consider the graph of the function $f(x) = a(x - p)(x - q)$.

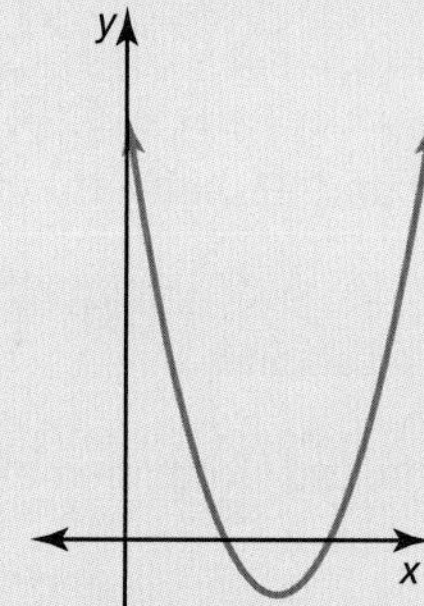

a. What do you know about the signs of a, p, and q?

b. Explain how the graph of f changes when the signs of a, p, and q change.

71. **MODELING REAL LIFE** A kernel of popcorn contains water that expands when the kernel is heated, causing it to pop. Each equation below represents the "popping volume" y (in cubic centimeters per gram) of popcorn with moisture content x (as a percent of the popcorn's weight).

Hot-air popping: $y = -0.761(x - 5.52)(x - 22.6)$

Hot-oil popping: $y = -0.652(x - 5.35)(x - 21.8)$

a. For hot-air popping, what moisture content maximizes popping volume? What is the maximum volume?

b. For hot-oil popping, what moisture content maximizes popping volume? What is the maximum volume?

c. Use technology to graph both functions in the same coordinate plane. What are the domain and range of each function in this situation? Explain.

72. THOUGHT PROVOKING An astronaut has n feet of rope to mark a rectangular dig site on the moon. What is the maximum area of the dig site in terms of n?

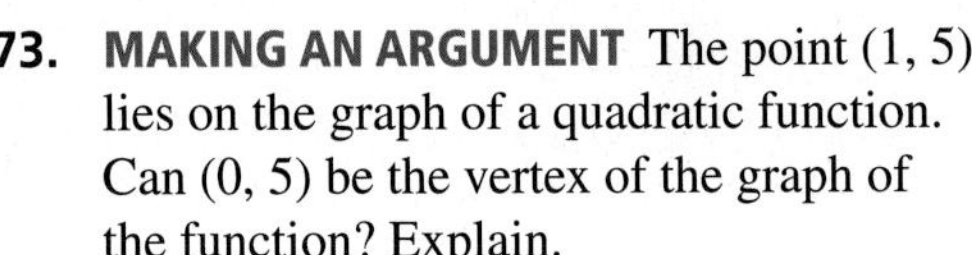

73. MAKING AN ARGUMENT The point $(1, 5)$ lies on the graph of a quadratic function. Can $(0, 5)$ be the vertex of the graph of the function? Explain.

74. CRITICAL THINKING Find the y-intercept in terms of a, p, and q for the quadratic function $f(x) = a(x - p)(x - q)$.

75. ABSTRACT REASONING A function is written in intercept form with $a > 0$. What happens to the vertex of the graph as a increases? as a approaches 0?

REVIEW & REFRESH

WATCH

In Exercises 76–79, solve the equation.

76. $2\sqrt{x - 4} - 2 = 2$

77. $\sqrt{5x} + 5 = 0$

78. $\sqrt{3x + 8} = \sqrt{x + 4}$

79. $\sqrt{5x + 6} = x$

In Exercises 80 and 81, solve the proportion.

80. $\dfrac{2}{3} = \dfrac{x}{9}$

81. $\dfrac{5}{2} = \dfrac{-20}{x}$

82. Describe the transformation of $f(x) = x^2$ represented by g.

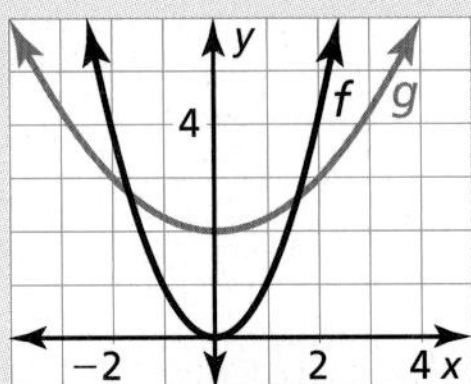

In Exercises 83 and 84, solve the system.

83. $x + 2y - z = 6$
$3x - y - 2z = -10$
$-2x - 4y + 2z = 12$

84. $2x - 5y - z = 3$
$-x + 3y + 2z = 10$
$4x - 2y - 3z = -16$

85. MODELING REAL LIFE The table shows the numbers of posts on a social media account and the numbers of months since opening the account. Do the data show a linear relationship? If so, write an equation of a line of fit and use it to estimate the number of posts on the account after 1 year.

Months, x	1	2	4	6	9
Number of posts, y	19	52	97	156	234

86. Solve $|3x + 5| = 2|x - 10|$.

In Exercises 87 and 88, graph the function. Label the x-intercept(s), vertex, and axis of symmetry.

87. $g(x) = -3(x + 2)(x + 4)$

88. $f(x) = 0.4x(x - 6)$

89. Find the volume of the pyramid.

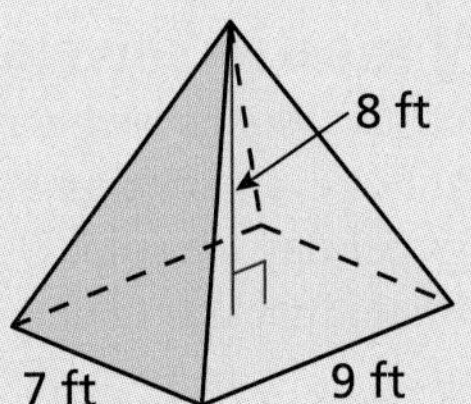

In Exercises 90 and 91, determine whether the function represents *exponential growth* or *exponential decay*. Identify the percent rate of change.

90. $y = 0.5(1.02)^t$

91. $y = 12(0.86)^t$

92. Analyze the data and then create a display that best represents the data. Explain your reasoning.

Natural Hair Color Survey	
Color	**Number of students**
black	14
brown	63
blonde	38
red	5

In Exercises 93 and 94, solve the inequality. Graph the solution.

93. $-7 < \frac{1}{2}(3n - 8) \leq 11$

94. $2(d + 5) \geq 50$ *or* $-4d - 1 > 23$

2.3 Focus of a Parabola

Learning Target Graph and write equations of parabolas.

Success Criteria

- I can explain the relationships among the focus, the directrix, and the graph of a parabola.
- I can graph parabolas.
- I can write equations of parabolas.

EXPLORE IT! Analyzing Graphs of Parabolas

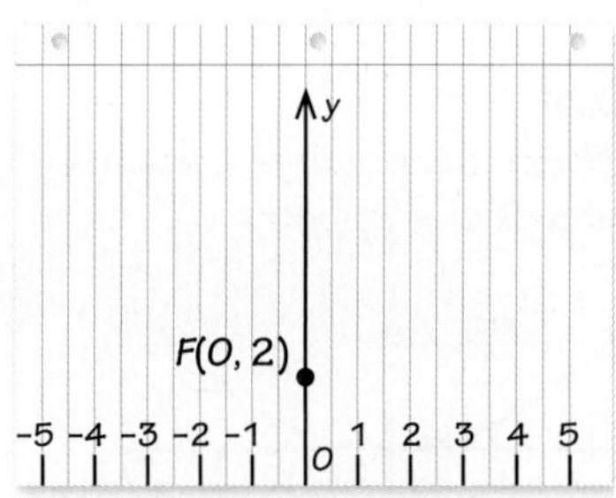

Work with a partner. Use dashes along the bottom of a piece of lined paper to mark and number equidistant points from -5 to 5 as shown. These dashes represent the units along the x-axis. Plot a point $F(0, 2)$ that is two units above 0. Draw a line through F to represent the y-axis.

a. Fold the paper so the point 0 (bottom of page) is on top of the plotted point. Unfold the paper and describe the line represented by the fold you made.

b. Repeat the process in part (a) with the points 1 and -1, 2 and -2, and so on. The diagrams below show the fold for the point 1. After you are done, examine the folds. What do you notice?

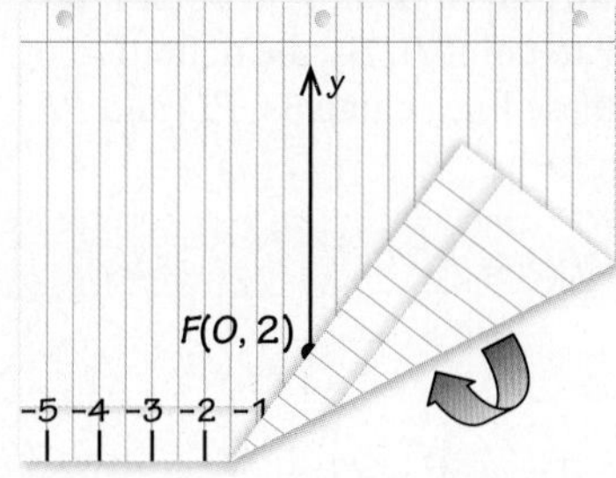

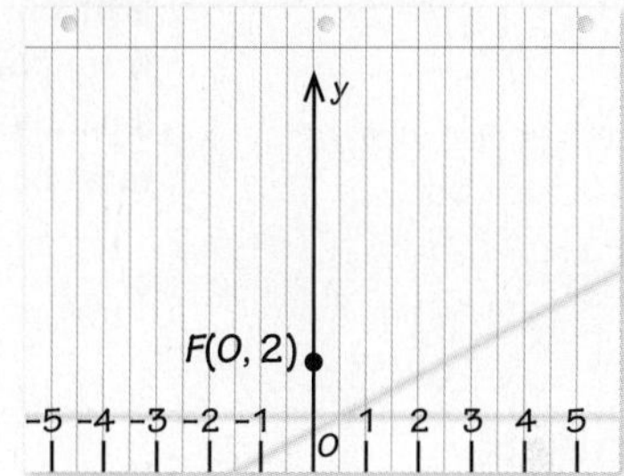

Math Practice

Construct Arguments
How does the shape of a parabola change as you move the focus closer and farther away from the vertex of the parabola?

c. On each fold for the points 0, 1, and 2, use the Pythagorean Theorem to find and label a point (x, y) that is equidistant from F and the x-axis. Then find an equation that represents the curve that passes through these points.

d. The parabola below represents the cross section of a satellite dish. When vertical rays enter the dish and hit the parabola, they reflect at the same angle at which they entered as shown. Draw the reflected rays so that they intersect the y-axis. What do you notice?

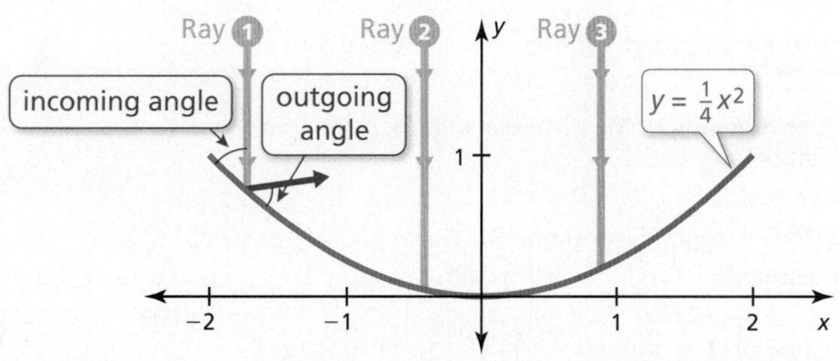

e. The optimal location for the receiver of the satellite dish in part (d) is at a point called the *focus* of the parabola. Determine the location of the focus.

Exploring the Focus and Directrix

Vocabulary
focus, *p. 64*
directrix, *p. 64*

Previously, you learned that the graph of a quadratic function is a parabola that opens up or down. A parabola can also be defined as the set of all points (x, y) in a plane that are equidistant from a fixed point called the **focus** and a fixed line called the **directrix**.

- The focus is in the interior of the parabola and lies on the axis of symmetry.
- The vertex lies halfway between the focus and the directrix.
- The directrix is perpendicular to the axis of symmetry.

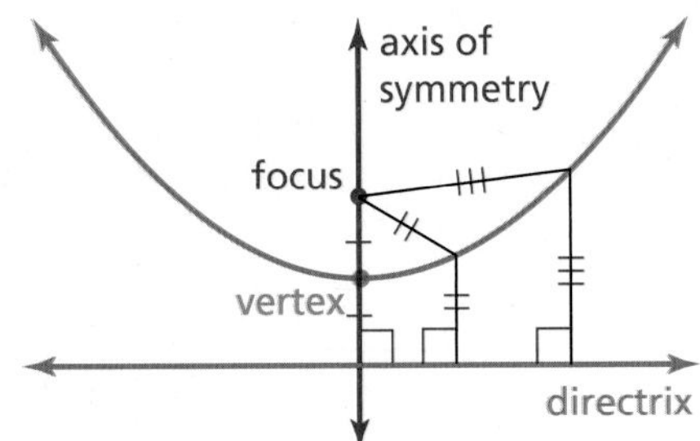

EXAMPLE 1 Deriving an Equation

Write an equation of the parabola with focus $F(0, 2)$ and directrix $y = -2$.

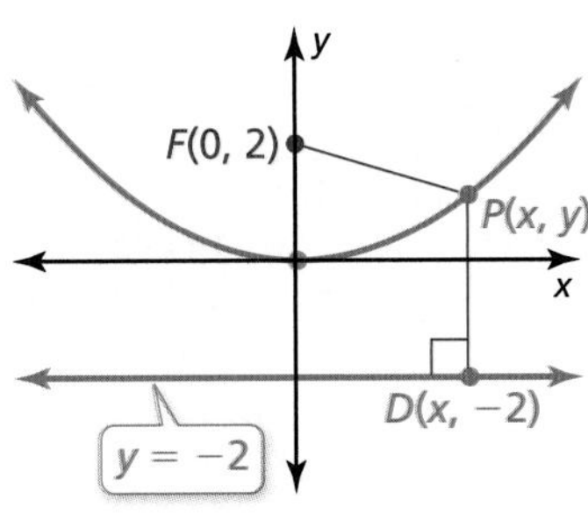

SOLUTION

The vertex is halfway between the focus and the directrix, at $(0, 0)$. Notice the line segments drawn from point F to point P and from point P to point D. By the definition of a parabola, these line segments, PD and PF, must be congruent.

STUDY TIP
The distance from a point to a line is defined as the length of the perpendicular segment from the point to the line.

$PD = PF$	Definition of a parabola
$\lvert y - (-2)\rvert = \sqrt{x^2 + (2 - y)^2}$	Write expressions for the lengths of the line segments.
$(y + 2)^2 = x^2 + (2 - y)^2$	Square each side.
$y^2 + 4y + 4 = x^2 + 4 - 4y + y^2$	Expand.
$8y = x^2$	Combine like terms.
$y = \frac{1}{8}x^2$	Divide each side by 8.

REMEMBER
You can use the Pythagorean Theorem to find distances in the coordinate plane.

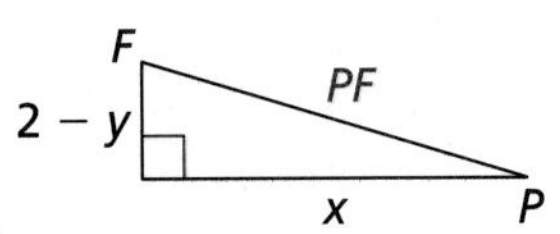

▶ So, an equation of the parabola is $y = \frac{1}{8}x^2$.

SELF-ASSESSMENT

1 I do not understand. 2 I can do it with help. 3 I can do it on my own. 4 I can teach someone else.

1. Write an equation of the parabola with focus $F(0, -3)$ and directrix $y = 3$.

2. **WRITING** Explain how to find the coordinates of the focus of a parabola with vertex $(0, 0)$ and directrix $y = 5$.

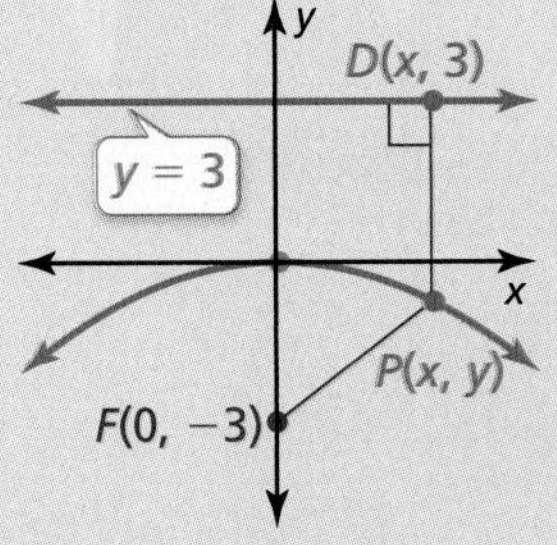

You can derive the equation of a parabola that opens up or down with vertex (0, 0), focus $(0, p)$, and directrix $y = -p$ using the procedure in Example 1.

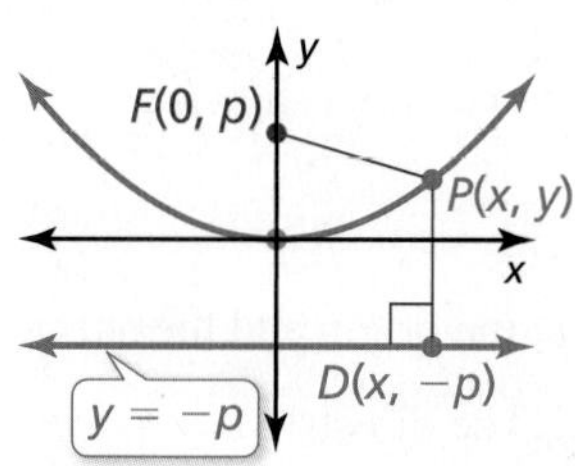

$$|y - (-p)| = \sqrt{x^2 + (p - y)^2}$$

$$(y + p)^2 = x^2 + (p - y)^2$$

$$y^2 + 2py + p^2 = x^2 + p^2 - 2py + y^2$$

$$4py = x^2$$

$$y = \frac{1}{4p}x^2$$

The focus and directrix each lie $|p|$ units from the vertex. Parabolas can also open left or right, in which case the equation has the form $x = \frac{1}{4p}y^2$ when the vertex is (0, 0).

KEY IDEA

Standard Equations of a Parabola with Vertex at the Origin

Math Practice

Look for Structure

How does changing the value of p affect the graph of $y = \frac{1}{4p}x^2$?

Vertical axis of symmetry ($x = 0$)

Equation: $y = \frac{1}{4p}x^2$

Focus: $(0, p)$

Directrix: $y = -p$

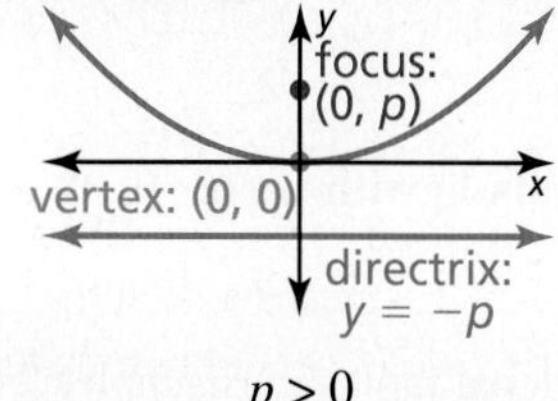

$p > 0$

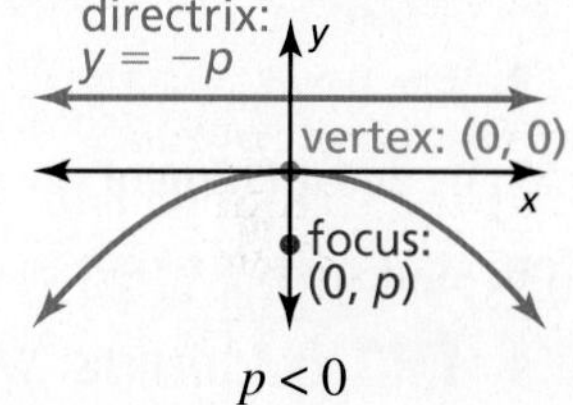

$p < 0$

Horizontal axis of symmetry ($y = 0$)

Equation: $x = \frac{1}{4p}y^2$

Focus: $(p, 0)$

Directrix: $x = -p$

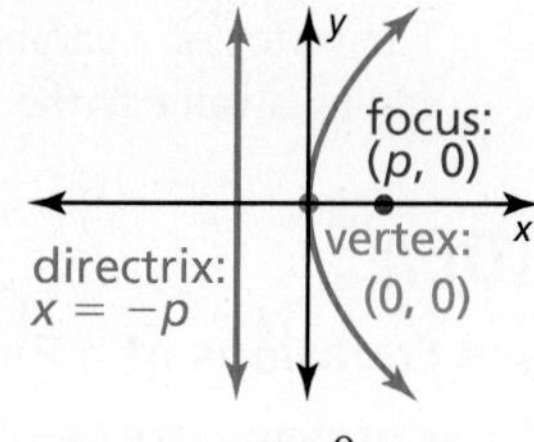

$p > 0$

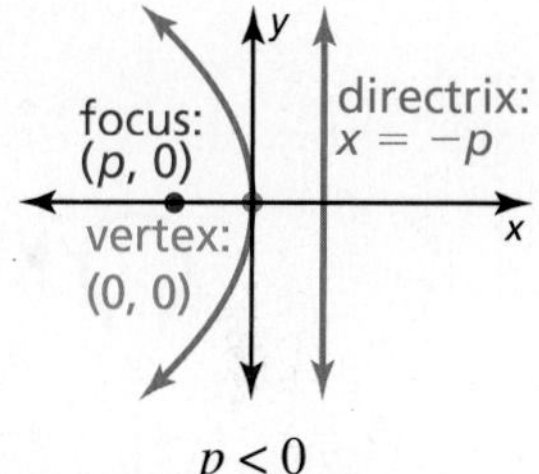

$p < 0$

EXAMPLE 2 Graphing an Equation of a Parabola

Identify the focus, directrix, and axis of symmetry of $-4x = y^2$. Graph the equation.

SOLUTION

Step 1 Rewrite the equation in standard form.

$-4x = y^2$ Write the original equation.

$x = -\frac{1}{4}y^2$ Divide each side by -4.

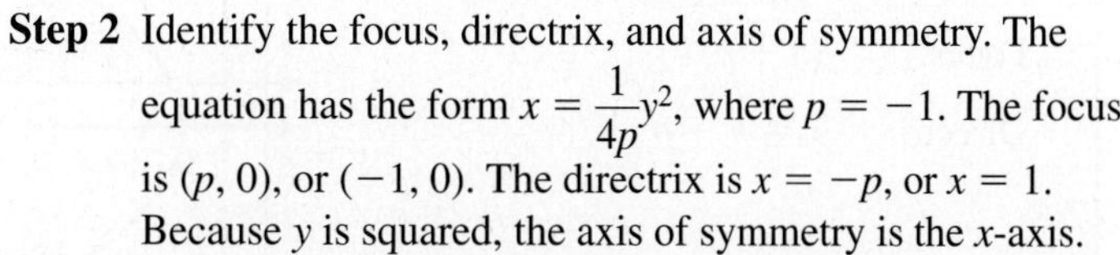

Step 2 Identify the focus, directrix, and axis of symmetry. The equation has the form $x = \frac{1}{4p}y^2$, where $p = -1$. The focus is $(p, 0)$, or $(-1, 0)$. The directrix is $x = -p$, or $x = 1$. Because y is squared, the axis of symmetry is the x-axis.

Step 3 Use a table of values to graph the equation. Notice that it is easier to substitute y-values and solve for x. Opposite y-values result in the same x-value.

y	x
0	0
±1	−0.25
±2	−1
±3	−2.25
±4	−4

Writing Equations of Parabolas

EXAMPLE 3 Writing an Equation of a Parabola

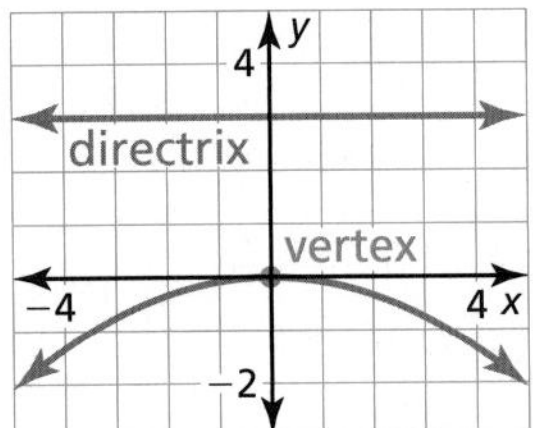

Write an equation of the parabola shown.

SOLUTION

Because the vertex is at the origin and the axis of symmetry is vertical, the equation has the form $y = \frac{1}{4p}x^2$. The directrix is $y = -p = 3$, so $p = -3$. Substitute -3 for p to write an equation of the parabola.

$$y = \frac{1}{4(-3)}x^2 = -\frac{1}{12}x^2$$

So, an equation of the parabola is $y = -\frac{1}{12}x^2$.

SELF-ASSESSMENT

1 I do not understand. 2 I can do it with help. 3 I can do it on my own. 4 I can teach someone else.

Identify the focus, directrix, and axis of symmetry of the parabola. Graph the equation.

3. $y = 0.5x^2$

4. $-y = x^2$

5. $y^2 = 10x$

Write an equation of the parabola with vertex (0, 0) and the given directrix or focus.

6. directrix: $x = -3$

7. focus: $(-2, 0)$

8. focus: $\left(0, \frac{3}{2}\right)$

9. **MP REASONING** Which parabolas in Examples 2 and 3 are functions? Explain.

The vertex of a parabola is not always at the origin. As in previous transformations, adding a value to the input or output translates the graph.

KEY IDEA

Standard Equations of a Parabola with Vertex at (*h*, *k*)

Vertical axis of symmetry ($x = h$)

Equation: $y = \frac{1}{4p}(x - h)^2 + k$

Focus: $(h, k + p)$

Directrix: $y = k - p$

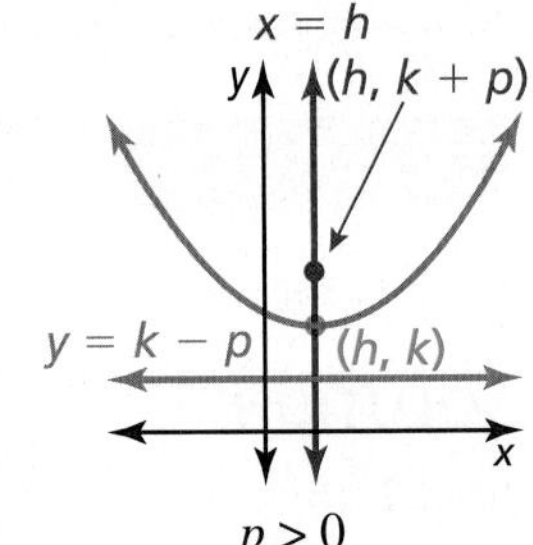

$p > 0$

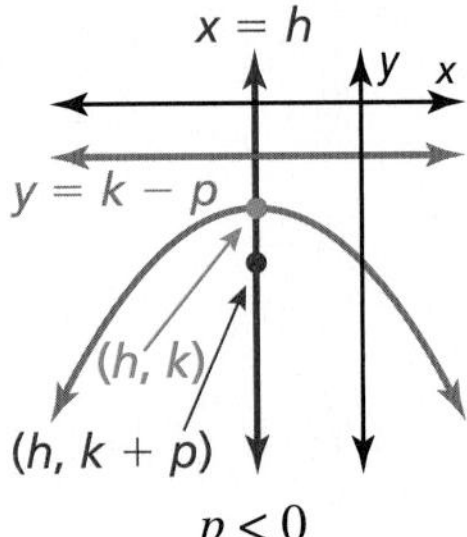

$p < 0$

Horizontal axis of symmetry ($y = k$)

Equation: $x = \frac{1}{4p}(y - k)^2 + h$

Focus: $(h + p, k)$

Directrix: $x = h - p$

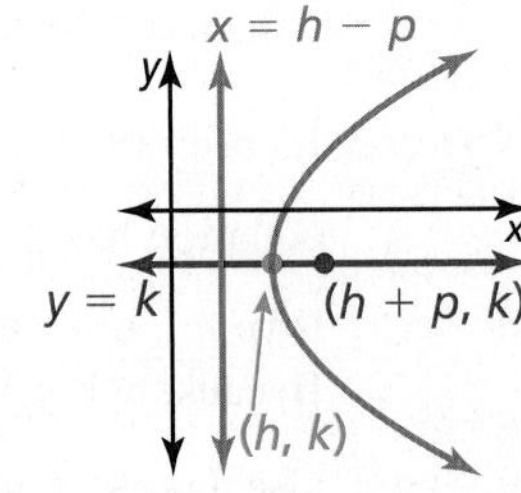

$p > 0$

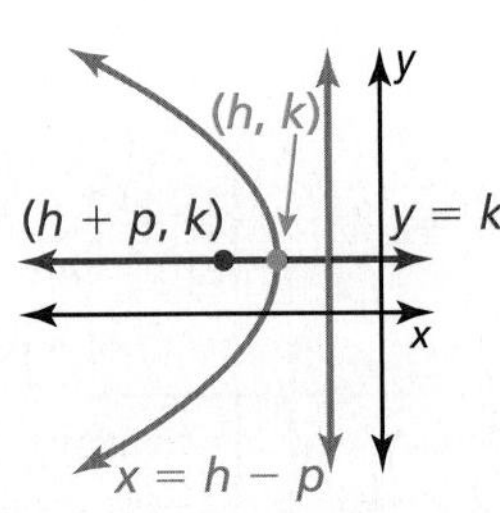

$p < 0$

Writing an Equation of a Translated Parabola

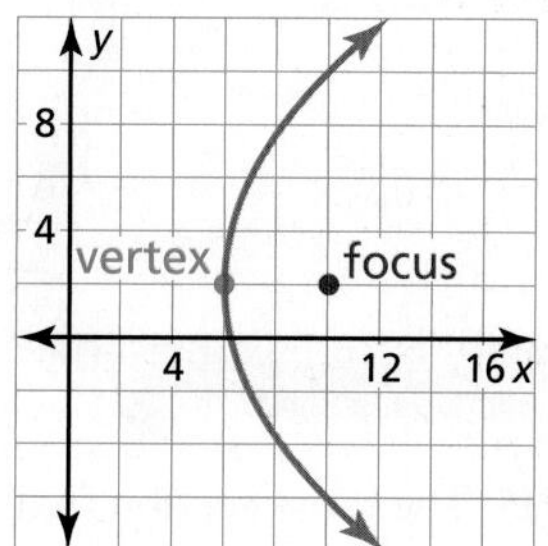

Write an equation of the parabola shown.

SOLUTION

Because the vertex is not at the origin and the axis of symmetry is horizontal, the equation has the form $x = \frac{1}{4p}(y - k)^2 + h$. The vertex (h, k) is $(6, 2)$ and the focus $(h + p, k)$ is $(10, 2)$, so $h = 6$, $k = 2$, and $p = 4$. Substitute these values to write an equation of the parabola.

$$x = \frac{1}{4(4)}(y - 2)^2 + 6 = \frac{1}{16}(y - 2)^2 + 6$$

▶ So, an equation of the parabola is $x = \frac{1}{16}(y - 2)^2 + 6$.

Solving Real-Life Problems

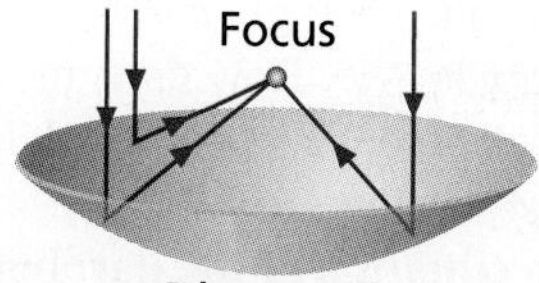

Diagram 1

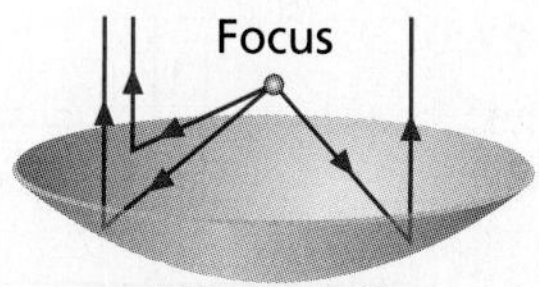

Diagram 2

Parabolic reflectors have cross sections that are parabolas to reflect sound, light, or other energy. Waves that hit a parabolic reflector parallel to the axis of symmetry are directed to the focus (Diagram 1). Similarly, waves that come from the focus and then hit the parabolic reflector are directed parallel to the axis of symmetry (Diagram 2).

EXAMPLE 5 **Modeling Real Life**

An electricity-generating dish uses a parabolic reflector to concentrate sunlight onto a high-frequency engine located at the focus of the reflector. The sunlight heats helium to 650°C to power the engine. Write an equation that represents the cross section of the dish shown with its vertex at (0, 0). What is the depth of the dish?

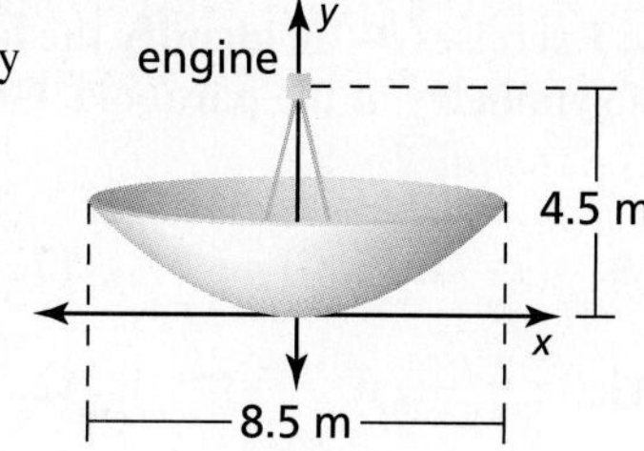

SOLUTION

Because the vertex is at the origin, and the axis of symmetry is vertical, the equation has the form $y = \frac{1}{4p}x^2$. The engine is at the focus, which is 4.5 meters above the vertex. So, $p = 4.5$. Substitute 4.5 for p to write the equation.

$$y = \frac{1}{4(4.5)}x^2 = \frac{1}{18}x^2$$

The depth of the dish is the y-value at the dish's outside edge. The dish extends $\frac{8.5}{2} = 4.25$ meters to either side of the vertex (0, 0), so find y when $x = 4.25$.

$$y = \frac{1}{18}(4.25)^2 \approx 1$$

▶ The depth of the dish is about 1 meter.

SELF-ASSESSMENT 1 I do not understand. 2 I can do it with help. 3 I can do it on my own. 4 I can teach someone else.

10. Write an equation of a parabola with vertex $(-1, 4)$ and focus $(-1, 2)$.

11. A parabolic microwave antenna is 16 feet in diameter. Write an equation that represents the cross section of the antenna with its vertex at (0, 0) and its focus 10 feet to the right of the vertex. What is the depth of the antenna?

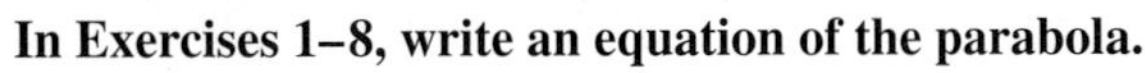

2.3 Practice WITH CalcChat® AND CalcView®

GO DIGITAL

In Exercises 1–8, write an equation of the parabola. *Example 1*

1.

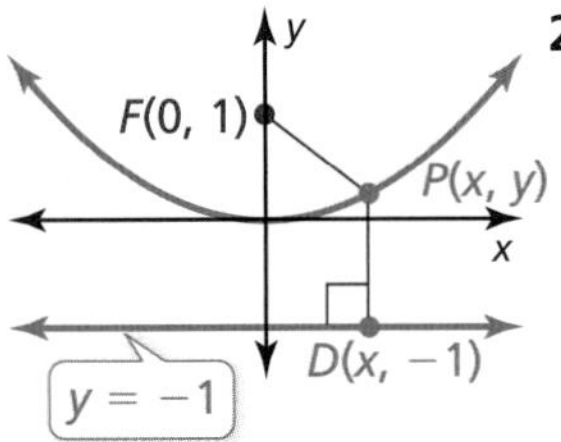

2.

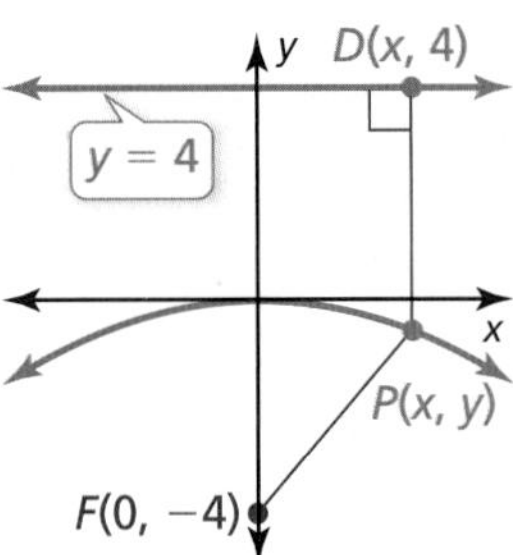

3. focus: $(0, -2)$
directrix: $y = 2$

4. directrix: $y = 7$
focus: $(0, -7)$

5. vertex: $(0, 0)$
directrix: $y = -6$

6. vertex: $(0, 0)$
focus: $(0, 5)$

7. vertex: $(0, 0)$
focus: $(0, -10)$

8. vertex: $(0, 0)$
directrix: $y = -9$

In Exercises 9–16, identify the focus, directrix, and axis of symmetry of the parabola. Graph the equation. *Example 2*

9. $y = \frac{1}{8}x^2$

10. $y = -\frac{1}{12}x^2$

11. $x = -\frac{1}{20}y^2$

12. $x = \frac{1}{24}y^2$

13. $y^2 = 16x$

14. $-x^2 = 48y$

15. $6x^2 + 3y = 0$

16. $8x^2 - y = 0$

ERROR ANALYSIS In Exercises 17 and 18, describe and correct the error in graphing the equation.

17. $-6x + y^2 = 0$

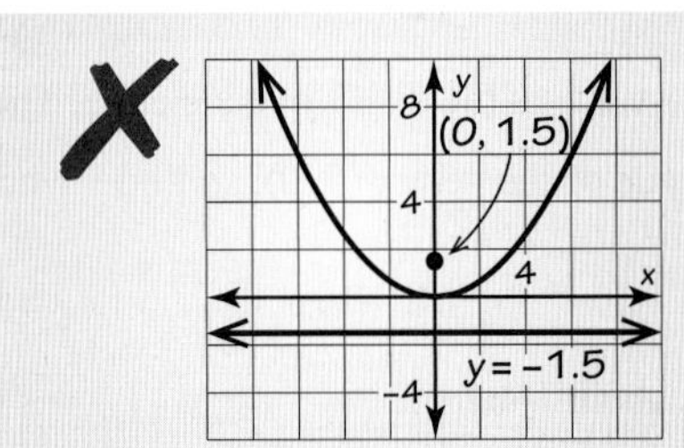

18. $0.5y^2 + x = 0$

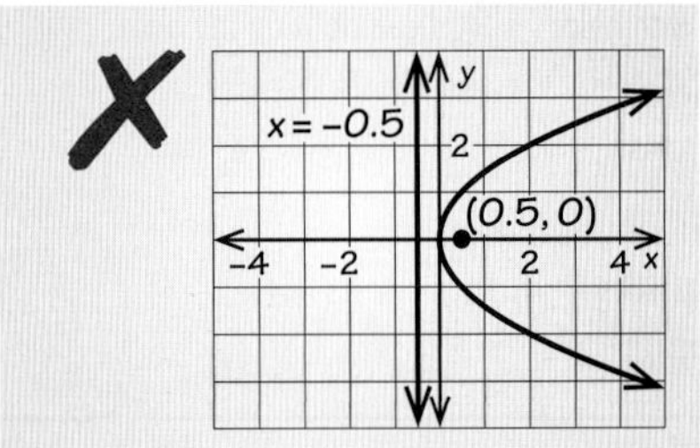

19. ANALYZING EQUATIONS The cross section (with units in inches) of a parabolic satellite dish can be modeled by the equation $y = \frac{1}{38}x^2$. How far is the focus from the vertex of the cross section? Explain.

20. ANALYZING EQUATIONS The cross section (with units in inches) of a parabolic spotlight can be modeled by the equation $x = \frac{1}{20}y^2$. How far is the focus from the vertex of the cross section? Explain.

In Exercises 21–24, write an equation of the parabola. *Example 3*

21.

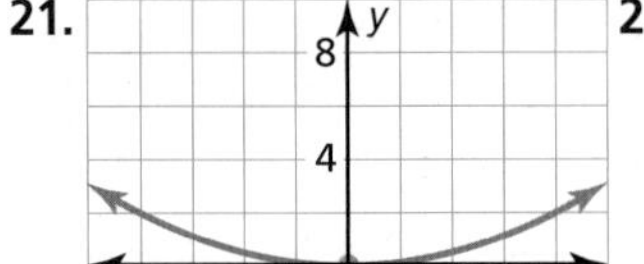

22.

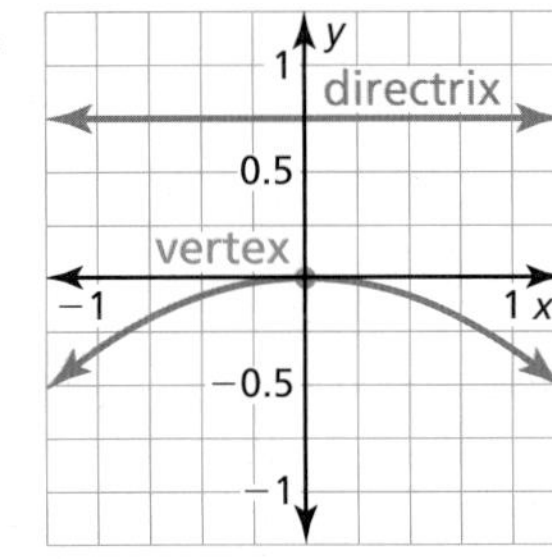

23.

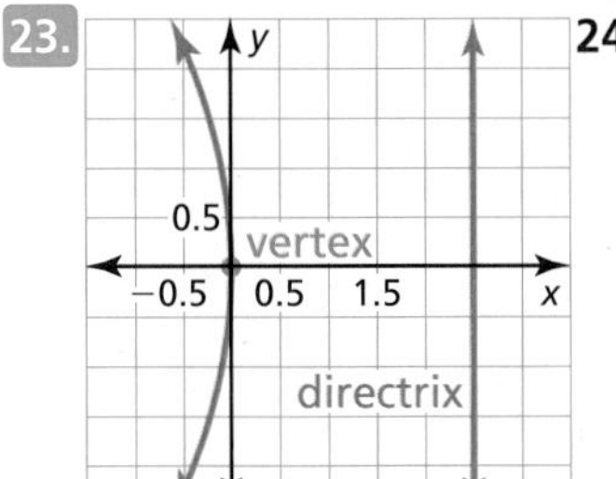

24.

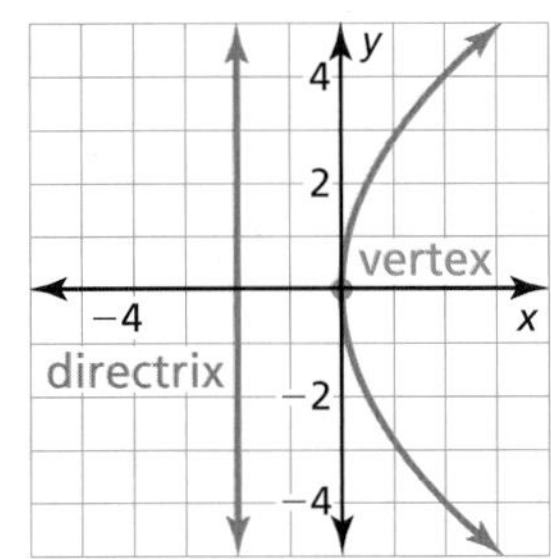

In Exercises 25–32, write an equation of the parabola with the given characteristics.

25. focus: $(-7, 0)$
directrix: $x = 7$

26. focus: $\left(\frac{2}{3}, 0\right)$
directrix: $x = -\frac{2}{3}$

27. directrix: $x = -10$
vertex: $(0, 0)$

28. directrix: $y = \frac{8}{3}$
vertex: $(0, 0)$

29. focus: $\left(0, -\frac{5}{3}\right)$
directrix: $y = \frac{5}{3}$

30. focus: $\left(0, \frac{5}{4}\right)$
directrix: $y = -\frac{5}{4}$

31. focus: $\left(0, \frac{6}{7}\right)$
vertex: $(0, 0)$

32. focus: $\left(-\frac{4}{5}, 0\right)$
vertex: $(0, 0)$

In Exercises 33–36, write an equation of the parabola. *Example 4*

33. 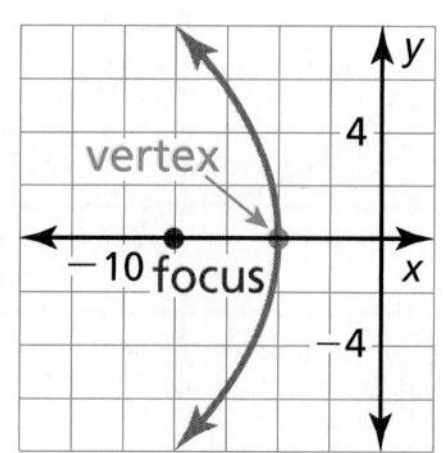

34. 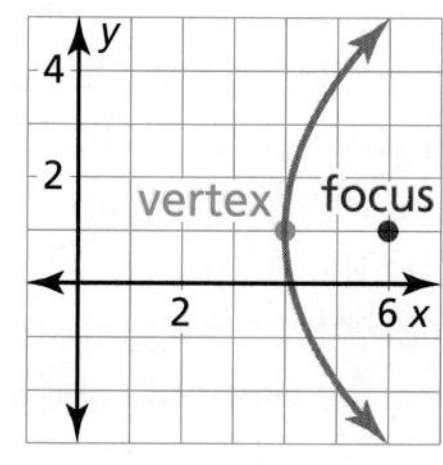

35. 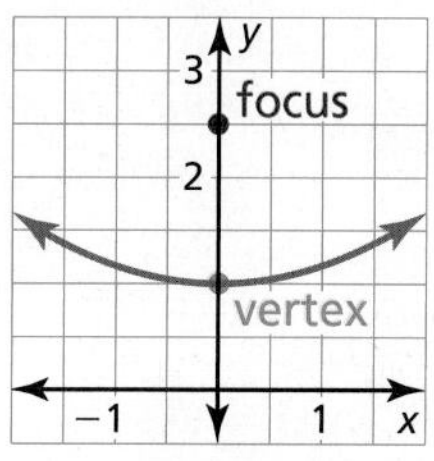

36. 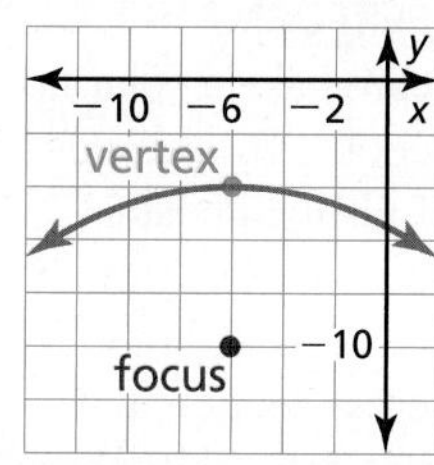

In Exercises 37–40, write an equation of the parabola with the given characteristics.

37. directrix: $y = 12$
vertex: $(2, 3)$

38. directrix: $x = 4$
vertex: $(-7, -5)$

39. focus: $\left(\frac{5}{4}, -1\right)$
directrix: $x = \frac{3}{4}$

40. focus: $\left(-3, \frac{11}{2}\right)$
directrix: $y = -\frac{3}{2}$

In Exercises 41–46, identify the vertex, focus, directrix, and axis of symmetry of the parabola. Describe the transformations of the graph of the standard equation with $p = 1$ and vertex $(0, 0)$.

41. $y = \frac{1}{8}(x - 3)^2 + 2$

42. $y = -\frac{1}{4}(x + 2)^2 + 1$

43. $x = \frac{1}{16}(y - 3)^2 + 1$

44. $y = (x + 3)^2 - 5$

45. $x = -3(y + 4)^2 + 2$

46. $x = 4(y + 5)^2 - 1$

47. **MODELING REAL LIFE** Scientists studying dolphin echolocation simulate a bottlenose dolphin's clicking sounds using computer models. The sounds originate at the focus of a parabolic reflector. The parabola represents the cross section of the reflector with focal length of 1.3 inches and aperture width of 8 inches. Write an equation of the parabola. What is the depth of the reflector? *Example 5*

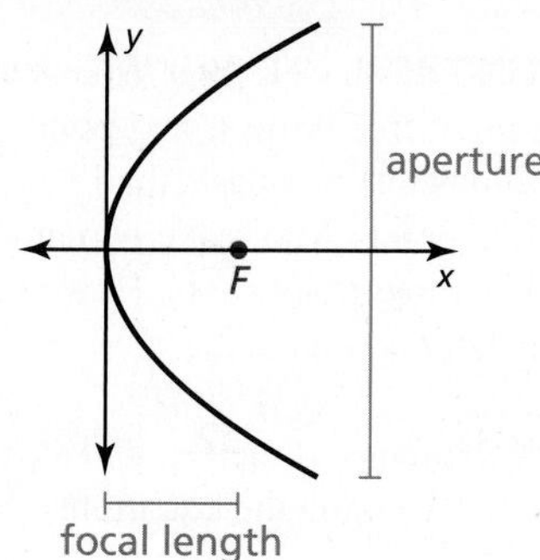

48. **MODELING REAL LIFE** Solar energy can be concentrated using a long trough that has a parabolic cross section, as shown in the figure. Write an equation that represents the cross section of the trough with its vertex at (0, 0). What are the domain and range in this situation? What do they represent?

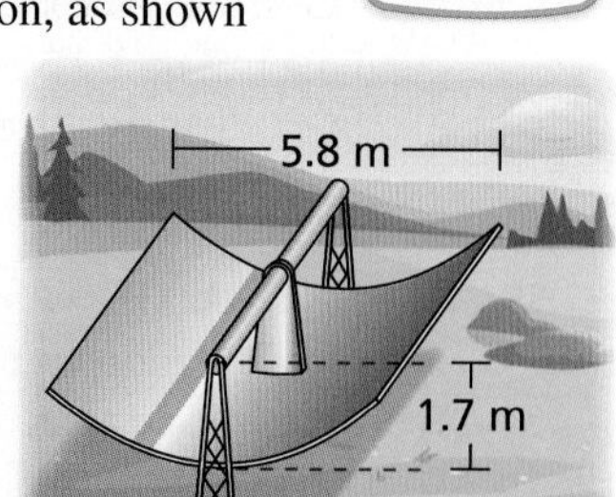

GO DIGITAL

49. **COLLEGE PREP** Which of the given characteristics describe parabolas that open down? Select all that apply.

Ⓐ focus: $(0, -6)$
directrix: $y = 6$

Ⓑ focus: $(0, -2)$
directrix: $y = 2$

Ⓒ focus: $(0, 6)$
directrix: $y = -6$

Ⓓ focus: $(0, -1)$
directrix: $y = 1$

50. **COLLEGE PREP** Which of the following are possible coordinates of the point P in the graph shown? Select all that apply.

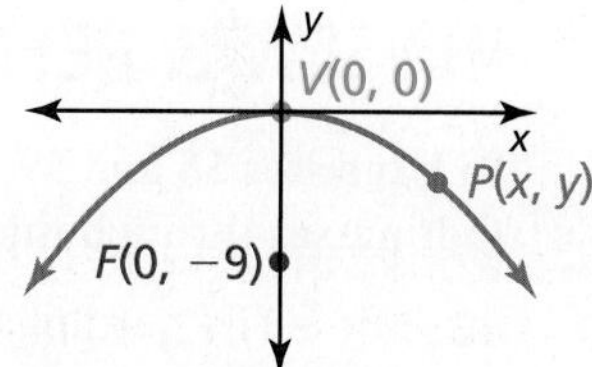

Ⓐ $(-6, -1)$ Ⓑ $\left(3, -\frac{1}{4}\right)$ Ⓒ $\left(4, -\frac{4}{9}\right)$
Ⓓ $\left(1, \frac{1}{36}\right)$ Ⓔ $(6, -1)$ Ⓕ $\left(2, -\frac{1}{18}\right)$

51. **ABSTRACT REASONING** As $|p|$ increases, how does the width of the graph of the equation $y = \frac{1}{4p}x^2$ change? Explain your reasoning.

52. **HOW DO YOU SEE IT?**
The graph shows the path of a volleyball served from an initial height of 6 feet as it travels over a net.

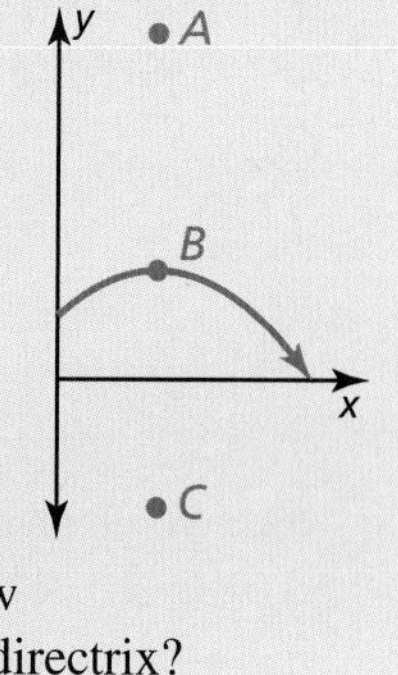

a. Label the vertex, focus, and a point on the directrix.

b. An underhand serve follows the same parabolic path but is hit from a height of 3 feet. How does this affect the focus? the directrix?

53. **CRITICAL THINKING**
The distance from point P to the directrix is 2 units. Write an equation of the parabola.

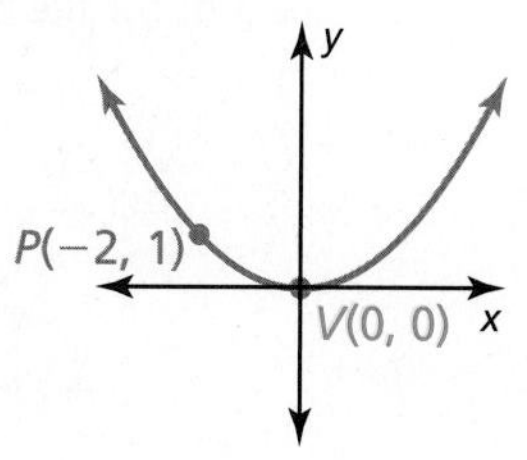

54. THOUGHT PROVOKING
Two parabolas have the same focus (a, b). The distance from the vertex to the focus of each parabola is 2 units. Write an equation of each parabola. Identify the directrix of each parabola.

55. **MP** **REPEATED REASONING** Derive the equation of a parabola that opens to the right with vertex $(0, 0)$, focus $(p, 0)$, and directrix $x = -p$.

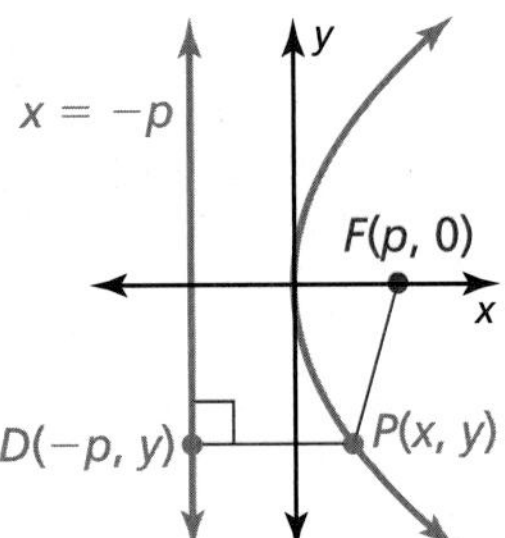

56. **DIG DEEPER** The *latus rectum* of a parabola is the line segment that is parallel to the directrix, passes through the focus, and has endpoints that lie on the parabola. Find the length of the latus rectum of the parabola shown.

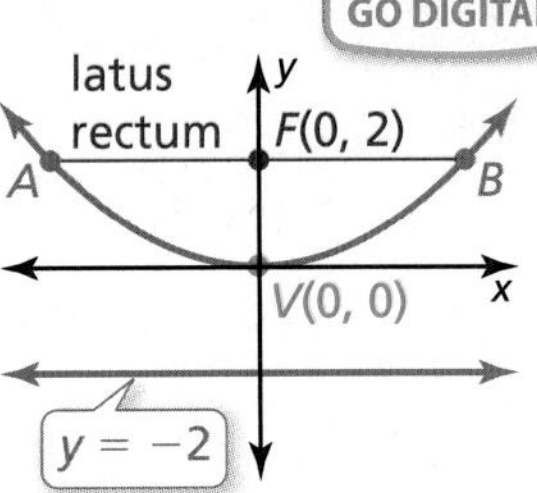

57. PERFORMANCE TASK You can make a solar hot dog cooker by shaping foil-lined poster board into a trough that has a parabolic cross section and passing a wire through each end piece. Design and construct your own hot dog cooker. Explain your process.

REVIEW & REFRESH

WATCH

In Exercises 58 and 59, write an equation of the line that passes through the given points.

58. $(1, -4), (2, -1)$ **59.** $(-3, 12), (0, 6)$

In Exercises 60 and 61, graph the inequality in a coordinate plane.

60. $y \leq -2.5$ **61.** $y > \frac{1}{2}x + 2$

62. The graph of square root function g is shown. Compare the average rate of change of g to the average rate of change of $h(x) = \sqrt[3]{\frac{3}{2}x}$ over the interval $x = 0$ to $x = 3$.

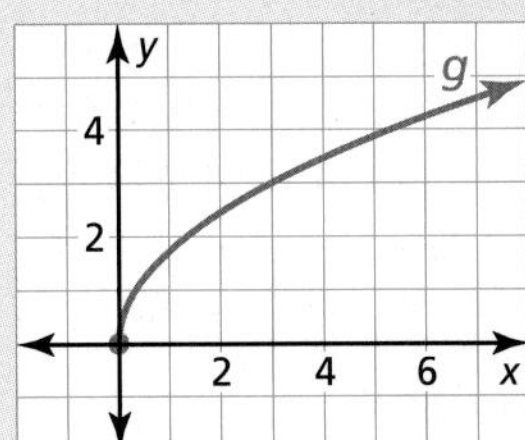

63. Write an equation of a parabola with vertex $(-2, -6)$ and focus $(-2, -1)$.

64. Use technology to find an equation of the line of best fit for the data.

x	0	3	6	7	11
y	4	9	24	29	46

65. **MP** **REASONING** A quadratic function has a minimum value at $x = -3$. When is the function increasing? decreasing?

66. Determine whether the table represents a *linear* or *nonlinear* function. Explain.

x	−1	1	3	5	7
y	6	3	−2	−9	−18

67. Let the graph of g be a translation 2 units up, followed by a reflection in the x-axis and a vertical stretch by a factor of 6 of the graph of $f(x) = x^2$. Write a rule for g and identify the vertex.

In Exercises 68–71, solve the equation.

68. $\frac{3}{5}n = -15$ **69.** $-2h + 17 = 12$

70. $3(2x - 4) = 3x + 9$

71. $4(2 - w) = -\frac{1}{2}(8w + 4)$

72. MODELING REAL LIFE You make a total of 11 one-point free throws, two-point shots, and three-point shots in a basketball game and score a total of 22 points. You make two more two-point shots than three-point shots. How many of each type of shot do you make?

73. Identify the focus, directrix, and axis of symmetry of $-3x = y^2$. Graph the equation.

2.4 Modeling with Quadratic Functions

Learning Target Write equations of quadratic functions using given characteristics.

Success Criteria
- I can write equations of quadratic functions using vertices, points, and *x*-intercepts.
- I can write quadratic equations to model data sets.
- I can use technology to find a quadratic model for a set of data.

EXPLORE IT! Modeling with Quadratic Functions

Math Practice

Use Other Resources How can you check your predictions when the values of *a*, *b*, or *c* change in the quadratic model?

Work with a partner.

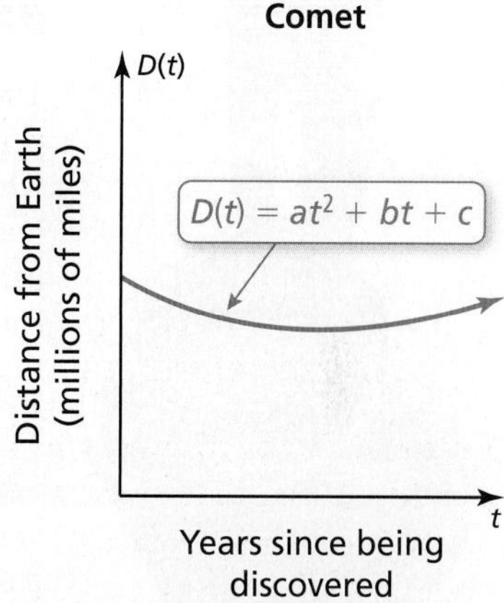

a. Explain what the graph represents.

b. What do you know about the value of *a*? How does the graph change if *a* is increased? decreased? What does this mean in this context? Explain your reasoning.

c. Write an expression that represents the year *t* when the comet is closest to Earth.

d. The comet is the same distance away from Earth in 2012 and 2020. Estimate the year when the comet is closest to Earth. Explain your reasoning.

e. What does *c* represent in this context? How does the graph change if *c* is increased? decreased? Explain.

f. Assume that the model is still valid today. Is the comet's distance from Earth currently increasing, decreasing, or constant? Explain.

g. The table shows the approximate distances *y* (in millions of miles) from Earth for a planetary object *m* months after being discovered. Can you use a quadratic function to model the data? How do you know? Is this the only type of function you can use to model the data? Explain your reasoning.

Months, *m*	0	1	2	3	4	5	6	7	8	9
Distance (millions of miles), *y*	50	57	65	75	86	101	115	130	156	175

h. Explain how you can find a quadratic model for the data. How do you know your model is a good fit?

Writing Quadratic Equations

KEY IDEA

Writing Quadratic Equations

Given a point and the vertex (h, k)	Use vertex form: $y = a(x - h)^2 + k$
Given a point and the x-intercepts p and q	Use intercept form: $y = a(x - p)(x - q)$
Given three points	Write and solve a system of three equations in three variables.

Writing an Equation Using the Vertex and a Point

WATCH

The graph shows the parabolic path of a performer who is shot out of a cannon, where y is the height (in feet) and x is the horizontal distance traveled (in feet). The performer lands in a net 90 feet from the cannon. What is the height of the net?

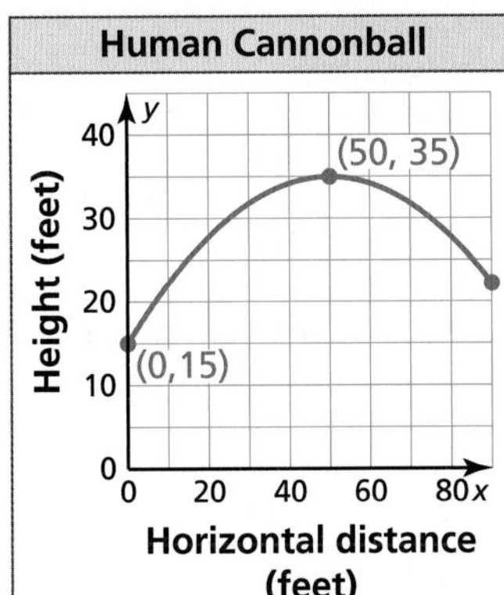

SOLUTION

From the graph, you can see that the vertex (h, k) is $(50, 35)$ and the parabola passes through the point $(0, 15)$. Use the vertex and the point to solve for a in vertex form. Then write an equation of the parabola.

$y = a(x - h)^2 + k$	Vertex form
$15 = a(0 - 50)^2 + 35$	Substitute for h, k, x, and y.
$-20 = 2500a$	Simplify.
$-0.008 = a$	Divide each side by 2500.

Because $a = -0.008$, $h = 50$, and $k = 35$, the path can be modeled by the equation $y = -0.008(x - 50)^2 + 35$, where $0 \le x \le 90$.

Find the height when $x = 90$.

$y = -0.008(90 - 50)^2 + 35$	Substitute 90 for x.
$= -0.008(1600) + 35$	Simplify.
$= 22.2$	Simplify.

▶ So, the height of the net is about 22 feet.

The world record for the farthest distance traveled by a human cannonball is almost 200 feet, achieved by David Smith Jr.

1 I do not understand. **2** I can do it with help. **3** I can do it on my own. **4** I can teach someone else.

1. **WHAT IF?** The vertex of the parabola is $(50, 37.5)$. What is the height of the net?

Write an equation of the parabola in vertex form.

2. passes through $(1, -7)$ and has vertex $(-2, 5)$
3. passes through $(0, 8)$ and has vertex $(-10, -3)$

EXAMPLE 2 Writing an Equation Using a Point and x-Intercepts

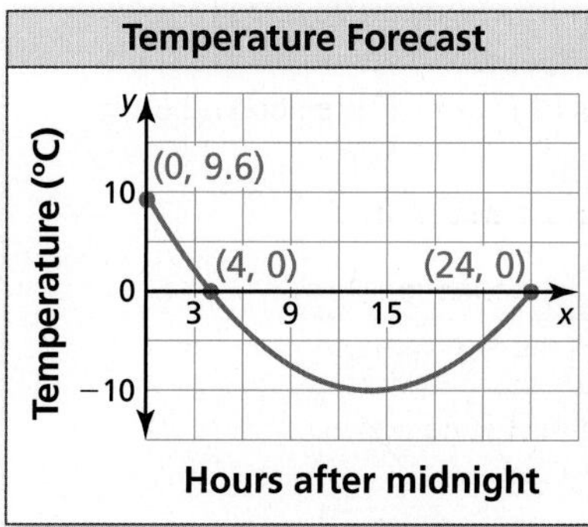

A meteorologist creates a parabola to predict the temperature tomorrow, where x is the number of hours after midnight and y is the temperature (in degrees Celsius).

a. Write a function f that models the temperature over time. What is the coldest temperature?

b. What is the average rate of change in temperature over the interval in which the temperature is decreasing? increasing? Compare the average rates of change.

SOLUTION

a. The x-intercepts are 4 and 24, and the parabola passes through (0, 9.6). Use the x-intercepts and the point to solve for a in intercept form.

$y = a(x - p)(x - q)$ Intercept form

$9.6 = a(0 - 4)(0 - 24)$ Substitute for p, q, x, and y.

$9.6 = 96a$ Simplify.

$0.1 = a$ Divide each side by 96.

Because $a = 0.1$, $p = 4$, and $q = 24$, the temperature over time can be modeled by $f(x) = 0.1(x - 4)(x - 24)$, where $0 \leq x \leq 24$.

The coldest temperature is the minimum value. Find $f(x)$ when $x = \frac{4 + 24}{2} = 14$.

$f(14) = 0.1(14 - 4)(14 - 24)$ Substitute 14 for x.

$= -10$ Simplify.

▶ So, the coldest temperature is −10°C at 14 hours after midnight, or 2 P.M.

b. The parabola opens up and the axis of symmetry is $x = 14$. So, the function is decreasing over the interval $0 < x < 14$ and increasing over the interval $14 < x < 24$.

Average rate of change over $0 < x < 14$:

$$\frac{f(14) - f(0)}{14 - 0} = \frac{-10 - 9.6}{14} = -1.4$$

Average rate of change over $14 < x < 24$:

$$\frac{f(24) - f(14)}{24 - 14} = \frac{0 - (-10)}{10} = 1$$

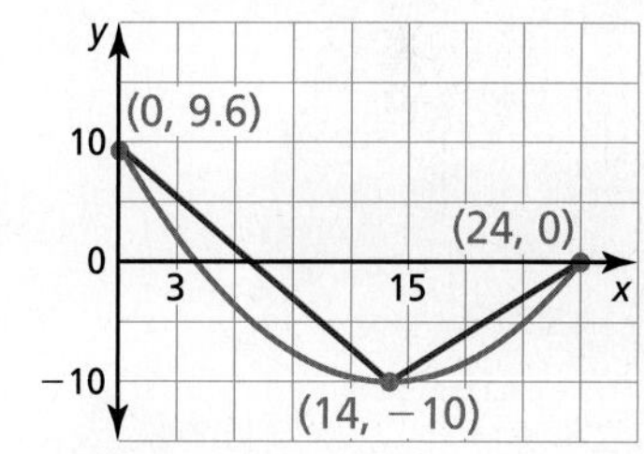

REMEMBER

The average rate of change of a function f from x_1 to x_2 is the slope of the line connecting $(x_1, f(x_1))$ and $(x_2, f(x_2))$: $\frac{f(x_2) - f(x_1)}{x_2 - x_1}$.

▶ Because $|-1.4| > |1|$, the average rate at which the temperature decreases from midnight to 2 P.M. is greater than the average rate at which it increases from 2 P.M. to midnight.

SELF-ASSESSMENT

1 I do not understand. 2 I can do it with help. 3 I can do it on my own. 4 I can teach someone else.

4. **WHAT IF?** The y-intercept is 4.8. How does this change your answers in parts (a) and (b)?

5. **MP REASONING** In Example 2, compare the average rates of change over the intervals in which the temperature is below zero and decreasing, and below zero and increasing.

6. Write an equation of the parabola that passes through the point (2, 5) and has x-intercepts −2 and 4.

GO DIGITAL

Writing Equations to Model Data

When data have equally-spaced inputs, you can analyze patterns in the differences of the outputs to determine what type of function can be used to model the data. Linear data have constant *first differences*. Quadratic data have constant *second differences*. The first and second differences of $f(x) = x^2$ are shown below.

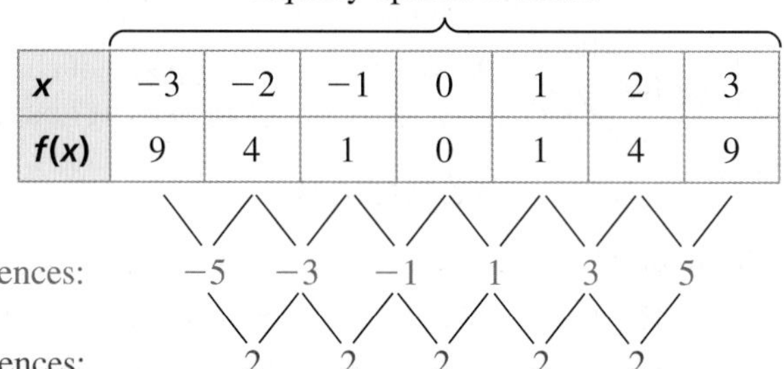

EXAMPLE 3 Writing a Quadratic Equation Using Three Points

Time, t	Height, $h(t)$
10	26,900
15	29,025
20	30,600
25	31,625
30	32,100
35	32,025
40	31,400

NASA can create a weightless environment by flying a plane in parabolic paths. The table shows the heights $h(t)$ (in feet) of a plane t seconds after starting the flight path. After about 20.8 seconds, passengers begin to experience a weightless environment. Write and evaluate a function to approximate the height at which this occurs.

SOLUTION

Step 1 The input values are equally spaced. So, analyze the differences in the outputs to determine what type of function you can use to model the data.

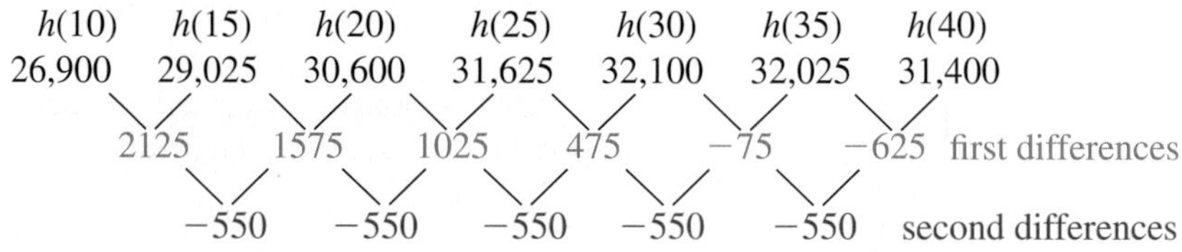

Because the second differences are constant, you can model the data with a quadratic function.

Step 2 Write a quadratic function of the form $h(t) = at^2 + bt + c$ that models the data. Use any three points $(t, h(t))$ from the table to write a system of equations.

Use (10, 26,900): $100a + 10b + c = 26{,}900$ Equation 1
Use (20, 30,600): $400a + 20b + c = 30{,}600$ Equation 2
Use (30, 32,100): $900a + 30b + c = 32{,}100$ Equation 3

Use the elimination method to solve the system.

Subtract Equation 1 from Equation 2. → $300a + 10b = 3700$ New Equation 1

Subtract Equation 1 from Equation 3. → $800a + 20b = 5200$ New Equation 2

$200a = -2200$ Subtract 2 times new Equation 1 from new Equation 2.

$a = -11$ Solve for a.

$b = 700$ Substitute into new Equation 1 to find b.

$c = 21{,}000$ Substitute into Equation 1 to find c.

The data can be modeled by the function $h(t) = -11t^2 + 700t + 21{,}000$.

Step 3 Evaluate the function when $t = 20.8$.

$$h(20.8) = -11(20.8)^2 + 700(20.8) + 21{,}000 = 30{,}800.96$$

▶ Passengers begin to experience a weightless environment at about 30,800 feet.

Real-life data that show a quadratic relationship usually do not have constant second differences because the data are not *exactly* quadratic. Relationships that are *approximately* quadratic have second differences that are relatively "close" in value. Many technology tools have a *quadratic regression* feature that you can use to find a quadratic function that best models a set of data.

EXAMPLE 4 Using Quadratic Regression

Miles per hour, x	Miles per gallon, y
20	14.5
24	17.5
30	21.2
36	23.7
40	25.2
45	25.8
50	25.8
56	25.1
60	24.0
70	19.5

The table shows fuel efficiencies of a vehicle at different speeds. Write a function that models the data. Use the model to approximate the best gas mileage.

SOLUTION

Because the x-values are not equally spaced, you cannot analyze the differences in the outputs. Use technology to find a function that models the data.

Step 1 Enter the data from the table and create a scatter plot. The data show a quadratic relationship.

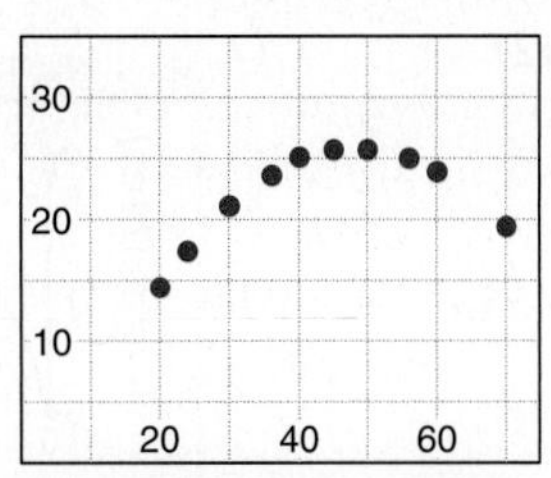

Step 2 Find the quadratic equation. The values in the equation can be rounded to obtain $y = -0.014x^2 + 1.37x - 7.1$.

$y = ax^2 + bx + c$

PARAMETERS

$a = -0.0141$ $b = 1.3662$

$c = -7.1441$

STATISTICS

$R^2 = 0.9992$

Step 3 Graph the regression equation with the scatter plot.

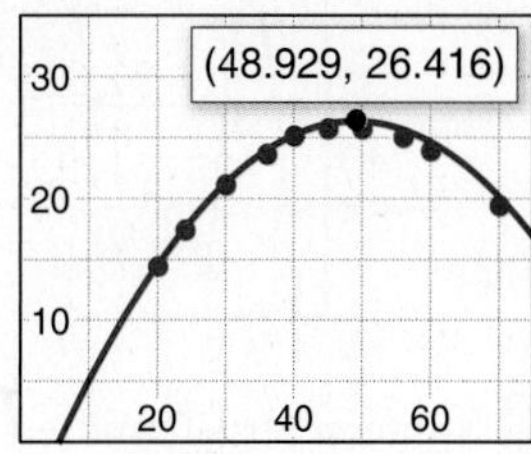

In this context, the best gas mileage is the maximum mileage per gallon. Using technology, you can see that the maximum mileage per gallon is about 26.4 miles per gallon when driving about 48.9 miles per hour.

▶ So, the best gas mileage is about 26.4 miles per gallon.

SELF-ASSESSMENT

1 I do not understand. 2 I can do it with help. 3 I can do it on my own. 4 I can teach someone else.

7. **WRITING** Explain when it is appropriate to use a quadratic model for a set of data.
8. Write an equation of the parabola that passes through the points $(-1, 4)$, $(0, 1)$, and $(2, 7)$.
9. The table shows the estimated profits y (in dollars) for a concert when the charge is x dollars per ticket. Write and evaluate a function to determine the maximum profit.

Ticket price, x	2	5	8	11	14	17
Profit, y	2600	6500	8600	8900	7400	4100

10. The table shows the results of an experiment testing the maximum weights y (in tons) supported by ice x inches thick. Write a function that models the data. How much weight can be supported by ice that is 22 inches thick?

Ice thickness, x	12	14	15	18	20	24	27
Maximum weight, y	3.4	7.6	10.0	18.3	25.0	40.6	54.3

2.4 Practice WITH CalcChat® AND CalcView®

GO DIGITAL

In Exercises 1–6, write an equation of the parabola in vertex form. ▷ *Example 1*

1.

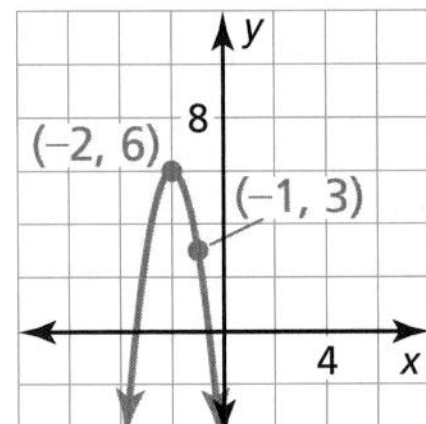

2.

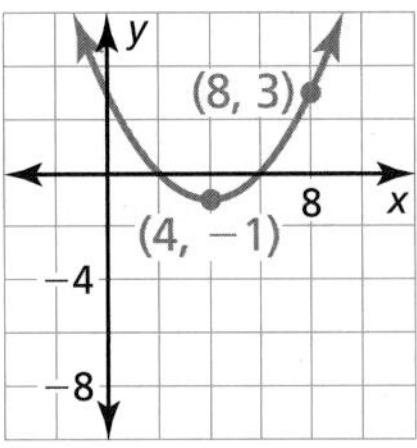

3. passes through (13, 8) and has vertex (3, 2)

4. passes through (−7, −15) and has vertex (−5, 9)

5. passes through (0, −24) and has vertex (−6, −12)

6. passes through (6, 35) and has vertex (−1, 14)

In Exercises 7–12, write an equation of the parabola in intercept form. ▷ *Example 2*

7.

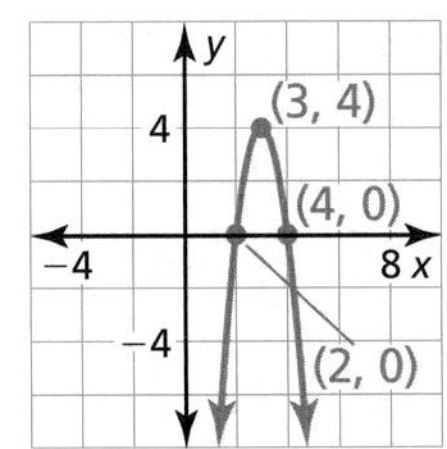

8.

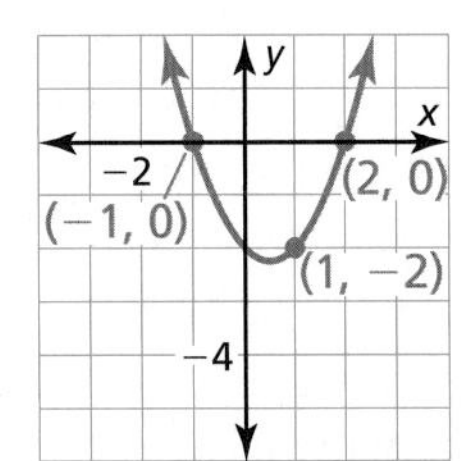

9. x-intercepts: 12 and −6; passes through (14, 4)

10. x-intercepts: 9 and 1; passes through (0, −18)

11. x-intercepts: −16 and −2; passes through (−18, 72)

12. x-intercepts: −7 and −3; passes through (−2, 0.05)

13. **WRITING** Explain when to use intercept form and when to use vertex form when writing an equation of a parabola.

14. **COLLEGE PREP** Which of the following equations represent the parabola? Select all that apply.

Ⓐ $y = 2(x - 2)(x + 1)$

Ⓑ $y = 2(x + 0.5)^2 - 4.5$

Ⓒ $y = 2(x - 0.5)^2 - 4.5$

Ⓓ $y = 2(x + 2)(x - 1)$

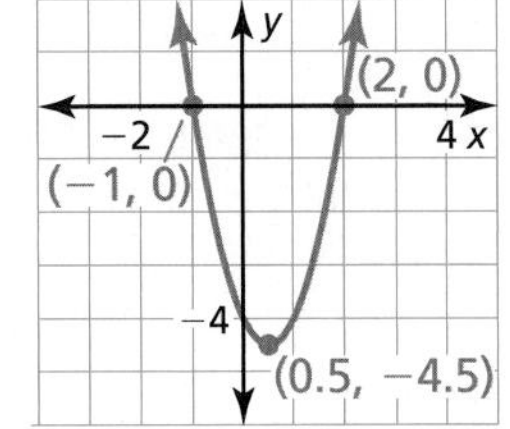

In Exercises 15–18, write an equation of the parabola in vertex form or intercept form.

15.

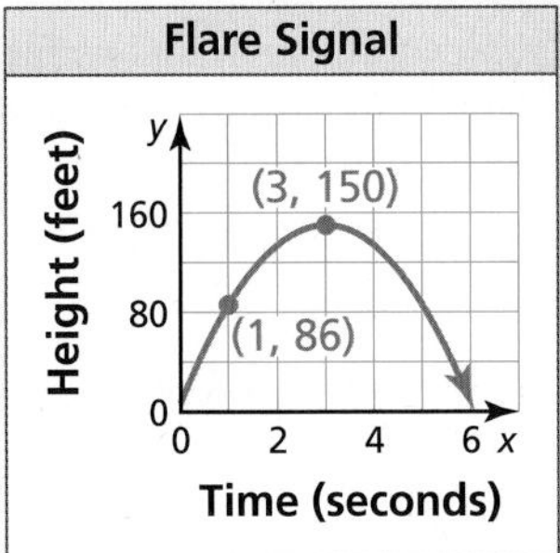

16.

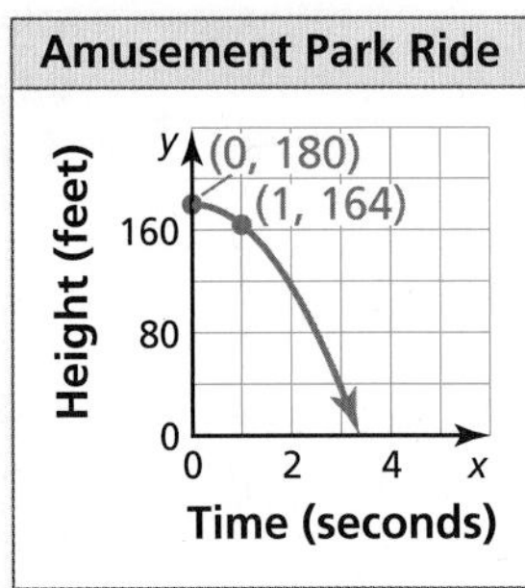

17.

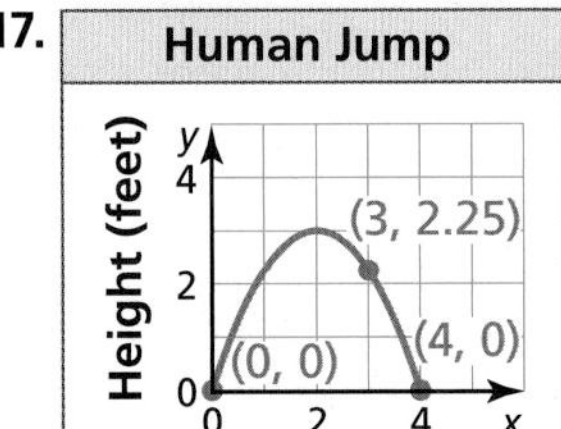

18.

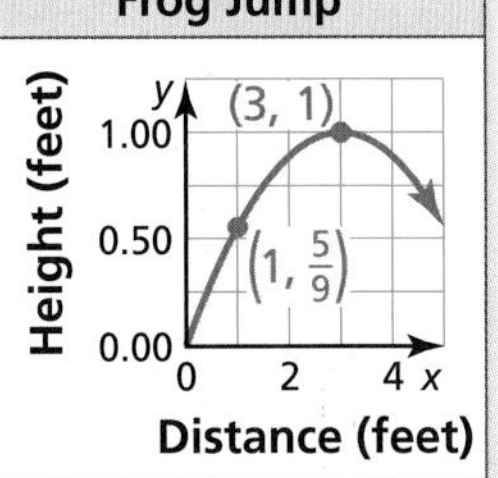

19. **ERROR ANALYSIS** Describe and correct the error in writing an equation of the parabola.

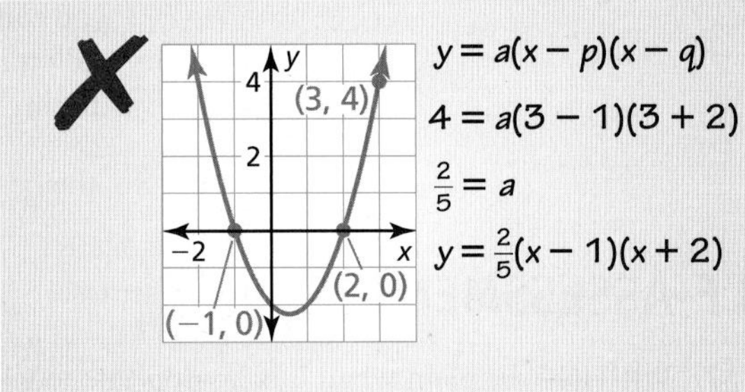

20. **CONNECTING CONCEPTS** The area of a rectangle is modeled by the graph, where y is the area (in square meters) and x is the width (in meters). Write an equation of the parabola. Find the dimensions and corresponding area of one possible rectangle. What dimensions result in the maximum area?

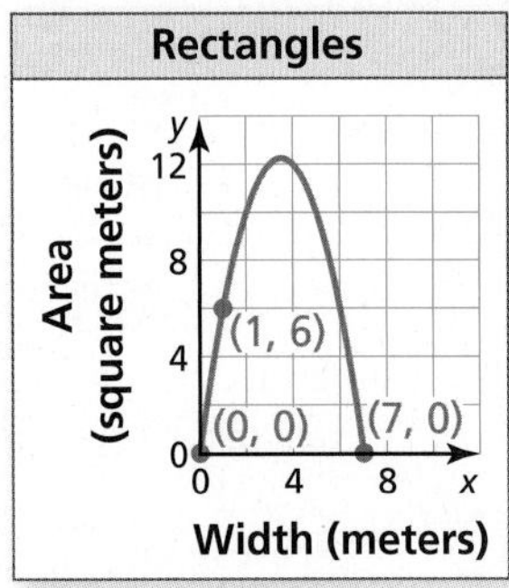

21. **MODELING REAL LIFE** Every rope has a safe working load. A rope should not be used to lift a weight greater than its safe working load. The table shows the safe working loads S (in pounds) for ropes with circumferences C (in inches). Write an equation for the safe working load for a rope. Find the safe working load for a rope that has a circumference of 10 inches. *Example 3*

Circumference, C	0	1	2	3
Safe working load, S	0	180	720	1620

22. **MODELING REAL LIFE** A baseball is thrown up in the air. The table shows the heights y (in feet) of the baseball after x seconds. Write an equation for the path of the baseball. Find the height of the baseball after 1.7 seconds.

Time, x	0.5	1	1.5	2
Baseball height, y	18	24	22	12

23. MP **USING TOOLS** The table shows the numbers y (in thousands) of people in a city who regularly use sharable electric scooters x weeks after the scooters are introduced. Write a function that models the data. Use the model to predict the number of users after 32 weeks. *Example 4*

Time, x	Number of users, y
1	1.5
4	2.2
6	2.4
10	3.9
12	5.5
15	6.8
20	12.3
24	16.4
25	17.6

24. MP **USING TOOLS** The table shows the numbers y of students absent from school x days after a flu outbreak. Write a function that models the data. Use the model to approximate the number of students absent 10 days after the outbreak.

Time (days), x	2	4	5	6	8	9	11
Number of students, y	11	17	19	19	17	14	7

25. **COMPARING METHODS** Which method is more efficient for finding an equation of the parabola that passes through the points $(-8, 0)$, $(2, -20)$, and $(1, 0)$: using a system of three equations in three variables or using intercept form? Justify your answer.

GO DIGITAL

26. **MAKING AN ARGUMENT** Do quadratic functions with the same x-intercepts have the same equations, vertex, and axis of symmetry? Explain your reasoning.

27. **MODELING REAL LIFE** The table shows the distances y a motorcyclist is from home after x hours.

Time (hours), x	0	1	2	3
Distance (miles), y	0	45	90	135

a. Determine what type of function you can use to model the data. Explain your reasoning.

b. Write and evaluate a function to determine the distance the motorcyclist is from home after 6 hours.

28. MP **PROBLEM SOLVING** The table shows the heights y of a competitive water-skier x seconds after jumping off a ramp. Write a function that models the height of the water-skier over time. When is the water-skier 5 feet above the water? How long is the skier in the air?

Time (seconds), x	0	0.25	0.75	1	1.1
Height (feet), y	22	22.5	17.5	12	9.24

In Exercises 29–32, analyze the differences in the outputs to determine whether the data are *linear*, *quadratic*, or *neither*. Explain. If the data are linear or quadratic, write a function that models the data.

29.

Price decrease (dollars), x	0	5	10	15	20
Revenue ($1000s), y	470	630	690	650	510

30.

Time (hours), x	0	1	2	3	4
Height (feet), y	40	42	44	46	48

31.

Time (hours), x	1	2	3	4	5
Population (hundreds), y	2	4	8	16	32

32.

Day, x	1	2	3	4
Balance (dollars), y	320	303	254	173

33. OPEN-ENDED Describe a real-life situation not mentioned in this chapter that can be modeled by a quadratic equation. Justify your answer.

34. HOW DO YOU SEE IT?
Use the graph to determine whether the average rate of change over each interval is *positive*, *negative*, or *zero*.

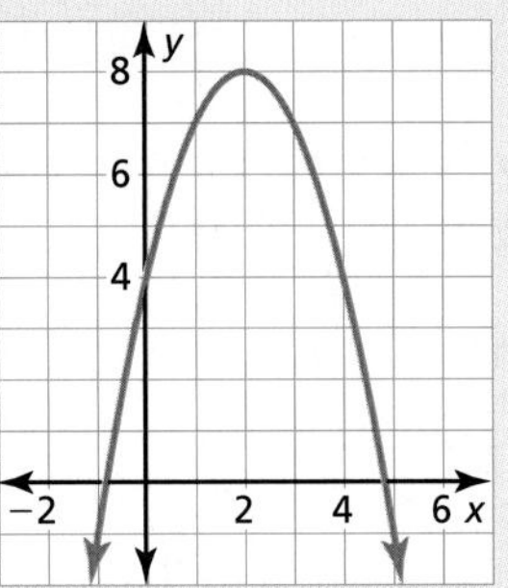

a. $0 \leq x \leq 2$ **b.** $2 \leq x \leq 5$

c. $2 \leq x \leq 4$ **d.** $0 \leq x \leq 4$

35. REPEATED REASONING The table shows the number of tiles in each figure. Verify that the data show a quadratic relationship. Predict the number of tiles in the 12th figure.

GO DIGITAL

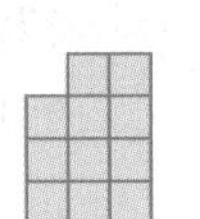
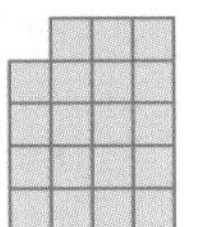

Figure 1 Figure 2 Figure 3 Figure 4

Figure	1	2	3	4
Number of tiles	1	5	11	19

36. THOUGHT PROVOKING
The table shows the temperatures y (in degrees Fahrenheit) of a cup of tea after x minutes. Write a function that models the data and can be used to predict the temperature of the tea after 20 minutes. Explain your reasoning.

Time, x	0	2	4	6	8	10
Temperature, y	190	164	146	131	120	111

REVIEW & REFRESH

WATCH

In Exercises 37–40, factor the polynomial.

37. $x^2 + 4x + 3$ **38.** $x^2 - 3x + 2$

39. $3x^2 - 15x + 12$ **40.** $x^2 + x - 6$

41. MODELING REAL LIFE The table shows the heights y (in feet) of a firework x seconds after it is launched. The firework explodes at its highest point. Write an equation for the path of the firework. Find the height at which the firework explodes.

Time, x	0	1	2	3
Height, y	0	112	192	240

42. Determine whether the graph represents a function. Explain.

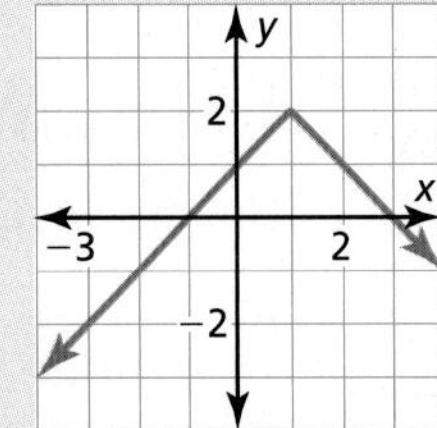

In Exercises 43 and 44, graph the function. Label the vertex and axis of symmetry.

43. $f(x) = 2(x - 1)^2 - 5$

44. $h(x) = 3x^2 + 6x - 2$

In Exercises 45 and 46, identify the focus, directrix, and axis of symmetry of the parabola. Graph the equation.

45. $x = -\frac{1}{12}y^2$ **46.** $16y = x^2$

47. Let the graph of g be a horizontal shrink by a factor of $\frac{1}{4}$, followed by a translation 1 unit up and 3 units right of the graph of $f(x) = (2x + 1)^2 - 11$. Write a rule for g and identify the vertex.

In Exercises 48–51, solve the inequality. Graph the solution.

48. $m + 9 \geq 13$ **49.** $15 - n < -6$

50. $5p > 10$ **51.** $-\frac{q}{4} \leq 3$

52. Determine whether the table represents a *linear* or an *exponential* function. Explain.

x	−1	0	1	2	3
y	$\frac{1}{8}$	$\frac{1}{2}$	2	8	32

In Exercises 53 and 54, write an equation in slope-intercept form of the line that passes through the given points.

53. $(4, -1), (0, 3)$ **54.** $(-3, -2), (1, 4)$

2 Chapter Review WITH CalcChat®

Chapter Learning Target Understand quadratic functions.

Chapter Success Criteria
- ◆ I can describe transformations of quadratic functions.
- ◆ I can identify characteristics of quadratic functions.
- ■ I can write equations of parabolas.
- ■ I can model with quadratic functions.

◆ Surface
■ Deep

SELF-ASSESSMENT 1 I do not understand. 2 I can do it with help. 3 I can do it on my own. 4 I can teach someone else.

2.1 Transformations of Quadratic Functions (pp. 45–52)

Learning Target: Describe and graph transformations of quadratic functions.

Vocabulary AZ VOCAB
quadratic function
parabola
vertex of a parabola
vertex form

Describe the transformation of $f(x) = x^2$ represented by g. Then graph each function.

1. $g(x) = (x + 4)^2$
2. $g(x) = -\frac{1}{5}x^2$
3. $g(x) = (x - 7)^2 + 2$
4. $g(x) = -3(x + 2)^2 - 1$

Write a rule for g.

5. The graph of g is a horizontal shrink by a factor of $\frac{2}{3}$, followed by a translation 5 units left and 2 units down of the graph of $f(x) = x^2$.

6. The graph of g is a translation 2 units left and 3 units up, followed by a reflection in the y-axis of the graph of $f(x) = x^2 - 2x$.

7. For each graph, determine whether h and k are *positive*, *negative*, or *zero*. Explain.

a.

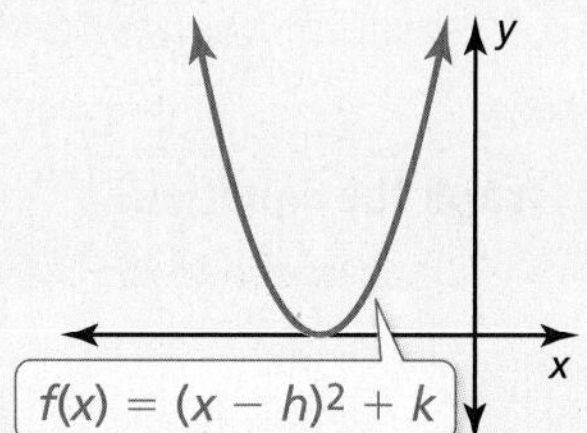

b.

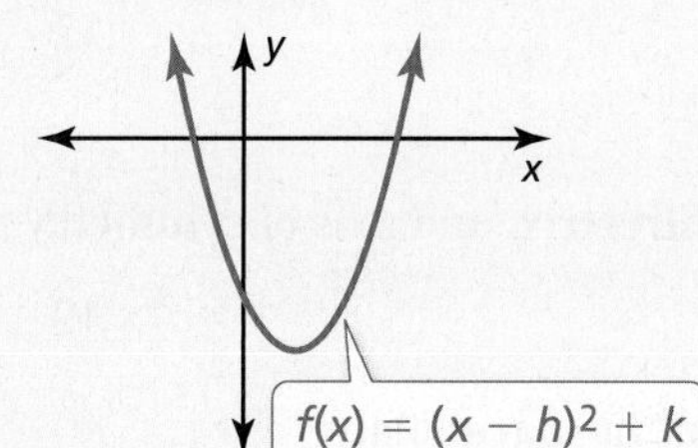

8. The graph represents the path of a football kicked by a player, where x is the horizontal distance (in yards) and y is the height (in yards). The player kicks the ball a second time so that it travels the same horizontal distance, but reaches a maximum height that is 6 yards greater than the maximum height of the first kick. Write a function that models the path of the second kick.

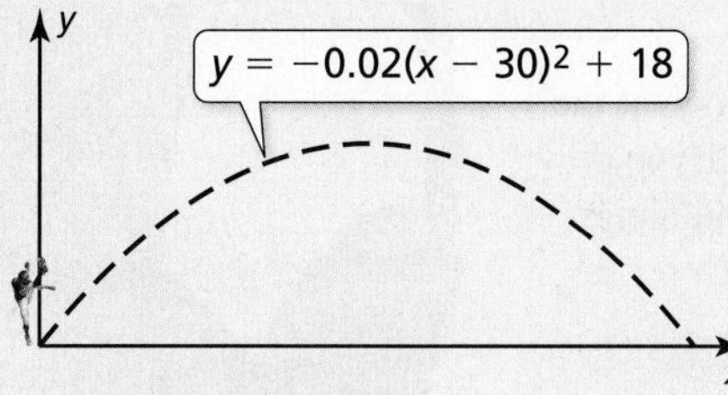

2.2 Characteristics of Quadratic Functions (pp. 53–62)

Learning Target: Graph and describe quadratic functions.

Vocabulary
axis of symmetry
standard form
minimum value
maximum value
intercept form

Graph the function. Label the vertex and axis of symmetry. Find the minimum value or maximum value of the function. Find when the function is increasing and decreasing.

9. $g(x) = (x + 5)^2 - 8$

10. $f(x) = 3(x - 1)^2 - 4$

11. $g(x) = -2x^2 + 16x + 3$

12. $h(x) = (x - 3)(x + 7)$

13. Find the vertex of the quadratic function represented by the table. Explain your reasoning.

x	−5	−2	1	4	7
g(x)	−68	−23	4	13	4

14. Write a quadratic function in standard form with axis of symmetry $x = -5$ and y-intercept 3.

15. You kick a kickball. The path of the ball is represented by $y = x(0.6 - 0.02x)$, where x is the horizontal distance (in feet) and y is the corresponding height (in feet). Your second kick reaches a maximum height of 7 feet, 12 feet away from you. Which kick travels farther before hitting the ground? Which kick travels higher?

2.3 Focus of a Parabola (pp. 63–70)

Learning Target: Graph and write equations of parabolas.

Vocabulary
focus
directrix

Write an equation of the parabola with the given characteristics.

16. vertex: (0, 0)
directrix: $x = 2$

17. focus: (2, 2)
vertex: (2, 6)

Identify the focus, directrix, and axis of symmetry of the parabola. Graph the equation.

18. $36y = x^2$

19. $64x + 8y^2 = 0$

Write an equation of the parabola.

20.

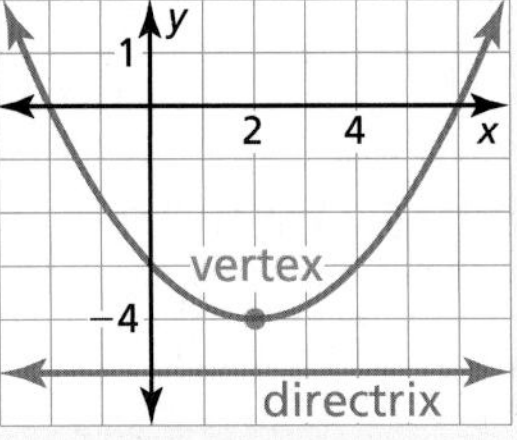

21.

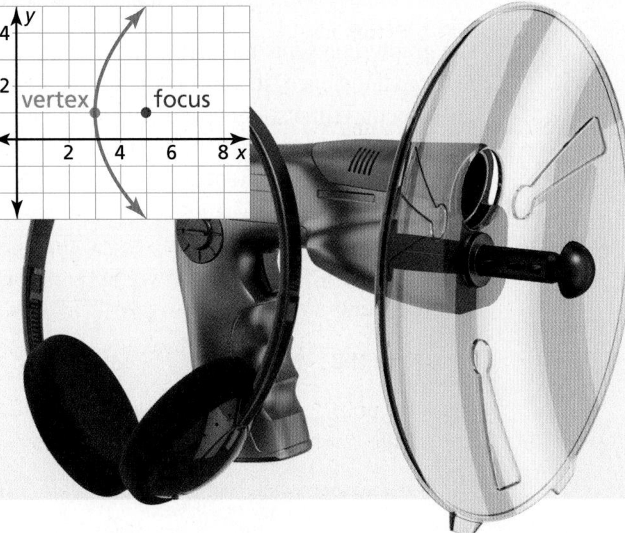

22. Parabolic microphones use a microphone at the focal point of a parabolic dish to amplify and record sound. One such device has a diameter of 20 inches and a depth of 6 inches. Describe the location of the microphone.

2.4 Modeling with Quadratic Functions (pp. 71–78)

Learning Target: Write equations of quadratic functions using given characteristics.

Write an equation of the parabola with the given characteristics.

23. passes through (1, 12) and has vertex (10, −4)

24. passes through (4, 3) and has x-intercepts −1 and 5

25. passes through (−2, 7), (1, 10), and (2, 27)

26. The graph shows the parabolic path of a stunt motorcyclist jumping off a ramp, where y is the height (in feet) and x is the horizontal distance traveled (in feet). Write an equation of the parabola. The motorcyclist lands on another ramp 160 feet from the first ramp. What is the height of the second ramp?

27. The table shows the heights y of a dropped object after x seconds. Verify that the data show a quadratic relationship. Write a function that models the data. How long is the object in the air?

Time (seconds), x	0	0.5	1	1.5	2	2.5
Height (feet), y	150	146	134	114	86	50

28. The table shows the average total stopping distances of a vehicle on dry pavement at different speeds.

Speed (miles per hour), x	20	30	40	55	65	70
Total stopping distance (feet), y	63	119	164	265	344	387

a. Use technology to write a function that models the data.

b. Estimate the total stopping distance of a vehicle traveling 45 miles per hour.

Mathematical Practices

Make Sense of Problems and Persevere in Solving Them

Mathematically proficient students consider analogous problems.

1. How did understanding transformations of linear functions help you to understand transformations of quadratic functions?

2. In Exercise 41 on page 59, you explained why you cannot use the axes of symmetry to distinguish between two quadratic functions whose graphs have vertices (2, 4) and (2, −3). Similarly, explain why you cannot use y-intercepts to distinguish between two linear functions whose graphs pass through the point (0, 2).

3. Complete the statement below. Explain your reasoning.

The point (−3, −1) on the graph of $y = (x + 3)^2 - 1$ is similar to the point ______ for the graph on $x = (y + 3)^2 - 1$.

2 Practice Test WITH CalcChat®

Describe the transformation of $f(x) = x^2$ represented by g. Then graph each function.

1. $g(x) = x^2 - 6$
2. $g(x) = (x + 1)^2$
3. $g(x) = \frac{1}{4}x^2$
4. $g(x) = (3x)^2$
5. $g(x) = -x^2 + 3$
6. $g(x) = (2x + 1)^2 - 4$
7. Identify the focus, directrix, and axis of symmetry of $x = 2y^2$. Graph the equation.
8. Graph $f(x) = 8x^2 - 4x + 3$. Label the vertex and axis of symmetry. Find when the function is increasing and decreasing.
9. A parabola has axis of symmetry $y = 3$ and passes through the point (2, 1). Find another point that lies on the parabola. Explain your reasoning.

Write an equation of the parabola.

10.

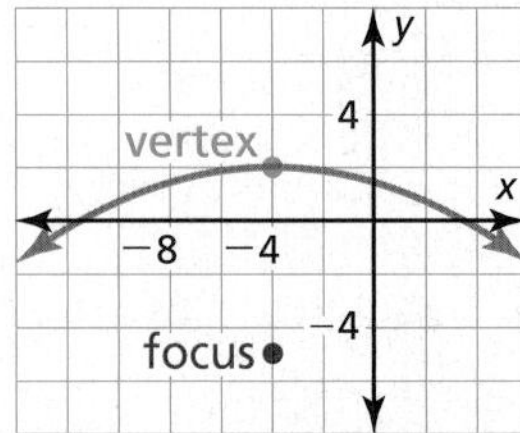

11.

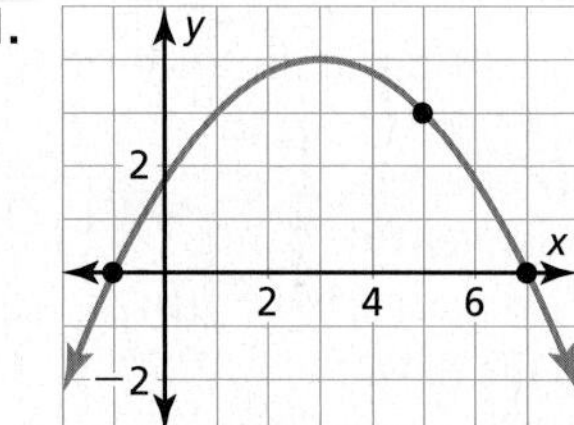

12.

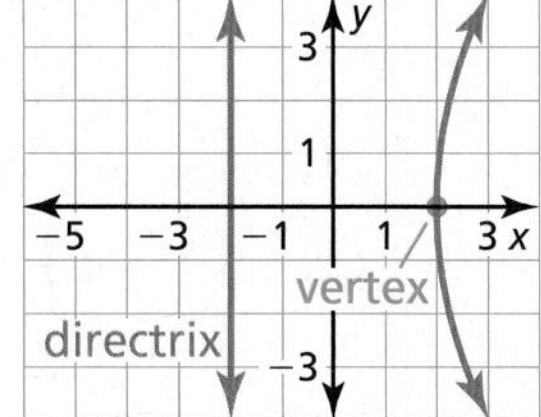

13. A surfboard shop sells 40 surfboards per month when it charges $500 per surfboard. Each time the shop decreases the price by $10, it sells 1 additional surfboard per month. How much should the shop charge per surfboard to maximize monthly revenue? What is the maximum monthly revenue? Explain.

14. Explain why a quadratic function models the data. Then use a linear system to find the model.

x	2	4	6	8	10
$f(x)$	0	−13	−34	−63	−100

15. The SG4 Big Dish is a machine with a parabolic cross section used to collect solar energy. The Sun's rays are reflected from the mirrors toward the focus of the parabola, where the heat produces steam. The steam can then be used to produce electricity.
    a. Write an equation that represents the cross section of the dish with its vertex at (0, 0).
    b. What is the depth of the SG4 Big Dish? Justify your answer.

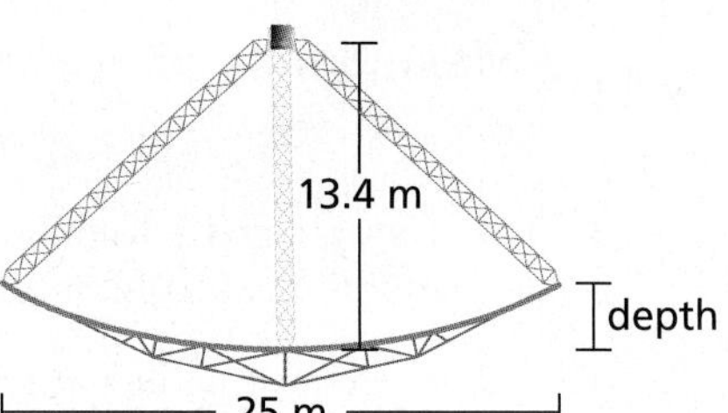

16. The table shows the speeds s (in feet per second) of sound in water at various temperatures t (in degrees Fahrenheit). Write a function that models the data. Use the model to approximate the speed of sound when the water temperature is 100°F.

Temperature (°F), t	32	50	90	120	180	212
Speed (ft/sec), s	4603	4748	4960	5049	5095	5062

2 Performance Task
Stargazing

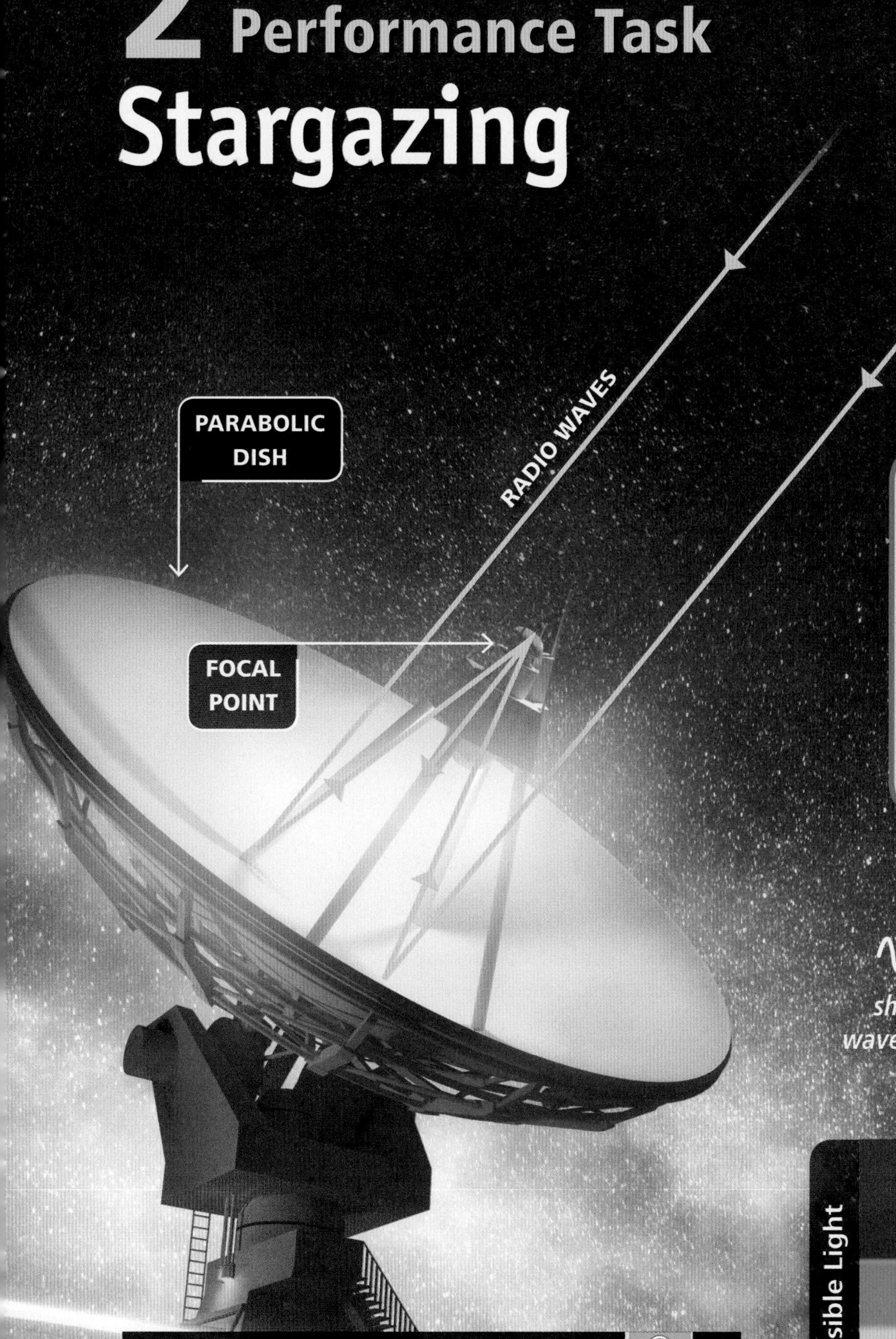

DISTANT RADIO SOURCE

RADIO WAVES

PARABOLIC DISH

FOCAL POINT

APPLICATIONS OF RADIO TELESCOPES

- search for extraterrestrial life
- study stars, black holes, and other celestial objects
- transmit radio light through our solar system
- detect ice on other planets
- track space probes

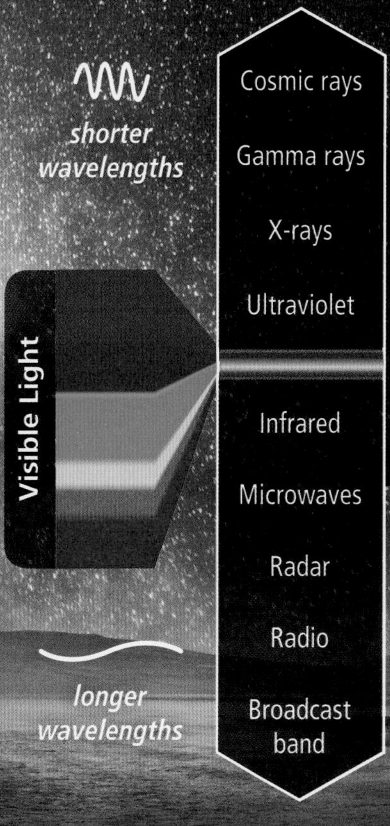

shorter wavelengths

Cosmic rays
Gamma rays
X-rays
Ultraviolet
Visible Light
Infrared
Microwaves
Radar
Radio
Broadcast band

longer wavelengths

Similar to how optical telescopes collect visible light waves, radio telescopes collect radio light waves.

TELESCOPE DESIGN

Design a parabolic radio telescope. Research existing telescopes to help you choose reasonable dimensions for your design. Write and graph an equation that represents the parabolic cross section of your telescope.

Radio telescopes are often arranged in an *array*. Describe the benefits of this kind of arrangement. Then determine whether your telescope will function independently or as part of an array.

2 College and Career Readiness WITH CalcChat®

Tutorial videos are available for each exercise.

1. Which of the following describes the transformation from the graph of $f(x) = |x|$ to the graph of $g(x) = \frac{1}{2}|x - 4| + 4$? Select all that apply.

   Ⓐ a translation 4 units right and a vertical shrink by a factor of $\frac{1}{2}$, followed by a translation 4 units up

   Ⓑ a translation 4 units right and 4 units up, followed by a vertical shrink by a factor of $\frac{1}{2}$

   Ⓒ a vertical shrink by a factor of $\frac{1}{2}$, followed by a translation 4 units up and 4 units right

   Ⓓ a translation 4 units right and 8 units up, followed by a vertical shrink by a factor of $\frac{1}{2}$

2. The table shows the profits y (in dollars) when x students attend a school dance and the school hires a DJ who charges $750.

Students, x	Profit, y
100	−250
200	250
300	750
400	1250
500	1750

   a. What is the cost of each ticket?

   b. Your school hires a different DJ who charges $650. Four hundred students are expected to attend the dance. How much should your school charge per ticket to make the same profit shown in the table?

3. Identify the focus and directrix of the graph of $x = \frac{1}{8}y^2$.

   Ⓐ focus: $(8, 0)$; directrix: $x = -8$

   Ⓑ focus: $\left(\frac{1}{8}, 0\right)$; directrix: $x = -\frac{1}{8}$

   Ⓒ focus: $(0, 2)$; directrix: $y = -2$

   Ⓓ focus: $(2, 0)$; directrix: $x = -2$

4. You and your friend throw a football. The parabola shows the path of your friend's throw, where x is the horizontal distance (in feet) and y is the height (in feet). The path of your throw is represented by $h(x) = -16x^2 + 65x + 5$. Complete the statement with <, =, or >. Explain your reasoning.

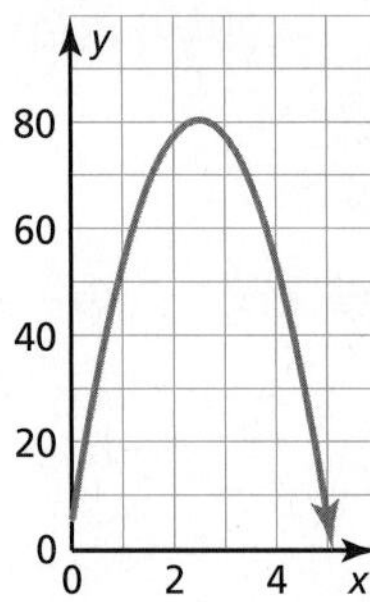

height of your throw ▒ height of your friend's throw

GO DIGITAL

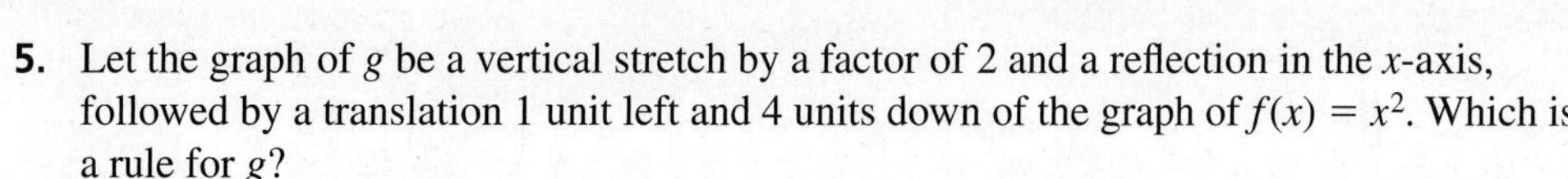

5. Let the graph of g be a vertical stretch by a factor of 2 and a reflection in the x-axis, followed by a translation 1 unit left and 4 units down of the graph of $f(x) = x^2$. Which is a rule for g?

Ⓐ $g(x) = -2(x + 1)^2 - 4$

Ⓑ $g(x) = -2(x + 1)^2 + 8$

Ⓒ $g(x) = 2(-x + 1)^2 - 4$

Ⓓ $g(x) = -2(x - 1)^2 - 4$

6. Two balls are thrown in the air. The height of the first ball over time is represented by the graph. The second ball is released 35 feet higher than the first ball, and reaches a maximum height that is 7 feet higher than the maximum height of the first ball after 1.5 seconds.

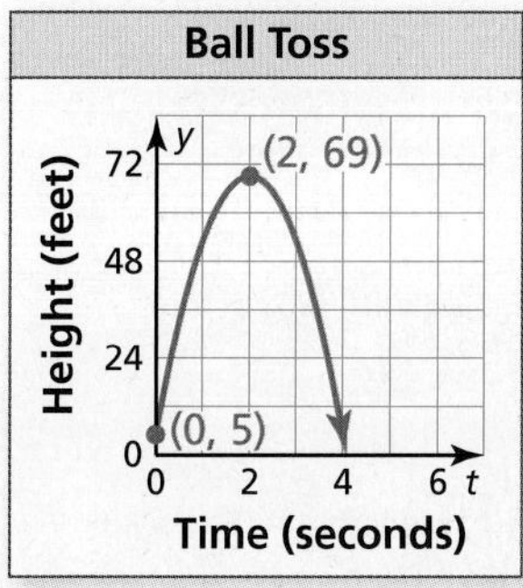

a. Write an equation that represents the height of the second ball over time.

b. Which ball hits the ground first? Explain your reasoning.

7. Let the graph of g be a translation 3 units right of the graph of f. The points $(-1, 6)$, $(3, 14)$, and $(6, 41)$ lie on the graph of f. Which points lie on the graph of g? Select all that apply.

Ⓐ $(-1, 9)$

Ⓑ $(2, 6)$

Ⓒ $(3, 17)$

Ⓓ $(6, 14)$

Ⓔ $(6, 44)$

Ⓕ $(9, 41)$

8. A system of three linear equations in three variables has infinitely many solutions. Two of the equations are shown below. Which of the following equations could be the third equation in the system? Select all that apply.

$$4x - 3y + z = 8$$

$$-8x + 6y + 4z = 12$$

Ⓐ $-4x + 3y - z = 8$

Ⓑ $12x + 3z = 24 + 9y$

Ⓒ $4x - 3y - 2z = -6$

Ⓓ $-2x + \frac{3}{2}y + z = 12$

9. Gym A charges \$10 per month plus a registration fee of \$100. Gym B charges \$30 per month, but does not charge a registration fee.

a. For each gym, write an equation that represents the total cost y of a membership after x months.

b. When is Gym A a better deal?

c. Gym A lowers its registration fee to \$25. Describe a transformation that represents this situation. How does this affect your answer in part (b)?

3 Quadratic Equations and Complex Numbers

NATIONAL GEOGRAPHIC EXPLORER

Leslie Dewan

Dr. Leslie Dewan believes that nuclear energy is a powerful tool to combat climate change. She has updated the design of the molten-salt reactor to keep its safety features and lower the cost of generating electricity. She hopes that this design can be used to generate electricity that is both carbon-free and cheaper than electricity generated from coal.

- What methods are used to generate electricity in the United States? Of these, which are classified as *renewable*?
- What percent of the electricity in the United States is generated from renewable energy sources?
- Is the Sun's heat a form of nuclear energy?

STEM

Nuclear fission has been used to generate electricity since the early 1950s. In the Performance Task, you will investigate how the number of operable nuclear reactors has grown over time.

Nuclear Engineering

Preparing for Chapter 3

Chapter Learning Target Understand quadratic equations and complex numbers.

Chapter Success Criteria

- ◆ I can perform operations with complex numbers.
- ◆ I can solve quadratic equations by completing the square.
- ■ I can describe how to use the Quadratic Formula.
- ■ I can solve nonlinear systems and quadratic inequalities.

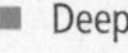

◆ Surface
■ Deep

Chapter Vocabulary

Work with a partner. Discuss each of the vocabulary terms.

quadratic equation in one variable	discriminant
zero of a function	system of nonlinear equations
completing the square	quadratic inequality in two variables
Quadratic Formula	quadratic inequality in one variable

Mathematical Practices

Make Sense of Problems and Persevere in Solving Them

Mathematically proficient students plan a solution pathway rather than simply jumping into a solution attempt.

Work with a partner. The table shows the amount of nuclear electricity generated for consumer use in the United States over time. Write a problem that can be solved using the given information. Then exchange problems with another pair of students.

Years since 1980	Electricity Generated by Nuclear Power (millions of kilowatt hours)	Percent of All Electricity Generated by Nuclear Power
0	251,116	11
5	383,691	15.5
10	576,862	19
15	673,402	20.1
20	753,893	19.8
25	781,986	19.3
30	806,968	19.6
35	797,178	19.6

1. Explain the problem.

a. What information is given?

b. What is being asked?

2. Make a plan for how to solve the problem. Describe any problem-solving strategies that you will use.

3. Use your plan to solve the problem. Then show that your solution is reasonable.

3 Prepare WITH CalcChat®

Simplifying Square Roots

Example 1 **Simplify $\sqrt{8}$.**

$\sqrt{8} = \sqrt{4 \cdot 2}$ — Factor using the greatest perfect square factor.

$= \sqrt{4} \cdot \sqrt{2}$ — Product Property of Square Roots

$= 2\sqrt{2}$ — Simplify.

Example 2 **Simplify $\sqrt{\frac{7}{36}}$.**

$\sqrt{\frac{7}{36}} = \frac{\sqrt{7}}{\sqrt{36}}$ — Quotient Property of Square Roots

$= \frac{\sqrt{7}}{6}$ — Simplify.

Simplify the expression.

1. $\sqrt{27}$ **2.** $-\sqrt{112}$ **3.** $\sqrt{\frac{11}{64}}$ **4.** $\sqrt{\frac{147}{100}}$

5. $\sqrt{\frac{18}{49}}$ **6.** $-\sqrt{\frac{65}{121}}$ **7.** $-\sqrt{80}$ **8.** $\sqrt{32}$

Factoring Special Products

Example 3 **Factor (a) $x^2 - 4$ and (b) $x^2 - 14x + 49$.**

a. $x^2 - 4 = x^2 - 2^2$ — Write as $a^2 - b^2$.

$= (x + 2)(x - 2)$ — Difference of two squares pattern

▶ So, $x^2 - 4 = (x + 2)(x - 2)$.

b. $x^2 - 14x + 49 = x^2 - 2(x)(7) + 7^2$ — Write as $a^2 - 2ab + b^2$.

$= (x - 7)^2$ — Perfect square trinomial pattern

▶ So, $x^2 - 14x + 49 = (x - 7)^2$.

Factor the polynomial.

9. $x^2 - 36$ **10.** $x^2 - 9$ **11.** $4x^2 - 25$

12. $x^2 - 22x + 121$ **13.** $x^2 + 28x + 196$ **14.** $49x^2 + 210x + 225$

15. MP **NUMBER SENSE** Determine the possible integer values of a and c for which the trinomial $ax^2 + 8x + c$ is factorable using the perfect square trinomial pattern. Explain your reasoning.

3.1 Solving Quadratic Equations

Learning Target Solve quadratic equations graphically and algebraically.

Success Criteria
- I can solve quadratic equations by graphing.
- I can solve quadratic equations algebraically.
- I can use quadratic equations to solve real-life problems.

EXPLORE IT! 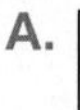 Solving Quadratic Equations

Math Practice

Find General Methods
Recall that when $ab = 0$, either a or b must be 0. How does this property help you solve quadratic equations?

Work with a partner.

a. Match each quadratic equation with the graph of its related function. Then use the graph to find the real solutions (if any) of each equation. Explain your reasoning.

i. $x^2 - 2x = 0$ **ii.** $x^2 - 2x + 1 = 0$

iii. $x^2 - 2x + 2 = 0$ **iv.** $-x^2 + 2x = 0$

v. $-x^2 + 2x - 1 = 0$ **vi.** $-x^2 + 2x - 2 = 0$

A.
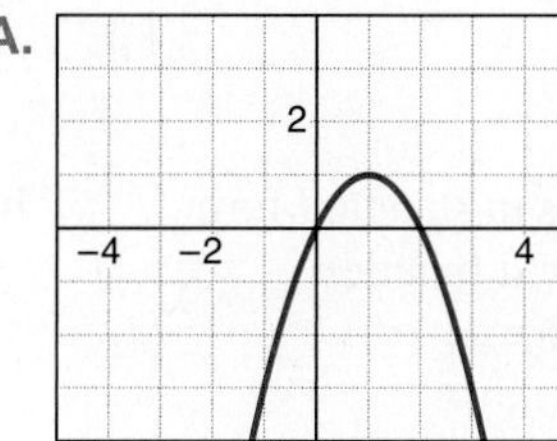

B.
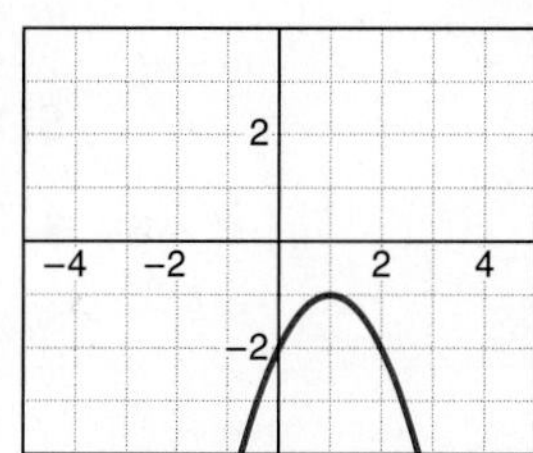

C.
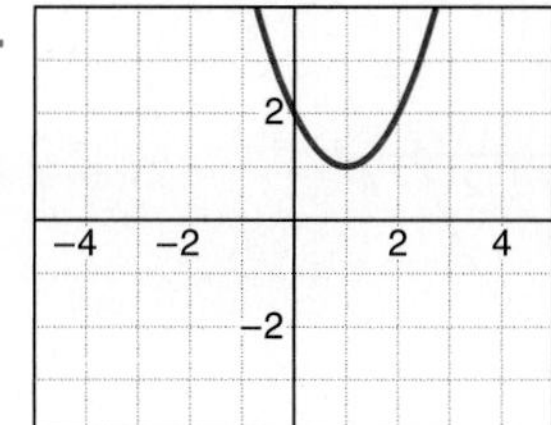

D.
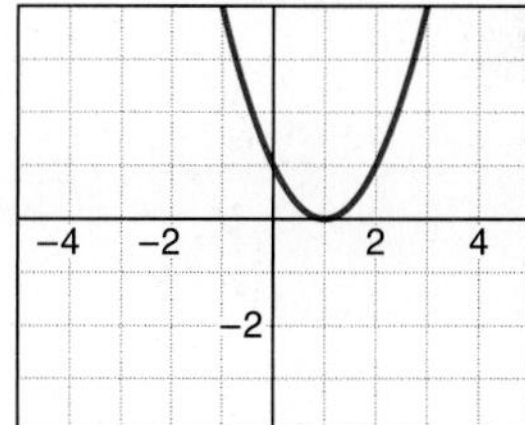

E.
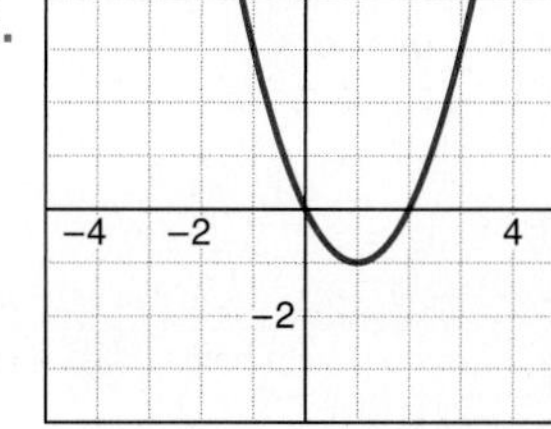

F.
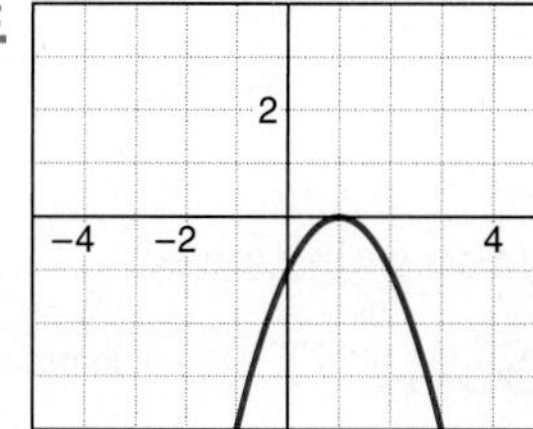

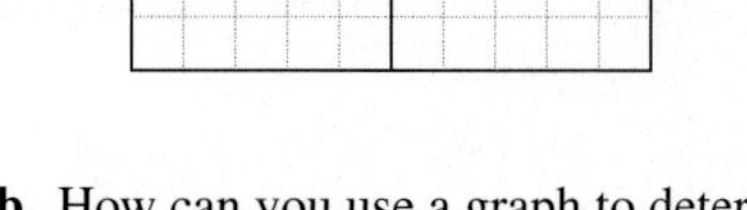

b. How can you use a graph to determine the number of real solutions of a quadratic equation?

c. What algebraic methods can you use to solve the equations in part (a)? Solve each equation using an algebraic method.

Solving Quadratic Equations by Graphing

A **quadratic equation in one variable** is an equation that can be written in the standard form $ax^2 + bx + c = 0$, where a, b, and c are real numbers and $a \neq 0$. A **root of an equation** is a solution of the equation. You can use various methods to solve quadratic equations.

Vocabulary (VOCAB)

quadratic equation in one variable, *p. 90*
root of an equation, *p. 90*
zero of a function, *p. 92*

STUDY TIP

Quadratic equations can have zero, one, or two real solutions.

KEY IDEA

Solving Quadratic Equations

By graphing Find the x-intercepts of the graph of the related function $y = ax^2 + bx + c$.

Using square roots Write the equation in the form $u^2 = d$, where u is an algebraic expression, and solve by taking the square root of each side.

By factoring Write the quadratic equation $ax^2 + bx + c = 0$ in factored form and solve using the Zero-Product Property.

EXAMPLE 1 Solving Quadratic Equations by Graphing

Solve each equation by graphing.

a. $x^2 - x - 6 = 0$ **b.** $-2x^2 - 2 = 4x$

SOLUTION

a. The equation is in standard form. Graph the related function $y = x^2 - x - 6$.

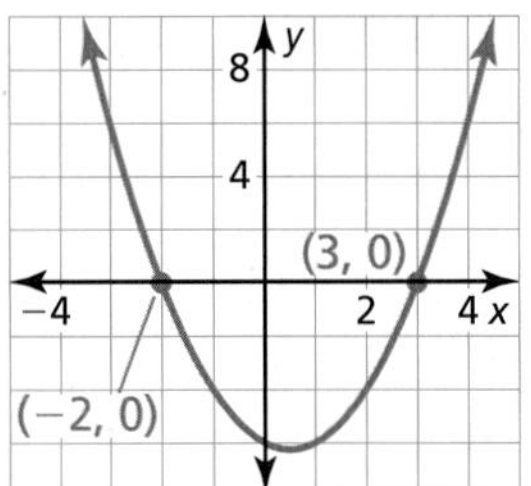

The x-intercepts are -2 and 3.

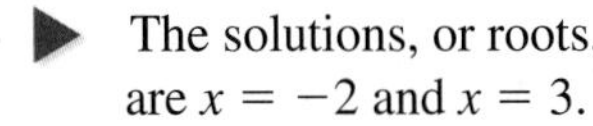

▶ The solutions, or roots, are $x = -2$ and $x = 3$.

Check

$$x^2 - x - 6 = 0$$
$$(-2)^2 - (-2) - 6 \stackrel{?}{=} 0$$
$$4 + 2 - 6 \stackrel{?}{=} 0$$
$$0 = 0 \checkmark$$

$$x^2 - x - 6 = 0$$
$$3^2 - 3 - 6 \stackrel{?}{=} 0$$
$$9 - 3 - 6 \stackrel{?}{=} 0$$
$$0 = 0 \checkmark$$

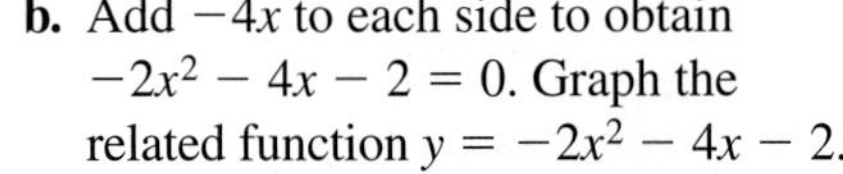

b. Add $-4x$ to each side to obtain $-2x^2 - 4x - 2 = 0$. Graph the related function $y = -2x^2 - 4x - 2$.

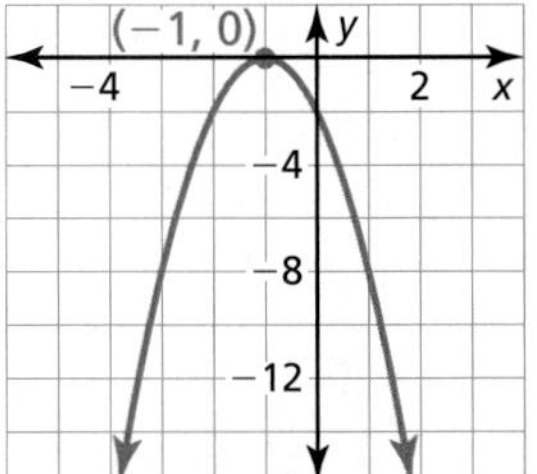

The x-intercept is -1.

▶ The solution, or root, is $x = -1$.

SELF-ASSESSMENT 1 I do not understand. 2 I can do it with help. 3 I can do it on my own. 4 I can teach someone else.

Solve the equation by graphing.

1. $x^2 - 8x + 12 = 0$ **2.** $4x^2 - 12x + 9 = 0$ **3.** $-\frac{1}{2}x^2 = 20 - 6x$

4. WRITING Explain how to use graphing to find the roots of the equation $ax^2 + bx + c = 0$.

5. MP STRUCTURE How many roots does $x^2 = 0$ have? Use your answer to determine the number of roots of $(x - 2)^2 = 0$. Explain your reasoning.

Solving Quadratic Equations Algebraically

GO DIGITAL

When solving quadratic equations using square roots, you can use properties of square roots to write your solutions in different forms. When a radicand in the denominator of a fraction is not a perfect square, you can multiply the fraction by an appropriate form of 1 to eliminate the radical from the denominator. This process is called *rationalizing the denominator*.

EXAMPLE 2 Solving Quadratic Equations Using Square Roots

Solve each equation using square roots.

a. $4x^2 - 31 = 49$ **b.** $3x^2 + 9 = 0$ **c.** $\frac{2}{5}(x + 3)^2 = 5$

SOLUTION

a. $4x^2 - 31 = 49$ Write the equation.

$4x^2 = 80$ Add 31 to each side.

$x^2 = 20$ Divide each side by 4.

$x = \pm\sqrt{20}$ Take square root of each side.

$x = \pm\sqrt{4} \cdot \sqrt{5}$ Product Property of Square Roots

$x = \pm 2\sqrt{5}$ Simplify.

▶ The solutions are $x = 2\sqrt{5}$ and $x = -2\sqrt{5}$.

b. $3x^2 + 9 = 0$ Write the equation.

$3x^2 = -9$ Subtract 9 from each side.

$x^2 = -3$ Divide each side by 3.

▶ The square of a real number cannot be negative. So, the equation has no real solution.

c. $\frac{2}{5}(x + 3)^2 = 5$ Write the equation.

$(x + 3)^2 = \frac{25}{2}$ Multiply each side by $\frac{5}{2}$.

$x + 3 = \pm\sqrt{\frac{25}{2}}$ Take square root of each side.

$x = -3 \pm \sqrt{\frac{25}{2}}$ Subtract 3 from each side.

$x = -3 \pm \frac{\sqrt{25}}{\sqrt{2}}$ Quotient Property of Square Roots

$x = -3 \pm \frac{\sqrt{25}}{\sqrt{2}} \cdot \frac{\sqrt{2}}{\sqrt{2}}$ Multiply by $\frac{\sqrt{2}}{\sqrt{2}}$.

$x = -3 \pm \frac{5\sqrt{2}}{2}$ Simplify.

▶ The solutions are $x = -3 + \frac{5\sqrt{2}}{2}$ and $x = -3 - \frac{5\sqrt{2}}{2}$.

STUDY TIP

Because $\frac{\sqrt{2}}{\sqrt{2}} = 1$, the value of $\frac{\sqrt{25}}{\sqrt{2}}$ does not change when you multiply by $\frac{\sqrt{2}}{\sqrt{2}}$.

SELF-ASSESSMENT 1 I do not understand. 2 I can do it with help. 3 I can do it on my own. 4 I can teach someone else.

Solve the equation using square roots.

6. $\frac{2}{3}x^2 + 14 = 20$ **7.** $-2x^2 + 1 = -6$ **8.** $2(x - 4)^2 = -5$

When the left side of $ax^2 + bx + c = 0$ is factorable, you can solve the equation using the *Zero-Product Property*.

KEY IDEA

Zero-Product Property

Words If the product of two expressions is zero, then one or both of the expressions equal zero.

Algebra If A and B are expressions and $AB = 0$, then $A = 0$ or $B = 0$.

EXAMPLE 3 Solving a Quadratic Equation by Factoring

Solve $x^2 - 4x = 45$ by factoring.

SOLUTION

$x^2 - 4x = 45$	Write the equation.
$x^2 - 4x - 45 = 0$	Write in standard form.
$(x - 9)(x + 5) = 0$	Factor the polynomial.
$x - 9 = 0$ or $x + 5 = 0$	Zero-Product Property
$x = 9$ or $x = -5$	Solve for x.

▶ The solutions are $x = -5$ and $x = 9$.

Math Practice

Understand Mathematical Terms

If a real number k is a zero of the function $f(x) = ax^2 + bx + c$, then k is an x-intercept of the graph of the function, and k is also a root of the equation $ax^2 + bx + c = 0$.

You know the x-intercepts of the graph of $f(x) = a(x - p)(x - q)$ are p and q. Because the value of the function is zero when $x = p$ and when $x = q$, the numbers p and q are also called *zeros* of the function. A **zero of a function** f is an x-value for which $f(x) = 0$.

EXAMPLE 4 Finding the Zeros of a Quadratic Function

Find the zeros of $f(x) = 2x^2 - 11x + 12$.

SOLUTION

To find the zeros of the function, find the x-values for which $f(x) = 0$.

$2x^2 - 11x + 12 = 0$	Set $f(x)$ equal to 0.
$(2x - 3)(x - 4) = 0$	Factor the polynomial.
$2x - 3 = 0$ or $x - 4 = 0$	Zero-Product Property
$x = 1.5$ or $x = 4$	Solve for x.

▶ The zeros of the function are $x = 1.5$ and $x = 4$.

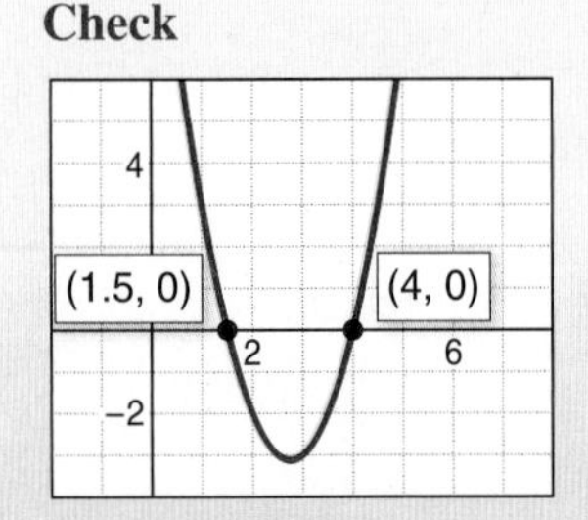

SELF-ASSESSMENT

1 I do not understand. 2 I can do it with help. 3 I can do it on my own. 4 I can teach someone else.

Solve the equation by factoring.

9. $x^2 + 12x + 35 = 0$ **10.** $2x^2 - 8x + 6 = 0$ **11.** $3x^2 - 5x = 2$

Find the zero(s) of the function.

12. $f(x) = x^2 - 8x$ **13.** $f(x) = x^2 + 2x - 8$ **14.** $f(x) = 4x^2 + 28x + 49$

Solving Real-Life Problems

One way to find the maximum value or minimum value of a quadratic function is to first write the function in intercept form $f(x) = a(x - p)(x - q)$. Because the vertex of the function lies on the axis of symmetry, $x = \frac{p + q}{2}$, the maximum value or minimum value occurs at the average of the zeros p and q.

Modeling Real Life

A streaming service company charges \$6 per month and has 15 million subscribers. For each \$1 increase in price, the company loses 1.5 million subscribers. How much should the company charge to maximize monthly revenue? What is the maximum monthly revenue?

SOLUTION

Step 1 Define the variables. Let x represent the price increase and $R(x)$ represent the monthly revenue.

Step 2 Write a verbal model. Then write a quadratic function in intercept form.

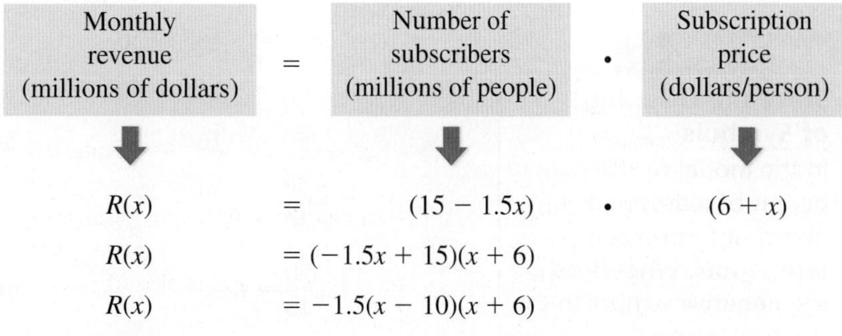

$$R(x) = (15 - 1.5x) \cdot (6 + x)$$

$$R(x) = (-1.5x + 15)(x + 6)$$

$$R(x) = -1.5(x - 10)(x + 6)$$

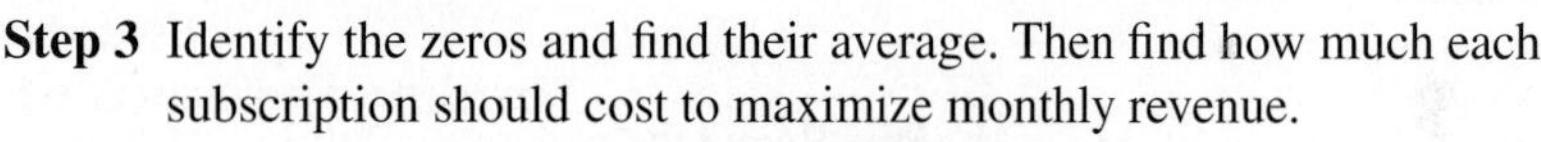

Step 3 Identify the zeros and find their average. Then find how much each subscription should cost to maximize monthly revenue.

The zeros of the revenue function are 10 and -6. The average of the zeros is $\frac{10 + (-6)}{2} = 2$.

To maximize revenue, each subscription should cost \$6 + \$2 = \$8.

Step 4 Find the maximum monthly revenue.

$$R(2) = -1.5(2 - 10)(2 + 6) = 96$$

▶ So, the company should charge \$8 per subscription to maximize monthly revenue. The maximum monthly revenue is \$96 million.

SELF-ASSESSMENT 1 I do not understand. 2 I can do it with help. 3 I can do it on my own. 4 I can teach someone else.

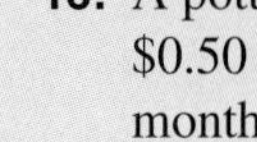

15. WHAT IF? The company charges \$8 per month and has 15 million subscribers. How much should the company charge to maximize monthly revenue? What is the maximum monthly revenue?

16. A pottery store charges \$10 per mug and sells 40 mugs per month. For each \$0.50 decrease in price, the store sells 5 more mugs. What is the maximum monthly profit for mugs when each mug costs \$3 to make?

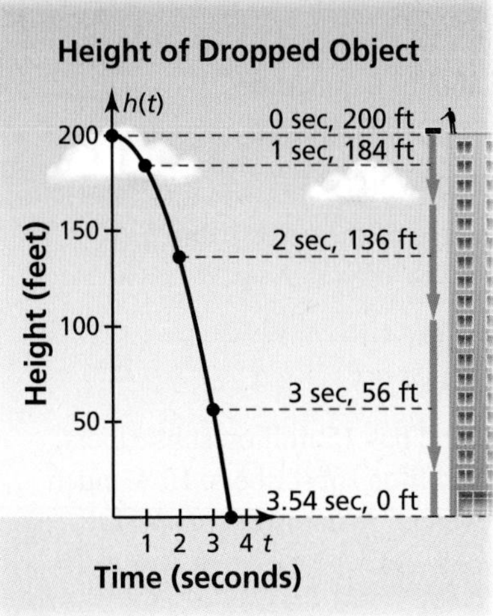

When an object is dropped, its height (in feet) above the ground after t seconds can be modeled by the function $h(t) = -16t^2 + s_0$, where s_0 is the initial height (in feet) of the object. The graph of $h(t) = -16t^2 + 200$, representing the height of an object dropped from an initial height of 200 feet, is shown at the left.

GO DIGITAL

The model $h(t) = -16t^2 + s_0$ assumes that the force of air resistance on the object is negligible. Also, this model applies only to objects dropped on Earth. For planets with stronger or weaker gravitational forces, different models are used.

EXAMPLE 6 Modeling Real Life

For a science competition, students must design a container that prevents an egg from breaking when dropped from a height of 50 feet.

a. Write a function h that gives the height (in feet) of the container after t seconds. How long does the container take to hit the ground?

b. Find and interpret $h(1) - h(1.5)$.

SOLUTION

a. The initial height is 50, so the model is $h(t) = -16t^2 + 50$. Find the zeros of the function.

$h(t) = -16t^2 + 50$ Write the function.

$0 = -16t^2 + 50$ Substitute 0 for $h(t)$.

$-50 = -16t^2$ Subtract 50 from each side.

$\frac{-50}{-16} = t^2$ Divide each side by -16.

$\pm\sqrt{\frac{50}{16}} = t$ Take square root of each side.

$\pm 1.8 \approx t$ Use technology.

▶ Reject the negative solution, -1.8, because time must be positive. The container will fall for about 1.8 seconds before it hits the ground.

Math Practice

State the Meaning of Symbols

In the model for the height of a dropped object, interpret the term $-16t^2$. What does the negative symbol in the term mean?

b. Find $h(1)$ and $h(1.5)$. These represent the heights after 1 and 1.5 seconds.

$$h(1) = -16(1)^2 + 50$$
$$= -16 + 50 = 34$$
$$h(1.5) = -16(1.5)^2 + 50$$
$$= -16(2.25) + 50$$
$$= -36 + 50 = 14$$
$$h(1) - h(1.5) = 34 - 14 = 20$$

▶ So, the container fell 20 feet between 1 and 1.5 seconds. You can check this by graphing the function. The points appear to be about 20 feet apart. So, the answer is reasonable.

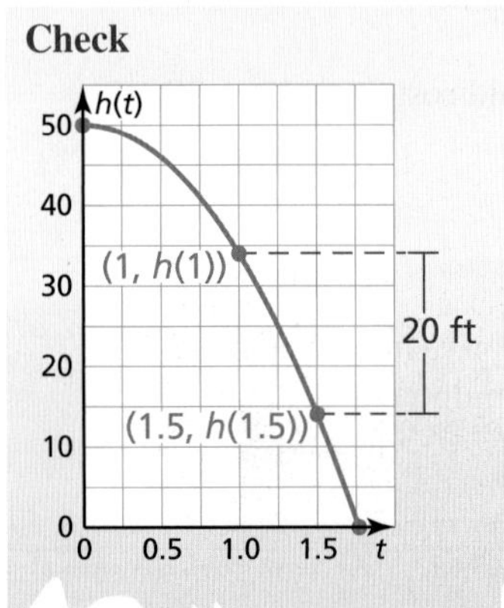

SELF-ASSESSMENT 1 I do not understand. 2 I can do it with help. 3 I can do it on my own. 4 I can teach someone else.

17. WHAT IF? The egg container is dropped from a height of 80 feet. How does this change your answers in parts (a) and (b)?

3.1 Practice WITH CalcChat® AND CalcView®

In Exercises 1–10, solve the equation by graphing. ▶ *Example 1*

1. $x^2 + 3x + 2 = 0$
2. $-x^2 + 2x + 3 = 0$
3. $0 = x^2 - 9$
4. $-8 = -x^2 - 4$
5. $8x = -4 - 4x^2$
6. $3x^2 = 6x - 3$
7. $7 = -x^2 - 4x$
8. $2x = x^2 + 2$
9. $\frac{1}{5}x^2 + 6 = 2x$
10. $3x = \frac{1}{4}x^2 + 5$

In Exercises 11–18, solve the equation using square roots. ▶ *Example 2*

11. $s^2 = 144$
12. $a^2 = 81$
13. $(z - 6)^2 = 25$
14. $(p - 4)^2 = 49$
15. $4(x - 1)^2 + 2 = 10$
16. $2(x + 2)^2 - 5 = 8$
17. $\frac{1}{2}r^2 - 10 = \frac{3}{2}r^2$
18. $\frac{1}{5}x^2 + 2 = \frac{3}{5}x^2$

ERROR ANALYSIS In Exercises 19 and 20, describe and correct the error in solving the equation.

19.

$$2(x + 1)^2 + 3 = 21$$
$$2(x + 1)^2 = 18$$
$$(x + 1)^2 = 9$$
$$x + 1 = 3$$
$$x = 2$$

20.

$$-2x^2 - 8 = 0$$
$$-2x^2 = 8$$
$$x^2 = -4$$
$$x = \pm 2$$

In Exercises 21–30, solve the equation by factoring. ▶ *Example 3*

21. $0 = x^2 + 6x + 9$
22. $0 = z^2 - 10z + 25$
23. $x^2 - 8x = -12$
24. $x^2 - 11x = -30$
25. $n^2 - 6n = 0$
26. $a^2 - 49 = 0$
27. $3p^2 + 11p = 4$
28. $6t^2 + 14 = -25t$
29. $2w^2 - 16w = 12w - 48$
30. $-y + 28 + y^2 = 2y + 2y^2$

In Exercises 31–38, solve the equation using any method. Explain your choice of method.

31. $u^2 = -9u$
32. $\frac{t^2}{20} + 8 = 15$
33. $-(x + 9)^2 = 64$
34. $-2(x + 2)^2 = 5$
35. $7(x - 4)^2 - 18 = 10$
36. $t^2 + 8t + 16 = 0$
37. $x^2 + 3x + \frac{5}{4} = 0$
38. $x^2 - 1.75 = 0.5$

In Exercises 39–48, find the zero(s) of the function. ▶ *Example 4*

39. $g(x) = x^2 + 6x + 8$
40. $f(x) = x^2 - 8x + 16$
41. $h(x) = x^2 + 7x - 30$
42. $g(x) = x^2 + 11x$
43. $g(x) = x^2 + 22x + 121$
44. $h(x) = x^2 + 19x + 84$
45. $f(x) = 2x^2 - 2x - 12$
46. $f(x) = 4x^2 - 12x + 9$
47. $p(x) = 8x^2 - 19x + 6$
48. $q(x) = 10x^2 - 3x - 4$

49. **MODELING REAL LIFE** A restaurant sells 330 sandwiches each day. For each $0.25 decrease in price, the restaurant sells 15 more sandwiches. How much should the restaurant charge to maximize daily revenue? What is the maximum daily revenue? ▶ *Example 5*

50. **MODELING REAL LIFE** An athletic store charges $120 per pair of basketball shoes and sells 200 pairs per month. For each $2 increase in price, the store sells two fewer pairs of shoes. How much should the store charge to maximize monthly revenue? What is the maximum monthly revenue?

51. **MODELING REAL LIFE** You drop a seashell into the ocean from a height of 40 feet above the water.
Example 6

a. Write a function h that gives the height (in feet) of the seashell above the water after t seconds. Interpret each term. How long does the seashell take to hit the water?

b. Find and interpret $h(0.5) - h(1)$.

52. **MODELING REAL LIFE** According to legend, in 1589, the Italian scientist Galileo Galilei dropped rocks of different weights from the top of the Leaning Tower of Pisa to prove his conjecture that the rocks would hit the ground at the same time.

a. The original height of the tower was about 196 feet. Write a function h that gives the height (in feet) of a rock dropped from the top of the original tower after t seconds. Interpret each term. How long does the rock take to hit the ground?

b. Find and interpret $h(1.25) - h(2.5)$.

53. **COLLEGE PREP** Which equations have roots that are equivalent to the x-intercepts of the graph shown?

Ⓐ $-x^2 - 6x - 8 = 0$

Ⓑ $0 = (x + 2)(x + 4)$

Ⓒ $0 = -(x + 2)^2 + 4$

Ⓓ $2x^2 - 4x - 6 = 0$

Ⓔ $4(x + 3)^2 - 4 = 0$

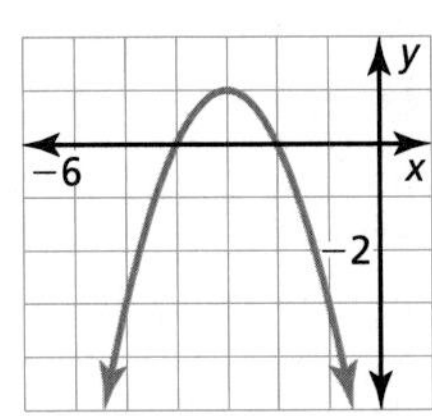

54. **COLLEGE PREP** Which graph has x-intercepts that are equivalent to the roots of the equation $\left(x - \frac{3}{2}\right)^2 = \frac{25}{4}$?

Ⓐ
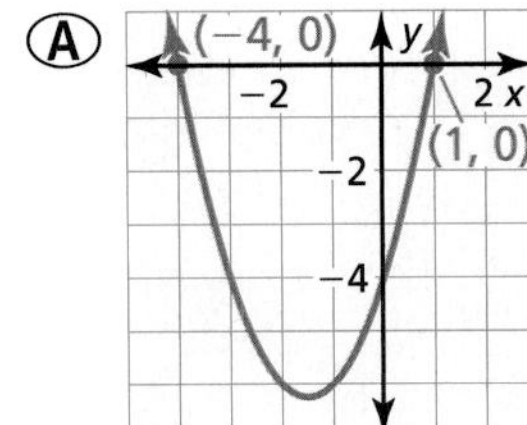

Ⓑ
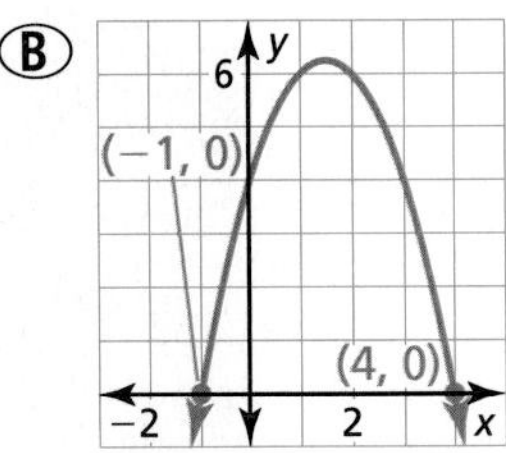

Ⓒ
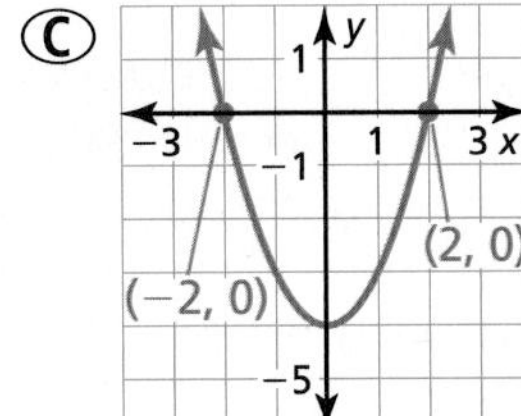

Ⓓ
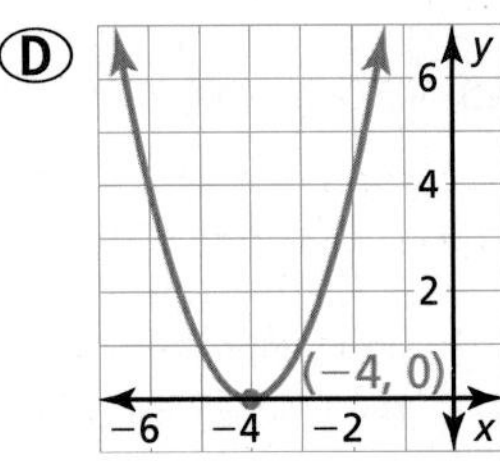

55. **MP REASONING** Write a quadratic function in the form $f(x) = x^2 + bx + c$ that has zeros 8 and 11.

56. **MP NUMBER SENSE** Write a quadratic equation in standard form that has roots equidistant from 10.

57. **OPEN-ENDED** Write a quadratic equation that has (a) one real solution, and (b) no real solution.

58. **MP PRECISION** Describe the relationship among zeros, x-intercepts, and roots.

CONNECTING CONCEPTS In Exercises 59–62, find the value of x.

59. Area of rectangle = 36

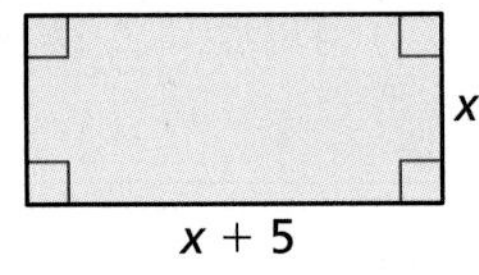

60. Area of circle = 25π

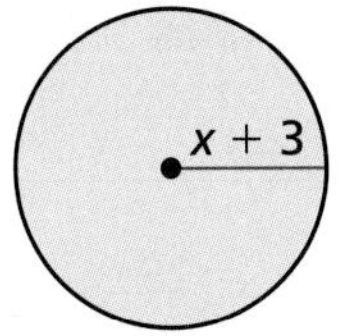

61. Area of triangle = 42

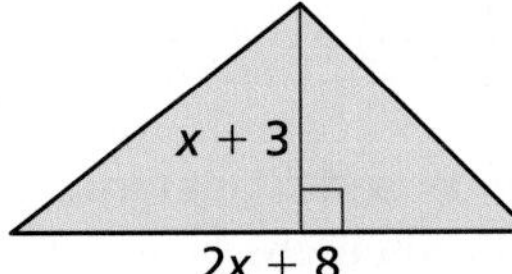

62. Area of trapezoid = 32

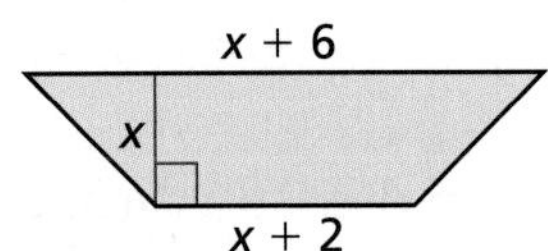

63. **MODELING REAL LIFE** The equation $h = 0.019s^2$ models the height h (in feet) of the largest ocean waves when the wind speed is s knots. Compare the wind speeds required to generate 5-foot waves and 20-foot waves.

64. **MP PROBLEM SOLVING** You make a rectangular quilt that is 5 feet by 4 feet. You use the remaining 10 square feet of fabric to add a border of uniform width to the quilt. What is the width of the border?

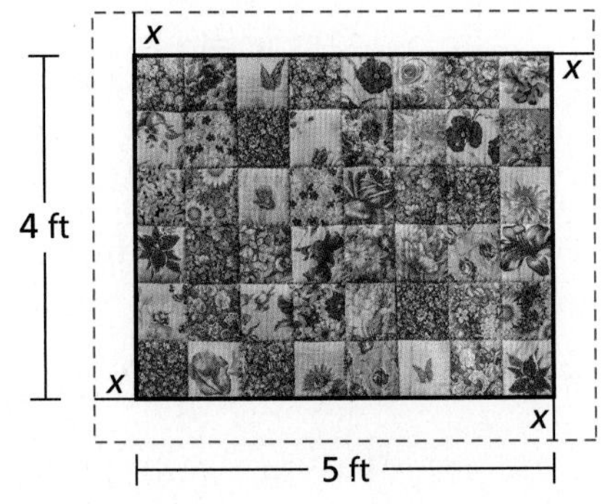

65. **CRITICAL THINKING** Use an equation to find two consecutive odd integers whose product is 143.

66. CONNECTING CONCEPTS A quadrilateral is divided into two right triangles as shown in the figure. What is the length of each side of the quadrilateral?

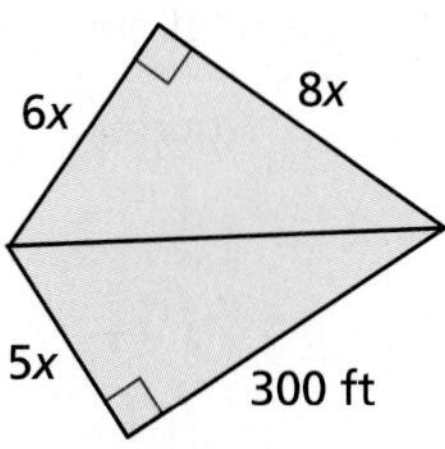

67. ABSTRACT REASONING An equation of the form $ax^2 + bx + c = 0$ has no real solution and a graph of the related function has a vertex that lies in the second quadrant.

a. Is the value of a positive or negative? Explain your reasoning.

b. The graph is translated so the vertex is in the fourth quadrant. Does the graph have any x-intercepts? Explain.

68. MP REASONING When an object is dropped on *any* planet, its height (in feet) after t seconds can be modeled by the function $h(t) = -\frac{g}{2}t^2 + s_0$, where s_0 is the object's initial height and g is the planet's acceleration due to gravity. Two rocks are dropped from the same initial height on Earth and Mars. Make a conjecture about which rock will hit the ground first. Justify your answer.

69. MP PROBLEM SOLVING A café has an outdoor, rectangular patio. The owner wants to add 329 square feet to the area of the patio by expanding the existing patio as shown. By what distance x should the patio be extended?

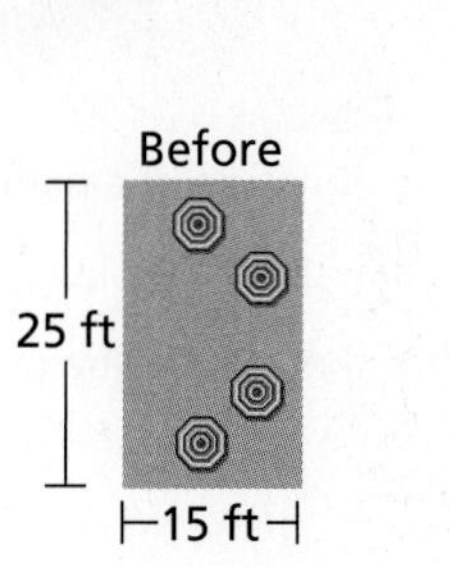

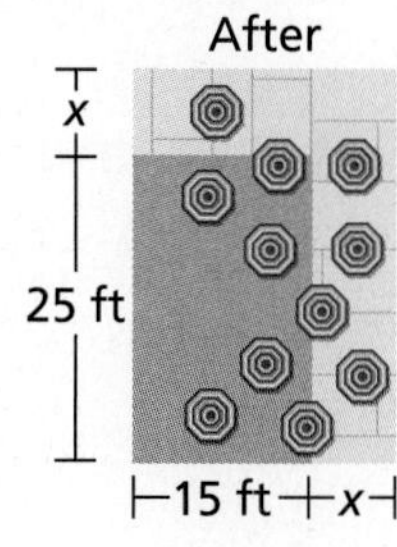

70. MP PROBLEM SOLVING A flea can jump very long distances relative to its size. The path of the jump of a flea can be modeled by the graph of the function $y = -0.189x^2 + 2.462x$, where x is the horizontal distance (in inches) and y is the vertical distance (in inches). Graph the function. Identify the vertex and zeros and interpret their meanings in this situation.

GO DIGITAL

71. MAKING AN ARGUMENT Your friend claims the equation $x^2 + 7x = -49$ can be solved by factoring and has the solutions $x = 0$ and $x = -7$. You solve the equation by graphing the related function and claim there is no solution. Who is correct? Explain.

72. HOW DO YOU SEE IT?
An artist is painting a mural and drops a paintbrush. The graph represents the height h (in feet) of the paintbrush after t seconds.

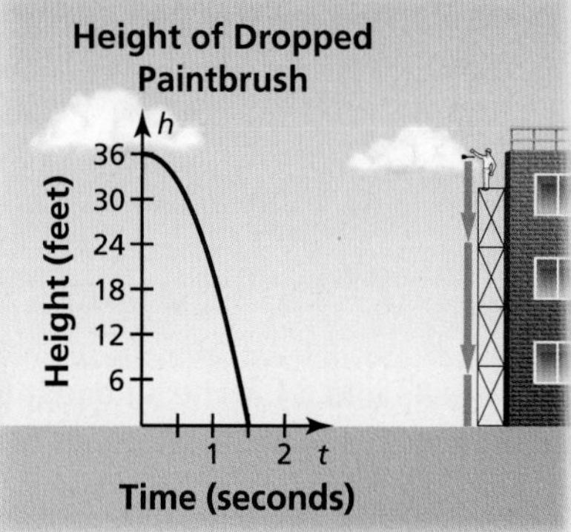

a. What is the initial height of the paintbrush?

b. How long does the paintbrush take to hit the ground?

73. CRITICAL THINKING The equation $x^2 - 2kx - 75 = 0$ has the solutions $x = k - 10$ and $x = k + 10$, where k is an integer. Find the possible values of k.

74. ABSTRACT REASONING Factor the expressions $x^2 - 4$ and $x^2 - 9$. Recall that an expression in this form is called a difference of two squares. Use your answers to factor the expression $x^2 - a^2$. Graph the related function $y = x^2 - a^2$. Label the vertex, x-intercepts, and axis of symmetry.

75. DRAWING CONCLUSIONS Consider the expression $x^2 + a^2$, where $a > 0$.

a. You want to rewrite the expression as $(x + m)(x + n)$. Write two equations that m and n must satisfy.

b. Use the equations you wrote in part (a) to solve for m and n. What can you conclude?

76. DIG DEEPER Officials at a school want to double the size of its parking lot by expanding the existing lot as shown. By what distance x should the lot be expanded?

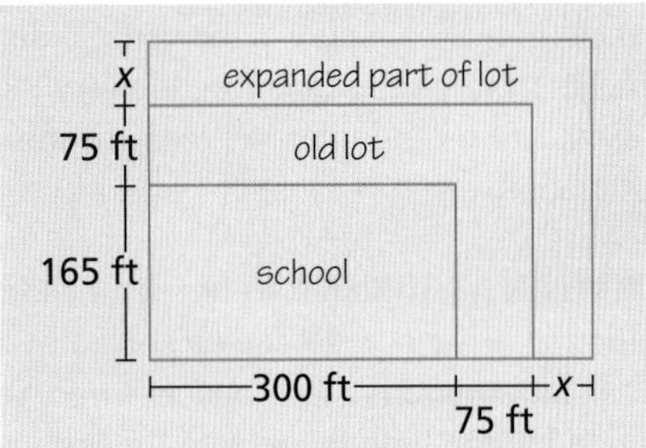

77. MP **REPEATED REASONING** The first three figures of a pattern are shown. Is there a figure with 480 dots in the pattern? If so, which figure is it? If not, explain why not.

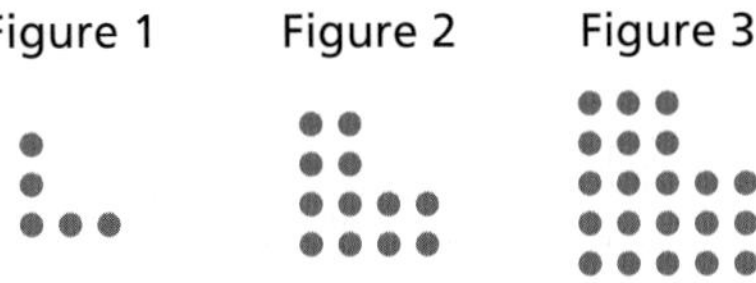

GO DIGITAL

78. THOUGHT PROVOKING
Write an equation of the form $ax^4 + bx^2 + c = 0$, where a, b, and c are real numbers, that can be solved by factoring and that has four real solutions. Explain how to solve your equation.

REVIEW & REFRESH

In Exercises 79–82, find the sum or difference.

79. $(x^2 + 2) + (2x^2 - x)$

80. $(-2x + 1) - (-3x^2 + x)$

81. $(x^3 + x^2 - 4) + (10 + 3x^2)$

82. $(-3x^3 + x^2 - 12x) - (3x - 6x^2 - 9)$

In Exercises 83 and 84, write an equation of the parabola in vertex form or intercept form.

83. x-intercepts of -8 and 4; passes through $(2, -12)$

84.

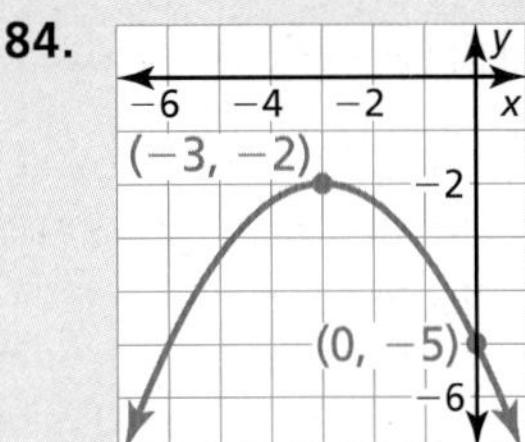

In Exercises 85–88, find the product.

85. $11x(-4x^2 + 3x + 8)$

86. $(7 - x)(x - 1)$

87. $(x + 2)(x - 2)$

88. $(3x + 5)^2$

In Exercises 89 and 90, solve the equation using any method. Explain your choice of method.

89. $2x^2 - 15 = 0$

90. $3x^2 - x - 2 = 0$

91. Write the sentence as an absolute value inequality. Then solve the inequality.

A number is more than 9 units from 3.

92. MODELING REAL LIFE The table shows the donations made by 12 people on a fundraising site.

Donations (dollars)			
25	20	25	10
50	15	100	25
50	30	25	75

a. Make a box-and-whisker plot that represents the data. Describe the shape of the distribution.

b. Does the data set contain any outliers?

In Exercises 93 and 94, find the minimum or maximum value of the function. Find the domain and range of the function, and when the function is increasing and decreasing.

93. $y = -x^2 - 4x + 6$

94. $y = \frac{1}{2}x^2 - 3x - 2$

95. What is the theoretical probability of spinning a multiple of 4 on the spinner?

96. MP **REASONING** The equation of a parabola is of the form $x = \frac{1}{4p}y^2$, and the parabola opens left. What can you conclude about the value of p?

3.2 Complex Numbers

Learning Target Understand the imaginary unit i and perform operations with complex numbers.

Success Criteria

- I can define the imaginary unit i and use it to rewrite the square root of a negative number.
- I can add, subtract, and multiply complex numbers.
- I can find complex solutions of quadratic equations and complex zeros of quadratic functions.

EXPLORE IT! Using Complex Numbers

Work with a partner.

a. A student solves the equations below as shown. Justify each solution step.

i.

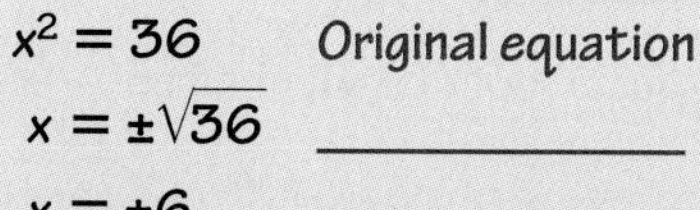

$x^2 = 36$ Original equation

$x = \pm\sqrt{36}$ ____________

$x = \pm 6$ ____________

ii.

$x^2 = -9$ Original equation

$x = \pm\sqrt{-9}$ ____________

$x = \pm\sqrt{9}\,\sqrt{-1}$ ____________

$x = \pm 3\sqrt{-1}$ ____________

> **Math Practice**
>
> **Look for Structure**
>
> How can you recognize when a quadratic equation of the form $x^2 + c = 0$ will have solutions that are not real numbers?

b. In your study of mathematics, you have probably worked with only real numbers, which can be represented graphically on the real number line. Describe the solutions of the equation $x^2 = c$ when $c > 0$, when $c = 0$, and when $c < 0$.

c. The solutions of the equation $x^2 = -9$ are *imaginary numbers*, and are typically written as $3i$ and $-3i$. Explain what i represents. What is the value of i^2?

d. In this lesson, the system of numbers is expanded to include imaginary numbers. The real numbers and imaginary numbers compose the set of *complex numbers*. Complete the diagram that shows the relationships among the number systems shown below.

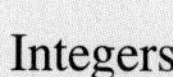

Integers
Natural Numbers
Rational Numbers
Whole Numbers
Real Numbers
Complex Numbers
Irrational Numbers
Imaginary Numbers

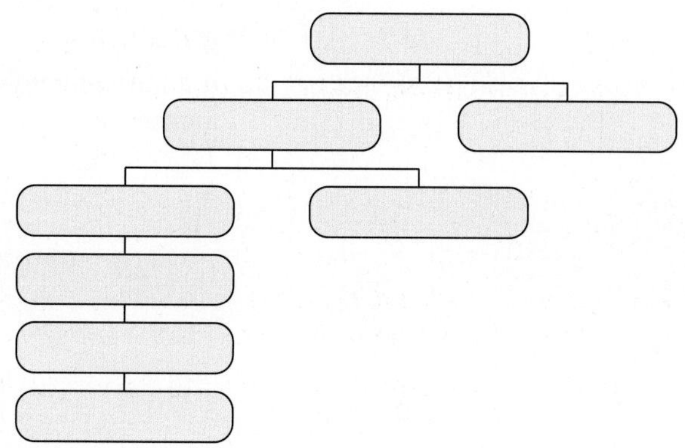

e. Determine which subsets of numbers in part (d) contain each number.

i. $\sqrt{9}$ **ii.** $\sqrt{0}$ **iii.** $-\sqrt{4}$ **iv.** $\sqrt{\dfrac{4}{9}}$ **v.** $\sqrt{2}$ **vi.** $\sqrt{-1}$

The Imaginary Unit i

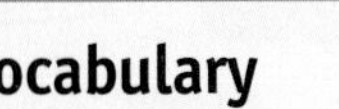 

Vocabulary

imaginary unit i, *p. 100*
complex number, *p. 100*
imaginary number, *p. 100*
pure imaginary number, *p. 100*
complex conjugates, *p. 102*

Not all quadratic equations have real-number solutions. For example, $x^2 = -3$ has no real-number solutions because the square of any real number is never a negative number.

To overcome this problem, mathematicians created an expanded system of numbers using the **imaginary unit *i***, defined as $i = \sqrt{-1}$. Note that $i^2 = -1$. The imaginary unit i can be used to write the square root of *any* negative number.

KEY IDEA

The Square Root of a Negative Number

Property	Example
1. If r is a positive real number, then $\sqrt{-r} = \sqrt{-1}\sqrt{r} = i\sqrt{r}$.	$\sqrt{-3} = \sqrt{-1}\sqrt{3} = i\sqrt{3}$
2. By the first property, it follows that $(i\sqrt{r})^2 = i^2 \cdot r = -r$.	$(i\sqrt{3})^2 = i^2 \cdot 3 = -1 \cdot 3 = -3$

EXAMPLE 1 Finding Square Roots of Negative Numbers

Find the square root of each number.

a. $\sqrt{-25}$ **b.** $\sqrt{-72}$ **c.** $-5\sqrt{-9}$

SOLUTION

a. $\sqrt{-25} = \sqrt{25} \cdot \sqrt{-1} = 5i$

b. $\sqrt{-72} = \sqrt{72} \cdot \sqrt{-1} = \sqrt{36} \cdot \sqrt{2} \cdot i = 6\sqrt{2}\, i = 6i\sqrt{2}$

c. $-5\sqrt{-9} = -5\sqrt{9} \cdot \sqrt{-1} = -5 \cdot 3 \cdot i = -15i$

WORDS AND MATH

Numbers of the form $a + bi$ are called *complex* because they have more than one part.

A **complex number** written in *standard form* is a number $a + bi$, where a and b are real numbers. The number a is the *real part*, and the number bi is the *imaginary part*.

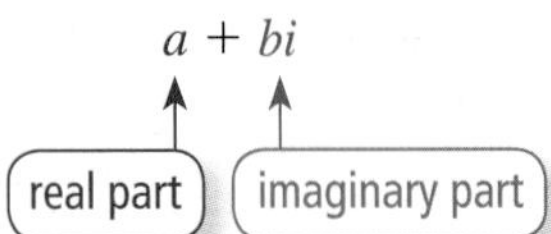

If $b \neq 0$, then $a + bi$ is an **imaginary number**. If $a = 0$ and $b \neq 0$, then $a + bi$ is a **pure imaginary number**. The diagram shows how different types of complex numbers are related.

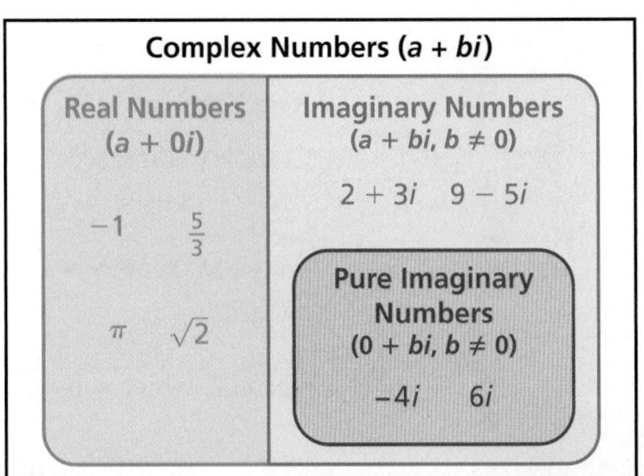

Two complex numbers $a + bi$ and $c + di$ are equal if and only if $a = c$ and $b = d$.

EXAMPLE 2 Equality of Two Complex Numbers

WATCH

Find the values of x and y that satisfy the equation $2x - 7i = 10 + yi$.

SOLUTION

Set the real parts equal to each other and the imaginary parts equal to each other.

$2x = 10$	Equate the real parts.	$-7i = yi$	Equate the imaginary parts.
$x = 5$	Solve for x.	$-7 = y$	Solve for y.

▶ So, $x = 5$ and $y = -7$.

SELF-ASSESSMENT

1 I do not understand. 2 I can do it with help. 3 I can do it on my own. 4 I can teach someone else.

1. **VOCABULARY** Define the imaginary unit i and explain how you use it.

2. **VOCABULARY** Identify the imaginary part and the real part of the complex number $5 - 2i$.

Find the square root of the number.

3. $\sqrt{-4}$
4. $\sqrt{-12}$
5. $-\sqrt{-36}$
6. $2\sqrt{-54}$

Find the values of x and y that satisfy the equation.

7. $x + 3i = 9 - yi$
8. $5x + 4i = 20 + 2yi$
9. $9 + 4yi = -2x + 3i$

Operations with Complex Numbers

KEY IDEA

Sums and Differences of Complex Numbers

To add (or subtract) two complex numbers, add (or subtract) their real parts and their imaginary parts separately.

Sum of complex numbers: $(a + bi) + (c + di) = (a + c) + (b + d)i$

Difference of complex numbers: $(a + bi) - (c + di) = (a - c) + (b - d)i$

EXAMPLE 3 Adding and Subtracting Complex Numbers

Add or subtract. Write the answer in standard form.

a. $(8 - i) + (5 + 4i)$

b. $(7 - 6i) - (3 - 6i)$

SOLUTION

a. $(8 - i) + (5 + 4i) = (8 + 5) + (-1 + 4)i$ — Definition of complex addition

$= 13 + 3i$ — Write in standard form.

b. $(7 - 6i) - (3 - 6i) = (7 - 3) + (-6 + 6)i$ — Definition of complex subtraction

$= 4 + 0i$ — Simplify.

$= 4$ — Write in standard form.

To multiply two complex numbers, use the Distributive Property, or the FOIL Method, just as you do when multiplying real numbers or algebraic expressions.

EXAMPLE 4 Multiplying Complex Numbers

Multiply. Write the answer in standard form.

a. $4i(-6 + i)$

b. $(9 - 2i)(-4 + 7i)$

SOLUTION

a. $4i(-6 + i) = -24i + 4i^2$ — Distributive Property

$= -24i + 4(-1)$ — Use $i^2 = -1$.

$= -4 - 24i$ — Write in standard form.

STUDY TIP

When simplifying an expression that involves complex numbers, be sure to simplify i^2 as -1.

b. $(9 - 2i)(-4 + 7i) = -36 + 63i + 8i - 14i^2$ — Multiply using FOIL.

$= -36 + 71i - 14(-1)$ — Simplify and use $i^2 = -1$.

$= -36 + 71i + 14$ — Simplify.

$= -22 + 71i$ — Write in standard form.

Pairs of complex numbers of the forms $a + bi$ and $a - bi$, where $b \neq 0$, are called **complex conjugates**. Consider the product of complex conjugates below.

$(a + bi)(a - bi) = a^2 - (ab)i + (ab)i - b^2i^2$ — Multiply using FOIL.

$= a^2 - b^2(-1)$ — Simplify and use $i^2 = -1$.

$= a^2 + b^2$ — Simplify.

Because a and b are real numbers, $a^2 + b^2$ is a real number. So, the product of complex conjugates is a real number.

EXAMPLE 5 Multiplying Complex Conjugates

Multiply $5 + 2i$ by its complex conjugate.

SOLUTION

The complex conjugate of $5 + 2i$ is $5 - 2i$.

Method 1 Use the FOIL Method.

$(5 + 2i)(5 - 2i) = 25 - 10i + 10i - 4i^2$ — Multiply using FOIL.

$= 25 - 4(-1)$ — Simplify and use $i^2 = -1$.

$= 29$ — Simplify.

Method 2 Use the pattern shown above, $(a + bi)(a - bi) = a^2 + b^2$ where $a = 5$ and $b = 2$.

$(5 + 2i)(5 - 2i) = 5^2 + 2^2$ — $a = 5, b = 2$

$= 25 + 4$ — Evaluate exponents.

$= 29$ — Add.

EXAMPLE 6 Modeling Real Life

Electrical circuit components, such as resistors, inductors, and capacitors, all oppose the flow of current. This opposition is called *resistance* for resistors and *reactance* for inductors and capacitors. Each of these quantities is measured in ohms. The symbol used for ohms is Ω, the uppercase Greek letter omega.

Component and symbol	Resistor	Inductor	Capacitor
Resistance or reactance (in ohms)	R	L	C
Impedance (in ohms)	R	Li	$-Ci$

The table shows the relationship between a component's resistance or reactance and its contribution to impedance. A *series circuit* is also shown with the resistance or reactance of each component labeled. The impedance for a series circuit is the sum of the impedances for the individual components. Find the impedance of the series circuit.

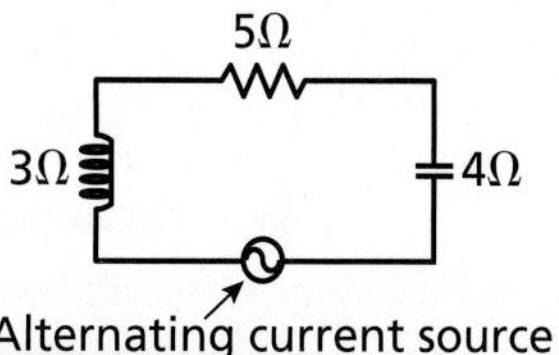

SOLUTION

The resistor has a resistance of 5 ohms, so its impedance is 5 ohms. The inductor has a reactance of 3 ohms, so its impedance is $3i$ ohms. The capacitor has a reactance of 4 ohms, so its impedance is $-4i$ ohms.

$$\text{Impedance of circuit} = 5 + 3i + (-4i)$$
$$= 5 - i$$

▶ The impedance of the circuit is $(5 - i)$ ohms.

SELF-ASSESSMENT

1 I do not understand. 2 I can do it with help. 3 I can do it on my own. 4 I can teach someone else.

Add or subtract. Write the answer in standard form.

10. $(9 - i) + (-6 + 7i)$ **11.** $(3 + 7i) - (8 - 2i)$ **12.** $-4 - (1 + i) - (5 + 9i)$

13. $5 + (-9 + 3i) + 6i$ **14.** $(2 - i) + (1 + i) - 7i$ **15.** $8i - (6 - 3i) + (4 - 4i)$

16. OPEN-ENDED Write two complex numbers with a difference of 9.

Multiply. Write the answer in standard form.

17. $(-3i)(10i)$ **18.** $i(8 - i)$ **19.** $(3 + i)(5 - i)$

Multiply the complex number by its complex conjugate.

20. $1 + i$ **21.** $4 - 7i$ **22.** $-3 - 2i$

23. WHAT IF? In Example 6, what is the impedance of the circuit when the capacitor is replaced with one having a reactance of 7 ohms?

Complex Solutions and Zeros

EXAMPLE 7 Solving Quadratic Equations

Solve (a) $x^2 + 4 = 0$ and (b) $2x^2 - 11 = -47$.

Math Practice

Look for Structure

How can you use the solutions in Example 7(a) to factor $x^2 + 4$?

SOLUTION

a. $x^2 + 4 = 0$ Write original equation.

$x^2 = -4$ Subtract 4 from each side.

$x = \pm\sqrt{-4}$ Take square root of each side.

$x = \pm 2i$ Write in terms of i.

▶ The solutions are $2i$ and $-2i$.

b. $2x^2 - 11 = -47$ Write original equation.

$2x^2 = -36$ Add 11 to each side.

$x^2 = -18$ Divide each side by 2.

$x = \pm\sqrt{-18}$ Take square root of each side.

$x = \pm i\sqrt{18}$ Write in terms of i.

$x = \pm 3i\sqrt{2}$ Simplify radical.

▶ The solutions are $3i\sqrt{2}$ and $-3i\sqrt{2}$.

EXAMPLE 8 Finding Zeros of a Quadratic Function

Math Practice

Use a Graph

A quadratic function without real zeros must have imaginary zeros. How can you use a graph to determine whether a quadratic function has imaginary zeros?

Find the zeros of the function.

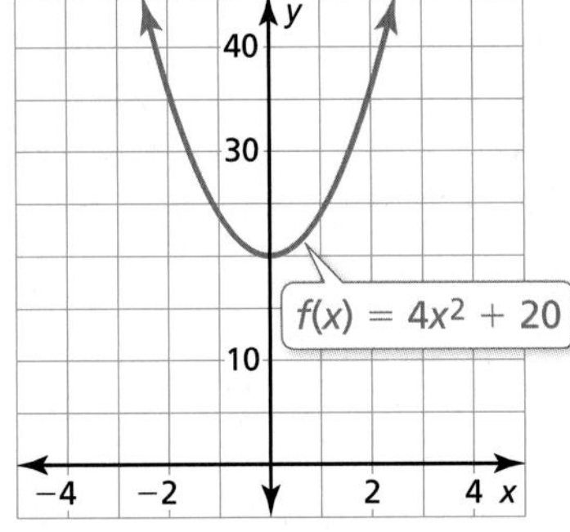

SOLUTION

$4x^2 + 20 = 0$ Set $f(x)$ equal to 0.

$4x^2 = -20$ Subtract 20 from each side.

$x^2 = -5$ Divide each side by 4.

$x = \pm\sqrt{-5}$ Take square root of each side.

$x = \pm i\sqrt{5}$ Write in terms of i.

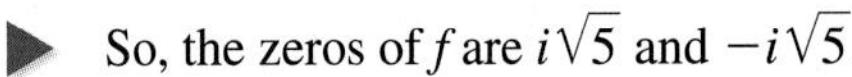

▶ So, the zeros of f are $i\sqrt{5}$ and $-i\sqrt{5}$.

Check

$f(i\sqrt{5}) = 4(i\sqrt{5})^2 + 20 = 4 \cdot 5i^2 + 20 = 4(-5) + 20 = 0$ ✓

$f(-i\sqrt{5}) = 4(-i\sqrt{5})^2 + 20 = 4 \cdot 5i^2 + 20 = 4(-5) + 20 = 0$ ✓

SELF-ASSESSMENT 1 I do not understand. 2 I can do it with help. 3 I can do it on my own. 4 I can teach someone else.

Solve the equation.

24. $x^2 = -13$ **25.** $x^2 - 8 = -36$ **26.** $3x^2 - 7 = -31$ **27.** $5x^2 + 33 = 3$

Find the zeros of the function.

28. $f(x) = x^2 + 7$ **29.** $f(x) = -x^2 - 4$ **30.** $f(x) = 9x^2 + 1$

3.2 Practice WITH CalcChat® AND CalcView®

GO DIGITAL

In Exercises 1–8, find the square root of the number. ▶ *Example 1*

1. $\sqrt{-36}$
2. $\sqrt{-64}$
3. $\sqrt{-18}$
4. $\sqrt{-24}$
5. $2\sqrt{-16}$
6. $-3\sqrt{-49}$
7. $-4\sqrt{-32}$
8. $6\sqrt{-63}$

In Exercises 9–16, find the values of *x* and *y* that satisfy the equation. ▶ *Example 2*

9. $4x + 2i = 8 + yi$
10. $3x + 6i = 27 + yi$
11. $-10x + 12i = 20 + 3yi$
12. $9x - 18i = -36 + 6yi$
13. $2x - yi = 14 + 12i$
14. $-12x + yi = 60 - 13i$
15. $54 - \frac{1}{7}yi = 9x - 4i$
16. $15 - 3yi = \frac{1}{2}x + 2i$

In Exercises 17–26, add or subtract. Write the answer in standard form. ▶ *Example 3*

17. $(6 - i) + (7 + 3i)$
18. $(9 + 5i) + (11 + 2i)$
19. $(12 + 4i) - (3 - 7i)$
20. $(2 - 15i) - (4 + 5i)$
21. $(12 - 3i) + (7 + 3i)$
22. $(16 - 9i) - (2 - 9i)$
23. $7 - (3 + 4i) + 6i$
24. $16 - (2 - 3i) - i$
25. $-10 + (6 - 5i) - 9i$
26. $-3 + (8 + 2i) + 7i$

27. **MP STRUCTURE** Write each expression as a complex number in standard form.

    a. $\sqrt{-9} + \sqrt{-4} - \sqrt{16}$

    b. $\sqrt{-16} + \sqrt{8} + \sqrt{-36}$

28. **MP REASONING** The additive inverse of a complex number *z* is a complex number z_a such that $z + z_a = 0$. Find the additive inverse of each complex number.

    a. $z = 1 + i$

    b. $z = 3 - i$

    c. $z = -2 + 8i$

In Exercises 29–36, multiply. Write the answer in standard form. ▶ *Example 4*

29. $3i(-5 + i)$
30. $2i(7 - i)$
31. $(3 - 2i)(4 + i)$
32. $(7 + 5i)(8 - 6i)$
33. $(5 - 2i)(-2 - 3i)$
34. $(-1 + 8i)(9 + 3i)$
35. $(3 - 6i)^2$
36. $(8 + 3i)^2$

ERROR ANALYSIS In Exercises 37 and 38, describe and correct the error in performing the operation and writing the answer in standard form.

37. ✗
$$(3 + 2i)(5 - i) = 15 - 3i + 10i - 2i^2$$
$$= 15 + 7i - 2i^2$$
$$= -2i^2 + 7i + 15$$

38. ✗

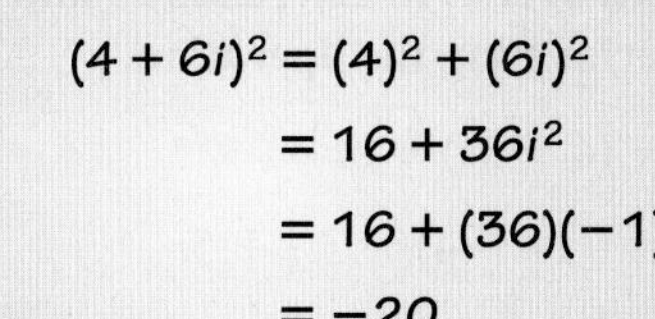

$$(4 + 6i)^2 = (4)^2 + (6i)^2$$
$$= 16 + 36i^2$$
$$= 16 + (36)(-1)$$
$$= -20$$

In Exercises 39–46, multiply the complex number by its complex conjugate. ▶ *Example 5*

39. $1 - i$
40. $8 + i$
41. $4 + 2i$
42. $5 - 6i$
43. $-2 + 2i$
44. $-1 - 9i$
45. $-3 - 5i$
46. $-7 + 4i$

MP REASONING In Exercises 47 and 48, use the given numbers to complete the equation.

47. $(\_\_\_\_ - \_\_\_\_i) - (\_\_\_\_ - \_\_\_\_i) = 2 - 4i$

7	4	3	6

48. $\_\_\_\_i(\_\_\_\_ + \_\_\_\_i) = -18 - 10i$

−5	9	2

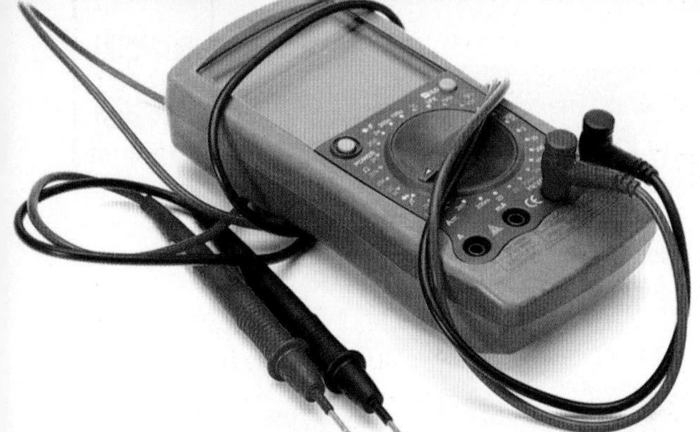

MODELING REAL LIFE In Exercises 49–52, find the impedance of the series circuit. ▷ *Example 6*

49. 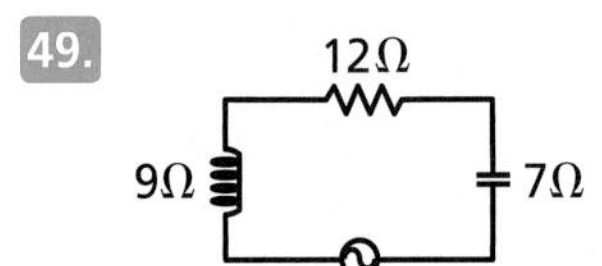

50. 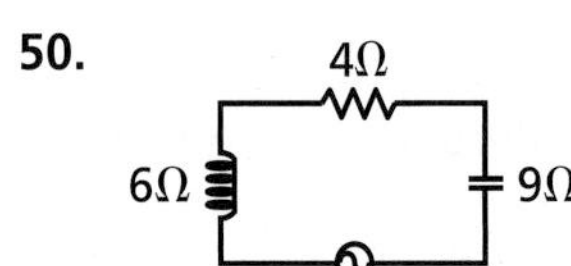

51. 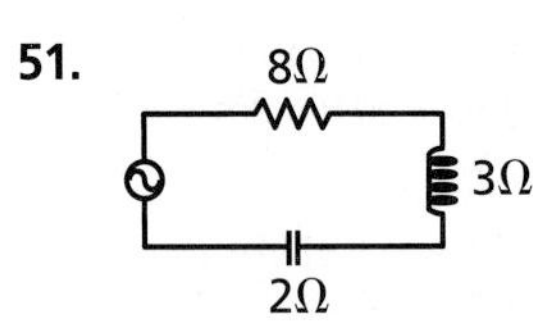

52. 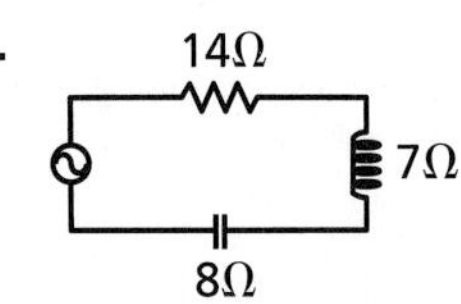

JUSTIFYING STEPS In Exercises 53 and 54, justify each step in performing the operation.

53. $11 - (4 + 3i) + 5i$

$= [(11 - 4) - 3i] + 5i$

$= (7 - 3i) + 5i$

$= 7 + (-3 + 5)i$

$= 7 + 2i$

54. $(3 + 2i)(7 - 4i)$

$= 21 - 12i + 14i - 8i^2$

$= 21 + 2i - 8(-1)$

$= 21 + 2i + 8$

$= 29 + 2i$

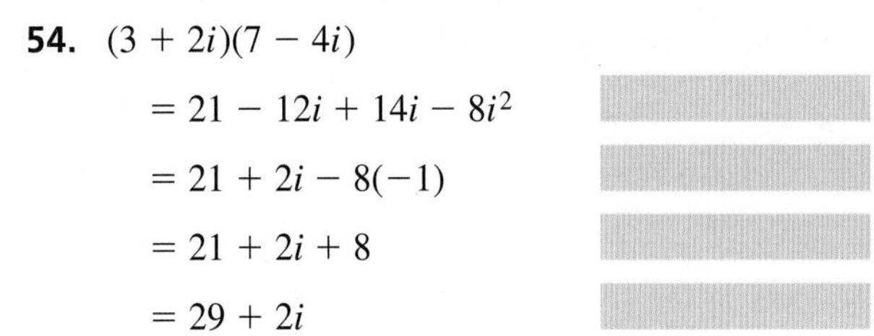

In Exercises 55–60, solve the equation. ▷ *Example 7*

55. $x^2 + 9 = 0$

56. $x^2 + 49 = 0$

57. $x^2 - 4 = -11$

58. $x^2 - 9 = -15$

59. $2x^2 + 6 = -34$

60. $x^2 + 7 = -47$

In Exercises 61–68, find the zeros of the function. ▷ *Example 8*

61. $f(x) = 3x^2 + 6$

62. $g(x) = 7x^2 + 21$

63. $h(x) = 2x^2 + 72$

64. $k(x) = -5x^2 - 125$

65. $m(x) = -x^2 - 27$

66. $p(x) = x^2 + 98$

67. $r(x) = -\frac{1}{2}x^2 - 24$

68. $f(x) = -\frac{1}{5}x^2 - 10$

69. **MP STRUCTURE** Expand $(a - bi)^2$ and write the result in standard form. Use your result to check your answer to Exercise 35.

70. **MP STRUCTURE** Expand $(a + bi)^2$ and write the result in standard form. Use your result to check your answer to Exercise 36.

71. **MP NUMBER SENSE** Write the complex conjugate of $1 - \sqrt{-12}$. Then find the product of the complex conjugates.

72. **MP NUMBER SENSE** Simplify each expression. Then classify your results in the table below.

a. $(-4 + 7i) + (-4 - 7i)$

b. $(2 - 6i) - (-10 + 4i)$

c. $(25 + 15i) - (25 - 6i)$

d. $(5 + i)(8 - i)$

e. $(17 - 3i) + (-17 - 6i)$

f. $(-1 + 2i)(11 - i)$

g. $(7 + 5i) + (7 - 5i)$

h. $(-3 + 6i) - (-3 - 8i)$

Real numbers	Imaginary numbers	Pure imaginary numbers

73.  **MP STRUCTURE** The coordinate system shown below is called the *complex plane*. In the complex plane, the point that corresponds to the complex number $a + bi$ is (a, b). Match each complex number with its corresponding point.

a. 2

b. $2i$

c. $4 - 2i$

d. $3 + 3i$

e. $-2 + 4i$

f. $-3 - 3i$

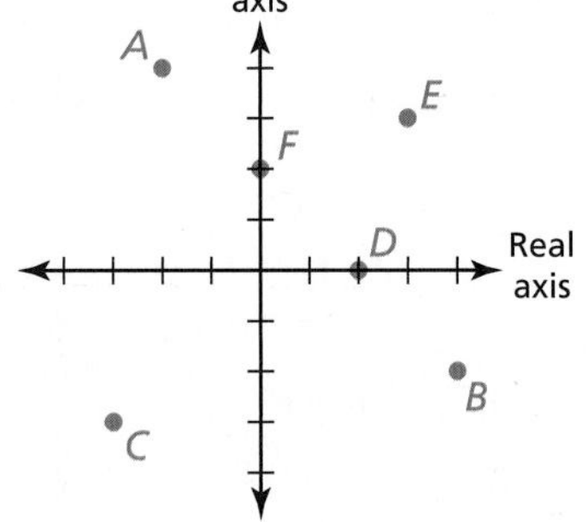

74. COMPARING METHODS Describe the methods shown for writing the complex expression in standard form. Which method do you prefer? Explain.

Method 1

$$4i(2-3i)+4i(1-2i)=8i-12i^2+4i-8i^2$$
$$=8i-12(-1)+4i-8(-1)$$
$$=20+12i$$

Method 2

$$4i(2-3i)+4i(1-2i)=4i[(2-3i)+(1-2i)]$$
$$=4i[3-5i]$$
$$=12i-20i^2$$
$$=12i-20(-1)$$
$$=20+12i$$

In Exercises 75–80, write the expression as a complex number in standard form.

75. $(3+4i)-(7-5i)+2i(9+12i)$

76. $3i(2+5i)+(6-7i)-(9+i)$

77. $(3+5i)(2-7i^4)$

78. $2i^3(5-12i)$

79. $(2+4i^5)+(1-9i^6)-(3+i^7)$

80. $(8-2i^4)+(3-7i^8)-(4+i^9)$

81. MP PATTERNS Make a table that shows the powers of i from i^1 to i^8 in the first row and the simplified forms of these powers in the second row. Describe the pattern you observe in the table. Then use the pattern to evaluate i^{25}, i^{50}, i^{75}, and i^{100}.

82. HOW DO YOU SEE IT?
The graphs of three functions are shown. Which function(s) have real zeros? imaginary zeros? Explain your reasoning.

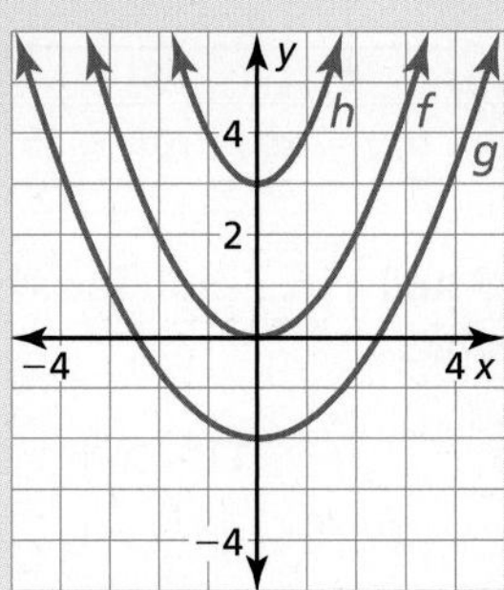

83. MP NUMBER SENSE Write each product as a complex number in standard form.

a. $(2-3i)^3$

b. $(3+i)^4$

84. MP REASONING Is it possible for a quadratic equation to have one real solution and one imaginary solution? Explain your reasoning.

85. COLLEGE PREP Which expressions are equivalent to $1+i$? Select all that apply.

(A) $(4-i)-(3+2i)$

(B) $-i(i^2+i)$

(C) $(2-i)(i+1)$

(D) $i^{20}-i^{21}$

86. MP NUMBER SENSE Write a pair of complex numbers whose sum is -4 and whose product is 53.

87. JUSTIFYING STEPS Justify each step in the simplification of i^2.

Algebraic Step	Justification
$i^2=(\sqrt{-1})^2$	
$=-1$	

88. MAKING AN ARGUMENT Your friend claims that the conclusion in Exercise 87 is incorrect because $i^2=i\cdot i=\sqrt{-1}\cdot\sqrt{-1}=\sqrt{-1(-1)}=\sqrt{1}=1$. Is your friend correct? Explain.

89. CRITICAL THINKING Rewrite each expression with a real denominator.

a. $\dfrac{1+3i}{2i}$ **b.** $\dfrac{4-2i}{1+i}$

90. MP LOGIC The sum of two complex numbers is $7+8i$. The difference of the numbers is $1-2i$. What is the product of the numbers?

91. CRITICAL THINKING Determine whether each statement is true or false. If it is true, give an example. If it is false, give a counterexample.

a. The sum of two imaginary numbers is always an imaginary number.

b. The product of two pure imaginary numbers is always a real number.

c. A pure imaginary number is an imaginary number.

d. A complex number is a real number.

92. **CRITICAL THINKING** The zeros of a quadratic function are $3 \pm 4i$.

a. What do you know about the vertex of the function? Explain.

b. Write and graph a quadratic function that has these zeros.

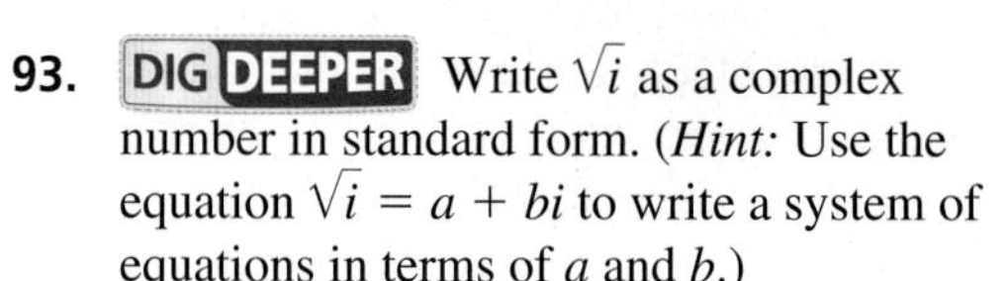

93. **DIG DEEPER** Write $\sqrt{i}$ as a complex number in standard form. (*Hint:* Use the equation $\sqrt{i} = a + bi$ to write a system of equations in terms of a and b.)

94. **THOUGHT PROVOKING**
Create a circuit that has an impedance of $14 - 3i$.

REVIEW & REFRESH

WATCH

In Exercises 95 and 96, graph the function and its parent function. Then describe the transformation.

95. $f(x) = \frac{1}{4}x^2 + 1$

96. $f(x) = -\frac{1}{2}x - 4$

In Exercises 97 and 98, simplify the expression. Write your answer using only positive exponents.

97. $\left(\dfrac{4c^4d^{-5}}{8c^0d^4}\right)^2$

98. $\left(\dfrac{3m^{-5}}{m^{-6}n}\right)^3 \cdot \left(\dfrac{-4m^3n^{-1}}{2mn^{-7}}\right)^4$

99. Write a quadratic function in vertex form whose graph is shown.

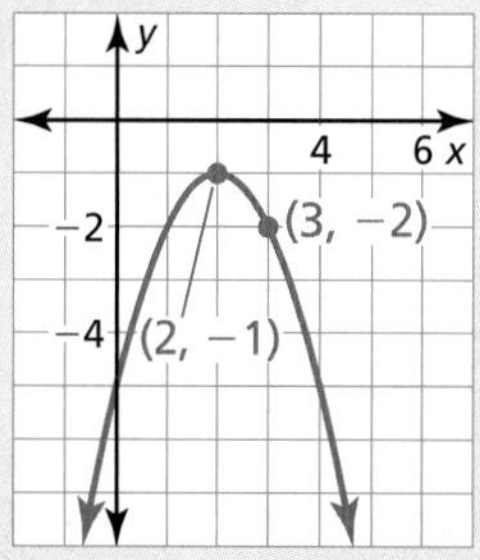

100. **MP REASONING** Find the zeros of the function $f(x) = 9x^2 + 2$. Does the graph of the function intersect the x-axis? Explain your reasoning.

In Exercises 101 and 102, write an equation of the parabola with the given characteristics.

101. focus: $(0, -2)$
directrix: $y = 2$

102. vertex: $(5, -4)$
directrix: $x = 2$

103. Make a scatter plot of the data. Then describe the relationship between the data.

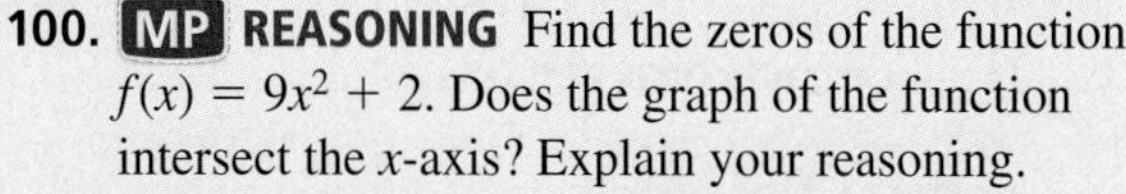

x	4	2	7	5	2	6	3	5
y	37	62	45	79	29	18	55	64

104. Find the circumference of the circle.

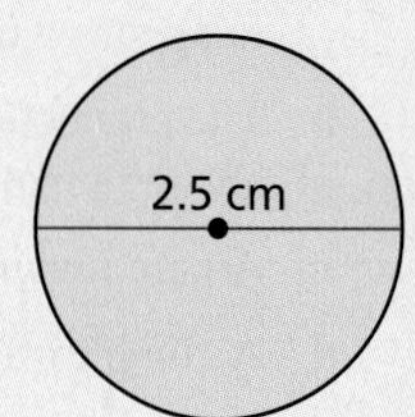

105. **MODELING REAL LIFE** A screen printing shop sells long-sleeved shirts and short-sleeved shirts. Order A includes 3 long-sleeved shirts and 12 short-sleeved shirts for a total cost of \$165. Order B includes 8 long-sleeved shirts and 2 short-sleeved shirts for a total cost of \$140. What is the cost of each type of shirt?

In Exercises 106–109, add, subtract, or multiply. Write the answer in standard form.

106. $-3i(9 - 4i)$

107. $(7 + 8i) - (-4 + 9i)$

108. $(5 - 2i)(1 - 12i)$

109. $(-15 - i) + (6 + 3i)$

In Exercises 110 and 111, write an inequality that represents the graph.

110. (number line from −5 to 5, open circle at −2, shaded to the right)

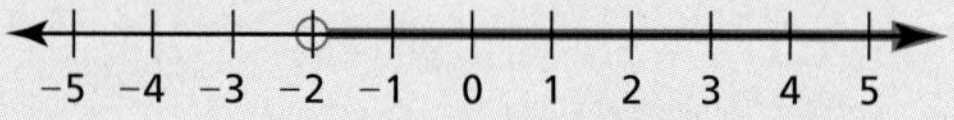

111. (number line from 3 to 13, closed circle at 9, shaded to the left)

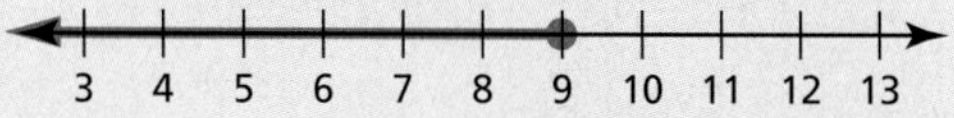

In Exercises 112 and 113, find the inverse of the function. Then graph the function and its inverse.

112. $f(x) = -3x + 6$

113. $f(x) = 2x^2 - 18, x \geq 0$

114. Use the graph to solve $x^2 - 10x + 25 = 0$.

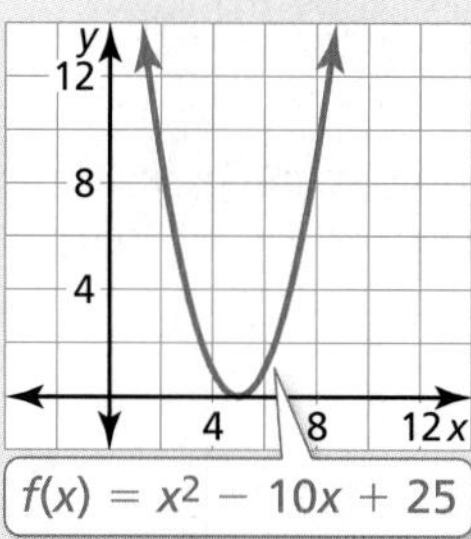

In Exercises 115 and 116, graph the system. Identify a solution, if possible.

115. $y > x - 1$
$y \leq -4$

116. $x + y \leq 3$
$y + 2 \geq -4x$

3.3 Completing the Square

Learning Target Solve quadratic equations and rewrite quadratic functions by completing the square.

Success Criteria

- I can solve quadratic equations using square roots.
- I can solve quadratic equations by completing the square.
- I can apply completing the square to write quadratic functions in vertex form.

EXPLORE IT! Using Algebra Tiles to Complete the Square

Work with a partner.

a. Write the expression modeled by the algebra tiles. How can you *complete the square*?

b. Use the model to find the value of c so that the expression

$$x^2 + 6x + c$$

is a perfect square trinomial. Then write the expression as the square of a binomial.

Math Practice

Find General Methods
How can completing the square help you solve quadratic equations?

c. Use the method outlined in parts (a) and (b) to complete the table.

Expression	Value of c needed to complete the square	Expression written as a binomial squared
$x^2 + 2x + c$		
$x^2 + 4x + c$		
$x^2 + 8x + c$		
$x^2 + 10x + c$		

d. Look for patterns in the table in part (c). Consider the general statement $x^2 + bx + c = (x + d)^2$. In each case,

- how are b and d related?
- how are c and d related?
- how are b and c related?

e. How can you complete the square for a quadratic expression of the form $x^2 + bx$?

f. Solve $x^2 + 8x + 16 = 9$ by taking the square root of each side. Can you use this method to solve the equivalent equation $x^2 + 8x = -7$? What does this imply about solving quadratic equations?

Solving Quadratic Equations Using Square Roots

Vocabulary

completing the square, *p. 110*

Previously, you have solved equations of the form $u^2 = d$ by taking the square root of each side. This method also works when one side of an equation is a perfect square trinomial and the other side is a constant.

EXAMPLE 1 Solving a Quadratic Equation Using Square Roots

Solve $x^2 - 16x + 64 = 100$ using square roots.

SOLUTION

$x^2 - 16x + 64 = 100$	Write the equation.
$(x - 8)^2 = 100$	Write the left side as a binomial squared.
$x - 8 = \pm 10$	Take square root of each side.
$x = 8 \pm 10$	Add 8 to each side.

So, the solutions are $x = 8 + 10 = 18$ and $x = 8 - 10 = -2$.

ANOTHER WAY

You can also solve the equation by writing it in standard form as $x^2 - 16x - 36 = 0$ and factoring.

SELF-ASSESSMENT 1 I do not understand. 2 I can do it with help. 3 I can do it on my own. 4 I can teach someone else.

Solve the equation using square roots. Check your solution(s).

1. $x^2 + 4x + 4 = 36$
2. $x^2 - 6x + 9 = 1$
3. $x^2 - 22x + 121 = 81$

Solving Quadratic Equations by Completing the Square

In Example 1, the expression $x^2 - 16x + 64$ is a perfect square trinomial because it can be written as $(x - 8)^2$. In some situations, you will need to add a constant to an expression of the form $x^2 + bx$ to make it a perfect square trinomial. This process is called **completing the square**.

KEY IDEA

Completing the Square

Words To complete the square for the expression $x^2 + bx$, add $\left(\frac{b}{2}\right)^2$.

Diagrams In each diagram, the combined area of the shaded regions is $x^2 + bx$. Adding $\left(\frac{b}{2}\right)^2$ completes the square in the second diagram.

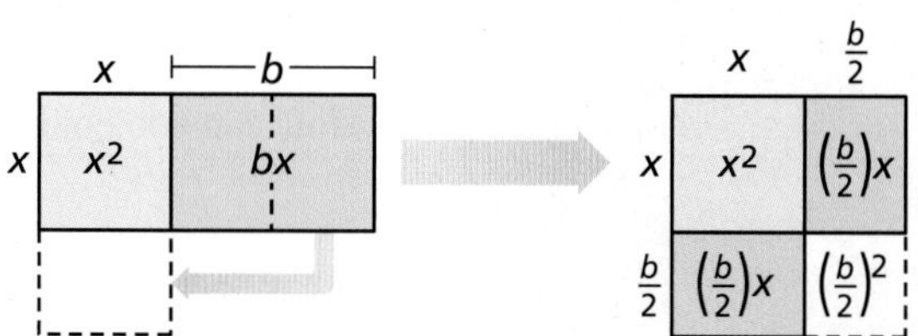

Algebra $x^2 + bx + \left(\frac{b}{2}\right)^2 = \left(x + \frac{b}{2}\right)\left(x + \frac{b}{2}\right) = \left(x + \frac{b}{2}\right)^2$

EXAMPLE 2 Completing the Square

Complete the square for $x^2 + 14x$. Then factor the trinomial.

SOLUTION

In this binomial, $b = 14$.

	x	7
x	x^2	$7x$
7	$7x$	49

Step 1 Find $\left(\frac{b}{2}\right)^2$. $\qquad \left(\frac{b}{2}\right)^2 = \left(\frac{14}{2}\right)^2 = 7^2 = 49$

Step 2 Add the result to $x^2 + bx$. $\qquad x^2 + 14x + 49$

▶ $x^2 + 14x + 49 = (x + 7)(x + 7) = (x + 7)^2$.

SELF-ASSESSMENT

1 I do not understand. 2 I can do it with help. 3 I can do it on my own. 4 I can teach someone else.

Complete the square for the expression. Then factor the trinomial.

4. $x^2 + 8x$ **5.** $x^2 - 2x$ **6.** $x^2 - 9x$

7. **MP REASONING** You complete the square for an expression of the form $x^2 + bx$ by adding 100. What is the value of b?

Completing the square can be used to solve any quadratic equation. First, write the equation in the form $x^2 + bx = d$. Then, when you complete the square, you must add the same number to *both* sides of the equation.

EXAMPLE 3 Solving $ax^2 + bx + c = 0$ when $a = 1$

Solve $x^2 - 10x + 7 = 0$ by completing the square.

SOLUTION

$x^2 - 10x + 7 = 0$	Write the equation.
$x^2 - 10x = -7$	Write left side in the form $x^2 + bx$.
$x^2 - 10x + 25 = -7 + 25$	Add $\left(\frac{b}{2}\right)^2 = \left(\frac{-10}{2}\right)^2 = 25$ to each side.
$(x - 5)^2 = 18$	Write left side as a binomial squared.
$x - 5 = \pm\sqrt{18}$	Take square root of each side.
$x = 5 \pm\sqrt{18}$	Add 5 to each side.
$x = 5 \pm 3\sqrt{2}$	Simplify radical.

Math Practice

Find Entry Points

How can you determine when it is convenient to solve by completing the square?

▶ The solutions are $x = 5 + 3\sqrt{2}$ and $x = 5 - 3\sqrt{2}$.

Check

You can check your solutions by graphing $y = x^2 - 10x + 7$.

$9.243 \approx 5 + 3\sqrt{2}$

$0.757 \approx 5 - 3\sqrt{2}$

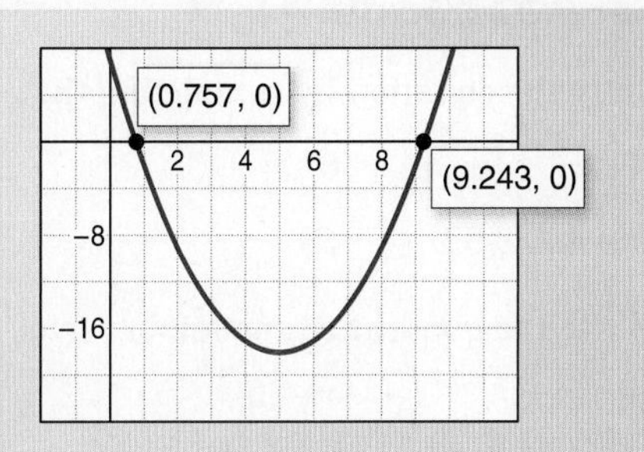

EXAMPLE 4 **Solving $ax^2 + bx + c = 0$ when $a \neq 1$**

Solve $3x^2 + 12x + 15 = 0$ by completing the square.

SOLUTION

The coefficient a is not 1, so you must first divide each side of the equation by a.

$3x^2 + 12x + 15 = 0$	Write the equation.
$x^2 + 4x + 5 = 0$	Divide each side by 3.
$x^2 + 4x = -5$	Write left side in the form $x^2 + bx$.
$x^2 + 4x + 4 = -5 + 4$	Add $\left(\frac{b}{2}\right)^2 = \left(\frac{4}{2}\right)^2 = 4$ to each side.
$(x + 2)^2 = -1$	Write left side as a binomial squared.
$x + 2 = \pm\sqrt{-1}$	Take square root of each side.
$x = -2 \pm \sqrt{-1}$	Subtract 2 from each side.
$x = -2 \pm i$	Write in terms of i.

▶ The solutions are $x = -2 + i$ and $x = -2 - i$.

Writing Quadratic Functions in Vertex Form

Recall that the vertex form of a quadratic function is $y = a(x - h)^2 + k$, where (h, k) is the vertex of the graph of the function. You can write a quadratic function in vertex form by completing the square.

EXAMPLE 5 **Writing a Quadratic Function in Vertex Form**

Write $y = x^2 - 12x + 18$ in vertex form. Then identify the vertex.

Check

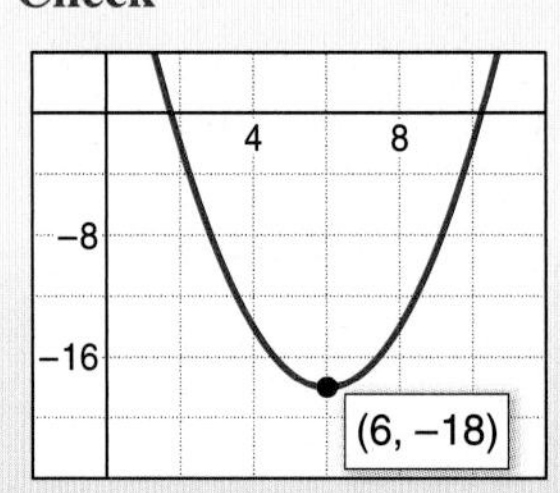

SOLUTION

$y = x^2 - 12x + 18$	Write the function.
$y + ? = (x^2 - 12x + ?) + 18$	Prepare to complete the square.
$y + 36 = (x^2 - 12x + 36) + 18$	Add $\left(\frac{b}{2}\right)^2 = \left(\frac{-12}{2}\right)^2 = 36$ to each side.
$y + 36 = (x - 6)^2 + 18$	Write $x^2 - 12x + 36$ as a binomial squared.
$y = (x - 6)^2 - 18$	Solve for y.

▶ The vertex form of the function is $y = (x - 6)^2 - 18$. The vertex is $(6, -18)$.

SELF-ASSESSMENT

1 I do not understand. 2 I can do it with help. 3 I can do it on my own. 4 I can teach someone else.

Solve the equation by completing the square.

8. $x^2 - 4x + 8 = 0$ **9.** $x^2 + 8x - 5 = 0$ **10.** $-3x^2 - 18x - 6 = 0$

11. $4x^2 + 32x = -68$ **12.** $6x(x + 2) = -42$ **13.** $2x(x - 2) = 200$

Write the quadratic function in vertex form. Then identify the vertex.

14. $y = x^2 - 8x + 18$ **15.** $y = x^2 + 6x + 4$ **16.** $f(x) = x^2 - 2x - 6$

 Modeling Real Life 

The height y (in feet) of a baseball t seconds after it is hit can be modeled by the function

$$y = -16t^2 + 96t + 3.$$

Find the maximum height of the baseball. How long does the ball take to hit the ground?

SOLUTION

1. **Understand the Problem** You are given a quadratic function that represents the height of a ball. You are asked to determine the maximum height of the ball and how long it is in the air.
2. **Make a Plan** Write the function in vertex form to identify the maximum height. Then find and interpret the zeros to determine how long the ball takes to hit the ground.
3. **Solve and Check** Write the function in vertex form by completing the square.

$y = -16t^2 + 96t + 3$	Write the function.
$y = -16(t^2 - 6t) + 3$	Factor -16 from first two terms.
$y + ? = -16(t^2 - 6t + ?) + 3$	Prepare to complete the square.
$y + (-16)(9) = -16(t^2 - 6t + 9) + 3$	Add $(-16)(9)$ to each side.
$y - 144 = -16(t - 3)^2 + 3$	Write $t^2 - 6t + 9$ as a binomial squared.
$y = -16(t - 3)^2 + 147$	Solve for y.

The vertex is (3, 147). Find the zeros of the function.

$0 = -16(t - 3)^2 + 147$	Substitute 0 for y.
$-147 = -16(t - 3)^2$	Subtract 147 from each side.
$9.1875 = (t - 3)^2$	Divide each side by -16.
$\pm\sqrt{9.1875} = t - 3$	Take square root of each side.
$3 \pm \sqrt{9.1875} = t$	Add 3 to each side.

Reject the negative solution, $3 - \sqrt{9.1875} \approx -0.03$, because time must be positive.

So, the maximum height of the ball is 147 feet, and it takes $3 + \sqrt{9.1875} \approx 6$ seconds for the ball to hit the ground.

ANOTHER WAY

You can use the coefficients of the original function $y = f(x)$ to find the maximum height.

$$f\left(-\frac{b}{2a}\right) = f\left(-\frac{96}{2(-16)}\right) = f(3) = 147$$

Math Practice

Interpret Results

The zeros can be written as $3 \pm \sqrt{9.1875}$ or as $3 \pm \frac{7\sqrt{3}}{4}$. Which form is more helpful when you interpret the solutions in this context?

Check The vertex indicates that the maximum height of 147 feet occurs when $t = 3$. This makes sense because the graph of the function is parabolic with zeros near $t = 0$ and $t = 6$. You can use a graph to check the maximum height.

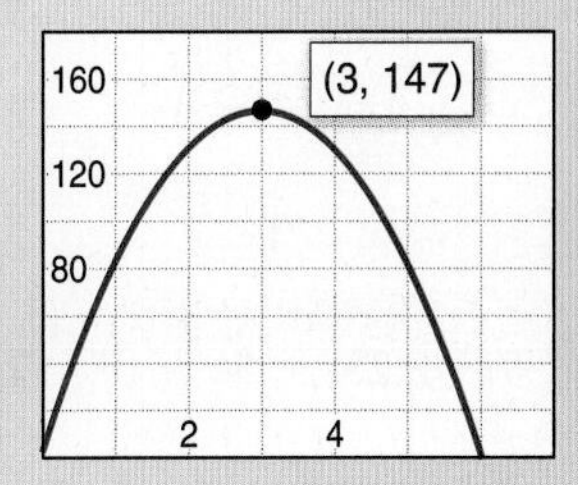

SELF-ASSESSMENT 1 I do not understand. 2 I can do it with help. 3 I can do it on my own. 4 I can teach someone else.

17. **WHAT IF?** The height of the baseball can be modeled by $y = -16t^2 + 80t + 2$. Find the maximum height of the baseball. How long does the ball take to hit the ground?

3.3 Practice WITH CalcChat® AND CalcView®

In Exercises 1–8, solve the equation using square roots. Check your solution(s). ▶ *Example 1*

1. $x^2 - 8x + 16 = 25$
2. $r^2 - 10r + 25 = 1$
3. $x^2 - 18x + 81 = 5$
4. $m^2 + 8m + 16 = 45$
5. $y^2 - 24y + 144 = -100$
6. $x^2 - 26x + 169 = -13$
7. $4w^2 + 4w + 1 = 75$
8. $4x^2 - 8x + 4 = 1$

In Exercises 9–18, complete the square for the expression. Then factor the trinomial. ▶ *Example 2*

9. $x^2 + 10x$
10. $x^2 + 20x$
11. $y^2 - 12y$
12. $t^2 - 22t$
13. $x^2 - 6x$
14. $x^2 + 24x$
15. $z^2 - 5z$
16. $x^2 + 9x$
17. $w^2 + 13w$
18. $s^2 - 17s$

In Exercises 19 and 20, find the value of c. Then write an expression represented by the diagram.

19.

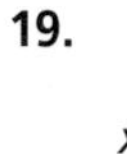

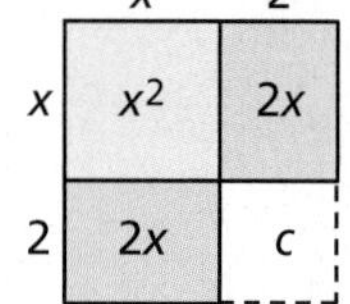

20.

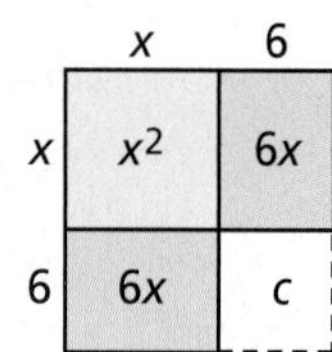

In Exercises 21–32, solve the equation by completing the square. ▶ *Examples 3 and 4*

21. $x^2 + 6x + 3 = 0$
22. $s^2 + 2s - 6 = 0$
23. $x^2 + 4x - 2 = 0$
24. $t^2 - 8t - 5 = 0$
25. $z(z + 9) = 1$
26. $x(x + 8) = -20$
27. $7t^2 + 28t + 56 = 0$
28. $6r^2 + 6r + 12 = 0$
29. $5x(x + 6) = -50$
30. $4w(w - 3) = 24$
31. $4x^2 - 30x = 12 + 10x$
32. $3s^2 + 8s = 2s - 9$

MP **STRUCTURE** In Exercises 33–42, decide whether to use factoring, square roots, or completing the square to solve the equation. Explain your reasoning. Then solve the equation.

33. $x^2 - 4x - 21 = 0$
34. $x^2 - 18x + 64 = 0$
35. $(x + 4)^2 = 16$
36. $(x - 7)^2 = -9$
37. $x^2 + 12x + 50 = 0$
38. $x^2 + 13x + 22 = 0$
39. $2x^2 + 4x - 3 = 0$
40. $3x^2 + 12x + 13 = 0$
41. $x^2 + 121 = 0$
42. $4x^2 - 20 = 0$

In Exercises 43–52, write the quadratic function in vertex form. Then identify the vertex. ▶ *Example 5*

43. $y = x^2 - 8x + 19$
44. $y = x^2 - 4x - 1$
45. $g(x) = x^2 + 12x + 37$
46. $h(x) = x^2 + 20x + 90$
47. $f(x) = x^2 - 3x + 4$
48. $g(x) = x^2 + 7x + 2$
49. $y = -x^2 - 2x - 9$
50. $y = -x^2 + 6x - 16$
51. $f(x) = 2x^2 - 8x - 13$
52. $g(x) = 5x^2 + 25x + 32$

53. **ERROR ANALYSIS** Describe and correct the error in completing the square for $x^2 + 30x$.

$x^2 + 30x$

$x^2 + 30x + \frac{30}{2}$

$x^2 + 30x + 15$

54. **ERROR ANALYSIS** Describe and correct the error in writing $y = 4x^2 + 24x - 11$ in vertex form.

$y = 4x^2 + 24x - 11$

$y = 4(x^2 + 6x) - 11$

$y + 9 = 4(x^2 + 6x + 9) - 11$

$y + 9 = 4(x + 3)^2 - 11$

$y = 4(x + 3)^2 - 20$

55. **MODELING REAL LIFE** The height h (in feet) of a badminton birdie t seconds after it is hit can be modeled by $h = -16t^2 + 32t + 4$. ▶ *Example 6*

 a. Find the maximum height of the birdie.

 b. How long does the birdie take to hit the ground?

56. **MODELING REAL LIFE** A drum major throws a baton into the air and catches it. The height h (in feet) of the baton t seconds after it is thrown can be modeled by $h = -16t^2 + 48t + 6$.

a. Find the maximum height of the baton.

b. The drum major catches the baton when it is 4 feet above the ground. How long is the baton in the air?

CONNECTING CONCEPTS In Exercises 57–60, find the value of x.

57. Area of rectangle = 50

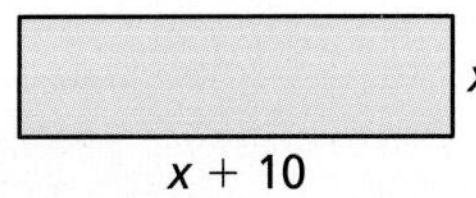

58. Area of parallelogram = 48

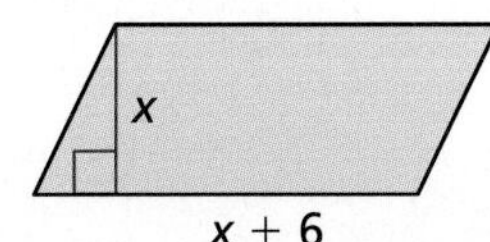

59. Area of triangle = 40

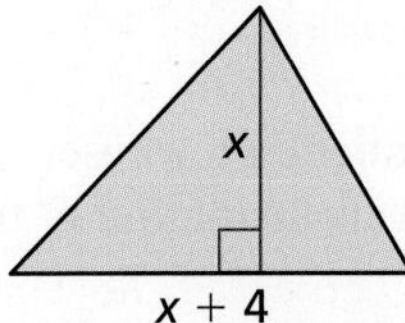

60. Area of trapezoid = 20

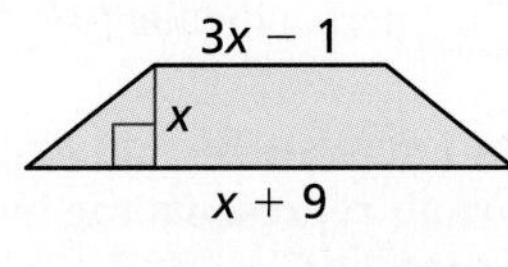

61. **COMPARING METHODS** An online skateboard shop charges \$70 per skateboard and sells 50 skateboards per week. For each \$1 decrease in price, one additional skateboard per week is sold. The shop's revenue can be modeled by $y = (70 - x)(50 + x)$.

a. Find the maximum weekly revenue by using the intercept form of the function and by writing the function in vertex form.

b. Which method do you prefer? Explain.

62. **WRITING** At Buckingham Fountain in Chicago, the height h (in feet) of the water above the main nozzle can be modeled by $h = -16t^2 + 89.6t$, where t is the time (in seconds) since the water has left the nozzle. Describe three different ways you can find the maximum height the water reaches. Then choose a method and find the maximum height of the water.

63. **MAKING AN ARGUMENT** Your friend says the equation $x^2 + 10x = -20$ can be solved by either completing the square or factoring. Is your friend correct? Explain.

64. **HOW DO YOU SEE IT?**
The diagram represents completing the square for an expression. What is the expression? Complete the diagram and write the resulting perfect square trinomial.

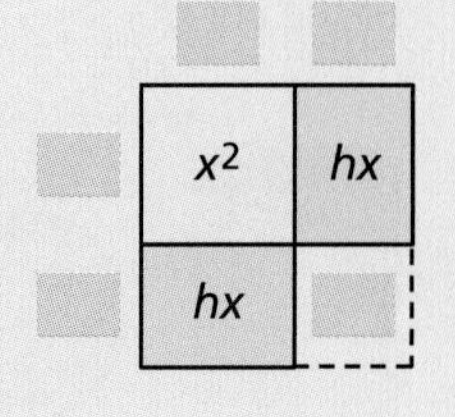

65. **COLLEGE PREP** Which of the following are solutions of the equation $x^2 - 2ax + a^2 = b^2$? Select all that apply.

Ⓐ ab Ⓑ $-a - b$
Ⓒ b Ⓓ a
Ⓔ $a - b$ Ⓕ $a + b$

66. **THOUGHT PROVOKING**
The equation of a parabola is $y^2 + 10y + 20x - 15 = 0$. Write the equation in standard form. Identify the vertex, focus, and directrix.

67. **CRITICAL THINKING** Write a function g in standard form whose graph has the same x-intercepts as the graph of $f(x) = 2x^2 + 8x + 2$. Find the zeros of each function by completing the square. Graph each function.

68. MP **PROBLEM SOLVING** A farmer is building a rectangular pen along the side of a barn for animals. The barn will serve as one side of the pen. The farmer has 120 feet of fence to enclose an area of 1512 square feet and wants each side of the pen to be at least 20 feet long. What are the dimensions of the pen?

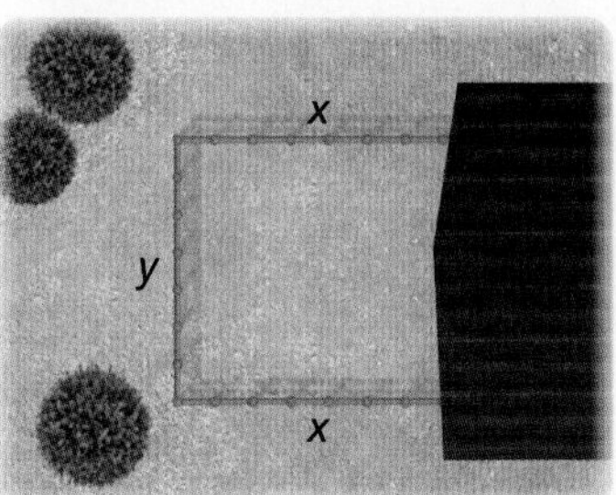

69. **CRITICAL THINKING** Solve $x^2 + bx + c = 0$ by completing the square. Your answer will be an expression for x in terms of b and c. What does your result represent?

70. DIG DEEPER In your pottery class, you are given a lump of clay with a volume of 200 cubic centimeters and are asked to make a cylindrical pencil holder. The pencil holder should be 9 centimeters high and have an inner radius of 3 centimeters. What thickness x should your pencil holder have if you want to use all of the clay?

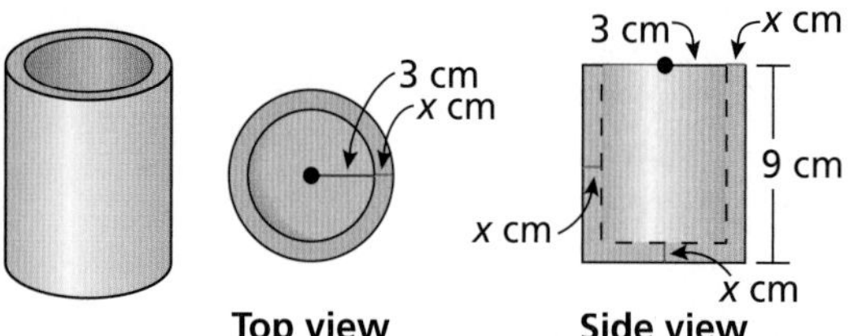

71. **PERFORMANCE TASK** A company wants to design a new smartphone. The ratio of the screen's height to its width should be 18 : 9. The total area of the screen and the border should be about 120 square centimeters.

GO DIGITAL

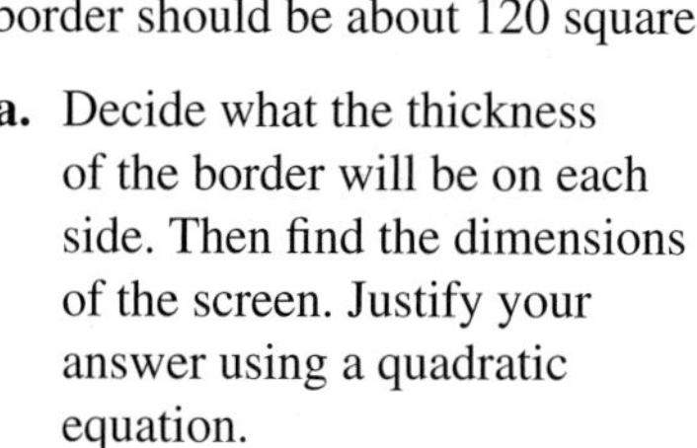

a. Decide what the thickness of the border will be on each side. Then find the dimensions of the screen. Justify your answer using a quadratic equation.

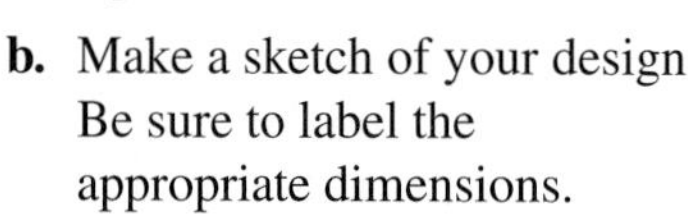

b. Make a sketch of your design. Be sure to label the appropriate dimensions.

REVIEW & REFRESH

WATCH

In Exercises 72–74, graph the function. Label the vertex, axis of symmetry, and x-intercepts.

72. $g(x) = 6(x - 4)^2$ **73.** $f(x) = x^2 + 2x + 5$

74. $f(x) = 2(x + 10)(x - 12)$

In Exercises 75–78, solve the inequality. Graph the solution.

75. $2x - 3 < 5$ **76.** $4 - 8y \geq 12$

77. $\frac{n}{3} + 6 > 1$ **78.** $-\frac{2s}{5} \leq 8$

In Exercises 79–82, perform the operation. Write the answer in standard form.

79. $(2 + 5i) + (-4 + 3i)$ **80.** $(3 + 9i) - (1 - 7i)$

81. $(2 + 4i)(-3 - 5i)$ **82.** $(9 - 2i)^2$

83. Identify the function family to which g belongs. Compare the graph of the function to the graph of its parent function.

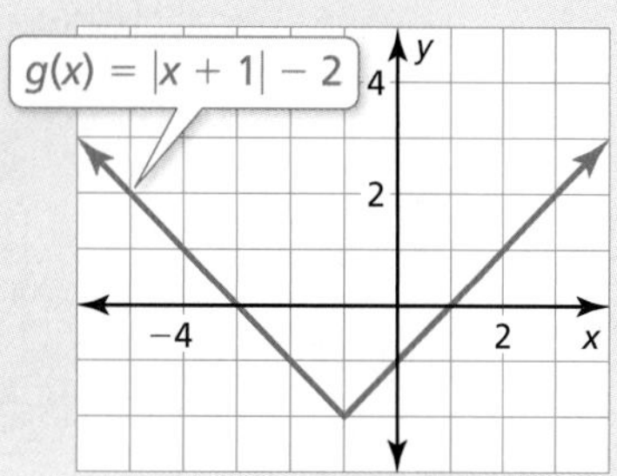

84. Write $y = x^2 + 2x - 48$ in vertex form. Then identify the vertex.

85. MP **STRUCTURE** For what value of m are the graphs of $-2y = 3x - 8$ and $y = mx - 6$ parallel? perpendicular?

In Exercises 86 and 87, write a function g whose graph represents the indicated transformation of the graph of f.

86. $f(x) = 3|x + 5|$; reflection in the x-axis

87. $f(x) = \frac{1}{3}x - \frac{2}{3}$; translation 4 units left

88. Write a function that models the data.

x	1	2	3	4	5
y	9	22	45	78	121

89. Solve $-4t^2 + 16t - 36 = 0$ by completing the square.

90. **MODELING REAL LIFE** A museum has a café with a rectangular patio. The museum wants to add 464 square feet to the area of the patio by expanding the existing patio as shown. By what distance x should the length of the patio be expanded?

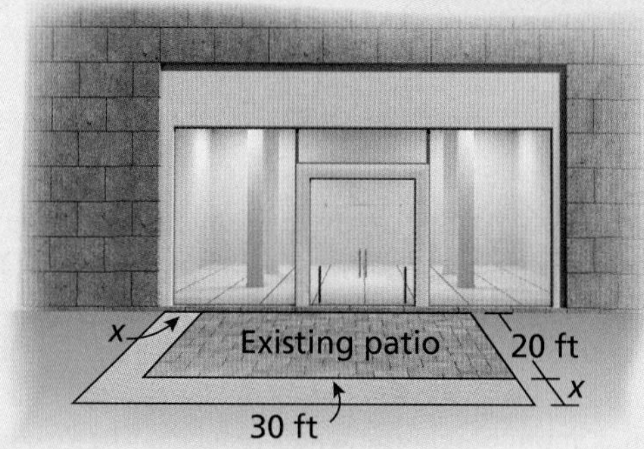

3.4 Using the Quadratic Formula

Learning Target Solve and analyze quadratic equations using the Quadratic Formula and discriminants.

Success Criteria
- I can solve quadratic equations using the Quadratic Formula.
- I can find and interpret the discriminant of an equation.
- I can write quadratic equations with different numbers of solutions using the discriminant.

EXPLORE IT! Analyzing the Quadratic Formula

Work with a partner. Recall the *Quadratic Formula*, which can be used to find the solutions of any quadratic equation of the form $ax^2 + bx + c = 0$, where a, b, and c are real numbers and $a \neq 0$.

$$x = \frac{-b \pm \sqrt{b^2 - 4ac}}{2a} \qquad \text{Quadratic Formula}$$

Math Practice

View as Components Can you write the right side of the formula as two fractions? If so, what does each fraction represent?

a. Show how to derive this formula by completing the square for $ax^2 + bx + c = 0$. The first step has been done for you.

Step	Justification
$ax^2 + bx + c = 0$	General equation
$ax^2 + bx = -c$	Subtract c from each side.

b. What part of the Quadratic Formula tells whether a quadratic equation has real solutions or imaginary solutions? When does the formula produce real solutions for a quadratic equation? When does it produce imaginary solutions? Explain.

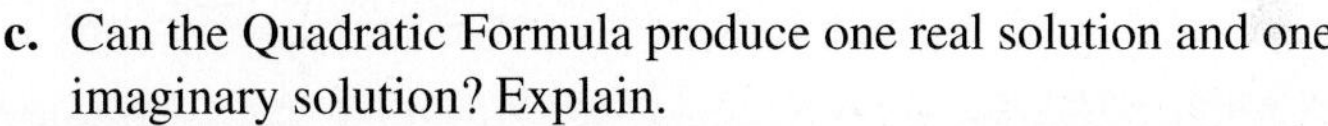

c. Can the Quadratic Formula produce one real solution and one imaginary solution? Explain.

d. Without solving, use your answer to part (b) to determine whether each equation has real solutions or imaginary solutions. What does this tell you about the graph of each equation?

i. $x^2 - 4x + 3 = 0$

ii. $x^2 + 4x + 6 = 0$

iii. $x^2 + 4x + 4 = 0$

iv. $x^2 - 6x + 10 = 0$

e. Solve the quadratic equation in as many ways as you can.

i. $x^2 + 2x - 3 = 0$

ii. $x^2 - 2x + 2 = 0$

f. Summarize the following methods you have learned for solving quadratic equations: graphing, using square roots, factoring, completing the square, and using the Quadratic Formula. Include when you would use each method.

Solving Equations Using the Quadratic Formula

Vocabulary 

Quadratic Formula, *p. 118*
discriminant, *p. 120*

You have already learned how to solve quadratic equations by graphing, using square roots, factoring, and completing the square. In the Explore It!, you derived the **Quadratic Formula** by completing the square. You can use the Quadratic Formula to find the solutions of any quadratic equation in standard form.

KEY IDEA

The Quadratic Formula

The solutions of the quadratic equation $ax^2 + bx + c = 0$ are

$$x = \frac{-b \pm \sqrt{b^2 - 4ac}}{2a} \qquad \text{Quadratic Formula}$$

where a, b, and c are real numbers and $a \neq 0$.

EXAMPLE 1 Solving an Equation with Two Real Solutions

Solve $x^2 + 3x = 5$ using the Quadratic Formula.

SOLUTION

Be sure to write the quadratic equation in standard form before applying the Quadratic Formula.

$$x^2 + 3x = 5 \qquad \text{Write original equation.}$$

$$x^2 + 3x - 5 = 0 \qquad \text{Write in standard form.}$$

$$x = \frac{-b \pm \sqrt{b^2 - 4ac}}{2a} \qquad \text{Quadratic Formula}$$

$$x = \frac{-3 \pm \sqrt{3^2 - 4(1)(-5)}}{2(1)} \qquad \text{Substitute 1 for } a\text{, 3 for } b\text{, and } -5 \text{ for } c.$$

$$x = \frac{-3 \pm \sqrt{29}}{2} \qquad \text{Simplify.}$$

▶ So, the solutions are $x = \dfrac{-3 + \sqrt{29}}{2}$ and $x = \dfrac{-3 - \sqrt{29}}{2}$.

Check
You can check your solutions by graphing $y = x^2 + 3x - 5$.

$$-4.193 \approx \frac{-3 - \sqrt{29}}{2}$$

$$1.193 \approx \frac{-3 + \sqrt{29}}{2}$$

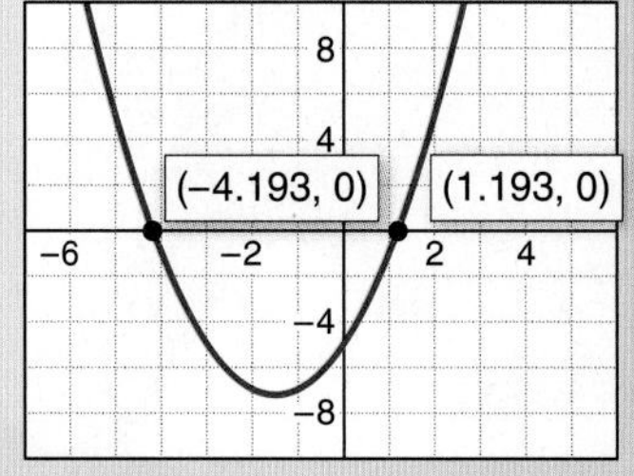

Math Practice

Calculate Accurately
In Example 1, can you say that $x = -4.193$ is a solution of the equation? Can you say that $x \approx 1.193$ is a solution? Explain.

SELF-ASSESSMENT

1 I do not understand. 2 I can do it with help. 3 I can do it on my own. 4 I can teach someone else.

1. MP **STRUCTURE** Explain how to identify a, b, and c when using the Quadratic Formula.

Solve the equation using the Quadratic Formula.

2. $x^2 - 6x + 4 = 0$
3. $2x^2 + 4 = -7x$
4. $5x^2 = x + 8$

EXAMPLE 2 Solving an Equation with One Real Solution

Solve $25x^2 - 8x = 12x - 4$ using the Quadratic Formula.

Check

Graph $y = 25x^2 - 20x + 4$. The only x-intercept is $\frac{2}{5}$.

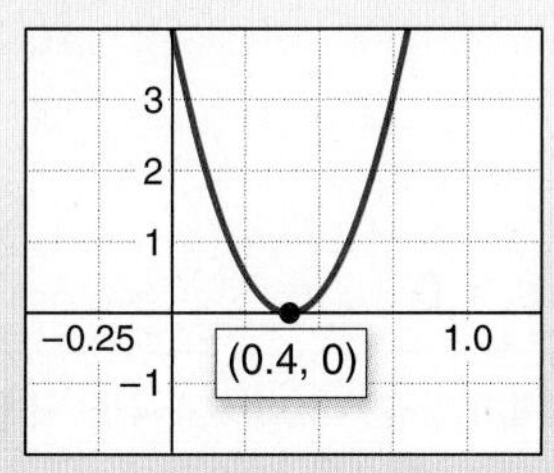

SOLUTION

$25x^2 - 8x = 12x - 4$ — Write original equation.

$25x^2 - 20x + 4 = 0$ — Write in standard form.

$x = \frac{-(-20) \pm \sqrt{(-20)^2 - 4(25)(4)}}{2(25)}$ — $a = 25, b = -20, c = 4$

$x = \frac{20 \pm \sqrt{0}}{50}$ — Simplify.

$x = \frac{2}{5}$ — Simplify.

▶ So, the solution is $x = \frac{2}{5}$.

EXAMPLE 3 Solving an Equation with Imaginary Solutions

Solve $-x^2 + 4x = 13$ using the Quadratic Formula.

SOLUTION

$-x^2 + 4x = 13$ — Write original equation.

$-x^2 + 4x - 13 = 0$ — Write in standard form.

$x = \frac{-4 \pm \sqrt{4^2 - 4(-1)(-13)}}{2(-1)}$ — $a = -1, b = 4, c = -13$

$x = \frac{-4 \pm \sqrt{-36}}{-2}$ — Simplify.

$x = \frac{-4 \pm 6i}{-2}$ — Write in terms of i.

$x = 2 \pm 3i$ — Simplify.

COMMON ERROR

Remember to divide the real part *and* the imaginary part by −2 when simplifying.

▶ The solutions are $x = 2 + 3i$ and $x = 2 - 3i$.

Check Graph $y = -x^2 + 4x - 13$. There are no x-intercepts. So, the original equation has no real solutions. An algebraic check for one of the imaginary solutions is shown.

$$-(2 + 3i)^2 + 4(2 + 3i) \stackrel{?}{=} 13$$
$$-(4 + 12i - 9) + 8 + 12i \stackrel{?}{=} 13$$
$$5 - 12i + 8 + 12i \stackrel{?}{=} 13$$
$$13 = 13 \checkmark$$

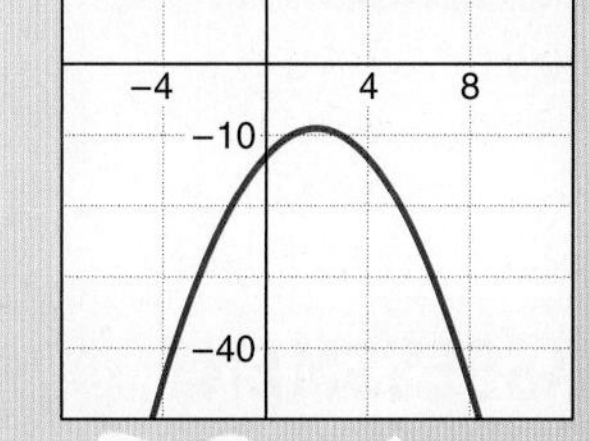

SELF-ASSESSMENT

1 I do not understand. 2 I can do it with help. 3 I can do it on my own. 4 I can teach someone else.

Solve the equation using the Quadratic Formula.

5. $x^2 + 41 = -8x$
6. $-9x^2 = 30x + 25$
7. $5x - 7x^2 = 3x + 4$
8. **MP REASONING** In Example 2, explain how you can use the solution to factor $25x^2 - 20x + 4$.

Analyzing the Discriminant

In the Quadratic Formula, the expression $b^2 - 4ac$ is called the **discriminant** of the associated equation $ax^2 + bx + c = 0$.

$$x = \frac{-b \pm \sqrt{b^2 - 4ac}}{2a}$$ ⟵ discriminant

WORDS AND MATH

Discriminate means to mark the distinguishing features of something. The *discriminant* of the Quadratic Formula can be used to discriminate between quadratic equations with different numbers and types of solutions.

You can analyze the discriminant of a quadratic equation to determine the number and type of solutions of the equation.

KEY IDEA

Analyzing the Discriminant of $ax^2 + bx + c = 0$

Value of discriminant	$b^2 - 4ac > 0$	$b^2 - 4ac = 0$	$b^2 - 4ac < 0$
Number and type of solutions	Two real solutions	One real solution	Two imaginary solutions
Graph of $y = ax^2 + bx + c$	Two x-intercepts	One x-intercept	No x-intercept

EXAMPLE 4 Analyzing the Discriminant

Find the discriminant of the quadratic equation and describe the number and type of solutions of the equation.

a. $x^2 - 6x + 10 = 0$ **b.** $x^2 - 6x + 9 = 0$ **c.** $x^2 - 6x + 8 = 0$

SOLUTION

Equation	**Discriminant**	**Solution(s)**
$ax^2 + bx + c = 0$	$b^2 - 4ac$	$x = \frac{-b \pm \sqrt{b^2 - 4ac}}{2a}$
a. $x^2 - 6x + 10 = 0$	$(-6)^2 - 4(1)(10) = -4$	Two imaginary: $3 \pm i$
b. $x^2 - 6x + 9 = 0$	$(-6)^2 - 4(1)(9) = 0$	One real: 3
c. $x^2 - 6x + 8 = 0$	$(-6)^2 - 4(1)(8) = 4$	Two real: 2, 4

SELF-ASSESSMENT

1 I do not understand. 2 I can do it with help. 3 I can do it on my own. 4 I can teach someone else.

Find the discriminant of the quadratic equation and describe the number and type of solutions of the equation.

9. $4x^2 + 8x + 4 = 0$ **10.** $\frac{1}{2}x^2 + x - 1 = 0$ **11.** $5x^2 = 8x - 13$

12. $7x^2 - 3x = 6$ **13.** $4x^2 + 6x = -9$ **14.** $-5x^2 + 1 = 6 - 10x$

15. MP **REASONING** What is the value of b^2 when a quadratic equation of the form $ax^2 + bx + c = 0$ has exactly one real solution? Explain your reasoning.

EXAMPLE 5 Writing Quadratic Equations

Find a possible pair of integer values for a and c so that the equation $ax^2 - 4x + c = 0$ has the given number and type of solution(s). Then write the equation.

a. one real solution

b. two imaginary solutions

SOLUTION

a. For the equation to have one real solution, the discriminant must equal 0.

$b^2 - 4ac = 0$	Write the discriminant.
$(-4)^2 - 4ac = 0$	Substitute -4 for b.
$16 - 4ac = 0$	Evaluate the power.
$-4ac = -16$	Subtract 16 from each side.
$ac = 4$	Divide each side by -4.

Because $ac = 4$, choose two integers whose product is 4, such as $a = 1$ and $c = 4$.

▶ So, one possible equation is $x^2 - 4x + 4 = 0$.

Check Graph $y = x^2 - 4x + 4$. The only x-intercept is 2. You can also check by factoring.

$$x^2 - 4x + 4 = 0$$
$$(x - 2)^2 = 0$$
$$x = 2 \checkmark$$

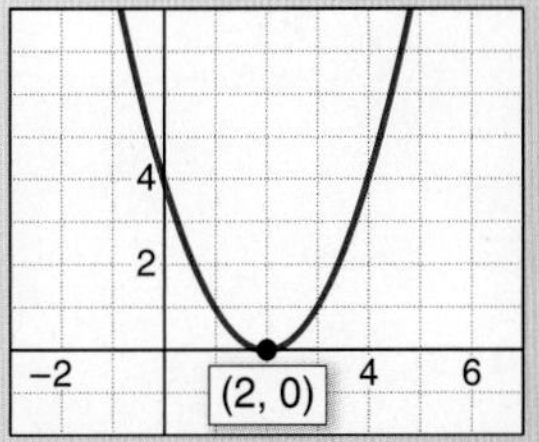

b. For the equation to have two imaginary solutions, the discriminant must be less than zero.

$b^2 - 4ac < 0$	Write the discriminant.
$(-4)^2 - 4ac < 0$	Substitute -4 for b.
$16 - 4ac < 0$	Evaluate the power.
$-4ac < -16$	Subtract 16 from each side.
$ac > 4$	Divide each side by -4. Reverse inequality symbol.

Because $ac > 4$, choose two integers whose product is greater than 4, such as $a = 2$ and $c = 3$.

▶ So, one possible equation is $2x^2 - 4x + 3 = 0$.

Check

The graph of $y = 2x^2 - 4x + 3$ does not have any x-intercepts. ✓

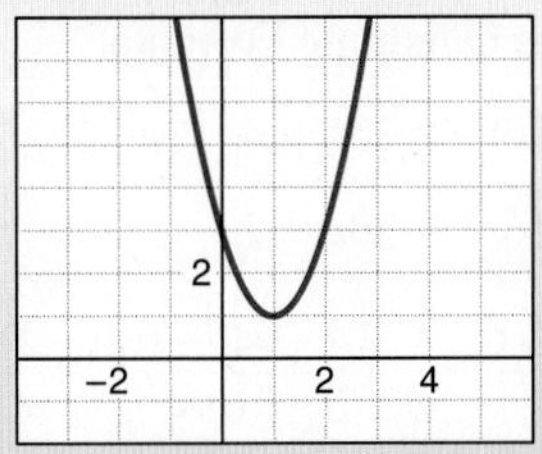

SELF-ASSESSMENT

1 I do not understand. 2 I can do it with help. 3 I can do it on my own. 4 I can teach someone else.

16. OPEN-ENDED Find another possible equation for Examples 5(a) and 5(b).

Find a possible pair of integer values for a and c so that the equation $ax^2 + 8x + c = 0$ has the given number and type of solution(s). Then write the equation.

17. two real solutions **18.** two imaginary solutions **19.** one real solution

Solving Real-Life Problems

The function $h = -16t^2 + s_0$ is used to model the height of a *dropped* object, where h is the height (in feet), t is the time in motion (in seconds), and s_0 is the initial height (in feet). For an object that is *launched* or *thrown*, an extra term $v_0 t$ must be added to the model to account for the object's initial vertical velocity v_0 (in feet per second).

$h = -16t^2 + s_0$ Object is dropped.

$h = -16t^2 + v_0 t + s_0$ Object is launched or thrown.

REMEMBER
These models assume that the force of air resistance on the object is negligible. Also, these models apply only to objects on Earth. For planets with stronger or weaker gravitational forces, different models are used.

As shown below, the value of v_0 can be positive, negative, or zero depending on whether the object is launched upward, downward, or parallel to the ground.

$v_0 > 0$

$v_0 < 0$

$v_0 = 0$

EXAMPLE 6 Modeling Real Life

A juggler tosses a ball into the air. The ball leaves the juggler's hand 4 feet above the ground and has an initial vertical velocity of 30 feet per second. Does the ball reach a height of 10 feet? 25 feet? Explain your reasoning.

SOLUTION

Because the ball is *thrown*, use the model $h = -16t^2 + v_0 t + s_0$ to write a function that represents the height of the ball.

$h = -16t^2 + v_0 t + s_0$ Write the height model.

$h = -16t^2 + 30t + 4$ Substitute 30 for v_0 and 4 for s_0.

To determine whether the ball reaches each height, substitute each height for h to create two equations. Then solve each equation using the Quadratic Formula.

$$10 = -16t^2 + 30t + 4 \qquad\qquad 25 = -16t^2 + 30t + 4$$

$$0 = -16t^2 + 30t - 6 \qquad\qquad 0 = -16t^2 + 30t - 21$$

$$t = \frac{-30 \pm \sqrt{30^2 - 4(-16)(-6)}}{2(-16)} \qquad\qquad t = \frac{-30 \pm \sqrt{30^2 - 4(-16)(-21)}}{2(-16)}$$

$$t = \frac{-30 \pm \sqrt{516}}{-32} \qquad\qquad t = \frac{-30 \pm \sqrt{-444}}{-32}$$

Check The graph shows that the ball reaches a height of 10 feet but not 25 feet. ✓

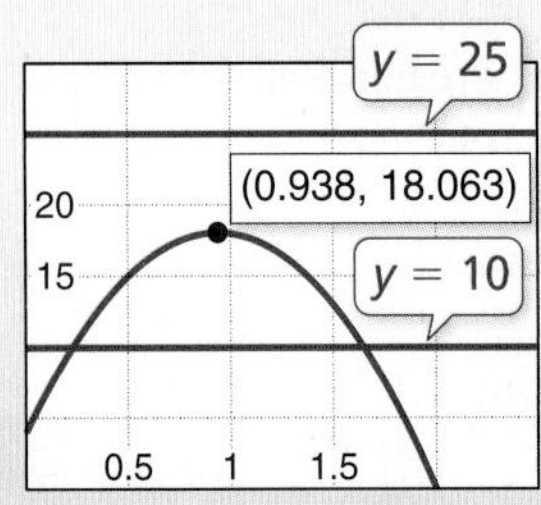

When $h = 10$, the equation has two real solutions, $t \approx 0.23$ and $t \approx 1.65$. When $h = 25$, the equation has two imaginary solutions because the discriminant is negative.

▶ So, the ball reaches a height of 10 feet, but it does not reach a height of 25 feet.

SELF-ASSESSMENT

20. **WHAT IF?** The ball leaves the juggler's hand with an initial vertical velocity of 40 feet per second. Does the ball reach a height of 20 feet? 30 feet? Explain.

3.4 Practice WITH CalcChat® AND CalcView®

In Exercises 1–14, solve the equation using the Quadratic Formula. Use technology to check your solution(s). ▷ *Examples 1, 2, and 3*

1. $x^2 - 4x + 3 = 0$
2. $3x^2 + 6x + 3 = 0$
3. $x^2 + 6x + 15 = 0$
4. $6x^2 - 2x + 1 = 0$
5. $x^2 - 14x = -49$
6. $2x^2 + 4x = 30$
7. $3x^2 + 5 = -2x$
8. $-3x = 2x^2 - 4$
9. $-10x = -25 - x^2$
10. $-5x^2 - 6 = -4x$
11. $-4x^2 + 3x = -5$
12. $x^2 + 121 = -22x$
13. $-z^2 = -12z + 6$
14. $-7w + 6 = -4w^2$

In Exercises 15–22, find the discriminant of the quadratic equation and describe the number and type of solutions of the equation. ▷ *Example 4*

15. $x^2 + 12x + 36 = 0$
16. $x^2 - x + 6 = 0$
17. $4n^2 - 4n - 24 = 0$
18. $-x^2 + 2x + 12 = 0$
19. $4x^2 = 5x - 10$
20. $-18p = p^2 + 81$
21. $24x = -48 - 3x^2$
22. $-2x^2 - 6 = x$

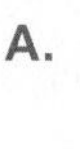

STRUCTURE In Exercises 23–26, use the discriminant to match each quadratic equation with the graph of its related function. Explain.

23. $x^2 - 6x + 25 = 0$
24. $2x^2 - 20x + 50 = 0$
25. $3x^2 + 6x - 9 = 0$
26. $-5x^2 + 10x + 35 = 0$

A. 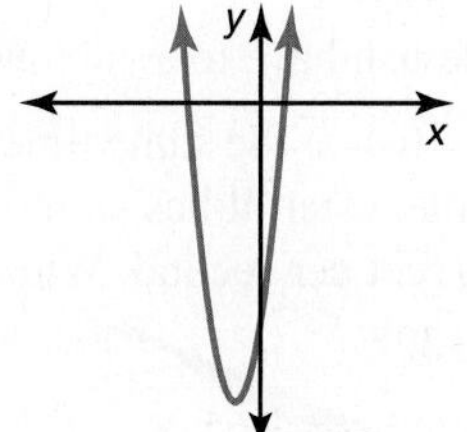

B. 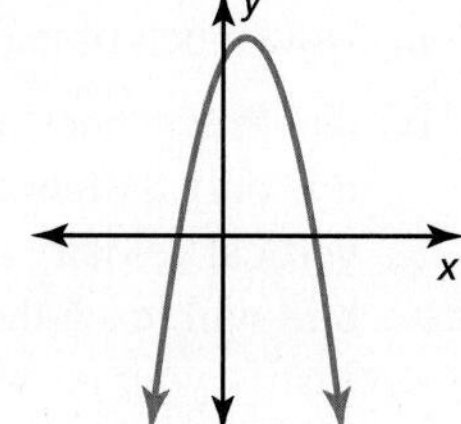

C. 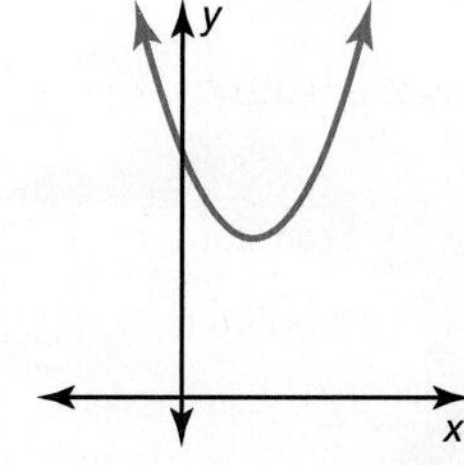

D. 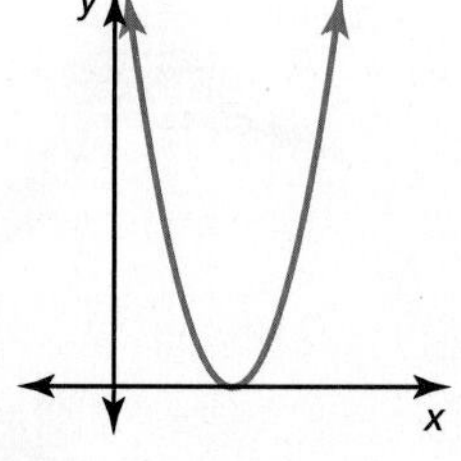

ERROR ANALYSIS In Exercises 27 and 28, describe and correct the error in solving the equation.

27. 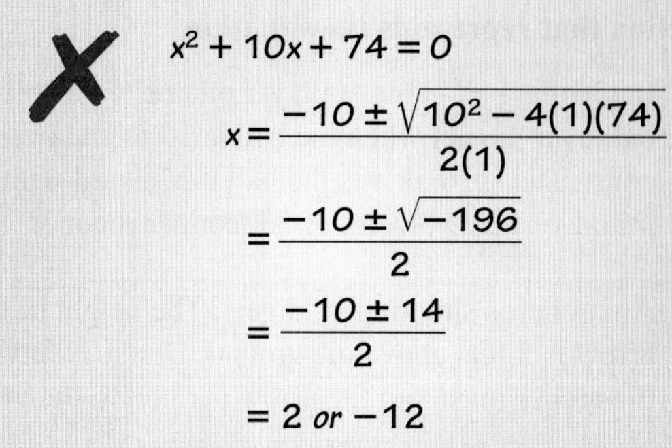

28. 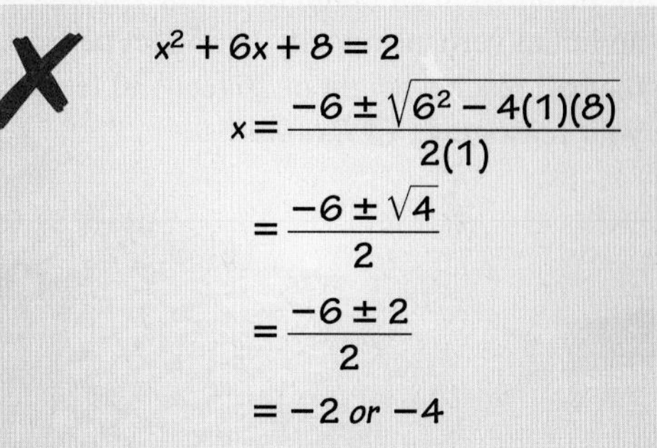

OPEN-ENDED In Exercises 29–34, find a possible pair of integer values for *a* and *c* so that the quadratic equation has the given number and type of solution(s). Then write the equation. ▷ *Example 5*

29. $ax^2 + 4x + c = 0$; two imaginary solutions
30. $ax^2 + 6x + c = 0$; two real solutions
31. $ax^2 - 8x + c = 0$; two real solutions
32. $ax^2 - 6x + c = 0$; one real solution
33. $ax^2 + 10x = c$; one real solution
34. $-4x + c = -ax^2$; two imaginary solutions
35. **COLLEGE PREP** Determine the number and type of solutions of the equation $x^2 + 7x = -11$.

    Ⓐ two real solutions

    Ⓑ one real solution

    Ⓒ two imaginary solutions

    Ⓓ one imaginary solution

36. **COLLEGE PREP** What are the solutions of the equation $2x^2 + 50 = 16x$?

Ⓐ $x = 4 \pm 3i$ Ⓑ $x = -4 \pm 3i$

Ⓒ $x = 1, x = 7$ Ⓓ $x = -7, x = -1$

MODELING REAL LIFE In Exercises 37 and 38, write a function that represents the situation.

37. In a volleyball game, a player on one team spikes the ball over the net when the ball is 10 feet above the court. The spike drives the ball downward with an initial vertical velocity of 55 feet per second.

38. An archer is shooting at targets. The height of the arrow is 5 feet above the ground. Due to safety rules, the archer must aim the arrow parallel to the ground.

39. **MODELING REAL LIFE** A lacrosse player throws a ball in the air from an initial height of 7 feet. The ball has an initial vertical velocity of 35 feet per second. Does the ball reach a height of 26 feet? 30 feet? Explain your reasoning. *Example 6*

40. **MODELING REAL LIFE** A rocketry club is launching model rockets. The launching pad is 30 feet above the ground. Your model rocket has an initial vertical velocity of 105 feet per second. Your friend's model rocket has an initial vertical velocity of 100 feet per second.

a. Does your rocket reach a height of 200 feet? Does your friend's rocket? Explain your reasoning.

b. Which rocket is in the air longer? How much longer?

MP STRUCTURE In Exercises 41–46, use the Quadratic Formula to write a quadratic equation that has the given solutions.

41. $x = \dfrac{-8 \pm \sqrt{-176}}{-10}$ **42.** $x = \dfrac{15 \pm \sqrt{-215}}{22}$

43. $x = \dfrac{-4 \pm \sqrt{-124}}{-14}$ **44.** $x = \dfrac{-9 \pm \sqrt{137}}{4}$

45. $x = \dfrac{-4 \pm 2}{6}$ **46.** $x = \dfrac{2 \pm 4}{-2}$

GO DIGITAL

COMPARING METHODS In Exercises 47–54, solve the quadratic equation using the Quadratic Formula. Then solve the equation using another method. Which method do you prefer? Explain.

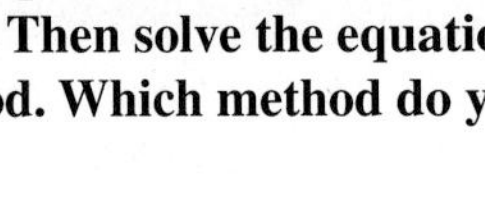

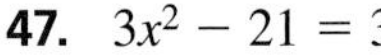

47. $3x^2 - 21 = 3$ **48.** $5x^2 + 38 = 3$

49. $2x^2 - 54 = 12x$ **50.** $x^2 = 3x + 15$

51. $x^2 + 8x - 13 = 0$ **52.** $x^2 - 7x + 12 = 0$

53. $8x^2 + 4x + 5 = 0$ **54.** $5x^2 - 50x = -135$

CONNECTING CONCEPTS In Exercises 55 and 56, find the value of x.

55. Area = 24 m^2 **56.** Area = 8 ft^2

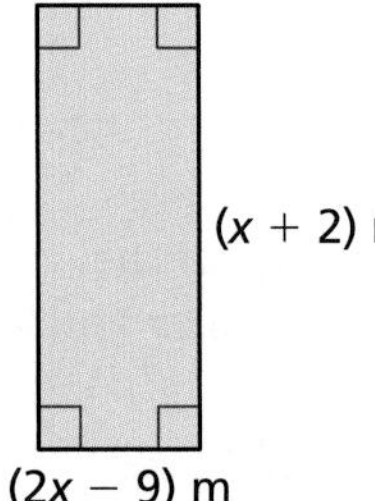

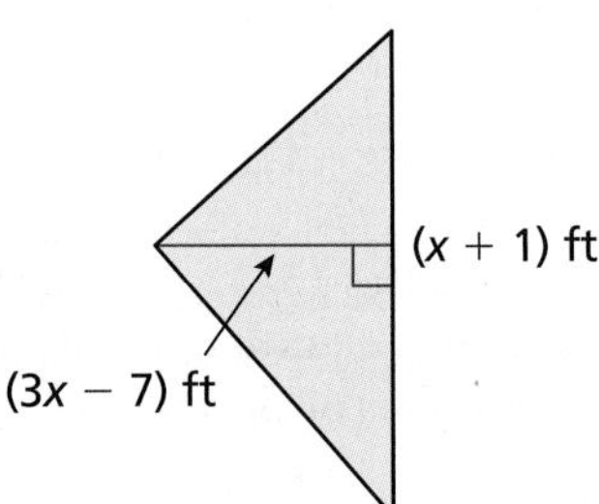

OPEN-ENDED In Exercises 57–60, find a possible pair of real number values for a and c so that the quadratic equation has one real solution. Then write the equation.

57. $ax^2 - 13x + c = 0$ **58.** $ax^2 - \sqrt{2}x + c = 0$

59. $\frac{1}{2}x + c = -ax^2$ **60.** $ax^2 + \pi x = -c$

61. **MP PROBLEM SOLVING** A gannet is a bird that feeds on fish by diving into the water. A gannet spots a fish on the surface of the water and flies down 100 feet to catch it. The bird plunges toward the water with an initial vertical velocity of −88 feet per second.

a. How much time does the fish have to swim away?

b. Another gannet spots the fish at the same time, but it is only 84 feet above the water. It has an initial vertical velocity of −70 feet per second. Which bird will reach the water first? Justify your answer.

62. **MP PROBLEM SOLVING** The amount A of nuclear energy (in billions of kilowatt hours) generated for consumer use in the United States can be modeled by the function $A = -0.6t^2 + 37.2t + 243$, where t represents the number of years after 1980.

 a. In what year did the amount of nuclear energy generated reach 800 billion kilowatt hours?

 b. Find the average rate of change from 2000 to 2015 and interpret the meaning in the context of the situation.

 c. Do you think this model will be accurate in 2030? Explain your reasoning.

63. **OPEN-ENDED** Describe a real-life situation that can be modeled by $h = -16t^2 + v_0t + s_0$. Write the height model for your situation and determine how long your object is in the air.

64. **HOW DO YOU SEE IT?**
The graphs of three quadratic functions are shown. For each graph, determine whether the discriminant of the associated equation is *positive*, *negative*, or *zero*. Then state the number and type of solution(s) of the associated equation. Explain your reasoning.

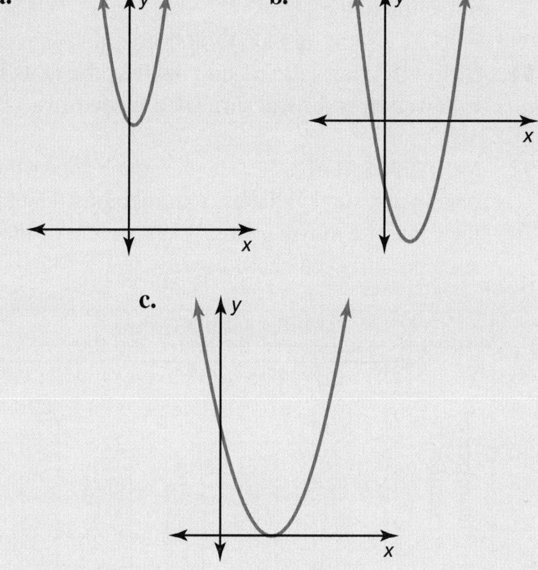

65. **MAKING AN ARGUMENT** Which method would you use to solve $4x^2 + 14x + 11 = 0$, completing the square or using the Quadratic Formula? Explain your reasoning.

66. **MP NUMBER SENSE** The quadratic equation $ax^2 + 5x + c = 0$ has one real solution. Is it possible for a and c to be integers? rational numbers? Explain your reasoning. Then describe the possible values of a and c.

67. **ABSTRACT REASONING** For a quadratic equation $ax^2 + bx + c = 0$ with two real solutions, show that the mean of the solutions is $-\frac{b}{2a}$. How is this fact related to the symmetry of the graph of $y = ax^2 + bx + c$?

68. **MODELING REAL LIFE** The Stratosphere Tower in Las Vegas is 921 feet tall and has a "needle" at its top that extends even higher into the air. A thrill ride called Big Shot catapults riders 160 feet up the needle and then lets them fall back to the launching pad.

 a. The height h (in feet) of a rider on the Big Shot can be modeled by $h = -16t^2 + v_0t + 921$, where t is the elapsed time (in seconds) after launch and v_0 is the initial vertical velocity (in feet per second). Find v_0 using the fact that the maximum value of h is $921 + 160 = 1081$ feet.

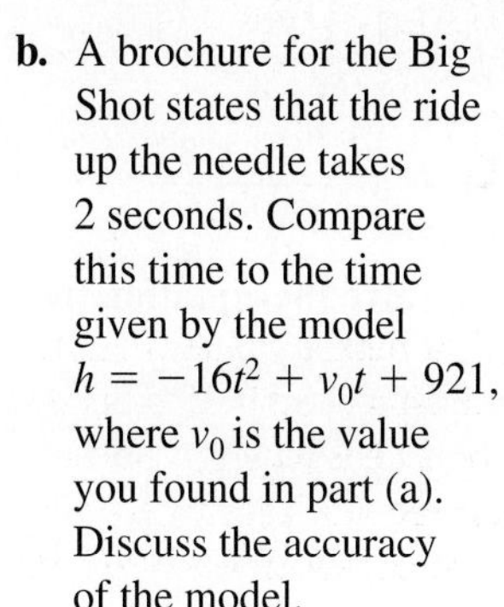

 b. A brochure for the Big Shot states that the ride up the needle takes 2 seconds. Compare this time to the time given by the model $h = -16t^2 + v_0t + 921$, where v_0 is the value you found in part (a). Discuss the accuracy of the model.

69. **ABSTRACT REASONING** For what value(s) of n does the equation $x^2 - 3x + n = -2$ have one real solution? Explain your reasoning.

70. CRITICAL THINKING Solve each absolute value equation.

a. $|x^2 - 3x - 14| = 4$ **b.** $x^2 = |x| + 6$

71. CRITICAL THINKING When a quadratic equation with real coefficients has imaginary solutions, why are the solutions complex conjugates? As part of your explanation, show that there is no such equation with solutions of $3i$ and $-2i$.

72. THOUGHT PROVOKING Show how you can use the Quadratic Formula to write the solutions of any quadratic equation of the form $a(x - h)^2 + k = 0$ in terms of a, h, and k.

73. DIG DEEPER Can you use the Quadratic Formula to find the solutions of $4x^4 + 35x^2 - 9 = 0$? If so, find the solutions. If not, explain why not.

REVIEW & REFRESH

WATCH

In Exercises 74–77, solve the system using any method. Explain your choice of method.

74. $-x + 2y = 6$
$x + 4y = 24$

75. $y = 2x - 1$
$y = x + 1$

76. $3x + y = 4$
$6x + 2y = -4$

77. $y = -x + 2$
$-5x + 5y = 10$

78. Use the graph to solve $x^2 = -2x + 8$.

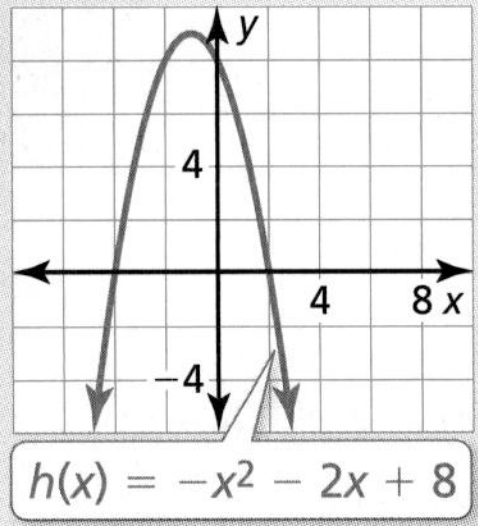

In Exercises 79 and 80, solve the equation by completing the square.

79. $x^2 - 6x + 10 = 0$ **80.** $9x^2 + 36x + 72 = 0$

81. Write $y = x^2 - 10x + 4$ in vertex form. Then identify the vertex.

82. Find the values of x and y that satisfy the equation $7x - 6i = 14 + yi$.

In Exercises 83 and 84, multiply the complex number by its complex conjugate.

83. $6 - 8i$ **84.** $-10 + 2i$

In Exercises 85 and 86, solve the equation by graphing.

85. $-2x + 5 = \frac{1}{3}x - 2$

86. $|4 - x| = |3x - 8|$

In Exercises 87 and 88, solve the equation using the Quadratic Formula.

87. $-3 = 4x^2 + 9x$ **88.** $x^2 = 1 - x$

89. Write an inequality that represents the graph.

In Exercises 90 and 91, write a function g whose graph represents the indicated transformations of the graph of f.

90. $f(x) = x$; translation 9 units down followed by a reflection in the y-axis

91. $f(x) = |x|$; translation 1 unit down and 2 units left followed by a vertical shrink by a factor of $\frac{1}{2}$

92. MODELING REAL LIFE The bar graph shows the results of a survey that asks a group of students their favorite movie genre. What percent of the students surveyed chose comedy?

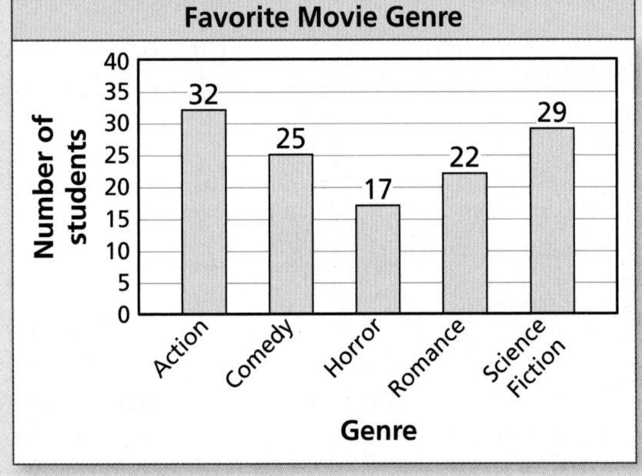

In Exercises 93–96, graph the function. Label the vertex and axis of symmetry.

93. $y = -(x - 1)^2 + 4$ **94.** $f(x) = (x + 1)(2x - 3)$

95. $y = 0.5x^2 + 2x + 5$ **96.** $g(x) = -3x^2 - 2$

3.5 Solving Nonlinear Systems of Equations

Learning Target Solve nonlinear systems graphically and algebraically.

Success Criteria

- I can describe what a nonlinear system of equations is.
- I can solve nonlinear systems using graphing, substitution, or elimination.
- I can solve quadratic equations by graphing each side of the equation.

EXPLORE IT! Solving Systems of Equations

Work with a partner.

a. Graph the equation $x^2 + y^2 = 4$. Make several observations about the graph.

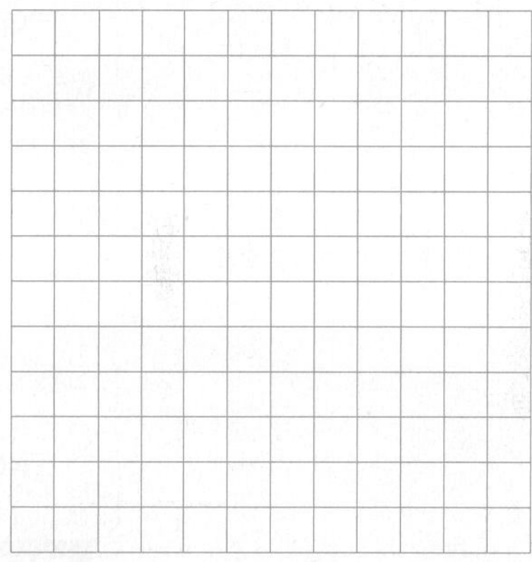

b. How many intersection points can the graphs of a line and a circle have? Use graphs to support your answers. What do the intersection points represent?

Math Practice

Look for Structure
How did you determine the ordered pairs used to graph the equation $x^2 + y^2 = 4$?

c. Consider the system below. Can you use a graph to solve the system? Explain.

$$x^2 + y^2 = 4$$

$$y = -\frac{1}{2}x + 1$$

d. MP **CHOOSE TOOLS** Find the points of intersection of the graphs of the equations in part (c). Explain your method.

e. Write the equation of a line that intersects the graph of $x^2 + y^2 = 4$ at only one point. Explain how you found your answer.

f. Think of all the ways that a parabola can intersect the graph of a circle. How many points of intersection are possible? Use graphs to support your answers.

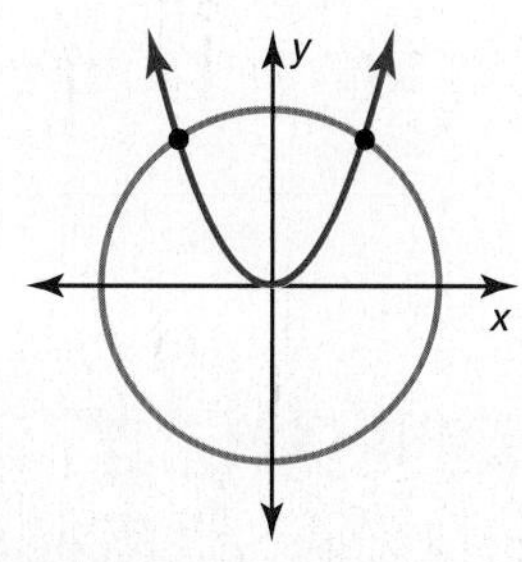

g. Use your answers in part (f) to write several equations of parabolas that have different numbers of intersection points with the graph of $x^2 + y^2 = 4$. Then compare your results with your classmates.

Solutions of Nonlinear Systems

GO DIGITAL

Vocabulary AZ VOCAB

system of nonlinear equations, *p. 128*

Previously, you solved systems of *linear* equations by graphing, substitution, and elimination. You can also use these methods to solve systems of *nonlinear* equations. A **system of nonlinear equations** is a system in which at least one of the equations is nonlinear. For instance, the nonlinear system shown consists of a quadratic equation and a linear equation.

$y = x^2 + 2x - 4$ Equation 1 is nonlinear.

$y = 2x + 5$ Equation 2 is linear.

When a nonlinear system consists of a linear equation and a quadratic equation, the graphs can intersect in zero, one, or two points. So, the system can have zero, one, or two real solutions, as shown.

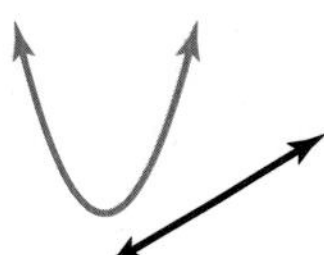

No real solution

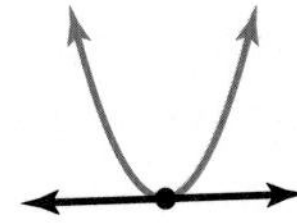

One real solution

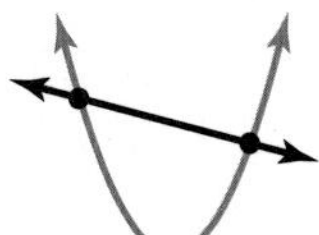

Two real solutions

When a nonlinear system consists of two parabolas that open up or open down, the graphs can intersect in zero, one, or two points. So, the system can have zero, one, or two real solutions, as shown.

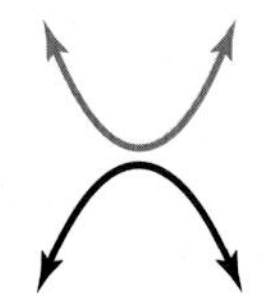

No real solution

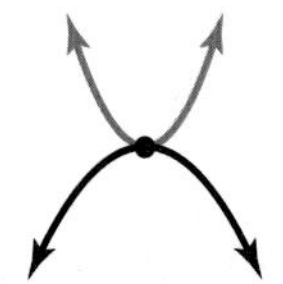

One real solution

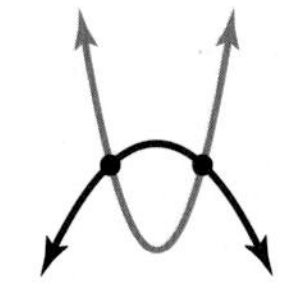

Two real solutions

EXAMPLE 1 Solving a Nonlinear System by Graphing

Solve the system by graphing.

$y = x^2 - 2x - 1$ Equation 1

$y = -2x - 1$ Equation 2

SOLUTION

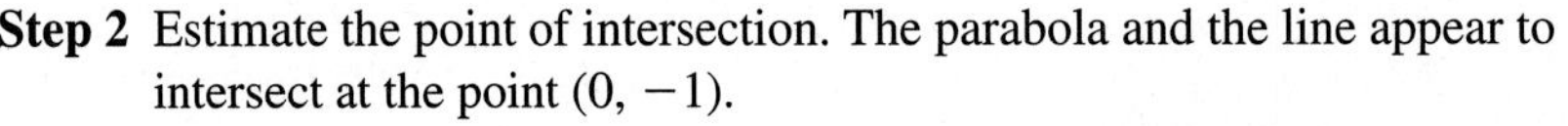

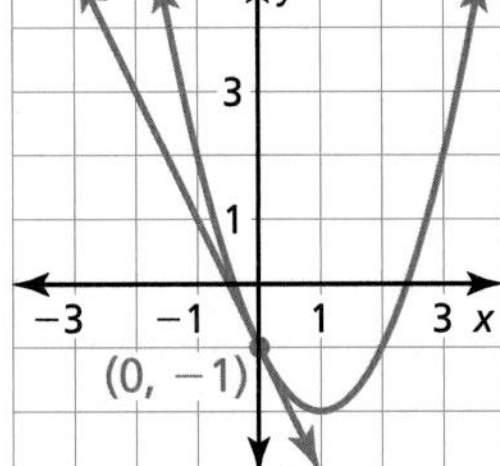

Step 1 Graph each equation.

Step 2 Estimate the point of intersection. The parabola and the line appear to intersect at the point $(0, -1)$.

Step 3 Check that $(0, -1)$ is a solution of each equation.

Equation 1

$y = x^2 - 2x - 1$

$-1 \stackrel{?}{=} (0)^2 - 2(0) - 1$

$-1 = -1$ ✓

Equation 2

$y = -2x - 1$

$-1 \stackrel{?}{=} -2(0) - 1$

$-1 = -1$ ✓

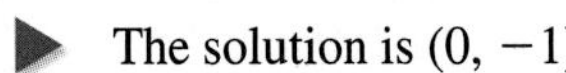

▶ The solution is $(0, -1)$.

SELF-ASSESSMENT 1 I do not understand. 2 I can do it with help. 3 I can do it on my own. 4 I can teach someone else.

Solve the system by graphing.

1. $y = x^2 - 4x - 2$
$y = x - 2$

2. $y = \frac{1}{2}x^2 - 2x + 4$
$x + y = 3$

3. $y = -3x + 8$
$y = -x^2 + 3x - 1$

EXAMPLE 2 Solving a Nonlinear System by Substitution

Solve the system by substitution.

$x^2 + x - y = -1$ Equation 1

$x + y = 4$ Equation 2

SOLUTION

Step 1 Solve for y in Equation 2.

$y = -x + 4$ Solve for y in Equation 2.

Step 2 Substitute $-x + 4$ for y in Equation 1 and solve for x.

$x^2 + x - y = -1$ Equation 1

$x^2 + x - (-x + 4) = -1$ Substitute $-x + 4$ for y.

$x^2 + 2x - 4 = -1$ Simplify.

$x^2 + 2x - 3 = 0$ Write in standard form.

$(x + 3)(x - 1) = 0$ Factor.

$x + 3 = 0$ *or* $x - 1 = 0$ Zero-Product Property

$x = -3$ *or* $x = 1$ Solve for x.

Check

(−3, 7)
(1, 3)

Step 3 Substitute -3 and 1 for x in $y = -x + 4$ and solve for y.

$y = -x + 4 = -(-3) + 4 = 7$ Substitute -3 for x.

$y = -x + 4 = -1 + 4 = 3$ Substitute 1 for x.

▶ So, the solutions are $(-3, 7)$ and $(1, 3)$.

EXAMPLE 3 Solving a Nonlinear System by Elimination

Solve the system by elimination.

$2x^2 - 5x - y = -2$ Equation 1

$x^2 + 2x + y = 0$ Equation 2

SOLUTION

The coefficients of the y-terms are opposites. So, add the equations to eliminate the y-terms and obtain a quadratic equation in x.

Check

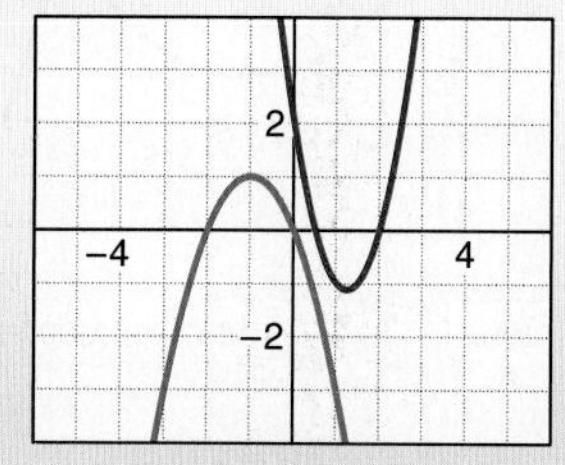

$$\begin{array}{r} 2x^2 - 5x - y = -2 \\ x^2 + 2x + y = 0 \\ \hline 3x^2 - 3x = -2 \end{array}$$ Add the equations.

$3x^2 - 3x + 2 = 0$ Write in standard form.

$$x = \frac{3 \pm \sqrt{-15}}{6}$$ Use the Quadratic Formula.

▶ Because the discriminant is negative, the equation $3x^2 - 3x + 2 = 0$ has no real solution. So, the original system has no real solution.

SELF-ASSESSMENT

1 I do not understand. 2 I can do it with help. 3 I can do it on my own. 4 I can teach someone else.

Solve the system using any method. Explain your choice of method.

4. $y = -x^2 + 4$
$y = -4x + 8$

5. $x^2 + 3x + y = 0$
$2x + y = 5$

6. $2x^2 + 4x - y = -2$
$x^2 + y = 2$

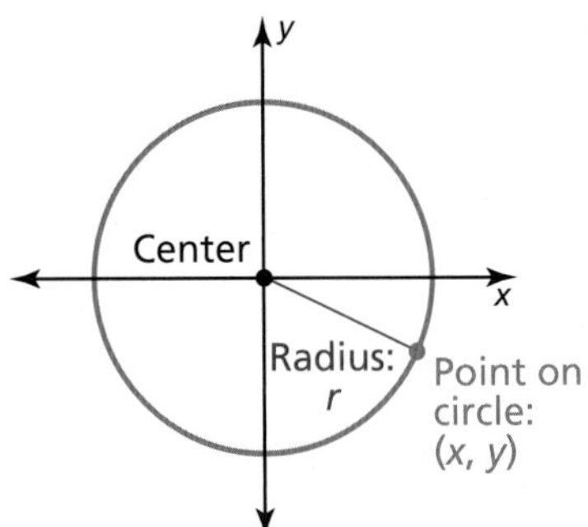

An equation of the form $x^2 + y^2 = r^2$ is the standard form of a circle with center (0, 0) and radius r. When a nonlinear system consists of the equation of a circle and a linear equation, the graphs can intersect in zero, one, or two points. So, the system can have zero, one, or two real solutions, as shown.

GO DIGITAL

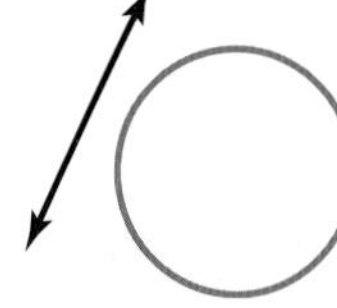
No real solution

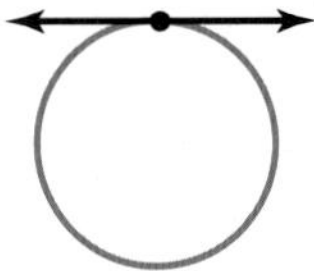
One real solution

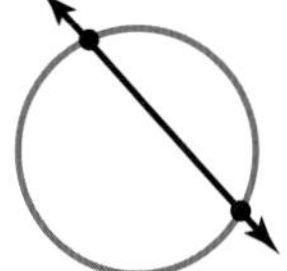
Two real solutions

EXAMPLE 4 Solving a Nonlinear System Involving a Circle

Solve the system by substitution.

$x^2 + y^2 = 10$ Equation 1

$y = -3x + 10$ Equation 2

SOLUTION

Step 1 Equation 2 is already solved for y. So, substitute $-3x + 10$ for y in Equation 1 and solve for x.

$x^2 + y^2 = 10$	Equation 1
$x^2 + (-3x + 10)^2 = 10$	Substitute $-3x + 10$ for y.
$x^2 + 9x^2 - 60x + 100 = 10$	Expand the power.
$10x^2 - 60x + 90 = 0$	Write in standard form.
$x^2 - 6x + 9 = 0$	Divide each side by 10.
$(x - 3)^2 = 0$	Perfect square trinomial pattern
$x = 3$	Zero-Product Property

COMMON ERROR

You can also substitute $x = 3$ in Equation 1 to find y. This yields two *apparent* solutions, (3, 1) and (3, −1). However, (3, −1) is *not* a solution because it does not satisfy Equation 2. You can also see (3, −1) is not a solution from the graph.

Step 2 Find the y-coordinate of the solution by substituting $x = 3$ in Equation 2.

$$y = -3(3) + 10 = 1$$

▶ So, the solution is (3, 1).

Check Use technology to check your answer.

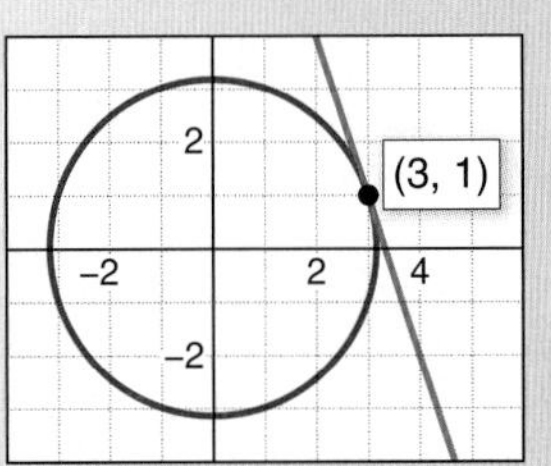

SELF-ASSESSMENT

1 I do not understand. 2 I can do it with help. 3 I can do it on my own. 4 I can teach someone else.

Solve the system.

7. $y = 4x + 17$
$x^2 + y^2 = 17$

8. $x^2 + y^2 = 4$
$y = x + 4$

9. $x^2 + y^2 = 1$
$y = \frac{1}{2}x + \frac{1}{2}$

10. WHICH ONE DOESN'T BELONG? Which system does *not* belong with the other three? Explain your reasoning.

$y = 3x + 4$ $y = x^2 + 1$	$y = 2x - 1$ $y = -3x + 6$	$y = 3x^2 + 4x + 1$ $y = -5x^2 - 3x + 1$	$x^2 + y^2 = 4$ $y = -x + 1$

STUDY TIP

You can think of this as solving the system of equations

$y = f(x)$

$y = g(x)$

by graphing.

Solving Equations by Graphing

KEY IDEA

Solving Equations by Graphing

Step 1 To solve the equation $f(x) = g(x)$, first write functions to represent each side of the equation, $y = f(x)$ and $y = g(x)$.

Step 2 Graph the functions $y = f(x)$ and $y = g(x)$. The x-value of an intersection point of the graphs of the functions is a solution of the equation $f(x) = g(x)$.

EXAMPLE 5 Solving Quadratic Equations by Graphing

Solve each equation by graphing.

a. $3x^2 + 5x - 1 = -x^2 + 2x + 1$

b. $-(x - 1.5)^2 + 2.25 = 2x(x + 1.5)$

SOLUTION

ANOTHER WAY

In Example 5(a), you can also find the solutions by writing the given equation as $4x^2 + 3x - 2 = 0$ and using the Quadratic Formula.

a. Step 1 Write functions to represent each side of the original equation.

Equation	*Functions*
$3x^2 + 5x - 1 = -x^2 + 2x + 1$	$y = 3x^2 + 5x - 1$ $y = -x^2 + 2x + 1$

Step 2 Use technology to graph the functions and find the x-coordinates of the intersection points of the graphs.

The points of intersection are about $(-1.175, -2.732)$ and $(0.425, 1.67)$.

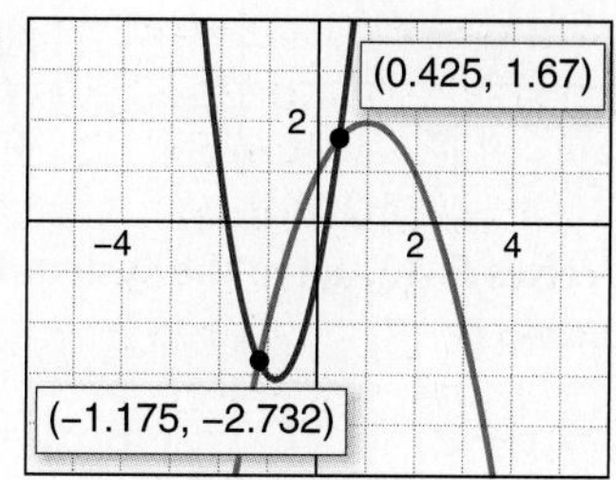

▶ So, the solutions of the equation are $x \approx -1.175$ and $x \approx 0.425$.

b. Step 1 Write functions to represent each side of the original equation.

Equation	*Functions*
$-(x - 1.5)^2 + 2.25 = 2x(x + 1.5)$	$y = -(x - 1.5)^2 + 2.25$ $y = 2x(x + 1.5)$

Step 2 Use technology to graph the functions and find the x-coordinate of the intersection point of the graphs. The graphs intersect at $(0, 0)$.

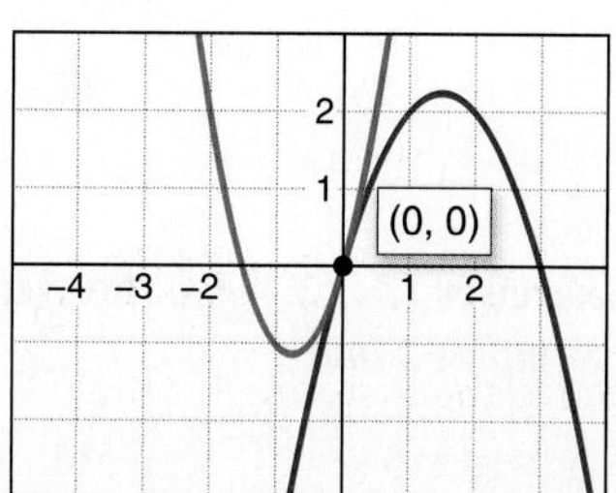

▶ So, the solution of the equation is $x = 0$.

SELF-ASSESSMENT 1 I do not understand. 2 I can do it with help. 3 I can do it on my own. 4 I can teach someone else.

Solve the equation by graphing.

11. $x^2 - 6x + 15 = -(x - 3)^2 + 6$

12. $(x + 4)(x - 1) = -x^2 + 3x + 4$

13. WRITING Explain why the x-coordinates of the points where the graphs of the equations $y = f(x)$ and $y = g(x)$ intersect are the solutions of the equation $f(x) = g(x)$.

3.5 Practice WITH CalcChat® AND CalcView®

In Exercises 1–4, use the graph to solve the system.

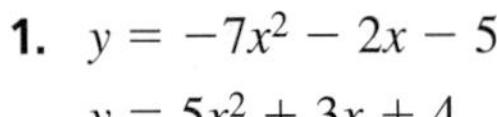

1. $y = -7x^2 - 2x - 5$
$y = 5x^2 + 3x + 4$

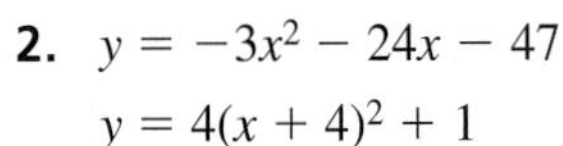

2. $y = -3x^2 - 24x - 47$
$y = 4(x + 4)^2 + 1$

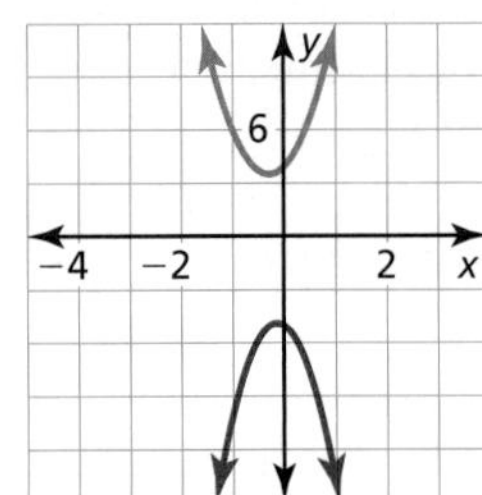

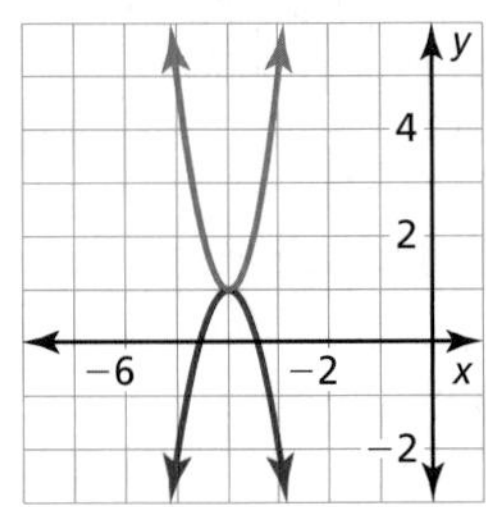

3. $y = x^2 + 8x + 15$
$y = \frac{1}{2}x^2 + 4x + 9$

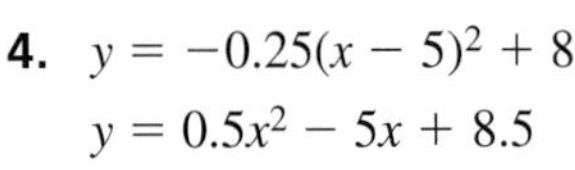

4. $y = -0.25(x - 5)^2 + 8$
$y = 0.5x^2 - 5x + 8.5$

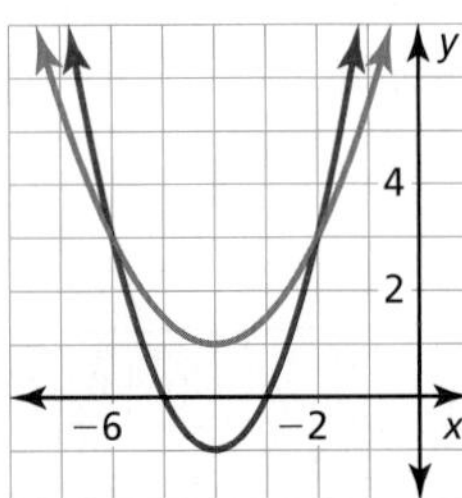

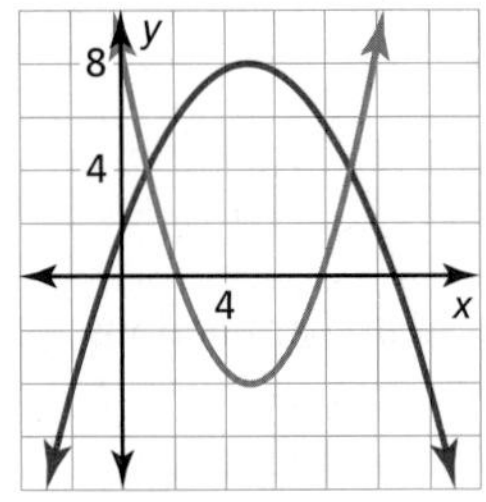

In Exercises 5–12, solve the system by graphing.
▶ *Example 1*

5. $y = x + 2$
$y = 0.5(x + 2)^2$

6. $y = (x - 3)^2 + 5$
$y = 5$

7. $y = \frac{1}{3}x + 2$
$y = -3x^2 - 5x - 4$

8. $y = -3x^2 - 30x - 71$
$y = -3x - 17$

9. $y = x^2 + 8x + 18$
$y = -2x^2 - 16x - 30$

10. $y = -2x^2 - 9$
$y = -x^2 - 1$

11. $y = (x - 2)^2$
$y = -x^2 + 4x - 2$

12. $y = \frac{1}{2}(x + 2)^2$
$y = -\frac{1}{2}x^2 + 2$

In Exercises 13–22, solve the system by substitution.
▶ *Examples 2 and 4*

13. $y = x + 5$
$y = x^2 - x + 2$

14. $x^2 + y^2 = 49$
$y = 7 - x$

15. $x^2 + y^2 = 20$
$y = 2x - 10$

16. $y = -2x - 5$
$-3x^2 + 4x - y = 8$

17. $2x^2 + 4x - y = -3$
$-2x + y = -4$

18. $2x - 3 = y + 5x^2$
$y = -3x - 3$

19. $y = x^2 - 1$
$-7 = -x^2 - y$

20. $y + 16x - 22 = 4x^2$
$4x^2 - 24x + 26 + y = 0$

21. $x^2 + y^2 = 7$
$x + 3y = 21$

22. $x^2 + y^2 = 5$
$-x + y = -1$

In Exercises 23–30, solve the system by elimination.
▶ *Example 3*

23. $2x^2 - 3x - y = -5$
$-x + y = 5$

24. $-3x^2 + 2x - 5 = y$
$-x + 2 = -y$

25. $-3x^2 + y = -18x + 29$
$-3x^2 - y = 18x - 25$

26. $y = -x^2 - 6x - 10$
$y = 3x^2 + 18x + 22$

27. $y + 2x = -14$
$-x^2 - y - 6x = 11$

28. $y = x^2 + 4x + 7$
$-y = 4x + 7$

29. $y = -3x^2 - 30x - 76$
$y = 2x^2 + 20x + 44$

30. $-10x^2 + y = -80x + 155$
$5x^2 + y = 40x - 85$

31. **ERROR ANALYSIS** Describe and correct the error in using elimination to solve for one of the variables in the system.

$y = 2x^2 - 26$
$\underline{-y = -x - 10}$
$0 = x^2 - 36$
$36 = x^2$
$\pm 6 = x$

32. **MP NUMBER SENSE** The table shows the inputs and outputs of two quadratic functions. Identify the solution(s) of the system. Explain your reasoning.

x	y_1	y_2
−3	29	−11
−1	9	9
1	−3	21
3	−7	25
7	9	9
11	57	−39

In Exercises 33–38, solve the system using any method. Explain your choice of method.

33. $y = x^2 - 1$
$-y = 2x^2 + 1$

34. $y = -4x^2 - 16x - 13$
$-3x^2 + y + 12x = 17$

35. $-2x + 10 + y = \frac{1}{3}x^2$
$y = 10$

36. $y = 0.5x^2 - 10$
$y = -x^2 + 14$

37. $y = -3(x - 4)^2 + 6$
$(x - 4)^2 + 2 - y = 0$

38. $-x^2 + y^2 = 100$
$y = -x + 14$

In Exercises 39–44, solve the equation by graphing.
Example 5

39. $x^2 + 2x = -\frac{1}{2}x^2 + 2x$

40. $2x^2 - 12x - 16 = -6x^2 + 60x - 144$

41. $(x + 2)(x - 2) = -x^2 + 6x - 7$

42. $-2x^2 - 16x - 25 = 6x^2 + 48x + 95$

43. $(x - 2)^2 - 3 = (x + 3)(-x + 9) - 38$

44. $(-x + 4)(x + 8) - 42 = (x + 3)(x + 1) - 1$

45. **COLLEGE PREP** Which ordered pairs are solutions of the nonlinear system?

$$y = \frac{1}{2}x^2 - 5x + \frac{21}{2}$$
$$y = -\frac{1}{2}x + \frac{13}{2}$$

Ⓐ (1, 6) Ⓑ (3, 0)
Ⓒ (8, 2.5) Ⓓ (7, 0)

46. **MP REASONING** A nonlinear system contains the equations of a constant function and a quadratic function. The system has one solution. Describe the relationship between the graphs.

47. **MODELING REAL LIFE** The range (in miles) of a broadcast signal from a radio tower is bounded by a circle given by the equation

$$x^2 + y^2 = 1620.$$

A straight highway can be modeled by the equation

$$y = -\frac{1}{3}x + 30.$$

For what length of the highway are cars able to receive the broadcast signal?

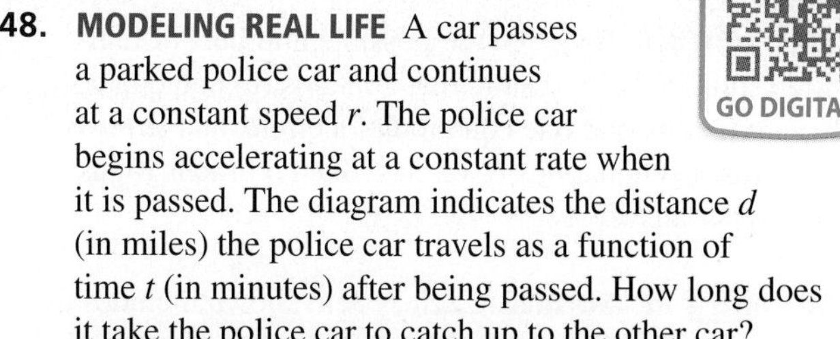

48. **MODELING REAL LIFE** A car passes a parked police car and continues at a constant speed r. The police car begins accelerating at a constant rate when it is passed. The diagram indicates the distance d (in miles) the police car travels as a function of time t (in minutes) after being passed. How long does it take the police car to catch up to the other car?

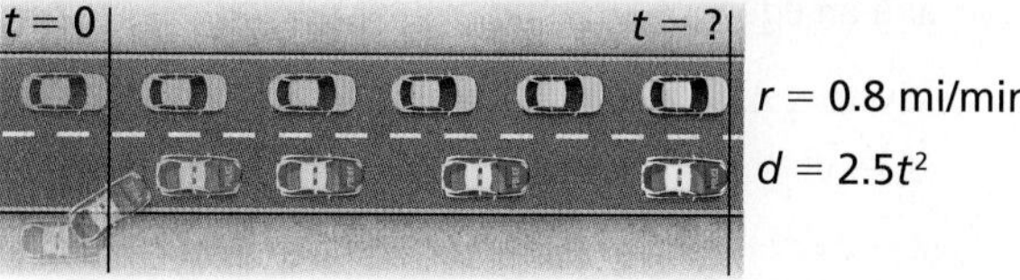

49. **COMPARING METHODS** Describe two different ways you can solve $-2x^2 + 12x - 17 = 2x^2 - 16x + 31$. Which way do you prefer? Explain your reasoning.

50. **OPEN-ENDED** Find a value for m so the system has (a) no real solution, (b) one real solution, and (c) two real solutions. Justify each answer using a graph.

$$3y = -x^2 + 8x - 7$$
$$y = mx + 3$$

51. **MAKING AN ARGUMENT** You and a friend solve the system shown and determine that $x = 3$ and $x = -3$. You use Equation 1 to obtain the solutions (3, 3), (3, −3), (−3, 3), and (−3, −3). Your friend uses Equation 2 to obtain the solutions (3, 3) and (−3, −3). Who is correct? Explain your reasoning.

$x^2 + y^2 = 18$ Equation 1
$x - y = 0$ Equation 2

52. **HOW DO YOU SEE IT?** The graph of a nonlinear system is shown. Estimate the solution(s). Then describe a transformation of the graph of the linear function that results in a system with no real solution.

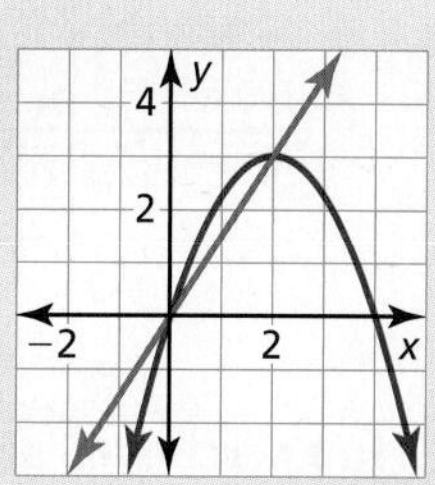

53. **ANALYZING RELATIONSHIPS** The graph of a line that passes through the origin intersects the graph of a circle with its center at the origin. When you know one of the points of intersection, explain how you can find the other point of intersection without performing any calculations.

54. **THOUGHT PROVOKING** Write a nonlinear system that has two different solutions with the same y-coordinate and does not include an equation of a constant function. Justify your answer by solving the system.

GO DIGITAL

55. **WRITING** Describe the possible numbers of real solutions of a system that contains (a) one quadratic equation and one equation of a circle, and (b) two distinct equations of circles. Sketch graphs to justify your answers.

56. **MP REASONING** Each system shown includes the equation of a circle with center (0, 0) and radius 1 and an equation of a line with a y-intercept of -1.

System A	System B	System C
$x^2 + y^2 = 1$	$x^2 + y^2 = 1$	$x^2 + y^2 = 1$
$y = 3x - 1$	$y = 4x - 1$	$y = 5x - 1$

a. Without solving, find one solution that all three systems have in common. Explain your reasoning.

b. Find the other solution of each system. What do you notice about the numerators and denominator of each solution?

57. **CRITICAL THINKING** Solve the system shown.

$$x^2 + y^2 = 4$$
$$2y = x^2 - 2x + 4$$
$$y = -x + 2$$

58. **DIG DEEPER** To be eligible for a parking pass on a college campus, a student must live at least 1 mile from the campus center. For what length of Oak Lane are students *not* eligible for a parking pass?

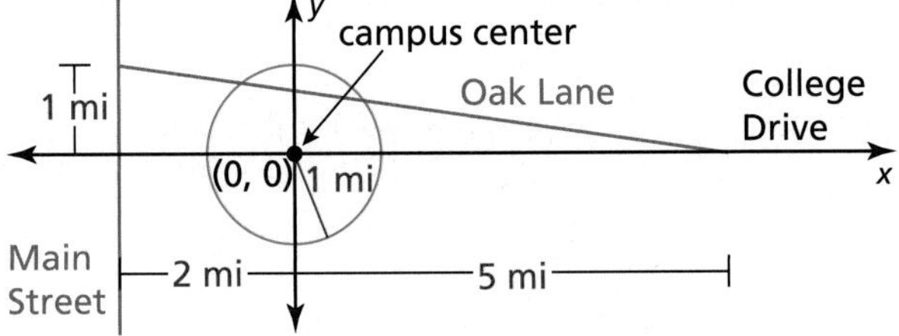

REVIEW & REFRESH

In Exercises 59–62, solve the inequality. Graph the solution.

59. $4x - 4 > 8$

60. $-x + 7 \leq 4 - 2x$

61. $-3(x - 4) \geq 24$

62. $3x - 2 < \frac{3}{2}(2x - 1)$

In Exercises 63 and 64, write an inequality that represents the graph.

63.

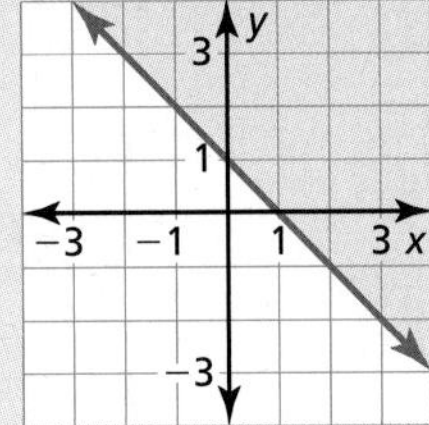

64.

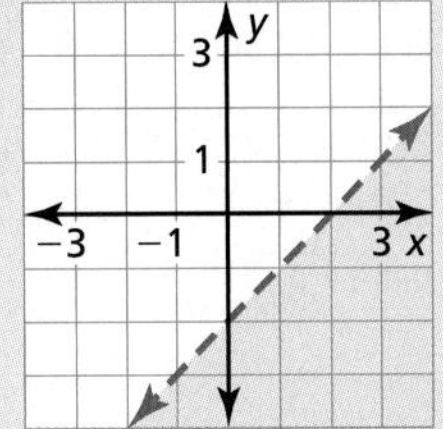

In Exercises 65 and 66, solve the system using any method. Explain your choice of method.

65. $2x^2 + 4x + y = -6$
$x^2 + 2x - y = 3$

66. $x^2 + y^2 = 25$
$y = x - 1$

67. Graph $y = \begin{cases} -\frac{1}{2}x + 6, & \text{if } x \leq 2 \\ 3x - 5, & \text{if } x > 2 \end{cases}$. Find the domain and range.

68. **MODELING REAL LIFE** You kick a soccer ball from an initial height of 2 feet. The ball has an initial vertical velocity of 45 feet per second. Does the ball reach a height of 35 feet? Explain your reasoning.

In Exercises 69 and 70, describe the transformation of $f(x) = x^2$ represented by g. Then graph each function.

69. $g(x) = (x - 5)^2 - 3$

70. $g(x) = \frac{1}{4}(x + 2)^2$

71. **MP NUMBER SENSE** For what values of b can you complete the square for $x^2 + bx$ by adding 81?

72. Use technology to find an equation of the line of best fit for the data. Identify and interpret the correlation coefficient.

x	0	5	10	12	16
y	18	15	9	7	2

In Exercises 73 and 74, find the square root of the number.

73. $\sqrt{-144}$

74. $\sqrt{-52}$

75. Approximate when the function is positive, negative, increasing, or decreasing.

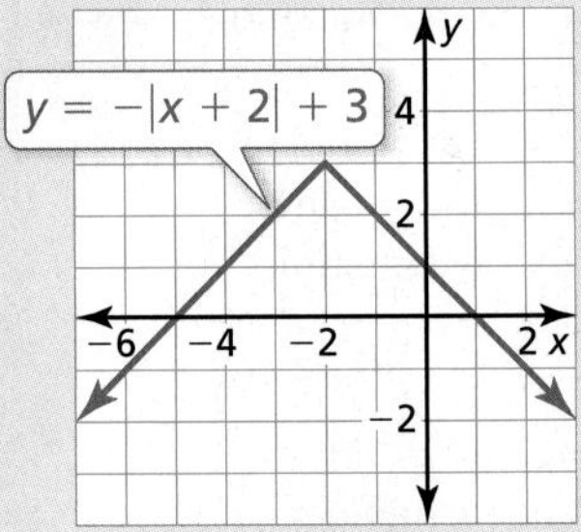

3.6 Quadratic Inequalities

Learning Target Graph quadratic inequalities in two variables and solve quadratic inequalities in one variable.

Success Criteria

- I can describe the graph of a quadratic inequality.
- I can graph quadratic inequalities.
- I can graph systems of quadratic inequalities.
- I can solve quadratic inequalities algebraically and graphically.

EXPLORE IT! Solving Quadratic Inequalities

Work with a partner. The figure shows the graph of $f(x) = x^2 + 2x - 3$.

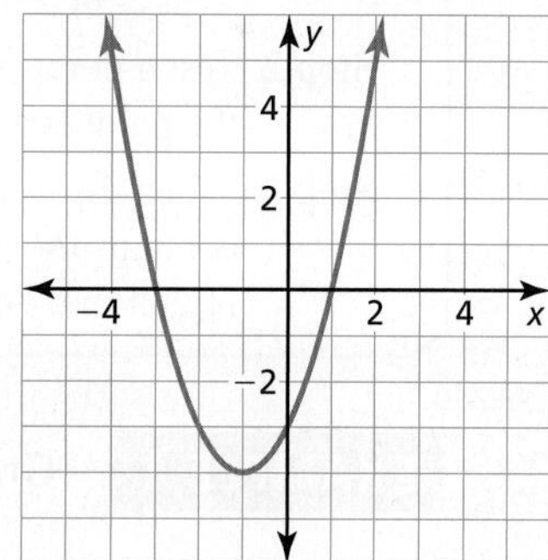

Math Practice

Consider Similar Problems

How is graphing a quadratic inequality in two variables similar to graphing a linear inequality in two variables?

a. Explain how you can use the graph to solve the inequality $0 > x^2 + 2x - 3$. Then graph the solutions of the inequality.

b. Explain how the inequality $y > x^2 + 2x - 3$ is different from the inequality in part (a).

c. Explain how you can use the graph above to represent the solutions of $y > x^2 + 2x - 3$. Then graph the inequality.

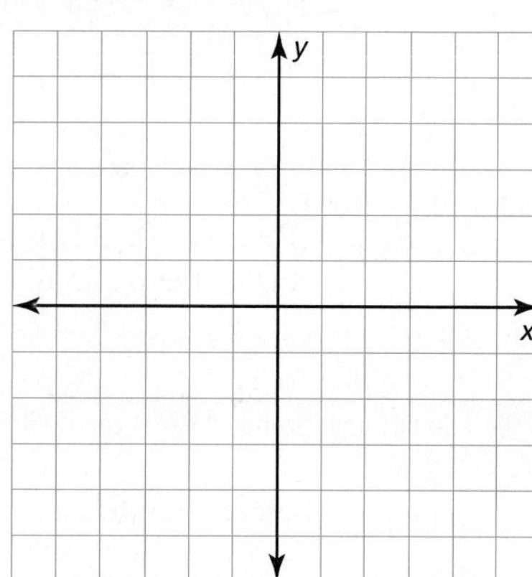

d. Repeat parts (a)–(c) by replacing > with ≤.

e. Compare the graphs of the solutions of quadratic inequalities in one variable to the graphs of the solutions of quadratic inequalities in two variables.

Graphing Quadratic Inequalities in Two Variables

Vocabulary

quadratic inequality in two variables, *p. 136*
system of quadratic inequalities, *p. 137*
quadratic inequality in one variable, *p. 138*

A **quadratic inequality in two variables**, x and y, can be written in one of the following forms, where a, b, and c are real numbers and $a \neq 0$.

$$y < ax^2 + bx + c \qquad y > ax^2 + bx + c$$

$$y \leq ax^2 + bx + c \qquad y \geq ax^2 + bx + c$$

The graph of any such inequality consists of all solutions (x, y) of the inequality.

Previously, you graphed linear inequalities in two variables. You can use a similar procedure to graph quadratic inequalities in two variables.

KEY IDEA

Graphing a Quadratic Inequality in Two Variables

Step 1 Graph the parabola with the equation $y = ax^2 + bx + c$. Make the parabola *dashed* for inequalities with $<$ or $>$ and *solid* for inequalities with $\leq$ or $\geq$.

Step 2 Test a point (x, y) that does not lie on the parabola to determine whether the point is a solution of the inequality.

Step 3 When the test point is a solution, shade the region of the plane that contains the point. When the test point is not a solution, shade the region that does not contain the point.

EXAMPLE 1 Graphing a Quadratic Inequality in Two Variables

Graph $y < -x^2 - 2x - 1$.

SOLUTION

Step 1 Graph $y = -x^2 - 2x - 1$. Because the inequality symbol is $<$, make the parabola dashed.

Step 2 Test a point that does not lie on the parabola, such as $(0, -3)$.

$y < -x^2 - 2x - 1$	Write the inequality.
$-3 \overset{?}{<} -0^2 - 2(0) - 1$	Substitute.
$-3 < -1$ ✓	Simplify.

Step 3 Because $(0, -3)$ is a solution, shade the region inside the parabola that contains $(0, -3)$.

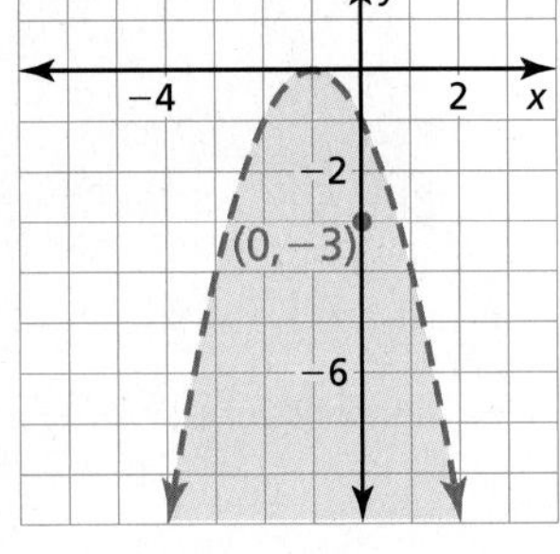

Math Practice

Look for Structure
Why is it convenient to choose a test point that is on the y-axis?

SELF-ASSESSMENT

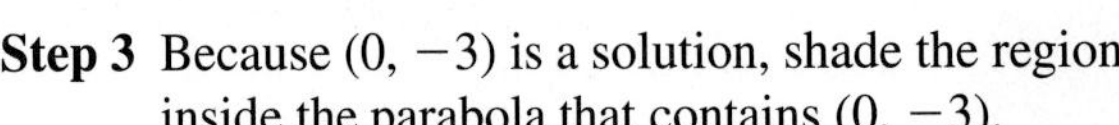

1. **WRITING** Explain how you can tell whether an ordered pair is a solution of a quadratic inequality.

Graph the inequality.

2. $y \geq x^2 + 2x - 8$
3. $y \leq 2x^2 - x - 1$
4. $y > -x^2 + 2x + 4$

5. **WRITING** When determining which region to shade in the graph of a quadratic inequality in two variables, why is it important to test a point that does not lie on the parabola?

EXAMPLE 2 Modeling Real Life

A manila rope used for rappelling down a cliff can safely support a weight W (in pounds) provided $W \leq 1480d^2$, where d is the diameter (in inches) of the rope. Graph the inequality and interpret the solution.

SOLUTION

Graph $W = 1480d^2$ for nonnegative values of d. Because the inequality symbol is $\leq$, make the parabola solid. Test a point that does not lie on the parabola, such as (1, 3000).

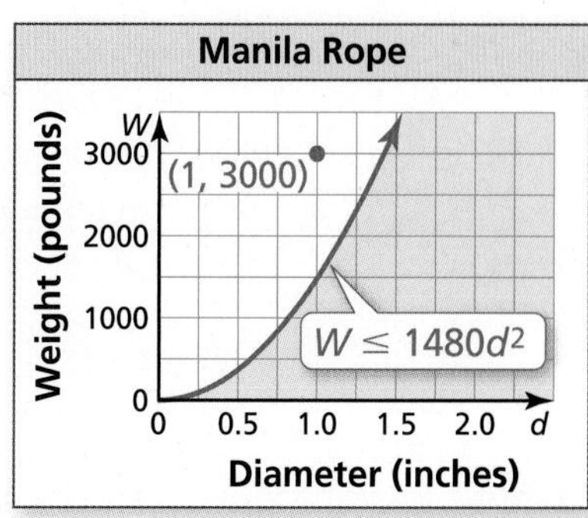

$$W \leq 1480d^2$$

$$3000 \overset{?}{\leq} 1480(1)^2$$

$$3000 \leq 1480$$

▶ Because (1, 3000) is not a solution, shade the region outside the parabola. The shaded region represents weights that can be supported by ropes with various diameters.

A **system of quadratic inequalities** is a set of two or more quadratic inequalities in the same variables. Graphing a system of quadratic inequalities is similar to graphing a system of linear inequalities. First graph each inequality in the same coordinate plane. Then identify the region in the coordinate plane common to all of the graphs. This region is called the *graph of the system.*

EXAMPLE 3 Graphing a System of Quadratic Inequalities

Graph the system of quadratic inequalities.

$y < -x^2 + 3$ Inequality 1

$y \geq x^2 + 2x - 3$ Inequality 2

SOLUTION

Step 1 Graph $y < -x^2 + 3$. The graph is the red region inside (but not including) the parabola $y = -x^2 + 3$.

Step 2 Graph $y \geq x^2 + 2x - 3$. The graph is the blue region inside and including the parabola $y = x^2 + 2x - 3$.

Step 3 Identify the purple region where the two graphs overlap. This region is the graph of the system.

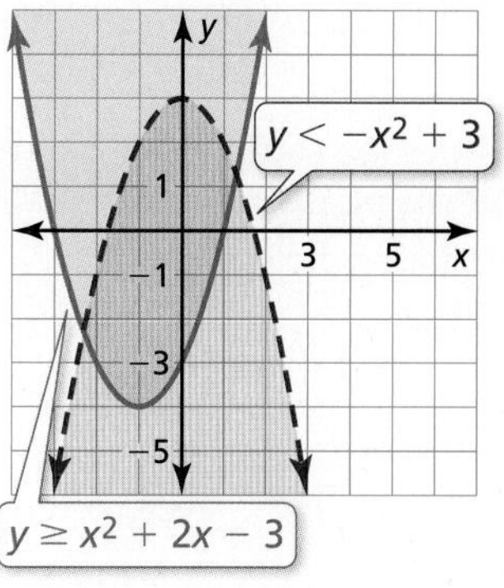

Check

Check that a point in the solution region, such as (0, 0), is a solution of the system.

$$y < -x^2 + 3$$

$$0 \overset{?}{<} -0^2 + 3$$

$$0 < 3 \checkmark$$

$$y \geq x^2 + 2x - 3$$

$$0 \overset{?}{\geq} 0^2 + 2(0) - 3$$

$$0 \geq -3 \checkmark$$

SELF-ASSESSMENT

1 I do not understand. 2 I can do it with help. 3 I can do it on my own. 4 I can teach someone else.

6. **MP REASONING** Can you use the graph in Example 2 to determine if a manila rope with a $\frac{3}{8}$-inch diameter can safely support a 200-pound person? Explain your reasoning. If not, show how you can solve the problem.

Graph the system of quadratic inequalities.

7. $y \leq -x^2$
   $y > x^2 - 3$

8. $y \geq x^2 + 2x - 1$
   $y \geq 2x^2 + 4x - 1$

9. $y > x^2 + 1$
   $y < -x^2 + x - 1$

Solving Quadratic Inequalities in One Variable

GO DIGITAL

A **quadratic inequality in one variable**, x, can be written in one of the following forms, where a, b, and c are real numbers and $a \neq 0$.

$ax^2 + bx + c < 0$ $\quad ax^2 + bx + c > 0$ $\quad ax^2 + bx + c \leq 0$ $\quad ax^2 + bx + c \geq 0$

You can solve quadratic inequalities using algebraic methods or graphs.

EXAMPLE 4 Solving a Quadratic Inequality Algebraically

Solve $x^2 - 3x - 4 < 0$ algebraically.

SOLUTION

First, write and solve the equation obtained by replacing $<$ with $=$.

$x^2 - 3x - 4 = 0$	Write the related equation.
$(x - 4)(x + 1) = 0$	Factor.
$x = 4$ or $x = -1$	Zero-Product Property

The numbers -1 and 4 are the *critical values* of the original inequality. Plot -1 and 4 on a number line, using open dots because the values do not satisfy the inequality. The critical values partition the number line into three intervals. Test an x-value in each interval to determine whether it satisfies the inequality.

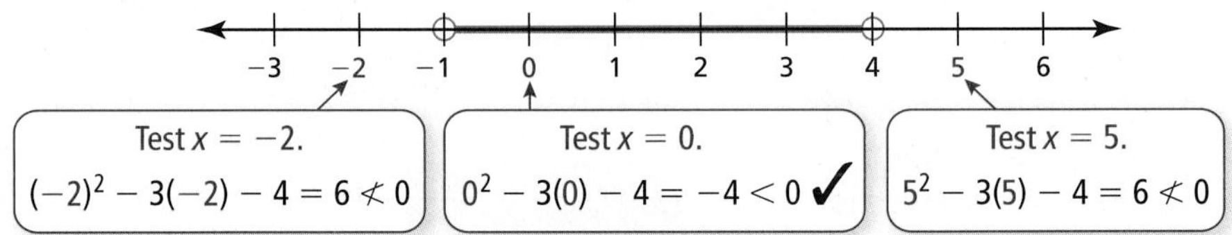

▶ So, the solution is $-1 < x < 4$.

Another way to solve $ax^2 + bx + c < 0$ is to first graph the related function $y = ax^2 + bx + c$. Then, because the inequality symbol is $<$, identify the x-values for which the graph lies *below* the x-axis. You can use a similar procedure to solve quadratic inequalities that involve $\leq$, $>$, or $\geq$.

EXAMPLE 5 Solving a Quadratic Inequality by Graphing

Solve $3x^2 - x - 5 \geq 0$ by graphing.

SOLUTION

The solution consists of the x-values for which the graph of $y = 3x^2 - x - 5$ lies on or above the x-axis. Find the x-intercepts of the graph by letting $y = 0$ and using the Quadratic Formula to solve $0 = 3x^2 - x - 5$ for x.

$$x = \frac{-(-1) \pm \sqrt{(-1)^2 - 4(3)(-5)}}{2(3)} \qquad a = 3, b = -1, c = -5$$

$$x = \frac{1 \pm \sqrt{61}}{6} \qquad \text{Simplify.}$$

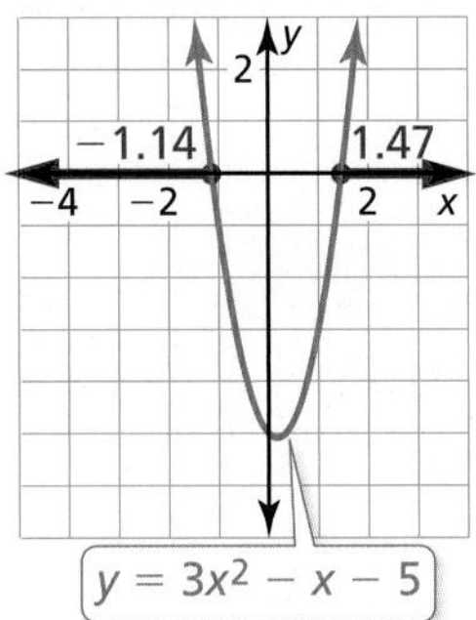

The solutions are $x \approx -1.14$ and $x \approx 1.47$. Sketch a parabola that opens up and has -1.14 and 1.47 as x-intercepts. The graph lies on or above the x-axis to the left of (and including) $x = -1.14$ and to the right of (and including) $x = 1.47$.

▶ The solution of the inequality is approximately $x \leq -1.14$ *or* $x \geq 1.47$.

EXAMPLE 6 Modeling Real Life

An archaeologist is roping off a rectangular region of land to dig for artifacts. The region must have a perimeter of 440 feet and an area of at least 8000 square feet. Describe the possible lengths of the archaeological region.

SOLUTION

1. **Understand the Problem** You are given the perimeter and the minimum area of a rectangular region. You are asked to determine the possible lengths of the region.
2. **Make a Plan** Use the perimeter and area formulas to write a quadratic inequality describing the possible lengths of the region. Then solve the inequality.
3. **Solve and Check** Let ℓ represent the length (in feet) and let w represent the width (in feet) of the region.

Perimeter $= 440$	Area ≥ 8000
$2\ell + 2w = 440$	$\ell w \geq 8000$

Solve the perimeter equation for w to obtain $w = 220 - \ell$. Substitute this into the area inequality to obtain a quadratic inequality in one variable.

$\ell w \geq 8000$	Write the area inequality.
$\ell(220 - \ell) \geq 8000$	Substitute $220 - \ell$ for w.
$220\ell - \ell^2 \geq 8000$	Distributive Property
$-\ell^2 + 220\ell - 8000 \geq 0$	Write in standard form.

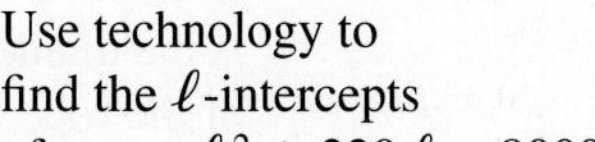

ANOTHER WAY

You can graph each side of $220\ell - \ell^2 = 8000$ and use the intersection points to determine when $220\ell - \ell^2$ is greater than or equal to 8000.

Use technology to find the ℓ-intercepts of $y = -\ell^2 + 220\ell - 8000$.

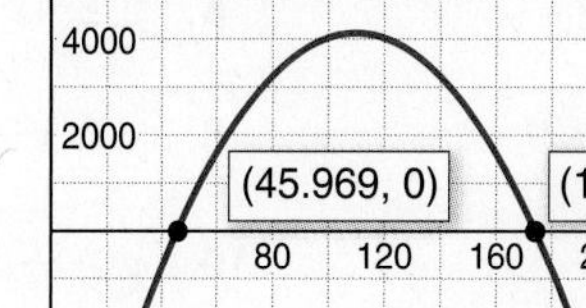

The ℓ-intercepts are $\ell \approx 45.969$ and $\ell \approx 174.031$. The solution consists of the ℓ-values for which the graph lies on or above the ℓ-axis. The graph lies on or above the ℓ-axis when $45.969 \leq \ell \leq 174.031$.

▶ So, the approximate lengths of the region are at least 46 feet and at most 174 feet.

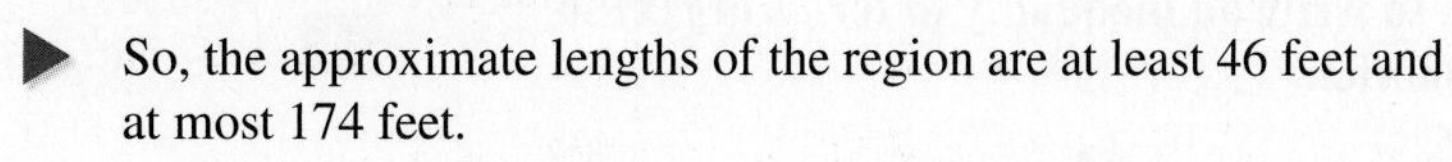

Check Choose a length in the solution region, such as $\ell = 100$, and find the width. Then check that the dimensions satisfy the original area inequality.

$2\ell + 2w = 440$	$\ell w \geq 8000$
$2(100) + 2w = 440$	$100(120) \overset{?}{\geq} 8000$
$w = 120$	$12{,}000 \geq 8000$ ✓

SELF-ASSESSMENT 1 I do not understand. 2 I can do it with help. 3 I can do it on my own. 4 I can teach someone else.

Solve the inequality using any method. Explain your choice of method.

10. $2x^2 + 3x \leq 2$ **11.** $-3x^2 - 4x + 1 < 0$ **12.** $4x^2 + 3 > -13x$ **13.** $x^2 + 6x - 8 < 0$

14. WHAT IF? In Example 6, the area must be at least 8500 square feet. Describe the possible lengths of the region.

3.6 Practice WITH CalcChat® AND CalcView®

In Exercises 1–4, match the inequality with its graph. Explain your reasoning.

1. $y \le x^2 + 4x + 3$
2. $y > -x^2 + 4x - 3$
3. $y < x^2 - 4x + 3$
4. $y \ge x^2 + 4x + 3$

A. 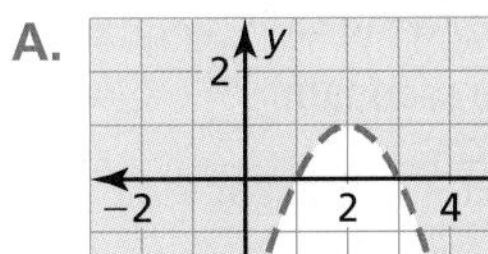

B. 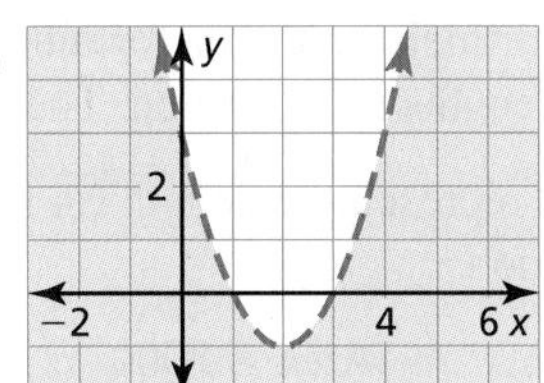

C. 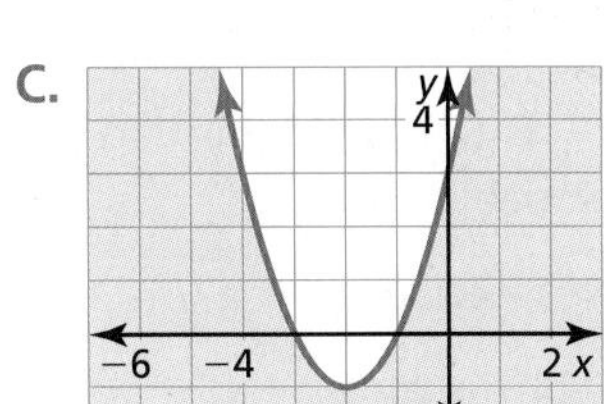

D. 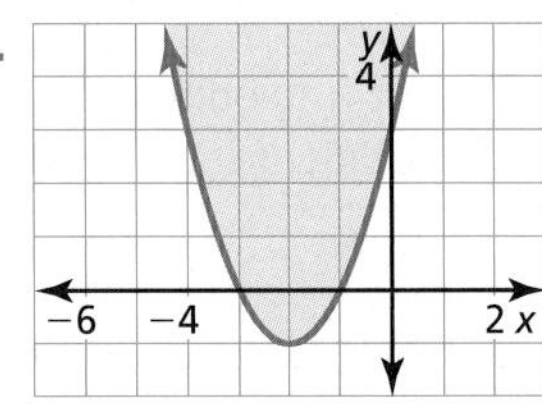

In Exercises 5–12, graph the inequality. *Example 1*

5. $y < -x^2$
6. $y \ge 4x^2$
7. $y > x^2 - 9$
8. $y < x^2 + 5$
9. $y \le x^2 + 5x$
10. $y \ge -2x^2 + 9x - 4$
11. $y > 2(x + 3)^2 - 1$
12. $y \le \left(x - \frac{1}{2}\right)^2 + \frac{5}{2}$

ANALYZING RELATIONSHIPS **In Exercises 13 and 14, use the graph to write an inequality in terms of $f(x)$ so point P is a solution.**

13. 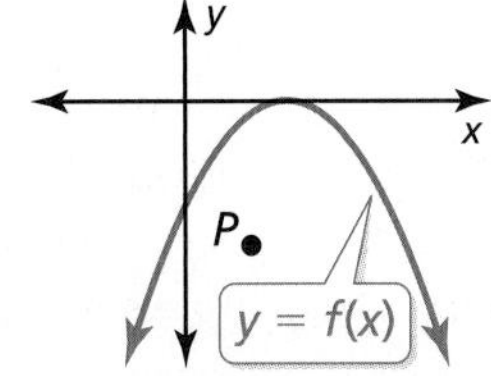

14. 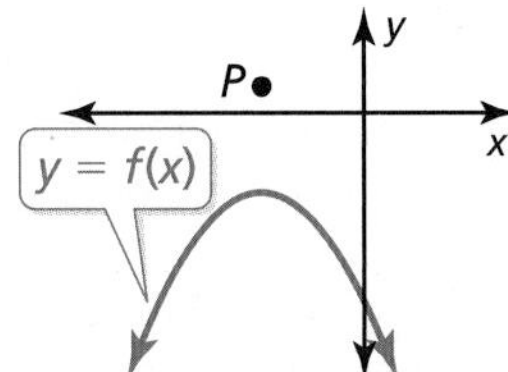

ERROR ANALYSIS **In Exercises 15 and 16, describe and correct the error in graphing $y \ge x^2 + 2$.**

15. 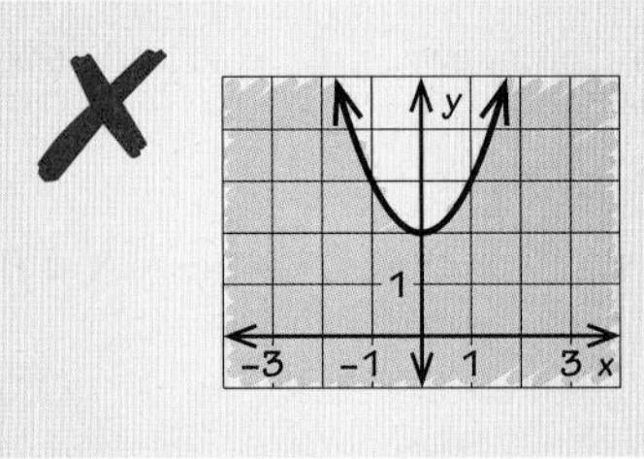

16. 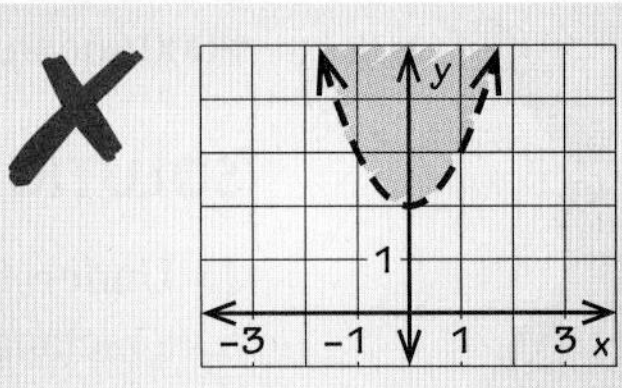

17. **MODELING REAL LIFE** A hardwood shelf in a wooden bookcase can safely support a weight W (in pounds) provided $W \le 115x^2$, where x is the thickness (in inches) of the shelf. Graph the inequality and interpret the solution. *Example 2*

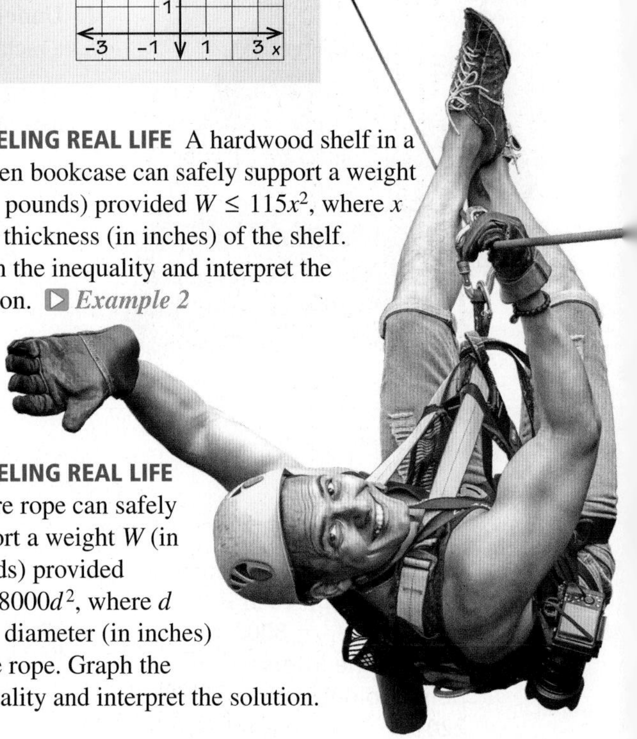

18. **MODELING REAL LIFE** A wire rope can safely support a weight W (in pounds) provided $W \le 8000d^2$, where d is the diameter (in inches) of the rope. Graph the inequality and interpret the solution.

In Exercises 19–26, graph the system of quadratic inequalities. *Example 3*

19. $y \ge 2x^2$
    $y < -x^2 + 1$
20. $y > -5x^2$
    $y > 3x^2 - 2$
21. $y \le -x^2 + 4x - 4$
    $y < x^2 + 2x - 8$
22. $y \ge x^2 - 4$
    $y \le -2x^2 + 7x + 4$
23. $y \ge 2x^2 + x - 5$
    $y < -x^2 + 5x + 10$
24. $y \ge x^2 - 3x - 6$
    $y \ge x^2 + 7x + 6$
25. $x^2 + y < 3x + 2$
    $y < -x^2 + 5x + 10$
26. $3x^2 + y \le -x - 3$
    $\frac{1}{2}x^2 + 2x \ge y - 2$

In Exercises 27–34, solve the inequality algebraically. *Example 4*

27. $4x^2 < 25$
28. $x^2 + 10x + 9 < 0$
29. $x^2 - 11x \ge -28$
30. $3x^2 - 13x > -10$
31. $2x^2 - 5x - 3 \le 0$
32. $4x^2 + 8x - 21 \ge 0$
33. $\frac{1}{2}x^2 - x > 4$
34. $-\frac{1}{2}x^2 + 4x \le 1$

In Exercises 35–42, solve the inequality by graphing.
Example 5

35. $x^2 - 3x + 1 < 0$ **36.** $x^2 - 4x + 2 > 0$

37. $x^2 + 8x > -7$ **38.** $x^2 + 6x < -3$

39. $3x^2 - 8 \leq -2x$ **40.** $3x^2 + 5x - 3 < 1$

41. $\frac{1}{3}x^2 + 2x \geq 2$ **42.** $\frac{3}{4}x^2 + 4x \geq 3$

43. **MODELING REAL LIFE** A rectangular fountain display has a perimeter of 400 feet and an area of at least 9100 square feet. Describe the possible widths of the fountain. *Example 6*

44. **MODELING REAL LIFE** An animal shelter director is planning to build a rectangular playpen. The playpen must have a perimeter of 150 feet and an area of at least 1000 square feet. Describe the possible lengths of the playpen.

45. **MP STRUCTURE** Consider the graph of the function $f(x) = ax^2 + bx + c$.

a. What are the solutions of $ax^2 + bx + c < 0$?

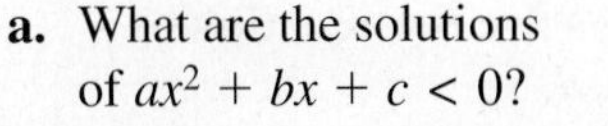

b. What are the solutions of $ax^2 + bx + c > 0$?

c. The graph of g represents a reflection in the x-axis of the graph of f. For which values of x is $g(x)$ positive?

46. **MODELING REAL LIFE** The arch of the Sydney Harbor Bridge in Sydney, Australia, can be modeled by $y = -0.00211x^2 + 1.06x$, where x is the distance (in meters) from the left pylons and y is the height (in meters) of the arch above the water. See photo at the bottom of the page. For what distances x is the arch above the road?

47. **MP PROBLEM SOLVING** The number of teams that have participated in an engineering competition for high-school students over a recent period of time x (in years) can be modeled by $T(x) = 17.155x^2 + 193.68x + 235.81, 0 \leq x \leq 6$. After how many years is the number of teams greater than 1000? Justify your answer.

GO DIGITAL

48. **MP PROBLEM SOLVING** A study found that a driver's reaction time $A(x)$ to audio stimuli and his or her reaction time $V(x)$ to visual stimuli (both in milliseconds) can be modeled by

$$A(x) = 0.0051x^2 - 0.319x + 15, 16 \leq x \leq 70$$

$$V(x) = 0.005x^2 - 0.23x + 22, 16 \leq x \leq 70$$

where x is the age (in years) of the driver.

a. Use technology to solve the inequality $A(x) < V(x)$. Explain how to use the domain to determine a reasonable solution.

b. Based on your result from part (a), do you think a driver reacts more quickly to a traffic light changing from green to yellow or to the siren of an approaching ambulance? Explain.

49. **MODELING REAL LIFE** The length (in millimeters) of the larvae of a black porgy fish can be modeled by

$$L(x) = 0.0058x^2 + 0.201x + 2.59, 0 \leq x \leq 44$$

where x is the age (in days) of the larvae. At what ages is a larva's length typically greater than 10 millimeters? Explain how the given domain affects the solution.

50. **HOW DO YOU SEE IT?**
The graph shows a system of quadratic inequalities.

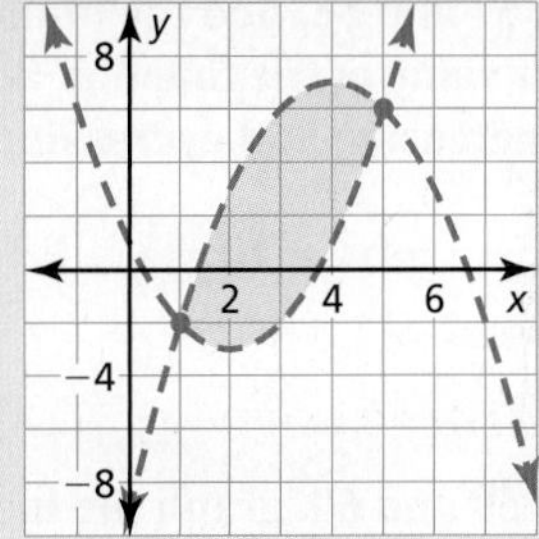

a. Identify two solutions of the system.

b. Are the points $(1, -2)$ and $(5, 6)$ solutions of the system? Explain.

c. Is it possible to change the inequality symbol(s) so that one, but not both, of the points in part (b) is a solution of the system? Explain.

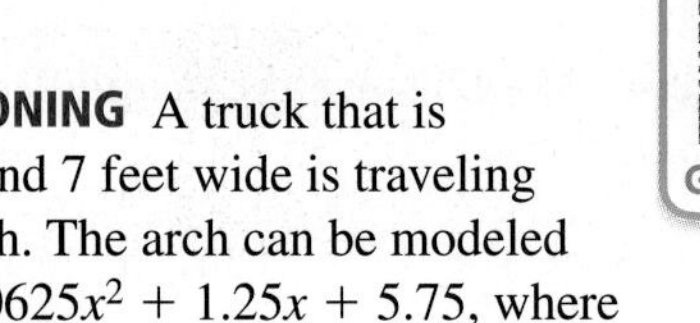

51. **CONNECTING CONCEPTS** The area A of the region bounded by a parabola and a horizontal line can be modeled by $A = \frac{2}{3}bh$, where b and h are as defined in the diagram. Find the area of the region determined by each pair of inequalities.

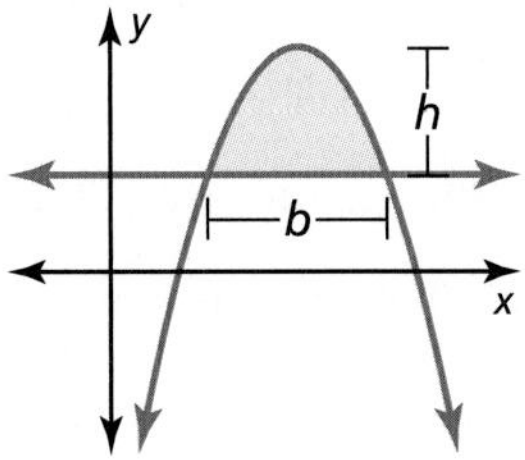

a. $y \leq -x^2 + 4x$
$y \geq 0$

b. $y \geq x^2 - 4x - 5$
$y \leq 7$

52. **OPEN-ENDED** Design a company logo that is created by the intersection of two quadratic inequalities. Justify your answer.

53. **MP REASONING** A truck that is 11 feet tall and 7 feet wide is traveling under an arch. The arch can be modeled by $y = -0.0625x^2 + 1.25x + 5.75$, where x and y are measured in feet.

a. Will the truck fit under the arch? Explain.

b. What is the maximum width that a truck 11 feet tall can have and still make it under the arch?

c. What is the maximum height that a truck 7 feet wide can have and still make it under the arch?

54. **THOUGHT PROVOKING**
Consider the system of inequalities below, where a, b, c, and d are real numbers, $a < b$, and $c < d$. Write the solutions of the system, if any, as an inequality.

$y \leq -ax^2 + c$
$y < -bx^2 + d$

REVIEW & REFRESH

WATCH

In Exercises 55 and 56, graph the function. Label the x-intercept(s) and the y-intercept.

55. $f(x) = (x + 7)(x - 9)$ 56. $h(x) = -x^2 + 5x - 6$

In Exercises 57 and 58, find the minimum value or maximum value of the function and when the function is increasing and decreasing.

57. $f(x) = -x^2 - 6x - 10$

58. $h(x) = \frac{1}{2}(x + 2)^2 - 1$

In Exercises 59 and 60, graph the inequality.

59. $y \geq \frac{1}{2}x^2 + 3$ 60. $y < -x^2 + 4x - 5$

61. Solve the system of nonlinear equations using the graph.

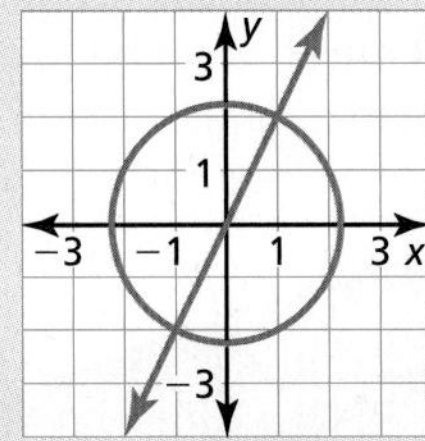

In Exercises 62 and 63, find the discriminant of the quadratic equation and describe the number and type of solutions of the equation.

62. $2x^2 - x + 7 = 0$ 63. $16x = -x^2 - 10$

In Exercises 64 and 65, solve the equation by completing the square.

64. $x^2 + 12x + 4 = 0$ 65. $4x(x + 6) = -40$

66. Write an equation for the nth term of the geometric sequence. Then find a_8.

n	1	2	3	4
a_n	6	18	54	162

67. **MODELING REAL LIFE** The linear function $y = 50 + 30x$ represents the cost y (in dollars) of renting a picnic pavilion for x hours. The pavilion can be rented for at most 24 hours.

a. Interpret the terms and coefficient in the equation.

b. Find the domain of the function. Is the domain discrete or continuous? Explain.

c. Graph the function using its domain.

In Exercises 68 and 69, solve the system.

68. $3x - y + 2z = 16$
$-2x + 4y + 3z = -2$
$6x + y - z = 0$

69. $2x + 3y + z = 7$
$-x - 5y + 4z = -6$
$6x + 9y + 3z = 14$

70. Write an equation of the line that passes through $(2, -2)$ and is perpendicular to $y = \frac{1}{3}x - 6$.

3 Chapter Review WITH CalcChat®

Chapter Learning Target Understand quadratic equations and complex numbers.

Chapter Success Criteria

- ◆ I can perform operations with complex numbers.
- ◆ I can solve quadratic equations by completing the square.
- ■ I can describe how to use the Quadratic Formula.
- ■ I can solve nonlinear systems and quadratic inequalities.

◆ Surface
■ Deep

SELF-ASSESSMENT 1 I do not understand. 2 I can do it with help. 3 I can do it on my own. 4 I can teach someone else.

3.1 Solving Quadratic Equations *(pp. 89–98)*

Learning Target: Solve quadratic equations graphically and algebraically.

Vocabulary (VOCAB)
quadratic equation in one variable
root of an equation
zero of a function

Solve the equation using any method. Explain your choice of method.

1. $6x^2 = 150$
2. $3x^2 - 4 = 8$
3. $x^2 + 6x - 16 = 0$
4. $2x^2 - 17x = -30$
5. A Rube Goldberg machine drops a ball from a 3-foot-tall table. Write a function that represents the height h (in feet) of the ball t seconds after it is dropped. How long is the ball in the air?
6. For each case, determine whether it is possible for $ax^2 + bx + c = 0$ to have no solutions. Explain your reasoning.
   a. $a > 0, c > 0$ **b.** $a > 0, c < 0$
   c. $a < 0, c > 0$ **d.** $a < 0, c < 0$
7. A rectangular enclosure at a zoo is 35 feet long by 18 feet wide. The zoo doubles the area of the enclosure by adding the same distance to the length and width. What are the new dimensions of the enclosure?

3.2 Complex Numbers *(pp. 99–108)*

Learning Target: Understand the imaginary unit i and perform operations with complex numbers.

Vocabulary (VOCAB)
imaginary unit i
complex number
imaginary number
pure imaginary number
complex conjugates

8. Find the values of x and y that satisfy the equation $36 - yi = 4x + 3i$.a

Perform the operation. Write the answer in standard form.

9. $(-2 + 3i) + (7 - 6i)$
10. $(9 + 3i) - (-2 - 7i)$
11. $(5 + 6i)(-4 + 7i)$
12. $(8 + 2i)(8 - 2i)$
13. Find the impedance of the series circuit.

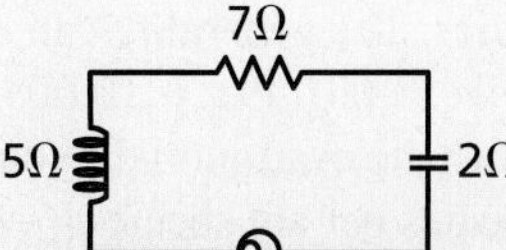

14. Solve $7x^2 + 21 = 0$.
15. Find the zeros of $f(x) = 2x^2 + 32$.

3.3 Completing the Square (pp. 109–116)

Learning Target: Solve quadratic equations and rewrite quadratic functions by completing the square.

Vocabulary
completing the square

Solve the equation using square roots or by completing the square. Explain your choice of method.

16. $x^2 + 6x + 9 = 49$

17. $x^2 + 16x + 17 = 0$

18. $4x^2 + 16x + 25 = 0$

19. $9x(x - 6) = 81$

20. Write $y = x^2 - 2x + 20$ in vertex form. Then identify the vertex.

21. The path of a T-shirt launched from a T-shirt cannon is modeled by the function shown, where x is the horizontal distance (in feet) and y is the vertical distance (in feet). Find the maximum height of the T-shirt.

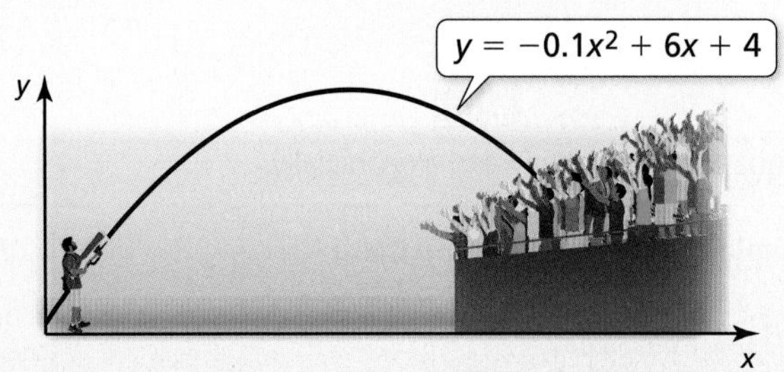

22. You plant a rectangular garden with an area of 80 square feet. You use 40 feet of fencing to enclose three sides of the garden. The fourth side is formed by the side of a shed. Find all possible dimensions of the garden.

3.4 Using the Quadratic Formula (pp. 117–126)

Learning Target: Solve and analyze quadratic equations using the Quadratic Formula and discriminants.

Vocabulary
Quadratic Formula
discriminant

Solve the equation using the Quadratic Formula.

23. $-x^2 + 5x = 2$

24. $2x^2 + 5x = 3$

25. $-x^2 + 3x = 2.25$

26. $3x^2 - 12x + 13 = 0$

Find the discriminant of the quadratic equation and describe the number and type of solutions of the equation.

27. $-x^2 - 6x - 9 = 0$

28. $x^2 - 2x - 9 = 0$

29. $x^2 + 6x + 5 = 0$

30. Find a pair of integer values for a and c so that the equation $ax^2 + 12x = -c$ has exactly one real solution. Then write the equation.

31. Write a quadratic equation that has solutions $\dfrac{3 \pm \sqrt{-131}}{10}$.

32. A researcher studies the *generality* of plant and ant species on Mount Wilhelm in Papua New Guinea. Generality is the number of plant species per ant species. The generality can be modeled by the function $g(x) = 0.000004x^2 - 0.0119x + 10.605$, where x is the elevation (in meters). At what elevation(s) do you expect to find a generality of 3 plant species per ant species?

3.5 Solving Nonlinear Systems of Equations (pp. 127–134)

Learning Target: Solve nonlinear systems graphically and algebraically.

Vocabulary

system of nonlinear equations

Solve the system by any method. Explain your choice of method.

33. $2x^2 - 2 = y$
$-2x + 2 = y$

34. $x^2 - 6x + 13 = y$
$-y = -2x + 3$

35. $x^2 + y^2 = 4$
$-15x + 5 = 5y$

36. Solve $-3x^2 + 5x - 1 = 5x^2 - 8x - 3$ by graphing.

37. The graph of quadratic function f has a vertex at (2, 5) and a y-intercept of 1. The graph of linear function g has a slope of $-\frac{1}{2}$ and passes through the point $(8, -3)$. Solve $f(x) = g(x)$.

3.6 Quadratic Inequalities (pp. 135–142)

Learning Target: Graph quadratic inequalities in two variables and solve quadratic inequalities in one variable.

Vocabulary

quadratic inequality in two variables
system of quadratic inequalities
quadratic inequality in one variable

Graph the inequality.

38. $y > x^2 + 8x + 16$

39. $y \geq x^2 + 6x + 8$

40. $x^2 + y \leq 7x - 12$

Graph the system of quadratic inequalities.

41. $x^2 - 4x + 8 > y$
$-x^2 + 4x + 2 \leq y$

42. $2x^2 - x \leq y + 5$
$0.5x^2 > y - 2x - 1$

Solve the inequality.

43. $3x^2 + 3x - 60 \geq 0$

44. $-x^2 - 10x < 21$

45. $3x^2 + 2 \leq 5x$

46. For each point, complete the inequality with $<$, $\leq$, $\geq$, or $>$ so that the point is a solution of the inequality. Justify your answers.

$$4x^2 - 3x \;\square\; y + 6$$

a. $(-1, -1)$ **b.** $(1, -4)$ **c.** $(2, 4)$

Mathematical Practices

Make Sense of Problems and Persevere in Solving Them

Mathematically proficient students plan a solution pathway rather than simply jumping into a solution attempt.

1. In Exercise 64 on page 96, why is it necessary to understand the problem and make a plan before solving? How does stating the given information and describing how it is related help you make a plan to solve the problem?

2. Make a plan that you can use to find the possible widths of the fountain in Exercise 43 on page 141.

3 Practice Test WITH CalcChat®

Solve the equation using any method. Explain your choice of method.

1. $x^2 + 49 = 85$
2. $0 = x^2 + 2x + 3$
3. $6x = x^2 + 7$
4. $(x + 4)(x - 1) = -x^2 + 3x + 4$

Explain how to use the graph to find the number and type of solutions of the quadratic equation. Justify your answer by using the discriminant.

5. $\frac{1}{2}x^2 + 3x + \frac{9}{2} = 0$

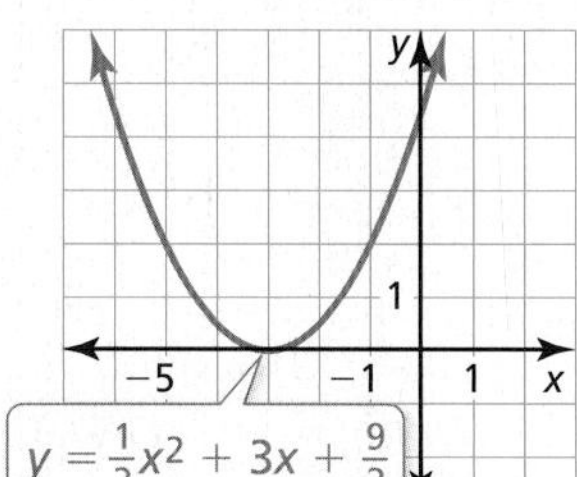

6. $4x^2 + 16x + 18 = 0$

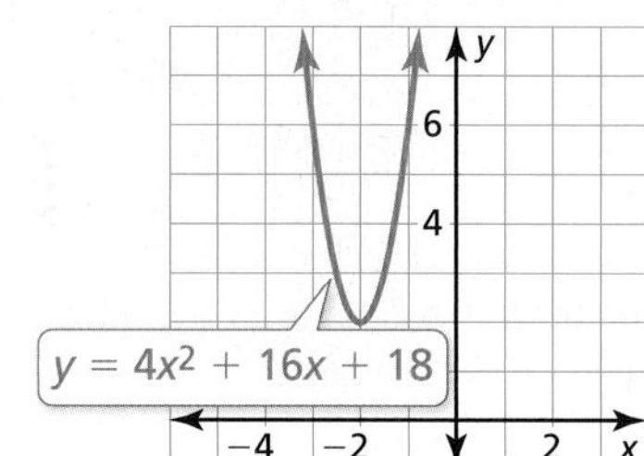

7. $-x^2 + \frac{1}{2}x + \frac{3}{2} = 0$

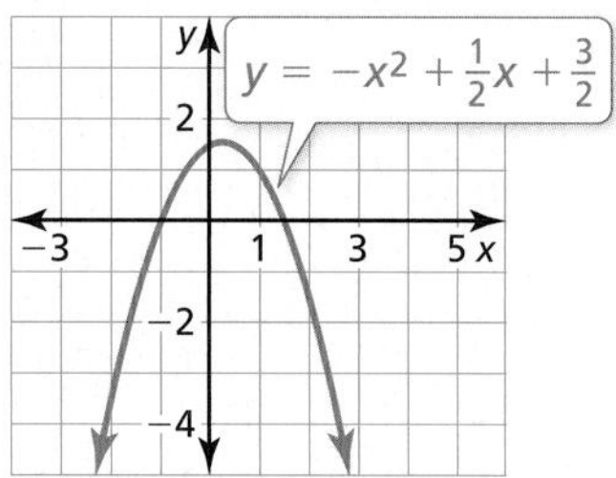

Solve the system of equations.

8. $x^2 + 66 = 16x - y$
   $2x - y = 18$
9. $0 = x^2 + y^2 - 40$
   $y = x + 4$

Graph the system of inequalities.

10. $y \leq x^2 - 5x + 4$
    $y < -(x - 3)(x + 1)$
11. $y \geq \frac{1}{4}x^2 - 2$
    $y < -(x + 3)^2 + 4$

12. Write $(3 + 4i)(4 - 6i)$ as a complex number in standard form.

13. You play a game of horseshoes. One of your tosses is modeled in the diagram, where x is the horseshoe's horizontal position (in feet) and y is the corresponding height (in feet). Find the maximum height of the horseshoe. Then find the horizontal distance the horseshoe travels. Justify your answer.

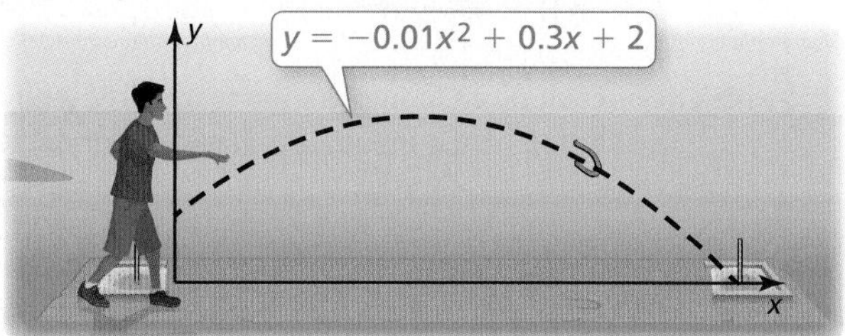

14. The shape of the Gateway Arch in St. Louis, Missouri, can be modeled by $y = -0.0063x^2 + 4x$, where x is the distance (in feet) from the left foot of the arch and y is the height (in feet) of the arch above the ground. For what distances x is the arch more than 200 feet above the ground? Justify your answer.

15. The *aspect ratio* of a TV is the ratio of the screen's width to its height. What are the width and the height of a 32-inch TV with an aspect ratio of 16 : 9? Justify your answer. (*Hint:* TV sizes refer to the diagonal length of the screen.)

3 Performance Task
Radioactive!

When a uranium atom absorbs an extra neutron inside the reactor, the atom becomes unstable and splits in a process called *nuclear fission*. Nuclear fission releases energy in the form of radiation and heat, which is used to produce steam. The steam turns large turbines that drive generators to make electricity. Some of the steam is turned back into liquid water in a cooling tower and recycled back into the system.

Electricity Generation in a Nuclear Power Plant

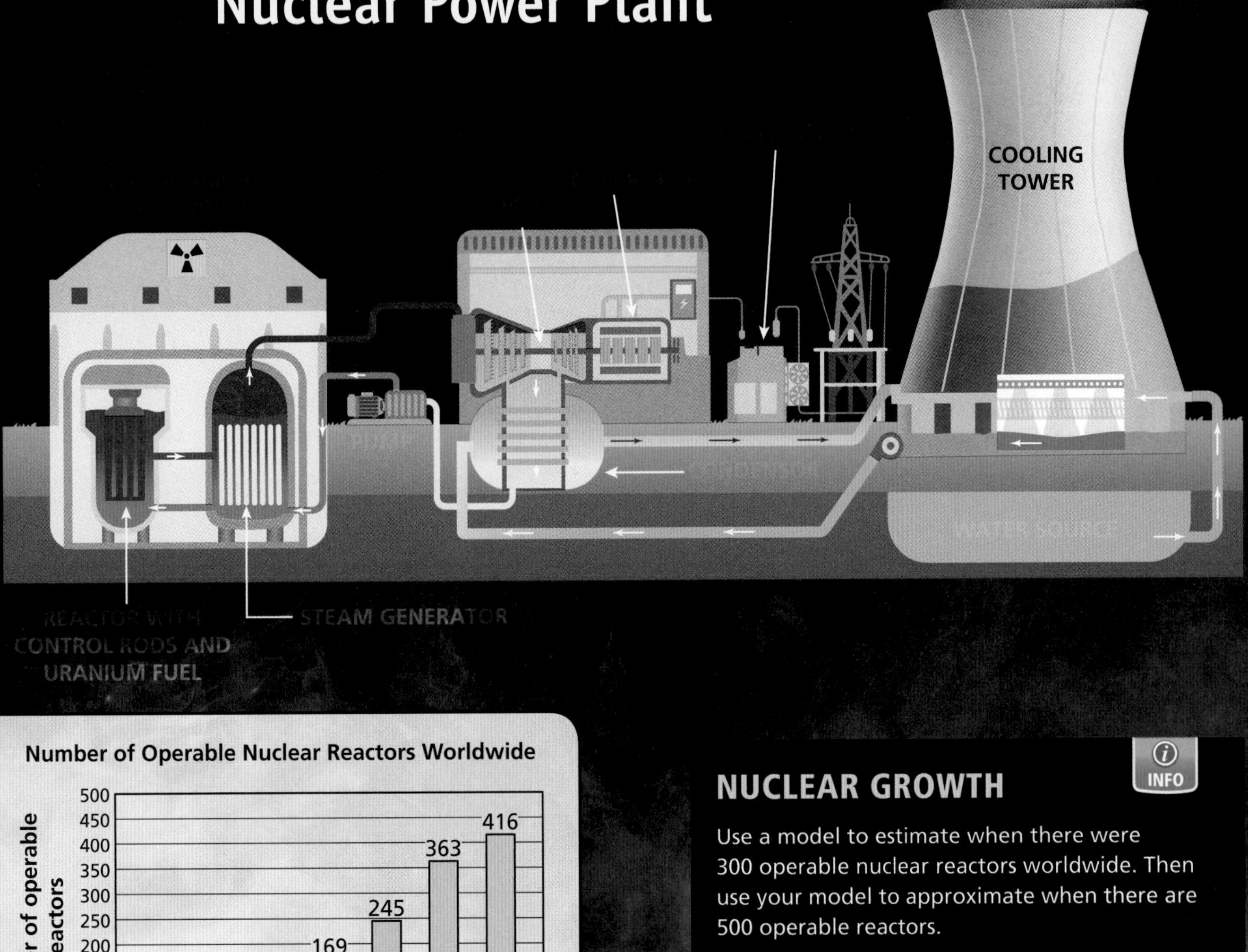

COOLING TOWER

PUMP

CONDENSER

WATER SOURCE

REACTOR WITH CONTROL RODS AND URANIUM FUEL

STEAM GENERATOR

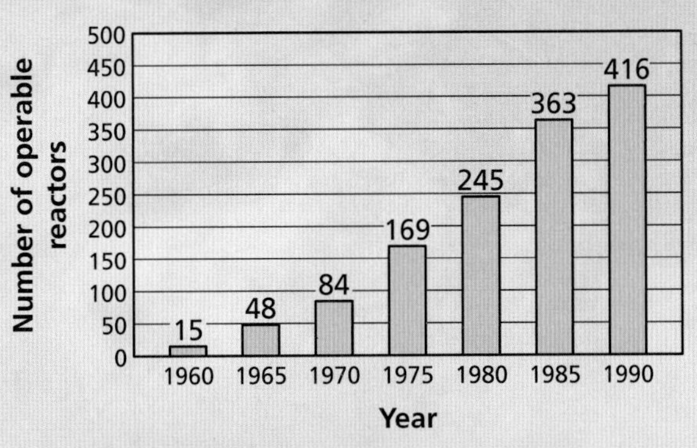

NUCLEAR GROWTH

Use a model to estimate when there were 300 operable nuclear reactors worldwide. Then use your model to approximate when there are 500 operable reactors.

Use the Internet to compare your estimates with actual data. Describe any significant differences. Explain what factors may have contributed to those differences.

3 College and Career Readiness WITH CalcChat®

Tutorial videos are available for each exercise.

1. The graph of which inequality is shown?

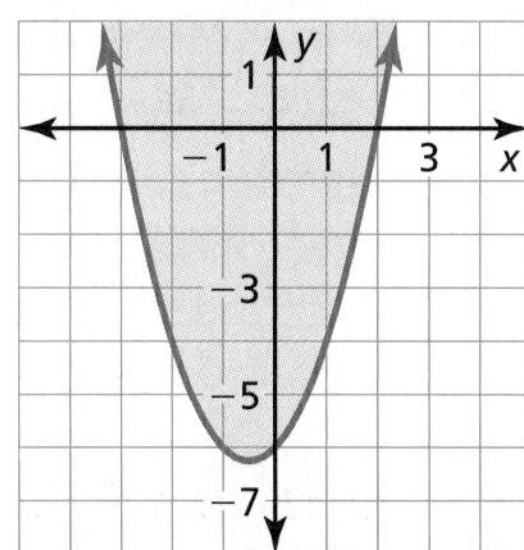

Ⓐ $y > x^2 + x - 6$

Ⓑ $y - x \geq x^2 - 6$

Ⓒ $y + 6 < x^2 + x$

Ⓓ $x^2 + x - 6 \geq y$

2. Which function is a translation 3 units right and 1 unit down of the graph of $f(x) = x^2$?

Ⓐ $y = (x + 3)^2 - 1$

Ⓑ $y = (x + 2)(x + 4)$

Ⓒ $y = x^2 - 6x + 8$

Ⓓ $y = (x - 3)^2 + 1$

3. Which function represents a parabola with focus $(-2, -2)$ and directrix $x = -6$?

Ⓐ

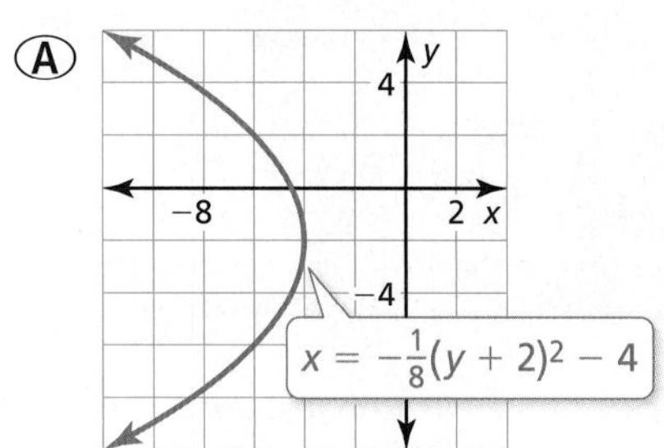

Ⓑ

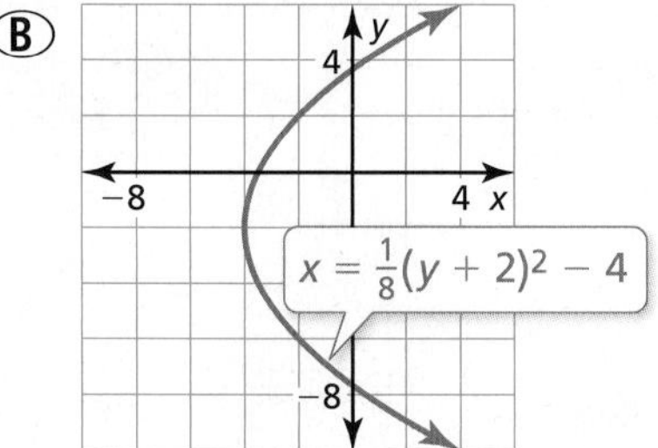

Ⓒ

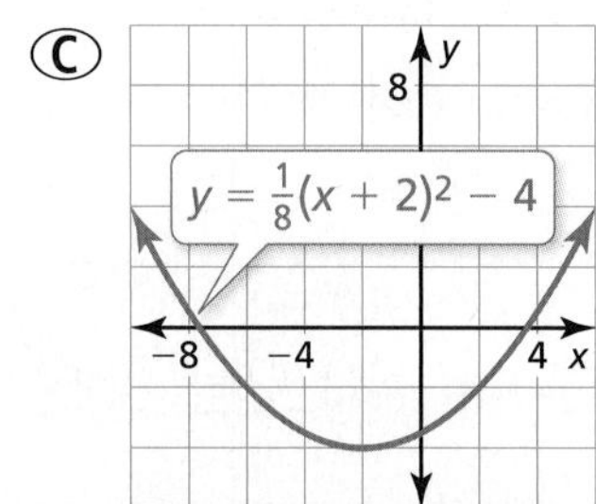

Ⓓ

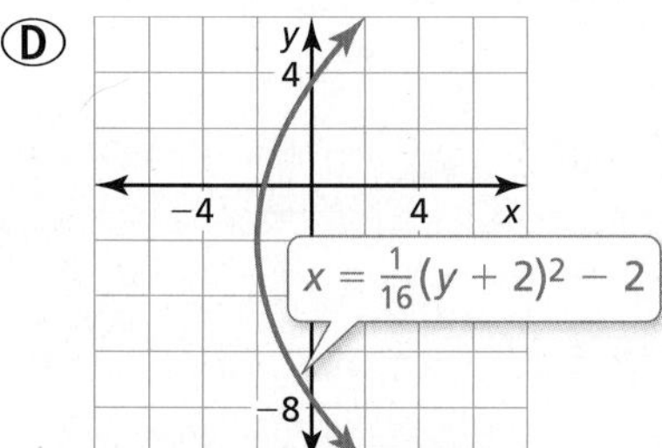

4. The table shows the average total stopping distances y (in feet) of a vehicle traveling x miles per hour.

Speed, x	10	20	30	40	50	60	70
Total stopping distance, y	27	63	109	164	229	304	388

a. Approximate the total stopping distance of a vehicle traveling 45 miles per hour.

b. Predict the total stopping distance of a vehicle traveling 80 miles per hour.

5. Which of the following points are solutions of the system? Select all that apply.

$y = x^2 - 6x + 14$

$y = 2x + 7$

Ⓐ $(-7, 105)$

Ⓑ $(1, 9)$

Ⓒ $(7, 21)$

Ⓓ no solution

6. Two equations form a linear system in two variables with no solution. One equation in the system is $y = -\frac{3}{5}x + 8$. Complete the second equation so that its graph passes through the point $(5, 9)$.

$y = \square x + \square$

7. The table shows the altitudes of a hang glider that descends at a constant rate. How long will it take for the hang glider to descend to an altitude of 100 feet?

Time (seconds), t	Altitude (feet), y
0	450
10	350
20	250
30	150

Ⓐ 10 seconds

Ⓑ 35 seconds

Ⓒ 45 seconds

Ⓓ 55 seconds

8. Choose values for the constants h and k in the equation $x = \frac{1}{4}(y - k)^2 + h$ so that each statement is true.

a. The graph of $x = \frac{1}{4}\left(y - \square\right)^2 + \square$ is a parabola with its vertex in the second quadrant.

b. The graph of $x = \frac{1}{4}\left(y - \square\right)^2 + \square$ is a parabola with its focus in the first quadrant.

c. The graph of $x = \frac{1}{4}\left(y - \square\right)^2 + \square$ is a parabola with its focus in the third quadrant.

9. A student solved the equation $\frac{1}{2}x^2 - 6x - 5 = 0$ as shown. Which statement accurately describes the student's work? Select all that apply.

$\frac{1}{2}x^2 - 6x - 5 = 0$

Step 1: $x^2 - 12x - 10 = 0$

Step 2: $x^2 - 12x = 10$

Step 3: $x^2 - 12x + 36 = 10$

Step 4: $(x - 6)^2 = 10$

Step 5: $x = 6 \pm \sqrt{10}$

Ⓐ The student made an error in Step 1.

Ⓑ The student made an error in Step 2.

Ⓒ The student made an error in Step 3.

Ⓓ The student made an error in Step 4.

Ⓔ The student made an error in Step 5.

Ⓕ The student's work is correct.

4 Polynomial Functions

GO DIGITAL

NATIONAL GEOGRAPHIC EXPLORER

Robert Lonsinger

Dr. Robert Lonsinger specializes in the conservation of endangered carnivore species. Dr. Lonsinger combines traditional approaches for monitoring wildlife populations with innovative conservation genetic techniques, noninvasive monitoring, and modeling platforms. He focuses on carnivores and their prey within desert and grassland communities.

- What are some examples of carnivorous mammals that live in deserts in the United States? in grasslands in the United States? Give examples of prey for each of these carnivore species.
- What is noninvasive monitoring of a species?

STEM

In 1995, wolves were reintroduced to Yellowstone National Park. In the Performance Task, you will study the effects wolves have on the elk population in Yellowstone.

Wildlife Conservation

Preparing for Chapter 4

Chapter Learning Target Understand polynomial functions.

Chapter Success Criteria
- ◆ I can graph polynomial functions.
- ◆ I can add, subtract, multiply, divide, and factor polynomials.
- ■ I can solve polynomial equations.
- ■ I can model with and analyze graphs of polynomial functions.

◆ Surface
■ Deep

Chapter Vocabulary

Work with a partner. Discuss each of the vocabulary terms.

polynomial
polynomial function
end behavior
polynomial long division
factored completely
factor by grouping
repeated solution
local maximum
local minimum

Mathematical Practices

Look for and Make Use of Structure

Mathematically proficient students look closely to discern a pattern or structure.

Work with a partner. A researcher studies the populations of carnivore and omnivore species in a region over time and records annual population estimates.

1. The table shows the numbers y of panthers in the region after x years.

Time (years), x	1	2	3	4	5
Number of panthers, y	24	20	24	36	56

   a. Write a model to represent the data. Explain how you used a pattern to determine which type of function to use for your model.
   b. When would you expect there to be 40 panthers in the region?

2. The table shows the numbers y of black bears in the region after x years.

Time (years), x	1	2	3	4	5
Number of black bears, y	618	631	644	657	670

   a. Write a model to represent the data. Explain how you used a pattern to determine which type of function to use for your model.
   b. When would you expect there to be 650 black bears in the region?

4 Prepare WITH CalcChat®

Adding and Subtracting Algebraic Expressions

Example 1 **Find $2(x + 4) + 3(6 - x)$.**

$$2(x + 4) + 3(6 - x) = 2(x) + 2(4) + 3(6) + 3(-x) \quad \text{Distributive Property}$$
$$= 2x + 8 + 18 - 3x \quad \text{Multiply.}$$
$$= (2x - 3x) + (8 + 18) \quad \text{Group like terms.}$$
$$= -x + 26 \quad \text{Simplify.}$$

WATCH

Example 2 **Find $(9x^2 + 4x) - (3x^2 - 6x + 3)$.**

$$(9x^2 + 4x) - (3x^2 - 6x + 3) = 9x^2 + 4x - 3x^2 + 6x - 3 \quad \text{Distributive Property}$$
$$= (9x^2 - 3x^2) + (4x + 6x) - 3 \quad \text{Group like terms.}$$
$$= 6x^2 + 10x - 3 \quad \text{Simplify.}$$

Find the sum or difference.

1. $3(y + 2) + 4y$

2. $9x - 4(2x - 1)$

3. $-(z + 2) - 2(1 - z)$

4. $-x^2 + 5x + x^2$

5. $(6x^2 - x + 9) + (5x - 4)$

6. $(-x^2 + 12) - (-3x^2 + 7)$

Finding Volume

Example 3 **Find the volume of a rectangular prism with a length of 10 centimeters, a width of 4 centimeters, and a height of 5 centimeters.**

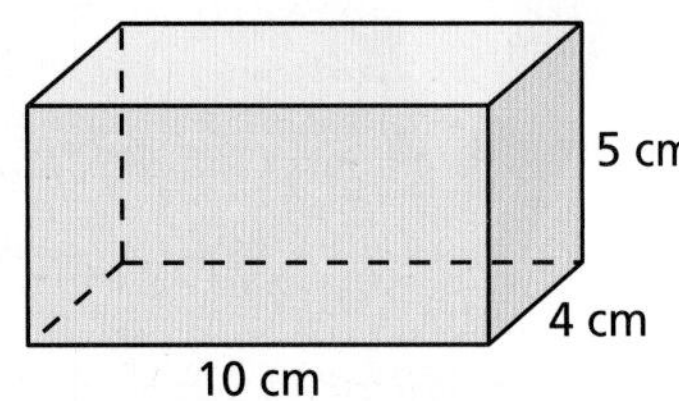

$$\text{Volume} = \ell wh \quad \text{Write the volume formula.}$$
$$= (10)(4)(5) \quad \text{Substitute 10 for } \ell\text{, 4 for } w\text{, and 5 for } h.$$
$$= 200 \quad \text{Multiply.}$$

▶ The volume is 200 cubic centimeters.

Find the volume of the solid.

7. cube with edge length 4 inches

8. sphere with radius 2 feet

9. rectangular prism with length 4 feet, width 2 feet, and height 6 feet

10. cylinder with radius 3 centimeters and height 5 centimeters

11. MP **REASONING** The edge length of a cube increases from a inches to ka inches, where $k > 0$. By how much does the volume increase?

4.1 Graphing Polynomial Functions

Learning Target Graph and describe polynomial functions.

Success Criteria

- I can identify and evaluate polynomial functions.
- I can graph polynomial functions.
- I can describe end behavior of polynomial functions.

EXPLORE IT! Graphing Polynomial Functions

MP CHOOSE TOOLS Work with a partner.

$f(x) = -x^2 - 1$	$f(x) = \dfrac{1}{x}$
$f(x) = 2^x$	$f(x) = -4x^3$
$f(x) = x^3 + 1$	$f(x) = \frac{1}{2}x^2 + x$
$f(x) = -\frac{1}{4}x^4 - x^3$	$f(x) = x^3 + x^2$
$f(x) = \sqrt{x}$	$f(x) = 2x^4 - x$

a. Identify each function in the list at the left in which $f(x)$ is a polynomial. Graph each function you identified. For each function,

- describe the end behavior.
- identify the term with the greatest exponent. How does the exponent affect the graph? How does the coefficient of this term affect the graph?

b. Graph $y = x^3$ and $y = x^4$. Compare the graphs. One of these graphs is *cubic* and the other is *quartic*. Which do you think is which? Explain.

c. Identify each function as cubic or quartic. Then match each function with its graph. Explain your reasoning.

i. $f(x) = x^3 - x$ **ii.** $f(x) = -x^3 + x$

iii. $f(x) = -x^4 + 1$ **iv.** $f(x) = x^4 - x^2$

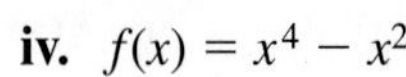

Math Practice

Find Entry Points
How can rewriting the functions help you match the functions with their graphs?

A.
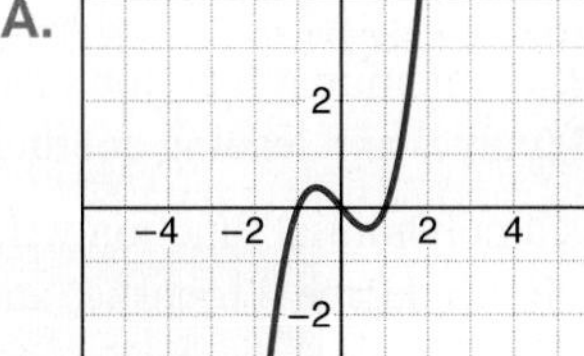

B.
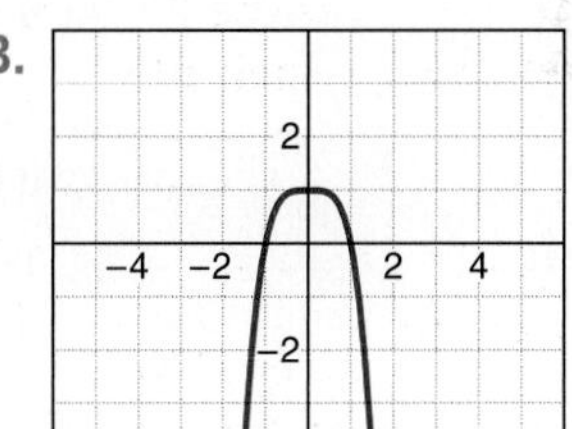

C.

D.
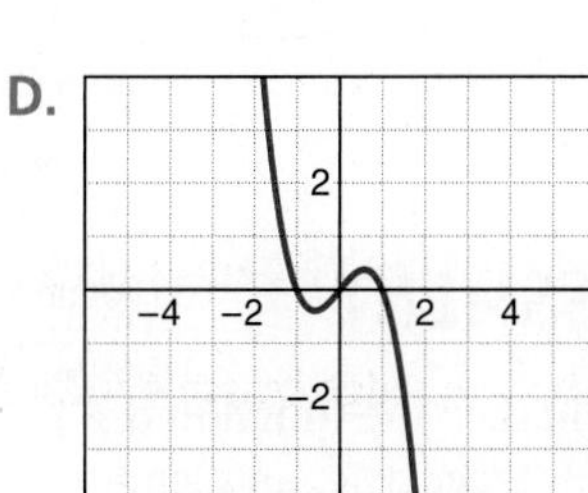

d. What are some characteristics of the graphs of cubic polynomial functions? quartic polynomial functions?

Polynomial Functions

GO DIGITAL

Vocabulary

AZ VOCAB

polynomial, *p. 154*
polynomial function, *p. 154*
end behavior, *p. 155*

A monomial is a number, a variable, or the product of a number and one or more variables with whole number exponents. A **polynomial** is a monomial or a sum of monomials. A **polynomial function** is a function of the form

$$f(x) = a_n x^n + a_{n-1}x^{n-1} + \cdots + a_1 x + a_0$$

where $a_n \neq 0$, the exponents are all whole numbers, and the coefficients are all real numbers. For this function, a_n is the leading coefficient, n is the degree, and a_0 is the constant term. A polynomial function is in *standard form* when its terms are written in descending order of exponents from left to right.

You are already familiar with some types of polynomial functions, such as linear and quadratic. Here is a summary of common types of polynomial functions.

Common Polynomial Functions			
Degree	**Type**	**Standard Form**	**Example**
0	Constant	$f(x) = a_0$	$f(x) = -14$
1	Linear	$f(x) = a_1x + a_0$	$f(x) = 5x - 7$
2	Quadratic	$f(x) = a_2x^2 + a_1x + a_0$	$f(x) = 2x^2 + x - 9$
3	Cubic	$f(x) = a_3x^3 + a_2x^2 + a_1x + a_0$	$f(x) = x^3 - x^2 + 3x$
4	Quartic	$f(x) = a_4x^4 + a_3x^3 + a_2x^2 + a_1x + a_0$	$f(x) = x^4 + 2x - 1$

EXAMPLE 1 Identifying Polynomial Functions

Determine whether each function is a polynomial function. If so, write it in standard form and state its degree, type, and leading coefficient.

a. $f(x) = -2x^3 + 5x + 8$

b. $g(x) = -0.8x^3 + \sqrt{2}x^4 - 12$

c. $h(x) = -x^2 + 7x^{-1} + 4x$

d. $k(x) = x^2 + 3^x$

SOLUTION

a. The function is a polynomial function that is already written in standard form. It has degree 3 (cubic) and leading coefficient -2.

b. The function is a polynomial function written as $g(x) = \sqrt{2}x^4 - 0.8x^3 - 12$ in standard form. It has degree 4 (quartic) and leading coefficient $\sqrt{2}$.

c. The function is not a polynomial function because the term $7x^{-1}$ has an exponent that is not a whole number.

d. The function is not a polynomial function because the term 3^x does not have a variable base and an exponent that is a whole number.

SELF-ASSESSMENT

1 I do not understand. 2 I can do it with help. 3 I can do it on my own. 4 I can teach someone else.

Determine whether the function is a polynomial function. If so, write it in standard form and state its degree, type, and leading coefficient.

1. $f(x) = 7 - 1.6x^2 - 5x$

2. $p(x) = x + 2x^{-2} + 9.5$

3. $q(x) = x^3 - 6x + 3x^4$

4. WHICH ONE DOESN'T BELONG? Which function does *not* belong with the other three? Explain your reasoning.

$f(x) = 7x^5 + 3x^2 - 2x$

$g(x) = 3x^3 - 2x^8 + \frac{3}{4}$

$h(x) = -3x^4 + 5x^{-1} - 3x^2$

$k(x) = \sqrt{3}x + 8x^4$

EXAMPLE 2 Evaluating a Polynomial Function

Evaluate $f(x) = 2x^4 - 8x^2 + 5x - 7$ when $x = 3$.

SOLUTION

$f(x) = 2x^4 - 8x^2 + 5x - 7$	Write the function.
$f(3) = 2(3)^4 - 8(3)^2 + 5(3) - 7$	Substitute 3 for x.
$= 162 - 72 + 15 - 7$	Evaluate powers and multiply.
$= 98$	Simplify.

The **end behavior** of a function is the behavior of the graph as x approaches positive infinity ($+\infty$) or negative infinity ($-\infty$). For a polynomial function, the end behavior is determined by the function's degree and the sign of its leading coefficient.

KEY IDEA

End Behavior of Polynomial Functions

REMEMBER

The expression "$x \to +\infty$" is read as "x approaches positive infinity."

Degree: odd
Leading coefficient: positive

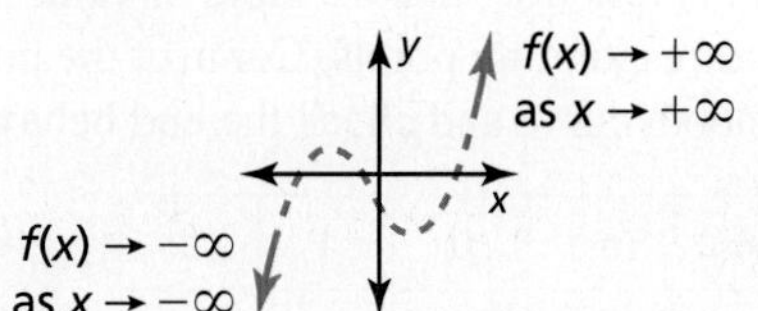

Degree: odd
Leading coefficient: negative

$f(x) \to +\infty$ as $x \to -\infty$

$f(x) \to -\infty$ as $x \to +\infty$

Degree: even
Leading coefficient: positive

$f(x) \to +\infty$ as $x \to -\infty$

$f(x) \to +\infty$ as $x \to +\infty$

Degree: even
Leading coefficient: negative

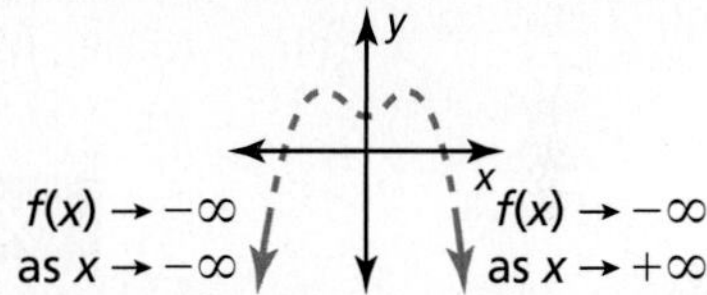

Check

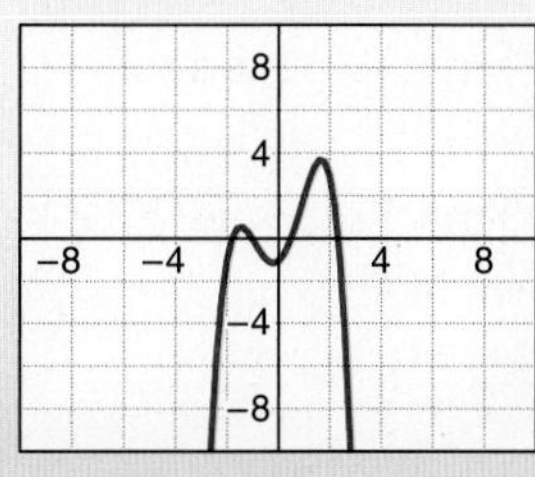

EXAMPLE 3 Describing End Behavior

Describe the end behavior of $f(x) = -0.5x^4 + 2.5x^2 + x - 1$.

SOLUTION

The function has degree 4 and leading coefficient -0.5. Because the degree is even and the leading coefficient is negative, $f(x) \to -\infty$ as $x \to -\infty$ and $f(x) \to -\infty$ as $x \to +\infty$.

SELF-ASSESSMENT

1 I do not understand. **2** I can do it with help. **3** I can do it on my own. **4** I can teach someone else.

Evaluate the function for the given value of x.

5. $f(x) = -x^3 + 3x^2 + 9; x = 4$

6. $f(x) = 3x^5 - x^4 - 6x + 10; x = -2$

7. WRITING Explain what is meant by the end behavior of a polynomial function.

8. Describe the end behavior of $f(x) = 0.25x^3 - x^2 - 1$.

Graphing Polynomial Functions

To graph a polynomial function, first plot points to determine the shape of the graph's middle portion. Then connect the points with a smooth continuous curve and use what you know about end behavior to sketch the graph.

EXAMPLE 4 Graphing Polynomial Functions

Graph (a) $f(x) = -x^3 + x^2 + 3x - 3$ and (b) $f(x) = x^4 - x^3 - 4x^2 + 4$.

SOLUTION

a. To graph the function, make a table of values and plot the corresponding points. Connect the points with a smooth curve and check the end behavior.

x	-2	-1	0	1	2
$f(x)$	3	-4	-3	0	-1

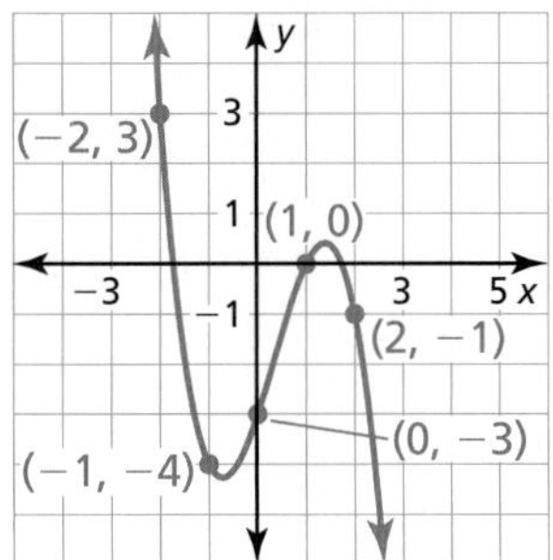

The degree is odd and the leading coefficient is negative. So, $f(x) \to +\infty$ as $x \to -\infty$ and $f(x) \to -\infty$ as $x \to +\infty$.

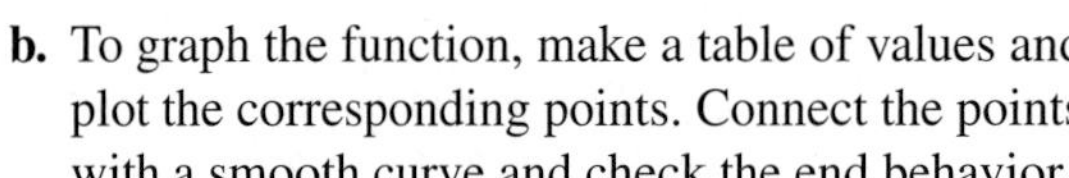

b. To graph the function, make a table of values and plot the corresponding points. Connect the points with a smooth curve and check the end behavior.

x	-2	-1	0	1	2
$f(x)$	12	2	4	0	-4

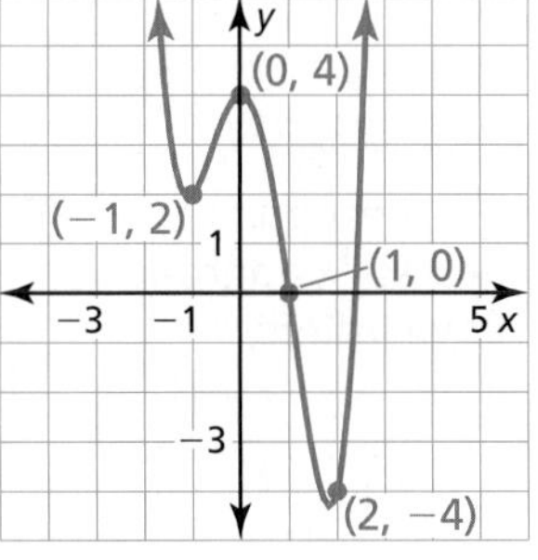

The degree is even and the leading coefficient is positive. So, $f(x) \to +\infty$ as $x \to -\infty$ and $f(x) \to +\infty$ as $x \to +\infty$.

EXAMPLE 5 Sketching a Graph

Sketch a graph of the polynomial function f with the following characteristics.

- f is increasing when $x < 0$ and $x > 4$.
- f is decreasing when $0 < x < 4$.
- $f(x) > 0$ when $-2 < x < 3$ and $x > 5$.
- $f(x) < 0$ when $x < -2$ and $3 < x < 5$.

Use the graph to describe the degree and leading coefficient of f.

SOLUTION

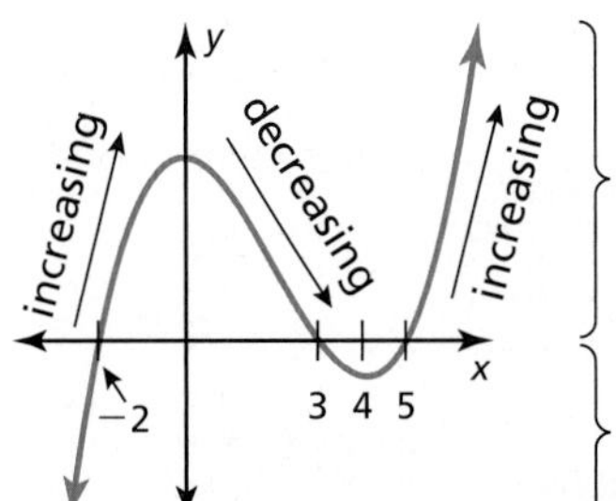

▶ From the graph, $f(x) \to -\infty$ as $x \to -\infty$ and $f(x) \to +\infty$ as $x \to +\infty$. So, the degree is odd and the leading coefficient is positive.

EXAMPLE 6 Modeling Real Life

The African wild dog is one of the most endangered carnivores on Earth. The estimated population of African wild dogs under human care can be modeled by the polynomial function

$$P(t) = 0.368t^3 - 11.45t^2 + 109.5t + 286$$

where t represents the number of years after 2000.

a. Use technology to graph the function for $1 \leq t \leq 18$. Describe the behavior of the graph on this interval.

b. What is the average rate of change in the number of dogs from 2001 to 2018?

c. Do you think this model can be used for years after 2018? Explain your reasoning.

SOLUTION

a. Using technology and the domain $1 \leq t \leq 18$, you obtain the graph shown.

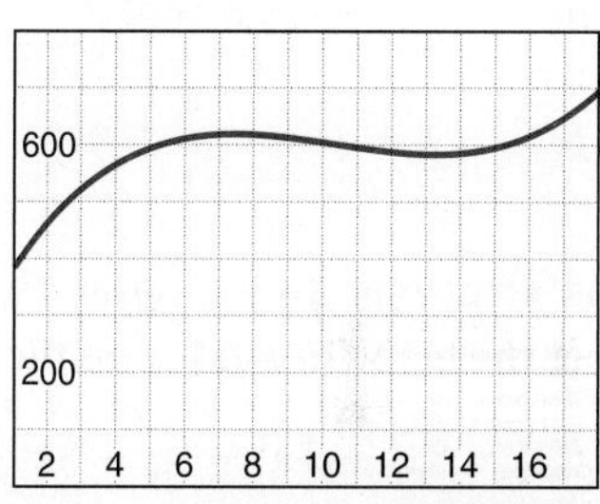

▶ The number of dogs increases from 2001 to 2007, decreases slightly from 2007 to 2013, and increases from 2013 to 2018.

b. The years 2001 and 2018 correspond to $t = 1$ and $t = 18$.

Average rate of change over $1 \leq t \leq 18$:

$$\frac{P(18) - P(1)}{18 - 1} = \frac{693.376 - 384.418}{17} = 18.174$$

▶ The average rate of change from 2001 to 2018 is about 18 dogs per year.

c. Because the degree is odd and the leading coefficient is positive, $P(t) \to -\infty$ as $t \to -\infty$ and $P(t) \to +\infty$ as $t \to +\infty$. The end behavior indicates that the model has unlimited growth as t increases. While the model may be valid for a few years after 2018, over time, unlimited growth is not reasonable.

SELF-ASSESSMENT

1 I do not understand. 2 I can do it with help. 3 I can do it on my own. 4 I can teach someone else.

Graph the polynomial function.

9. $f(x) = x^4 + x^2 - 3$

10. $f(x) = 4 - x^3$

11. $f(x) = x^3 - x^2 + x - 1$

12. Sketch a graph of the polynomial function f with the following characteristics.

- f is decreasing when $x < -1.5$ and $x > 2.5$; f is increasing when $-1.5 < x < 2.5$.
- $f(x) > 0$ when $x < -3$ and $1 < x < 4$; $f(x) < 0$ when $-3 < x < 1$ and $x > 4$.

Use the graph to describe the degree and leading coefficient of f.

13. WHAT IF? Repeat Example 6 using the following model for the African wild dog population.

$$P(t) = 0.0012t^4 + 0.321t^3 - 10.86t^2 + 106.8t + 289$$

4.1 Practice WITH CalcChat® AND CalcView®

In Exercises 1–6, determine whether the function is a polynomial function. If so, write it in standard form and state its degree, type, and leading coefficient. *Example 1*

1. $f(x) = -3x + 5x^3 - 6x^2 + 2$

2. $p(x) = \frac{1}{2}x^2 + 3x - 4x^3 + 6x^4 - 1$

3. $f(x) = 9x^4 + 8x^3 - 6x^{-2} + 2x$

4. $g(x) = \sqrt{3} - 12x + 13x^2$

5. $h(x) = \frac{5}{3}x^2 - \sqrt{7}x^4 + 8x^3 - \frac{1}{2} + x$

6. $h(x) = 3x^4 + 2x - \frac{5}{x} + 9x^3 - 7$

ERROR ANALYSIS In Exercises 7 and 8, describe and correct the error in analyzing the function.

7. $f(x) = 8x^3 - 7x^4 - 9x - 3x^2 + 11$

f is a polynomial function.
The degree is 3 and f is a cubic function.
The leading coefficient is 8.

8. $f(x) = 2x^4 + 4x - 9\sqrt{x} + 3x^2 - 8$

f is a polynomial function.
The degree is 4 and f is a quartic function.
The leading coefficient is 2.

In Exercises 9–16, evaluate the function for the given value of *x*. *Example 2*

9. $f(x) = 2x^3 - 5x^2 + 16; x = -4$

10. $p(x) = -x^5 + 11x^3 + 7; x = 3$

11. $h(x) = -3x^4 + 2x^3 - 12x - 6; x = -2$

12. $f(x) = 7x^4 - 10x^2 + 14x - 26; x = -7$

13. $g(x) = x^6 - 64x^4 + x^2 - 7x - 51; x = 8$

14. $g(x) = -x^3 + 3x^2 + 5x + 1; x = -12$

15. $p(x) = 2x^3 + 4x^2 + 6x + 7; x = \frac{1}{2}$

16. $h(x) = 5x^3 - 3x^2 + 2x + 4; x = -\frac{1}{3}$

17. **WRITING** Let $f(x) = 13$. State the degree, type, and leading coefficient. Describe the end behavior of the function. Explain your reasoning.

18. **MODELING REAL LIFE** The weight of an ideal round-cut diamond can be modeled by

$$w = 0.00583d^3 - 0.0125d^2 + 0.022d - 0.01$$

where w is the weight of the diamond (in carats) and d is the diameter (in millimeters). According to the model, what is the weight of a diamond with a diameter of 12 millimeters?

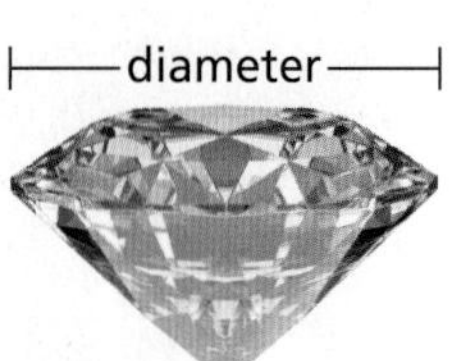

In Exercises 19–22, describe the end behavior of the function. *Example 3*

19. $h(x) = -5x^4 + 7x^3 - 6x^2 + 9x + 2$

20. $g(x) = 7x^7 + 12x^5 - 6x^3 - 2x - 18$

21. $f(x) = -2x^4 + 12x^8 + 17 + 15x^2$

22. $f(x) = 11 - 18x^2 - 5x^5 - 12x^4 - 2x$

In Exercises 23 and 24, use the graph to describe the degree and leading coefficient of *f*.

23.

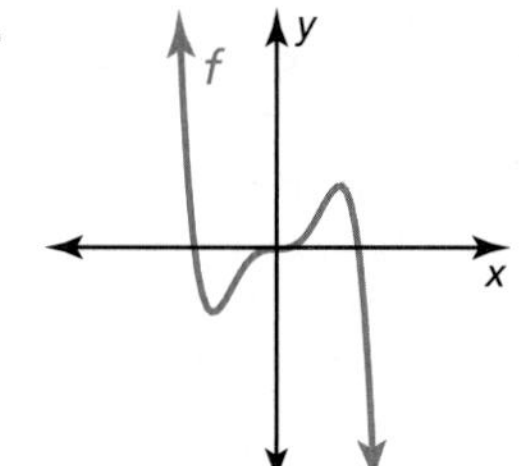

24.

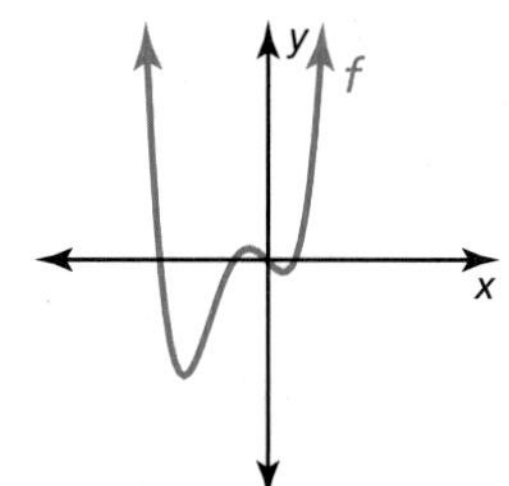

In Exercises 25–32, graph the polynomial function. *Example 4*

25. $p(x) = 3 - x^4$

26. $g(x) = x^3 + x + 3$

27. $f(x) = 4x - 9 - x^3$

28. $p(x) = x^5 - 3x^3 + 2$

29. $h(x) = x^4 - 2x^3 + 3x$

30. $h(x) = 5 + 3x^2 - x^4$

31. $g(x) = x^5 - 3x^4 + 2x - 4$

32. $p(x) = x^6 - 2x^5 - 2x^3 + x + 5$

ANALYZING RELATIONSHIPS In Exercises 33 and 34, describe the x-values for which (a) f is increasing, (b) f is decreasing, (c) $f(x) > 0$, and (d) $f(x) < 0$.

33. 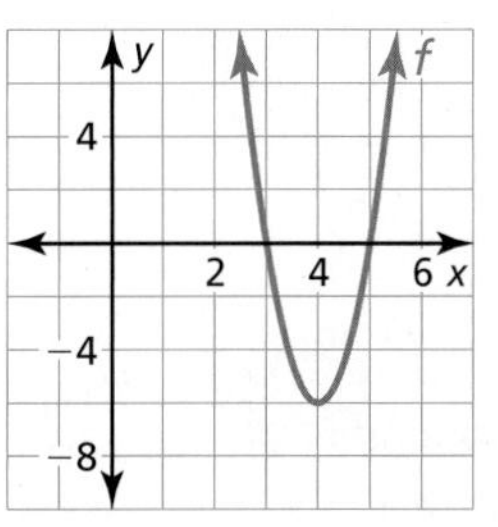

34. 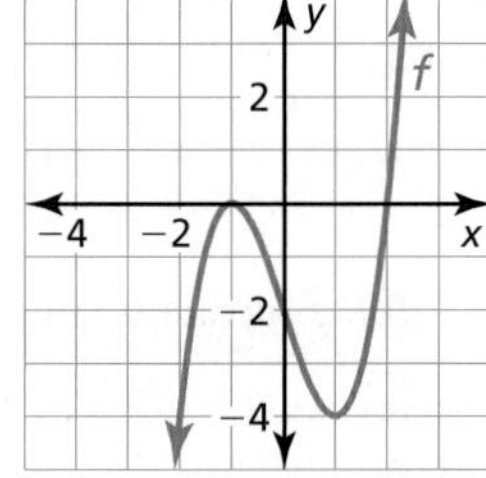

In Exercises 35–38, sketch a graph of the polynomial function f with the given characteristics. Use the graph to describe the degree and leading coefficient of the function f. *Example 5*

35.
- f is increasing when $x > 0.5$; f is decreasing when $x < 0.5$.
- $f(x) > 0$ when $x < -2$ and $x > 3$; $f(x) < 0$ when $-2 < x < 3$.

36.
- f is increasing when $-2 < x < 3$; f is decreasing when $x < -2$ and $x > 3$.
- $f(x) > 0$ when $x < -4$ and $1 < x < 5$; $f(x) < 0$ when $-4 < x < 1$ and $x > 5$.

37.
- f is increasing when $-2 < x < 0$ and $x > 2$; f is decreasing when $x < -2$ and $0 < x < 2$.
- $f(x) > 0$ when $x < -3$, $-1 < x < 1$, and $x > 3$; $f(x) < 0$ when $-3 < x < -1$ and $1 < x < 3$.

38.
- f is increasing when $x < -1$ and $x > 1$; f is decreasing when $-1 < x < 1$.
- $f(x) > 0$ when $-1.5 < x < 0$ and $x > 1.5$; $f(x) < 0$ when $x < -1.5$ and $0 < x < 1.5$.

39. MODELING REAL LIFE The estimated population of Sumatran tigers can be modeled by the function

$$P(t) = -0.077t^3 + 2.11t^2 - 7.1t + 166$$

where t is the number of years after 2000. *Example 6*

a. Use technology to graph the function for $1 \leq t \leq 18$. Describe the behavior of the graph on this interval.

b. What is the average rate of change in the number of tigers from 2001 to 2018?

c. Do you think this model can be used for years after 2018? Explain your reasoning.

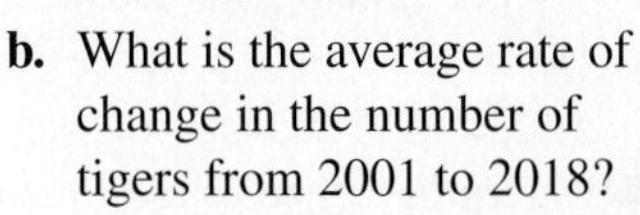

40. MODELING REAL LIFE The number of drive-in movie theaters in the United States from 1995 to 2018 can be modeled by the function

$$d(t) = -0.086t^3 + 3.71t^2 - 53.7t + 643$$

where t is the number of years after 1995.

a. Use technology to graph the function for $1 \leq t \leq 23$. Describe the behavior of the graph on this interval.

b. Find and interpret the average rates of change in the number of drive-in movie theaters from 1996 to 2006 and from 2006 to 2018.

c. Do you think this model can be used for years before 1995 or after 2018? Explain.

41. MP USING TOOLS Your friend uses technology to graph $f(x) = (x - 1)(x - 2)(x + 12)$ in the viewing window $-10 \leq x \leq 10$, $-10 \leq y \leq 10$, and says the graph is a parabola. Is your friend correct? Explain.

42. HOW DO YOU SEE IT?
The graph of a polynomial function is shown.

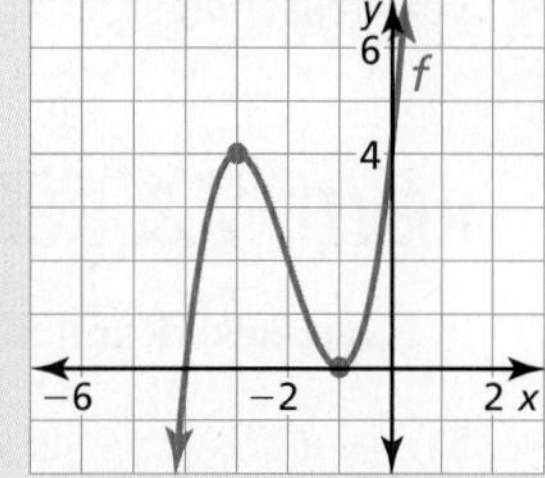

a. State the degree and leading coefficient of f.

b. Describe the intervals for which the function is increasing and decreasing.

c. What is the constant term of the polynomial function? Explain.

43. ABSTRACT REASONING The end behavior of a polynomial function f is described by $f(x) \to +\infty$ as $x \to -\infty$ and $f(x) \to -\infty$ as $x \to +\infty$. Describe the end behavior of $g(x) = -f(x)$. Justify your answer.

44. THOUGHT PROVOKING
The end behavior of a polynomial function f is described by $f(x) \to -\infty$ as $x \to -\infty$ and $f(x) \to +\infty$ as $x \to +\infty$. Is it possible that f has no zeros? one zero? more than one zero? Explain your reasoning.

45. ANALYZING RELATIONSHIPS Use technology to graph $f(x) = x^2$, $g(x) = x^4$, and $h(x) = x^6$ in the same coordinate plane.

a. What do you notice about the functions and their points of intersection? Does the pattern continue for greater, even powers of x? Explain.

b. Is there a similar pattern for functions with odd powers of x? Explain.

46. **DRAWING CONCLUSIONS** The graph of a function is symmetric about the y-axis if for each point (a, b) on the graph, $(-a, b)$ is also a point on the graph. It is symmetric about the origin if for each point (a, b) on the graph, $(-a, -b)$ is also a point on the graph.

   a. Use technology to graph the function $y = x^n$ when $n = 1, 2, 3, 4, 5$, and 6. In each case, identify the symmetry of the graph.

   b. Predict the symmetry of the graphs of $y = x^{10}$ and $y = x^{11}$. Explain your reasoning. Then confirm your predictions by graphing the functions.

47. **MAKING AN ARGUMENT** Can you use the table to determine whether the polynomial function f has an even degree or an odd degree? Explain.

x	−5	−1	0	1	5
$f(x)$	92.5	58.9	55	58.9	92.5

48. **DIG DEEPER** A cubic polynomial function f has a leading coefficient of 2 and a constant term of −5. When $f(1) = 0$ and $f(2) = 3$, what is $f(-5)$? Explain your reasoning.

49. **COLLEGE PREP** The function f represented by the table is a polynomial function. Which statement is true?

x	2	5	8	11	13
$f(x)$	−75	39	−22	−47	−9

Ⓐ f has a maximum value of 39.

Ⓑ $f(x) = 0$ for at least one value of x.

Ⓒ f is increasing when $2 < x < 5$.

Ⓓ $f(x) \to -\infty$ as $x \to -\infty$ and $f(x) \to +\infty$ as $x \to +\infty$.

50. **CRITICAL THINKING** The weight y (in pounds) of a rainbow trout can be modeled by $y = 0.000304x^3$, where x is the length (in inches) of the trout.

   a. Write a function that relates the weight y and length x of a rainbow trout when y is measured in kilograms and x is measured in centimeters.

   b. Graph the original function and the function from part (a) in the same coordinate plane. What type of transformation can you apply to the original function to produce the graph from part (a)?

REVIEW & REFRESH

In Exercises 51 and 52, simplify the expression.

51. $-wk + 3kz - 2kw + 9zk - kw$

52. $a^2(m - 7a^3) - m(a^2 - 10)$

53. Write a function g whose graph represents the indicated transformation of the graph of $f(x) = -|x - 1| + 3$.

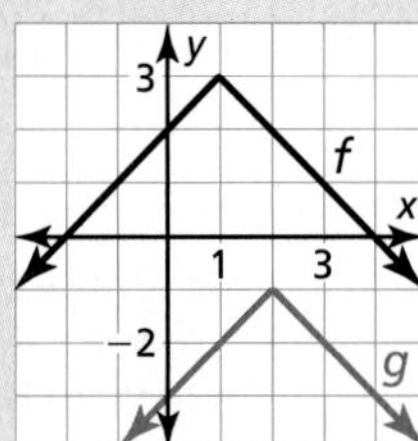

In Exercises 54 and 55, describe the transformation of $f(x) = x^2$ represented by g. Then graph each function.

54. $g(x) = (x + 5)^2$

55. $g(x) = -\frac{3}{2}x^2$

In Exercises 56 and 57, solve the system using any method. Explain your choice of method.

56. $y = x^2 + x - 6$
$y = 2x^2 + x - 10$

57. $x^2 - 7x = y - 6$
$y = -8$

58. **MODELING REAL LIFE** You toss a penny into a park fountain. The penny leaves your hand 4 feet above the ground and has an initial vertical velocity of 25 feet per second. Does the penny reach a height of 10 feet? 15 feet? Explain your reasoning.

In Exercises 59 and 60, solve the inequality using any method. Explain your choice of method.

59. $2x^2 - 7x - 4 \leq 0$

60. $5x + 1 > 3x^2$

61. Write an inequality that represents the graph.

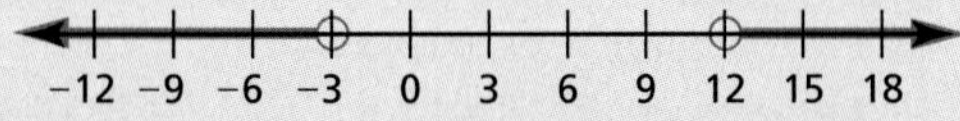

In Exercises 62 and 63, graph the polynomial function.

62. $g(x) = -x^4 + 3x^2 - 5$

63. $h(x) = 2x^2 - 7x + \frac{1}{2}x^3 + 4$

64. **MP STRUCTURE** Determine whether the function is a polynomial function. If so, write it in standard form and state its degree, type, and leading coefficient.

$f(x) = 5x^3x + \frac{5}{2}x^3 - 9x^4 + \sqrt{2}x^2 + 4x - 1 - x^{-5}x^5 - 4$

4.2 Adding, Subtracting, and Multiplying Polynomials

Learning Target Add, subtract, and multiply polynomials.

Success Criteria
- I can add and subtract polynomials.
- I can multiply polynomials and use special product patterns.
- I can use Pascal's Triangle to expand binomials.

EXPLORE IT! Expanding Binomials

Work with a partner.

a. Copy the diagram. Find the value of each expression. Write one digit of the value in each box.

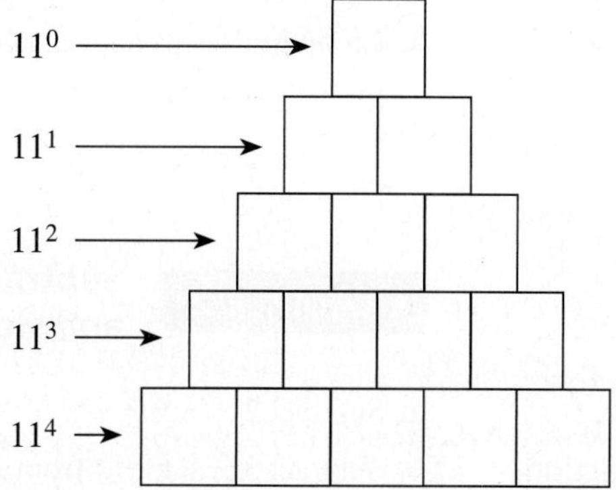

What pattern(s) do you notice?

b. Find each product. Explain your steps.

$(x + 1)^2$ $\qquad$ $(x + 1)^3$

What pattern do you notice between the values of 11^n and the terms of $(x + 1)^n$ for $0 \leq n \leq 3$? Does this pattern continue for $(x + 1)^4$? Explain your reasoning.

c. Find each product. Explain your steps.

$(a + b)^3$ $\qquad$ $(a - b)^3$

What other pattern(s) do you notice when cubing these binomials?

d. Explain how you can use Pascal's Triangle to find each product. Then find the product.

i. $(x + 2)^3$

ii. $(2x - 3)^3$

Pascal's Triangle

Math Practice

Look for Patterns

How can you extend Pascal's Triangle and use it to expand a binomial with a greater exponent, such as $(2x + 1)^5$?

Adding and Subtracting Polynomials

GO DIGITAL

Vocabulary 

Pascal's Triangle, *p. 165*

The set of integers is *closed* under addition and subtraction because every sum or difference results in an integer. To add or subtract polynomials, add or subtract the coefficients of like terms. Because adding or subtracting polynomials results in a polynomial, the set of polynomials is also closed under addition and subtraction.

EXAMPLE 1 Adding Polynomials Vertically and Horizontally

a. Add $3x^3 + 2x^2 - x - 7$ and $x^3 - 10x^2 + 8$ in a vertical format.

b. Add $9y^3 + 3y^2 - 2y + 1$ and $-5y^2 + y - 4$ in a horizontal format.

STUDY TIP

When a power of the variable appears in one polynomial but not the other, leave a space in that column, or write the term with a coefficient of 0.

SOLUTION

a. Align like terms vertically and add.

$$\begin{array}{r} 3x^3 + 2x^2 - x - 7 \\ +\ \ x^3 - 10x^2 + 8 \\ \hline 4x^3 - 8x^2 - x + 1 \end{array}$$

b. Group like terms and simplify.

$$\begin{aligned}(9y^3 + 3y^2 - 2y + 1) + (-5y^2 + y - 4) &= 9y^3 + 3y^2 - 5y^2 - 2y + y + 1 - 4 \\ &= 9y^3 - 2y^2 - y - 3\end{aligned}$$

EXAMPLE 2 Subtracting Polynomials Vertically and Horizontally

COMMON ERROR

A common mistake is to forget to change signs correctly when subtracting one polynomial from another. Be sure to add the opposite of *every* term of the subtracted polynomial.

a. Subtract $2x^3 + 6x^2 - x + 1$ from $8x^3 - 3x^2 - 2x + 9$ in a vertical format.

b. Subtract $3z^2 + z - 4$ from $2z^2 + 3z$ in a horizontal format.

SOLUTION

a. Align like terms vertically, then add the opposite of the subtracted polynomial.

$$\begin{array}{r} 8x^3 - 3x^2 - 2x + 9 \\ -\ (2x^3 + 6x^2 - \ \ x + 1) \\ \hline \end{array} \quad \Rightarrow \quad \begin{array}{r} 8x^3 - 3x^2 - 2x + 9 \\ +\ \ -2x^3 - 6x^2 + \ \ x - 1 \\ \hline 6x^3 - 9x^2 - \ \ x + 8 \end{array}$$

b. Write the opposite of the subtracted polynomial, then add like terms.

$$\begin{aligned}(2z^2 + 3z) - (3z^2 + z - 4) &= 2z^2 + 3z - 3z^2 - z + 4 \\ &= -z^2 + 2z + 4\end{aligned}$$

SELF-ASSESSMENT

1 I do not understand. 2 I can do it with help. 3 I can do it on my own. 4 I can teach someone else.

Find the sum or difference.

1. $(2x^2 - 6x + 5) + (7x^2 - x - 9)$
2. $(6z^4 + 3z^2 - 10) + (6z^3 - 4z^2 + z - 10)$
3. $(3t^3 + 8t^2 - t - 4) - (5t^3 - t^2 + 17)$
4. $(p^5 + 2p^3 - 8p^2 + 7) - (9p^5 + 12p^2 - p)$
5. **OPEN-ENDED** Write two trinomials whose sum has (a) four terms, (b) two terms, and (c) one term.
6. **MP STRUCTURE** In your own words, explain why the set of polynomials is closed under addition and subtraction.

GO DIGITAL

Multiplying Polynomials

To multiply two polynomials, multiply each term of the first polynomial by each term of the second polynomial. As with addition and subtraction, the set of polynomials is closed under multiplication.

EXAMPLE 3 Multiplying Polynomials Vertically and Horizontally

WATCH

a. Multiply $-x^2 + 2x + 4$ and $x - 3$ in a vertical format.

b. Multiply $y + 5$ and $3y^2 - 2y + 2$ in a horizontal format.

REMEMBER

The Product of Powers Property states that

$a^m \cdot a^n = a^{m+n}$

where a is a real number and m and n are integers.

SOLUTION

a.

$$\begin{array}{r} -x^2 + 2x + 4 \\ \times \qquad\quad x - 3 \\ \hline 3x^2 - 6x - 12 \\ -x^3 + 2x^2 + 4x \qquad \\ \hline -x^3 + 5x^2 - 2x - 12 \end{array}$$

Multiply $-x^2 + 2x + 4$ by -3.

Multiply $-x^2 + 2x + 4$ by x.

Combine like terms.

b. $(y + 5)(3y^2 - 2y + 2) = (y + 5)3y^2 - (y + 5)2y + (y + 5)2$

$= 3y^3 + 15y^2 - 2y^2 - 10y + 2y + 10$

$= 3y^3 + 13y^2 - 8y + 10$

EXAMPLE 4 Multiplying Three Binomials

WATCH

Multiply $x - 1$, $x + 4$, and $x + 5$ in a horizontal format.

SOLUTION

$(x - 1)(x + 4)(x + 5) = (x^2 + 3x - 4)(x + 5)$

$= (x^2 + 3x - 4)x + (x^2 + 3x - 4)5$

$= x^3 + 3x^2 - 4x + 5x^2 + 15x - 20$

$= x^3 + 8x^2 + 11x - 20$

Some binomial products occur so frequently that it is worth memorizing their patterns. You can verify these polynomial identities by multiplying.

KEY IDEA

Special Product Patterns

Sum and Difference	**Example**
$(a + b)(a - b) = a^2 - b^2$	$(x + 3)(x - 3) = x^2 - 9$
Square of a Binomial	**Example**
$(a + b)^2 = a^2 + 2ab + b^2$	$(y + 4)^2 = y^2 + 8y + 16$
$(a - b)^2 = a^2 - 2ab + b^2$	$(2t - 5)^2 = 4t^2 - 20t + 25$
Cube of a Binomial	**Example**
$(a + b)^3 = a^3 + 3a^2b + 3ab^2 + b^3$	$(z + 3)^3 = z^3 + 9z^2 + 27z + 27$
$(a - b)^3 = a^3 - 3a^2b + 3ab^2 - b^3$	$(m - 2)^3 = m^3 - 6m^2 + 12m - 8$

COMMON ERROR

In general,

$(a \pm b)^2 \neq a^2 \pm b^2$

and

$(a \pm b)^3 \neq a^3 \pm b^3$.

EXAMPLE 5 Proving a Polynomial Identity

a. Prove the polynomial identity for the cube of a binomial representing a sum:

$(a + b)^3 = a^3 + 3a^2b + 3ab^2 + b^3$.

b. Use the cube of a binomial in part (a) to calculate 11^3.

SOLUTION

a. Expand and simplify the expression on the left side of the equation.

$$\begin{aligned}(a + b)^3 &= (a + b)(a + b)(a + b)\\ &= (a^2 + 2ab + b^2)(a + b)\\ &= (a^2 + 2ab + b^2)a + (a^2 + 2ab + b^2)b\\ &= a^3 + 2a^2b + ab^2 + a^2b + 2ab^2 + b^3\\ &= a^3 + 3a^2b + 3ab^2 + b^3 \checkmark\end{aligned}$$

▶ The simplified left side equals the right side of the original identity. So, the identity $(a + b)^3 = a^3 + 3a^2b + 3ab^2 + b^3$ is true.

b. To calculate 11^3 using the cube of a binomial, note that $11 = 10 + 1$.

$11^3 = (10 + 1)^3$	Write 11 as 10 + 1.
$= 10^3 + 3(10)^2(1) + 3(10)(1)^2 + 1^3$	Cube of a binomial pattern
$= 1000 + 300 + 30 + 1$	Simplify.
$= 1331$	Add.

EXAMPLE 6 Using Special Product Patterns

REMEMBER

The Power of a Product Property states that

$(ab)^m = a^mb^m$

where a and b are real numbers and m is an integer.

Find each product.

a. $(4n + 5)(4n - 5)$ **b.** $(9y - 2)^2$ **c.** $(ab + 4)^3$

SOLUTION

a. $(4n + 5)(4n - 5) = (4n)^2 - 5^2$	Sum and difference pattern
$= 16n^2 - 25$	Simplify.
b. $(9y - 2)^2 = (9y)^2 - 2(9y)(2) + 2^2$	Square of a binomial pattern
$= 81y^2 - 36y + 4$	Simplify.
c. $(ab + 4)^3 = (ab)^3 + 3(ab)^2(4) + 3(ab)(4)^2 + 4^3$	Cube of a binomial pattern
$= a^3b^3 + 12a^2b^2 + 48ab + 64$	Simplify.

SELF-ASSESSMENT

1 I do not understand. 2 I can do it with help. 3 I can do it on my own. 4 I can teach someone else.

Find the product.

7. $(4x^2 + x - 5)(2x + 1)$ **8.** $(y - 2)(5y^2 + 3y - 1)$ **9.** $(m - 2)(m - 1)(m + 3)$

10. $(3t - 2)(3t + 2)$ **11.** $(5a + 2)^2$ **12.** $(xy - 3)^3$

13. MP **STRUCTURE** In your own words, explain why the set of polynomials is closed under multiplication.

14. a. Prove the polynomial identity for the cube of a binomial representing a difference: $(a - b)^3 = a^3 - 3a^2b + 3ab^2 - b^3$.

b. Use the cube of a binomial in part (a) to calculate 9^3.

Pascal's Triangle

Consider the expansion of the binomial $(a + b)^n$ for whole number values of n. When you arrange the coefficients of the variables in the expansion of $(a + b)^n$, you will see a special pattern called **Pascal's Triangle**. Pascal's Triangle is named after French mathematician Blaise Pascal (1623–1662).

KEY IDEA

Pascal's Triangle

In Pascal's Triangle, the first and last numbers in each row are 1. Every number other than 1 is the sum of the closest two numbers in the row directly above it. The numbers in Pascal's Triangle are the same numbers that are the coefficients of binomial expansions, as shown in the first six rows.

	n	$(a + b)^n$	Binomial Expansion	Pascal's Triangle
0th row	0	$(a + b)^0 =$	1	1
1st row	1	$(a + b)^1 =$	$1a + 1b$	1 1
2nd row	2	$(a + b)^2 =$	$1a^2 + 2ab + 1b^2$	1 2 1
3rd row	3	$(a + b)^3 =$	$1a^3 + 3a^2b + 3ab^2 + 1b^3$	1 3 3 1
4th row	4	$(a + b)^4 =$	$1a^4 + 4a^3b + 6a^2b^2 + 4ab^3 + 1b^4$	1 4 6 4 1
5th row	5	$(a + b)^5 =$	$1a^5 + 5a^4b + 10a^3b^2 + 10a^2b^3 + 5ab^4 + 1b^5$	1 5 10 10 5 1

Blaise Pascal (1623–1662)

In general, the nth row in Pascal's Triangle gives the coefficients of $(a + b)^n$. Here are some other observations about the expansion of $(a + b)^n$.

1. An expansion has $n + 1$ terms.
2. The power of a begins with n, decreases by 1 in each successive term, and ends with 0.
3. The power of b begins with 0, increases by 1 in each successive term, and ends with n.
4. The sum of the powers of each term is n.

EXAMPLE 7 Using Pascal's Triangle to Expand Binomials

Use Pascal's Triangle to expand (a) $(x - 2)^5$ and (b) $(3y + 1)^3$.

SOLUTION

a. The coefficients from the fifth row of Pascal's Triangle are 1, 5, 10, 10, 5, and 1.

$$(x - 2)^5 = 1x^5 + 5x^4(-2) + 10x^3(-2)^2 + 10x^2(-2)^3 + 5x(-2)^4 + 1(-2)^5$$
$$= x^5 - 10x^4 + 40x^3 - 80x^2 + 80x - 32$$

b. The coefficients from the third row of Pascal's Triangle are 1, 3, 3, and 1.

$$(3y + 1)^3 = 1(3y)^3 + 3(3y)^2(1) + 3(3y)(1)^2 + 1(1)^3$$
$$= 27y^3 + 27y^2 + 9y + 1$$

SELF-ASSESSMENT

1 I do not understand. 2 I can do it with help. 3 I can do it on my own. 4 I can teach someone else.

15. Use Pascal's Triangle to expand (a) $(z + 3)^4$ and (b) $(2t - 1)^5$.

16. WRITING Describe three different methods to expand $(x + 3)^3$.

4.2 Practice WITH CalcChat® AND CalcView®

In Exercises 1–6, find the sum. ▶ *Example 1*

1. $(3x^2 + 4x - 1) + (-2x^2 - 3x + 2)$
2. $(-5x^2 + 4x - 2) + (-8x^2 + 2x + 1)$
3. $(12x^5 - 3x^4 + 2x - 5) + (8x^4 - 3x^3 + 4x + 1)$
4. $(8x^4 + 2x^2 - 1) + (3x^3 - 5x^2 + 7x + 1)$
5. $(2x^5 + 7x^6 - 3x^2 + 9x) + (5x^5 + 8x^3 - 6x^2 + 2x - 5)$
6. $(9x^4 - 3x^3 + 4x^2 + 5x + 7) + (11x^4 - 9 - 4x^2 - 11x)$

In Exercises 7–12, find the difference. ▶ *Example 2*

7. $(3x^3 - 2x^2 + 4x - 8) - (5x^3 + 12x^2 - 3x - 4)$
8. $(7x^4 - 9x^3 - 4x^2 + 5x + 6) - (2x^4 + 3x^3 - x^2 + x - 4)$
9. $(5x^6 - 2x^4 + 9x^3 + 2x - 4) - (7x^5 - 8x^4 + 2x - 11)$
10. $(4x^5 - 7x^3 - 9x^2 + 18) - (14x^5 - 8x^4 + 11x^2 + x)$
11. $(8x^5 + 6x^3 - 2x^2 + 10x) - (4 + 9x^5 - x^3 - 13x^2)$
12. $(3x - 9x^2 + 11x^4 + 11) - (2x^4 + 6x^3 + 2x - 9)$

In Exercises 13–20, find the product. ▶ *Example 3*

13. $7x^3(5x^2 + 3x + 1)$
14. $-4x^5(11x^3 + 2x^2 + 9x + 1)$
15. $(5x^2 - 4x + 6)(-2x + 3)$
16. $(-x - 3)(2x^2 + 5x + 8)$
17. $(x^2 - 2x - 4)(x^2 - 3x - 5)$
18. $(3x^2 + x - 2)(-4x^2 - 2x - 1)$
19. $(3x^3 - 9x + 7)(x^2 - 2x + 1)$
20. $(4x^2 - 8x - 2)(x^4 + 3x^2 + 4x)$

In Exercises 21–26, find the product of the binomials. ▶ *Example 4*

21. $(x - 3)(x + 2)(x + 4)$
22. $(x - 5)(x + 2)(x - 6)$
23. $(x - 2)(3x + 1)(4x - 3)$
24. $(2x + 5)(x - 2)(3x + 4)$
25. $(3x - 4)(5 - 2x)(4x + 1)$
26. $(4 - 5x)(1 - 2x)(3x + 2)$

27. **MP REASONING** Prove the polynomial identity $(a + b)(a - b) = a^2 - b^2$. Then give an example of two whole numbers greater than 10 that can be multiplied using mental math and the given identity. Justify your answer. ▶ *Example 5*

28. **MP NUMBER SENSE** Your Spanish club wants to order 29 hooded sweatshirts that cost \$31 each. Explain how you can use the polynomial identity $(a + b)(a - b) = a^2 - b^2$ and mental math to find the total cost of the hooded sweatshirts.

In Exercises 29–38, find the product. ▶ *Example 6*

29. $(x - 9)(x + 9)$
30. $(m + 6)^2$
31. $(3c - 5)^2$
32. $(2y - 5)(2y + 5)$
33. $(7h + 4)^2$
34. $(9g - 4)^2$
35. $(2k + 6)^3$
36. $(4n - 3)^3$
37. $(pq - 2)^3$
38. $(wz + 8)^3$

ERROR ANALYSIS In Exercises 39 and 40, describe and correct the error in performing the operation.

39.

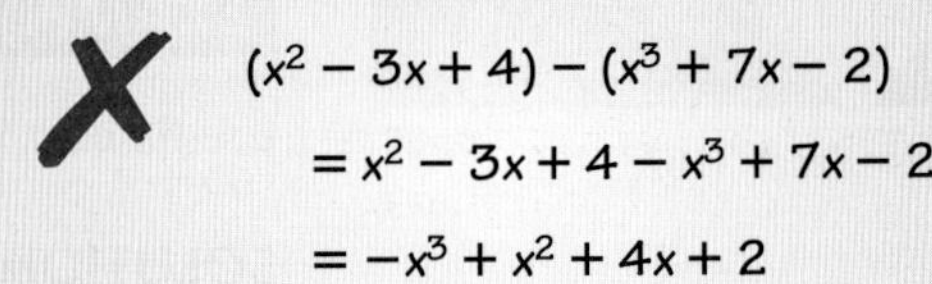

40.

✗ $(2x - 7)^3 = (2x)^3 - 7^3$
$= 8x^3 - 343$

In Exercises 41–46, use Pascal's Triangle to expand the binomial. ▶ *Example 7*

41. $(6m + 2)^2$
42. $(2t + 4)^3$
43. $(2q - 3)^4$
44. $(g + 2)^5$
45. $(yz + 1)^5$
46. $(np - 1)^4$

47. MODELING REAL LIFE During a recent period of time, the numbers (in thousands) of males M and females F who attend degree-granting institutions in the United States can be modeled by

$$M = 0.75t^2 - 79.5t + 9020$$

$$F = 22.44t^2 - 264.1t + 11{,}971$$

where t is time in years. Write a polynomial to model the total number of people attending degree-granting institutions. Interpret its constant term.

48. MODELING REAL LIFE You throw a ball up into the air. The velocity v (in meters per second) of the ball after t seconds is given by $v = -9.8t + 10$. The mass m of the ball is 0.5 kilogram.

a. Use the formula $K = \frac{1}{2}mv^2$ to write a polynomial in standard form that represents the kinetic energy K (in joules) of the ball after t seconds.

b. The potential energy U (in joules) of the ball after t seconds is given by

$$U = -24.01t^2 + 49t + 4.9.$$

Write a polynomial that represents the total kinetic and potential energy. Interpret your result.

CONNECTING CONCEPTS In Exercises 49 and 50, write an expression for the volume of the figure as a polynomial in standard form.

49.

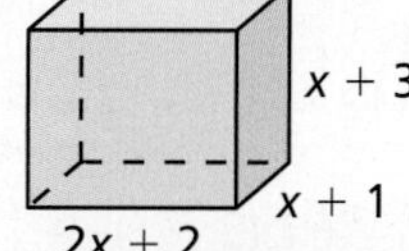

50.

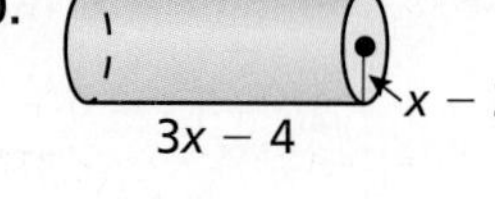

51. **MP REASONING** Is it possible for $x^2 + 3x + 2x^{-1}$ to be the sum, difference, or product of two polynomials? Explain your reasoning.

52. COMPARING METHODS Find the product $(a^2 + 4b^2)^2(3a^2 - b^2)^2$ using two different methods. Which method do you prefer? Explain.

53. **MP PROBLEM SOLVING** The sphere is centered in the cube. Write an expression for the volume of the cube outside the sphere as a polynomial in standard form.

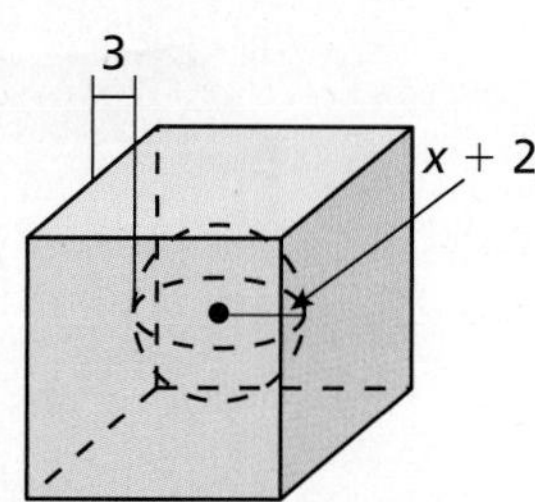

54. MAKING AN ARGUMENT Is the sum of two binomials always a binomial? Is the product of two binomials always a trinomial? Explain your reasoning.

55. MODELING REAL LIFE Two people make three deposits into their bank accounts. The accounts earn interest at the same rate r at the end of each year.

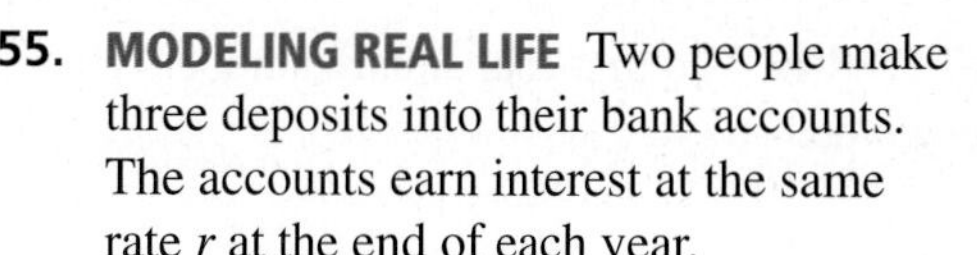

http://www.anytow

Person A — Account No. 2-5384100608

Date	Transaction	Amount
01/01/2018	Deposit	\$2000.00
01/01/2019	Deposit	\$3000.00
01/01/2020	Deposit	\$1000.00

http://www.anytow

Person B — Account No. 1-5233032905

Date	Transaction	Amount
01/01/2018	Deposit	\$5000.00
01/01/2019	Deposit	\$1000.00
01/01/2020	Deposit	\$4000.00

On January 1, 2021, Person A's account is worth

$$2000(1 + r)^3 + 3000(1 + r)^2 + 1000(1 + r).$$

a. Write a polynomial for the value of Person B's account on January 1, 2021.

b. Write the total value of the two accounts as a polynomial in standard form. Then interpret the coefficients of the polynomial.

c. What is the total value of the two accounts on January 1, 2021 when the interest rate is 0.01?

56. HOW DO YOU SEE IT? What polynomials are being multiplied in the table? What is the degree of the product?

	$2x^2$	$-x$	4
$3x$	$6x^3$	$-3x^2$	$12x$
-7	$-14x^2$	$7x$	-28

57. **MP REASONING** Copy Pascal's Triangle and include rows for $n = 6, 7, 8, 9$, and 10. Use the new rows to expand $(x + 3)^7$ and $(x - 5)^9$.

58. ABSTRACT REASONING You are given the function $f(x) = (x + a)(x + b)(x + c)(x + d)$. When $f(x)$ is written in standard form, show that the coefficient of x^3 is the sum of a, b, c, and d, and the constant term is the product of a, b, c, and d.

59. DRAWING CONCLUSIONS Let $g(x) = 12x^4 + 8x + 9$ and $h(x) = 3x^5 + 2x^3 - 7x + 4$.

a. What is the degree of the polynomial $g(x) + h(x)$? $g(x) - h(x)$? $g(x) \cdot h(x)$?

b. In general, if $g(x)$ and $h(x)$ are polynomials such that $g(x)$ has degree m and $h(x)$ has degree n, and $m > n$, what is the degree of $g(x) + h(x)$? $g(x) - h(x)$? $g(x) \cdot h(x)$?

60. **MP PATTERNS** The first four square numbers are represented below.

1 4 9 16

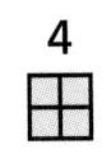

a. Find the differences between consecutive square numbers. What do you notice?

b. Show how the polynomial identity $(n + 1)^2 - n^2 = 2n + 1$ models the differences between consecutive square numbers.

c. Prove the polynomial identity in part (b).

In Exercises 61 and 62, simplify the expression.

61. $(1 + i)^5$

62. $(3 - i)^6$

63. **CRITICAL THINKING** Recall that a Pythagorean triple is a set of positive integers a, b, and c such that $a^2 + b^2 = c^2$. You can use the polynomial identity $(x^2 - y^2)^2 + (2xy)^2 = (x^2 + y^2)^2$ to generate Pythagorean triples.

GO DIGITAL

a. Prove the polynomial identity.

b. Use the identity to generate the Pythagorean triple when $x = 6$ and $y = 5$. Then verify that your answer satisfies $a^2 + b^2 = c^2$.

64. **THOUGHT PROVOKING**
Is the square of an odd number odd or even? Prove your answer.

REVIEW & REFRESH

WATCH

65. Solve $x^2 - 7x + 2 = -2x^2 + 10x - 9$ by graphing.

In Exercises 66–69, perform the operation.

66. $(7x^2 - 4) - (3x^2 - 5x + 1)$

67. $(-5x^4 + 6x^3 + x - 12) + (4x^4 - 15x^3 + 2x^2 - 3)$

68. $(x^2 - 3x + 2)(3x - 1)$

69. $(x - 4)^3$

70. Write an equation of the parabola.

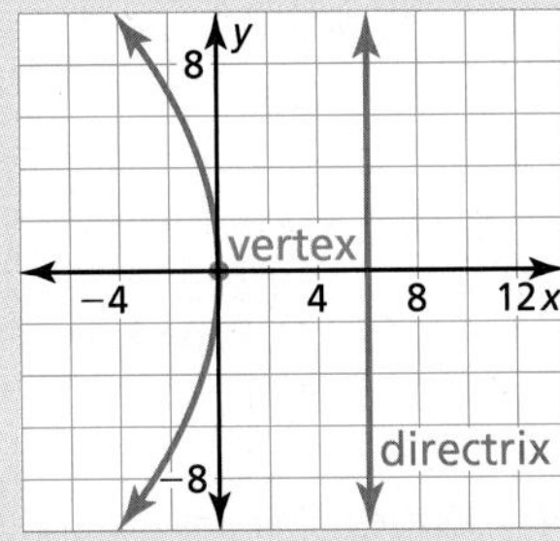

In Exercises 71 and 72, describe the end behavior of the function.

71. $f(x) = -2x^5 + 4x^3 - x^2 - 8$

72. $g(x) = 3x^6 - x^5 - 5x^2 + 4x + 1$

73. **MP REASONING** The vertex of a parabola is $(-3, 4)$ and one x-intercept is 2. What is the other x-intercept? Explain your reasoning.

74. Graph the system of quadratic inequalities.

$$y > x^2 + 4x + 5$$
$$y \leq x^2 - 1$$

In Exercises 75 and 76, evaluate the function for the given value of x.

75. $y = 2(0.5)^x$; $x = 3$

76. $y = -9(3)^x$; $x = -1$

In Exercises 77–80, perform the operation. Write the answer in standard form.

77. $(3 - 2i) + (5 + 9i)$

78. $(12 + 3i) - (7 - 8i)$

79. $7i(-3i)$

80. $(4 + i)(2 - i)$

81. **MODELING REAL LIFE** A contractor is hired to build an apartment complex. Each unit has a bedroom, kitchen, and bathroom. The bedroom will have the same area as the kitchen. The owner orders 980 square feet of tile to completely cover the floors of two kitchens and two bathrooms. Determine how many square feet of carpet is needed for each bedroom.

4.3 Dividing Polynomials

Learning Target Divide polynomials by other polynomials and use the Remainder Theorem.

Success Criteria

- I can use long division to divide polynomials by other polynomials.
- I can divide polynomials by binomials of the form $x - k$ using synthetic division.
- I can explain the Remainder Theorem.

EXPLORE IT! Dividing Polynomials

Work with a partner.

a. Consider the polynomial $x^3 + 2x^2 - x - 2$. Use technology to explore the graph of the polynomial divided by the binomial $x + a$ for the given values of a. What do you notice? What can you conclude?

i. $a = 1$ **ii.** $a = 2$

iii. $a = 3$ **iv.** $a = -1$

v. $a = -2$ **vi.** $a = 4$

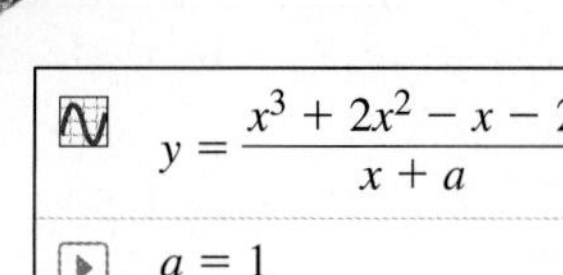

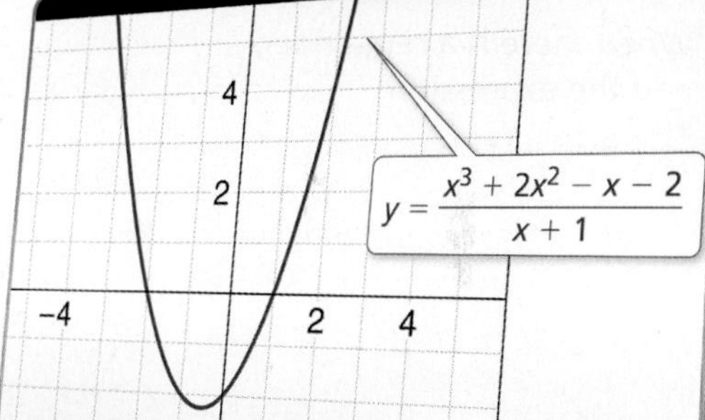

Math Practice

Make Conjectures What do you notice about the degree of the resulting polynomial when a linear binomial divides evenly into a cubic polynomial?

b. Repeat part (a) for the polynomial $x^3 - 3x^2 - 10x + 24$ and the given values of a. What do you notice? What can you conclude?

i. $a = -1$ **ii.** $a = 2$

iii. $a = -2$ **iv.** $a = 3$

v. $a = -3$ **vi.** $a = 4$

c. Use technology to explore the graph of the polynomial $x^4 + 7x^3 + 9x^2 - 7x - 10$ divided by the binomial $x + a$ for several values of a. Make several observations about the graphs.

Long Division of Polynomials

Vocabulary 

polynomial long division, *p. 170*
synthetic division, *p. 171*

When you divide a polynomial $f(x)$ by a nonzero polynomial divisor $d(x)$, you get a quotient polynomial $q(x)$ and a remainder polynomial $r(x)$.

$$\frac{f(x)}{d(x)} = q(x) + \frac{r(x)}{d(x)}$$

The degree of the divisor $d(x)$ is less than or equal to the degree of the dividend $f(x)$. Also, the degree of the remainder $r(x)$ must be less than the degree of the divisor. When the remainder is 0, the divisor *divides evenly* into the dividend. One way to divide polynomials is called **polynomial long division**.

EXAMPLE 1 Using Polynomial Long Division 

Divide $2x^4 + 3x^3 + 5x - 1$ by $x^2 + 3x + 2$.

SOLUTION

Write polynomial division in the same format you use when dividing numbers. Include a "0" as the coefficient of x^2 in the dividend. At each step, divide the term with the highest power in what is left of the dividend by the first term of the divisor. This gives the next term of the quotient.

$$\begin{array}{rll}
 & 2x^2 - 3x + 5 & \leftarrow \text{quotient} \\
x^2 + 3x + 2 \,\big)\!\! & 2x^4 + 3x^3 + 0x^2 + 5x - 1 & \\
 & \underline{2x^4 + 6x^3 + 4x^2} & \text{Multiply divisor by } \frac{2x^4}{x^2} = 2x^2. \\
 & -3x^3 - 4x^2 + 5x & \text{Subtract. Bring down next term.} \\
 & \underline{-3x^3 - 9x^2 - 6x} & \text{Multiply divisor by } \frac{-3x^3}{x^2} = -3x. \\
 & 5x^2 + 11x - 1 & \text{Subtract. Bring down next term.} \\
 & \underline{5x^2 + 15x + 10} & \text{Multiply divisor by } \frac{5x^2}{x^2} = 5. \\
 & -4x - 11 & \leftarrow \text{remainder}
\end{array}$$

COMMON ERROR
When there is a remainder, add the expression $\frac{r(x)}{d(x)}$, not just $r(x)$.

▶ $$\frac{2x^4 + 3x^3 + 5x - 1}{x^2 + 3x + 2} = 2x^2 - 3x + 5 + \frac{-4x - 11}{x^2 + 3x + 2}$$

Check You can check the result of a division problem by multiplying the quotient by the divisor and adding the remainder. The result should be the dividend.

$$\begin{aligned}
&(2x^2 - 3x + 5)(x^2 + 3x + 2) + (-4x - 11) \\
&\quad = (2x^2)(x^2 + 3x + 2) - (3x)(x^2 + 3x + 2) + (5)(x^2 + 3x + 2) - 4x - 11 \\
&\quad = 2x^4 + 6x^3 + 4x^2 - 3x^3 - 9x^2 - 6x + 5x^2 + 15x + 10 - 4x - 11 \\
&\quad = 2x^4 + 3x^3 + 5x - 1 \ \checkmark
\end{aligned}$$

SELF-ASSESSMENT 1 I do not understand. 2 I can do it with help. 3 I can do it on my own. 4 I can teach someone else.

Divide using polynomial long division.

1. $(2x^2 - 5x - 3) \div (x - 3)$

2. $(4x^2 + 3x - 11) \div (x + 1)$

3. $(x^3 - x^2 - 2x + 8) \div (x - 1)$

4. $(x^4 + 2x^2 - x + 5) \div (x^2 - x + 1)$

5. **MP REASONING** Write a trinomial that can be divided evenly by $x - 4$. Explain how you found your answer.

Synthetic Division

Synthetic division is a shortcut for dividing polynomials by binomials of the form $x - k$.

EXAMPLE 2 Using Synthetic Division

Divide $-x^3 + 4x^2 + 9$ by $x - 3$.

SOLUTION

Step 1 Write the coefficients of the dividend in order of descending exponents. Include a "0" for the missing x-term. Because the divisor is $x - 3$, $k = 3$. Write the k-value to the left of the vertical bar.

$$\text{k-value} \rightarrow \begin{array}{r|rrrr} 3 & -1 & 4 & 0 & 9 \\ & & & & \\ \hline & & & & \end{array} \leftarrow \text{coefficients of } -x^3 + 4x^2 + 9$$

Step 2 Bring down the leading coefficient. Multiply the leading coefficient by k. Write the product under the second coefficient. Add.

$$\begin{array}{r|rrrr} 3 & -1 & 4 & 0 & 9 \\ & & -3 & & \\ \hline & -1 & 1 & & \end{array}$$

Step 3 Multiply the previous sum by k. Write the product under the third coefficient. Add. Repeat this process for the remaining coefficient. The first three numbers in the bottom row are the coefficients of the quotient, and the last number is the remainder.

$$\text{coefficients of quotient} \rightarrow \begin{array}{r|rrrr} 3 & -1 & 4 & 0 & 9 \\ & & -3 & 3 & 9 \\ \hline & -1 & 1 & 3 & 18 \end{array} \leftarrow \text{remainder}$$

▶ $$\frac{-x^3 + 4x^2 + 9}{x - 3} = -x^2 + x + 3 + \frac{18}{x - 3}$$

EXAMPLE 3 Using Synthetic Division

Divide $3x^3 - 2x^2 + 2x - 5$ by $x + 1$.

SOLUTION

Use synthetic division. Because the divisor is $x + 1 = x - (-1)$, $k = -1$.

$$\begin{array}{r|rrrr} -1 & 3 & -2 & 2 & -5 \\ & & -3 & 5 & -7 \\ \hline & 3 & -5 & 7 & -12 \end{array}$$

▶ $$\frac{3x^3 - 2x^2 + 2x - 5}{x + 1} = 3x^2 - 5x + 7 - \frac{12}{x + 1}$$

SELF-ASSESSMENT 1 I do not understand. 2 I can do it with help. 3 I can do it on my own. 4 I can teach someone else.

6. Divide (a) $(x^3 - 3x^2 - 7x + 6) \div (x - 2)$ and (b) $(2x^3 - x - 7) \div (x + 3)$ using synthetic division.

7. **MP REASONING** Explain why you can simply "bring down" the leading coefficient of the dividend when using synthetic division.

The Remainder Theorem

The remainder in the synthetic division process has an important interpretation. When you divide a polynomial $f(x)$ by $d(x) = x - k$, the result is

$\dfrac{f(x)}{d(x)} = q(x) + \dfrac{r(x)}{d(x)}$ Polynomial division

$\dfrac{f(x)}{x - k} = q(x) + \dfrac{r(x)}{x - k}$ Substitute $x - k$ for $d(x)$.

$f(x) = (x - k)q(x) + r(x).$ Multiply both sides by $x - k$.

Because either $r(x) = 0$ *or* the degree of $r(x)$ is less than the degree of $x - k$, you know that $r(x)$ is a constant function. So, let $r(x) = r$, where r is a real number, and evaluate $f(x)$ when $x = k$.

$f(k) = (k - k)q(k) + r$ Substitute k for x and r for $r(x)$.

$f(k) = r$ Simplify.

This result is stated in the *Remainder Theorem.*

KEY IDEA

The Remainder Theorem

If a polynomial $f(x)$ is divided by $x - k$, then the remainder is $r = f(k)$.

The Remainder Theorem tells you that synthetic division can be used to evaluate a polynomial function. So, to evaluate $f(x)$ when $x = k$, divide $f(x)$ by $x - k$. The remainder will be $f(k)$.

EXAMPLE 4 Evaluating a Polynomial

Use synthetic division to evaluate $f(x) = 5x^3 - x^2 + 13x + 29$ when $x = -4$.

SOLUTION

$$\begin{array}{r|rrrr} -4 & 5 & -1 & 13 & 29 \\ & & -20 & 84 & -388 \\ \hline & 5 & -21 & 97 & -359 \end{array}$$

▶ The remainder is -359. So, you can conclude from the Remainder Theorem that $f(-4) = -359$.

Check Check this by substituting $x = -4$ in the original function.

$$\begin{aligned} f(-4) &= 5(-4)^3 - (-4)^2 + 13(-4) + 29 \\ &= -320 - 16 - 52 + 29 \\ &= -359 \ ✓ \end{aligned}$$

SELF-ASSESSMENT 1 I do not understand. 2 I can do it with help. 3 I can do it on my own. 4 I can teach someone else.

Use synthetic division to evaluate the function for the indicated value of x.

8. $f(x) = 4x^2 - 10x - 21$; $x = 5$

9. $f(x) = 5x^4 + 2x^3 - 20x - 6$; $x = 2$

10. **MP REASONING** Is the set of polynomials closed under division? Justify your answer.

4.3 Practice WITH CalcChat® AND CalcView®

In Exercises 1–8, divide using polynomial long division. *Example 1*

1. $(x^2 + x - 17) \div (x - 4)$
2. $(3x^2 - 14x - 5) \div (x - 5)$
3. $(x^3 + x^2 + x + 2) \div (x^2 - 1)$
4. $(7x^3 + x^2 + x) \div (x^2 + 1)$
5. $(8x^3 - 3x + 1) \div (4x^3 + x^2 - 2x - 3)$
6. $(10x^3 + 5x^2 - 1) \div (2x^3 - 4x^2 - x + 2)$
7. $(5x^4 - 2x^3 - 7x^2 - 39) \div (x^2 + 2x - 4)$
8. $(4x^4 + 5x - 4) \div (x^2 - 3x - 2)$

In Exercises 9–16, divide using synthetic division. *Examples 2 and 3*

9. $(x^2 + 8x + 1) \div (x - 4)$
10. $(4x^2 - 13x - 5) \div (x - 2)$
11. $(2x^2 - x + 7) \div (x + 5)$
12. $(x^2 + 9) \div (x + 4)$
13. $(x^3 - 4x + 6) \div (x + 3)$
14. $(3x^3 - 5x^2 - 2) \div (x - 1)$
15. $(x^4 - 5x^3 - 8x^2 + 13x - 12) \div (x - 6)$
16. $(x^4 + 4x^3 + 16x - 35) \div (x + 5)$

ANALYZING RELATIONSHIPS In Exercises 17–20, match the equivalent expressions. Justify your answers.

17. $(x^2 + x - 3) \div (x - 2)$
18. $(x^2 - x - 3) \div (x - 2)$
19. $(x^2 - x + 3) \div (x - 2)$
20. $(x^2 + x + 3) \div (x - 2)$

A. $x + 1 - \dfrac{1}{x - 2}$ B. $x + 3 + \dfrac{9}{x - 2}$

C. $x + 1 + \dfrac{5}{x - 2}$ D. $x + 3 + \dfrac{3}{x - 2}$

ERROR ANALYSIS In Exercises 21 and 22, describe and correct the error in using synthetic division to divide $x^3 - 5x + 3$ by $x - 2$.

21.

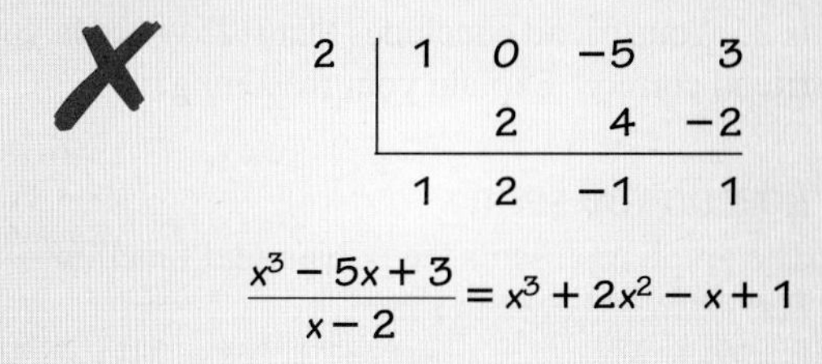

22.

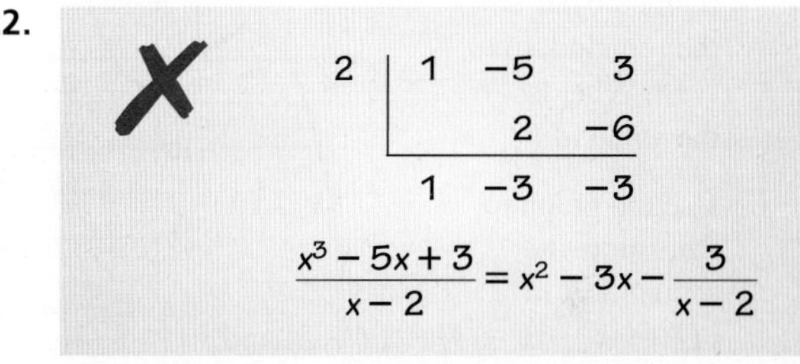

In Exercises 23–30, use synthetic division to evaluate the function for the indicated value of x. *Example 4*

23. $f(x) = -x^2 - 8x + 30;\ x = -1$
24. $f(x) = 3x^2 + 2x - 20;\ x = 3$
25. $f(x) = x^3 - 2x^2 + 4x + 3;\ x = 2$
26. $f(x) = x^3 + x^2 - 3x + 9;\ x = -4$
27. $f(x) = x^3 - 6x + 1;\ x = 6$
28. $f(x) = x^3 - 9x - 7;\ x = 10$
29. $f(x) = x^4 + 6x^2 - 7x + 1;\ x = 3$
30. $f(x) = -x^4 - x^3 - 2;\ x = 5$

31. **MODELING REAL LIFE** You are making a blanket with a fringe border of equal width on each side. The length of the blanket without the fringe border is 72 inches. The combined area A (in square inches) of the blanket and the fringe border is represented by $A = 4x^2 + 240x + 3456$. What is the width of the blanket without the fringe border?

32. MODELING REAL LIFE The profit P (in millions of dollars) earned by a company x years since 2014 can be modeled by $P = 0.1x^3 - x^2 + 2.5x + 1.7$, where $0 < x < 6$. Use synthetic division to show that the company earned a profit of \$2.3 million in 2020.

33. MAKING AN ARGUMENT You use synthetic division to divide $f(x)$ by $x - a$ and find that the remainder is 25. Your friend concludes that $f(25) = a$. Is your friend correct? Explain your reasoning.

34. HOW DO YOU SEE IT?
The graph represents the polynomial function $f(x) = x^3 + 3x^2 - x - 3$.

a. When $f(x)$ is divided by $x - k$, the remainder is -15. What is the value of k?

b. Use the graph to determine the remainders of $(x^3 + 3x^2 - x - 3) \div (x + 3)$ and $(x^3 + 3x^2 - x - 3) \div (x + 1)$.

35. COLLEGE PREP What is the value of k such that $(x^3 - x^2 + kx - 30) \div (x - 5)$ has a remainder of 0?

Ⓐ -14 Ⓑ -2

Ⓒ 26 Ⓓ 32

36. CONNECTING CONCEPTS
The volume V of the triangular prism is given by $V = 2x^3 - 5x^2 - 19x + 42$. Find an expression for the missing dimension.

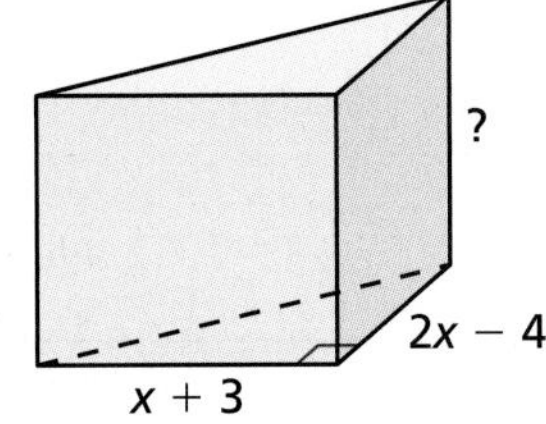

37. MP STRUCTURE You divide two polynomials and obtain the result $5x^2 - 13x + 47 - \frac{102}{x + 2}$. What is the dividend? How did you find it?

38. THOUGHT PROVOKING
Explain how to use synthetic division to divide $4x^3 - 3x^2 + 3x - 7$ by $4x + 1$. Then find the quotient.

REVIEW & REFRESH

In Exercises 39–42, find the zero(s) of the function.

39. $f(x) = x^2 - 6x + 9$

40. $g(x) = 3(x + 6)(x - 2)$

41. $g(x) = x^2 + 14x + 45$

42. $h(x) = 4x^2 + 36$

43. Use synthetic division to evaluate $f(x) = x^3 - 3x + 12$ when $x = -5$.

44. Write an equation of the parabola in vertex form.

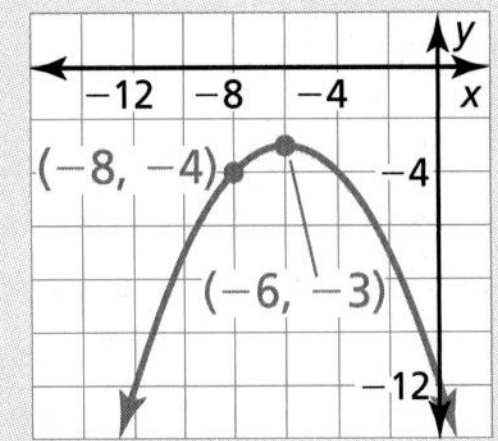

45. MP STRUCTURE For what value of k is the expression $(x + 3)(kx^2 - 4x + 1) - (2x^3 + 9x^2 - 7)$ equal to $4x^3 + 5x^2 - 11x + 10$?

46. Graph $f(x) = x^3 - 3x + 1$.

47. Divide $4x^4 - 2x^3 + x^2 - 5x + 8$ by $x^2 - 2x - 1$.

In Exercises 48 and 49, solve the equation.

48. $5^{2x} = 5^{x+4}$ **49.** $2^{x-3} = 16$

50. The table shows the results of flipping a penny 50 times. What is the experimental probability of flipping heads?

Heads	Tails
23	27

In Exercises 51–54, simplify the expression.

51. $\sqrt{300x^3}$ **52.** $\sqrt{\frac{10}{49}}$

53. $2\sqrt{3} - 6\sqrt{5} + 7\sqrt{3}$ **54.** $5\sqrt{2} - \sqrt{8}$

55. MODELING REAL LIFE City officials want to build a rectangular flower bed in a downtown park. The flower bed must have a perimeter of 50 feet and an area of at least 100 square feet. Describe the possible lengths of the flower bed.

4.4 Factoring Polynomials

Learning Target Factor polynomials and use the Factor Theorem.

Success Criteria
- I can find common monomial factors of polynomials.
- I can factor polynomials.
- I can use the Factor Theorem.

EXPLORE IT! Factoring Polynomials

Work with a partner.

a. When sketching the graph of the function $f(x) = x^3 + 7x^2 + 7x - 15$, you notice that the sum of the coefficients of the terms is zero.

$$1 + 7 + 7 + (-15) = 0$$

What does this tell you about $f(1)$?

b. How can you use the result of part (a) to algebraically find other zeros of the function?

c. Find all the zeros of $f(x) = x^3 + 7x^2 + 7x - 15$. Use the zeros to sketch a graph of f.

d. Use technology to match each polynomial function with its graph. Then write each polynomial function in factored form. Explain your reasoning.

i. $f(x) = x^2 + 5x + 4$ **ii.** $f(x) = x^3 - 2x^2 - x + 2$

iii. $f(x) = x^3 + x^2 - 2x$ **iv.** $f(x) = x^3 - x$

v. $f(x) = x^4 - 5x^2 + 4$ **vi.** $f(x) = x^4 - 2x^3 - x^2 + 2x$

Math Practice

Justify Conclusions Given that $x - k$ is a factor of a polynomial $f(x)$, what can you determine about the value $f(k)$? Justify your answer.

A. 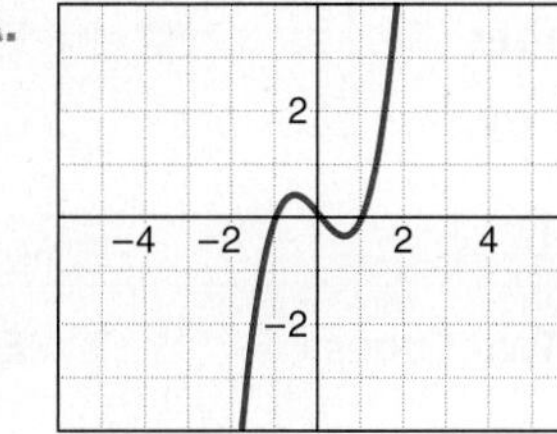

B. 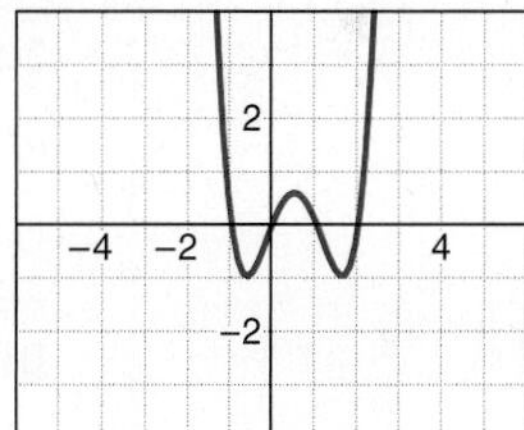

C. 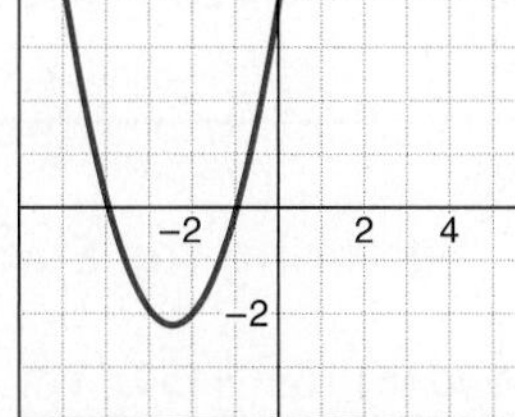

D. 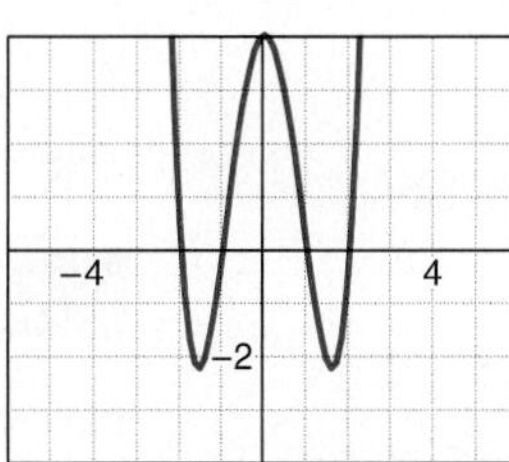

E. 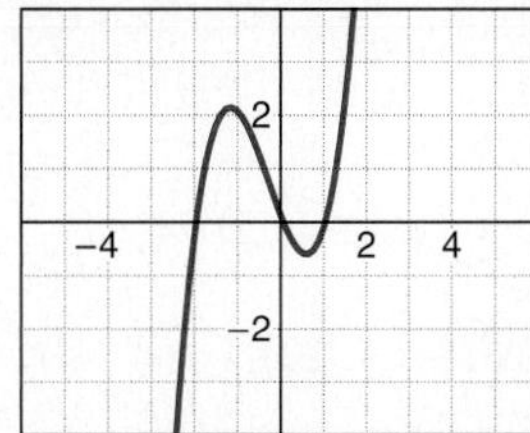

F. 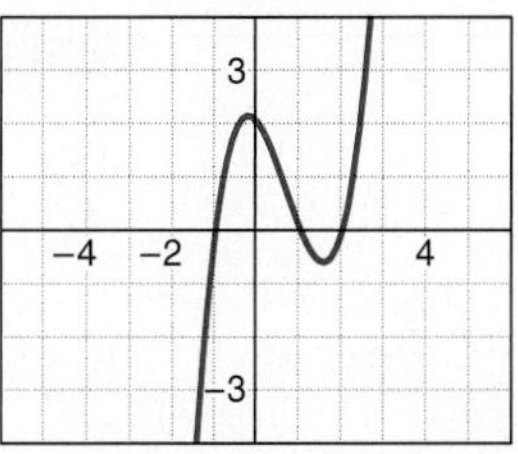

e. What information can you obtain about the graph of a polynomial function written in factored form?

Factoring Polynomials

Vocabulary

factored completely, *p. 176*
factor by grouping, *p. 177*
quadratic form, *p. 177*

Previously, you factored quadratic polynomials. You can also factor polynomials with degree greater than 2. Some of these polynomials can be *factored completely* using techniques you have previously learned. A factorable polynomial with integer coefficients is **factored completely** when it is written as a product of unfactorable polynomials with integer coefficients.

EXAMPLE 1 Finding a Common Monomial Factor

Factor each polynomial completely.

a. $x^3 - 4x^2 - 5x$ **b.** $3y^5 - 48y^3$ **c.** $5z^4 + 30z^3 + 45z^2$

SOLUTION

a. $x^3 - 4x^2 - 5x = x(x^2 - 4x - 5)$ Factor common monomial.

$= x(x - 5)(x + 1)$ Factor trinomial.

b. $3y^5 - 48y^3 = 3y^3(y^2 - 16)$ Factor common monomial.

$= 3y^3(y - 4)(y + 4)$ Difference of two squares pattern

c. $5z^4 + 30z^3 + 45z^2 = 5z^2(z^2 + 6z + 9)$ Factor common monomial.

$= 5z^2(z + 3)^2$ Perfect square trinomial pattern

In part (b) of Example 1, the special factoring pattern for the difference of two squares was used to factor the expression completely. There are also factoring patterns that you can use to factor the sum or difference of two *cubes*.

KEY IDEA

Special Factoring Patterns

Sum of Two Cubes

$a^3 + b^3 = (a + b)(a^2 - ab + b^2)$

Example

$64x^3 + 1 = (4x)^3 + 1^3$

$= (4x + 1)(16x^2 - 4x + 1)$

Difference of Two Cubes

$a^3 - b^3 = (a - b)(a^2 + ab + b^2)$

Example

$27x^3 - 8 = (3x)^3 - 2^3$

$= (3x - 2)(9x^2 + 6x + 4)$

EXAMPLE 2 Factoring the Sum or Difference of Two Cubes

Factor (a) $x^3 - 125$ and (b) $16s^5 + 54s^2$ completely.

SOLUTION

a. $x^3 - 125 = x^3 - 5^3$ Write as $a^3 - b^3$.

$= (x - 5)(x^2 + 5x + 25)$ Difference of two cubes pattern

b. $16s^5 + 54s^2 = 2s^2(8s^3 + 27)$ Factor common monomial.

$= 2s^2[(2s)^3 + 3^3]$ Write $8s^3 + 27$ as $a^3 + b^3$.

$= 2s^2(2s + 3)(4s^2 - 6s + 9)$ Sum of two cubes pattern

For some polynomials, you can **factor by grouping** pairs of terms that have a common monomial factor. The pattern for factoring by grouping is shown below.

$$ra + rb + sa + sb = r(a + b) + s(a + b)$$
$$= (r + s)(a + b)$$

EXAMPLE 3 Factoring by Grouping

Factor $z^3 + 5z^2 - 4z - 20$ completely.

SOLUTION

$z^3 + 5z^2 - 4z - 20 = z^2(z + 5) - 4(z + 5)$	Factor by grouping.
$= (z^2 - 4)(z + 5)$	Distributive Property
$= (z - 2)(z + 2)(z + 5)$	Difference of two squares pattern

An expression of the form $au^2 + bu + c$, where u is an algebraic expression, is said to be in **quadratic form**. The factoring techniques you have studied can sometimes be used to factor such expressions.

EXAMPLE 4 Factoring Polynomials in Quadratic Form

Factor (a) $16x^4 - 81$ and (b) $3p^8 + 15p^5 + 18p^2$ completely.

SOLUTION

a. $16x^4 - 81 = (4x^2)^2 - 9^2$	Write as $a^2 - b^2$.
$= (4x^2 + 9)(4x^2 - 9)$	Difference of two squares pattern
$= (4x^2 + 9)(2x - 3)(2x + 3)$	Difference of two squares pattern
b. $3p^8 + 15p^5 + 18p^2 = 3p^2(p^6 + 5p^3 + 6)$	Factor common monomial.
$= 3p^2(p^3 + 3)(p^3 + 2)$	Factor trinomial in quadratic form.

Math Practice

Look for Structure

The expression $16x^4 - 81$ is in quadratic form because it can be written as $u^2 - 81$ where $u = 4x^2$.

SELF-ASSESSMENT

1 I do not understand. 2 I can do it with help. 3 I can do it on my own. 4 I can teach someone else.

Factor the polynomial completely.

1. $x^3 - 7x^2 + 10x$
2. $3n^7 - 75n^5$
3. $8m^5 - 16m^4 + 8m^3$
4. $a^3 + 27$
5. $6z^5 - 750z^2$
6. $x^3 + 4x^2 - x - 4$
7. $3y^3 + y^2 + 9y + 3$
8. $-16n^4 + 625$
9. $5w^6 - 25w^4 + 30w^2$
10. **WRITING** How do you know when a polynomial is factored completely?
11. **VOCABULARY** Explain when you should try factoring a polynomial by grouping.
12. **WHICH ONE DOESN'T BELONG?** Which expression does *not* belong with the other three? Explain your reasoning.

$12x^4 - 3x^2$	$3x^2(4x^2 - 1)$	$3x^2(2x + 1)(2x - 1)$	$3x^2(2x - 1)^2$

The Factor Theorem

When dividing polynomials in the previous section, the examples had nonzero remainders. Suppose the remainder is 0 when a polynomial $f(x)$ is divided by $x - k$. Then,

$$\frac{f(x)}{x-k} = q(x) + \frac{0}{x-k} = q(x)$$

where $q(x)$ is the quotient polynomial. Therefore, $f(x) = (x - k) \cdot q(x)$, so that $x - k$ is a factor of $f(x)$. This result is summarized by the *Factor Theorem*, which is a special case of the Remainder Theorem.

READING

In other words, $x - k$ is a factor of $f(x)$ if and only if k is a zero of f.

KEY IDEA

The Factor Theorem

A polynomial $f(x)$ has a factor $x - k$ if and only if $f(k) = 0$.

EXAMPLE 5 Determining Whether a Linear Binomial is a Factor

Determine whether (a) $x - 2$ is a factor of $f(x) = x^2 + 2x - 4$ and (b) $x + 5$ is a factor of $f(x) = 3x^4 + 15x^3 - x^2 + 25$.

SOLUTION

a. Find $f(2)$ by direct substitution.

$$\begin{aligned} f(2) &= 2^2 + 2(2) - 4 \\ &= 4 + 4 - 4 \\ &= 4 \end{aligned}$$

▶ Because $f(2) \neq 0$, the binomial $x - 2$ is not a factor of $f(x) = x^2 + 2x - 4$.

b. Find $f(-5)$ by synthetic division.

$$\begin{array}{r|rrrrr} -5 & 3 & 15 & -1 & 0 & 25 \\ & & -15 & 0 & 5 & -25 \\ \hline & 3 & 0 & -1 & 5 & 0 \end{array}$$

▶ Because $f(-5) = 0$, the binomial $x + 5$ is a factor of $f(x) = 3x^4 + 15x^3 - x^2 + 25$.

STUDY TIP

In part (b), notice that direct substitution would have resulted in more difficult computations than synthetic division.

EXAMPLE 6 Factoring a Polynomial

Show that $x + 3$ is a factor of $f(x) = x^4 + 3x^3 - x - 3$. Then factor $f(x)$ completely.

SOLUTION

Show that $f(-3) = 0$ by synthetic division.

$$\begin{array}{r|rrrrr} -3 & 1 & 3 & 0 & -1 & -3 \\ & & -3 & 0 & 0 & 3 \\ \hline & 1 & 0 & 0 & -1 & 0 \end{array}$$

Because $f(-3) = 0$, you can conclude that $x + 3$ is a factor of $f(x)$ by the Factor Theorem. Use the result to write $f(x)$ as a product of two factors and then factor completely.

$f(x) = x^4 + 3x^3 - x - 3$	Write original polynomial.
$= (x + 3)(x^3 - 1)$	Write as a product of two factors.
$= (x + 3)(x - 1)(x^2 + x + 1)$	Difference of two cubes pattern

Because the x-intercepts of the graph of a function are the zeros of the function, you can use the graph to approximate the zeros. You can check the approximations using the Factor Theorem.

EXAMPLE 7 Modeling Real Life

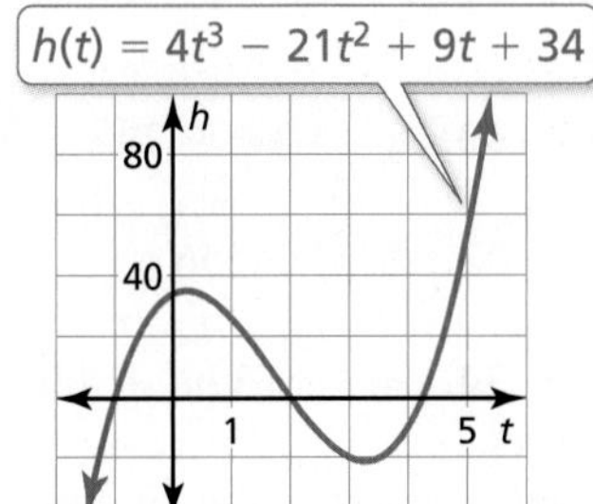

A roller coaster starts at a height of 34 feet and then goes through an underground tunnel. The function $h(t) = 4t^3 - 21t^2 + 9t + 34$ represents the coaster's height h (in feet) after t seconds, where $0 \le t \le 5$. How long is the coaster in the tunnel?

SOLUTION

1. **Understand the Problem** You are given a function rule and a graph that represent the height of a roller coaster. You are asked to determine how long the roller coaster is in an underground tunnel.

2. **Make a Plan** Use the graph to estimate the zeros of the function and check using the Factor Theorem. Then use the zeros to describe where the graph lies below the t-axis.

3. **Solve and Check** From the graph, two of the zeros appear to be -1 and 2. The third zero is between 4 and 5.

STUDY TIP

You could also check that 2 is a zero using the original function, but using the resulting quotient polynomial helps you find the remaining factor.

Step 1 Determine whether -1 is a zero using synthetic division.

$$\begin{array}{r|rrrr} -1 & 4 & -21 & 9 & 34 \\ & & -4 & 25 & -34 \\ \hline & 4 & -25 & 34 & 0 \end{array}$$

$h(-1) = 0$, so -1 is a zero of h and $t + 1$ is a factor of $h(t)$.

Step 2 Determine whether 2 is a zero. If 2 is also a zero, then $t - 2$ is a factor of the resulting quotient polynomial. Check using synthetic division.

$$\begin{array}{r|rrr} 2 & 4 & -25 & 34 \\ & & 8 & -34 \\ \hline & 4 & -17 & 0 \end{array}$$

The remainder is 0, so $t - 2$ is a factor of $h(t)$ and 2 is a zero of h.

So, $h(t) = (t + 1)(t - 2)(4t - 17)$. The factor $4t - 17$ indicates that the zero between 4 and 5 is $\frac{17}{4}$, or 4.25.

▶ The zeros are -1, 2, and 4.25. Only $t = 2$ and $t = 4.25$ are in the given domain. The graph shows that the roller coaster is in the underground tunnel for $4.25 - 2 = 2.25$ seconds.

Check

Use technology to analyze function values.

t	$h(t)$	
0.5	33.75	
1.25	20.25	
2	0	zero
2.75	−16.88	negative
3.5	−20.25	negative
4.25	0	zero
5	54	

SELF-ASSESSMENT

1 I do not understand. 2 I can do it with help. 3 I can do it on my own. 4 I can teach someone else.

13. Determine whether $x - 4$ is a factor of $f(x) = 2x^2 + 5x - 12$.

14. Show that $x - 6$ is a factor of $f(x) = x^3 - 5x^2 - 6x$. Then factor $f(x)$ completely.

15. In Example 7, does your answer change when you first determine whether 2 is a zero and then whether -1 is a zero? Justify your answer.

16. WRITING Explain the Factor Theorem and why it is useful.

4.4 Practice WITH CalcChat® AND CalcView®

In Exercises 1–8, factor the polynomial completely. *Example 1*

1. $x^3 - 2x^2 - 24x$
2. $4k^5 - 100k^3$
3. $3p^5 - 192p^3$
4. $2m^6 - 24m^5 + 64m^4$
5. $2q^4 + 9q^3 - 18q^2$
6. $3r^6 - 11r^5 - 20r^4$
7. $10w^{10} - 19w^9 + 6w^8$
8. $18v^9 + 33v^8 + 14v^7$

In Exercises 9–16, factor the polynomial completely. *Example 2*

9. $x^3 + 64$
10. $y^3 + 512$
11. $g^3 - 343$
12. $c^3 - 27$
13. $4h^9 - 256h^6$
14. $9n^6 - 6561n^3$
15. $16t^7 + 250t^4$
16. $270z^{11} - 80z^8$

ERROR ANALYSIS In Exercises 17 and 18, describe and correct the error in factoring the polynomial completely.

17.

$3x^3 + 27x = 3x(x^2 + 9)$

$= 3x(x + 3)(x - 3)$

18.

✗ $x^9 + 8x^3 = (x^3)^3 + (2x)^3$

$= (x^3 + 2x)[(x^3)^2 - (x^3)(2x) + (2x)^2]$

$= (x^3 + 2x)(x^6 - 2x^4 + 4x^2)$

In Exercises 19–26, factor the polynomial completely. *Example 3*

19. $y^3 - 5y^2 + 6y - 30$
20. $m^3 - m^2 + 7m - 7$
21. $3a^3 + 18a^2 + 8a + 48$
22. $2k^3 - 20k^2 + 5k - 50$
23. $x^3 - 8x^2 - 4x + 32$
24. $z^3 - 5z^2 - 9z + 45$
25. $4q^3 - 16q^2 - 9q + 36$
26. $16n^3 + 32n^2 - n - 2$

In Exercises 27–34, factor the polynomial completely. *Example 4*

27. $49k^4 - 9$
28. $4m^4 - 25$
29. $c^4 + 9c^2 + 20$
30. $y^4 - 3y^2 - 28$
31. $16z^4 - 625$
32. $81a^4 - 256$
33. $3r^8 + 3r^5 - 60r^2$
34. $4n^{12} - 32n^7 + 48n^2$

In Exercises 35–40, determine whether the binomial is a factor of the polynomial. *Example 5*

35. $f(x) = 2x^3 + 5x^2 - 37x - 60;\ x - 4$
36. $g(x) = 3x^3 - 28x^2 + 29x + 140;\ x + 7$
37. $h(x) = 6x^5 - 15x^4 - 9x^3;\ x + 3$
38. $g(x) = 8x^5 - 58x^4 + 60x^3 + 140;\ x - 6$
39. $h(x) = 6x^4 - 6x^3 - 84x^2 + 144x;\ x + 4$
40. $t(x) = 48x^4 + 36x^3 - 138x^2 - 36x;\ x + 2$

In Exercises 41–46, show that the binomial is a factor of the polynomial. Then factor the polynomial completely. *Example 6*

41. $g(x) = x^3 - x^2 - 20x;\ x + 4$
42. $t(x) = x^3 - 5x^2 - 9x + 45;\ x - 5$
43. $f(x) = x^4 - 6x^3 - 8x + 48;\ x - 6$
44. $s(x) = x^4 + 4x^3 - 64x - 256;\ x + 4$
45. $r(x) = x^3 - 37x + 84;\ x + 7$
46. $h(x) = x^3 - x^2 - 24x - 36;\ x + 2$

MP STRUCTURE In Exercises 47–54, use the method of your choice to factor the polynomial completely. Explain your reasoning.

47. $a^6 + a^5 - 30a^4$
48. $8m^3 - 343$
49. $z^3 - 7z^2 - 9z + 63$
50. $2p^8 - 12p^5 + 16p^2$
51. $64r^3 + 729$
52. $5x^5 - 10x^4 - 40x^3$
53. $16n^4 - 1$
54. $9k^3 - 24k^2 + 3k - 8$

ANALYZING RELATIONSHIPS In Exercises 55–58, match the function with the correct graph. Explain your reasoning.

55. $f(x) = (x - 2)(x - 3)(x + 1)$

56. $g(x) = x(x + 2)(x + 1)(x - 2)$

57. $h(x) = (x + 2)(x + 3)(x - 1)$

58. $k(x) = x(x - 2)(x - 1)(x + 2)$

A.
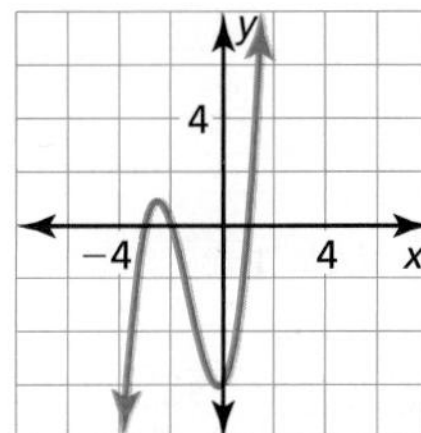

B.
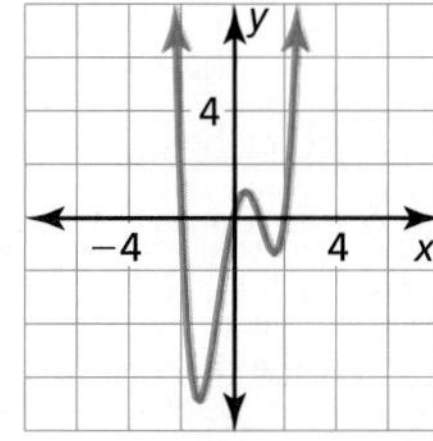

C.
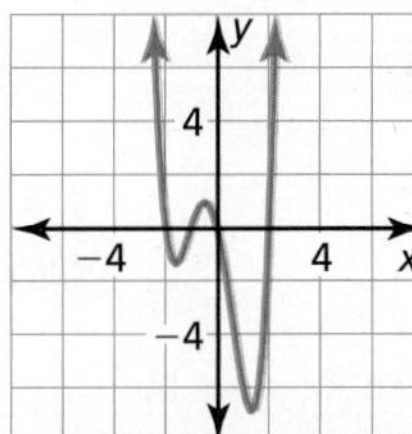

D.
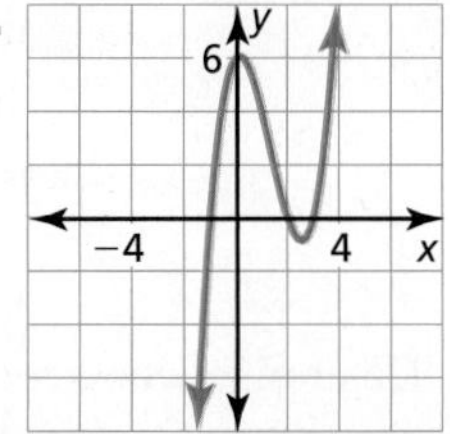

59. MODELING REAL LIFE The volume (in cubic inches) of a shipping box is modeled by $V = 2x^3 - 19x^2 + 39x$, where x is the length (in inches). Determine the values of x for which the model makes sense. Explain your reasoning. *Example 7*

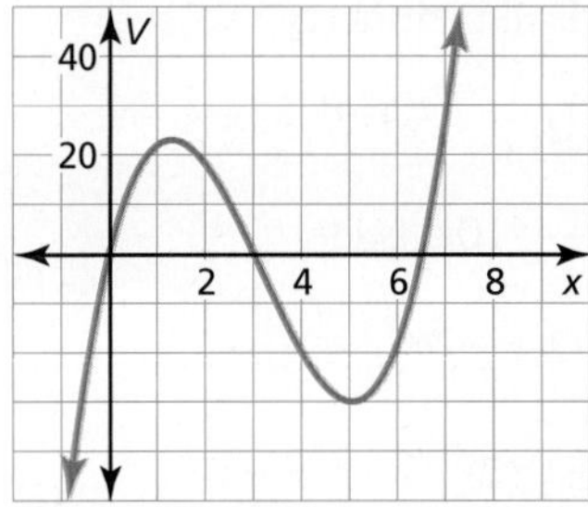

60. MODELING REAL LIFE The profit P (in millions of dollars) for a smart speaker manufacturer can be modeled by $P = -21x^3 + 46x$, where x is the number (in millions) of speakers produced. The company now produces 1 million speakers and makes a profit of \$25 million, but it would like to cut back production. What lesser number of speakers could the company produce and still make the same profit?

61. MP REASONING Determine whether each polynomial is factored completely. If not, factor completely.

GO DIGITAL

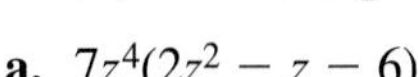

a. $7z^4(2z^2 - z - 6)$

b. $(2 - n)(n^2 + 6n)(3n - 11)$

c. $3(4y - 5)(9y^2 - 6y - 4)$

62. COLLEGE PREP Consider the function $f(x) = x^3 - 3x^2 - 4x$. For what value of k does $\frac{f(x)}{x - k}$ have a remainder not equal to 0? Explain.

Ⓐ -1 Ⓑ 0

Ⓒ 1 Ⓓ 4

63. MAKING AN ARGUMENT You divide $f(x)$ by $x - a$ and find that the remainder does not equal 0. Does this mean that $f(x)$ cannot be factored? Explain.

64. HOW DO YOU SEE IT?
Use the graph to write an equation of the cubic function in factored form. Explain your reasoning.

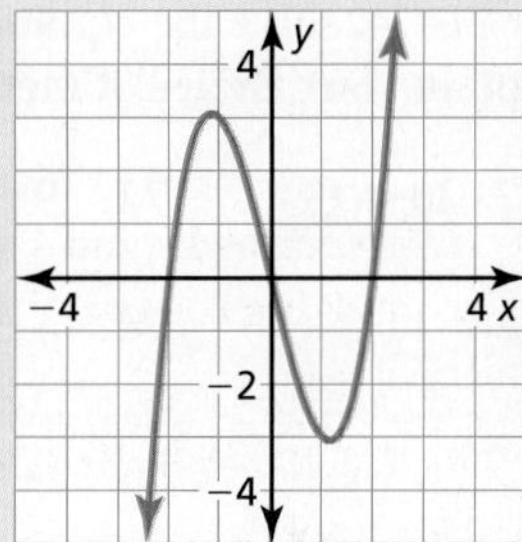

65. ABSTRACT REASONING Factor each polynomial completely.

a. $7ac^2 + bc^2 - 7ad^2 - bd^2$

b. $x^{2n} - 2x^n + 1$

c. $a^5b^2 - a^2b^4 + 2a^4b - 2ab^3 + a^3 - b^2$

66. MP REASONING The graph of the function $f(x) = x^4 + 3x^3 + 2x^2 + x + 3$ is shown. Can you use the Factor Theorem to factor $f(x)$? Explain.

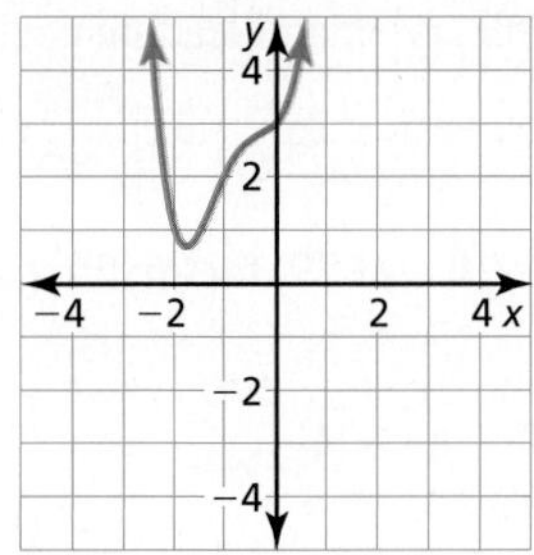

67. **DIG DEEPER** What is the value of k such that $x - 7$ is a factor of $h(x) = 2x^3 - 13x^2 - kx + 105$? Justify your answer.

68. **CONNECTING CONCEPTS** The standard equation of a circle with radius r and center (h, k) is $(x - h)^2 + (y - k)^2 = r^2$. Rewrite each equation of a circle in standard form. Identify the center and radius of the circle. Then graph the circle.

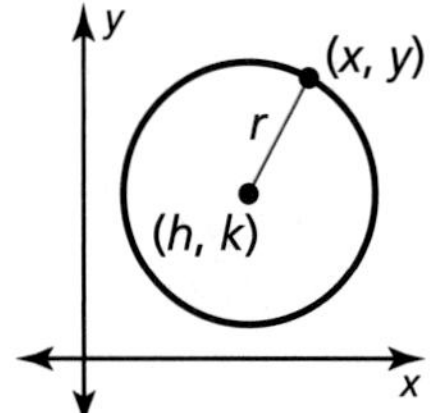

a. $x^2 + 6x + 9 + y^2 = 25$

b. $x^2 - 4x + 4 + y^2 = 9$

c. $x^2 - 8x + 16 + y^2 + 2y + 1 = 36$

69. **CRITICAL THINKING** Use the diagram to complete parts (a)–(c).

a. Explain why $a^3 - b^3$ is equal to the sum of the volumes of the solids I, II, and III.

b. Write an algebraic expression for the volume of each of the three solids. Leave your expressions in factored form.

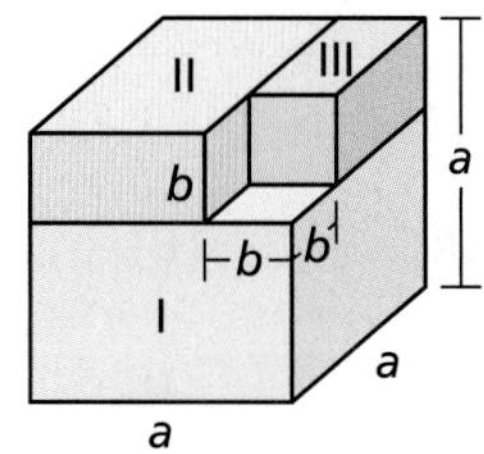

c. Use the results from parts (a) and (b) to derive the difference of two cubes pattern $a^3 - b^3$.

70. **THOUGHT PROVOKING**

Consider the equation $\frac{a^3 - b^3}{(a - b)^3} = \frac{31}{3}$, where a and b are real numbers and $a > b > 0$. Find $\frac{b}{a}$.

REVIEW & REFRESH

In Exercises 71–74, solve the equation using any method. Explain your choice of method.

71. $x^2 \quad x \quad 30 = 0$

72. $9x^2 - 28x + 3 = 0$

73. $x^2 - 8x = 11$

74. $4x^2 + 36x - 4 = 0$

75. Divide $-x^3 + x^2 - 2x - 16$ by $x + 2$.

76. Write an expression for the area and perimeter of the figure shown.

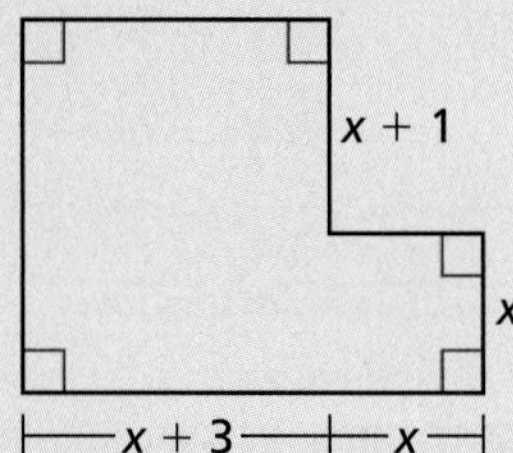

77. Determine whether the function is a polynomial function. If so, write it in standard form and state its degree, type, and leading coefficient.

$$f(x) = 5 + 2x^2 - 3x^4 - 2x - x^3$$

In Exercises 78 and 79, factor the polynomial completely.

78. $z^3 + z^2 - 4z - 4$

79. $49b^4 - 64$

80. Determine whether the table represents an *exponential growth function*, an *exponential decay function*, or *neither*. Explain.

x	−1	0	1	2
y	80	20	5	1.25

In Exercises 81–84, graph the function. Label the vertex and axis of symmetry.

81. $f(x) = -(x - 4)^2 + 3$

82. $g(x) = x^2 - 10x + 11$

83. $h(x) = -2(x - 7)(x + 3)$

84. $j(x) = \frac{1}{4}x(x + 5)$

85. **MODELING REAL LIFE** Determine whether the data show a linear relationship. If so, write an equation of a line of fit. Then estimate y when $x = 60$ and explain its meaning in the context of the situation.

Minutes skating, x	10	15	25	30	45
Distance (miles), y	2.2	3.1	5.0	5.8	8.5

86. Write the sentence as an inequality.

A number n plus 8.5 is no more than 17.

4.5 Solving Polynomial Equations

Learning Target Solve polynomial equations and find zeros of polynomial functions.

Success Criteria

- I can explain how solutions of equations and zeros of functions are related.
- I can solve polynomial equations.
- I can write a polynomial function when given information about its zeros.

EXPLORE IT! Solving Polynomial Equations with Repeated Solutions

Work with a partner. Polynomial equations can have distinct solutions or *repeated solutions*. In parts (a)–(f), solve the equation algebraically. Then use the graph to describe the behavior of the related function near any repeated zeros. What do you notice?

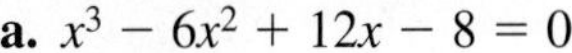

Math Practice

Make Conjectures
What conjecture can you make about the graph of a polynomial function f near the x-axis when a factor of $f(x)$ is raised to an odd power? to an even power?

a. $x^3 - 6x^2 + 12x - 8 = 0$

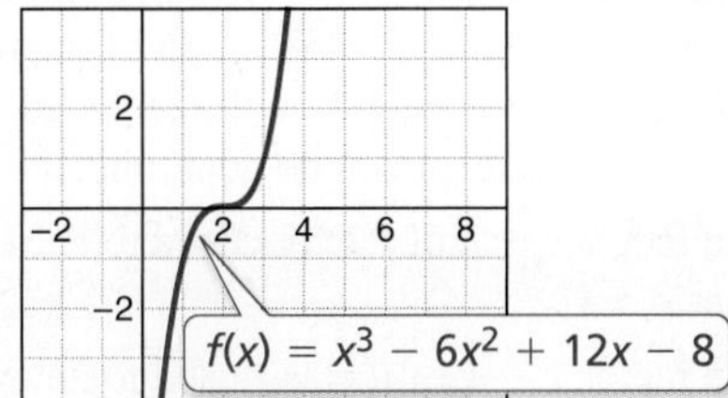

b. $x^3 + 3x^2 + 3x + 1 = 0$

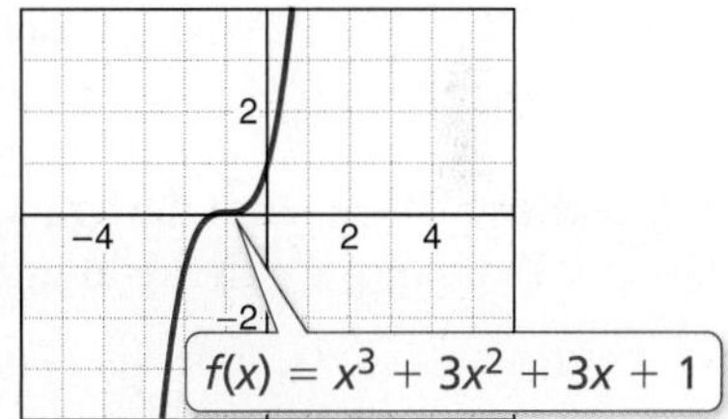

c. $x^3 - 3x + 2 = 0$

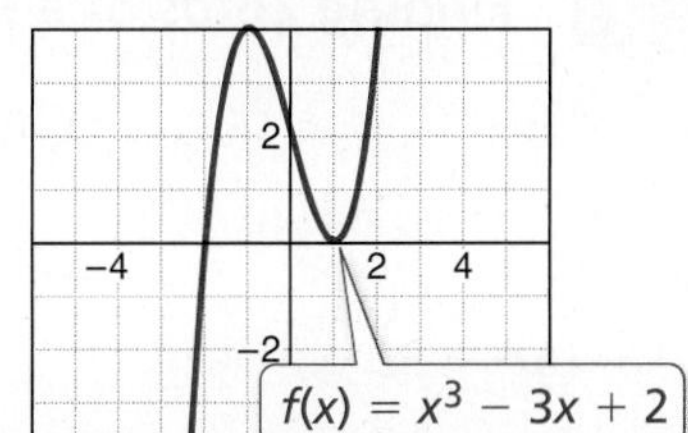

d. $x^3 + x^2 - 2x = 0$

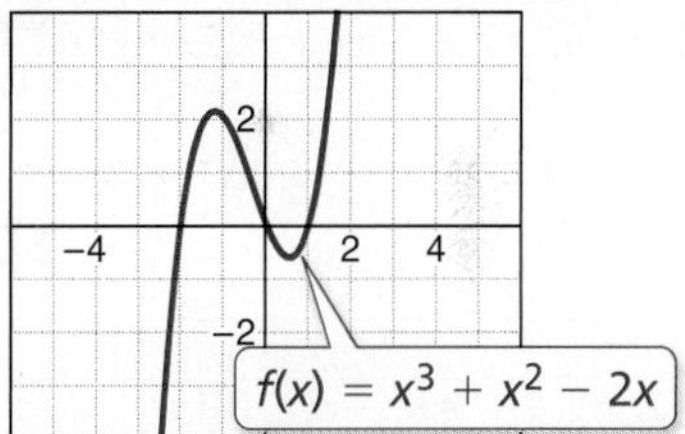

e. $x^3 - 3x - 2 = 0$

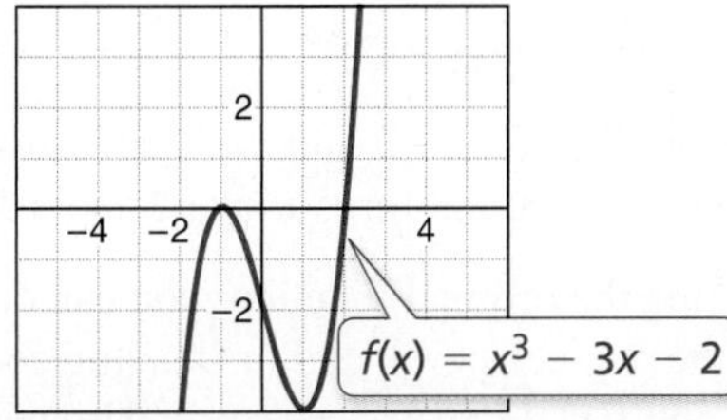

f. $x^3 - 3x^2 + 2x = 0$

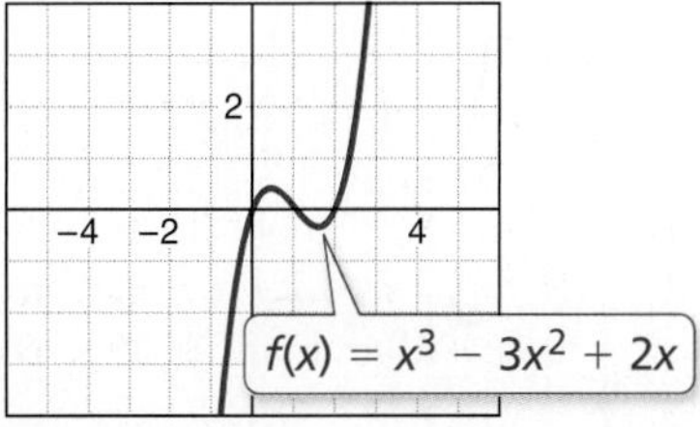

g. MP **CHOOSE TOOLS** Graph the related function for each quartic equation and describe the behavior of the function near its zeros.

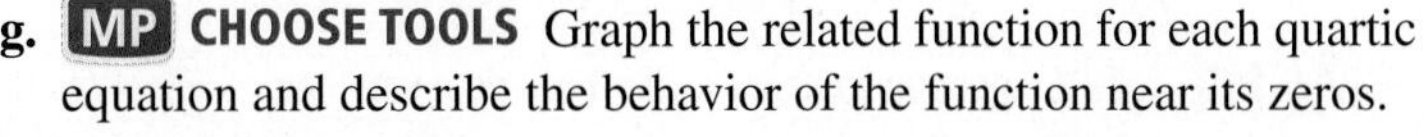

i. $x^4 - 4x^3 + 5x^2 - 2x = 0$ **ii.** $x^4 - 2x^3 - x^2 + 2x = 0$

iii. $x^4 - 4x^3 + 4x^2 = 0$ **iv.** $x^4 + 3x^3 = 0$

h. Describe what it means when a polynomial equation has a repeated solution. How can you determine whether a polynomial equation has a repeated solution?

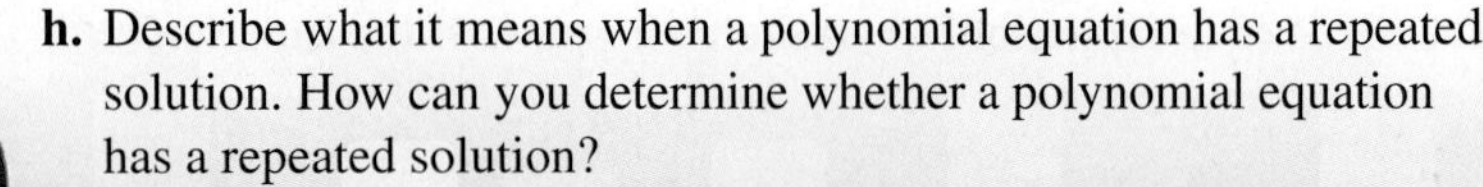

Finding Solutions and Zeros

Vocabulary

repeated solution, *p. 184*

You have used the Zero-Product Property and factoring to solve quadratic equations. You can extend this technique to solve some higher-degree polynomial equations.

EXAMPLE 1 Solving a Polynomial Equation by Factoring

Solve $2x^3 - 12x^2 + 18x = 0$.

SOLUTION

$2x^3 - 12x^2 + 18x = 0$	Write the equation.
$2x(x^2 - 6x + 9) = 0$	Factor common monomial.
$2x(x - 3)^2 = 0$	Perfect square trinomial pattern
$2x = 0$ or $(x - 3)^2 = 0$	Zero-Product Property
$x = 0$ or $x = 3$	Solve for x.

Check

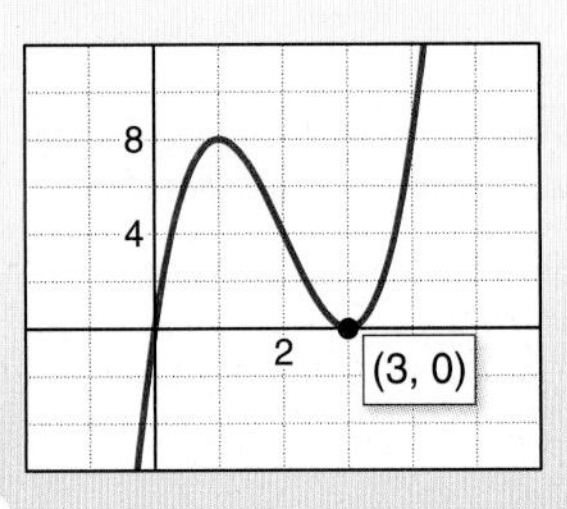

▶ The solutions, or roots, are $x = 0$ and $x = 3$.

In Example 1, the factor $x - 3$ appears more than once. This creates a **repeated solution** of $x = 3$. Note that the graph of the related function touches the x-axis (but does not cross the x-axis) at the repeated zero $x = 3$, and crosses the x-axis at the zero $x = 0$. This concept can be generalized for a polynomial function f as follows.

- When a factor $x - k$ of $f(x)$ is raised to an odd power, the graph of f *crosses* the x-axis at $x = k$.
- When a factor $x - k$ of $f(x)$ is raised to an even power, the graph of f *touches* the x-axis (but does not cross the x-axis) at $x = k$.

EXAMPLE 2 Finding Zeros of a Polynomial Function

Find the zeros of $f(x) = -2x^4 + 16x^2 - 32$. Then sketch a graph of the function.

SOLUTION

$0 = -2x^4 + 16x^2 - 32$	Set $f(x)$ equal to 0.
$0 = -2(x^4 - 8x^2 + 16)$	Factor out -2.
$0 = -2(x^2 - 4)(x^2 - 4)$	Factor trinomial in quadratic form.
$0 = -2(x + 2)(x - 2)(x + 2)(x - 2)$	Difference of two squares pattern
$0 = -2(x + 2)^2(x - 2)^2$	Rewrite using exponents.

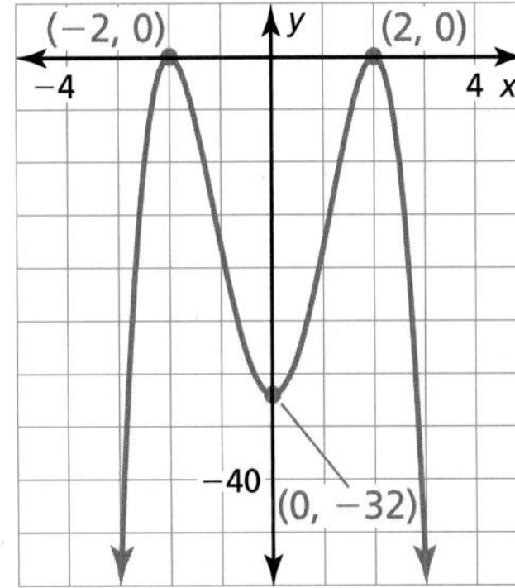

Because both factors $x + 2$ and $x - 2$ are raised to an even power, the graph of f touches the x-axis at the zeros $x = -2$ and $x = 2$.

By analyzing the original function, you can determine that the y-intercept is -32. Because the degree is even and the leading coefficient is negative, $f(x) \to -\infty$ as $x \to -\infty$ and $f(x) \to -\infty$ as $x \to +\infty$. Use these characteristics to sketch a graph of f.

SELF-ASSESSMENT

1 I do not understand. 2 I can do it with help. 3 I can do it on my own. 4 I can teach someone else.

Solve the equation.

1. $4x^4 - 40x^2 + 36 = 0$
2. $-3n^3 + 24n^2 - 48n = 0$
3. $2x^5 + 24x = 14x^3$

Find the zeros of the function. Then sketch a graph of the function.

4. $f(x) = 3x^4 - 6x^2 + 3$
5. $f(x) = x^3 + x^2 - 6x$
6. $h(x) = -x^3 - 2x^2 + 9x + 18$

The Rational Root Theorem

GO DIGITAL

The solutions of the equation $64x^3 + 152x^2 - 62x - 105 = 0$ are $-\frac{5}{2}$, $-\frac{3}{4}$, and $\frac{7}{8}$. Notice that the numerators (5, 3, and 7) of the zeros are factors of the constant term, -105. Also notice that the denominators (2, 4, and 8) are factors of the leading coefficient, 64. These observations are generalized by the *Rational Root Theorem.*

KEY IDEA

The Rational Root Theorem

If $f(x) = a_nx^n + \cdots + a_1x + a_0$ has *integer* coefficients, then every rational solution of $f(x) = 0$ has the following form.

$$\frac{p}{q} = \frac{\text{factor of constant term } a_0}{\text{factor of leading coefficient } a_n}$$

The Rational Root Theorem can be a starting point for finding solutions of polynomial equations. However, the theorem lists only *possible* solutions. In order to find the *actual* solutions, you must test values from the list of possible solutions.

EXAMPLE 3 Using the Rational Root Theorem

Find all the real solutions of $x^3 - 8x^2 + 11x + 20 = 0$.

Math Practice

Look for Structure
What do you notice about the possible rational solutions when the leading coefficient is 1?

SOLUTION

The polynomial that defines the function $f(x) = x^3 - 8x^2 + 11x + 20$ is not easily factorable. Begin by using the Rational Root Theorem.

Step 1 List the possible rational solutions. The leading coefficient of $f(x)$ is 1 and the constant term is 20. So, the possible rational solutions of $f(x) = 0$ are

$$x = \pm\frac{1}{1}, \pm\frac{2}{1}, \pm\frac{4}{1}, \pm\frac{5}{1}, \pm\frac{10}{1}, \pm\frac{20}{1}.$$

STUDY TIP
You can use direct substitution to test possible solutions, but synthetic division helps you identify other factors of the polynomial.

Step 2 Test possible solutions using synthetic division until a solution is found.

Test $x = 1$:

1	1	−8	11	20
		1	−7	4
	1	−7	4	24

$f(1) \neq 0$, so $x - 1$ is not a factor of $f(x)$.

Test $x = -1$:

−1	1	−8	11	20
		−1	9	−20
	1	−9	20	0

$f(-1) = 0$, so $x + 1$ is a factor of $f(x)$.

Step 3 Factor completely using the result of the synthetic division.

$(x + 1)(x^2 - 9x + 20) = 0$ — Write as a product of factors.

$(x + 1)(x - 4)(x - 5) = 0$ — Factor the trinomial.

▶ So, the solutions are $x = -1$, $x = 4$, and $x = 5$.

SELF-ASSESSMENT 1 I do not understand. 2 I can do it with help. 3 I can do it on my own. 4 I can teach someone else.

7. MP **STRUCTURE** Use the Rational Root Theorem to list the possible rational solutions of $x^3 + 14x^2 + 55x + 42 = 0$.

Find all the real solutions of the equation.

8. $x^3 + 2x^2 - 13x + 10 = 0$

9. $x^3 - 5x^2 - 2x + 24 = 0$

In Example 3, the leading coefficient of the polynomial is 1. When the leading coefficient is not 1, the list of possible rational solutions or zeros can increase dramatically. In such cases, the search can be shortened by using a graph.

EXAMPLE 4 Finding Zeros of a Polynomial Function

WATCH

Find all the real zeros of $f(x) = 10x^4 - 11x^3 - 42x^2 + 7x + 12$.

SOLUTION

Step 1 List the possible rational zeros of f: $\pm\frac{1}{1}, \pm\frac{2}{1}, \pm\frac{3}{1}, \pm\frac{4}{1}, \pm\frac{6}{1}, \pm\frac{12}{1}$, $\pm\frac{1}{2}, \pm\frac{3}{2}, \pm\frac{1}{5}, \pm\frac{2}{5}, \pm\frac{3}{5}, \pm\frac{4}{5}, \pm\frac{6}{5}, \pm\frac{12}{5}, \pm\frac{1}{10}, \pm\frac{3}{10}$.

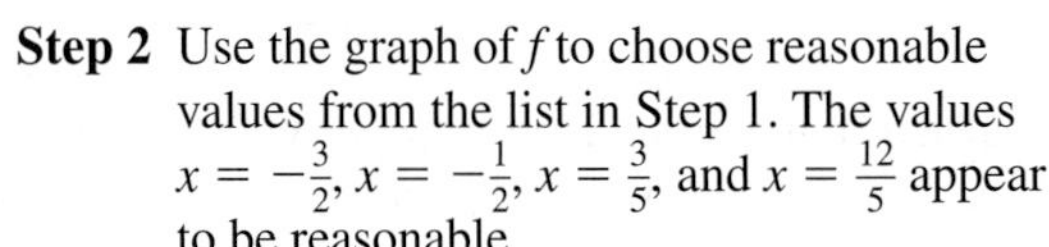

Step 2 Use the graph of f to choose reasonable values from the list in Step 1. The values $x = -\frac{3}{2}$, $x = -\frac{1}{2}$, $x = \frac{3}{5}$, and $x = \frac{12}{5}$ appear to be reasonable.

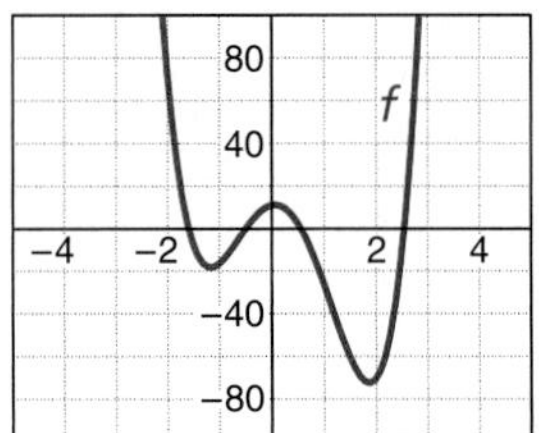

Step 3 Test the values using synthetic division until a zero is found.

$-\frac{3}{2}$	10	−11	−42	7	12
		−15	39	$\frac{9}{2}$	$-\frac{69}{4}$
	10	−26	−3	$\frac{23}{2}$	$-\frac{21}{4}$

$-\frac{3}{2}$ is *not* a zero.

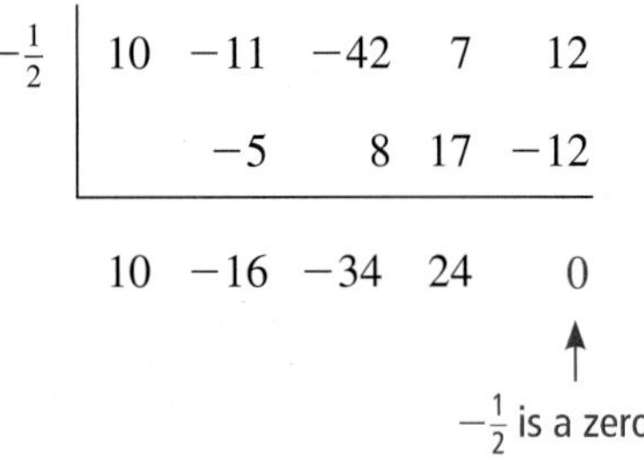

$-\frac{1}{2}$	10	−11	−42	7	12
		−5	8	17	−12
	10	−16	−34	24	0

$-\frac{1}{2}$ is a zero.

Step 4 Factor out a binomial using the result of the synthetic division.

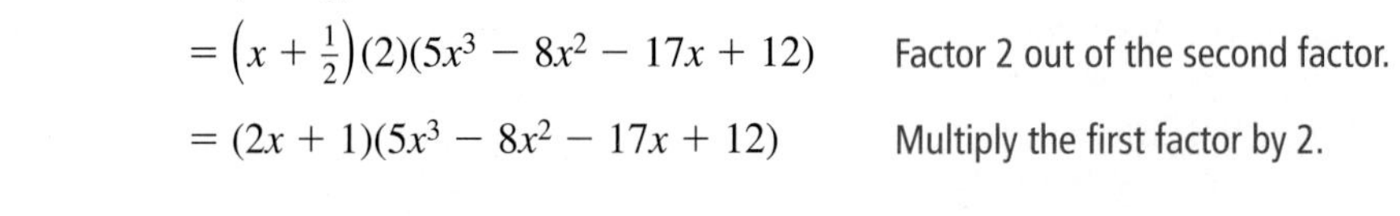

$f(x) = \left(x + \frac{1}{2}\right)(10x^3 - 16x^2 - 34x + 24)$ Write as a product of factors.

$= \left(x + \frac{1}{2}\right)(2)(5x^3 - 8x^2 - 17x + 12)$ Factor 2 out of the second factor.

$= (2x + 1)(5x^3 - 8x^2 - 17x + 12)$ Multiply the first factor by 2.

Step 5 Repeat the steps above for $g(x) = 5x^3 - 8x^2 - 17x + 12$. Any zero of g will also be a zero of f. The possible rational zeros of g are

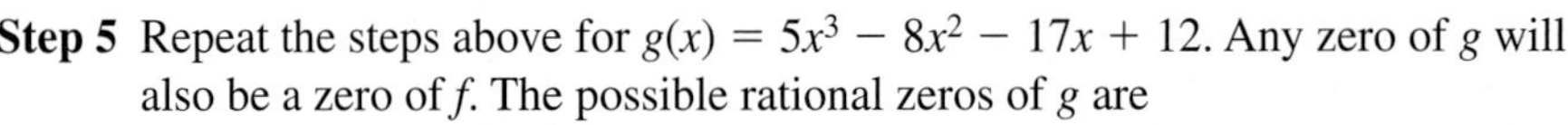

$$x = \pm1, \pm2, \pm3, \pm4, \pm6, \pm12, \pm\frac{1}{5}, \pm\frac{2}{5}, \pm\frac{3}{5}, \pm\frac{4}{5}, \pm\frac{6}{5}, \pm\frac{12}{5}.$$

The graph of g shows that $\frac{3}{5}$ may be a zero. Synthetic division shows that $\frac{3}{5}$ *is* a zero and $g(x) = \left(x - \frac{3}{5}\right)(5x^2 - 5x - 20) = (5x - 3)(x^2 - x - 4)$. It follows that $f(x) = (2x + 1) \cdot g(x) = (2x + 1)(5x - 3)(x^2 - x - 4)$.

Step 6 Find the remaining zeros of f by solving $x^2 - x - 4 = 0$.

$$x = \frac{-(-1) \pm \sqrt{(-1)^2 - 4(1)(-4)}}{2(1)}$$ Substitute 1 for a, −1 for b, and −4 for c in the Quadratic Formula.

$$x = \frac{1 \pm \sqrt{17}}{2}$$ Simplify.

▶ The real zeros of f are $-\frac{1}{2}$, $\frac{3}{5}$, $\frac{1 + \sqrt{17}}{2}$, and $\frac{1 - \sqrt{17}}{2}$.

The Irrational Conjugates Theorem

In Example 4, notice that the irrational zeros are *conjugates* of the form $a + \sqrt{b}$ and $a - \sqrt{b}$. This illustrates the theorem below.

KEY IDEA

The Irrational Conjugates Theorem

Let f be a polynomial function with rational coefficients, and let a and b be rational numbers such that $\sqrt{b}$ is irrational. If $a + \sqrt{b}$ is a zero of f, then $a - \sqrt{b}$ is also a zero of f.

EXAMPLE 5 Using Zeros to Write a Polynomial Function

Write a polynomial function f of least degree that has rational coefficients, a leading coefficient of 1, and the zeros 3 and $2 + \sqrt{5}$.

SOLUTION

Because the coefficients are rational and $2 + \sqrt{5}$ is a zero, $2 - \sqrt{5}$ must also be a zero by the Irrational Conjugates Theorem. Use the three zeros and the Factor Theorem to write $f(x)$ as a product of three factors.

$$f(x) = (x - 3)[x - (2 + \sqrt{5})][x - (2 - \sqrt{5})]$$ Write $f(x)$ in factored form.

$$= (x - 3)[(x - 2) - \sqrt{5}][(x - 2) + \sqrt{5}]$$ Regroup terms.

$$= (x - 3)[(x - 2)^2 - 5]$$ Multiply.

$$= (x - 3)[(x^2 - 4x + 4) - 5]$$ Expand binomial.

$$= (x - 3)(x^2 - 4x - 1)$$ Simplify.

$$= x^3 - 4x^2 - x - 3x^2 + 12x + 3$$ Multiply.

$$= x^3 - 7x^2 + 11x + 3$$ Combine like terms.

Check You can check this result by evaluating f at each of the given zeros.

$$f(3) = 3^3 - 7(3)^2 + 11(3) + 3 = 27 - 63 + 33 + 3 = 0 \checkmark$$

$$f(2 + \sqrt{5}) = (2 + \sqrt{5})^3 - 7(2 + \sqrt{5})^2 + 11(2 + \sqrt{5}) + 3$$

$$= 38 + 17\sqrt{5} - 63 - 28\sqrt{5} + 22 + 11\sqrt{5} + 3$$

$$= 0 \checkmark$$

Because $f(2 + \sqrt{5}) = 0$, by the Irrational Conjugates Theorem $f(2 - \sqrt{5}) = 0$. ✓

SELF-ASSESSMENT

1 I do not understand. 2 I can do it with help. 3 I can do it on my own. 4 I can teach someone else.

Find all the real zeros of the function.

10. $h(x) = 16x^3 - 44x^2 + 8x + 5$

11. $f(x) = 3x^4 - 2x^3 - 37x^2 + 24x + 12$

Write a polynomial function f of least degree that has rational coefficients, a leading coefficient of 1, and the given zero(s).

12. $3 + \sqrt{2}$

13. $4, 1 - \sqrt{5}$

14. $0, 2, 6 + \sqrt{3}$

4.5 Practice WITH CalcChat® AND CalcView®

In Exercises 1–10, solve the equation. *Example 1*

1. $z^3 - z^2 - 12z = 0$
2. $a^3 - 4a^2 + 4a = 0$
3. $2x^4 - 4x^3 = -2x^2$
4. $v^3 - 2v^2 - 16v = -32$
5. $5w^3 = 50w$
6. $9m^5 = 27m^3$
7. $2c^4 - 6c^3 = 12c^2 - 36c$
8. $p^4 + 40 = 14p^2$
9. $12n^2 + 48n = -n^3 - 64$
10. $y^3 - 27 = 9y^2 - 27y$

In Exercises 11–18, find the zeros of the function. Then sketch a graph of the function. *Example 2*

11. $h(x) = x^4 + x^3 - 6x^2$
12. $f(x) = x^4 - 18x^2 + 81$
13. $p(x) = x^6 - 11x^5 + 30x^4$
14. $g(x) = -2x^5 + 2x^4 + 40x^3$
15. $g(x) = -4x^4 + 8x^3 + 60x^2$
16. $h(x) = -x^3 - 2x^2 + 15x$
17. $h(x) = -x^3 - x^2 + 9x + 9$
18. $p(x) = x^3 - 5x^2 - 4x + 20$

In Exercises 19 and 20, determine whether $f(x) = 0$ has any repeated real solutions. Explain your reasoning.

19.

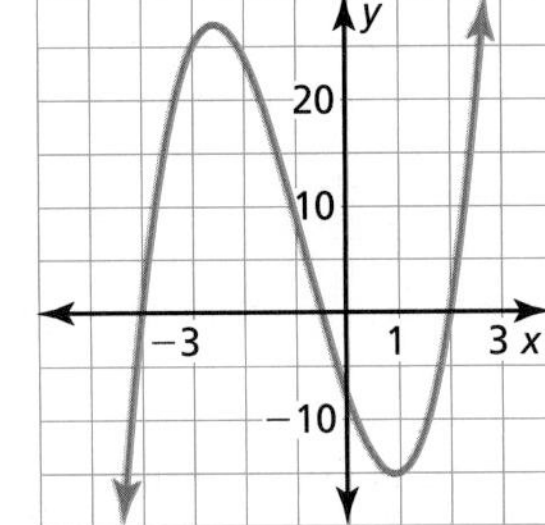

20.

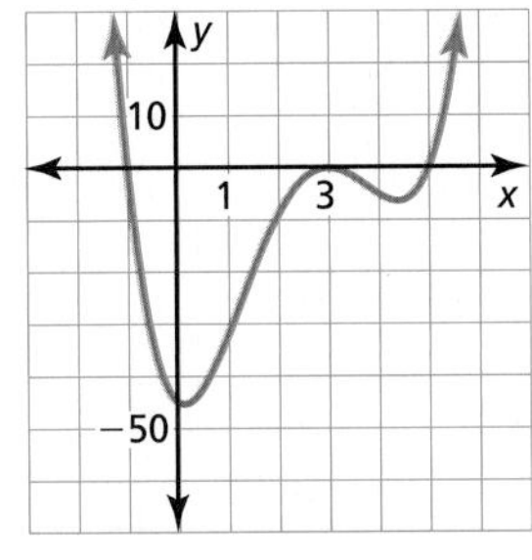

In Exercises 21–28, find all the real solutions of the equation. *Example 3*

21. $x^3 + x^2 - 17x + 15 = 0$
22. $x^3 - 2x^2 - 5x + 6 = 0$
23. $x^3 - 10x^2 + 19x + 30 = 0$
24. $x^3 + 4x^2 - 11x - 30 = 0$
25. $x^3 - 6x^2 - 7x + 60 = 0$
26. $x^3 - 16x^2 + 55x + 72 = 0$
27. $2x^3 - 3x^2 - 50x - 24 = 0$
28. $3x^3 + x^2 - 38x + 24 = 0$

29. **COLLEGE PREP** According to the Rational Root Theorem, which is *not* a possible solution of the equation $2x^4 - 5x^3 + 10x^2 - 9 = 0$?

    Ⓐ $x = -9$

    Ⓑ $x = -\frac{1}{2}$

    Ⓒ $x = \frac{2}{9}$

    Ⓓ $x = 3$

30. **COLLEGE PREP** According to the Rational Root Theorem, which is *not* a possible zero of the function $f(x) = 40x^5 - 42x^4 - 107x^3 + 107x^2 + 33x - 36$?

    Ⓐ $-\frac{2}{3}$

    Ⓑ $-\frac{3}{8}$

    Ⓒ $\frac{3}{4}$

    Ⓓ $\frac{4}{5}$

ERROR ANALYSIS In Exercises 31 and 32, describe and correct the error in listing the possible rational zeros of the function.

31.

$f(x) = x^3 + 5x^2 - 9x - 45$

Possible rational zeros of f:

$1, 3, 5, 9, 15, 45$

32.

$f(x) = 3x^3 + 13x^2 - 41x + 8$

Possible rational zeros of f:

$\pm 1, \pm 3, \pm\frac{1}{2}, \pm\frac{1}{4}, \pm\frac{1}{8}, \pm\frac{3}{2}, \pm\frac{3}{4}, \pm\frac{3}{8}$

In Exercises 33–40, find all the real zeros of the function. *Example 4*

33. $f(x) = x^3 - 3x - 2$

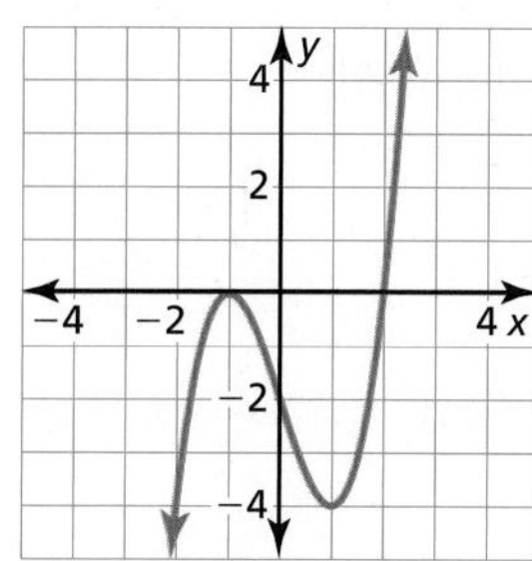

34. $f(x) = x^3 - 28x - 48$

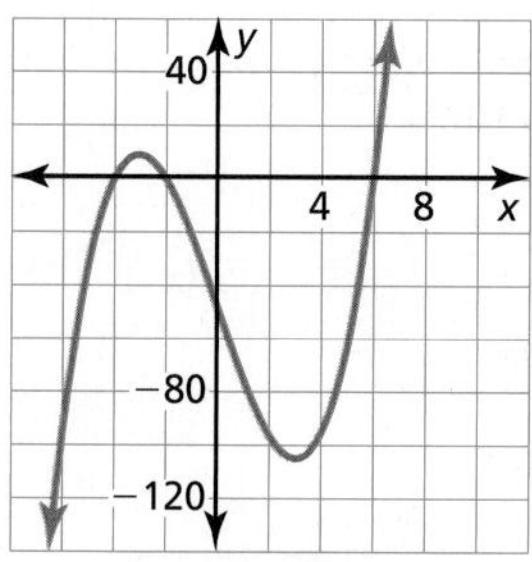

35. $p(x) = 2x^3 - x^2 - 27x + 36$

36. $g(x) = 3x^3 - 25x^2 + 58x - 40$

37. $f(x) = 4x^3 - 20x + 16$

38. $f(x) = 4x^3 - 49x - 60$

39. $h(x) = 64x^4 + 32x^3 - 44x^2 - 12x + 9$

40. $f(x) = 3x^4 - 2x^3 - 25x^2 - 20x - 4$

In Exercises 41–48, write a polynomial function f of least degree that has rational coefficients, a leading coefficient of 1, and the given zero(s). *Example 5*

41. $-2, 3, 6$

42. $-4, -2, 5$

43. $6 - \sqrt{7}$

44. $-2 + \sqrt{5}$

45. $-2, 1 + \sqrt{7}$

46. $4, 6 - \sqrt{7}$

47. $-6, 0, 3 - \sqrt{5}$

48. $0, 5, -5 + \sqrt{8}$

49. **MP REASONING** According to the Rational Root Theorem, ± 1 and ± 2 are possible rational zeros of a function f. The graph of f does *not* have x-intercepts of ± 1 or ± 2. Does this contradict the Rational Root Theorem? Explain.

50. **COMPARING METHODS** Solve the equation $x^3 - 4x^2 - 9x + 36 = 0$ using two different methods. Which method do you prefer? Explain your reasoning.

51. **MODELING REAL LIFE** Archaeologists discovered several huge concrete blocks at the ruins of Caesarea. One of the blocks has a volume of 180 cubic meters and the dimensions shown. Find the value of x.

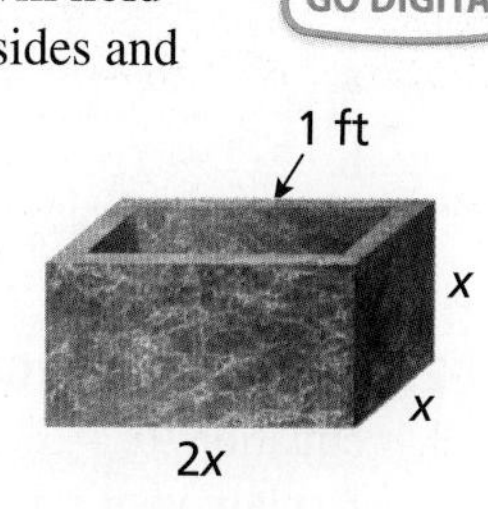

52. **MP PROBLEM SOLVING** You are designing a marble basin that will hold a fountain for a city park. The sides and bottom of the basin should be 1 foot thick. Its outer length should be twice its outer width and outer height. What should the outer dimensions of the basin be if it is to hold 36 cubic feet of water?

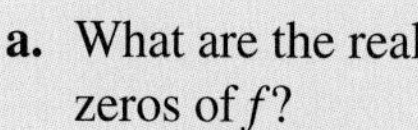

53. **MP REASONING** Is it possible for a cubic function to have more than three real zeros? Explain.

54. **HOW DO YOU SEE IT?** The graph of a quartic function f is shown.

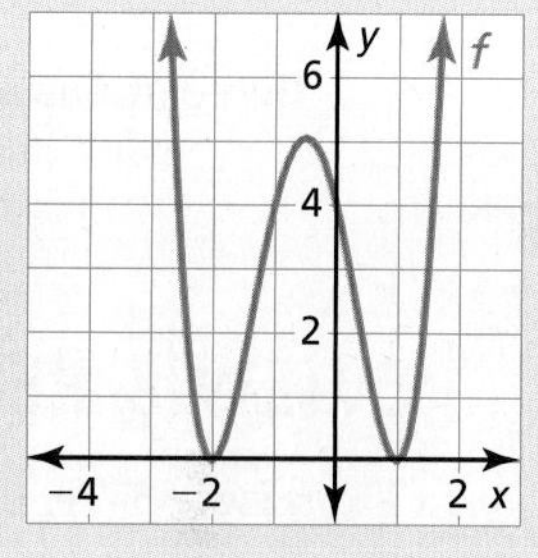

a. What are the real zeros of f?

b. Write an equation of the function in factored form.

55. **MODELING REAL LIFE** During a 10-year period, the amount (in millions of dollars) of athletic equipment E sold domestically can be modeled by $E(t) = -20t^3 + 252t^2 - 280t + 21{,}614$, where t is in years. When is about \$24,014,000,000 of athletic equipment sold?

56. **THOUGHT PROVOKING** All the possible rational solutions and actual rational solutions of the equation below are shown. Complete the equation.

Possible: $x = \pm 1, \pm 2, \pm 4, \pm 8, \pm 16$

Actual: $x = -1, 2$

$$(x + \square)(x + \square)(x^2 + \square) = 0$$

In Exercises 57–60, solve $f(x) = g(x)$ by graphing and algebraic methods.

57. $f(x) = x^3 + x^2 - x - 1$; $g(x) = -x + 1$

58. $f(x) = x^3 - 4x^2 + 4x$; $g(x) = -2x + 4$

59. $f(x) = x^4 - 5x^3 + 2x^2 + 8x$; $g(x) = -x^2 + 6x - 8$

60. $f(x) = x^4 + 2x^3 - 11x^2 - 12x + 36$; $g(x) = -x^2 - 6x - 9$

61. **MP REASONING** Determine the value of k for each equation so that the given x-value is a solution.

a. $x^3 - 6x^2 - 7x + k = 0; x = 4$

b. $2x^3 + 7x^2 - kx - 18 = 0; x = -6$

c. $kx^3 - 35x^2 + 19x + 30 = 0; x = 5$

62. **MAKING AN ARGUMENT** A student solves the equation $9x = x^3$ as shown. Is the solution correct? Explain your reasoning.

$9x = x^3$
$9 = x^2$
$\pm\sqrt{9} = x$
$\pm 3 = x$
The solutions are $x = -3$ and $x = 3$.

63. **MODELING REAL LIFE** Some ice sculptures are made by filling a mold and then freezing it. You make the ice mold shown. The mold is in the shape of a square pyramid and can hold a maximum of 30 gallons of water. What are the dimensions of the mold?

GO DIGITAL

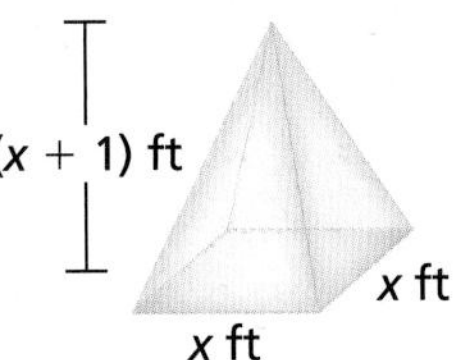

64. **DIG DEEPER** Let a_n be the leading coefficient of a polynomial function f and a_0 be the constant term. If a_n has r factors and a_0 has s factors, what is the greatest number of possible rational zeros of f that can be generated by the Rational Root Theorem? Explain your reasoning.

REVIEW & REFRESH

WATCH

In Exercises 65–70, find the product or quotient.

65. $(2b + 3)(2b - 3)$

66. $(5x + 8)^2$

67. $(4p - 2)^3$

68. $(mn + 6)^3$

69. $(x^4 + 2x^3 - 25x^2 - 2x + 24) \div (x^2 + 5x - 6)$

70. $(x^4 + 4x^3 - 10x^2 - 28x - 15) \div (x - 3)$

In Exercises 71 and 72, identify the function family to which f belongs. Describe the transformation from the graph of the parent function to the graph of f.

71.

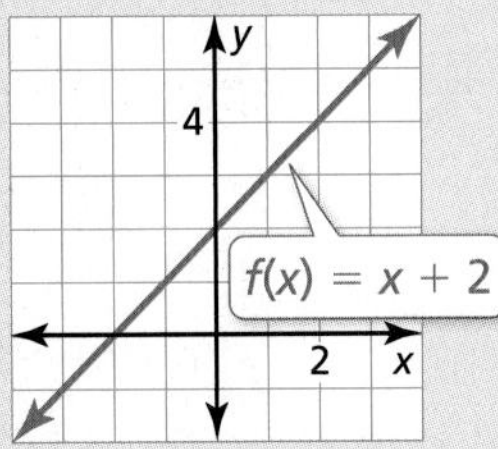

72.

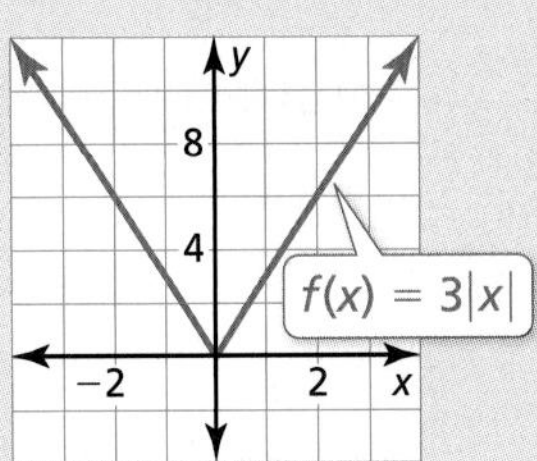

73. Write a function to model the data.

x	−1	0	1	2	3
y	4.5	8	10.5	12	12.5

74. Write the function $f(x) = x^2 + 7x + 13$ in vertex form. Then identify the vertex.

In Exercises 75 and 76, find all the real zeros of the function.

75. $f(x) = x^3 - 3x^2 - 6x + 8$

76. $g(x) = 45x^3 - 69x^2 + 32x - 4$

In Exercises 77–80, solve the equation.

77. $8x^2 - 1 = 0$

78. $7x^2 + 42 = 0$

79. $-5 = 3x^2 + 7$

80. $9 = \frac{1}{2}(x - 4)^2 - 6$

81. **MODELING REAL LIFE** The profit P (in millions of dollars) for a manufacturer of cell phone grips can be modeled by $P = -\frac{1}{4}(x^3 - 49x)$, where x is the number (in tens of millions) of grips produced. Currently, the company produces 50 million grips and makes a profit of \$30 million. What lesser number of grips could the company produce and still make the same profit?

In Exercises 82 and 83, write an equation of the parabola.

82.

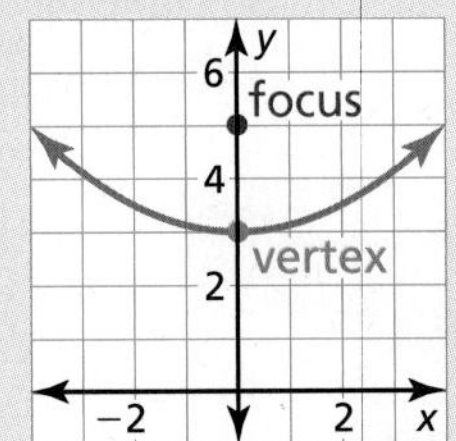

83.

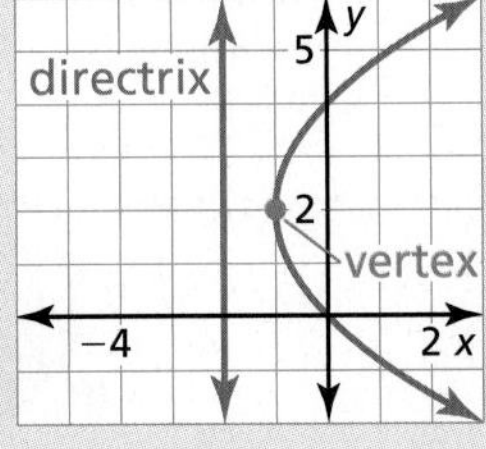

4.6 The Fundamental Theorem of Algebra

Learning Target Use the Fundamental Theorem of Algebra to find all complex roots of polynomial equations.

Success Criteria
- I can identify the degree of a polynomial.
- I can explain the Fundamental Theorem of Algebra.
- I can find all the zeros of a polynomial function.

EXPLORE IT! Finding Zeros of Functions

Work with a partner.

a. Use technology to explore each function for several values of a, b, c, and d.

$$f(x) = (x + a)(x + b)$$

$$g(x) = (x + a)(x + b)(x + c)$$

$$h(x) = (x + a)(x + b)(x + c)(x + d)$$

How does the graph change when you change the values of a, b, c, and d? Does the number of real zeros change?

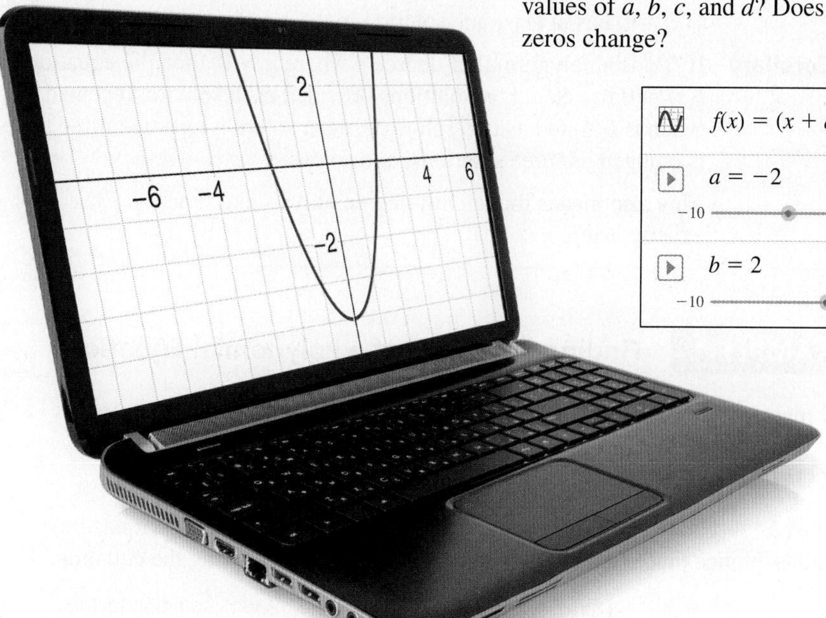

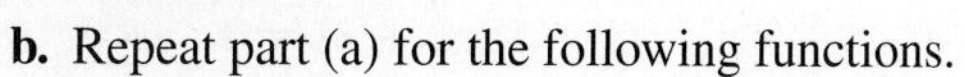

b. Repeat part (a) for the following functions.

$$m(x) = ax^2 + bx + c$$

$$n(x) = ax^3 + bx^2 + cx + d$$

$$p(x) = ax^4 + bx^3 + cx^2 + dx + e$$

c. Make a conjecture about the number of real zeros of $y = f(x)$ when the degree of $f(x)$ is a positive number n.

Math Practice

Analyze Conjectures
How can you justify your conjecture algebraically?

The Fundamental Theorem of Algebra

The table shows several polynomial equations and their solutions, including repeated solutions. Notice that for the last equation, the repeated solution $x = -1$ is counted twice.

Equation	Degree	Solution(s)	Number of solutions
$2x - 1 = 0$	1	$\frac{1}{2}$	1
$x^2 - 2 = 0$	2	$\pm\sqrt{2}$	2
$x^3 - 8 = 0$	3	$2, -1 \pm i\sqrt{3}$	3
$x^3 + x^2 - x - 1 = 0$	3	$-1, -1, 1$	3

In the table, note the relationship between the degree of the polynomial $f(x)$ and the number of solutions of $f(x) = 0$. This relationship is generalized by the *Fundamental Theorem of Algebra*, first proven by German mathematician Carl Friedrich Gauss (1777–1855).

KEY IDEA

The Fundamental Theorem of Algebra

Theorem If $f(x)$ is a polynomial of degree n where $n > 0$, then the equation $f(x) = 0$ has at least one solution in the set of complex numbers.

Corollary If $f(x)$ is a polynomial of degree n where $n > 0$, then the equation $f(x) = 0$ has exactly n solutions provided each solution repeated twice is counted as two solutions, each solution repeated three times is counted as three solutions, and so on.

This also means that an nth-degree polynomial function f has exactly n zeros.

Math Practice

Understand Mathematical Terms

Compare the statements "the polynomial equation $f(x) = 0$ has exactly n solutions" and "the polynomial function f has exactly n zeros."

EXAMPLE 1 Finding Solutions of a Polynomial Equation

How many solutions does $x^4 + x^3 + 8x + 8 = 0$ have? Find all the solutions.

SOLUTION

Because $x^4 + x^3 + 8x + 8 = 0$ is a polynomial equation of degree 4, it has four solutions. Notice that you can factor by grouping to begin solving the equation.

$$(x^4 + x^3) + (8x + 8) = 0 \quad \text{Group terms with common factors.}$$

$$x^3(x + 1) + 8(x + 1) = 0 \quad \text{Factor out GCF of each pair of terms.}$$

$$(x + 1)(x^3 + 8) = 0 \quad \text{Distributive Property}$$

$$(x + 1)(x + 2)(x^2 - 2x + 4) = 0 \quad \text{Sum of two cubes pattern}$$

The linear factors indicate that -2 and -1 are solutions. To find the remaining two solutions, solve $x^2 - 2x + 4 = 0$ by using the Quadratic Formula.

$$x = \frac{-(-2) \pm \sqrt{(-2)^2 - 4(1)(4)}}{2(1)} = 1 \pm i\sqrt{3}$$

▶ The solutions are $-2, -1, 1 - i\sqrt{3}$, and $1 + i\sqrt{3}$.

EXAMPLE 2 Finding the Zeros of a Polynomial Function

Find all the zeros of $f(x) = x^5 + x^3 - 2x^2 - 12x - 8$.

SOLUTION

Step 1 Find the rational zeros of f. Because f is a polynomial function of degree 5, it has five zeros. The possible rational zeros are ± 1, ± 2, ± 4, and ± 8. Using synthetic division, you can determine that -1 is a zero repeated twice and 2 is also a zero.

Step 2 Write $f(x)$ in factored form. Dividing $f(x)$ by its known factors $x + 1$, $x + 1$, and $x - 2$ gives a quotient of $x^2 + 4$. So,

$$f(x) = (x + 1)^2(x - 2)(x^2 + 4).$$

Step 3 Find the imaginary zeros of f. Solving $x^2 + 4 = 0$, you get $x = \pm 2i$. This means $x^2 + 4 = (x + 2i)(x - 2i)$.

$$f(x) = (x + 1)^2(x - 2)(x + 2i)(x - 2i)$$

REMEMBER
You can use imaginary numbers to write $x^2 + 4$ as $(x + 2i)(x - 2i)$. In general, $a^2 + b^2 = (a + bi)(a - bi)$.

▶ From the factorization, there are five zeros. The zeros of f are

-1, -1, 2, $-2i$, and $2i$.

Check The graph of f and the real zeros are shown. Notice that only the *real* zeros appear as x-intercepts. Also, the graph of f touches the x-axis at the repeated zero $x = -1$ and crosses the x-axis at $x = 2$.

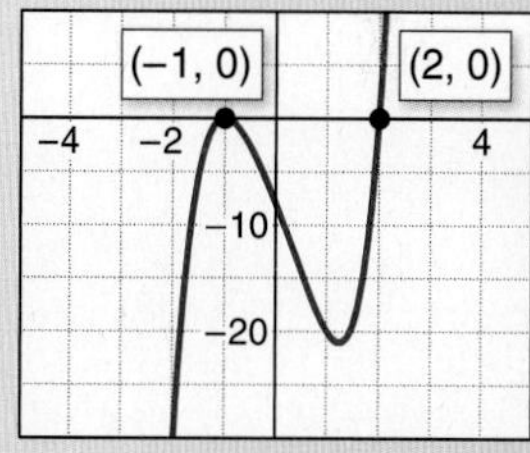

SELF-ASSESSMENT

1 I do not understand. 2 I can do it with help. 3 I can do it on my own. 4 I can teach someone else.

Identify the number of solutions of the polynomial equation. Then find all the solutions.

1. $x^5 - 4x^3 - x^2 + 4 = 0$
2. $x^4 + 7x^2 - 144 = 0$

Find all the zeros of the polynomial function.

3. $f(x) = x^3 + 7x^2 + 16x + 12$
4. $f(x) = x^5 - 3x^4 + 5x^3 - x^2 - 6x + 4$
5. **WRITING** Show why the Fundamental Theorem of Algebra is true for all quadratic equations.

Complex Conjugates

Pairs of complex numbers of the forms $a + bi$ and $a - bi$, where $b \neq 0$, are called complex conjugates. In Example 2, notice that the zeros $2i$ and $-2i$ are complex conjugates. This illustrates the next theorem.

KEY IDEA

The Complex Conjugates Theorem

If f is a polynomial function with real coefficients, and $a + bi$ is an imaginary zero of f, then $a - bi$ is also a zero of f.

EXAMPLE 3 Using Zeros to Write a Polynomial Function

Write a polynomial function f of least degree that has rational coefficients, a leading coefficient of 1, and the zeros 2 and $3 + i$.

SOLUTION

Because the coefficients are rational and $3 + i$ is a zero, $3 - i$ must also be a zero by the Complex Conjugates Theorem. Use the three zeros and the Factor Theorem to write $f(x)$ as a product of three factors.

$f(x) = (x - 2)[x - (3 + i)][x - (3 - i)]$	Write $f(x)$ in factored form.
$= (x - 2)[(x - 3) - i][(x - 3) + i]$	Regroup terms.
$= (x - 2)[(x - 3)^2 - i^2]$	Multiply.
$= (x - 2)[(x^2 - 6x + 9) - (-1)]$	Expand binomial and use $i^2 = -1$.
$= (x - 2)(x^2 - 6x + 10)$	Simplify.
$= x^3 - 6x^2 + 10x - 2x^2 + 12x - 20$	Multiply.
$= x^3 - 8x^2 + 22x - 20$	Combine like terms.

Check

You can check this result by evaluating f at each of the given zeros.

$$f(2) = 2^3 - 8(2)^2 + 22(2) - 20 = 8 - 32 + 44 - 20 = 0 \checkmark$$

$$f(3 + i) = (3 + i)^3 - 8(3 + i)^2 + 22(3 + i) - 20$$
$$= 18 + 26i - 64 - 48i + 66 + 22i - 20$$
$$= 0 \checkmark$$

Because $f(3 + i) = 0$, by the Complex Conjugates Theorem $f(3 - i) = 0$. ✓

SELF-ASSESSMENT  1 I do not understand. 2 I can do it with help. 3 I can do it on my own. 4 I can teach someone else.

Write a polynomial function f of least degree that has rational coefficients, a leading coefficient of 1, and the given zeros.

6. $-1, 4i$ **7.** $3, 1 + i\sqrt{5}$ **8.** $\sqrt{2}, 1 - 3i$ **9.** $2, 2i, 4 - \sqrt{6}$

Descartes's Rule of Signs

French mathematician René Descartes (1596–1650) found the following relationship between the coefficients of a polynomial function and the number of positive and negative zeros of the function.

KEY IDEA

Descartes's Rule of Signs

Let $f(x) = a_nx^n + a_{n-1}x^{n-1} + \cdots + a_2x^2 + a_1x + a_0$ be a polynomial function with real coefficients.

- The number of *positive real zeros* of f is equal to the number of changes in sign of the coefficients of $f(x)$ or is less than this by an even number.
- The number of *negative real zeros* of f is equal to the number of changes in sign of the coefficients of $f(-x)$ or is less than this by an even number.

EXAMPLE 4 Using Descartes's Rule of Signs

Determine the possible numbers of positive real zeros, negative real zeros, and imaginary zeros for $f(x) = x^6 - 2x^5 + 3x^4 - 10x^3 - 6x^2 - 8x - 8$.

SOLUTION

$$f(x) = x^6 - 2x^5 + 3x^4 - 10x^3 - 6x^2 - 8x - 8$$

The coefficients in $f(x)$ have 3 sign changes, so f has 3 or 1 positive real zero(s).

$$f(-x) = (-x)^6 - 2(-x)^5 + 3(-x)^4 - 10(-x)^3 - 6(-x)^2 - 8(-x) - 8$$
$$= x^6 + 2x^5 + 3x^4 + 10x^3 - 6x^2 + 8x - 8$$

The coefficients in $f(-x)$ have 3 sign changes, so f has 3 or 1 negative real zero(s).

▶ The possible numbers of zeros for f are summarized in the table below.

Positive real zeros	Negative real zeros	Imaginary zeros	Total zeros
3	3	0	6
3	1	2	6
1	3	2	6
1	1	4	6

EXAMPLE 5 Modeling Real Life

A tachometer measures the speed (in revolutions per minute, or RPMs) at which an engine shaft rotates. For a certain boat, the speed x (in hundreds of RPMs) of the engine shaft and the speed s (in miles per hour) of the boat are modeled by

$$s(x) = 0.00547x^3 - 0.225x^2 + 3.62x - 11.0.$$

What is the tachometer reading when the boat travels 15 miles per hour?

SOLUTION

Substitute 15 for $s(x)$ in the function. You can rewrite the resulting equation as

$$0 = 0.00547x^3 - 0.225x^2 + 3.62x - 26.0.$$

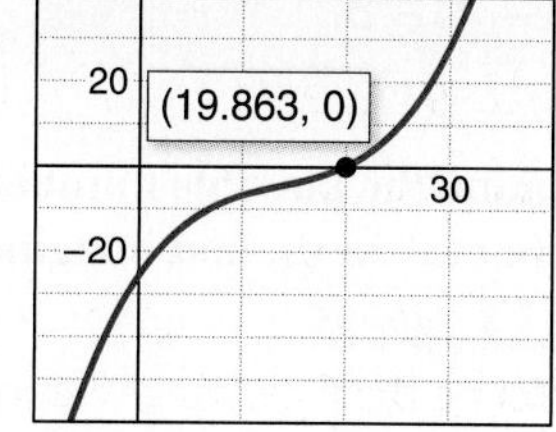

The related function is $f(x) = 0.00547x^3 - 0.225x^2 + 3.62x - 26.0$. By Descartes's Rule of Signs, you know f has 3 or 1 positive real zero(s). In the context of speed, negative real zeros and imaginary zeros do not make sense, so you do not need to check for them. To approximate the positive real zeros of f, use technology. From the graph, there is 1 real zero, $x \approx 19.9$.

▶ The tachometer reading is about 1990 RPMs.

SELF-ASSESSMENT

1 I do not understand. 2 I can do it with help. 3 I can do it on my own. 4 I can teach someone else.

Determine the possible numbers of positive real zeros, negative real zeros, and imaginary zeros for the function.

10. $f(x) = x^3 + 9x - 25$

11. $f(x) = 3x^4 - 7x^3 + x^2 - 13x + 8$

12. WHAT IF? In Example 5, what is the tachometer reading when the boat travels 20 miles per hour?

4.6 Practice WITH CalcChat® AND CalcView®

In Exercises 1–6, identify the number of solutions of the polynomial equation. Then find all the solutions. *Example 1*

1. $x^3 + 4x^2 - 11x - 30 = 0$

2. $z^3 + 10z^2 + 28z + 24 = 0$

3. $4x^5 - 8x^4 + 6x^3 = 0$

4. $-2x^6 - 8x^5 - x^4 = 0$

5. $t^4 - 2t^3 + t = 2$

6. $y^4 + 5y^3 - 125y = 625$

In Exercises 7–14, find all the zeros of the polynomial function. *Example 2*

7. $f(x) = x^4 - 6x^3 + 7x^2 + 6x - 8$

8. $f(x) = x^4 + 5x^3 - 7x^2 - 29x + 30$

9. $g(x) = x^4 - 9x^2 - 4x + 12$

10. $h(x) = x^3 + 5x^2 - 4x - 20$

11. $g(x) = x^4 + 4x^3 + 7x^2 + 16x + 12$

12. $h(x) = x^4 - x^3 + 7x^2 - 9x - 18$

13. $g(x) = x^5 + 3x^4 - 4x^3 - 2x^2 - 12x - 16$

14. $f(x) = x^5 - 20x^3 + 20x^2 - 21x + 20$

ANALYZING RELATIONSHIPS In Exercises 15–18, determine the number of imaginary zeros for the function with the given degree and graph. Explain your reasoning.

15. Degree: 4

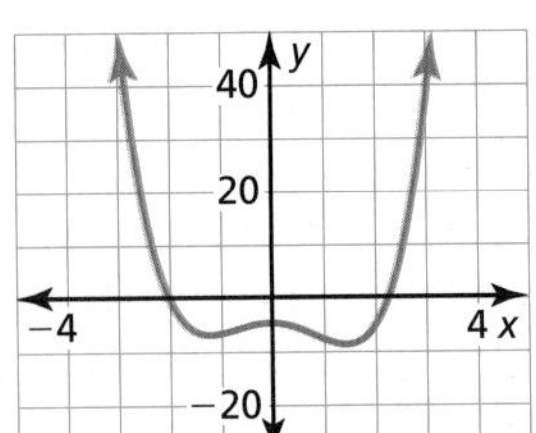

16. Degree: 5

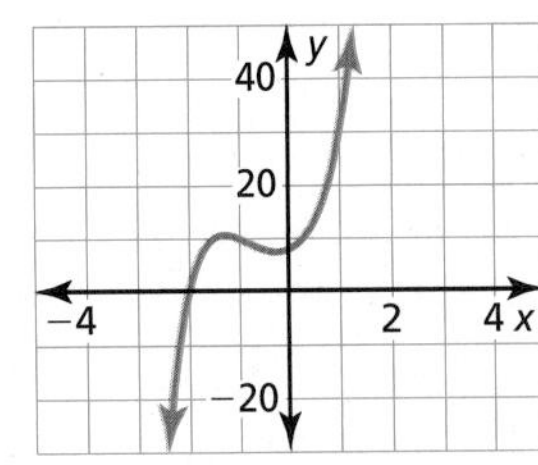

17. Degree: 2

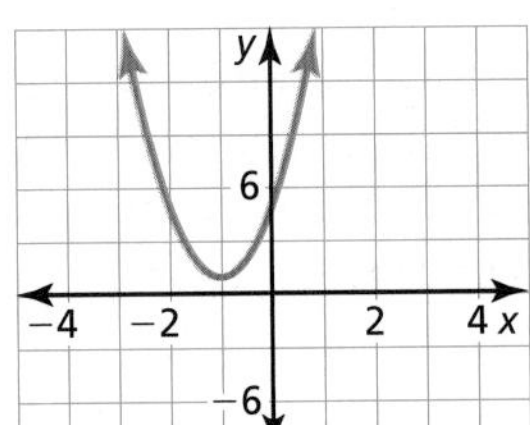

18. Degree: 3

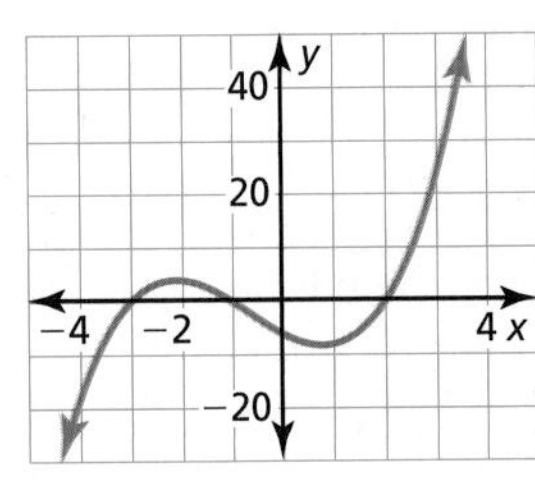

In Exercises 19–26, write a polynomial function *f* of least degree that has rational coefficients, a leading coefficient of 1, and the given zeros. *Example 3*

19. $-5, -1, 2$

20. $-2, 1, 3$

21. $3, 4 + i$

22. $2, 5 - i$

23. $4, -\sqrt{5}$

24. $3, 2 - \sqrt{3}$

25. $2, 1 + i, 2 - \sqrt{3}$

26. $3, 4 + 2i, 1 + \sqrt{7}$

ERROR ANALYSIS In Exercises 27 and 28, describe and correct the error in writing a polynomial function with rational coefficients and the given zero(s).

27. Zeros: $2, 1 + i$

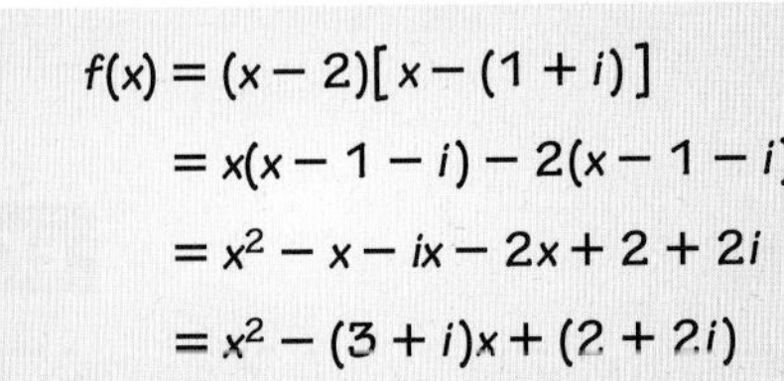

$$\begin{aligned} f(x) &= (x - 2)[x - (1 + i)] \\ &= x(x - 1 - i) - 2(x - 1 - i) \\ &= x^2 - x - ix - 2x + 2 + 2i \\ &= x^2 - (3 + i)x + (2 + 2i) \end{aligned}$$

28. Zero: $2 + i$

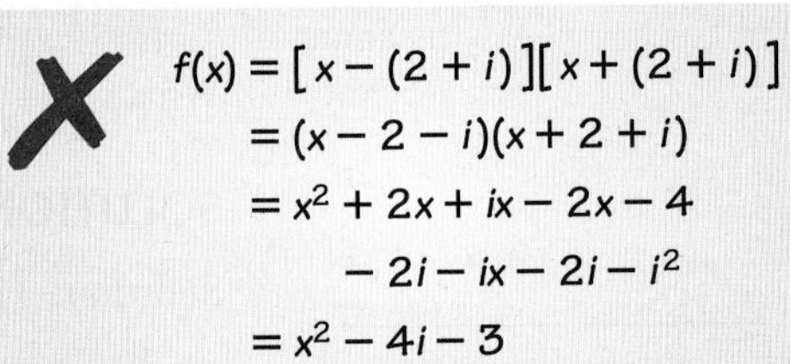

$$\begin{aligned} f(x) &= [x - (2 + i)][x + (2 + i)] \\ &= (x - 2 - i)(x + 2 + i) \\ &= x^2 + 2x + ix - 2x - 4 \\ &\quad - 2i - ix - 2i - i^2 \\ &= x^2 - 4i - 3 \end{aligned}$$

In Exercises 29–36, determine the possible numbers of positive real zeros, negative real zeros, and imaginary zeros for the function. *Example 4*

29. $g(x) = x^4 - x^2 - 6$

30. $g(x) = -x^3 + 5x^2 + 12$

31. $g(x) = x^3 - 4x^2 + 8x + 7$

32. $g(x) = x^5 - 2x^3 - x^2 + 6$

33. $g(x) = x^5 - 3x^3 + 8x - 10$

34. $g(x) = x^5 + 7x^4 - 4x^3 - 3x^2 + 9x - 15$

35. $g(x) = x^6 + x^5 - 3x^4 + x^3 + 5x^2 + 9x - 18$

36. $g(x) = x^7 + 4x^4 - 10x + 25$

37. **MODELING REAL LIFE** From 1900 to 2017, the number P (in thousands) of immigrants residing in the United States can be modeled by

$$P = 0.0757t^3 - 7.893t^2 + 187.10t + 11{,}757.7$$

where t is the number of years since 1900. In which year did the number of immigrants reach 43 million? *Example 5*

38. **MODELING REAL LIFE** A state maintains a list of the bodies of water infested by zebra mussels. The number N of bodies of water that have been on the list since year t can be modeled by

$$N = 0.0004t^4 + 0.042t^3 + 0.35t^2 - 1.0t + 14$$

where $0 \le t \le 18$. A researcher studies the 25 bodies of water that have been infested the longest. Since what year have these 25 bodies of water been infested?

39. **MODELING REAL LIFE** For the 12 years that a grocery store has been open, its annual revenue R (in millions of dollars) can be modeled by the function

$$R = 0.0001(-t^4 + 12t^3 - 77t^2 + 600t + 13{,}650)$$

where t is the number of years since the store opened. In which year(s) was the revenue \$1.5 million?

40. **CONNECTING CONCEPTS** A solid monument with the dimensions shown is to be built using 1000 cubic feet of marble. What is the value of x?

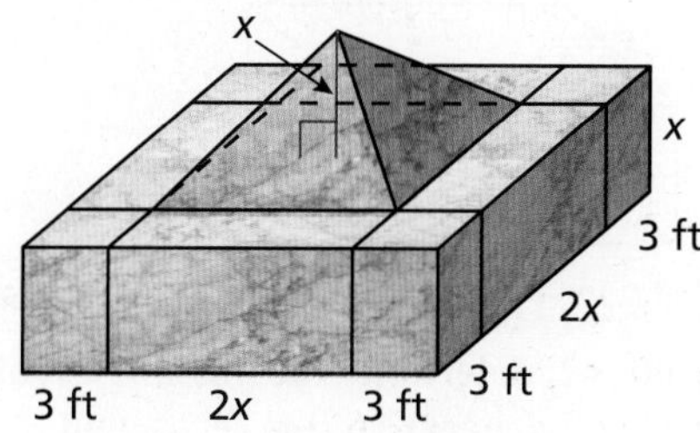

41. **MP STRUCTURE** What is the least number of possible terms of an nth-degree polynomial function with root $4i$? Justify your answer.

42. **OPEN-ENDED** Write a polynomial function of degree 6 with zeros 1, 2, and $-i$. Justify your answer.

43. **COLLEGE PREP** Which is *not* a possible classification of the zeros for $f(x) = x^5 - 4x^3 + 6x^2 + 2x - 6$? Explain.

Ⓐ three positive real zeros, two negative real zeros, and no imaginary zeros

Ⓑ three positive real zeros, no negative real zeros, and two imaginary zeros

Ⓒ one positive real zero, four negative real zeros, and no imaginary zeros

Ⓓ one positive real zero, two negative real zeros, and two imaginary zeros

44. **COLLEGE PREP** Use Descartes's Rule of Signs to determine which functions could have 1 positive real zero. Select all that apply.

Ⓐ $f(x) = x^4 + 2x^3 - 9x^2 - 2x - 8$

Ⓑ $f(x) = x^4 + 4x^3 + 8x^2 + 16x$

Ⓒ $f(x) = -x^4 + 5x^2 - 4$

Ⓓ $f(x) = -x^4 + 4x^3 - 7x^2 + 12x + 12$

45. **MP REASONING** Two zeros of

$$f(x) = x^3 - 6x^2 - 16x + 96$$

are 4 and -4. Is the third zero *real* or *imaginary*? Explain your reasoning.

46. **HOW DO YOU SEE IT?**
The graph represents a polynomial function of degree 6.

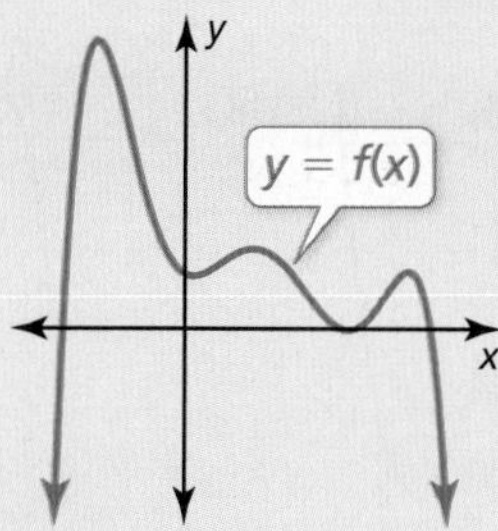

a. How many positive real zeros does the function have? negative real zeros? imaginary zeros?

b. Use Descartes's Rule of Signs and your answers in part (a) to describe the possible sign changes in the coefficients of $f(x)$.

47. **MAKING AN ARGUMENT** The graph of the constant polynomial function $f(x) = 2$ is a line that does not have any x-intercepts. Does the function contradict the Fundamental Theorem of Algebra? Explain your reasoning.

48. THOUGHT PROVOKING
Find the zeros of several polynomial functions with leading coefficients of 1. For functions of this form, make a conjecture about the relationship between (a) the sum of the zeros and the coefficients, and (b) the product of the zeros and the coefficients.

49. **MP USING TOOLS** Use technology to graph f for $n = 2, 3, 4, 5, 6$, and 7.

$$f(x) = (x + 3)^n$$

a. Compare the graphs when n is even and n is odd.

b. Describe the behavior of the graph near $x = -3$ as n increases.

c. Use your results from parts (a) and (b) to describe the behavior of the graph of $g(x) = (x - 4)^{20}$ near $x = 4$.

50. **DIG DEEPER** You want to save money so you can buy a used car in four years. At the end of each summer, you deposit \$1000 earned from summer jobs into your bank account. The table shows the values of your deposits over the four-year period. In the table, g is the growth factor $1 + r$, where r is the annual interest rate expressed as a decimal.

GO DIGITAL

Deposit	Year 1	Year 2	Year 3	Year 4
1st Deposit	1000	$1000g$	$1000g^2$	$1000g^3$
2nd Deposit	–	1000		
3rd Deposit	–	–	1000	
4th Deposit	–	–	–	1000

a. Copy and complete the table.

b. What annual interest rate do you need in order to pay cash for a car that costs \$4300?

REVIEW & REFRESH

In Exercises 51–54, match the function with the correct graph. Explain your reasoning.

51. $f(x) = x(x - 3)(x + 1)$

52. $g(x) = (x + 3)(x - 1)(x - 2)$

53. $h(x) = x(x + 3)(x - 1)$

54. $k(x) = (x - 3)(x + 1)(x + 2)$

A.
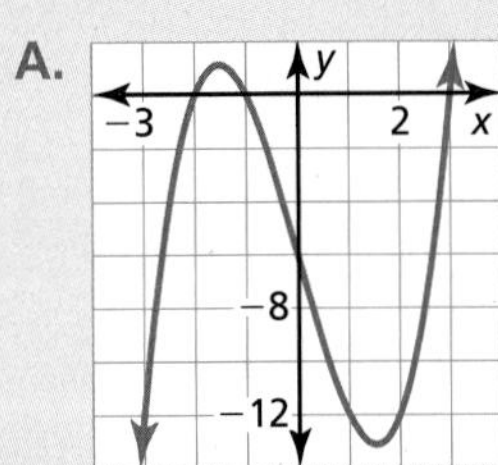

B.
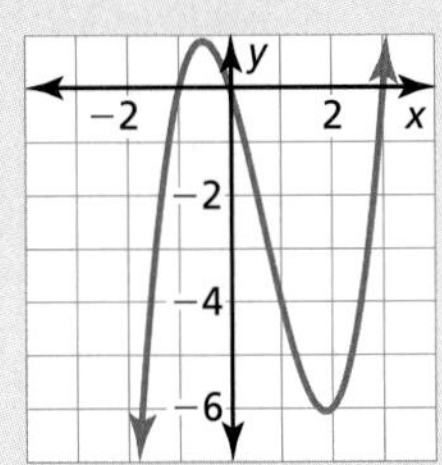

C.
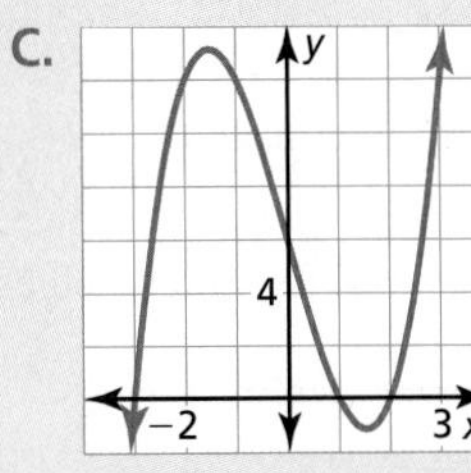

D.
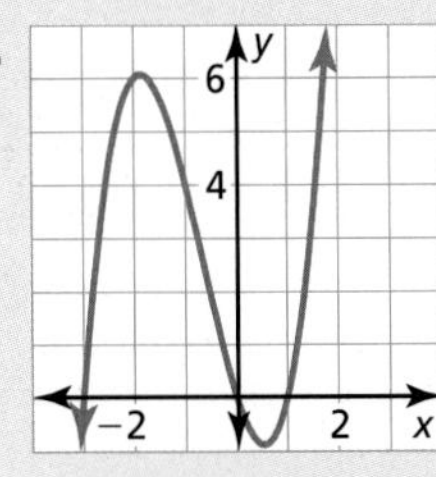

55. MODELING REAL LIFE Solution A is 10% acid and Solution B is 35% acid. How much of each solution should a chemist mix to make 2 cups of a solution that is 15% acid?

In Exercises 56–58, write a function g whose graph represents the indicated transformation of the graph of f.

56. $f(x) = x$; vertical shrink by a factor of $\frac{1}{3}$ and a reflection in the y-axis

57. $f(x) = |x + 1| - 3$; horizontal stretch by a factor of 9

58. $f(x) = x^2$; reflection in the x-axis, followed by a translation 2 units right and 7 units up

59. The volume V of the rectangular prism is given by $V = 2x^3 + 17x^2 + 46x + 40$. Find an expression for the missing dimension.

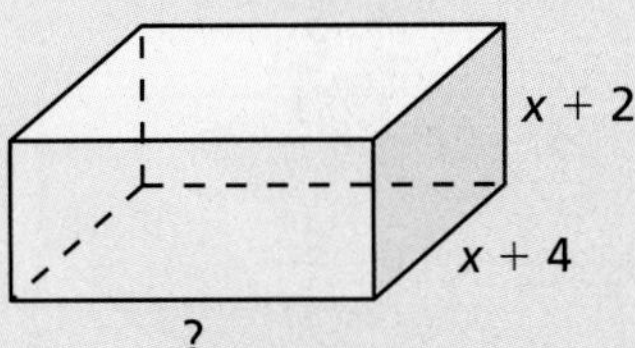

In Exercises 60–62, determine the possible numbers of positive real zeros, negative real zeros, and imaginary zeros for the function. Then find the zeros.

60. $f(x) = 2x^3 - 5x^2 - x + 6$

61. $h(x) = x^4 - 18x^2 + 81$

62. $g(x) = x^4 + x^3 + 4x^2 + 4x$

4.7 Transformations of Polynomial Functions

Learning Target Describe and graph transformations of polynomial functions.

Success Criteria

- I can describe transformations of polynomial functions.
- I can graph transformations of polynomial functions.
- I can write functions that represent transformations of polynomial functions.

EXPLORE IT! Transforming Graphs of Cubic and Quartic Functions

Work with a partner. The graphs of the parent cubic function $f(x) = x^3$ and the parent quartic function $g(x) = x^4$ are shown.

Math Practice

Construct Arguments Why does the range of f include negative numbers, but the range of g does not?

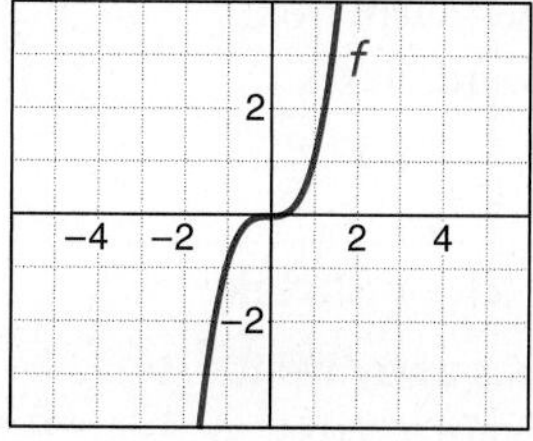

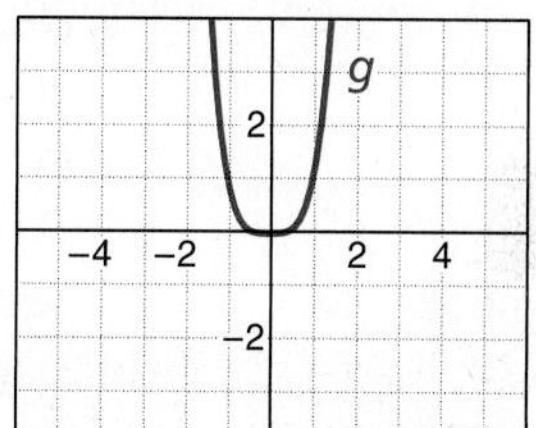

In parts (a)–(h), use technology to explore each function for several values of k, h, and a. How does the graph change when you change the values of k, h, and a?

a. $y = f(x) + k$

b. $y = f(x - h)$

c. $y = a \cdot f(x)$

d. $y = f(ax)$

e. $y = g(x) + k$

f. $y = g(x - h)$

g. $y = a \cdot g(x)$

h. $y = g(ax)$

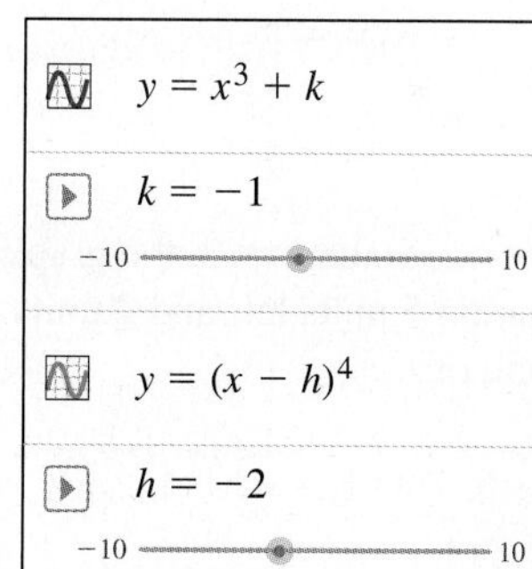

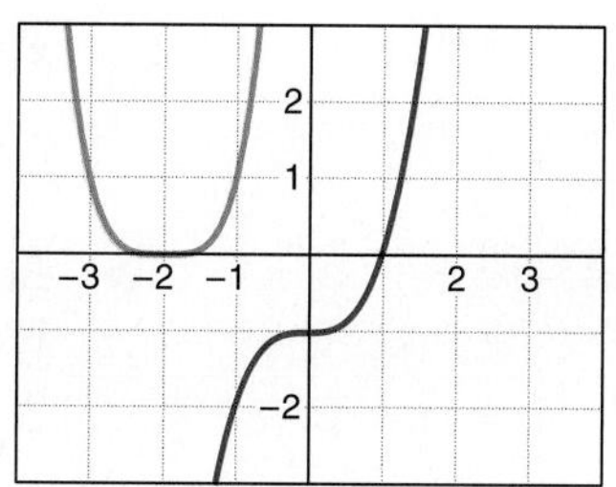

Describing Transformations of Polynomial Functions

GO DIGITAL

You can transform graphs of polynomial functions in the same way you transformed graphs of linear functions, absolute value functions, and quadratic functions. Examples of transformations of the graph of $f(x) = x^4$ are shown below.

KEY IDEAS

Transformation	$f(x)$ Notation	Examples	
Horizontal Translation Graph shifts left or right.	$f(x - h)$	$g(x) = (x - 5)^4$ $g(x) = (x + 2)^4$	5 units right 2 units left
Vertical Translation Graph shifts up or down.	$f(x) + k$	$g(x) = x^4 + 1$ $g(x) = x^4 - 4$	1 unit up 4 units down
Reflection Graph flips over a line.	$f(-x)$ $-f(x)$	$g(x) = (-x)^4 = x^4$ $g(x) = -x^4$	in the y-axis in the x-axis
Horizontal Stretch or Shrink Graph stretches away from or shrinks toward y-axis by a factor of $\frac{1}{a}$.	$f(ax)$	$g(x) = (2x)^4$ $g(x) = \left(\frac{1}{2}x\right)^4$	shrink by a factor of $\frac{1}{2}$ stretch by a factor of 2
Vertical Stretch or Shrink Graph stretches away from or shrinks toward x-axis by a factor of a.	$a \cdot f(x)$	$g(x) = 8x^4$ $g(x) = \frac{1}{4}x^4$	stretch by a factor of 8 shrink by a factor of $\frac{1}{4}$

EXAMPLE 1 Translating a Polynomial Function

WATCH

Describe the transformation of $f(x) = x^3$ represented by $g(x) = (x + 5)^3 + 2$. Then graph each function.

SOLUTION

Notice that the function is of the form $g(x) = (x - h)^3 + k$. Rewrite the function to identify h and k.

$$g(x) = (x - \underset{\substack{\uparrow \\ h}}{(-5)})^3 + \underset{\substack{\uparrow \\ k}}{2}$$

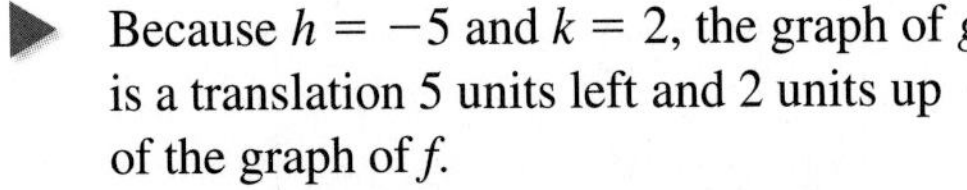

▶ Because $h = -5$ and $k = 2$, the graph of g is a translation 5 units left and 2 units up of the graph of f.

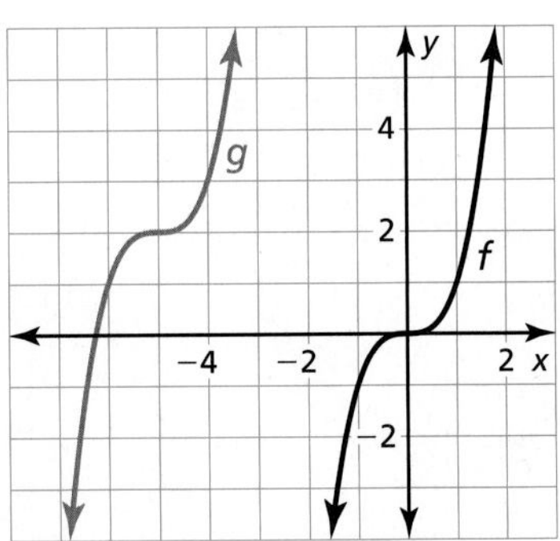

SELF-ASSESSMENT

1 I do not understand. 2 I can do it with help. 3 I can do it on my own. 4 I can teach someone else.

Describe the transformation of f represented by g. Then graph each function.

1. $f(x) = x^3$, $g(x) = x^3 - 2$

2. $f(x) = x^4$, $g(x) = (x - 3)^4 - 1$

3. MP **STRUCTURE** Describe the transformation of $f(x) = x^4$ represented by $g(x) = (x^2 - 1)(x^2 + 1)$.

EXAMPLE 2 Transforming Polynomial Functions

Describe the transformation of f represented by g. Then graph each function.

a. $f(x) = x^4,\ g(x) = -\frac{1}{4}x^4$

b. $f(x) = x^5,\ g(x) = (2x)^5 - 3$

SOLUTION

a. Notice that the function is of the form $g(x) = -ax^4$, where $a = \frac{1}{4}$.

▶ So, the graph of g is a reflection in the x-axis and a vertical shrink by a factor of $\frac{1}{4}$ of the graph of f.

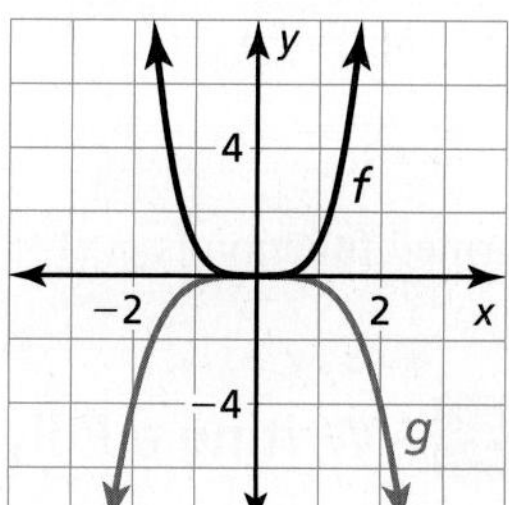

b. Notice that the function is of the form $g(x) = (ax)^5 + k$, where $a = 2$ and $k = -3$.

▶ So, the graph of g is a horizontal shrink by a factor of $\frac{1}{2}$ and a translation 3 units down of the graph of f.

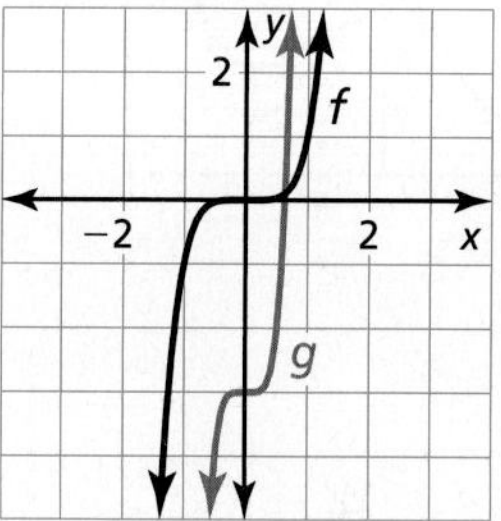

SELF-ASSESSMENT

1 I do not understand. 2 I can do it with help. 3 I can do it on my own. 4 I can teach someone else.

4. Describe the transformation of $f(x) = x^3$ represented by $g(x) = 4(x + 2)^3$. Then graph each function.

5. **VOCABULARY** Describe how the vertex form of a quadratic function is similar to the form $f(x) = a(x - h)^3 + k$ for a cubic function.

Writing Transformations of Polynomial Functions

EXAMPLE 3 Writing Transformed Polynomial Functions

Let $f(x) = x^3 + x^2 + 1$. Write a rule for g and then graph each function. Describe the graph of g as a transformation of the graph of f.

a. $g(x) = f(-x)$

b. $g(x) = 3f(x)$

SOLUTION

a. $g(x) = f(-x) = (-x)^3 + (-x)^2 + 1$

$= -x^3 + x^2 + 1$

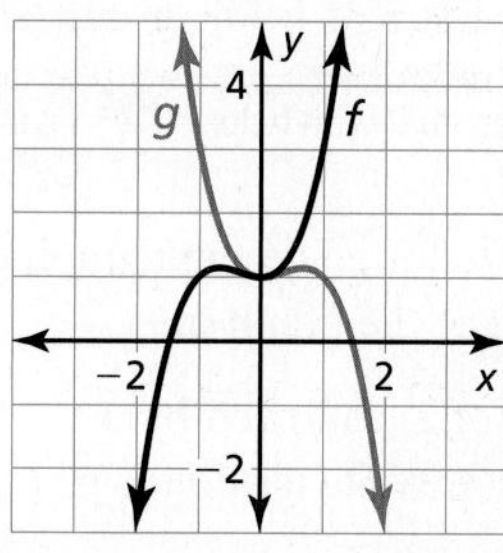

▶ The graph of g is a reflection in the y-axis of the graph of f.

b. $g(x) = 3f(x) = 3(x^3 + x^2 + 1)$

$= 3x^3 + 3x^2 + 3$

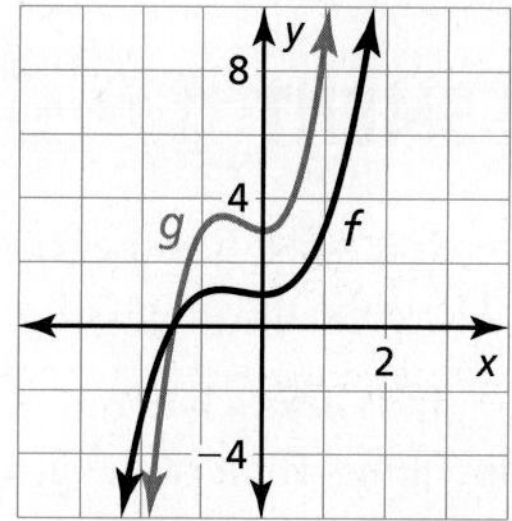

▶ The graph of g is a vertical stretch by a factor of 3 of the graph of f.

REMEMBER

Vertical stretches and shrinks do not change the x-intercept(s) of a graph. You can observe this using the graph in Example 3(b).

EXAMPLE 4 Writing a Transformed Polynomial Function

Let the graph of g be a vertical stretch by a factor of 2, followed by a translation 3 units up of the graph of $f(x) = x^4 - 2x^2$. Write a rule for g.

SOLUTION

Step 1 First write a function h that represents the vertical stretch of f.

$h(x) = 2 \cdot f(x)$	Multiply the output by 2.
$= 2(x^4 - 2x^2)$	Substitute $x^4 - 2x^2$ for $f(x)$.
$= 2x^4 - 4x^2$	Distributive Property

Step 2 Then write a function g that represents the translation of h.

$g(x) = h(x) + 3$	Add 3 to the output.
$= 2x^4 - 4x^2 + 3$	Substitute $2x^4 - 4x^2$ for $h(x)$.

▶ The transformed function is $g(x) = 2x^4 - 4x^2 + 3$.

Check

EXAMPLE 5 Writing a Polynomial Model

The function $V(x) = \frac{1}{3}x^3 - x^2$ represents the volume (in cubic feet) of the square pyramid shown. The function $W(x) = V(3x)$ represents the volume (in cubic feet) when x is measured in yards. Write a rule for W. Find and interpret $W(10)$.

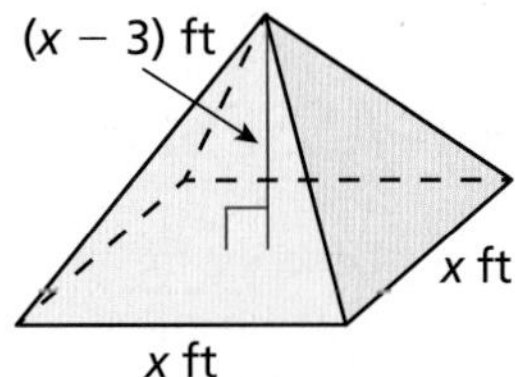

SOLUTION

1. **Understand the Problem** You are given two volume functions V and W whose inputs have different units. The horizontal shrink shown by $W(x) = V(3x)$ makes sense because there are 3 feet in 1 yard. You are asked to write a rule for W and interpret the output for a given input.

2. **Make a Plan** Write the transformed function W and then find $W(10)$.

3. **Solve and Check** $W(x) = V(3x)$

$= \frac{1}{3}(3x)^3 - (3x)^2$	Replace x with $3x$ in $V(x)$.
$= 9x^3 - 9x^2$	Simplify.

Next, find $W(10)$.

$$W(10) = 9(10)^3 - 9(10)^2 = 9000 - 900 = 8100$$

▶ When x is 10 yards, the volume of the pyramid is 8100 cubic feet.

Check Because $W(x) = V(3x)$, you can determine that $W(10) = V(30)$. Check that your solution is correct by verifying that $V(30) = 8100$.

$$V(30) = \frac{1}{3}(30)^3 - 30^2$$
$$= 9000 - 900$$
$$= 8100 \checkmark$$

SELF-ASSESSMENT

1 I do not understand. 2 I can do it with help. 3 I can do it on my own. 4 I can teach someone else.

6. Let $f(x) = x^5 - 4x + 6$ and $g(x) = -f(x)$. Write a rule for g and then graph each function. Describe the graph of g as a transformation of the graph of f.

7. Let the graph of g be a horizontal stretch by a factor of 2, followed by a translation 3 units right of the graph of $f(x) = 8x^3 + 3$. Write a rule for g.

8. **WHAT IF?** In Example 5, the height of the pyramid is $6x$ feet, and the volume (in cubic feet) is represented by $V(x) = 2x^3$. Write a rule for W. Find and interpret $W(7)$.

4.7 Practice WITH CalcChat® AND CalcView®

In Exercises 1–4, describe the transformation of f represented by g. Then graph each function. *Example 1*

1. $f(x) = x^4$, $g(x) = x^4 + 3$

2. $f(x) = x^4$, $g(x) = (x - 5)^4$

3. $f(x) = x^5$, $g(x) = (x - 2)^5 - 1$

4. $f(x) = x^6$, $g(x) = (x + 1)^6 - 4$

ANALYZING RELATIONSHIPS In Exercises 5–8, match the function with the correct transformation of the graph of f. Explain your reasoning.

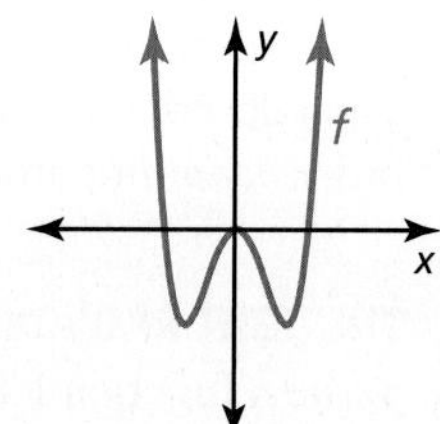

5. $y = f(x - 2)$

6. $y = f(x + 2) + 2$

7. $y = f(x - 2) + 2$

8. $y = f(x) - 2$

A.
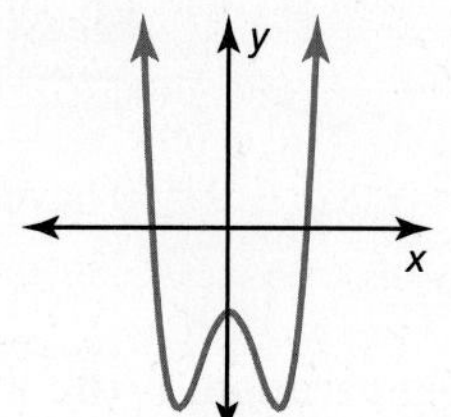

B.
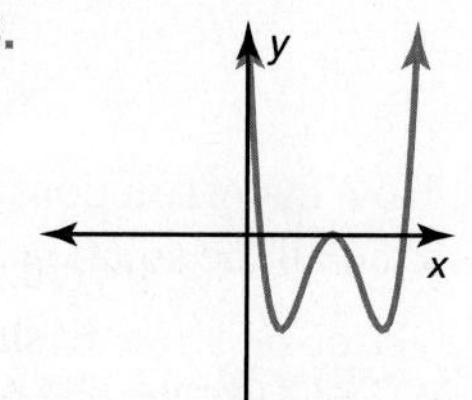

C.
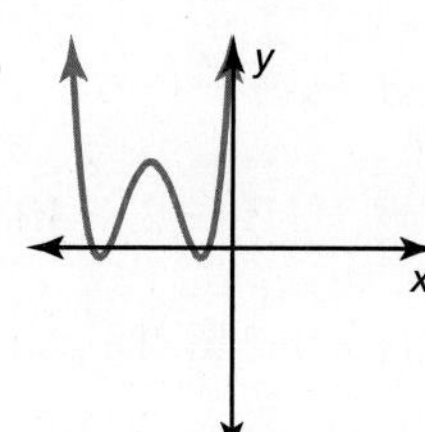

D.
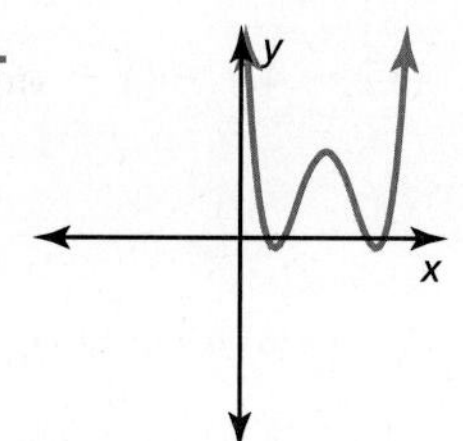

In Exercises 9–14, describe the transformation of f represented by g. Then graph each function. *Example 2*

9. $f(x) = x^4$, $g(x) = -2x^4$

10. $f(x) = x^6$, $g(x) = -\frac{1}{4}x^6$

11. $f(x) = x^3$, $g(x) = 5x^3 + 1$

12. $f(x) = x^4$, $g(x) = \frac{1}{2}x^4 + 5$

13. $f(x) = x^5$, $g(x) = \frac{3}{4}(x + 4)^5$

14. $f(x) = x^4$, $g(x) = (3x)^4 - 2$

In Exercises 15–20, write a rule for g and then graph each function. Describe the graph of g as a transformation of the graph of f. *Example 3*

15. $f(x) = x^4 + 1$, $g(x) = f(x + 2)$

16. $f(x) = x^6 - 3x^3 + 2$, $g(x) = f(x) - 3$

17. $f(x) = x^5 - 2x + 3$, $g(x) = 3f(x)$

18. $f(x) = 2x^3 - 2x^2 + 6$, $g(x) = -\frac{1}{2}f(x)$

19. $f(x) = x^4 + x^3 - 1$, $g(x) = f(-x) - 5$

20. $f(x) = \frac{1}{2}x^5 + x^3 - 4x - 4$, $g(x) = -f(2x) + 1$

21. **ERROR ANALYSIS** Describe and correct the error in graphing the transformation of $f(x) = x^4$ represented by $g(x) = (x + 2)^4 - 6$.

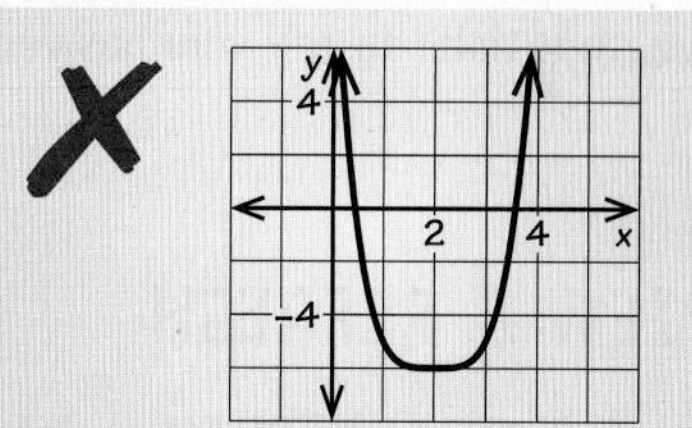

22. **ERROR ANALYSIS** Describe and correct the error in describing the transformation of $f(x) = x^5$ represented by $g(x) = (3x)^5 - 4$.

The graph of g is a horizontal shrink by a factor of 3, followed by a translation 4 units down of the graph of f.

In Exercises 23–26, write a rule for g that represents the indicated transformations of the graph of f. *Example 4*

23. $f(x) = x^3 - 6$; translation 3 units left, followed by a reflection in the y-axis

24. $f(x) = x^4 + 2x + 6$; vertical stretch by a factor of 2, followed by a translation 4 units right

25. $f(x) = x^3 + 2x^2 - 9$; horizontal shrink by a factor of $\frac{1}{3}$ and a translation 2 units up, followed by a reflection in the x-axis

26. $f(x) = 2x^5 - x^3 + x^2 + 4$; reflection in the y-axis and a vertical stretch by a factor of 3, followed by a translation 1 unit down

27. CONNECTING CONCEPTS The function $V(x) = x^3 - 4x$ represents the volume (in cubic feet) of the pyramid. The function $W(x) = V(3x)$ represents the volume (in cubic feet) of the pyramid when x is measured in yards. Write a rule for W. Find and interpret $W(5)$.
▶ *Example 5*

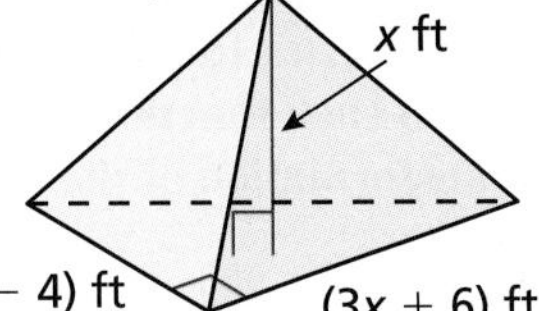

28. CONNECTING CONCEPTS Write a function V for the volume (in cubic yards) of the right circular cone shown. Then write a function W that represents the volume (in cubic yards) of the cone when x is measured in feet. Find and interpret $W(3)$.

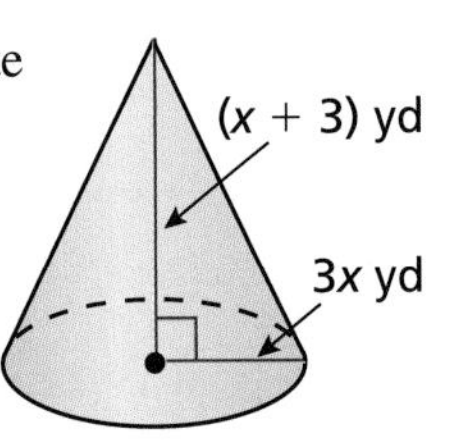

29. MAKING AN ARGUMENT The function $V(x) = x^3$ represents the volume of a cube with edge length x. Does the volume decrease by a greater amount when you divide the volume in half or when you divide each side length in half? Justify your answer.

30. HOW DO YOU SEE IT?
Describe the transformation of the graph of f represented by the graph of g.

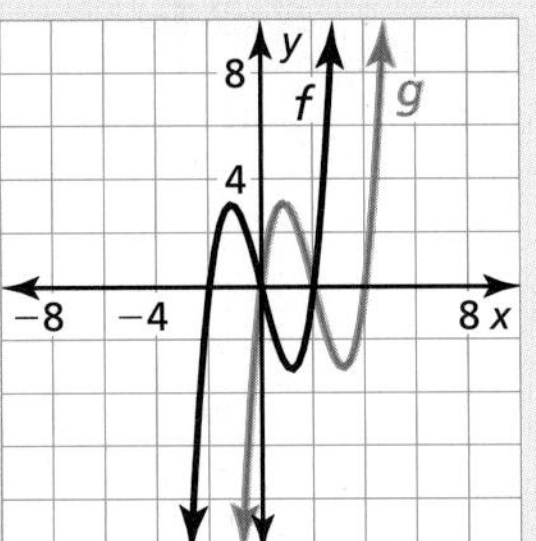

31. OPEN-ENDED Describe two transformations of $f(x) = x^5$ where the order in which the transformations are performed is important. Then describe two transformations where the order is *not* important. Explain your reasoning.

32. THOUGHT PROVOKING
Write a function g that has a y-intercept of -2 and is a transformation of $f(x) = -\frac{1}{4}(2x^2 - 3)(x + 2)^2$.

REVIEW & REFRESH

WATCH

In Exercises 33 and 34, find the minimum value or maximum value of the function. Find the domain and range of the function, and when the function is increasing and decreasing.

33. $h(x) = (x + 5)^2 - 7$ **34.** $f(x) = -2x^2 + 4x - 1$

35. Find all the real zeros of $f(x) = 2x^3 - 21x^2 + 12x + 72$.

36. MODELING REAL LIFE The volume (in cubic feet) of a dog kennel in the shape of a rectangular prism can be modeled by $V = 3x^3 - 17x^2 + 29x - 15$, where x is the length (in feet). Determine the values of x for which the model makes sense. Explain.

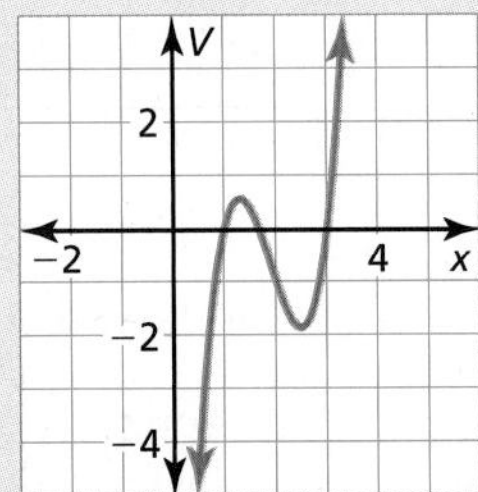

37. Write an equation in intercept form of the parabola that passes through $(-10, 10)$ and has x-intercepts -11 and -5.

38. How many solutions does $x^4 + 8x^2 - 9 = 0$ have? Find all the solutions.

In Exercises 39–42, perform the operation. Write the answer in standard form.

39. $(12 - 4i) + (1 - i)$ **40.** $(3 + 8i) - (-6 + 2i)$

41. $7i(5 - 3i)$ **42.** $(9 - 11i)(-2 + 4i)$

43. Write an inequality that is represented by the graph.

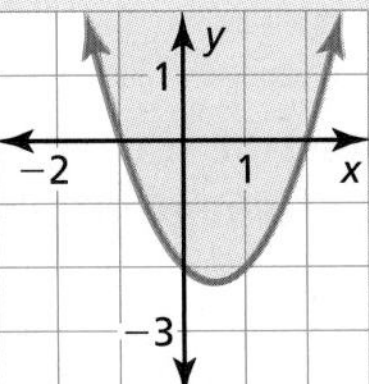

44. Let $f(x) = -x^4 + 2x^2 - 3$ and $g(x) = 2f(x)$. Write a rule for g and then graph each function. Describe the graph of g as a transformation of the graph of f.

In Exercises 45 and 46, graph the function and its parent function. Then describe the transformation.

45. $g(x) = |x + 3|$ **46.** $h(x) = \frac{3}{2}x^2$

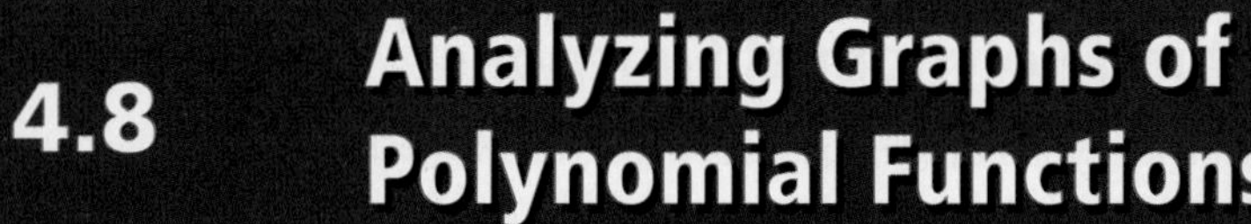

4.8 Analyzing Graphs of Polynomial Functions

Learning Target Analyze graphs of polynomial functions.

Success Criteria
- I can identify a turning point of a polynomial function.
- I can analyze real zeros and turning points numerically.
- I can explain the relationship among the degree of a polynomial function, real zeros, and turning points.

EXPLORE IT! Approximating Turning Points

Work with a partner.

a. The graph of the function at the left has two *turning points*. What is meant by a turning point?

b. Use technology to approximate the coordinates of the turning points of the graph of each function. Round your answers to the nearest hundredth.

i.
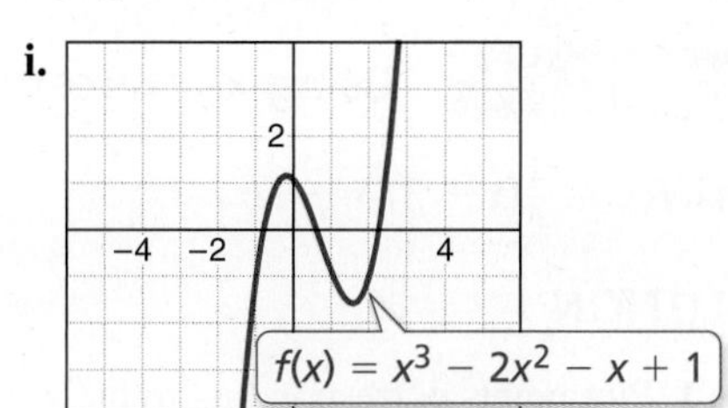

ii.
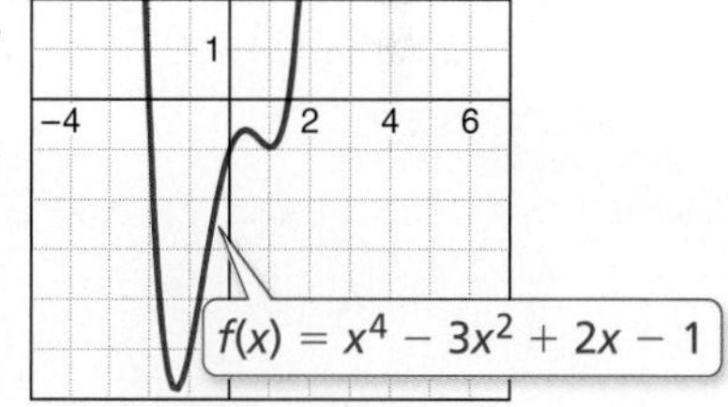

iii.
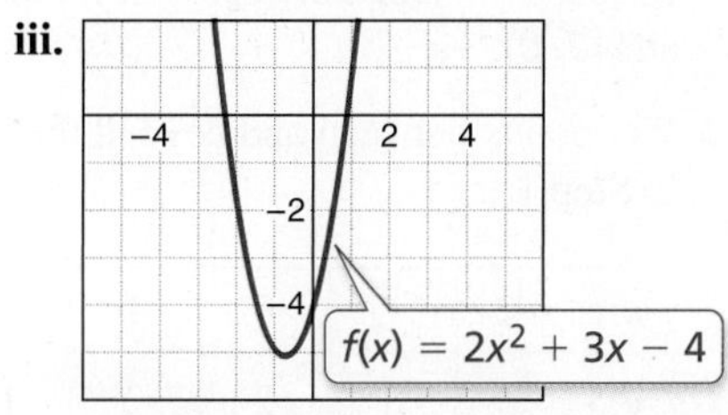

iv.
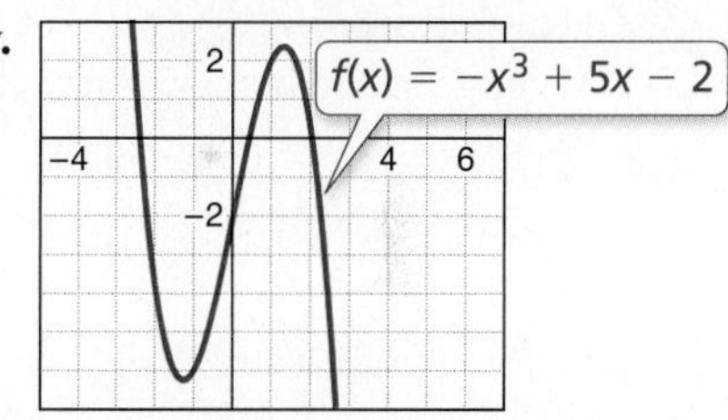

v.
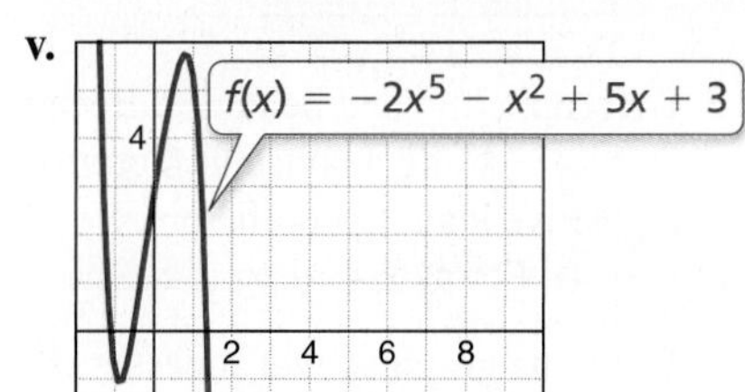

vi.
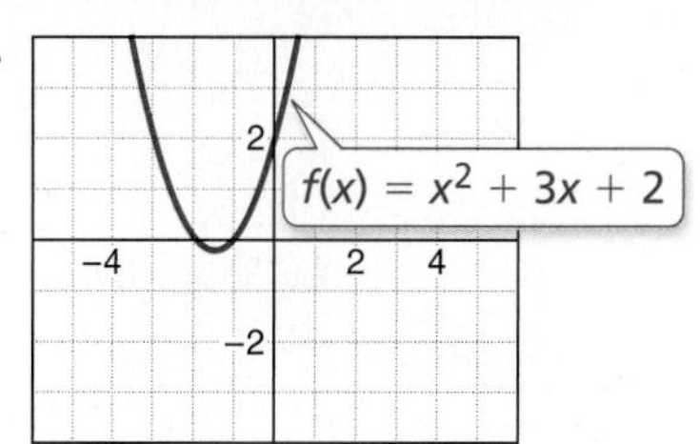

vii.
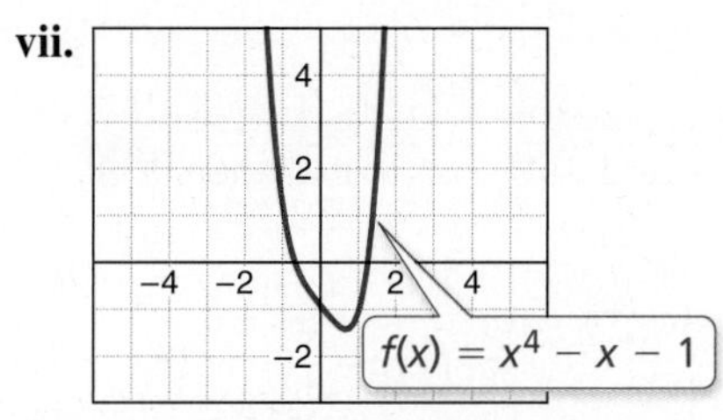

viii.
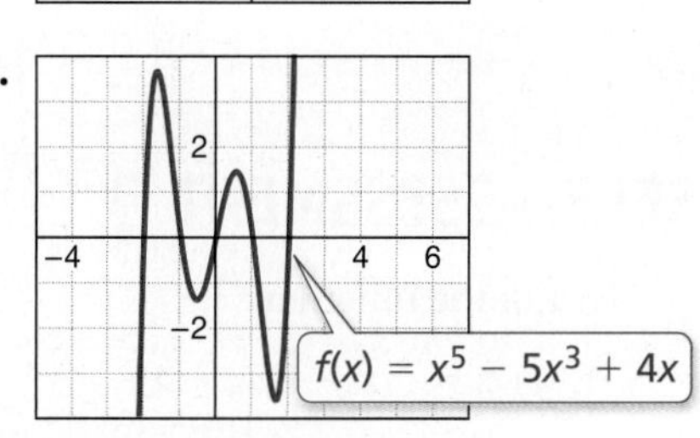

c. Make a conjecture about the number of turning points of the graph of a polynomial function of degree n. Explain your reasoning.

Math Practice

Use a Graph
How can turning points help you identify intervals on which a function is increasing or decreasing?

Graphing Polynomial Functions

Vocabulary 

local maximum, *p. 208*
local minimum, *p. 208*
even function, *p. 209*
odd function, *p. 209*

In this chapter, you have learned that zeros, factors, solutions, and x-intercepts are closely related concepts. Here is a summary of these relationships.

CONCEPT SUMMARY

Zeros, Factors, Solutions, and *x*-Intercepts

Let $f(x) = a_n x^n + a_{n-1}x^{n-1} + \cdots + a_1 x + a_0$ be a polynomial function. The following statements are equivalent.

Zero: k is a zero of the polynomial function f.

Factor: $x - k$ is a factor of the polynomial $f(x)$.

Solution: k is a solution (or root) of the polynomial equation $f(x) = 0$.

x-Intercept: If k is a real number, then k is an x-intercept of the graph of the polynomial function f. The graph of f passes through $(k, 0)$.

EXAMPLE 1 Using *x*-intercepts to Graph a Polynomial Function

Graph $f(x) = \frac{1}{6}(x + 3)(x - 2)^2$.

SOLUTION

Step 1 Plot points corresponding to the x-intercepts. Because -3 and 2 are zeros of f, plot $(-3, 0)$ and $(2, 0)$.

Step 2 Plot points between and beyond the points in Step 1.

x	-2	-1	0	1	3
y	$\frac{8}{3}$	3	2	$\frac{2}{3}$	1

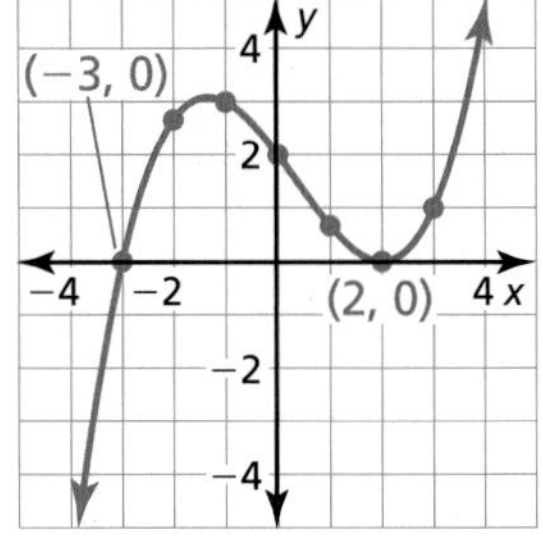

Step 3 Determine the end behavior. Because $f(x)$ has three factors of the form $x - k$ and a constant factor of $\frac{1}{6}$, f is a cubic function with a positive leading coefficient. So, $f(x) \rightarrow -\infty$ as $x \rightarrow -\infty$ and $f(x) \rightarrow +\infty$ as $x \rightarrow +\infty$.

Step 4 Draw the graph so that it passes through the plotted points and has the appropriate end behavior.

SELF-ASSESSMENT

1 I do not understand. 2 I can do it with help. 3 I can do it on my own. 4 I can teach someone else.

Graph the function.

1. $f(x) = \frac{1}{2}(x + 1)(x - 4)^2$

2. $f(x) = \frac{1}{4}(x + 2)(x - 1)(x - 3)$

3. MP **REASONING** The graph of a function g crosses the x-axis at $(-1, 0)$ and touches but does not cross the x-axis at $(-10, 0)$. Can you determine any solutions of $g(x) = 0$? Can there be more solutions? Explain your reasoning.

The Location Principle

You can use the *Location Principle* to help you find real zeros of polynomial functions.

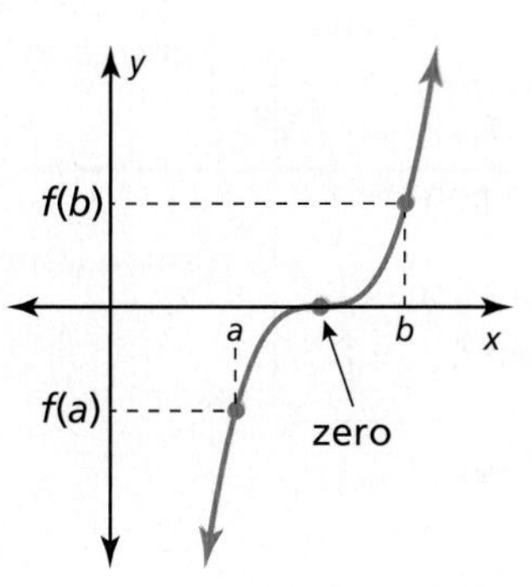

KEY IDEA

The Location Principle

If f is a polynomial function, and a and b are two real numbers such that $f(a) < 0$ and $f(b) > 0$, then f has at least one real zero between a and b.

To use this principle to locate real zeros of a polynomial function, find a value a at which the polynomial function is negative and another value b at which the function is positive. You can conclude that the function has *at least* one real zero between a and b.

EXAMPLE 2 Finding Real Zeros of a Polynomial Function

Find all the real zeros of $f(x) = 6x^3 + 5x^2 - 17x - 6$.

SOLUTION

x	$f(x)$
0	−6
1	−12
2	28
3	150
4	390
5	784
6	1368

Step 1 Use technology to make a table.

Step 2 Use the Location Principle. From the table shown, you can see that $f(1) < 0$ and $f(2) > 0$. So, by the Location Principle, f has at least one real zero between 1 and 2. Because f is a polynomial function of degree 3, it has three zeros. By the Rational Root Theorem, the only possible *rational* zero between 1 and 2 is $\frac{3}{2}$. Use synthetic division to confirm that $\frac{3}{2}$ is a zero.

$$\begin{array}{r|rrrr} \frac{3}{2} & 6 & 5 & -17 & -6 \\ & & 9 & 21 & 6 \\ \hline & 6 & 14 & 4 & 0 \end{array}$$

The remainder is 0, so $x - \frac{3}{2}$ is a factor of $f(x)$.

Check

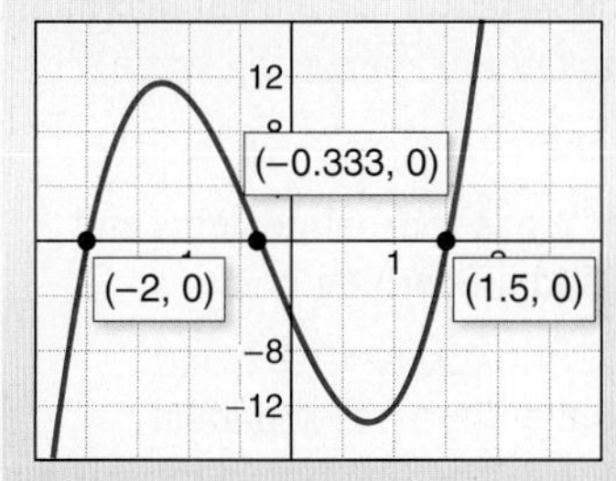

Step 3 Write $f(x)$ in factored form using its known factor $x - \frac{3}{2}$ and the quotient polynomial $6x^2 + 14x + 4$.

$$\begin{aligned} f(x) &= \left(x - \tfrac{3}{2}\right)(6x^2 + 14x + 4) \\ &= 2\left(x - \tfrac{3}{2}\right)(3x^2 + 7x + 2) \\ &= 2\left(x - \tfrac{3}{2}\right)(3x + 1)(x + 2) \end{aligned}$$

▶ From the factorization, there are three zeros. The zeros of f are $\frac{3}{2}$, $-\frac{1}{3}$, and -2.

SELF-ASSESSMENT 1 I do not understand. 2 I can do it with help. 3 I can do it on my own. 4 I can teach someone else.

Find all the real zeros of the function.

4. $f(x) = 18x^3 + 21x^2 - 13x - 6$

5. $f(x) = 2x^4 + x^3 - 9x^2 - 13x - 5$

6. **MP PRECISION** In your own words, explain why the Location Principle is true.

Turning Points

Another important characteristic of graphs of polynomial functions is that they have *turning points* corresponding to local maximum and minimum values.

> **READING**
> Local maximum and local minimum are sometimes referred to as *relative maximum* and *relative minimum*.

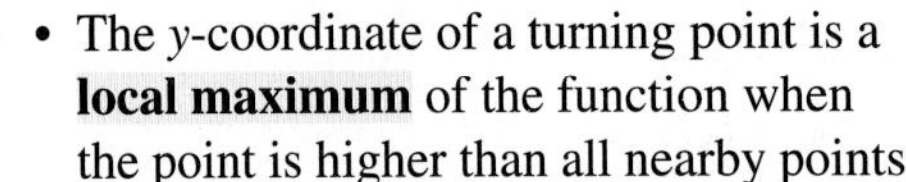

- The y-coordinate of a turning point is a **local maximum** of the function when the point is higher than all nearby points.

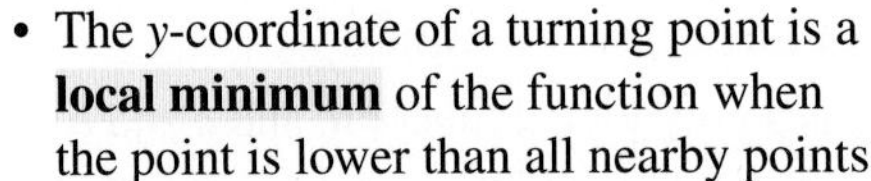

- The y-coordinate of a turning point is a **local minimum** of the function when the point is lower than all nearby points.

A turning point of a graph of a function is a point on the graph at which the function changes from increasing to decreasing, or decreasing to increasing.

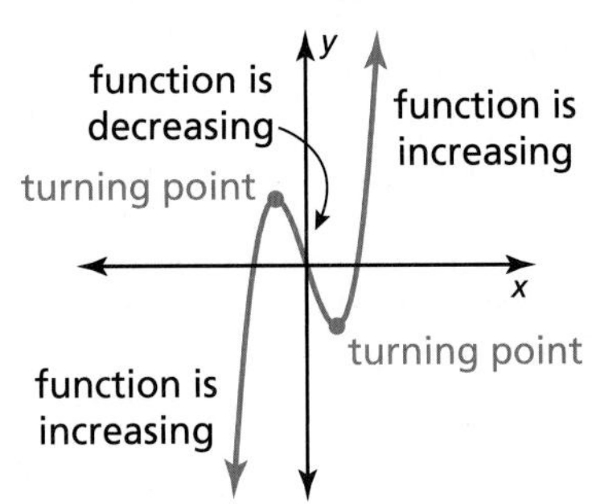

> **WORDS AND MATH**
> In everyday life, *turning point* refers to a point in time or to an event that changes the course of action.

KEY IDEA

Turning Points of Polynomial Functions

1. The graph of every polynomial function of degree n has *at most* $n - 1$ turning points.
2. If a polynomial function of degree n has n distinct real zeros, then its graph has *exactly* $n - 1$ turning points.

EXAMPLE 3 **Finding Turning Points**

Graph each function. Identify the x-intercepts and the points where the local maximums and local minimums occur. Determine the intervals for which each function is increasing or decreasing.

a. $f(x) = x^3 - 3x^2 + 6$ **b.** $g(x) = x^4 - 6x^3 + 3x^2 + 10x - 3$

SOLUTION

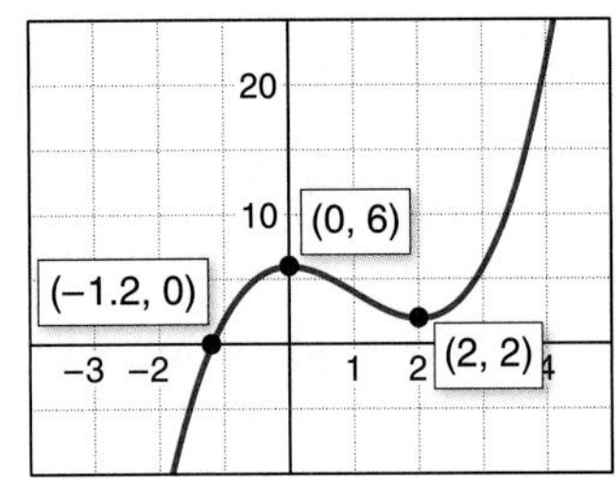

a. Use technology to graph the function. The graph of f has one x-intercept and two turning points. Approximate the x-intercept and the turning points.

▶ The x-intercept of the graph is $x \approx -1.20$. The function has a local maximum at $(0, 6)$ and a local minimum at $(2, 2)$. The function is increasing when $x < 0$ and $x > 2$ and decreasing when $0 < x < 2$.

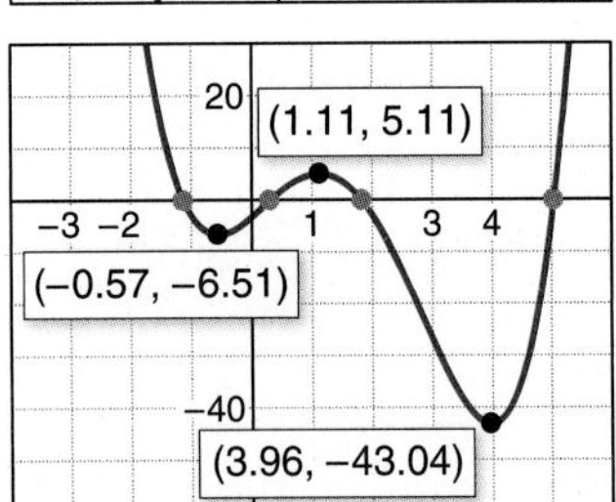

b. Use technology to graph the function. The graph of g has four x-intercepts and three turning points. Approximate the x-intercepts and the turning points.

▶ The x-intercepts of the graph are $x \approx -1.14$, $x \approx 0.29$, $x \approx 1.82$, and $x \approx 5.03$. The function has a local maximum at $(1.11, 5.11)$ and local minimums at $(-0.57, -6.51)$ and $(3.96, -43.04)$. The function is increasing when $-0.57 < x < 1.11$ and $x > 3.96$ and decreasing when $x < -0.57$ and $1.11 < x < 3.96$.

SELF-ASSESSMENT 1 I do not understand. 2 I can do it with help. 3 I can do it on my own. 4 I can teach someone else.

7. Graph $f(x) = 0.5x^3 + x^2 - x + 2$. Identify the x-intercepts and the points where the local maximums and local minimums occur. Determine the intervals for which the function is increasing or decreasing.

8. **WRITING** Explain the local maximum of a function and how it may be different from the maximum value of the function.

Even and Odd Functions

KEY IDEA

Even and Odd Functions

A function f is an **even function** when $f(-x) = f(x)$ for all x in its domain. The graph of an even function is *symmetric about the y-axis.*

A function f is an **odd function** when $f(-x) = -f(x)$ for all x in its domain. The graph of an odd function is *symmetric about the origin.* One way to recognize a graph as symmetric about the origin is that it looks the same after a 180° rotation about the origin.

Even Function

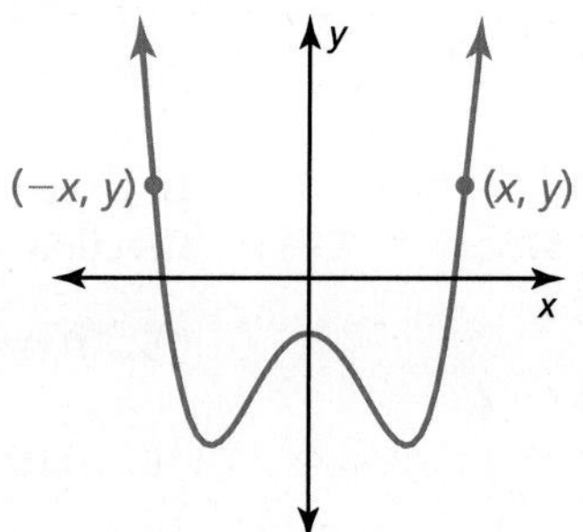

For an even function, if (x, y) is on the graph, then $(-x, y)$ is also on the graph.

Odd Function

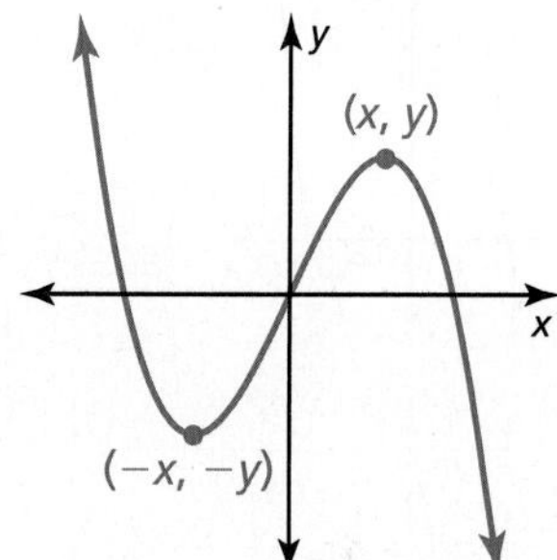

For an odd function, if (x, y) is on the graph, then $(-x, -y)$ is also on the graph.

EXAMPLE 4 Identifying Even and Odd Functions

Determine whether each function is *even*, *odd*, or *neither*.

a. $f(x) = x^3 - 7x$ **b.** $g(x) = x^4 + x^2 - 1$ **c.** $h(x) = x^3 + 2$

SOLUTION

a. Replace x with $-x$ in the equation for f, and then simplify.

$$f(-x) = (-x)^3 - 7(-x) = -x^3 + 7x = -(x^3 - 7x) = -f(x)$$

▶ Because $f(-x) = -f(x)$, the function is odd.

b. Replace x with $-x$ in the equation for g, and then simplify.

$$g(-x) = (-x)^4 + (-x)^2 - 1 = x^4 + x^2 - 1 = g(x)$$

▶ Because $g(-x) = g(x)$, the function is even.

c. Replacing x with $-x$ in the equation for h produces

$$h(-x) = (-x)^3 + 2 = -x^3 + 2.$$

▶ Because $h(x) = x^3 + 2$ and $-h(x) = -x^3 - 2$, you can conclude that $h(-x) \neq h(x)$ and $h(-x) \neq -h(x)$. So, the function is neither even nor odd.

SELF-ASSESSMENT

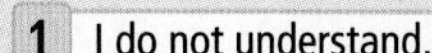

1 I do not understand. 2 I can do it with help. 3 I can do it on my own. 4 I can teach someone else.

Determine whether the function is *even*, *odd*, or *neither*.

9. $f(x) = -x^2 + 5$ **10.** $f(x) = x^4 - 5x^3$ **11.** $f(x) = 2x^5$ **12.** $f(x) = |2x^3|$

4.8 Practice WITH CalcChat® AND CalcView®

ANALYZING RELATIONSHIPS In Exercises 1–4, match the function with its graph.

1. $f(x) = (x - 1)^2(x + 2)$
2. $h(x) = (x + 2)^2(x + 1)$
3. $f(x) = (x - 1)(x - 2)(x + 2)$
4. $g(x) = (x + 1)(x - 1)(x + 2)$

A. 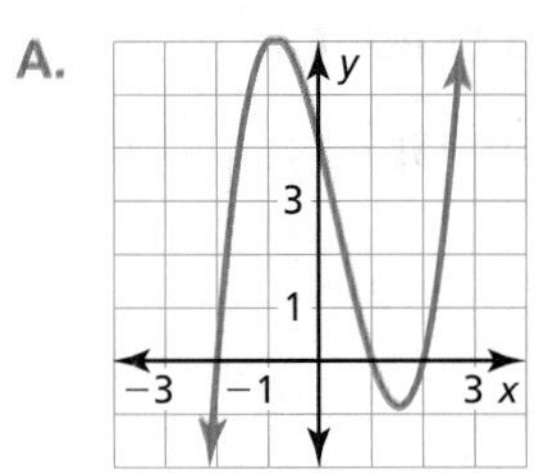

B. 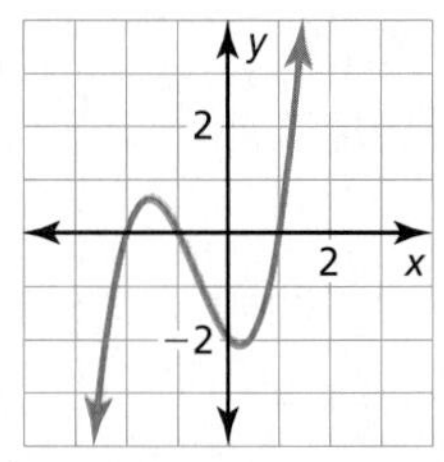

C. 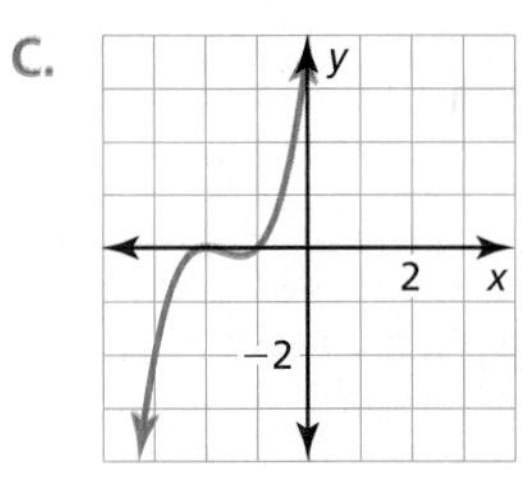

D. 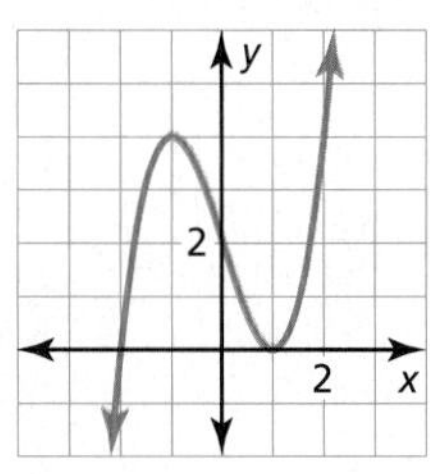

In Exercises 5–12, graph the function. *Example 1*

5. $f(x) = (x - 2)^2(x + 1)$
6. $f(x) = (x + 2)^2(x + 4)^2$
7. $h(x) = (x + 1)^2(x - 1)(x - 3)$
8. $g(x) = 4(x + 1)(x + 2)(x - 1)$
9. $h(x) = \frac{1}{3}(x - 5)(x + 2)(x - 3)$
10. $g(x) = \frac{1}{12}(x + 4)(x + 8)(x - 1)$
11. $h(x) = (x - 3)(x^2 + x + 1)$
12. $f(x) = (x - 4)(2x^2 - 2x + 1)$

ERROR ANALYSIS In Exercises 13 and 14, describe and correct the error in using factors to graph *f*.

13. $f(x) = (x + 2)(x - 1)^2$

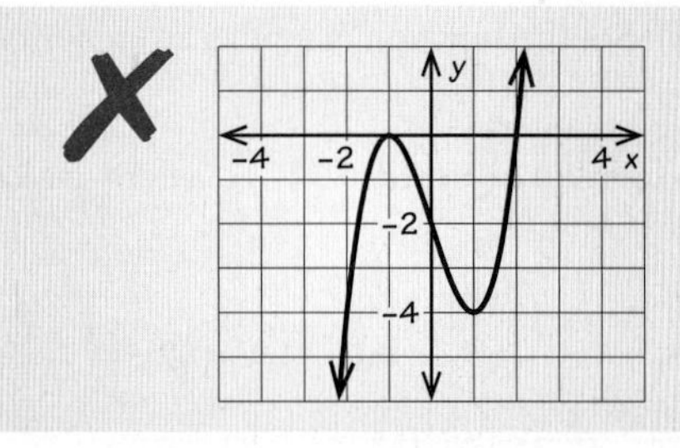

14. $f(x) = x^2(x - 3)^3$

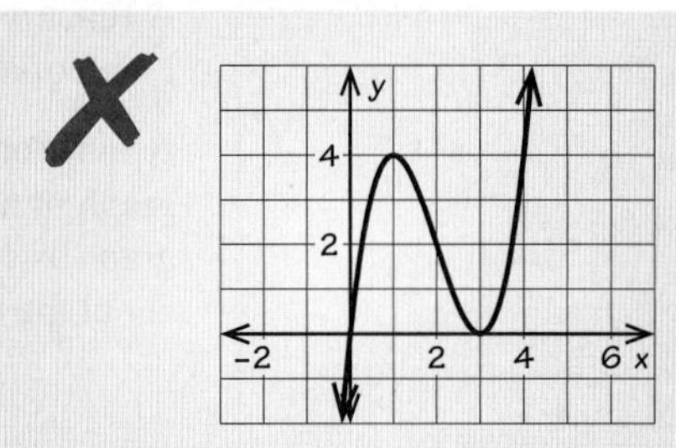

In Exercises 15–22, find all the real zeros of the function. *Example 2*

15. $f(x) = x^3 - 4x^2 - x + 4$
16. $f(x) = x^3 - 3x^2 - 4x + 12$
17. $h(x) = 2x^3 + 7x^2 - 5x - 4$
18. $h(x) = 4x^3 - 2x^2 - 24x - 18$
19. $g(x) = 4x^3 + x^2 - 51x + 36$
20. $f(x) = 2x^3 - 3x^2 - 32x - 15$
21. $p(x) = 2x^4 + 5x^3 - 18x^2 - 68x - 56$
22. $m(x) = 24x^4 - 14x^3 - 37x^2 + 4x + 3$

In Exercises 23–30, graph the function. Identify the *x*-intercepts and the points where the local maximums and local minimums occur. Determine the intervals for which the function is increasing or decreasing. *Example 3*

23. $g(x) = 2x^3 + 8x^2 - 3$
24. $g(x) = -x^4 + 3x$
25. $h(x) = x^4 - 3x^2 + x$
26. $f(x) = x^5 - 4x^3 + x^2 + 2$
27. $f(x) = 0.5x^3 - 2x + 2.5$
28. $f(x) = 0.7x^4 - 3x^3 + 5x$
29. $h(x) = x^5 + 2x^2 - 17x - 4$
30. $g(x) = x^4 - 5x^3 + 2x^2 + x - 3$

In Exercises 31–34, determine the least possible degree of *f*.

31.

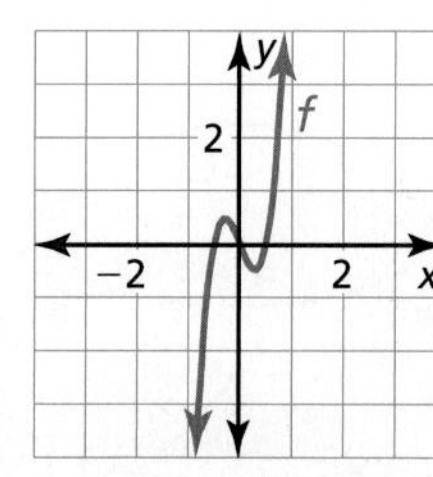

32.

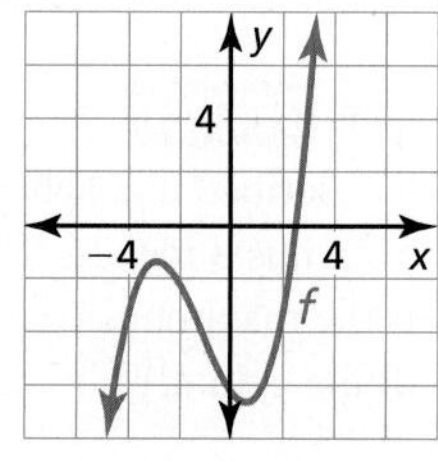

33.

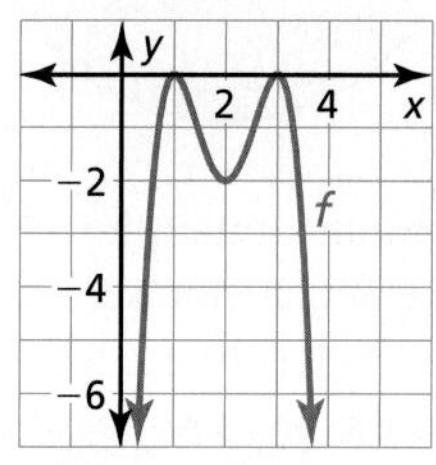

34.

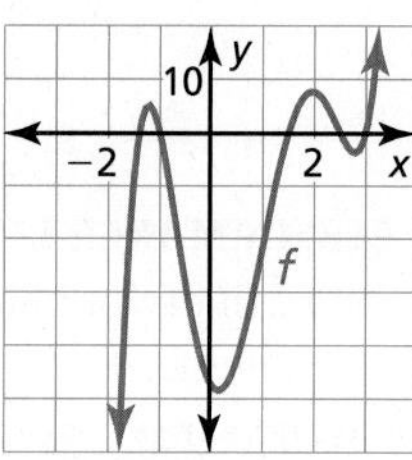

In Exercises 35 and 36, sketch a graph of a polynomial function *f* having the given characteristics.

35. • The graph of f has x-intercepts of -4, 0, and 2.

• f has a local maximum when $x = 1$.

• f has a local minimum when $x = -2$.

36. • The graph of f has x-intercepts of -3, 1, and 5.

• f has a local maximum when $x = 1$.

• f has a local minimum when $x = -2$ and when $x = 4$.

In Exercises 37–44, determine whether the function is *even, odd,* or *neither.* *Example 4*

37. $h(x) = 4x^7$

38. $g(x) = -2x^6 + x^2$

39. $f(x) = x^4 + 3x^2 - 2$

40. $f(x) = x^5 + 3x^3 - x$

41. $g(x) = x^2 + 5x + 1$

42. $f(x) = -x^3 + 2x - 9$

43. $f(x) = x^4 - 12x^2$

44. $h(x) = x^5 + 3x^4$

45. MODELING REAL LIFE When a swimmer does the breaststroke, the function

$$S = -241t^7 + 1060t^6 - 1870t^5 + 1650t^4 - 737t^3 + 144t^2 - 2.43t$$

models the speed S (in meters per second) of the swimmer during one complete stroke, where t is the number of seconds since the start of the stroke and $0 \le t \le 1.22$. Use technology to graph the function. At what time during the stroke is the swimmer traveling the fastest?

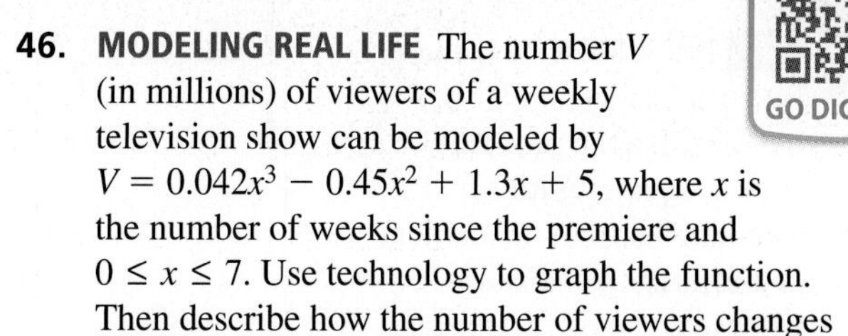

46. MODELING REAL LIFE The number V (in millions) of viewers of a weekly television show can be modeled by $V = 0.042x^3 - 0.45x^2 + 1.3x + 5$, where x is the number of weeks since the premiere and $0 \le x \le 7$. Use technology to graph the function. Then describe how the number of viewers changes over this period of time.

47. WRITING Why is the adjective *local*, used to describe the maximums and minimums of cubic functions, not required for quadratic functions?

48. HOW DO YOU SEE IT?
The graph of a polynomial function is shown.

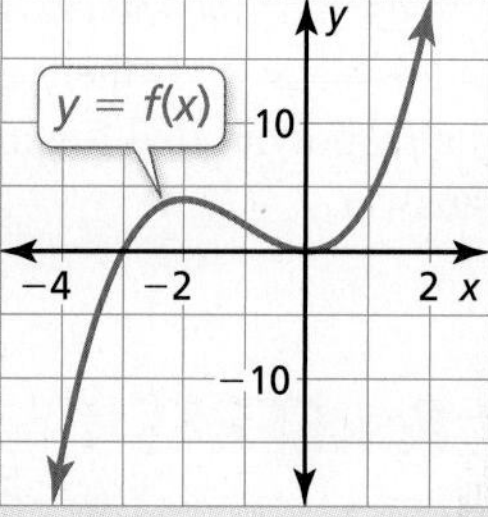

a. Approximate the real zeros of the function and the points where the local maximum and local minimum occur.

b. Compare the x-intercepts of the graphs of $y = f(x)$ and $y = -f(x)$.

c. Compare the local maximums and local minimums of the functions $y = f(x)$ and $y = -f(x)$.

49. MP REASONING Is it possible to sketch the graph of a cubic polynomial function that has *no* turning points? Explain your reasoning.

50. MP PROBLEM SOLVING Quonset huts are temporary, all-purpose structures shaped like half cylinders. You have 1100 square feet of material to build a quonset hut.

STEM

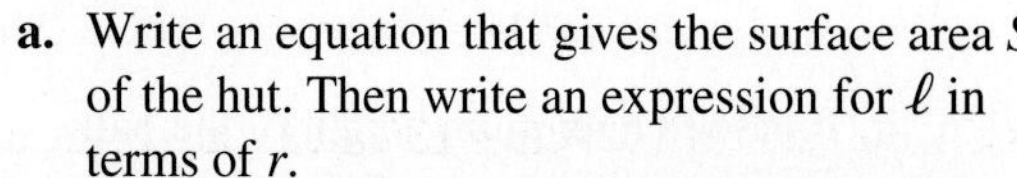

a. Write an equation that gives the surface area S of the hut. Then write an expression for ℓ in terms of r.

b. Write an equation that gives the volume V of a quonset hut as a function of r only. Then find the value of r that maximizes the volume of the hut.

51. **MP PRECISION** You can construct a rectangular box out of a sheet of paper by cutting squares with equal side lengths from the corners and folding up the sides. Choose a piece of paper and construct a box with the greatest possible volume that can be obtained. Explain how you determined the length you should make the cuts and your choice of units. State the volume of your box.

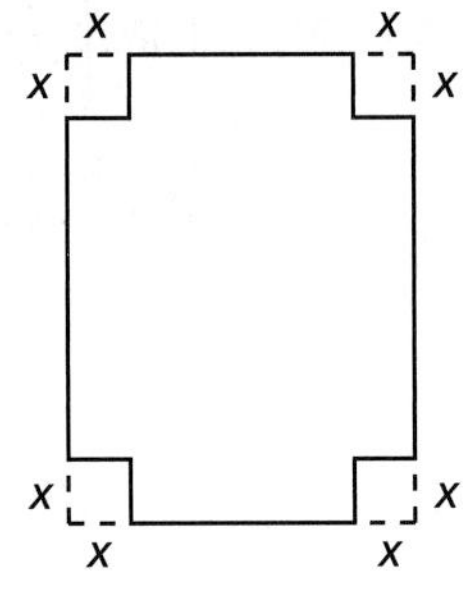

52. **THOUGHT PROVOKING**
Write and graph a polynomial function that has one real zero in each of the intervals $-2 < x < -1$, $0 < x < 1$, and $4 < x < 5$. Is there a maximum degree that such a polynomial function can have? Justify your answer.

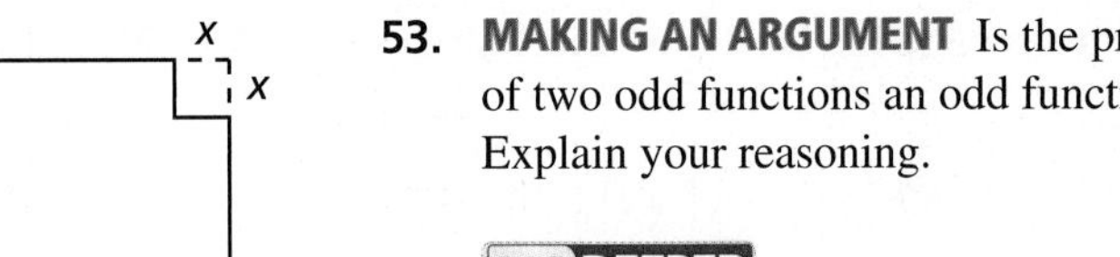

53. **MAKING AN ARGUMENT** Is the product of two odd functions an odd function? Explain your reasoning.

54. **DIG DEEPER** A cylinder is inscribed in a sphere of radius 8 inches. What is the maximum volume of the cylinder?

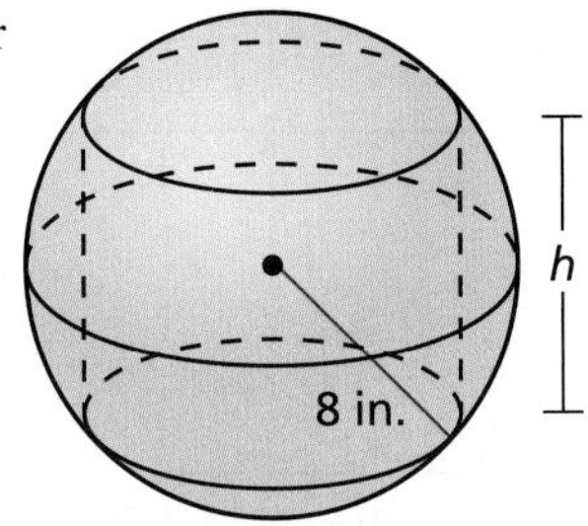

55. **PERFORMANCE TASK** Measure the dimensions of a food can of your choice, and calculate the surface area and volume. The manufacturer wants to use a can that has the same surface area and the greatest possible volume. Write a recommendation to the manufacturer describing a design for the can.

REVIEW & REFRESH

In Exercises 56 and 57, solve the equation.

56. $n^3 + n^2 - 6n = 0$

57. $2m^4 + 10m^3 = 4m^2 + 20m$

In Exercises 58 and 59, determine whether the data are *linear*, *quadratic*, or *neither*. Explain.

58.

Month, x	0	1	2	3
Savings (dollars), y	100	150	200	250

59.

Time (seconds), x	0	1	2	3
Height (feet), y	300	284	236	156

60. **MODELING REAL LIFE** During a game of "Spud," a kickball is thrown straight up into the air. The height h (in feet) of the ball t seconds after it is thrown can be modeled by $h = -16t^2 + 24t + 5$.

  a. Find the maximum height of the ball.

  b. A chosen player catches the ball when it is 5 feet above the ground. How long is the ball in the air?

In Exercises 61 and 62, describe the transformation of *f* represented by *g*. Then graph each function.

61. $f(x) = x^3, g(x) = (x + 2)^3 - 5$

62. $f(x) = x^4, g(x) = -\frac{1}{2}x^4$

In Exercises 63 and 64, divide.

63. $(2x^2 + 9x - 5) \div (x + 3)$

64. $(7x^3 - 2x^2 + 4x + 6) \div (x^2 - x + 2)$

65. **MP REASONING** The graph of $g(x) = x - 5$ is a vertical translation 2 units down of the graph of $f(x) = x - 3$. How can you obtain the graph of g from the graph of f using a horizontal translation? Explain.

66. Find all the zeros of $f(x) = x^5 + 3x^4 + 9x^3 + 23x^2 - 36$.

67. Use the graph to solve $2x^2 + 16 = 12x$.

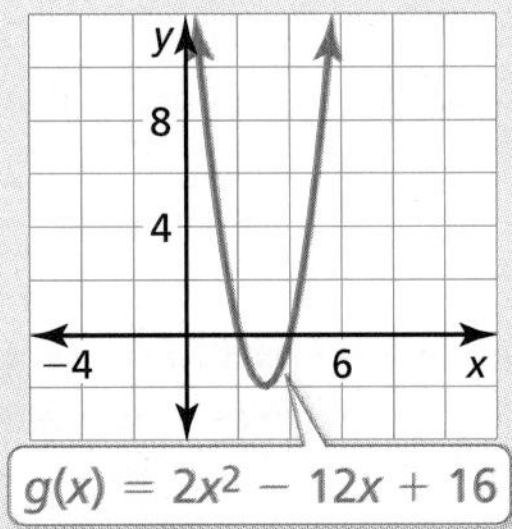

68. Graph $f(x) = 2x^4 - 3x^3 - 9x^2 + 6x - 4$. Identify the x-intercepts and the points where the local maximums and local minimums occur. Determine the intervals for which the function is increasing or decreasing.

In Exercises 69 and 70, find the product.

69. $(3z + 4)(3z - 4)$

70. $(6y - 10)^2$

4.9 Modeling with Polynomial Functions

Learning Target Write polynomial functions.

Success Criteria

- I can write a polynomial function given a graph or a set of points.
- I can write a polynomial function using finite differences.
- I can use technology to find a polynomial model for a set of data.

EXPLORE IT! Modeling Real-Life Data

Work with a partner. The data show the prices per share y (in dollars) for Amazon.com, Inc. stock t years after 2000.

t	0	1	2	3	4	5	6
y	81.50	15.81	10.93	19.19	52.76	44.95	47.47

t	7	8	9	10	11	12	13
y	38.68	95.35	51.35	136.25	181.37	175.89	256.08

t	14	15	16	17	18	19
y	398.80	312.58	656.29	757.92	1172.00	1465.20

a. Use technology to make a scatter plot of the data. Describe the scatter plot.

b. Use technology to find a linear model and a quadratic model to represent the data. Is either model a good fit? How can you tell?

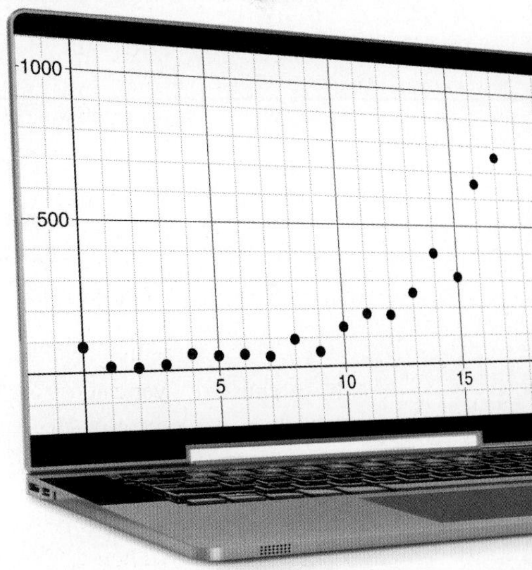

c. Is there another type of model you can use that better represents the data in the table? Use technology to find the model and explain why it is a better fit. Compare your results with your classmates.

d. Can you use the model you found in part (c) to make predictions about the share prices for Amazon.com, Inc. for future years? Explain your reasoning.

e. How can you tell when a model fits a set of data *exactly*?

Math Practice

Evaluate Results

How can you determine whether one model is a better fit for a set of data than another model?

Writing a Polynomial Function for a Set of Points

Vocabulary 

finite differences, *p. 214*

You know that two points determine a line and three points not on a line determine a parabola. In Example 1, you will see that four points not on a line or a parabola determine the graph of a cubic function.

EXAMPLE 1 Writing a Cubic Function

Write the cubic function whose graph is shown.

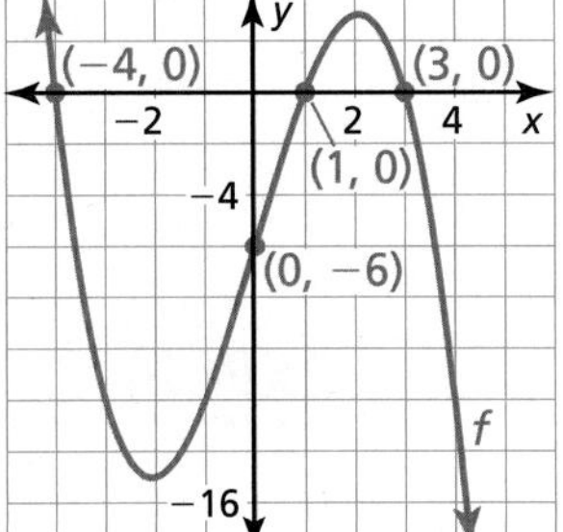

SOLUTION

Step 1 Use the three x-intercepts to write the function in intercept form.

$$f(x) = a(x + 4)(x - 1)(x - 3)$$

Step 2 Find the value of a by substituting the coordinates of the point $(0, -6)$.

$$-6 = a(0 + 4)(0 - 1)(0 - 3)$$

$$-6 = 12a$$

$$-\frac{1}{2} = a$$

▶ The function is $f(x) = -\frac{1}{2}(x + 4)(x - 1)(x - 3)$.

REMEMBER

The intercept form of a cubic function is

$$f(x) = a(x - p)(x - q)(x - r)$$

where $a \neq 0$, and the x-intercepts of the graph of f are p, q, and r.

Check

Check the end behavior of f. The degree of f is odd and $a < 0$. So, $f(x) \to +\infty$ as $x \to -\infty$ and $f(x) \to -\infty$ as $x \to +\infty$, which matches the graph. 

SELF-ASSESSMENT 1 I do not understand. 2 I can do it with help. 3 I can do it on my own. 4 I can teach someone else.

Write a cubic function whose graph passes through the given points.

1. $(-4, 0), (0, 10), (2, 0), (5, 0)$
2. $(-1, 0), (0, -12), (2, 0), (3, 0)$

Finite Differences

When the x-values in a data set are equally spaced, the differences of consecutive y-values are called **finite differences**. Recall from Section 2.4 that the first and second differences of $y = x^2$ are:

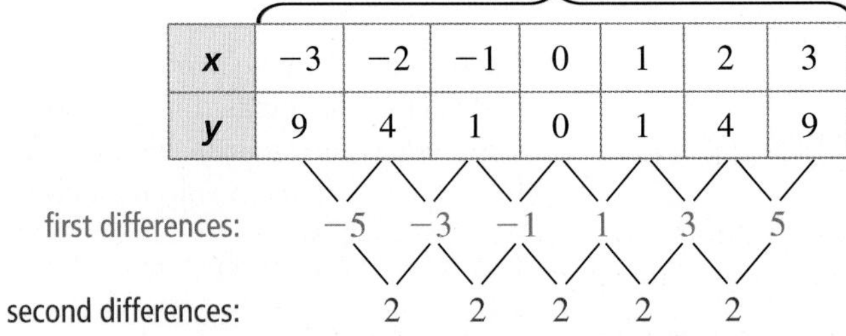

Equally-spaced x-values

x	−3	−2	−1	0	1	2	3
y	9	4	1	0	1	4	9

first differences: −5 −3 −1 1 3 5

second differences: 2 2 2 2 2

Notice that $y = x^2$ has degree *two* and that the *second* differences are constant and nonzero. This illustrates the first of the two properties of finite differences shown on the next page.

KEY IDEA

Properties of Finite Differences

1. If a polynomial function $y = f(x)$ has degree n, then the nth differences of function values for equally-spaced x-values are nonzero and constant.
2. Conversely, if the nth differences of equally-spaced data are nonzero and constant, then the data can be represented by a polynomial function of degree n.

The second property of finite differences allows you to write a polynomial function that models a set of equally-spaced data.

EXAMPLE 2 Writing a Function Using Finite Differences

Use finite differences to determine the degree of the polynomial function that fits the data. Then use technology to find the polynomial function.

x	1	2	3	4	5	6	7
$f(x)$	1	4	10	20	35	56	84

SOLUTION

Step 1 Write the function values. Find the first differences by subtracting consecutive values. Then find the second differences by subtracting consecutive first differences. Continue until you obtain differences that are nonzero and constant.

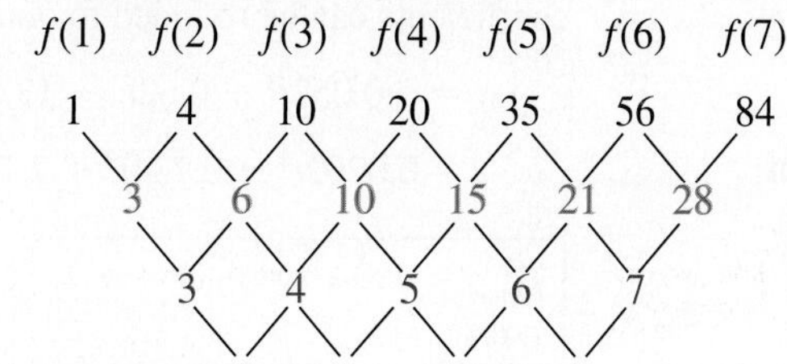

Because the third differences are nonzero and constant, you can model the data *exactly* with a cubic function.

Step 2 Use technology to enter the data from the table. Then use *cubic regression* to obtain a polynomial function.

$y = ax^3 + bx^2 + cx + d$
PARAMETERS
$a = 0.166667$ $b = 0.5$
$c = 0.333333$ $d = 0$
STATISTICS
$R^2 = 1$

▶ Because $0.166667 \approx \frac{1}{6}$, $0.5 = \frac{1}{2}$, and $0.333333 \approx \frac{1}{3}$, a cubic function that fits the data exactly is

$$f(x) = \frac{1}{6}x^3 + \frac{1}{2}x^2 + \frac{1}{3}x.$$

SELF-ASSESSMENT

1 I do not understand. 2 I can do it with help. 3 I can do it on my own. 4 I can teach someone else.

3. **WRITING** Explain how you know when a set of data can be modeled by a polynomial function of degree n.
4. Use finite differences to determine the degree of the polynomial function that fits the data. Then use technology to find the polynomial function.

x	−3	−2	−1	0	1	2
$f(x)$	6	15	22	21	6	−29

Finding Models Using Technology

In Examples 1 and 2, you found a cubic model that *exactly* fits a set of data. In many real-life situations, you cannot find models to fit data exactly. Despite this limitation, you can still use technology to approximate the data with a polynomial model.

EXAMPLE 3 **Modeling Real Life**  

The data show the numbers y of bald eagle nests counted in Ohio t years after 2000. Find a model for the data. Use the model to estimate the number of bald eagle nests in 2015.

t	0	1	2	3	4	5	6
y	63	73	79	88	108	125	150

t	7	8	9	12	14	17
y	164	184	215	213	200	221

On August 9, 2007, the bald eagle was removed from the federal list of threatened and endangered species.

SOLUTION

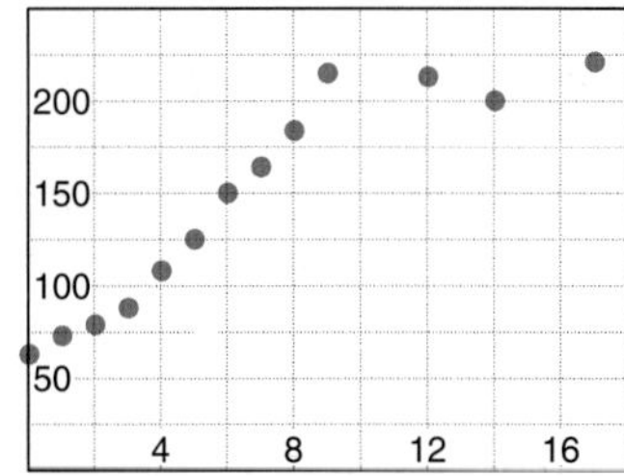

Step 1 Use technology to make a scatter plot of the data. The data suggest some type of polynomial model such as a cubic or quartic function.

Step 2 Use *cubic* and *quartic regression*. The coefficients can be rounded to obtain:

$$y = -0.052t^3 + 0.62t^2 + 13.6t + 55 \quad \text{Cubic model}$$

$$y = 0.0202t^4 - 0.734t^3 + 7.79t^2 - 11.0t + 70 \quad \text{Quartic model}$$

$y = ax^3 + bx^2 + cx + d$
PARAMETERS
$a = -0.0516199$ $b = 0.618239$
$c = 13.5523$ $d = 54.9467$
STATISTICS
$R^2 = 0.9569$

$y = ax^4 + bx^3 + cx^2 + dx + f$
PARAMETERS
$a = 0.020226$ $b = -0.733573$
$c = 7.79139$ $d = -11.0265$
$f = 69.7095$
STATISTICS
$R^2 = 0.9876$

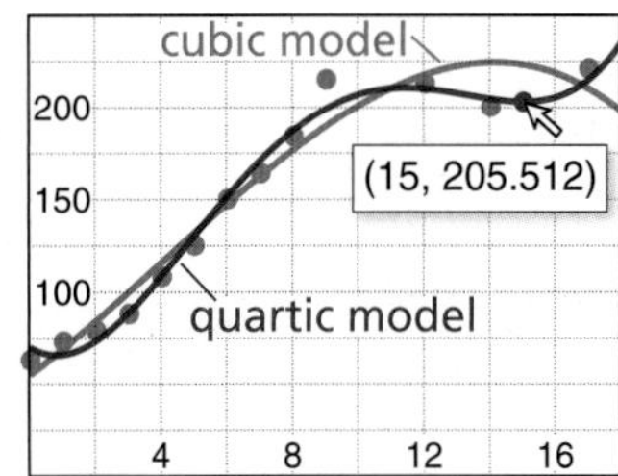

Step 3 Graph the equations with the data and compare the models. The graph of the quartic model appears to be closer to the data points than the graph of the cubic model. So, a good model for the data is $y = 0.0202t^4 - 0.734t^3 + 7.79t^2 - 11.0t + 70$.

Step 4 Find y when $t = 15$. It is about 206.

▶ The number of bald eagle nests in 2015 was about 206.

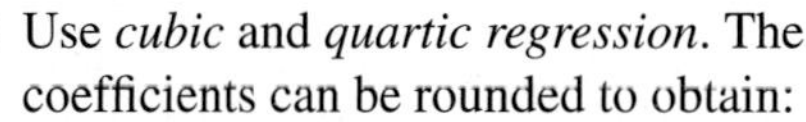

SELF-ASSESSMENT

1 I do not understand. 2 I can do it with help. 3 I can do it on my own. 4 I can teach someone else.

5. Use technology to find a polynomial function that fits the data.

x	1	2	3	4	5	6
y	5	13	17	11	11	56

6. MP **REASONING** Use the cubic model in Example 3 to estimate the number of bald eagle nests in 2015. What do you notice?

4.9 Practice WITH CalcChat® AND CalcView®

In Exercises 1–4, write a cubic function whose graph passes through the given points. *Example 1*

1.

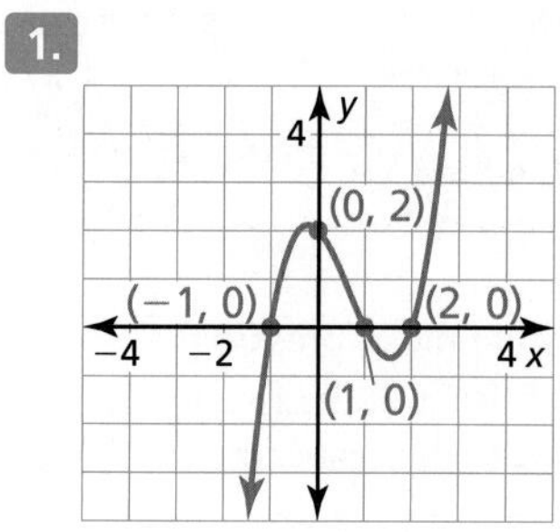

2.

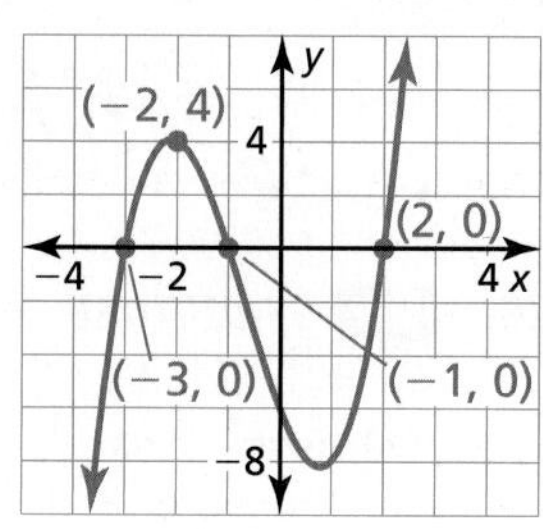

3. (−5, 0), (1, 0), (2, −2), (4, 0)

4. (−6, 0), (−3, 0), (0, −9), (3, 0)

In Exercises 5–10, use finite differences to determine the degree of the polynomial function that fits the data. Then use technology to find the polynomial function. *Example 2*

5.

x	−6	−3	0	3	6	9
$f(x)$	−2	15	−4	49	282	803

6.

x	−1	0	1	2	3	4
$f(x)$	−14	−5	−2	7	34	91

7. (−4, −317), (−3, −37), (−2, 21), (−1, 7), (0, −1), (1, 3), (2, −47), (3, −289), (4, −933)

8. (−6, 744), (−4, 154), (−2, 4), (0, −6), (2, 16), (4, 154), (6, 684), (8, 2074), (10, 4984)

9. (−2, 968), (−1, 422), (0, 142), (1, 26), (2, −4), (3, −2), (4, 2), (5, 2), (6, 16)

10. (1, 0), (2, 6), (3, 2), (4, 6), (5, 12), (6, −10), (7, −114), (8, −378), (9, −904)

11. ERROR ANALYSIS Describe and correct the error in writing a cubic function whose graph passes through the given points.

> ✗ (−6, 0), (1, 0), (3, 0), (0, 54)
>
> $54 = a(0 - 6)(0 + 1)(0 + 3)$
>
> $54 = -18a$
>
> $-3 = a$
>
> $f(x) = -3(x - 6)(x + 1)(x + 3)$

12. MAKING AN ARGUMENT Is it possible to determine the degree of a polynomial function given only the first differences? Explain your reasoning.

13. MODELING REAL LIFE The table shows the total U.S. biomass energy consumptions y (in trillions of British thermal units, or Btus) t years after 2000. Find a model for the data. Use the model to estimate the total U.S. biomass energy consumption in 2017. *Example 3*

t	0	1	2	3	4
y	3008	2622	2701	2806	3008

t	5	10	15	16	18
y	3114	4506	4983	5020	5128

14. MODELING REAL LIFE The data in the table show the average speeds y (in miles per hour) of a pontoon boat for several different engine speeds x (in hundreds of revolutions per minute, or RPMs). Find a model for the data. Use the model to estimate the average speed of the pontoon boat when the engine speed is 2800 RPMs.

x	10	20	25	30	45	55
y	4.5	8.9	13.8	18.9	29.9	37.7

15. WRITING Explain why you cannot always use finite differences to find models for real-life data sets.

16. HOW DO YOU SEE IT?
The graph shows typical speeds y (in feet per second) of a space shuttle x seconds after it is launched.

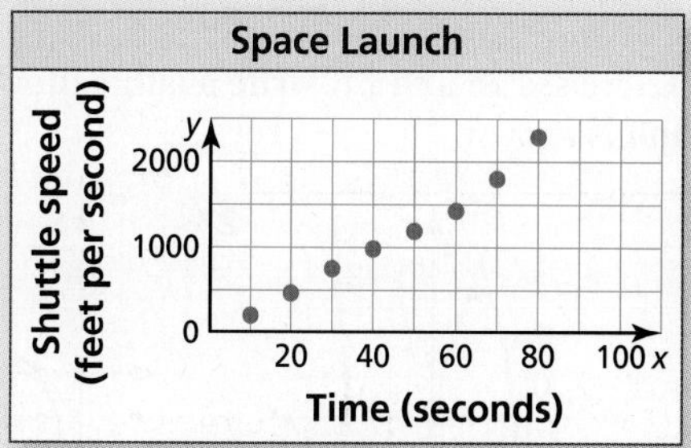

a. Do the data appear to be best represented by a *linear*, *quadratic*, or *cubic* function? Explain.

b. Which nth differences should be constant for the function in part (a)? Explain.

17. ANALYZING RELATIONSHIPS The table shows the numbers of diagonals for polygons with n sides. Find a polynomial function that fits the data. Determine the number of diagonals in the decagon shown.

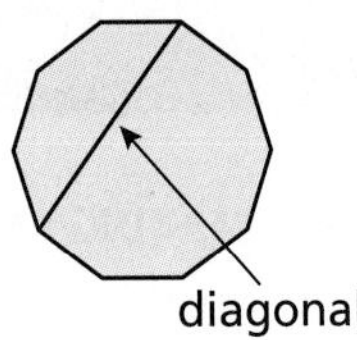

Sides, n	3	4	5	6	7	8
Diagonals, d	0	2	5	9	14	20

18. THOUGHT PROVOKING
Write a polynomial function that has constant fourth differences of -2. Justify your answer.

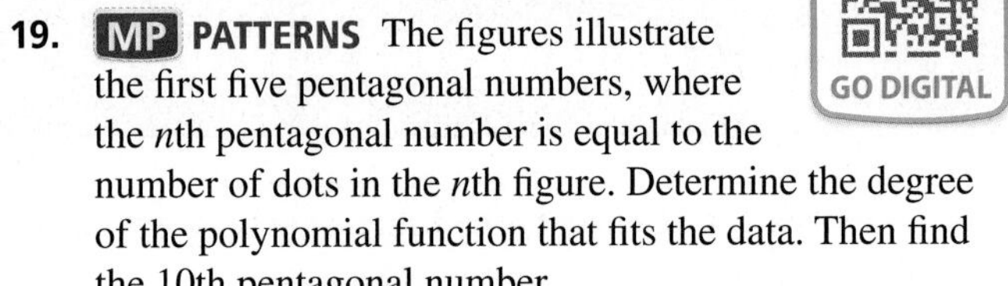

19. MP PATTERNS The figures illustrate the first five pentagonal numbers, where the nth pentagonal number is equal to the number of dots in the nth figure. Determine the degree of the polynomial function that fits the data. Then find the 10th pentagonal number.

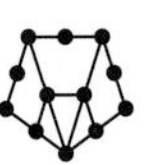
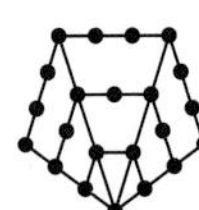
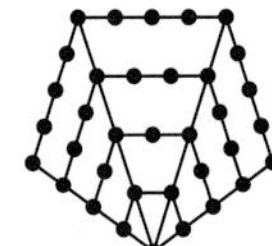

20. MP STRUCTURE Substitute the expressions $z, z + 1, z + 2, \ldots, z + 5$ for x in the function $f(x) = ax^3 + bx^2 + cx + d$ to generate six equally-spaced ordered pairs. Then show that the third differences are constant.

REVIEW & REFRESH

In Exercises 21 and 22, use the graph to describe the degree and leading coefficient of f.

21.

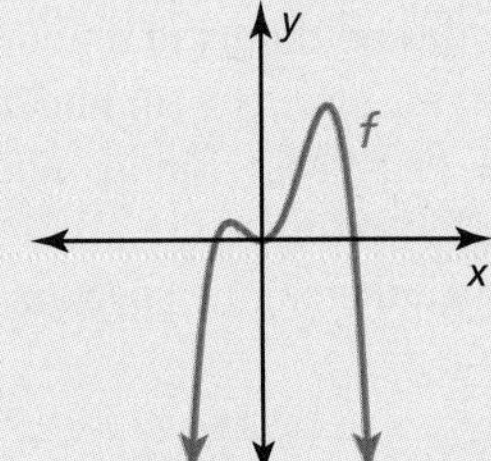

22.

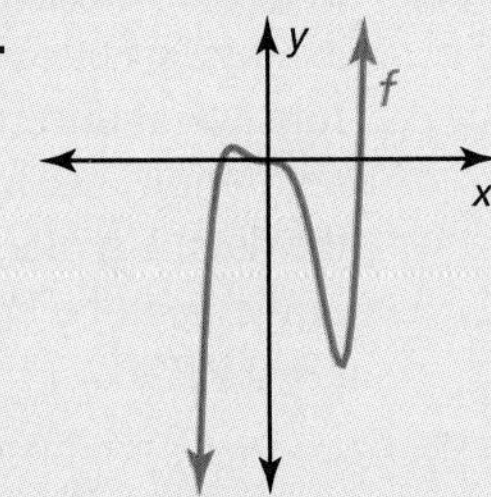

23. Let the graph of g be a translation 2 units left and 5 units down, followed by a reflection in the x-axis of the graph of $f(x) = (x + 1)^3 + 3$. Write a rule for g.

In Exercises 24 and 25, solve the system using any method. Explain your choice of method.

24. $y = -2x + 5$
$x^2 + y^2 = 5$

25. $x^2 - 3x - y = -3$
$3x^2 - 8x - y = -5$

In Exercises 26 and 27, write a cubic function whose graph is shown.

26.

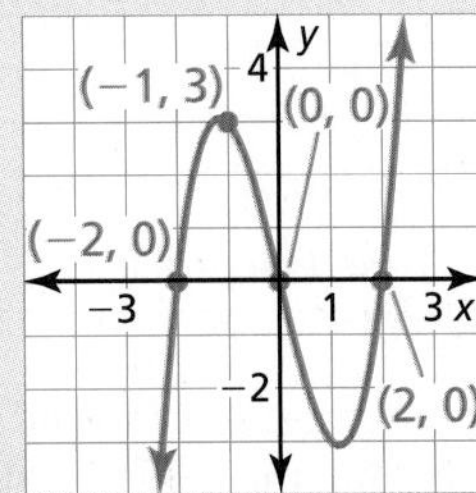

27.

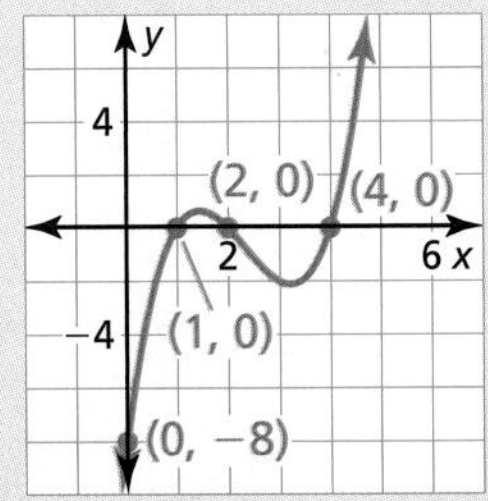

28. MP REASONING Identify the focus and the directrix of $y = ax^2 + c$ in terms of a and c.

29. Determine the possible numbers of positive real zeros, negative real zeros, and imaginary zeros for the function $g(x) = -x^5 - 2x^4 + 7x^2 - 3x + 8$.

30. MODELING REAL LIFE The table shows the total numbers y of species added to the Endangered Species Act x years since 2010. Use technology to find an equation of the line of best fit. Interpret the slope and y-intercept in this situation.

Years since 2010, x	Species added, y
0	54
1	73
2	124
3	213
4	279
5	310
6	384
7	395

In Exercises 31–34, solve the equation.

31. $x^2 - 6 = 30$

32. $5x^2 - 38 = 187$

33. $2x^2 + 3x = -3x^2 + 1$

34. $4x - 20 = x^2$

35. Write an expression for the volume of the rectangular prism as a polynomial in standard form.

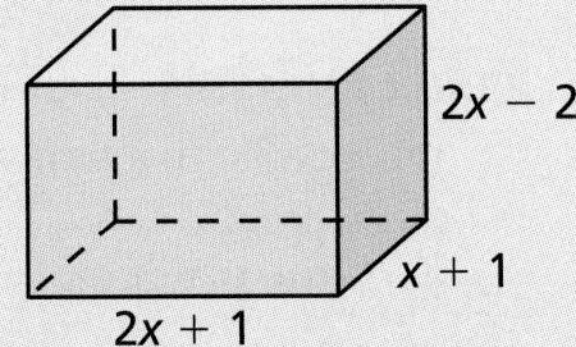

36. Graph $f(x) = -x^4 + 4x^3 - 8x$. Identify the x-intercepts and the points where the local maximums and local minimums occur. Determine the intervals for which the function is increasing or decreasing.

4 Chapter Review WITH CalcChat®

Chapter Learning Target Understand polynomial functions.

Chapter Success Criteria
- ◆ I can graph polynomial functions.
- ◆ I can add, subtract, multiply, and divide, and factor polynomials.
- ■ I can solve polynomial equations.
- ■ I can model with and analyze graphs of polynomial functions.

◆ Surface
■ Deep

SELF-ASSESSMENT 1 I do not understand. 2 I can do it with help. 3 I can do it on my own. 4 I can teach someone else.

4.1 Graphing Polynomial Functions (pp. 153–160)

Learning Target: Graph and describe polynomial functions.

Vocabulary AZ VOCAB
polynomial
polynomial function
end behavior

Graph the polynomial function.

1. $h(x) = x^2 + 6x^5 - 5$
2. $p(x) = 2x^3 - 4x + 6$
3. $f(x) = 3x^4 - 5x^2 + 1$
4. $g(x) = -x^4 + x + 2$
5. The life expectancy (in years) at birth of a person in the United States t years after 2000 can be modeled by the polynomial function $f(t) = -0.0013t^3 + 0.023t^2 + 0.09t + 76.8$.
   a. Use technology to graph the function for $0 \le t \le 16$. Describe the behavior of the graph on this interval.
   b. What was the average rate of change in life expectancy at birth from 2000 to 2016?
   c. Do you think this model can be used for years after 2016? Explain your reasoning.

4.2 Adding, Subtracting, and Multiplying Polynomials (pp. 161–168)

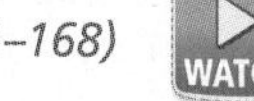

Learning Target: Add, subtract, and multiply polynomials.

Vocabulary AZ VOCAB
Pascal's Triangle

Find the sum or difference.

6. $(4x^3 - 12x^2 - 5) - (-8x^2 + 4x + 3)$
7. $(x^4 + 3x^3 - x^2 + 6) + (2x^4 - 3x + 9)$
8. $(3x^2 + 9x + 13) - (x^2 - 2x + 12)$

Find the product.

9. $(2y^2 + 4y - 7)(y + 3)$
10. $(2m + n)^3$
11. $(s + 2)(s + 4)(s - 3)$

Use Pascal's Triangle to expand the binomial.

12. $(m + 4)^4$
13. $(3s + 2)^5$
14. $(z + 1)^6$

4.3 Dividing Polynomials *(pp. 169–174)* WATCH

Learning Target: Divide polynomials by other polynomials and use the Remainder Theorem.

Divide using polynomial long division or synthetic division.

Vocabulary VOCAB
polynomial long division
synthetic division

15. $(x^3 + x^2 + 3x - 4) \div (x^2 + 2x + 1)$

16. $(x^4 + 3x^3 - 4x^2 + 5x + 3) \div (x^2 + x + 4)$

17. $(-2x^3 + 3x - 5) \div (x - 2)$

18. $(x^4 - x^2 - 7) \div (x + 4)$

Use synthetic division to evaluate the function for the indicated value of *x*.

19. $f(x) = 4x^3 + 2x^2 - 4;\ x = 5$

20. $f(x) = -x^4 - 3x^3 + 6x;\ x = -3$

21. Find the missing values. Then write the dividend, divisor, and quotient represented by the synthetic division.

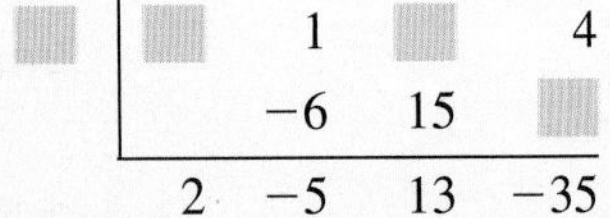

22. The total numbers N (in thousands) of overnight stays at Zion National Park x years after 2000 can be modeled by

$$N = -0.032x^3 + 0.73x^2 + 2.2x + 248$$

where $0 \le x \le 18$. Use synthetic division to find the total number of overnight stays in 2018. Justify your answer.

4.4 Factoring Polynomials *(pp. 175–182)*

Learning Target: Factor polynomials and use the Factor Theorem.

Factor the polynomial completely.

23. $64x^3 - 8$

24. $8y^3 + 125y^6$

25. $2z^5 - 12z^3 + 10z$

26. $2a^3 - 7a^2 - 8a + 28$

Vocabulary

factored completely
factor by grouping
quadratic form

27. Show that $x + 2$ is a factor of $f(x) = x^4 + 2x^3 - 27x - 54$. Then factor $f(x)$ completely.

28. A rectangular prism has a volume of $x^3 + 13x^2 + 34x - 48$ cubic inches. Give one possible set of dimensions for the prism in terms of x. Justify your answer.

29. The profit P (in millions of dollars) for a game company can be modeled by $P = -x^3 + 3x^2 + 3$, where x is the number (in millions) of copies of a new game produced. The company now produces 1 million copies of the new game and makes a profit of \$5 million, but it would like to increase production. What greater number of copies could the company produce and still make the same profit?

4.5 Solving Polynomial Equations (pp. 183–190)

Learning Target: Solve polynomial equations and find zeros of polynomial functions.

Vocabulary AZ VOCAB

repeated solution

Find all the real solutions of the equation.

30. $x^3 + 3x^2 - 10x - 24 = 0$

31. $x^3 + 5x^2 - 2x - 24 = 0$

Find the zeros of the function. Then sketch a graph of the function.

32. $f(x) = -3x^3 - 6x^2$

33. $f(x) = -x^4 + 18x^2 - 81$

Write a polynomial function *f* of least degree that has rational coefficients, a leading coefficient of 1, and the given zeros.

34. $1, 2 - \sqrt{3}$

35. $2, 3, \sqrt{5}$

36. $-2, 5, 3 + \sqrt{6}$

37. You use 240 cubic inches of clay to make a sculpture shaped like a rectangular prism. The width is 4 inches less than the length, and the height is 2 inches more than three times the length. What are the dimensions of the sculpture? Justify your answer.

38. The Willis Tower in Chicago is composed of nine rectangular prisms with square bases and varying heights. A model of one of the two tallest prisms is shown.

a. The volume of the prism in the model is 522 cubic inches. What are the dimensions?

b. The height of the actual prism is about 1450 feet. Use the model to approximate the volume of the actual prism.

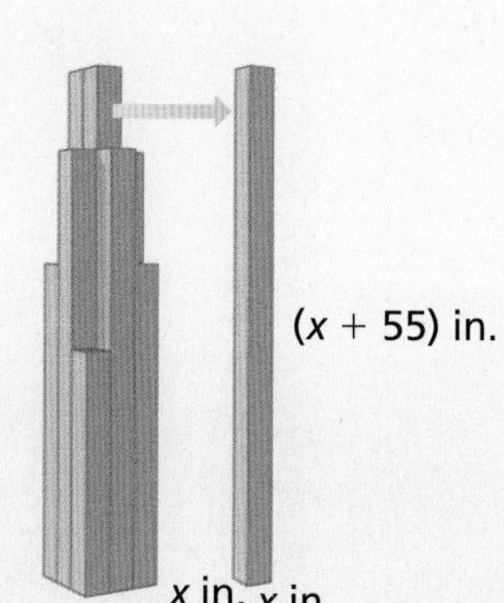

4.6 The Fundamental Theorem of Algebra (pp. 191–198)

WATCH

Learning Target: Use the Fundamental Theorem of Algebra to find all complex roots of polynomial equations.

Find all the zeros of the polynomial function.

39. $h(x) = x^4 - 4x^3 - x^2 - 16x - 20$

40. $f(x) = x^5 + 5x^4 + 8x^3 + 8x^2 + 7x + 3$

Write a polynomial function *f* of least degree that has rational coefficients, a leading coefficient of 1, and the given zeros.

41. $3, 1 + 2i$

42. $-1, 2, 4i$

43. $-5, -4, 1 - i\sqrt{3}$

Determine the possible numbers of positive real zeros, negative real zeros, and imaginary zeros for the function.

44. $f(x) = x^4 - 10x + 8$

45. $f(x) = -6x^4 - x^3 + 3x^2 + 2x + 18$

46. The average monthly low temperature (in degrees Celsius) in Fargo, North Dakota, can be modeled by $f(t) = 0.0226t^4 - 0.645t^3 + 5.15t^2 - 8.0t - 14$, where $t = 1$ represents January. For what month(s) is the average low temperature about 8 degrees Celsius?

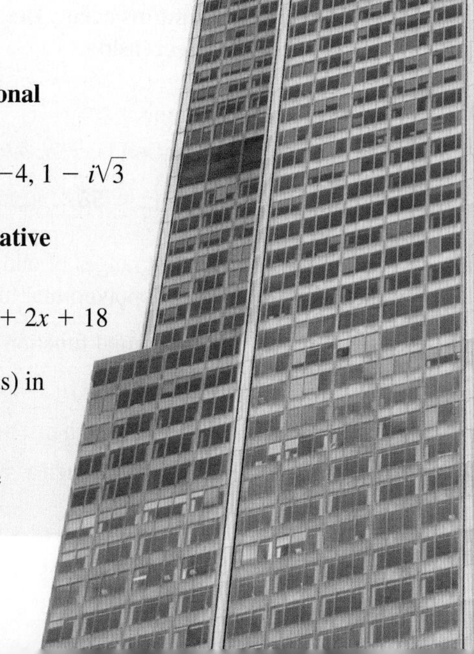

4.7 Transformations of Polynomial Functions (pp. 199–204)

Learning Target: Describe and graph transformations of polynomial functions.

Describe the transformation of f represented by g. Then graph each function.

47. $f(x) = x^3, g(x) = (-x)^3 + 2$

48. $f(x) = x^4, g(x) = -(x + 9)^4$

Write a rule for g.

49. Let the graph of g be a horizontal stretch by a factor of 4, followed by a translation 3 units right and 5 units down of the graph of $f(x) = x^5 + 3x$.

50. Let the graph of g be a translation 5 units up, followed by a reflection in the y-axis of the graph of $f(x) = x^4 - 2x^3 - 12$.

Match the function with the correct transformation of the graph of f.

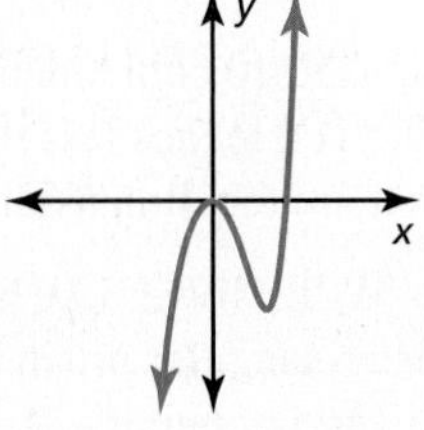

51. $y = f(2x)$

52. $y = -2f(x)$

53. $y = f(-2x)$

54. $y = 2f(-x)$

A.

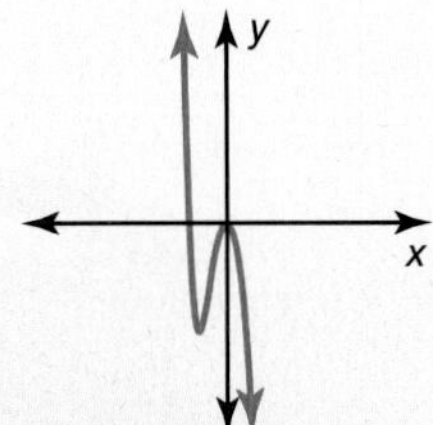

B.

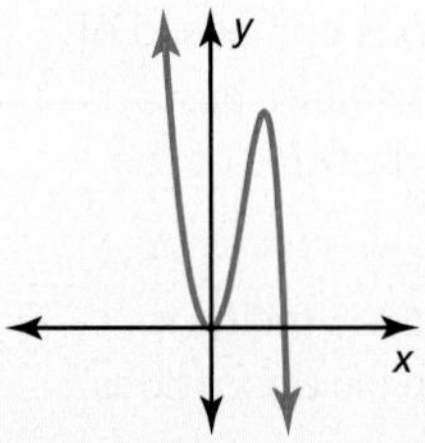

C.

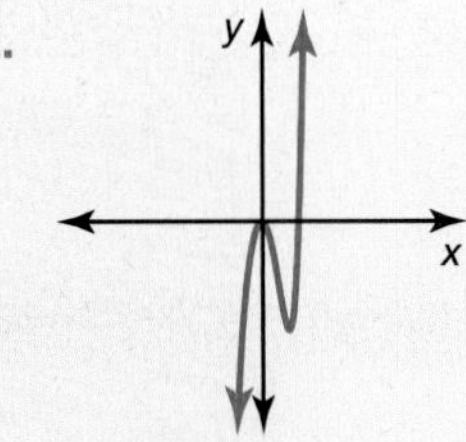

D.

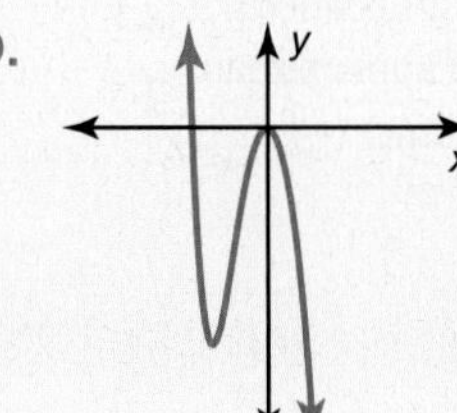

4.8 Analyzing Graphs of Polynomial Functions (pp. 205–212)

Learning Target: Analyze graphs of polynomial functions.

Vocabulary AZ VOCAB
- local maximum
- local minimum
- even function
- odd function

Graph the function. Identify the x-intercepts and the points where the local maximums and local minimums occur. Determine the intervals for which the function is increasing or decreasing.

55. $f(x) = -2x^3 - 3x^2 - 1$

56. $f(x) = x^4 + 3x^3 - x^2 - 8x + 2$

Determine whether the function is *even*, *odd*, or *neither*.

57. $f(x) = 2x^3 + 3x$

58. $g(x) = 3x^2 - 7$

59. $h(x) = x^6 + 3x^5$

60. Compare the domains and ranges of odd-degree polynomial functions with the domains and ranges of even-degree polynomial functions.

61. Sketch a graph of a polynomial function f having the given characteristics.

- The graph of f has x-intercepts of $x = -1$, $x = 3$, and $x = 5$.
- f has a local maximum value when $x = 0$ and when $x = 4$.
- f has a local minimum value when $x = 3$.

4.9 Modeling with Polynomial Functions (pp. 213–218)

Learning Target: Write polynomial functions.

Vocabulary

finite differences

Write a cubic function whose graph is shown.

62.

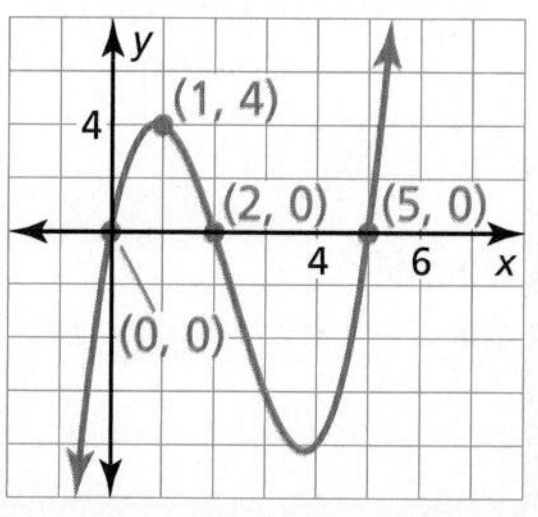

63.

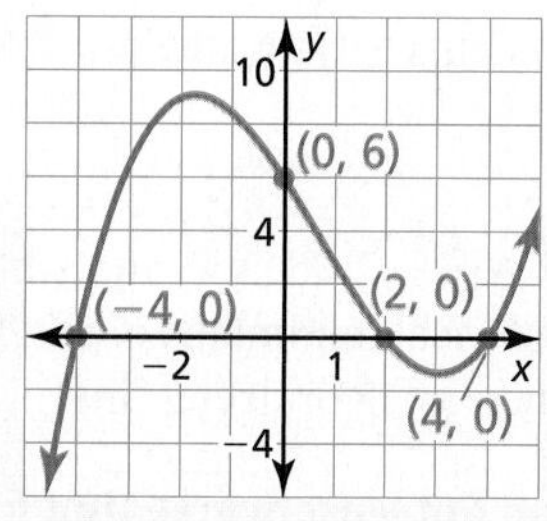

Use finite differences to determine the degree of the polynomial function that fits the data. Then use technology to find the polynomial function.

64.

x	1	2	3	4	5	6	7
$f(x)$	−11	−24	−27	−8	45	144	301

65.

x	−4	−2	0	2	4	6	8
$f(x)$	−60	10	4	−6	4	10	−60

66. The table shows the numbers y of moose on Isle Royale in Michigan in the year t, where $t = 0$ corresponds to 2010. Find a model for the data. Use the model to predict the number of moose on Isle Royale in 2019.

t	0	1	2	3	4	5	6	7	8
y	510	515	750	975	1050	1250	1300	1600	1500

Mathematical Practices

Look for and Make Use of Structure

Mathematically proficient students look closely to discern a pattern or structure.

1. Describe any patterns that you see in the diagonals of Pascal's Triangle.

2. In Exercise 65(c) on page 181, explain how you used the structure of the polynomial $a^5b^2 - a^2b^4 + 2a^4b - 2ab^3 + a^3 - b^2$ to factor it completely.

3. Explain how you used a pattern to write the polynomial function in Exercise 18 on page 218.

4 Practice Test WITH CalcChat®

Determine whether the function is a polynomial function. If so, write it in standard form and state its degree, type, and leading coefficient.

1. $f(x) = x^2 - 2^x + 9$

2. $g(x) = -\frac{1}{2}x + 3x^4 - 2x^3$

3. Graph $y = -x^4 + x^3 - 6x^2 - 2$. Identify the x-intercepts and the points where the local maximums and local minimums occur. Determine the intervals for which the function is increasing or decreasing.

Write a polynomial function f of least degree that has rational coefficients, a leading coefficient of 1, and the given zeros.

4. $3, 1 - \sqrt{2}$

5. $-2, 4, 3i$

Find the product or quotient.

6. $(x^6 - 4)(x^2 - 7x + 5)$

7. $(2x + 3)^3$

8. $(2x^3 - 3x^2 + 5x - 1) \div (x + 2)$

9. $(3x^4 - 2x^3 - x - 1) \div (x^2 - 2x + 1)$

Factor the polynomial completely.

10. $27x^3 + 64$

11. $8x^2 - 125x^5$

12. $16x^4 - 1$

13. $2x^9 - 4x^5 - 16x$

14. The graphs of $f(x) = x^4$ and $g(x) = (x - 3)^4$ are shown.

a. How many zeros does each function have? Explain.

b. Describe the transformation of f represented by g.

c. Determine the intervals for which the function g is increasing or decreasing.

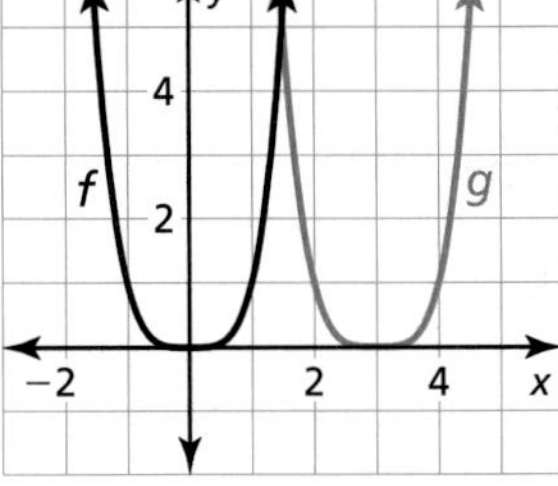

15. Solve the system. Explain your method.

$$y = -3x^2 + 5x - 9$$
$$y = x^3 - 4x^2 - 11x + 7$$

16. The number P (in thousands) of passenger cars, and the number C (in thousands) of commercial vehicles, produced each year in the United States in a 9-year period can be modeled by the equations shown, where t is time (in years). Write a model for the total number T of passenger cars and commercial vehicles produced each year. Then find the total number of passenger cars and commercial vehicles produced in the third year.

$$P = 11t^4 - 208t^3 + 1288t^2 - 2438t + 3695$$
$$C = 9t^4 - 166t^3 + 989t^2 - 1480t + 4754$$

17. Your friend starts a golf caddy business. The table shows the profit p (in dollars) of the business each month t for the first five months. Use finite differences to determine the degree of the polynomial function that fits the data. Then use technology to find the polynomial function. Use the model to predict the profit in the seventh month.

t	1	2	3	4	5	6
p	65	86	129	200	305	450

4 Performance Task
Thrown to the Wolves

BEFORE	1995 The gray wolf is reintroduced to Yellowstone National Park.	AFTER
Elk feed heavily along rivers and streams, drastically reducing vegetation.		Elk spend less time feeding in exposed areas along rivers and streams, allowing vegetation to flourish.
With reduced vegetation, riverbanks are exposed and erode easily.		Willows and other plants stabilize the soil along rivers and streams, preventing erosion.
The population of beavers decreases and dams cease to be constructed.		Vegetation attracts beavers, who return to the area and build dams, increasing water quality.
Scavengers such as ravens, eagles, and coyotes must hunt for their own food supplies.		Wolves leave a leftover food supply for scavengers.
Coyotes multiply, and dominate the food supply.		The number of coyotes decreases, increasing the amount of prey available to other animals.

YELLOWSTONE WOLF REINTRODUCTION

As a researcher, you want to understand how the number of wolves in Yellowstone impacts the population of the northern Yellowstone elk herd. You conduct 10 surveys of the populations over several years. The results are shown in the table.

Explore several different models that relate the populations. Then decide which model best represents the situation. Explain how you chose the best model. Then summarize how the number of wolves impacts the elk herd population.

Wolves	Northern Yellowstone elk herd
132	13,400
148	11,950
174	9,100
171	8,400
118	9,600
171	6,900
96	7,100
97	6,050
98	4,800
83	4,150

4 College and Career Readiness WITH CalcChat®

Tutorial videos are available for each exercise.

1. Choose a value for m in the function $f(x) = x^3 - 3x^2 + mx + 3$ so that $f(x) \div (x - 4)$ has a remainder of 15. Justify your answer.

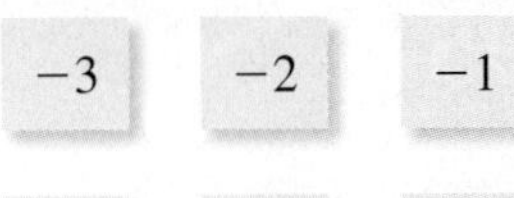

2. Analyze the graph of the polynomial function to determine the sign of the leading coefficient, the least possible degree, and the number of real zeros of the function. Explain.

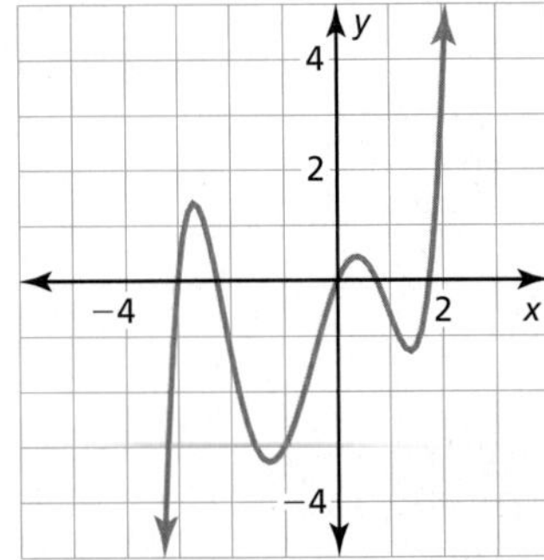

3. A parabola has focus (3.5, 4) and directrix $x = 2.5$. What is the equation of the parabola?

Ⓐ $x = -\frac{1}{2}(y - 4)^2 + 3$

Ⓑ $y = \frac{1}{3}(x - 3.5)^2 + 3.25$

Ⓒ $x = \frac{1}{2}(y - 4)^2 + 3$

Ⓓ $x = \frac{1}{4}(y - 4)^2 + 3.5$

4. A parabola passes through the point shown in the graph. The equation of the axis of symmetry is $x = -a$. (a) Which of the given points could lie on the parabola? (b) If the axis of symmetry was $x = a$, then which of the given points could lie on the parabola? Explain your reasoning.

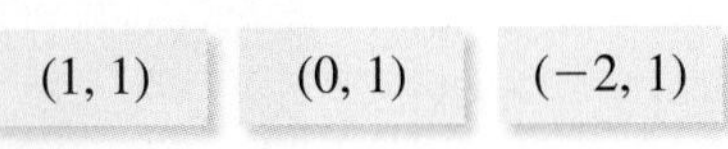

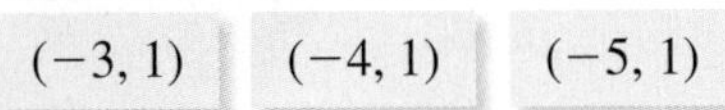

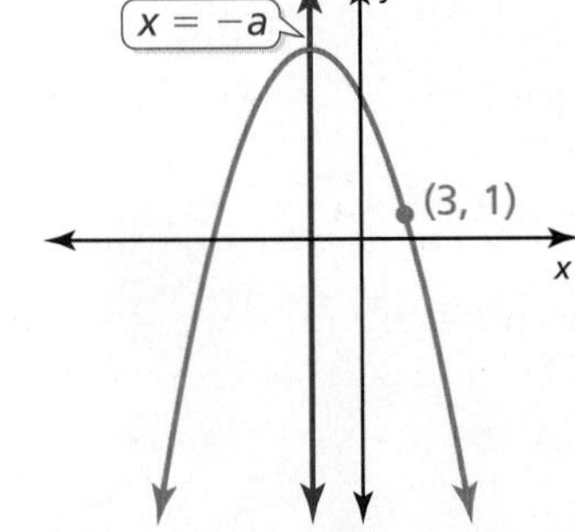

5. Select values for the function to model each transformation of the graph of $f(x) = x$.

$$g(x) = \boxed{}\left(x - \boxed{}\right) + \boxed{}$$

a. The graph is a translation 2 units up and 3 units left.

b. The graph is a translation 2 units right and 3 units down.

c. The graph is a vertical stretch by a factor of 2, followed by a translation 2 units up.

d. The graph is a translation 3 units right and a vertical shrink by a factor of $\frac{1}{2}$, followed by a translation 4 units down.

6. The diagram shows a circle inscribed in a square. The area of the shaded region is 21.5 square meters. To the nearest tenth of a meter, how long is each side of the square?

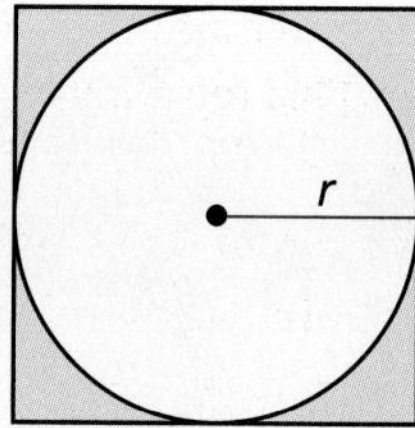

Ⓐ 4.6 meters　Ⓑ 5.0 meters　Ⓒ 5.2 meters　Ⓓ 10.0 meters

7. The table shows the femur lengths (in millimeters) and the total lengths (in millimeters) of several alligators. Write a function that models the data. Use the model to predict the total length of an alligator with a femur length of 250 millimeters.

Femur length (millimeters)	55	82	105	150	162	197	236
Total length (millimeters)	829	1218	1496	2026	2283	2768	3382

8. The volume of the rectangular prism shown is given by $V = 2x^3 + 7x^2 - 18x - 63$. Which polynomial represents the area of the base of the prism?

Ⓐ $2x^2 + x - 21$

Ⓑ $-2x^2 - 21 - 13x$

Ⓒ $13x + 21 + 2x^2$

Ⓓ $2x^3 + 13x^2 + 21x$

$x - 3$

9. The number R (in tens of thousands) of retirees receiving Social Security benefits is modeled by the function

$$R = 0.138t^3 + 0.92t^2 - 6.8t + 300, \quad 0 \le t \le 7$$

where t represents the number of years since 2010. Identify any turning points on the given interval. What does a turning point represent in this situation?

5 Rational Exponents and Radical Functions

GO DIGITAL

NATIONAL GEOGRAPHIC EXPLORER

Ben Mirin

Ben Mirin is an acoustic biologist, sound artist, and science communicator. He is the creator and host of the digital series WILD BEATS. Ben travels the world recording animal sounds and samples them to create music that connects people to nature. He leads expeditions to record and catalog acoustic data from many of the planet's most endangered ecosystems.

- Give examples of animal sounds you can hear where you live. Do you have a favorite animal sound?
- What are some animal species that sing?
- Why do you think animals sing? Use the Internet or another resource to find at least two reasons.

STEM

Have you ever heard of a song being played in a certain *octave*? In the Performance Task, you will compare the sounds of notes in different octaves. Then you will explain properties of the sound waves that produce those notes.

Sound Art

Preparing for Chapter 5

Chapter Learning Target Understand rational exponents and radical functions.

Chapter Success Criteria

- ◆ I can represent roots using rational exponents.
- ◆ I can describe the properties of rational exponents and radicals.
- ■ I can solve radical equations and inequalities.
- ■ I can find compositions and inverses of functions.

◆ Surface
■ Deep

Chapter Vocabulary

Work with a partner. Discuss each of the vocabulary terms.

*n*th root of *a*
simplest form of a radical
like radicals
radical function
radical equation
extraneous solutions
inverse functions

Mathematical Practices

Model with Mathematics

Mathematically proficient students identify important quantities in practical situations and map their relationships using such tools as diagrams, two-way tables, graphs, flowcharts, and formulas.

Work with a partner. You use a microphone to record the sound of an owl that is 500 meters away. You want to determine whether it is possible for the sound to reach your microphone in less than 1.25 seconds. The speed of sound in air can be approximated by the function shown.

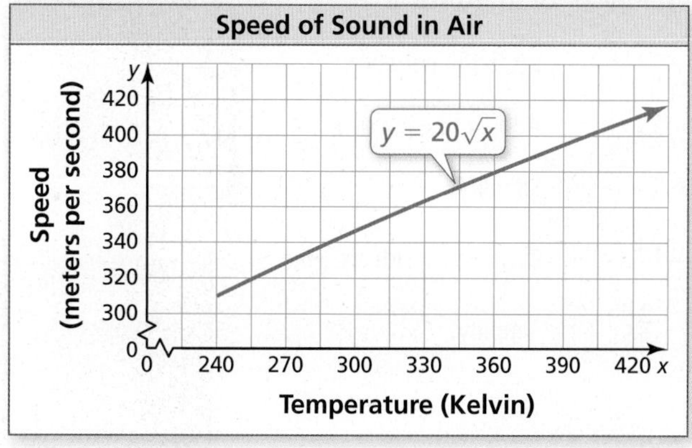

1. Identify the important quantities in this situation.
2. Describe any relationships among the important quantities.
3. Use the relationships you described in Exercise 2 to solve the problem by (a) estimating using the graph and (b) solving algebraically. Justify your answers.

5 Prepare WITH CalcChat®

Properties of Integer Exponents

WATCH

Example 1 Simplify the expression $\frac{x^5 \cdot x^2}{x^3}$.

$$\frac{x^5 \cdot x^2}{x^3} = \frac{x^{5+2}}{x^3} \qquad \text{Product of Powers Property}$$

$$= \frac{x^7}{x^3} \qquad \text{Simplify.}$$

$$= x^{7-3} \qquad \text{Quotient of Powers Property}$$

$$= x^4 \qquad \text{Simplify.}$$

Example 2 Simplify the expression $\left(\frac{2s^3}{t}\right)^2$.

$$\left(\frac{2s^3}{t}\right)^2 = \frac{(2s^3)^2}{t^2} \qquad \text{Power of a Quotient Property}$$

$$= \frac{2^2 \cdot (s^3)^2}{t^2} \qquad \text{Power of a Product Property}$$

$$= \frac{4s^6}{t^2} \qquad \text{Power of a Power Property}$$

Simplify. Write the expression using only positive exponents.

1. $y^6 \cdot y$

2. $\frac{n^4}{n^3}$

3. $\frac{x^5}{x^6 \cdot x^2}$

4. $\frac{x^6}{x^5} \cdot 3x^2$

5. $\left(\frac{4w^3}{2z^2}\right)^3$

6. $\left(\frac{m^7 \cdot m}{z^2 \cdot m^3}\right)^2$

Rewriting Literal Equations

Example 3 Solve the literal equation $-5y - 2x = 10$ for y.

$$-5y - 2x = 10 \qquad \text{Write the equation.}$$

$$-5y - 2x + 2x = 10 + 2x \qquad \text{Add } 2x \text{ to each side.}$$

$$-5y = 10 + 2x \qquad \text{Simplify.}$$

$$\frac{-5y}{-5} = \frac{10 + 2x}{-5} \qquad \text{Divide each side by } -5.$$

$$y = -2 - \frac{2}{5}x \qquad \text{Simplify.}$$

Solve the literal equation for *y*.

7. $4x + y = 2$

8. $x - \frac{1}{3}y = -1$

9. $2y - 9 = 13x$

10. $2xy + 6y = 10$

11. $8x - 4xy = 3$

12. $6x + 7xy = 15$

13. **MP REASONING** Is the order in which you apply properties of exponents important? Explain your reasoning.

5.1 *n*th Roots and Rational Exponents

Learning Target Evaluate expressions and solve equations containing *n*th roots and rational exponents.

Success Criteria
- I can explain the meaning of a rational exponent.
- I can evaluate expressions with rational exponents.
- I can solve equations using *n*th roots.

Previously, you learned that the *n*th root of a is

$\sqrt[n]{a} = a^{1/n}$ Definition of rational exponent

for any real number a and integer n greater than 1.

EXPLORE IT! Writing Expressions in Different Forms

Work with a partner.

a. Use the definition of a rational exponent and the properties of exponents to write each expression as a base with a single rational exponent or as a radical raised to an exponent.

	Radical raised to an exponent	Base with a single rational exponent
i.	$(\sqrt{5})^3$	
ii.	$(\sqrt[4]{4})^2$	
iii.	$(\sqrt[3]{9})^2$	
iv.	$(\sqrt[5]{10})^4$	
v.	$(\sqrt{15})^3$	
vi.	$(\sqrt[3]{27})^4$	
vii.		$8^{2/3}$
viii.		$6^{5/2}$
ix.		$12^{3/4}$
x.		$10^{3/2}$
xi.		$16^{3/2}$
xii.		$20^{6/5}$

Math Practice

Look for Structure
How do you know when the value of $a^{1/n}$ is an integer?

b. Use technology to evaluate each expression in part (a). Round your answer to two decimal places, if necessary.

c. Simplify $\sqrt[n]{a^n}$. What does this imply about the relationship between raising an expression to the *n*th power and taking the *n*th root? How can you use this result to solve the equation $x^4 = 6$?

Finding *n*th Roots

Vocabulary
*n*th root of *a*, *p. 232*
index of a radical, *p. 232*

You can extend the concept of a square root to other types of roots. For example, 2 is a cube root of 8 because $2^3 = 8$. In general, for an integer n greater than 1, if $b^n = a$, then b is an **nth root of a**. An nth root of a is written as $\sqrt[n]{a}$, where n is the **index of the radical**.

You can also write an nth root of a as a power of a. If you assume the Power of a Power Property applies to rational exponents, then the following is true.

$$(a^{1/2})^2 = a^{(1/2) \cdot 2} = a^1 = a$$

$$(a^{1/3})^3 = a^{(1/3) \cdot 3} = a^1 = a$$

$$(a^{1/4})^4 = a^{(1/4) \cdot 4} = a^1 = a$$

Because $a^{1/2}$ is a number whose square is a, you can write $\sqrt{a} = a^{1/2}$. Similarly, $\sqrt[3]{a} = a^{1/3}$ and $\sqrt[4]{a} = a^{1/4}$. In general, $\sqrt[n]{a} = a^{1/n}$ for any integer n greater than 1.

KEY IDEA

Real *n*th Roots of *a*

Let n be an integer greater than 1 and let a be a real number.

	***n* is an even integer.**		***n* is an odd integer.**
$a < 0$	No real nth roots	$a < 0$	One real nth root: $\sqrt[n]{a} = a^{1/n}$
$a = 0$	One real nth root: $\sqrt[n]{0} = 0$	$a = 0$	One real nth root: $\sqrt[n]{0} = 0$
$a > 0$	Two real nth roots: $\pm\sqrt[n]{a} = \pm a^{1/n}$	$a > 0$	One real nth root: $\sqrt[n]{a} = a^{1/n}$

STUDY TIP

When n is even and $a > 0$, there are two real roots. The positive root is called the *principal root*.

EXAMPLE 1 Finding *n*th Roots

Find the indicated real nth root(s) of a.

a. $n = 3, a = -216$

b. $n = 4, a = 81$

SOLUTION

a. Because $n = 3$ is odd and $a = -216 < 0$, -216 has one real cube root. Because $(-6)^3 = -216$, you can write

$$\sqrt[3]{-216} = -6 \text{ or } (-216)^{1/3} = -6.$$

b. Because $n = 4$ is even and $a = 81 > 0$, 81 has two real fourth roots. Because $3^4 = 81$ and $(-3)^4 = 81$, you can write

$$\pm\sqrt[4]{81} = \pm 3 \text{ or } \pm 81^{1/4} = \pm 3.$$

SELF-ASSESSMENT 1 I do not understand. 2 I can do it with help. 3 I can do it on my own. 4 I can teach someone else.

Find the indicated real *n*th root(s) of *a*.

1. $n = 4, a = 16$

2. $n = 2, a = -49$

3. $n = 3, a = -125$

4. $n = 5, a = 243$

5. COMPLETE THE SENTENCE For an integer n greater than 1, if $b^n = a$, then b is a(n) ___________ of a.

6. WRITING Explain how to use the sign of a to determine the number of real fourth roots of a and the number of real fifth roots of a.

Rational Exponents

A rational exponent does not have to be of the form $1/n$. Other rational numbers, such as $3/2$ and $-1/2$, can also be exponents. Two properties of rational exponents are shown below.

KEY IDEA

Rational Exponents

Let $a^{1/n}$ be an nth root of a, and let m be a positive integer.

$$a^{m/n} = (a^{1/n})^m = (\sqrt[n]{a})^m \quad \text{or} \quad a^{m/n} = (a^m)^{1/n} = \sqrt[n]{a^m}$$

$$a^{-m/n} = \frac{1}{a^{m/n}} = \frac{1}{(a^{1/n})^m} = \frac{1}{(\sqrt[n]{a})^m}, \ a \neq 0 \quad \text{or} \quad a^{-m/n} = \frac{1}{(a^m)^{1/n}} = \frac{1}{\sqrt[n]{a^m}}, \ a \neq 0$$

EXAMPLE 2 Evaluating Expressions with Rational Exponents

Evaluate (a) $16^{3/2}$ and (b) $32^{-3/5}$.

SOLUTION

	Rational Exponent Form	Radical Form
a.	$16^{3/2} = (16^{1/2})^3 = 4^3 = 64$	$16^{3/2} = (\sqrt{16})^3 = 4^3 = 64$
b.	$32^{-3/5} = \frac{1}{32^{3/5}} = \frac{1}{(32^{1/5})^3} = \frac{1}{2^3} = \frac{1}{8}$	$32^{-3/5} = \frac{1}{32^{3/5}} = \frac{1}{(\sqrt[5]{32})^3} = \frac{1}{2^3} = \frac{1}{8}$

EXAMPLE 3 Approximating Expressions with Rational Exponents

Evaluate each expression using technology. Round your answer to two decimal places.

a. $9^{1/5}$ **b.** $12^{3/8}$ **c.** $(\sqrt[4]{7})^3$

SOLUTION

a. $9^{1/5} \approx 1.55$

b. $12^{3/8} \approx 2.54$

c. Before evaluating $(\sqrt[4]{7})^3$, rewrite the expression in rational exponent form.

$$(\sqrt[4]{7})^3 = 7^{3/4} \approx 4.30$$

$9^{\frac{1}{5}}$	= 1.55184557392
$12^{\frac{3}{8}}$	= 2.53917695148
$7^{\frac{3}{4}}$	= 4.30351707066

SELF-ASSESSMENT 1 I do not understand. 2 I can do it with help. 3 I can do it on my own. 4 I can teach someone else.

Evaluate the expression without using technology.

7. $4^{5/2}$ **8.** $9^{-1/2}$ **9.** $81^{3/4}$ **10.** $1^{7/8}$

Evaluate the expression using technology. Round your answer to two decimal places, if necessary.

11. $6^{2/5}$ **12.** $64^{-2/3}$ **13.** $(\sqrt[4]{16})^5$ **14.** $(\sqrt[3]{-30})^2$

15. WHICH ONE DOESN'T BELONG? Which expression does *not* belong with the other three? Explain your reasoning.

$(a^{1/n})^m$ $(\sqrt[n]{a})^m$ $(\sqrt[m]{a})^{-n}$ $a^{m/n}$

Solving Equations Using *n*th Roots

Raising to the *n*th power and taking the *n*th root are inverse operations.

$$\sqrt[n]{a^n} = (a^n)^{1/n} = a^{n \cdot 1/n} = a^1 = a$$

So, you can solve an equation of the form $u^n = d$, where u is an algebraic expression and d is a real number, by taking the *n*th root of each side.

EXAMPLE 4 Solving Equations Using *n*th Roots

Find the real solution(s) of (a) $4x^5 = 128$ and (b) $(x - 3)^4 = 21$. Round your answer to two decimal places, if necessary.

SOLUTION

a.

$4x^5 = 128$	Write original equation.
$x^5 = 32$	Divide each side by 4.
$x = \sqrt[5]{32}$	Take fifth root of each side.
$x = 2$	Simplify.

▶ The solution is $x = 2$.

COMMON ERROR

When *n* is even and *a* > 0, be sure to consider both the positive and negative *n*th roots of *a*.

b.

$(x - 3)^4 = 21$	Write original equation.
$x - 3 = \pm\sqrt[4]{21}$	Take fourth root of each side.
$x = 3 \pm \sqrt[4]{21}$	Add 3 to each side.

▶ The solutions are $x = 3 + \sqrt[4]{21} \approx 5.14$ and $x = 3 - \sqrt[4]{21} \approx 0.86$.

EXAMPLE 5 Modeling Real Life

A hospital purchases an ultrasound machine for \$50,000. The hospital expects the useful life of the machine to be 10 years, at which time its value will have depreciated to \$8000. The hospital uses the declining balances method for depreciation, so the annual depreciation rate r (in decimal form) is given by the formula

$$r = 1 - \left(\frac{S}{C}\right)^{1/n}.$$

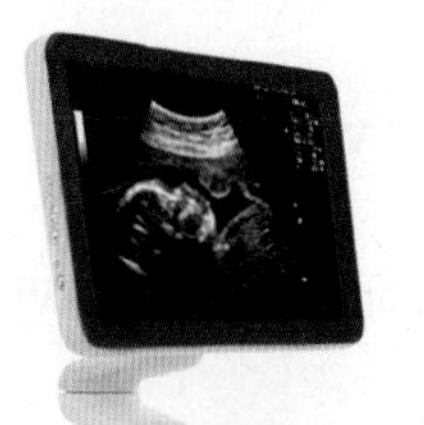

In the formula, n is the useful life of the item (in years), S is the salvage value (in dollars), and C is the original cost (in dollars). What annual depreciation rate did the hospital use?

SOLUTION

The useful life is 10 years, so $n = 10$. The machine depreciates to \$8000, so $S = 8000$. The original cost is \$50,000, so $C = 50,000$. So, the annual depreciation rate is

$$r = 1 - \left(\frac{S}{C}\right)^{1/n} = 1 - \left(\frac{8000}{50,000}\right)^{1/10} = 1 - \left(\frac{4}{25}\right)^{1/10} \approx 0.167.$$

▶ The annual depreciation rate is about 0.167, or 16.7%.

SELF-ASSESSMENT

1 I do not understand. 2 I can do it with help. 3 I can do it on my own. 4 I can teach someone else.

Find the real solution(s) of the equation. Round your answer to two decimal places, if necessary.

16. $8x^3 = 64$ **17.** $\frac{1}{2}x^5 = 512$ **18.** $(x + 5)^4 = 16$ **19.** $(x - 2)^3 = -14$

20. WHAT IF? In Example 5, what is the annual depreciation rate when the salvage value is \$6000?

5.1 Practice WITH CalcChat® AND CalcView®

In Exercises 1–6, find the indicated real nth root(s) of a. *Example 1*

1. $n = 3, a = 8$
2. $n = 5, a = -1$
3. $n = 2, a = 0$
4. $n = 4, a = 256$
5. $n = 5, a = -32$
6. $n = 6, a = -729$

In Exercises 7–14, evaluate the expression without using technology. *Example 2*

7. $64^{1/6}$
8. $8^{1/3}$
9. $25^{3/2}$
10. $32^{4/5}$
11. $(-243)^{1/5}$
12. $(-64)^{4/3}$
13. $8^{-2/3}$
14. $16^{-7/4}$

ERROR ANALYSIS In Exercises 15 and 16, describe and correct the error in evaluating the expression.

15. ✗
$$-27^{5/3} = (-27^{1/3})^5$$
$$= 3^5$$
$$= 243$$

16.

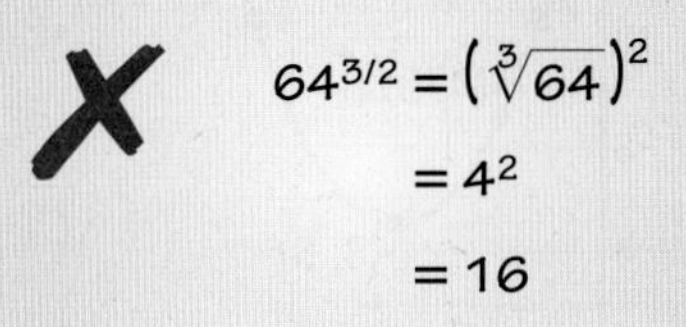

MP STRUCTURE In Exercises 17–20, match the equivalent expressions. Explain your reasoning.

17. $(\sqrt[3]{5})^4$
18. $(\sqrt[4]{5})^3$
19. $\dfrac{1}{\sqrt[4]{5}}$
20. $-\sqrt[4]{5}$

A. $5^{-1/4}$
B. $5^{4/3}$
C. $-5^{1/4}$
D. $5^{3/4}$

In Exercises 21–28, evaluate the expression using technology. Round your answer to two decimal places, if necessary. *Example 3*

21. $\sqrt[5]{32{,}768}$
22. $\sqrt[7]{1695}$
23. $25^{-1/3}$
24. $85^{1/6}$
25. $20{,}736^{4/5}$
26. $86^{-5/6}$
27. $(\sqrt[4]{187})^3$
28. $(\sqrt[5]{-8})^8$

In Exercises 29–38, find the real solution(s) of the equation. Round your answer to two decimal places, if necessary. *Example 4*

29. $x^3 = 125$
30. $5x^3 = 1080$
31. $(x + 10)^5 = 70$
32. $(x - 5)^4 = 256$
33. $x^5 = -48$
34. $7x^4 = 56$
35. $x^6 + 36 = 100$
36. $x^3 + 40 = 25$
37. $\frac{1}{3}x^4 = 27$
38. $\frac{1}{6}x^3 = -36$

39. **MODELING REAL LIFE** When the average price of an item increases from p_1 to p_2 over a period of n years, the annual rate of inflation r (in decimal form) is given by $r = \left(\dfrac{p_2}{p_1}\right)^{1/n} - 1$. Find the rate of inflation for each item in the table. *Example 5*

Item	Price per pound in 2009	Price per pound in 2019
Potatoes	\$0.620	\$0.749
Oranges	\$0.910	\$1.280
Ground beef	\$2.251	\$3.775

40. **MODELING REAL LIFE** A *weir* is a dam that is built across a river to regulate the flow of water. The flow rate Q (in cubic feet per second) can be calculated using the formula $Q = 3.367\ell h^{3/2}$, where ℓ is the length (in feet) of the bottom of the spillway and h is the depth (in feet) of the water on the spillway. Determine the flow rate of a weir with a spillway that is 20 feet long and has a water depth of 5 feet.

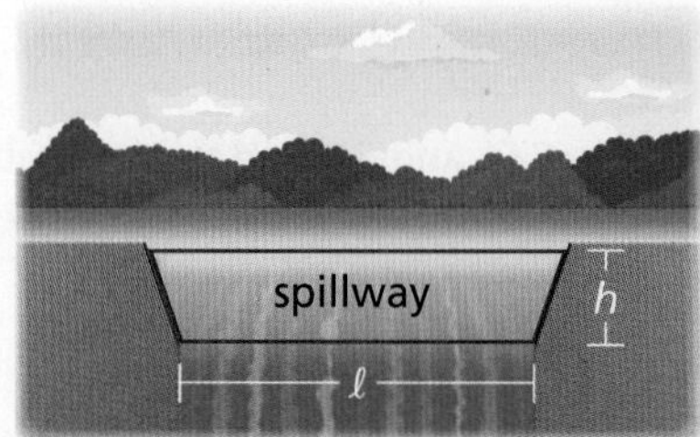

41. **MP NUMBER SENSE** Between which two consecutive integers does $\sqrt[4]{125}$ lie? Explain your reasoning.

42. HOW DO YOU SEE IT?
The graph of $y = x^n$ is shown in red. What can you conclude about the value of n? Determine the number of real nth roots of a. Explain your reasoning.

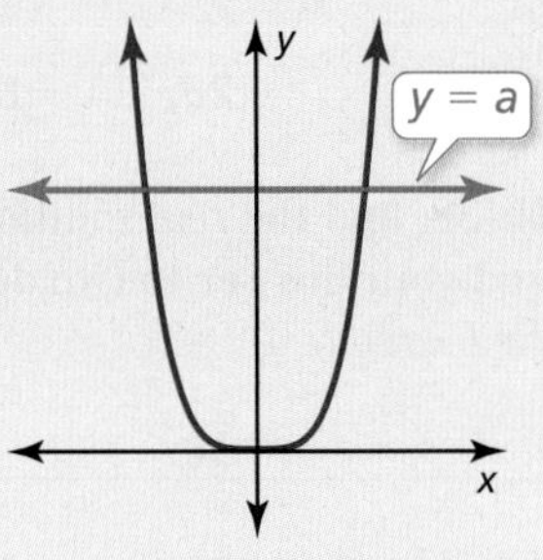

CONNECTING CONCEPTS In Exercises 43 and 44, find the radius of the figure with the given volume.

43. $V = 216 \text{ ft}^3$ **44.** $V = 1332 \text{ cm}^3$

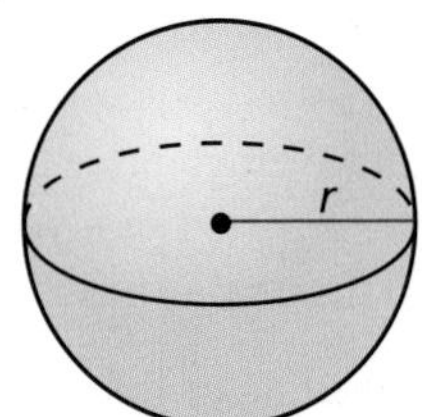

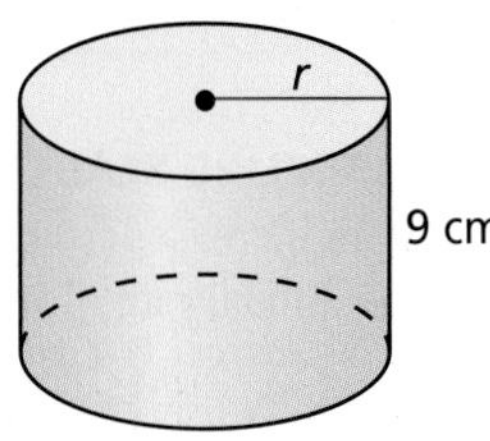

45. MP **REPEATED REASONING** The mass of the particles that a river can transport is proportional to the sixth power of the speed of the river. A certain river normally flows at a speed of 1 meter per second. What must its speed be in order to transport particles that are twice as massive as usual? 10 times as massive? 100 times as massive?

GO DIGITAL

46. THOUGHT PROVOKING
In 1619, Johannes Kepler published his third law, which can be given by $d^3 = t^2$, where d is the mean distance (in astronomical units) of a planet from the Sun and t is the time (in years) it takes the planet to orbit the Sun. It takes Mars 1.88 years to orbit the Sun. Graph a possible location of Mars. Justify your answer. (The diagram shows the Sun at the origin of the xy-plane and a possible location of Earth.)

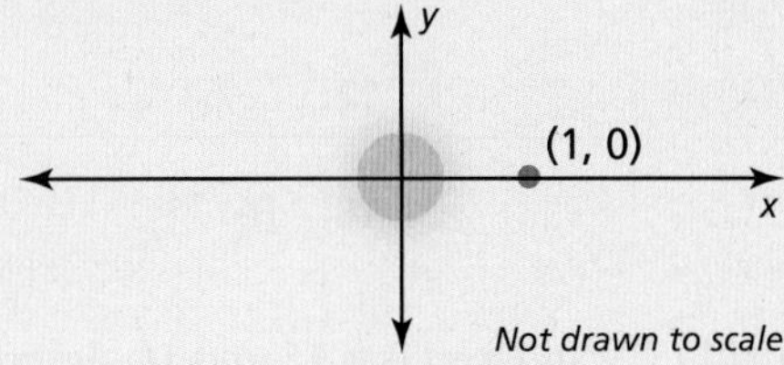

REVIEW & REFRESH

In Exercises 47 and 48, graph the function.

47. $f(x) = (x + 1)(x - 2)(x - 4)$

48. $g(x) = 2(x + 2)^2(x - 1)(x + 5)$

49. Use finite differences to determine the degree of the polynomial function that fits the data. Then use technology to find the polynomial function.

x	−2	−1	0	1	2	3
$f(x)$	1	9	1	1	9	1

50. Find all zeros of
$f(x) = x^4 - 9x^3 + 19x^2 - 9x + 18$.

In Exercises 51 and 52, find the real solution(s) of the equation. Round your answer to two decimal places, if necessary.

51. $2x^4 = 1250$ **52.** $(x - 8)^3 = 144$

53. Let the graph of g be a translation 3 units left, followed by a vertical shrink by a factor of $\frac{1}{2}$ of the graph of $f(x) = x^3 - 4x$. Write a rule for g.

54. Write an equation of the parabola in vertex form.

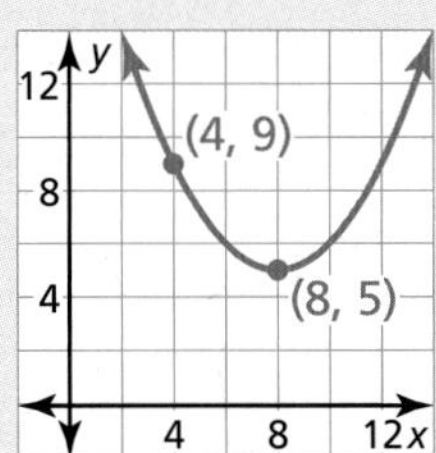

55. Write $(1 + 7i) + (10 - 2i) - 3i(2 + 9i)$ as a complex number in standard form.

56. MODELING REAL LIFE The table shows the distances run by an athlete on a treadmill over time. What type of function can you use to model the data? Predict the distance traveled by the runner after 30 minutes.

Time (minutes), x	Distance (miles), y
5	0.5
10	1.0
15	1.5
20	2.0
25	2.5

5.2 Properties of Rational Exponents and Radicals

Learning Target Simplify radical expressions.

Success Criteria
- I can simplify radical expressions with rational exponents.
- I can explain when radical expressions are in simplest form.
- I can simplify variable expressions containing rational exponents and radicals.

EXPLORE IT! Reviewing Properties of Exponents

Work with a partner.

a. The Product Property of Square Roots states that the square root of a product equals the product of the square roots of the factors.

$\sqrt{64x^2} = \sqrt{64} \cdot \sqrt{x^2}$ Product Property of Square Roots

$= 8x$ Simplify.

Describe the behavior of the graphs of $y = \sqrt{64x^2}$ and $y = 8x$. What do you notice? Use technology to check your graphs and explain the results.

b. You can extend the Product Property of Square Roots to other radicals, such as cube roots.

$\sqrt[3]{64x^3} = \sqrt[3]{64} \cdot \sqrt[3]{x^3}$ Product Property of Cube Roots

$= 4x$ Simplify.

Describe the behavior of the graphs of $y = \sqrt[3]{64x^3}$ and $y = 4x$. What do you notice? Use technology to check your graphs and explain the results.

c. How can you change the function $y = 8x$ so that it coincides with the graph of $y = \sqrt{64x^2}$ for all values of x? Explain your reasoning.

d. Determine the values of n for which $\sqrt[n]{x^n} = x$ and $\sqrt[n]{x^n} = |x|$.

Math Practice

Use Technology to Explore
How can you use technology to help you determine the values of n in part (d)?

Properties of Rational Exponents

GO DIGITAL

The properties of integer exponents can also be applied to rational exponents.

Vocabulary AZ VOCAB

simplest form of a radical, *p. 239*
like radicals, *p. 240*

KEY IDEA

Properties of Rational Exponents

Let a and b be real numbers and let m and n be rational numbers, such that the quantities in each property are real numbers.

Property Name	Definition	Example
Product of Powers	$a^m \cdot a^n = a^{m+n}$	$5^{1/2} \cdot 5^{3/2} = 5^{(1/2+3/2)} = 5^2 = 25$
Power of a Power	$(a^m)^n = a^{mn}$	$(3^{5/2})^2 = 3^{(5/2 \cdot 2)} = 3^5 = 243$
Power of a Product	$(ab)^m = a^m b^m$	$(16 \cdot 9)^{1/2} = 16^{1/2} \cdot 9^{1/2} = 4 \cdot 3 = 12$
Negative Exponent	$a^{-m} = \frac{1}{a^m}, a \neq 0$	$36^{-1/2} = \frac{1}{36^{1/2}} = \frac{1}{6}$
Zero Exponent	$a^0 = 1, a \neq 0$	$213^0 = 1$
Quotient of Powers	$\frac{a^m}{a^n} = a^{m-n}, a \neq 0$	$\frac{4^{5/2}}{4^{1/2}} = 4^{(5/2-1/2)} = 4^2 = 16$
Power of a Quotient	$\left(\frac{a}{b}\right)^m = \frac{a^m}{b^m}, b \neq 0$	$\left(\frac{27}{64}\right)^{1/3} = \frac{27^{1/3}}{64^{1/3}} = \frac{3}{4}$

COMMON ERROR

When you multiply powers, *do not* multiply the exponents, add them. For example, $3^2 \cdot 3^5 = 3^7$, not 3^{10}.

EXAMPLE 1 Using Properties of Exponents

WATCH

Use the properties of rational exponents to simplify each expression.

a. $7^{1/4} \cdot 7^{1/2} = 7^{(1/4+1/2)} = 7^{3/4}$ — Product of Powers Property

b. $(6^{1/2} \cdot 4^{1/3})^2 = (6^{1/2})^2 \cdot (4^{1/3})^2$ — Power of a Product Property
$= 6^{(1/2 \cdot 2)} \cdot 4^{(1/3 \cdot 2)}$ — Power of a Power Property
$= 6 \cdot 4^{2/3}$ — Simplify.

c. $(4^5 \cdot 3^5)^{-1/5} = [(4 \cdot 3)^5]^{-1/5}$ — Power of a Product Property
$= (12^5)^{-1/5}$ — Multiply.
$= 12^{[5 \cdot (-1/5)]}$ — Power of a Power Property
$= 12^{-1}$ — Simplify.
$= \frac{1}{12}$ — Definition of negative exponent

d. $\frac{5}{5^{1/3}} = \frac{5^1}{5^{1/3}} = 5^{(1-1/3)} = 5^{2/3}$ — Quotient of Powers Property

e. $\left(\frac{42^{1/3}}{6^{1/3}}\right)^2 = \left[\left(\frac{42}{6}\right)^{1/3}\right]^2$ — Power of a Quotient Property
$= (7^{1/3})^2$ — Divide.
$= 7^{2/3}$ — Power of a Power Property

WORDS AND MATH

In everyday life, a property of an object or idea is a quality or attribute of it. A mathematical property describes attributes of numbers and expressions.

SELF-ASSESSMENT 1 I do not understand. 2 I can do it with help. 3 I can do it on my own. 4 I can teach someone else.

Simplify the expression.

1. $2^{3/4} \cdot 2^{1/2}$

2. $\frac{3}{3^{1/4}}$

3. $\left(\frac{20^{1/2}}{5^{1/2}}\right)^3$

4. $(5^{1/3} \cdot 7^{1/4})^3$

Simplifying Radical Expressions

The Power of a Product and Power of a Quotient properties can be expressed using radical notation when $m = \frac{1}{n}$ for some integer n greater than 1.

GO DIGITAL

KEY IDEA

Properties of Radicals

Let a and b be real numbers such that the indicated roots are real numbers, and let n be an integer greater than 1.

Property Name	Definition	Example
Product Property	$\sqrt[n]{a \cdot b} = \sqrt[n]{a} \cdot \sqrt[n]{b}$	$\sqrt[3]{4} \cdot \sqrt[3]{2} = \sqrt[3]{8} = 2$
Quotient Property	$\sqrt[n]{\frac{a}{b}} = \frac{\sqrt[n]{a}}{\sqrt[n]{b}}, b \neq 0$	$\frac{\sqrt[4]{162}}{\sqrt[4]{2}} = \sqrt[4]{\frac{162}{2}} = \sqrt[4]{81} = 3$

EXAMPLE 2 Using Properties of Radicals

Use the properties of radicals to simplify each expression.

a. $\sqrt[3]{12} \cdot \sqrt[3]{18} = \sqrt[3]{12 \cdot 18} = \sqrt[3]{216} = 6$ — Product Property of Radicals

b. $\frac{\sqrt[4]{80}}{\sqrt[4]{5}} = \sqrt[4]{\frac{80}{5}} = \sqrt[4]{16} = 2$ — Quotient Property of Radicals

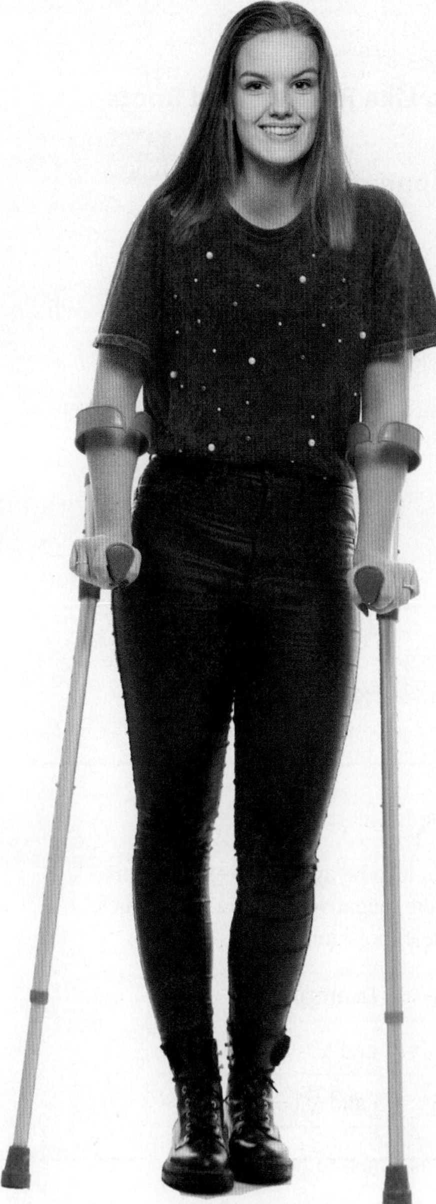

An expression involving a radical with index n is in **simplest form** when these three conditions are met.

- No radicands have perfect nth powers as factors other than 1.
- No radicands contain fractions.
- No radicals appear in the denominator of a fraction.

To meet the last two conditions, rationalize the denominator by multiplying the expression by an appropriate form of 1 that eliminates the radical from the denominator.

EXAMPLE 3 Writing Radicals in Simplest Form

Write the expressions (a) $\sqrt[3]{135}$ and (b) $\frac{\sqrt[5]{7}}{\sqrt[5]{8}}$ in simplest form.

SOLUTION

a. $\sqrt[3]{135} = \sqrt[3]{27 \cdot 5}$ — Factor out perfect cube.

$= \sqrt[3]{27} \cdot \sqrt[3]{5}$ — Product Property of Radicals

$= 3\sqrt[3]{5}$ — Simplify.

b. $\frac{\sqrt[5]{7}}{\sqrt[5]{8}} = \frac{\sqrt[5]{7}}{\sqrt[5]{8}} \cdot \frac{\sqrt[5]{4}}{\sqrt[5]{4}}$ — Make the radicand in the denominator a perfect fifth power.

$= \frac{\sqrt[5]{28}}{\sqrt[5]{32}}$ — Product Property of Radicals

$= \frac{\sqrt[5]{28}}{2}$ — Simplify.

For a denominator that is a sum or difference involving square roots, multiply both the numerator and denominator by the *conjugate* of the denominator. The expressions $a\sqrt{b} + c\sqrt{d}$ and $a\sqrt{b} - c\sqrt{d}$ are conjugates of each other, where *a*, *b*, *c*, and *d* are rational numbers.

EXAMPLE 4 Writing a Radical Expression in Simplest Form

Write $\dfrac{1}{5 + \sqrt{3}}$ in simplest form.

SOLUTION

$$\frac{1}{5+\sqrt{3}} = \frac{1}{5+\sqrt{3}} \cdot \frac{5-\sqrt{3}}{5-\sqrt{3}}$$ The conjugate of $5 + \sqrt{3}$ is $5 - \sqrt{3}$.

$$= \frac{1(5-\sqrt{3})}{5^2 - (\sqrt{3})^2}$$ Sum and Difference Pattern

$$= \frac{5-\sqrt{3}}{22}$$ Simplify.

Radical expressions with the same index and radicand are **like radicals**. To add or subtract like radicals, use the Distributive Property.

EXAMPLE 5 Adding and Subtracting Like Radicals and Roots

Simplify each expression.

a. $\sqrt[4]{10} + 7\sqrt[4]{10}$ **b.** $2(8^{1/5}) + 10(8^{1/5})$ **c.** $\sqrt[3]{54} - \sqrt[3]{2}$

SOLUTION

a. $\sqrt[4]{10} + 7\sqrt[4]{10} = (1 + 7)\sqrt[4]{10} = 8\sqrt[4]{10}$

b. $2(8^{1/5}) + 10(8^{1/5}) = (2 + 10)(8^{1/5}) = 12(8^{1/5})$

c. $\sqrt[3]{54} - \sqrt[3]{2} = \sqrt[3]{27} \cdot \sqrt[3]{2} - \sqrt[3]{2} = 3\sqrt[3]{2} - \sqrt[3]{2} = (3 - 1)\sqrt[3]{2} = 2\sqrt[3]{2}$

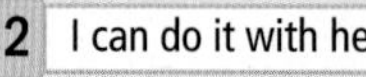

SELF-ASSESSMENT 1 I do not understand. 2 I can do it with help. 3 I can do it on my own. 4 I can teach someone else.

Simplify the expression.

5. $\sqrt[4]{27} \cdot \sqrt[4]{3}$ **6.** $\dfrac{\sqrt[3]{250}}{\sqrt[3]{2}}$ **7.** $\sqrt[3]{104}$ **8.** $\sqrt[5]{\dfrac{3}{4}}$

9. $\dfrac{3}{6 - \sqrt{2}}$ **10.** $7\sqrt[5]{12} - \sqrt[5]{12}$ **11.** $4(9^{2/3}) + 8(9^{2/3})$ **12.** $\sqrt[3]{5} + \sqrt[3]{40}$

Simplifying Variable Expressions

The properties of rational exponents and radicals can also be applied to expressions involving variables. Because a variable can be positive, negative, or zero, sometimes absolute value is needed when simplifying a variable expression.

	Rule	Example
When *n* is odd	$\sqrt[n]{x^n} = x$	$\sqrt[7]{5^7} = 5$ and $\sqrt[7]{(-5)^7} = -5$
When *n* is even	$\sqrt[n]{x^n} = \lvert x \rvert$	$\sqrt[4]{3^4} = 3$ and $\sqrt[4]{(-3)^4} = 3$

Absolute value is not needed when all variables are assumed to be positive.

EXAMPLE 6 Simplifying Variable Expressions

Simplify each expression.

a. $\sqrt[3]{64y^6}$ b. $\sqrt[4]{\dfrac{x^4}{y^8}}$

STUDY TIP

You do not need to take the absolute value of y^2 because it is always positive.

SOLUTION

a. $\sqrt[3]{64y^6} = \sqrt[3]{4^3(y^2)^3} = \sqrt[3]{4^3} \cdot \sqrt[3]{(y^2)^3} = 4y^2$

b. $\sqrt[4]{\dfrac{x^4}{y^8}} = \dfrac{\sqrt[4]{x^4}}{\sqrt[4]{y^8}} = \dfrac{\sqrt[4]{x^4}}{\sqrt[4]{(y^2)^4}} = \dfrac{|x|}{y^2}$

EXAMPLE 7 Writing Variable Expressions in Simplest Form

Write each expression in simplest form. Assume all variables are positive.

a. $\sqrt[4]{16a^7b^{11}c^4}$ b. $\dfrac{x}{\sqrt[3]{y^8}}$ c. $\dfrac{14xy^{1/3}}{2x^{3/4}z^{-6}}$

SOLUTION

a. $\sqrt[4]{16a^7b^{11}c^4} = \sqrt[4]{16a^4a^3b^8b^3c^4}$ Factor out perfect fourth powers.

$= \sqrt[4]{16a^4b^8c^4} \cdot \sqrt[4]{a^3b^3}$ Product Property of Radicals

$= 2ab^2c\sqrt[4]{a^3b^3}$ Simplify.

b. $\dfrac{x}{\sqrt[3]{y^8}} = \dfrac{x}{\sqrt[3]{y^8}} \cdot \dfrac{\sqrt[3]{y}}{\sqrt[3]{y}}$ Make denominator a perfect cube.

$= \dfrac{x\sqrt[3]{y}}{\sqrt[3]{y^9}}$ Product Property of Radicals

$= \dfrac{x\sqrt[3]{y}}{y^3}$ Simplify.

COMMON ERROR

You must multiply both the numerator *and* denominator of the fraction by $\sqrt[3]{y}$ so that the value of the fraction does not change.

c. $\dfrac{14xy^{1/3}}{2x^{3/4}z^{-6}} = 7x^{(1-3/4)}y^{1/3}z^{-(-6)} = 7x^{1/4}y^{1/3}z^6$

EXAMPLE 8 Adding and Subtracting Variable Expressions

Perform each indicated operation. Assume all variables are positive.

a. $5\sqrt{y} + 6\sqrt{y}$ b. $12\sqrt[3]{2z^5} - z\sqrt[3]{54z^2}$

SOLUTION

a. $5\sqrt{y} + 6\sqrt{y} = (5 + 6)\sqrt{y} = 11\sqrt{y}$

b. $12\sqrt[3]{2z^5} - z\sqrt[3]{54z^2} = 12z\sqrt[3]{2z^2} - 3z\sqrt[3]{2z^2} = (12z - 3z)\sqrt[3]{2z^2} = 9z\sqrt[3]{2z^2}$

SELF-ASSESSMENT

1 I do not understand. 2 I can do it with help. 3 I can do it on my own. 4 I can teach someone else.

13. Simplify (a) $\sqrt[3]{27q^3}$ and (b) $\sqrt[4]{\dfrac{a^8}{256b^4}}$.

Simplify the expression. Assume all variables are positive.

14. $\sqrt[6]{36p^6q^8r^{10}}$ **15.** $\sqrt[5]{\dfrac{x^{10}}{y^5}}$ **16.** $\dfrac{6xy^{3/4}}{3x^{1/2}y^{1/2}}$ **17.** $\sqrt{9w^5} - w\sqrt{w^3}$

5.2 Practice WITH CalcChat® AND CalcView®

In Exercises 1–10, use the properties of rational exponents to simplify the expression. ▶ *Example 1*

1. $(9^2)^{1/3}$
2. $(12^2)^{1/4}$
3. $\dfrac{6}{6^{1/4}}$
4. $\dfrac{7}{7^{1/3}}$
5. $\left(\dfrac{8^4}{10^4}\right)^{-1/4}$
6. $\left(\dfrac{9^3}{6^3}\right)^{-1/3}$
7. $(3^{-2/3} \cdot 3^{1/3})^{-1}$
8. $(5^{1/2} \cdot 5^{-3/2})^{-1/4}$
9. $\dfrac{2^{2/3} \cdot 16^{2/3}}{4^{2/3}}$
10. $\dfrac{49^{3/8} \cdot 49^{7/8}}{7^{5/4}}$

In Exercises 11–18, use the properties of radicals to simplify the expression. ▶ *Example 2*

11. $\sqrt{2} \cdot \sqrt{72}$
12. $\sqrt[3]{16} \cdot \sqrt[3]{32}$
13. $\sqrt[4]{5} \cdot \sqrt[4]{125}$
14. $\sqrt[4]{2} \cdot \sqrt[4]{128}$
15. $\dfrac{\sqrt[5]{486}}{\sqrt[5]{2}}$
16. $\dfrac{\sqrt{2}}{\sqrt{32}}$
17. $\dfrac{\sqrt[3]{6} \cdot \sqrt[3]{72}}{\sqrt[3]{2}}$
18. $\dfrac{\sqrt[3]{3} \cdot \sqrt[3]{18}}{\sqrt[6]{2} \cdot \sqrt[6]{2}}$

In Exercises 19–26, write the expression in simplest form. ▶ *Example 3*

19. $\sqrt[4]{567}$
20. $\sqrt[5]{288}$
21. $\dfrac{\sqrt[3]{5}}{\sqrt[3]{4}}$
22. $\dfrac{\sqrt[4]{4}}{\sqrt[4]{27}}$
23. $\sqrt{\dfrac{3}{8}}$
24. $\sqrt[3]{\dfrac{7}{4}}$
25. $\sqrt[3]{\dfrac{64}{49}}$
26. $\sqrt[4]{\dfrac{1296}{25}}$

In Exercises 27–34, write the expression in simplest form. ▶ *Example 4*

27. $\dfrac{1}{1 + \sqrt{3}}$
28. $\dfrac{1}{2 + \sqrt{5}}$
29. $\dfrac{5}{3 - \sqrt{2}}$
30. $\dfrac{11}{9 - \sqrt{6}}$
31. $\dfrac{9}{\sqrt{3} + \sqrt{7}}$
32. $\dfrac{2}{\sqrt{8} + \sqrt{7}}$
33. $\dfrac{\sqrt{6}}{\sqrt{3} - \sqrt{5}}$
34. $\dfrac{\sqrt{7}}{\sqrt{10} - \sqrt{2}}$

In Exercises 35–44, simplify the expression. ▶ *Example 5*

35. $9\sqrt[3]{11} + 3\sqrt[3]{11}$
36. $8\sqrt[6]{5} - 12\sqrt[6]{5}$
37. $3(14^{1/4}) + 9(14^{1/4})$
38. $13(8^{3/4}) - 4(8^{3/4})$
39. $5\sqrt{12} - 19\sqrt{3}$
40. $27\sqrt{6} + 7\sqrt{150}$
41. $\sqrt[5]{224} + 3\sqrt[5]{7}$
42. $7\sqrt[3]{2} - \sqrt[3]{128}$
43. $5(24^{1/3}) - 4(3^{1/3})$
44. $5^{1/4} + 6(405^{1/4})$

In Exercises 45–50, simplify the expression. ▶ *Example 6*

45. $\sqrt[4]{81y^8}$
46. $\sqrt[3]{64r^3t^6}$
47. $\sqrt[5]{\dfrac{m^{10}}{n^5}}$
48. $\sqrt[4]{\dfrac{k^{16}}{16z^4}}$
49. $\sqrt[6]{\dfrac{g^6h}{h^7}}$
50. $\sqrt[8]{\dfrac{n^2p^{-1}}{n^{18}p^7}}$

ERROR ANALYSIS In Exercises 51 and 52, describe and correct the error in simplifying the expression.

51.

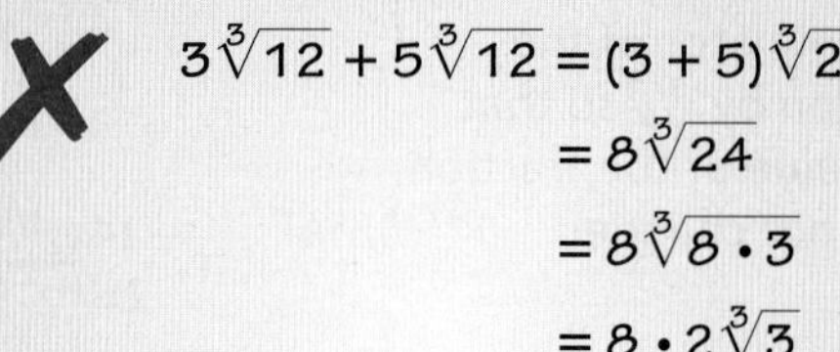

52.

✗ $\sqrt[6]{\dfrac{64}{w^6}} = \dfrac{\sqrt[6]{64}}{\sqrt[6]{w^6}} = \dfrac{\sqrt[6]{2^6}}{\sqrt[6]{w^6}} = \dfrac{2}{w}$

53. **OPEN-ENDED** Write two variable expressions involving radicals, one that needs absolute value when simplifying and one that does not need absolute value. Justify your answers.

54. COLLEGE PREP When each expression is simplified and written in radical form, which expressions are like radicals?

Ⓐ $(5^{2/9})^{3/2}$ Ⓑ $\dfrac{5^3}{5^{8/3}}$

Ⓒ $\sqrt[3]{625}$ Ⓓ $\sqrt[3]{960} - \sqrt[3]{120}$

Ⓔ $\sqrt[3]{40} + 3\sqrt[3]{320}$ Ⓕ $7\sqrt[4]{80} - 2\sqrt[4]{405}$

In Exercises 55–62, write the expression in simplest form. Assume all variables are positive. ▶ *Example 7*

55. $\sqrt{81a^7b^{12}c^9}$ **56.** $\sqrt[3]{125r^4s^9t^7}$

57. $\dfrac{c^3}{\sqrt[4]{d^7}}$ **58.** $\dfrac{w^7}{\sqrt[5]{z^{13}}}$

59. $\sqrt[5]{\dfrac{160m^6}{n^7}}$ **60.** $\sqrt[4]{\dfrac{405x^3y^3}{5x^{-1}y}}$

61. $\dfrac{18w^{1/3}v^{5/4}}{27w^{4/3}v^{1/2}}$ **62.** $\dfrac{7x^{3/4}y^{5/2}}{56x^{-1/2}y^{1/4}z^{-2/3}}$

In Exercises 63–68, perform the indicated operation. Assume all variables are positive. ▶ *Example 8*

63. $12\sqrt[3]{y} + 9\sqrt[3]{y}$ **64.** $11\sqrt{2z} - 5\sqrt{2z}$

65. $3x^{7/2} - 5x^{7/2}$ **66.** $7m^{7/3} + 3m^{7/3}$

67. $\sqrt[4]{16w^{10}} + 2w\sqrt[4]{w^6}$

68. $\sqrt[3]{32p^{10}} - 9p^2\sqrt[3]{4p^4}$

CONNECTING CONCEPTS In Exercises 69 and 70, find simplified expressions for the perimeter and area of the given figure.

69.

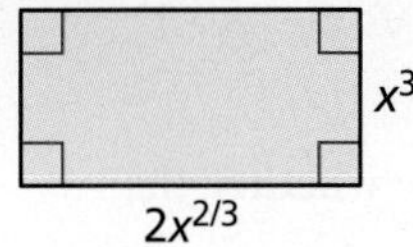

70.

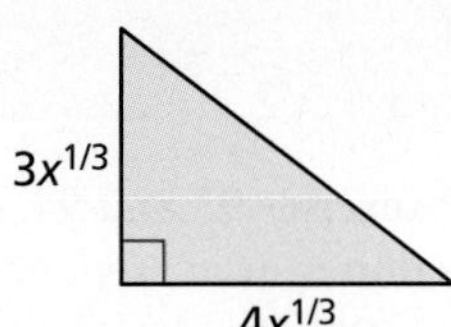

71. MODELING REAL LIFE The optimum diameter d (in millimeters) of the pinhole in a pinhole camera can be modeled by $d = 1.9[(5.5 \times 10^{-4})\ell]^{1/2}$, where ℓ is the length (in millimeters) of the camera box. Find the optimum pinhole diameter for a camera box with a length of 10 centimeters.

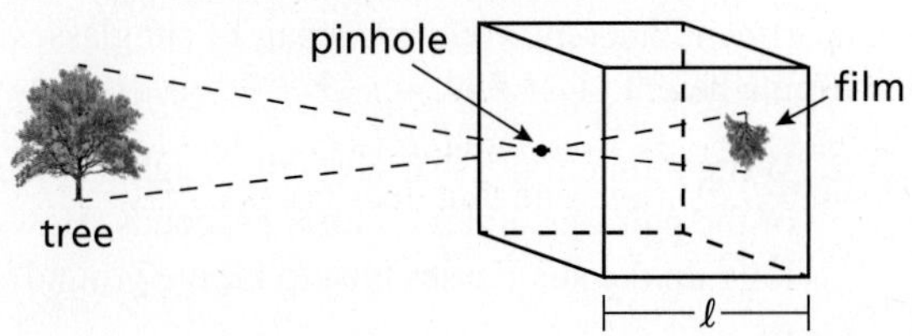

72. MODELING REAL LIFE The apparent magnitude of a star is a number that indicates how faint the star is in relation to other stars. The expression $\dfrac{2.512^{m_1}}{2.512^{m_2}}$ tells how many times fainter a star with apparent magnitude m_1 is than a star with apparent magnitude m_2.

Star	Apparent magnitude	Constellation
Vega	0.03	Lyra
Altair	0.77	Aquila
Deneb	1.25	Cygnus

a. How many times fainter is Altair than Vega?

b. How many times fainter is Deneb than Altair?

c. How many times fainter is Deneb than Vega?

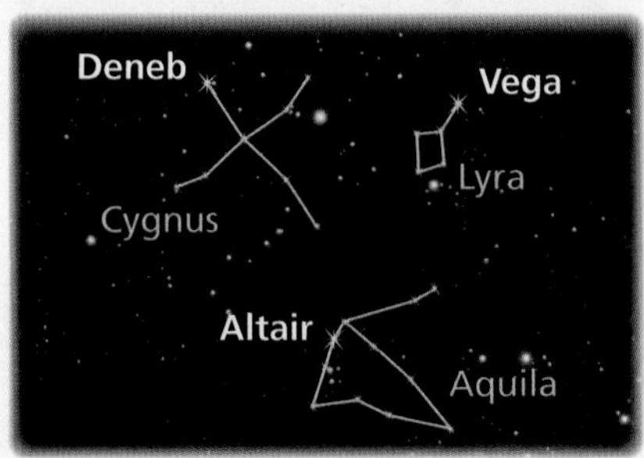

73. MAKING AN ARGUMENT Your friend claims it is not possible to simplify the expression $7\sqrt{11} - 9\sqrt{44}$ because it does not contain like radicals. Is your friend correct? Explain your reasoning.

74. MP PROBLEM SOLVING The surface area S (in square centimeters) of a mammal can be modeled by $S = km^{2/3}$, where m is the mass (in grams) of the mammal and k is a constant. The table shows the values of k for different mammals.

Mammal	Rabbit	Human	Bat
Value of k	9.75	11.0	57.5

a. Find the surface area of a bat whose mass is 32 grams.

b. Find the surface area of a rabbit whose mass is 3.4 kilograms (3.4×10^3 grams).

c. Which mammal has the greatest mass per square centimeter of surface area, the bat in part (a), the rabbit in part (b), or a human whose mass is 59 kilograms?

d. Rewrite the formula so that one side is $\dfrac{m}{S}$. Use this formula to justify your answer in part (c).

75. CONNECTING CONCEPTS Find a simplified radical expression for the perimeter of the triangle inscribed in the square. Is the inscribed triangle a right triangle?

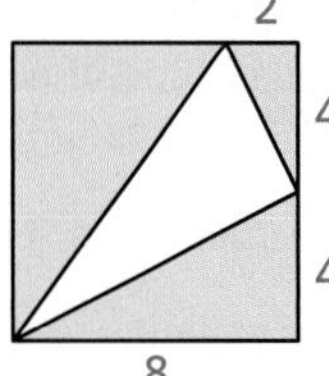

76. HOW DO YOU SEE IT?

Without finding points, match the functions $f(x) = \sqrt{x^2}$ and $g(x) = \sqrt[3]{x^3}$ with their graphs. Explain your reasoning.

A. 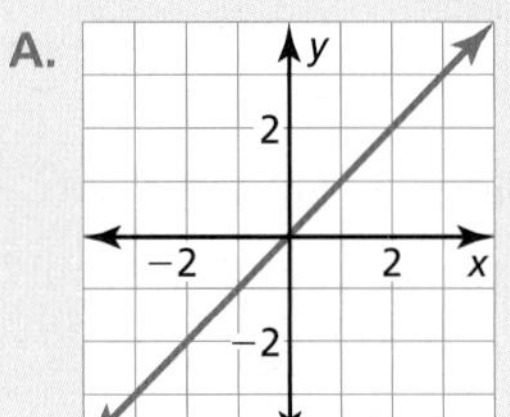

B. 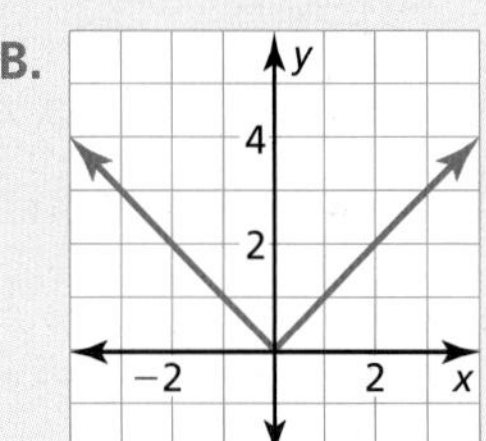

77. REWRITING A FORMULA You fill two round balloons with water. One balloon contains twice as much water as the other balloon.

a. Solve the formula for the volume of a sphere, $V = \frac{4}{3}\pi r^3$, for r.

b. Use your result from part (a) and the formula for the surface area of a sphere, $S = 4\pi r^2$, to show that $S = (4\pi)^{1/3}(3V)^{2/3}$.

c. Compare the surface areas of the two water balloons using the formula in part (b).

78. THOUGHT PROVOKING

Determine whether the expressions $(x^2)^{1/6}$ and $(x^{1/6})^2$ are equivalent for all values of x. Explain your reasoning.

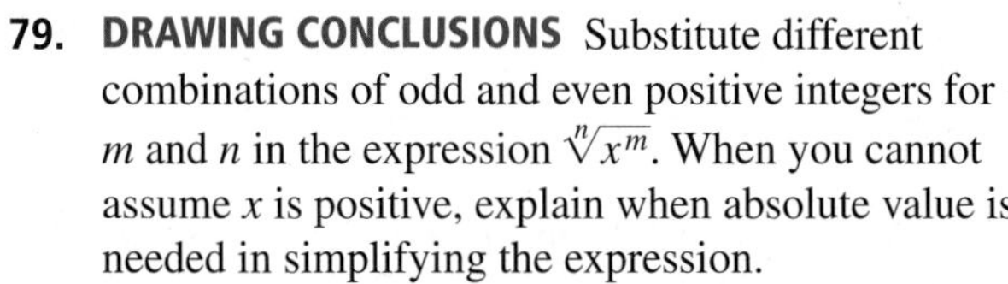

79. DRAWING CONCLUSIONS Substitute different combinations of odd and even positive integers for m and n in the expression $\sqrt[n]{x^m}$. When you cannot assume x is positive, explain when absolute value is needed in simplifying the expression.

REVIEW & REFRESH

In Exercises 80–83, write a rule for g. Describe the graph of g as a transformation of the graph of f.

80. $f(x) = x^4 - 3x^2 - 2x,\ g(x) = -f(x)$

81. $f(x) = x^3 - x,\ g(x) = f(x) - 3$

82. $f(x) = x^3 - 4,\ g(x) = f(x - 2)$

83. $f(x) = x^4 + 2x^3 - 4x^2,\ g(x) = f(2x)$

In Exercises 84 and 85, identify the focus, directrix, and axis of symmetry of the parabola. Then graph the equation.

84. $y = 2x^2$

85. $y^2 = -x$

86. Write the cubic function whose graph is shown.

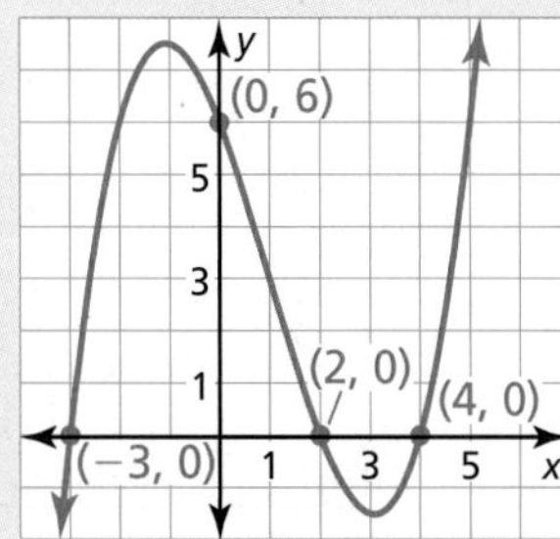

87. Is $f(x) = 4x^3 + 2^x - 5x$ a polynomial function? Explain.

88. Determine whether the sequence is *arithmetic*, *geometric*, or *neither*. Explain your reasoning.

4, 12, 36, 108, . . .

In Exercises 89–92, simplify the expression.

89. $\left(\frac{48^{1/4}}{6^{1/4}}\right)^6$

90. $\sqrt[4]{3} \cdot \sqrt[4]{432}$

91. $\frac{1}{3 + \sqrt{2}}$

92. $\sqrt[3]{16} - 5\sqrt[3]{2}$

In Exercises 93 and 94, determine whether the function is *even*, *odd*, or *neither*.

93. $f(x) = 3x^4 - 5$

94. $g(x) = x^5 + 2x - 3$

In Exercises 95 and 96, evaluate the expression without using technology.

95. $16^{3/4}$

96. $125^{2/3}$

97. MODELING REAL LIFE While standing on an apartment balcony, you drop a pair of sunglasses from a height of 25 feet.

a. Write a function h that gives the height (in feet) of the pair of sunglasses after t seconds. How long do the sunglasses take to hit the ground?

b. Find and interpret $h(0.25) - h(1)$.

5.3 Graphing Radical Functions

Learning Target Describe and graph transformations of radical functions.

Success Criteria
- I can graph radical functions.
- I can describe transformations of radical functions.
- I can write functions that represent transformations of radical functions.

EXPLORE IT! Graphing Radical Functions

Work with a partner.

a. In your own words, define a *radical* function. Give several examples.

b. MP **CHOOSE TOOLS** Graph each function. How are the graphs alike? How are they different?

i. $f(x) = \sqrt{x}$ **ii.** $f(x) = \sqrt[3]{x}$ **iii.** $f(x) = \sqrt[4]{x}$ **iv.** $f(x) = \sqrt[5]{x}$

Math Practice

Use Technology to Explore
How are the domain and range of a radical function related to the index of the radical?

c. Match each function with its graph. Explain your reasoning. Then describe g as a transformation of its parent function f.

i. $g(x) = \sqrt{x+2}$ **ii.** $g(x) = \sqrt{x-2}$

iii. $g(x) = \sqrt[3]{x} + 2$ **iv.** $g(x) = \sqrt[4]{x} - 2$

v. $g(x) = \sqrt[3]{x+2} - 2$ **vi.** $g(x) = -\sqrt[5]{x+2}$

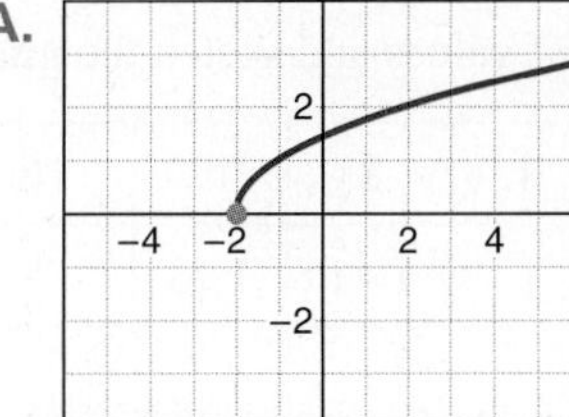

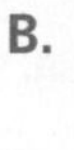

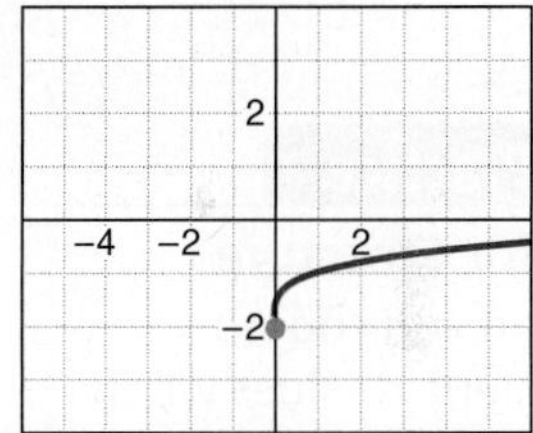

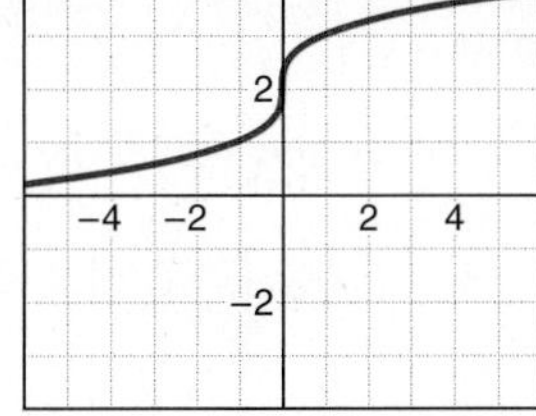

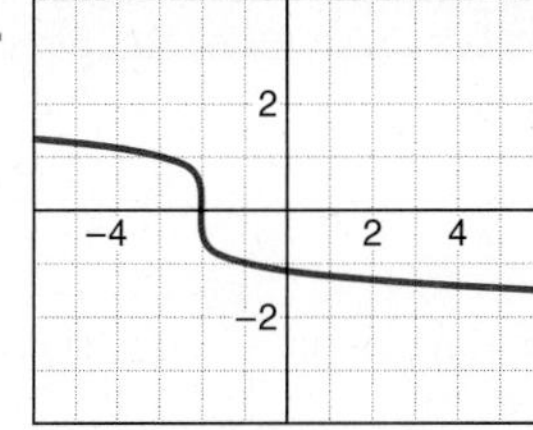

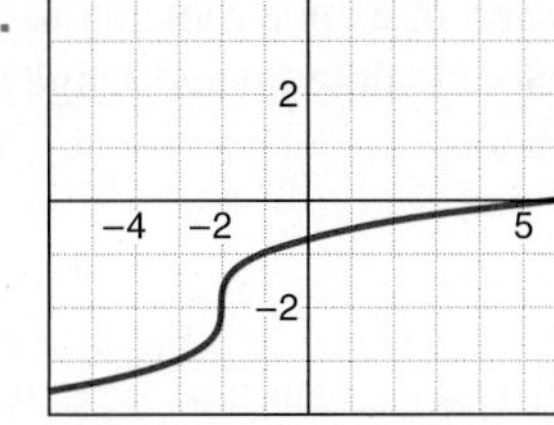

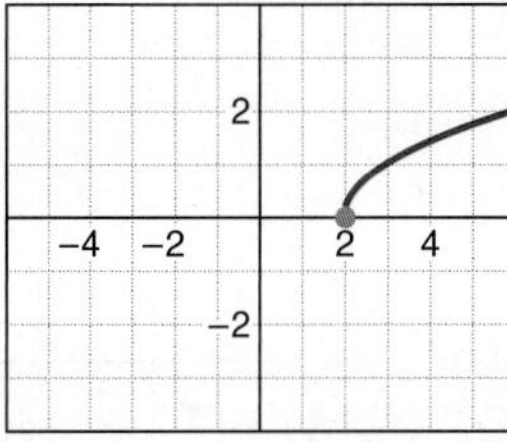

d. Describe the transformation of $f(x) = \sqrt{x}$ represented by $g(x) = -\sqrt{x} + 1$. Then graph each function.

Graphing Radical Functions

Vocabulary 

radical function, p. 246

A **radical function** contains a radical expression with the independent variable in the radicand. When the radical is a square root, the function is called a *square root function*. When the radical is a cube root, the function is called a *cube root function*.

KEY IDEA

Parent Functions for Square Root and Cube Root Functions

The parent function for the family of square root functions is $f(x) = \sqrt{x}$.

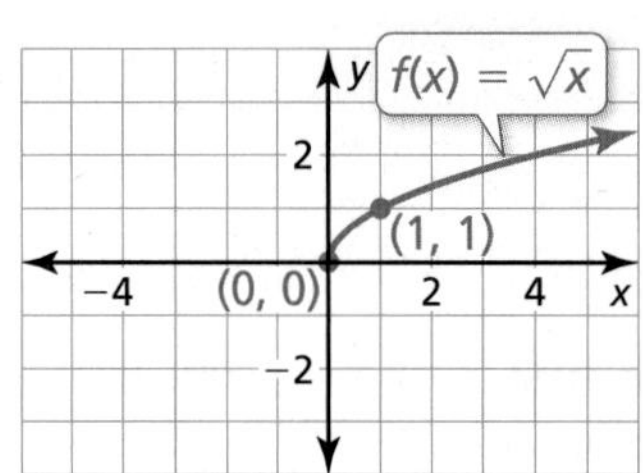

Domain: $x \geq 0$, Range: $y \geq 0$

The parent function for the family of cube root functions is $f(x) = \sqrt[3]{x}$.

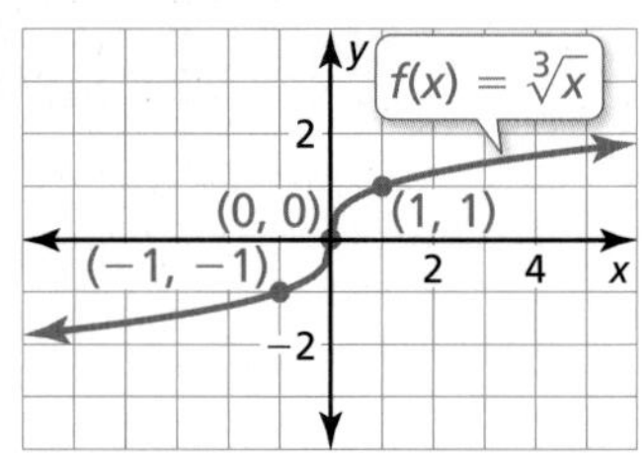

Domain and range: All real numbers

STUDY TIP

A *power function* has the form $y = ax^b$, where a is a real number and b is a rational number. Notice that the parent square root function is a power function, where $a = 1$ and $b = \frac{1}{2}$.

EXAMPLE 1 Graphing Radical Functions

Graph each function. Find the domain and range of each function.

a. $f(x) = \sqrt{\frac{1}{4}x}$ **b.** $g(x) = -3\sqrt[3]{x}$

SOLUTION

a. Make a table of values and sketch the graph.

x	0	4	8	12	16
y	0	1	1.41	1.73	2

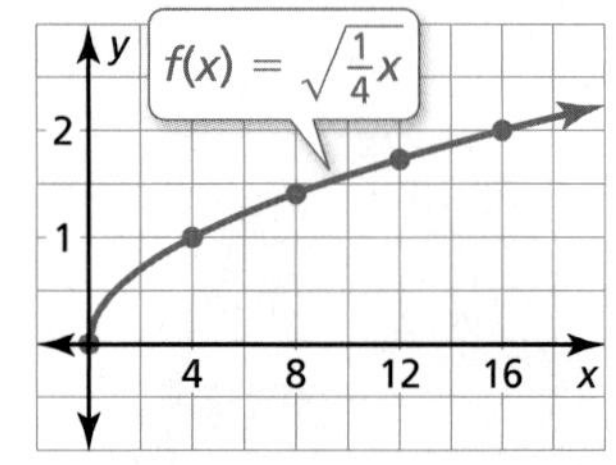

▶ The radicand of a square root must be nonnegative. So, the domain is $x \geq 0$. The range is $y \geq 0$.

Math Practice

Look for Structure

How can you choose convenient x-values when making a table for a radical function?

b. Make a table of values and sketch the graph.

x	−2	−1	0	1	2
y	3.78	3	0	−3	−3.78

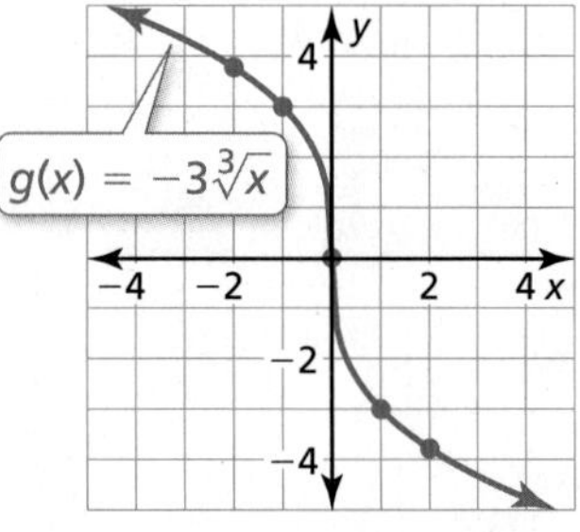

▶ The radicand of a cube root can be any real number. So, the domain and range are all real numbers.

SELF-ASSESSMENT 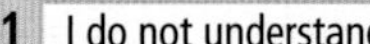 1 I do not understand. 2 I can do it with help. 3 I can do it on my own. 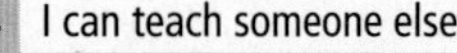 4 I can teach someone else.

Graph the function. Find the domain and range of the function.

1. $g(x) = \sqrt{x + 1}$ **2.** $f(x) = \sqrt[3]{2x}$ **3.** $h(x) = -\frac{1}{2}\sqrt{x - 3}$

Graphing Transformations of Radical Functions

In Example 1, notice that the graph of f is a horizontal stretch of the graph of the parent square root function. The graph of g is a vertical stretch and a reflection in the x-axis of the graph of the parent cube root function. You can transform graphs of radical functions in the same way you transformed graphs of functions previously.

KEY IDEAS

Transformation	$f(x)$ Notation	Examples	
Horizontal Translation Graph shifts left or right.	$f(x-h)$	$g(x) = \sqrt{x-2}$ $g(x) = \sqrt{x+3}$	2 units right 3 units left
Vertical Translation Graph shifts up or down.	$f(x)+k$	$g(x) = \sqrt{x} + 7$ $g(x) = \sqrt{x} - 1$	7 units up 1 unit down
Reflection Graph flips over a line.	$f(-x)$ $-f(x)$	$g(x) = \sqrt{-x}$ $g(x) = -\sqrt{x}$	in the y-axis in the x-axis
Horizontal Stretch or Shrink Graph stretches away from or shrinks toward y-axis by a factor of $\frac{1}{a}$.	$f(ax)$	$g(x) = \sqrt{3x}$ $g(x) = \sqrt{\frac{1}{2}x}$	shrink by a factor of $\frac{1}{3}$ stretch by a factor of 2
Vertical Stretch or Shrink Graph stretches away from or shrinks toward x-axis by a factor of a.	$a \cdot f(x)$	$g(x) = 4\sqrt{x}$ $g(x) = \frac{1}{5}\sqrt{x}$	stretch by a factor of 4 shrink by a factor of $\frac{1}{5}$

EXAMPLE 2 Transforming Radical Functions

Describe the transformation of f represented by g. Then graph each function.

a. $f(x) = \sqrt{x}$, $g(x) = \sqrt{x-3} + 4$ **b.** $f(x) = \sqrt[3]{x}$, $g(x) = \sqrt[3]{-8x}$

SOLUTION

a. Notice that the function is of the form $g(x) = \sqrt{x-h} + k$, where $h = 3$ and $k = 4$.

▶ So, the graph of g is a translation 3 units right and 4 units up of the graph of f.

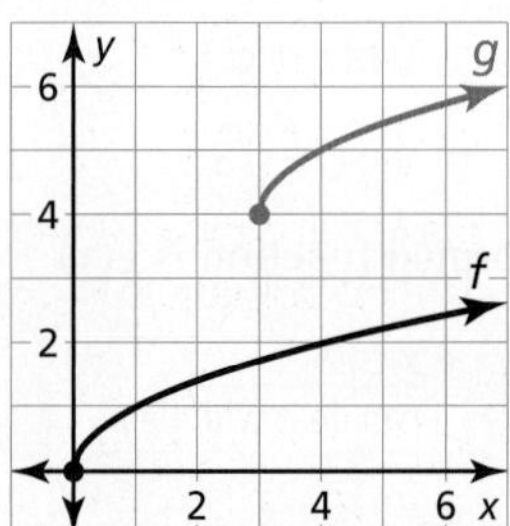

b. Notice that the function is of the form $g(x) = \sqrt[3]{ax}$, where $a = -8$.

▶ So, the graph of g is a horizontal shrink by a factor of $\frac{1}{8}$ and a reflection in the y-axis of the graph of f.

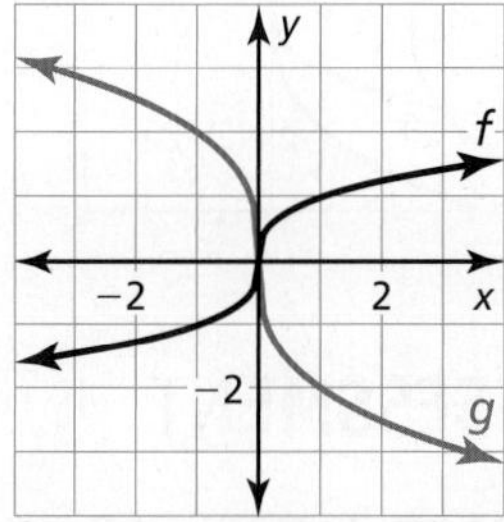

Math Practice

Look for Structure

In Example 2(b), how can you rewrite g to describe the transformation a different way?

SELF-ASSESSMENT 1 I do not understand. 2 I can do it with help. 3 I can do it on my own. 4 I can teach someone else.

4. Describe the transformation of $f(x) = \sqrt[3]{x}$ represented by $g(x) = -\sqrt[3]{x} - 2$. Then graph each function.

Writing Transformations of Radical Functions

EXAMPLE 3 Modeling Real Life

The function $E(d) = 0.25\sqrt{d}$ approximates the number of seconds it takes a dropped object to fall d feet on Earth. The function $M(d) = 1.6 \bullet E(d)$ approximates the number of seconds it takes a dropped object to fall d feet on Mars. How long does it take a dropped object to fall 64 feet on Mars?

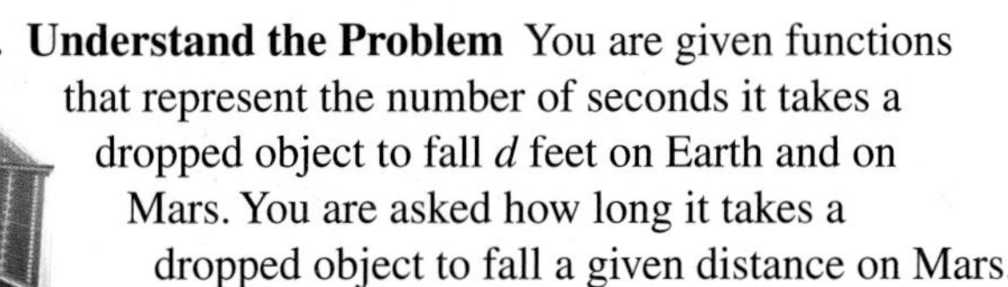

Mars lander InSight took this self-portrait of one of its 7-foot-wide solar panels in December 2018.

SOLUTION

1. **Understand the Problem** You are given functions that represent the number of seconds it takes a dropped object to fall d feet on Earth and on Mars. You are asked how long it takes a dropped object to fall a given distance on Mars.
2. **Make a Plan** Multiply $E(d)$ by 1.6 to write a rule for M. Then find $M(64)$.
3. **Solve and Check** $M(d) = 1.6 \bullet E(d)$

$= 1.6 \bullet 0.25\sqrt{d}$ — Substitute $0.25\sqrt{d}$ for $E(d)$.

$= 0.4\sqrt{d}$ — Simplify.

$M(64) = 0.4\sqrt{64} = 0.4(8) = 3.2$

▶ It takes a dropped object about 3.2 seconds to fall 64 feet on Mars.

Check
Use the original functions to check your solution.

$E(64) = 0.25\sqrt{64} = 2$ ✓

$M(64) = 1.6 \bullet E(64)$

$= 1.6 \bullet 2 = 3.2$ ✓

EXAMPLE 4 Writing a Transformed Radical Function

Let the graph of g be a horizontal shrink by a factor of $\frac{1}{6}$, followed by a translation 3 units left of the graph of $f(x) = \sqrt[3]{x}$. Write a rule for g.

SOLUTION

Step 1 First write a function h that represents the horizontal shrink of f.

$h(x) = f(6x)$ — Multiply the input by $1 \div \frac{1}{6} = 6$.

$= \sqrt[3]{6x}$ — Replace x with $6x$ in $f(x)$.

Step 2 Then write a function g that represents the translation of h.

$g(x) = h(x + 3)$ — Subtract -3, or add 3, to the input.

$= \sqrt[3]{6(x + 3)}$ — Replace x with $x + 3$ in $h(x)$.

$= \sqrt[3]{6x + 18}$ — Distributive Property

▶ The transformed function is $g(x) = \sqrt[3]{6x + 18}$.

Check

SELF-ASSESSMENT

1 I do not understand. 2 I can do it with help. 3 I can do it on my own. 4 I can teach someone else.

5. **WHAT IF?** In Example 3, the function $N(d) = 2.4 \bullet E(d)$ approximates the number of seconds it takes a dropped object to fall d feet on the Moon. How long does it take a dropped object to fall 25 feet on the Moon?
6. **WRITING** In Example 4, is the transformed function the same when you perform the translation followed by the horizontal shrink? Explain your reasoning.

Graphing Parabolas and Circles

You can use radical functions to graph circles and parabolas that open left or right.

EXAMPLE 5 **Graphing a Parabola (Horizontal Axis of Symmetry)**

Use radical functions to graph $\frac{1}{2}y^2 = x$. Identify the vertex and the direction that the parabola opens.

SOLUTION

Step 1 Solve for y.

$\frac{1}{2}y^2 = x$ Write the original equation.

$y^2 = 2x$ Multiply each side by 2.

$y = \pm\sqrt{2x}$ Take square root of each side.

STUDY TIP

Notice that y_1 is a function and y_2 is a function, but $\frac{1}{2}y^2 = x$ is not a function.

Step 2 Graph both radical functions.

$y_1 = \sqrt{2x}$

$y_2 = -\sqrt{2x}$

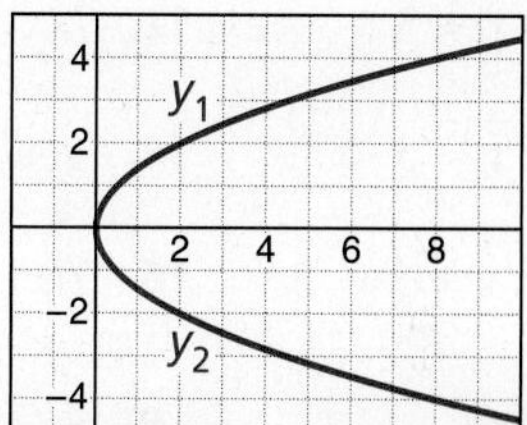

▶ The vertex is (0, 0) and the parabola opens right.

EXAMPLE 6 **Graphing a Circle (Center at the Origin)**

Use radical functions to graph $x^2 + y^2 = 16$. Identify the radius and the intercepts.

SOLUTION

Step 1 Solve for y.

$x^2 + y^2 = 16$ Write the original equation.

$y^2 = 16 - x^2$ Subtract x^2 from each side.

$y = \pm\sqrt{16 - x^2}$ Take square root of each side.

Step 2 Graph both radical functions.

$y_1 = \sqrt{16 - x^2}$

$y_2 = -\sqrt{16 - x^2}$

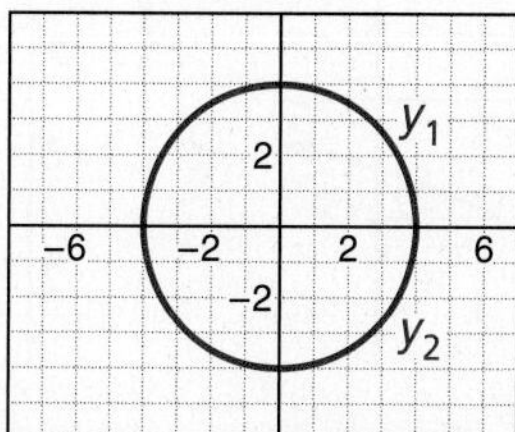

▶ The radius is 4 units. The x-intercepts are ±4. The y-intercepts are also ±4.

SELF-ASSESSMENT

1 I do not understand. 2 I can do it with help. 3 I can do it on my own. 4 I can teach someone else.

Use radical functions to graph the equation of the parabola. Identify the vertex and the direction that the parabola opens.

7. $x = 2y^2$ **8.** $-4y^2 = x + 1$ **9.** $\frac{1}{3}x = 1 - y^2$

Use radical functions to graph the equation of the circle. Identify the radius and the intercepts.

10. $x^2 + y^2 = 25$ **11.** $y^2 = 49 - x^2$ **12.** $4x^2 + 4y^2 = 1$

5.3 Practice WITH CalcChat® AND CalcView®

In Exercises 1–10, graph the function. Find the domain and range of the function. *Example 1*

1. $h(x) = \sqrt{x} + 4$
2. $g(x) = \sqrt{x} - 5$
3. $g(x) = -\sqrt[3]{2x}$
4. $f(x) = \sqrt[3]{-5x}$
5. $g(x) = \frac{1}{5}\sqrt{x - 3}$
6. $f(x) = \frac{1}{2}\sqrt[3]{x + 6}$
7. $f(x) = (6x)^{1/2} + 3$
8. $g(x) = -3(x + 1)^{1/3}$
9. $h(x) = -\sqrt[4]{x}$
10. $h(x) = \sqrt[5]{2x}$

In Exercises 11–16, match the function with its graph.

11. $f(x) = \sqrt{x + 3}$
12. $h(x) = \sqrt{x} + 3$
13. $f(x) = \sqrt{x - 3}$
14. $g(x) = \sqrt{x} - 3$
15. $h(x) = \sqrt{x + 3} - 3$
16. $f(x) = \sqrt{x - 3} + 3$

A. 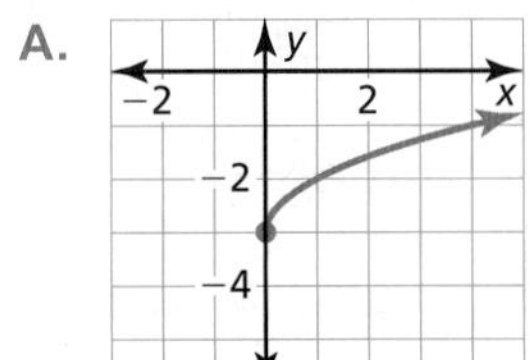

B. 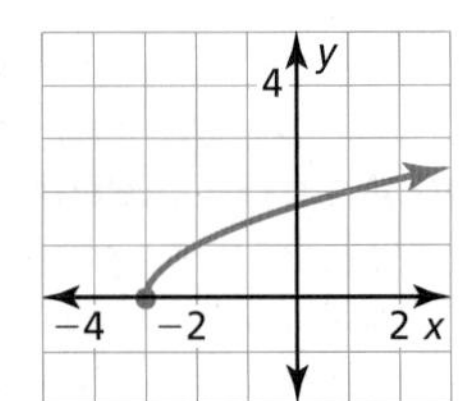

C. 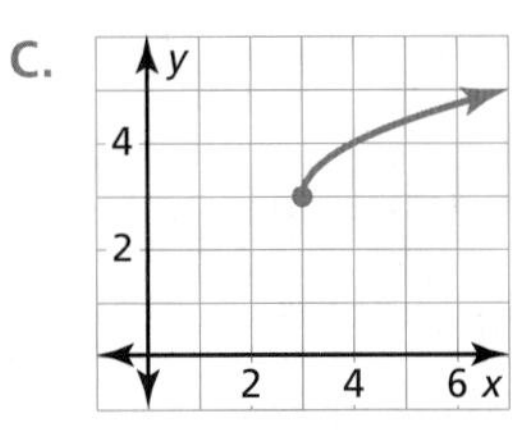

D. 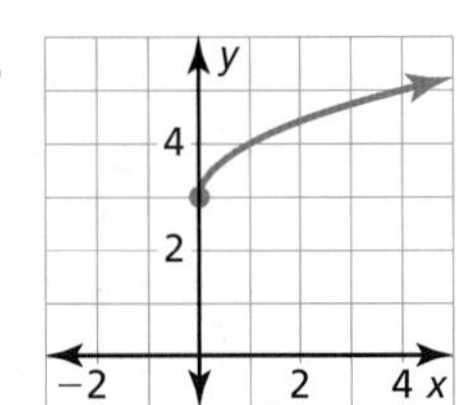

E. 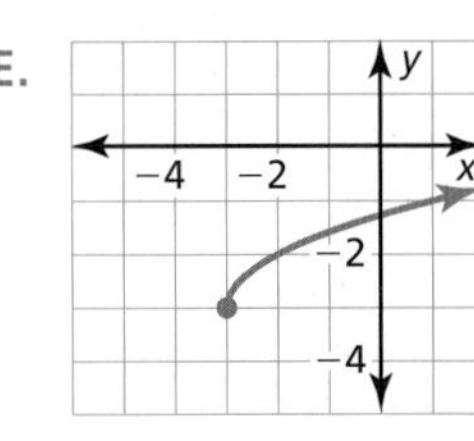

F. 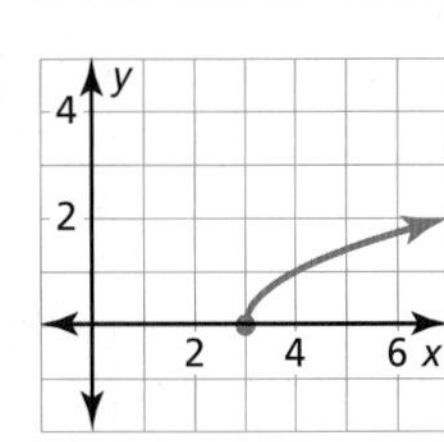

In Exercises 17–24, describe the transformation of f represented by g. Then graph each function. *Example 2*

17. $f(x) = \sqrt{x}$, $g(x) = \sqrt{x + 1} + 8$
18. $f(x) = \sqrt{x}$, $g(x) = 2\sqrt{x - 1}$
19. $f(x) = \sqrt[3]{x}$, $g(x) = -\sqrt[3]{x} - 1$
20. $f(x) = \sqrt[3]{x}$, $g(x) = \sqrt[3]{x + 4} - 5$
21. $f(x) = x^{1/2}$, $g(x) = \frac{1}{4}(-x)^{1/2}$
22. $f(x) = x^{1/3}$, $g(x) = \frac{1}{3}x^{1/3} + 6$
23. $f(x) = \sqrt[4]{x}$, $g(x) = 2\sqrt[4]{x + 5} - 4$
24. $f(x) = \sqrt[5]{x}$, $g(x) = \sqrt[5]{-32x} + 3$

25. **ERROR ANALYSIS** Describe and correct the error in graphing $f(x) = \sqrt{x - 2} - 2$.

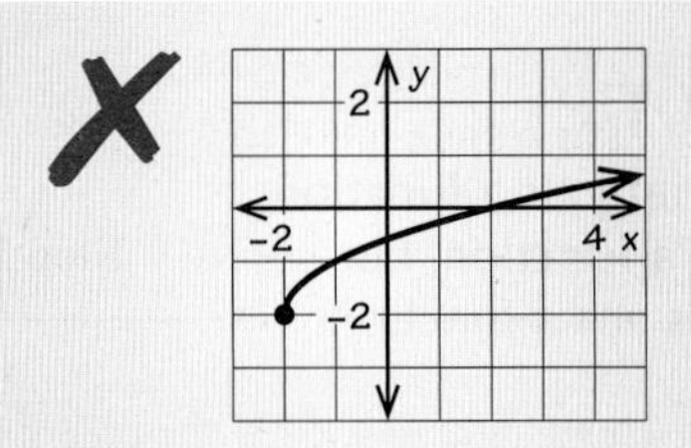

26. **ERROR ANALYSIS** Describe and correct the error in describing the transformation of $f(x) = \sqrt{x}$ represented by $g(x) = \sqrt{\frac{1}{2}x} + 3$.

The graph of g is a horizontal shrink by a factor of $\frac{1}{2}$ and a translation 3 units up of the graph of f.

MP USING TOOLS In Exercises 27–32, use technology to graph the function. Then find the domain and range of the function.

27. $g(x) = \sqrt{x^2 + x}$
28. $h(x) = \sqrt{x^2 - 2x}$
29. $f(x) = \sqrt[3]{x^2 + 2x}$
30. $f(x) = \sqrt[3]{2x^2 - x}$
31. $f(x) = \sqrt{x^2 - 4x + 6}$
32. $h(x) = \sqrt[3]{\frac{1}{2}x^2 - 3x + 4}$

33. **MODELING REAL LIFE** The functions approximate the velocity (in feet per second) of an object dropped from a height of x feet right before it hits the ground on Earth and on Mars.

Earth: $E(x) = 8\sqrt{x}$

Mars: $M(x) = 0.6 \cdot E(x)$

What is the velocity of an object dropped from a height of 25 feet right before it hits the ground on Mars? *Example 3*

34. **MODELING REAL LIFE** The speed (in knots) of sound waves in air can be modeled by

$$v(K) = 643.855\sqrt{\frac{K}{273.15}}$$

where K is the air temperature (in Kelvin). The speed (in meters per second) of sound waves in air can be modeled by

$$s(K) = \frac{v(K)}{1.944}.$$

What is the speed (in meters per second) of sound waves when the air temperature is 305 Kelvin?

In Exercises 35–38, write a rule for g described by the transformations of the graph of f. *Example 4*

35. Let g be a vertical stretch by a factor of 2, followed by a translation 2 units up of the graph of $f(x) = \sqrt{x} + 3$.

36. Let g be a reflection in the y-axis, followed by a translation 1 unit right of the graph of $f(x) = 2\sqrt[3]{x - 1}$.

37. Let g be a horizontal shrink by a factor of $\frac{2}{3}$, followed by a translation 4 units left of the graph of $f(x) = \sqrt{6x}$.

38. Let g be a translation 1 unit down and 5 units right, followed by a reflection in the x-axis of the graph of $f(x) = -\frac{1}{2}\sqrt[4]{x} + \frac{3}{2}$.

In Exercises 39 and 40, write a rule for g.

39. 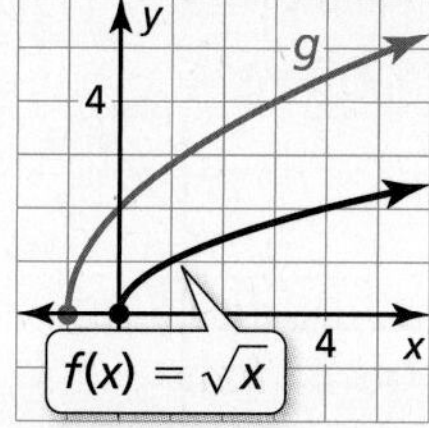

40. 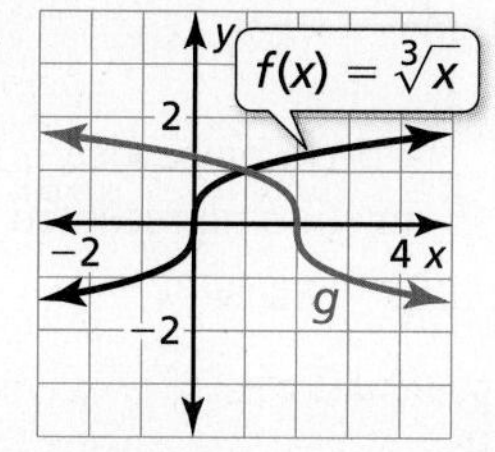

In Exercises 41–44, write a rule for g that represents the indicated transformation of the graph of f.

41. $f(x) = 2\sqrt{x}$, $g(x) = f(x + 3)$

42. $f(x) = \frac{1}{3}\sqrt{x - 1}$, $g(x) = -f(x) + 9$

43. $f(x) = -\sqrt{x^2 - 2}$, $g(x) = -2f(x + 5)$

44. $f(x) = \sqrt[3]{x^2 + 10x}$, $g(x) = \frac{1}{4}f(-x) + 6$

In Exercises 45–50, use radical functions to graph the equation of the parabola. Identify the vertex and the direction that the parabola opens. *Example 5*

45. $\frac{1}{4}y^2 = x$

46. $3y^2 = x$

47. $-8y^2 + 2 = x$

48. $2y^2 = x - 4$

49. $x + 8 = \frac{1}{5}y^2$

50. $\frac{1}{2}x = y^2 - 4$

In Exercises 51–56, use radical functions to graph the equation of the circle. Identify the radius and the intercepts. *Example 6*

51. $x^2 + y^2 = 9$

52. $x^2 + y^2 = 4$

53. $1 - y^2 = x^2$

54. $64 - x^2 = y^2$

55. $-y^2 = x^2 - 36$

56. $x^2 = 100 - y^2$

ABSTRACT REASONING **In Exercises 57–60, complete the statement with *sometimes*, *always*, or *never*.**

57. The domain of the function $y = a\sqrt{x}$ is ______ $x \geq 0$.

58. The range of the function $y = a\sqrt{x}$ is ______ $y \geq 0$.

59. The domain and range of the function $y = \sqrt[3]{x - h} + k$ are ________ all real numbers.

60. The domain of the function $y = a\sqrt{-x} + k$ is ________ $x \geq 0$.

61. **MODELING REAL LIFE** The *period* of a pendulum is the time the pendulum takes to complete one back-and-forth swing. The period T (in seconds) can be modeled by the function $T = 1.11\sqrt{\ell}$, where ℓ is the length (in feet) of the pendulum. Estimate the length of a pendulum with a period of 2 seconds.

62. **HOW DO YOU SEE IT?** Does the graph represent a square root function or a cube root function? Explain. What are the domain and range of the function?

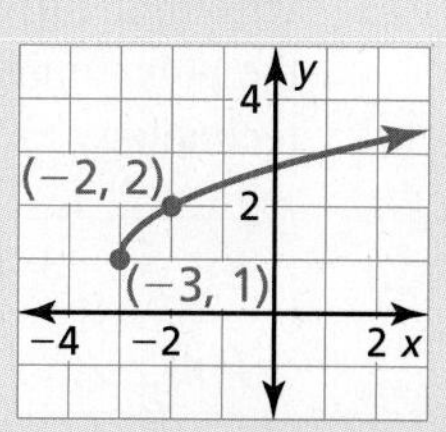

63. **MP PROBLEM SOLVING** For a drag race car with a total weight of 3500 pounds, the speed s (in miles per hour) at the end of a race can be modeled by $s = 14.8\sqrt[3]{p}$, where p is the power (in horsepower).

a. Determine the power of a 3500-pound car that reaches a speed of 200 miles per hour.

b. What is the average rate of change in speed as the power changes from 1000 horsepower to 1500 horsepower?

64. MULTIPLE REPRESENTATIONS The terminal velocity v_t (in feet per second) of a skydiver who weighs 140 pounds is given by

$$v_t = 33.7\sqrt{\frac{140}{A}}$$

where A is the cross-sectional surface area (in square feet) of the skydiver. The table shows the terminal velocities (in feet per second) for various surface areas (in square feet) of a skydiver who weighs 165 pounds. Which skydiver has a greater terminal velocity for each value of A given in the table? How is it possible for the value of A to vary for one skydiver?

Cross-sectional surface area, A	Terminal velocity, v_t
1	432.9
3	249.9
5	193.6
7	163.6

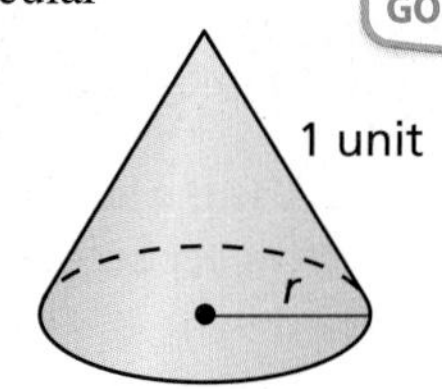

65. CONNECTING CONCEPTS The surface area S of a right circular cone with a slant height of 1 unit is given by $S = \pi r + \pi r^2$, where r is the radius of the cone.

a. Use completing the square to show that

$$r = \frac{1}{\sqrt{\pi}}\sqrt{S + \frac{\pi}{4}} - \frac{1}{2}.$$

b. Use technology to graph the equation in part (a). Then find the radius of a right circular cone with a slant height of 1 unit and a surface area of $\frac{3\pi}{4}$ square units.

66. THOUGHT PROVOKING
The graph of a radical function f passes through the points (3, 1) and (4, 0). Write two different functions that can represent $f(x + 2) + 1$.

REVIEW & REFRESH

WATCH

In Exercises 67 and 68, solve the inequality.

67. $x^2 + 7x + 12 < 0$ **68.** $x^2 - 10x + 25 \geq 4$

In Exercises 69–72, write the expression in simplest form. Assume all variables are positive.

69. $\sqrt[3]{216p^9}$ **70.** $\dfrac{\sqrt[5]{32}}{\sqrt[5]{m^3}}$

71. $\sqrt[4]{n^4q} + 7n\sqrt[4]{q}$ **72.** $\dfrac{21ab^{3/2}}{3a^{1/3}b^{1/2}c^{-1/4}}$

73. Use finite differences to determine the degree of the polynomial function that fits the data. Then use technology to find the polynomial function.

x	−3	−2	−1	0	1	2
f(x)	−7	−3	−2	−1	3	13

In Exercises 74 and 75, graph the function. Label the vertex and axis of symmetry.

74. $g(x) = -(x + 4)^2 - 1$ **75.** $h(x) = 4x^2 + 8x - 5$

76. Evaluate $10^{2/3}$ using technology. Round your answer to two decimal places.

77. Graph $f(x) = -2\sqrt{x + 3}$. Find the domain and range of the function.

In Exercises 78–81, solve the equation.

78. $|3x + 2| = 5$ **79.** $|4x + 9| = -7$

80. $|x - 9| = 2x$ **81.** $|x + 8| = |2x + 2|$

82. Write a piecewise function represented by the graph.

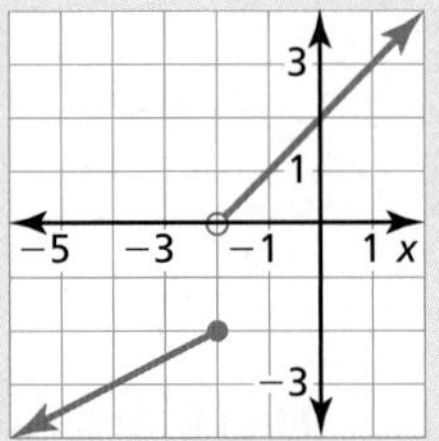

83. MODELING REAL LIFE The prices of smartphone cases at a store have a median of \$29.99 and a range of \$40. The manager considers decreasing all prices by either \$5 or 15%. Which decrease results in a lesser median price? a lesser range of prices?

84. Solve the system.

$$3x + 2y - z = -11$$
$$2x + y + 2z = 3$$
$$4x - 5y + z = -13$$

85. Describe the transformation of $f(x) = \sqrt[3]{x}$ represented by $g(x) = \sqrt[3]{x - 2} - 4$. Then graph each function.

5.4 Solving Radical Equations and Inequalities

Learning Target Solve equations and inequalities containing radicals and rational exponents.

Success Criteria
- I can identify radical equations and inequalities.
- I can solve radical equations and inequalities.
- I can identify extraneous solutions of radical equations.
- I can solve real-life problems involving radical equations.

EXPLORE IT! Solving Radical Equations

Work with a partner.

a. Two students solve the equation $x + 2 = \sqrt{5x + 16}$ as shown. Justify each solution step in the first student's solution. Then describe each student's method. Are the methods valid? Explain.

Math Practice

Understand Mathematical Terms

The solution $x = -3$ is called an *extraneous solution*. Why is it called *extraneous*?

Student 1

$x + 2 = \sqrt{5x + 16}$	Write the equation.
$(x + 2)^2 = (\sqrt{5x + 16})^2$	______
$x^2 + 4x + 4 = 5x + 16$	______
$x^2 - x - 12 = 0$	______
$(x - 4)(x + 3) = 0$	______
$x - 4 = 0$ or $x + 3 = 0$	______
$x = 4$ or $x = -3$	______

Student 2

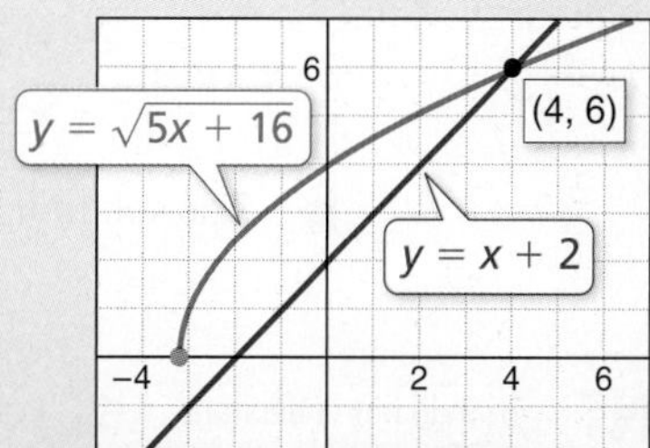

The graphs intersect at the point (4, 6). So, the only solution is $x = 4$.

b. Which student is correct? Explain why the other student's solution is incorrect and how the student arrived at an incorrect answer.

c. Explain how you might solve the equation $(9n)^{3/2} - 7 = 20$.

GO DIGITAL

Solving Equations

A **radical equation** contains radicals that have variables in the radicands. An example of a radical equation is $2\sqrt{x+1} = 4$.

Vocabulary 

radical equation, *p. 254*
extraneous solution, *p. 255*

KEY IDEA

Solving Radical Equations

Step 1 Isolate the radical on one side of the equation, if necessary.

Step 2 Raise each side of the equation to the same exponent to eliminate the radical and obtain a linear, quadratic, or other polynomial equation.

Step 3 Solve the resulting equation using techniques you learned in previous chapters. Check your solution.

EXAMPLE 1 Solving Radical Equations 

Solve each equation.

a. $2\sqrt{x+1} = 4$ **b.** $\sqrt[3]{2x-9} - 1 = 2$

SOLUTION

a.

$2\sqrt{x+1} = 4$ Write the equation.

$\sqrt{x+1} = 2$ Divide each side by 2.

$(\sqrt{x+1})^2 = 2^2$ Square each side to eliminate the radical.

$x + 1 = 4$ Simplify.

$x = 3$ Subtract 1 from each side.

▶ The solution is $x = 3$.

Check

$2\sqrt{3+1} \stackrel{?}{=} 4$

$2\sqrt{4} \stackrel{?}{=} 4$

$4 = 4$ ✓

b.

$\sqrt[3]{2x-9} - 1 = 2$ Write the equation.

$\sqrt[3]{2x-9} = 3$ Add 1 to each side.

$(\sqrt[3]{2x-9})^3 = 3^3$ Cube each side to eliminate the radical.

$2x - 9 = 27$ Simplify.

$2x = 36$ Add 9 to each side.

$x = 18$ Divide each side by 2.

▶ The solution is $x = 18$.

Check

$\sqrt[3]{2(18)-9} - 1 \stackrel{?}{=} 2$

$\sqrt[3]{27} - 1 \stackrel{?}{=} 2$

$2 = 2$ ✓

SELF-ASSESSMENT 1 I do not understand. 2 I can do it with help. 3 I can do it on my own. 4 I can teach someone else.

Solve the equation. Check your solution.

1. $\sqrt[3]{x} - 9 = -6$ **2.** $\sqrt{x+25} = 2$ **3.** $2\sqrt[3]{x-3} = 4$

4. WHICH ONE DOESN'T BELONG? Which equation does *not* belong with the other three? Explain your reasoning.

$\sqrt[3]{x} + 7 = 11$ $3\sqrt{x+5} = 21$ $3x - \sqrt{2} = 6$ $\sqrt[3]{x-1} = 5$

EXAMPLE 2 Modeling Real Life

The mean sustained wind velocity (in meters per second) of a hurricane is modeled by $v(p) = 6.3\sqrt{1013 - p}$, where p is the air pressure (in millibars) at the center of the hurricane. Estimate the air pressure at the center of the hurricane when the mean sustained wind velocity is 54.5 meters per second.

SOLUTION

$v(p) = 6.3\sqrt{1013 - p}$	Write the function.
$54.5 = 6.3\sqrt{1013 - p}$	Substitute 54.5 for $v(p)$.
$8.65 \approx \sqrt{1013 - p}$	Divide each side by 6.3.
$8.65^2 \approx \left(\sqrt{1013 - p}\right)^2$	Square each side.
$74.8 \approx 1013 - p$	Simplify.
$-938.2 \approx -p$	Subtract 1013 from each side.
$938.2 \approx p$	Divide each side by -1.

▶ The air pressure at the center of the hurricane is about 938 millibars.

Math Practice

Explain the Meaning

To understand how extraneous solutions can be introduced, consider the equation $\sqrt{x} = -3$. This equation has no real solution, however, you obtain $x = 9$ after squaring each side.

Raising each side of an equation to the same exponent may introduce solutions that are *not* solutions of the original equation. These solutions are called **extraneous solutions**. When you use this procedure, you should always check each apparent solution in the *original* equation.

EXAMPLE 3 Solving an Equation with an Extraneous Solution

Solve $x + 1 = \sqrt{7x + 15}$.

SOLUTION

$x + 1 = \sqrt{7x + 15}$	Write the equation.
$(x + 1)^2 = \left(\sqrt{7x + 15}\right)^2$	Square each side.
$x^2 + 2x + 1 = 7x + 15$	Expand left side and simplify right side.
$x^2 - 5x - 14 = 0$	Write in standard form.
$(x - 7)(x + 2) = 0$	Factor.
$x - 7 = 0$ or $x + 2 = 0$	Zero-Product Property
$x = 7$ or $x = -2$	Solve for x.

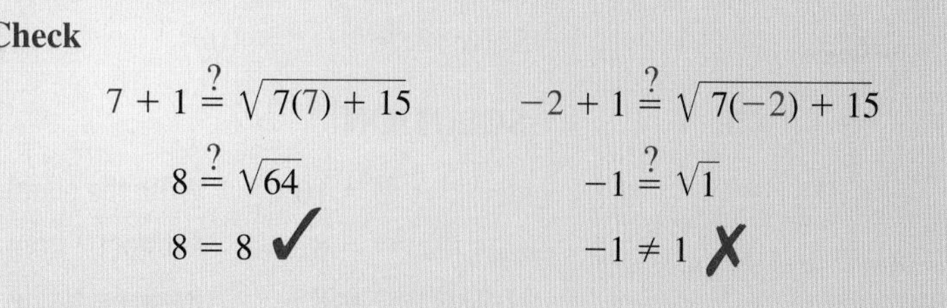

Check

$7 + 1 \stackrel{?}{=} \sqrt{7(7) + 15}$ $\qquad$ $-2 + 1 \stackrel{?}{=} \sqrt{7(-2) + 15}$

$8 \stackrel{?}{=} \sqrt{64}$ $\qquad$ $-1 \stackrel{?}{=} \sqrt{1}$

$8 = 8$ ✓ $\qquad$ $-1 \neq 1$ ✗

▶ The apparent solution $x = -2$ is extraneous. So, the only solution is $x = 7$.

EXAMPLE 4 Solving an Equation with Two Radicals

Solve $\sqrt{x+2} + 1 = \sqrt{3-x}$.

SOLUTION

$\sqrt{x+2} + 1 = \sqrt{3-x}$	Write the equation.
$\left(\sqrt{x+2} + 1\right)^2 = \left(\sqrt{3-x}\right)^2$	Square each side.
$x + 2 + 2\sqrt{x+2} + 1 = 3 - x$	Expand left side and simplify right side.
$2\sqrt{x+2} = -2x$	Isolate radical expression.
$\sqrt{x+2} = -x$	Divide each side by 2.
$\left(\sqrt{x+2}\right)^2 = (-x)^2$	Square each side.
$x + 2 = x^2$	Simplify.
$0 = x^2 - x - 2$	Write in standard form.
$0 = (x-2)(x+1)$	Factor.
$x - 2 = 0$ or $x + 1 = 0$	Zero-Product Property
$x = 2$ or $x = -1$	Solve for x.

ANOTHER WAY

You can also graph each side of the equation and find the x-value where the graphs intersect.

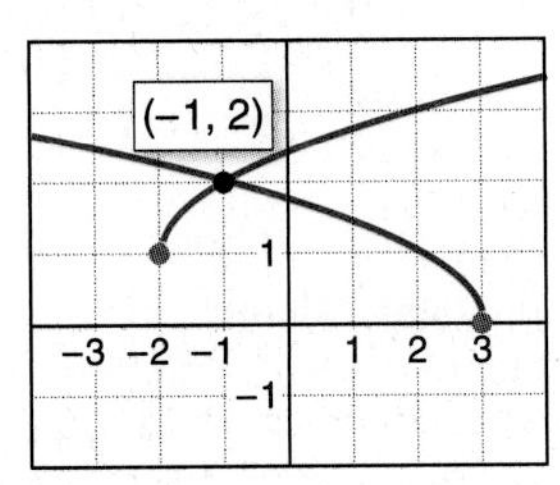

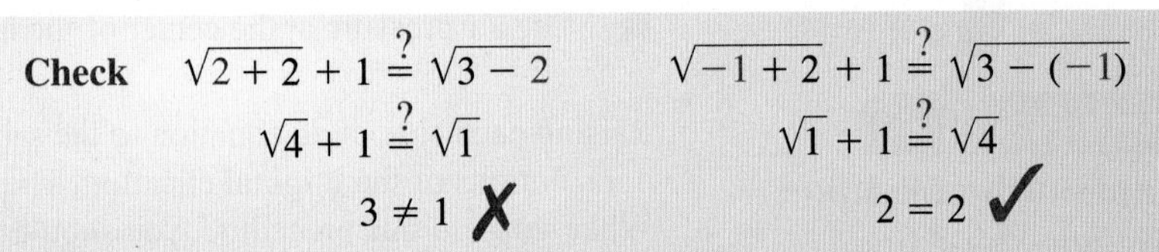

Check $\sqrt{2+2} + 1 \stackrel{?}{=} \sqrt{3-2}$ $\qquad$ $\sqrt{-1+2} + 1 \stackrel{?}{=} \sqrt{3-(-1)}$

$\sqrt{4} + 1 \stackrel{?}{=} \sqrt{1}$ $\qquad$ $\sqrt{1} + 1 \stackrel{?}{=} \sqrt{4}$

$3 \neq 1$ ✗ $\qquad$ $2 = 2$ ✓

▶ The apparent solution $x = 2$ is extraneous. So, the only solution is $x = -1$.

SELF-ASSESSMENT

1 I do not understand. 2 I can do it with help. 3 I can do it on my own. 4 I can teach someone else.

5. **WHAT IF?** In Example 2, estimate the air pressure at the center of the hurricane when the mean sustained wind velocity is 48.3 meters per second.

Solve the equation. Check your solution(s).

6. $\sqrt{10x + 9} = x + 3$

7. $\sqrt{2x+5} = \sqrt{x+7}$

8. $\sqrt{x+6} - 2 = \sqrt{x-2}$

When an equation contains a power with a rational exponent, you can solve the equation using a procedure similar to the one for solving radical equations. In this case, first isolate the power and then raise each side of the equation to the reciprocal of the rational exponent.

EXAMPLE 5 Solving an Equation with a Rational Exponent

Solve $(2x)^{3/4} + 2 = 10$.

SOLUTION

$(2x)^{3/4} + 2 = 10$	Write the equation.
$(2x)^{3/4} = 8$	Subtract 2 from each side.
$[(2x)^{3/4}]^{4/3} = 8^{4/3}$	Raise each side to the four-thirds.
$2x = 16$	Simplify.
$x = 8$	Divide each side by 2.

▶ The solution is $x = 8$.

Check

$(2 \cdot 8)^{3/4} + 2 \stackrel{?}{=} 10$

$16^{3/4} + 2 \stackrel{?}{=} 10$

$10 = 10$ ✓

EXAMPLE 6 Solving an Equation with a Rational Exponent

Solve $(x + 30)^{1/2} = x$.

SOLUTION

$(x + 30)^{1/2} = x$	Write the equation.
$[(x + 30)^{1/2}]^2 = x^2$	Square each side.
$x + 30 = x^2$	Simplify.
$0 = x^2 - x - 30$	Write in standard form.
$0 = (x - 6)(x + 5)$	Factor.
$x - 6 = 0$ or $x + 5 = 0$	Zero-Product Property
$x = 6$ or $x = -5$	Solve for x.

▶ The apparent solution $x = -5$ is extraneous. So, the only solution is $x = 6$.

Check

$(6 + 30)^{1/2} \stackrel{?}{=} 6$

$36^{1/2} \stackrel{?}{=} 6$

$6 = 6$ ✓

$(-5 + 30)^{1/2} \stackrel{?}{=} -5$

$25^{1/2} \stackrel{?}{=} -5$

$5 \neq -5$ ✗

Solving Radical Inequalities

To solve a simple radical inequality of the form $\sqrt[n]{u} < d$, where u is an algebraic expression and d is a nonnegative number, raise each side to the exponent n. This procedure also works for $>$, $\leq$, and $\geq$. Be sure to consider the possible values of the radicand.

EXAMPLE 7 Solving a Radical Inequality

Solve $3\sqrt{x - 1} \leq 12$.

SOLUTION

Step 1 Solve for x.

$3\sqrt{x - 1} \leq 12$	Write the inequality.
$\sqrt{x - 1} \leq 4$	Divide each side by 3.
$x - 1 \leq 16$	Square each side.
$x \leq 17$	Add 1 to each side.

Step 2 Consider the radicand.

$x - 1 \geq 0$	The radicand cannot be negative.
$x \geq 1$	Add 1 to each side.

▶ So, the solution is $1 \leq x \leq 17$.

Check

The graph of $y = 3\sqrt{x - 1}$ is on or below the graph of $y = 12$ when $1 \leq x \leq 17$.

y = 12
(17, 12)
y = 3√(x − 1)

SELF-ASSESSMENT

1 I do not understand. 2 I can do it with help. 3 I can do it on my own. 4 I can teach someone else.

Solve the equation. Check your solution(s).

9. $(3x)^{1/3} = -3$

10. $(x + 20)^{1/2} = x$

11. $(x + 2)^{3/4} = 8$

Solve the inequality.

12. $2\sqrt{x} - 3 \geq 3$

13. $4\sqrt[3]{x + 1} < 8$

14. $\frac{1}{2}\sqrt{6 - x} \leq 5$

15. MP **REASONING** How does changing 8 to -8 change the solution in Exercise 13? cut.

5.4 Practice WITH CalcChat® AND CalcView®

In Exercises 1–10, solve the equation. Check your solution. *Example 1*

1. $\sqrt{5x+1} = 6$
2. $\sqrt{3x+10} = 8$
3. $\sqrt[3]{x-16} = 2$
4. $\sqrt[3]{x} - 10 = -7$
5. $-2\sqrt{24x} + 13 = -11$
6. $\sqrt{2x} - \frac{2}{3} = 0$
7. $8\sqrt[3]{10x} - 15 = 17$
8. $\frac{1}{5}\sqrt[3]{3x} + 10 = 8$
9. $2\sqrt[5]{x} + 7 = 15$
10. $\sqrt[4]{4x} - 13 = -15$

11. **MODELING REAL LIFE** The maximum speed v (in meters per second) of a trapeze artist is represented by $v = \sqrt{2gh}$, where g is the acceleration due to gravity ($g \approx 9.8$ m/sec^2) and h is the height (in meters) of the swing path. Find the height of the swing path for a performer whose maximum speed is 7 meters per second. *Example 2*

12. **MODELING REAL LIFE** The shoulder height h (in centimeters) of a male Asian elephant can be modeled by $h = 62.5\sqrt[3]{t} + 75.8$, where t is the age (in years) of the elephant. Determine the age of an elephant with a shoulder height of 250 centimeters.

In Exercises 13–22, solve the equation. Check your solution(s). *Examples 3 and 4*

13. $x - 6 = \sqrt{3x}$
14. $x - 10 = \sqrt{9x}$
15. $\sqrt{44-2x} = x - 10$
16. $\sqrt{2x+30} = x + 3$
17. $\sqrt[3]{2x^3-1} = x$
18. $\sqrt[3]{3-8x^2} = 2x$
19. $\sqrt{4x+1} = \sqrt{x+10}$
20. $\sqrt{3x-3} = \sqrt{x+12}$
21. $\sqrt[3]{2x-5} - \sqrt[3]{8x+1} = 0$
22. $\sqrt[3]{x+5} - 2\sqrt[3]{2x+6} = 0$

In Exercises 23–30, solve the equation. Check your solution(s). *Examples 5 and 6*

23. $2x^{2/3} = 8$
24. $4x^{3/2} = 32$
25. $x^{1/4} + 3 = 0$
26. $2x^{3/4} - 14 = 40$
27. $(x+6)^{1/2} = x$
28. $(5-x)^{1/2} - 2x = 0$
29. $2(x+11)^{1/2} = x + 3$
30. $(5x^2-4)^{1/4} = x$

ERROR ANALYSIS In Exercises 31 and 32, describe and correct the error in solving the equation.

31.
✗
$$\sqrt[3]{3x-8} = 4$$
$$\left(\sqrt[3]{3x-8}\right)^3 = 4$$
$$3x - 8 = 4$$
$$3x = 12$$
$$x = 4$$

32.
✗
$$8x^{3/2} = 1000$$
$$8(x^{3/2})^{2/3} = 1000^{2/3}$$
$$8x = 100$$
$$x = \frac{25}{2}$$

In Exercises 33–40, solve the inequality. *Example 7*

33. $4\sqrt{x} - 2 > 18$
34. $7\sqrt{x} + 1 < 9$
35. $\sqrt[3]{x-5} \ge 3$
36. $\sqrt[3]{x-4} \le 5$
37. $4\sqrt[3]{x+7} \ge 8$
38. $-2\sqrt[3]{x+4} < 12$
39. $2\sqrt{x} + 3 \le 8$
40. $-0.25\sqrt{x} - 6 \le -3$

41. **MODELING REAL LIFE** The least possible frequency of a string is its *fundamental frequency*. The fundamental frequency n (in hertz) of a certain string on a violin is represented by $n = \sqrt{\frac{T}{0.0054}}$, where T is the tension (in newtons). The fundamental frequency of the string is 196 hertz. What is the tension of the string?

42. **MP REASONING** A company finds that the function $p = 70 - \sqrt{0.02x+1}$ relates the price p of an item and the number x of units demanded per day. Explain how changing the price affects the number of units demanded.

MP USING TOOLS In Exercises 43–46, solve the nonlinear system. Justify your answer with a graph.

43. $y = \sqrt{x - 3}$
$y = x - 3$

44. $y = \sqrt{4x + 17}$
$y = x + 5$

45. $y = \pm\sqrt{-x^2 + 1}$
$y = \frac{1}{2}x^2 - 1$

46. $x^2 + y^2 = 4$
$y = \pm\sqrt{x + 2}$

47. **MP PROBLEM SOLVING** The speed s (in miles per hour) of a car is given by $s = \sqrt{30fd}$, where f is the coefficient of friction and d is the stopping distance (in feet). The table shows the coefficient of friction for different surfaces.

Surface	Coefficient of friction, f
dry asphalt	0.75
wet asphalt	0.60
snow	0.30
ice	0.15

a. Compare the stopping distances of a car traveling 45 miles per hour on the surfaces given in the table.

b. You are driving 35 miles per hour on an icy road when a deer jumps in front of your car. How far away must you begin to brake to avoid hitting the deer? Justify your answer.

48. **MODELING REAL LIFE** The Beaufort wind scale was devised to measure wind speed. The Beaufort numbers B, which range from 0 to 12, can be modeled by $B = 1.69\sqrt{s + 4.25} - 3.55$, where s is the wind speed (in miles per hour).

Beaufort number	Force of wind
0	calm
3	gentle breeze
6	strong breeze
9	strong gale
12	hurricane

a. What is the wind speed for $B = 0$? $B = 3$?

b. Write an inequality that describes the range of wind speeds represented by the Beaufort model.

49. **MP STRUCTURE** Without performing any calculations, explain how you know that the radical equation $\sqrt{x + 4} = -5$ has no real solution.

50. **HOW DO YOU SEE IT?**
Use the graph to find the solution of the equation $2\sqrt{x - 4} = -\sqrt{x - 1} + 4$. Justify your answer.

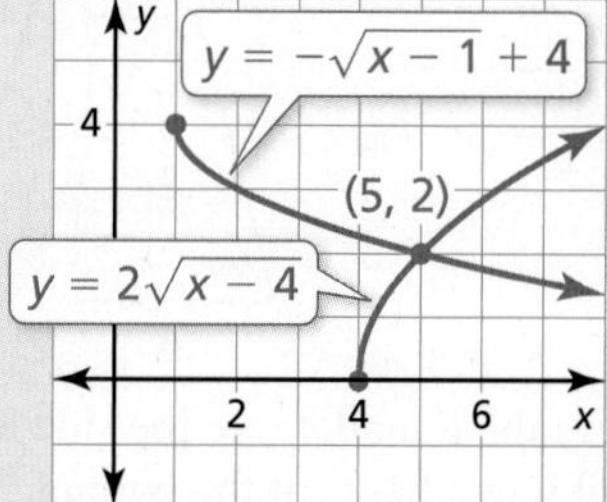

51. **MODELING REAL LIFE** The Moeraki Boulders are stone spheres along the coast of New Zealand. A formula for the radius of a sphere is $r = \frac{1}{2}\sqrt{\frac{S}{\pi}}$ where S is the surface area of the sphere. Find the surface area of a Moeraki Boulder with a radius of 3 feet.

52. **DRAWING CONCLUSIONS** "Hang time" is the time you are suspended in the air during a jump. Your hang time t (in seconds) is given by the function $t = 0.5\sqrt{h}$, where h is the height (in feet) of the jump. Suppose a wallaby and a skier jump with the hang times shown.

a. Find the heights that the wallaby and the skier jump.

b. If the hang time doubles, does the height of the jump double? Justify your answer.

53. **MAKING AN ARGUMENT** Is it possible for a radical equation to have two extraneous solutions? Justify your answer.

54. **THOUGHT PROVOKING**
City officials rope off a circular area to prepare for a concert in a park. They estimate that each person occupies 6 square feet. Describe how you can use a radical inequality to determine the possible radius of the region when P people are expected to attend the concert.

55. MP PROBLEM SOLVING The height h and slant height ℓ of a truncated square pyramid are related by the formula shown.

$$\ell = \sqrt{h^2 + \frac{1}{4}(b_2 - b_1)^2}$$

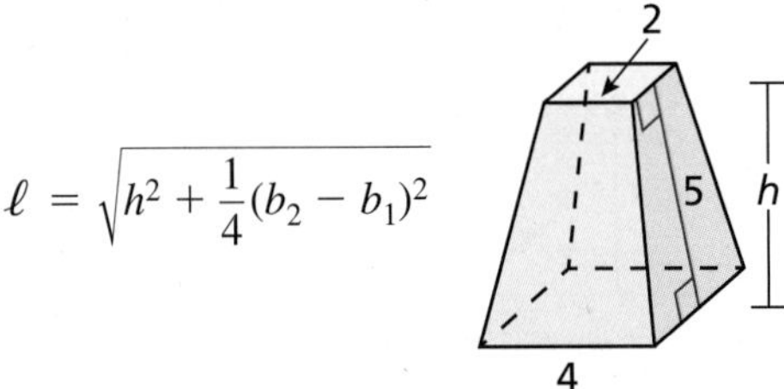

In the given formula, b_1 and b_2 are the side lengths of the upper and lower bases of the pyramid, respectively. What is the height of the truncated square pyramid shown?

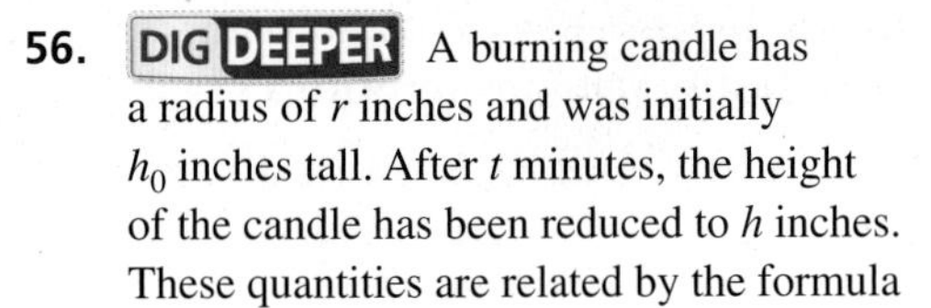

56. DIG DEEPER A burning candle has a radius of r inches and was initially h_0 inches tall. After t minutes, the height of the candle has been reduced to h inches. These quantities are related by the formula

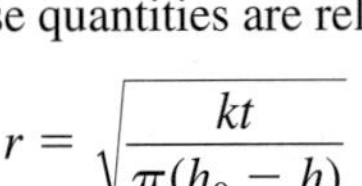

$$r = \sqrt{\frac{kt}{\pi(h_0 - h)}}$$

where k is a constant. Suppose the radius of a candle is 0.875 inch, its initial height is 6.5 inches, and $k = 0.04$.

a. Rewrite the formula, solving for h in terms of t.

b. Use your formula in part (a) to determine the height of the candle after it burns for 45 minutes.

GO DIGITAL

REVIEW & REFRESH

In Exercises 57–60, perform the operation.

57. $(x^3 - 2x^2 + 3x + 1) + (x^4 - 7x)$

58. $(2x^5 + x^4 - 4x^2) - (x^5 - 3)$

59. $(x^3 + 2x^2 + 1)(x^2 + 5)$

60. $(x^4 + 2x^3 + 11x^2 + 14x - 16) \div (x + 2)$

In Exercises 61 and 62, write a rule for g.

61.

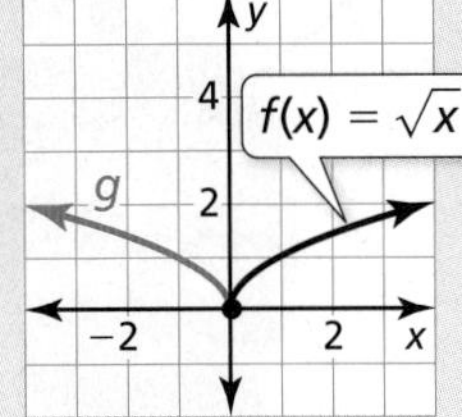

62.

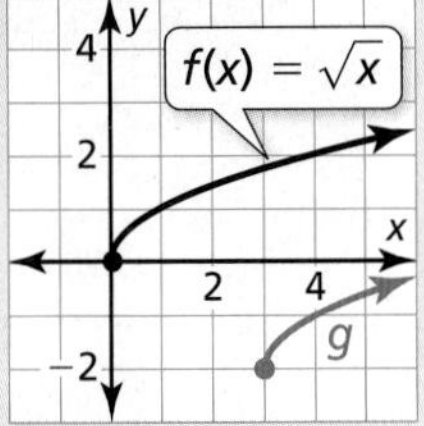

In Exercises 63–66, simplify the expression.

63. $\sqrt[3]{64p^9}$

64. $\sqrt[4]{81m^4n^8}$

65. $\sqrt[4]{\frac{y^{16}}{z^4}}$

66. $\sqrt[7]{\frac{g^5k^{17}}{g^{-2}k^3}}$

67. MP REASONING The graph of f is a parabola with axis of symmetry $x = -3$ that passes through the point $(-7, 12)$. Solve $f(x) = 12$. Explain your reasoning.

In Exercises 68–71, let $f(x) = x^3 - 4x^2 + 6$. Write a rule for g. Describe the graph of g as a transformation of the graph of f.

68. $g(x) = f(-x) + 4$

69. $g(x) = \frac{1}{2}f(x) - 3$

70. $g(x) = -f(x - 1)$

71. $g(x) = f\left(\frac{1}{4}x\right) + 5$

In Exercises 72–75, solve the inequality.

72. $6\sqrt{x - 1} \leq 18$

73. $4\sqrt[3]{x} + 7 > 23$

74. $-\sqrt[3]{x} + 6 < 11$

75. $-4\sqrt{x - 1} \geq -3$

76. MODELING REAL LIFE Some countries use the Fujita scale to describe the potential damage inflicted by tornados. The number for the rating on the scale can be found using the equation $y = \left(\frac{w}{14.1}\right)^{2/3} - 2$, where w is the wind speed (in miles per hour). What is the rating for a tornado with wind speeds of 200 miles per hour?

y	Rating
$y < 1$	F0
$1 \leq y < 2$	F1
$2 \leq y < 3$	F2
$3 \leq y < 4$	F3
$4 \leq y < 5$	F4
$5 \leq y$	F5

In Exercises 77–80, solve the equation by completing the square.

77. $x^2 - 8x = 6$

78. $2x^2 + 4x = 16$

79. $x^2 + 4x + 11 = 0$

80. $-x^2 + 3x + 1 = 4$

81. Solve the system using any method. Explain your choice of method.

$$3x - y + 4z = 14$$
$$-x - 2y + 3z = 25$$
$$-5x + 3y - 2z = 24$$

5.5 Performing Function Operations

Learning Target Perform arithmetic operations on two functions.

Success Criteria
- I can explain what it means to perform an arithmetic operation on two functions.
- I can find arithmetic combinations of two functions.
- I can state the domain of an arithmetic combination of two functions.
- I can evaluate an arithmetic combination of two functions for a given input.

Just as two real numbers can be combined by the operations of addition, subtraction, multiplication, and division to form other real numbers, two functions can be combined to form other functions.

EXPLORE IT! Graphing Arithmetic Combinations of Two Functions

Work with a partner. Consider the graphs of f and g.

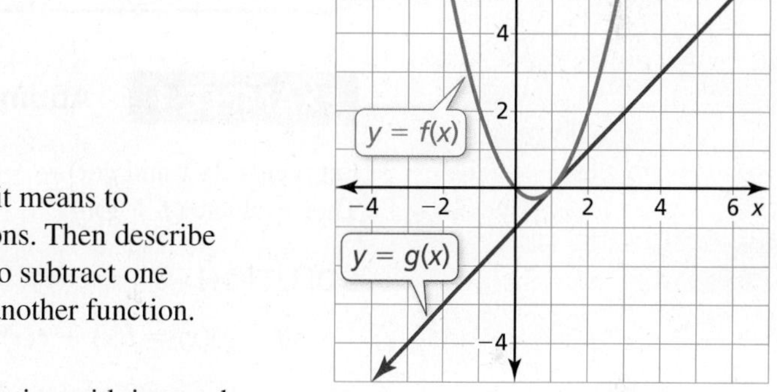

Math Practice

Use a Table
How can you use a table to organize your work in part (b)?

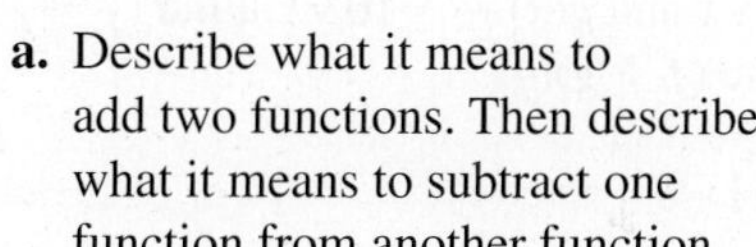

a. Describe what it means to add two functions. Then describe what it means to subtract one function from another function.

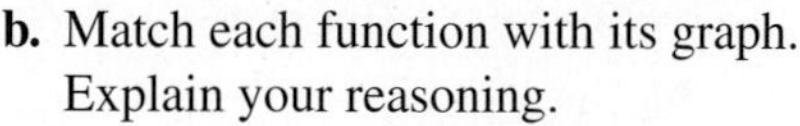

b. Match each function with its graph. Explain your reasoning.

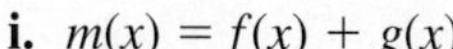

i. $m(x) = f(x) + g(x)$

ii. $n(x) = f(x) - g(x)$

iii. $p(x) = f(x) \cdot g(x)$

iv. $q(x) = f(x) \div g(x)$

A. 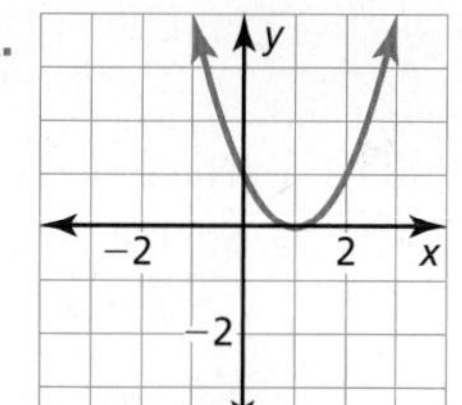

B. 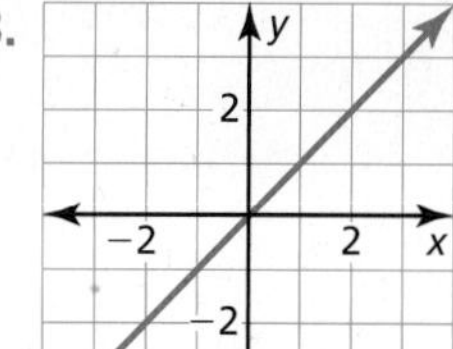

C. 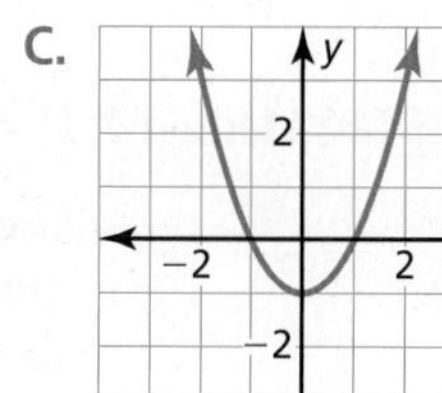

D. 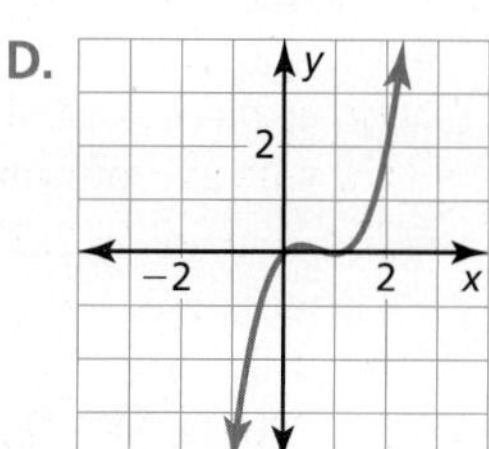

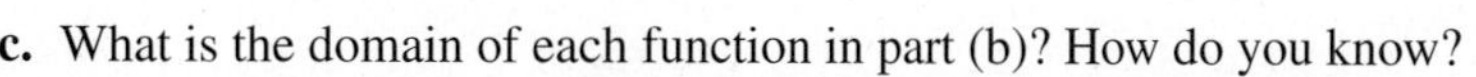

c. What is the domain of each function in part (b)? How do you know?

d. Check your answers in part (b) by writing function rules for f and g, performing each arithmetic combination, and graphing the results.

Operations on Functions

You have learned how to add, subtract, multiply, and divide polynomial expressions. These operations are also defined for functions.

KEY IDEA

Operations on Functions

Let f and g be any two functions. A new function can be defined by performing any of the four basic operations on f and g.

Operation	Definition	Example: $f(x) = 5x$, $g(x) = x + 2$
Addition	$(f + g)(x) = f(x) + g(x)$	$(f + g)(x) = 5x + (x + 2) = 6x + 2$
Subtraction	$(f - g)(x) = f(x) - g(x)$	$(f - g)(x) = 5x - (x + 2) = 4x - 2$
Multiplication	$(fg)(x) = f(x) \cdot g(x)$	$(fg)(x) = 5x(x + 2) = 5x^2 + 10x$
Division	$\left(\frac{f}{g}\right)(x) = \frac{f(x)}{g(x)}$	$\left(\frac{f}{g}\right)(x) = \frac{5x}{x + 2}$

The domains of the sum, difference, product, and quotient functions consist of the x-values that are in the domains of both f and g. Additionally, the domain of the quotient does not include x-values for which $g(x) = 0$.

EXAMPLE 1 Adding Two Functions

Let $f(x) = 3\sqrt{x}$ and $g(x) = -10\sqrt{x}$. Find $(f + g)(x)$ and state the domain. Then evaluate $(f + g)(4)$.

SOLUTION

$$(f + g)(x) = f(x) + g(x) \quad \text{Definition of function addition}$$
$$= 3\sqrt{x} + (-10\sqrt{x}) \quad \text{Write sum of } f(x) \text{ and } g(x).$$
$$= (3 - 10)\sqrt{x} \quad \text{Distributive Property}$$
$$= -7\sqrt{x} \quad \text{Subtract.}$$

The functions f and g each have the same domain: all nonnegative real numbers. So, the domain of $f + g$ also consists of all nonnegative real numbers. To evaluate $f + g$ when $x = 4$, you can use several methods. Here are two:

Method 1 Use an algebraic approach.

$$(f + g)(4) = -7\sqrt{4} = -14$$

Method 2 Use a graphical approach.

Use technology to graph the sum of the functions. The graph shows that $(f + g)(4) = -14$.

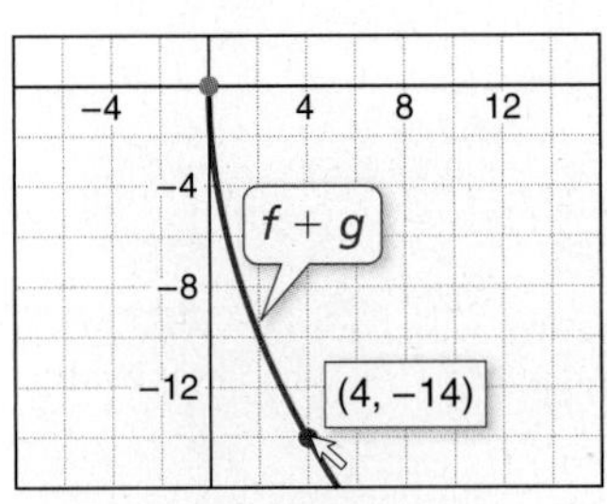

EXAMPLE 2 Subtracting Two Functions

Let $f(x) = 3x^3 - 2x^2 + 5$ and $g(x) = x^3 - 3x^2 + 4x - 2$. Find $(f - g)(x)$ and state the domain. Then evaluate $(f - g)(-2)$.

SOLUTION

$$\begin{aligned}(f - g)(x) &= f(x) - g(x)\\ &= 3x^3 - 2x^2 + 5 - (x^3 - 3x^2 + 4x - 2)\\ &= 2x^3 + x^2 - 4x + 7\end{aligned}$$

The functions f and g each have the same domain: all real numbers. So, the domain of $f - g$ also consists of all real numbers.

$$(f - g)(-2) = 2(-2)^3 + (-2)^2 - 4(-2) + 7 = 3$$

EXAMPLE 3 Multiplying Two Functions

Let $f(x) = x^2$ and $g(x) = \sqrt{x}$. Find $(fg)(x)$ and state the domain. Then evaluate $(fg)(9)$.

SOLUTION

$$(fg)(x) = f(x) \cdot g(x) = x^2(\sqrt{x}) = x^2(x^{1/2}) = x^{(2 + 1/2)} = x^{5/2}$$

The domain of f consists of all real numbers, and the domain of g consists of all nonnegative real numbers. So, the domain of fg consists of all nonnegative real numbers.

$$(fg)(9) = 9^{5/2} = (9^{1/2})^5 = 3^5 = 243$$

Check

The domain of fg is all nonnegative real numbers.

EXAMPLE 4 Dividing Two Functions

WATCH

Let $f(x) = 6x$ and $g(x) = x^{3/4}$. Find $\left(\frac{f}{g}\right)(x)$ and state the domain. Then evaluate $\left(\frac{f}{g}\right)(16)$.

SOLUTION

$$\left(\frac{f}{g}\right)(x) = \frac{f(x)}{g(x)} = \frac{6x}{x^{3/4}} = 6x^{(1 - 3/4)} = 6x^{1/4}$$

The domain of f consists of all real numbers, the domain of g consists of all nonnegative real numbers, and $g(0) = 0$. So, the domain of $\frac{f}{g}$ is restricted to all *positive* real numbers.

$$\left(\frac{f}{g}\right)(16) = 6(16)^{1/4} = 6(2^4)^{1/4} = 12$$

ANOTHER WAY

In Example 4, you can also evaluate $\left(\frac{f}{g}\right)(16)$ as

$$\begin{aligned}\left(\frac{f}{g}\right)(16) &= \frac{f(16)}{g(16)}\\ &= \frac{6(16)}{(16)^{3/4}}\\ &= \frac{96}{8}\\ &= 12.\end{aligned}$$

SELF-ASSESSMENT

1 I do not understand. 2 I can do it with help. 3 I can do it on my own. 4 I can teach someone else.

1. Let $f(x) = -2x^{2/3}$ and $g(x) = 7x^{2/3}$. Find $(f + g)(x)$ and $(f - g)(x)$ and state the domain of each. Then evaluate $(f + g)(8)$ and $(f - g)(8)$.

2. Let $f(x) = 3x$ and $g(x) = x^{1/5}$. Find $(fg)(x)$ and $\left(\frac{f}{g}\right)(x)$ and state the domain of each. Then evaluate $(fg)(32)$ and $\left(\frac{f}{g}\right)(32)$.

$f(x) = \sqrt{x}$
$g(x) = \sqrt{9 - x^2}$
$f(2) + g(2)$
$= 3.65028153987$
$f(2) - g(2)$
$= -0.821854415127$
$f(2) \cdot g(2)$
$= 3.16227766017$
$\dfrac{f(2)}{g(2)}$
$= 0.632455532034$

EXAMPLE 5 Performing Function Operations Using Technology

Let $f(x) = \sqrt{x}$ and $g(x) = \sqrt{9 - x^2}$. Use technology to evaluate $(f + g)(x)$, $(f - g)(x)$, $(fg)(x)$, and $\left(\dfrac{f}{g}\right)(x)$ when $x = 2$. Round your answers to two decimal places.

SOLUTION

Enter f and g. From the screen, you can see that $f(2) + g(2) \approx 3.65$, so $(f + g)(2) \approx 3.65$. Similarly,

$$(f - g)(2) \approx -0.82, (fg)(2) \approx 3.16, \text{ and } \left(\frac{f}{g}\right)(2) \approx 0.63.$$

EXAMPLE 6 Modeling Real Life

For a white rhino, heart rate (in beats per minute) and life span (in minutes) are related to body mass m (in kilograms) by the following functions.

Heart rate: $r(m) = 241m^{-0.25}$

Life span: $s(m) = (6 \times 10^6)m^{0.2}$

Find $(rs)(m)$ and explain what it represents.

SOLUTION

$(rs)(m) = r(m) \cdot s(m)$	Definition of function multiplication
$= 241m^{-0.25}[(6 \times 10^6)m^{0.2}]$	Write product of $r(m)$ and $s(m)$.
$= 241(6 \times 10^6)m^{-0.25 + 0.2}$	Product of Powers Property
$= (1446 \times 10^6)m^{-0.05}$	Simplify.
$= (1.446 \times 10^9)m^{-0.05}$	Use scientific notation.

▶ So, $(rs)(m) = (1.446 \times 10^9)m^{-0.05}$. Multiplying heart rate by life span gives the total number of heartbeats over the lifetime of a white rhino with body mass m.

SELF-ASSESSMENT

1 I do not understand. 2 I can do it with help. 3 I can do it on my own. 4 I can teach someone else.

3. Let $f(x) = 8x$ and $g(x) = 2x^{5/6}$. Use technology to evaluate $(f + g)(x)$, $(f - g)(x)$, $(fg)(x)$, and $\left(\dfrac{f}{g}\right)(x)$ when $x = 5$. Round your answers to two decimal places.

4. **WRITING** In Example 5, explain why you can evaluate $(f + g)(3)$, $(f - g)(3)$, and $(fg)(3)$ but not $\left(\dfrac{f}{g}\right)(3)$.

5. Use the answer in Example 6 to find the total number of heartbeats over the lifetime of a white rhino when its body mass is 1.7×10^5 kilograms.

6. The cost (in dollars) to rent a scooter for x minutes in City A is represented by $A(x) = 0.15x + 1$. The cost (in dollars) in City B is represented by $B(x) = 0.29x + 1$. Find $(B - A)(x)$ and explain what it represents.

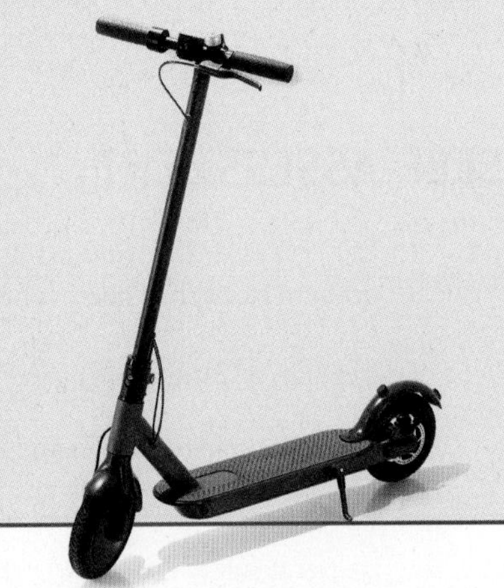

5.5 Practice WITH CalcChat® AND CalcView®

In Exercises 1–4, find $(f + g)(x)$ and $(f - g)(x)$ and state the domain of each. Then evaluate $f + g$ and $f - g$ for the given value of x. *Examples 1 and 2*

1. $f(x) = -5\sqrt[4]{x}$, $g(x) = 19\sqrt[4]{x}$; $x = 16$

2. $f(x) = \sqrt[3]{2x}$, $g(x) = -11\sqrt[3]{2x}$; $x = -4$

3. $f(x) = 6x - 4x^2 - 7x^3$, $g(x) = 9x^2 - 5x$; $x = -1$

4. $f(x) = 11x + 2x^2$, $g(x) = -7x - 3x^2 + 4$; $x = 2$

In Exercises 5–10, find $(fg)(x)$ and $\left(\frac{f}{g}\right)(x)$ and state the domain of each. Then evaluate fg and $\frac{f}{g}$ for the given value of x. *Examples 3 and 4*

5. $f(x) = 2x^3$, $g(x) = \sqrt[3]{x}$; $x = -27$

6. $f(x) = x^4$, $g(x) = 3\sqrt{x}$; $x = 4$

7. $f(x) = 4x$, $g(x) = 9x^{1/2}$; $x = 9$

8. $f(x) = 11x^3$, $g(x) = 7x^{7/3}$; $x = -8$

9. $f(x) = 7x^{3/2}$, $g(x) = -14x^{1/3}$; $x = 64$

10. $f(x) = 4x^{5/4}$, $g(x) = 2x^{1/2}$; $x = 16$

MP USING TOOLS In Exercises 11–14, use technology to evaluate $(f + g)(x)$, $(f - g)(x)$, $(fg)(x)$, and $\left(\frac{f}{g}\right)(x)$ when $x = 5$. Round your answers to two decimal places. *Example 5*

11. $f(x) = 4x^4$; $g(x) = 24x^{1/3}$

12. $f(x) = 7x^{5/3}$; $g(x) = 49x^{2/3}$

13. $f(x) = -2x^{1/3}$; $g(x) = 5x^{1/2}$

14. $f(x) = 4x^{1/2}$; $g(x) = 6x^{3/4}$

ERROR ANALYSIS In Exercises 15 and 16, describe and correct the error in stating the domain.

15.

$f(x) = x^3$ and $g(x) = x^2 - 4$

The domain of $\left(\frac{f}{g}\right)(x) = \frac{x^3}{x^2 - 4}$ is all real numbers except $x = 2$.

16.

$f(x) = x^{1/2}$ and $g(x) = x^{3/2}$

The domain of $(fg)(x) = x^2$ is all real numbers.

17. **MODELING REAL LIFE** Over a period of 8 years, the numbers (in millions) of female and male employees in the United States over the age of 16 can be modeled by $F(t) = 0.0134t^3 - 0.160t^2 + 0.98t + 72.9$ and $M(t) = 0.0093t^3 - 0.078t^2 + 0.58t + 82.3$, where t is the number of years since 2010. *Example 6*

    a. Find $(F + M)(t)$.

    b. Explain what $(F + M)(t)$ represents.

18. **MODELING REAL LIFE** For a mammal that weighs w grams, the volume b (in milliliters) of air breathed in and the volume d (in milliliters) of "dead space" (the portion of the lungs not filled with air) can be modeled by

$$b(w) = 0.007w \text{ and } d(w) = 0.002w.$$

The breathing rate r (in breaths per minute) of a mammal that weighs w grams can be modeled by

$$r(w) = \frac{1.1w^{0.734}}{b(w) - d(w)}.$$

Simplify $r(w)$ and calculate the breathing rate for body weights of 6.5 grams, 300 grams, and 70,000 grams.

19. **MAKING AN ARGUMENT** Is the addition of functions commutative? the multiplication of functions? Explain your reasoning.

20. **HOW DO YOU SEE IT?** The graphs of the functions $f(x) = 3x^2 - 2x - 1$ and $g(x) = 3x + 4$ are shown. Which graph represents the function $f + g$? the function $f - g$? Explain.

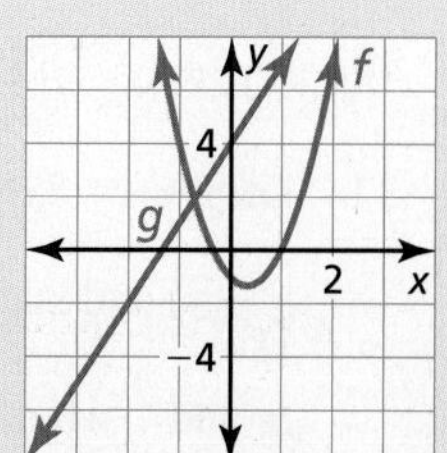

A.
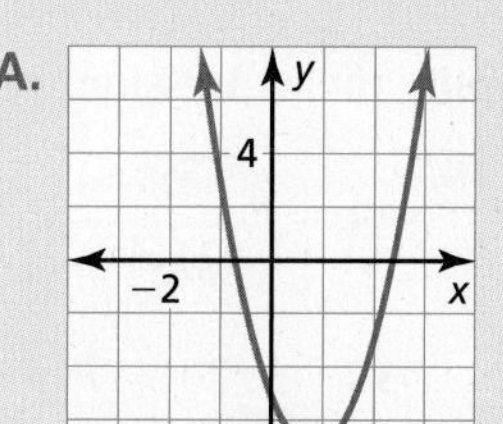

B.
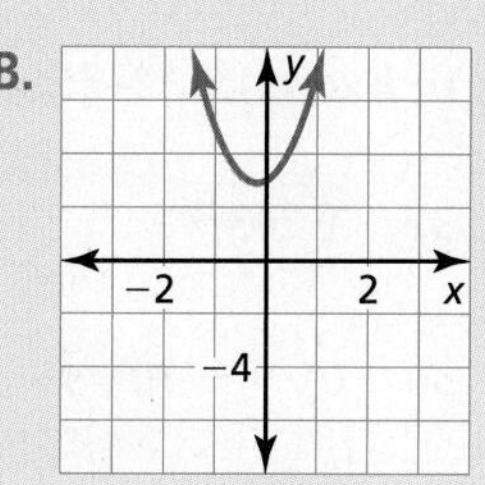

21. **MP REASONING** The table shows the outputs of the two functions f and g. Use the table to find each value.

x	0	1	2	3	4
$f(x)$	-2	-4	0	10	26
$g(x)$	-1	-3	-13	-31	-57

a. $(f + g)(3)$ **b.** $(f - g)(1)$

c. $(fg)(2)$ **d.** $\left(\frac{f}{g}\right)(0)$

22. THOUGHT PROVOKING
Is it possible to write two functions whose sum contains radicals, but whose product does not? Justify your answers.

23. **DIG DEEPER** For the functions f and g, $(f + g)(-1) = 4$ and $\left(\frac{f}{g}\right)(-1) = -\frac{3}{2}$. Find $f(-1)$ and $g(-1)$.

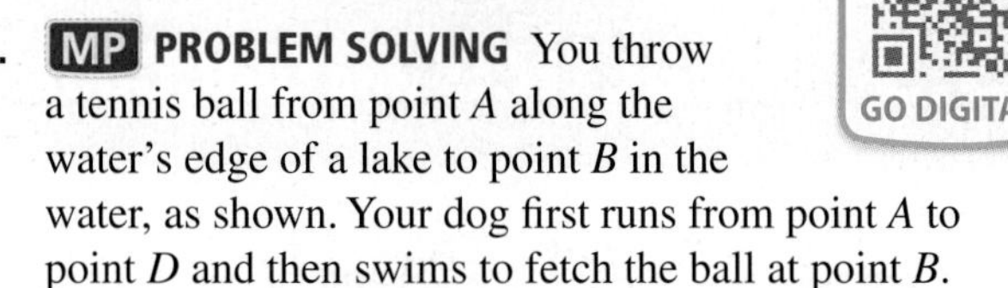

24. **MP PROBLEM SOLVING** You throw a tennis ball from point A along the water's edge of a lake to point B in the water, as shown. Your dog first runs from point A to point D and then swims to fetch the ball at point B.

GO DIGITAL

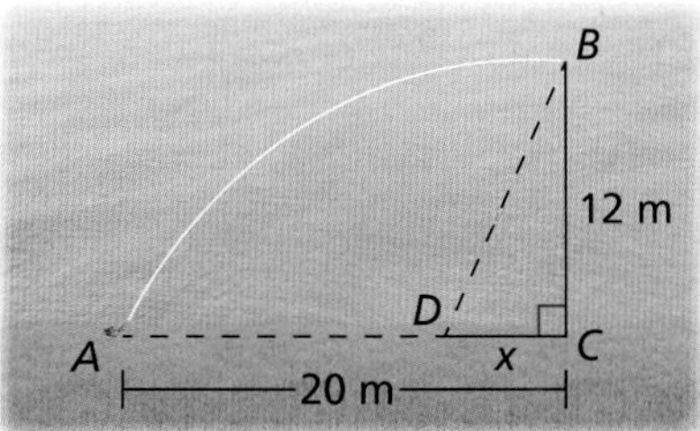

a. Your dog runs at a speed of about 6.4 meters per second and swims at a speed of about 0.9 meter per second. Write a function r in terms of x that represents the time he spends running. Write a function s in terms of x that represents the time he spends swimming.

b. Write a function t in terms of x that represents how long it takes your dog to reach the ball.

c. Use technology to graph t. Find the value of x that minimizes t. Explain the meaning of this value.

REVIEW & REFRESH

WATCH

In Exercises 25 and 26, solve the equation.

25. $3\sqrt{2x} - 5 = 9$ **26.** $\sqrt{-x - 3} = x + 5$

In Exercises 27 and 28, solve the literal equation for n.

27. $3xn - 9 = 6y$ **28.** $\frac{3 + 4n}{n} = 7b$

In Exercises 29 and 30, determine whether the relation is a function. Explain.

29. $(1, 6), (7, -3), (4, 0), (3, 0)$

30. $(3, 8), (2, 5), (9, 5), (2, -3)$

31. Let $f(x) = 8x^3$ and $g(x) = -2x^{3/2}$. Find $(fg)(x)$ and $\left(\frac{f}{g}\right)(x)$ and state the domain of each. Then evaluate fg and $\frac{f}{g}$ when $x = 4$.

In Exercises 32–35, simplify the expression.

32. $\sqrt[5]{243z^8}$ **33.** $\sqrt[4]{\frac{y^{12}}{625y^8}}$

34. $6\sqrt[3]{9} - 10\sqrt[3]{9}$ **35.** $3\sqrt{20} + 7\sqrt{5}$

In Exercises 36 and 37, describe the transformation of f represented by g. Then graph each function.

36. $f(x) = \sqrt{x}$, $g(x) = -\sqrt{x + 2}$

37. $f(x) = \sqrt[3]{x}$, $g(x) = 4\sqrt[3]{x} - 6$

38. Determine whether the table represents a *linear* or *nonlinear* function. Explain.

x	12	9	6	3
y	-1	0	1	2

39. **MODELING REAL LIFE** The number A of commercial drones sold (in thousands) can be modeled by the function $A = 19t^2 + 30t + 110$, where t represents the number of years after 2016.

a. In what year did commercial drone sales reach 200,000?

b. Find and interpret the average rate of change from 2016 to 2018.

c. Do you think this model will be accurate after 20 years? Explain your reasoning.

5.6 Composition of Functions

Learning Target Evaluate and find compositions of functions.

Success Criteria
- I can evaluate a composition of functions.
- I can find a composition of functions.
- I can state the domain of a composition of functions.

EXPLORE IT! Finding a Composition of Functions

Work with a partner. The formulas below represent the temperature F (in degrees Fahrenheit) when the temperature is C degrees Celsius, and the temperature C when the temperature is K (Kelvin).

$$F = \frac{9}{5}C + 32 \qquad C = K - 273$$

Math Practice

Make Sense of Quantities

Does $g(f(x))$ make sense in this context? Explain.

a. Write an expression for F in terms of K.

b. Given that

$$f(x) = \frac{9}{5}x + 32$$

and

$$g(x) = x - 273$$

write an expression for $f(g(x))$. What does $f(g(x))$ represent in this situation?

c. Water freezes at about 273 Kelvin. Find $f(g(273))$. Does your answer make sense? Explain your reasoning.

d. Interpret the point shown on the graph.

Temperature Conversion

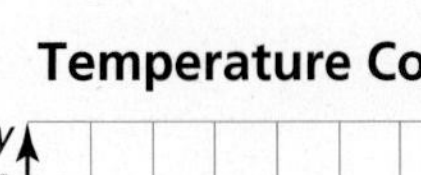
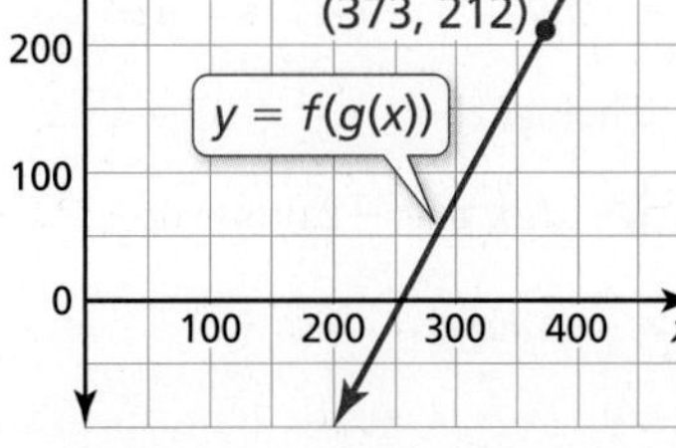

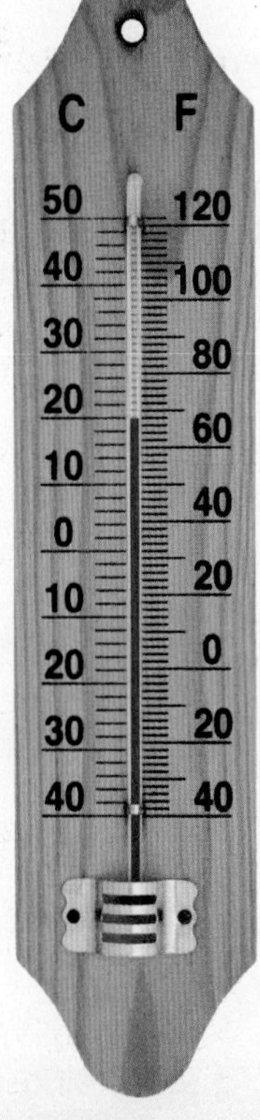

Evaluating Compositions of Functions

Vocabulary 

composition, *p. 268*

You have combined functions by finding sums, differences, products, and quotients of functions. Another way of combining two functions is to form a *composition*.

READING

The composition $g(f(x))$ can be read as "g of f of x."

KEY IDEA

Composition of Functions

The **composition** of a function g with a function f is

$$h(x) = g(f(x)).$$

The domain of h is the set of all x-values such that x is in the domain of f and $f(x)$ is in the domain of g.

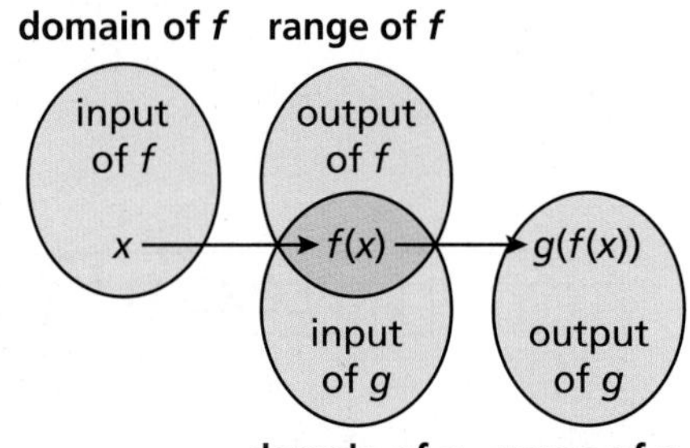

EXAMPLE 1 Evaluating Compositions of Functions

Let $f(x) = \sqrt{2x + 1}$ and $g(x) = x^2 - 4$. Find the indicated value.

a. $g(f(4))$ **b.** $f(g(2))$ **c.** $g(g(-2))$

SOLUTION

a. To evaluate $g(f(4))$, first find $f(4)$.

$$f(4) = \sqrt{2(4) + 1} = \sqrt{8 + 1} = \sqrt{9} = 3$$

Then $g(f(4)) = g(3) = 3^2 - 4 = 9 - 4 = 5$.

▶ So, $g(f(4))$ is 5.

b. To evaluate $f(g(2))$, first find $g(2)$.

$$g(2) = 2^2 - 4 = 4 - 4 = 0$$

Then $f(g(2)) = f(0) = \sqrt{2(0) + 1} = \sqrt{0 + 1} = \sqrt{1} = 1$.

▶ So, $f(g(2))$ is 1.

READING

As with subtraction and division of functions, you need to be aware of the order of functions when they are composed. In general, $f(g(x)) \neq g(f(x))$.

c. To evaluate $g(g(-2))$, first find $g(-2)$.

$$g(-2) = (-2)^2 - 4 = 4 - 4 = 0$$

Then $g(g(-2)) = g(0) = 0^2 - 4 = 0 - 4 = -4$.

▶ So, $g(g(-2))$ is -4.

SELF-ASSESSMENT 1 I do not understand. 2 I can do it with help. 3 I can do it on my own. 4 I can teach someone else.

Let $f(x) = x - 2$, $g(x) = x^2$, and $h(x) = \dfrac{x + 5}{2}$. Find the indicated value.

1. $f(g(-1))$
2. $g(h(-7))$
3. $h(g(5))$
4. $f(f(0))$
5. **MP STRUCTURE** For functions f and g, $f(2) = -3$ and $g(-3) = 10$. Find $g(f(2))$.

GO DIGITAL

Finding Compositions of Functions

EXAMPLE 2 **Finding Compositions of Functions**

WATCH

Let $f(x) = 5x^{-1}$ and $g(x) = 3x - 3$. Perform the indicated composition and state the domain.

a. $f(g(x))$

b. $g(f(x))$

c. $f(f(x))$

SOLUTION

STUDY TIP

$g(1) = 0$ is not in the domain of f because $f(0) = \frac{5}{0}$, which is undefined.

a. $f(g(x)) = f(3x - 3)$ — Substitute $3x - 3$ for $g(x)$.

$= 5(3x - 3)^{-1}$ — Replace x with $3x - 3$ in $f(x)$.

$= \dfrac{5}{3x - 3}$ — Definition of negative exponents

▶ The domain of $y = f(g(x))$ is all real numbers except $x = 1$, because $g(1) = 0$ is not in the domain of f.

b. $g(f(x)) = g(5x^{-1})$ — Substitute $5x^{-1}$ for $f(x)$.

$= 3(5x^{-1}) - 3$ — Replace x with $5x^{-1}$ in $g(x)$.

$= 15x^{-1} - 3$ — Multiply.

$= \dfrac{15}{x} - 3$ — Definition of negative exponents

▶ The domain of $y = g(f(x))$ is all real numbers except $x = 0$, because 0 is not in the domain of f.

c. $f(f(x)) = f(5x^{-1})$ — Substitute $5x^{-1}$ for $f(x)$.

$= 5(5x^{-1})^{-1}$ — Replace x with $5x^{-1}$ in $f(x)$.

$= 5(5^{-1}x^{1})$ — Use properties of exponents.

$= 5\left(\frac{1}{5}x\right)$ — Definition of negative exponents

$= x$ — Multiply.

▶ The domain of $y = f(f(x))$ is all real numbers except $x = 0$, because 0 is not in the domain of f.

SELF-ASSESSMENT 1 I do not understand. 2 I can do it with help. 3 I can do it on my own. 4 I can teach someone else.

Let $f(x) = 2x^{-1}$, $g(x) = 4x - 3$, and $h(x) = 0.5x + 2$. Perform the indicated composition and state the domain.

6. $f(g(x))$

7. $g(f(x))$

8. $f(f(x))$

9. $h(h(x))$

10. **MP REASONING** Let f and g be linear functions. Is $y = f(g(x))$ a linear function? Explain your reasoning.

Solving Real-Life Problems

EXAMPLE 3 **Modeling Real Life** 

The function $C(m) = 15 - 10.5m$ approximates the temperature (in degrees Celsius) at an altitude of m miles. The diagram shows the altitude (in miles) of an airplane t minutes after taking off, where $0 \leq t \leq 30$. Find $C(m(t))$. Evaluate $C(m(30))$ and explain what it represents.

SOLUTION

The composition $C(m(t))$ represents the temperature at the airplane's altitude t minutes after taking off. Find $C(m(t))$.

$C(m(t)) = C(0.2t)$	Substitute $0.2t$ for $m(t)$.
$= 15 - 10.5(0.2t)$	Replace m with $0.2t$ in $C(m)$.
$= 15 - 2.1t$	Multiply.

Evaluate $C(m(30))$.

$C(m(30)) = 15 - 2.1(30)$	Substitute 30 for t.
$= 15 - 63$	Multiply.
$= -48$	Subtract.

▶ So, $C(m(30)) = -48$ indicates that after 30 minutes, the airplane is at an altitude that has a temperature of about $-48°C$.

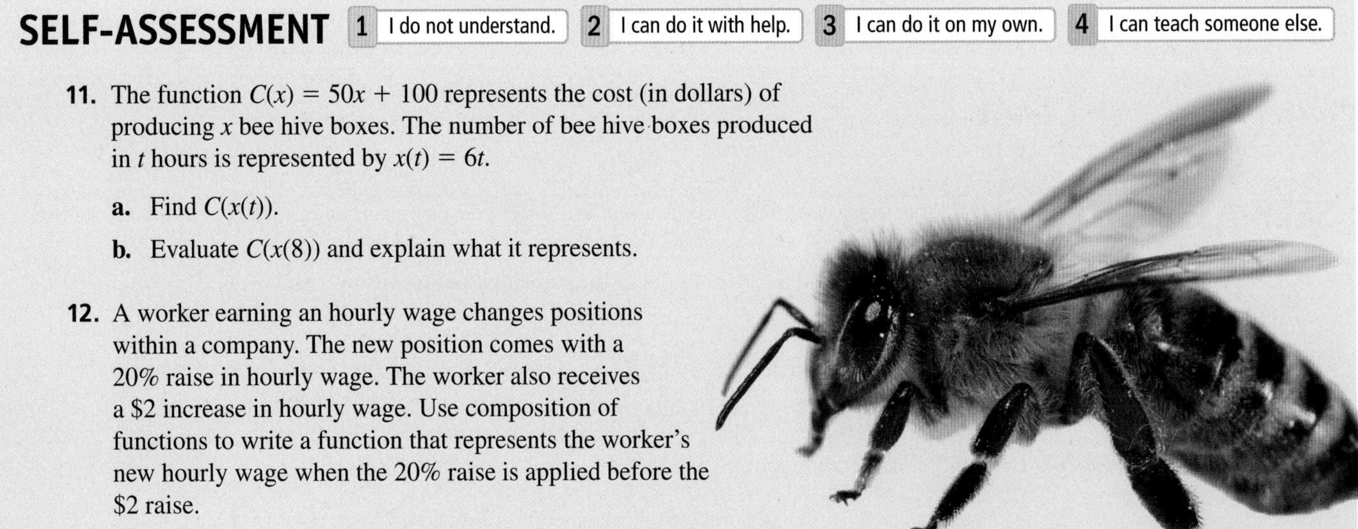

SELF-ASSESSMENT **1** I do not understand. **2** I can do it with help. **3** I can do it on my own. **4** I can teach someone else.

11. The function $C(x) = 50x + 100$ represents the cost (in dollars) of producing x bee hive boxes. The number of bee hive boxes produced in t hours is represented by $x(t) = 6t$.

a. Find $C(x(t))$.

b. Evaluate $C(x(8))$ and explain what it represents.

12. A worker earning an hourly wage changes positions within a company. The new position comes with a 20% raise in hourly wage. The worker also receives a \$2 increase in hourly wage. Use composition of functions to write a function that represents the worker's new hourly wage when the 20% raise is applied before the \$2 raise.

5.6 Practice WITH CalcChat® AND CalcView®

In Exercises 1–8, let $f(x) = \sqrt{x+1}$, $g(x) = 2x - 5$, and $h(x) = 3x^2 - 3$. Find the indicated value. *Example 1*

1. $f(g(4))$
2. $g(f(0))$
3. $g(h(-2))$
4. $h(g(-1))$
5. $h(f(10))$
6. $f(h(-3))$
7. $g(g(-2.5))$
8. $h\left(h\left(\frac{2}{3}\right)\right)$

In Exercises 9–20, find (a) $f(g(x))$, (b) $g(f(x))$, and (c) $f(f(x))$. State the domain of each composition. *Example 2*

9. $f(x) = -5x$, $g(x) = x + 6$
10. $f(x) = x - 9$, $g(x) = |x + 2|$
11. $f(x) = 2x^2$, $g(x) = x - 1$
12. $f(x) = x^2 + 7$, $g(x) = 2x + 5$
13. $f(x) = 3x^{-1}$, $g(x) = 4x + 8$
14. $f(x) = 10x^{-1}$, $g(x) = x^2 - 9$
15. $f(x) = 3x - 7$, $g(x) = \sqrt{x+7}$
16. $f(x) = 4x + 2$, $g(x) = \sqrt{x-6}$
17. $f(x) = -x + 11$, $g(x) = \sqrt[3]{x-3}$
18. $f(x) = -6x - 5$, $g(x) = \sqrt[3]{x+4}$
19. $f(x) = 2x + 1$, $g(x) = x^2 + 6x - 10$
20. $f(x) = 3x - 1$, $g(x) = x^3 - 2x + 4$

ERROR ANALYSIS In Exercises 21 and 22, let $f(x) = x^2 - 3$ and $g(x) = 4x$. Describe and correct the error in performing the composition.

21. ✗
$$f(g(x)) = (x^2 - 3)(4x)$$
$$= 4x^3 - 12x$$

22. 
$$g(f(x)) = g(x^2 - 3)$$
$$= 4x^2 - 3$$

23. **MODELING REAL LIFE** The function $C(g) = 2.75g$ represents the cost (in dollars) of g gallons of gasoline at a gas station. The function $g(m) = 0.04m$ approximates the number of gallons of gasoline a vehicle uses to travel m miles. *Example 3*

 a. Find $C(g(m))$. Interpret the coefficient.

 b. Evaluate $C(g(100))$ and explain what it represents.

24. **MODELING REAL LIFE** The function $p(d) = 0.03d + 1$ approximates the pressure (in atmospheres) at a depth of d feet below sea level. The function $d(t) = 60t$ represents the depth (in feet) of a diver t minutes after beginning a descent from sea level, where $0 \le t \le 2$.

 a. Find $p(d(t))$. Interpret the terms and coefficient.

 b. Evaluate $p(d(1.5))$ and explain what it represents.

25. **MP REASONING** The table shows the inputs and outputs of two functions f and g. Use the table to find each value.

x	−2	−1	0	1	2	3
f(x)	7	5	3	2	0	−2
g(x)	1	−2	−1	5	2	0

 a. $f(g(-1))$ b. $g(f(2))$

 c. $f(f(0))$ d. $g(g(-2))$

26. **HOW DO YOU SEE IT?**
Use the graphs of f and g to find each value.

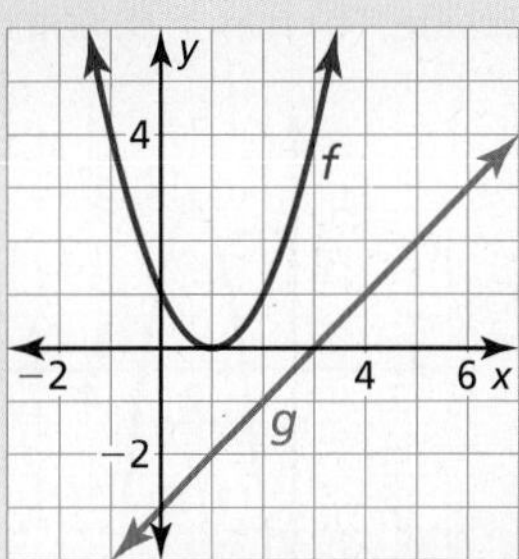

 a. $f(g(6))$ b. $g(f(-1))$

 c. $f(f(2))$ d. $g(g(3))$

27. **MP REASONING** Functions f and g consist only of the ordered pairs shown. Find the ordered pairs for $y = f(g(x))$.

f: (−12, 11), (−4, 9), (1, 3), (2, −4), (6, −5)

g: (−10, 6), (−3, 1), (0, −4), (5, 2), (8, −12)

28. **COLLEGE PREP** Let $f(x) = x^2 + 1$ and $g(x) = 3x + 1$. What is $f(f(x)) - g(f(x))$?

Ⓐ $x^2 - 3x$

Ⓑ $x^4 - x^2 - 2$

Ⓒ $x^4 - 7x^2 - 6x$

Ⓓ $x^4 - 3x^3 + x^2 - 3x$

29. **CONNECTING CONCEPTS** The radius of a circular region increases at a rate of 2 inches per minute. Use composition of functions to write a function that represents the area A (in square inches) of the region after t minutes.

30. **MP PROBLEM SOLVING** You have two coupons for a store, one for \$10 off your entire purchase and another for 20% off your entire purchase. Both coupons can be used on the same purchase. Which order of discounts results in a lesser total? Use composition of functions to justify your answer.

MP STRUCTURE In Exercises 31–34, find functions f and g such that $f(g(x)) = h(x)$, $f(x) \neq x$, and $g(x) \neq x$.

31. $h(x) = \frac{1}{2}x + 6$

32. $h(x) = |2x + 9|$

33. $h(x) = \sqrt[3]{x + 2}$

34. $h(x) = \dfrac{4}{3x^2 + 7}$

35. **MP LOGIC** Complete the table using the following information.

- f and g are linear functions.
- $f(g(1)) = 6.5$
- $g(f(2)) = -5$

x	$f(x)$	$g(x)$
1		
2		
4		-5
7	6.5	

36. **THOUGHT PROVOKING**
Write two different nonlinear functions f and g such that $f(g(x)) = x$ and $g(f(x)) = x$.

In Exercises 37–40, let $f(x) = 3x + 5$, $g(x) = x^2$, and $h(x) = -2x - 1$. Perform the indicated composition.

37. $f(g(h(x)))$

38. $h(g(f(x)))$

39. $f(f(f(x)))$

40. $g(h(g(x)))$

41. **DIG DEEPER** Show that the function $f(x) = \frac{1}{3}\sqrt{x - 2} + 3$ is a composition, in some order, of functions g, h, p, and q.

$g(x) = \frac{1}{3}x$ $\quad$ $h(x) = x - 2$

$p(x) = x + 9$ $\quad$ $q(x) = \sqrt{x}$

REVIEW & REFRESH

In Exercises 42 and 43, solve the inequality.

42. $5\sqrt{x} - 3 < 17$

43. $\sqrt[3]{x + 1} + 4 \geq -2$

44. Describe the x-values for which (a) f is increasing or decreasing, (b) $f(x) > 0$, and (c) $f(x) < 0$.

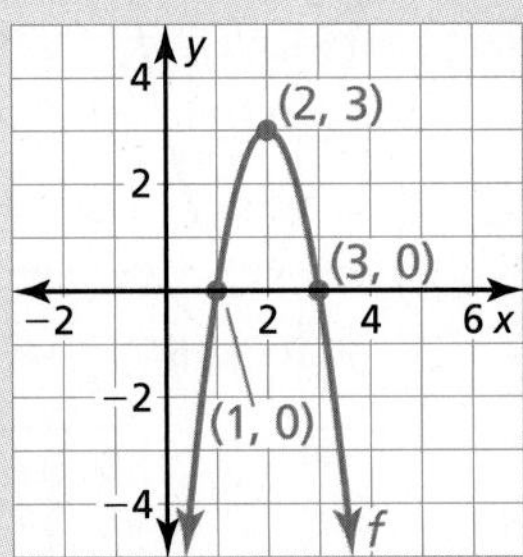

In Exercises 45 and 46, let $f(x) = -x + 4$ and $g(x) = \dfrac{2x - 1}{3}$. Find the indicated value.

45. $f(g(5))$

46. $g(f(-4))$

47. Let g be a horizontal stretch by a factor of 2, followed by a translation 3 units up of the graph of $f(x) = \sqrt{4x}$. Write a rule for g.

In Exercises 48 and 49, solve the system using any method. Explain your choice of method.

48. $2x^2 + 4x - y = -5$
$2x + y = 1$

49. $x^2 - 3x - y = 4$
$-x^2 + 7x + y = 10$

50. **MODELING REAL LIFE** From 2012 to 2017, the United States population (in millions) ages 5 and over can be modeled by

$$P(t) = 0.0208t^4 - 0.203t^3 + 0.56t^2 + 2.1t + 289$$

and the number of people in that group that speak a language other than English at home can be modeled by

$$S(t) = 0.0037t^3 - 0.042t^2 + 1.08t + 59.4$$

where t is the number of years since 2012. Find $(P - S)(t)$. Explain what $(P - S)(t)$ represents.

51. Find the volume of the cone. Round your answer to the nearest tenth.

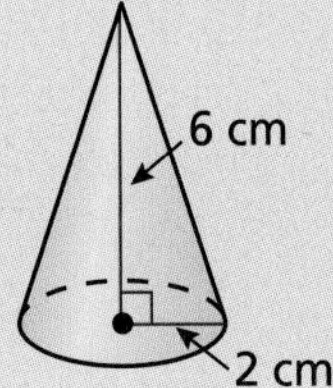

5.7 Inverse of a Function

Learning Target Understand the relationship between inverse functions.

Success Criteria
- I can explain what inverse functions are.
- I can find inverses of linear and nonlinear functions.
- I can determine whether a pair of functions are inverses.

EXPLORE IT! Describing Functions and Their Inverses

Work with a partner.

a. Consider each pair of functions, f and g, below. For each pair, create an input-output table of values for each function. Use the outputs of f as the inputs of g. What do you notice about the relationship between the equations of f and g?

i. $f(x) = 4x + 3$
$g(x) = \dfrac{x - 3}{4}$

ii. $f(x) = x^3 + 1$
$g(x) = \sqrt[3]{x - 1}$

iii. $f(x) = \sqrt{x - 3}$
$g(x) = x^2 + 3, x \geq 0$

b. What do you notice about the graphs of each pair of functions in part (a)?

c. For each pair of functions in part (a), find $f(g(x))$ and $g(f(x))$. What do you notice?

Math Practice

Build Arguments

In part (c), why do you think this occurs when you find the compositions of these functions?

d. The functions h and j are inverses of each other. Use the graph of h to find the given value. Explain how you found your answers.

i. $j(-6)$

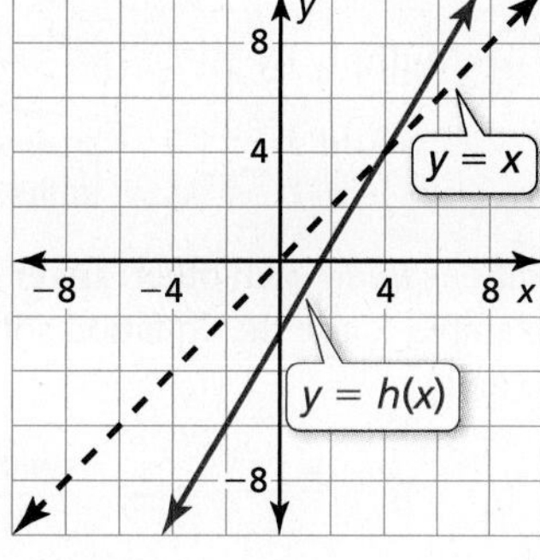

ii. $j(4)$

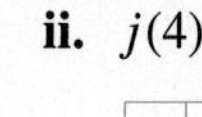

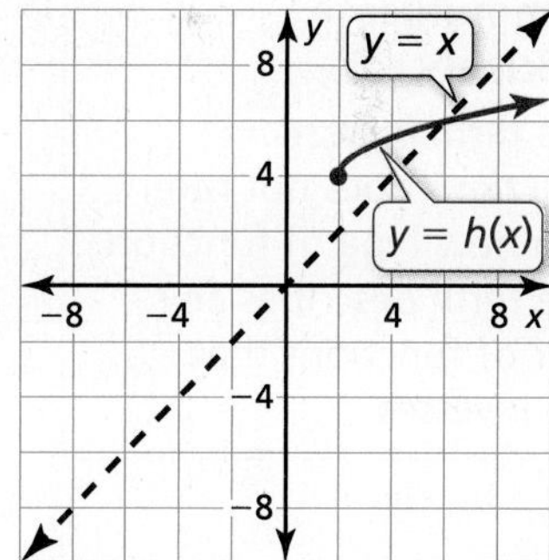

iii. $j(-6)$

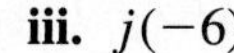

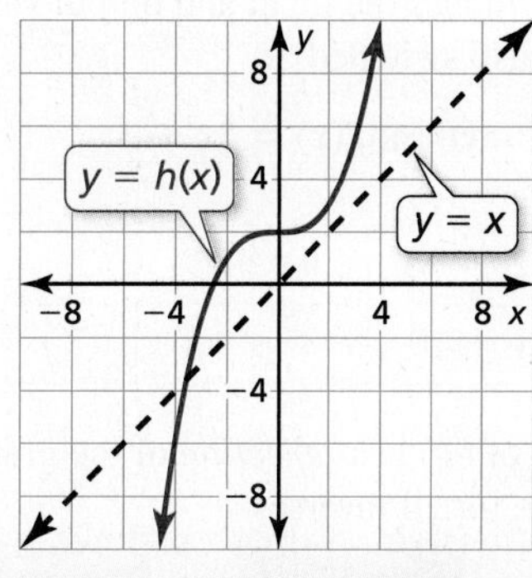

iv. $j(2)$

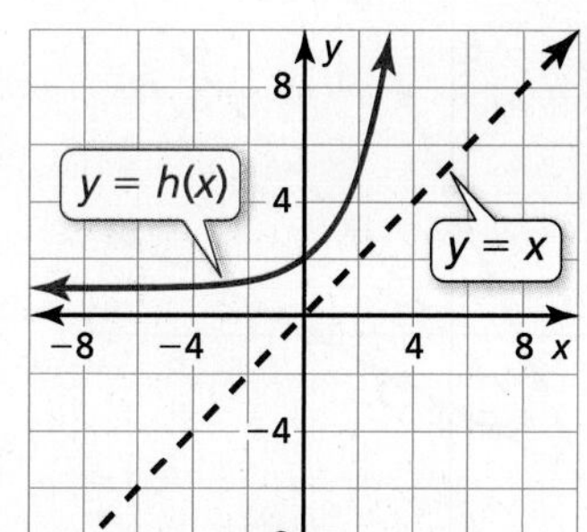

Exploring Inverses of Functions

Vocabulary 

Inverse functions, *p. 274*

You can solve equations of the form $y = f(x)$ for x to obtain an equation that gives the input for a specific output of f.

EXAMPLE 1 Writing a Formula for the Input of a Function

Let $f(x) = 2x + 3$. Solve $y = f(x)$ for x. Then find the input when the output is -7.

SOLUTION

$y = 2x + 3$ Set y equal to $f(x)$.

$y - 3 = 2x$ Subtract 3 from each side.

$\dfrac{y-3}{2} = x$ Divide each side by 2.

Find the input when $y = -7$.

$x = \dfrac{-7-3}{2}$ Substitute -7 for y.

$= \dfrac{-10}{2}$ Subtract.

$= -5$ Divide.

Check

$f(-5) = 2(-5) + 3$

$= -10 + 3$

$= -7$ ✓

▶ So, the input is -5 when the output is -7.

In Example 1, notice the operations in the equations $y = 2x + 3$ and $x = \dfrac{y-3}{2}$.

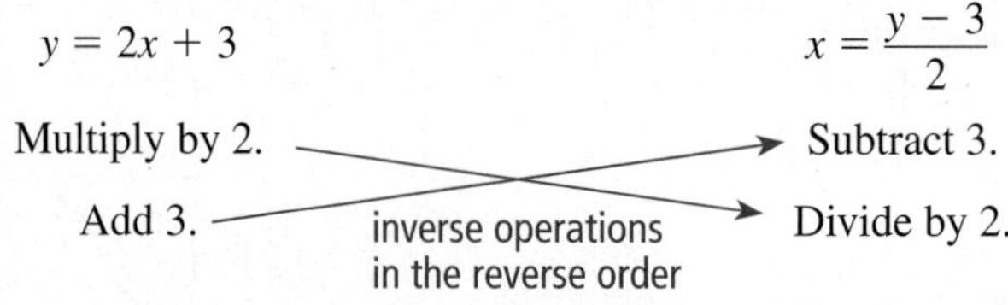

Math Practice

Communicate Precisely

The term *inverse functions* does not refer to a new type of function. The term describes any pair of functions that are inverses.

These operations *undo* each other. **Inverse functions** are functions that undo each other. In Example 1, use the equation solved for x to write the inverse of f by switching x and y.

$$x = \frac{y-3}{2} \xrightarrow{\text{switch } x \text{ and } y} y = \frac{x-3}{2}$$

An inverse function can be denoted by f^{-1}, read as "f inverse." Because an inverse function switches the input and output values of the original function, the domain and range are also switched.

Original function: $f(x) = 2x + 3$

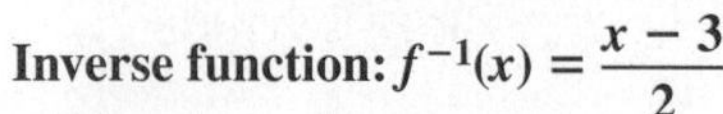
Inverse function: $f^{-1}(x) = \dfrac{x-3}{2}$

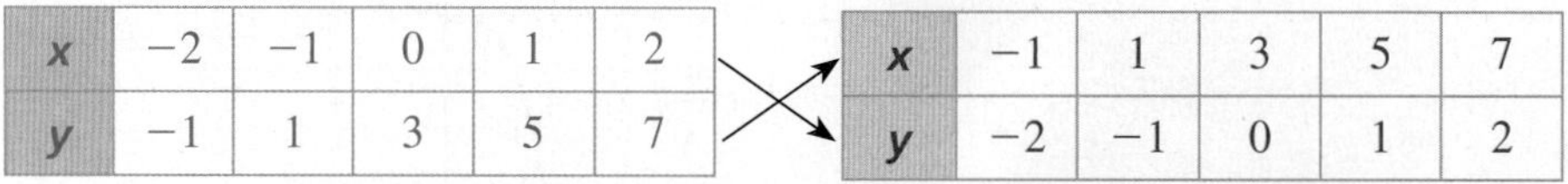

x	-2	-1	0	1	2
y	-1	1	3	5	7

x	-1	1	3	5	7
y	-2	-1	0	1	2

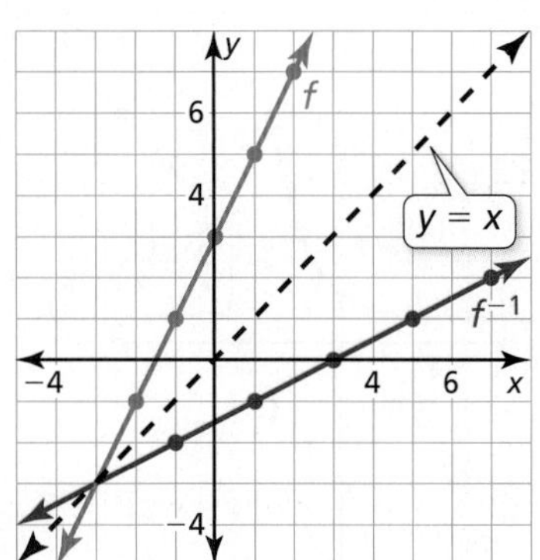

The graph of f^{-1} is a *reflection* of the graph of f. The *line of reflection* is $y = x$. This is true for all inverses.

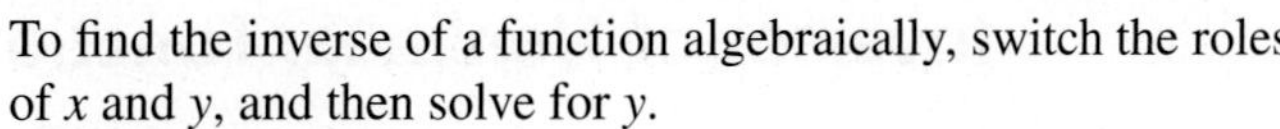

To find the inverse of a function algebraically, switch the roles of x and y, and then solve for y.

GO DIGITAL

EXAMPLE 2 Finding the Inverse of a Linear Function

Find the inverse of $f(x) = 3x - 1$.

SOLUTION

Method 1 Use inverse operations in the reverse order.

$f(x) = 3x - 1$ Multiply the input x by 3 and then subtract 1.

To find the inverse, apply inverse operations in the reverse order.

$f^{-1}(x) = \dfrac{x+1}{3}$ Add 1 to the input x and then divide by 3.

> **READING**
> The -1 in f^{-1} is not an exponent. It indicates that the function is an inverse, *not* that it is equal to $\dfrac{1}{f(x)}$.

▶ The inverse of f is $f^{-1}(x) = \dfrac{x+1}{3}$.

Method 2 Set y equal to $f(x)$. Switch the roles of x and y and solve for y.

$y = 3x - 1$ Set y equal to $f(x)$.

$x = 3y - 1$ Switch x and y.

$x + 1 = 3y$ Add 1 to each side.

$\dfrac{x+1}{3} = y$ Divide each side by 3.

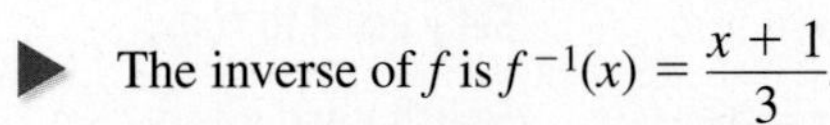

▶ The inverse of f is $f^{-1}(x) = \dfrac{x+1}{3}$.

Check

Use technology to graph f and f^{-1}.

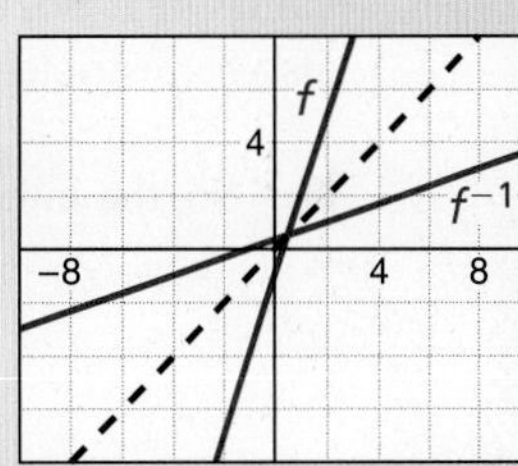

The graph of f^{-1} appears to be a reflection of the graph of f in the line $y = x$. ✓

SELF-ASSESSMENT

1 I do not understand. 2 I can do it with help. 3 I can do it on my own. 4 I can teach someone else.

Solve $y = f(x)$ for x. Then find the input(s) when the output is 2.

1. $f(x) = x - 2$ **2.** $f(x) = 2x^2$ **3.** $f(x) = -x^3 + 3$

4. VOCABULARY In your own words, state the definition of inverse functions.

Find the inverse of the function. Then graph the function and its inverse.

5. $f(x) = 2x$ **6.** $f(x) = -x + 1$ **7.** $f(x) = \frac{1}{3}x - 2$

Inverses of Nonlinear Functions

In the previous examples, the inverses of the linear functions were also functions. However, inverses of functions are *not* always functions. The graphs of $f(x) = x^2$ and $f(x) = x^3$ are shown along with their reflections in the line $y = x$. Notice that the inverse of $f(x) = x^3$ is a function, but the inverse of $f(x) = x^2$ is *not* a function.

REMEMBER

You can use the Vertical Line Test to check whether the inverse is a function.

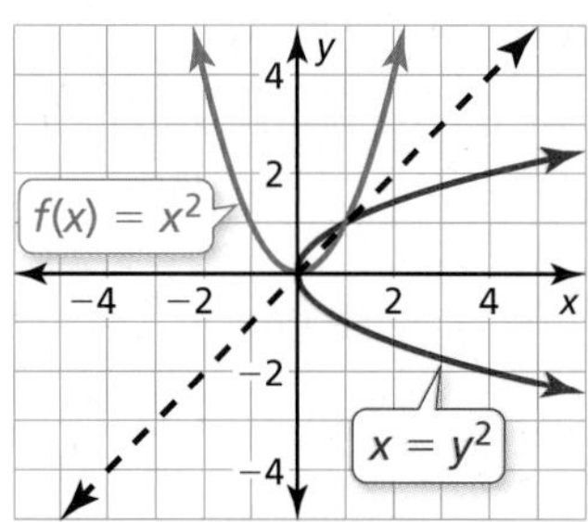

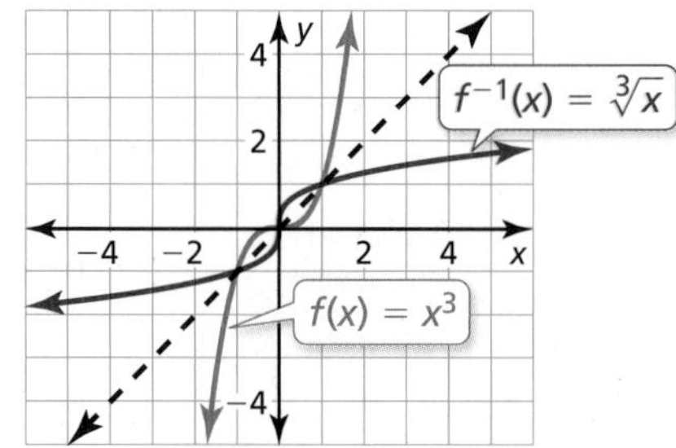

When the domain of $f(x) = x^2$ is *restricted* to only nonnegative real numbers, the inverse of f *is* a function, as shown in the next example.

EXAMPLE 3 Finding the Inverse of a Quadratic Function

Find the inverse of $f(x) = x^2$, $x \geq 0$. Then graph the function and its inverse.

SOLUTION

$f(x) = x^2$	Write the original function.
$y = x^2$	Set y equal to $f(x)$.
$x = y^2$	Switch x and y.
$\pm\sqrt{x} = y$	Take square root of each side.

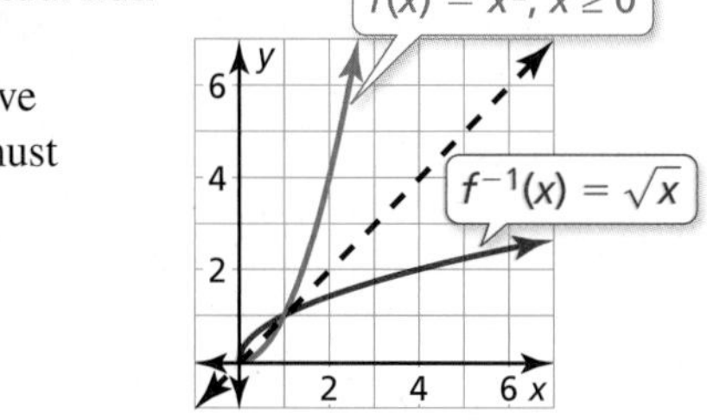

The domain of f is restricted to nonnegative values of x. So, the range of the inverse must also be restricted to nonnegative values.

▶ So, the inverse of f is $f^{-1}(x) = \sqrt{x}$.

STUDY TIP

If the domain of f is instead restricted to $x \leq 0$, then the inverse is $f^{-1}(x) = -\sqrt{x}$.

You can use the graph of a function f to determine whether the inverse of f is a function by applying the *Horizontal Line Test.*

KEY IDEA

Horizontal Line Test

The inverse of a function f is also a function if and only if no horizontal line intersects the graph of f more than once.

Inverse is a function **Inverse is not a function**

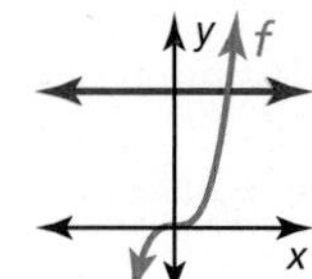

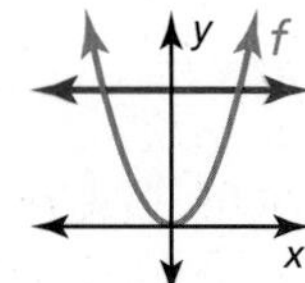

EXAMPLE 4 Finding the Inverse of a Cubic Function

Consider the function $f(x) = 2x^3 + 1$. Determine whether the inverse of f is a function. Then find the inverse.

SOLUTION

Graph the function f. Notice that no horizontal line intersects the graph more than once. So, the inverse of f is a function. Find the inverse.

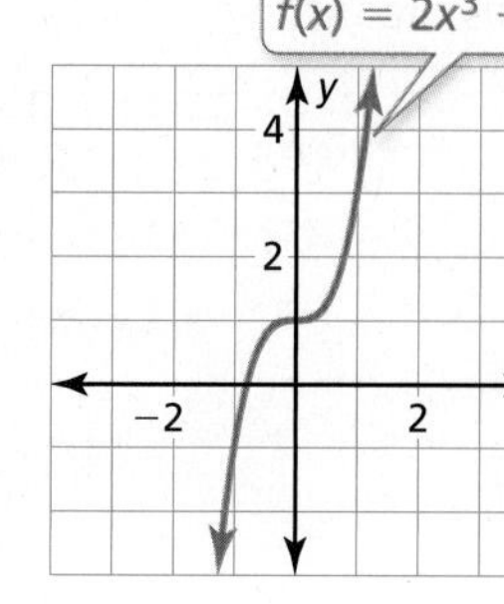

$y = 2x^3 + 1$	Set y equal to $f(x)$.
$x = 2y^3 + 1$	Switch x and y.
$x - 1 = 2y^3$	Subtract 1 from each side.
$\dfrac{x-1}{2} = y^3$	Divide each side by 2.
$\sqrt[3]{\dfrac{x-1}{2}} = y$	Take cube root of each side.

Check

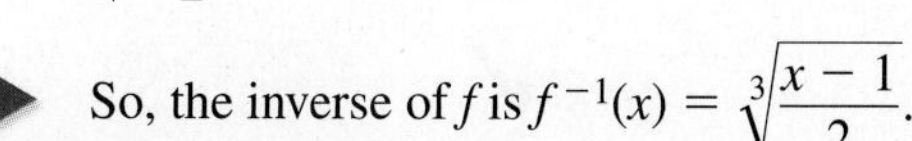

▶ So, the inverse of f is $f^{-1}(x) = \sqrt[3]{\dfrac{x-1}{2}}$.

EXAMPLE 5 Finding the Inverse of a Radical Function

Consider the function $f(x) = 2\sqrt{x-3}$. Determine whether the inverse of f is a function. Then find the inverse.

SOLUTION

Graph the function f. Notice that no horizontal line intersects the graph more than once. So, the inverse of f is a function. Find the inverse.

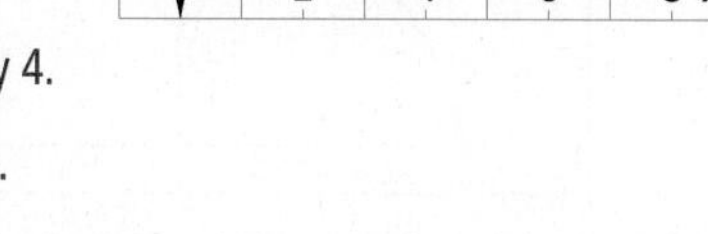

$y = 2\sqrt{x-3}$	Set y equal to $f(x)$.
$x = 2\sqrt{y-3}$	Switch x and y.
$x^2 = \left(2\sqrt{y-3}\right)^2$	Square each side.
$x^2 = 4(y-3)$	Simplify.
$\frac{1}{4}x^2 = y - 3$	Divide each side by 4.
$\frac{1}{4}x^2 + 3 = y$	Add 3 to each side.

Check

Because the range of f is $y \geq 0$, the domain of the inverse must be restricted to $x \geq 0$.

▶ So, the inverse of f is $f^{-1}(x) = \frac{1}{4}x^2 + 3, x \geq 0$.

SELF-ASSESSMENT

1 I do not understand. 2 I can do it with help. 3 I can do it on my own. 4 I can teach someone else.

8. Find the inverse of $f(x) = -x^2, x \leq 0$. Then graph the function and its inverse.

Determine whether the inverse of f is a function. Then find the inverse.

9. $f(x) = -x^3 + 4$

10. $f(x) = \dfrac{1}{x^2 + 1}$

11. $f(x) = \sqrt{x+2}$

12. WRITING Explain why you can use horizontal lines to determine whether the inverse of a function is also a function.

Math Practice

Communicate Precisely

Inverse functions *undo* each other. In your own words, explain what this means.

Let f and g be inverse functions. If $f(a) = b$, then $g(b) = a$. So, in general,

$$f(g(x)) = x \quad \text{and} \quad g(f(x)) = x.$$

EXAMPLE 6 Determining Whether Functions Are Inverses

Determine whether $f(x) = 3x - 1$ and $g(x) = \dfrac{x+1}{3}$ are inverse functions.

SOLUTION

Use compositions to determine whether f and g are inverse functions.

Step 1 Find $f(g(x))$.

$$\begin{aligned} f(g(x)) &= f\left(\frac{x+1}{3}\right) \\ &= 3\left(\frac{x+1}{3}\right) - 1 \\ &= x + 1 - 1 \\ &= x \ ✓ \end{aligned}$$

Step 2 Find $g(f(x))$.

$$\begin{aligned} g(f(x)) &= g(3x - 1) \\ &= \frac{3x - 1 + 1}{3} \\ &= \frac{3x}{3} \\ &= x \ ✓ \end{aligned}$$

▶ So, f and g are inverse functions.

EXAMPLE 7 Modeling Real Life

The speed of sound (in meters per second) through air is approximated by $f(x) = 20\sqrt{x + 273}$ where x is the temperature in degrees Celsius. Find and interpret $f^{-1}(340)$.

SOLUTION

Graph the function f. Notice that no horizontal line intersects the graph more than once. So, the inverse of f is a function. Find the inverse.

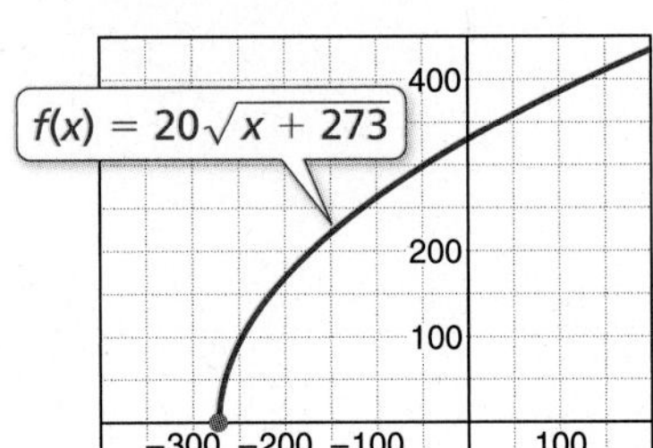

$y = 20\sqrt{x + 273}$	Set y equal to $f(x)$.
$x = 20\sqrt{y + 273}$	Switch x and y.
$x^2 = \left(20\sqrt{y + 273}\right)^2$	Square each side.
$x^2 = 400(y + 273)$	Simplify.
$\frac{1}{400}x^2 = y + 273$	Divide each side by 400.
$\frac{1}{400}x^2 - 273 = y$	Subtract 273 from each side.

Because the range of f is $y \geq 0$, the domain of the inverse must be restricted to $x \geq 0$. The inverse of f is $f^{-1}(x) = \frac{1}{400}x^2 - 273$, $x \geq 0$.

▶ Using $f^{-1}(x)$, you obtain $f^{-1}(340) = 16$. This represents that the temperature is 16 degrees Celsius when the speed of sound through air is 340 meters per second.

SELF-ASSESSMENT 1 I do not understand. 2 I can do it with help. 3 I can do it on my own. 4 I can teach someone else.

Determine whether the functions are inverse functions.

13. $f(x) = x + 5$, $g(x) = x - 5$

14. $f(x) = 8x^3$, $g(x) = \sqrt[3]{2x}$

15. WHAT IF? In Example 7, find and interpret $f^{-1}(350)$.

5.7 Practice WITH CalcChat® AND CalcView®

In Exercises 1–8, solve $y = f(x)$ for x. Then find the input(s) when the output is -3. *Example 1*

1. $f(x) = 3x + 5$
2. $f(x) = -7x - 2$
3. $f(x) = \frac{1}{2}x - 3$
4. $f(x) = -\frac{2}{3}x + 1$
5. $f(x) = 3x^3$
6. $f(x) = 2x^4 - 5$
7. $f(x) = (x - 2)^2 - 7$
8. $f(x) = (x - 5)^3 - 1$

In Exercises 9–16, find the inverse of the function. Then graph the function and its inverse. *Example 2*

9. $f(x) = 6x$
10. $f(x) = -3x$
11. $f(x) = -2x + 5$
12. $f(x) = 6x - 3$
13. $f(x) = -\frac{1}{2}x + 4$
14. $f(x) = \frac{1}{3}x - 1$
15. $f(x) = \frac{2}{3}x - \frac{1}{3}$
16. $f(x) = -\frac{4}{5}x + \frac{1}{5}$

MP REASONING In Exercises 17 and 18, determine whether functions f and g are inverses. Explain your reasoning.

17.

x	-2	-1	0	1	2
$f(x)$	-2	1	4	7	10

x	-2	1	4	7	10
$g(x)$	-2	-1	0	1	2

18.

x	2	3	4	5	6
$f(x)$	8	6	4	2	0

x	2	3	4	5	6
$g(x)$	-8	-6	-4	-2	0

In Exercises 19–24, find the inverse of the function. Then graph the function and its inverse. *Example 3*

19. $f(x) = 4x^2,\ x \le 0$
20. $f(x) = 9x^2,\ x \le 0$
21. $f(x) = (x - 3)^2,\ x \ge 3$
22. $f(x) = (x + 4)^2,\ x \ge -4$
23. $f(x) = -(x - 1)^2 + 6,\ x \ge 1$
24. $f(x) = 2(x + 5)^2 - 2,\ x \le -5$

ERROR ANALYSIS In Exercises 25 and 26, describe and correct the error in finding the inverse of the function.

25.

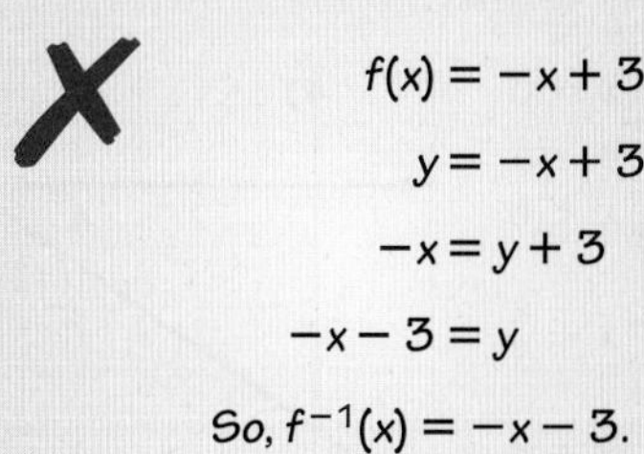

26.

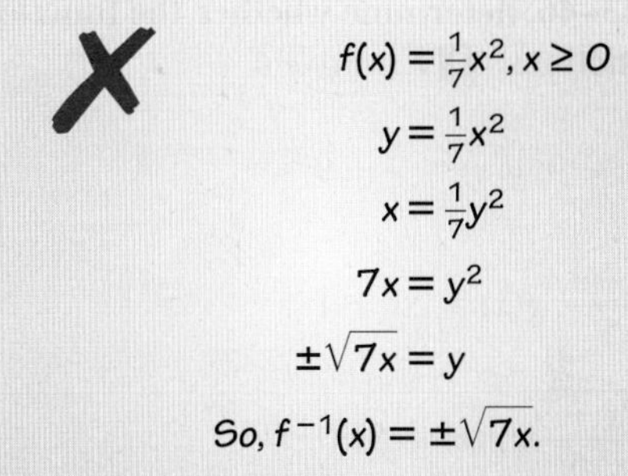

MP USING TOOLS In Exercises 27 and 28, use the graph to determine whether the inverse of f is a function. Explain your reasoning.

27.

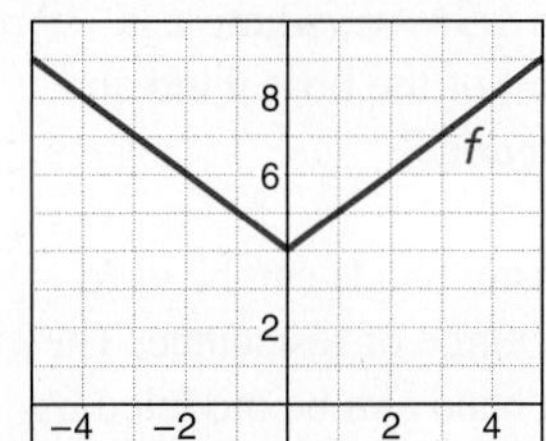

28.

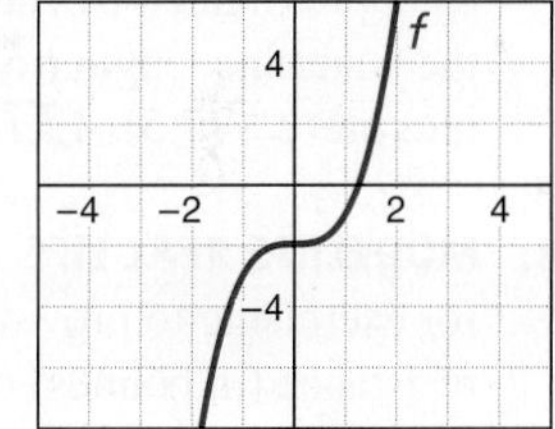

In Exercises 29–40, find the inverse of the function. Then graph the function and its inverse. *Examples 4 and 5*

29. $f(x) = x^3 - 1$
30. $f(x) = -x^3 + 3$
31. $f(x) = -x^3 + 2$
32. $f(x) = 2x^3 - 5$
33. $f(x) = \sqrt{x + 4}$
34. $f(x) = \sqrt{x - 6}$
35. $f(x) = 2\sqrt[3]{x - 5}$
36. $f(x) = 3\sqrt[3]{x + 1}$
37. $f(x) = \frac{2}{3}(x + 1)^3 + 8$
38. $f(x) = -\frac{2}{5}(x - 2)^3 - 4$
39. $f(x) = -\sqrt[3]{\dfrac{2x + 4}{3}}$
40. $f(x) = -3\sqrt{\dfrac{4x - 7}{3}}$

41. **COLLEGE PREP** What is the inverse of $f(x) = -\frac{1}{64}x^3$?

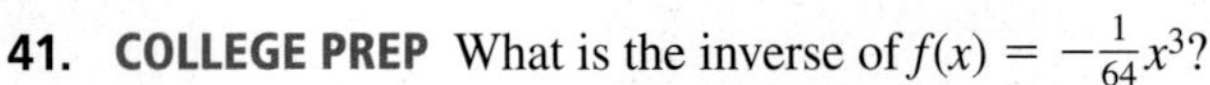

Ⓐ $g(x) = -4x^3$ Ⓑ $g(x) = 4\sqrt[3]{x}$

Ⓒ $g(x) = -4\sqrt[3]{x}$ Ⓓ $g(x) = \sqrt[3]{-4x}$

42. **COLLEGE PREP** What is the inverse of the function whose graph is shown?

Ⓐ $g(x) = \frac{3}{2}x - 6$

Ⓑ $g(x) = \frac{3}{2}x + 6$

Ⓒ $g(x) = \frac{2}{3}x + \frac{8}{3}$

Ⓓ $g(x) = \frac{3}{2}x + 4$

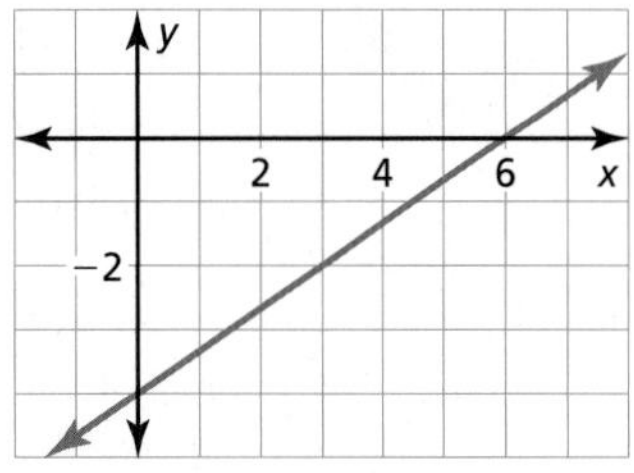

In Exercises 43–46, determine whether the functions are inverse functions. ▶ *Example 6*

43. $f(x) = 2x - 9$, $g(x) = \dfrac{x}{2} + 9$

44. $f(x) = \dfrac{x-1}{5}$, $g(x) = 5x + 1$

45. $f(x) = \sqrt[5]{\dfrac{x+9}{5}}$, $g(x) = 5x^5 - 9$

46. $f(x) = 7x^{3/2} - 4$, $g(x) = \left(\dfrac{x+4}{7}\right)^{3/2}$

47. **MODELING REAL LIFE** The maximum hull speed (in knots) of a boat with a displacement hull can be approximated by $f(x) = 1.34\sqrt{x}$, where x is the waterline length (in feet) of the boat. Find and interpret $f^{-1}(7.5)$. ▶ *Example 7*

48. **MODELING REAL LIFE** Elastic bands can be used for exercising to provide a range of resistance. The resistance (in pounds) of a band can be modeled by $r(x) = \frac{3}{8}x - 5$, where x is the total length (in inches) of the stretched band. Find and interpret $r^{-1}(19)$.

ANALYZING RELATIONSHIPS

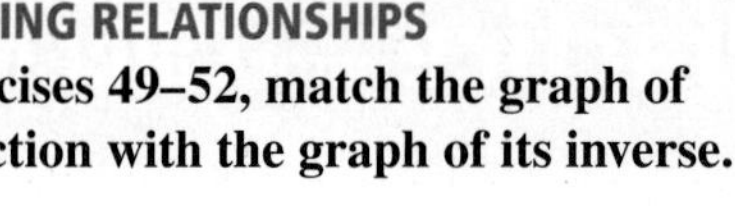

In Exercises 49–52, match the graph of the function with the graph of its inverse.

49.

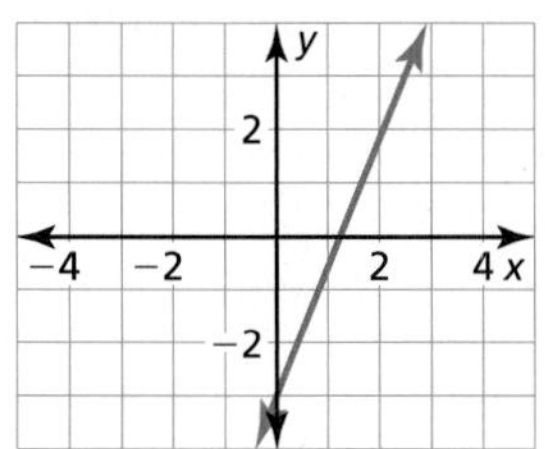

50.

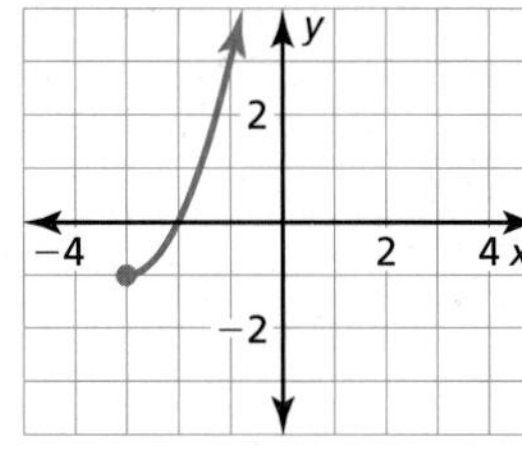

51.

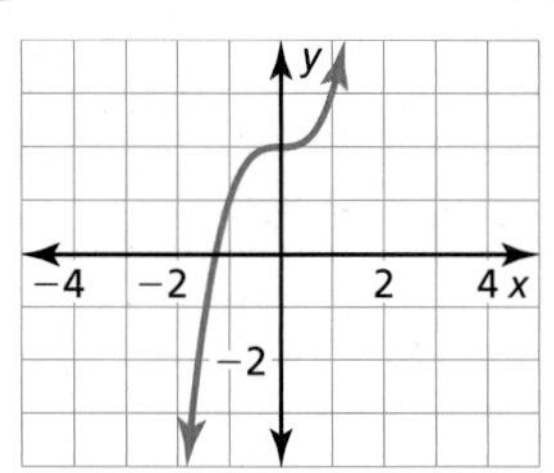

52.

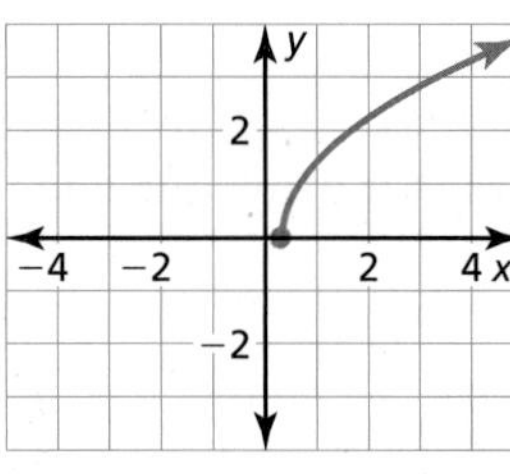

A.

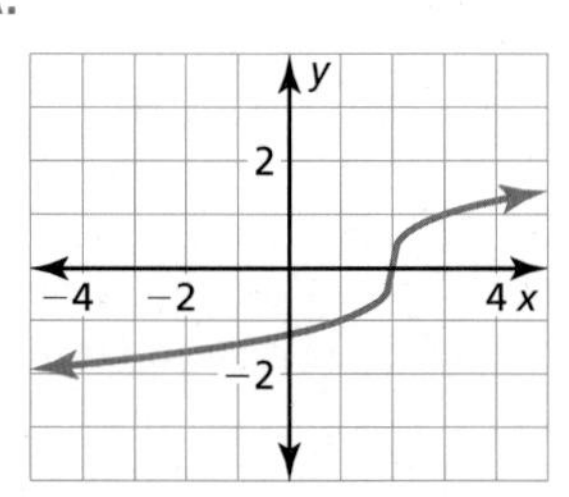

B.

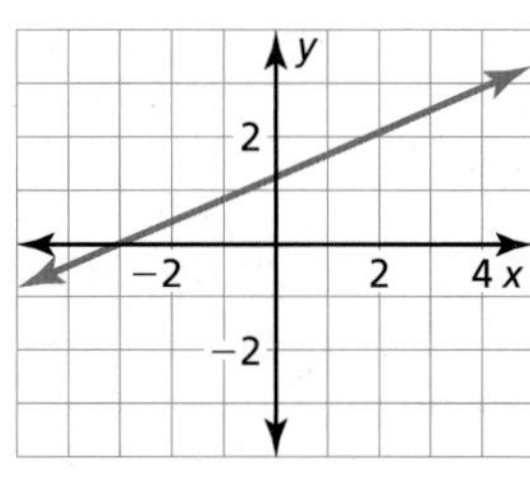

C.

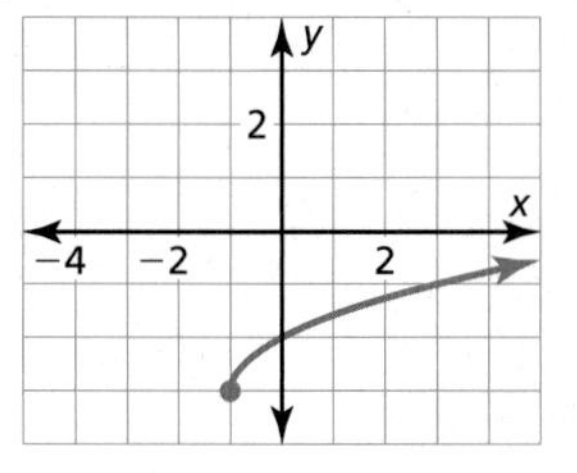

D.

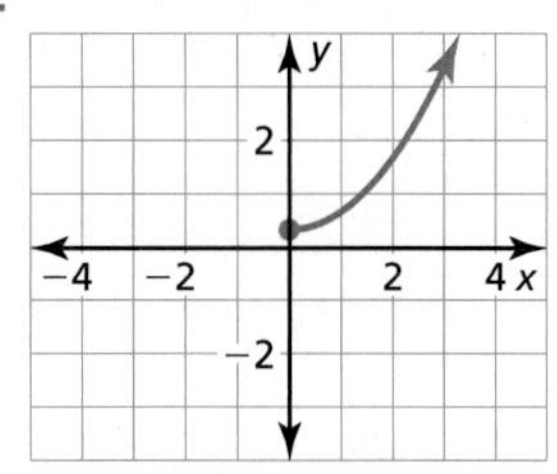

In Exercises 53 and 54, use the table or graph to find $f^{-1}(-2)$. Explain your reasoning.

53.

x	−2	−1	0	1	2	3
f(x)	−1	−2	1	4	7	10

54.

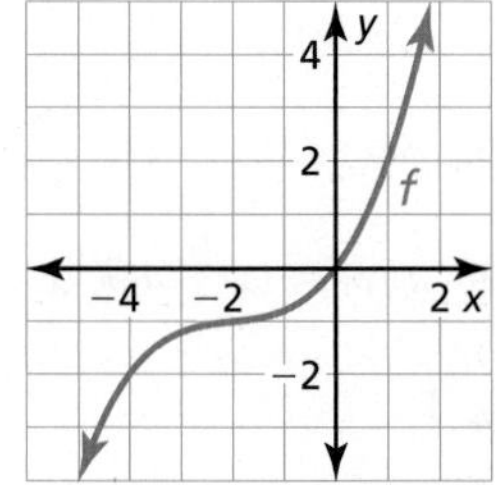

55. COMPARING METHODS Find the inverse of $f(x) = -3x + 4$ by switching the roles of x and y and solving for y. Then find the inverse of f by using inverse operations in the reverse order. Which method do you prefer? Explain.

56. MP REASONING The graph of a function passes through the points $(-2, 5)$, $(0, 1)$, $(3, -6)$, and $(7, n)$. For what values of n is the inverse a function? Explain your reasoning.

MP STRUCTURE In Exercises 57–60, match the function with the graph of its inverse.

57. $f(x) = \sqrt[3]{x - 4}$ **58.** $f(x) = \sqrt[3]{x + 4}$

59. $f(x) = \sqrt{x + 1} - 3$ **60.** $f(x) = \sqrt{x - 1} + 3$

A.
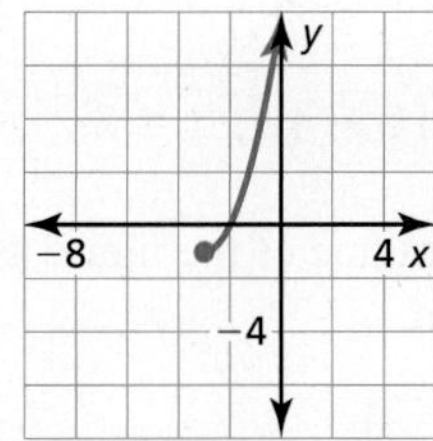

B.
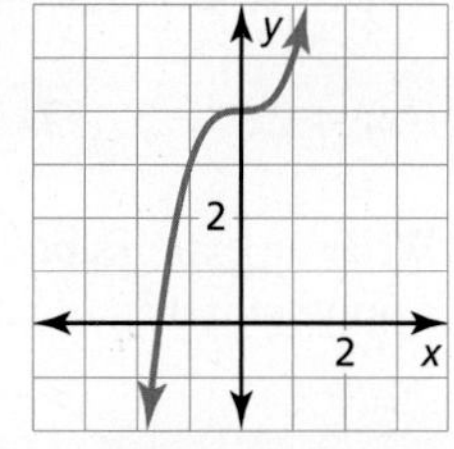

C.
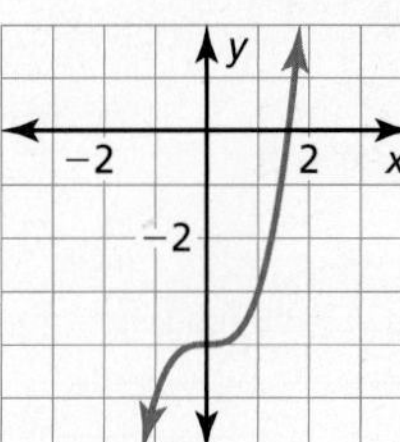

D.
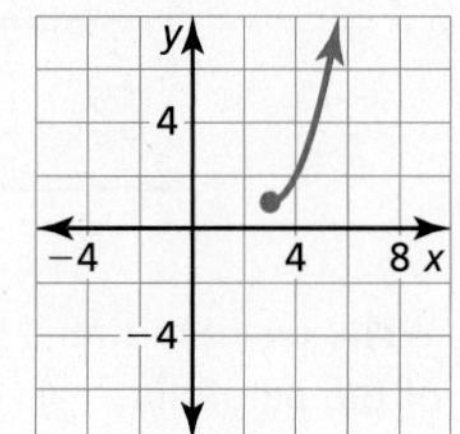

61. MP PROBLEM SOLVING When calibrating a spring scale, you need to know how far the spring stretches for various weights. Hooke's Law states that the distance a spring stretches is proportional to the weight attached to it. The length (in inches) of the spring on a certain scale is represented by $h(x) = 0.5x + 3$, where x is the weight (in pounds) of the object.

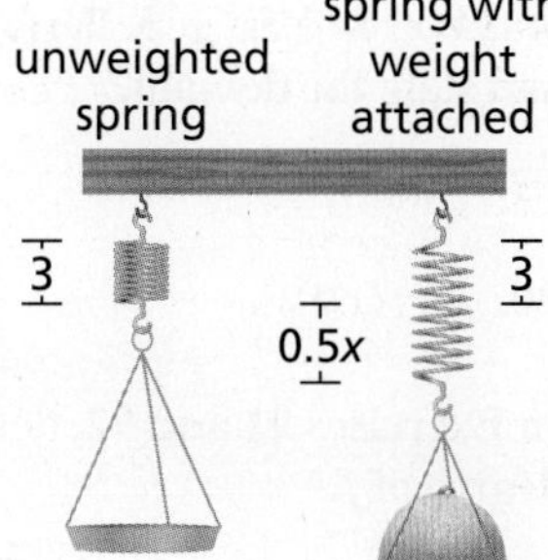

a. Find the inverse function. Describe what it represents.

b. You place a melon on the scale, and the spring stretches to a total length of 5.5 inches. Determine the weight of the melon.

c. Verify that h and the function you found in part (a) are inverse functions.

62. MP PROBLEM SOLVING The surface area (in square meters) of a person with a mass of 60 kilograms can be approximated by $s(x) = 0.2195x^{0.3964}$, where x is the height (in centimeters) of the person.

a. Find the inverse function. Then estimate the height of a 60-kilogram person who has a body surface area of 1.6 square meters.

b. Verify that s and the function you found in part (a) are inverse functions.

63. MODELING REAL LIFE At the start of a dog sled race in Anchorage, Alaska, the temperature was 5°C. By the end of the race, the temperature was -10°C. The temperature in degrees Celsius is represented by $C(x) = \frac{5}{9}(x - 32)$, where x is the temperature in degrees Fahrenheit.

a. Find the inverse function. Describe what it represents.

b. Find the Fahrenheit temperatures at the start and end of the race.

64. HOW DO YOU SEE IT? The graph of the function f is shown. Name three points that lie on the graph of the inverse of f. Explain your reasoning.

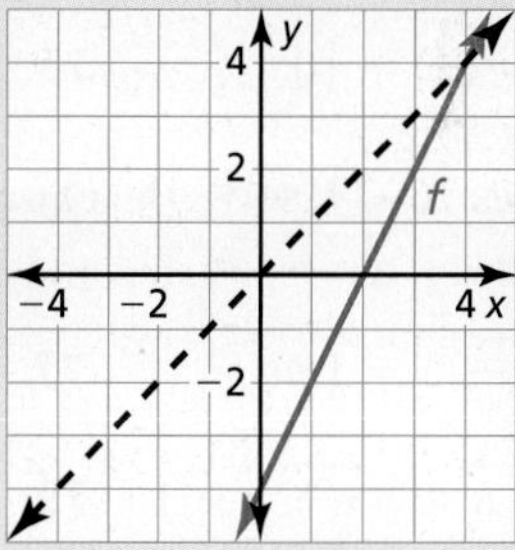

65. MAKING AN ARGUMENT Does every quadratic function whose domain is restricted to nonnegative values have an inverse function? Explain your reasoning.

66. THOUGHT PROVOKING Do functions of the form $y = \sqrt[n]{x^m}$, where m and n are positive integers, have inverse functions? Justify your answer with examples.

67. ABSTRACT REASONING Compare the slope and the y-intercept of a linear function with the slope and the y-intercept of its inverse. Is the inverse of any linear function also a linear function? Explain.

68. **PERFORMANCE TASK** When communicating by a secret code, the sender and the receiver of a message each use the same *key*. The sender uses the key to encode the message, and the receiver uses the key to decipher the message. This process is called *cryptography*. Work with a partner to write a function that can be used as the key for a secret code. Each of you encode a message and then decipher your partner's message. Explain how inverse functions are used in this process.

69. **DRAWING CONCLUSIONS** Determine whether the statement is *true* or *false*. Explain your reasoning.

a. If $f(x) = x^n$ and n is a positive even integer, then the inverse of f is a function.

b. If $f(x) = x^n$ and n is a positive odd integer, then the inverse of f is a function.

c. If $f(x) = x^n$, where $x \leq 0$ and n is a positive even integer, then the inverse of f is a function.

REVIEW & REFRESH

In Exercises 70 and 71, describe the x-values for which the function is increasing, decreasing, positive, and negative.

70.

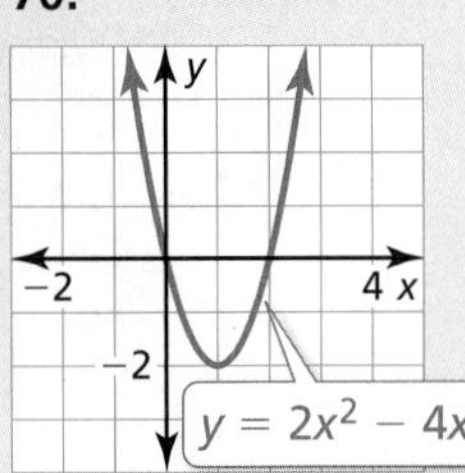

71.

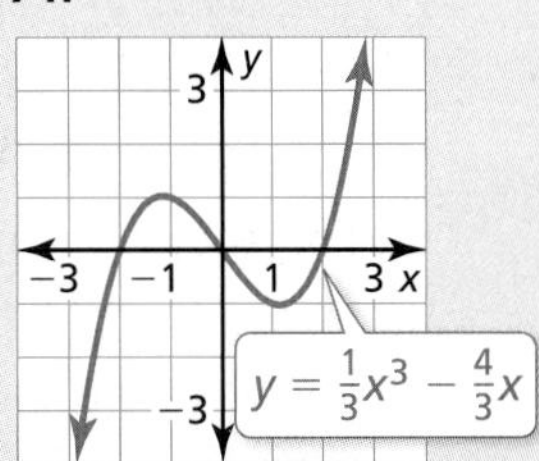

In Exercises 72–75, find the inverse of the function. Then graph the function and its inverse.

72. $f(x) = -4x + 7$

73. $f(x) = -3x^2 - 9,\ x \geq 0$

74. $f(x) = 2x^3 - 10$

75. $f(x) = 5\sqrt{x + 3}$

In Exercises 76–79, solve the equation. Check your solution(s).

76. $3\sqrt{4x - 3} = 15$

77. $x + 3 = \sqrt{4x + 17}$

78. $\sqrt{x - 8} = \sqrt{x + 3} - 1$

79. $(3x)^{2/3} - 6 = 3$

80. Write an equation that represents the data in the table.

x	1	2	3	4	5	6
y	12	10	0	−18	−44	−78

81. Write a quadratic equation that has the given solutions.

$$x = \frac{-5 \pm \sqrt{89}}{4}$$

82. Find the values of x and y that satisfy the equation $7yi + 3 = 18x + 14i$.

In Exercises 83 and 84, find $(f + g)(x)$ and $(f - g)(x)$ and state the domain of each. Then evaluate $f + g$ and $f - g$ for the given value of x.

83. $f(x) = 3\sqrt[3]{x},\ g(x) = -12\sqrt[3]{x};\ x = 64$

84. $f(x) = 2x^2 - 3 + 7x,\ g(x) = 11 + 4x^2;\ x = 3$

85. Write an expression for the volume of the figure as a polynomial in standard form.

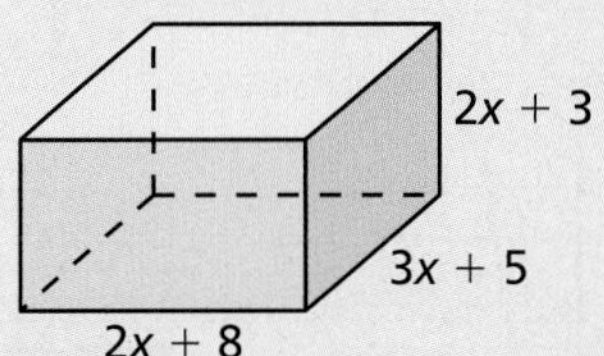

86. Write an equation of the parabola.

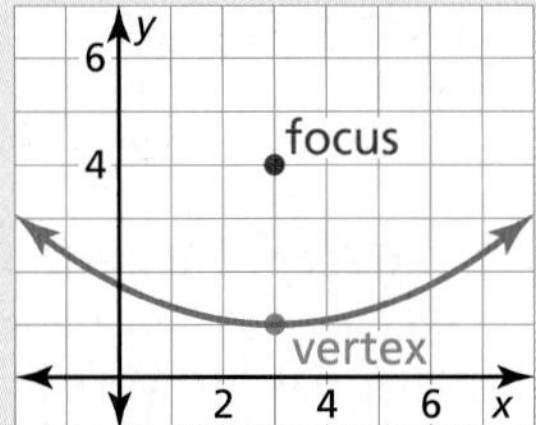

In Exercises 87–90, let $f(x) = 6x - 2$, $g(x) = 2x^{-1}$, and $h(x) = 1.5x + 3$. Perform the indicated operation and state the domain.

87. $f(h(x))$

88. $h(f(x))$

89. $g(f(x))$

90. $f(g(x))$

In Exercises 91 and 92, determine the least possible degree of f.

91.

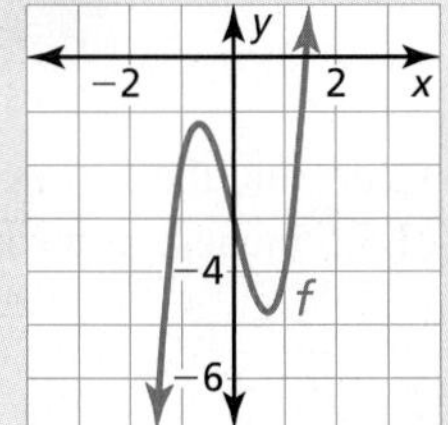

92.

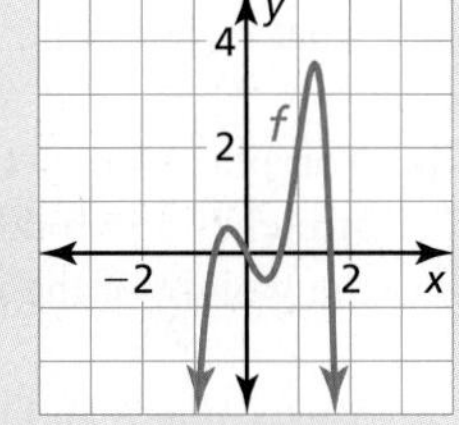

5 Chapter Review WITH CalcChat®

Chapter Learning Target Understand rational exponents and radical functions.

Chapter Success Criteria
- ◆ I can represent roots using rational exponents.
- ◆ I can describe the properties of rational exponents and radicals.
- ■ I can solve radical equations and inequalities.
- ■ I can find compositions and inverses of functions.

◆ Surface
■ Deep

SELF-ASSESSMENT 1 I do not understand. 2 I can do it with help. 3 I can do it on my own. 4 I can teach someone else.

5.1 *n*th Roots and Rational Exponents (pp. 231–236)

Learning Target: Evaluate expressions and solve equations containing *n*th roots and rational exponents.

Vocabulary
*n*th root of *a*
index of a radical

Find the indicated *n*th root(s) of *a*.

1. $n = 4, a = 1296$
2. $n = 5, a = -1024$

Evaluate the expression without using technology.

3. $8^{7/3}$
4. $9^{5/2}$
5. $(-27)^{-2/3}$

Find the real solution(s) of the equation. Round your answer to two decimal places when appropriate.

6. $x^5 + 17 = 35$
7. $7x^3 = 189$
8. $(x + 8)^4 = 16$

9. Without using technology, show that $3^{1.45}$ must be less than 6.

10. A diamond has eight equilateral triangles as faces. The formula $V = 0.47s^3$ approximates the volume V (in cubic millimeters) of the diamond, where s is the side length (in millimeters) of each edge. Approximate the length of each edge of the diamond.

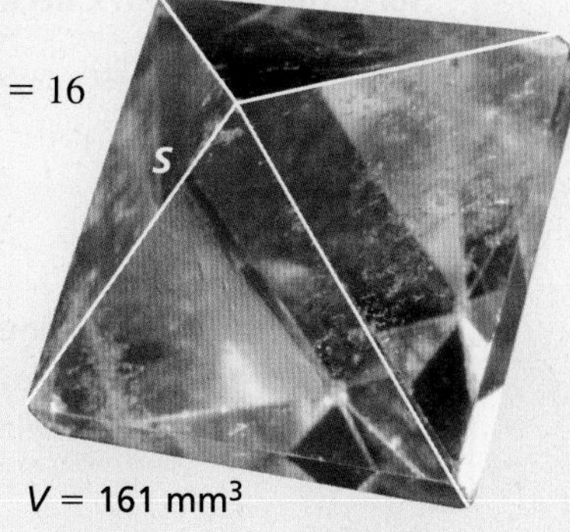

$V = 161$ mm^3

5.2 Properties of Rational Exponents and Radicals (pp. 237–244)

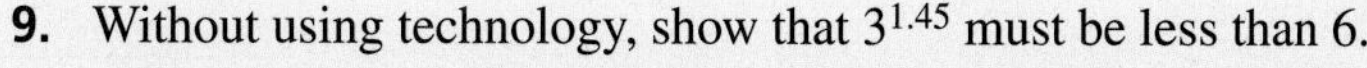

Learning Target: Simplify radical expressions.

Vocabulary
simplest form of a radical
like radicals

Simplify the expression.

11. $\left(\dfrac{6^{2/5}}{6^{1/5}}\right)^3$
12. $\sqrt[4]{32} \cdot \sqrt[4]{8}$
13. $\dfrac{1}{2 - \sqrt{7}}$
14. $4\sqrt[5]{8} + 3\sqrt[5]{8}$
15. $2\sqrt{48} - \sqrt{3}$
16. $(5^{2/3} \cdot 2^{3/2})^{1/2}$

Simplify the expression. Assume all variables are positive.

17. $\sqrt[3]{125z^9}$
18. $\dfrac{2^{1/4}z^{5/4}}{6z}$
19. $\sqrt{10z^5} - z^2\sqrt{40z}$

5.3 Graphing Radical Functions (pp. 245–252)

WATCH

Learning Target: Describe and graph transformations of radical functions.

Vocabulary VOCAB

radical function

Describe the transformation of f represented by g. Then graph each function.

20. $f(x) = \sqrt{x}$, $g(x) = -2\sqrt{x}$

21. $f(x) = \sqrt[3]{x}$, $g(x) = \sqrt[3]{-x} - 6$

22. Let the graph of g be a reflection in the y-axis, followed by a translation 7 units right of the graph of $f(x) = \sqrt[3]{x}$. Write a rule for g.

23. Use technology to graph $2y^2 = x - 8$. Identify the vertex and the direction the parabola opens.

24. Use technology to graph $x^2 + y^2 = 81$. Identify the radius and the intercepts.

25. An investigator uses the model $s = 4\sqrt{d}$ to estimate the speed s (in miles per hour) of a car just prior to an accident, where d is the length (in feet) of the skid marks. Graph the model. The skid marks are 90 feet long. Was the car traveling at the posted speed limit prior to the accident? Explain your reasoning.

5.4 Solving Radical Equations and Inequalities (pp. 253–260)

Learning Target: Solve equations and inequalities containing radicals and rational exponents.

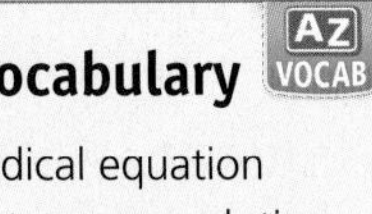

Vocabulary VOCAB

radical equation
extraneous solution

Solve the equation. Check your solution.

26. $4\sqrt[3]{2x + 1} = 20$

27. $\sqrt{4x - 4} = \sqrt{5x - 1} - 1$

28. $(6x)^{2/3} = 36$

Solve the inequality.

29. $5\sqrt{x} + 2 > 17$

30. $2\sqrt{x - 8} < 24$

31. $7\sqrt[3]{x - 3} \geq 21$

32. In a tsunami, the wave speeds (in meters per second) can be modeled by $s(d) = \sqrt{9.8d}$, where d is the depth (in meters) of the water. Estimate the depth of the water when the wave speed is 200 meters per second.

5.5 Performing Function Operations (pp. 261–266)

Learning Target: Perform arithmetic operations on two functions.

33. Let $f(x) = 2\sqrt{3 - x}$ and $g(x) = 4\sqrt[3]{3 - x}$. Find $(fg)(x)$ and $\left(\frac{f}{g}\right)(x)$ and state the domain of each. Then evaluate $(fg)(2)$ and $\left(\frac{f}{g}\right)(2)$.

34. Let $f(x) = 3x^2 + 1$ and $g(x) = x + 4$. Find $(f + g)(x)$ and $(f - g)(x)$ and state the domain of each. Then evaluate $(f + g)(-5)$ and $(f - g)(-5)$.

Determine whether the statement is *always*, *sometimes*, or *never* true. Explain your reasoning.

35. For two quadratic functions f and g, $f + g$ is also a quadratic function.

36. For two functions f and g, when $f(a) = 3$ and $g(a) = 4$, $(fg)(a) = 12$.

5.6 Composition of Functions (pp. 267–272)

Learning Target: Evaluate and find compositions of functions.

Vocabulary
composition

Let $f(x) = x + 3$, $g(x) = 4x^2$, and $h(x) = \sqrt{x - 7}$. Find the indicated value.

37. $f(h(11))$ **38.** $g(f(-8))$ **39.** $h(g(2))$

Let $f(x) = 2x - 5$, $g(x) = x^{-2}$, and $h(x) = 3x + 4$. Perform the indicated composition and state the domain.

40. $f(g(x))$ **41.** $h(f(x))$ **42.** $g(h(x))$

43. Let f be a radical function and let g be a linear function with a nonzero slope. What type of function results when you compose f and g?

44. You have the coupons shown to use for a purchase at an online store. Use a composition of functions to determine which coupon you should apply first. Explain.

5.7 Inverse of a Function (pp. 273–282)

Learning Target: Understand the relationship between inverse functions.

Vocabulary
inverse functions

Find the inverse of the function. Then graph the function and its inverse.

45. $f(x) = -\frac{1}{2}x + 10$ **46.** $f(x) = x^2 + 8, x \geq 0$

47. $f(x) = -x^3 - 9$ **48.** $f(x) = 3\sqrt{x} + 5$

Determine whether the functions are inverse functions.

49. $f(x) = 4(x - 11)^2$, $g(x) = \frac{1}{4}(x + 11)^2$ **50.** $f(x) = -2x + 6$, $g(x) = -\frac{1}{2}x + 3$

51. On a certain day, the function that gives U.S. dollars in terms of British pounds is $d(p) = 0.777p$, where p represents British pounds. Find and interpret $d^{-1}(100)$.

Mathematical Practices

Model with Mathematics

Mathematically proficient students identify important quantities in practical situations and map their relationships using such tools as diagrams, two-way tables, graphs, flowcharts, and formulas.

1. Explain how the equation you used to solve Exercise 45 on page 236 demonstrates the relationship among the given information.

2. In Example 3 on page 248, the relationship between time (in seconds) and the distance (in feet) that an object falls on Mars is represented by a function. Represent this relationship in two other ways.

5 Practice Test WITH CalcChat®

1. Solve the inequality $5\sqrt{x-3} - 2 \leq 13$ and the equation $5\sqrt{x-3} - 2 = 13$. Describe the similarities and differences in solving radical equations and radical inequalities.

Describe the transformation of *f* represented by *g*. Then write a rule for *g*.

2. $f(x) = \sqrt{x}$

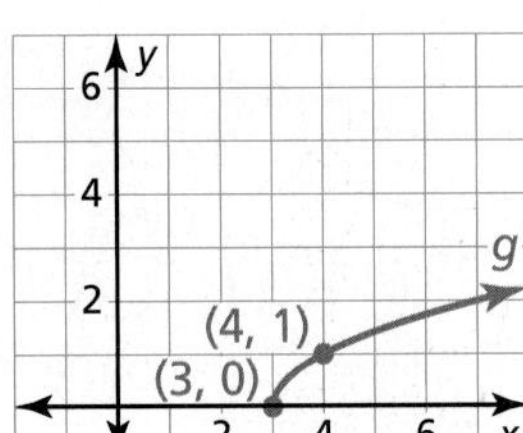

3. $f(x) = \sqrt[3]{x}$

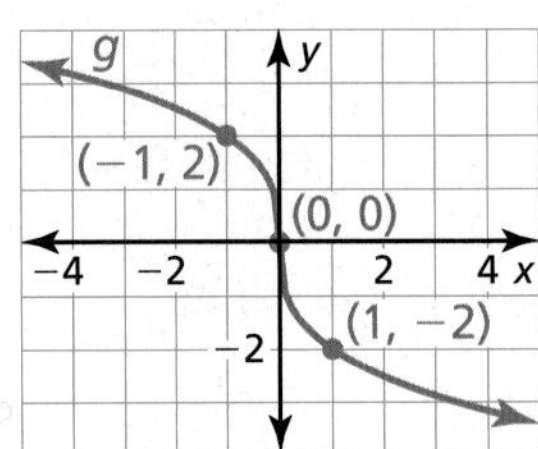

4. $f(x) = \sqrt[5]{x}$

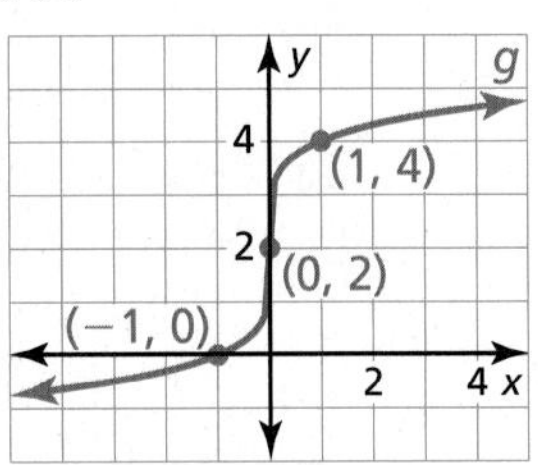

Simplify the expression. Explain your reasoning.

5. $64^{2/3}$

6. $(-27)^{5/3}$

7. $\sqrt[4]{48xy^{11}z^3}$

8. $\dfrac{\sqrt[3]{256}}{\sqrt[3]{32}}$

Let $f(x) = \frac{1}{4}x + 6$, $g(x) = 3x^{-1}$, and $h(x) = 4x + 12$. Perform the indicated composition and state the domain.

9. $f(h(x))$

10. $h(g(x))$

11. $g(f(x))$

12. $f(f(x))$

13. The graph of quadratic function f has focus $(-2, -7)$ and directrix $y = -1$. Find the focus and the directrix of the graph of the inverse of f.

14. The basal metabolic rate of an animal is a measure of the amount of calories burned at rest for basic functioning. Kleiber's law states that an animal's basal metabolic rate R (in kilocalories per day) can be modeled by $R = 73.3w^{3/4}$, where w is the mass (in kilograms) of the animal. Find the basal metabolic rates of each animal in the table.

Animal	Mass (kilograms)
rabbit	2.5
sheep	50
human	70
lion	210

15. Let $f(x) = 6x^{3/5}$ and $g(x) = -x^{3/5}$. Find $(f + g)(x)$ and $(f - g)(x)$ and state the domain of each. Then evaluate $(f + g)(32)$ and $(f - g)(32)$.

16. Let $f(x) = \frac{1}{2}x^{3/4}$ and $g(x) = 8x$. Find $(fg)(x)$ and $\left(\frac{f}{g}\right)(x)$ and state the domain of each. Then evaluate $(fg)(16)$ and $\left(\frac{f}{g}\right)(16)$.

17. The fork length r (in centimeters) of a requiem shark can be approximated by $r = 0.83t + 1.13$, where t is the total length (in centimeters) of the shark. Find the inverse of the function. Use the inverse to approximate the total length of a requiem shark whose fork length is 250 centimeters.

5 Performance Task
The Sounds of Music

Sound is transmitted in waves.

Each sound wave has a frequency, in hertz (Hz), that determines its pitch.

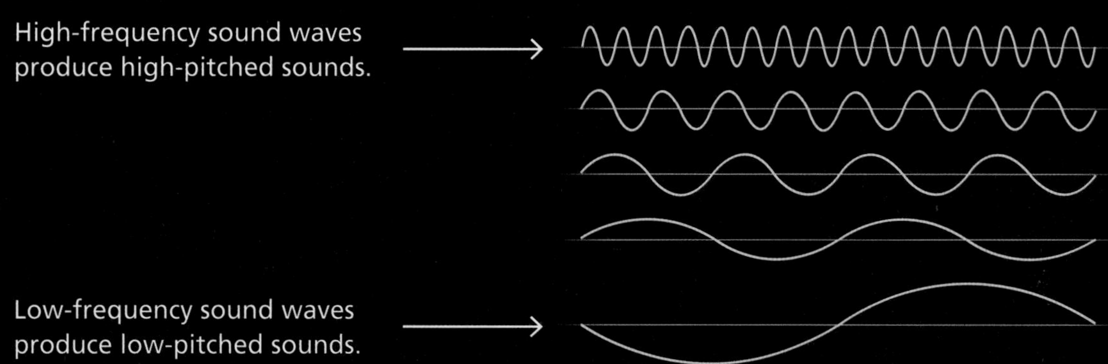

Each white key and each black key on a piano represents a distinct musical note. The frequency of a sound wave produced by each note is $2^{1/12}$ times the frequency of a sound wave produced by the previous note.

27.5 Hz

4186 Hz

A B C D E F G A B C D E F G A B C D E F G A B C D E F G A B C D E F G A B C D E F G A B C D E F G A B C D E F G A B C

1st octave | 2nd octave | 3rd octave | 4th octave | 5th octave | 6th octave | 7th octave

Musical tones are separated into groups called *octaves*. On a piano, 7 white keys and 5 black keys make up each octave.

COMPARING OCTAVES

Use a musical instrument or the Internet to listen to the same tone in different octaves. Compare and contrast their sounds. Then explain how the frequencies of the sound waves in the second octave on a piano compare to the frequencies of the sound waves in the first and third octaves. Justify your answers.

Which key on a piano is referred to as *middle C*? Show how you can use the information above to quickly find the frequency of a sound wave produced by middle C. Then find the frequencies of every note in the same octave as middle C.

5 College and Career Readiness WITH CalcChat®

Tutorial videos are available for each exercise.

1. Identify three pairs of equivalent expressions. Assume all variables are positive. Justify your answer.

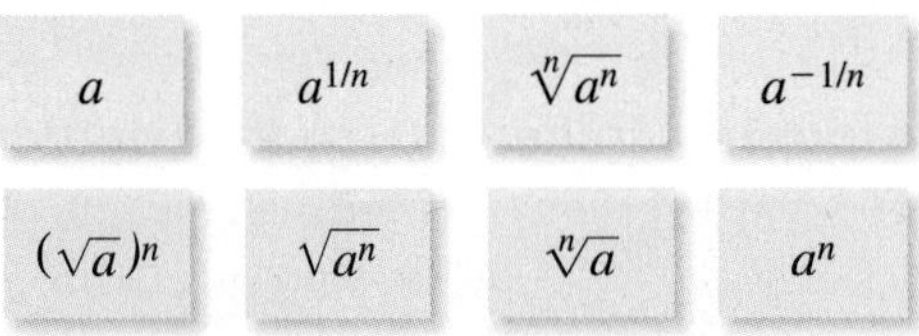

2. The graph represents the function $f(x) = (x - \square)^2 + \square$. Choose the correct values to complete the function.

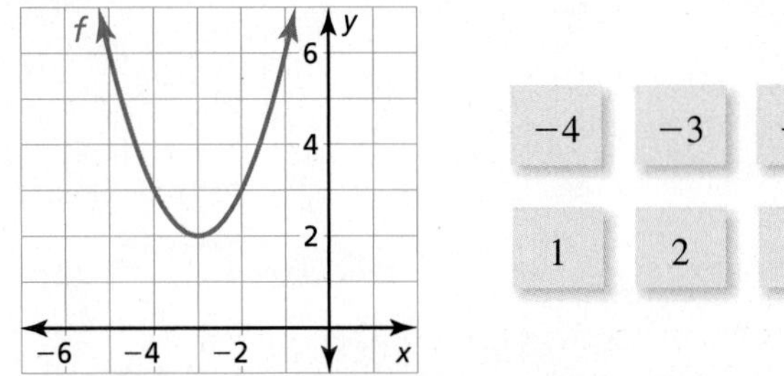

3. Which of the following are zeros of $f(x) = x^3 + 2x^2 + 9x + 18$? Select all that apply.

Ⓐ -3
Ⓑ -2
Ⓒ 2
Ⓓ 3
Ⓔ $-3i$
Ⓕ $3i$

4. A polynomial function fits the data shown. Complete the table. Justify your answers.

x	−7	−6	−5	−4	−3	−2	−1
f(x)	−15	−6	1	6	−9		

5. Which expression is equivalent to $8x^3 - 1$?

Ⓐ $(8x - 1)(64x^2 + 8x + 1)$

Ⓑ $(2x - 1)(4x^2 + 2x + 1)$

Ⓒ $(2x + 1)(4x^2 - 2x + 1)$

Ⓓ none of the above

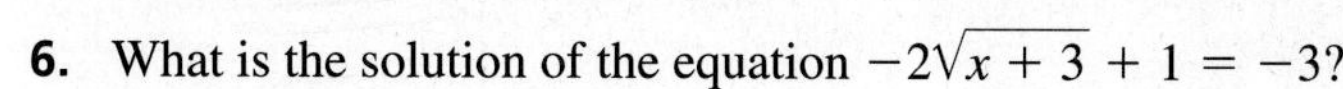

6. What is the solution of the equation $-2\sqrt{x+3} + 1 = -3$?

Ⓐ $x = -2$

Ⓑ $x = \sqrt{2} - 3$

Ⓒ $x = 1$

Ⓓ no solution

7. Which function does the graph represent?

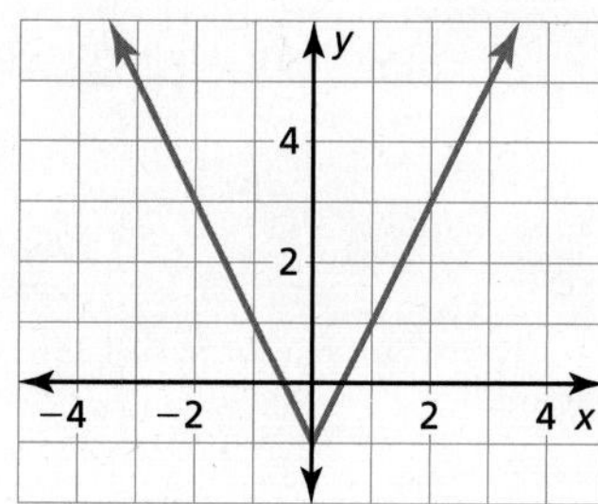

Ⓐ $y = -|2x| - 1$

Ⓑ $y = |x| - 1$

Ⓒ $y = |2x| - 1$

Ⓓ $y = |2x + 1|$

8. Your friend releases a weather balloon 50 feet from you. The balloon rises vertically. When the balloon is at height h, the distance d between you and the balloon is given by $d = \sqrt{2500 + h^2}$, where h and d are measured in feet. Find the inverse of the function. What is the height of the balloon when the distance between you and the balloon is 100 feet?

9. The area of the triangle is 42 square inches. Find the value of x.

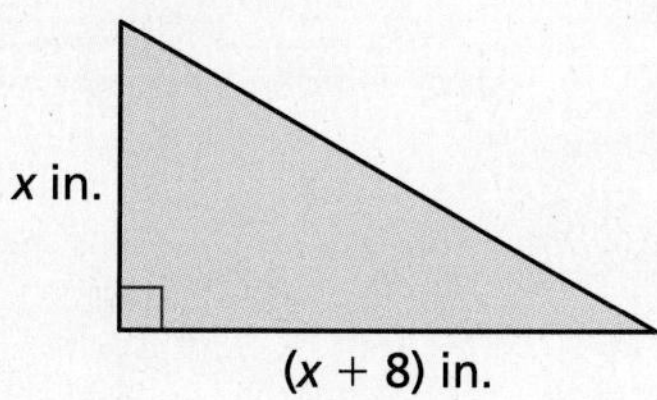

10. Which is the graph of $f(x) = (x - 2)(x + 1)(x - 1)^2$?

Ⓐ

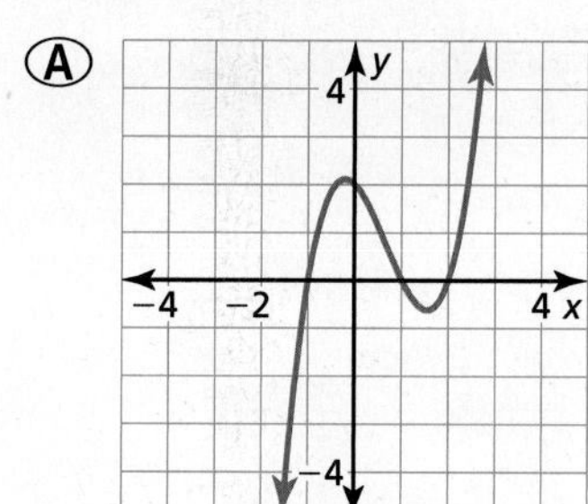

Ⓑ

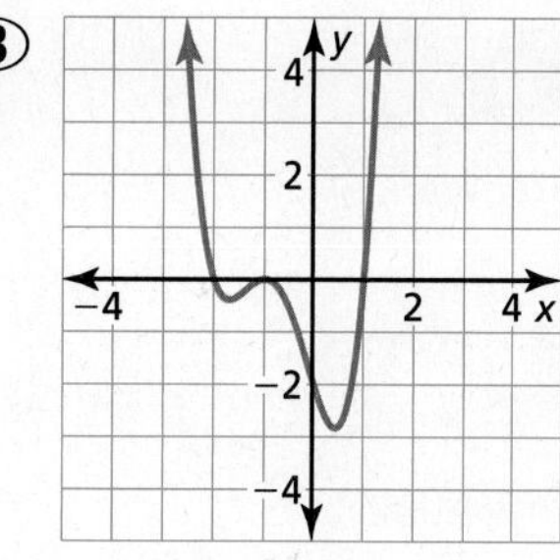

Ⓒ

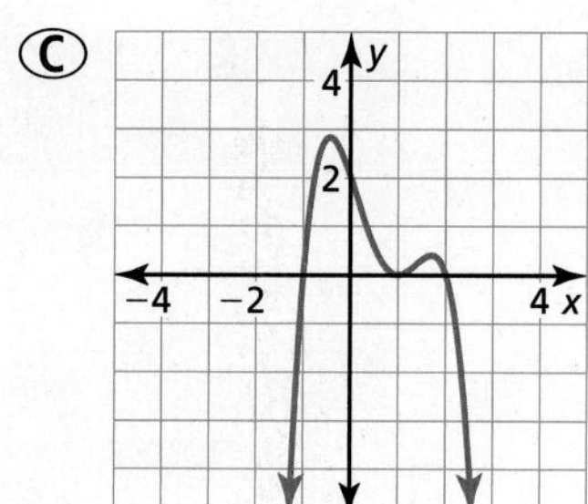

Ⓓ

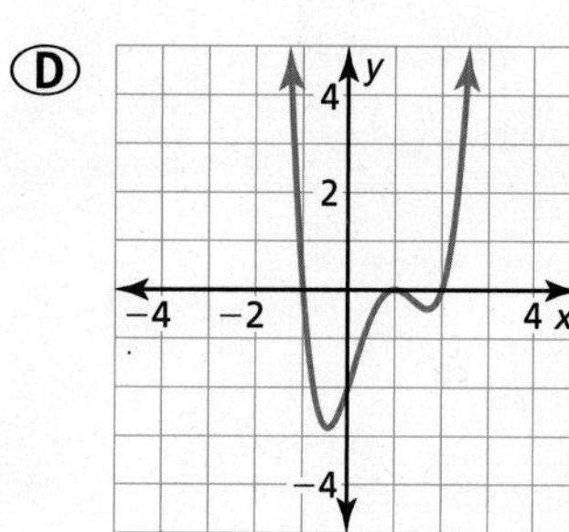

6 Exponential and Logarithmic Functions

NATIONAL GEOGRAPHIC EXPLORER

Matthew Piscitelli

Dr. Matthew Piscitelli is an archaeologist who researches an early civilization in the Norte Chico region of Peru. Dr. Piscitelli writes that during the Late Archaic Period, people in the Norte Chico region changed from being hunter-gatherers to being farmers. They built cities and ceremonial structures. Their civilization is one of the oldest in the Americas.

- What is archaeology?
- When was the Late Archaic Period?
- Which crops did the ancient Peruvians grow?
- Describe some of the large ceremonial structures that the ancient Peruvians built during the Late Archaic Period.

STEM

When archaeologists discover organic matter, they can use carbon dating to approximate when the organic matter died. In the Performance Task, you will use carbon dating to approximate the age of an ancient manuscript made from a plant called papyrus.

Andean Prehistory

Preparing for Chapter 6

Chapter Learning Target Understand exponential and logarithmic functions.

Chapter Success Criteria

- ◆ I can determine whether a function represents exponential growth or decay.
- ◆ I can simplify exponential and logarithmic expressions.
- ■ I can solve exponential and logarithmic equations.
- ■ I can model exponential and logarithmic functions.

◆ Surface
■ Deep

Chapter Vocabulary

Work with a partner. Discuss each of the vocabulary terms.

exponential growth function
growth factor
exponential decay function
decay factor
exponential equations

Mathematical Practices

Look for and Express Regularity in Repeated Reasoning

Mathematically proficient students notice if calculations are repeated, and look both for general methods and for shortcuts.

Work with a partner. The table shows the percents y of carbon-14 remaining in an organism, where t is the amount of time (in thousands of years) since the organism died.

Time (thousands of years), t	0	1	2	3	4	5
Percent remaining, y	100	88.61	78.51	69.57	61.64	54.62

1. Describe the relationships between consecutive t- and y-values in the table.

2. Use the relationships that you described in Exercise 1 to find the percents of carbon-14 remaining after 6000, 7000, and 8000 years.

3. Write an equation that represents the percent y of carbon-14 remaining after t thousand years. Explain your reasoning.

6 Prepare WITH CalcChat®

Using Properties of Exponents

Example 1 **Simplify** $\left(\frac{4p}{3}\right)^3$.

$$\left(\frac{4p}{3}\right)^3 = \frac{(4p)^3}{3^3}$$ Power of a Quotient Property

$$= \frac{4^3p^3}{3^3}$$ Power of a Product Property

$$= \frac{64p^3}{27}$$ Simplify.

Simplify the expression. Write your answer using only positive exponents.

1. $6b^0$

2. $(-2n)^5$

3. $\left(\frac{3w}{2x}\right)^4$

4. $\frac{3g}{4^{-2}}$

Finding the Domain and Range of a Function

Example 2 **Find the domain and range of the function represented by the graph.**

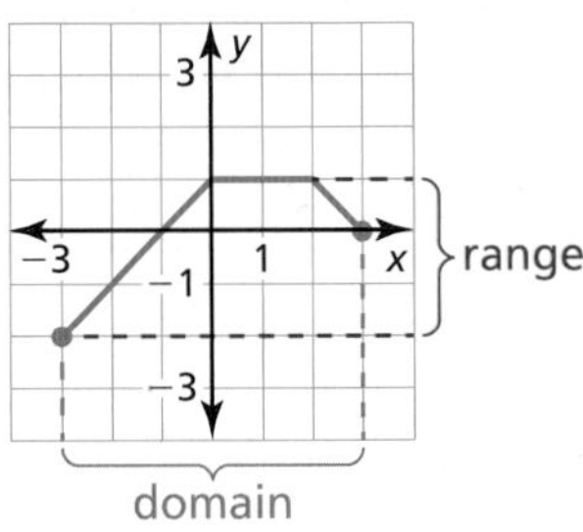

▶ The domain is $-3 \le x \le 3$.
The range is $-2 \le y \le 1$.

Find the domain and range of the function represented by the graph.

5.

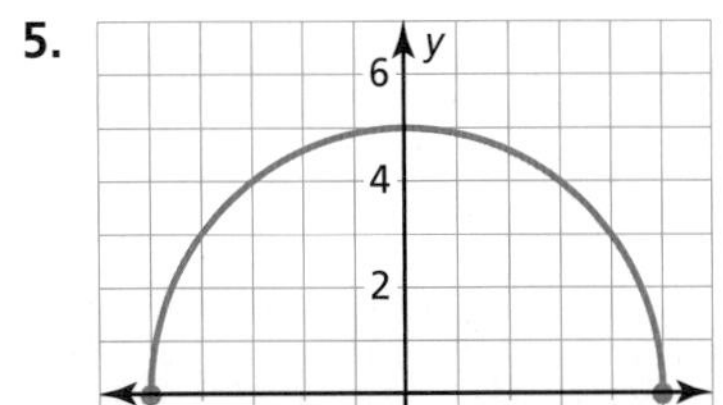

6.

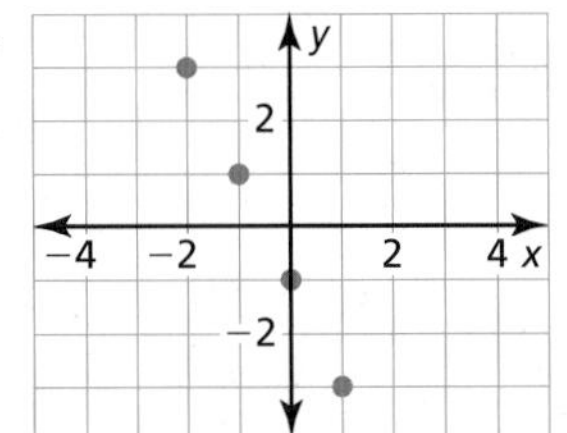

7.

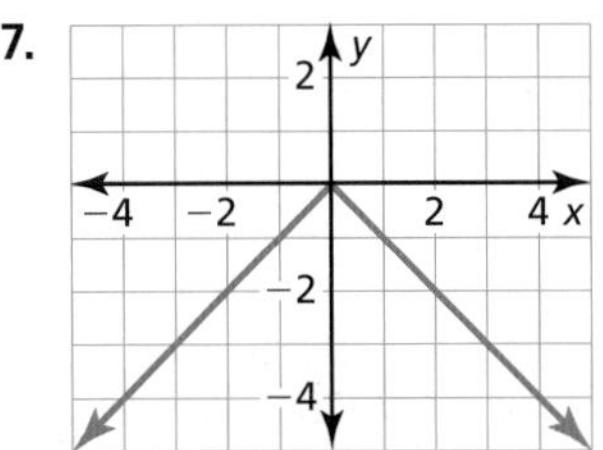

8. **MP STRUCTURE** Consider the expressions $-a^n$ and $(-a)^n$, where $a > 0$ and n is an integer. For what values of n is each expression negative? positive? Explain your reasoning.

6.1 Exponential Growth and Decay Functions

Learning Target Write and graph exponential growth and decay functions.

Success Criteria

- I can identify and graph exponential growth and decay functions.
- I can write exponential growth and decay functions.
- I can solve real-life problems using exponential growth and decay functions.

EXPLORE IT! Describing Exponential Growth

Work with a partner. You are studying bacteria growth in a laboratory.

a. The study starts with a population of 100 bacteria. You notice that the population doubles every hour. Complete the table.

Time (hours), t	0	1	2	3	4	5
Population, P						

b. Write a model that represents the population P of the bacteria after t hours.

c. Use the model in part (b) to complete the table. By what factor does the population increase every half hour? Explain your reasoning.

Time (hours), t	0	$\frac{1}{2}$	1	$\frac{3}{2}$	2	$\frac{5}{2}$	3
Population, P							

d. Use the model in part (b) to complete the table. By what factor does the population increase every 20 minutes? Explain your reasoning.

Time (hours), t	0	$\frac{1}{3}$	$\frac{2}{3}$	1	$\frac{4}{3}$	$\frac{5}{3}$	2
Population, P							

e. Create a graph that shows the population P after t hours. Would you expect the actual bacteria population to closely follow this model as t increases? Explain your reasoning.

f. MP **CHOOSE TOOLS** The population P of a different type of bacteria after t hours can be represented by

$$P = 10(3)^t.$$

How does the growth pattern of this bacteria compare with the growth rate of the bacteria in parts (a)–(e)?

Math Practice

Construct Arguments
Will the two bacteria populations ever be equal? Explain.

Exponential Growth and Decay Functions

Vocabulary

exponential function, *p. 294*
exponential growth function, *p. 294*
growth factor, *p. 294*
asymptote, *p. 294*
exponential decay function, *p. 294*
decay factor, *p. 294*

An **exponential function** has the form $y = ab^x$, where $a \neq 0$ and the base b is a positive real number other than 1. If $a > 0$ and $b > 1$, then $y = ab^x$ is an **exponential growth function**, and b is called the **growth factor**. The simplest type of exponential growth function has the form $y = b^x$.

KEY IDEA

Parent Function for Exponential Growth Functions

The function $f(x) = b^x$, where $b > 1$, is the parent function for the family of exponential growth functions with base b. The graph shows the general shape of an exponential growth function.

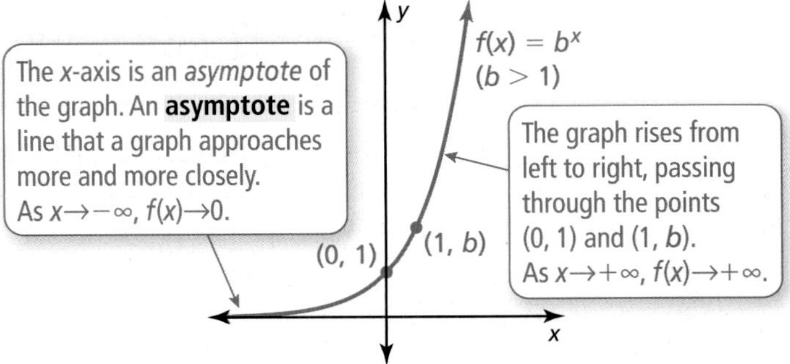

The domain of $f(x) = b^x$ is all real numbers. The range is $y > 0$.

If $a > 0$ and $0 < b < 1$, then $y = ab^x$ is an **exponential decay function**, and b is called the **decay factor**.

KEY IDEA

Parent Function for Exponential Decay Functions

The function $f(x) = b^x$, where $0 < b < 1$, is the parent function for the family of exponential decay functions with base b. The graph shows the general shape of an exponential decay function.

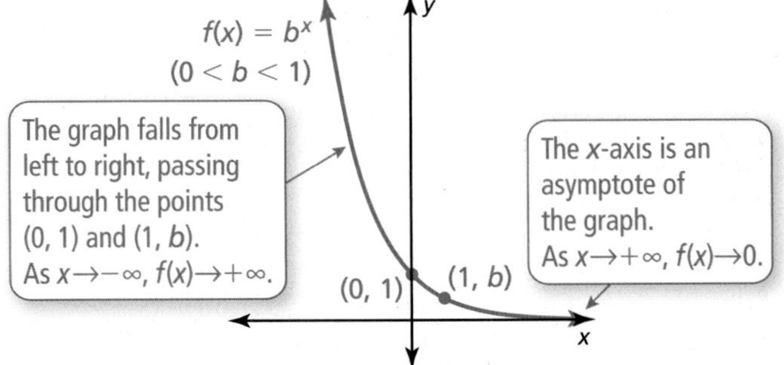

The domain of $f(x) = b^x$ is all real numbers. The range is $y > 0$.

EXAMPLE 1 **Graphing Exponential Growth and Decay Functions**

Determine whether each function represents *exponential growth* or *exponential decay*. Then graph the function.

a. $y = 2^x$ **b.** $y = \left(\frac{1}{2}\right)^x$

SOLUTION

a. Step 1 Identify the value of the base. The base, 2, is greater than 1, so the function represents exponential growth.

Step 2 Make a table of values.

x	−2	−1	0	1	2	3
y	$\frac{1}{4}$	$\frac{1}{2}$	1	2	4	8

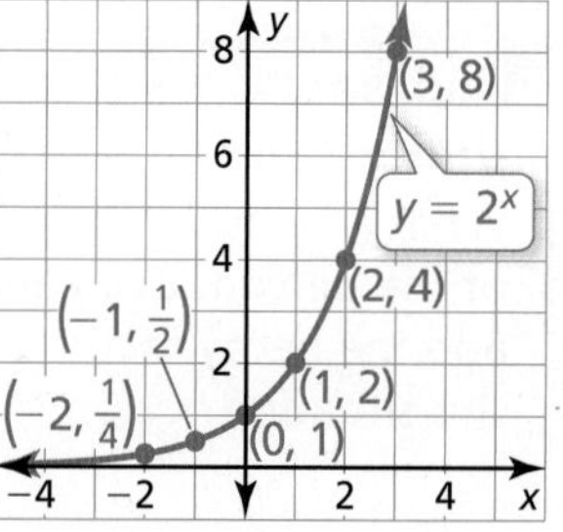

Step 3 Plot the points from the table.

Step 4 Draw, from *left to right*, a smooth curve that begins just above the x-axis, passes through the plotted points, and moves up to the right.

b. Step 1 Identify the value of the base. The base, $\frac{1}{2}$, is greater than 0 and less than 1, so the function represents exponential decay.

Step 2 Make a table of values.

x	−3	−2	−1	0	1	2
y	8	4	2	1	$\frac{1}{2}$	$\frac{1}{4}$

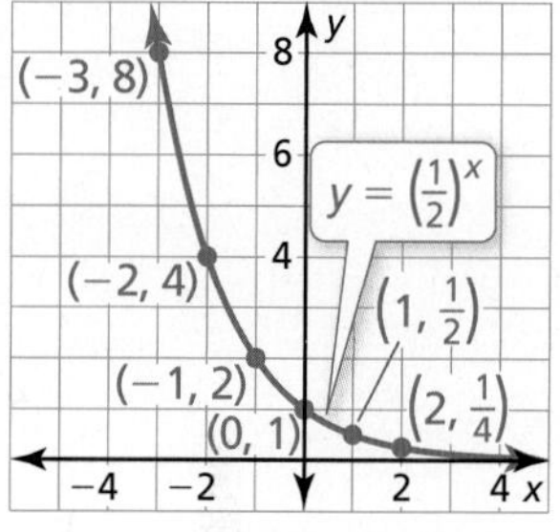

Step 3 Plot the points from the table.

Step 4 Draw, from *right to left*, a smooth curve that begins just above the x-axis, passes through the plotted points, and moves up to the left.

SELF-ASSESSMENT 1 I do not understand. 2 I can do it with help. 3 I can do it on my own. 4 I can teach someone else.

Determine whether the function represents *exponential growth* or *exponential decay*. Then graph the function.

1. $y = 4^x$
2. $y = \left(\frac{2}{3}\right)^x$
3. $f(x) = (0.25)^x$
4. $f(x) = (1.5)^x$
5. **MP STRUCTURE** Let $f(x) = 3^x$. What transformations of f result in exponential growth functions? What transformations result in exponential decay functions? Explain your reasoning.

Exponential Models

Some real-life quantities increase or decrease by a fixed percent each year (or some other time period). The amount y of such a quantity after t years can be modeled by one of these equations:

Exponential Growth Model	Exponential Decay Model
$y = a(1 + r)^t$	$y = a(1 - r)^t$

Note that a is the initial amount and r is the percent increase or decrease written as a decimal. The quantity $1 + r$ is the growth factor, and $1 - r$ is the decay factor.

Modeling Real Life

The value of a car y (in thousands of dollars) can be approximated by the model $y = 25(0.85)^t$, where t is the number of years since the car was purchased.

a. Determine whether the model represents *exponential growth* or *exponential decay.*

b. Identify the annual percent increase or decrease in the value of the car.

c. Estimate when the value of the car will be $8000.

SOLUTION

a. The base, 0.85, is greater than 0 and less than 1, so the model represents exponential decay.

b. Because t is given in years and the decay factor $0.85 = 1 - 0.15$, the annual percent decrease is 0.15, or 15%.

c. Use technology to determine that $y \approx 8$ when $t = 7$. After 7 years, the value of the car will be about $8000.

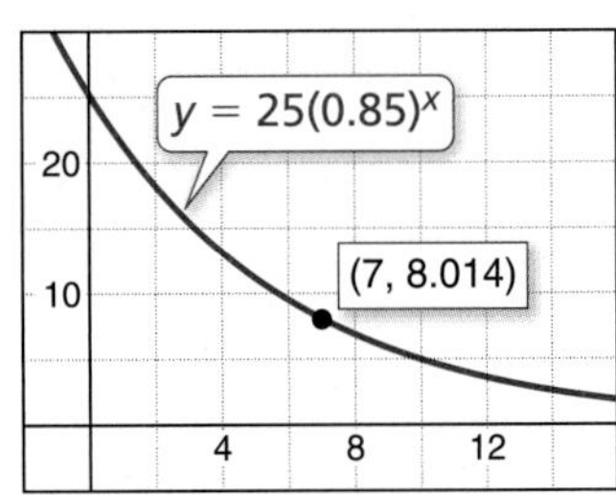

Math Practice

Understand Quantities

What are the meanings of the percent decrease and the decay factor in this situation?

EXAMPLE 3

Writing an Exponential Model

In 2015, the world population was about 7.38 billion. During the next 5 years, the world population increased by about 1.09% each year. Write an exponential model that represents the population y (in billions) t years after 2015. Then estimate the world population in 2020.

SOLUTION

The initial amount is $a = 7.38$. The percent increase is $r = 0.0109$, so use an exponential growth model.

$y = a(1 + r)^t$	Write exponential growth model.
$= 7.38(1 + 0.0109)^t$	Substitute 7.38 for *a* and 0.0109 for *r*.
$= 7.38(1.0109)^t$	Simplify.

To estimate the world population in 2020, evaluate the model when $t = 5$.

$$y = 7.38(1.0109)^5 \approx 7.79 \text{ billion}$$

SELF-ASSESSMENT

1 I do not understand. **2** I can do it with help. **3** I can do it on my own. **4** I can teach someone else.

6. WHAT IF? In Example 2, the value of the car can be approximated by the model $y = 25(0.9)^t$. Identify the annual percent decrease in the value of the car. Estimate when the value of the car will be $8000.

7. WHAT IF? In Example 3, assume that starting in 2020, the world population increases by 0.98% each year for the next 5 years. Use a model to estimate when the world population will be 8 billion.

8. WHICH ONE DOESN'T BELONG? Which characteristic of an exponential decay function does *not* belong with the other three? Explain your reasoning.

base of 0.8	percent decrease of 20%	decay factor of 0.8	80% decrease

GO DIGITAL

EXAMPLE 4 Rewriting an Exponential Function

The amount y (in grams) of the radioactive isotope chromium-51 remaining after t days is $y = a(0.5)^{t/28}$, where a is the initial amount (in grams). What percent of the chromium-51 decays each day?

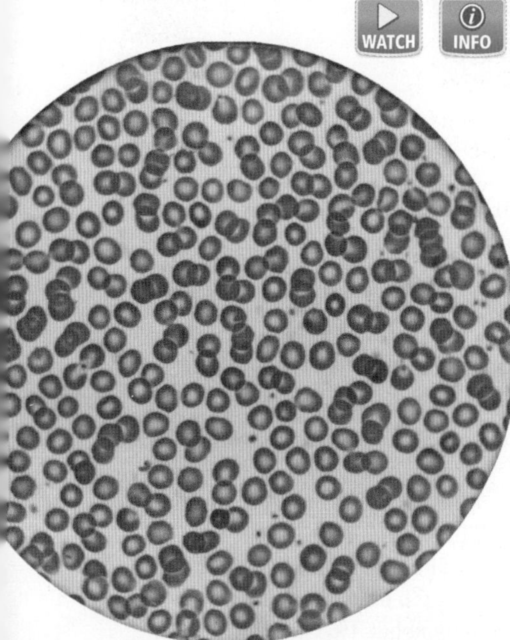

Chromium-51 is used in medical research. It can be used as a tracer in blood for studies of red blood cells.

SOLUTION

$y = a(0.5)^{t/28}$ Write original function.

$= a[(0.5)^{1/28}]^t$ Power of a Power Property

$\approx a(0.9755)^t$ Evaluate power.

$= a(1 - 0.0245)^t$ Rewrite in form $y = a(1 - r)^t$.

▶ The daily decay rate is about 0.0245, or 2.45%.

Compound interest is interest paid on an initial investment, called the *principal*, and on previously earned interest. Interest earned is often expressed as an *annual* percent, but the interest is usually compounded more than once per year. So, the exponential growth model $y = a(1 + r)^t$ must be modified for compound interest problems.

KEY IDEA

Compound Interest

Consider an initial principal P deposited in an account that pays interest at an annual rate r (expressed as a decimal), compounded n times per year. The amount A in the account after t years is given by

$$A = P\left(1 + \frac{r}{n}\right)^{nt}.$$

EXAMPLE 5 Finding the Balance in an Account

You deposit $9000 in an account that pays 1.46% annual interest. Find the balance after 3 years when the interest is compounded quarterly.

SOLUTION

Use the compound interest formula.

$A = P\left(1 + \frac{r}{n}\right)^{nt}$ Write compound interest formula.

$= 9000\left(1 + \frac{0.0146}{4}\right)^{4 \cdot 3}$ $P = 9000, r = 0.0146, n = 4, t = 3$ (compounded quarterly)

≈ 9402.21 Use technology.

▶ The balance after 3 years is $9402.21.

Math Practice

View as Components

You can write the formula as $A = 9000(1.00365)^{4t}$. Notice that this formula consists of the product of the principal, 9000, and a factor independent of the principal, $(1.00365)^{4t}$.

SELF-ASSESSMENT

1 I do not understand. 2 I can do it with help. 3 I can do it on my own. 4 I can teach someone else.

9. The amount y (in grams) of the radioactive isotope iodine-123 remaining after t hours is $y = a(0.5)^{t/13}$, where a is the initial amount (in grams). What percent of the iodine-123 decays each hour?

10. You deposit $500 in an account that pays 2.5% annual interest. Find the balance after 2 years when the interest is compounded daily.

6.1 Practice WITH CalcChat® AND CalcView®

GO DIGITAL

In Exercises 1–6, evaluate the expression for (a) $x = -2$ and (b) $x = 3$.

1. 2^x
2. $\left(\frac{1}{4}\right)^x$
3. $8(3)^x$
4. $6\left(\frac{1}{2}\right)^x$
5. $5(1.03)^x$
6. $-2(0.8)^x$

In Exercises 7–16, determine whether the function represents *exponential growth* or *exponential decay*. Then graph the function. *Example 1*

7. $y = 6^x$
8. $y = 7^x$
9. $f(x) = \left(\frac{1}{6}\right)^x$
10. $f(x) = \left(\frac{1}{8}\right)^x$
11. $y = \left(\frac{4}{3}\right)^x$
12. $y = \left(\frac{2}{5}\right)^x$
13. $f(x) = (1.2)^x$
14. $f(x) = (0.75)^x$
15. $y = (0.6)^x$
16. $y = (1.8)^x$

ANALYZING RELATIONSHIPS In Exercises 17 and 18, use the graph of $f(x) = b^x$ to identify the value of the base b.

17.

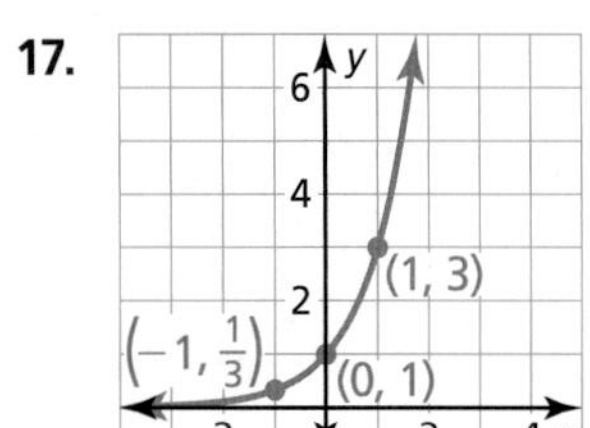

18.

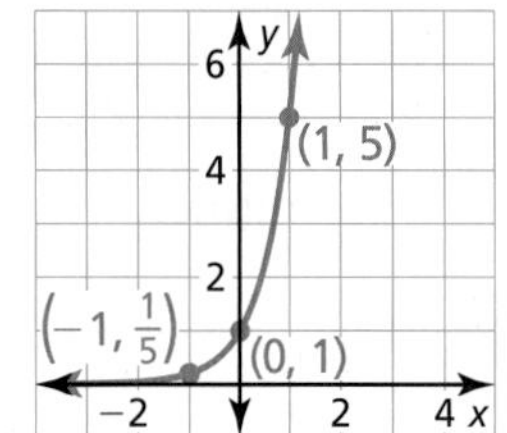

19. **MODELING REAL LIFE** The value of a mountain bike y (in dollars) can be approximated by the model $y = 200(0.65)^t$, where t is the number of years since the bike was purchased. *Example 2*

   a. Determine whether the model represents *exponential growth* or *exponential decay*.

   b. Identify the annual percent increase or decrease in the value of the bike.

   c. Estimate when the value of the bike will be \$50.

20. **MODELING REAL LIFE** The population P (in millions) of Peru during a recent decade can be approximated by $P = 28.22(1.01)^t$, where t is the number of years since the beginning of the decade.

   a. Determine whether the model represents *exponential growth* or *exponential decay*.

   b. Identify the annual percent increase or decrease in population.

   c. Estimate when the population was about 30 million.

21. **MODELING REAL LIFE** In 2012, there were about 6.26 billion cell phone subscribers in the world. During the next 5 years, the number of cell phone subscribers increased by about 4% each year. *Example 3*

   a. Write an exponential model that represents the number of cell phone subscribers y (in billions) t years after 2012. Then estimate the number of cell phone subscribers in 2016.

   b. Estimate when the number of cell phone subscribers was about 7 billion.

22. **MODELING REAL LIFE** You take a 325-milligram dosage of ibuprofen. The amount of medication in your bloodstream decreases by about 29% each hour.

   a. Write an exponential model that represents the amount y (in milligrams) of ibuprofen in your bloodstream t hours after the initial dose.

   b. Estimate when you will have 100 milligrams of ibuprofen in your bloodstream.

JUSTIFYING STEPS In Exercises 23 and 24, justify each step in rewriting the exponential function.

23. $y = a(3)^{t/14}$ Write original function.

   $= a[(3)^{1/14}]^t$

   $\approx a(1.0816)^t$

   $= a(1 + 0.0816)^t$

24. $y = a(0.1)^{t/3}$ Write original function.

   $= a[(0.1)^{1/3}]^t$

   $\approx a(0.4642)^t$

   $= a(1 - 0.5358)^t$

25. MODELING REAL LIFE When a plant or an animal dies, it stops acquiring carbon-14 from the atmosphere. The amount y (in grams) of carbon-14 in the body of an organism t years after the organism dies is $y = a(0.5)^{t/5730}$, where a is the initial amount (in grams). What percent of the carbon-14 is released each year? *Example 4*

26. MODELING REAL LIFE The number y of Salmonella cells on an egg after t minutes is $y = a(4.7)^{t/45}$, where a is the initial number of cells. By what percent does the number of Salmonella cells increase each minute?

In Exercises 27–34, rewrite the function in the form $y = a(1 + r)^t$ or $y = a(1 - r)^t$. State the growth or decay rate, and describe the end behavior of the function.

27. $y = a(2)^{t/3}$

28. $y = a(4)^{t/6}$

29. $y = a(0.5)^{t/12}$

30. $y = a(0.25)^{t/9}$

31. $y = a\left(\frac{2}{3}\right)^{t/10}$

32. $y = a\left(\frac{5}{4}\right)^{t/22}$

33. $y = a(2)^{8t}$

34. $y = a\left(\frac{1}{3}\right)^{3t}$

35. MP PROBLEM SOLVING You deposit \$5000 in an account that pays 2.25% annual interest. Find the balance after 5 years when the interest is compounded quarterly. *Example 5*

36. DRAWING CONCLUSIONS You deposit \$2200 into each of three separate bank accounts that pay 3% annual interest. Interest is compounded quarterly in Account 1, monthly in Account 2, and daily in Account 3. How much interest does each account earn after 6 years?

37. ERROR ANALYSIS You invest \$500 in the stock of a company. The value of the stock decreases 2% each year. Describe and correct the error in writing a model for the value of the stock after t years.

> ✗ $y = \left(\text{Initial amount}\right)\left(\text{Decay factor}\right)^t$
>
> $y = 500(0.02)^t$

38. ERROR ANALYSIS You deposit \$250 in an account that pays 1.25% annual interest. Describe and correct the error in finding the balance after 3 years when the interest is compounded quarterly.

> ✗ $A = 250\left(1 + \frac{1.25}{4}\right)^{4 \cdot 3}$
>
> $= \$6533.29$

In Exercises 39–42, use the given information to find the balance in the account earning compound interest after 6 years when the principal is \$3500.

39. $r = 2.16\%$, compounded quarterly

40. $r = 2.29\%$, compounded monthly

41. $r = 1.26\%$, compounded monthly

42. $r = 1.83\%$, compounded daily

43. MP STRUCTURE In the compound interest formula for interest compounded yearly, $A = P(1 + r)^t$, what does P represent? What does $(1 + r)^t$ represent? Does P depend on $(1 + r)^t$? Does $(1 + r)^t$ depend on P? Explain.

44. MP STRUCTURE A website recorded the number y of referrals it received from social media websites over a 10-year period. The results can be modeled by $y = 2500(1.50)^t$, where t is the year and $0 \leq t \leq 9$. Interpret what the numbers 2500 and 1.50 represent in this situation. What is the annual percent increase? Explain.

45. COMPARING FUNCTIONS Compare the graph of $f(x) = 2(1.5)^x$ to the graph of g. Which graph has a greater y-intercept? Which graph is increasing at a faster rate? Explain your reasoning.

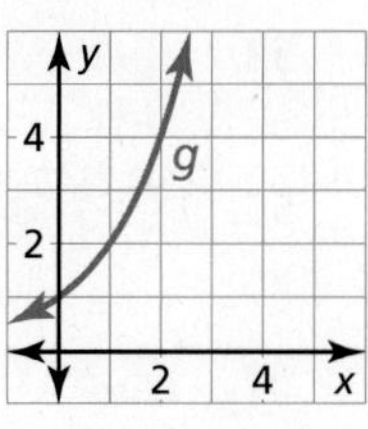

46. HOW DO YOU SEE IT? The graph shows an exponential function of the form $f(x) = ab^x$.

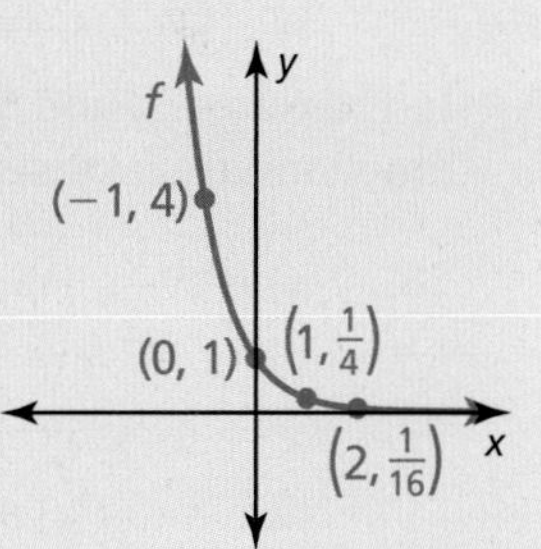

a. Determine whether f represents *exponential growth* or *exponential decay*.

b. What are the domain and range of the function? Explain.

47. MP PROBLEM SOLVING The population p of a small town after x years can be modeled by the function $p = 6850(1.03)^x$. What is the average rate of change in the population over the first 6 years? Justify your answer.

48. THOUGHT PROVOKING The function $f(x) = b^x$ represents exponential decay. Write another exponential decay function in terms of b and x.

49. **COLLEGE PREP** The radioactive isotope phosphorus-32 has a daily decay rate of 4.8%. After 1 week, there are 7.1 grams of phosphorus-32 remaining. About how many grams were there initially?

Ⓐ 1.2 g Ⓑ 5.1 g
Ⓒ 10.0 g Ⓓ 1209.4 g

50. **MP REASONING** Consider the exponential function $f(x) = ab^x$.

a. Show that $\frac{f(x+1)}{f(x)} = b$.

b. Use the equation in part (a) to explain why there is no exponential function of the form $f(x) = ab^x$ whose graph passes through the points in the table.

x	0	1	2	3	4
y	4	4	8	24	72

51. **MP PROBLEM SOLVING** The number E of eggs a Leghorn chicken produces per year can be modeled by the equation $E = 179.2(0.89)^{w/52}$, where w is the age (in weeks) of the chicken and $w \geq 22$.

a. Identify the decay factor and the percent decrease.

b. Graph the equation.

c. Estimate the egg production of a chicken that is 2.5 years old.

d. Explain how you can rewrite the given equation so that time is measured in years rather than in weeks.

52. **DIG DEEPER** You buy a new laptop for \$1300 and sell it 4 years later for \$275. Assume that the resale value of the laptop decays exponentially with time. Write an equation that represents the resale value V (in dollars) of the laptop as a function of the time t (in years) since it was purchased.

REVIEW & REFRESH

In Exercises 53–56, simplify the expression.

53. $x^9 \cdot x^2$

54. $(2x \cdot 3x^5)^3$

55. $\left(\frac{4x^8}{2x^6}\right)^4$

56. $\frac{12x}{4x} + 5x$

57. **MP STRUCTURE** In the exponential model $y = 2.4(1.5)^x$, identify the initial amount, the growth or decay factor, and the percent increase or decrease.

In Exercises 58 and 59, determine whether the functions are inverse functions.

58. $f(x) = -\frac{1}{2}x + 5$, $g(x) = -2x + 10$

59. $f(x) = \sqrt[3]{4x}$, $g(x) = \frac{x^3}{64}$

60. Let $f(x) = -x^3$ and $g(x) = 4\sqrt{x}$. Find $(fg)(x)$ and $\left(\frac{f}{g}\right)(x)$ and state the domain of each. Then evaluate $(fg)(4)$ and $\left(\frac{f}{g}\right)(4)$.

In Exercises 61–64, let $f(x) = x^2 - 6$, $g(x) = -\frac{1}{2}x + 5$, and $h(x) = 4x^{-1}$. Perform the indicated composition and state the domain.

61. $g(h(x))$

62. $f(g(x))$

63. $g(g(x))$

64. $h(f(x))$

In Exercises 65 and 66, determine whether the function represents *exponential growth* or *exponential decay*. Then graph the function.

65. $y = (3.25)^x$

66. $y = \left(\frac{3}{4}\right)^x$

67. Describe the x-values for which (a) f is increasing, (b) f is decreasing, (c) $f(x) > 0$, and (d) $f(x) < 0$.

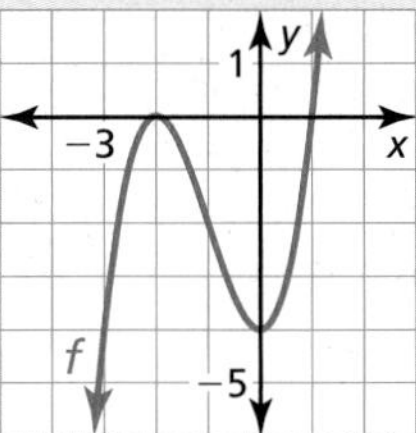

68. **MODELING REAL LIFE** The distances traveled (in miles) by several people on a given day, as recorded by their fitness trackers, are shown.

1.86, 5.31, 7.18, 5.20, 1.49, 2.25,
3.43, 3.93, 4.70, 6.18, 12.28

a. Make a box-and-whisker plot that represents the data. Describe the shape of the distribution.

b. Does the data set contain any outliers? If so, explain how the outlier(s) affect the mean and five-number summary.

6.2 The Natural Base e

Learning Target Use the natural base *e* and graph natural base functions.

Success Criteria
- I can explain the natural base *e*.
- I can simplify natural base expressions.
- I can graph natural base functions.
- I can solve real-life problems using exponential growth and decay functions.

EXPLORE IT! Approximating the Natural Base e

Work with a partner. So far in your study of mathematics, you have worked with special numbers such as π and i. Another special number is called the *natural base* and is denoted by e.

a. One way to approximate the natural base e is to approximate the sum

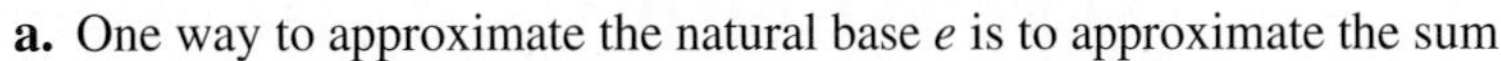

$$1 + \frac{1}{1} + \frac{1}{1 \cdot 2} + \frac{1}{1 \cdot 2 \cdot 3} + \frac{1}{1 \cdot 2 \cdot 3 \cdot 4} + \cdots.$$

Approximate this sum and explain your method. Then compare your result with those of your classmates.

b. Another way to approximate the natural base e is to consider the expression

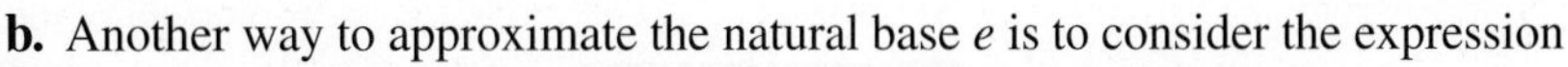

$$\left(1 + \frac{1}{x}\right)^x.$$

Complete the table. What do you notice as x increases?

x	10^1	10^2	10^3	10^4	10^5	10^6
$\left(1 + \frac{1}{x}\right)^x$						

Use your results to approximate e. Compare this approximation to the one in part (a).

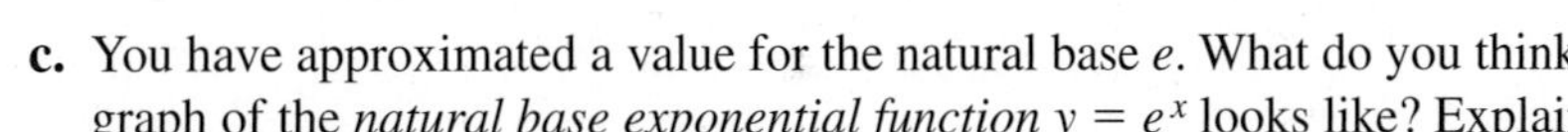

c. You have approximated a value for the natural base e. What do you think the graph of the *natural base exponential function* $y = e^x$ looks like? Explain.

d. Use your result in part (a) or part (b) to complete the table. Then graph $y = e^x$. Find the domain and range. Make several observations about the graph.

x	-2	-1	0	1	2
$y = e^x$					

e. Repeat part (d) for the natural base exponential function $y = e^{-x}$. Compare the graphs of $y = e^x$ and $y = e^{-x}$.

Math Practice

Understand Mathematical Terms

Do you think the natural base e is rational or irrational?

The Natural Base e

Vocabulary 

natural base e, *p. 302*

The history of mathematics is marked by the discovery of special numbers, such as π and i. Another special number is denoted by the letter e. The number is called the **natural base** e. The expression

$$\left(1 + \frac{1}{x}\right)^x$$

approaches e as x increases, as shown in the graph and table.

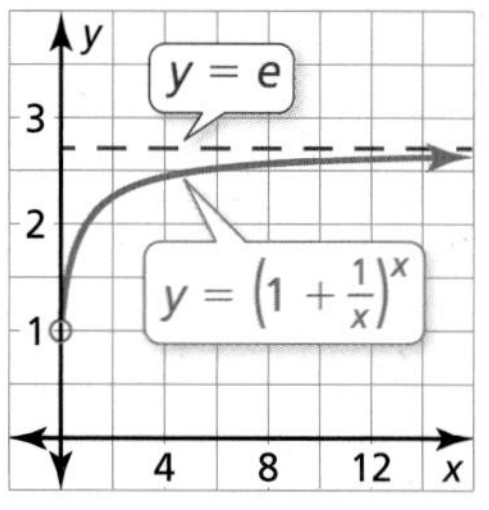

x	10^1	10^2	10^3	10^4	10^5	10^6
$\left(1 + \frac{1}{x}\right)^x$	2.59374	2.70481	2.71692	2.71815	2.71827	2.71828

KEY IDEA

The Natural Base e

The natural base e is irrational. It is defined as follows:

As x approaches $+\infty$, $\left(1 + \frac{1}{x}\right)^x$ approaches $e \approx 2.71828182846$.

EXAMPLE 1 Simplifying Natural Base Expressions

Simplify each expression.

a. $e^3 \cdot e^6$

b. $\dfrac{16e^5}{4e^4}$

c. $(3e^{-4x})^2$

d. $\sqrt{4e^{2x}}$

Check

You can use technology to check the equivalence of numerical expressions involving e.

$e^3 \cdot e^6$	= 8103.08392758
e^9	= 8103.08392758

SOLUTION

a. $e^3 \cdot e^6 = e^{3+6}$

$= e^9$

b. $\dfrac{16e^5}{4e^4} = 4e^{5-4}$

$= 4e$

c. $(3e^{-4x})^2 = 3^2(e^{-4x})^2$

$= 9e^{-8x}$

$= \dfrac{9}{e^{8x}}$

d. $\sqrt{4e^{2x}} = \sqrt{4} \cdot \sqrt{e^{2x}}$

$= 2 \cdot (e^{2x})^{1/2}$

$= 2e^x$

SELF-ASSESSMENT

1 I do not understand. 2 I can do it with help. 3 I can do it on my own. 4 I can teach someone else.

1. VOCABULARY What is the natural base e?

Simplify the expression.

2. $e^7 \cdot e^4$

3. $\dfrac{24e^8}{8e^5}$

4. $(10e^{-3x})^3$

5. $\sqrt{\frac{1}{9}e^{8x}}$

6. MP **REASONING** Can the natural base e be written as $\dfrac{271{,}801}{99{,}990}$? Explain.

Graphing Natural Base Functions

KEY IDEA

Natural Base Functions

A function of the form $y = ae^{rx}$ is called a *natural base exponential function.*

- When $a > 0$ and $r > 0$, the function is an exponential growth function.
- When $a > 0$ and $r < 0$, the function is an exponential decay function.

The graphs of the basic functions $y = e^x$ and $y = e^{-x}$ are shown.

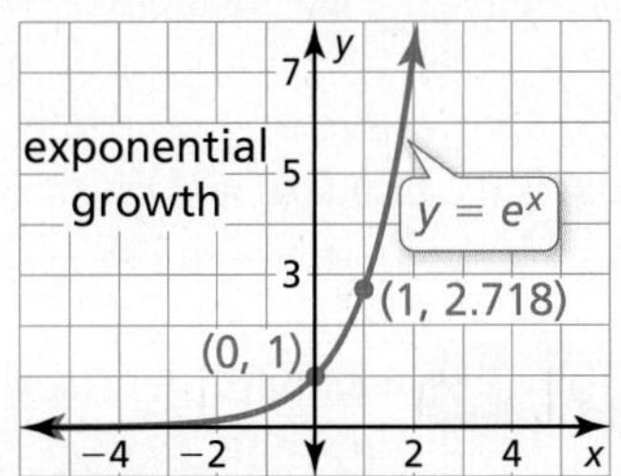

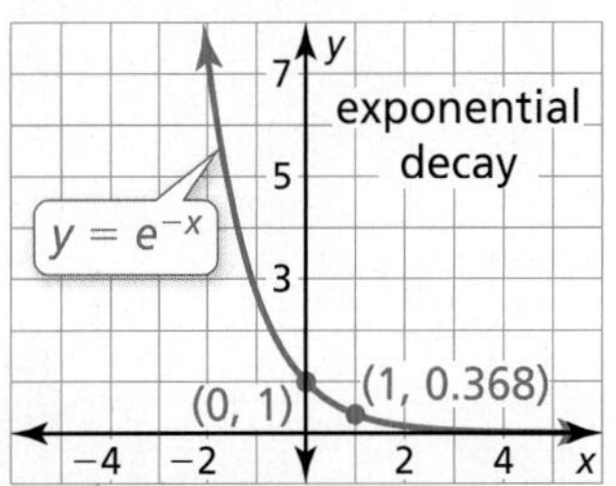

EXAMPLE 2 Graphing Natural Base Functions

Determine whether each function represents *exponential growth* or *exponential decay.* Then graph the function.

a. $y = 3e^x$

b. $f(x) = e^{-0.5x}$

SOLUTION

a. Because $a = 3$ is positive and $r = 1$ is positive, the function is an exponential growth function. Use a table to graph the function.

x	−2	−1	0	1
y	0.41	1.10	3	8.15

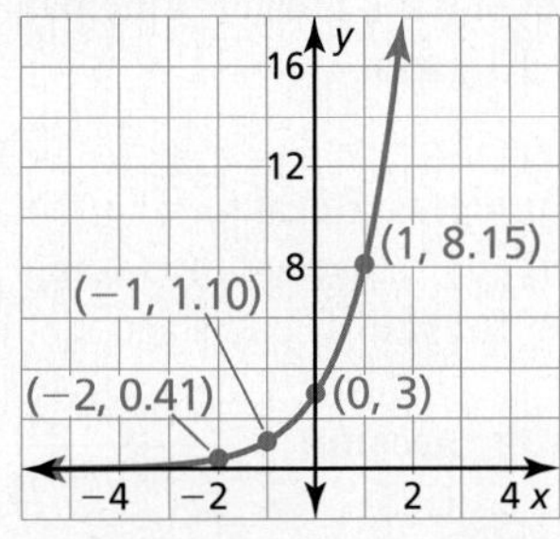

b. Because $a = 1$ is positive and $r = -0.5$ is negative, the function is an exponential decay function. Use a table to graph the function.

x	−4	−2	0	2
$f(x)$	7.39	2.72	1	0.37

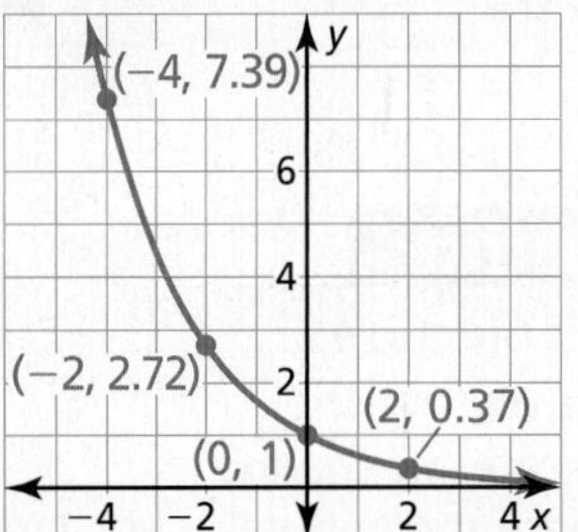

Math Practice

Look for Structure

Show how you can rewrite the function in Example 2(b) to find the percent rate of change.

SELF-ASSESSMENT

1 I do not understand. 2 I can do it with help. 3 I can do it on my own. 4 I can teach someone else.

Determine whether the function represents *exponential growth* or *exponential decay.* Then graph the function.

7. $y = \frac{1}{2}e^x$

8. $y = 4e^{-x}$

9. $g(x) = \frac{1}{3}e^{-4x}$

10. $f(x) = 2e^{2x}$

Solving Real-Life Problems

You have learned that the balance of an account earning compound interest is given by $A = P\left(1 + \frac{r}{n}\right)^{nt}$. As the frequency n of compounding approaches positive infinity, the compound interest formula approximates the following formula.

KEY IDEA

Continuously Compounded Interest

When interest is compounded *continuously*, the amount A in an account after t years is given by the formula

$$A = Pe^{rt}$$

where P is the principal and r is the annual interest rate expressed as a decimal.

EXAMPLE 3 **Modeling Real Life** 

You and your friend each have accounts that earn annual interest compounded continuously. The balance A (in dollars) of your account after t years can be modeled by $A = 4500e^{0.04t}$. The graph shows the balance of your friend's account over time. Which account has a greater principal? Which has a greater balance after 10 years?

Your Friend's Account

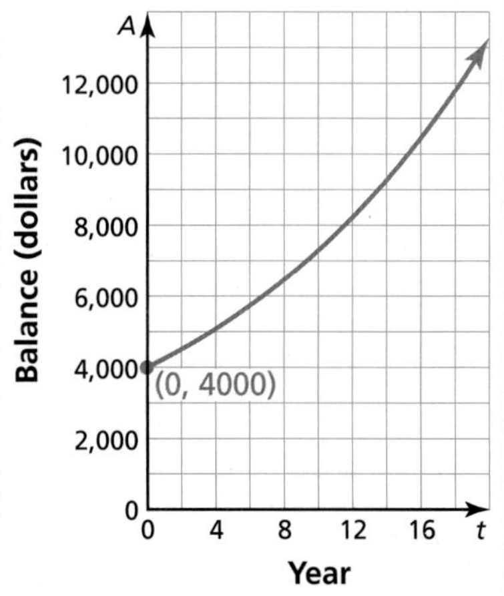

(Graph: Balance (dollars), A, from 0 to 12,000 versus Year, t, from 0 to 16; curve passes through (0, 4000).)

SOLUTION

1. **Understand the Problem** You are given a graph and an equation that represent account balances. You are asked to identify the account with the greater principal and the account with the greater balance after 10 years.
2. **Make a Plan** Use the equation to find your principal and account balance after 10 years. Then compare these values to the graph that shows your friend's account.
3. **Solve and Check** The equation $A = 4500e^{0.04t}$ is of the form $A = Pe^{rt}$, where $P = 4500$. So, your principal is \$4500. Your balance A when $t = 10$ is

$$A = 4500e^{0.04(10)} = \$6713.21.$$

Because the graph passes through (0, 4000), your friend's principal is \$4000. The graph also shows that the balance is about \$7250 when $t = 10$.

▶ So, your account has a greater principal, but your friend's account has a greater balance after 10 years.

Check Reasonableness Because your friend's account has a lesser principal but a greater balance after 10 years, the average rate of change from $t = 0$ to $t = 10$ should be greater for your friend's account than for your account.

Your account: $\dfrac{A(10) - A(0)}{10 - 0} = \dfrac{6713.21 - 4500}{10} = 221.321$

Your friend's account: $\dfrac{A(10) - A(0)}{10 - 0} \approx \dfrac{7250 - 4000}{10} = 325$ ✓

Math Practice

Make Conjectures

How can you use the average rates of change to compare the annual interest rates of the accounts?

SELF-ASSESSMENT 1 I do not understand. 2 I can do it with help. 3 I can do it on my own. 4 I can teach someone else.

11. You deposit \$4250 in an account that earns 5% annual interest compounded continuously.
    a. Compare the balance after 10 years with the balances of the accounts in Example 3.
    b. How much more money does this account earn after 10 years with interest compounded continuously than with interest compounding monthly? yearly?

6.2 Practice WITH CalcChat® AND CalcView®

GO DIGITAL

In Exercises 1–10, simplify the expression. ▶ *Example 1*

1. $e^3 \cdot e^5$
2. $e^{-4} \cdot e^6$
3. $\dfrac{11e^9}{22e^{10}}$
4. $\dfrac{27e^7}{3e^4}$
5. $(5e^{7x})^4$
6. $(4e^{-2x})^3$
7. $\sqrt{9e^{6x}}$
8. $\sqrt[3]{8e^{12x}}$
9. $e^x \cdot e^{-6x} \cdot e^8$
10. $e^x \cdot e^4 \cdot e^{x+3}$

ERROR ANALYSIS In Exercises 11 and 12, describe and correct the error in simplifying the expression.

11. 

$$(4e^{3x})^2 = 4e^{(3x)(2)}$$
$$= 4e^{6x}$$

12. 

$$\frac{e^{5x}}{e^{-2x}} = e^{5x-2x}$$
$$= e^{3x}$$

ANALYZING EQUATIONS In Exercises 13–16, match the function with its graph. Explain your reasoning.

13. $y = e^{2x}$
14. $y = e^{-2x}$
15. $y = 4e^{-0.5x}$
16. $y = 0.75e^x$

A. 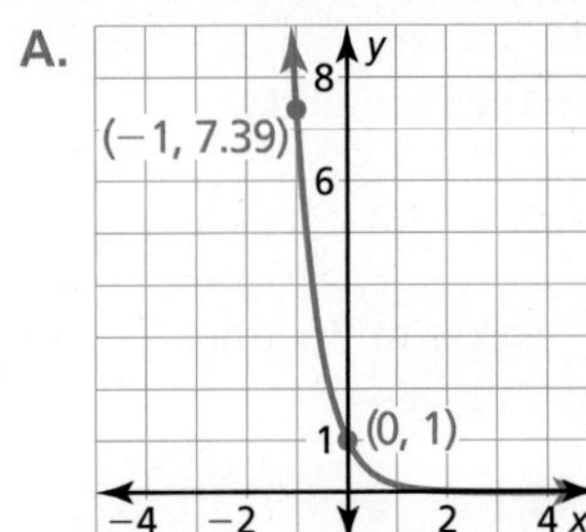

B. 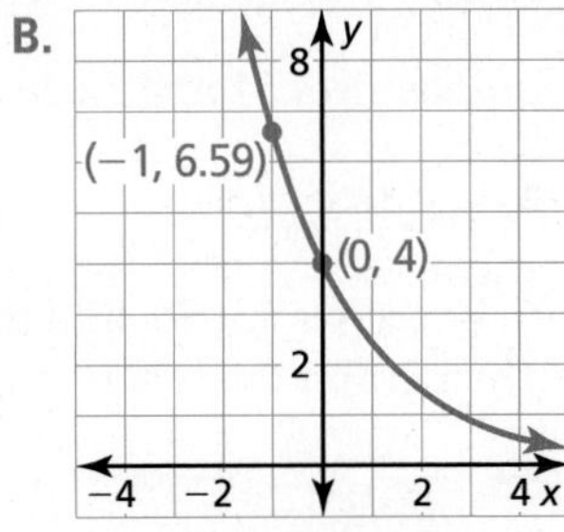

C. 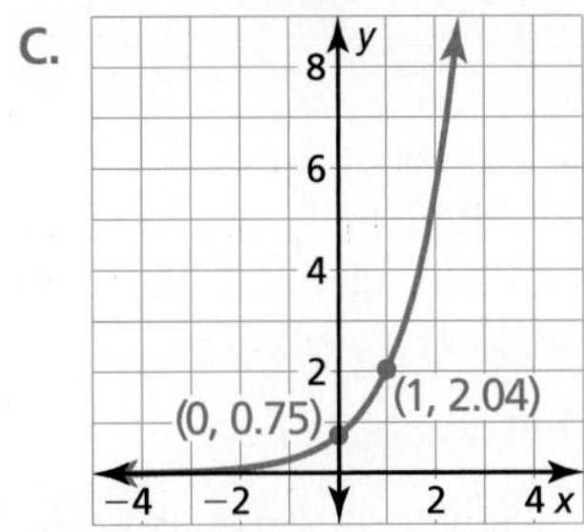

D. 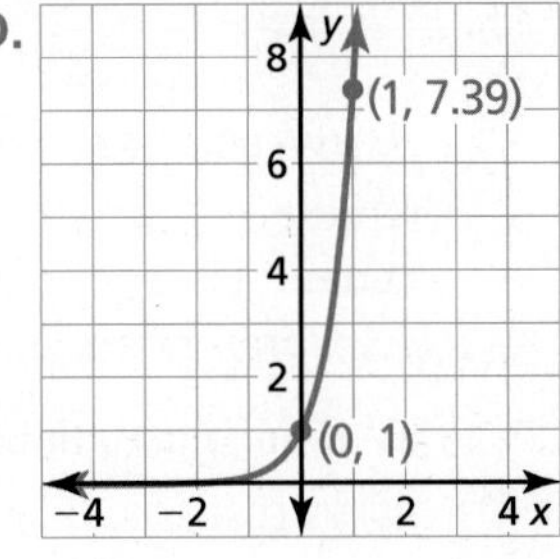

In Exercises 17–24, determine whether the function represents *exponential growth* or *exponential decay*. Then graph the function. ▶ *Example 2*

17. $y = e^{3x}$
18. $y = e^{-0.8x}$
19. $y = 2e^{-x}$
20. $y = 3e^{2x}$
21. $y = \frac{1}{2}e^x$
22. $y = \frac{1}{4}e^{-3x}$
23. $y = 0.4e^{-0.25x}$
24. $y = 0.6e^{0.5x}$

MP STRUCTURE In Exercises 25–28, use the properties of exponents to rewrite the function in the form $y = a(1 + r)^t$ or $y = a(1 - r)^t$. Then find the percent rate of change.

25. $y = e^{-0.75t}$
26. $y = e^{-0.25t}$
27. $y = 2e^{0.4t}$
28. $y = 0.5e^{0.8t}$

MP USING TOOLS In Exercises 29–32, use a table of values or technology to graph the function. Then find the domain and range.

29. $y = e^{x-2}$
30. $y = e^{x+1}$
31. $y = 2e^x + 1$
32. $y = 3e^x - 5$

33. **MODELING REAL LIFE** Investment accounts for a house and education earn annual interest compounded continuously. The balance A (in dollars) of the house account after t years can be modeled by $A = 3224e^{0.05t}$. The graph shows the balance of the education account over time. Which account has a greater principal? Which account has a greater balance after 12 years? ▶ *Example 3*

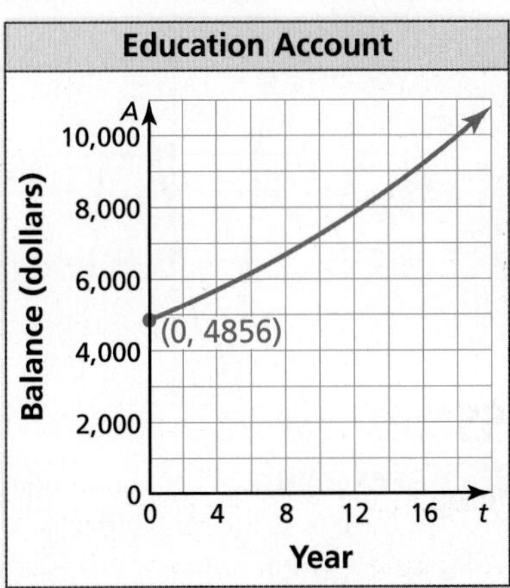

34. MODELING REAL LIFE Tritium and sodium-22 decay over time. In a sample of tritium, the amount y (in milligrams) remaining after t years is given by $y = 10e^{-0.0562t}$. The graph shows the amount of sodium-22 remaining in a sample over time. Which sample has a greater initial amount? Which sample has a greater amount remaining after 5 years?

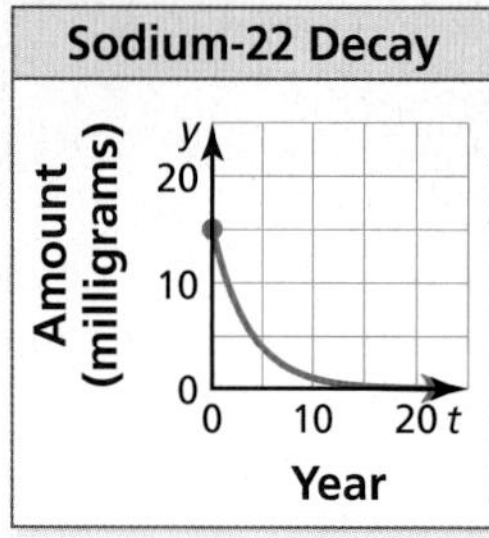

35. OPEN-ENDED Find values of a, b, r, and q such that $f(x) = ae^{rx}$ and $g(x) = be^{qx}$ are exponential decay functions, but $\frac{f(x)}{g(x)}$ represents exponential growth.

36. DRAWING CONCLUSIONS You want to invest \$2500 in an account to save for college. Account 1 pays 6% annual interest compounded quarterly. Account 2 pays 4% annual interest compounded continuously. Which account should you choose to obtain the greater amount in 10 years? Justify your answer.

37. MAKING AN ARGUMENT Your friend evaluates $f(x) = e^{-x}$ when $x = 1000$ and concludes that the graph of $y = f(x)$ has an x-intercept of 1000. Is your friend correct? Explain your reasoning.

38. HOW DO YOU SEE IT?
Use the graph to complete each statement.

a. $f(x)$ approaches ____ as x approaches $+\infty$.

b. $f(x)$ approaches ____ as x approaches $-\infty$.

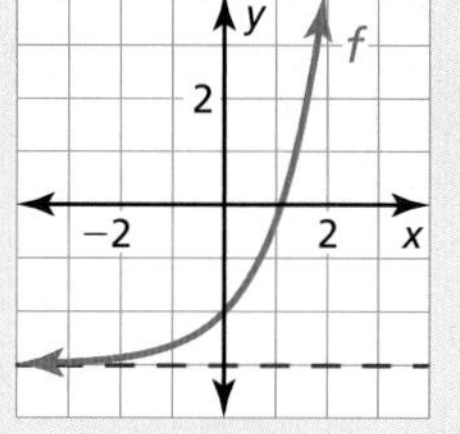

39. MP PROBLEM SOLVING The number of *Mycobacterium tuberculosis* bacteria after t hours can be modeled by the function $N(t) = ae^{0.166t}$, where a is the number of bacteria at 12:00 P.M. At 1:00 P.M., there are 30 *M. tuberculosis* bacteria in a sample. Find the number of bacteria in the sample at 3:45 P.M.

40. THOUGHT PROVOKING
Explain why $A = P\left(1 + \frac{r}{n}\right)^{nt}$ approximates $A = Pe^{rt}$ as n approaches positive infinity.

REVIEW & REFRESH

In Exercises 41 and 42, write the number in scientific notation.

41. 26,000,000 **42.** 0.000000047

In Exercises 43 and 44, graph the function. Label the vertex and axis of symmetry.

43. $y = 3(x + 2)(x - 2)$ **44.** $y = -(x + 6)^2 + 1$

45. Write the cubic function whose graph is shown.

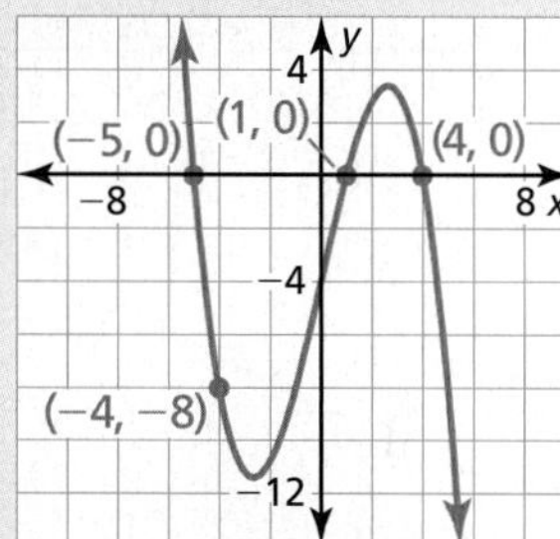

46. MP REASONING When a polynomial $f(x)$ is divided by $x - 2$, the remainder is -11. Find one point on the graph of $y = f(x)$.

In Exercises 47–50, determine whether the function represents *exponential growth* or *exponential decay*. Then graph the function.

47. $f(x) = (4.25)^x$ **48.** $y = \left(\frac{3}{8}\right)^x$

49. $y = e^{0.6x}$ **50.** $f(x) = 5e^{-2x}$

In Exercises 51 and 52, graph the inequality.

51. $y < x^2 - 6x$ **52.** $y \geq x^2 + 3x - 4$

In Exercises 53–56, find the inverse of the function. Then graph the function and its inverse.

53. $y = 3x + 5$ **54.** $y = x^2 - 1, x \leq 0$

55. $y = \sqrt{x + 6}$ **56.** $y = x^3 - 2$

57. MODELING REAL LIFE The function $f(t) = 9.75t$ represents your earnings (in dollars) for working t hours. The function $t(x) = 15x$ represents the total number of hours you work after x weeks.

a. Find $f(t(x))$. Interpret the coefficient.

b. Evaluate $f(t(12))$ and explain what it represents.

6.3 Logarithms and Logarithmic Functions

Learning Target Understand logarithms and graph logarithmic functions.

Success Criteria
- I can explain the meaning of a logarithm with base b.
- I can evaluate logarithmic expressions.
- I can graph logarithmic functions.

EXPLORE IT! Understanding Logarithmic Functions

Work with a partner.

a. Look for a pattern and complete each statement.

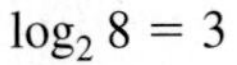

$\log_2 8 = 3$ $\log_3 27 =$ ______

$\log_5 25 = 2$ $\log_2 32 =$ ______

$\log_{10} 1000 = 3$ $\log_4 64 =$ ______

$\log_7 49 =$ ______ $\log_2 \frac{1}{2} =$ ______

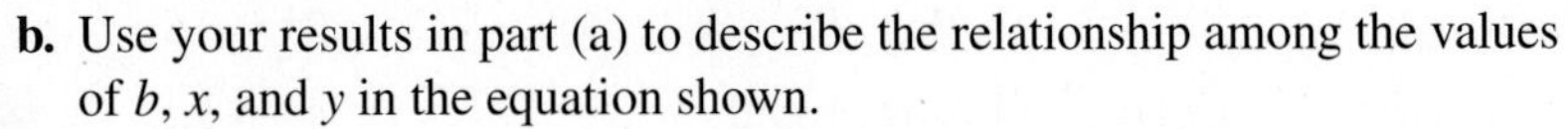

b. Use your results in part (a) to describe the relationship among the values of b, x, and y in the equation shown.

$$\log_b y = x$$

c. Use your results above to complete the table of values.

x		$\frac{1}{10}$				1000
$\log_{10} x$	−2	−1	0	1	2	3

d. Plot the points $(x, \log_{10} x)$ from part (c). Draw a smooth curve through the points. Make several observations about the graph.

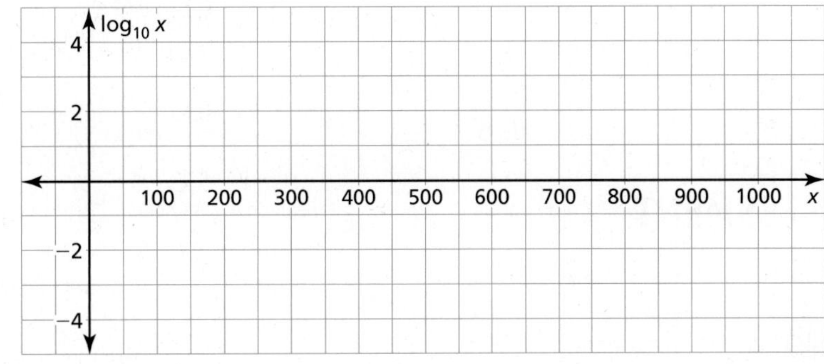

Math Practice

Find General Methods
How can you use the graph of an exponential function to sketch the graph of a logarithmic function?

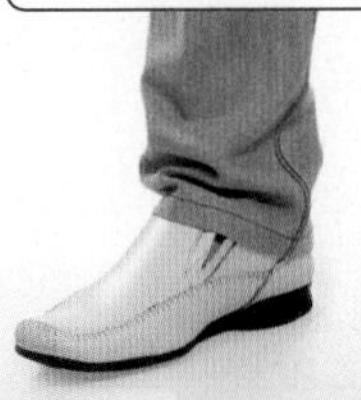

Logarithms

GO DIGITAL

Vocabulary AZ VOCAB

logarithm of *y* with base *b*, *p. 308*
common logarithm, *p. 309*
natural logarithm, *p. 309*

You know that $2^2 = 4$ and $2^3 = 8$. However, for what value of x does $2^x = 6$? Mathematicians define this x-value using a *logarithm* and write $x = \log_2 6$. The definition of a logarithm can be generalized as follows.

KEY IDEA

Definition of Logarithm with Base *b*

Let b and y be positive real numbers with $b \neq 1$. The **logarithm of *y* with base *b*** is denoted by $\log_b y$ and is defined as

$$\log_b y = x \qquad \text{if and only if} \qquad b^x = y.$$

The expression $\log_b y$ is read as "log base b of y." This definition tells you that the equations $\log_b y = x$ and $b^x = y$ are equivalent. The first is in *logarithmic form*, and the second is in *exponential form.*

EXAMPLE 1 Rewriting Logarithmic Equations

Rewrite each equation in exponential form.

a. $\log_2 16 = 4$ **b.** $\log_4 1 = 0$ **c.** $\log_{12} 12 = 1$ **d.** $\log_{1/4} 4 = -1$

SOLUTION

Logarithmic Form	Exponential Form
a. $\log_2 16 = 4$	$2^4 = 16$
b. $\log_4 1 = 0$	$4^0 = 1$
c. $\log_{12} 12 = 1$	$12^1 = 12$
d. $\log_{1/4} 4 = -1$	$\left(\frac{1}{4}\right)^{-1} = 4$

EXAMPLE 2 Rewriting Exponential Equations

Rewrite each equation in logarithmic form.

a. $5^2 = 25$ **b.** $10^{-1} = 0.1$ **c.** $8^{2/3} = 4$ **d.** $6^{-3} = \frac{1}{216}$

SOLUTION

Exponential Form	Logarithmic Form
a. $5^2 = 25$	$\log_5 25 = 2$
b. $10^{-1} = 0.1$	$\log_{10} 0.1 = -1$
c. $8^{2/3} = 4$	$\log_8 4 = \frac{2}{3}$
d. $6^{-3} = \frac{1}{216}$	$\log_6 \frac{1}{216} = -3$

SELF-ASSESSMENT

1 I do not understand. 2 I can do it with help. 3 I can do it on my own. 4 I can teach someone else.

Rewrite the equation in exponential form.

1. $\log_3 81 = 4$ **2.** $\log_7 7 = 1$ **3.** $\log_{14} 1 = 0$ **4.** $\log_{1/2} 32 = -5$

Rewrite the equation in logarithmic form.

5. $7^2 = 49$ **6.** $50^0 = 1$ **7.** $4^{-1} = \frac{1}{4}$ **8.** $256^{1/8} = 2$

Parts (b) and (c) of Example 1 illustrate two special logarithm values that you should learn to recognize. Let b be a positive real number such that $b \neq 1$.

Logarithm of 1	**Logarithm of *b* with Base *b***
$\log_b 1 = 0$ because $b^0 = 1$.	$\log_b b = 1$ because $b^1 = b$.

EXAMPLE 3 Evaluating Logarithmic Expressions

Evaluate each logarithm.

a. $\log_4 64$ **b.** $\log_5 0.2$ **c.** $\log_{1/5} 125$ **d.** $\log_{36} 6$

SOLUTION

To help you find the value of $\log_b y$, ask yourself "What power of b gives you y?"

a. What power of 4 gives you 64? $4^3 = 64$, so $\log_4 64 = 3$.

b. What power of 5 gives you 0.2? $5^{-1} = 0.2$, so $\log_5 0.2 = -1$.

c. What power of $\frac{1}{5}$ gives you 125? $\left(\frac{1}{5}\right)^{-3} = 125$, so $\log_{1/5} 125 = -3$.

d. What power of 36 gives you 6? $36^{1/2} = 6$, so $\log_{36} 6 = \frac{1}{2}$.

A **common logarithm** is a logarithm with base 10. It is denoted by $\log_{10}$ or simply by log. A **natural logarithm** is a logarithm with base e. It can be denoted by $\log_e$ but is usually denoted by ln.

Common Logarithm	**Natural Logarithm**
$\log_{10} x = \log x$	$\log_e x = \ln x$

EXAMPLE 4 Evaluating Common and Natural Logarithms

Evaluate (a) log 8 and (b) ln 0.3 using technology. Round your answer to three decimal places.

SOLUTION

a. $\log 8 \approx 0.903$

b. $\ln 0.3 \approx -1.204$

log 8	= 0.903089987
ln 0.3	= −1.203972804

Check Rewrite each logarithm in exponential form and evaluate.

$10^{0.903}$	= 7.99834255
$e^{-1.204}$	= 0.2999918414

SELF-ASSESSMENT

1 I do not understand. 2 I can do it with help. 3 I can do it on my own. 4 I can teach someone else.

Evaluate the logarithm. If necessary, use technology and round your answer to three decimal places.

9. $\log_2 32$ **10.** $\log_{27} 3$ **11.** $\log 12$ **12.** $\ln 0.75$

13. DIFFERENT WORDS, SAME QUESTION Which is different? Find "both" answers.

What power of 4 gives you 16?	What is log base 4 of 16?
Evaluate 4^2.	Evaluate $\log_4 16$.

Using Inverse Properties

By the definition of logarithm, it follows that the logarithmic function $g(x) = \log_b x$ is the inverse of the exponential function $f(x) = b^x$. This means that

$$g(f(x)) = \log_b b^x = x \qquad \text{and} \qquad f(g(x)) = b^{\log_b x} = x.$$

In other words, exponential functions and logarithmic functions "undo" each other.

EXAMPLE 5 Using Inverse Properties

Simplify (a) $10^{\log 4}$ and (b) $\log_5 25^x$.

SOLUTION

a. $10^{\log 4} = 4$ — $b^{\log_b x} = x$

b. $\log_5 25^x = \log_5(5^2)^x$ — Express 25 as a power with base 5.

$= \log_5 5^{2x}$ — Power of a Power Property

$= 2x$ — $\log_b b^x = x$

EXAMPLE 6 Finding Inverse Functions

Find the inverse of each function.

a. $f(x) = 6^x$

b. $f(x) = \ln(x + 3)$

SOLUTION

a. From the definition of logarithm, the inverse of $f(x) = 6^x$ is $f^{-1}(x) = \log_6 x$.

b. Set y equal to $f(x)$. Switch the roles of x and y and solve for y.

$y = \ln(x + 3)$ — Set y equal to $f(x)$.

$x = \ln(y + 3)$ — Switch x and y.

$e^x = y + 3$ — Write in exponential form.

$e^x - 3 = y$ — Subtract 3 from each side.

▶ The inverse of f is $f^{-1}(x) = e^x - 3$.

STUDY TIP

From the definition of $\ln x$, $x = \log_e(y + 3)$. In exponential form, this is written as $e^x = y + 3$.

Check

a. $f(f^{-1}(x)) = 6^{\log_6 x} = x$ ✓

$f^{-1}(f(x)) = \log_6 6^x = x$ ✓

b. $f(f^{-1}(x)) = \ln(e^x - 3 + 3) = \ln e^x = x$ ✓

$f^{-1}(f(x)) = e^{\ln(x+3)} - 3 = x + 3 - 3 = x$ ✓

SELF-ASSESSMENT 1 I do not understand. 2 I can do it with help. 3 I can do it on my own. 4 I can teach someone else.

Simplify the expression.

14. $8^{\log_8 x}$

15. $\log_7 7^{-3x}$

16. $\log_2 64^x$

17. $e^{\ln 20}$

18. Find the inverse of (a) $f(x) = 4^x$ and (b) $f(x) = \ln(x - 5)$.

Graphing Logarithmic Functions

You can use the inverse relationship between exponential and logarithmic functions to graph logarithmic functions.

KEY IDEA

Graphing Logarithmic Functions

The graph of $f(x) = \log_b x$ is shown below for $b > 1$ and for $0 < b < 1$. Because $f(x) = \log_b x$ and $g(x) = b^x$ are inverse functions, you can graph f by reversing coordinates of points on the graph of g. The graph of f is the reflection of the graph of g in the line $y = x$.

Graph of $f(x) = \log_b x$ for $b > 1$

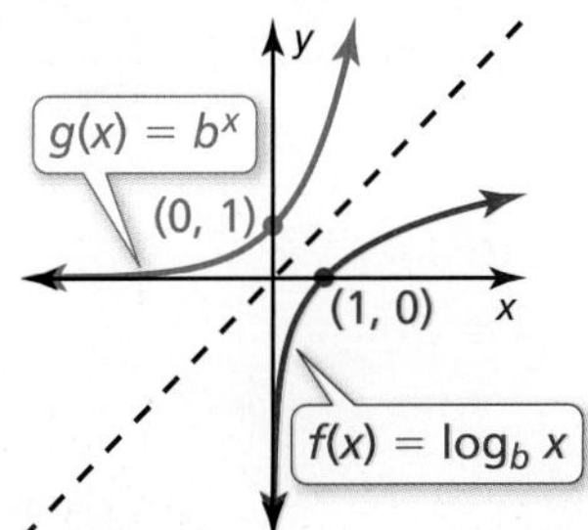

Graph of $f(x) = \log_b x$ for $0 < b < 1$

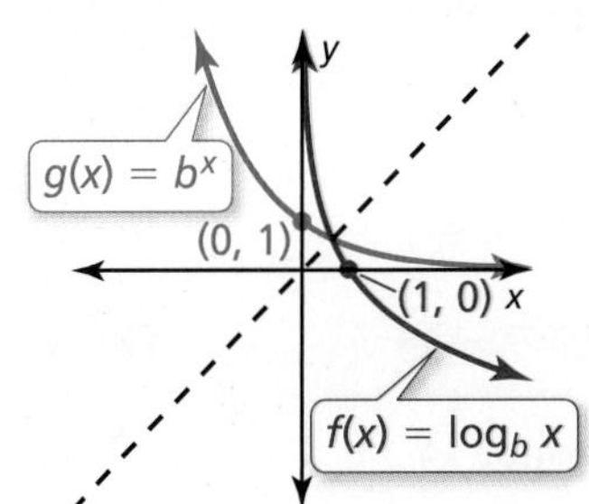

Note that the y-axis is a vertical asymptote of the graph of $f(x) = \log_b x$. The domain of $f(x) = \log_b x$ is $x > 0$, and the range is all real numbers.

EXAMPLE 7 Graphing a Logarithmic Function

Graph $f(x) = \log_3 x$.

SOLUTION

Step 1 Find the inverse of f. From the definition of logarithm, the inverse of $f(x) = \log_3 x$ is $f^{-1}(x) = 3^x$.

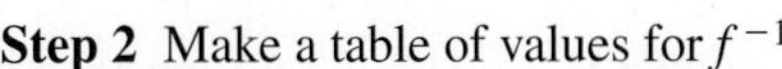

Step 2 Make a table of values for f^{-1}.

x	-2	-1	0	1	2
$f^{-1}(x)$	$\frac{1}{9}$	$\frac{1}{3}$	1	3	9

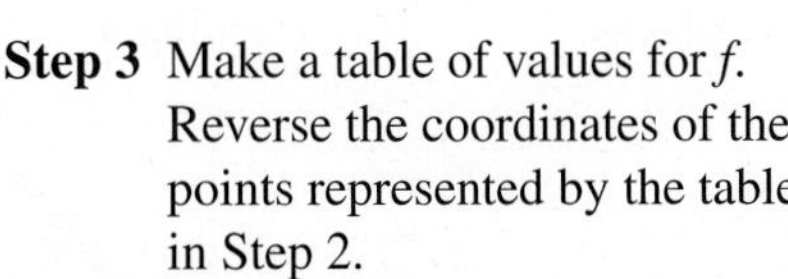

Step 3 Make a table of values for f. Reverse the coordinates of the points represented by the table in Step 2.

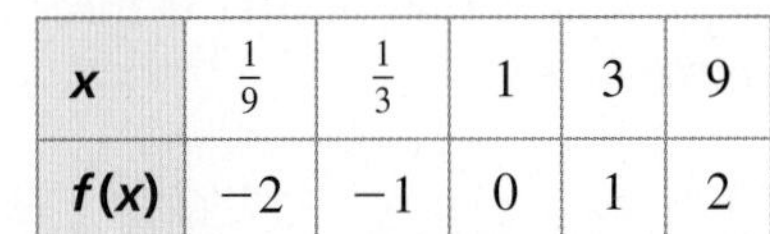

x	$\frac{1}{9}$	$\frac{1}{3}$	1	3	9
$f(x)$	-2	-1	0	1	2

Step 4 Plot the points from each table. Connect each set of points with a smooth curve.

SELF-ASSESSMENT 1 I do not understand. 2 I can do it with help. 3 I can do it on my own. 4 I can teach someone else.

Graph the function.

19. $y = \log_2 x$

20. $f(x) = \log_5 x$

21. $y = \log_{1/2} x$

6.3 Practice WITH CalcChat® AND CalcView®

In Exercises 1–6, rewrite the equation in exponential form. ▶ *Example 1*

1. $\log_3 9 = 2$
2. $\log_4 4 = 1$
3. $\log_6 1 = 0$
4. $\log_7 343 = 3$
5. $\log_{1/2} 16 = -4$
6. $\log_3 \frac{1}{3} = -1$

In Exercises 7–12, rewrite the equation in logarithmic form. ▶ *Example 2*

7. $6^2 = 36$
8. $12^0 = 1$
9. $16^{-1} = \frac{1}{16}$
10. $5^{-2} = \frac{1}{25}$
11. $125^{2/3} = 25$
12. $49^{-1/2} = \frac{1}{7}$

In Exercises 13–20, evaluate the logarithm. ▶ *Example 3*

13. $\log_3 81$
14. $\log_7 49$
15. $\log_3 3$
16. $\log_{1/2} 1$
17. $\log_5 \frac{1}{625}$
18. $\log_8 \frac{1}{512}$
19. $\log_4 0.25$
20. $\log_{10} 0.001$

21. **MP NUMBER SENSE** Order the logarithms from least value to greatest value.

$\log_5 23$	$\log_6 38$	$\log_7 8$	$\log_2 10$

22. **MP STRUCTURE** How many times greater is the value of $\log_{10} 10^{20}$ than the value of $\log_{10} 10^5$?

In Exercises 23–28, evaluate the logarithm using technology. Round your answer to three decimal places. ▶ *Example 4*

23. $\log 6$
24. $\ln 12$
25. $\ln \frac{1}{3}$
26. $\log \frac{2}{7}$
27. $3 \ln 0.5$
28. $\log 0.6 + 1$

29. **MODELING REAL LIFE** The pH value for a substance measures how acidic or alkaline the substance is. It is given by the formula $\text{pH} = -\log[\text{H}^+]$, where H^+ is the hydrogen ion concentration (in moles per liter). Find the pH of vinegar, which has a hydrogen ion concentration of $[\text{H}^+] = 10^{-3}$ mole per liter.

30. **MODELING REAL LIFE** Skydivers use an *altimeter* to track their altitudes as they fall. The altimeter determines altitude by measuring air pressure. The altitude h (in meters) above sea level is related to the air pressure P (in pascals) by the function shown in the diagram. What is the altitude above sea level when the air pressure is 57,000 pascals?

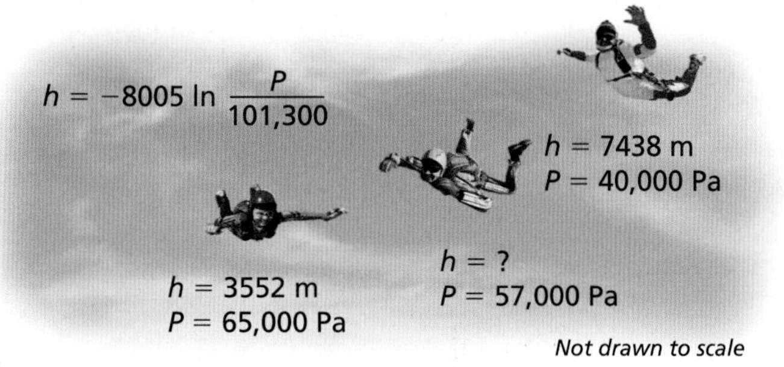

$h = -8005 \ln \frac{P}{101,300}$

$h = 7438$ m
$P = 40,000$ Pa

$h = 3552$ m
$P = 65,000$ Pa

$h = ?$
$P = 57,000$ Pa

Not drawn to scale

In Exercises 31–38, simplify the expression. ▶ *Example 5*

31. $7^{\log_7 x}$
32. $3^{\log_3 5x}$
33. $e^{\ln 4}$
34. $10^{\log 15}$
35. $\log_3 3^{2x}$
36. $\log_2 8^{3x}$
37. $\ln e^{-x}$
38. $\ln e^{4 + 5x}$

39. **WRITING** Describe the relationship between $y = 7^x$ and $y = \log_7 x$.

40. **COLLEGE PREP** Which expression is equal to 1?

Ⓐ $\log 1$ Ⓑ $\log_2 1$
Ⓒ $\ln 1$ Ⓓ $\log_2 2$

41. **ERROR ANALYSIS** Describe and correct the error in rewriting $4^{-3} = \frac{1}{64}$ in logarithmic form.

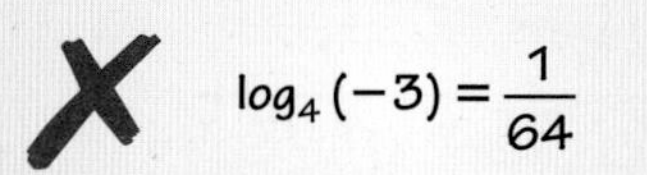

42. **ERROR ANALYSIS** Describe and correct the error in simplifying the expression $\log_4 64^x$.

✗
$$\begin{aligned}\log_4 64^x &= \log_4(16 \cdot 4^x)\\ &= \log_4(4^2 \cdot 4^x)\\ &= \log_4 4^{2+x}\\ &= 2 + x\end{aligned}$$

In Exercises 43–52, find the inverse of the function. *Example 6*

43. $f(x) = 0.3^x$

44. $y = 11^x$

45. $y = \log_2 x$

46. $f(x) = \log_{1/5} x$

47. $y = \ln(x - 1)$

48. $y = \ln 2x$

49. $f(x) = e^{3x}$

50. $y = e^{x-4}$

51. $y = 5^x - 9$

52. $y = 13 + \log x$

53. MODELING REAL LIFE The wind speed (in miles per hour) near the center of a tornado can be modeled by $f(x) = 93 \log x + 65$, where x is the distance (in miles) the tornado travels.

a. In 2019, a tornado traveled 2.05 miles through Georgia. Estimate the wind speed near the center of the tornado.

b. Find and interpret $f^{-1}(x)$.

54. MODELING REAL LIFE The energy magnitude of an earthquake can be modeled by $f(x) = \frac{2}{3} \log x - 9.9$, where x is the amount of energy released (in ergs).

a. In 2019, an earthquake near Ridgecrest, California released 3.16×10^{25} ergs. What was the energy magnitude of the earthquake?

b. Find and interpret $f^{-1}(x)$.

In Exercises 55–60, graph the function. *Example 7*

55. $f(x) = \log_4 x$

56. $y = \log_6 x$

57. $y = \log_{1/3} x$

58. $y = \log_{1/4} x$

59. $y = \log_2 x - 1$

60. $f(x) = \log_3(x + 2)$

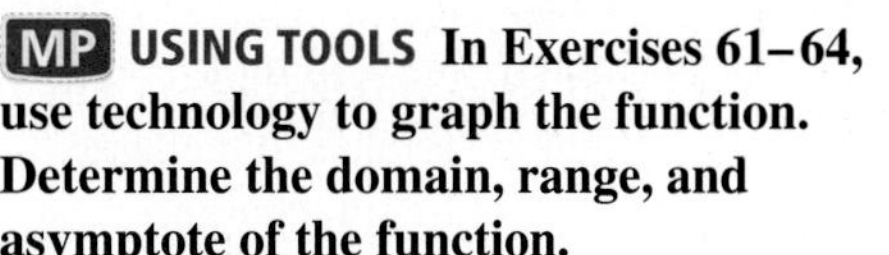

MP USING TOOLS In Exercises 61–64, use technology to graph the function. Determine the domain, range, and asymptote of the function.

61. $y = \log(x + 2)$

62. $y = -\ln x$

63. $y = \ln(-x)$

64. $y = 3 - \log x$

65. MAKING AN ARGUMENT Does the graph of every function of the form $y = \log_b x$ pass through the point $(1, 0)$? Explain your reasoning.

66. ANALYZING RELATIONSHIPS Order the functions from the least average rate of change to the greatest average rate of change when $1 \le x \le 10$.

a. $y = \log_6 x$

b. $y = \log_{3/5} x$

c.

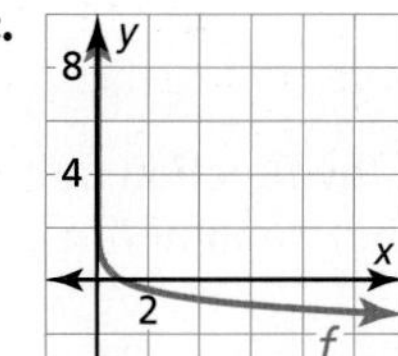

d.

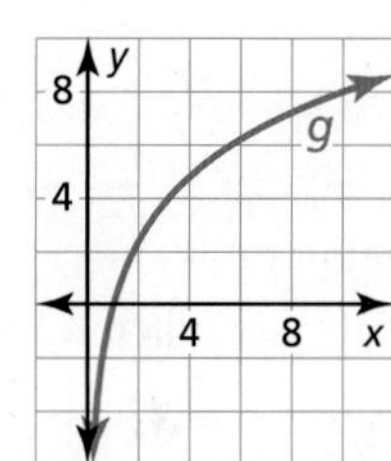

67. MP PROBLEM SOLVING Biologists have found that the length ℓ (in inches) of an alligator and its weight w (in pounds) are related by the function $\ell = 27.1 \ln w - 32.8$.

a. Use technology to graph the function.

b. Use your graph to estimate the weight of an alligator that is 10 feet long.

c. Find the x-intercept of the graph of the function. Does this x-value make sense in this situation? Explain.

68. HOW DO YOU SEE IT?
The figure shows the graphs of the two functions f and g.

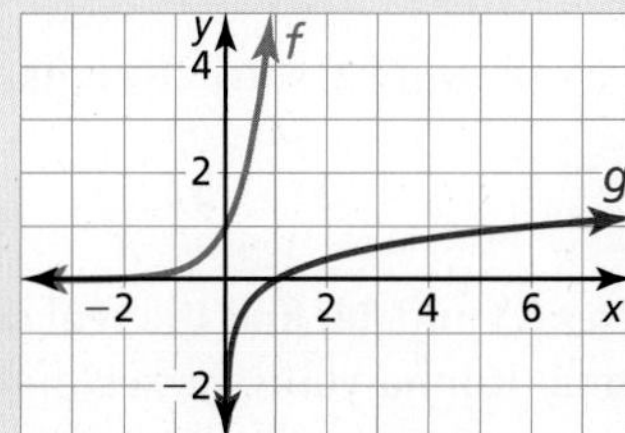

a. Compare the end behavior of the logarithmic function g to that of the exponential function f.

b. Determine whether the functions are inverse functions. Explain.

c. What is the base of each function? Explain.

69. **DIG DEEPER** The function $t(r) = -35 \ln\left(1 - \frac{r}{100}\right)$ represents the time (in minutes) it takes to recharge a tablet battery from 0% to r% of its full charge.

a. Use technology to graph t for $0 < r < 100$ and for $0 < t < 350$.

b. How long will it take to recharge the battery to 40% of its full charge?

c. Describe what happens to $t(r)$ as r increases in this situation.

70. **THOUGHT PROVOKING** Explain why a base of 1 is excluded from the definition of logarithm.

71. **CRITICAL THINKING** Evaluate each logarithm. (*Hint*: For each logarithm $\log_b x$, rewrite b and x as powers of the same base.)

a. $\log_{125} 25$ b. $\log_8 32$

c. $\log_{27} 81$ d. $\log_4 128$

72. **OPEN-ENDED** Write a logarithmic function f that satisfies both characteristics. Then graph the function.

$f(0) = -3$; end behavior: as $x \to +\infty$, $f(x) \to +\infty$

REVIEW & REFRESH

In Exercises 73–76, identify the function family to which f belongs. Compare the graph of f to the graph of its parent function.

73.
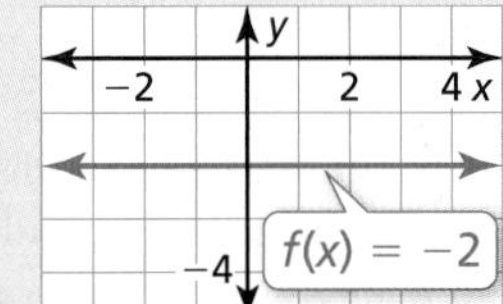

74.
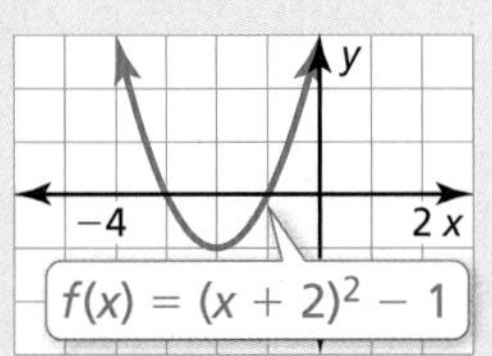

75.
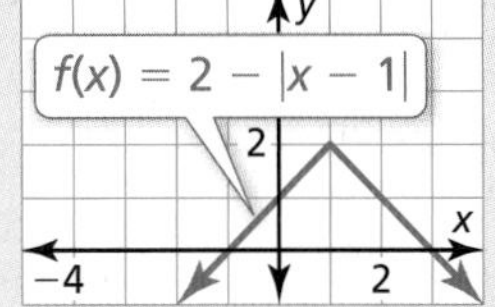

76.
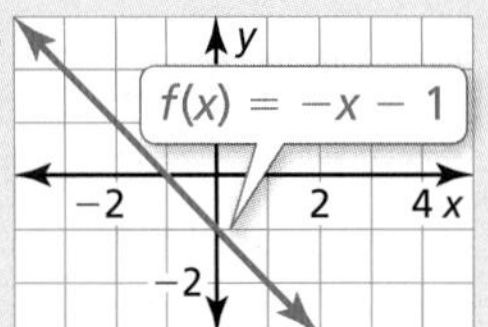

In Exercises 77–80, simplify the expression.

77. $-e^2 \cdot e^9$

78. $\frac{3e^2}{15e^4}$

79. $(2e^x)^4$

80. $\sqrt{4e^{8x}}$

In Exercises 81 and 82, solve the equation.

81. $0 = x^2 + 12x + 11$

82. $n^2 - n = 0$

In Exercises 83 and 84, find the real solution(s) of the equation. Round your answer(s) to two decimal places when appropriate.

83. $x^3 = -343$

84. $y^6 + 1 = 71$

In Exercises 85 and 86, determine whether the inverse of f is a function. Then find the inverse.

85. $f(x) = 3x^3 + 2$

86. $f(x) = \sqrt{x + 1}$

87. The two-way table shows the results of a survey. Find and interpret the marginal frequencies.

		Support Motor Contest		
		Yes	No	Undecided
Gender	Male	12	3	5
	Female	10	5	5

In Exercises 88 and 89, determine whether the function represents *exponential growth* or *exponential decay*. Then graph the function.

88. $y = (0.8)^x$

89. $y = \left(\frac{6}{5}\right)^x$

In Exercises 90 and 91, graph the function.

90. $y = 3 - \log_4 x$

91. $f(x) = \log_7(x - 1)$

92. **MODELING REAL LIFE** The volume of the largest of the six pyramids constructed by the Norte Chico people in Caral, Peru is about 4,500,000 cubic feet. What is the height of the pyramid?

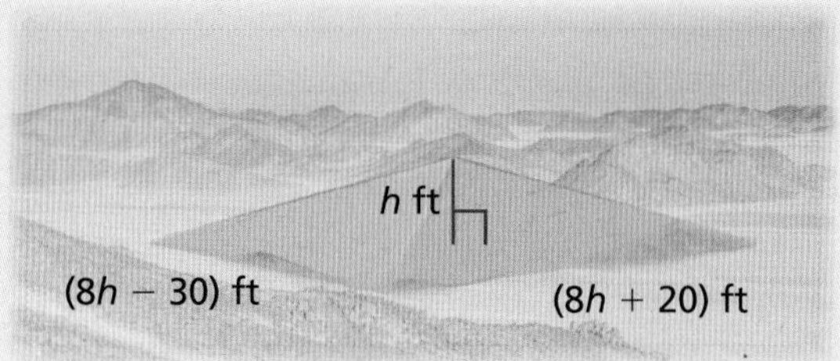

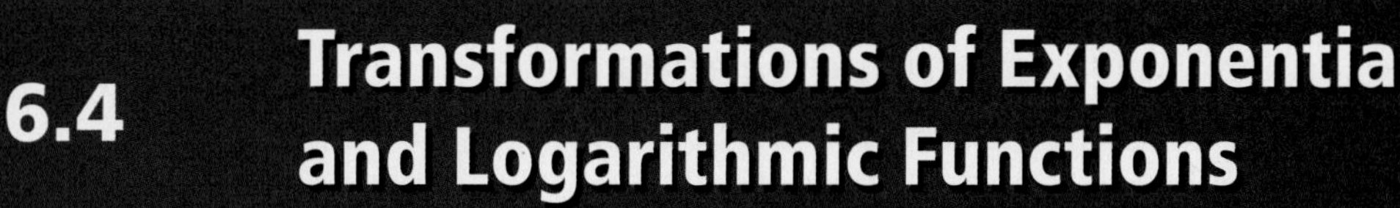

6.4 Transformations of Exponential and Logarithmic Functions

Learning Target Describe and graph transformations of exponential and logarithmic functions.

Success Criteria
- I can describe transformations of exponential and logarithmic functions.
- I can graph transformations of exponential and logarithmic functions.
- I can write functions that represent transformations of exponential and logarithmic functions.

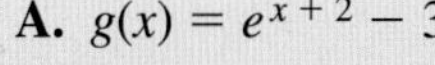

EXPLORE IT! Identifying Transformations

Work with a partner. You can transform graphs of exponential and logarithmic functions in the same way you transformed graphs of functions previously. Each graph shown is a transformation of the parent function

$$f(x) = e^x \qquad \text{or} \qquad f(x) = \ln x.$$

In parts (a)–(f), match each graph with one of the functions in the list at the left. Explain your reasoning. Then describe the transformation of f represented by g.

A. $g(x) = e^{x+2} - 3$

B. $g(x) = -e^{x+2} + 1$

C. $g(x) = -e^{x-2} + 3$

D. $g(x) = e^{x-2} - 1$

E. $g(x) = \ln(x + 2)$

F. $g(x) = \ln(x - 2)$

G. $g(x) = 2 + \ln x$

H. $g(x) = 2 + \ln(-x)$

a.

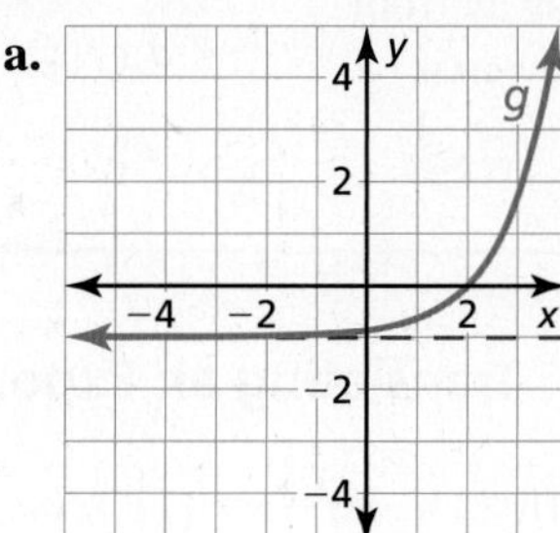

b.

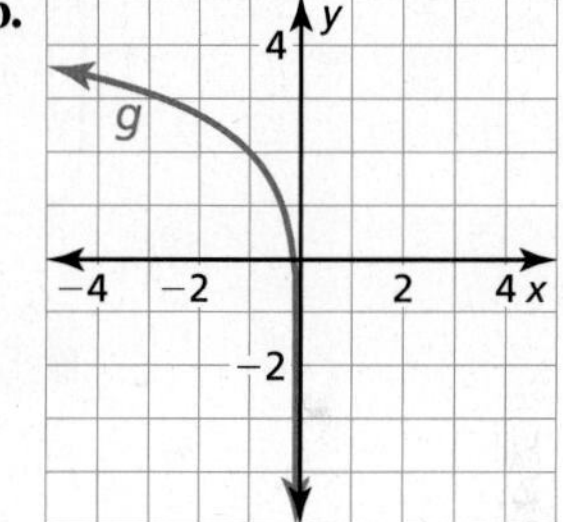

c.

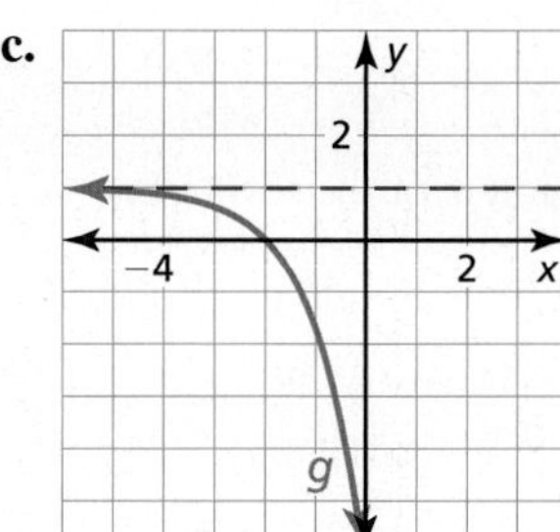

d.

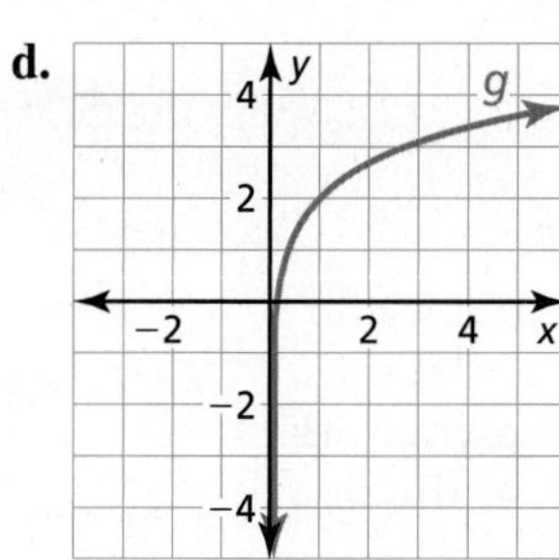

Math Practice

Look for Structure
How can you use the asymptotes to match the functions and graphs?

e.

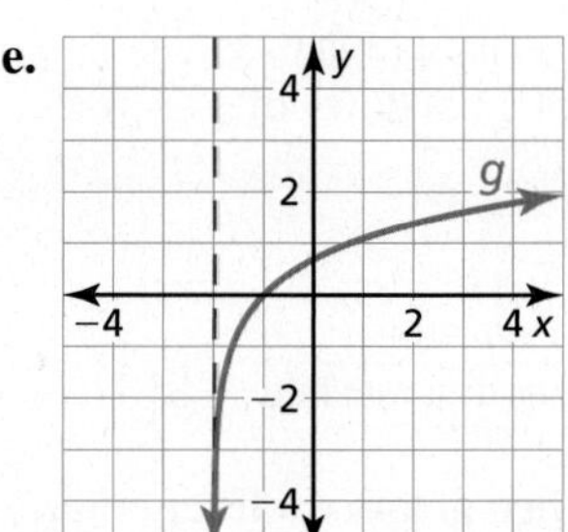

f.

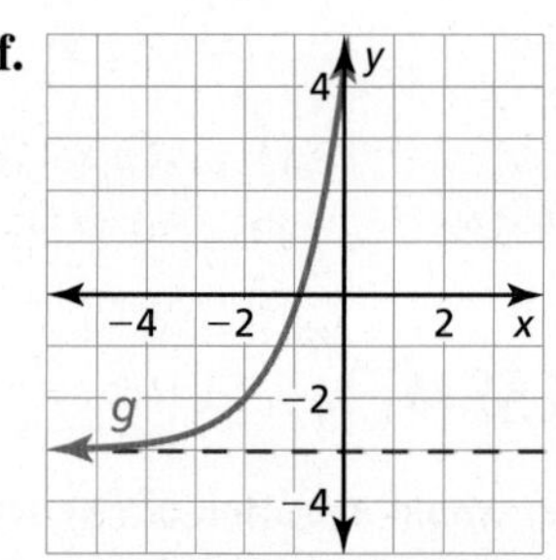

g. The graph of h is a translation 4 units right and 1 unit up of the graph of $f(x) = e^x$. Write a rule for h. Then graph each function.

Transforming Graphs of Exponential Functions

You can transform graphs of exponential and logarithmic functions in the same way you transformed graphs of functions in previous chapters. Examples of transformations of the graph of $f(x) = 4^x$ are shown below.

KEY IDEAS

Transformation	f(x) Notation	Examples	
Horizontal Translation Graph shifts left or right.	$f(x - h)$	$g(x) = 4^{x-3}$ $g(x) = 4^{x+2}$	3 units right 2 units left
Vertical Translation Graph shifts up or down.	$f(x) + k$	$g(x) = 4^x + 5$ $g(x) = 4^x - 1$	5 units up 1 unit down
Reflection Graph flips over a line.	$f(-x)$ $-f(x)$	$g(x) = 4^{-x}$ $g(x) = -4^x$	in the y-axis in the x-axis
Horizontal Stretch or Shrink Graph stretches away from or shrinks toward y-axis by a factor of $\frac{1}{a}$.	$f(ax)$	$g(x) = 4^{2x}$ $g(x) = 4^{x/2}$	shrink by a factor of $\frac{1}{2}$ stretch by a factor of 2
Vertical Stretch or Shrink Graph stretches away from or shrinks toward x-axis by a factor of a.	$a \cdot f(x)$	$g(x) = 3(4^x)$ $g(x) = \frac{1}{4}(4^x)$	stretch by a factor of 3 shrink by a factor of $\frac{1}{4}$

EXAMPLE 1 Translating an Exponential Function

Describe the transformation of $f(x) = \left(\frac{1}{2}\right)^x$ represented by $g(x) = \left(\frac{1}{2}\right)^x - 4$. Then graph each function.

SOLUTION

Notice that the function is of the form $g(x) = \left(\frac{1}{2}\right)^x + k$.

Rewrite the function to identify k.

$$g(x) = \left(\frac{1}{2}\right)^x + \underset{k}{\underset{\uparrow}{(-4)}}$$

▶ Because $k = -4$, the graph of g is a translation 4 units down of the graph of f.

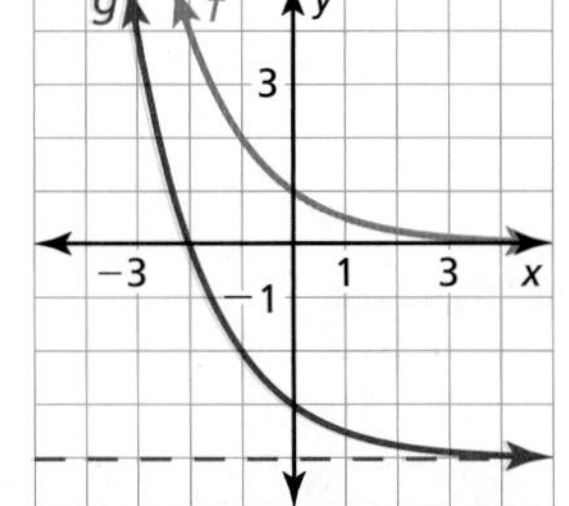

STUDY TIP

Notice in the graph that the vertical translation also shifts the asymptote 4 units down, so the range of g is $y > -4$.

SELF-ASSESSMENT 1 I do not understand. 2 I can do it with help. 3 I can do it on my own. 4 I can teach someone else.

Describe the transformation of f represented by g. Then graph each function.

1. $f(x) = 3^x$, $g(x) = 3^x + 2$
2. $f(x) = \left(\frac{1}{4}\right)^x$, $g(x) = \left(\frac{1}{4}\right)^{x-2}$
3. $f(x) = 0.5^x$, $g(x) = 0.5^{x+1} - 6$
4. $f(x) = 2^x$, $g(x) = 2^{x-3} + 1$

EXAMPLE 2 Translating a Natural Base Exponential Function

Describe the transformation of $f(x) = e^x$ represented by $g(x) = e^{x+3} + 2$. Then graph each function.

SOLUTION

Notice that the function is of the form $g(x) = e^{x-h} + k$. Rewrite the function to identify h and k.

$$g(x) = e^{x-(-3)} + 2$$

(↑ h, ↑ k)

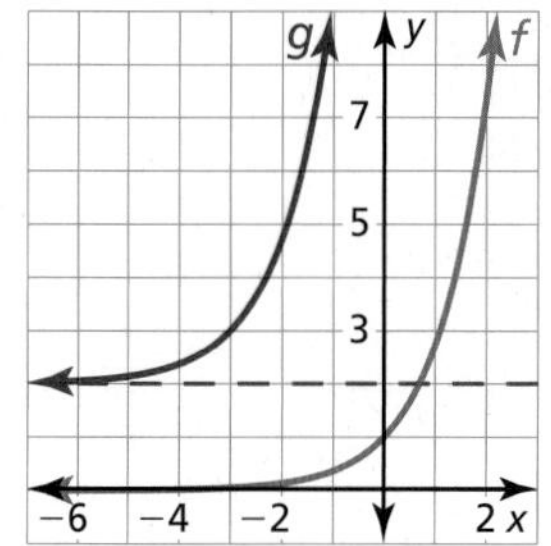

▶ Because $h = -3$ and $k = 2$, the graph of g is a translation 3 units left and 2 units up of the graph of f.

STUDY TIP

Notice in the graph that the vertical translation also shifts the asymptote 2 units up, so the range of g is $y > 2$.

EXAMPLE 3 Transforming Exponential Functions

Describe the transformation of f represented by g. Then graph each function.

a. $f(x) = 3^x$, $g(x) = 3^{3x-5}$

b. $f(x) = e^{-x}$, $g(x) = -\frac{1}{8}e^{-x}$

SOLUTION

a. Notice that the function is of the form $g(x) = 3^{ax-h}$, where $a = 3$ and $h = 5$.

▶ So, the graph of g is a translation 5 units right, followed by a horizontal shrink by a factor of $\frac{1}{3}$ of the graph of f.

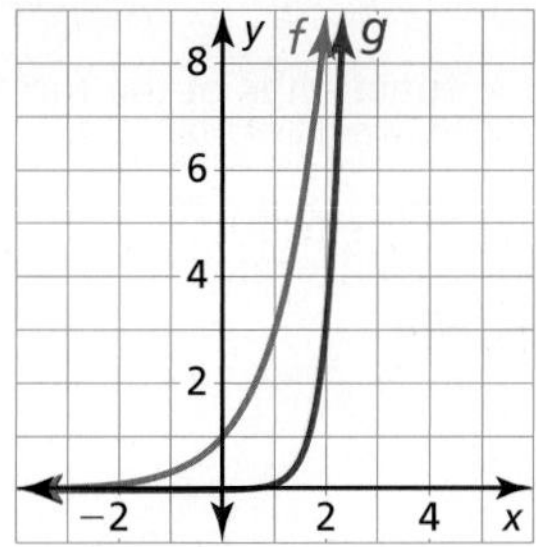

b. Notice that the function is of the form $g(x) = ae^{-x}$, where $a = -\frac{1}{8}$.

▶ So, the graph of g is a reflection in the x-axis and a vertical shrink by a factor of $\frac{1}{8}$ of the graph of f.

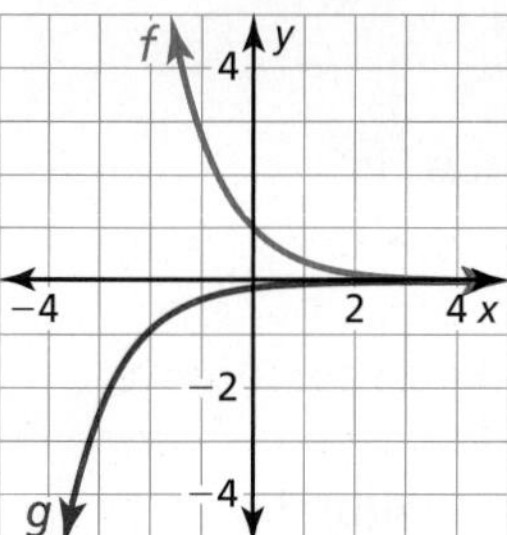

Math Practice

Look for Structure

Compare the transformation in Example 3(a) with the transformation of f represented by $h(x) = 3^{3(x-5)}$.

SELF-ASSESSMENT

1 I do not understand. 2 I can do it with help. 3 I can do it on my own. 4 I can teach someone else.

Describe the transformation of f represented by g. Then graph each function.

5. $f(x) = e^x$, $g(x) = e^{x-3}$
6. $f(x) = e^{-x}$, $g(x) = e^{-x} - 5$
7. $f(x) = 0.4^x$, $g(x) = 0.4^{-2x}$
8. $f(x) = e^x$, $g(x) = -e^{x+6}$
9. **WRITING** Given the function $f(x) = ab^{x-h} + k$, describe the effects of a, h, and k on the graph of the function.

Transforming Graphs of Logarithmic Functions

Examples of transformations of the graph of $f(x) = \log x$ are shown below.

KEY IDEAS

Transformation	$f(x)$ Notation	Examples	
Horizontal Translation Graph shifts left or right.	$f(x - h)$	$g(x) = \log(x - 4)$ $g(x) = \log(x + 7)$	4 units right 7 units left
Vertical Translation Graph shifts up or down.	$f(x) + k$	$g(x) = \log x + 3$ $g(x) = \log x - 1$	3 units up 1 unit down
Reflection Graph flips over a line.	$f(-x)$ $-f(x)$	$g(x) = \log(-x)$ $g(x) = -\log x$	in the y-axis in the x-axis
Horizontal Stretch or Shrink Graph stretches away from or shrinks toward y-axis by a factor of $\frac{1}{a}$.	$f(ax)$	$g(x) = \log(4x)$ $g(x) = \log\left(\frac{1}{3}x\right)$	shrink by a factor of $\frac{1}{4}$ stretch by a factor of 3
Vertical Stretch or Shrink Graph stretches away from or shrinks toward x-axis by a factor of a.	$a \cdot f(x)$	$g(x) = 5 \log x$ $g(x) = \frac{2}{3} \log x$	stretch by a factor of 5 shrink by a factor of $\frac{2}{3}$

EXAMPLE 4 Transforming Logarithmic Functions

Describe the transformation of f represented by g. Then graph each function.

a. $f(x) = \log x$, $g(x) = \log\left(-\frac{1}{2}x\right)$ **b.** $f(x) = \log_{1/2} x$, $g(x) = 2 \log_{1/2}(x + 4)$

SOLUTION

a. Notice that the function is of the form $g(x) = \log(ax)$, where $a = -\frac{1}{2}$.

▶ So, the graph of g is a reflection in the y-axis and a horizontal stretch by a factor of 2 of the graph of f.

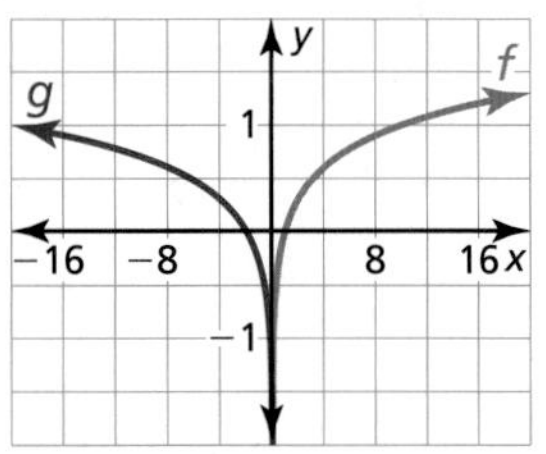

STUDY TIP

In Example 4(b), notice in the graph that the horizontal translation also shifts the asymptote 4 units left, so the domain of g is $x > -4$.

b. Notice that the function is of the form $g(x) = a \log_{1/2}(x - h)$, where $a = 2$ and $h = -4$.

▶ So, the graph of g is a horizontal translation 4 units left and a vertical stretch by a factor of 2 of the graph of f.

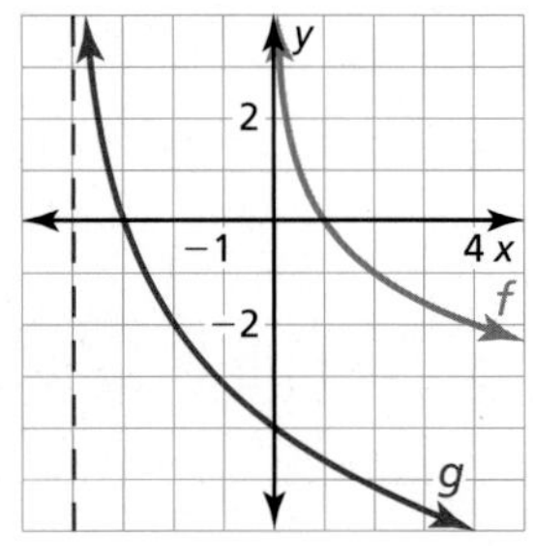

Writing Transformations of Graphs of Functions

EXAMPLE 5 Writing a Transformed Exponential Function

Let the graph of g be a reflection in the x-axis, followed by a translation 4 units right of the graph of $f(x) = 2^x$. Write a rule for g.

SOLUTION

Step 1 First write a function h that represents the reflection of f.

$$h(x) = -f(x) \qquad \text{Multiply the output by } -1.$$
$$= -2^x \qquad \text{Substitute } 2^x \text{ for } f(x).$$

Step 2 Then write a function g that represents the translation of h.

$$g(x) = h(x - 4) \qquad \text{Subtract 4 from the input.}$$
$$= -2^{x-4} \qquad \text{Replace } x \text{ with } x - 4 \text{ in } h(x).$$

▶ The transformed function is $g(x) = -2^{x-4}$.

Check

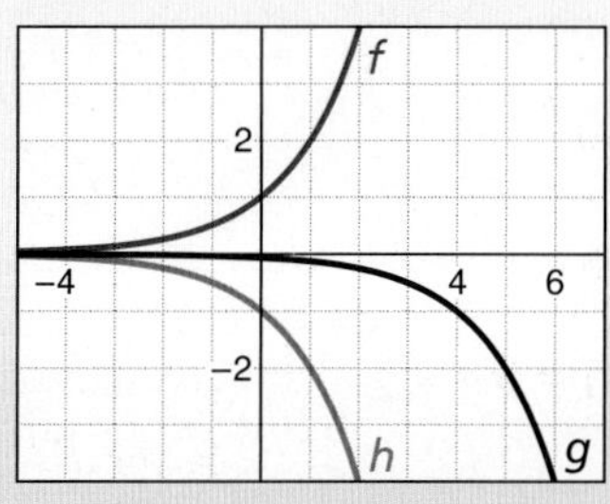

EXAMPLE 6 Writing a Transformed Logarithmic Function

Let the graph of g be a translation 2 units up, followed by a vertical stretch by a factor of 2 of the graph of $f(x) = \log_{1/3} x$. Write a rule for g.

SOLUTION

Step 1 First write a function h that represents the translation of f.

$$h(x) = f(x) + 2 \qquad \text{Add 2 to the output.}$$
$$= \log_{1/3} x + 2 \qquad \text{Substitute } \log_{1/3} x \text{ for } f(x).$$

Step 2 Then write a function g that represents the vertical stretch of h.

$$g(x) = 2 \cdot h(x) \qquad \text{Multiply the output by 2.}$$
$$= 2 \cdot (\log_{1/3} x + 2) \qquad \text{Substitute } \log_{1/3} x + 2 \text{ for } h(x).$$
$$= 2 \log_{1/3} x + 4 \qquad \text{Distributive Property}$$

▶ The transformed function is $g(x) = 2 \log_{1/3} x + 4$.

Check

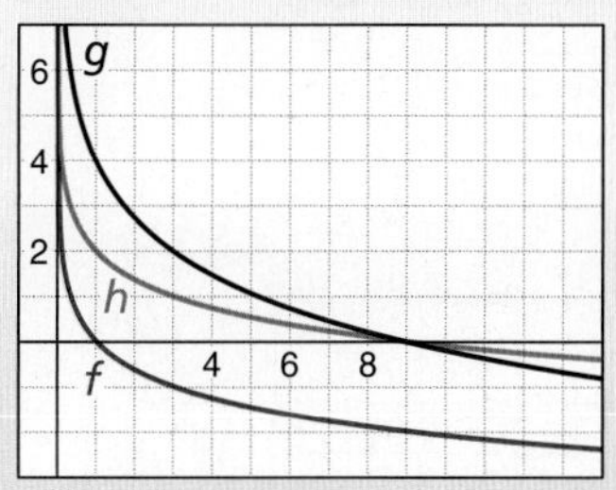

SELF-ASSESSMENT

1 I do not understand. | 2 I can do it with help. | 3 I can do it on my own. | 4 I can teach someone else.

Describe the transformation of f represented by g. Then graph each function.

10. $f(x) = \log_2 x$, $g(x) = -3 \log_2 x$

11. $f(x) = \log_{1/4} x$, $g(x) = \log_{1/4}(4x) - 5$

12. Let the graph of g be a horizontal stretch by a factor of 3, followed by a translation 2 units up of the graph of $f(x) = e^{-x}$. Write a rule for g.

13. Let the graph of g be a reflection in the y-axis, followed by a translation 4 units left of the graph of $f(x) = \log x$. Write a rule for g.

6.4 Practice WITH CalcChat® AND CalcView®

GO DIGITAL

In Exercises 1–4, match the function with its graph. Explain your reasoning.

1. $y = 2^{x+2} - 2$

2. $y = 2^{x+2} + 2$

3. $y = 2^{x-2} - 2$

4. $y = 2^{x-2} + 2$

A.

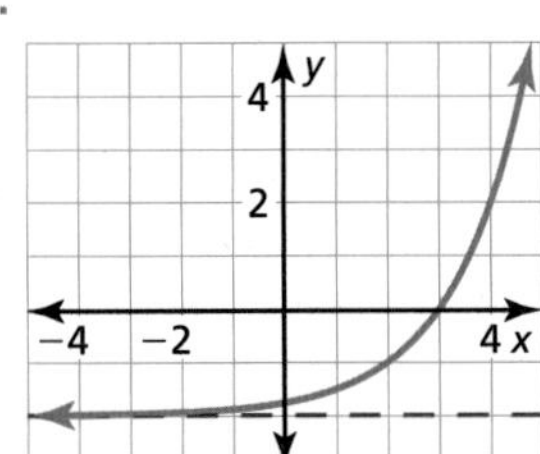

B.

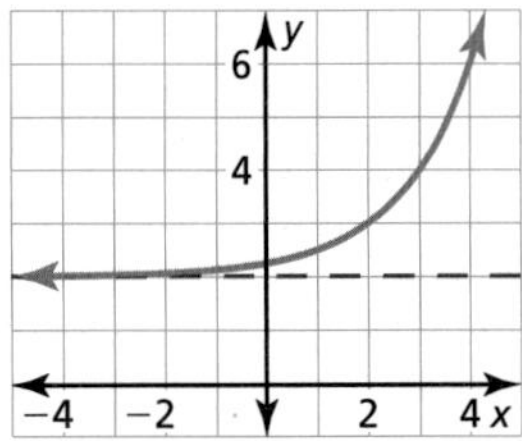

C.

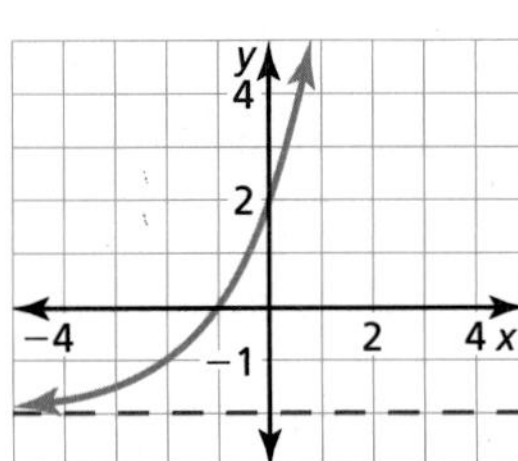

D.

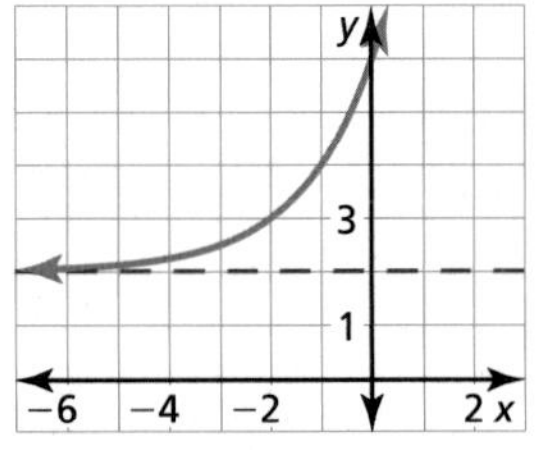

In Exercises 5–14, describe the transformation of *f* represented by *g*. Then graph each function. *Examples 1 and 2*

5. $f(x) = 3^x, g(x) = 3^x + 5$

6. $f(x) = 4^x, g(x) = 4^x - 8$

7. $f(x) = e^x, g(x) = e^x - 1$

8. $f(x) = e^x, g(x) = e^x + 4$

9. $f(x) = 2^x, g(x) = 2^{x-7}$

10. $f(x) = 5^x, g(x) = 5^{x+1}$

11. $f(x) = e^{-x}, g(x) = e^{-x} + 6$

12. $f(x) = e^{-x}, g(x) = e^{-x} - 9$

13. $f(x) = 0.25^x, g(x) = 0.25^{x-3} + 12$

14. $f(x) = \left(\frac{1}{3}\right)^x, g(x) = \left(\frac{1}{3}\right)^{x+2} - \frac{2}{3}$

In Exercises 15–22, describe the transformation of *f* represented by *g*. Then graph each function. *Example 3*

15. $f(x) = e^x, g(x) = e^{2x}$

16. $f(x) = e^x, g(x) = \frac{4}{3}e^x$

17. $f(x) = 2^x, g(x) = -2^{x-3}$

18. $f(x) = 4^x, g(x) = 4^{0.5x-5}$

19. $f(x) = e^{-x}, g(x) = 3e^{-6x}$

20. $f(x) = e^{-x}, g(x) = e^{-5x} + 2$

21. $f(x) = 0.5^x, g(x) = 6(0.5)^{x+5} - 2$

22. $f(x) = \left(\frac{3}{4}\right)^x, g(x) = -\left(\frac{3}{4}\right)^{x-7} + 1$

ERROR ANALYSIS In Exercises 23 and 24, describe and correct the error in graphing the transformation of *f* represented by *g*.

23. $g(x) = 2^x + 3$

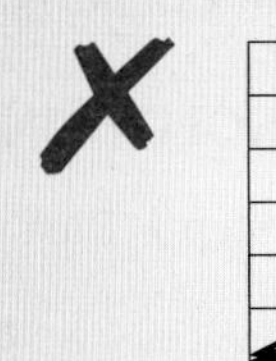
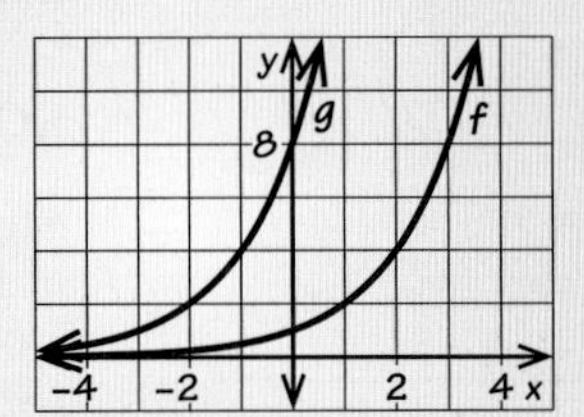

24. $g(x) = 3^{-x}$

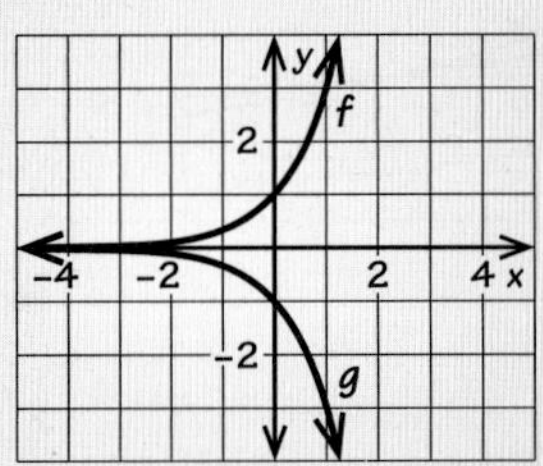

In Exercises 25–28, describe the transformation of *f* represented by *g*. Then graph each function. *Example 4*

25. $f(x) = \log_4 x, g(x) = 3\log_4 x - 5$

26. $f(x) = \log_{1/3} x, g(x) = \log_{1/3}(-x) + 6$

27. $f(x) = \log_{1/5} x, g(x) = -\log_{1/5}(x - 7)$

28. $f(x) = \log_2 x, g(x) = \log_2(x + 2) - 3$

ANALYZING RELATIONSHIPS **In Exercises 29–32, use the graph of *f* to match the transformation of *f* with its graph.**

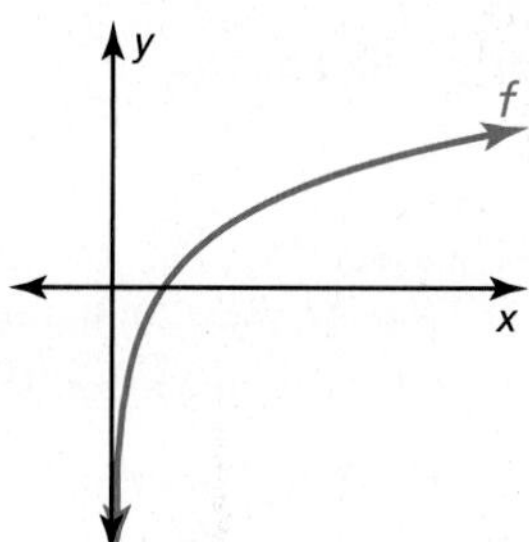

29. $y = f(x - 2)$

30. $y = f(x + 2)$

31. $y = 2f(x)$

32. $y = f(2x)$

A.

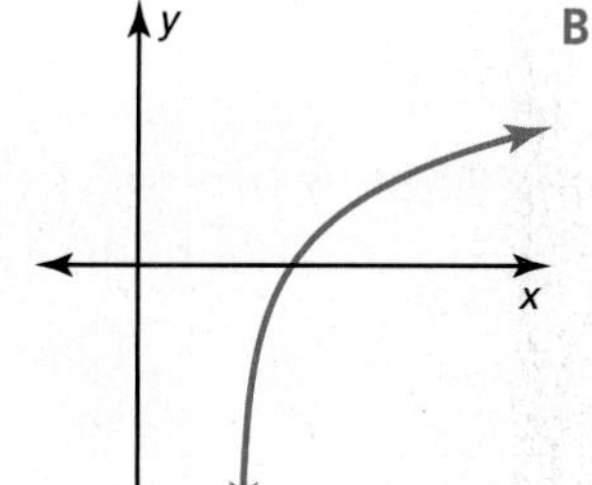

B.

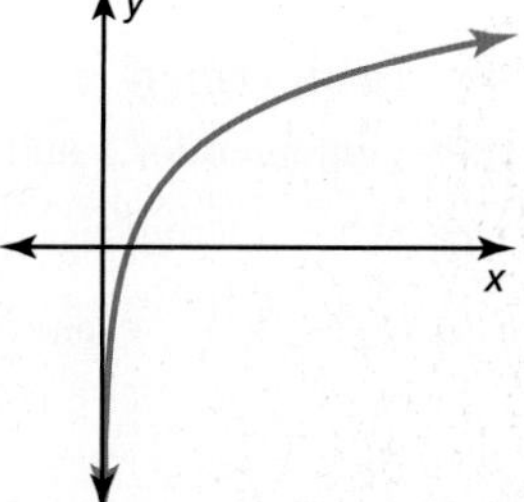

C.

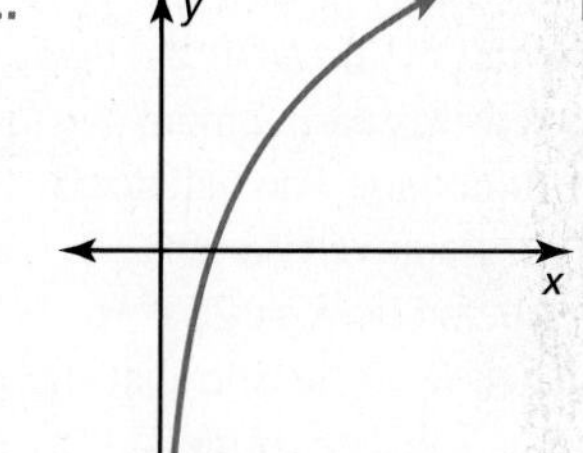

D.

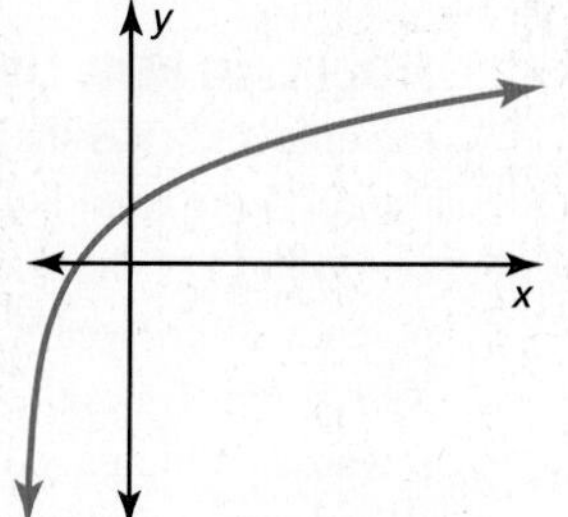

JUSTIFYING STEPS **In Exercises 33 and 34, justify each step in writing a rule for *g* that represents the indicated transformations of the graph of *f*.**

33. $f(x) = \log_7 x$; reflection in the x-axis, followed by a translation 6 units down

$h(x) = -f(x)$

$= -\log_7 x$

$g(x) = h(x) - 6$

$= -\log_7 x - 6$

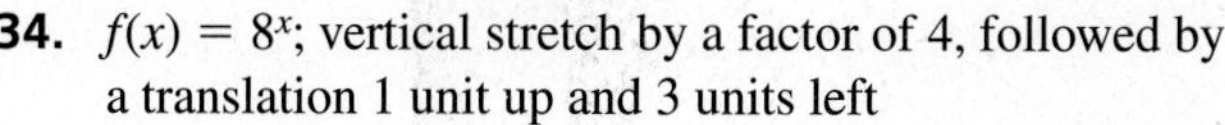

34. $f(x) = 8^x$; vertical stretch by a factor of 4, followed by a translation 1 unit up and 3 units left

$h(x) = 4 \cdot f(x)$

$= 4 \cdot 8^x$

$g(x) = h(x + 3) + 1$

$= 4 \cdot 8^{x+3} + 1$

In Exercises 35–38, write a rule for *g* that represents the indicated transformations of the graph of *f*. *Example 5*

35. $f(x) = 5^x$; translation 2 units down, followed by a reflection in the y-axis

36. $f(x) = \left(\frac{2}{3}\right)^x$; reflection in the x-axis, followed by a vertical stretch by a factor of 6 and a translation 4 units left

37. $f(x) = e^x$; horizontal shrink by a factor of $\frac{1}{2}$, followed by a translation 5 units up

38. $f(x) = e^{-x}$; translation 4 units right and 1 unit down, followed by a vertical shrink by a factor of $\frac{1}{3}$

In Exercises 39–42, write a rule for *g* that represents the indicated transformations of the graph of *f*. *Example 6*

39. $f(x) = \log_6 x$; vertical stretch by a factor of 6, followed by a translation 5 units down

40. $f(x) = \log_5 x$; reflection in the x-axis, followed by a translation 9 units left

41. $f(x) = \log_{1/2} x$; translation 3 units left and 2 units up, followed by a reflection in the y-axis

42. $f(x) = \ln x$; translation 3 units right and 1 unit up, followed by a horizontal stretch by a factor of 8

MP STRUCTURE **In Exercises 43 and 44, describe the transformation of the graph of *f* represented by the graph of *g*. Then give an equation of the asymptote.**

43. $f(x) = 3^x$, $g(x) = 3^{x-9}$

44. $f(x) = \log_{1/5} x$, $g(x) = \log_{1/5} x + 13$

45. **MODELING REAL LIFE** The speed (in miles per hour) of a hoverboard can be modeled by the function $g(t) = 9 - 9e^{-at}$, where t is the number of seconds since activation and $0 < a < 1$. Describe how changing the value of a affects the graph of g. What does this mean in terms of the speed of the hoverboard?

46. **MODELING REAL LIFE** Explain why the advertisement below is misleading for the hoverboard modeled in Exercise 45.

47. **MAKING AN ARGUMENT** Does a horizontal stretch by a factor of 4 have the same result as a vertical shrink by a factor of $\frac{1}{4}$ for $f(x) = \log_4 x$? Explain.

48. **HOW DO YOU SEE IT?** The graphs of $f(x) = b^x$ and $g(x) = \left(\frac{1}{b}\right)^x$ are shown for $b = 2$. Use the graphs to describe a transformation of the graph of f that results in the graph of g.

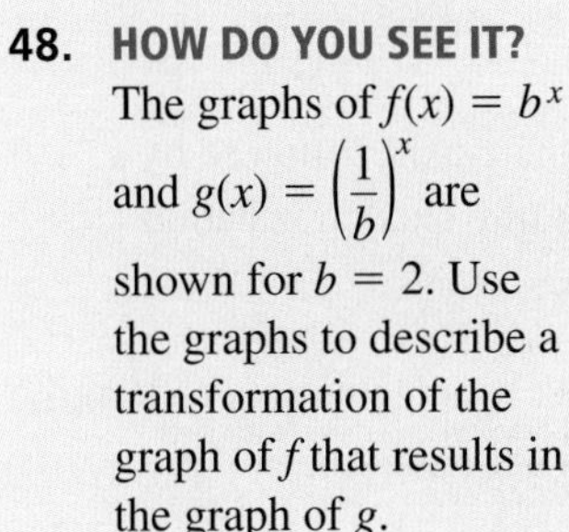

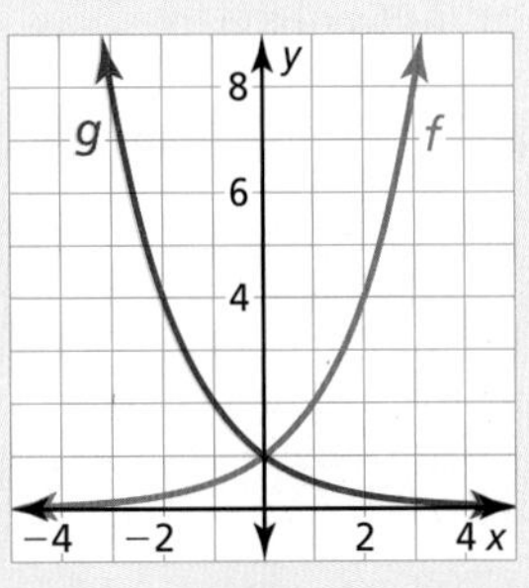

49. **CRITICAL THINKING** Consider the graph of the function $h(x) = e^{-x-2}$. Describe the transformation of the graph of $f(x) = e^{-x}$ represented by the graph of h. Then describe the transformation of the graph of $g(x) = e^x$ represented by the graph of h.

50. **THOUGHT PROVOKING** Consider the functions $f(x) = \log_a x$ and $g(x) = \frac{1}{\log a} \log x + k$. How are the graphs of f and g related?

51. **MP PROBLEM SOLVING** The amount P (in grams) of 100 grams of plutonium-239 that remains after t years can be modeled by $P = 100(0.99997)^t$.

    a. How much plutonium-239 remains after 12,000 years?

    b. Describe the transformation of the function when the initial amount of plutonium-239 is 550 grams.

    c. Does the transformation in part (b) affect the domain and range of the function? Explain.

52. **OPEN-ENDED** Write a function whose graph has a y-intercept of 5 and an asymptote of $y = 2$.

REVIEW & REFRESH

WATCH

In Exercises 53–56, simplify the expression.

53. $9^{\log_9 x}$

54. $e^{\ln 9}$

55. $\log_2 2^{2x}$

56. $10^{\log (x-3)}$

In Exercises 57 and 58, determine whether the data show a linear relationship. If so, write an equation of a line of fit. Then estimate y when $x = 20$ and explain its meaning in the context of the situation.

57.

Minutes gliding, x	1	4	8	12
Calories burned, y	8	32	64	96

58.

Months, x	3	6	9	12
Attendance (thousands), y	2	2.1	2.2	2.3

In Exercises 59 and 60, write a rule for g that represents the indicated transformations of the graph of f.

59. $f(x) = e^x$; horizontal shrink by a factor of $\frac{1}{3}$, followed by a translation 1 unit down

60. $f(x) = \log_2 x$; reflection in the y-axis, followed by a translation 3 units right

61. Find the zeros of $h(x) = x^4 + x^3 - 12x^2$. Then sketch the graph of h.

62. Solve $\sqrt{2x + 11} = 5$. Check your solution.

63. **MODELING REAL LIFE** Social media advertisement revenue and ride sharing rewards earn annual interest compounded continuously. The balance S (in dollars) of the social media advertisement revenue after t years is modeled by $S = 25e^{0.1t}$. The graph shows the balance R of the ride sharing rewards. Which account has a greater principal? Which account has a greater balance after 6 years?

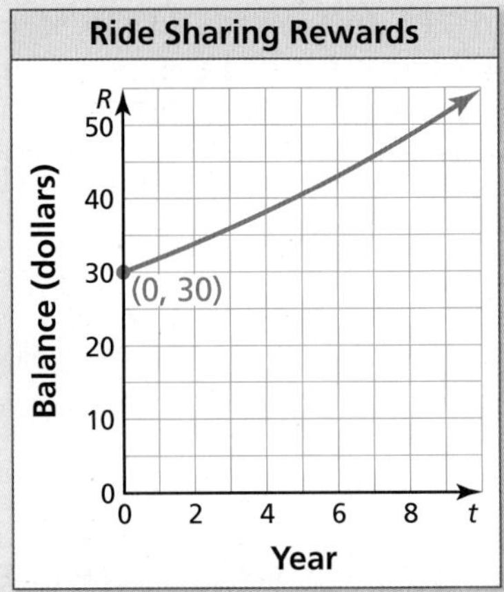

In Exercises 64 and 65, rewrite the function in the form $y = a(1 + r)^t$ or $y = a(1 - r)^t$. State the growth or decay rate, and describe the end behavior of the function.

64. $y = a(2)^{t/4}$

65. $y = a\left(\frac{1}{3}\right)^{2t}$

6.5 Properties of Logarithms

Learning Target Use properties of logarithms.

Success Criteria
- I can evaluate logarithms.
- I can expand or condense logarithmic expressions.
- I can explain how to use the change-of-base formula.

EXPLORE IT! Deriving Properties of Logarithms

Work with a partner. You can use properties of exponents to derive several properties of logarithms. Let $x = \log_b m$ and $y = \log_b n$. The corresponding exponential forms of these two equations are

$$b^x = m \quad \text{and} \quad b^y = n.$$

a. The diagram shows a way to derive the Product Property of Logarithms. Complete and explain the diagram.

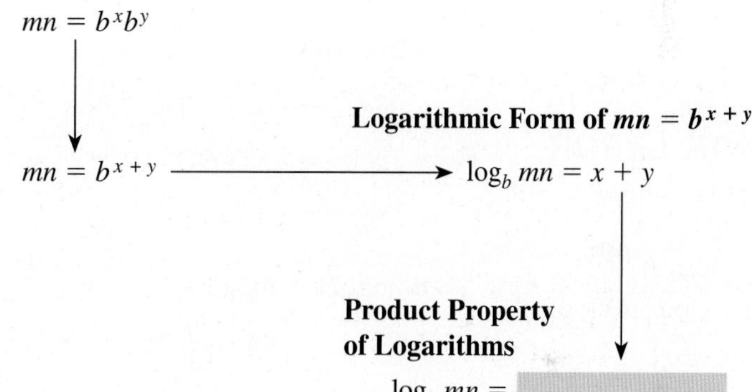

Math Practice

Make Conjectures
Do you think you can extend the Product Property of Logarithms to more than two factors?

b. Derive the Quotient Property of Logarithms shown below using a diagram similar to that in part (a). Explain your reasoning.

$$\log_b \frac{m}{n} = \log_b m - \log_b n \qquad \text{Quotient Property of Logarithms}$$

Give some examples to show that the property works. Revise your work if needed.

c. Use the substitution $m = b^x$ to derive the Power Property of Logarithms shown below.

$$\log_b m^n = n \log_b m \qquad \text{Power Property of Logarithms}$$

d. How are these three properties of logarithms similar to properties of exponents?

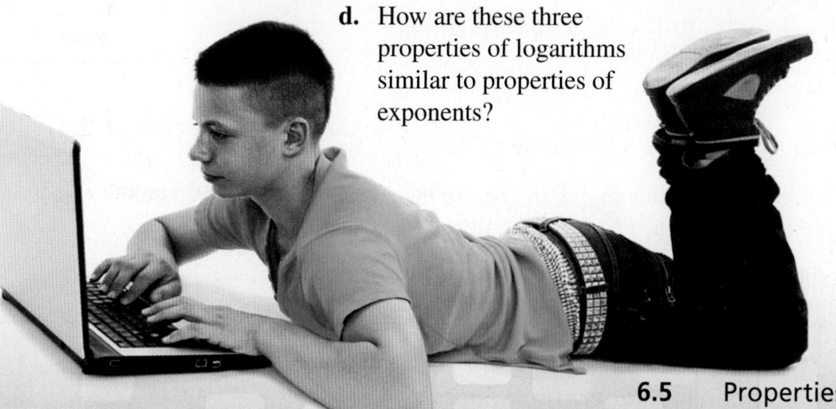

GO DIGITAL

Properties of Logarithms

You know that the logarithmic function with base b is the inverse function of the exponential function with base b. Because of this relationship, it makes sense that logarithms have properties similar to properties of exponents.

KEY IDEA

Properties of Logarithms

Let b, m, and n be positive real numbers with $b \neq 1$.

Product Property $\log_b mn = \log_b m + \log_b n$

Quotient Property $\log_b \frac{m}{n} = \log_b m - \log_b n$

Power Property $\log_b m^n = n \log_b m$

STUDY TIP

These three properties of logarithms correspond to these three properties of exponents.

$a^m a^n = a^{m+n}$

$\frac{a^m}{a^n} = a^{m-n}$

$(a^m)^n = a^{mn}$

EXAMPLE 1 Using Properties of Logarithms

Use $\log_2 3 \approx 1.585$ and $\log_2 7 \approx 2.807$ to evaluate each logarithm.

a. $\log_2 \frac{3}{7}$ **b.** $\log_2 21$ **c.** $\log_2 49$

SOLUTION

a. $\log_2 \frac{3}{7} = \log_2 3 - \log_2 7$ Quotient Property

$\approx 1.585 - 2.807$ Use the given values of $\log_2 3$ and $\log_2 7$.

$= -1.222$ Subtract.

b. $\log_2 21 = \log_2(3 \cdot 7)$ Write 21 as $3 \cdot 7$.

$= \log_2 3 + \log_2 7$ Product Property

$\approx 1.585 + 2.807$ Use the given values of $\log_2 3$ and $\log_2 7$.

$= 4.392$ Add.

c. $\log_2 49 = \log_2 7^2$ Write 49 as 7^2.

$= 2 \log_2 7$ Power Property

$\approx 2(2.807)$ Use the given value of $\log_2 7$.

$= 5.614$ Multiply.

COMMON ERROR

Note that in general

$\log_b \frac{m}{n} \neq \frac{\log_b m}{\log_b n}$ and

$\log_b mn \neq (\log_b m)(\log_b n)$.

SELF-ASSESSMENT

1 I do not understand. 2 I can do it with help. 3 I can do it on my own. 4 I can teach someone else.

Use $\log_6 5 \approx 0.898$ and $\log_6 8 \approx 1.161$ to evaluate the logarithm.

1. $\log_6 \frac{5}{8}$

2. $\log_6 40$

3. $\log_6 64$

4. $\log_6 125$

5. **MP STRUCTURE** Without using technology, can you use the approximations given below to evaluate $\ln x$ for all integer values of x between 1 and 10? Explain your reasoning.

$\ln 2 \approx 0.6931, \quad \ln 3 \approx 1.0986, \quad \ln 5 \approx 1.6094$

Expanding and Condensing Logarithmic Expressions

EXAMPLE 2 **Expanding a Logarithmic Expression** 

Expand $\ln \frac{5x^7}{y}$.

STUDY TIP

When you are expanding or condensing an expression involving logarithms, you can assume that any variables are positive.

SOLUTION

$$\ln \frac{5x^7}{y} = \ln 5x^7 - \ln y \qquad \text{Quotient Property}$$
$$= \ln 5 + \ln x^7 - \ln y \qquad \text{Product Property}$$
$$= \ln 5 + 7 \ln x - \ln y \qquad \text{Power Property}$$

EXAMPLE 3 **Condensing a Logarithmic Expression** 

Condense $\log 9 + 3 \log 2 - \log 3$.

SOLUTION

$$\log 9 + 3 \log 2 - \log 3 = \log 9 + \log 2^3 - \log 3 \qquad \text{Power Property}$$
$$= \log(9 \cdot 2^3) - \log 3 \qquad \text{Product Property}$$
$$= \log \frac{9 \cdot 2^3}{3} \qquad \text{Quotient Property}$$
$$= \log 24 \qquad \text{Simplify.}$$

SELF-ASSESSMENT 1 I do not understand. 2 I can do it with help. 3 I can do it on my own. 4 I can teach someone else.

Expand the logarithmic expression.

6. $\log_6 3x^4$ **7.** $\ln \frac{5}{12x}$ **8.** $\log_5 2\sqrt{x}$

9. **MP REASONING** Which property of logarithms do you need to use to condense the expression $\log_3 2x + \log_3 y$?

Condense the logarithmic expression.

10. $\log x - \log 9$ **11.** $4 \ln x + 8 \ln y$ **12.** $\ln 4 + 3 \ln 3 - \ln 12$

Change-of-Base Formula

Logarithms with any base other than 10 or e can be written in terms of common or natural logarithms using the *change-of-base formula*. This allows you to evaluate any logarithm using a calculator.

KEY IDEA

Change-of-Base Formula

If a, b, and c are positive real numbers with $b \neq 1$ and $c \neq 1$, then

$$\log_c a = \frac{\log_b a}{\log_b c}.$$

In particular, $\log_c a = \frac{\log a}{\log c}$ and $\log_c a = \frac{\ln a}{\ln c}$.

EXAMPLE 4 Changing a Base Using Common Logarithms

Evaluate $\log_3 8$ using common logarithms.

SOLUTION

$$\log_3 8 = \frac{\log 8}{\log 3} \qquad \log_c a = \frac{\log a}{\log c}$$

$$\approx 1.893 \qquad \text{Use technology.}$$

ANOTHER WAY

You can also evaluate $\log_3 8$ using natural logarithms.

$$\log_3 8 = \frac{\ln 8}{\ln 3} \approx 1.893$$

Notice that you get the same answer whether you use natural logarithms or common logarithms in the change-of-base formula.

EXAMPLE 5 Changing a Base Using Natural Logarithms

Evaluate $\log_6 24$ using natural logarithms.

SOLUTION

$$\log_6 24 = \frac{\ln 24}{\ln 6} \qquad \log_c a = \frac{\ln a}{\ln c}$$

$$\approx 1.774 \qquad \text{Use technology.}$$

EXAMPLE 6 Modeling Real Life

For a sound with intensity I (in watts per square meter), the loudness $L(I)$ of the sound (in decibels) is given by the function

$$L(I) = 10 \log \frac{I}{I_0}$$

where I_0 is the intensity of a barely audible sound (about 10^{-12} watt per square meter). An artist in a recording studio turns up the volume of a track so that the intensity of the sound doubles. By how many decibels does the loudness increase?

SOLUTION

Let I be the original intensity, so that $2I$ is the doubled intensity.

$$\text{increase in loudness} = L(2I) - L(I) \qquad \text{Write an expression.}$$

$$= 10 \log \frac{2I}{I_0} - 10 \log \frac{I}{I_0} \qquad \text{Substitute.}$$

$$= 10\left(\log \frac{2I}{I_0} - \log \frac{I}{I_0}\right) \qquad \text{Distributive Property}$$

$$= 10\left(\log 2 + \log \frac{I}{I_0} - \log \frac{I}{I_0}\right) \qquad \text{Product Property}$$

$$= 10 \log 2 \qquad \text{Simplify.}$$

▶ The loudness increases by 10 log 2 decibels, or about 3 decibels.

SELF-ASSESSMENT 1 I do not understand. 2 I can do it with help. 3 I can do it on my own. 4 I can teach someone else.

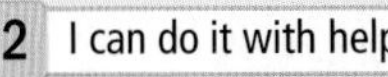

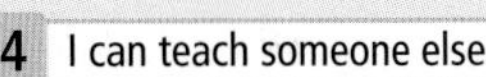

Use the change-of-base formula to evaluate the logarithm.

13. $\log_5 8$ **14.** $\log_8 14$ **15.** $\log_{26} 9$ **16.** $\log_{12} 30$

17. **MP REASONING** Describe two ways to evaluate $\log_7 12$ using a calculator.

18. **WHAT IF?** In Example 6, the artist turns up the volume so that the intensity of the sound triples. By how many decibels does the loudness increase?

6.5 Practice WITH CalcChat® AND CalcView®

In Exercises 1–4, match the expression with the logarithm that has the same value. Justify your answer.

1. $\log_3 6 - \log_3 2$	**A.** $\log_3 64$
2. $2 \log_3 6$	**B.** $\log_3 3$
3. $6 \log_3 2$	**C.** $\log_3 12$
4. $\log_3 6 + \log_3 2$	**D.** $\log_3 36$

In Exercises 5–10, use $\log_7 4 \approx 0.712$ and $\log_7 12 \approx 1.277$ to evaluate the logarithm. *Example 1*

5. $\log_7 3$

6. $\log_7 48$

7. $\log_7 16$

8. $\log_7 64$

9. $\log_7 \frac{1}{4}$

10. $\log_7 \frac{1}{3}$

In Exercises 11–18, expand the logarithmic expression. *Example 2*

11. $\log_3 2x$

12. $\log_8 3x$

13. $\log 10x^5$

14. $\ln 3x^4$

15. $\ln \frac{x}{3y}$

16. $\ln \frac{6x^2}{y^4}$

17. $\log_7 5\sqrt{x}$

18. $\log_5 \sqrt[3]{x^2y}$

ERROR ANALYSIS In Exercises 19 and 20, describe and correct the error in expanding the logarithmic expression.

19.

$\log_2 5x = (\log_2 5)(\log_2 x)$

20.

$$\begin{aligned} \ln 7x^3 &= 3 \ln 7x \\ &= 3(\ln 7 + \ln x) \\ &= 3 \ln 7 + 3 \ln x \end{aligned}$$

In Exercises 21–28, condense the logarithmic expression. *Example 3*

21. $\log_4 7 - \log_4 10$

22. $\ln 12 - \ln 4$

23. $6 \ln x + 4 \ln y$

24. $2 \log x + \log 11$

25. $\log_5 4 + \frac{1}{3} \log_5 x$

26. $6 \ln 2 - 4 \ln y$

27. $5 \ln 2 + 7 \ln x + 4 \ln y$

28. $\log_3 4 + 2 \log_3 \frac{1}{2} + \log_3 x$

In Exercises 29–36, use the change-of-base formula to evaluate the logarithm. *Examples 4 and 5*

29. $\log_4 7$

30. $\log_5 13$

31. $\log_9 15$

32. $\log_8 22$

33. $\log_6 17$

34. $\log_2 28$

35. $\log_7 \frac{3}{16}$

36. $\log_3 \frac{9}{40}$

MODELING REAL LIFE In Exercises 37 and 38, use the function $L(I) = 10 \log \frac{I}{I_0}$ given in Example 6.

37. The intensity of the sound of a television commercial is 10 times greater than the intensity of the television program it follows. By how many decibels does the loudness increase? *Example 6*

38. The blue whale can produce sound with an intensity that is 1 million times greater than the intensity of the loudest sound a human can make. Find the difference in the loudness of the sounds made by a blue whale and a human.

39. COLLEGE PREP Which of the following is *not* equivalent to $\log_5 \frac{y^4}{3x}$?

Ⓐ $4 \log_5 y - \log_5 3x$

Ⓑ $4 \log_5 y - \log_5 3 + \log_5 x$

Ⓒ $4 \log_5 y - \log_5 3 - \log_5 x$

Ⓓ $\log_5 y^4 - \log_5 3 - \log_5 x$

40. **COLLEGE PREP** Which of the following equations is true?

Ⓐ $\log_7 x + 2 \log_7 y = \log_7(x + y^2)$

Ⓑ $9 \log x - 2 \log y = \log \frac{x^9}{y^2}$

Ⓒ $5 \log_4 x + 7 \log_2 y = \log_6 x^5y^7$

Ⓓ $\log_9 x - 5 \log_9 y = \log_9 \frac{x}{5y}$

41. **REWRITING A FORMULA** Under certain conditions, the wind speed (in knots) at an altitude of h meters above a grassy plain can be modeled by the function $s(h) = 2 \ln 100h$.

a. By what amount does the wind speed increase when the altitude doubles?

b. Show that the given function can be written in terms of common logarithms as

$s(h) = \frac{2}{\log e}(\log h + 2)$.

42. **HOW DO YOU SEE IT?**

Use the graph to determine the value of $\frac{\log 8}{\log 2}$.

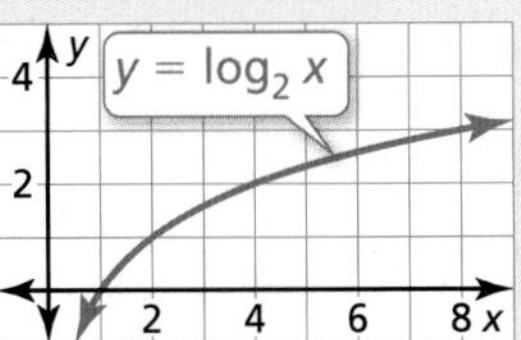

43. **MP REASONING** Determine whether $\log_b(M + N) = \log_b M + \log_b N$ is true for all positive, real values of M, N, and b (with $b \neq 1$). Justify your answer.

44. **THOUGHT PROVOKING**
Use properties of exponents to prove the change-of-base formula. (*Hint:* Let $x = \log_b a$, $y = \log_b c$, and $z = \log_c a$.)

45. 

Describe three ways to transform the graph of $f(x) = \log x$ to obtain the graph of $g(x) = \log 100x - 1$. Justify your answers.

REVIEW & REFRESH

WATCH

In Exercises 46 and 47, rewrite the equation in exponential or logarithmic form.

46. $\log_4 1024 = 5$

47. $7^4 = 2401$

48. Write an equation of the parabola in vertex form.

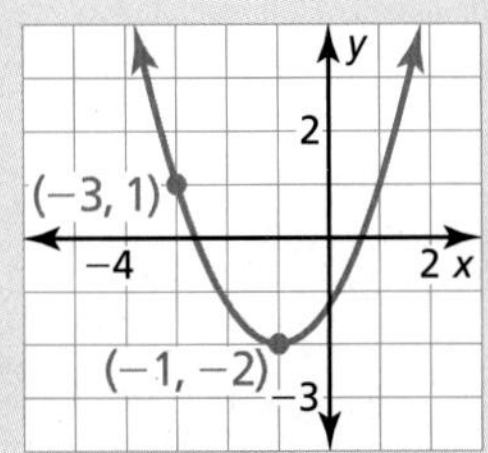

49. Use the change-of-base formula to evaluate $\log_5 20$.

In Exercises 50 and 51, solve the equation by graphing.

50. $4x^2 - 3x - 6 = -x^2 + 5x + 3$

51. $-(x + 3)(x + 2) = x^2 - 6x$

52. **MODELING REAL LIFE** At a frozen yogurt stand, two small cones, one medium cone, and two large cones cost $14.60. One small cone, one medium cone, and one large cone cost $8.70. Three small cones, two medium cones, and one large cone cost $16.50. How much does each cone size cost?

In Exercises 53 and 54, solve the inequality by graphing.

53. $x^2 + 13x + 42 < 0$

54. $-x^2 - 4x + 6 \leq -6$

55. Expand $\log \frac{y^3}{x^5}$.

56. 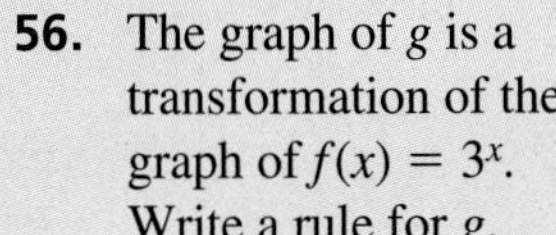
The graph of g is a transformation of the graph of $f(x) = 3^x$. Write a rule for g.

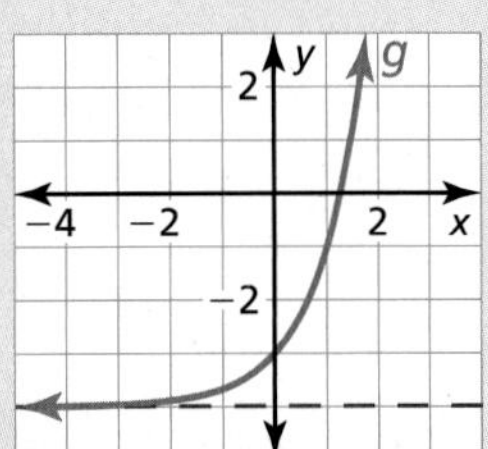

In Exercises 57 and 58, perform the operation. Write the answer in standard form.

57. $(3 - i)(8 + 2i)$

58. $(6 + 11i) - (13 - 4i)$

In Exercises 59–62, simplify the expression.

59. $e^8 \cdot e^4$

60. $\frac{15e^3}{3e}$

61. $(5e^{4x})^3$

62. $\frac{e^{11} \cdot e^{-3}}{e^2}$

6.6 Solving Exponential and Logarithmic Equations

Learning Target Solve exponential and logarithmic equations and inequalities.

Success Criteria
- I can solve exponential equations.
- I can solve logarithmic equations.
- I can solve exponential and logarithmic inequalities.

EXPLORE IT! Solving Exponential and Logarithmic Equations

Work with a partner.

a. Find the intersection point of the graphs. Explain how this point can be used to solve each equation.

i. $4^x = 2$ **ii.** $\log_4 x = 1$

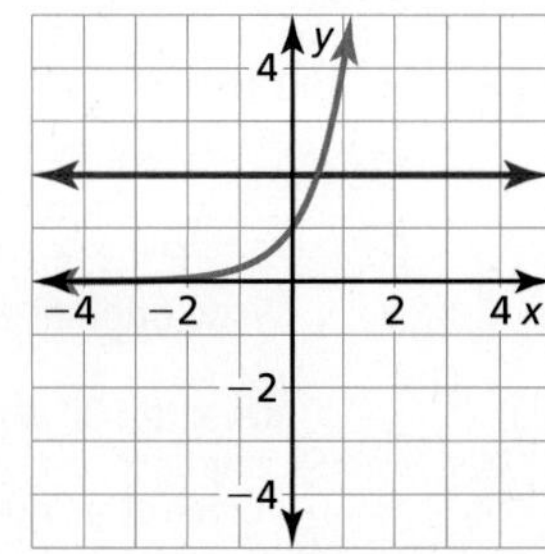

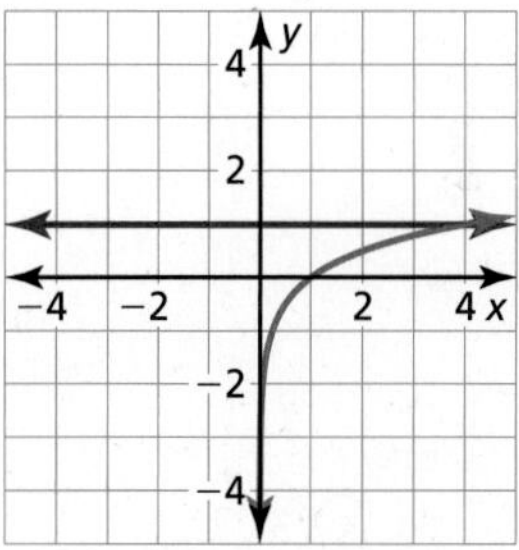

b. Solve each equation by graphing.

i. $e^x = 2$

ii. $\ln x = -1$

iii. $2^x = 3^{-x}$

iv. $\log_5 x = \frac{1}{2}$

c. MP **CHOOSE TOOLS** Solve one of the equations in part (b) using a *numerical approach*, such as using a table or a spreadsheet. Explain your reasoning.

d. Solve one of the equations in part (b) using an *analytical approach*, such as using properties of exponents and logarithms. Explain your reasoning.

e. What are some of the advantages and disadvantages of the solution methods in parts (b)–(d)?

Math Practice

Look for Structure
What are some characteristics of an equation that can help you choose your solution method?

Solving Exponential Equations

Vocabulary

exponential equations, *p. 330*
logarithmic equations, *p. 331*

Exponential equations are equations in which variable expressions occur as exponents. You can use the following property to solve some exponential equations.

KEY IDEA

Property of Equality for Exponential Equations

Algebra If b is a positive real number other than 1, then $b^x = b^y$ if and only if $x = y$.

Example If $3^x = 3^5$, then $x = 5$. If $x = 5$, then $3^x = 3^5$.

The property above is useful for solving an exponential equation when each side has the same base (or can be rewritten using the same base). When it is not convenient to rewrite each side of an exponential equation using the same base, you can try to solve the equation by taking a logarithm of each side.

EXAMPLE 1 Solving Exponential Equations

Solve (a) $100^x = \left(\frac{1}{10}\right)^{x-3}$ and (b) $2^x = 7$.

SOLUTION

a. $100^x = \left(\frac{1}{10}\right)^{x-3}$ Write original equation.

$(10^2)^x = (10^{-1})^{x-3}$ Rewrite 100 and $\frac{1}{10}$ as powers with base 10.

$10^{2x} = 10^{-x+3}$ Power of a Power Property

$2x = -x + 3$ Property of Equality for Exponential Equations

$x = 1$ Solve for x.

Check

$100^1 \stackrel{?}{=} \left(\frac{1}{10}\right)^{1-3}$

$100 \stackrel{?}{=} \left(\frac{1}{10}\right)^{-2}$

$100 = 100$ ✓

b. $2^x = 7$ Write original equation.

$\log_2 2^x = \log_2 7$ Take $\log_2$ of each side.

$x = \log_2 7$ $\log_b b^x = x$

$x \approx 2.807$ Use technology.

Check

Use technology to graph $y = 2^x$ and $y = 7$. Then find the intersection point of the graphs. The graphs intersect at about (2.807, 7). ✓

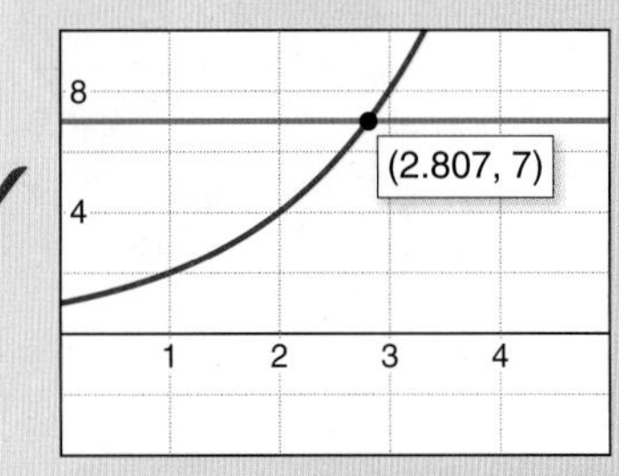

SELF-ASSESSMENT 1 I do not understand. 2 I can do it with help. 3 I can do it on my own. 4 I can teach someone else.

Solve the equation.

1. $\left(\frac{1}{5}\right)^{1-x} = 25^{2x+1}$
2. $8^{2x-1} = 2^{4x-4}$
3. $2^x = 5$
4. $7^{9x} = 15$

GO DIGITAL

Math Practice

Look for Structure

Notice that Newton's Law of Cooling models the temperature of a cooling body by adding a constant function, T_R, to a decaying exponential function, $(T_0 - T_R)e^{-rt}$.

An important application of exponential equations is *Newton's Law of Cooling*. This law states that for a cooling substance with initial temperature T_0, the temperature T after t minutes can be modeled by

$$T = (T_0 - T_R)e^{-rt} + T_R$$

where T_R is the surrounding temperature and r is the cooling rate of the substance.

EXAMPLE 2 Modeling Real LIfe

You are cooking *aleecha*, an Ethiopian stew. When you take it off the stove, its temperature is 212°F. The room temperature is 70°F, and the cooling rate of the stew is $r = 0.046$. How long will it take to cool the stew to a serving temperature of 100°F?

SOLUTION

Use Newton's Law of Cooling with $T = 100$, $T_0 = 212$, $T_R = 70$, and $r = 0.046$.

$T = (T_0 - T_R)e^{-rt} + T_R$	Newton's Law of Cooling
$100 = (212 - 70)e^{-0.046t} + 70$	Substitute for T, T_0, T_R, and r.
$30 = 142e^{-0.046t}$	Subtract 70 from each side.
$0.211 \approx e^{-0.046t}$	Divide each side by 142.
$\ln 0.211 \approx \ln e^{-0.046t}$	Take natural log of each side.
$-1.556 \approx -0.046t$	$\ln e^x = \log_e e^x = x$
$33.8 \approx t$	Divide each side by -0.046.

▶ You should wait about 34 minutes before serving the stew.

SELF-ASSESSMENT 1 I do not understand. 2 I can do it with help. 3 I can do it on my own. 4 I can teach someone else.

5. **WHAT IF?** Use the information in Example 2.

   a. How long will it take to cool the stew to 100°F when the room temperature is 75°F?

   b. How much sooner can your guests begin to eat when the serving temperature is 140°F instead of 100°F? Explain your reasoning.

Solving Logarithmic Equations

Logarithmic equations are equations that involve one or more logarithms of variable expressions. You can use the following property to solve some logarithmic equations.

KEY IDEA

Property of Equality for Logarithmic Equations

Algebra If b, x, and y are positive real numbers with $b \neq 1$, then $\log_b x = \log_b y$ if and only if $x = y$.

Example If $\log_2 x = \log_2 7$, then $x = 7$. If $x = 7$, then $\log_2 x = \log_2 7$.

The property above implies that if you are given an equation $x = y$, then you can exponentiate each side to obtain an equation of the form $b^x = b^y$.

EXAMPLE 3 Solving Logarithmic Equations

Solve (a) $\ln(4x - 7) = \ln(x + 5)$ and (b) $\log_2(5x - 17) = 3$.

SOLUTION

a. $\ln(4x - 7) = \ln(x + 5)$ Write original equation.

$4x - 7 = x + 5$ Property of Equality for Logarithmic Equations

$3x - 7 = 5$ Subtract x from each side.

$x = 4$ Solve for x.

Check

$\ln(4 \cdot 4 - 7) \stackrel{?}{=} \ln(4 + 5)$

$\ln(16 - 7) \stackrel{?}{=} \ln 9$

$\ln 9 = \ln 9$ ✓

b. $\log_2(5x - 17) = 3$ Write original equation.

$2^{\log_2(5x - 17)} = 2^3$ Exponentiate each side using base 2.

$5x - 17 = 8$ $b^{\log_b x} = x$

$x = 5$ Solve for x.

Check

$\log_2(5 \cdot 5 - 17) \stackrel{?}{=} 3$

$\log_2(25 - 17) \stackrel{?}{=} 3$

$\log_2 8 \stackrel{?}{=} 3$

Because $2^3 = 8$, $\log_2 8 = 3$. ✓

EXAMPLE 4 Solving an Equation with an Extraneous Solution

Solve $\log 2x + \log(x - 5) = 2$.

SOLUTION

$\log 2x + \log(x - 5) = 2$ Write original equation.

$\log[2x(x - 5)] = 2$ Product Property of Logarithms

$10^{\log[2x(x - 5)]} = 10^2$ Exponentiate each side using base 10.

$2x(x - 5) = 100$ $b^{\log_b x} = x$

$2x^2 - 10x - 100 = 0$ Use Distributive Property and write in standard form.

$x^2 - 5x - 50 = 0$ Divide each side by 2.

$(x - 10)(x + 5) = 0$ Factor.

$x = 10$ or $x = -5$ Zero-Product Property

STUDY TIP

Because the domain of a logarithmic function generally does not include all real numbers, be sure to check for extraneous solutions of logarithmic equations. You can do this algebraically or graphically.

Check $\log(2 \cdot 10) + \log(10 - 5) \stackrel{?}{=} 2$

$\log 20 + \log 5 \stackrel{?}{=} 2$

$\log 100 \stackrel{?}{=} 2$

$2 = 2$ ✓

$\log[2 \cdot (-5)] + \log(-5 - 5) \stackrel{?}{=} 2$

$\log(-10) + \log(-10) \stackrel{?}{=} 2$

Because $\log(-10)$ is not defined, -5 is not a solution. ✗

▶ The apparent solution $x = -5$ is extraneous. So, the only solution is $x = 10$.

SELF-ASSESSMENT

1 I do not understand. 2 I can do it with help. 3 I can do it on my own. 4 I can teach someone else.

Solve the equation. Check your solution(s).

6. $\ln(7x - 4) = \ln(2x + 11)$

7. $\log_7(4x - 1) = \log_7 23$

8. $\log_2(x - 6) = 5$

9. $\log 5x + \log(x - 1) = 2$

10. $\log_4(x + 12) + \log_4 x = 3$

11. $\ln(x + 4) + \ln x = 6$

12. WRITING When do logarithmic equations have extraneous solutions?

Solving Exponential and Logarithmic Inequalities

Exponential inequalities are inequalities in which variable expressions occur as exponents, and *logarithmic inequalities* are inequalities that involve logarithms of variable expressions. To solve exponential and logarithmic inequalities algebraically, use the following properties. Note that the properties are true for $\leq$ and $\geq$.

STUDY TIP

Be sure you understand that these properties of inequality are only true for values of $b > 1$.

Exponential Property of Inequality: If b is a positive real number greater than 1, then $b^x > b^y$ if and only if $x > y$, and $b^x < b^y$ if and only if $x < y$.

Logarithmic Property of Inequality: If b, x, and y are positive real numbers with b greater than 1, then $\log_b x > \log_b y$ if and only if $x > y$, and $\log_b x < \log_b y$ if and only if $x < y$.

You can also solve an inequality by taking a logarithm of each side or by exponentiating each side.

EXAMPLE 5 Solving an Exponential Inequality

Solve $3^x < 20$.

SOLUTION

$3^x < 20$	Write original inequality.
$\log_3 3^x < \log_3 20$	Take $\log_3$ of each side.
$x < \log_3 20$	$\log_b b^x = x$

▶ The solution is $x < \log_3 20$. Because $\log_3 20 \approx 2.727$, the approximate solution is $x < 2.727$.

EXAMPLE 6 Solving a Logarithmic Inequality

Solve $\log x \leq 2$.

SOLUTION

Method 1 Use an algebraic approach.

$\log x \leq 2$	Write original inequality.
$10^{\log_{10} x} \leq 10^2$	Exponentiate each side using base 10.
$x \leq 100$	$b^{\log_b x} = x$

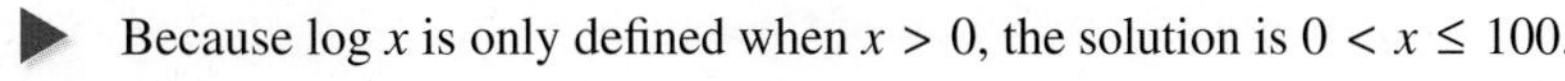
▶ Because $\log x$ is only defined when $x > 0$, the solution is $0 < x \leq 100$.

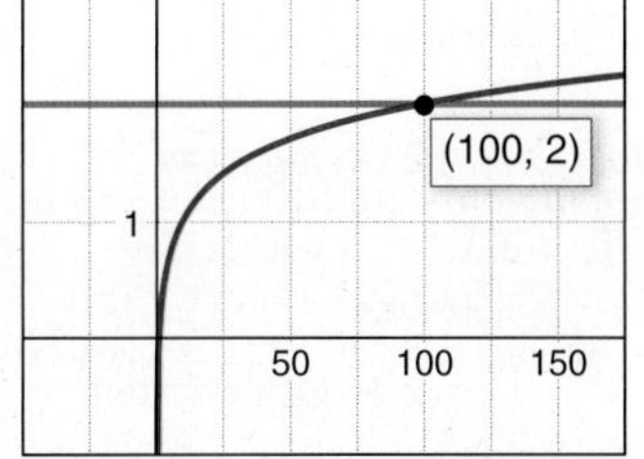

Method 2 Use a graphical approach.

Use technology to graph $y = \log x$ and $y = 2$. Then find the intersection point of the graphs. The graphs intersect at $(100, 2)$. The graph of $y = \log x$ is on or below the graph of $y = 2$ when $0 < x \leq 100$.

▶ The solution is $0 < x \leq 100$.

SELF-ASSESSMENT 1 I do not understand. 2 I can do it with help. 3 I can do it on my own. 4 I can teach someone else.

Solve the inequality.

13. $e^x < 2$ **14.** $10^{2x-6} > 3$ **15.** $\log x + 9 < 45$ **16.** $2 \ln x - 1 > 4$

In Exercises 1–12, solve the equation. ▶ *Example 1*

1. $2^{3x+5} = 2^{1-x}$
2. $e^{2x} = e^{3x-1}$
3. $5^{x-3} = 25^{x-5}$
4. $6^{2x-6} = 36^{3x-5}$
5. $3^x = 7$
6. $10^x = 33$
7. $100^{5x+2} = \left(\frac{1}{10}\right)^{11-x}$
8. $512^{5x-1} = \left(\frac{1}{8}\right)^{-4-x}$
9. $5(7)^{5x} = 60$
10. $3(2)^{6x} = 99$
11. $3e^{4x} + 9 = 15$
12. $2e^{2x} - 7 = 5$

13. **MODELING REAL LIFE** The length ℓ (in centimeters) of a scalloped hammerhead shark can be modeled by the function

$$\ell = 266 - 219e^{-0.05t}$$

where t is the age (in years) of the shark. How old is a shark that is 175 centimeters long?

14. **MODELING REAL LIFE** One hundred grams of radium are stored in a container. The amount R (in grams) of radium present after t years is modeled by $R = 100e^{-0.00043t}$. After how many years will only 5 grams of radium be present?

In Exercises 15 and 16, use Newton's Law of Cooling to solve the problem. ▶ *Example 2*

15. You are driving on a hot day when your car overheats and stops running. The car overheats at 280°F and can be driven again at 230°F. When it is 80°F outside, the cooling rate of the car is $r = 0.0058$. How long do you have to wait until you can continue driving?

16. You cook a turkey until the internal temperature reaches 180°F. The turkey is placed on the table until the internal temperature reaches 100°F and it can be carved. When the room temperature is 72°F, the cooling rate of the turkey is $r = 0.067$. How long do you have to wait until you can carve the turkey?

In Exercises 17–26, solve the equation. ▶ *Example 3*

17. $\ln(4x - 12) = \ln x$
18. $\ln(2x - 4) = \ln(x + 6)$
19. $\log_2(3x - 4) = \log_2 5$
20. $\log(7x + 3) = \log 38$
21. $\log_2(4x + 8) = 5$
22. $\log_3(2x + 1) = 2$
23. $\log(12x - 9) = \log 3x$
24. $\log_6(5x + 9) = \log_6 6x$
25. $\log_2(x^2 - x - 6) = 2$
26. $\log_3(x^2 + 9x + 27) = 2$

In Exercises 27–34, solve the equation. Check your solution(s). ▶ *Example 4*

27. $\log_2 x + \log_2(x - 2) = 3$
28. $\log_6 3x + \log_6(x - 1) = 3$
29. $\ln x + \ln(x + 3) = 4$
30. $\ln x + \ln(x - 2) = 5$
31. $\log_3 3x^2 + \log_3 3 = 2$
32. $\log_4(-x) + \log_4(x + 10) = 2$
33. $\log_3(x - 9) + \log_3(x - 3) = 2$
34. $\log_5(x + 4) + \log_5(x + 1) = 2$

ERROR ANALYSIS In Exercises 35 and 36, describe and correct the error in solving the equation.

35.

$$\log_3(5x - 1) = 4$$
$$3^{\log_3(5x-1)} = 4^3$$
$$5x - 1 = 64$$
$$5x = 65$$
$$x = 13$$

36.

$$\log_4(x + 12) + \log_4 x = 3$$
$$\log_4[(x + 12)(x)] = 3$$
$$4^{\log_4[(x+12)(x)]} = 4^3$$
$$(x + 12)(x) = 64$$
$$x^2 + 12x - 64 = 0$$
$$(x + 16)(x - 4) = 0$$
$$x = -16 \quad \text{or} \quad x = 4$$

The only solution is $x = -16$.

37. MP **PROBLEM SOLVING** You deposit \$100 in an account that pays 6% annual interest. How long will it take for the balance to reach \$1000 for quarterly compounding? continuous compounding?

38. **MODELING REAL LIFE** The *apparent magnitude* of a star is a measure of the brightness of the star viewed from Earth. The apparent magnitude M of the dimmest star that can be seen with a telescope is $M = 5 \log D + 2$, where D is the diameter (in millimeters) of the telescope's objective lens. What is the diameter of the objective lens of a telescope that can reveal stars with an apparent magnitude of 12?

39. **ANALYZING RELATIONSHIPS** Approximate the solution of each equation using the graph.

 a. $1 - 5^{5-x} = -9$ b. $\log_2 5x = 2$

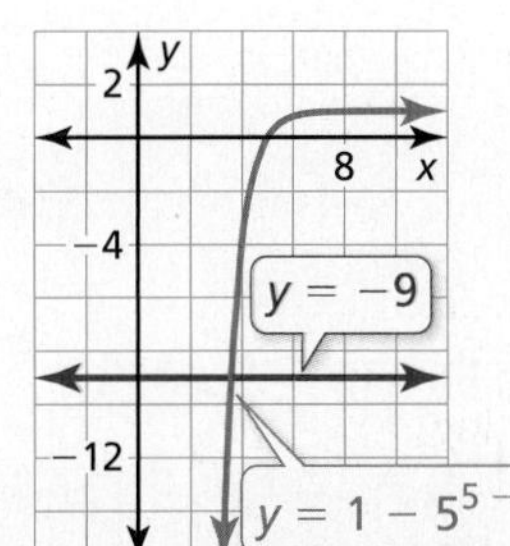

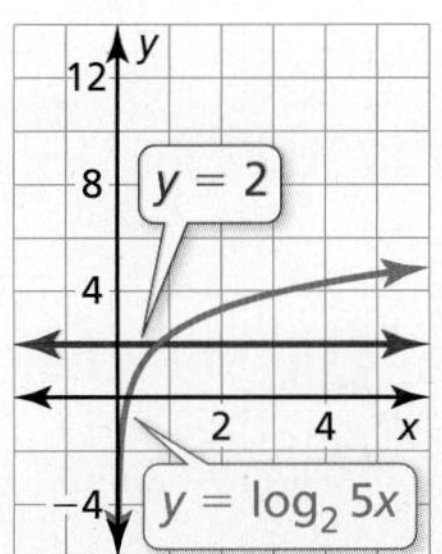

40. **MAKING AN ARGUMENT** Your friend states that a logarithmic equation cannot have a negative solution because logarithmic functions are not defined for negative numbers. Is your friend correct? Explain.

In Exercises 41–52, solve the inequality.
Examples 5 and 6

41. $2^x < 8$ 42. $9^x > 27$

43. $7^x > 54$ 44. $4^x \leq 36$

45. $\log(x - 1) > \log 2$ 46. $\ln 3 > \ln(x + 2)$

47. $\ln x \geq 3$ 48. $\log_4 x < 4$

49. $3^{4x-5} < 8$ 50. $e^{3x+4} > 11$

51. $-3 \log_5 x + 6 \leq 9$ 52. $-4 \log_5 x - 5 \geq 3$

53. **COMPARING METHODS** Solve $\log_5 x < 2$ algebraically and graphically. Which method do you prefer? Explain your reasoning.

54. MP **PROBLEM SOLVING** You buy an autographed jersey for \$55. The value of the jersey is expected to increase by 8% each year. How long will it take the jersey to double in value?

55. MP **PROBLEM SOLVING** An investment that earns a rate of return r doubles in value in t years, where $t = \frac{\ln 2}{\ln(1 + r)}$ and r is expressed as a decimal. What rates of return will double the value of an investment in less than 10 years?

56. MP **PROBLEM SOLVING** A phone case sells for \$48. The value of the phone case decreases by 25% each year. When does the value of the phone case exceed \$20.25?

MP **USING TOOLS In Exercises 57–60, use technology to solve the equation.**

57. $\ln 2x = 3^{-x+2}$ 58. $\log x = 7^{-x}$

59. $\log x = 3^{x-3}$ 60. $\ln 2x = e^{x-3}$

61. **REWRITING A FORMULA** A biologist estimates the age a (in years) of an African elephant by measuring the length ℓ (in centimeters) of its footprint and using the equation

$$\ell = 45 - 25.7e^{-0.09a}.$$

Find the ages of the elephants whose footprints are shown.

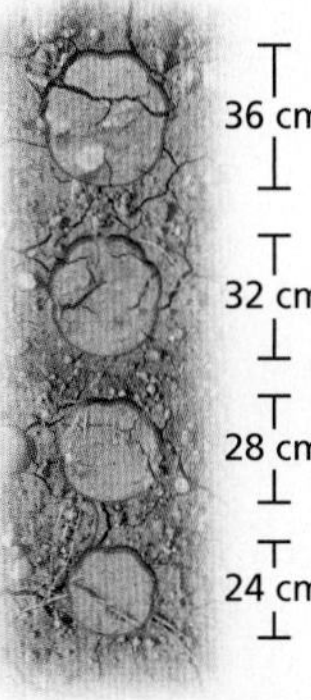

62. **HOW DO YOU SEE IT?** Use the graph to approximate the solution of $4 \ln x + 6 > 9$. Explain.

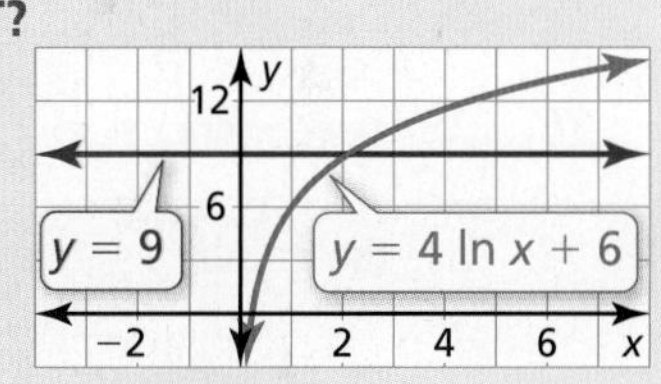

63. **OPEN-ENDED** Write an exponential or logarithmic equation that has a solution of $x = 4$.

64. **THOUGHT PROVOKING** Give an example of an exponential or logarithmic inequality that has no solution.

CRITICAL THINKING In Exercises 65–70, solve the equation.

65. $2^{x+3} = 5^{3x-1}$ 66. $10^{3x-8} = 2^{5-x}$

67. $\log_3(x - 6) = \log_9 2x$ 68. $\log_4 x = \log_8 4x$

69. $2^{2x} - 7 \cdot 2^x + 6 = 0$ 70. $5^{2x} + 3 \cdot 5^x - 40 = 0$

71. WRITING In Exercises 65–68, you solved exponential and logarithmic equations with different bases. Describe general methods for solving such equations.

72. PERFORMANCE TASK You find reward apps to help you resist using your phone during school. Points from an app are redeemable for prizes.

Option A	Option B
• Earns 5% per hour • 20-point penalty for checking phone during school SELECT	• Earns 4% per hour • 10-point penalty for checking phone during school SELECT

Research other aspects of reward apps. Then create a plan for an app to compete with the ones above, including a model for the number of points earned over time.

73. MP PROBLEM SOLVING When X-rays of a fixed wavelength strike a material x centimeters thick, the intensity $I(x)$ of the X-rays transmitted through the material is given by $I(x) = I_0e^{-\mu x}$, where I_0 is the initial intensity and μ is a value that depends on the type of material and the wavelength of the X-rays. The table shows the values of μ for various materials and X-rays of medium wavelength.

Material	Aluminum	Copper	Lead
Value of μ	0.43	3.2	43

You wear a lead apron to protect you from harmful radiation while your dentist takes X-rays of your teeth. Explain why lead is a better material to use than aluminum or copper.

REVIEW & REFRESH

WATCH

74. MODELING REAL LIFE The intensity of the sound of a musical overture is 5 times greater than the intensity of a sensory friendly musical overture. Use the function $L(I) = 10 \log \frac{I}{I_0}$ to determine the loudness increase (in decibels).

In Exercises 75 and 76, describe the transformation of *f* represented by *g*. Then graph each function.

75. $f(x) = 3^x$, $g(x) = 3^x + 7$

76. $f(x) = e^{-x}$, $g(x) = e^{-x-2}$

77. Use the graph to solve $3 = x^2 - 2x$.

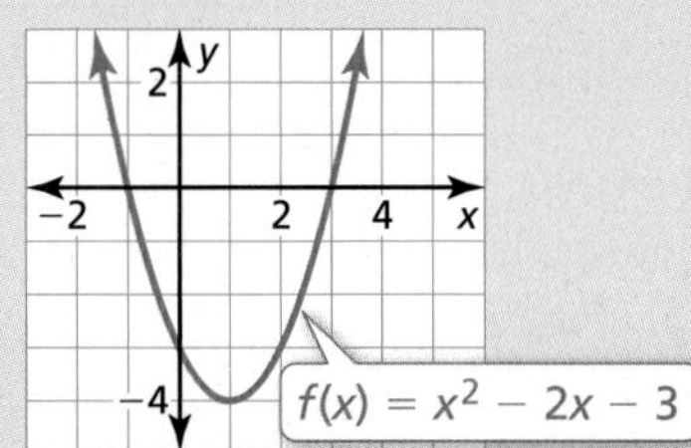

78. Describe the transformation of $f(x) = x^3$ represented by $g(x) = 2(x + 1)^3$. Then graph each function.

In Exercises 79 and 80, simplify the expression.

79. $4\sqrt[3]{17} + 3\sqrt[3]{17}$

80. $\sqrt[5]{\frac{m^{25}}{n^5}}$

81. MP STRUCTURE For the functions f and g, $\left(\frac{f}{g}\right)(2) = 2$ and $(f + g)(2) = 12$. Find the values of $f(2)$ and $g(2)$.

In Exercises 82 and 83, solve the quadratic equation.

82. $2x^2 - 10 = 4$

83. $x^2 + 3x - 11 = 0$

In Exercises 84 and 85, solve the equation. Check your solution(s).

84. $\log_4 x + \log_4(x - 1) = 2$

85. $\log_5 2x^2 + \log_5 4 = 4$

In Exercises 86 and 87, evaluate the logarithm.

86. $\log_3 729$

87. $\log_{1/2} 8$

In Exercises 88 and 89, solve the system.

88. $3x + 2y + z = 9$
$-x + 2y + 5z = 5$
$x + y - 2z = -2$

89. $x - y - z = -4$
$x + y - 2z = 3$
$-x + 2y - 4z = 3$

90. Use the table to find the product of $3x^2 - x + 1$ and $2x - 1$.

	$3x^2$	$-x$	1
$2x$		$-2x^2$	$2x$
-1	$-3x^2$		

6.7 Modeling with Exponential and Logarithmic Functions

Learning Target Write exponential and logarithmic functions to model sets of data.

Success Criteria
- I can use a common ratio to determine whether data can be represented by an exponential function.
- I can write an exponential function using two points.
- I can use technology to find exponential models and logarithmic models for sets of data.

EXPLORE IT! Writing Exponential Functions

Work with a partner. In parts (a) and (b), the graph of a function of the form $f(x) = ab^x$ is shown.

a. Write an exponential function that passes through the points. Explain your reasoning.

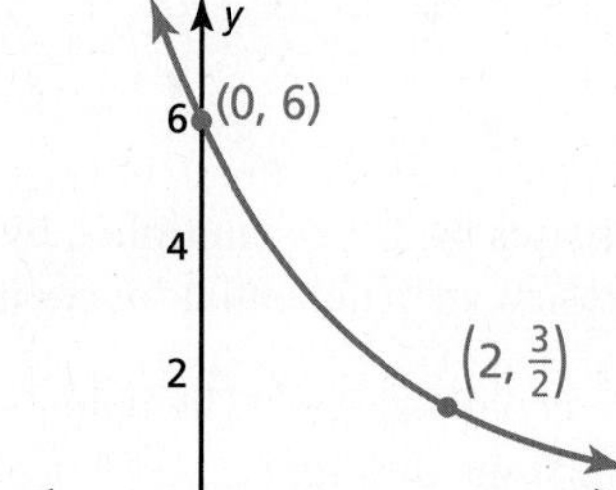

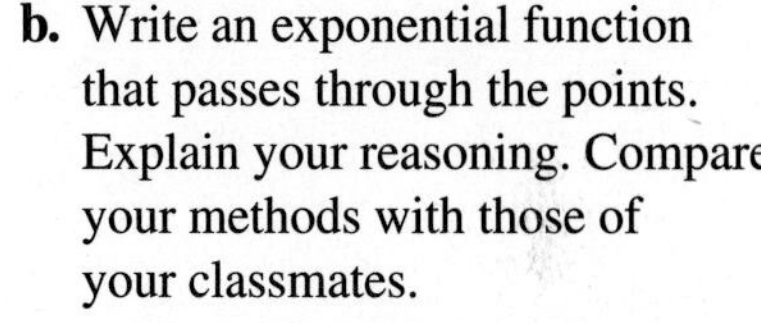

b. Write an exponential function that passes through the points. Explain your reasoning. Compare your methods with those of your classmates.

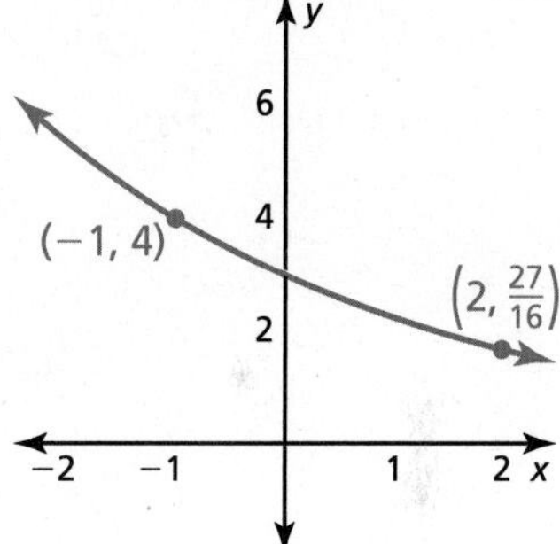

Math Practice

Construct Arguments

Do two points always determine an exponential function of the form $f(x) = ab^x$?

c. A function f is of the form $f(x) = ab^x$, where a is a real number and $b > 0$. Can you find the values of a and b so that f passes through the points (0, 4) and (2, −2)? Explain your reasoning.

d. You perform an experiment where you measure the temperature T (in degrees Fahrenheit) of coffee m minutes after it is poured into a cup. The temperature of the coffee is initially 185°F. After 5 minutes, the temperature of the coffee is about 150°F. Can you use a model of the form $y = ab^x$ to model this situation? Explain. If not, sketch a graph that could model the temperature of the coffee over time. Make several observations about your graph.

Choosing Functions to Model Data

You have analyzed *finite differences* of data with equally-spaced inputs to determine what type of polynomial function can be used to model the data. To determine whether an exponential function can be used to model the data, the outputs must be multiplied by a constant factor. So, consecutive outputs form equivalent ratios.

EXAMPLE 1 Using Differences or Ratios to Identify Functions

Determine the type of function represented by each table.

a.

x	−2	−1	0	1	2	3	4
y	0.5	1	2	4	8	16	32

b.

x	−8	−6	−4	−2	0	2	4
y	−1	8	7	2	−1	4	23

SOLUTION

a. The inputs are equally spaced. Look for a pattern in the outputs.

x	−2	−1	0	1	2	3	4
y	0.5	1	2	4	8	16	32

×2 ×2 ×2 ×2 ×2 ×2

▶ As x increases by 1, y is multiplied by 2. So, the common ratio is 2, and the data represent an exponential function.

b. The inputs are equally spaced. The outputs do not have a common ratio. So, analyze the finite differences.

x	−8	−6	−4	−2	0	2	4
y	−1	8	7	2	−1	4	23

9 −1 −5 −3 5 19 first differences

−10 −4 2 8 14 second differences

6 6 6 6 third differences

▶ The third differences are nonzero and constant. So, the data represent a cubic function.

REMEMBER

First differences of linear functions are constant, second differences of quadratic functions are constant, and so on.

SELF-ASSESSMENT

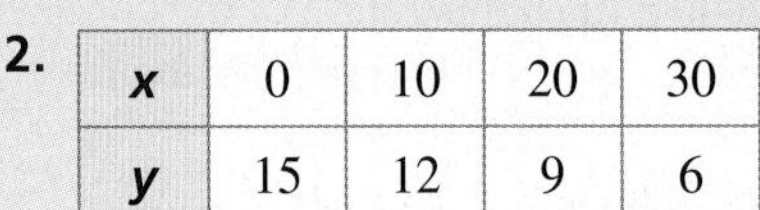

1 I do not understand. 2 I can do it with help. 3 I can do it on my own. 4 I can teach someone else.

1. **WRITING** Given a table of values, explain how you can determine whether an exponential function can be used to model the data.

Determine the type of function represented by the table. Explain your reasoning.

2.

x	0	10	20	30
y	15	12	9	6

3.

x	0	2	4	6
y	27	9	3	1

Writing Exponential Functions

Math Practice

Consider Similar Problems

Two points can determine an exponential curve. What other type of function can be determined by two points?

EXAMPLE 2 Writing an Exponential Function Using Two Points

Write an exponential function $y = ab^x$ whose graph passes through (1, 6) and (3, 54).

SOLUTION

Step 1 Substitute the coordinates of the two given points into $y = ab^x$.

$6 = ab^1$ Equation 1: Substitute 6 for y and 1 for x.

$54 = ab^3$ Equation 2: Substitute 54 for y and 3 for x.

Step 2 Solve for a in Equation 1 to obtain $a = \frac{6}{b}$ and substitute this expression for a in Equation 2.

$54 = \left(\frac{6}{b}\right)b^3$ Substitute $\frac{6}{b}$ for a in Equation 2.

$54 = 6b^2$ Simplify.

$9 = b^2$ Divide each side by 6.

$3 = b$ Take the positive square root because $b > 0$.

REMEMBER

By the definition of an exponential function, b must be positive.

Step 3 Substitute 3 for b to determine that $a = \frac{6}{b} = \frac{6}{3} = 2$.

▶ So, the exponential function is $y = 2(3)^x$.

Data do not always show an *exact* exponential relationship. When the data in a scatter plot show an *approximately* exponential relationship, you can model the data with an exponential function.

EXAMPLE 3 Finding an Exponential Model

The table shows the numbers y (in thousands) of people who visit Machu Picchu x years after 1990. Write a function that models the data.

Years after 1990, x	0	4	8	12	16	20	24	28
Number of visitors, y	150	210	360	470	700	700	1150	1580

SOLUTION

Step 1 Make a scatter plot of the data. The data appear exponential.

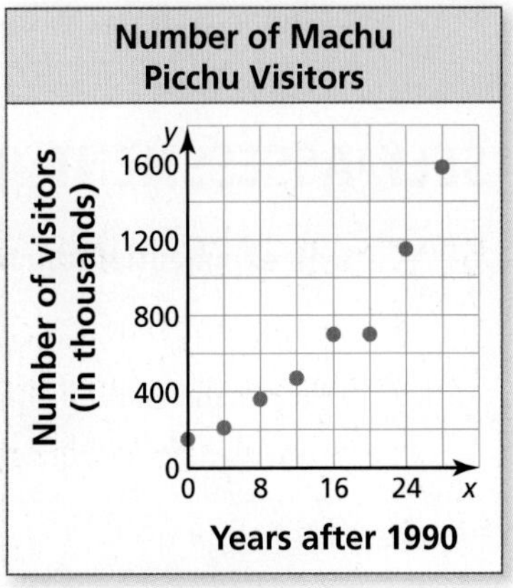

Number of Machu Picchu Visitors

(Scatter plot: y-axis "Number of visitors (in thousands)" 0, 400, 800, 1200, 1600; x-axis "Years after 1990" 0, 8, 16, 24)

Step 2 Choose any two points to write a function, such as (0, 150) and (20, 700). Substitute the coordinates of these two points into $y = ab^x$.

$150 = ab^0$

$700 = ab^{20}$

The first equation shows that $a = 150$.

Substitute 150 for a in the second equation to obtain $b = \sqrt[20]{\frac{700}{150}} \approx 1.08$.

▶ So, an exponential function that models the data is $y = 150(1.08)^x$.

A set of more than two points (x, y) fits an exponential pattern if and only if the set of transformed points $(x, \ln y)$ fits a linear pattern.

Graph of points (x, y)

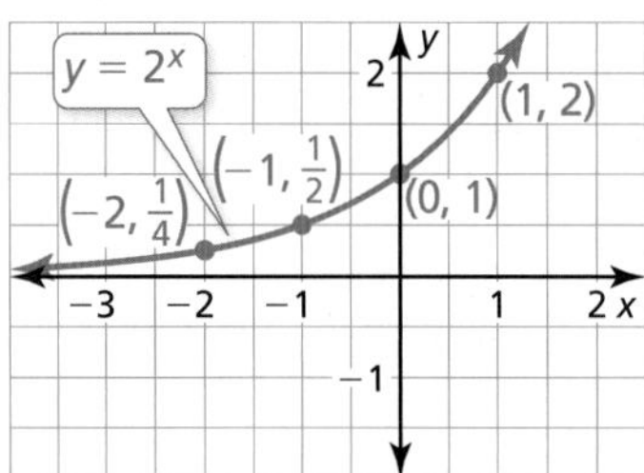

The graph is an exponential curve.

Graph of points $(x, \ln y)$

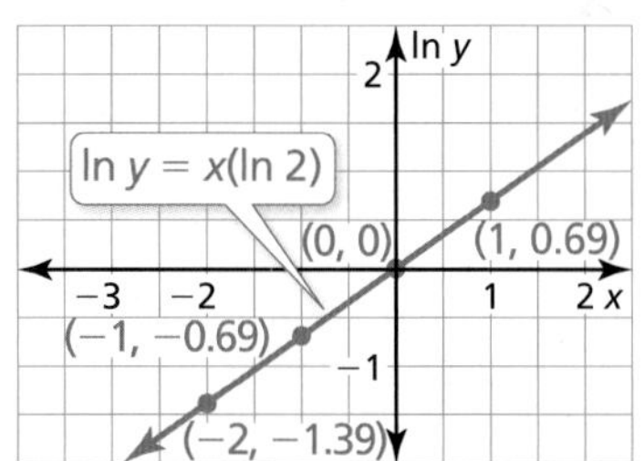

The graph is a line.

EXAMPLE 4 Writing a Model Using Transformed Points

Use the data from Example 3. Create a scatter plot of the data pairs $(x, \ln y)$ to show that an exponential model should be a good fit for the original data pairs (x, y). Then write an exponential model for the original data.

SOLUTION

Step 1 Create a table of data pairs $(x, \ln y)$.

x	0	4	8	12	16	20	24	28
$\ln y$	5.01	5.35	5.89	6.15	6.55	6.55	7.05	7.37

Step 2 Plot the transformed points as shown. The points lie close to a line, so an exponential model should be a good fit for the original data.

Step 3 Find an exponential model $y = ab^x$ by choosing any two points on the line, such as (0, 5.01) and (20, 6.55). Use these points to write an equation of the line. Then solve for y.

$\ln y - 5.01 = 0.08(x - 0)$ Equation of line

$\ln y = 0.08x + 5.01$ Simplify.

$y = e^{0.08x + 5.01}$ Exponentiate each side using base e.

$y = e^{0.08x}(e^{5.01})$ Use properties of exponents.

$y = 149.90(1.08)^x$ Simplify.

▶ So, an exponential function that models the data is $y = 149.90(1.08)^x$.

Math Practice

Communicate Precisely

Explain why the line can be represented by the equation $\ln y - 5.01 = 0.08(x - 0)$.

SELF-ASSESSMENT

1 I do not understand. 2 I can do it with help. 3 I can do it on my own. 4 I can teach someone else.

Write an exponential function $y = ab^x$ whose graph passes through the given points.

4. (2, 12), (3, 24)

5. (1, 2), (3, 32)

6. (2, 16), (5, 2)

7. A store sells gaming laptops. The table shows the numbers y of gaming laptops sold during the xth month that the store has been open. Repeat Examples 3 and 4 using these data.

Month, x	1	2	3	4	5	6	7
Number of gaming laptops, y	12	16	25	36	50	67	96

Using Technology

You can use technology to find models for exponential and logarithmic data.

EXAMPLE 5 Finding an Exponential Model

Use technology to find an exponential model for the data in Example 3. Then use this model and the models in Examples 3 and 4 to estimate the number of visitors in 2020. Compare the estimates.

SOLUTION

Use technology to enter the data and perform an exponential regression. The model is $y = 163.73(1.08)^x$.

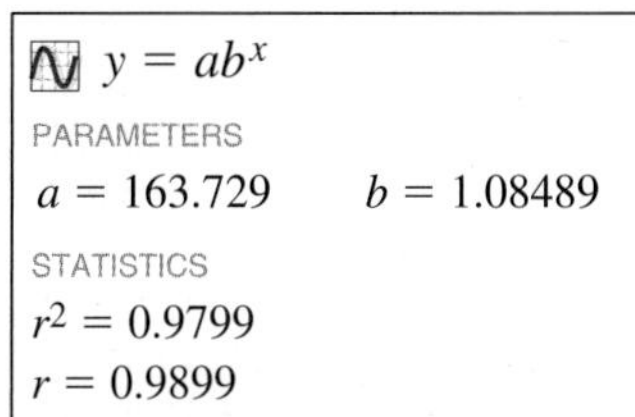

Substitute $x = 30$ into each model to estimate the number of visitors in 2020.

$$\text{Example 3: } y = 150(1.08)^{30} \approx 1509$$

$$\text{Example 4: } y = 149.90(1.08)^{30} \approx 1508$$

$$\text{Regression model: } y = 163.73(1.08)^{30} \approx 1648$$

▶ The estimates for the models in Examples 3 and 4 are close to each other. These estimates are less than the estimate for the regression model.

EXAMPLE 6 Finding a Logarithmic Model

The atmospheric pressure decreases with increasing altitude. At sea level, the average air pressure is 1 atmosphere (1.033227 kilograms per square centimeter). The table shows the air pressures p (in atmospheres) at several altitudes h (in kilometers). Use technology to find a logarithmic model of the form $h = a + b \ln p$ that represents the data. Estimate the altitude when the air pressure is 0.75 atmosphere.

Air pressure, *p*	1	0.55	0.25	0.12	0.06	0.02
Altitude, *h*	0	5	10	15	20	25

SOLUTION

Use technology to enter the data and perform a logarithmic regression. The model is $h = 0.86 - 6.45 \ln p$.

$y = a + b \ln(x)$
PARAMETERS
$a = 0.862658$ $b = -6.44738$
STATISTICS
$R^2 = 0.9926$

Substitute $p = 0.75$ into the model to obtain

$$h = 0.86 - 6.45 \ln 0.75 \approx 2.7.$$

▶ So, when the air pressure is 0.75 atmosphere, the altitude is about 2.7 kilometers.

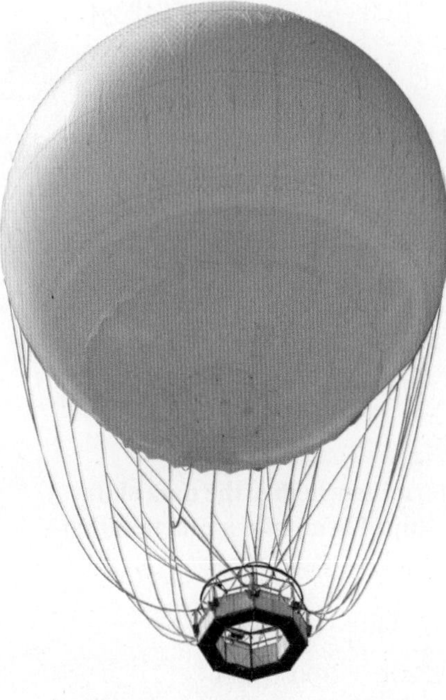

Weather balloons carry instruments that send back information such as wind speed, temperature, and air pressure.

SELF-ASSESSMENT 1 I do not understand. 2 I can do it with help. 3 I can do it on my own. 4 I can teach someone else.

8. Use technology to find an exponential model for the data in Exercise 7. Then use this model and the models you found in Exercise 7 to predict the number of gaming laptops sold during the eighth month. Compare the predictions.

9. Use technology to find a logarithmic model of the form $p = a + b \ln h$ for the data in Example 6. Explain why the result is an error message.

6.7 Practice WITH CalcChat® AND CalcView®

GO DIGITAL

In Exercises 1–4, determine the type of function represented by the table. Explain your reasoning.
▶ *Example 1*

1.

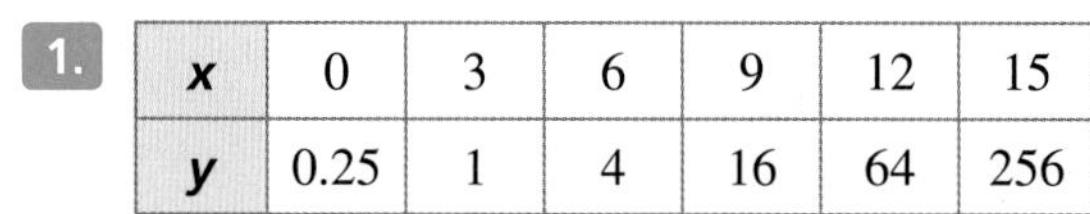

x	0	3	6	9	12	15
y	0.25	1	4	16	64	256

2.

x	−4	−3	−2	−1	0	1	2
y	16	8	4	2	1	$\frac{1}{2}$	$\frac{1}{4}$

3.

x	5	10	15	20	25	30
y	4	3	7	16	30	49

4.

x	−3	−1	1	3	5	7
y	61	5	5	13	−19	−139

In Exercises 5–14, write an exponential function $y = ab^x$ whose graph passes through the given points.
▶ *Example 2*

5. (1, 3), (2, 12)

6. (2, 24), (3, 144)

7. (−1, 4), (1, 1)

8. (−2, 96), (1, 1.5)

9. (1, 2), (3, 50)

10. (−4, 32), (−2, 2)

11. (−1, 10), (4, 0.31)

12. (2, 6.4), (5, 409.6)

13.

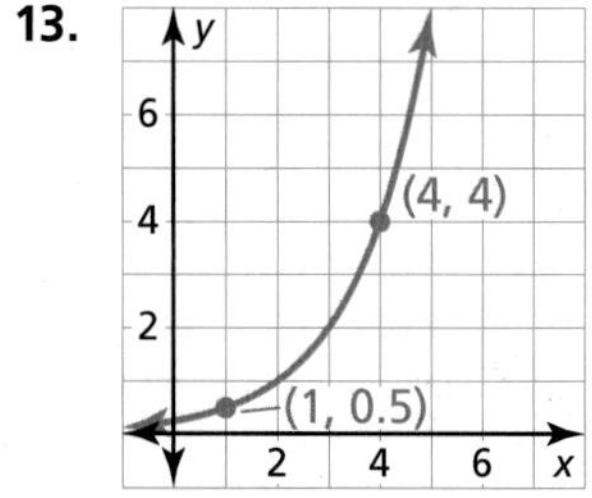

14.

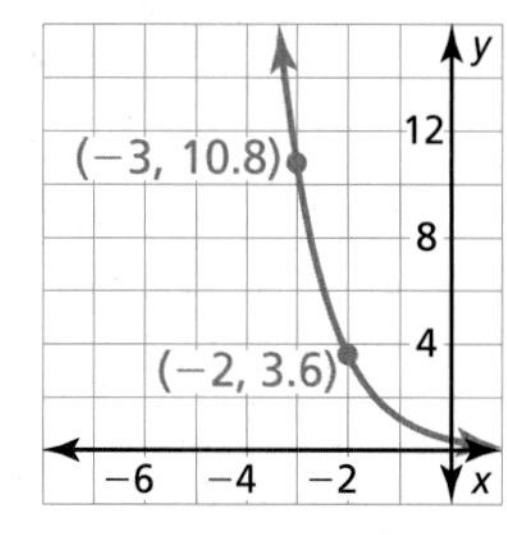

ERROR ANALYSIS In Exercises 15 and 16, describe and correct the error in determining the type of function represented by the table.

15.

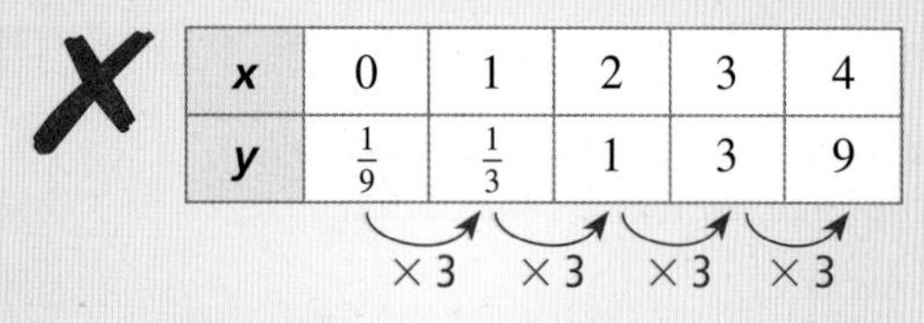

x	0	1	2	3	4
y	$\frac{1}{9}$	$\frac{1}{3}$	1	3	9

×3 ×3 ×3 ×3

The outputs have a common ratio of 3, so the data represent a linear function.

16.

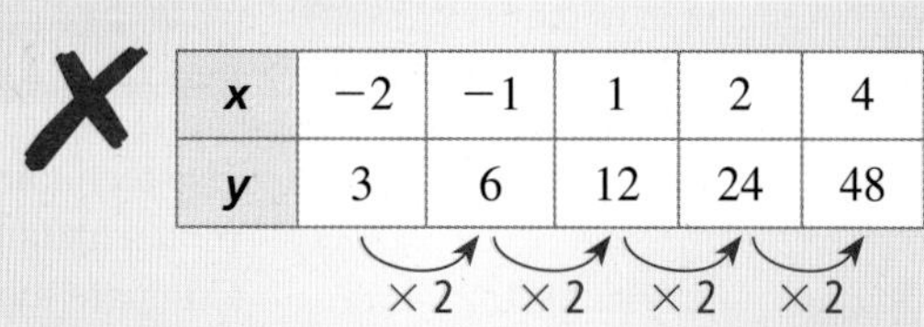

x	−2	−1	1	2	4
y	3	6	12	24	48

×2 ×2 ×2 ×2

The outputs have a common ratio of 2, so the data represent an exponential function.

17. **MODELING REAL LIFE** A store sells electric scooters. The table shows the numbers y of scooters sold during the xth year that the store has been open. Write a function that models the data.
▶ *Example 3*

x	1	2	3	4	5	6	7
y	9	14	19	25	37	53	71

18. **MODELING REAL LIFE** The table shows the numbers y (in thousands) of visits to a website during the xth month. Write a function that models the data. Then use your model to predict the number of visits after 1 year.

x	1	2	3	4	5	6	7
y	22	39	70	126	227	408	735

In Exercises 19–22, determine whether the data show an exponential relationship. Then write a function that models the data.

19.

x	1	6	11	16	21
y	12	28	76	190	450

20.

x	−3	−1	1	3	5
y	2	7	24	68	194

21.

x	0	10	20	30	40	50	60
y	66	58	48	42	31	26	21

22.

x	−20	−13	−6	1	8	15
y	25	19	14	11	8	6

23. MODELING REAL LIFE Your visual near point is the closest point at which your eyes can see an object distinctly. The diagram shows the near point y (in centimeters) at age x (in years). Create a scatter plot of the data pairs $(x, \ln y)$ to show that an exponential model should be a good fit for the original data pairs (x, y). Then write an exponential model for the original data. *Example 4*

Visual Near Point Distances
Age 20, 12 cm
Age 30, 15 cm
Age 40, 25 cm
Age 50, 40 cm
Age 60, 100 cm

24. MODELING REAL LIFE Use the data from Exercise 17. Create a scatter plot of the data pairs $(x, \ln y)$ to show that an exponential model should be a good fit for the original data pairs (x, y). Then write an exponential model for the original data.

In Exercises 25–28, create a scatter plot of the points $(x, \ln y)$ to determine whether an exponential model fits the data. If so, find an exponential model for the data.

25.

x	1	2	3	4	5
y	18	36	72	144	288

26.

x	1	4	7	10	13
y	3.3	10.1	30.6	92.7	280.9

27.

x	−13	−6	1	8	15
y	9.8	12.2	15.2	19	23.8

28.

x	−8	−5	−2	1	4
y	1.4	1.67	5.32	6.41	7.97

29. MP USING TOOLS Use technology to find an exponential model for the data in Exercise 17. Then use the model to predict the number of electric scooters sold during the tenth year. *Example 5*

GO DIGITAL

30. MP USING TOOLS A doctor measures an astronaut's heart rate y (in beats per minute) at various times x (in minutes) after the astronaut finishes exercising. The results are shown in the table. Use technology to find an exponential model for the data. Then use the model to predict the astronaut's heart rate after 16 minutes.

x	0	2	4	6	8	10	12
y	172	132	110	92	84	78	75

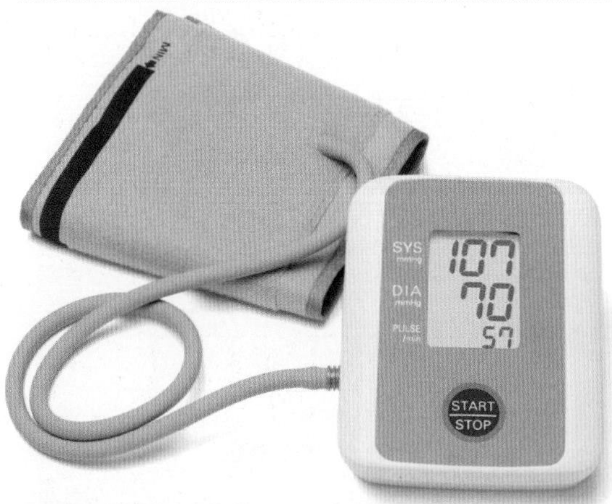

31. MP USING TOOLS A clay pot with a temperature of 160°C is removed from a kiln and placed in a room with a temperature of 20°C. The table shows the temperatures d (in degrees Celsius) of the clay pot at several times t (in hours) after it is removed from the kiln. Use technology to find a logarithmic model of the form $t = a + b \ln d$ that represents the data. Estimate how long it takes for the clay pot to cool to 50°C. *Example 6*

d	160	90	56	38	29	24
t	0	1	2	3	4	5

32. MP USING TOOLS The f-stops on a camera control the amount of light that enters the camera. Let s be a measure of the amount of light that strikes the film and let f be the f-stop. The table shows several f-stops on a 35-millimeter camera. Use technology to find a logarithmic model of the form $s = a + b \ln f$ that represents the data. Estimate the amount of light that strikes the film when $f = 5.657$.

f	s
1.414	1
2.000	2
2.828	3
4.000	4
11.314	7

33. **MAKING AN ARGUMENT** Is it possible to find a logarithmic model of the form $d = a + b \ln t$ for the data in Exercise 31? Explain.

34. **HOW DO YOU SEE IT?**
The graph shows a set of data pairs $(x, \ln y)$. Do the data pairs (x, y) fit an exponential pattern? Explain your reasoning.

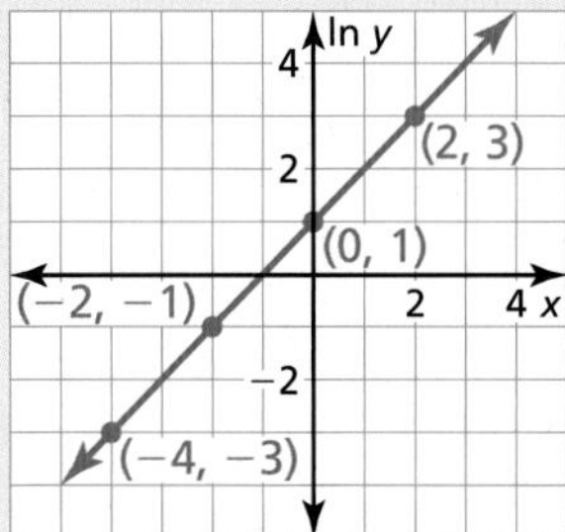

35. **CRITICAL THINKING** You plant a sunflower seedling in a community garden. The height (in centimeters) of the sunflower after t weeks can be modeled by the *logistic function*

$$h(t) = \frac{256}{1 + 13e^{-0.65t}}.$$

a. Find the time it takes the sunflower to reach a height of 200 centimeters.

b. Use technology to graph the function. Interpret the meaning of the asymptote(s) in this situation.

GO DIGITAL

36. **THOUGHT PROVOKING**
Is it possible to write y as an exponential function of x when p is positive? If so, write the function. If not, explain why not.

x	1	2	3	4	5
y	p	$2p$	$4p$	$8p$	$16p$

REVIEW & REFRESH

WATCH

In Exercises 37 and 38, tell whether x and y are in a proportional relationship. Explain your reasoning.

37. $y = \frac{x}{2}$

38. $y = 3x - 12$

39. **MODELING REAL LIFE** You brew a cup of coffee at a temperature of 200°F. You place the cup on a table until it reaches a drinking temperature of 130°F. When the room temperature is 72°F, the cooling rate of the coffee is $r = 0.04$. Use Newton's Law of Cooling, $T = (T_0 - T_R)e^{-rt} + T_R$, to determine how long you should wait to drink the coffee.

40. Determine whether functions f and g are inverses. Explain your reasoning.

x	−2	−1	0	1	2
$f(x)$	15	11	7	3	−1

x	15	11	7	3	−1
$g(x)$	−2	−1	0	1	2

In Exercises 41 and 42, use the change-of-base formula to evaluate the logarithm.

41. $\log_3 20$

42. $\log_4 \frac{5}{12}$

In Exercises 43 and 44, write an exponential function $y = ab^x$ whose graph passes through the given points.

43. (3, 1), (5, 4)

44. (−1, 4), (7, 0.4)

In Exercises 45 and 46, identify the focus, directrix, and axis of symmetry of the parabola. Graph the equation.

45. $x = \frac{1}{8}y^2$

46. $y^2 = \frac{2}{5}x$

47. The function g is a transformation of $f(x) = \log_3 x$. Write a rule for g.

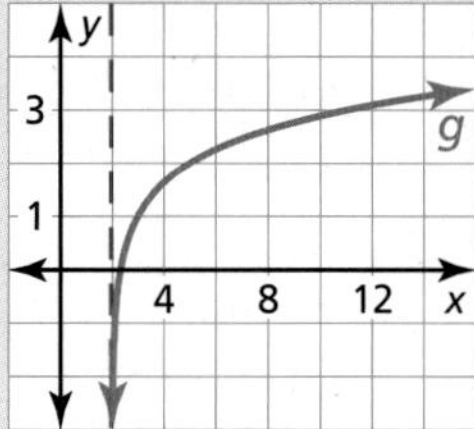

48. Describe the transformation of $f(x) = x^4$ represented by $g(x) = 2x^4 - 1$. Then graph each function.

In Exercises 49–52, solve the equation.

49. $4^x = 9$

50. $e^{3x} = e^{5x-6}$

51. $\ln(8x + 5) = \ln 9$

52. $\log_2(3x - 1) = 5$

53. Show that $x + 5$ is a factor of $f(x) = x^3 - 2x^2 - 23x + 60$. Then factor $f(x)$ completely.

54. Complete the square for $x^2 - 4x$. Then factor the trinomial.

6 Chapter Review WITH CalcChat®

Chapter Learning Target Understand exponential and logarithmic functions.

Chapter Success Criteria

- ◆ I can determine whether a function represents exponential growth or decay.
- ◆ I can simplify exponential and logarithmic expressions.
- ■ I can solve exponential and logarithmic equations.
- ■ I can model exponential and logarithmic functions.

◆ Surface
■ Deep

SELF-ASSESSMENT 1 I do not understand. 2 I can do it with help. 3 I can do it on my own. 4 I can teach someone else.

6.1 Exponential Growth and Decay Functions (pp. 293–300)

Learning Target: Write and graph exponential growth and decay functions.

Vocabulary 

exponential function
exponential growth function
growth factor
asymptote
exponential decay function
decay factor

Determine whether the function represents *exponential growth* or *exponential decay*. Then graph the function.

1. $f(x) = \left(\frac{1}{3}\right)^x$ **2.** $y = 5^x$ **3.** $f(x) = (0.2)^x$

4. You deposit \$1500 in an account that pays 7% annual interest. Find the balance after 2 years when the interest is compounded daily.

5. Consider two exponential decay functions f and g. Determine whether each statement is *always*, *sometimes*, or *never* true. Justify your answers.

a. $(fg)(x)$ is an exponential decay function.

b. $\left(\frac{f}{g}\right)(x)$ is an exponential decay function.

6. A substance decays 10% each year. Find the initial amount of the substance when there are about 5.8 grams remaining after 9 years.

6.2 The Natural Base *e* (pp. 301–306)

WATCH

Learning Target: Use the natural base *e* and graph natural base functions.

Vocabulary 

natural base e

Simplify the expression.

7. $e^4 \cdot e^{11}$ **8.** $\frac{20e^3}{10e^6}$ **9.** $(-3e^{-5x})^2$

Determine whether the function represents *exponential growth* or *exponential decay*. Then graph the function.

10. $f(x) = \frac{1}{3}e^x$ **11.** $y = 6e^{-x}$ **12.** $y = 3e^{-0.75x}$

13. An account earns 3% annual interest compounded continuously. Find the principal when the balance is \$100 after 10 years.

6.3 Logarithms and Logarithmic Functions (pp. 307–314)

WATCH

Learning Target: Understand logarithms and graph logarithmic functions.

Vocabulary

VOCAB

logarithm of y with base b
common logarithm
natural logarithm

Evaluate the logarithm.

14. $\log_2 8$

15. $\log_6 \frac{1}{36}$

16. $\log_5 1$

Find the inverse of the function.

17. $f(x) = 8^x$

18. $y = \ln(x - 4)$

19. $y = \log(x + 9)$

20. Graph $y = \log_{1/5} x$.

21. The Richter scale is used for measuring the magnitude of an earthquake. The Richter magnitude R is given by $R = 0.67 \ln E + 1.17$, where E is the energy (in kilowatt-hours) released by the earthquake. To the nearest tenth, what is the Richter magnitude of an earthquake that releases 23,000 kilowatt-hours of energy?

6.4 Transformations of Exponential and Logarithmic Functions (pp. 315–322)

Learning Target: Describe and graph transformations of exponential and logarithmic functions.

Describe the transformation of f represented by g. Then graph each function.

22. $f(x) = e^{-x}$, $g(x) = e^{-5x} - 8$

23. $f(x) = \log_4 x$, $g(x) = \frac{1}{2}\log_4(x + 5)$

24. Find the domain and range of $f(x) = a(e^{x+h} - k)$, where $a < 0$.

Write a rule for g.

25. Let the graph of g be a vertical stretch by a factor of 3, followed by a translation 6 units left and 3 units up of the graph of $f(x) = e^x$.

26. Let the graph of g be a translation 2 units down, followed by a reflection in the y-axis of the graph of $f(x) = \log x$.

6.5 Properties of Logarithms (pp. 323–328)

Learning Target: Use properties of logarithms.

Expand or condense the logarithmic expression.

27. $\log_8 3xy$

28. $\log 10x^3y$

29. $\ln \frac{3y}{x^5}$

30. $3 \log_7 4 + \log_7 6$

31. $\log_2 12 - 2 \log_2 x$

32. $2 \ln x + 5 \ln 2 - \ln 8$

Use the change-of-base formula to evaluate the logarithm.

33. $\log_2 10$

34. $\log_7 9$

35. $\log_{23} 42$

6.6 Solving Exponential and Logarithmic Equations (pp. 329–336)

Learning Target: Solve exponential and logarithmic equations and inequalities.

Vocabulary
exponential equations
logarithmic equations

Solve the equation. Check your solution(s).

36. $5^x = 8$

37. $\log_3(2x - 5) = 2$

38. $\ln x + \ln(x + 2) = 3$

Solve the inequality.

39. $6^x > 12$

40. $\ln x \leq 9$

41. $e^{4x-2} \geq 16$

42. The equation $y = 0.95^x$ represents the percent chance y (in decimal form) that a player on a football team successfully kicks x extra points in a row. For what number x does the percent chance fall to 25%?

43. A scientist studying memory determines that the percent y of new information that a certain individual remembers after x minutes can be modeled by $y = \dfrac{184}{(\log x)^{1.25} + 1.84}$. After how long does the person remember 50% of new information?

6.7 Modeling with Exponential and Logarithmic Functions (pp. 337–344)

Learning Target: Write exponential and logarithmic functions to model sets of data.

Write an exponential function $y = ab^x$ whose graph passes through the given points.

44. (3, 8), (5, 2)

45. (1, 3), (4, 648)

46. (−1, 16), (2, 6.75)

47. A shoe store sells a new type of basketball shoe. The table shows the pairs sold s over time t (in weeks). Use technology to find a logarithmic model of the form $s = a + b \ln t$ that represents the data. Estimate the number of pairs of shoes sold after 6 weeks.

Week, t	1	3	5	7	9
Pairs sold, s	5	32	48	58	65

Mathematical Practices

Look for and Express Regularity in Repeated Reasoning

Mathematically proficient students notice if calculations are repeated, and look both for general methods and for shortcuts.

1. In Exercise 71 on page 314, you evaluated expressions of the form $\log_b x$, where b and x can be rewritten as powers of the same base. In general, what is the value of a logarithmic expression of this form? Justify your answer.

2. Explain how you can distinguish among data that are represented by a linear, a quadratic, or an exponential function.

6 Practice Test WITH CalcChat®

Graph the equation. Find the domain, range, and asymptote.

1. $y = \left(\frac{3}{4}\right)^x$

2. $y = \log_{2/3} x$

3. $y = 4e^{-2x}$

Describe the transformation of f represented by g. Then write a rule for g.

4. $f(x) = \log x$

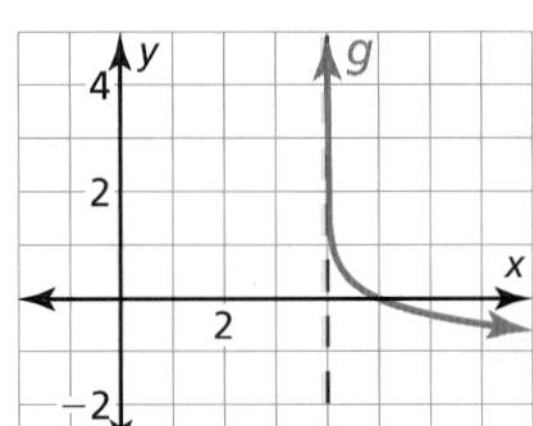

5. $f(x) = e^x$

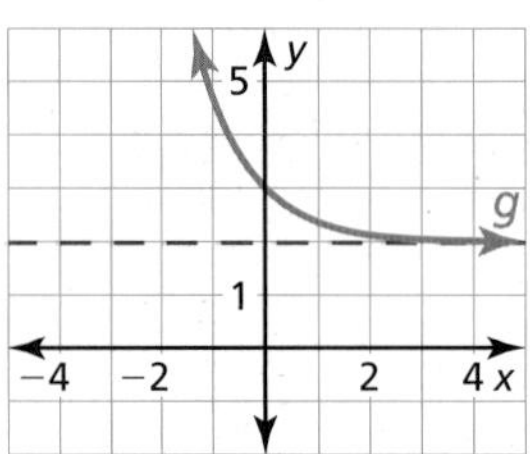

6. $f(x) = \left(\frac{1}{4}\right)^x$

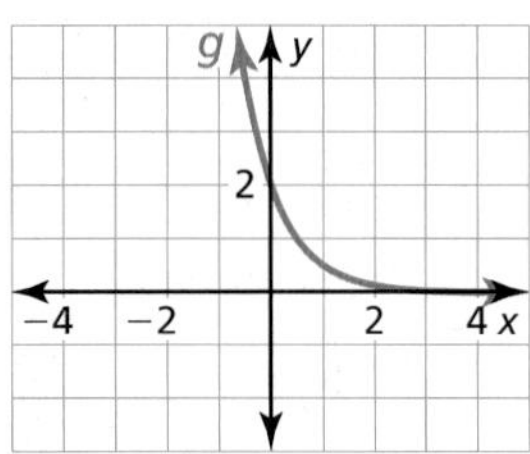

Use $\log_3 4 \approx 1.262$ and $\log_3 13 \approx 2.335$ to evaluate the logarithm.

7. $\log_3 52$

8. $\log_3 \frac{13}{9}$

9. $\log_3 16$

10. $\log_3 8 + \log_3 \frac{1}{2}$

11. The percent L of surface light that filters down through a particular body of water can be modeled by the exponential function $L(x) = 100e^{-0.1x}$, where x is the depth (in meters) below the surface.

    a. Determine whether the model represents *exponential growth* or *exponential decay*. Explain your reasoning.

    b. Find the percent of surface light available at a depth of 40 meters.

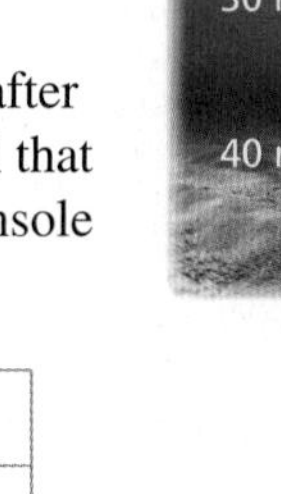

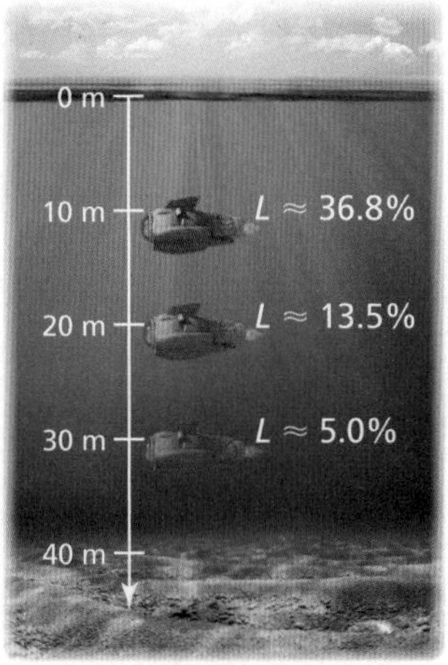

12. Without calculating, determine whether $\log_5 11$, $\frac{\log 11}{\log 5}$, and $\frac{\ln 11}{\ln 5}$ are equivalent expressions. Explain your reasoning.

13. The table shows the values y (in dollars) of a video game console x years after it is purchased. Describe three different ways to find an exponential model that represents the data. Then write and use a model to determine when the console is worth \$150.

Year, x	0	2	4	6	8
Value, y	250	202.50	164.03	132.86	107.62

14. Consider functions f and g. Solve $f(g(x)) = g(f(x))$. Justify your answer.

    $f(x) = 2(3)^x$

    $g(x) = 4x$

15. The amount of oil and gas (in billions of barrels of oil equivalent) discovered after drilling x wells in a region can be modeled by $f(x) = 3.4 \ln x - 14.3$, where $0 \le x \le 3000$.

    a. About how much oil and gas were discovered after drilling 1000 wells?

    b. Find the inverse of the given function. Describe what the inverse represents.

6 Performance Task
Carbon Dating

Carbon dating is a process that measures the amount of carbon-14 in an organism in order to approximate when it died.

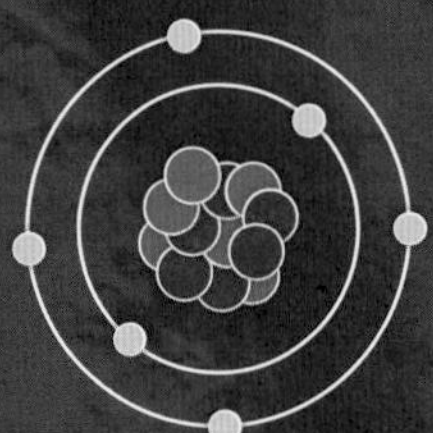

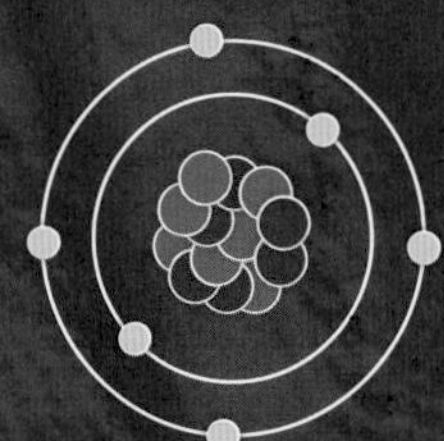

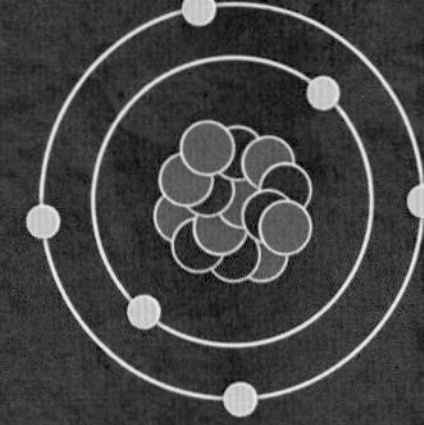

Carbon-12
- 6 Protons
- 6 Neutrons
- 6 Electrons

Carbon-13
- 6 Protons
- 7 Neutrons
- 6 Electrons

Carbon-14
- 6 Protons
- 8 Neutrons
- 6 Electrons

Radioactive

Concentration: 1.2 parts per trillion

There are about 1.2 atoms of carbon-14 in the atmosphere for every 1 trillion atoms of non-radioactive carbon.

The concentration of carbon-14 in living organic matter is equal to the concentration found in the atmosphere.

Half-life of Carbon-14: 5730 years

Due to radioactive decay, the amount of carbon-14 in a sample is halved every 5730 years after an organism dies.

Radioactive Decay of Carbon-14

Carbon-14 remaining: 100%, 50%, 25%, 12.5%, 6.25%, 0%

Time (years): 0, 5730, 11,460, 17,190, 22,920

ANCIENT DISCOVERY

You discover an ancient manuscript at an archaeological site. The manuscript is written on an organic material made from a plant called papyrus. You determine that the concentration of carbon-14 in the papyrus is about 0.93 part per trillion. Use a model to approximate the number of years since the papyrus plant died. Explain your reasoning.

Use the Internet or another resource to research carbon dating. What are some of its limitations? What assumptions do scientists make when using this dating method?

6 College and Career Readiness WITH CalcChat®

Tutorial videos are available for each exercise.

1. Select each value of b for the equation $y = b^x$ that could result in the graph shown.

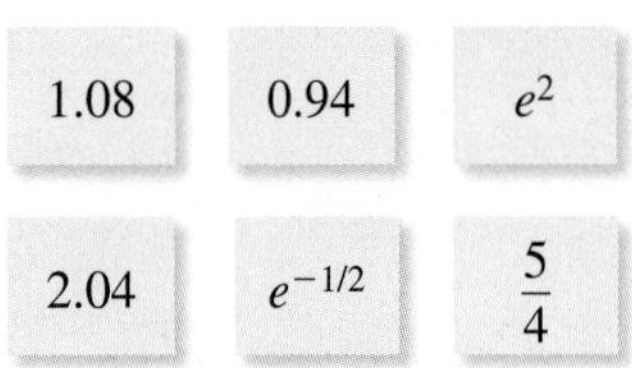

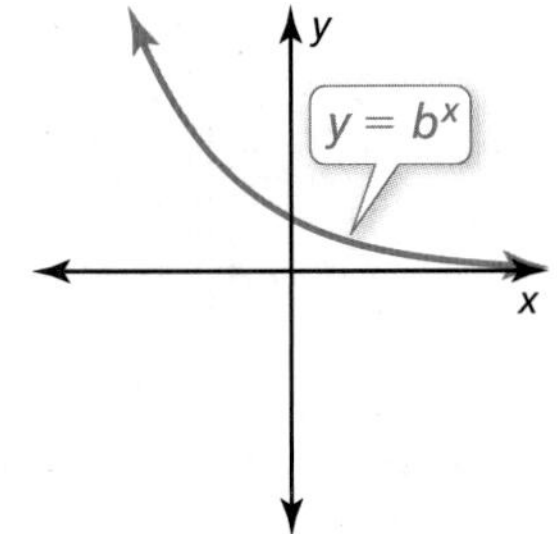

2. What is the solution of the equation $e^{3x+2} = 8$?

Ⓐ $x = \ln 8$

Ⓑ $x = \dfrac{\log 8 - 2}{3}$

Ⓒ $x = \dfrac{e^8 - 2}{3}$

Ⓓ $x = \dfrac{\ln 8 - 2}{3}$

3. Which describes the transformation of the graph of $f(x) = \log_2 x$ represented by the graph of g?

Ⓐ The graph of g is a reflection in the y-axis, followed by a translation 3 units left of the graph of f.

Ⓑ The graph of g is a reflection in the y-axis, followed by a translation 2 units down of the graph of f.

Ⓒ The graph of g is a reflection in the y-axis, followed by a translation 2 units up of the graph of f.

Ⓓ The graph of g is a reflection in the x-axis, followed by a translation 2 units down of the graph of f.

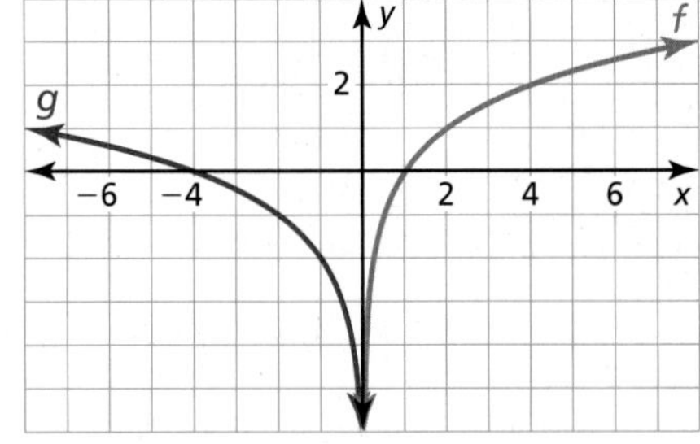

4. Let $f(x) = 2x^3 - 4x^2 + 8x - 1$, $g(x) = 2x - 3x^4 - 6x^3 + 5$, and $h(x) = -7 + x^2 + x$. Order the following functions from least degree to greatest degree.

A. $(f + g)(x)$ **B.** $(hg)(x)$

C. $(h - f)(x)$ **D.** $(fh)(x)$

5. Which statement describes the end behavior of $f(x) = -4x^5 + 6x^2 + 7x - 5$?

Ⓐ $f(x) \to -\infty$ as $x \to -\infty$ and $f(x) \to +\infty$ as $x \to +\infty$.

Ⓑ $f(x) \to +\infty$ as $x \to -\infty$ and $f(x) \to -\infty$ as $x \to +\infty$.

Ⓒ $f(x) \to +\infty$ as $x \to -\infty$ and $f(x) \to +\infty$ as $x \to +\infty$.

Ⓓ $f(x) \to -\infty$ as $x \to -\infty$ and $f(x) \to -\infty$ as $x \to +\infty$.

6. Write exponential functions represented by the graph and table. Compare the y-intercepts and the growth factors.

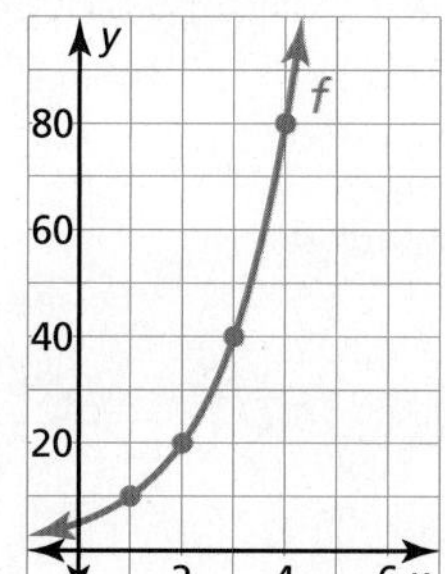

x	2	3	4	5	6
$g(x)$	4.5	13.5	40.5	121.5	364.5

7. Which graph represents $f(x) = \sqrt{x - 3} + 2$?

Ⓐ 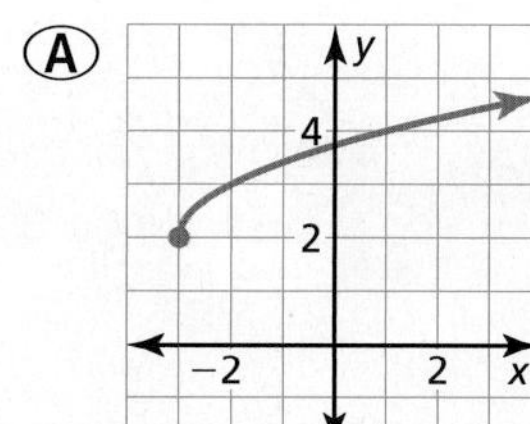

Ⓑ 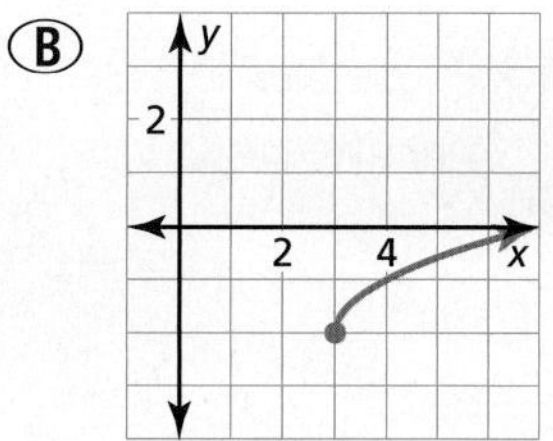

Ⓒ 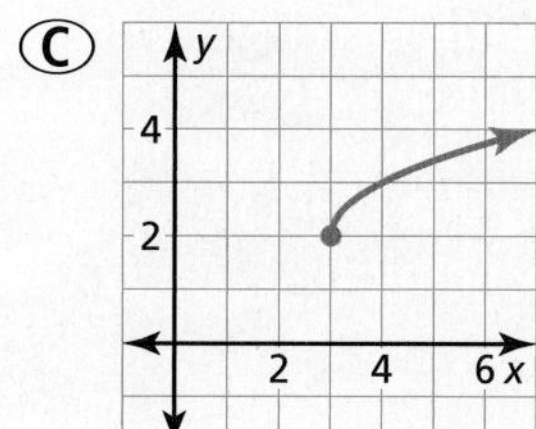

Ⓓ 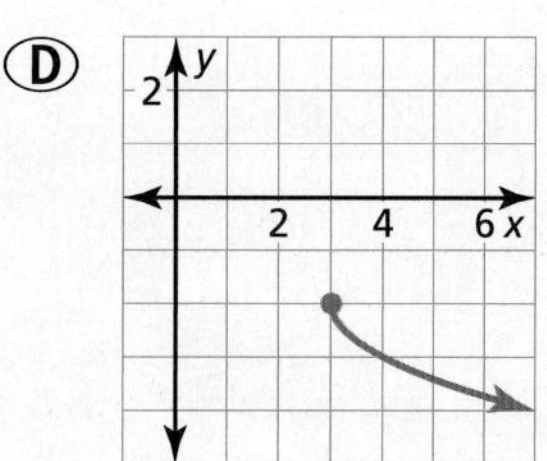

8. Which inequality is represented by the graph?

Ⓐ $-(x + 3)(x - 1) \geq y$

Ⓑ $-(x + 3)(x - 1) < y$

Ⓒ $y < (x + 3)(x - 1)$

Ⓓ $y < -(x + 3)(x - 1)$

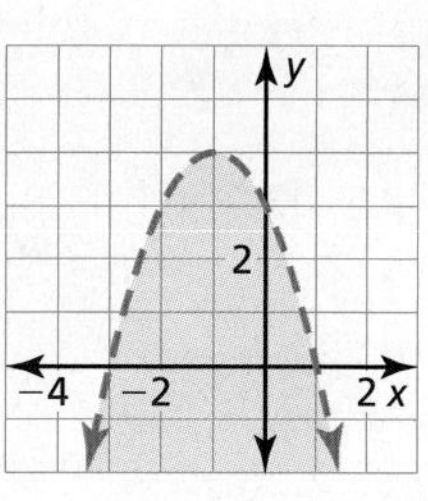

9. At a pumpkin-launching contest, contestants compete to see who can catapult a pumpkin the longest distance. The table shows the horizontal distances y (in feet) pumpkins travel when launched at different angles x (in degrees). Do the data represent a *linear*, *quadratic*, or *exponential* relationship? Use technology to find a model for the data. Then find the angle(s) at which a launched pumpkin travels 500 feet.

Angle (degrees), x	20	30	40	50	60	70
Distance (feet), y	372	462	509	501	437	323

7 Rational Functions

GO DIGITAL

NATIONAL GEOGRAPHIC EXPLORER

Skylar Tibbits

Skylar Tibbits is the founder of the Self-Assembly Lab at the Massachusetts Institute of Technology's International Design Center. His invention of 4-D printing involves programmable materials that can sense and respond to internal or external stimuli. His research aims to apply principles of self-assembly to construction and manufacturing: for example, a cell phone that can build itself or a chair that self-assembles.

- What is self-assembly?
- How are 3-D printing and 4-D printing similar? How are they different?
- What kinds of stimuli can be used to trigger a material to self-assemble?

STEM

As 3-D printing becomes more and more affordable, many people are starting their own 3-D printing business. In the Performance Task, you will analyze the costs and profits of creating and selling your own 3-D-printed object.

3-D and 4-D Printing

Preparing for Chapter 7

Chapter Learning Target Understand rational functions.

Chapter Success Criteria

- ◆ I can determine whether an equation represents direct variation or inverse variation.
- ◆ I can graph rational functions.
- ■ I can add, subtract, multiply, and divide rational expressions.
- ■ I can solve rational equations.

◆ Surface
■ Deep

Chapter Vocabulary

Work with a partner. Discuss each of the vocabulary terms.

inverse variation   rational function   rational expression

Mathematical Practices

Reason Abstractly and Quantitatively

Mathematically proficient students make sense of quantities and their relationships in problem situations.

Work with a partner. An entrepreneur sells 3-D-printed cell phone cases. The 3-D printer costs \$300 and materials for each case cost \$1.50.

1. Complete the table. Then plot the points in a coordinate plane.

Number of cases, x	Average cost per case (dollars), y
20	
40	
60	
80	
100	
120	

2. What is the minimum average cost per case? Explain your reasoning.

3. Your friend buys a 3-D printer for \$500 and materials for each case cost \$1.25. Will your friend's average cost per case ever be less than the entrepreneur's? Explain your reasoning.

7 Prepare WITH CalcChat®

Adding and Subtracting Rational Numbers

Example 1 **Find $-\frac{7}{4} + \frac{3}{4}$.**

Because the signs are different and $\left|-\frac{7}{4}\right| > \left|\frac{3}{4}\right|$, subtract $\left|\frac{3}{4}\right|$ from $\left|-\frac{7}{4}\right|$.

$\left|-\frac{7}{4}\right| - \left|\frac{3}{4}\right| = \frac{7}{4} - \frac{3}{4}$ Find the absolute values.

$= \frac{7-3}{4}$ Write the difference of the numerators over the common denominator.

$= 1$ Simplify.

Because $\left|-\frac{7}{4}\right| > \left|\frac{3}{4}\right|$, use the sign of $-\frac{7}{4}$.

▶ So, $-\frac{7}{4} + \frac{3}{4} = -1$.

Example 2 **Find $-\frac{7}{8} - \frac{5}{16}$.**

Rewrite the difference as a sum by adding the opposite.

$$-\frac{7}{8} - \frac{5}{16} = -\frac{7}{8} + \left(-\frac{5}{16}\right)$$

Because the signs are the same, add $\left|-\frac{7}{8}\right|$ and $\left|-\frac{5}{16}\right|$.

$\left|-\frac{7}{8}\right| + \left|-\frac{5}{16}\right| = \frac{7}{8} + \frac{5}{16}$ Find the absolute values.

$= \frac{14}{16} + \frac{5}{16}$ Rewrite $\frac{7}{8}$ as $\frac{14}{16}$.

$= \frac{14+5}{16}$ Write the sum of the numerators over the common denominator.

$= \frac{19}{16}$, or $1\frac{3}{16}$ Simplify.

Because $-\frac{7}{8}$ and $-\frac{5}{16}$ are both negative, use a negative sign in the difference.

▶ So, $-\frac{7}{8} - \frac{5}{16} = -1\frac{3}{16}$.

Find the sum or difference.

1. $\frac{7}{9} - \frac{4}{9}$

2. $\frac{3}{5} + \frac{2}{3}$

3. $-\frac{4}{7} + \frac{1}{6}$

4. $\frac{5}{12} - \left(-\frac{1}{2}\right)$

5. $\frac{2}{7} + \frac{1}{7} - \frac{6}{7}$

6. $\frac{3}{10} - \frac{3}{4} + \frac{2}{5}$

7. **MP STRUCTURE** How can you find a common denominator for the expressions $\frac{1}{a}$ and $\frac{1}{b}$, where a and b are nonzero integers?

7.1 Inverse Variation

Learning Target Understand inverse variation.

Success Criteria

- I can identify equations and data sets that show direct variation.
- I can identify equations and data sets that show inverse variation.
- I can write inverse variation equations.
- I can solve real-life problems using inverse variation functions.

EXPLORE IT! Describing Types of Variation

Work with a partner.

a. The table represents the side length s (in inches) and the perimeter P (in inches) of a square. Complete the table. Describe the relationship between s and P. Explain why the perimeter P is said to vary *directly* with the side length s.

s	1	2	3	4	5	6
P						

b. Make a scatter plot of the data. What are some characteristics of the graph?

c. Write an equation that represents P as a function of s.

d. The table represents the length ℓ (in inches) and the width w (in inches) of a rectangle that has an area of 64 square inches. Complete the table. Describe the relationship between ℓ and w. Explain why the width w is said to vary *inversely* with the length ℓ.

ℓ	1	2	4	8	16	32	64
w							

w 64 in.^{2} ℓ

e. Make a scatter plot of the data. Compare the characteristics of the graph with the graph in part (b).

f. Write an equation that represents w as a function of ℓ. Compare it with the equation in part (c).

g. How can you recognize when two quantities vary directly or inversely?

Math Practice

Communicate Precisely

How can you explain to a friend the difference between two quantities that vary directly and two quantities that vary inversely? Give real-life situations to support your explanation.

Classifying Direct and Inverse Variation

Recall that two variables x and y are in a proportional relationship when $y = ax$ for some nonzero constant a. When this occurs, x and y are said to show *direct variation*. Another type of variation is *inverse* variation.

Vocabulary 

direct variation, *p. 356*
constant of variation, *p. 356*
inverse variation, *p. 356*

WORDS AND MATH

A *variation* is a change in an amount or quantity. *Direct variation* and *inverse variation* describe relationships where a change in one quantity causes a predictable change in another quantity.

KEY IDEAS

Direct Variation

Two variables x and y show **direct variation** when they are related as follows:

$y = ax, a \neq 0$ Direct variation

The constant a is the **constant of variation**, and y is said to *vary directly* with x.

Inverse Variation

Two variables x and y show **inverse variation** when they are related as follows:

$y = \frac{a}{x}, a \neq 0$ Inverse variation

The constant a is the constant of variation, and y is said to *vary inversely* with x.

EXAMPLE 1 Classifying Equations

Tell whether x and y show *direct variation*, *inverse variation*, or *neither*.

a. $xy = 5$ **b.** $y = x - 4$ **c.** $\frac{y}{2} = x$

SOLUTION

	Given Equation	Solved for y	Type of Variation
a.	$xy = 5$	$y = \frac{5}{x}$	inverse
b.	$y = x - 4$	$y = x - 4$	neither
c.	$\frac{y}{2} = x$	$y = 2x$	direct

SELF-ASSESSMENT 1 I do not understand. 2 I can do it with help. 3 I can do it on my own. 4 I can teach someone else.

1. **MP REASONING** Describe the relationship the equation in Example 1(b) represents. Explain why it does not show direct or inverse variation.

Tell whether x and y show *direct variation*, *inverse variation*, or *neither*.

2. $6x = y$
3. $xy = -0.25$
4. $y + x = 10$

The general equation $y = ax$ for direct variation can be rewritten as $\frac{y}{x} = a$. So, a set of data pairs (x, y) shows direct variation when the ratios $\frac{y}{x}$ are constant.

The general equation $y = \frac{a}{x}$ for inverse variation can be rewritten as $xy = a$. So, a set of data pairs (x, y) shows inverse variation when the products xy are constant.

GO DIGITAL

EXAMPLE 2 **Classifying Data** 

Tell whether x and y show *direct variation, inverse variation,* or *neither.*

a.

x	2	4	6	8
y	-12	-6	-4	-3

b.

x	1	2	3	4
y	2	4	8	16

SOLUTION

a. Find the products xy and ratios $\frac{y}{x}$.

xy	-24	-24	-24	-24	The products are constant.
$\frac{y}{x}$	$\frac{-12}{2} = -6$	$\frac{-6}{4} = -\frac{3}{2}$	$\frac{-4}{6} = -\frac{2}{3}$	$-\frac{3}{8}$	The ratios are not constant.

▶ So, x and y show inverse variation.

b. Find the products xy and ratios $\frac{y}{x}$.

xy	2	8	24	64	The products are not constant.
$\frac{y}{x}$	$\frac{2}{1} = 2$	$\frac{4}{2} = 2$	$\frac{8}{3}$	$\frac{16}{4} = 4$	The ratios are not constant.

▶ So, x and y show neither direct nor inverse variation.

SELF-ASSESSMENT 1 I do not understand. 2 I can do it with help. 3 I can do it on my own. 4 I can teach someone else.

5. **VOCABULARY** Explain how a set of data pairs that shows direct variation is different from a set of data pairs that shows inverse variation.

Tell whether x and y show *direct variation, inverse variation,* or *neither.*

6.

x	-4	-3	-2	-1
y	20	15	10	5

7.

x	1	2	3	4
y	60	30	20	15

Writing Inverse Variation Equations

EXAMPLE 3 **Writing an Inverse Variation Equation** 

The variables x and y vary inversely, and $y = 4$ when $x = 3$. Write an equation that relates x and y. Then find y when $x = -2$.

SOLUTION

$y = \frac{a}{x}$ Write general equation for inverse variation.

$4 = \frac{a}{3}$ Substitute 4 for y and 3 for x.

$12 = a$ Multiply each side by 3.

▶ The inverse variation equation is $y = \frac{12}{x}$. When $x = -2$, $y = \frac{12}{-2} = -6$.

ANOTHER WAY

Because x and y vary inversely, the products xy are constant. This product equals the constant of variation a. So, you can quickly determine that $a = xy = 3(4) = 12$.

EXAMPLE 4 Modeling Real Life

The time t (in hours) that it takes a group of volunteers to build a playground varies inversely with the number n of volunteers. It takes a group of 10 volunteers 8 hours to build the playground.

- Make a table showing the times that it takes to build the playground when the number of volunteers is 15, 20, 25, and 30.
- What happens to the time it takes to build the playground as the number of volunteers increases?

SOLUTION

1. **Understand the Problem** You are given a description of two quantities that vary inversely and one pair of data values. You are asked to create a table that gives additional data pairs and determine what happens to the building time as the number of volunteers increases.
2. **Make a Plan** Use the time that it takes 10 volunteers to build the playground to find the constant of variation. Then write an inverse variation equation and substitute for the different numbers of volunteers to find the corresponding times.
3. **Solve and Check**

$t = \frac{a}{n}$ Write general equation for inverse variation.

$8 = \frac{a}{10}$ Substitute 8 for t and 10 for n.

$80 = a$ Multiply each side by 10.

The inverse variation equation is $t = \frac{80}{n}$. Make a table of values.

n	15	20	25	30
t	$\frac{80}{15} = 5$ h 20 min	$\frac{80}{20} = 4$ h	$\frac{80}{25} = 3$ h 12 min	$\frac{80}{30} = 2$ h 40 min

▶ As the number of volunteers increases, the time it takes to build the playground decreases.

Check Because the time decreases as the number of volunteers increases, the time for 5 volunteers to build the playground should be greater than 8 hours.

$t = \frac{80}{5} = 16$ hours ✓

Math Practice

Look for Patterns

Will the time change more when increasing from 30 to 35 volunteers or when increasing from 55 to 60 volunteers? Explain.

SELF-ASSESSMENT

1 I do not understand. 2 I can do it with help. 3 I can do it on my own. 4 I can teach someone else.

The variables x and y vary inversely. Use the given values to write an equation relating x and y. Then find y when $x = 2$.

8. $x = 4, y = 5$

9. $x = 6, y = -1$

10. $x = \frac{1}{2}, y = 16$

11. **WHAT IF?** In Example 4, it takes a group of 10 volunteers 12 hours to build the playground. How long does it take a group of 15 volunteers?

12. A company determines that the demand d for one of its products varies inversely with the price p of the product. When the price is \$2.75, the demand is 550 units. When the price is doubled, is the demand for the product halved? Justify your answer.

7.1 Practice WITH CalcChat® AND CalcView®

In Exercises 1–8, tell whether x and y show *direct variation, inverse variation,* or *neither*. *Example 1*

1. $y = \frac{2}{x}$
2. $xy = 12$
3. $\frac{y}{x} = 8$
4. $4x = y$
5. $y = x + 4$
6. $x + y = 6$
7. $8y = x$
8. $xy = \frac{1}{5}$

In Exercises 9–12, tell whether x and y show *direct variation, inverse variation,* or *neither*. *Example 2*

9.

x	12	18	23	29	34
y	132	198	253	319	374

10.

x	1.5	2.5	4	7.5	10
y	13.5	22.5	36	67.5	90

11.

x	4	6	8	8.4	12
y	21	14	10.5	10	7

12.

x	4	5	6.2	7	11
y	16	11	10	9	6

In Exercises 13–20, the variables x and y vary inversely. Use the given values to write an equation relating x and y. Then find y when $x = 3$. *Example 3*

13. $x = 5, y = -4$
14. $x = 1, y = 9$
15. $x = -3, y = 8$
16. $x = 7, y = 2$
17. $x = \frac{3}{4}, y = 28$
18. $x = -4, y = -\frac{5}{4}$
19. $x = -12, y = -\frac{1}{6}$
20. $x = \frac{5}{3}, y = -7$

21. **COLLEGE PREP** In which equation do the variables x and y *not* show inverse variation?

Ⓐ $y = -\frac{4}{x}$ Ⓑ $y = \frac{x}{3}$

Ⓒ $xy = 7$ Ⓓ $x = \frac{6}{y}$

22. **MP STRUCTURE** The variable P varies inversely with t, and $P = -8$ when $t = -2$. Find P when $t = 4$.

ERROR ANALYSIS In Exercises 23 and 24, the variables x and y vary inversely. Describe and correct the error in writing an equation relating x and y.

23. $x = 8, y = 5$

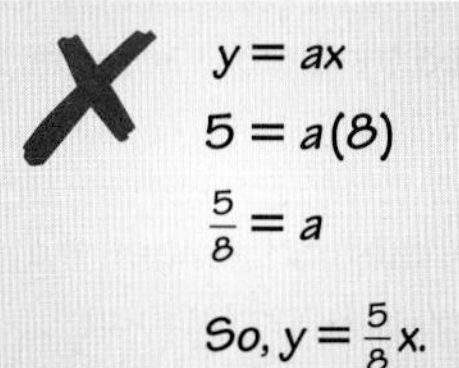

24. $x = 5, y = 2$

✗

$xy = a$

$5 \cdot 2 = a$

$10 = a$

So, $y = 10x$.

25. **MODELING REAL LIFE** The number y of apps that can be stored on a tablet varies inversely with the average size x of an app. A certain tablet can store 200 apps when the average size of an app is 28 megabytes (MB). *Example 4*

   a. Make a table showing the numbers of apps that will fit on the tablet when the average size of an app is 20 MB, 25 MB, 30 MB, and 50 MB.

   b. What happens to the number of apps as the average app size increases?

26. **MODELING REAL LIFE** When you stand on snow, the average pressure P (in pounds per square inch) that you exert on the snow varies inversely with the total surface area A (in square inches) of the soles of your footwear. Write an equation that gives P as a function of A when a hiker wears the snowshoes shown and the pressure is 0.43 pound per square inch. Then find the pressure when the hiker wears the boots shown.

27. **MP PROBLEM SOLVING** Computer chips are etched onto silicon wafers. The table compares the areas A (in square millimeters) of computer chips with the number c of chips that can be obtained from a silicon wafer. Write a model that gives c as a function of A. Then predict the number of chips per wafer when the area of a chip is 81 square millimeters.

Area (mm²), A	58	62	66	70
Number of chips, c	448	424	392	376

28. HOW DO YOU SEE IT? Does the graph of f represent inverse variation or direct variation? Explain your reasoning.

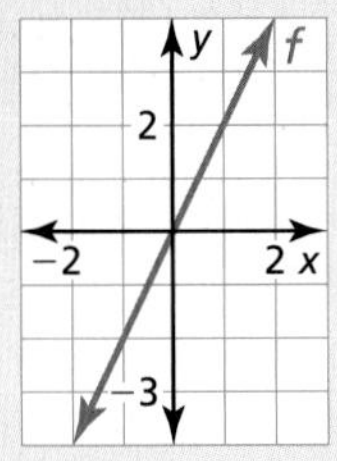

29. MAKING AN ARGUMENT You download y movies for x dollars each. You have enough money to download 5 movies for \$8 each or 8 movies for \$5 each. Can this situation be represented by direct variation or inverse variation? Explain.

30. OPEN-ENDED Describe a real-life situation that can be modeled by an inverse variation equation.

31. CONNECTING CONCEPTS Consider the formula for the volume of a rectangular prism, $V = Bh$. How does the area of the base vary with the height of the prism? What is the constant of variation? Explain your reasoning.

32. THOUGHT PROVOKING The weight w (in pounds) of an object varies inversely with the square of the distance d (in miles) of the object from the center of Earth. At sea level (3978 miles from the center of the Earth), an astronaut weighs 210 pounds. How much does the astronaut weigh 200 miles above sea level?

GO DIGITAL

33. CRITICAL THINKING Suppose x varies inversely with y and y varies inversely with z. How does x vary with z? Justify your answer.

34. DIG DEEPER To balance the board in the diagram, the distances (in feet) of the animals from the fulcrum must vary directly. How far is each animal from the fulcrum when they move so they are 6 feet apart and the board remains balanced? Justify your answer.

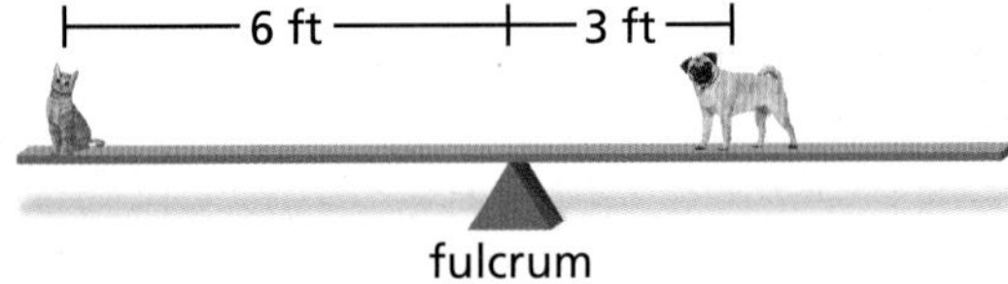

REVIEW & REFRESH

In Exercises 35 and 36, divide.

35. $(x^2 + 2x - 99) \div (x + 11)$

36. $(3x^4 - 13x^2 - x^3 + 6x - 30) \div (3x^2 - x + 5)$

37. MODELING REAL LIFE The table shows the heights y of a skateboard x seconds after jumping off the ground. What type of function can you use to model the data? Estimate the height after 0.75 second.

Time (seconds), x	Height (inches), y
0	0
0.5	12
1.0	16
1.5	12
2.0	0

In Exercises 38 and 39, solve the equation.

38. $64^x = \left(\frac{1}{4}\right)^{2x+15}$

39. $\log(x + 6) = \log 7x$

40. MP REASONING Which properties of logarithms can you use to condense the expression $3 \ln 0.5x - \ln 6$?

41. Tell whether x and y show *direct variation*, *inverse variation*, or *neither*.

x	−5	−1	2	8	11
y	40	8	−16	−64	−88

In Exercises 42–45, graph the function. Then state the domain and range.

42. $f(x) = 5^x + 4$

43. $g(x) = e^{x-1}$

44. $y = \log 3x - 6$

45. $h(x) = 2 \ln(x + 9)$

46. Create a scatter plot of the points $(x, \ln y)$ to determine whether an exponential model fits the data. If so, find an exponential model for the data.

x	2	5	8	11	14
y	1.8	5.4	16.2	48.6	145.8

In Exercises 47–50, simplify the expression.

47. $8^{3/2} \cdot 8^{1/4}$

48. $5\sqrt{48} - 9\sqrt{3}$

49. $\dfrac{\sqrt[3]{54}}{\sqrt[3]{2}}$

50. $\sqrt[4]{\dfrac{a^{12}}{81b^{16}}}$

7.2 Graphing Rational Functions

Learning Target Describe and graph rational functions.

Success Criteria

- I can graph rational functions.
- I can describe transformations of rational functions.
- I can explain how to find the asymptotes of a rational function from an equation.
- I can write rational functions in different forms.

EXPLORE IT! Graphing Rational Functions

Work with a partner. The function $f(x) = \frac{1}{x}$ is a simple *rational* function.

Math Practice

Look for Structure How do the values of *h* and *k* affect the asymptotes?

a. What does the graph of f look like? How is the graph similar to other functions you have studied? How is it different?

b. Describe the end behavior of f. Then describe the behavior of the graph when x is between -1 and 1. Why is there an asymptote at the y-axis?

c. Use technology to explore the graph of $y = f(x - h)$ for several values of h. How does the graph change when you change the value of h?

$f(x) = \frac{1}{x}$

$y = \frac{1}{x - h}$

$h = 3$

−10 10

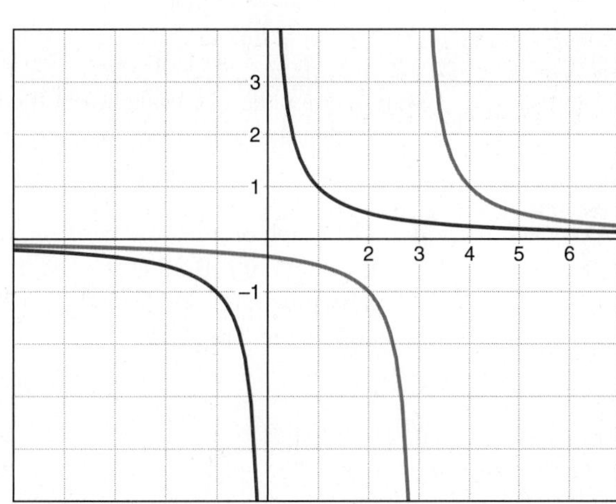

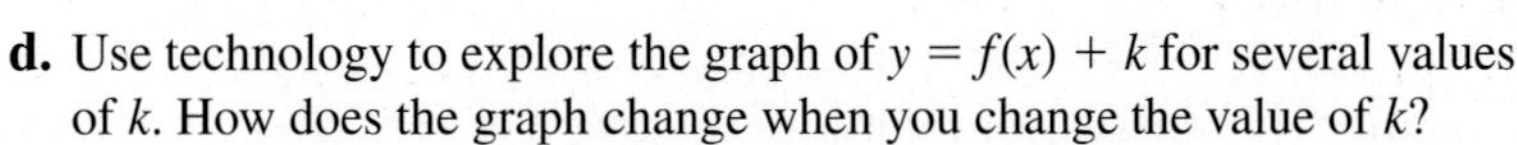

d. Use technology to explore the graph of $y = f(x) + k$ for several values of k. How does the graph change when you change the value of k?

Graphing Simple Rational Functions

Vocabulary AZ VOCAB

rational function, *p. 362*

A **rational function** has the form $f(x) = \frac{p(x)}{q(x)}$, where $p(x)$ and $q(x)$ are polynomials and $q(x) \neq 0$. The inverse variation function $f(x) = \frac{a}{x}$ is a rational function.

STUDY TIP

Notice that $\frac{1}{x} \to 0$ as $x \to +\infty$ and as $x \to -\infty$. This explains why $y = 0$ is a horizontal asymptote of the graph of $f(x) = \frac{1}{x}$. You can also analyze y-values as x approaches 0 to see why $x = 0$ is a vertical asymptote.

KEY IDEA

Parent Function for Simple Rational Functions

The graph of the parent function $f(x) = \frac{1}{x}$ is a *hyperbola*, which consists of two symmetrical parts called branches. The domain and range are all nonzero real numbers.

Any function of the form $g(x) = \frac{a}{x}$ $(a \neq 0)$ has the same asymptotes, domain, and range as the function $f(x) = \frac{1}{x}$.

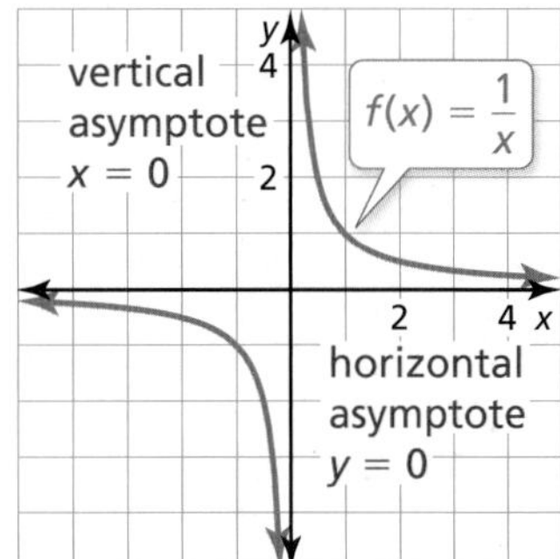

EXAMPLE 1 Graphing a Rational Function of the Form $y = \frac{a}{x}$

Graph $g(x) = \frac{4}{x}$. Compare the graph with the graph of $f(x) = \frac{1}{x}$.

SOLUTION

Step 1 The function is of the form $g(x) = \frac{a}{x}$, so the asymptotes are $x = 0$ and $y = 0$. Draw the asymptotes.

Step 2 Make a table of values and plot the points. Include both positive and negative values of x.

x	-3	-2	-1	1	2	3
y	$-\frac{4}{3}$	-2	-4	4	2	$\frac{4}{3}$

Step 3 Draw the two branches of the hyperbola so that they pass through the plotted points and approach the asymptotes.

▶ The graph of g lies farther from the axes than the graph of f. Both graphs lie in the first and third quadrants and have the same asymptotes, domain, and range.

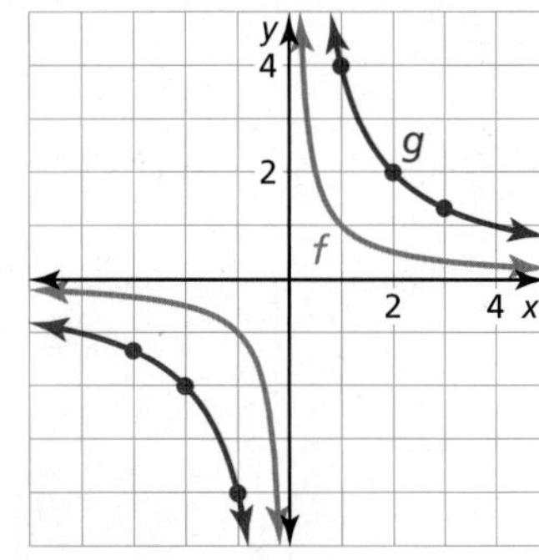

SELF-ASSESSMENT 1 I do not understand. 2 I can do it with help. 3 I can do it on my own. 4 I can teach someone else.

Graph the function. Compare the graph with the graph of $f(x) = \frac{1}{x}$.

1. $g(x) = \frac{2}{x}$

2. $g(x) = \frac{-6}{x}$

3. $g(x) = -\frac{3}{x}$

Translating Simple Rational Functions

KEY IDEA

Graphing Translations of Simple Rational Functions

To graph a rational function of the form $y = \dfrac{a}{x-h} + k$, follow these steps.

Step 1 Draw the asymptotes $x = h$ and $y = k$.

Step 2 Plot points to the left and to the right of the vertical asymptote.

Step 3 Draw the two branches of the hyperbola so that they pass through the plotted points and approach the asymptotes.

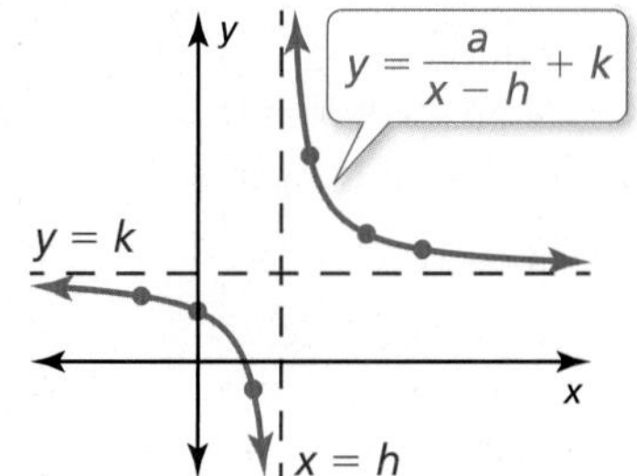

EXAMPLE 2 Graphing a Translation of a Rational Function

Graph $g(x) = \dfrac{-4}{x+2} - 1$. Find the domain and range.

SOLUTION

Step 1 Draw the asymptotes $x = -2$ and $y = -1$.

Step 2 Plot points to the left of the vertical asymptote, such as $(-3, 3)$, $(-4, 1)$, and $(-6, 0)$. Plot points to the right of the vertical asymptote, such as $(-1, -5)$, $(0, -3)$, and $(2, -2)$.

Step 3 Draw the two branches of the hyperbola so that they pass through the plotted points and approach the asymptotes.

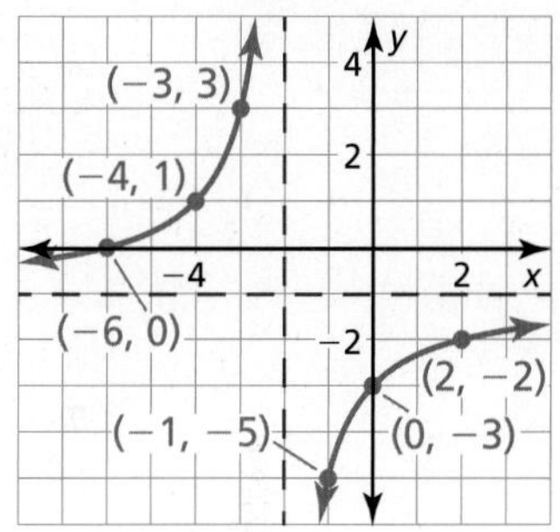

▶ The domain is all real numbers except $x = -2$ and the range is all real numbers except $y = -1$.

Math Practice

Look for Structure

Compare the graph of g to the graph of $f(x) = \dfrac{-4}{x}$. Explain your reasoning.

SELF-ASSESSMENT

1 I do not understand. 2 I can do it with help. 3 I can do it on my own. 4 I can teach someone else.

Graph the function. Find the domain and range.

4. $y = \dfrac{3}{x} - 2$

5. $y = \dfrac{-1}{x+4}$

6. $y = \dfrac{1}{x-1} + 5$

7. **MP STRUCTURE** Which functions have the same asymptotes as $h(x) = \dfrac{7}{x+4} + 3$?

$m(x) = \dfrac{1}{x+3} + 4$

$n(x) = \dfrac{1}{x+4} + 3$

$p(x) = \dfrac{7}{x-4} - 3$

$q(x) = \dfrac{-2}{x+4} + 3$

Graphing Other Rational Functions

All rational functions of the form $y = \dfrac{ax + b}{cx + d}$ also have graphs that are hyperbolas.

- The vertical asymptote of the graph is the line $x = -\dfrac{d}{c}$ because the function is undefined when the denominator $cx + d$ is zero.
- The horizontal asymptote is the line $y = \dfrac{a}{c}$.

EXAMPLE 3 Graphing a Rational Function of the Form $y = \dfrac{ax + b}{cx + d}$

Graph $f(x) = \dfrac{2x + 1}{x - 3}$. Find the domain and range.

SOLUTION

Step 1 Draw the asymptotes. Solve $x - 3 = 0$ for x to find the vertical asymptote $x = 3$. The horizontal asymptote is $y = \dfrac{a}{c} = \dfrac{2}{1} = 2$.

Step 2 Plot points to the left of the vertical asymptote, such as $(2, -5)$, $\left(0, -\dfrac{1}{3}\right)$, and $\left(-2, \dfrac{3}{5}\right)$. Plot points to the right of the vertical asymptote, such as $(4, 9)$, $\left(6, \dfrac{13}{3}\right)$, and $\left(8, \dfrac{17}{5}\right)$.

Step 3 Draw the two branches of the hyperbola so that they pass through the plotted points and approach the asymptotes.

▶ The domain is all real numbers except $x = 3$ and the range is all real numbers except $y = 2$.

Rewriting a rational function may reveal properties of the function and its graph. For example, rewriting a rational function in the form $y = \dfrac{a}{x - h} + k$ reveals that it is a translation of $y = \dfrac{a}{x}$ with vertical asymptote $x = h$ and horizontal asymptote $y = k$.

EXAMPLE 4 Rewriting and Graphing a Rational Function

Rewrite $g(x) = \dfrac{3x + 5}{x + 1}$ in the form $g(x) = \dfrac{a}{x - h} + k$. Graph the function. Describe the graph of g as a transformation of the graph of $f(x) = \dfrac{a}{x}$.

SOLUTION

Rewrite the function by using polynomial long division.

$$\begin{array}{r} 3 \\ x + 1 \enclose{longdiv}{3x + 5} \\ \underline{3x + 3} \\ 2 \end{array}$$

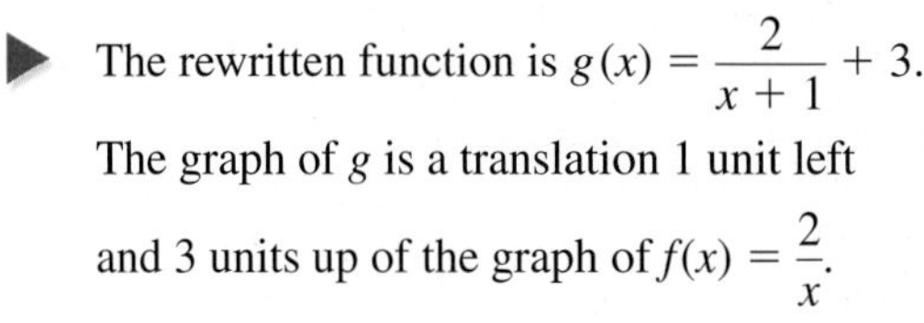

▶ The rewritten function is $g(x) = \dfrac{2}{x + 1} + 3$. The graph of g is a translation 1 unit left and 3 units up of the graph of $f(x) = \dfrac{2}{x}$.

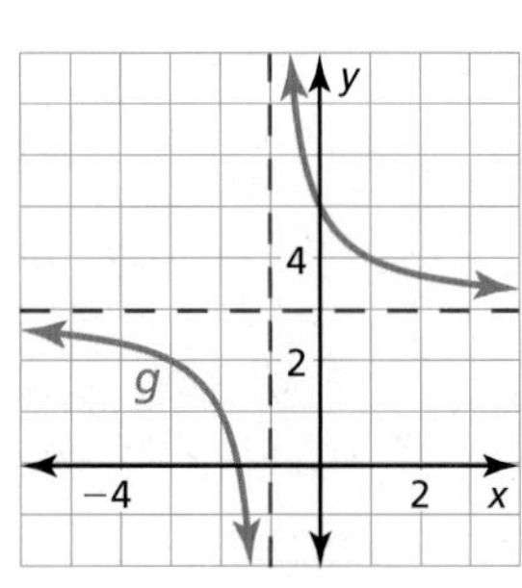

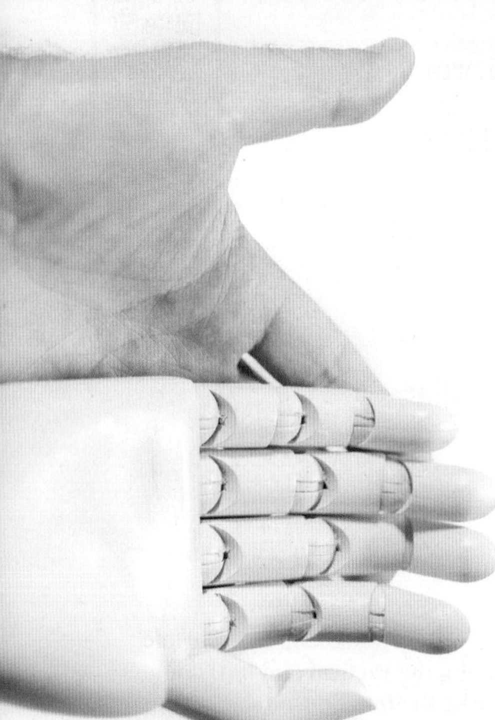

EXAMPLE 5 Modeling Real Life

A 3-D printer builds objects by depositing material one layer at a time. The layers are bonded together, creating a solid object. A medical researcher makes prosthetic hands using a 3-D printer. The printer costs \$1000 and the material for each hand costs \$50.

- How many prosthetic hands must be printed for the average cost per hand to fall to \$90?
- What happens to the average cost as more prosthetic hands are printed?

SOLUTION

1. **Understand the Problem** You are given the cost of a printer and the cost to create a prosthetic hand using the printer. You are asked to find the number of hands for which the average cost falls to \$90.

2. **Make a Plan** Write an equation that represents the average cost. Use technology to estimate the number of hands for which the average cost is \$90. Then analyze the graph to determine what happens to the average cost as more hands are printed.

3. **Solve and Check** Let $c(x)$ be the average cost (in dollars) for printing x hands.

$$c(x) = \frac{\text{(Unit cost)(Number printed)} + \text{(Cost of printer)}}{\text{Number printed}} = \frac{50x + 1000}{x}$$

Use technology to graph the function. Because the number of hands and average cost cannot be negative, graph the function in the first quadrant.

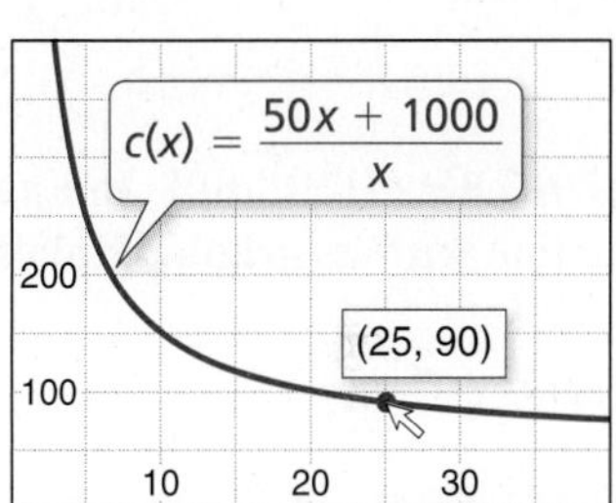

▶ The graph shows that the average cost falls to \$90 per hand after 25 hands are printed. Because the horizontal asymptote is $c(x) = 50$, the average cost approaches \$50 as more hands are printed.

Check Use technology to create a table for large values of x. The table shows that the average cost approaches \$50 as more hands are printed.

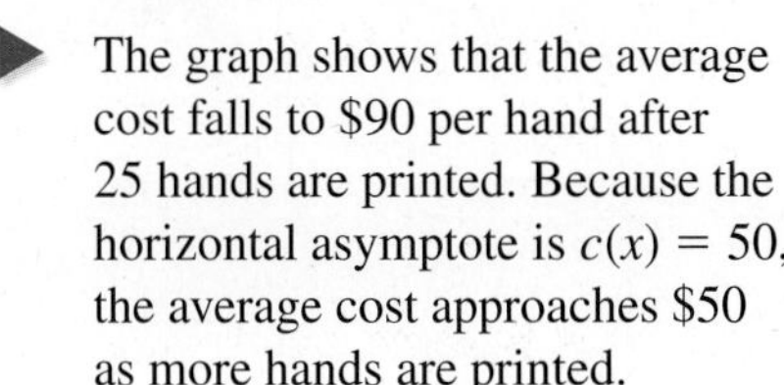

x	$c(x)$
10	150
100	60
1000	51
10000	50.1
100000	50.01

SELF-ASSESSMENT

1 I do not understand. 2 I can do it with help. 3 I can do it on my own. 4 I can teach someone else.

Graph the function. Find the domain and range.

8. $f(x) = \dfrac{x - 1}{x + 3}$

9. $f(x) = \dfrac{2x + 1}{4x - 2}$

10. $f(x) = \dfrac{-3x + 2}{-x - 1}$

11. Rewrite $g(x) = \dfrac{2x + 3}{x + 1}$ in the form $g(x) = \dfrac{a}{x - h} + k$. Graph the function. Describe the graph of g as a transformation of the graph of $f(x) = \dfrac{a}{x}$.

12. WHAT IF? How do the answers in Example 5 change when the cost of the 3-D printer is \$800?

7.2 Practice WITH CalcChat® AND CalcView®

In Exercises 1–8, graph the function. Compare the graph with the graph of $f(x) = \frac{1}{x}$. *Example 1*

1. $g(x) = \frac{3}{x}$
2. $g(x) = \frac{10}{x}$
3. $g(x) = \frac{-5}{x}$
4. $g(x) = \frac{-9}{x}$
5. $g(x) = \frac{15}{x}$
6. $g(x) = \frac{-12}{x}$
7. $g(x) = \frac{-0.5}{x}$
8. $g(x) = \frac{0.1}{x}$

In Exercises 9–16, graph the function. Find the domain and range. *Example 2*

9. $g(x) = \frac{4}{x} + 3$
10. $y = \frac{2}{x} - 3$
11. $h(x) = \frac{6}{x - 1}$
12. $y = \frac{1}{x + 2}$
13. $h(x) = \frac{-3}{x + 2}$
14. $f(x) = \frac{-2}{x - 7}$
15. $g(x) = \frac{-3}{x - 4} - 1$
16. $y = \frac{10}{x + 7} - 5$

ANALYZING RELATIONSHIPS In Exercises 17–20, match the function with its graph. Explain your reasoning.

17. $g(x) = \frac{2}{x - 3} + 1$
18. $h(x) = \frac{2}{x + 3} + 1$
19. $f(x) = \frac{2}{x - 3} - 1$
20. $y = \frac{2}{x + 3} - 1$

A.
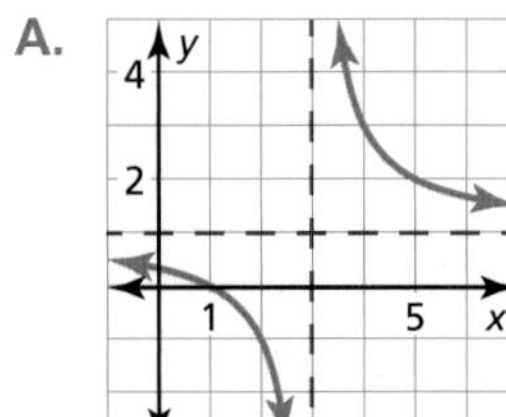

B.
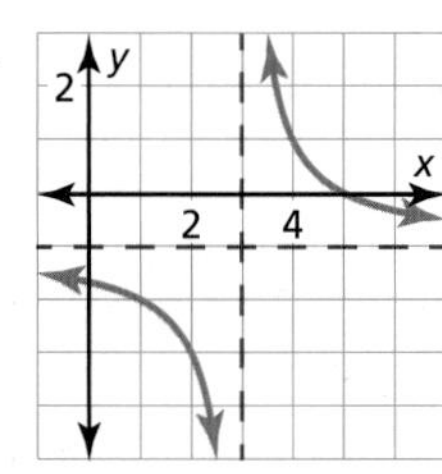

C.
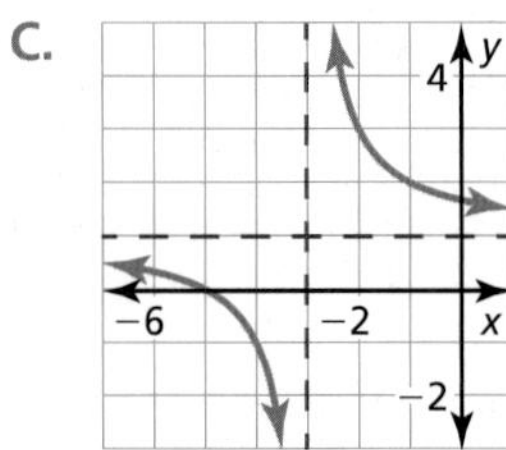

D.
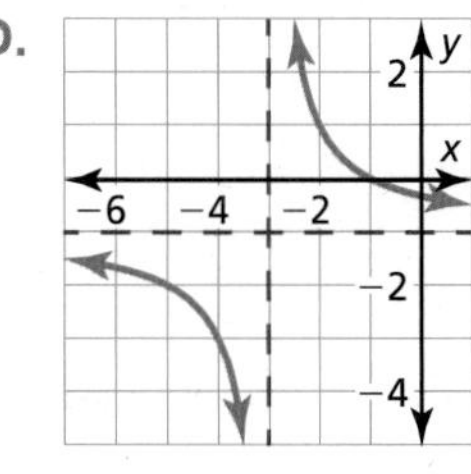

In Exercises 21–28, graph the function. Find the domain and range. *Example 3*

21. $f(x) = \frac{x + 4}{x - 3}$
22. $y = \frac{x - 1}{x + 5}$
23. $y = \frac{x + 6}{4x - 8}$
24. $h(x) = \frac{8x + 3}{2x - 6}$
25. $f(x) = \frac{-5x + 2}{4x + 5}$
26. $g(x) = \frac{6x - 1}{3x - 1}$
27. $h(x) = \frac{-5x}{-2x - 3}$
28. $y = \frac{-2x + 3}{-x + 10}$

ERROR ANALYSIS In Exercises 29 and 30, describe and correct the error in finding the vertical and horizontal asymptotes of the graph of the function.

29. $f(x) = \frac{3}{x + 6} - 2$

The vertical asymptote is $x = 6$. The horizontal asymptote is $y = -2$.

30. $g(x) = \frac{10x + 9}{2x + 1}$

$2x + 1 = 0$

$2x = -1$

$x = -\frac{1}{2}$

The vertical asymptote is $x = -\frac{1}{2}$. The horizontal asymptote is $y = \frac{9}{1} = 9$.

In Exercises 31–38, rewrite the function in the form $g(x) = \frac{a}{x - h} + k$. Graph the function. Describe the graph of g as a transformation of the graph of $f(x) = \frac{a}{x}$. *Example 4*

31. $g(x) = \frac{5x + 6}{x + 1}$
32. $g(x) = \frac{7x + 4}{x - 3}$
33. $g(x) = \frac{2x - 4}{x - 5}$
34. $g(x) = \frac{4x - 11}{x - 2}$
35. $g(x) = \frac{x + 18}{x - 6}$
36. $g(x) = \frac{x + 2}{x - 8}$
37. $g(x) = \frac{7x - 20}{x + 13}$
38. $g(x) = \frac{9x - 3}{x + 7}$

39. **MODELING REAL LIFE** Your school purchases a math software application. The program has an initial cost of \$500 plus \$20 for each student who subscribes. *Example 5*

a. How many students must subscribe for the average cost per student to fall to \$30?

b. What happens to the average cost as more students subscribe?

40. **MODELING REAL LIFE** To join a rock climbing gym, you must pay an initial fee of \$100 and a monthly fee of \$59.

a. How many months must you have a membership for the average cost per month to fall to \$69?

b. What happens to the average cost as the number of months that you are a member increases?

41. **COLLEGE PREP** What is the x-intercept of the graph of the function $y = \dfrac{x-5}{x-2}$?

Ⓐ −5 Ⓑ −2 Ⓒ 2 Ⓓ 5

42. **MP USING TOOLS** The time t (in seconds) it takes for sound to travel 1 kilometer can be modeled by $t = \dfrac{1000}{0.6T + 331}$, where T is the air temperature (in degrees Celsius).

a. You are 1 kilometer from a lightning strike. You hear thunder 2.9 seconds later. Use a graph to find the approximate air temperature.

b. Find the average rate of change in the time it takes sound to travel 1 kilometer as the air temperature increases from 0°C to 10°C.

43. **MODELING REAL LIFE** A business is studying the cost to remove a pollutant from the ground at its site. The function $y = \dfrac{15x}{1.1 - x}$ models the estimated cost y (in thousands of dollars) to remove x percent (expressed as a decimal) of the pollutant.

a. Graph the function. Describe a reasonable domain and range.

b. How much does it cost to remove 20% of the pollutant? 40% of the pollutant? 80% of the pollutant? Does doubling the percent of the pollutant removed double the cost? Explain.

44. **MAKING AN ARGUMENT** Is it possible for a rational function to have two vertical asymptotes? Justify your answer.

MP USING TOOLS In Exercises 45–48, use technology to graph the function. Then determine whether the function is *even*, *odd*, or *neither*.

45. $h(x) = \dfrac{6}{x^2 + 1}$

46. $f(x) = \dfrac{2x^2}{x^2 - 9}$

47. $y = \dfrac{x^3}{3x^2 + x^4}$

48. $f(x) = \dfrac{4x^2}{2x^3 - x}$

49. **MP PROBLEM SOLVING** Internet service provider A charges a \$50 installation fee and a monthly fee of \$43. The table shows the average monthly costs y of provider B for x months of service. Which provider would you choose if you plan to stay with the provider for 12 months? 18 months? 24 months?

Months, x	Average monthly cost (dollars), y
12	\$46.92
18	\$45.94
24	\$45.46

50. **HOW DO YOU SEE IT?**

The graph of $f(x) = \dfrac{1}{x-h} + k$ is shown. Find the values of h and k. Then describe the end behavior of f.

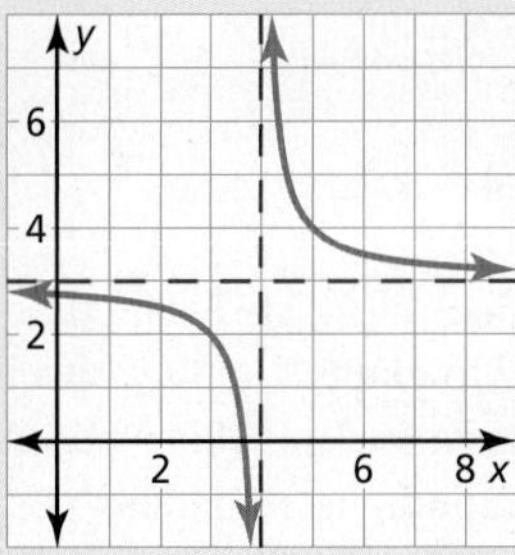

In Exercises 51 and 52, sketch a graph of the rational function f with the given characteristics.

51.
- The domain of f is all real numbers except $x = 1$.
- $f(x) \to -5$ as $x \to -\infty$ and as $x \to +\infty$.

52.
- The graph of f does not have a y-intercept.
- The range of f is all real numbers except $y = 6$.

53. **MP REASONING** A rational function f is of the form $f(x) = \frac{a}{x - h} + k$. The asymptotes of the graph of f intersect at (3, 2). The point (2, 1) is on the graph of f. Find three other points on the graph of f. Explain your reasoning.

54. **DRAWING CONCLUSIONS** In what line(s) is the graph of $y = \frac{1}{x}$ symmetric? What does this symmetry tell you about the inverse of the function $f(x) = \frac{1}{x}$?

55. **ABSTRACT REASONING** Describe the intervals where the graph of $y = \frac{a}{x}$ is increasing or decreasing when (a) $a > 0$ and (b) $a < 0$. Explain your reasoning.

56. **THOUGHT PROVOKING** There are four basic types of conic sections: parabolas, circles, ellipses, and hyperbolas. Each of these can be represented by the intersection of a double-napped cone and a plane. Three of them are shown. Sketch the intersection for a hyperbola.

GO DIGITAL

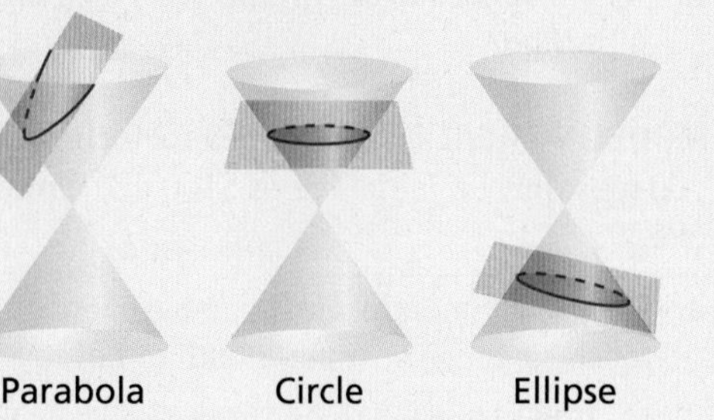

REVIEW & REFRESH

WATCH

In Exercises 57 and 58, write a function g whose graph represents the indicated transformations of the graph of f.

57. $f(x) = x$; translation 6 units down, followed by a reflection in the x-axis

58. $f(x) = |x|$; translation 4 units left, followed by a horizontal stretch by a factor of 3

In Exercises 59–64, factor the polynomial completely.

59. $4x^2 - 4x - 80$

60. $10x^2 + 31x - 14$

61. $x^2 + 20x + 100$

62. $x^3 - 216$

63. $x^3 + 11x^2 + 28x$

64. $2x^3 - 14x^2 + 5x - 35$

65. **MODELING REAL LIFE** The time t (in minutes) required to empty a tank varies inversely with the pumping rate r (in gallons per minute). The rate of a certain pump is 70 gallons per minute. It takes the pump 20 minutes to empty the tank. Complete the table for the times it takes the pump to empty a tank for the given pumping rates.

Pumping rate (gal/min)	Time (min)
50	
56	

66. Find the discriminant of the equation $4x^2 - 10x + 7 = 0$ and describe the number and type of solutions of the equation.

In Exercises 67 and 68, solve the equation.

67. $4^x = 21$

68. $\log_3(5x + 1) = 4$

In Exercises 69 and 70, simplify the expression.

69. $2^{1/2} \cdot 2^{3/5}$

70. $\frac{6^{5/6}}{6^{1/6}}$

71. Rewrite $g(x) = \frac{2x + 9}{x + 8}$ in the form $g(x) = \frac{a}{x - h} + k$. Graph the function. Describe the graph of g as a transformation of the graph of $f(x) = \frac{a}{x}$.

72. Determine the type of function represented by the table. Explain your reasoning.

x	-3	-2	-1	0	1	2
y	128	32	8	2	$\frac{1}{2}$	$\frac{1}{8}$

73. **MP STRUCTURE** Which functions do *not* have a domain of all real numbers?

$f(x) = (x - 8)^2 - 5$ $\qquad$ $g(x) = \sqrt{x - 8} - 5$

$h(x) = \sqrt[3]{x - 8} - 5$ $\qquad$ $p(x) = \frac{1}{x - 8} - 5$

7.3 Multiplying and Dividing Rational Expressions

Learning Target Multiply and divide rational expressions.

Success Criteria

- I can simplify rational expressions and identify any excluded values.
- I can multiply rational expressions.
- I can divide rational expressions.

EXPLORE IT! Analyzing Rational Expressions

Work with a partner.

a. A student divides $2x^2 + 9x + 4$ by $x + 4$ below as shown. Justify each solution step and describe the method.

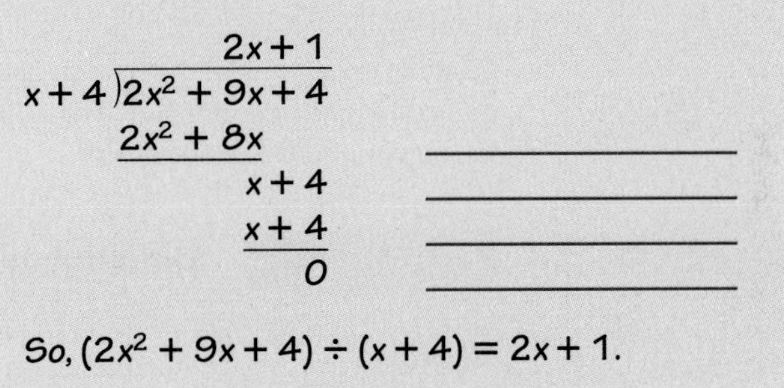

What other methods can you use to divide these polynomials?

Math Practice

Use a Graph
How does the graph of $y = \dfrac{2x^2 + 9x + 4}{x + 4}$ compare to the graph of $y = 2x + 1$?

b. **MP CHOOSE TOOLS** Create a table of values for $\dfrac{2x^2 + 9x + 4}{x + 4}$ and $2x + 1$. What happens when $x = -4$? Why does this happen? Explain how this affects your answer in part (a).

c. You can multiply and divide rational expressions in the same way that you multiply and divide fractions. Find each product or quotient. Determine whether you need to restrict the domains for any of the products or quotients.

Expression	Product or Quotient
i. $\dfrac{x}{x+1} \cdot \dfrac{1}{x}$	
ii. $\dfrac{1}{x-2} \cdot \dfrac{x-2}{x+1}$	
iii. $\dfrac{1}{x} \div \dfrac{x}{x+1}$	
iv. $\dfrac{x}{x+2} \div \dfrac{x}{x-1}$	

d. Is the set of rational expressions closed under multiplication? under division? Justify your answer.

Simplifying Rational Expressions

A **rational expression** is a fraction whose numerator and denominator are nonzero polynomials. The *domain* of a rational expression excludes values that make the denominator zero. A rational expression is in **simplified form** when its numerator and denominator have no common factors (other than ± 1).

Vocabulary

rational expression, p. 370
simplified form of a rational expression, p. 370

KEY IDEA

Simplifying Rational Expressions

Let a, b, and c be expressions with $b \neq 0$ and $c \neq 0$.

Property $\dfrac{a\cancel{c}}{b\cancel{c}} = \dfrac{a}{b}$ Divide out common factor c.

Examples $\dfrac{15}{65} = \dfrac{3 \cdot \cancel{5}}{13 \cdot \cancel{5}} = \dfrac{3}{13}$ Divide out common factor 5.

$\dfrac{4\cancel{(x+3)}}{(x+3)\cancel{(x+3)}} = \dfrac{4}{x+3}$ Divide out common factor $x + 3$.

Simplifying a rational expression usually requires two steps. First, factor the numerator and denominator. Then divide out any factors that are common to both the numerator and denominator.

EXAMPLE 1 Simplifying a Rational Expression

Simplify $\dfrac{x^2 - 4x - 12}{x^2 - 4}$.

SOLUTION

$\dfrac{x^2 - 4x - 12}{x^2 - 4} = \dfrac{(x+2)(x-6)}{(x+2)(x-2)}$ Factor numerator and denominator.

$= \dfrac{\cancel{(x+2)}(x-6)}{\cancel{(x+2)}(x-2)}$ Divide out common factor.

$= \dfrac{x-6}{x-2},\quad x \neq -2$ Simplified form

COMMON ERROR
Do not divide out variable terms that are not factors.

$$\frac{x-6}{x-2} \neq \frac{-6}{-2}$$

The original expression is undefined when $x = -2$. To make the original and simplified expressions equivalent, restrict the domain of the simplified expression by excluding $x = -2$. Both expressions are undefined when $x = 2$, so it is not necessary to list it.

SELF-ASSESSMENT 1 I do not understand. 2 I can do it with help. 3 I can do it on my own. 4 I can teach someone else.

Simplify the rational expression, if possible.

1. $\dfrac{2(x+1)}{(x+1)(x+3)}$
2. $\dfrac{x+4}{x^2-16}$
3. $\dfrac{4}{x(x+2)}$
4. $\dfrac{x^2-2x-3}{x^2-x-6}$
5. **WRITING** When simplifying rational expressions, explain why you must restrict the domain of the simplified expression in some cases.

Multiplying Rational Expressions

The rule for multiplying rational expressions is the same as the rule for multiplying numerical fractions: multiply numerators, multiply denominators, and write the new fraction in simplified form. Similar to rational numbers, rational expressions are closed under multiplication.

KEY IDEA

Multiplying Rational Expressions

Let a, b, c, and d be expressions with $b \neq 0$ and $d \neq 0$.

Property $\frac{a}{b} \cdot \frac{c}{d} = \frac{ac}{bd}$ Simplify $\frac{ac}{bd}$ if possible.

Example $\frac{5x^2}{2xy^2} \cdot \frac{6xy^3}{10y} = \frac{30x^3y^3}{20xy^3} = \frac{\cancel{10} \cdot 3 \cdot \cancel{x} \cdot x^2 \cdot \cancel{y^3}}{\cancel{10} \cdot 2 \cdot \cancel{x} \cdot \cancel{y^3}} = \frac{3x^2}{2}, \quad x \neq 0, y \neq 0$

ANOTHER WAY

In Example 2, you can simplify each rational expression before multiplying, and then simplify the result.

$$\frac{8x^3y}{2xy^2} \cdot \frac{7x^4y^3}{4y}$$

$$= \frac{4x^2}{y} \cdot \frac{7x^4y^2}{4}$$

$$= \frac{\cancel{4} \cdot 7 \cdot x^6 \cdot \cancel{y} \cdot y}{\cancel{4} \cdot \cancel{y}}$$

$$= 7x^6y, \quad x \neq 0, y \neq 0$$

EXAMPLE 2 Multiplying Rational Expressions

Find the product $\frac{8x^3y}{2xy^2} \cdot \frac{7x^4y^3}{4y}$.

SOLUTION

$$\frac{8x^3y}{2xy^2} \cdot \frac{7x^4y^3}{4y} = \frac{56x^7y^4}{8xy^3}$$ Multiply numerators and denominators.

$$= \frac{\cancel{8} \cdot 7 \cdot \cancel{x} \cdot x^6 \cdot \cancel{y^3} \cdot y}{\cancel{8} \cdot \cancel{x} \cdot \cancel{y^3}}$$ Factor and divide out common factors.

$$= 7x^6y, \quad x \neq 0, y \neq 0$$ Simplified form

EXAMPLE 3 Multiplying Rational Expressions

Find the product $\frac{3x - 3x^2}{x^2 + 4x - 5} \cdot \frac{x^2 + x - 20}{3x}$.

SOLUTION

$$\frac{3x - 3x^2}{x^2 + 4x - 5} \cdot \frac{x^2 + x - 20}{3x} = \frac{3x(1 - x)}{(x - 1)(x + 5)} \cdot \frac{(x + 5)(x - 4)}{3x}$$ Factor numerators and denominators.

$$= \frac{3x(1 - x)(x + 5)(x - 4)}{(x - 1)(x + 5)(3x)}$$ Multiply numerators and denominators.

$$= \frac{3x(-1)(x - 1)(x + 5)(x - 4)}{(x - 1)(x + 5)(3x)}$$ Rewrite $1 - x$ as $(-1)(x - 1)$.

$$= \frac{\cancel{3x}(-1)\cancel{(x - 1)}\cancel{(x + 5)}(x - 4)}{\cancel{(x - 1)}\cancel{(x + 5)}\cancel{(3x)}}$$ Divide out common factors.

$$= -x + 4, \quad x \neq -5, x \neq 0, x \neq 1$$ Simplified form

Check Use technology to check your answer. The values are the same, except when $x = -5$, $x = 0$, and $x = 1$.

x	$\frac{3x - 3x^2}{x^2 + 4x - 5} \cdot \frac{x^2 + x - 20}{3x}$	$-x + 4$
−5	undefined	9
−4	8	8
−3	7	7
−2	6	6
−1	5	5
0	undefined	4
1	undefined	3
2	2	2

EXAMPLE 4 Multiplying a Rational Expression by a Polynomial

STUDY TIP

Notice that $x^2 + 3x + 9$ does not equal zero for any real value of x. So, no values must be excluded from the domain to make the simplified form equivalent to the original.

Find the product $\frac{x+2}{x^3-27} \cdot (x^2+3x+9)$.

SOLUTION

$$\frac{x+2}{x^3-27} \cdot (x^2+3x+9) = \frac{x+2}{x^3-27} \cdot \frac{x^2+3x+9}{1}$$ Write polynomial as a rational expression.

$$= \frac{(x+2)(x^2+3x+9)}{(x-3)(x^2+3x+9)}$$ Multiply. Factor denominator.

$$= \frac{(x+2)\cancel{(x^2+3x+9)}}{(x-3)\cancel{(x^2+3x+9)}}$$ Divide out common factor.

$$= \frac{x+2}{x-3}$$ Simplified form

SELF-ASSESSMENT

1 I do not understand. 2 I can do it with help. 3 I can do it on my own. 4 I can teach someone else.

Find the product.

6. $\frac{3x^5y^2}{8xy} \cdot \frac{6xy^2}{9x^3y}$

7. $\frac{2x^2-10x}{x^2-25} \cdot \frac{x+3}{2x^2}$

8. $\frac{x+5}{x^3-1} \cdot (x^2+x+1)$

Dividing Rational Expressions

The rule for dividing rational expressions is the same as the rule for dividing fractions: multiply the first by the reciprocal of the second, and write the result in simplified form. Rational expressions are closed under nonzero division.

KEY IDEA

Dividing Rational Expressions

Let a, b, c, and d be expressions with $b \neq 0$, $c \neq 0$, and $d \neq 0$.

Property $\frac{a}{b} \div \frac{c}{d} = \frac{a}{b} \cdot \frac{d}{c} = \frac{ad}{bc}$ Simplify $\frac{ad}{bc}$ if possible.

Example $\frac{7}{x+1} \div \frac{x+2}{2x-3} = \frac{7}{x+1} \cdot \frac{2x-3}{x+2} = \frac{7(2x-3)}{(x+1)(x+2)}, \; x \neq \frac{3}{2}$

EXAMPLE 5 Dividing Rational Expressions

Find the quotient $\frac{7x}{2x-10} \div \frac{x^2-6x}{x^2-11x+30}$.

SOLUTION

$$\frac{7x}{2x-10} \div \frac{x^2-6x}{x^2-11x+30} = \frac{7x}{2x-10} \cdot \frac{x^2-11x+30}{x^2-6x}$$ Multiply by reciprocal.

$$= \frac{7x}{2(x-5)} \cdot \frac{(x-5)(x-6)}{x(x-6)}$$ Factor.

$$= \frac{7\cancel{x}\cancel{(x-5)}\cancel{(x-6)}}{2\cancel{(x-5)}(\cancel{x})\cancel{(x-6)}}$$ Multiply. Divide out common factors.

$$= \frac{7}{2}, \quad x \neq 0, x \neq 5, x \neq 6$$ Simplified form

EXAMPLE 6 Dividing a Rational Expression by a Polynomial

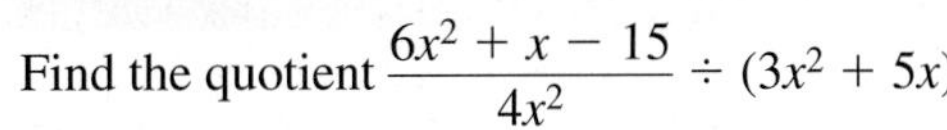

Find the quotient $\dfrac{6x^2 + x - 15}{4x^2} \div (3x^2 + 5x)$.

SOLUTION

$$\frac{6x^2 + x - 15}{4x^2} \div (3x^2 + 5x) = \frac{6x^2 + x - 15}{4x^2} \cdot \frac{1}{3x^2 + 5x}$$ Multiply by reciprocal.

$$= \frac{(3x + 5)(2x - 3)}{4x^2} \cdot \frac{1}{x(3x + 5)}$$ Factor.

$$= \frac{\cancel{(3x + 5)}(2x - 3)}{4x^2(x)\cancel{(3x + 5)}}$$ Multiply. Divide out common factor.

$$= \frac{2x - 3}{4x^3}, \quad x \neq -\frac{5}{3}$$ Simplified form

EXAMPLE 7 Modeling Real Life

The total amount E (in millions of dollars) of healthcare expenditures and the residential population P (in millions) of the United States can be modeled by

$$E = \frac{111{,}082t + 1{,}422{,}329}{1 - 0.002t} \quad \text{and} \quad P = 2.515t + 283.37$$

where t represents the number of years since 2000. Estimate the annual healthcare expenditures per resident in 2022.

SOLUTION

Find a model M for the annual healthcare expenditures per resident by dividing the total amount E by the population P.

$$M = \frac{111{,}082t + 1{,}422{,}329}{1 - 0.002t} \div (2.515t + 283.37)$$ Divide E by P.

$$= \frac{111{,}082t + 1{,}422{,}329}{1 - 0.002t} \cdot \frac{1}{2.515t + 283.37}$$ Multiply by reciprocal.

$$= \frac{111{,}082t + 1{,}422{,}329}{(1 - 0.002t)(2.515t + 283.37)}$$ Multiply.

To estimate the annual healthcare expenditures per resident in 2022, let $t = 22$ in the model.

$$M = \frac{111{,}082 \cdot 22 + 1{,}422{,}329}{(1 - 0.002 \cdot 22)(2.515 \cdot 22 + 283.37)}$$ Substitute 22 for t.

$$\approx 11{,}940$$ Use technology.

▶ In 2022, the annual healthcare expenditures per resident was about \$11,940.

SELF-ASSESSMENT

1 I do not understand. 2 I can do it with help. 3 I can do it on my own. 4 I can teach someone else.

9. Find (a) $\dfrac{4x}{5x - 20} \div \dfrac{x^2 - 2x}{x^2 - 6x + 8}$ and (b) $\dfrac{2x^2 + 3x - 5}{6x} \div (2x^2 + 5x)$.

10. **WHAT IF?** In Example 7, estimate the annual healthcare expenditures per resident in 2022 when $P = -0.028t^2 + 3.03t + 281.8$.

7.3 Practice WITH CalcChat® AND CalcView®

In Exercises 1–8, simplify the expression, if possible.
Example 1

1. $\frac{2x^2}{3x^2 - 4x}$

2. $\frac{-x^2}{2x^2 + 5x}$

3. $\frac{x^2 - 3x - 18}{x^2 - 7x + 6}$

4. $\frac{x^2 + 13x + 36}{x^2 - 7x + 10}$

5. $\frac{x^2 + 11x + 18}{x^3 + 8}$

6. $\frac{x^2 - 7x + 12}{x^3 - 27}$

7. $\frac{32x^4 - 50}{4x^3 - 12x^2 - 5x + 15}$

8. $\frac{3x^3 - 3x^2 + 7x - 7}{27x^4 - 147}$

In Exercises 9–18, find the product.
Examples 2, 3 and 4

9. $\frac{4xy^3}{x^2y} \cdot \frac{y}{8x}$

10. $\frac{3x^3y}{xy^2} \cdot \frac{x}{9y}$

11. $\frac{x^2(x - 4)}{x - 3} \cdot \frac{(x - 3)(x + 6)}{x^3}$

12. $\frac{x^3(x + 5)}{x - 9} \cdot \frac{(x - 9)(x + 8)}{3x^3}$

13. $\frac{x^2 - 3x}{x - 2} \cdot \frac{x^2 + x - 6}{x}$

14. $\frac{x^2 - 4x}{x - 1} \cdot \frac{x^2 + 3x - 4}{2x}$

15. $\frac{x^2 + 3x - 4}{x^2 + 4x + 4} \cdot \frac{2x^2 + 4x}{x^2 - 4x + 3}$

16. $\frac{x^2 - x - 6}{4x^3} \cdot \frac{2x^2 + 2x}{x^2 + 5x + 6}$

17. $\frac{x^2 + 5x - 36}{x^2 - 49} \cdot (x^2 - 11x + 28)$

18. $\frac{x^2 - x - 12}{x^2 - 16} \cdot (x^2 + 2x - 8)$

19. **ERROR ANALYSIS** Describe and correct the error in simplifying the rational expression.

✗ $\frac{x^2 + \overset{2}{\cancel{16}}x + \overset{3}{\cancel{48}}}{x^2 + \underset{1}{\cancel{8}}x + \underset{1}{\cancel{16}}} = \frac{x^2 + 2x + 3}{x^2 + x + 1}$

20. **ERROR ANALYSIS** Describe and correct the error in finding the product.

✗ $\frac{x^2 - 25}{3 - x} \cdot \frac{x - 3}{x + 5}$
$= \frac{(x + 5)(x - 5)}{3 - x} \cdot \frac{x - 3}{x + 5}$
$= \frac{\cancel{(x + 5)}(x - 5)\cancel{(x - 3)}}{\cancel{(3 - x)}\cancel{(x + 5)}}$
$= x - 5, x \neq 3, x \neq -5$

21. **COMPARING METHODS** Find the product below by multiplying the numerators and denominators, then simplifying. Then find the product by simplifying each expression, then multiplying. Which method do you prefer? Explain.

$$\frac{4x^2y}{2x^3} \cdot \frac{12y^4}{24x^2}$$

22. **COLLEGE PREP** For what value of k is $2(y + 1)$, $x \neq 0$, $y \neq -3$ the simplified form of $\frac{y^2 + 4y + 3}{x} \cdot \frac{2x}{y + k}$?

Ⓐ $k = -3$ Ⓑ $k = -1$

Ⓒ $k = 1$ Ⓓ $k = 3$

In Exercises 23–30, find the quotient.
Examples 5 and 6

23. $\frac{32x^3y}{y^8} \div \frac{y^7}{8x^4}$

24. $\frac{2xyz}{x^3z^3} \div \frac{6y^4}{2x^2z^2}$

25. $\frac{x^2 - x - 6}{2x^4 - 6x^3} \div \frac{x + 2}{4x^3}$

26. $\frac{2x^2 - 12x}{x^2 - 7x + 6} \div \frac{2x}{3x - 3}$

27. $\frac{x^2 - x - 6}{x + 4} \div (x^2 - 6x + 9)$

28. $\frac{x^2 - 5x - 36}{x + 2} \div (x^2 - 18x + 81)$

29. $\frac{x^2 + 9x + 18}{x^2 + 6x + 8} \div \frac{x^2 - 3x - 18}{x^2 + 2x - 8}$

30. $\frac{x^2 - 3x - 40}{x^2 + 8x - 20} \div \frac{x^2 + 13x + 40}{x^2 + 12x + 20}$

In Exercises 31 and 32, use the following information.

Manufacturers often package products in a way that uses the least amount of material. One measure of the efficiency of a package is the ratio of its surface area S to its volume V. The smaller the ratio, the more efficient the packaging.

31. You are examining three cylindrical containers.

a. Write an expression for the efficiency ratio of a cylinder with height h and radius r.

b. Find the efficiency ratio for each cylindrical can listed in the table. Rank the three cans according to efficiency.

	Soup	Coffee	Paint
Height, *h*	10.2 cm	15.9 cm	19.4 cm
Radius, *r*	3.4 cm	7.8 cm	8.4 cm

32. A popcorn company is designing a new tin with the same square base and twice the height of the old tin.

a. Write an expression for the efficiency ratio of each tin.

b. Did the company make a good decision by creating the new tin? Explain.

33. MODELING REAL LIFE The total amount E (in thousands of dollars) of educational technology expenditures and the total number of students P (in thousands) in a school system is modeled by

$$E = \frac{-6.984t + 550}{1 - 0.027t}$$

and

$$P = 0.006t + 2.09$$

where t represents the number of years since 2000. Estimate the annual educational technology expenditures per student in 2022. *Example 7*

34. MODELING REAL LIFE The total amount S (in millions of dollars) of revenue and the number of users U (in millions) of a social media platform is modeled by

$$S = \frac{3.520t - 3.33}{1 - 0.066t}$$

and

$$U = 0.203t + 0.48$$

where t represents the number of years since 2010. Estimate the revenue per user in 2022.

35. MP STRUCTURE Refer to the population model P in Exercise 33.

a. Interpret the meaning of the coefficient of t.

b. Interpret the meaning of the constant term.

36. CRITICAL THINKING Find the expression that makes the following statement true. Assume $x \neq -2$ and $x \neq 5$.

$$\frac{x - 5}{x^2 + 2x - 35} \div \frac{\square}{x^2 - 3x - 10} = \frac{x + 2}{x + 7}$$

37. DRAWING CONCLUSIONS Complete the table for the function $y = \frac{x + 4}{x^2 - 16}$. Then use technology to explain the behavior of the function at $x = -4$.

x	y
−3.5	
−3.8	
−3.9	
−4.1	
−4.2	

38. HOW DO YOU SEE IT?
Use the graphs of f and g to determine the excluded values of each function.

a. $h(x) = (fg)(x)$

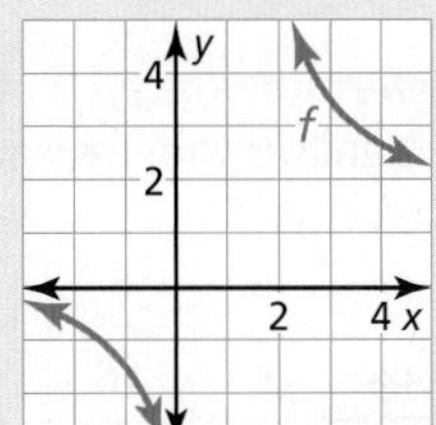

b. $k(x) = \left(\frac{f}{g}\right)(x)$

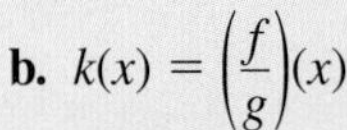

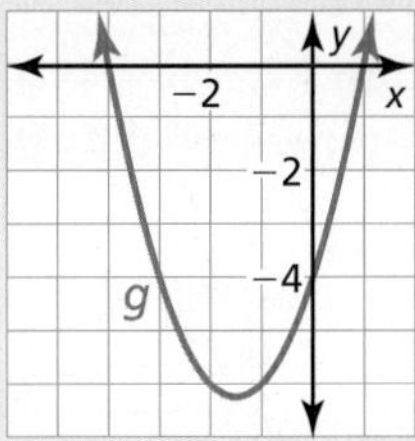

39. **CONNECTING CONCEPTS** Find the ratio of the perimeter to the area of the triangle shown.

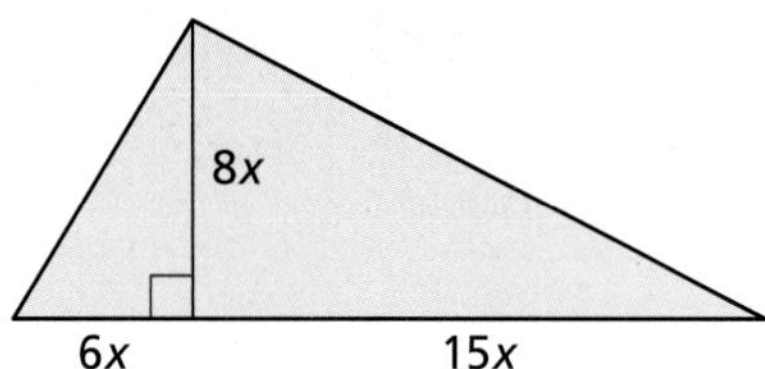

40. **THOUGHT PROVOKING**
Is it possible to write two radical functions whose product represents a parabola and whose quotient represents a hyperbola? Justify your answer.

41. **REASONING** Find two rational functions f and g that have the stated product and quotient.

$$(fg)(x) = x^2; \left(\frac{f}{g}\right)(x) = \frac{(x-1)^2}{(x+2)^2}$$

42. **PERFORMANCE TASK** Animals can better conserve body heat as their surface area to volume ratios decrease.

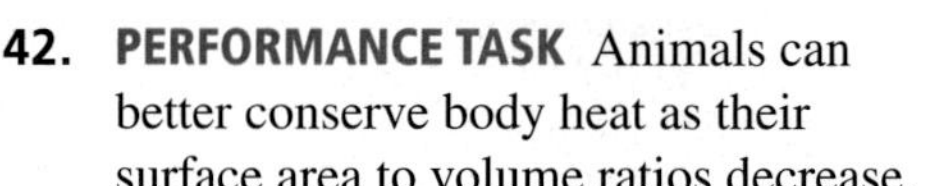

a. Which penguin below is better equipped to live in a colder climate? Explain your reasoning.

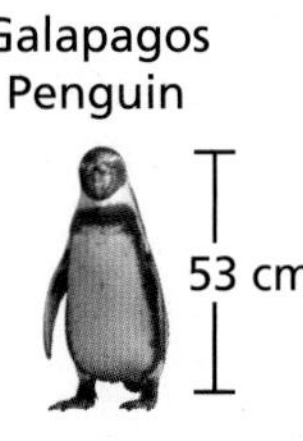

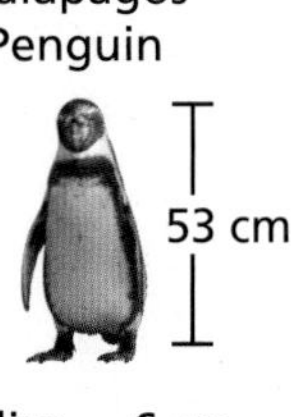

Not drawn to scale

b. Research other factors that influence the survival of penguins in cold climates. How might these factors support or change your answer?

REVIEW & REFRESH

43. Describe the transformation of $f(x) = x^2$ represented by g.

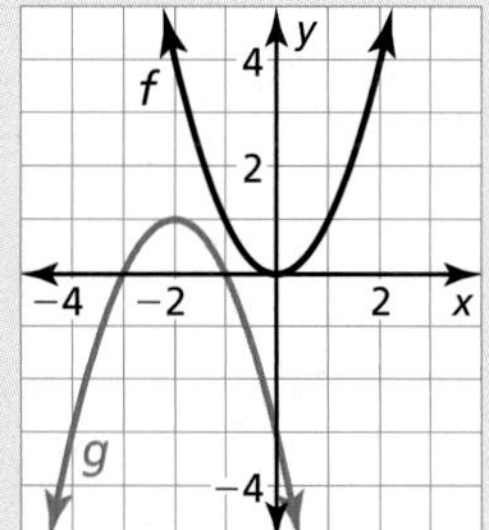

In Exercises 44 and 45, graph the function. Find the domain and range.

44. $f(x) = \dfrac{x+1}{x-1}$

45. $y = \dfrac{-2x+5}{-x+10}$

In Exercises 46 and 47, the variables x and y vary inversely. Use the given values to write an equation relating x and y. Then find y when x = 6.

46. $x = 1, y = -4$

47. $x = 4, y = 3$

In Exercises 48 and 49 determine the type of function represented by the data. Explain your reasoning.

48.

x	0	2	4	6	8
y	1	2	4	8	16

49. $(-4, 48), (-3, 43), (-2, 38), (-1, 33), (0, 28)$

In Exercises 50 and 51, find the product or quotient.

50. $\dfrac{3xy^2}{xy^4} \cdot \dfrac{y}{6x}$

51. $\dfrac{4xyz}{x^5z^3} \div \dfrac{8y^2}{4x^2z^3}$

52. **MODELING REAL LIFE** A mobile provider maintains a list of active cell phones. The number N (in hundreds) of active cell phones of a particular model since year t can be modeled by

$$N = 0.622t^3 + 0.31t^2 - 1.1t + 20$$

where $0 \leq t \leq 12$. Since what year are there at least 10,000 active phones of the particular model?

In Exercises 53 and 54, factor the polynomial completely.

53. $8x^3 + 27$

54. $3y^6 - 15y^4 + 18y^2$

55. Write an exponential growth function represented by the graph.

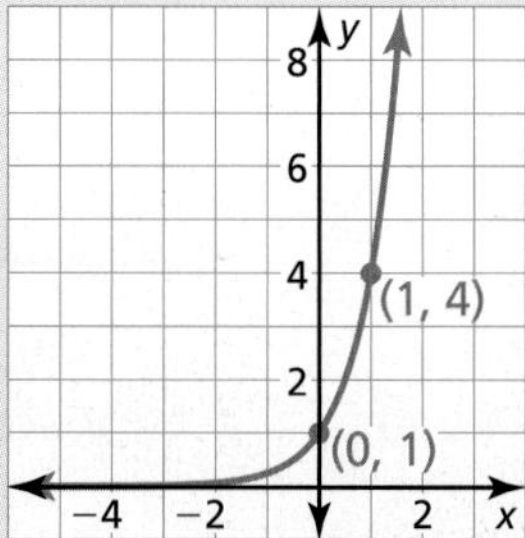

7.4 Adding and Subtracting Rational Expressions

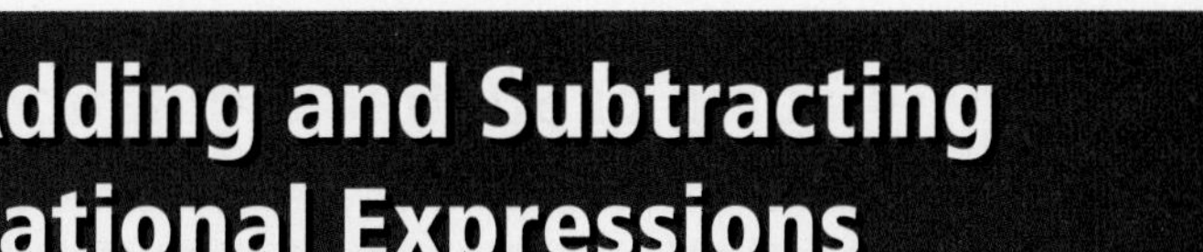

Learning Target Add and subtract rational expressions.

Success Criteria

- I can add and subtract rational expressions with like denominators.
- I can explain how to find a common denominator for rational expressions.
- I can add and subtract rational expressions with unlike denominators.

EXPLORE IT! Adding and Subtracting Rational Expressions

Work with a partner.

a. Explain how to find each sum or difference.

i. $\frac{3}{8} + \frac{1}{8}$ **ii.** $\frac{9}{10} - \frac{3}{10}$

iii. $\frac{1}{2} + \frac{3}{4}$ **iv.** $\frac{5}{8} - \frac{7}{12}$

b. You can add and subtract rational expressions in the same way that you add and subtract fractions. Find each sum or difference. Explain your methods.

Math Practice

View as Components
How is it helpful to view denominators of rational expressions in terms of their factors?

Expression	Sum or Difference
i. $\frac{3}{x} + \frac{1}{x}$	
ii. $\frac{9}{x} - \frac{3}{x}$	
iii. $\frac{1}{x} + \frac{3}{2x}$	
iv. $\frac{5}{x+1} - \frac{7}{x+1}$	
v. $\frac{7}{x+2} + \frac{3}{x-4}$	
vi. $\frac{4}{x+1} - \frac{3x-3}{x^2-1}$	

c. Is it necessary to restrict the domain for any of the sums or differences in part (b)? Explain.

d. Is the set of rational expressions closed under addition and subtraction? Justify your answer.

Vocabulary

complex fraction, *p. 381*

Adding or Subtracting Rational Expressions

As with numerical fractions, the procedure used to add or subtract two rational expressions depends upon whether the expressions have like or unlike denominators. To add or subtract rational expressions with like denominators, simply add or subtract their numerators. Then write the result over the common denominator.

KEY IDEA

Adding or Subtracting with Like Denominators

Let a, b, and c be expressions with $c \neq 0$.

Addition

$$\frac{a}{c} + \frac{b}{c} = \frac{a + b}{c}$$

Subtraction

$$\frac{a}{c} - \frac{b}{c} = \frac{a - b}{c}$$

EXAMPLE 1 Adding or Subtracting with Like Denominators

Find each sum or difference.

a. $\dfrac{7}{4x} + \dfrac{3}{4x}$

b. $\dfrac{2x}{x + 6} - \dfrac{5}{x + 6}$

SOLUTION

a. $\dfrac{7}{4x} + \dfrac{3}{4x} = \dfrac{7 + 3}{4x} = \dfrac{10}{4x} = \dfrac{5}{2x}$ Add numerators and simplify.

b. $\dfrac{2x}{x + 6} - \dfrac{5}{x + 6} = \dfrac{2x - 5}{x + 6}$ Subtract numerators.

To add or subtract rational expressions with *unlike* denominators, find a common denominator. Rewrite each rational expression using the common denominator. Then add or subtract.

KEY IDEA

Adding or Subtracting with Unlike Denominators

Let a, b, c, and d be expressions with $c \neq 0$ and $d \neq 0$.

Addition

$$\frac{a}{c} + \frac{b}{d} = \frac{ad}{cd} + \frac{bc}{cd} = \frac{ad + bc}{cd}$$

Subtraction

$$\frac{a}{c} - \frac{b}{d} = \frac{ad}{cd} - \frac{bc}{cd} = \frac{ad - bc}{cd}$$

You can always find a common denominator of rational expressions by multiplying the denominators, as shown above. However, when you use the least common denominator (LCD), which is the least common multiple (LCM) of the denominators, simplifying your answer may take fewer steps.

To find the LCM of two (or more) expressions, factor the expressions completely. The LCM is the product of the highest power of each factor that appears in either of the expressions.

EXAMPLE 2 Finding a Least Common Multiple (LCM)

Find the least common multiple of $4x^2 - 16$ and $6x^2 - 24x + 24$.

SOLUTION

Step 1 Factor each polynomial. Write numerical factors as products of primes.

$$4x^2 - 16 = 4(x^2 - 4)$$
$$= (2^2)(x + 2)(x - 2)$$
$$6x^2 - 24x + 24 = 6(x^2 - 4x + 4)$$
$$= (2)(3)(x - 2)^2$$

Step 2 The LCM is the product of the highest power of each factor that appears in either polynomial.

$$\text{LCM} = (2^2)(3)(x + 2)(x - 2)^2$$
$$= 12(x + 2)(x - 2)^2$$

EXAMPLE 3 Adding with Unlike Denominators

Find the sum $\frac{7}{9x^2} + \frac{x}{3x^2 + 3x}$.

SOLUTION

Method 1 Multiply the denominators to find a common denominator and then add.

$$\frac{7}{9x^2} + \frac{x}{3x^2 + 3x} = \frac{7(3x^2 + 3x) + x(9x^2)}{9x^2(3x^2 + 3x)} \qquad \frac{a}{c} + \frac{b}{d} = \frac{ad + bc}{cd}$$

$$= \frac{21x^2 + 21x + 9x^3}{9x^2(3x^2 + 3x)} \qquad \text{Distributive Property}$$

$$= \frac{\cancel{3x}(3x^2 + 7x + 7)}{9x^2(x + 1)(\cancel{3x})} \qquad \text{Factor. Divide out common factors.}$$

$$= \frac{3x^2 + 7x + 7}{9x^2(x + 1)} \qquad \text{Simplify.}$$

Method 2 Find the LCD and then add. To find the LCD, find the LCM of the denominators. Note that $9x^2 = 3^2x^2$ and $3x^2 + 3x = 3x(x + 1)$, so the LCD is $(3^2)(x^2)(x + 1) = 9x^2(x + 1)$.

$$\frac{7}{9x^2} + \frac{x}{3x^2 + 3x} = \frac{7}{9x^2} + \frac{x}{3x(x + 1)} \qquad \text{Factor second denominator.}$$

$$= \frac{7}{9x^2} \cdot \frac{x + 1}{x + 1} + \frac{x}{3x(x + 1)} \cdot \frac{3x}{3x} \qquad \text{LCD is } 9x^2(x + 1).$$

$$= \frac{7x + 7}{9x^2(x + 1)} + \frac{3x^2}{9x^2(x + 1)} \qquad \text{Multiply.}$$

$$= \frac{3x^2 + 7x + 7}{9x^2(x + 1)} \qquad \text{Add numerators.}$$

Note in Examples 1 and 3 that when adding or subtracting rational expressions, the result is a rational expression. Similar to rational numbers, rational expressions are closed under addition and subtraction.

EXAMPLE 4 **Subtracting with Unlike Denominators**

Find the difference $\dfrac{x+2}{2x-2} - \dfrac{-2x-1}{x^2-4x+3}$.

SOLUTION

$$\frac{x+2}{2x-2} - \frac{-2x-1}{x^2-4x+3} = \frac{x+2}{2(x-1)} - \frac{-2x-1}{(x-1)(x-3)}$$ Factor each denominator.

$$= \frac{x+2}{2(x-1)} \cdot \frac{x-3}{x-3} - \frac{-2x-1}{(x-1)(x-3)} \cdot \frac{2}{2}$$ LCD is $2(x-1)(x-3)$.

$$= \frac{x^2-x-6}{2(x-1)(x-3)} - \frac{-4x-2}{2(x-1)(x-3)}$$ Multiply.

$$= \frac{x^2-x-6-(-4x-2)}{2(x-1)(x-3)}$$ Subtract numerators.

$$= \frac{x^2+3x-4}{2(x-1)(x-3)}$$ Simplify numerator.

$$= \frac{\cancel{(x-1)}(x+4)}{2\cancel{(x-1)}(x-3)}$$ Factor numerator. Divide out common factor.

$$= \frac{x+4}{2(x-3)}, \quad x \neq 1$$ Simplify.

COMMON ERROR

When subtracting rational expressions, remember to distribute the negative sign to all the terms in the quantity that is being subtracted.

Rewriting Rational Functions

Rewriting a rational function may reveal properties of the function and its graph. In Example 4 of Section 7.2, you used long division to rewrite a rational function. In the next example, you will use inspection.

EXAMPLE 5 **Rewriting and Graphing a Rational Function**

Rewrite $g(x) = \dfrac{3x+5}{x+1}$ in the form $g(x) = \dfrac{a}{x-h} + k$. Graph the function. Describe the graph of g as a transformation of the graph of $f(x) = \dfrac{a}{x}$.

SOLUTION

Rewrite by inspection.

$$\frac{3x+5}{x+1} = \frac{3x+3+2}{x+1} = \frac{3(x+1)+2}{x+1} = \frac{3\cancel{(x+1)}}{\cancel{x+1}} + \frac{2}{x+1} = 3 + \frac{2}{x+1}$$

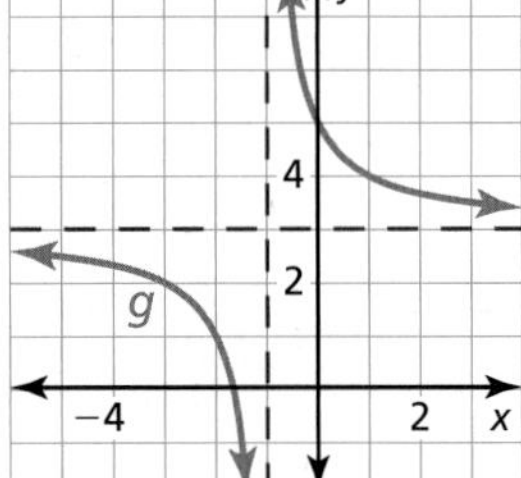

▶ The rewritten function is $g(x) = \dfrac{2}{x+1} + 3$. The graph of g is a translation 1 unit left and 3 units up of the graph of $f(x) = \dfrac{2}{x}$.

SELF-ASSESSMENT 1 I do not understand. 2 I can do it with help. 3 I can do it on my own. 4 I can teach someone else.

Find the sum or difference.

1. $\dfrac{2}{3x^2} + \dfrac{1}{3x^2}$

2. $\dfrac{4x}{x-2} - \dfrac{x}{x-2}$

3. $\dfrac{3}{4x} - \dfrac{1}{7}$

4. $\dfrac{1}{3x^2} + \dfrac{x}{9x^2-12}$

5. Rewrite $g(x) = \dfrac{2x-4}{x-3}$ in the form $g(x) = \dfrac{a}{x-h} + k$. Graph the function. Describe the graph of g as a transformation of the graph of $f(x) = \dfrac{a}{x}$.

Complex Fractions

A **complex fraction** is a fraction that contains a fraction in its numerator or denominator. A complex fraction can be simplified using either of the methods below.

KEY IDEA

Simplifying Complex Fractions

Method 1 If necessary, simplify the numerator and denominator by writing each as a single fraction. Then divide by multiplying the numerator by the reciprocal of the denominator.

Method 2 Multiply the numerator and the denominator by the LCD of *every* fraction in the numerator and denominator. Then simplify.

EXAMPLE 6 Simplifying a Complex Fraction

Simplify $\dfrac{\frac{5}{x+4}}{\frac{1}{x+4}+\frac{2}{x}}$.

SOLUTION

Method 1 $\dfrac{\frac{5}{x+4}}{\frac{1}{x+4}+\frac{2}{x}} = \dfrac{\frac{5}{x+4}}{\frac{3x+8}{x(x+4)}}$ — Add fractions in denominator.

$= \dfrac{5}{x+4} \cdot \dfrac{x(x+4)}{3x+8}$ — Multiply by reciprocal.

$= \dfrac{5x\cancel{(x+4)}}{\cancel{(x+4)}(3x+8)}$ — Multiply. Divide out common factors.

$= \dfrac{5x}{3x+8}, \quad x \neq -4, x \neq 0$ — Simplify.

Method 2 The LCD of all the fractions in the numerator and denominator is $x(x+4)$.

$\dfrac{\frac{5}{x+4}}{\frac{1}{x+4}+\frac{2}{x}} = \dfrac{\frac{5}{x+4}}{\frac{1}{x+4}+\frac{2}{x}} \cdot \dfrac{x(x+4)}{x(x+4)}$ — Multiply numerator and denominator by the LCD.

$= \dfrac{\frac{5}{\cancel{x+4}} \cdot x\cancel{(x+4)}}{\frac{1}{\cancel{x+4}} \cdot x\cancel{(x+4)} + \frac{2}{\cancel{x}} \cdot \cancel{x}(x+4)}$ — Multiply. Divide out common factors.

$= \dfrac{5x}{x+2(x+4)}$ — Simplify.

$= \dfrac{5x}{3x+8}, \quad x \neq -4, x \neq 0$ — Simplify.

SELF-ASSESSMENT 1 I do not understand. 2 I can do it with help. 3 I can do it on my own. 4 I can teach someone else.

Simplify the complex fraction.

6. $\dfrac{\frac{x}{6}-\frac{x}{3}}{\frac{x}{5}-\frac{7}{10}}$

7. $\dfrac{\frac{2}{x}-4}{\frac{2}{x}+3}$

8. $\dfrac{\frac{3}{x+5}}{\frac{2}{x-3}+\frac{1}{x+5}}$

7.4 Practice WITH CalcChat® AND CalcView®

In Exercises 1–6, find the sum or difference. *Example 1*

1. $\dfrac{15}{4x} + \dfrac{5}{4x}$

2. $\dfrac{9}{16x^2} - \dfrac{4}{16x^2}$

3. $\dfrac{9}{x+1} - \dfrac{2x}{x+1}$

4. $\dfrac{3x^2}{x-8} + \dfrac{6x}{x-8}$

5. $\dfrac{5x}{x+3} + \dfrac{15}{x+3}$

6. $\dfrac{4x^2}{2x-1} - \dfrac{1}{2x-1}$

In Exercises 7–14, find the least common multiple of the expressions. *Example 2*

7. $3x, 3(x-2)$

8. $2x, 2(x+6)$

9. $5x, 5x-10$

10. $4x, 4x-4$

11. $2x^2 - 18, x^2 + x - 12$

12. $4x^2 - 16, x^2 + 9x + 14$

13. $x^2 + 3x - 40, x - 8$

14. $x^2 - 2x - 63, x + 7$

In Exercises 15–22, find the sum or difference. *Examples 3 and 4*

15. $\dfrac{12}{5x} - \dfrac{7}{6x}$

16. $\dfrac{8}{3x} + \dfrac{5}{4x}$

17. $\dfrac{3}{x+4} - \dfrac{1}{x+6}$

18. $\dfrac{9}{x-3} + \dfrac{2x}{x+1}$

19. $\dfrac{12}{x^2+5x-24} + \dfrac{3}{x-3}$

20. $\dfrac{x^2-5}{x^2+5x-14} - \dfrac{x+3}{x+7}$

21. $\dfrac{x+2}{x-4} + \dfrac{2}{x} + \dfrac{5x}{3x-1}$

22. $\dfrac{x+3}{x^2-25} - \dfrac{x-1}{x-5} + \dfrac{3}{x+3}$

ERROR ANALYSIS In Exercises 23 and 24, describe and correct the error in finding the sum.

23.

$$\frac{2}{5x} + \frac{4}{x^2} = \frac{2+4}{5x+x^2} = \frac{6}{x(5+x)}$$

24.

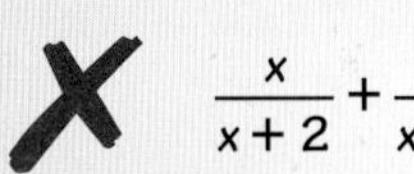

$$\frac{x}{x+2} + \frac{4}{x-5} = \frac{x+4}{(x+2)(x-5)}$$

25. **MP REASONING** Tell whether the statement is *always, sometimes,* or *never* true. Explain.

a. The LCD of two rational expressions is the product of the denominators.

b. The LCD of two rational expressions will have a degree greater than or equal to that of the denominator with the higher degree.

26. **COLLEGE PREP** Which expression is not equivalent to $\dfrac{x-a}{x^2-a^2}$?

Ⓐ $\dfrac{x}{x-a} - \dfrac{a}{x+a}$

Ⓑ $\dfrac{1}{x+a}, x \neq a$

Ⓒ $\dfrac{x}{x^2-a^2} - \dfrac{a}{x^2-a^2}$

Ⓓ $\dfrac{x}{x^2-a^2} + \dfrac{a}{a^2-x^2}$

In Exercises 27–34, rewrite the function in the form $g(x) = \dfrac{a}{x-h} + k$. Graph the function. Describe the graph of g as a transformation of the graph of $f(x) = \dfrac{a}{x}$. *Example 5*

27. $g(x) = \dfrac{5x-7}{x-1}$

28. $g(x) = \dfrac{6x+4}{x+5}$

29. $g(x) = \dfrac{12x}{x-5}$

30. $g(x) = \dfrac{8x}{x+13}$

31. $g(x) = \dfrac{2x+3}{x}$

32. $g(x) = \dfrac{4x-6}{x}$

33. $g(x) = \dfrac{3x+11}{x-3}$

34. $g(x) = \dfrac{7x-9}{x+10}$

In Exercises 35–40, simplify the complex fraction. *Example 6*

35. $\dfrac{\frac{x}{3} - 6}{10 + \frac{4}{x}}$

36. $\dfrac{15 - \frac{2}{x}}{\frac{x}{5} + 4}$

37. $\dfrac{\frac{1}{2x-5} - \frac{7}{8x-20}}{\frac{x}{2x-5}}$

38. $\dfrac{\frac{16}{x-2}}{\frac{4}{x+1} + \frac{6}{x}}$

39. $\dfrac{\frac{1}{3x^2-3}}{\frac{5}{x+1} - \frac{x+4}{x^2-3x-4}}$

40. $\dfrac{\frac{3}{x-2} - \frac{6}{x^2-4}}{\frac{3}{x+2} + \frac{1}{x-2}}$

41. **MP PROBLEM SOLVING** The total time T (in hours) needed to fly from New York to Los Angeles and back can be modeled by the equation below, where d is the distance (in miles) each way, a is the average airplane speed (in miles per hour), and j is the average speed (in miles per hour) of the jet stream. Simplify the equation. Then find the total time it takes to fly 2468 miles when $a = 510$ and $j = 115$.

$$T = \frac{d}{a - j} + \frac{d}{a + j}$$

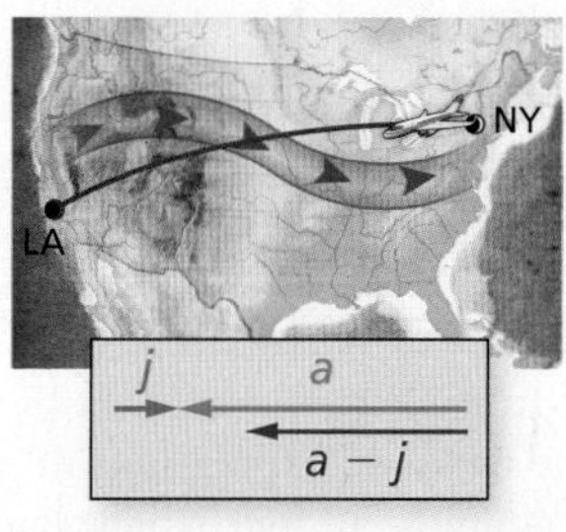

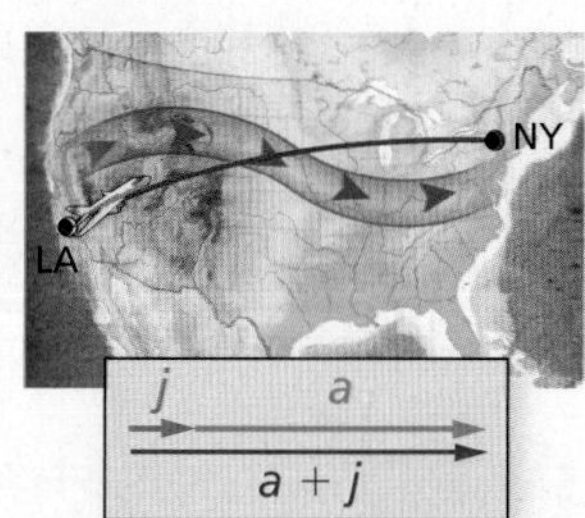

42. **REWRITING A FORMULA** The total resistance R_t of two resistors in a parallel circuit with resistances R_1 and R_2 (in ohms) is given by the equation shown. Simplify the complex fraction. Then find the total resistance when $R_1 = 2000$ and $R_2 = 5600$.

$$R_t = \frac{1}{\frac{1}{R_1} + \frac{1}{R_2}}$$

R_t = R_1, R_2 (parallel)

43. **MP PROBLEM SOLVING** You participate in a sprint triathlon that involves swimming, bicycling, and running. The table shows the distances (in miles) and your average speed for each portion of the race.

	Distance (miles)	Speed (miles per hour)
Swimming	0.5	r
Bicycling	12.4	$9r$
Running	3.1	$r + 5$

a. Write a model in simplified form for the total time (in hours) it takes to complete the race.

b. How long does it take to complete the race if you can swim at an average speed of 2 miles per hour?

44. **MP PROBLEM SOLVING** A trip involves a 40-mile bus ride and a train ride. The entire trip is 140 miles. The time (in hours) the bus travels is $y_1 = \frac{40}{x}$, where x is the average speed (in miles per hour) of the bus. The time (in hours) the train travels is $y_2 = \frac{100}{x + 30}$. Write and simplify a model that shows the total time y (in hours) of the trip.

45. **MAKING AN ARGUMENT** Is the least common multiple of two expressions always greater than each of the expressions? Explain.

46. **HOW DO YOU SEE IT?**
Use the graph to write a function of the form $f(x) = \frac{a}{x - h} + k$.

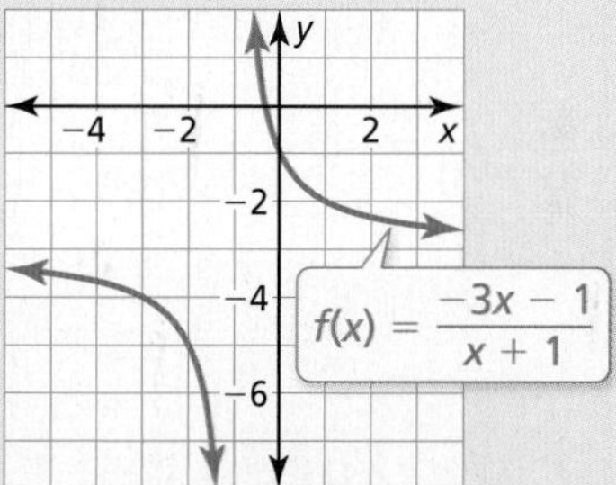

47. **MP STRUCTURE** A family borrows P dollars to pay for orthodontics. The family agrees to repay the loan over t years at a monthly interest rate of i (expressed as a decimal). The monthly payment M is given by either formula below.

$$M = \frac{Pi}{1 - \left(\frac{1}{1 + i}\right)^{12t}} \quad \text{or} \quad M = \frac{Pi(1 + i)^{12t}}{(1 + i)^{12t} - 1}$$

a. Show that the formulas are equivalent by simplifying the first formula.

b. Find the monthly payment when the family borrows $5000 at a monthly interest rate of 0.5% and repays the loan over 4 years.

48. **THOUGHT PROVOKING**
Is it possible to write two rational functions whose sum is a quadratic function? Justify your answer.

49. **OPEN ENDED** Write a complex fraction that has a value of 3 when $x = 2$ and is undefined when $x = -3$ and $x = 1$.

50. CONNECTING CONCEPTS Find an expression for the surface area of the box.

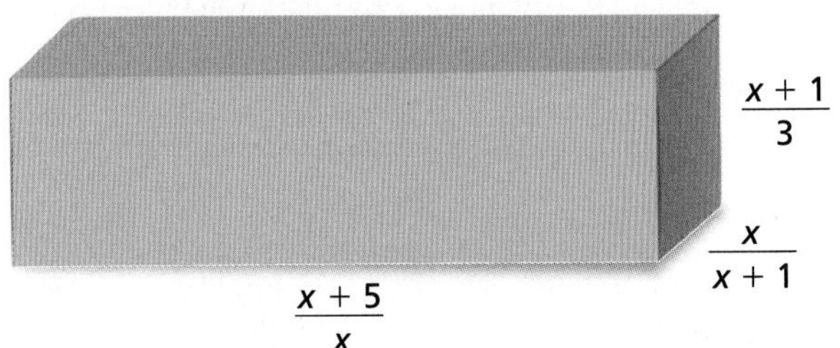

51. MP PROBLEM SOLVING One 3-D printer creates 10% of a medical instrument in one minute. Another 3-D printer takes x minutes to create a medical instrument of the same design. Write an expression for the number of instruments the two printers create in one hour when both printers operate for the full hour.

52. MP STRUCTURE Find the value of b that completes the equation.

$$\frac{3x - 1}{(x + 1)(x - 3)} = \frac{1}{x + 1} + \frac{b}{x - 3}$$

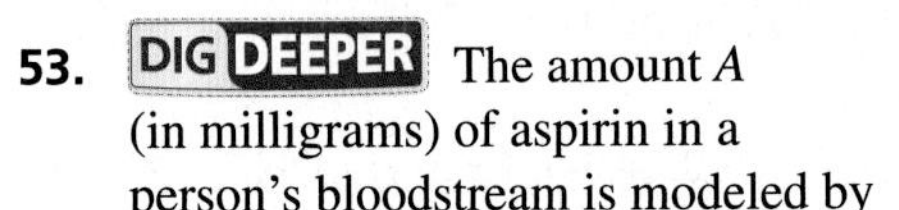

53. DIG DEEPER The amount A (in milligrams) of aspirin in a person's bloodstream is modeled by

$$A = \frac{391t^2 + 0.112}{0.218t^4 + 0.991t^2 + 1}$$

where t is the time (in hours) after one dose is taken. A second dose is taken 1 hour after the first dose. Write an equation for the total amount of aspirin in the bloodstream after the second dose is taken.

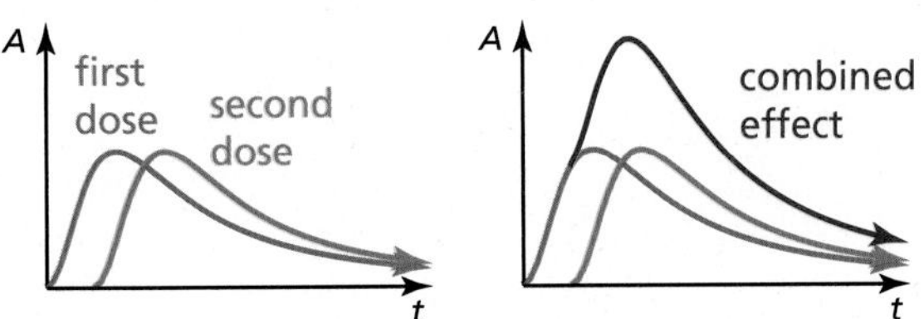

54. MP PATTERNS Find the next two expressions in the pattern shown. Then simplify all five expressions. What value do the expressions approach?

$$1 + \cfrac{1}{2 + \cfrac{1}{2}},\ 1 + \cfrac{1}{2 + \cfrac{1}{2 + \cfrac{1}{2}}},\ 1 + \cfrac{1}{2 + \cfrac{1}{2 + \cfrac{1}{2 + \cfrac{1}{2}}}},\ \ldots$$

REVIEW & REFRESH

WATCH

In Exercises 55 and 56, graph the function. Find the domain and range.

55. $g(x) = \frac{4}{x} + 1$

56. $g(x) = \frac{-2}{x - 6}$

57. Tell whether x and y show *direct variation, inverse variation,* or *neither*.

x	6	8	10	12	14
y	15	20	25	30	35

In Exercises 58 and 59, find the product or quotient.

58. $\frac{2x}{4x} \cdot \frac{1}{3y}$

59. $\frac{xy^3}{x^2} \div \frac{y^4}{x^3}$

60. MODELING REAL LIFE An app store sells 60 apps each day and charges \$8.00 per download. For each \$0.50 decrease in price, the store sells 10 more apps. How much should the store charge to maximize daily revenue?

In Exercises 61 and 62, solve the equation.

61. $|m + 2| = 0$

62. $\left|\frac{x}{3}\right| = 3$

63. Write an equation of the parabola.

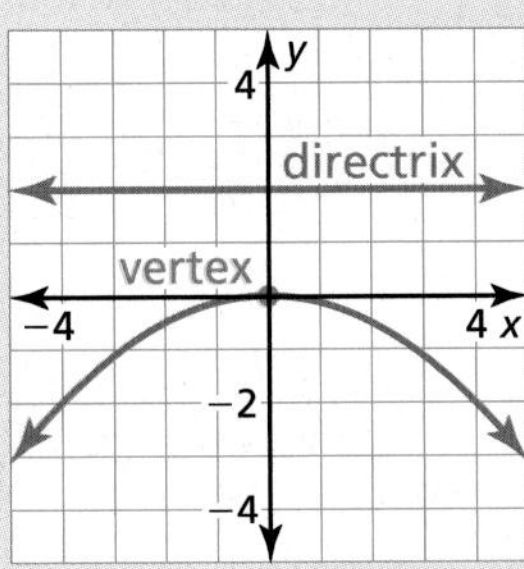

64. Graph $y \geq 2x^2 - 5x - 3$

In Exercises 65 and 66, describe the transformation of f represented by g. Then graph each function.

65. $f(x) = \sqrt{x}$, $g(x) = \sqrt{x} + 1$

66. $f(x) = \sqrt{x}$, $g(x) = 2\sqrt{x - 3}$

In Exercises 67 and 68, find the sum or difference.

67. $\frac{11}{4x} - \frac{1}{2x}$

68. $\frac{1}{x^3} + \frac{5}{4x}$

7.5 Solving Rational Equations

Learning Target Solve rational equations.

Success Criteria
- I can solve rational equations by cross multiplying and by using least common denominators.
- I can identify extraneous solutions of rational equations.
- I can solve real-life problems using inverses of rational functions.

EXPLORE IT! Solving Rational Equations

Work with a partner.

a. Match each equation with its related graph. Explain your reasoning. Then use the graph to approximate the solution(s) of the equation.

i. $\frac{2}{x-1} = 1$ **ii.** $\frac{-x-1}{x-3} = x + 1$

iii. $\frac{1}{x} = x^2$ **iv.** $\frac{1}{x} = \frac{-1}{x-2}$

A.
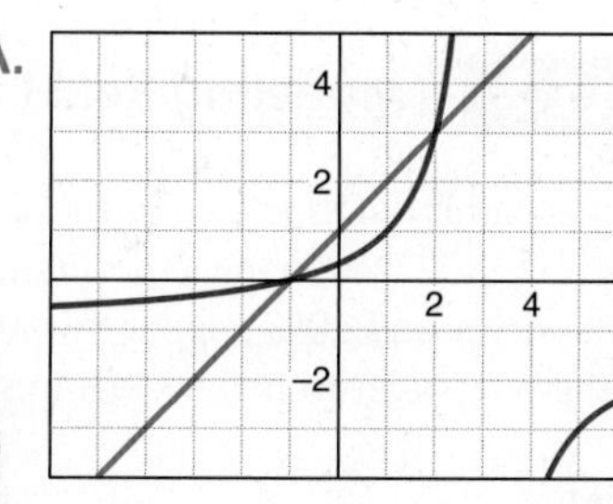

B.
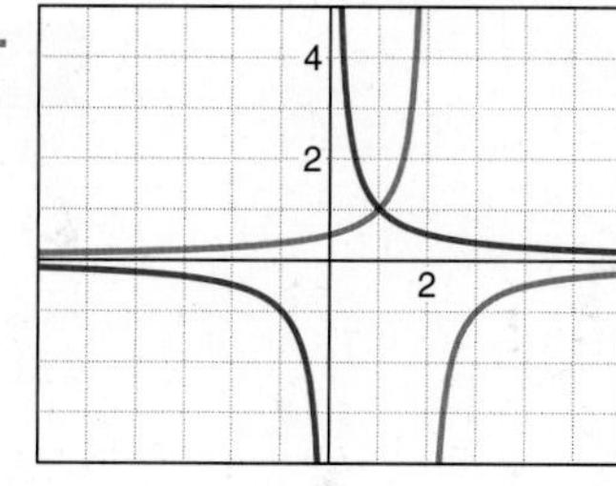

C.
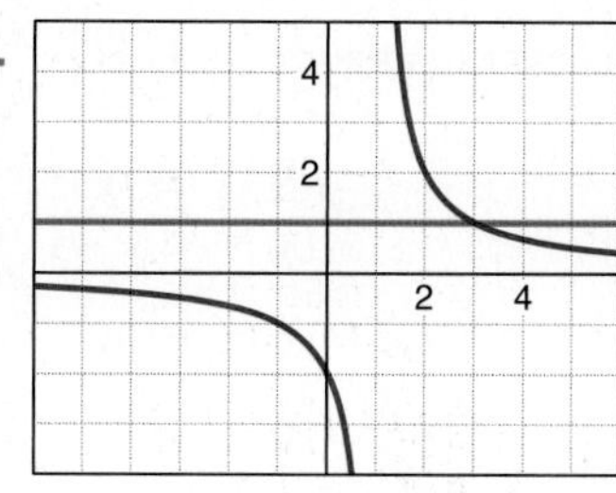

D.
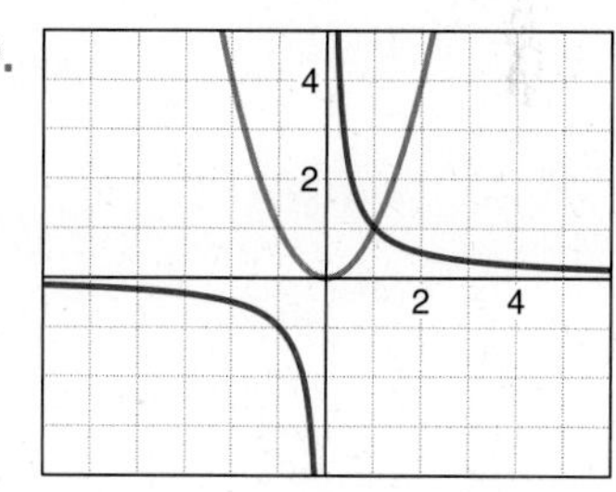

b. Solve the proportion $\frac{3}{4} = \frac{8}{x}$ algebraically. Explain your method. Then solve the rational equations in part (a) using the same algebraic method. Compare your answers with your approximations in part (a).

c. A student solves the equation $\frac{5x}{x^2-4} = \frac{3}{x+2}$ as shown. Explain the student's method. Is the answer correct? Explain.

$$\frac{5x}{x^2-4} = \frac{3}{x+2}$$
$$5x^2 + 10x = 3x^2 - 12$$
$$2x^2 + 10x + 12 = 0$$
$$2(x+3)(x+2) = 0$$
So, $x = -3$ and $x = -2$.

Math Practice
Evaluate Results
Why is it always important to check your solutions in the original equation?

Solving by Cross Multiplying

You can *cross multiply* to solve a rational equation when each side of the equation is a single rational expression.

EXAMPLE 1 **Solving a Rational Equation by Cross Multiplying** 

Solve $\frac{3}{x+1} = \frac{9}{4x+5}$.

SOLUTION

$\frac{3}{x+1} = \frac{9}{4x+5}$	Write original equation.
$3(4x+5) = 9(x+1)$	Cross multiply.
$12x + 15 = 9x + 9$	Distributive Property
$3x + 15 = 9$	Subtract $9x$ from each side.
$3x = -6$	Subtract 15 from each side.
$x = -2$	Divide each side by 3.

▶ The solution is $x = -2$. Check this in the original equation.

Check

$$\frac{3}{-2+1} \stackrel{?}{=} \frac{9}{4(-2)+5}$$

$$\frac{3}{-1} \stackrel{?}{=} \frac{9}{-3}$$

$$-3 = -3 \checkmark$$

EXAMPLE 2 **Modeling Real Life**  

An *alloy* is formed by mixing two or more metals. Sterling silver is an alloy composed of 92.5% silver and 7.5% copper by weight. You have 15 ounces of 800 grade silver, which is 80% silver and 20% copper by weight. How much pure silver should you mix with the 800 grade silver to make sterling silver?

SOLUTION

$$\text{percent of copper in mixture} = \frac{\text{weight of copper in mixture}}{\text{total weight of mixture}}$$

$\frac{7.5}{100} = \frac{(0.2)(15)}{15+x}$	x is the amount of silver added.
$7.5(15+x) = 100(0.2)(15)$	Cross multiply.
$112.5 + 7.5x = 300$	Simplify.
$7.5x = 187.5$	Subtract 112.5 from each side.
$x = 25$	Divide each side by 7.5.

▶ You should mix 25 ounces of pure silver with the 15 ounces of 800 grade silver.

SELF-ASSESSMENT 1 I do not understand. 2 I can do it with help. 3 I can do it on my own. 4 I can teach someone else.

Solve the equation by cross multiplying. Check your solution(s).

1. $\frac{3}{5x} = \frac{2}{x-7}$

2. $\frac{-4}{x+3} = \frac{5}{x-3}$

3. $\frac{1}{2x+5} = \frac{x}{11x+8}$

4. **WHAT IF?** You have 12 ounces of an alloy that is 90% silver and 10% copper by weight. How much pure silver should you mix with the alloy to make sterling silver?

GO DIGITAL

Solving by Using the Least Common Denominator

When a rational equation is not expressed as a proportion, you can solve it by multiplying each side of the equation by the least common denominator of the rational expressions.

EXAMPLE 3 Solving Rational Equations by Using the LCD

Solve each equation.

a. $\frac{5}{x} + \frac{7}{4} = -\frac{9}{x}$ **b.** $1 - \frac{8}{x-5} = \frac{3}{x}$

SOLUTION

a. $\frac{5}{x} + \frac{7}{4} = -\frac{9}{x}$ Write original equation.

$4x\left(\frac{5}{x} + \frac{7}{4}\right) = 4x\left(-\frac{9}{x}\right)$ Multiply each side by the LCD, $4x$.

$20 + 7x = -36$ Simplify.

$7x = -56$ Subtract 20 from each side.

$x = -8$ Divide each side by 7.

▶ The solution is $x = -8$. Check this in the original equation.

Check

$\frac{5}{-8} + \frac{7}{4} \stackrel{?}{=} -\frac{9}{-8}$

$-\frac{5}{8} + \frac{14}{8} \stackrel{?}{=} \frac{9}{8}$

$\frac{9}{8} = \frac{9}{8}$ ✓

b. $1 - \frac{8}{x-5} = \frac{3}{x}$ Write original equation.

$x(x-5)\left(1 - \frac{8}{x-5}\right) = x(x-5) \cdot \frac{3}{x}$ Multiply each side by the LCD, $x(x - 5)$.

$x(x-5) - 8x = 3(x-5)$ Simplify.

$x^2 - 5x - 8x = 3x - 15$ Distributive Property

$x^2 - 16x + 15 = 0$ Write in standard form.

$(x-1)(x-15) = 0$ Factor.

$x = 1$ or $x = 15$ Zero-Product Property

▶ The solutions are $x = 1$ and $x = 15$. Check these in the original equation.

Check

$1 - \frac{8}{1-5} \stackrel{?}{=} \frac{3}{1}$	Substitute for x.	$1 - \frac{8}{15-5} \stackrel{?}{=} \frac{3}{15}$
$1 + 2 \stackrel{?}{=} 3$	Simplify.	$1 - \frac{4}{5} \stackrel{?}{=} \frac{1}{5}$
$3 = 3$ ✓		$\frac{1}{5} = \frac{1}{5}$ ✓

SELF-ASSESSMENT 1 I do not understand. 2 I can do it with help. 3 I can do it on my own. 4 I can teach someone else.

Solve the equation by using the LCD. Check your solution(s).

5. $\frac{15}{x} + \frac{4}{5} = \frac{7}{x}$

6. $\frac{3x}{x+1} - \frac{5}{2x} = \frac{3}{2x}$

7. $\frac{4x+1}{x+1} = \frac{12}{x^2-1} + 3$

When solving a rational equation, you may obtain solutions that are extraneous. Be sure to check for extraneous solutions by checking your solutions in the *original* equation.

EXAMPLE 4 Solving an Equation with an Extraneous Solution

Solve $\frac{6}{x-3} = \frac{8x^2}{x^2-9} - \frac{4x}{x+3}$.

SOLUTION

Write each denominator in factored form. The LCD is $(x+3)(x-3)$.

$$\frac{6}{x-3} = \frac{8x^2}{(x+3)(x-3)} - \frac{4x}{x+3}$$

$$(x+3)(x-3) \cdot \frac{6}{x-3} = (x+3)(x-3) \cdot \frac{8x^2}{(x+3)(x-3)} - (x+3)(x-3) \cdot \frac{4x}{x+3}$$

$$6(x+3) = 8x^2 - 4x(x-3)$$

$$6x + 18 = 8x^2 - 4x^2 + 12x$$

$$0 = 4x^2 + 6x - 18$$

$$0 = 2x^2 + 3x - 9$$

$$0 = (2x-3)(x+3)$$

$$2x - 3 = 0 \quad \text{or} \quad x + 3 = 0$$

$$x = \frac{3}{2} \quad \text{or} \quad x = -3$$

Check

Check $x = \frac{3}{2}$:

$$\frac{6}{\frac{3}{2} - 3} \stackrel{?}{=} \frac{8\left(\frac{3}{2}\right)^2}{\left(\frac{3}{2}\right)^2 - 9} - \frac{4\left(\frac{3}{2}\right)}{\frac{3}{2} + 3}$$

$$\frac{6}{-\frac{3}{2}} \stackrel{?}{=} \frac{18}{-\frac{27}{4}} - \frac{6}{\frac{9}{2}}$$

$$-4 \stackrel{?}{=} -\frac{8}{3} - \frac{4}{3}$$

$$-4 = -4 \checkmark$$

Check $x = -3$:

$$\frac{6}{-3-3} \stackrel{?}{=} \frac{8(-3)^2}{(-3)^2 - 9} - \frac{4(-3)}{-3+3}$$

$$\frac{6}{-6} \stackrel{?}{=} \frac{72}{0} - \frac{-12}{0} \ \text{✗}$$

Division by zero is undefined.

ANOTHER WAY

You can also graph each side of the equation and find the *x*-value where the graphs intersect.

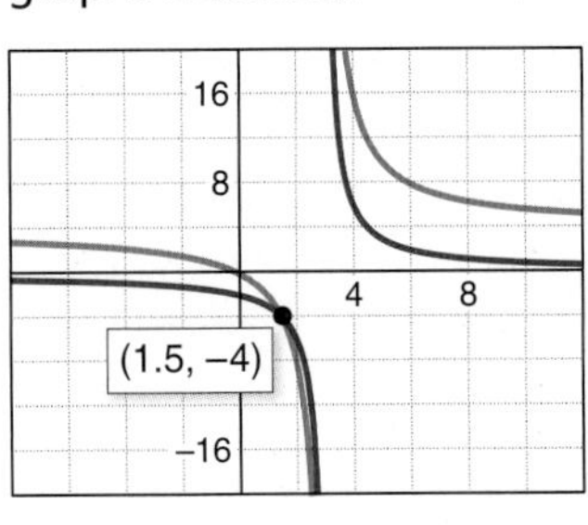

▶ The apparent solution $x = -3$ is extraneous. So, the only solution is $x = \frac{3}{2}$.

SELF-ASSESSMENT

1 I do not understand. 2 I can do it with help. 3 I can do it on my own. 4 I can teach someone else.

Solve the equation. Check your solution(s).

8. $\frac{3}{x-1} - 1 = \frac{6}{x^2-1}$

9. $\frac{9}{x-2} + \frac{6x}{x+2} = \frac{9x^2}{x^2-4}$

Using Inverses of Functions

EXAMPLE 5 Finding the Inverse of a Rational Function

Consider the function $f(x) = \dfrac{2}{x+3}$. Determine whether the inverse of f is a function. Then find the inverse.

SOLUTION

Graph the function f. Notice that no horizontal line intersects the graph more than once. So, the inverse of f is a function. Find the inverse.

$y = \dfrac{2}{x+3}$ Set y equal to $f(x)$.

$x = \dfrac{2}{y+3}$ Switch x and y.

$x(y+3) = 2$ Cross multiply.

$y + 3 = \dfrac{2}{x}$ Divide each side by x.

$y = \dfrac{2}{x} - 3$ Subtract 3 from each side.

$f(x) = \dfrac{2}{x+3}$

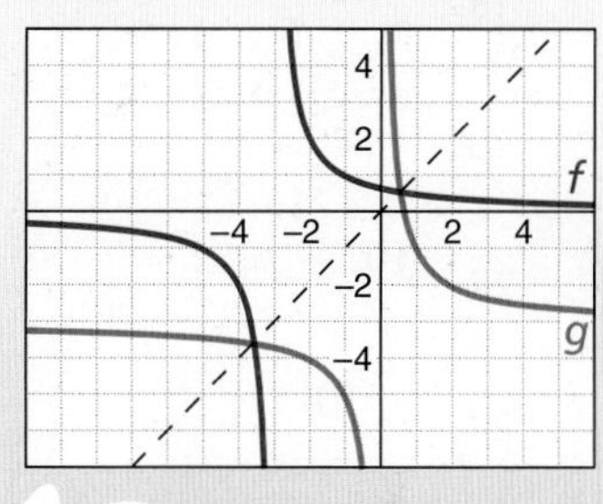

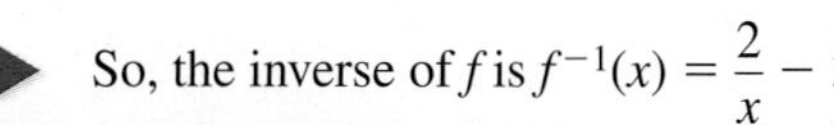

▶ So, the inverse of f is $f^{-1}(x) = \dfrac{2}{x} - 3$.

EXAMPLE 6 Modeling Real Life

In Section 7.2 Example 5, you wrote the function $c(x) = \dfrac{50x + 1000}{x}$ to represent the average cost (in dollars) of making x prosthetic hands using a 3-D printer. How many hands must be printed for the average cost per hand to fall to \$90?

SOLUTION

Method 1 Substitute 90 for $c(x)$ and solve.

$$90 = \frac{50x + 1000}{x}$$

$$90x = 50x + 1000$$

$$40x = 1000$$

$$x = 25$$

Method 2 Find $c^{-1}(x)$. Then evaluate $c^{-1}(90)$.

$y = \dfrac{50x + 1000}{x}$ Set y equal to $c(x)$.

$x = \dfrac{50y + 1000}{y}$ Switch x and y.

$xy = 50y + 1000$ Cross multiply.

$y = \dfrac{1000}{x - 50}$ Solve for y.

The inverse of c is $c^{-1}(x) = \dfrac{1000}{x - 50}$.

$$c^{-1}(90) = \frac{1000}{90 - 50} = 25$$

▶ So, the average cost falls to \$90 per hand after 25 hands are printed.

SELF-ASSESSMENT 1 I do not understand. 2 I can do it with help. 3 I can do it on my own. 4 I can teach someone else.

10. Consider the function $f(x) = \dfrac{1}{x} - 2$. Determine whether the inverse of f is a function. Then find the inverse.

11. WHAT IF? How does the answer in Example 6 change when $c(x) = \dfrac{50x + 800}{x}$?

7.5 Practice WITH CalcChat® AND CalcView®

In Exercises 1–8, solve the equation by cross multiplying. Check your solution(s). *Example 1*

1. $\frac{4}{2x} = \frac{5}{x+6}$

2. $\frac{9}{3x} = \frac{4}{x+2}$

3. $\frac{6}{x-1} = \frac{9}{x+1}$

4. $\frac{8}{3x-2} = \frac{2}{x-1}$

5. $\frac{x}{2x+7} = \frac{x-5}{x-1}$

6. $\frac{-2}{x-1} = \frac{x-8}{x+1}$

7. $\frac{x^2-3}{x+2} = \frac{x-3}{2}$

8. $\frac{-1}{x-3} = \frac{x-4}{x^2-27}$

9. **MP PROBLEM SOLVING** A game show contestant has answered 37 out of 44 trivia questions correctly so far. Solve the equation $\frac{90}{100} = \frac{37+x}{44+x}$ to find the number of consecutive questions the contestant needs to answer correctly to raise the correct answer percentage to 90%.

10. **MP PROBLEM SOLVING** Your friend has 12 hits out of 60 times at-bat so far this baseball season. Solve the equation $0.360 = \frac{12+x}{60+x}$ to find the number of consecutive hits your friend needs to raise his batting average to 0.360.

11. **MODELING REAL LIFE** Brass is an alloy composed of 55% copper and 45% zinc by weight. You have 25 ounces of copper. How many ounces of zinc do you need to make brass? *Example 2*

12. **MODELING REAL LIFE** You have 0.2 liter of an acid solution whose acid concentration is 16 moles per liter. You want to dilute the solution with water so that its acid concentration is only 12 moles per liter. Use the given model to determine how many liters of water you should add to the solution.

$$\text{Concentration of new solution} = \frac{\text{Concentration of original solution} \cdot \text{Volume of original solution}}{\text{Volume of original solution} + \text{Volume of water added}}$$

MP STRUCTURE In Exercises 13–16, identify the LCD of the rational expressions in the equation.

13. $\frac{x}{x+3} + \frac{1}{x} = \frac{3}{x}$

14. $\frac{5x}{x-1} - \frac{7}{x} = \frac{9}{x}$

15. $\frac{2}{x+1} + \frac{x}{x+4} = \frac{1}{2}$

16. $\frac{4}{x+9} + \frac{3x}{2x-1} = \frac{10}{3}$

In Exercises 17–28, solve the equation by using the LCD. Check your solution(s). *Examples 3 and 4*

17. $\frac{3}{2} + \frac{1}{x} = 2$

18. $\frac{2}{3x} + \frac{1}{6} = \frac{4}{3x}$

19. $\frac{8}{x-4} + \frac{4}{x} = \frac{2x}{x-4}$

20. $\frac{2}{x-3} + \frac{1}{x} = \frac{x-1}{x-3}$

21. $\frac{6x}{x+4} + 4 = \frac{2x+2}{x-1}$

22. $\frac{10}{x} + 3 = \frac{x+9}{x-4}$

23. $\frac{18}{x^2-3x} - \frac{6}{x-3} = \frac{5}{x}$

24. $\frac{10}{x^2-2x} + \frac{4}{x} = \frac{5}{x-2}$

25. $\frac{x+1}{x+6} + \frac{1}{x} = \frac{2x+1}{x+6}$

26. $\frac{x+3}{x-3} + \frac{x}{x-5} = \frac{x+5}{x-5}$

27. $\frac{5}{x} - 2 = \frac{2}{x+3}$

28. $\frac{5}{x^2+x-6} = 2 + \frac{x-3}{x-2}$

ERROR ANALYSIS In Exercises 29 and 30, describe and correct the error in the first step of solving the equation.

29.

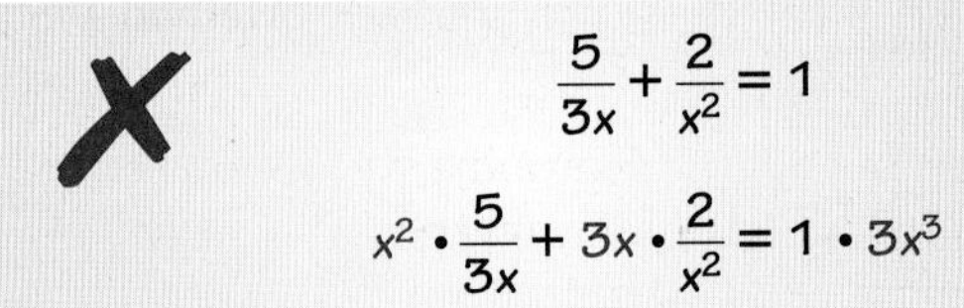

30.

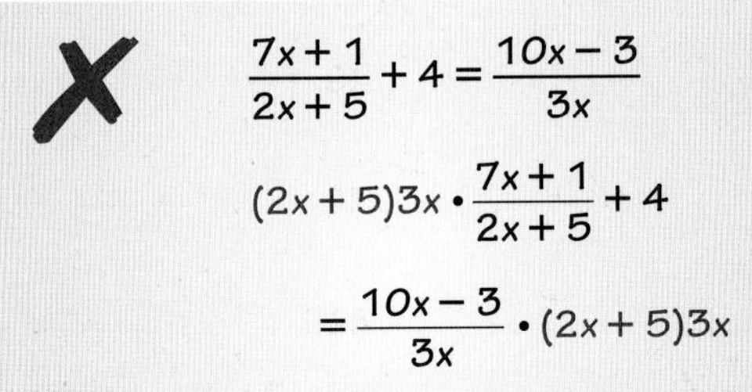

31. **COLLEGE PREP** Which of the following equations have an extraneous solution? Select all that apply.

(A) $\frac{x}{2x+3} = \frac{x-2}{x-6}$

(B) $\frac{5}{x-2} - \frac{2}{x} = \frac{x+3}{x-2}$

(C) $\frac{x+8}{x-4} - 1 = \frac{6}{x}$

(D) $\frac{15}{x^2-3x} - \frac{5}{x-3} = \frac{7}{x}$

32. **OPEN-ENDED** Give an example of a rational equation that you would solve using cross multiplication and one that you would solve using the LCD. Explain your reasoning.

33. **MP PROBLEM SOLVING** You can clean a park in 2 hours. Working together, you and your friend can clean the park in 1.2 hours.

a. Let t be the time (in hours) your friend takes to clean the park when working alone. Complete the table. (*Hint*: (Work done) = (Work rate) × (Time))

	Work rate	Time	Work done
You	$\frac{1 \text{ park}}{2 \text{ hours}}$	1.2 hours	
Friend		1.2 hours	

b. Explain what the sum of the expressions represents in the last column. Write and solve an equation to find how long your friend takes to clean the park when working alone.

34. **DIG DEEPER** A kayaker paddles upstream for 2 miles and downstream for 2 miles. The speed of the current is 1 mile per hour. The entire trip takes 2 hours and 40 minutes. Write and solve an equation to find the average speed at which the kayaker paddles.

In Exercises 35–42, determine whether the inverse of f is a function. Then find the inverse. *Example 5*

35. $f(x) = \frac{2}{x - 4}$

36. $f(x) = \frac{7}{x + 6}$

37. $f(x) = \frac{3}{x} - 2$

38. $f(x) = \frac{5}{x} - 6$

39. $f(x) = \frac{4}{11 - 2x}$

40. $f(x) = \frac{8}{9 + 5x}$

41. $f(x) = \frac{1}{x^2} + 4$

42. $f(x) = \frac{1}{x^4} - 7$

43. **MODELING REAL LIFE** The recommended percent (in decimal form) of nitrogen (by volume) in the air that a diver breathes is given by $p(d) = \frac{105.07}{d + 33}$, where d is the depth (in feet) of the diver. Find the depth when the air contains 47% recommended nitrogen by (i) solving an equation, and (ii) using the inverse of the function. *Example 6*

GO DIGITAL

44. **MODELING REAL LIFE** The model shown gives the cost of fueling a car for 1 year. Last year your friend drove 9000 miles, paid an average of \$2.89 per gallon of gasoline, and spent a total of \$1239 on gasoline.

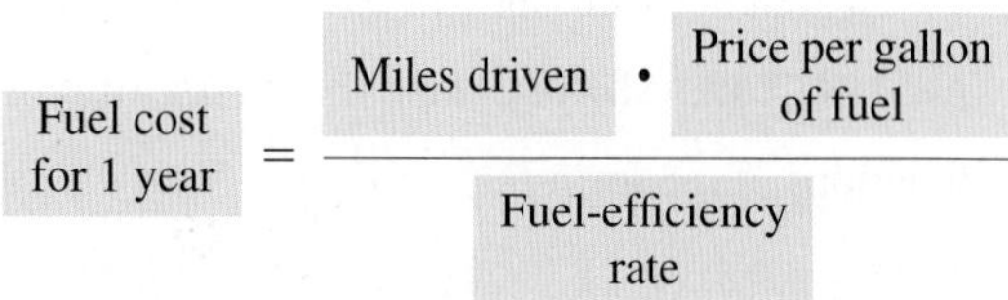

a. Use the model to write a function c that represents the fuel cost for 1 year in terms of the fuel-efficiency rate r.

b. Find the fuel-efficiency rate of the car by (i) solving an equation and (ii) using the inverse of the function you wrote in part (a).

MP USING TOOLS In Exercises 45–48, use technology to solve the equation $f(x) = g(x)$.

45. $f(x) = \frac{2}{3x}$, $g(x) = x$

46. $f(x) = -\frac{3}{5x}$, $g(x) = -x$

47. $f(x) = \frac{1}{x} + 1$, $g(x) = x^2$

48. $f(x) = \frac{2}{x} + 1$, $g(x) = x^2 + 1$

49. **CONNECTING CONCEPTS** *Golden rectangles* are rectangles for which the ratio of the width w to the length ℓ is equal to the ratio of ℓ to $\ell + w$. The ratio of the length to the width for these rectangles is called the golden ratio. Find the value of the golden ratio using a rectangle with a width of 1 unit.

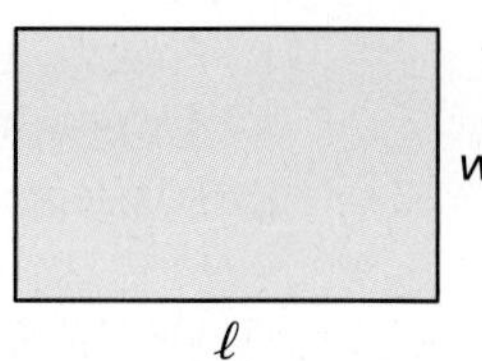

50. **HOW DO YOU SEE IT?**
Use the graph to identify the solution(s) of $\frac{4(x-1)}{x-1} = \frac{2x-2}{x+1}$. Explain your reasoning.

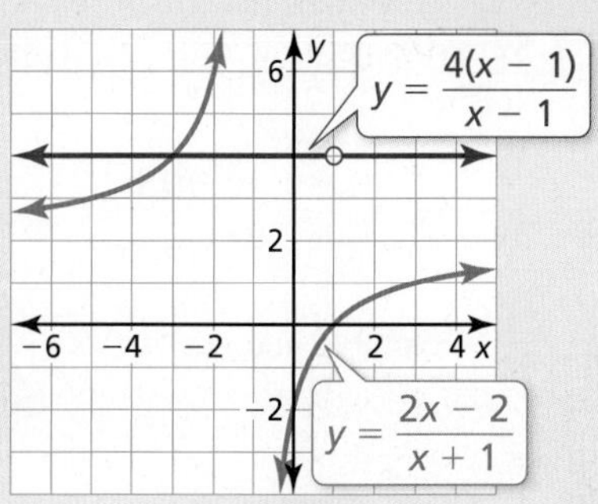

MP STRUCTURE In Exercises 51 and 52, find the inverse of the function. (*Hint:* Try rewriting the function by using either inspection or long division.)

51. $f(x) = \dfrac{3x + 1}{x - 4}$ **52.** $f(x) = \dfrac{4x - 7}{2x + 3}$

53. ABSTRACT REASONING Find the inverse of rational functions of the form $f(x) = \dfrac{ax + b}{cx + d}$. Verify your answer is correct by using it to find $f^{-1}(x)$ in Exercises 51 and 52.

54. THOUGHT PROVOKING
Is it possible to write a rational equation that has the given number of solutions? Justify your answers.

a. no solution **b.** exactly one solution

c. exactly two solutions

d. infinitely many solutions

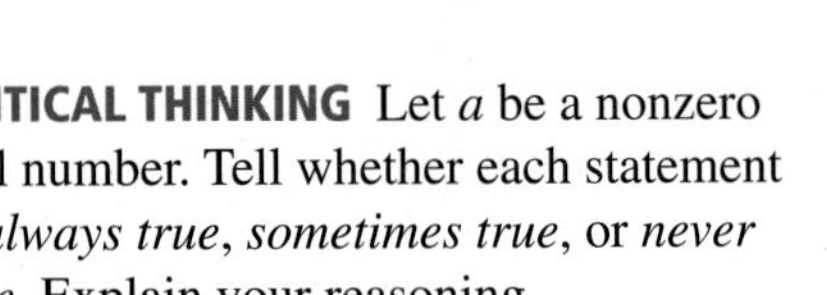

55. CRITICAL THINKING Let a be a nonzero real number. Tell whether each statement is *always true*, *sometimes true*, or *never true*. Explain your reasoning.

a. For the equation $\dfrac{1}{x - a} = \dfrac{x}{x - a}$, $x = a$ is an extraneous solution.

b. The equation $\dfrac{3}{x - a} = \dfrac{x}{x - a}$ has exactly one solution.

c. The equation $\dfrac{1}{x - a} = \dfrac{2}{x + a} + \dfrac{2a}{x^2 - a^2}$ has no solution.

56. MAKING AN ARGUMENT Is it possible for a rational equation of the form $\dfrac{x - a}{b} = \dfrac{x - c}{d}$, where a, b, c, and d are constants, $b \neq 0$, and $d \neq 0$, to have extraneous solutions? Explain your reasoning.

REVIEW & REFRESH

In Exercises 57 and 58, evaluate the function for the given value of x.

57. $f(x) = x^3 - 2x + 7;\ x = -2$

58. $g(x) = -2x^4 + 7x^3 + x - 2;\ x = 3$

59. MODELING REAL LIFE The linear function $t = 2p$ represents the total cost t (in dollars) of p pounds of broccoli.

a. Find the domain of the function. Is the domain discrete or continuous? Explain.

b. Graph the function using its domain.

In Exercises 60–63, perform the operation.

60. $\dfrac{x^2}{x + 2} - \dfrac{4}{x + 2}$

61. $\dfrac{x - 1}{-2x + 6} + \dfrac{2x + 3}{x^2 + 3x - 18}$

62. $\dfrac{x^2 + 5x - 14}{4x^3 + 28x^2} \div \dfrac{x - 2}{2x^3}$

63. $\dfrac{2x^2 + 4x}{x^2 - 3x - 10} \cdot \dfrac{x^2 - 8x + 15}{2x}$

64. Let $f(x) = 3x^2 + 1$ and $g(x) = \sqrt{x - 4}$. Find $f(g(8))$ and $g(f(-2))$.

MP STRUCTURE In Exercises 65–68, match the function with its graph. Explain your reasoning.

65. $g(x) = \dfrac{-2}{x}$ **66.** $f(x) = \dfrac{3}{x} + 2$

67. $y = \dfrac{-2}{x + 3} - 2$ **68.** $h(x) = \dfrac{2x + 2}{3x + 1}$

A.

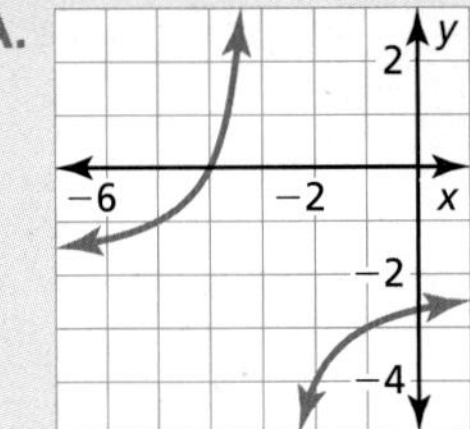

B.

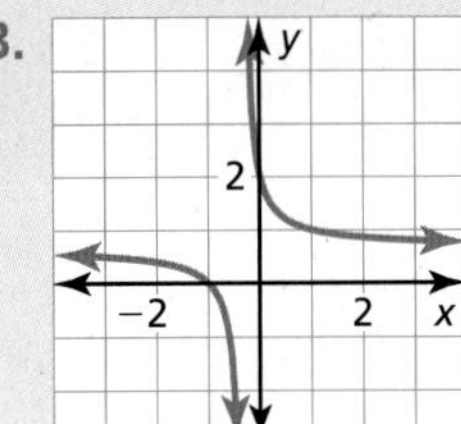

C.

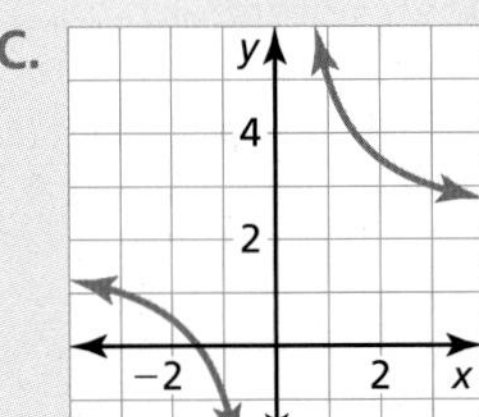

D.

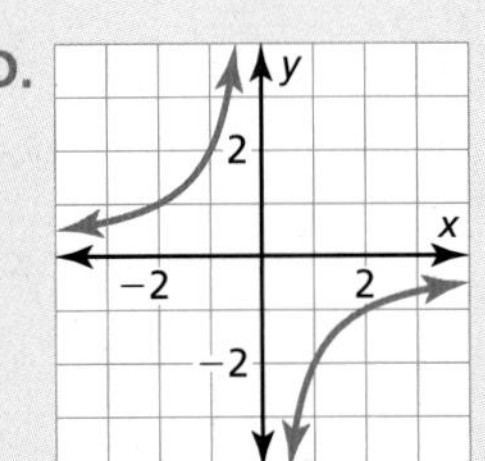

In Exercises 69 and 70, solve the equation. Check your solution(s).

69. $\dfrac{-3}{x - 1} = \dfrac{6}{x + 4}$

70. $\dfrac{x}{x^2 - 2x} + \dfrac{4}{x} = \dfrac{x - 4}{x - 2}$

7 Chapter Review WITH CalcChat®

Chapter Learning Target Understand rational functions.

Chapter Success Criteria

- ◆ I can determine whether an equation represents direct variation or inverse variation.
- ◆ I can graph rational functions.
- ■ I can add, subtract, multiply, and divide rational expressions.
- ■ I can solve rational equations.

◆ Surface
■ Deep

SELF-ASSESSMENT 1 I do not understand. 2 I can do it with help. 3 I can do it on my own. 4 I can teach someone else.

7.1 Inverse Variation (pp. 355–360)

Vocabulary

direct variation
constant of variation
inverse variation

Learning Target: Understand inverse variation.

Tell whether *x* and *y* show *direct variation*, *inverse variation*, or *neither*.

1. $xy = 5$
2. $5y = 6x$
3. $15 = \frac{x}{y}$
4. $y - 3 = 2x$
5.

x	7	11	15	20
y	35	55	75	100

6.

x	5	8	10	20
y	6.4	4	3.2	1.6

The variables *x* and *y* vary inversely. Use the given values to write an equation relating *x* and *y*. Then find *y* when $x = -3$.

7. $x = 1, y = 5$
8. $x = -4, y = -6$
9. $x = \frac{5}{2}, y = 18$
10. $x = -12, y = \frac{2}{3}$

7.2 Graphing Rational Functions (pp. 361–368)

Vocabulary

rational function

Learning Target: Describe and graph rational functions.

Graph the function. State the domain and range.

11. $y = \frac{4}{x - 3}$
12. $y = \frac{1}{x + 5} + 2$
13. $f(x) = \frac{3x - 2}{x - 4}$
14. $y = -\frac{1}{x} - 1$
15. A teacher orders tablet stands. There is a delivery fee of \$10 and each stand costs \$2. How many stands must the teacher buy for the average cost per stand to fall to \$2.50?

7.3 Multiplying and Dividing Rational Expressions (pp. 369–376)

Learning Target: Multiply and divide rational expressions.

Vocabulary

rational expression
simplified form of a rational expression

Find the product or quotient.

16. $\frac{80x^4}{y^3} \cdot \frac{xy}{5x^2}$

17. $\frac{x-3}{2x-8} \cdot \frac{6x^2-96}{x^2-9}$

18. $\frac{16x^2-8x+1}{x^3-7x^2+12x} \div \frac{20x^2-5x}{15x^3}$

19. $\frac{x^2-13x+40}{x^2-2x-15} \div (x^2-5x-24)$

20. Find an expression that completes the equation below.

$$\frac{3-x}{x^2+3x-18} \div \frac{\blacksquare}{x^2+7x+6} = x+1$$

21. What is the domain of $g(x) = \frac{2+x}{8-2x^2}$?

7.4 Adding and Subtracting Rational Expressions (pp. 377–384)

Learning Target: Add and subtract rational expressions.

Vocabulary

complex fraction

Find the sum or difference.

22. $\frac{5}{6(x+3)} + \frac{x+4}{2x}$

23. $\frac{5x}{x+8} + \frac{4x-9}{x^2+5x-24}$

24. $\frac{x+2}{x^2+4x+3} - \frac{5x}{x^2-9}$

25. $\frac{1}{2} + \frac{x^2+4}{x-2}$

Rewrite the function in the form $g(x) = \frac{a}{x-h} + k$. Graph the function. Describe the graph of g as a transformation of the graph of $f(x) = \frac{a}{x}$.

26. $g(x) = \frac{5x+1}{x-3}$

27. $g(x) = \frac{4x+2}{x+7}$

28. $g(x) = \frac{9x-10}{x-1}$

29. $g(x) = \frac{-1}{2+x}$

30. Let f be the focal length of a thin camera lens, p be the distance between the lens and an object being photographed, and q be the distance between the lens and the film. For the photograph to be in focus, the variables should satisfy the lens equation to the right. Simplify the complex fraction.

$$f = \frac{1}{\frac{1}{p} + \frac{1}{q}}$$

31. Members of a student council prepare banners, balloons, and party bags for a school celebration. The table shows the rates of completion for the requested materials. Write a model in simplified form for the total time (in minutes) it takes to prepare the materials.

	Number	Rate (objects per minute)
Banners	10	x
Balloons	50	$x - 10$
Party Bags	80	$x + 5$

GO DIGITAL

7.5 Solving Rational Equations (pp. 385–392)

Learning Target: Solve rational equations.

Solve the equation. Check your solution(s).

32. $\frac{5}{x} = \frac{7}{x+2}$

33. $\frac{8(x-1)}{x^2-4} = \frac{4}{x+2}$

34. $\frac{2(x+7)}{x+4} - 2 = \frac{2x+20}{2x+8}$

35. $\frac{2}{x+1} = x - 1$

Determine whether the inverse of *f* is a function. Then find the inverse.

36. $f(x) = \frac{3}{x+6}$

37. $f(x) = \frac{10}{x-7}$

38. $f(x) = \frac{1}{x} + 8$

39. $f(x) = \frac{x}{1-x}$

40. You play 30 levels of a video game and achieve an expert rating in 11 of those levels. Solve the equation $0.5 = \frac{11+x}{30+x}$ to find the number of consecutive expert ratings you need to achieve so that you have achieved an expert rating on half of the levels you have played.

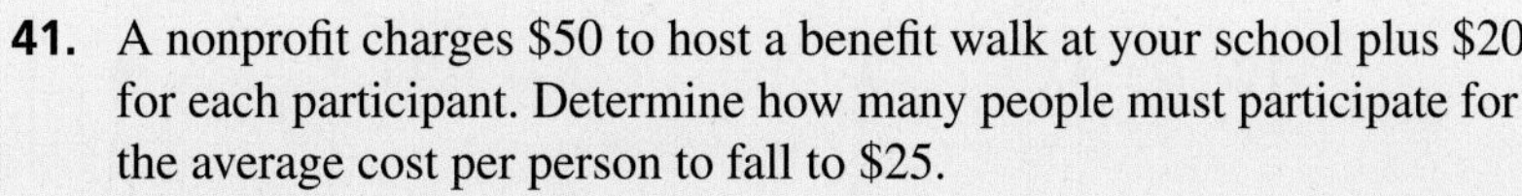

41. A nonprofit charges \$50 to host a benefit walk at your school plus \$20 for each participant. Determine how many people must participate for the average cost per person to fall to \$25.

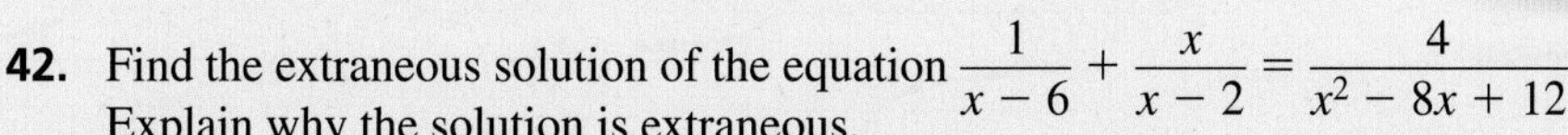

42. Find the extraneous solution of the equation $\frac{1}{x-6} + \frac{x}{x-2} = \frac{4}{x^2-8x+12}$. Explain why the solution is extraneous.

Mathematical Practices

Reason Abstractly and Quantitatively

Mathematically proficient students make sense of quantities and their relationships in problem situations.

1. In Exercise 47 on page 383, you calculated a monthly payment M for a given principal and interest rate. In general, what happens to the value of M when you double P? Explain your reasoning.

2. In Example 7 on page 373, total healthcare expenditures over time is described by a function. How does this model change if E were given in billions?

3. Consider the function $c(x) = \frac{ax+b}{x}$ where $c(x)$ is the average cost of purchasing x items for a dollars per item with an initial fee of b dollars. Create an average cost function for a situation for which the average cost is within 10 cents of \$50 after about 40 items are purchased. How do the relationships between a, b, and x affect your model?

7 Practice Test WITH CalcChat®

1. The variables x and y vary inversely, and $y = 2$ when $x = 5$. Write an equation that relates x and y. Then find y when $x = 4$.

2. Graph $f(x) = \dfrac{5x + 7}{x + 1}$. Find the domain and range.

Perform the indicated operation.

3. $\dfrac{3x^2y}{4x^3y^5} \div \dfrac{6y^2}{2xy^3}$

4. $\dfrac{3x}{x^2 + x - 12} - \dfrac{6}{x + 4}$

5. $\dfrac{x^2 - 3x - 4}{x^2 - 3x - 18} \bullet \dfrac{x - 6}{x + 1}$

6. $\dfrac{4}{x + 5} + \dfrac{2x}{x^2 - 25}$

Solve the equation.

7. $\dfrac{15}{2x - 1} = \dfrac{x + 11}{x - 1}$

8. $\dfrac{x}{x + 4} = \dfrac{16}{x^2 + 4x} + \dfrac{2}{x}$

The graph shows the function $y = \dfrac{1}{x - h} + k$. Determine whether the value of each constant h and k is *positive*, *negative*, or *zero*. Explain your reasoning.

9.

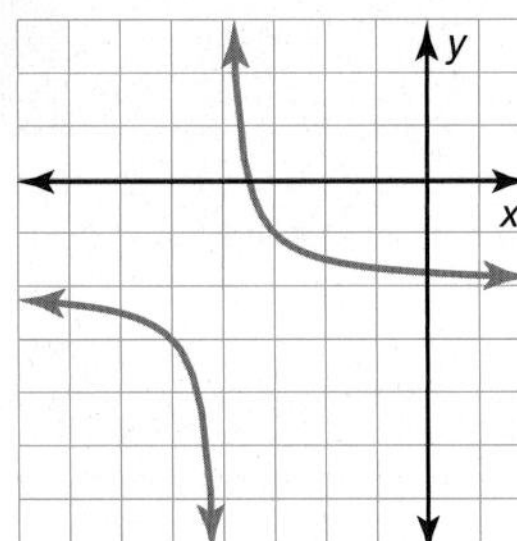

10.

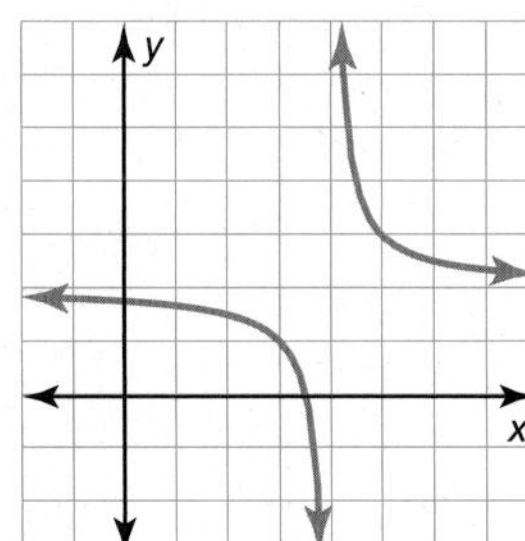

11.

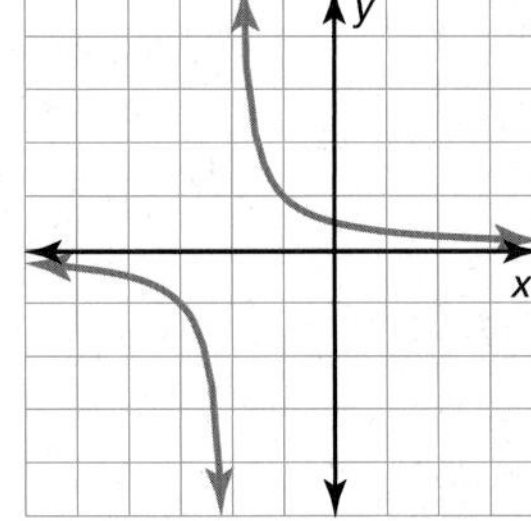

12. Let $g(x) = \dfrac{(x + 3)(x - 2)}{x + 3}$. Simplify $g(x)$. Determine whether the graph of $f(x) = x - 2$ and the graph of g are different. Explain your reasoning.

13. The asymptote of the graph of $g(x) = 3^x + 4$ is the same as the horizontal asymptote of the graph of $f(x) = \dfrac{ax + 1}{2x - 3}$. Find the value of a.

14. The initial cost to start a beekeeping business is \$500. The cost to collect, clean, bottle, and label the honey is \$1.25 per pound. How many pounds of honey must be produced for the average cost per pound to fall to \$1.75? Justify your answer.

15. You can use a simple lever to lift a 300-pound rock. The force F (in foot-pounds) needed to lift the rock is inversely related to the distance d (in feet) from the pivot point of the lever. To lift the rock, you need 60 pounds of force applied to a lever with a distance of 10 feet from the pivot point. What force is needed when you increase the distance to 15 feet from the pivot point? Justify your answer.

7 Performance Task
3-D Printing

In 3-D printing, a blueprint is created using computer-aided design software. The blueprint data is then uploaded to the printer, and an object is built by depositing material one layer at a time.

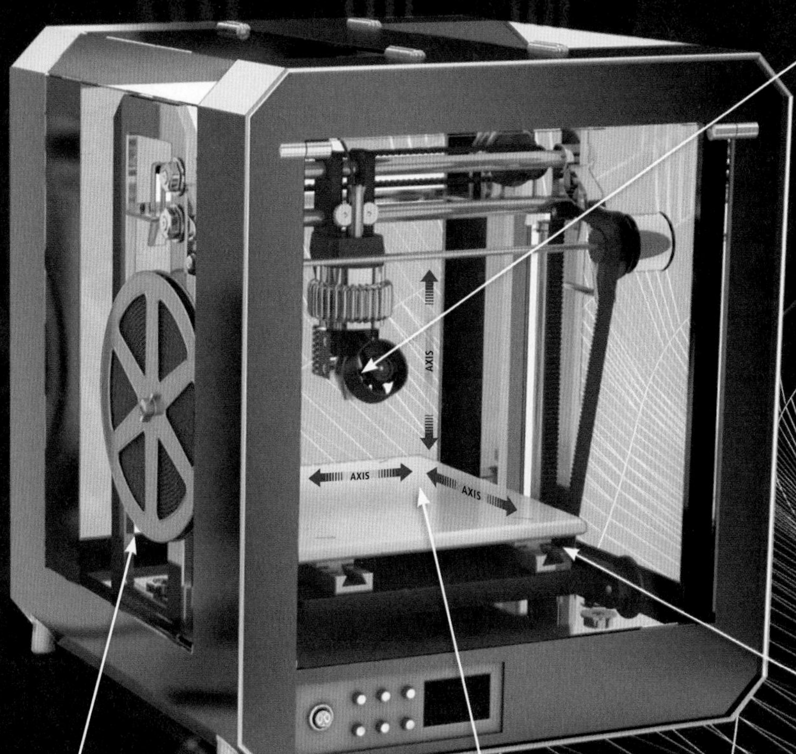

Print Head

Filament is heated and passes through the print head.

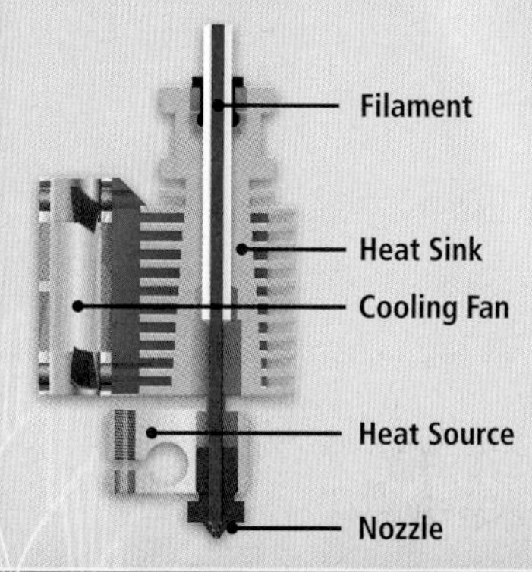

Print Bed

The print bed is the surface that objects are printed on.

Axes

Unlike ink printers, which use two axes, a 3-D printer moves along three axes.

Filament

Filaments used in 3-D printing include:

- plastics
- metals
- clay
- nylon
- wax
- and many others.

STARTING A BUSINESS

You want to start a business selling 3-D printed items. Choose an object to print and then sketch a design. Research the costs associated with starting your business, including the cost of the printer and the estimated cost of materials to print each copy of your object. Finally, determine the selling price of each copy.

Write and graph several functions that represent the following relationships. Describe each relationship as the number of copies increases.

- the average cost per copy when n copies are printed
- the cost of printing n copies compared to your revenue after selling n copies
- your average profit or loss per copy after printing and selling n copies

7 College and Career Readiness WITH CalcChat®

Tutorial videos are available for each exercise.

1. Which of the following functions are shown in the graph? Select all that apply.

Ⓐ $y = -2x^2 + 12x - 10$

Ⓑ $y = 2(x - 1)(x - 5)$

Ⓒ $y = -(x - 1)(x - 5)$

Ⓓ $y = -2(x - 3)^2 + 8$

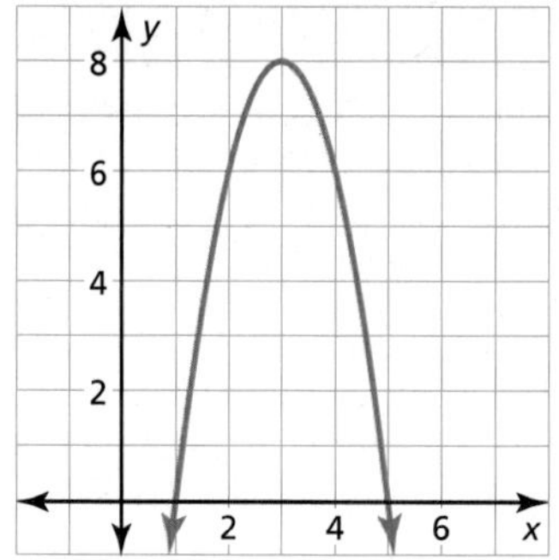

2. Which expression is the simplified form of $(x + 3)^2(x - 2) - (x^2 + 7x - 12)$?

Ⓐ $x^3 - 3x^2 + 2x - 6$

Ⓑ $x^3 + 3x^2 + 4x - 30$

Ⓒ $x^3 + 3x^2 - 10x - 6$

Ⓓ $-x^4 - 12x^3 - 35x^2 + 6x + 90$

3. The tables give the amounts A (in dollars) of money in two different bank accounts over time t (in years).

	Checking Account			
t	1	2	3	4
A	5000	5110	5220	5330

	Savings Account			
t	1	2	3	4
A	5000	5100	5202	5306.04

a. Determine the type of function represented by the data in each table.

b. Which account has a greater value after 10 years? after 15 years? Justify your answers.

4. The graph of a rational function of the form $f(x) = \dfrac{1}{x - h} + k$ has asymptotes that intersect in the second quadrant. Which of the following are possible values of h and k?

Ⓐ $h = -6, k = -3$

Ⓑ $h = -6, k = 3$

Ⓒ $h = 6, k = -3$

Ⓓ $h = 6, k = 3$

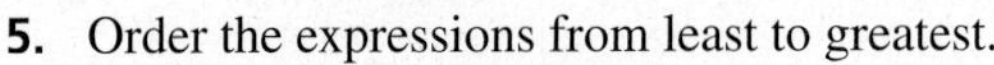

5. Order the expressions from least to greatest.

$(\sqrt{5})^3$ $\quad$ $(\sqrt[3]{125})^2$

$125^{3/2}$ $\quad$ $25^{1/2}$

6. A movie grosses \$37 million in its opening week. The weekly gross sales decrease by 30% each week. Which function represents the weekly gross sales y (in millions) x weeks after opening week?

Ⓐ $y = 37 - 0.3x$

Ⓑ $y = 37(0.3)^x$

Ⓒ $y = 37(0.7)^x$

Ⓓ $y = 37(1.3)^x$

7. The variable p varies inversely with the difference of q and r. Write an equation that relates p, q, and r. Then complete the table.

p	q	r
−12	20	17
	−2	−8
4		10
18	3	

8. A basketball player has made 13 out of 20 free throws so far this season. How many consecutive free throws must the basketball player make to raise the free throw average to 0.75? Justify your answer.

9. The graph of function f is shown. Let $g(x) = 3\sqrt[3]{x}$. Which function has a greater rate of change over the interval $x = 1$ to $x = 8$?

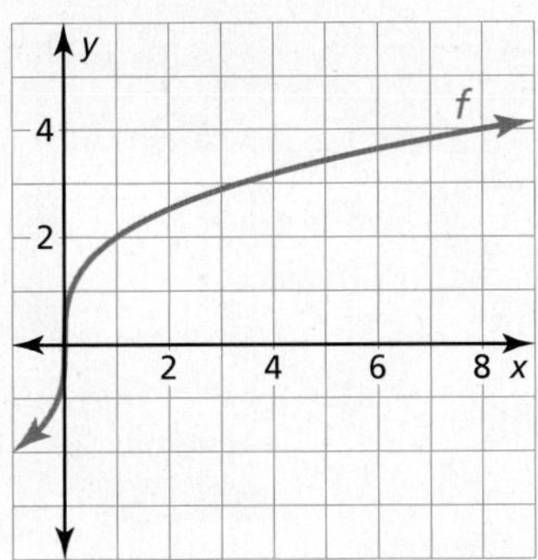

8 Probability

NATIONAL GEOGRAPHIC EXPLORER

Jeffrey Ian Rose

Dr. Jeffrey Ian Rose is a prehistoric archaeologist specializing in the Paleolithic and Neolithic periods of the Arabian Peninsula. His areas of interest include modern human origins, Neolithization, stone tool technology, human genetics, rock art, geoarchaeology, underwater archaeology, and comparative religions.

- When did the Paleolithic and Neolithic periods occur?
- Which modern countries are in the Arabian Peninsula?
- Describe different types of stone tools that have been discovered from the Neolithic period. Are these different from the stone tools that have been discovered from the Paleolithic period?

STEM

Archaeologists use probability to help determine where to excavate. In the Performance Task, you will help a team of archaeologists choose between three potential excavation sites.

Prehistoric Archaeology

Preparing for Chapter 8

Chapter Learning Target Understand probability.

Chapter Success Criteria
- ◆ I can define theoretical and experimental probability.
- ◆ I can use two-way tables to find probabilities.
- ■ I can compare independent and dependent events.
- ■ I can construct and interpret probability and binomial distributions.

◆ Surface
■ Deep

Chapter Vocabulary

Work with a partner. Discuss each of the vocabulary terms.

outcome
event
theoretical probability
geometric probability
experimental probability
independent events
dependent events
two-way table

Mathematical Practices

Model with Mathematics

Mathematically proficient students apply the mathematics they know to solve problems arising in everyday life, society, and the workplace.

Work with a partner. During an interview, an archaeologist is asked about the experimental probabilities of finding several different objects during past expeditions. The answers are recorded in the table.

Object	Probability
tools	*"about nine times out of ten"*
pottery	*"about 70 percent of the time"*
religious objects	*"about three tenths of the time"*
bones	*"one hundred percent"*
intact human skeleton	*"less than one percent"*
walls or other parts of structures	*"about one out of four times"*

1. Order the objects by probability from least to greatest. Explain your method.
2. Compare the probability that the archaeologist finds religious objects with the probability that the archaeologist does *not* find pottery. Explain your reasoning.
3. Describe the likelihood of each event in the table.

8 Prepare WITH CalcChat®

Using the Percent Proportion

Example 1 What percent of 12 is 9?

$$\frac{a}{w} = \frac{p}{100}$$ Write the percent proportion.

$$\frac{9}{12} = \frac{p}{100}$$ Substitute 9 for *a* and 12 for *w*.

$$100 \cdot \frac{9}{12} = 100 \cdot \frac{p}{100}$$ Multiplication Property of Equality

$$75 = p$$ Simplify.

► So, 9 is 75% of 12.

Write and solve a proportion to answer the question.

1. What percent of 30 is 6? **2.** What number is 68% of 25? **3.** 34.4 is what percent of 86?

Making a Histogram

Example 2 The frequency table shows the ages of people at a gym. Display the data in a histogram.

Age	Frequency
10–19	7
20–29	12
30–39	6
40–49	4
50–59	0
60–69	3

Step 1 Draw and label the axes.

Step 2 Draw a bar to represent the frequency of each interval.

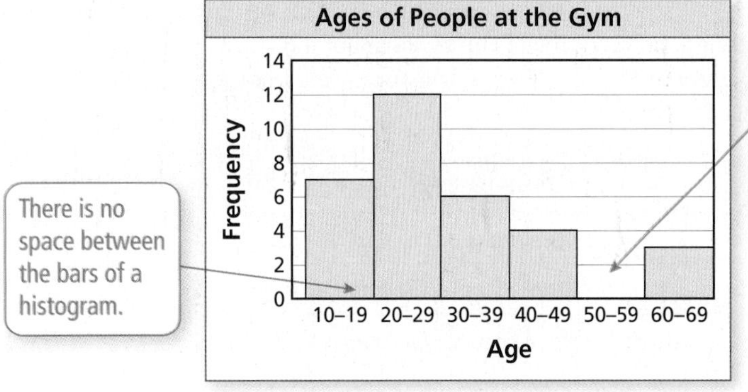

4. Display the data in a histogram.

	Movies Watched per Week		
Movies	0–1	2–3	4–5
Frequency	35	11	6

5. **MP REASONING** A sofa and an arm chair are the same price at a furniture store. The sofa is 20% off. The arm chair is 10% off, and a coupon applies an additional 10% off the discounted price of the chair. Are the items equally priced after the discounts are applied? Explain.

8.1 Sample Spaces and Probability

Learning Target Find sample spaces and probabilities of events.

Success Criteria
- I can list the possible outcomes in a sample space.
- I can find theoretical probabilities.
- I can find experimental probabilities.

EXPLORE IT! Finding Sample Spaces and Describing Events

Work with a partner.

a. Describe the set of all possible outcomes for each experiment.

i. Three coins are flipped.

ii. One six-sided die is rolled.

iii. Two six-sided dice are rolled.

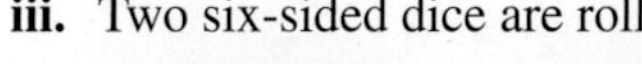

Math Practice

Understand Mathematical Terms

Can the likelihood of an event be impossible? Can the likelihood of an event be certain?

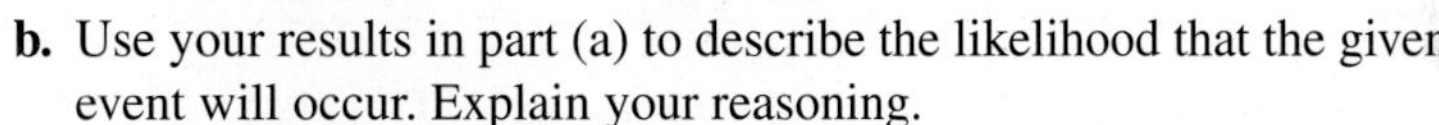

b. Use your results in part (a) to describe the likelihood that the given event will occur. Explain your reasoning.

i. You flip three tails.

ii. You roll an odd number.

iii. You roll a sum greater than 3.

c. Use your results in part (a) to determine which event is more likely to occur. Explain your reasoning.

i. **Event A:** flip exactly two heads
Event B: flip three heads

ii. **Event A:** roll an even number
Event B: roll a number less than 3

iii. **Event A:** roll "doubles"
Event B: roll a sum less than 6

d. Describe a real-life situation where it is important to know the likelihood of an event.

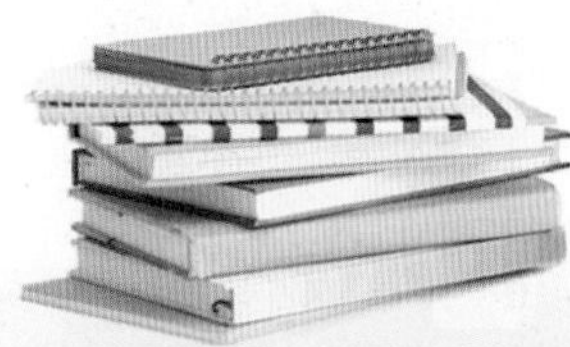

Sample Spaces

A **probability experiment** is an action, or trial, that has varying results. The possible results of a probability experiment are **outcomes**. A collection of one or more outcomes is an **event**. The set of all possible outcomes is called a **sample space**. Here are some examples.

Probability experiment: rolling a six-sided die

Sample space: 1, 2, 3, 4, 5, 6

Event: rolling an even number

Outcome: rolling a 4

Vocabulary

AZ VOCAB

probability experiment, p. 404
outcome, p. 404
event, p. 404
sample space, p. 404
probability of an event, p. 404
theoretical probability, p. 405
geometric probability, p. 406
experimental probability, p. 407

EXAMPLE 1 Finding a Sample Space

You flip a coin and roll a six-sided die. How many possible outcomes are in the sample space? List the possible outcomes.

SOLUTION

Use a tree diagram to find the outcomes in the sample space.

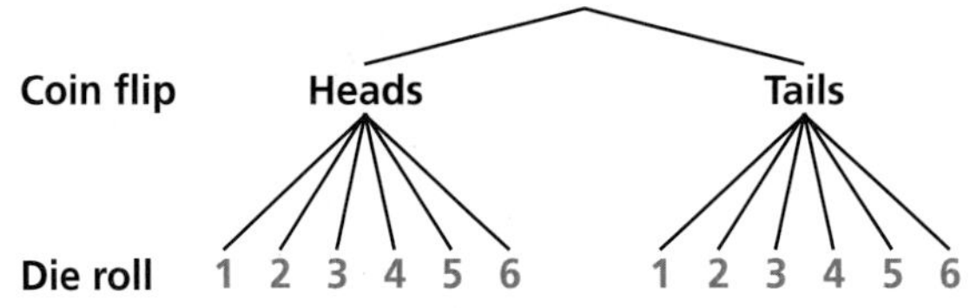

▶ The sample space has 12 possible outcomes. They are listed below.

Heads, 1	Heads, 2	Heads, 3	Heads, 4	Heads, 5	Heads, 6
Tails, 1	Tails, 2	Tails, 3	Tails, 4	Tails, 5	Tails, 6

Math Practice

State the Meaning of Symbols

Using H for "heads" and T for "tails," you can list the outcomes as shown below.

H1	H2	H3	H4	H5	H6
T1	T2	T3	T4	T5	T6

SELF-ASSESSMENT

1 I do not understand. 2 I can do it with help. 3 I can do it on my own. 4 I can teach someone else.

Find the number of possible outcomes in the sample space. Then list the possible outcomes.

1. You flip two coins.
2. You flip two coins and roll a six-sided die.
3. **WRITING** Explain the difference between an outcome and an event.

Theoretical Probabilities

The **probability of an event** is a measure of the likelihood, or chance, that the event will occur. Probability is a number from 0 to 1, including 0 and 1, and can be expressed as a decimal, fraction, or percent.

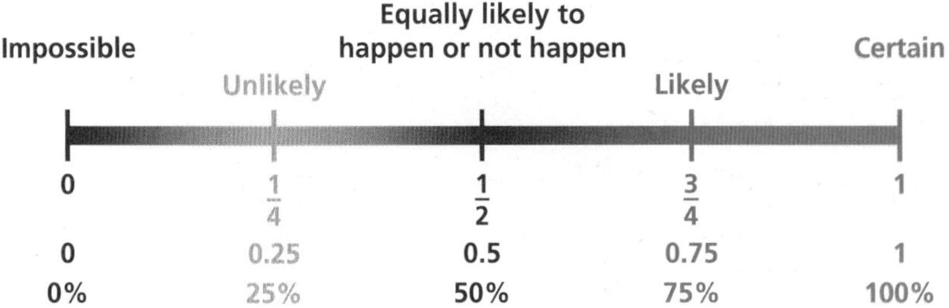

The outcomes for a specified event are called *favorable outcomes*. When all outcomes are equally likely, the **theoretical probability** of the event can be found using the following.

$$\text{Theoretical probability} = \frac{\text{Number of favorable outcomes}}{\text{Total number of outcomes}}$$

The probability of event A is written as $P(A)$.

EXAMPLE 2 Finding a Theoretical Probability

Math Practice

Communicate Precisely

Why is it more precise to use the phrase "exactly two answers" than the phrase "two answers?"

A student taking a quiz randomly guesses the answers to four true-false questions. What is the probability of the student guessing exactly two correct answers?

SOLUTION

Step 1 Identify the sample space. Let C represent a correct answer and I represent an incorrect answer. The possible outcomes are shown in the table.

Number correct	Outcome
0	IIII
1	CIII ICII IICI IIIC
2 (exactly two correct)	IICC ICIC ICCI CIIC CICI CCII
3	ICCC CICC CCIC CCCI
4	CCCC

Step 2 Identify the number of favorable outcomes and the total number of outcomes. There are 6 favorable outcomes with exactly two correct answers and the total number of outcomes is 16.

Step 3 Find the probability of the student guessing exactly two correct answers. Because the student is randomly guessing, the outcomes should be equally likely. So, use the theoretical probability formula.

$$P(\text{exactly two correct answers}) = \frac{\text{Number of favorable outcomes}}{\text{Total number of outcomes}}$$
$$= \frac{6}{16}$$
$$= \frac{3}{8}$$

▶ The probability of the student guessing exactly two correct answers is $\frac{3}{8}$, or 37.5%.

The sum of the probabilities of all outcomes in a sample space is 1. So, when you know the probability of event A, you can find the probability of the *complement* of event A. The *complement* of event A consists of all outcomes that are not in A and is denoted by $\overline{A}$. The notation $\overline{A}$ is read as "A bar." You can use the following formula to find $P(\overline{A})$.

WORDS AND MATH

Complements are parts that combine to create a whole. The probabilities of an event and its complement sum to 1.

KEY IDEA

Probability of the Complement of an Event

The probability of the complement of event A is

$$P(\overline{A}) = 1 - P(A).$$

EXAMPLE 3 Finding Probabilities of Complements

When two six-sided dice are rolled, there are 36 possible outcomes, as shown. Find the probability of each event.

a. The sum is *not* 6.

b. The sum is less than or equal to 9.

SOLUTION

a. $P(\text{sum is not } 6) = 1 - P(\text{sum is } 6) = 1 - \frac{5}{36} = \frac{31}{36} \approx 0.861$

b. $P(\text{sum} \leq 9) = 1 - P(\text{sum} > 9) = 1 - \frac{6}{36} = \frac{30}{36} = \frac{5}{6} \approx 0.833$

Some probabilities are found by calculating a ratio of two lengths, areas, or volumes. Such probabilities are called **geometric probabilities**.

EXAMPLE 4 Using Area to Find Probability

You throw a dart at the board shown. Your dart is equally likely to hit any point inside the square board. Are you more likely to get 10 points or 0 points?

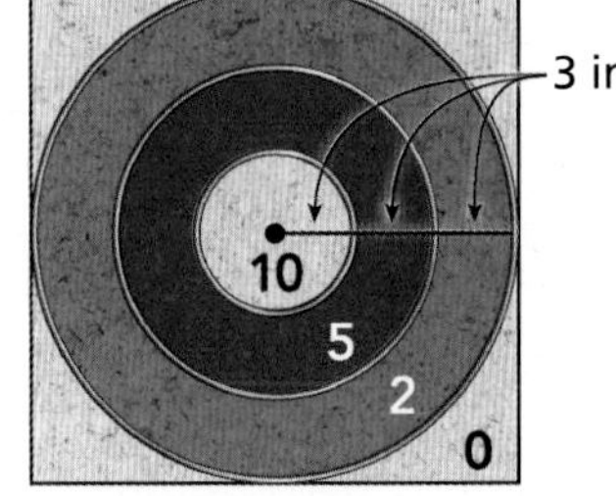

SOLUTION

The radius of the largest circle is 9 inches, so the side length of the board is 18 inches.

The probability of getting 10 points is

$$P(10 \text{ points}) = \frac{\text{Area of smallest circle}}{\text{Area of entire board}} = \frac{\pi \cdot 3^2}{18^2} = \frac{9\pi}{324} \approx 0.087.$$

REMEMBER

The area A of a circle with radius r is $A = \pi r^2$.

The probability of getting 0 points is

$$P(0 \text{ points}) = \frac{\text{Area outside largest circle}}{\text{Area of entire board}}$$

$$= \frac{18^2 - (\pi \cdot 9^2)}{18^2}$$

$$= \frac{324 - 81\pi}{324}$$

$$\approx 0.215.$$

▶ Because 0.215 > 0.087, you are more likely to get 0 points.

SELF-ASSESSMENT

1 I do not understand. 2 I can do it with help. 3 I can do it on my own. 4 I can teach someone else.

4. You flip a coin and roll a six-sided die. What is the probability that the coin shows tails and the die shows 4?

Use the information in Example 3 to find the probability of each event.

5. The sum is *not* 11.

6. The sum is greater than 3.

7. In Example 4, are you more likely to get 5 points or 0 points?

8. In Example 4, are you more likely to score more than 2 points or exactly 2 points?

Experimental Probabilities

An **experimental probability** is based on repeated *trials* of a probability experiment. The number of trials is the number of times the probability experiment is performed. Each trial in which a favorable outcome occurs is called a *success*. The experimental probability can be found using the following.

$$\text{Experimental probability} = \frac{\text{Number of successes}}{\text{Number of trials}}$$

EXAMPLE 5 Finding an Experimental Probability

Spinner Results			
red	**green**	**blue**	**yellow**
5	9	3	3

Each section of the spinner shown has the same area. The spinner is spun 20 times. The table shows the results. For which color is the experimental probability of stopping on the color the same as the theoretical probability?

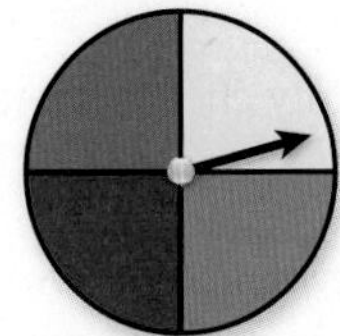

SOLUTION

The theoretical probability of stopping on each of the four colors is $\frac{1}{4}$. Use the outcomes in the table to find the experimental probabilities.

$P(\text{red}) = \frac{5}{20} = \frac{1}{4}$ $\quad P(\text{green}) = \frac{9}{20}$ $\quad P(\text{blue}) = \frac{3}{20}$ $\quad P(\text{yellow}) = \frac{3}{20}$

▶ The experimental probability of stopping on red is the same as the theoretical probability.

EXAMPLE 6 Modeling Real Life

A research team finds that 368 out of 490 crustaceans have ingested plastic. The types of crustaceans that ingested plastic are shown. The team randomly selects a crustacean that ingested plastic to demonstrate their findings. What is the probability that they choose a crayfish?

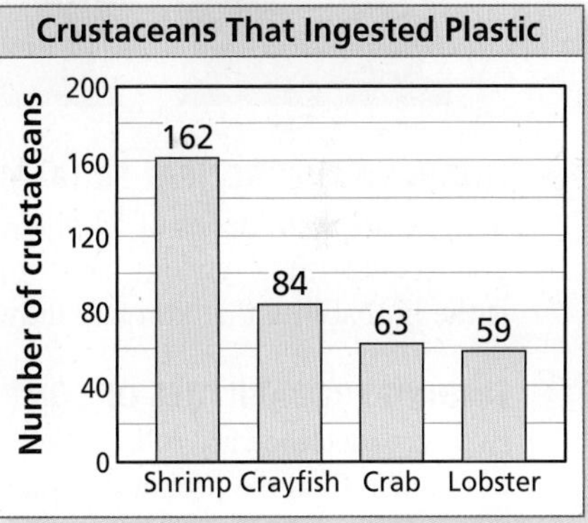

SOLUTION

The number of trials is the number of crustaceans that ingested plastic, 368. A success is a crustacean that ingested plastic is a crayfish. From the figure, there are 84 crayfish.

$$P(\text{crustacean that ingested plastic is a crayfish}) = \frac{84}{368} = \frac{21}{92} \approx 0.228$$

▶ The probability that they choose a crayfish is about 23%.

SELF-ASSESSMENT 1 I do not understand. 2 I can do it with help. 3 I can do it on my own. 4 I can teach someone else.

9. In Example 5, for which color is the experimental probability of stopping on the color greater than the theoretical probability?

10. **WHAT IF?** In Example 6, what is the probability that they randomly select a lobster?

8.1 Practice WITH CalcChat® AND CalcView®

In Exercises 1–4, find the number of possible outcomes in the sample space. Then list the possible outcomes. *Example 1*

1. You flip a coin and draw a marble at random from a bag containing two purple marbles and one white marble.

2. You flip four coins.

3. You randomly choose a letter from A to F and a whole number from 1 to 3.

4. You draw two marbles without replacement from a bag containing three green marbles and three black marbles.

5. **FINDING A THEORETICAL PROBABILITY** A game show airs five days per week. Each day, a prize is randomly placed behind one of two doors. The contestant wins the prize by selecting the correct door. What is the probability that exactly two of the five contestants win a prize during a week? *Example 2*

6. **FINDING A THEORETICAL PROBABILITY** Your friend has two standard decks of 52 playing cards and asks you to randomly draw one card from each deck. What is the probability that you will draw two spades?

7. **FINDING PROBABILITIES OF COMPLEMENTS** When two six-sided dice are rolled, there are 36 possible outcomes. Find the probability that (a) the sum is *not* 4 and (b) the sum is greater than 5. *Example 3*

8. **FINDING PROBABILITIES OF COMPLEMENTS** The age distribution of guests at a cultural festival is shown. Find the probability that (a) a person chosen at random is at least 15 years old and (b) a person chosen at random is *not* 25 to 44 years old.

Age Distribution

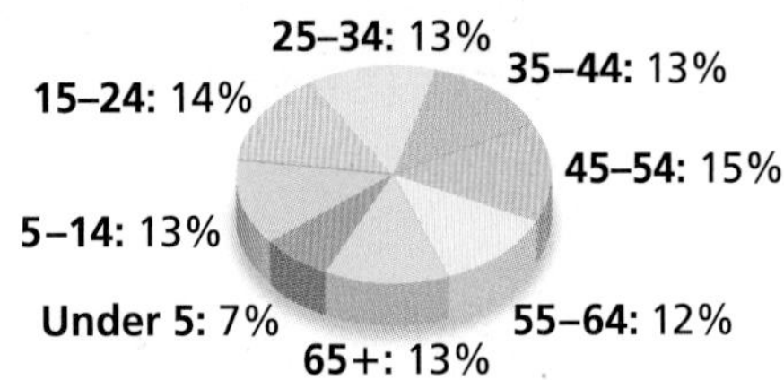

9. **ERROR ANALYSIS** A student randomly guesses the answers to two true-false questions. Describe and correct the error in finding the probability of the student guessing both answers correctly.

The student can either guess two incorrect answers, two correct answers, or one of each. So the probability of guessing both answers correctly is $\frac{1}{3}$.

10. **ERROR ANALYSIS** A student randomly draws a whole number between 1 and 30. Describe and correct the error in finding the probability that the number drawn is greater than 4.

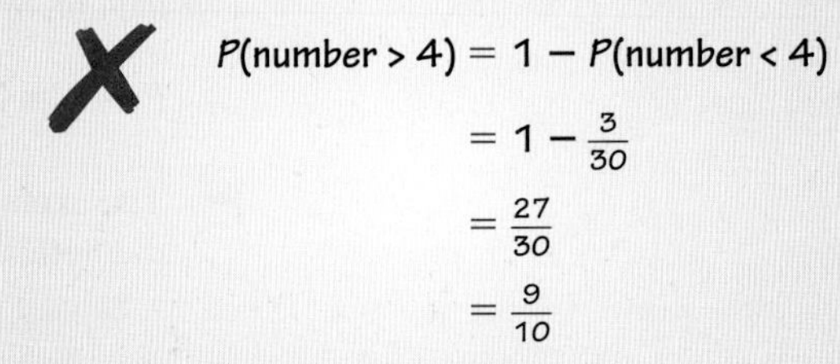

$$P(\text{number} > 4) = 1 - P(\text{number} < 4)$$
$$= 1 - \frac{3}{30}$$
$$= \frac{27}{30}$$
$$= \frac{9}{10}$$

11. **FINDING A GEOMETRIC PROBABILITY** You throw a dart at the board shown. Your dart is equally likely to hit any point inside the square board. What is the probability your dart lands in the yellow region? *Example 4*

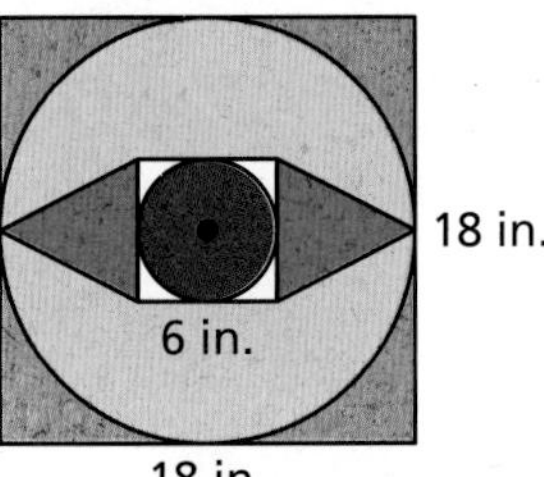

12. **FINDING A GEOMETRIC PROBABILITY** A student loses his earbuds while walking home from school. The earbuds are equally likely to be at any point along the path shown. What is the probability that the earbuds are on Cherry Street?

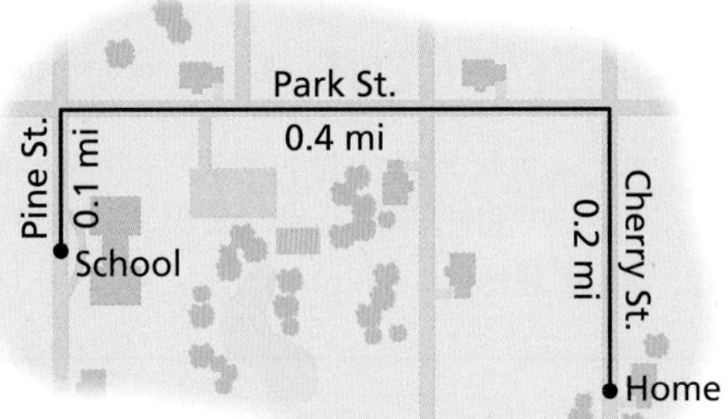

13. **DRAWING CONCLUSIONS** You roll a six-sided die 60 times. The table shows the results. For which number is the experimental probability of rolling the number the same as the theoretical probability? *Example 5*

Six-sided Die Results					
⚀	⚁	⚂	⚃	⚄	⚅
11	14	7	10	6	12

14. **DRAWING CONCLUSIONS** A bag contains 5 marbles that are each a different color. A marble is drawn, its color is recorded, and then the marble is placed back in the bag. The table shows the results after 30 draws. For which marble(s) is the experimental probability of drawing the marble greater than the theoretical probability?

Drawing Results				
white	**black**	**red**	**green**	**blue**
5	6	8	2	9

15. **MODELING REAL LIFE** An archaeologist uncovers 26 artifacts from a site. The types of artifacts are shown. An artifact is randomly selected for display. What is the probability that a piece of pottery is selected? *Example 6*

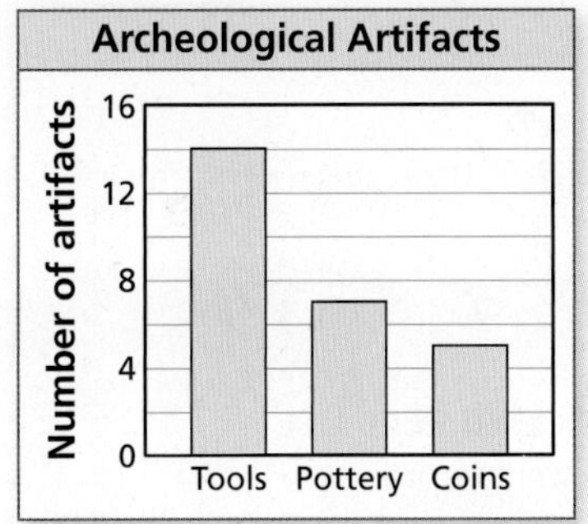

16. **MODELING REAL LIFE** A survey of 140 teenagers asked what type of food they like best. The results are shown. What is the probability that a randomly selected teenager from the survey likes Mexican food best?

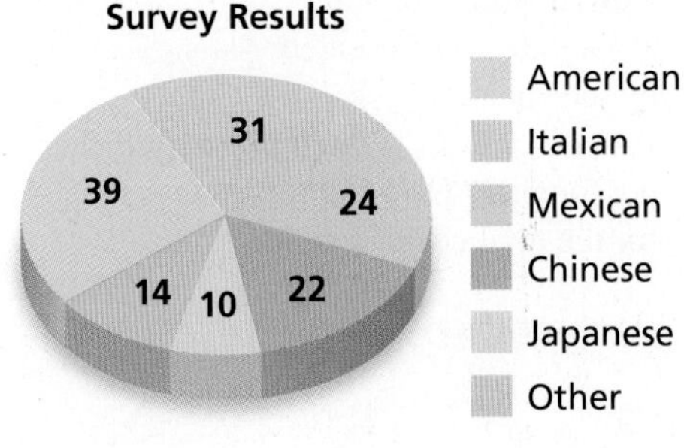

17. **MAKING AN ARGUMENT** You flip a coin three times. It lands on heads twice and on tails once. Your friend concludes that the theoretical probability of the coin landing heads up is $\frac{2}{3}$. Is your friend correct? Explain your reasoning.

18. **OPEN-ENDED** Describe a real-life event that has a probability of 0. Then describe a real-life event that has a probability of 1.

19. **ANALYZING RELATIONSHIPS** Refer to the board in Exercise 11. Order the likelihoods that the dart lands in the given region from least likely to most likely.

    A. green

    B. *not* blue

    C. red

    D. *not* yellow

20. **ANALYZING RELATIONSHIPS** Refer to the chart below. Order the following events from least likely to most likely.

    A. It rains on Sunday.

    B. It does *not* rain on Saturday.

    C. It rains on Monday.

    D. It does *not* rain on Friday.

21. **MP USING TOOLS** Use the figure in Example 3.

    a. List the possible sums that result from rolling two six-sided dice.

    b. Find the theoretical probability of rolling each sum.

    c. The table shows a simulation of rolling two six-sided dice three times. Use a random number generator to simulate rolling two six-sided dice 50 times. Compare the experimental probabilities of rolling each possible sum with the theoretical probabilities.

	A	B	C
1	**First Die**	**Second Die**	**Sum**
2	4	6	10
3	3	5	8
4	1	6	7
5			

22. HOW DO YOU SEE IT? Consider the graph of f shown. What is the probability that the graph of $y = f(x) + c$ intersects the x-axis when c is a randomly chosen integer from 1 to 6? Explain.

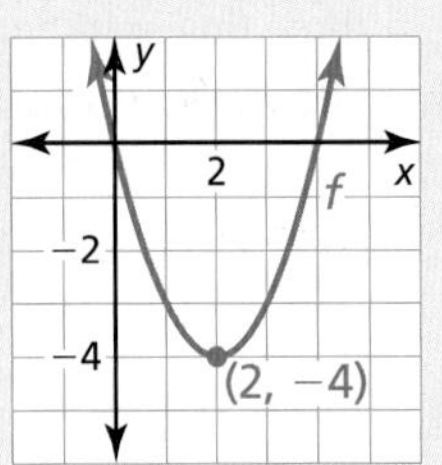

23. CONNECTING CONCEPTS A sphere fits inside a cube so that it touches each side, as shown. What is the probability a point chosen at random inside the cube is also inside the sphere?

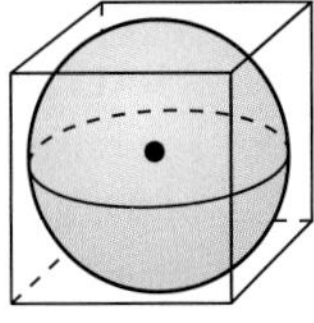

24. THOUGHT PROVOKING Describe a probability experiment that involves more than one action and has 48 possible outcomes in the sample space.

25. DRAWING CONCLUSIONS A manufacturer tests 1200 computers and finds that 9 of them have defects. Predict the number of computers with defects in a shipment of 15,000 computers. Explain your reasoning.

26. DIG DEEPER A test contains n true-false questions. A student randomly guesses the answer to each question. Write an expression that gives the probability of correctly answering all n questions.

27. PERFORMANCE TASK You are in charge of designing a game of chance for a fundraising event. You will charge a fee to play, and each winner will receive a cash prize. You expect about 200 people to play. Write a proposal in which you describe your game. Be sure to include how much you will charge to play, how much each winner will receive, the theoretical probability of winning, and how much you expect to raise (after prizes are deducted).

REVIEW & REFRESH

WATCH

In Exercises 28 and 29, simplify the expression.

28. $e^{\ln 9}$

29. $\log_3 81^{-2x}$

In Exercises 30 and 31, describe the transformation of f represented by g. Then graph each function.

30. $f(x) = x^3$, $g(x) = -0.5x^3$

31. $f(x) = x^4$, $g(x) = (x + 1)^4 - 2$

32. The spinner is divided into sections with the same area. You spin the spinner 25 times. It stops on a multiple of 3 twenty times. Compare the experimental probability of spinning a multiple of 3 with the theoretical probability.

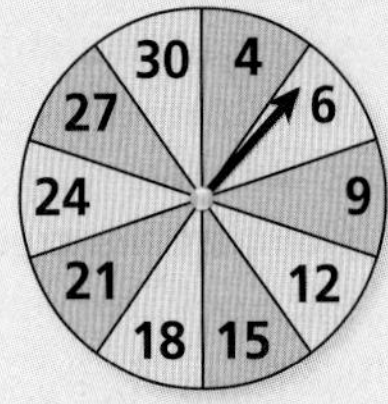

33. Solve $\frac{x}{x-3} - \frac{4}{x} = \frac{12}{x}$.

34. MP REASONING A polynomial function f has rational coefficients and zeros of $2i$, $5 - i$, and -3. What is the least possible degree of f?

In Exercises 35–40, perform the indicated operation.

35. $\frac{4x^9y}{3x^3} \cdot \frac{2xy}{8y^2}$

36. $\frac{2y}{5x} \div \frac{y}{6x}$

37. $\frac{7}{x-2} + \frac{3x}{x+1}$

38. $\frac{4}{3x^2} - \frac{1}{x^2 + 5x}$

39. $\frac{x+8}{x^2 - x - 30} \cdot (x^2 - 7x + 6)$

40. $\frac{x^2 + 9x + 14}{x^2 - 9} \div \frac{x+7}{5x + 15}$

41. MODELING REAL LIFE You want to order a pizza from one of two pizza shops. The table shows the total costs of a pizza with different numbers of toppings at Shop A. The total cost y (in dollars) of a pizza with x toppings at Shop B is represented by the equation $y = 1.75x + 11$. Which pizza shop charges less per topping? How many toppings must you order for the total costs to be the same?

Shop A

Number of toppings, x	Total cost, y
1	13.50
2	15.00
3	16.50
4	18.00
5	19.50

42. Evaluate $625^{3/4}$.

8.2 Two-Way Tables and Probability

Learning Target Use two-way tables to represent data and find probabilities.

Success Criteria
- I can make two-way tables.
- I can find and interpret relative frequencies and conditional relative frequencies.
- I can use conditional relative frequencies to find probabilities.

EXPLORE IT! Finding Probabilities Using a Two-Way Table

Math Practice

Look for Structure What are some advantages and disadvantages of organizing data in a Venn diagram? in a table?

Work with a partner. A survey of 80 students at a high school asks whether they participate in outside of school activities and whether they participate in inside of school activities. The results are shown in the Venn diagram.

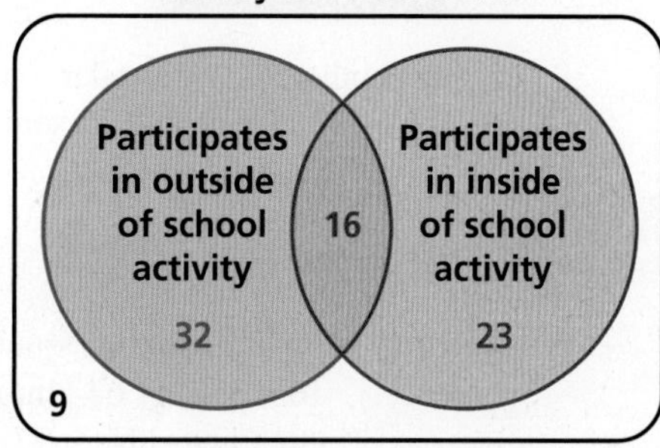

a. Show how you can represent the data in the Venn diagram using a single table.

b. One student is selected at random from the 80 students who took the survey. Find the probability that the student

i. participates in an outside of school activity.

ii. participates in an outside of school activity and participates in an inside of school activity.

iii. participates in an outside of school activity and does not participate in an inside of school activity.

c. Conduct a survey of the students in your class. Choose two categories that are different from those given above. Then summarize the results in both a Venn diagram and a table similar to the one above. Discuss the results and find a probability using your table.

Making Two-Way Tables

Vocabulary

two-way table, *p. 412*
joint frequency, *p. 412*
marginal frequency, *p. 412*
joint relative frequency, *p. 413*
marginal relative frequency, *p. 413*
conditional relative frequency, *p. 414*

A **two-way table** is a frequency table that displays data collected from one source that belong to two different categories. One category of data is represented by rows and the other is represented by columns. For instance, the two-way table below shows the results of a survey that asked freshmen and sophomores whether they are attending a school concert.

Each entry in the table is called a **joint frequency**. The sums of the rows and columns are called **marginal frequencies**, which you will find in Example 1.

		Attendance	
		Attending	Not Attending
Class	Freshman	25	44
	Sophomore	80	32

joint frequency

EXAMPLE 1 Making a Two-Way Table

In another survey similar to the one above, 106 juniors and 114 seniors respond. Of those, 42 juniors and 77 seniors plan on attending. Organize these results in a two-way table. Then find and interpret the marginal frequencies.

SOLUTION

Step 1 Find the joint frequencies. Because 42 of the 106 juniors are attending, $106 - 42 = 64$ juniors are not attending. Because 77 of the 114 seniors are attending, $114 - 77 = 37$ seniors are not attending. Place each joint frequency in its corresponding cell.

Step 2 Find the marginal frequencies. Create a new column and row for the sums. Then add the entries and interpret the results.

Step 3 Find the sums of the marginal frequencies. Notice the sums $106 + 114 = 220$ and $119 + 101 = 220$ are equal. Place this value at the bottom right.

READING

A two-way table is also called a *contingency table*, or a *two-way frequency table*.

		Attendance		
		Attending	Not Attending	Total
Class	Junior	42	64	106
	Senior	77	37	114
	Total	119	101	220

106 juniors responded.
114 seniors responded.
220 students were surveyed.
119 students are attending.
101 students are not attending.

SELF-ASSESSMENT

1 I do not understand. 2 I can do it with help. 3 I can do it on my own. 4 I can teach someone else.

1. You randomly survey students about whether they are in favor of planting a community garden at school. Of 96 boys surveyed, 61 are in favor. Of 88 girls surveyed, 17 are against. Organize the results in a two-way table. Then find and interpret the marginal frequencies.

Finding Relative and Conditional Relative Frequencies

GO DIGITAL

You can display values in a two-way table as frequency counts (as in Example 1) or as *relative frequencies*.

STUDY TIP

You can interpret relative frequencies as probabilities.

KEY IDEA

Relative Frequencies

A **joint relative frequency** is the ratio of a joint frequency to the total number of values or observations.

A **marginal relative frequency** is the sum of the joint relative frequencies in a row or a column.

EXAMPLE 2 **Finding Joint and Marginal Relative Frequencies**

Use the survey results in Example 1 to make a two-way table that shows the joint and marginal relative frequencies. Interpret one of the joint relative frequencies and one of the marginal relative frequencies.

SOLUTION

To find the joint relative frequencies, divide each frequency by the total number of students in the survey. Then find the sum of each row and each column to find the marginal relative frequencies.

		Attendance		
		Attending	Not Attending	Total
Class	Junior	$\frac{42}{220} \approx 0.191$	$\frac{64}{220} \approx 0.291$	0.482
	Senior	$\frac{77}{220} = 0.35$	$\frac{37}{220} \approx 0.168$	0.518
	Total	0.541	0.459	1

▶ The joint relative frequency 0.291 means that about 29.1% of the students in the survey are juniors who are not attending the concert. So, the probability that a randomly selected student from the survey is a junior who is not attending the concert is about 29.1%.

The marginal relative frequency 0.518 means that about 51.8% of the students in the survey are seniors. So, the probability that a randomly selected student from the survey is a senior is about 51.8%.

SELF-ASSESSMENT 1 I do not understand. 2 I can do it with help. 3 I can do it on my own. 4 I can teach someone else.

2. Use the survey results in Exercise 1 to make a two-way table that shows the joint and marginal relative frequencies. Interpret one of the joint relative frequencies and one of the marginal relative frequencies.

3. **WRITING** Explain the differences between joint relative frequencies and marginal relative frequencies.

KEY IDEA

Conditional Relative Frequencies

A **conditional relative frequency** is the ratio of a joint relative frequency to the marginal relative frequency. You can find a conditional relative frequency using a row total or a column total of a two-way table.

EXAMPLE 3 Finding Conditional Relative Frequencies

Use the survey results in Example 1. Make a two-way table that shows the conditional relative frequencies based on (a) the row totals and (b) the column totals. Interpret one of the conditional relative frequencies in each table.

SOLUTION

a. Use the marginal relative frequency of each *row* in Example 2 to calculate the conditional relative frequencies.

		Attendance	
		Attending	Not Attending
Class	Junior	$\frac{0.191}{0.482} \approx 0.396$	$\frac{0.291}{0.482} \approx 0.604$
	Senior	$\frac{0.35}{0.518} \approx 0.676$	$\frac{0.168}{0.518} \approx 0.324$

▶ The conditional relative frequency 0.604 means that about 60.4% of the juniors in the survey are not attending the concert. So, the probability that a randomly selected junior from the survey is not attending the concert is about 60.4%.

b. Use the marginal relative frequency of each *column* in Example 2 to calculate the conditional relative frequencies.

		Attendance	
		Attending	Not Attending
Class	Junior	$\frac{0.191}{0.541} \approx 0.353$	$\frac{0.291}{0.459} \approx 0.634$
	Senior	$\frac{0.35}{0.541} \approx 0.647$	$\frac{0.168}{0.459} \approx 0.366$

▶ The conditional relative frequency 0.634 means that of the students in the survey who are not attending the concert, about 63.4% are juniors. So, given that a randomly selected student in the survey is not attending the concert, the probability that the student is a junior is about 63.4%.

SELF-ASSESSMENT

1 I do not understand. 2 I can do it with help. 3 I can do it on my own. 4 I can teach someone else.

4. Use the survey results in Exercise 1 to make a two-way table that shows the conditional relative frequencies based on the column totals. Interpret one of the conditional relative frequencies.

5. Use the relative frequencies in Example 2 or 3 to find the probability that a randomly selected student from the survey is a senior who is attending the concert.

8.2 Practice WITH CalcChat® AND CalcView®

In Exercises 1 and 2, complete the two-way table.

1.

		Preparation		
		Studied	Did Not Study	Total
Grade	Pass		6	
	Fail			10
	Total	38		50

2.

		Response		
		Yes	No	Total
Role	Student	56		
	Teacher		7	10
	Total		49	

3. MAKING TWO-WAY TABLES You survey 171 males and 180 females at Grand Central Station in New York City. Of those, 132 males and 151 females wash their hands after using the public restrooms. Organize these results in a two-way table. Then find and interpret the marginal frequencies. *Example 1*

4. MAKING TWO-WAY TABLES A survey asks 80 seniors and 66 juniors whether they have a curfew. Of those, 59 seniors and 28 juniors say they have a curfew. Organize these results in a two-way table. Then find and interpret the marginal frequencies.

5. MODELING REAL LIFE Use the survey results from Exercise 3 to make a two-way table that shows the joint and marginal relative frequencies. Interpret one of the joint relative frequencies and one of the marginal relative frequencies. *Example 2*

6. MODELING REAL LIFE In a survey, 49 people received a flu vaccine before the flu season and 63 people did not receive the vaccine. Of those who received the flu vaccine, 16 people got the flu. Of those who did not receive the vaccine, 17 got the flu. Make a two-way table that shows the joint and marginal relative frequencies. Interpret one of the joint relative frequencies and one of the marginal relative frequencies.

7. MODELING REAL LIFE A survey finds that 73 people like horror movies and 87 people do not. Of those who like horror movies, 39 people have visited a haunted house. Of those who do not like horror movies, 42 people have visited a haunted house. Make a two-way table that shows the conditional relative frequencies based on (a) the horror movie totals and (b) the haunted house totals. Interpret one of the conditional relative frequencies in each table. *Example 3*

8. MODELING REAL LIFE Use the survey results from Exercise 6 to make a two-way table that shows the conditional relative frequencies based on (a) the flu vaccine totals and (b) the flu totals. Interpret one of the conditional relative frequencies in each table.

9. ERROR ANALYSIS The table shows the conditional relative frequencies for the results of a survey based on the row totals. Describe and correct the error in interpreting the data.

		Roller Coasters	
		Like	Dislike
Grade	Upperclassmen	0.729	0.271
	Underclassmen	0.707	0.293

0.271 means that about 27.1% of the students surveyed who dislike roller coasters are upperclassmen.

10. MAKING AN ARGUMENT The results of a survey are organized in a two-way table. Can you find the conditional relative frequencies without calculating the joint and marginal relative frequencies? Explain.

11. MP PROBLEM SOLVING Students in a history class are writing reports about either the Paleolithic era or the Neolithic era. Of the 14 boys and 17 girls in the class, 8 boys are writing their reports about the Paleolithic era and 9 girls are writing their reports about the Neolithic era. Find the probability that a randomly selected student from the class is a boy who is writing his report about the Neolithic era.

12. **MP PROBLEM SOLVING** Use the survey results in Exercise 4 to find the probability that a randomly selected senior from the survey has a curfew.

13. **MODELING REAL LIFE** A survey asks students whether they prefer math class or science class. Of the 150 male students surveyed, 62% prefer math class over science class. Of the female students surveyed, 74% prefer math class. Make a two-way table to show the number of students in each category if 350 students were surveyed.

14. **HOW DO YOU SEE IT?**
A survey asks teenagers and adults about whether their state should increase the minimum driving age. The two-way table shows the results.

		Age Group		
		Teenager	Adult	Total
Response	Yes	45	880	925
	No	456	120	576
	Total	501	1000	1501

a. What does 120 represent?

b. What does 925 represent?

c. What does 1501 represent?

15. **MP STRUCTURE** A survey asks 481 students their gender and blood type. The two-way table shows the results.

		Blood Type			
		A	B	AB	O
Gender	Male	93	50	14	79
	Female	89	50	30	76

a. Find the probability that a randomly selected student from the survey has blood type AB.

b. Find the probability that a randomly selected student from the survey with blood type O is male.

16. **THOUGHT PROVOKING**
Provide an example of a three-way table. Explain how you can find conditional relative frequencies for the data in the table. Then find and interpret one of the conditional relative frequencies.

17. **OPEN-ENDED** Create and conduct a survey in your class. Organize the results in a two-way table. Then create a two-way table that shows the joint and marginal relative frequencies. Use the relative frequencies to find a probability.

REVIEW & REFRESH

In Exercises 18 and 19, determine whether the inverse of *f* is a function. Then find the inverse.

18. $f(x) = \dfrac{6}{13 - x}$

19. $f(x) = \dfrac{1}{x^2} + 5$

20. **MODELING REAL LIFE** A survey finds that 110 people ate breakfast and 30 people skipped breakfast. Of those who ate breakfast, 10 people felt tired. Of those who skipped breakfast, 10 people felt tired. Make a two-way table that shows the conditional relative frequencies based on the breakfast totals. Then interpret one of the conditional relative frequencies.

21. Simplify $\dfrac{\dfrac{2}{x-3}}{\dfrac{4}{x} + \dfrac{1}{x-3}}$.

22. When two six-sided dice are rolled, there are 36 possible outcomes. Find the probability that the sum is *not* 7.

23. Write a rule for g.

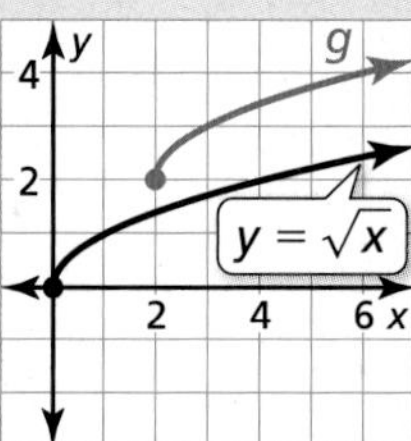

In Exercises 24 and 25, tell whether the function represents *exponential growth* or *exponential decay*. Then graph the function.

24. $f(x) = (0.4)^x$

25. $y = 2e^{3x}$

26. Expand $\log_4 9x^3$.

27. Factor $a^3 - 2a^2 - 9a + 18$ completely.

In Exercises 28 and 29, solve the equation using any method. Explain your choice of method.

28. $2x^2 + 10 = 9x$

29. $3x^2 + 14x - 1 = 0$

8.3 Conditional Probability

Learning Target Find and use conditional probabilities.

Success Criteria

- I can explain the meaning of conditional probability.
- I can find conditional probabilities.
- I can make decisions using probabilities.

EXPLORE IT! Finding Conditional Probabilities

Work with a partner. Six pieces of paper, numbered 1 through 6, are placed in a bag. You draw two pieces of paper one at a time without replacing the first.

a. Use a tree diagram to find the outcomes in the sample space.

b. What is the probability that you draw two odd numbers?

c. When the first number you draw is odd, what is the probability that the second number you draw is also odd? Explain.

d. Compare and contrast the questions in parts (b) and (c).

e. The probability in part (c) is called a *conditional probability*. How would you define conditional probability?

f. The probability that event B occurs given that event A has occurred is called the conditional probability of B given A and is written as $P(B|A)$. The probability that both events A and B occur is written as $P(A \text{ and } B)$.

Find $P(B|A)$, $P(A \text{ and } B)$, and $P(A)$ for the following pair of events.

Event A: The first number is divisible by 3.

Event B: The second number is greater than 2.

g. Use your answers in part (f) to write a formula for $P(B|A)$ in terms of $P(A \text{ and } B)$ and $P(A)$.

Math Practice

Justify Conclusions
Explain why your formula makes sense in part (g).

Understanding Conditional Probability

GO DIGITAL

Vocabulary AZ VOCAB

conditional probability, *p. 418*

The probability that event B occurs given that event A has occurred is called the **conditional probability** of B given A and is written as $P(B \mid A)$. You can use sample spaces and two-way tables to find conditional probabilities.

EXAMPLE 1 Using a Sample Space to Find a Conditional Probability

A family has two dogs and two cats. They randomly select a pet to get brushed and then randomly select a different pet to get a treat. Find the probability that they select a cat to get a treat given that they selected a dog to get brushed.

Outcome	
C_1D_1	D_1C_1
C_1D_2	D_1C_2
C_1C_2	D_1D_2
C_2C_1	D_2D_1
C_2D_1	D_2C_1
C_2D_2	D_2C_2

SOLUTION

Let C_1 and C_2 represent the two cats, and D_1 and D_2 represent the two dogs. Use a table to list the outcomes in the sample space.

Use the sample space to find $P(\text{cat second} \mid \text{dog first})$. There are 6 outcomes for choosing a dog first. A cat is second in 4 of these 6 outcomes.

▶ So, $P(\text{cat second} \mid \text{dog first}) = \frac{4}{6} = \frac{2}{3} \approx 0.667$, or about 66.7%.

EXAMPLE 2 Using a Two-way Table to Find Conditional Probabilities

A quality-control inspector checks for defective parts. The two-way table shows the results. Find each probability.

a. $P(\text{pass} \mid \text{defective})$

b. $P(\text{fail} \mid \text{non-defective})$

		Result	
		Pass	**Fail**
Part Type	**Defective**	3	36
	Non-defective	450	11

SOLUTION

a. Find the probability that a defective part passes.

$$P(\text{pass} \mid \text{defective}) = \frac{\text{Number of defective parts passed}}{\text{Total number of defective parts}}$$

$$= \frac{3}{3+36} = \frac{3}{39} = \frac{1}{13} \approx 0.077, \text{ or about } 7.7\%$$

READING

You can think of $P(B \mid A)$ as the fraction of A's outcomes that are also in B. So, you can think of $P(\text{pass} \mid \text{defective})$ as the fraction of defective parts that pass the inspection.

b. Find the probability that a non-defective part fails.

$$P(\text{fail} \mid \text{non-defective}) = \frac{\text{Number of non-defective parts failed}}{\text{Total number of non-defective parts}}$$

$$= \frac{11}{450+11} = \frac{11}{461} \approx 0.024, \text{ or about } 2.4\%$$

SELF-ASSESSMENT 1 I do not understand. 2 I can do it with help. 3 I can do it on my own. 4 I can teach someone else.

1. In Example 1, what is the probability that they select a dog to get a treat given that they selected a dog to get brushed?

2. In Example 2, find (a) the probability that a non-defective part passes, and (b) the probability that a defective part fails.

KEY IDEA

Conditional Probability Formula

READING

The probability that both events *A* and *B* occur is written as *P*(*A* and *B*).

Words For two events *A* and *B*, the conditional probability of the second event given the first event is the probability that both events occur divided by the probability of the first event.

Symbols $P(B|A) = \dfrac{P(A \text{ and } B)}{P(A)}$

EXAMPLE 3 Using a Formula to Find a Conditional Probability

Find the probability in Example 2(a) using the formula for conditional probability.

SOLUTION

Find the joint and marginal relative frequencies.

		Result		
		Pass	Fail	Total
Part Type	Defective	$\frac{3}{500} = 0.006$	$\frac{36}{500} = 0.072$	0.078
	Non-defective	$\frac{450}{500} = 0.9$	$\frac{11}{500} = 0.022$	0.922
	Total	0.906	0.094	1

Use the formula for conditional probability. Let event *A* be "part is defective" and let event *B* be "part passes."

$$P(B|A) = \frac{P(A \text{ and } B)}{P(A)}$$ Write formula for conditional probability.

$$= \frac{0.006}{0.078}$$ Substitute 0.006 for *P*(*A* and *B*) and 0.078 for *P*(*A*).

$$= \frac{6}{78}$$ Rewrite fraction.

$$= \frac{1}{13} \approx 0.077$$ Simplify.

▶ So, the probability that a defective part passes is about 7.7%.

SELF-ASSESSMENT

1 I do not understand. 2 I can do it with help. 3 I can do it on my own. 4 I can teach someone else.

3. Find the probability in Example 2(b) using the formula for conditional probability.

4. You study survival statistics of adults from the Titanic shipwreck. The two-way table shows the joint and marginal relative frequencies. Find and compare *P*(female | did not survive) and *P*(female | survived).

		Result		
		Survived	Did Not Survive	Total
Gender	Male	0.160	0.639	0.799
	Female	0.149	0.052	0.201
	Total	0.309	0.691	1

EXAMPLE 4 Finding Conditional Probabilities

At a school, 60% of students buy a school lunch, 18% of students buy a dessert, and 10% of students buy a lunch and a dessert.

a. What is the probability that a student who buys lunch also buys dessert?

b. What is the probability that a student who buys dessert also buys lunch?

SOLUTION

Math Practice

Use a Diagram

Draw a Venn diagram that represents the values of $P(A)$, $P(B)$, $P(A \text{ and } B)$, and $P(\text{neither } A \text{ nor } B)$.

Let event A be "buys lunch" and let event B be "buys dessert."

a. You are given $P(A) = 0.6$ and $P(A \text{ and } B) = 0.1$. Use the formula to find $P(B|A)$.

$$P(B|A) = \frac{P(A \text{ and } B)}{P(A)}$$ Write formula for conditional probability.

$$= \frac{0.1}{0.6}$$ Substitute 0.1 for $P(A \text{ and } B)$ and 0.6 for $P(A)$.

$$= \frac{1}{6}$$ Rewrite fraction.

$$\approx 0.167$$ Simplify.

▶ So, the probability that a student who buys lunch also buys dessert is about 16.7%.

b. You are given $P(B) = 0.18$ and $P(A \text{ and } B) = 0.1$. Use the formula to find $P(A|B)$.

$$P(A|B) = \frac{P(A \text{ and } B)}{P(B)}$$ Write formula for conditional probability.

$$= \frac{0.1}{0.18}$$ Substitute 0.1 for $P(A \text{ and } B)$ and 0.18 for $P(B)$.

$$= \frac{10}{18}$$ Rewrite fraction.

$$= \frac{5}{9} \approx 0.556$$ Simplify.

▶ So, the probability that a student who buys dessert also buys lunch is about 55.6%.

SELF-ASSESSMENT

1 I do not understand. 2 I can do it with help. 3 I can do it on my own. 4 I can teach someone else.

5. At a coffee shop, 80% of customers order coffee, 15% of customers order coffee and a bagel, and 20% of customers order coffee and a sandwich.

a. What is the probability that a customer who orders coffee also orders a bagel?

b. What is the probability that a customer who orders coffee also orders a sandwich?

c. What information do you need to find the probability that a customer who orders a bagel also orders coffee? Explain.

Make Decisions Using Conditional Probabilities

EXAMPLE 5 Using Conditional Probabilities to Make a Decision

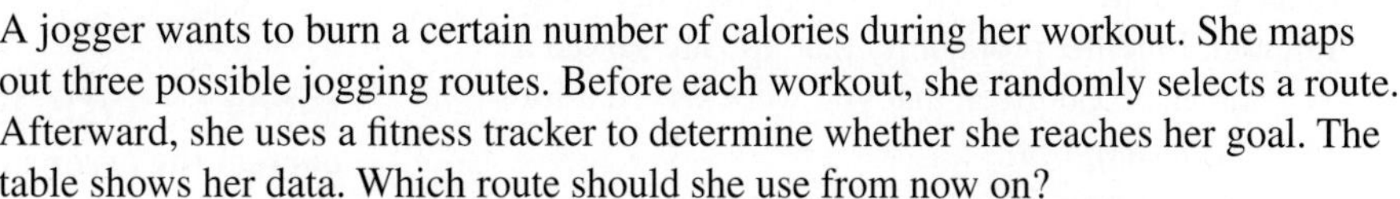

A jogger wants to burn a certain number of calories during her workout. She maps out three possible jogging routes. Before each workout, she randomly selects a route. Afterward, she uses a fitness tracker to determine whether she reaches her goal. The table shows her data. Which route should she use from now on?

Route	Reaches Goal	Does Not Reach Goal
A	𝍸 𝍸 I	𝍸 I
B	𝍸 𝍸 I	IIII
C	𝍸 𝍸 II	𝍸 I

SOLUTION

Step 1 Use the data to make a two-way table that shows the joint and marginal relative frequencies. There are a total of 50 observations in the table.

Step 2 Find the conditional probabilities by dividing each joint relative frequency in the "Reaches Goal" column by the marginal relative frequency in its corresponding row.

		Result		
		Reaches Goal	Does Not Reach Goal	Total
Route	A	0.22	0.12	0.34
	B	0.22	0.08	0.30
	C	0.24	0.12	0.36
	Total	0.68	0.32	1

$$P(\text{reaches goal} \mid \text{Route A}) = \frac{P(\text{Route A and reaches goal})}{P(\text{Route A})} = \frac{0.22}{0.34} \approx 0.647$$

$$P(\text{reaches goal} \mid \text{Route B}) = \frac{P(\text{Route B and reaches goal})}{P(\text{Route B})} = \frac{0.22}{0.30} \approx 0.733$$

$$P(\text{reaches goal} \mid \text{Route C}) = \frac{P(\text{Route C and reaches goal})}{P(\text{Route C})} = \frac{0.24}{0.36} \approx 0.667$$

▶ Based on the sample, the probability that she reaches her goal is greatest when she uses Route B. So, she should use Route B from now on.

SELF-ASSESSMENT

1 I do not understand. 2 I can do it with help. 3 I can do it on my own. 4 I can teach someone else.

6. A manager is assessing three employees in order to offer one of them a promotion. Over a period of time, the manager records whether the employees meet or exceed expectations on their assigned tasks. The table shows the manager's results. Which employee should be offered the promotion? Explain.

Employee	Exceed Expectations	Meet Expectations
A	𝍸 IIII	𝍸 I
B	𝍸 𝍸 II	𝍸 III
C	𝍸 𝍸 I	𝍸 II

8.3 Practice WITH CalcChat® AND CalcView®

GO DIGITAL

1. **FINDING A PROBABILITY** A school lunch offers three different fruits and two different vegetables as side dishes. You are served two different side dishes at random. Find the probability that you are served a vegetable second given that you were served a fruit first. *Example 1*

2. **FINDING A PROBABILITY** A movie complex is showing three action films and three comedy films. You randomly select two different films to watch. Find the probability that you select a comedy to watch second given that you randomly selected a comedy to watch first.

3. **MODELING REAL LIFE** A teacher administers three different versions of a test to his students. The two-way table shows the results. Find each probability. *Example 2*

		Grade	
		Pass	Fail
Test	A	49	7
	B	46	6
	C	34	12

a. $P(\text{pass} \mid \text{Test A})$ b. $P(\text{Test C} \mid \text{fail})$

4. **MODELING REAL LIFE** The two-way table shows the numbers of tropical cyclones that formed during the hurricane seasons over a 12-year period. Find each probability.

		Location	
		Northern Hemisphere	Southern Hemisphere
Type of Tropical Cyclone	Tropical depression	100	107
	Tropical storm	342	487
	Hurricane	379	525

a. $P(\text{hurricane} \mid \text{Northern Hemisphere})$

b. $P(\text{Southern Hemisphere} \mid \text{hurricane})$

5. **USING A FORMULA** Find the probability in Exercise 3(a) using the formula for conditional probability. *Example 3*

6. **USING A FORMULA** Find the probability in Exercise 4(a) using the formula for conditional probability.

ERROR ANALYSIS In Exercises 7 and 8, describe and correct the error in finding the given conditional probability.

		City			
		Tokyo	London	Washington, D.C.	Total
Satisfied Resident	Yes	0.049	0.136	0.171	0.356
	No	0.341	0.112	0.191	0.644
	Total	0.39	0.248	0.362	1

7. $P(\text{yes} \mid \text{Tokyo})$

✗
$$P(\text{yes} \mid \text{Tokyo}) = \frac{P(\text{Tokyo and yes})}{P(\text{Tokyo})} = \frac{0.049}{0.356} \approx 0.138$$

8. $P(\text{London} \mid \text{no})$

✗
$$P(\text{London} \mid \text{no}) = \frac{P(\text{no and London})}{P(\text{London})} = \frac{0.112}{0.248} \approx 0.452$$

9. **MODELING REAL LIFE** At a school, 43% of students attend the homecoming football game, 48% of students attend the homecoming dance, and 23% of students attend the game and the dance. *Example 4*

a. What is the probability that a student who attends the football game also attends the dance?

b. What is the probability that a student who attends the dance also attends the football game?

10. **MODELING REAL LIFE** At a gas station, 84% of customers buy gasoline, 9% of customers buy gasoline and a beverage, and 5% of customers buy gasoline and a snack.

a. What is the probability that a customer who buys gasoline also buys a beverage?

b. What is the probability that a customer who buys gasoline also buys a snack?

11. **MP PROBLEM SOLVING** You want to find the quickest route to school. You map out three routes. Before school, you randomly select a route and record whether you are late or on time. The table shows your findings. Assuming you leave at the same time each morning, which route should you use? Explain.
Example 5

Route	On Time	Late
A	𝍸 II	IIII
B	𝍸 𝍸 I	III
C	𝍸 𝍸 II	IIII

12. **MP PROBLEM SOLVING** A teacher is assessing three groups of students in order to award one group a prize. Over a period of time, the teacher records whether the groups meet or exceed expectations on their assigned tasks. The table shows the results. Which group should be awarded the prize? Explain.

Group	Exceed Expectations	Meet Expectations
1	𝍸 𝍸 II	IIII
2	𝍸 III	𝍸
3	𝍸 IIII	𝍸 I

13. **COLLEGE PREP** Let $P(A) = 0.6$, $P(B) = 0.8$, and $P(A \text{ and } B) = 0.24$. What is $P(A|B)$?

Ⓐ 0.3 Ⓑ 0.4

Ⓒ 0.48 Ⓓ 0.75

14. **MP STRUCTURE** Show that $P(B|A) \cdot P(A) = P(A|B) \cdot P(B)$.

15. **MULTIPLE REPRESENTATIONS** The Venn diagram shows the results of a survey. Use the Venn diagram to construct a two-way table. Then use your table to answer each question.

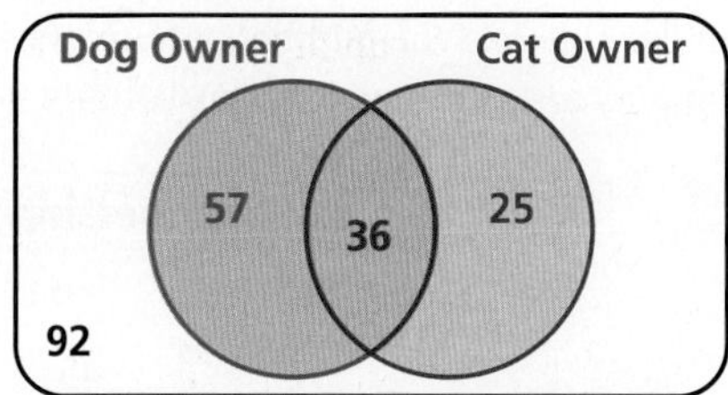

a. What is the probability that a randomly selected person from the survey does not own either pet?

b. What is the probability that a randomly selected person from the survey who owns a dog also owns a cat?

16. **HOW DO YOU SEE IT?**
You randomly select two marbles from a bag, one at a time. The sample space is shown, with each first selection on the left. What is the probability that you select a red marble second given that you randomly selected a blue marble first?

GO DIGITAL

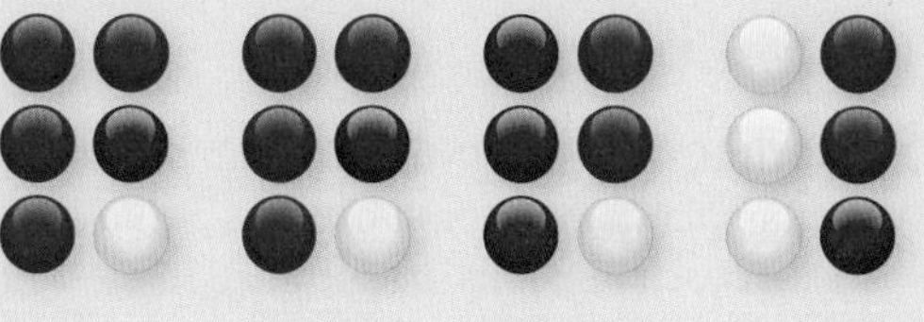

17. **MAKING AN ARGUMENT** Your friend uses the table to determine which dance routine meets the required time limit for a competition. Your friend decides that Routine B is the best option because it has the fewest tally marks in the "Does Not Meet Time Limit" column. Is your friend correct? Explain.

Routine	Meets Time Limit	Does Not Meet Time Limit
A	𝍸	III
B	IIII	II
C	𝍸 II	IIII

18. **MP PROBLEM SOLVING** A pharmaceutical company conducts a voluntary study of 500 teenagers with acne to determine the effectiveness of a new medication. The two-way table shows the results. The company claims that the medicine is effective in 94% of cases. Do the data support this claim? Explain your reasoning.

		Took Medicine	
		Yes	No
Acne Remaining	Yes	98	134
	No	187	81

19. **CRITICAL THINKING** In a survey, 53% of respondents have a music streaming subscription, 68% have a video streaming subscription, and 47% of the respondents who have video streaming also have music streaming.

a. What is the probability that a person from the survey has both video and music streaming?

b. What is the probability that a person from the survey who has music streaming also has video streaming?

20. THOUGHT PROVOKING Bayes' Theorem is given by

$$P(A|B) = \frac{P(B|A) \cdot P(A)}{P(B)}.$$

Use a two-way table to write an example of Bayes' Theorem.

21. ABSTRACT REASONING The Venn diagram represents the sample space S for two events X and Y. The area of each region is proportional to the number of outcomes within the region. Determine whether the statement $P(X|Y) > P(Y|X)$ is *true* or *false*. Explain.

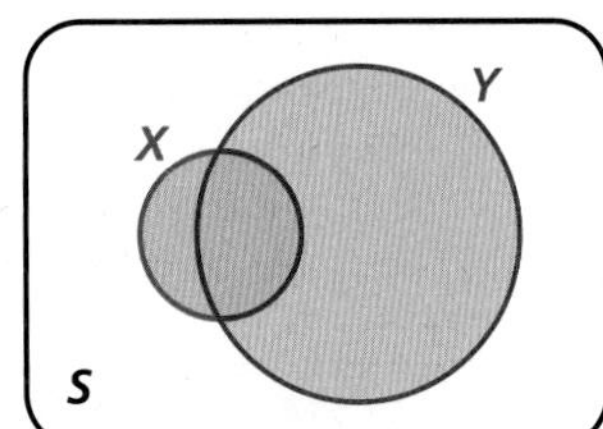

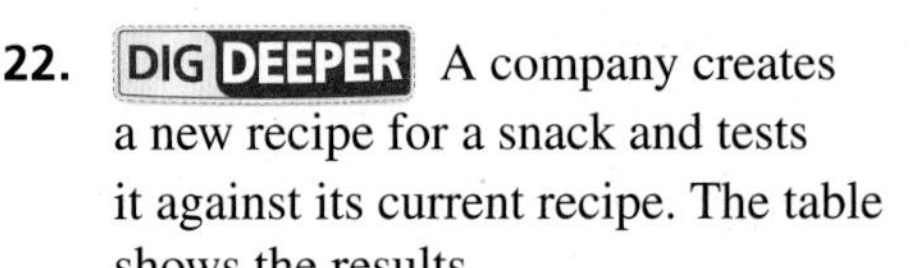

22. DIG DEEPER A company creates a new recipe for a snack and tests it against its current recipe. The table shows the results.

		Recipe Preference	
		Current	New
Current Consumer of Snack	Yes	72	46
	No	52	114

The company is deciding whether it should change the snack's recipe, and to whom the snack should be marketed. Use probability to explain the decisions the company should make when the total size of the snack's market is expected to (a) change very little, and (b) expand very rapidly.

REVIEW & REFRESH

WATCH

In Exercises 23 and 24, solve the equation.

23. $\frac{9}{10}x = 0.18$

24. $\frac{1}{4}x + 0.5x = 1.5$

In Exercises 25 and 26, identify the focus, directrix, and axis of symmetry of the parabola. Graph the equation.

25. $x = \frac{1}{12}y^2$

26. $y = \frac{1}{4}(x + 3)^2 - 2$

27. Use the data to create a two-way table that shows the joint and marginal relative frequencies.

		Dominant Hand		
		Left	Right	Total
Gender	Female	11	104	115
	Male	24	92	116
	Total	35	196	231

28. Solve $\frac{3}{x + 4} + \frac{2x^2}{x^2 - 16} = \frac{1}{x - 4}$.

In Exercises 29 and 30, find $(f + g)(x)$ and $(f - g)(x)$ and state the domain of each. Then evaluate $f + g$ and $f - g$ for the given value of x.

29. $f(x) = 6\sqrt[3]{4x}$, $g(x) = -12\sqrt[3]{4x}$; $x = -16$

30. $f(x) = 4x + 9x^2 - 2$, $g(x) = 10 - 3x^2$; $x = 1$

In Exercises 31–34, find the product.

31. $5x^2(2x^3 - x^2 + 13)$

32. $(2x + 7)(2x - 7)$

33. $(x^2 - 8x + 7)(x^2 + 2x - 3)$

34. $(x - 4)(2x + 3)(x + 1)$

35. You roll a six-sided die 30 times. A 5 is rolled 8 times. What is the theoretical probability of rolling a 5? What is the experimental probability of rolling a 5?

36. Find the zeros of $f(x) = 2x^3 + 9x^2 - 5x$. Then sketch a graph of the function.

37. MODELING REAL LIFE The two-way table shows the numbers of juniors at a school who have a gym membership and the numbers of juniors at a school who play a sport. Find each probability.

		Gym Membership	
		Yes	No
Plays a Sport	Yes	57	45
	No	34	41

a. $P(\text{membership}|\text{sport})$

b. $P(\text{no sport}|\text{no membership})$

8.4 Independent and Dependent Events

Learning Target Understand and find probabilities of independent and dependent events.

Success Criteria
- I can explain how independent events and dependent events are different.
- I can determine whether events are independent.
- I can find probabilities of independent and dependent events.

EXPLORE IT! Identifying Independent and Dependent Events

Work with a partner.

a. Two events are either *independent* or *dependent*. Which pair of events below are independent? Which are dependent? Explain your reasoning.

i. You roll a six-sided die twice.

Event *A*: The first number is even.

Event *B*: The second number is a 6.

ii. Six pieces of paper, numbered 1 through 6, are placed in a bag. Two pieces of paper are selected one at a time without replacement.

Event *A*: The first number is even.

Event *B*: The second number is a 6.

b. Complete the table for each set of events in part (a).

Experiment	Rolling Die	Selecting Papers
$P(A)$		
$P(B)$		
$P(B \mid A)$		
$P(A \text{ and } B)$		

c. Write a formula that relates $P(A \text{ and } B)$, $P(B \mid A)$, and $P(A)$.

$P(A \text{ and } B) =$ ______

Math Practice

Interpret Results
In the first experiment, $P(B \mid A) = P(B)$, but that is not true in the second experiment. Why? What does this imply about events A and B?

Determining Whether Events Are Independent

Vocabulary

independent events, *p. 426*
dependent events, *p. 428*

Two events are **independent events** when the occurrence of one event does not affect the occurrence of the other event.

KEY IDEA

Probability of Independent Events

Words Two events A and B are independent events if and only if the probability that both events occur is the product of the probabilities of the events.

Symbols $P(A \text{ and } B) = P(A) \cdot P(B)$

EXAMPLE 1 Determining Whether Events Are Independent

A student taking a quiz randomly guesses the answers to four true-false questions. Use a sample space to determine whether guessing the correct answer to Question 1 and guessing the correct answer to Question 2 are independent events.

SOLUTION

Outcomes			
IIII	IIIC	CIIC	CICC
CIII	IICC	CICI	CCIC
ICII	ICIC	CCII	CCCI
IICI	ICCI	ICCC	CCCC

Use a table to list the outcomes in the sample space. Using the sample space:

$P(\text{correct on Question 1}) = \frac{8}{16} = \frac{1}{2}$

$P(\text{correct on Question 2}) = \frac{8}{16} = \frac{1}{2}$

$P(\text{correct on Question 1 and correct on Question 2}) = \frac{4}{16} = \frac{1}{4}$

▶ Because $\frac{1}{2} \cdot \frac{1}{2} = \frac{1}{4}$, the events are independent.

EXAMPLE 2 Determining Whether Events Are Independent

A group of four students includes one boy and three girls. The teacher randomly selects one of the students to be the speaker and a different student to be the recorder. Use a sample space to determine whether randomly selecting a girl first and randomly selecting a girl second are independent events.

SOLUTION

Let B represent the boy. Let G_1, G_2, and G_3 represent the three girls. Use a table to list the outcomes in the sample space.

Number of girls	Outcome	
1	G_1B	BG_1
1	G_2B	BG_2
1	G_3B	BG_3
2	G_1G_2	G_2G_1
2	G_1G_3	G_3G_1
2	G_2G_3	G_3G_2

Using the sample space:

$P(\text{girl first}) = \frac{9}{12} = \frac{3}{4}$

$P(\text{girl second}) = \frac{9}{12} = \frac{3}{4}$

$P(\text{girl first and girl second}) = \frac{6}{12} = \frac{1}{2}$

▶ Because $\frac{3}{4} \cdot \frac{3}{4} \neq \frac{1}{2}$, the events are not independent.

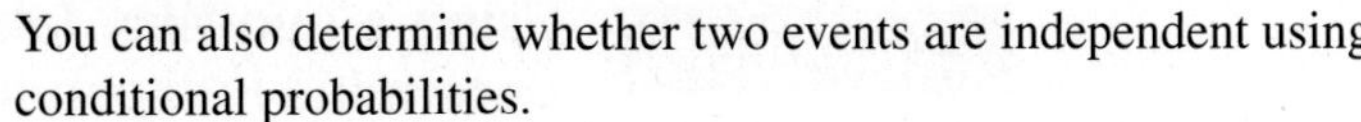

You can also determine whether two events are independent using conditional probabilities.

KEY IDEA

Conditional Probability and Independent Events

Words When two events A and B are independent, the conditional probability of A given B is equal to the probability of A, and the conditional probability of B given A is equal to the probability of B.

Symbols $P(A|B) = P(A)$ and $P(B|A) = P(B)$

EXAMPLE 3 Determining Whether Events Are Independent

Use conditional probabilities to determine whether the events are independent in (a) Example 1 and (b) Example 2.

SOLUTION

a. Determine whether $P(B|A) = P(B)$.

$$P(\text{correct on Question 2} \mid \text{correct on Question 1}) = \frac{4}{8} = \frac{1}{2}$$

$$P(\text{correct on Question 2}) = \frac{8}{16} = \frac{1}{2}$$

▶ This shows that being correct on the first question does not affect the probability of being correct on the second question. Because $P(B|A) = P(B)$, the events are independent.

b. Determine whether $P(B|A) = P(B)$.

$$P(\text{girl second} \mid \text{girl first}) = \frac{6}{9} = \frac{2}{3}$$

$$P(\text{girl second}) = \frac{9}{12} = \frac{3}{4}$$

▶ This shows that the first selection affects the outcome of the second selection. Because $P(B|A) \neq P(B)$, the events are not independent.

SELF-ASSESSMENT

1 I do not understand. 2 I can do it with help. 3 I can do it on my own. 4 I can teach someone else.

1. In Example 1, determine whether guessing Question 1 incorrectly and guessing Question 2 correctly are independent events.
2. In Example 2, determine whether randomly selecting a girl first and randomly selecting a boy second are independent events.
3. Five out of eight tiles in a bag have numbers on them. You randomly draw a tile, set it aside, and then randomly draw another tile. Use a conditional probability to determine whether selecting a numbered tile first and a numbered tile second are independent events.

EXAMPLE 4 Using a Two-Way Table to Determine Independence

WATCH GO DIGITAL

A satellite TV provider surveys customers in three cities. The survey asks whether they would recommend the TV provider to a friend. The results, given as joint relative frequencies, are shown in the two-way table. Determine whether recommending the provider to a friend and living in Long Beach are independent events.

		Location		
		Glendale	Santa Monica	Long Beach
Response	Yes	0.29	0.27	0.32
	No	0.05	0.03	0.04

SOLUTION

Use the formula $P(B) = P(B|A)$ and compare $P(\text{Long Beach})$ and $P(\text{Long Beach}|\text{yes})$.

$$P(\text{Long Beach}) = 0.32 + 0.04$$
$$= 0.36$$

$$P(\text{Long Beach}|\text{yes}) = \frac{P(\text{yes and Long Beach})}{P(\text{yes})}$$
$$= \frac{0.32}{0.29 + 0.27 + 0.32}$$
$$\approx 0.36$$

▶ Because $P(\text{Long Beach}) \approx P(\text{Long Beach}|\text{yes})$, the two events are independent.

SELF-ASSESSMENT

1 I do not understand. 2 I can do it with help. 3 I can do it on my own. 4 I can teach someone else.

4. In Example 4, determine whether recommending the provider to a friend and living in Santa Monica are independent events. Explain your reasoning.

Finding Probabilities of Events

In Example 1, it makes sense that the events are independent because the second guess should not be affected by the first guess. In Example 2, however, the selection of the second person *depends* on the selection of the first person because the same person cannot be selected twice. These events are *dependent*. Two events are **dependent events** when the occurrence of one event *does* affect the occurrence of the other event.

KEY IDEA

Probability of Dependent Events

Words If two events A and B are dependent events, then the probability that both events occur is the product of the probability of the first event and the conditional probability of the second event given the first event.

Symbols $P(A \text{ and } B) = P(A) \bullet P(B|A)$

EXAMPLE 5 Finding the Probability of Independent Events

A spinner is divided into equal parts. Find the probability that you get a 5 on your first spin and a number greater than 3 on your second spin.

SOLUTION

Let event A be "5 on first spin" and let event B be "greater than 3 on second spin."

The events are independent because the outcome of your second spin is not affected by the outcome of your first spin. Find the probability of each event and then multiply the probabilities.

$P(A) = \frac{1}{8}$ 1 of the 8 sections is a "5."

$P(B) = \frac{5}{8}$ 5 of the 8 sections (4, 5, 6, 7, 8) are greater than 3.

$$P(A \text{ and } B) = P(A) \cdot P(B) = \frac{1}{8} \cdot \frac{5}{8} = \frac{5}{64} \approx 0.078$$

▶ So, the probability that you get a 5 on your first spin and a number greater than 3 on your second spin is about 7.8%.

EXAMPLE 6 Finding the Probability of Dependent Events

A bag contains twenty \$1 bills and five \$10 bills. You randomly draw a bill from the bag, set it aside, and then randomly draw another bill from the bag. Find the probability that both events A and B will occur.

Event A: The first bill is \$10.

Event B: The second bill is \$10.

SOLUTION

The events are dependent because there is one less bill in the bag on your second draw than on your first draw. Find $P(A)$ and $P(B|A)$. Then multiply the probabilities.

$P(A) = \frac{5}{25}$ 5 of the 25 bills are \$10 bills.

$P(B|A) = \frac{4}{24}$ When the first bill is \$10, 4 of the remaining 24 bills are \$10 bills.

$$P(A \text{ and } B) = P(A) \cdot P(B|A) = \frac{5}{25} \cdot \frac{4}{24} = \frac{1}{5} \cdot \frac{1}{6} = \frac{1}{30} \approx 0.033.$$

▶ So, the probability that you draw two \$10 bills is about 3.3%.

SELF-ASSESSMENT

1 I do not understand. 2 I can do it with help. 3 I can do it on my own. 4 I can teach someone else.

5. In Example 5, what is the probability that you spin an even number and then an odd number?

6. In Example 6, what is the probability that both bills are \$1 bills?

8.4 Practice WITH CalcChat® AND CalcView®

In Exercises 1–6, use a sample space to determine whether the events are independent. *Examples 1 and 2*

1. You play a game that involves spinning the spinner shown. Each section of the spinner has the same area. Determine whether randomly spinning blue and then green are independent events.

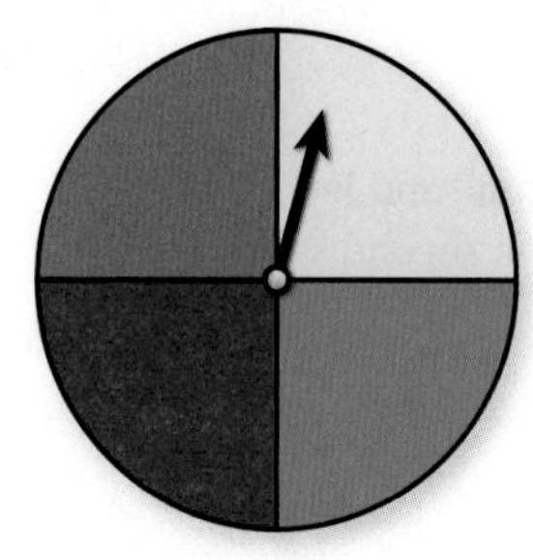

2. There are three green apples and one red apple in a bowl. You randomly select one apple to eat now and another apple to eat with lunch. Determine whether randomly selecting a green apple first and randomly selecting a green apple second are independent events.

3. A student is taking a multiple-choice quiz where each question has four choices. The student randomly guesses the answers to the three-question quiz. Determine whether guessing the correct answer to Question 1 and guessing the correct answer to Question 2 are independent events.

4. A bag contains four quarters and one nickel. You randomly select two coins. Determine whether randomly selecting a quarter first and randomly selecting a quarter second are independent events.

5. You randomly select two gift cards from a bag that contains three restaurant gift cards and two department store gift cards. Determine whether randomly selecting a restaurant gift card first and randomly selecting a department store gift card second are independent events.

6. You roll a six-sided die two times. Determine whether getting a 6 and then getting a 1 are independent events.

In Exercises 7–10, use a conditional probability to determine whether the events are independent. *Example 3*

7. Determine whether the events in Exercise 1 are independent.

8. Determine whether the events in Exercise 2 are independent.

9. You have six solid and three striped cell phone cases. You randomly select a case, set it aside, and then randomly select another case. Determine whether randomly selecting a striped case first and a striped case second are independent events.

10. You flip a coin and roll a six-sided die. Determine whether getting tails and getting a 4 are independent events.

11. **MODELING REAL LIFE** Three different local hospitals in New York surveyed their patients. The survey asked whether the patient's physician communicated efficiently. The results, given as joint relative frequencies, are shown in the two-way table. Determine whether being satisfied with the communication of the physician and living in Saratoga are independent events. *Example 4*

		Location		
		Glens Falls	**Saratoga**	**Albany**
Response	**Yes**	0.123	0.289	0.338
	No	0.042	0.095	0.113

12. **MODELING REAL LIFE** A researcher surveys a random sample of high school students in seven states. The survey asks whether students plan to stay in their home state after graduation. The results, given as joint relative frequencies, are shown in the two-way table. Determine whether planning to stay in their home state and living in Nebraska are independent events.

		Location		
		Nebraska	**North Carolina**	**Other States**
Response	**Yes**	0.044	0.051	0.056
	No	0.400	0.193	0.256

13. **MP PROBLEM SOLVING** You play a game that involves spinning the money wheel shown. You spin the wheel twice. Find the probability that you get more than \$500 on your first spin and then go bankrupt on your second spin.
Example 5

14. **MP PROBLEM SOLVING** You play a game that involves drawing two numbers from a hat. There are 25 pieces of paper numbered from 1 to 25 in the hat. Each number is replaced after it is drawn. Find the probability that you will draw the 3 on your first draw and a number greater than 10 on your second draw.

15. **MP PROBLEM SOLVING** A bag contains 12 movie tickets and 8 concert tickets. You randomly choose 1 ticket and do not replace it. Then you randomly choose another ticket. Find the probability that both events A and B will occur. *Example 6*

Event A: The first ticket is a concert ticket.

Event B: The second ticket is a concert ticket.

16. **MP PROBLEM SOLVING** A word game has 100 tiles, 98 of which are letters and 2 of which are blank. The numbers of tiles of each letter are shown. You randomly draw 1 tile, set it aside, and then randomly draw another tile. Find the probability that both events A and B will occur.

Event A: The first tile is a consonant.

Event B: The second tile is a vowel.

A – 9	H – 2	O – 8	V – 2
B – 2	I – 9	P – 2	W – 2
C – 2	J – 1	Q – 1	X – 1
D – 4	K – 1	R – 6	Y – 2
E – 12	L – 4	S – 4	Z – 1
F – 2	M – 2	T – 6	– 2 Blank
G – 3	N – 6	U – 4	

17. **ERROR ANALYSIS** A video streaming queue shows 3 animated movies and 4 adventure movies. You randomly choose two movies to watch. Describe and correct the error in finding the probability that both events A and B occur.

Event A: The first movie is animated.

Event B: The second movie is adventure.

✗ $P(A) = \frac{3}{7}$ $\quad P(B|A) = \frac{4}{7}$

$P(A \text{ and } B) = \frac{3}{7} \cdot \frac{4}{7} = \frac{12}{49} \approx 0.245$

18. **ERROR ANALYSIS** Events A and B are independent. Describe and correct the error in finding $P(A \text{ and } B)$.

✗ $P(A) = 0.6$

$P(B) = 0.2$

$P(A \text{ and } B) = 0.6 + 0.2 = 0.8$

19. **MP NUMBER SENSE** Events A and B are independent. Let $P(B) = 0.4$ and $P(A \text{ and } B) = 0.13$. Find $P(A)$.

20. **MP NUMBER SENSE** Events A and B are dependent. Let $P(B|A) = 0.6$ and $P(A \text{ and } B) = 0.15$. Find $P(A)$.

21. **ANALYZING RELATIONSHIPS** A bin contains orange, blue, green, and yellow water balloons. You randomly select two balloons to toss. Are events A and B independent or dependent? Explain your reasoning.

Event A: You choose a green balloon first.

Event B: You choose a yellow balloon second.

22. **HOW DO YOU SEE IT?**
A bag contains one red marble and one blue marble. The diagrams show the possible outcomes of randomly choosing two marbles using different methods. For each method, determine whether the marbles were selected with or without replacement.

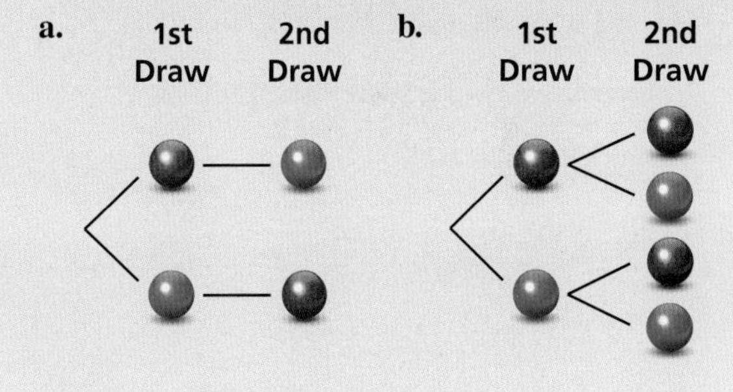

23. **MP REASONING** You enter to win a contest in which the winners are selected by a random drawing. There is a 5% chance of winning the grand prize, a 20% chance of winning a door prize, and a 1% chance of winning the grand prize and a door prize. Determine whether winning the grand prize and winning a door prize are independent events. Justify your answer.

24. **CRITICAL THINKING** You randomly select three cards from a standard deck of 52 playing cards. What is the probability that all three cards are face cards when (a) you replace each card before selecting the next card, and (b) you do not replace each card before selecting the next card?

25. MAKING AN ARGUMENT A meteorologist claims that there is a 70% chance of rain. When it rains, there is a 75% chance that your softball game will be rescheduled. Is the game more likely to be rescheduled than played? Explain your reasoning.

26. THOUGHT PROVOKING
Two six-sided dice are rolled once. Events A and B are represented by the diagram. Describe each event. Are the two events dependent or independent? Justify your reasoning.

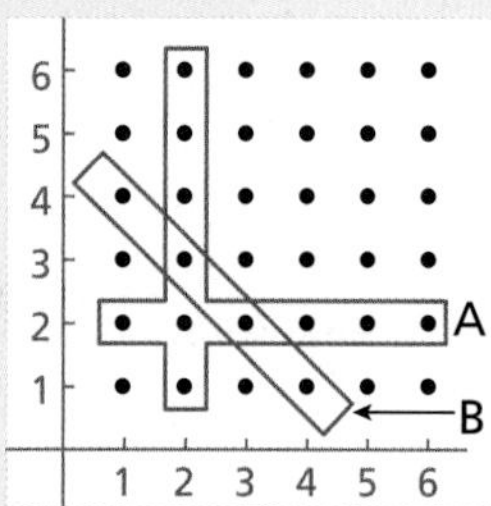

27. ABSTRACT REASONING Assume that A and B are independent events.

a. Explain why $P(B) = P(B|A)$ and $P(A) = P(A|B)$.

b. Can $P(A \text{ and } B)$ also be defined as $P(B) \cdot P(A|B)$? Justify your reasoning.

28. DIG DEEPER A football team is losing by 14 points near the end of a game. The team scores two touchdowns (worth 6 points each) before the end of the game. After each touchdown, the coach must decide whether to go for 1 point with a kick (which is successful 99% of the time) or 2 points with a run or pass (which is successful 45% of the time).

a. If the team goes for 1 point after each touchdown, what is the probability that the team wins? loses? ties?

b. If the team goes for 2 points after each touchdown, what is the probability that the team wins? loses? ties?

c. Can you develop a strategy so that the team has a probability of winning the game that is greater than the probability of losing? If so, explain your strategy and calculate the probabilities of winning and losing the game.

REVIEW & REFRESH

In Exercises 29–32, solve the equation.

29. $2x^2 + 17 = 71$

30. $3(4)^{10x} = 48$

31. $\log_4 x + \log_4 (x - 12) = 3$

32. $0.3x - \frac{3}{5}x + 1.6 = 1.555$

33. You roll a six-sided die and flip a coin. Find the probability that you get a 2 when rolling the die and heads when flipping the coin.

34. MODELING REAL LIFE A survey asks 68 males and 57 females whether they have been to an escape room. Complete the two-way table. Then interpret the marginal frequencies.

		Escape Room		
		Yes	No	Total
Gender	Male	35		
	Female		28	
	Total			

In Exercises 35 and 36, simplify the expression.

35. $\sqrt[3]{5} \cdot \sqrt[3]{25}$

36. $3\sqrt{32} + 6\sqrt{2}$

37. Tell whether x and y show *direct variation*, *inverse variation*, or *neither*.

x	1	2	3	4
y	12	6	4	3

In Exercises 38 and 39, graph the function. Label the vertex and axis of symmetry.

38. $y = -(x + 6)^2 - 1$

39. $f(x) = x^2 + 4x - 5$

40. Let $P(A) = 0.4$, $P(B) = 0.88$, and $P(A \text{ and } B) = 0.22$. Find $P(B|A)$ and $P(A|B)$.

41. You randomly draw a marble out of a bag containing 8 green marbles, 4 blue marbles, 12 yellow marbles, and 10 red marbles. Find the probability of drawing a marble that is not yellow.

8.5 Probability of Disjoint and Overlapping Events

Learning Target Find probabilities of disjoint and overlapping events.

Success Criteria
- I can explain how disjoint events and overlapping events are different.
- I can find probabilities of disjoint events.
- I can find probabilities of overlapping events.
- I can solve real-life problems using more than one probability rule.

EXPLORE IT! Identifying Overlapping and Disjoint Events

Math Practice

Understand Mathematical Terms
What are some other examples of disjoint events and overlapping events that do not involve dice?

Work with a partner.

a. You roll two six-sided dice. Which pair of events below are *overlapping*? Which are *disjoint*? Use Venn diagrams to support your answers.

i. Event A: The sum is an even number.
Event B: The sum is 7.

ii. Event A: The sum is less than 7.
Event B: The sum is a prime number.

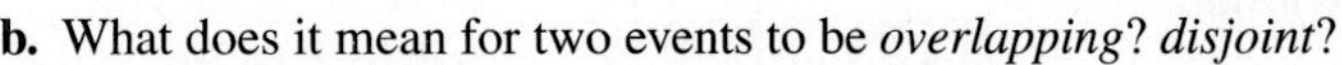

b. What does it mean for two events to be *overlapping*? *disjoint*?

c. Complete the table for each set of events in part (a).

Experiment	Events in (i)	Events in (ii)
$P(A)$		
$P(B)$		
$P(A \text{ and } B)$		
$P(A \text{ or } B)$		

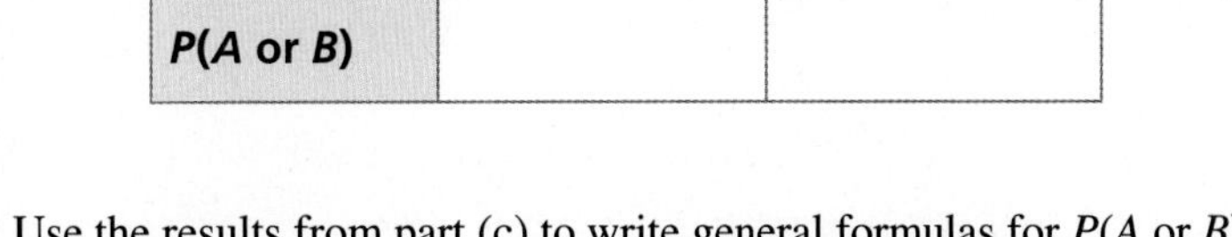

d. Use the results from part (c) to write general formulas for $P(A \text{ or } B)$.

Events are disjoint: $P(A \text{ or } B) =$

Events are overlapping: $P(A \text{ or } B) =$

Compound Events

GO DIGITAL

Vocabulary 

compound event, *p. 434*
overlapping events, *p. 434*
disjoint events, *p. 434*

When you consider only the outcomes shared by both A and B, you form the *intersection* of A and B, as shown in the first diagram. Similarly, when you consider all the outcomes that belong to A, B, or both, you form the *union* of A and B, as shown in the second diagram. The probability that an outcome is in the union of A and B is written as $P(A \text{ or } B)$. The union or intersection of two events is called a **compound event**.

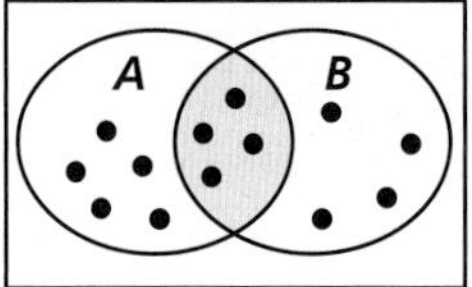

Intersection of A and B

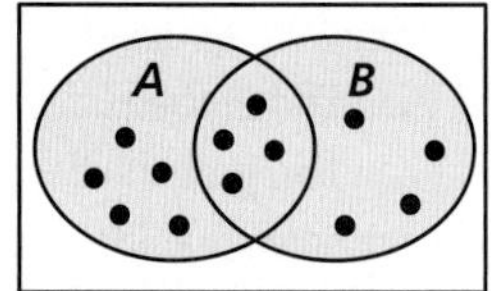

Union of A and B

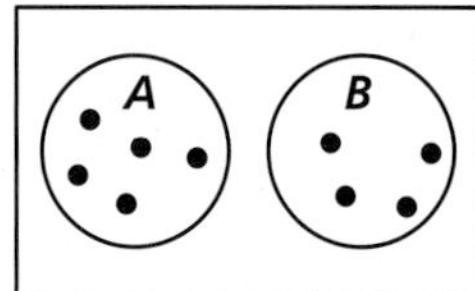

Intersection of A and B is empty.

To find $P(A \text{ or } B)$ you must consider the number of outcomes in the intersection of A and B. Two events are **overlapping** when they have one or more outcomes in common. Two events are **disjoint**, or *mutually exclusive*, when they have no outcomes in common, as shown in the third diagram.

KEY IDEA

Probability of Compound Events

If A and B are any two events, then the probability of A or B is

$$P(A \text{ or } B) = P(A) + P(B) - P(A \text{ and } B).$$

If A and B are disjoint events, then $P(A \text{ and } B) = 0$ and the probability of A or B is

$$P(A \text{ or } B) = P(A) + P(B).$$

STUDY TIP

If two events A and B are overlapping, then the outcomes in the intersection of A and B are counted *twice* when $P(A)$ and $P(B)$ are added. So, $P(A \text{ and } B)$ must be subtracted from the sum.

EXAMPLE 1 Finding the Probability of Disjoint Events

A card is randomly selected from a standard deck of 52 playing cards. What is the probability that it is a 10 *or* a face card?

SOLUTION

Let event A be selecting a 10 and event B be selecting a face card. Event A has 4 outcomes and event B has 12 outcomes. Because A and B are disjoint, use the disjoint probability formula.

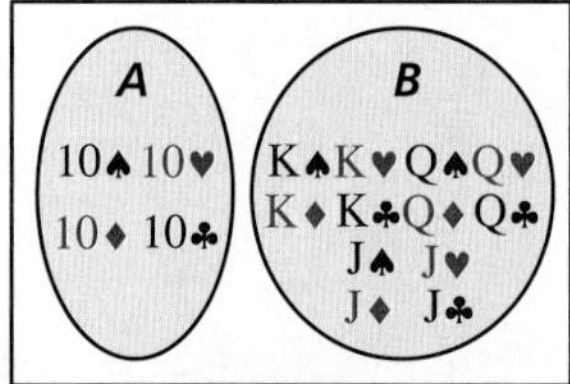

$$P(A \text{ or } B) = P(A) + P(B)$$ Write disjoint probability formula.

$$= \frac{4}{52} + \frac{12}{52}$$ Substitute known probabilities.

$$= \frac{16}{52}$$ Add.

$$= \frac{4}{13} \approx 0.308$$ Simplify and use technology.

▶ So, the probability that a randomly selected card is a 10 or a face card is about 30.8%.

EXAMPLE 2 Finding the Probability of Overlapping Events

WATCH

GO DIGITAL

A card is randomly selected from a standard deck of 52 playing cards. What is the probability that it is a face card *or* a spade?

SOLUTION

> **COMMON ERROR**
> When two events A and B overlap, as in Example 2, $P(A \text{ or } B)$ does not equal $P(A) + P(B)$.

Let event A be selecting a face card and event B be selecting a spade. Event A has 12 outcomes and event B has 13 outcomes. Of these, 3 outcomes are common to A and B. Find $P(A \text{ or } B)$.

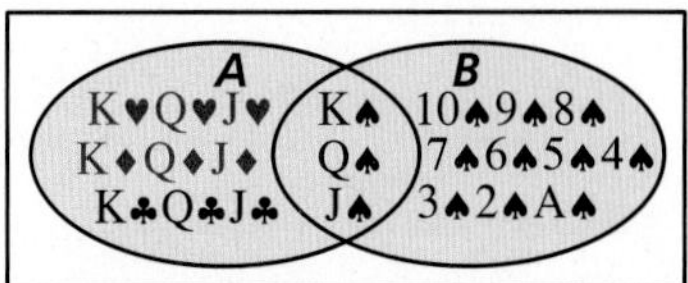

$$P(A \text{ or } B) = P(A) + P(B) - P(A \text{ and } B) \qquad \text{Write general formula.}$$

$$= \frac{12}{52} + \frac{13}{52} - \frac{3}{52} \qquad \text{Substitute known probabilities.}$$

$$= \frac{22}{52} \qquad \text{Add.}$$

$$= \frac{11}{26} \approx 0.423 \qquad \text{Simplify and use technology.}$$

EXAMPLE 3 Modeling Real Life

WATCH

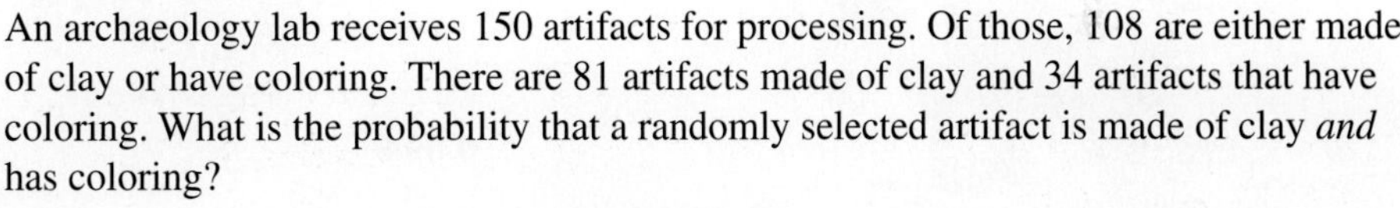

An archaeology lab receives 150 artifacts for processing. Of those, 108 are either made of clay or have coloring. There are 81 artifacts made of clay and 34 artifacts that have coloring. What is the probability that a randomly selected artifact is made of clay *and* has coloring?

SOLUTION

Let event A be selecting an artifact that is made of clay and event B be selecting an artifact that has coloring. From the given information, you know that $P(A) = \frac{81}{150}$, $P(B) = \frac{34}{150}$, and $P(A \text{ or } B) = \frac{108}{150}$. The probability that a randomly selected artifact is both made of clay *and* has coloring is $P(A \text{ and } B)$.

$$P(A \text{ or } B) = P(A) + P(B) - P(A \text{ and } B) \qquad \text{Write general formula.}$$

$$\frac{108}{150} = \frac{81}{150} + \frac{34}{150} - P(A \text{ and } B) \qquad \text{Substitute known probabilities.}$$

$$P(A \text{ and } B) = \frac{81}{150} + \frac{34}{150} - \frac{108}{150} \qquad \text{Solve for } P(A \text{ and } B).$$

$$P(A \text{ and } B) = \frac{7}{150} \qquad \text{Simplify.}$$

$$P(A \text{ and } B) \approx 0.047 \qquad \text{Use technology.}$$

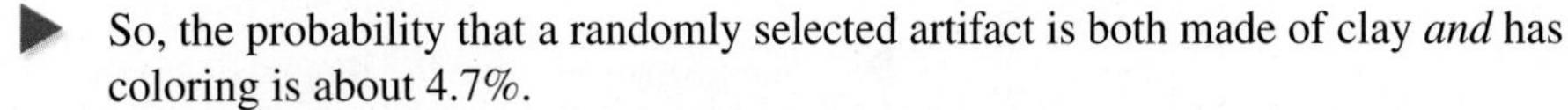

▶ So, the probability that a randomly selected artifact is both made of clay *and* has coloring is about 4.7%.

SELF-ASSESSMENT

1 I do not understand. 2 I can do it with help. 3 I can do it on my own. 4 I can teach someone else.

A card is randomly selected from a standard deck of 52 playing cards. Find the probability of the event.

1. selecting an ace *or* an 8
2. selecting a 10 *or* a diamond
3. Out of 200 students in a senior class, 113 students are either varsity athletes or on the honor roll. There are 74 seniors who are varsity athletes and 51 seniors who are on the honor roll. What is the probability that a randomly selected senior is both a varsity athlete *and* on the honor roll?

Using More Than One Probability Rule

The solution to some real-life problems may require the use of two or more probability rules, as shown in the next example.

EXAMPLE 4 Modeling Real Life

The American Diabetes Association estimates that 9.4% of people in the United States have diabetes. A medical lab has developed a simple diagnostic test for diabetes that is 98% accurate for people who have the disease and 95% accurate for people who do not have it. The medical lab gives the test to a randomly selected person. What is the probability that the diagnosis is correct?

SOLUTION

Let event A be "person has diabetes" and event B be "correct diagnosis." Notice that the probability of B depends on the occurrence of A, so the events are dependent. When A occurs, $P(B) = 0.98$. When A does not occur, $P(B) = 0.95$.

A probability tree diagram, where the probabilities are given along the branches, can help you see the different ways to obtain a correct diagnosis. Use the complements of events A and B to complete the diagram, where $\overline{A}$ is "person does not have diabetes" and $\overline{B}$ is "incorrect diagnosis." Notice that the probabilities for all branches from the same point must sum to 1.

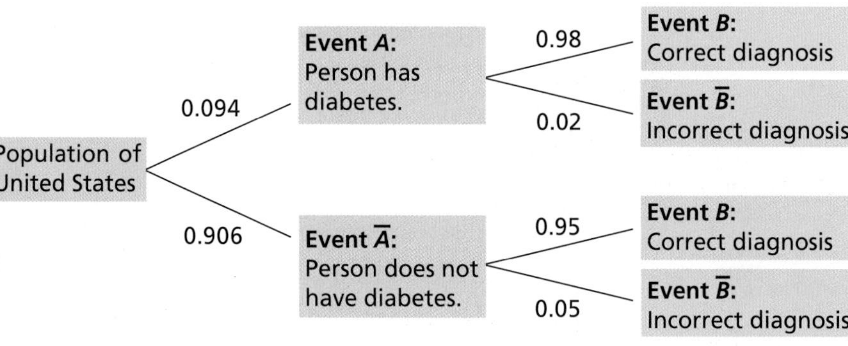

To find the probability that the diagnosis is correct, follow the branches leading to event B.

$$P(B) = P(A \text{ and } B) + P(\overline{A} \text{ and } B) \quad \text{Use tree diagram.}$$
$$= P(A) \cdot P(B|A) + P(\overline{A}) \cdot P(B|\overline{A}) \quad \text{Probability of dependent events}$$
$$= (0.094)(0.98) + (0.906)(0.95) \quad \text{Substitute.}$$
$$\approx 0.953 \quad \text{Use technology.}$$

▶ The probability that the diagnosis is correct is about 0.953, or 95.3%.

SELF-ASSESSMENT

1 I do not understand. 2 I can do it with help. 3 I can do it on my own. 4 I can teach someone else.

4. In Example 4, what is the probability that a randomly selected person diagnosed with diabetes actually has the disease?

5. A high school basketball team leads at halftime in 60% of the games in a season. The team wins 80% of the time when they have the halftime lead, but only 10% of the time when they do not. What is the probability that the team wins a particular game during the season?

8.5 Practice WITH CalcChat® AND CalcView®

GO DIGITAL

In Exercises 1 and 2, events *A* and *B* are disjoint. Find *P*(*A* or *B*).

1. $P(A) = 0.3, P(B) = 0.1$ 2. $P(A) = \frac{2}{3}, P(B) = \frac{1}{5}$

In Exercises 3–8, each section of the spinner shown has the same area. Find the probability of the event.

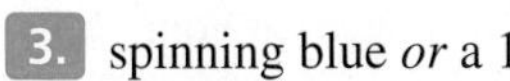

Examples 1 and 2

3. spinning blue *or* a 1

4. spinning green *or* a multiple of 4

5. spinning red *or* an odd number

6. spinning yellow *or* a number less than 5

7. spinning a factor of 6 *or* a number greater than 9

8. spinning an even number *or* a prime number

ERROR ANALYSIS In Exercises 9 and 10, describe and correct the error in finding the probability of randomly drawing the given card from a standard deck of 52 playing cards.

9. ✗
$$P(\text{heart or face card}) = P(\text{heart}) + P(\text{face card}) = \frac{13}{52} + \frac{12}{52} = \frac{25}{52}$$

10. ✗
$$P(\text{club or } 9) = P(\text{club}) + P(9) + P(\text{club and } 9) = \frac{13}{52} + \frac{4}{52} + \frac{1}{52} = \frac{9}{26}$$

11. **MP PROBLEM SOLVING** You perform an experiment for your science project to determine how well plants grow under different light sources. Of the 30 plants in the experiment, 12 receive visible light, 15 receive ultraviolet light, and 6 receive both visible and ultraviolet light. What is the probability that a plant in the experiment receives visible *or* ultraviolet light?

12. **MP PROBLEM SOLVING** Of 162 students honored at an academic awards banquet, 48 won awards for mathematics and 78 won awards for English. There are 14 students who won awards for both mathematics and English. A student is selected at random for an interview. What is the probability that the student won an award for English *or* mathematics?

13. **MODELING REAL LIFE** A group of 40 trees in a forest are not growing properly. A botanist determines that 34 of the trees have a disease or are being damaged by insects, with 18 trees having a disease and 20 being damaged by insects. What is the probability that a randomly selected tree has both a disease *and* is being damaged by insects? *Example 3*

STEM

14. **MODELING REAL LIFE** Out of 55 teenagers enrolled in dance classes, 30 teenagers take either hip hop or jazz classes. There are 13 teenagers who take hip hop classes and 24 teenagers who take jazz classes. What is the probability that a randomly selected teenager takes both hip hop *and* jazz classes?

15. **DRAWING CONCLUSIONS** A company is focus testing a new type of fruit drink. The focus group is 47% male. Of the responses, 40% of the males and 54% of the females said they would buy the fruit drink. What is the probability that a randomly selected person would buy the fruit drink? *Example 4*

16. **DRAWING CONCLUSIONS** The Redbirds trail the Bluebirds by one goal with 1 minute left in the hockey game. The Redbirds' coach must decide whether to remove the goalie and add a frontline player. The probabilities of each team scoring are shown in the table.

	Goalie	No goalie
Redbirds score	0.1	0.3
Bluebirds score	0.1	0.6

a. Find the probability that the Redbirds score and the Bluebirds do not score when the coach leaves the goalie in.

b. Find the probability that the Redbirds score and the Bluebirds do not score when the coach takes the goalie out.

c. Based on parts (a) and (b), what should the coach do?

17. **MP PROBLEM SOLVING** You can win concert tickets from a radio station if you are the first person to call when the song of the day is played, or if you are the first person to correctly answer a daily trivia question. The song of the day is announced at a random time between 7:00 and 7:30 A.M. The trivia question is asked at a random time between 7:15 and 7:45 A.M. You begin listening to the radio station at 7:20 A.M. Find the probability that you miss the announcement of the song of the day *or* the trivia question.

18. **HOW DO YOU SEE IT?**
Are events A and B disjoint events? Explain your reasoning.

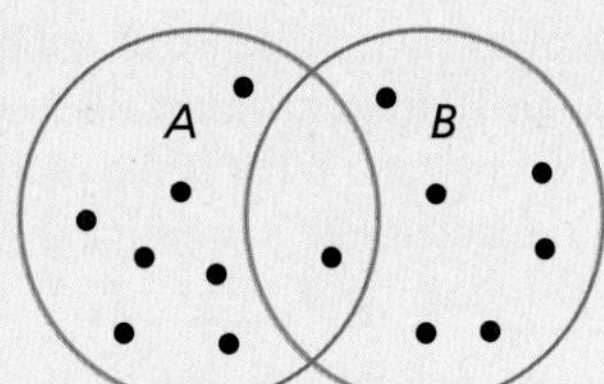

GO DIGITAL

19. **MP PROBLEM SOLVING** You take a bus from your neighborhood to a store. The express bus arrives at your neighborhood at a random time between 7:30 and 7:36 A.M. The local bus arrives at your neighborhood at a random time between 7:30 and 7:40 A.M. You arrive at the bus stop at 7:33 A.M. Find the probability that you miss the express bus *or* the local bus.

20. **THOUGHT PROVOKING**
Write a general rule for finding $P(A \text{ or } B \text{ or } C)$ for (a) disjoint and (b) overlapping events A, B, and C.

REVIEW & REFRESH

WATCH

In Exercises 21 and 22, write the function in vertex form. Then identify the vertex.

21. $y = x^2 + 6x - 4$

22. $y = 3x^2 - 12x + 11$

23. You randomly draw a card from a standard deck of 52 playing cards, set it aside, and then randomly draw another card from the deck. Find the probability that both cards are hearts.

24. Use the graph to solve $\log_5 (2x - 1) = 1$.

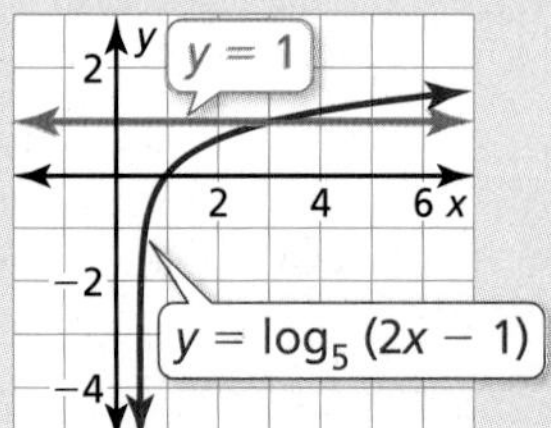

25. **MODELING REAL LIFE** A group of people wants to equally share the cost of a gift. The cost per person c (in dollars) varies inversely with the number n of people sharing the cost. When 3 people share the cost, the cost per person is $40. What is the cost per person when 5 people share the cost?

In Exercises 26 and 27, find the missing probability.

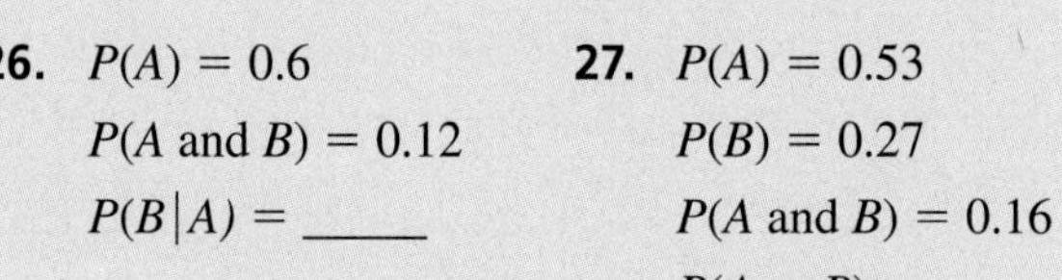

26. $P(A) = 0.6$
$P(A \text{ and } B) = 0.12$
$P(B|A) =$ _____

27. $P(A) = 0.53$
$P(B) = 0.27$
$P(A \text{ and } B) = 0.16$
$P(A \text{ or } B) =$ _____

In Exercises 28 and 29, find the inverse of the function.

28. $f(x) = \frac{1}{4}x + 3$

29. $f(x) = \sqrt{x} + 7$

30. A teacher asks students to vote on whether they want to take a test Friday or Monday. The results are shown in the two-way table. Make a two-way table that shows the joint and marginal relative frequencies. Then interpret one of the joint relative frequencies and one of the marginal relative frequencies.

		Vote	
		Friday	**Monday**
Gender	**Male**	7	8
	Female	5	6

8.6 Permutations and Combinations

Learning Target Count permutations and combinations.

Success Criteria

- I can explain the difference between permutations and combinations.
- I can find numbers of permutations and combinations.
- I can find probabilities using permutations and combinations.

EXPLORE IT! Counting Outcomes

Work with a partner.

a. A fair conducts three obstacle course races. In how many different orders can the dogs finish in each race? Justify your answers.

Race 1

Labrador Retriever

Golden Retriever

Race 2

Golden Retriever

Labrador Retriever

German Shepherd

Race 3

Dalmation

German Shepherd

Golden Retriever

Labrador Retriever

b. For each race in part (a), in how many different ways can the dogs finish first and second? Justify your answers.

c. For each race in part (a), how many different pairs of dogs can you form?

d. Explain why your answers in part (c) are different from your answers in part (b).

Math Practice

Reason Abstractly

In how many different orders can n dogs finish in a race? Explain your reasoning.

Permutations

GO DIGITAL

Vocabulary AZ VOCAB

permutation, *p. 440*
n factorial, *p. 440*
combination, *p. 442*
Binomial Theorem, *p. 444*

A **permutation** is an arrangement of objects in which order is important. For instance, the 6 possible permutations of the letters A, B, and C are shown.

ABC ACB BAC BCA CAB CBA

EXAMPLE 1 **Counting Permutations**

Consider the letters in the word JULY.

a. In how many ways can you arrange all of the letters?

b. In how many ways can you arrange 2 of the letters?

SOLUTION

a. Because the order of the letters is important, use the Fundamental Counting Principle to find the number of permutations of the letters in the word JULY.

$$\text{Number of permutations} = \begin{pmatrix}\text{Choices for}\\ \text{1st letter}\end{pmatrix}\begin{pmatrix}\text{Choices for}\\ \text{2nd letter}\end{pmatrix}\begin{pmatrix}\text{Choices for}\\ \text{3rd letter}\end{pmatrix}\begin{pmatrix}\text{Choices for}\\ \text{4th letter}\end{pmatrix}$$

$$= 4 \cdot 3 \cdot 2 \cdot 1$$

$$= 24$$

▶ There are 24 ways you can arrange all of the letters in the word JULY.

REMEMBER

Fundamental Counting Principle: If one event can occur in m ways and another event can occur in n ways, then the number of ways that both events can occur is $m \cdot n$. The Fundamental Counting Principle can be extended to three or more events.

b. When arranging 2 letters of the word JULY, you have 4 choices for the first letter and 3 choices for the second letter.

$$\text{Number of permutations} = \begin{pmatrix}\text{Choices for}\\ \text{1st letter}\end{pmatrix}\begin{pmatrix}\text{Choices for}\\ \text{2nd letter}\end{pmatrix}$$

$$= 4 \cdot 3$$

$$= 12$$

▶ There are 12 ways you can arrange 2 of the letters in the word JULY.

In Example 1(a), you evaluated the expression $4 \cdot 3 \cdot 2 \cdot 1$. This expression can be written as 4! and is read "4 *factorial*." For any positive integer n, the product of the integers from 1 to n is called ***n* factorial** and is written as

$$n! = n \cdot (n-1) \cdot (n-2) \cdot \cdots \cdot 3 \cdot 2 \cdot 1.$$

As a special case, the value of 0! is defined to be 1.

In Example 1(b), you found the permutations of 4 objects taken 2 at a time. You can also find the number of permutations using the following formula.

KEY IDEA

Permutations

Formula

The number of permutations of n objects taken r at a time, where $r \le n$, is given by

$${}_nP_r = \frac{n!}{(n-r)!}.$$

Example

The number of permutations of 4 objects taken 2 at a time is

$${}_4P_2 = \frac{4!}{(4-2)!} = \frac{4 \cdot 3 \cdot \cancel{2!}}{\cancel{2!}} = 12.$$

EXAMPLE 2 Using the Permutations Formula

Ten horses run in a race. In how many different ways can the horses finish first, second, and third? (Assume there are no ties.)

SOLUTION

To find the number of permutations of 3 horses chosen from 10, find ${}_{10}P_3$.

$${}_{10}P_3 = \frac{10!}{(10-3)!}$$ Permutations formula

$$= \frac{10!}{7!}$$ Subtract.

$$= \frac{10 \cdot 9 \cdot 8 \cdot \cancel{7!}}{\cancel{7!}}$$ Expand 10!. Divide out the common factor, 7!.

$$= 720$$ Simplify.

▶ There are 720 ways for the horses to finish first, second, and third.

Check

nPr(10,3) = 720

EXAMPLE 3 Finding a Probability Using Permutations

You ride on a float with your soccer team in a parade. There are 12 floats in the parade, and their order is chosen at random. Find the probability that your float is first and the float with the school chorus is second.

SOLUTION

Step 1 Write the number of possible ways that two of the floats can be first and second as the number of permutations of the 12 floats taken 2 at a time.

$${}_{12}P_2 = \frac{12!}{(12-2)!}$$ Permutations formula

$$= \frac{12!}{10!}$$ Subtract.

$$= \frac{12 \cdot 11 \cdot \cancel{10!}}{\cancel{10!}}$$ Expand 12!. Divide out the common factor, 10!.

$$= 132$$ Simplify.

Step 2 Find the number of favorable outcomes.

Only one of the possible permutations includes your float first and the float with the school chorus second.

Step 3 Find the probability.

$$P(\text{soccer team is 1st, chorus is 2nd}) = \frac{1}{132}$$

▶ The probability is $\frac{1}{132}$.

SELF-ASSESSMENT

1 I do not understand. 2 I can do it with help. 3 I can do it on my own. 4 I can teach someone else.

1. Consider the letters in the word MARCH. In how many ways can you arrange (a) all of the letters and (b) 3 of the letters?
2. **WHAT IF?** In Example 3, there are 14 floats in the parade. Find the probability that the soccer team is first and the chorus is second.
3. **MP STRUCTURE** Find the number of permutations of n objects taken n at a time. Justify your answer.

Combinations

A **combination** is a selection of objects in which order is *not* important. For instance, in a drawing for 3 identical prizes, the order of the winners does not matter. If the prizes were different, then the order would matter.

EXAMPLE 4 Counting Combinations

Count the possible combinations of 2 letters chosen from the list A, B, C, D.

SOLUTION

List all of the permutations of 2 letters from the list A, B, C, D. Because order is not important in a combination, cross out any duplicate pairs.

AB	AC	AD	~~BA~~	BC	BD
~~CA~~	~~CB~~	CD	~~DA~~	~~DB~~	~~DC~~

BD and DB are the same pair.

▶ There are 6 possible combinations of 2 letters from the list A, B, C, D.

In Example 4, you found the number of combinations of objects by making an organized list. You can also find the number of combinations using the following formula.

KEY IDEA

Combinations

Formula

The number of combinations of n objects taken r at a time, where $r \le n$, is given by

$${}_nC_r = \frac{n!}{(n-r)! \cdot r!}.$$

Example

The number of combinations of 4 objects taken 2 at a time is

$${}_4C_2 = \frac{4!}{(4-2)! \cdot 2!} = \frac{4 \cdot 3 \cdot \cancel{2!}}{\cancel{2!} \cdot (2 \cdot 1)} = 6.$$

EXAMPLE 5 Using the Combinations Formula

You order a sandwich at a restaurant. You can choose 2 side dishes from a list of 8. How many combinations of side dishes are possible?

SOLUTION

The order in which you choose the side dishes is not important. So, to find the number of combinations of 8 side dishes taken 2 at a time, find ${}_8C_2$.

$${}_8C_2 = \frac{8!}{(8-2)! \cdot 2!}$$ Combinations formula

$$= \frac{8!}{6! \cdot 2!}$$ Subtract.

$$= \frac{8 \cdot 7 \cdot \cancel{6!}}{\cancel{6!} \cdot (2 \cdot 1)}$$ Expand 8! and 2!. Divide out the common factor, 6!.

$$= 28$$ Simplify.

▶ There are 28 different combinations of side dishes.

Check

```
nCr(8,2)
                 = 28
```

EXAMPLE 6 Finding a Probability Using Combinations

A yearbook editor has selected 14 photos, including one of you and one of your friend, to use in a collage for the yearbook. The photos are placed at random. There is room for 2 photos at the top of the page. What is the probability that your photo and your friend's photo are the 2 placed at the top of the page?

SOLUTION

1. **Understand the Problem** You are given the total number of photos in the collage and the number of photos placed at the top of the page. You are asked to find the probability that your photo and your friend's photo are placed at the top of the page.

2. **Make a Plan** The order in which the photos are chosen is not important. Find the number of possible outcomes and the number of favorable outcomes. Then use these numbers to find the probability.

3. **Solve and Check**

Step 1 Write the number of possible outcomes as the number of combinations of 14 photos taken 2 at a time, or ${}_{14}C_2$.

$${}_{14}C_2 = \frac{14!}{(14-2)! \bullet 2!}$$ Combinations formula

$$= \frac{14!}{12! \bullet 2!}$$ Subtract.

$$= \frac{14 \bullet 13 \bullet \cancel{12!}}{\cancel{12!} \bullet (2 \bullet 1)}$$ Expand 14! and 2!. Divide out the common factor, 12!.

$$= 91$$ Simplify.

Check

nCr(14,2)	=91

Step 2 Find the number of favorable outcomes.

Only one of the possible combinations includes your photo and your friend's photo.

Step 3 Find the probability.

$$P(\text{your photo and your friend's photo are chosen}) = \frac{1}{91}$$

▶ The probability is $\frac{1}{91}$.

SELF-ASSESSMENT

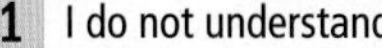

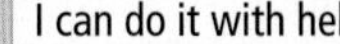

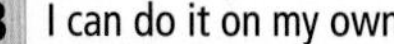

4. Count the possible combinations of 3 letters chosen from the list A, B, C, D, E.

5. **WHICH ONE DOESN'T BELONG?** Which expression does *not* belong with the other three? Explain your reasoning.

$\frac{7!}{2! \bullet 5!}$	${}_7C_5$	${}_7C_2$	$\frac{7!}{(7-2)!}$

6. **WHAT IF?** In Example 5, you can choose 3 side dishes out of the list of 8 side dishes. How many combinations are possible?

7. **WHAT IF?** In Example 6, there are 20 photos in the collage. Find the probability that your photo and your friend's photo are the 2 placed at the top of the page.

GO DIGITAL

Binomial Expansions

In Section 4.2, you used Pascal's Triangle to find binomial expansions. The table shows that the coefficients in the expansion of $(a + b)^n$ correspond to combinations.

	n	Pascal's Triangle as Numbers	Pascal's Triangle as Combinations	Binomial Expansion
0th row	0	1	${}_0C_0$	$(a + b)^0 = 1$
1st row	1	1 1	${}_1C_0 \quad {}_1C_1$	$(a + b)^1 = 1a + 1b$
2nd row	2	1 2 1	${}_2C_0 \quad {}_2C_1 \quad {}_2C_2$	$(a + b)^2 = 1a^2 + 2ab + 1b^2$
3rd row	3	1 3 3 1	${}_3C_0 \quad {}_3C_1 \quad {}_3C_2 \quad {}_3C_3$	$(a + b)^3 = 1a^3 + 3a^2b + 3ab^2 + 1b^3$

The results in the table are generalized in the **Binomial Theorem**.

KEY IDEA

The Binomial Theorem

For any positive integer n, the binomial expansion of $(a + b)^n$ is

$$(a + b)^n = {}_nC_0\, a^nb^0 + {}_nC_1\, a^{n-1}b^1 + {}_nC_2\, a^{n-2}b^2 + \cdots + {}_nC_n\, a^0b^n.$$

Notice that each term in the expansion of $(a + b)^n$ has the form ${}_nC_r\, a^{n-r}b^r$, where r is an integer from 0 to n.

EXAMPLE 7 Using the Binomial Theorem

WATCH

a. Use the Binomial Theorem to write the expansion of $(x^2 + y)^3$.

b. Find the coefficient of x^4 in the expansion of $(3x + 2)^{10}$.

SOLUTION

a. $(x^2 + y)^3 = {}_3C_0(x^2)^3y^0 + {}_3C_1(x^2)^2y^1 + {}_3C_2(x^2)^1y^2 + {}_3C_3(x^2)^0y^3$

$= (1)(x^6)(1) + (3)(x^4)(y^1) + (3)(x^2)(y^2) + (1)(1)(y^3)$

$= x^6 + 3x^4y + 3x^2y^2 + y^3$

b. From the Binomial Theorem, you know

$$(3x + 2)^{10} = {}_{10}C_0(3x)^{10}(2)^0 + {}_{10}C_1(3x)^9(2)^1 + \cdots + {}_{10}C_{10}(3x)^0(2)^{10}.$$

Each term in the expansion has the form ${}_{10}C_r(3x)^{10-r}(2)^r$. The term containing x^4 occurs when $r = 6$.

$${}_{10}C_6(3x)^4(2)^6 = (210)(81x^4)(64) = 1{,}088{,}640x^4$$

▶ The coefficient of x^4 is 1,088,640.

SELF-ASSESSMENT 1 I do not understand. 2 I can do it with help. 3 I can do it on my own. 4 I can teach someone else.

8. Use the Binomial Theorem to write the expansion of (a) $(x + 3)^5$ and (b) $(2p - q)^4$.

9. Find the coefficient of x^5 in the expansion of $(x - 3)^7$.

10. Find the coefficient of x^3 in the expansion of $(2x + 5)^8$.

8.6 Practice WITH CalcChat® AND CalcView®

GO DIGITAL

In Exercises 1–6, find the number of ways you can arrange (a) all of the letters and (b) 2 of the letters in the given word. *Example 1*

1. AT

2. TRY

3. ROCK

4. WATER

5. FAMILY

6. FLOWERS

In Exercises 7–12, evaluate the expression.

7. ${}_5P_2$

8. ${}_7P_3$

9. ${}_9P_1$

10. ${}_6P_5$

11. ${}_8P_6$

12. ${}_{12}P_0$

13. MODELING REAL LIFE Eleven students are competing in a graphic design contest. In how many different ways can the students finish first, second, and third? *Example 2*

14. MODELING REAL LIFE Six friends go to a movie theater. In how many different ways can they sit together in a row of 6 empty seats?

15. MODELING REAL LIFE You and your friend are 2 of 8 servers working a shift in a restaurant. At the beginning of the shift, the manager randomly assigns one section to each server. Find the probability that you are assigned Section 1 and your friend is assigned Section 2. *Example 3*

16. MODELING REAL LIFE You make 6 posters to hold up at a basketball game. Each poster has a letter of the word TIGERS. You and 5 friends sit next to each other in a row. The posters are distributed at random. Find the probability that TIGERS is spelled correctly when you hold up the posters.

In Exercises 17–20, count the possible combinations of *r* letters chosen from the given list. *Example 4*

17. A, B, C, D; $r = 3$

18. L, M, N, O; $r = 2$

19. U, V, W, X, Y, Z; $r = 3$

20. D, E, F, G, H; $r = 4$

In Exercises 21–26, evaluate the expression.

21. ${}_5C_1$

22. ${}_8C_5$

23. ${}_9C_9$

24. ${}_8C_6$

25. ${}_{12}C_3$

26. ${}_{11}C_4$

27. MODELING REAL LIFE A team of 25 rowers attends a rowing tournament. Five rowers compete at a time. How many combinations of 5 rowers are possible? *Example 5*

28. MODELING REAL LIFE A grocery store sells 7 different flavors of vegetable dip. You have enough money to purchase 2 flavors. How many combinations of 2 flavors of vegetable dip are possible?

ERROR ANALYSIS In Exercises 29 and 30, describe and correct the error in evaluating the expression.

29.

✗ $${}_{11}P_7 = \frac{11!}{(11-7)} = \frac{11!}{4} = 9{,}979{,}200$$

30.

✗ $${}_9C_4 = \frac{9!}{(9-4)!} = \frac{9!}{5!} = 3024$$

31. COLLEGE PREP Which expression has the greatest value, where $n > 4$?

Ⓐ ${}_nP_{n-1}$

Ⓑ ${}_nP_{n-2}$

Ⓒ ${}_nP_{n-3}$

Ⓓ ${}_nP_{n-4}$

32. COLLEGE PREP What is the solution of ${}_nC_{n-2} = {}_nC_{n-3}$?

Ⓐ $n = 3$

Ⓑ $n = 5$

Ⓒ $n = 6$

Ⓓ $n = 14$

MP REASONING In Exercises 33–36, tell whether the question can be answered using *permutations* or *combinations*. Explain your reasoning. Then answer the question.

33. To complete an exam, you must answer 8 questions from a list of 10 questions. In how many ways can you complete the exam?

34. Ten students are auditioning for 3 different roles in a play. In how many ways can the 3 roles be filled?

35. Fifty-two athletes are competing in a bicycle race. In how many orders can the bicyclists finish first, second, and third? (Assume there are no ties.)

36. An employee at a pet store needs to catch 5 tetras in an aquarium containing 27 tetras. In how many groupings can the employee capture 5 tetras?

37. MODELING REAL LIFE You and your friend are in the studio audience on a game show. From an audience of 300 people, 2 people are randomly selected as contestants. What is the probability that you and your friend are chosen? *Example 6*

38. MODELING REAL LIFE You work 5 evenings each week at a bookstore. Your supervisor assigns you 5 evenings at random from the 7 possibilities. What is the probability that your schedule does not include working on the weekend?

39. MP PATTERNS Describe why it makes sense to define 0! as 1.

40. CRITICAL THINKING Show that each identity is true for any whole numbers r and n, where $0 \le r \le n$.

a. ${}_nC_n = 1$

b. ${}_{n+1}C_r = {}_nC_r + {}_nC_{r-1}$

41. OPEN-ENDED Describe a real-life situation where the number of possibilities is given by ${}_5P_2$. Then describe a real-life situation where the number of possibilities is given by ${}_5C_2$.

42. MP REASONING Consider a set of 4 objects.

a. Are there more permutations of all 4 of the objects or of 3 of the objects? Explain your reasoning.

b. Are there more combinations of all 4 of the objects or of 3 of the objects? Explain your reasoning.

c. Compare your answers to parts (a) and (b).

43. MP REPEATED REASONING Complete the table for each given value of r. Then write an inequality relating ${}_nP_r$ and ${}_nC_r$. Explain your reasoning.

	$r = 0$	$r = 1$	$r = 2$	$r = 3$
${}_3P_r$				
${}_3C_r$				

44. MP REASONING Write an equation that relates ${}_nP_r$ and ${}_nC_r$. Then use your equation to find and interpret the value of $\frac{{}_{182}P_4}{{}_{182}C_4}$.

MP REASONING In Exercises 45 and 46, find the probability of winning a lottery using the given rules. Assume that lottery numbers are selected at random.

45. You must correctly select 6 numbers, each an integer from 0 to 49. The order is not important.

46. You must correctly select 4 numbers, each an integer from 0 to 9. The order is important.

In Exercises 47–54, use the Binomial Theorem to write the binomial expansion. *Example 7a*

47. $(x + 2)^3$

48. $(c - 4)^5$

49. $(a + 3b)^4$

50. $(4p - q)^6$

51. $(w^3 - 3)^4$

52. $(2s^4 + 5)^5$

53. $(3u + v^2)^6$

54. $(x^3 - y^2)^4$

In Exercises 55–60, use the given value of n to find the coefficient of x^n in the expansion of the binomial. *Example 7b*

55. $(x - 2)^{10}, n = 5$

56. $(x - 3)^7, n = 4$

57. $(2x + 5)^{12}, n = 7$

58. $(3x - 1)^9, n = 2$

59. $\left(\frac{1}{2}x - 4\right)^{11}, n = 4$

60. $\left(\frac{1}{4}x + 6\right)^6, n = 3$

61. MP REASONING Write the eighth row of Pascal's Triangle as combinations and as numbers.

62. **MP PROBLEM SOLVING** The triangular numbers are a sequence of numbers found in Pascal's Triangle. The first four triangular numbers are 1, 3, 6, and 10.

a. Use Pascal's Triangle to write the first four triangular numbers as combinations.

1
1 1
1 2 1
1 3 3 1
1 4 6 4 1
1 5 10 10 5 1

b. Use your result from part (a) to write an explicit rule for the nth triangular number T_n.

63. **CONNECTING CONCEPTS**
A polygon is convex when no line that contains a side of the polygon contains a point in the interior of the polygon. Consider a convex polygon with n sides.

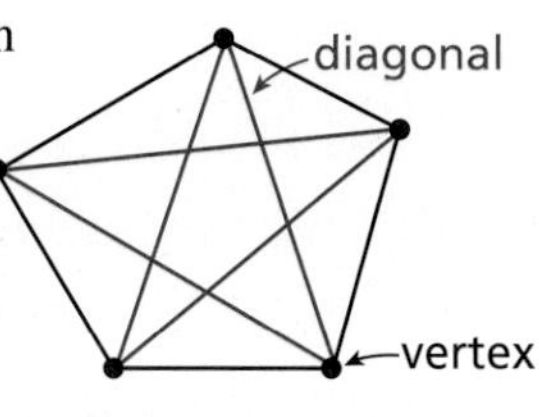

a. Use the combinations formula to write an expression for the number of diagonals in an n-sided polygon.

b. Use your result from part (a) to write a formula for the number of diagonals of an n-sided convex polygon.

64. **MP PROBLEM SOLVING** You are ordering a burrito with 2 main ingredients and 3 toppings. The menu below shows the possible choices. How many different burritos are possible?

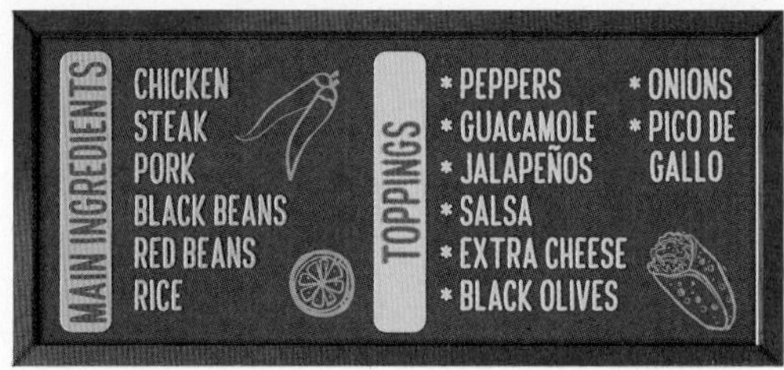

65. **MP PROBLEM SOLVING** You select 2 different contemporary music playlists and 1 classical music playlist from the music collection shown. How many different sets of playlists can you select?

GO DIGITAL

66. **MP PROBLEM SOLVING** Every student in your history class is required to present a project in front of the class. Each day, 4 students present in an order chosen at random by the teacher. You present on the first day.

a. What is the probability that you are chosen to be the first or second presenter on the first day?

b. What is the probability that you are chosen to be the second or third presenter on the first day? Compare your answer with that in part (a).

67. **MP PROBLEM SOLVING** The organizer of a cast party for a drama club asks each of the 6 cast members to bring 1 food item from a list of 10 items. Assuming each member randomly chooses a food item to bring, what is the probability that at least 2 of the 6 cast members bring the same item?

68. **HOW DO YOU SEE IT?**
A bag contains one green marble, one red marble, and one blue marble. The diagram shows the possible outcomes of randomly drawing three marbles from the bag without replacement.

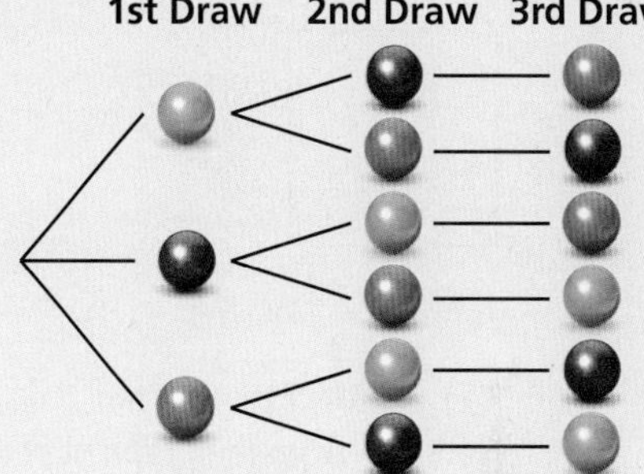

a. How many combinations of three marbles can be drawn from the bag? Explain.

b. How many permutations of three marbles can be drawn from the bag? Explain.

69. **MP PROBLEM SOLVING** You and a friend are two of 10 students performing in a school talent show. The order of the performances is determined at random. The first 5 performers go on stage before the intermission.

a. What is the probability that you are the last performer before the intermission and your friend performs immediately before you?

b. What is the probability that you are *not* the first performer?

70. **THOUGHT PROVOKING**
How many integers, greater than 999 but not greater than 4000, can be formed with the digits 0, 1, 2, 3, and 4? Repetition of digits is allowed.

71. **MP PROBLEM SOLVING** Consider a standard deck of 52 playing cards. The order in which the cards are dealt for a "hand" does not matter. How many different 5-card hands have all 5 cards of a single suit?

72. **MP PROBLEM SOLVING** There are 30 students in your class. Your science teacher chooses 5 students at random to complete a group project. Find the probability that you and your 2 best friends in the science class are chosen to work in the group. Explain how you found your answer.

73. **CONNECTING CONCEPTS** Use combinations to determine how many lines can be drawn through each pair of points below.

E•

A• *B*• *D*•
C•

74. **DIG DEEPER** Follow the steps below to explore a famous probability problem called the *birthday problem*. (Assume there are 365 equally likely birthdays possible.)

GO DIGITAL

a. What is the probability that at least 2 people share the same birthday in a group of 6 randomly chosen people? in a group of 10 randomly chosen people?

b. Generalize the results from part (a) by writing a formula for the probability $P(n)$ that at least 2 people in a group of n people share the same birthday. (*Hint:* Use ${}_nP_r$ notation in your formula.)

c. Use technology to determine by what group size the probability that at least 2 people share the same birthday first exceeds 50%.

REVIEW & REFRESH

75. Find the dimensions of the cube.

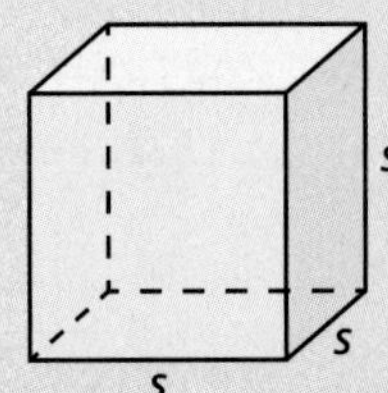

Volume = 343 cm³

76. Graph $f(x) = |x - 2| + 1$. Then describe the transformations from the graph of $f(x) = |x|$ to the graph of the function.

In Exercises 77 and 78, use the Binomial Theorem to write the binomial expansion

77. $(x + 6)^3$

78. $(2x - 3y)^3$

79. You spin the wheel shown. Each section of the wheel has the same area. Use a sample space to determine whether randomly spinning red and then blue are independent events.

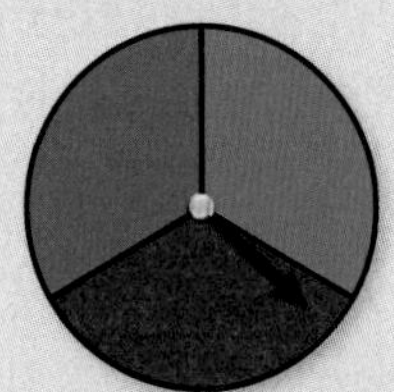

80. **MP NUMBER SENSE** Events A and B are dependent. Suppose $P(A \text{ and } B) = 0.04$ and $P(A) = 0.16$. Find $P(B \mid A)$.

In Exercises 81 and 82, graph the function. Find the domain and range of the function.

81. $g(x) = -(x)^{1/4} + 2$

82. $f(x) = \frac{1}{2}\sqrt[3]{x} + 1$

83. Determine the type of function represented by the table. Explain your reasoning.

x	−2	−1	0	1	2	3
y	1	2	4	8	16	32

84. Use the graphs of f and r to describe the transformation from the graph of f to the graph of r.

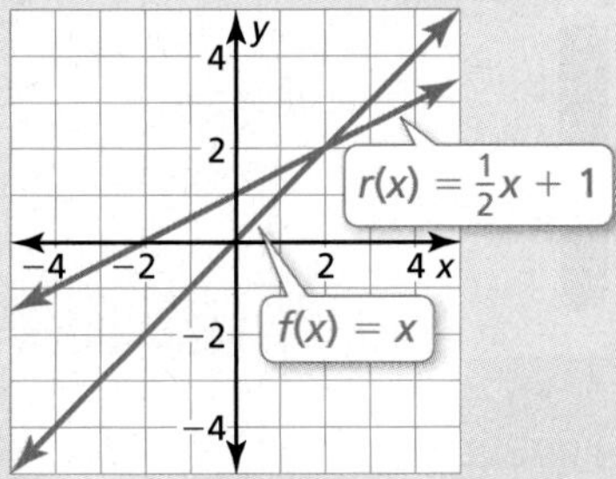

85. Solve the equation $x^2 + 3x = 5x^2 + 2x$ by graphing.

86. Events A and B are disjoint. Find $P(A \text{ or } B)$ when $P(A) = 0.4$ and $P(B) = 0.6$.

87. Determine whether the function $y = (1.5)^x$ represents *exponential growth* or *exponential decay*. Then graph the function.

8.7 Binomial Distributions

Learning Target Understand binomial distributions.

Success Criteria

- I can explain the meaning of a probability distribution.
- I can construct and interpret probability distributions.
- I can find probabilities using binomial distributions.

EXPLORE IT! Counting Outcomes

Work with a partner. The diagrams represent the possible outcomes when flipping n coins.

STUDY TIP

When 4 coins are flipped, the possible outcomes are

TTTT TTTH TTHT THTT
HTTT TTHH THTH THHT
HTTH HTHT HHTT THHH
HTHH HHTH HHHT HHHH.

The diagram shows the numbers of outcomes having 0, 1, 2, 3, and 4 heads.

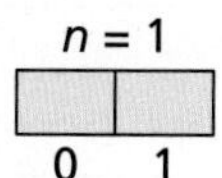

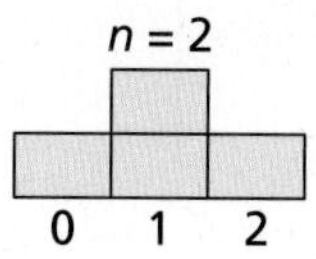

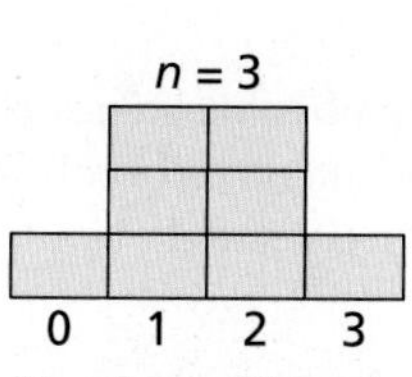

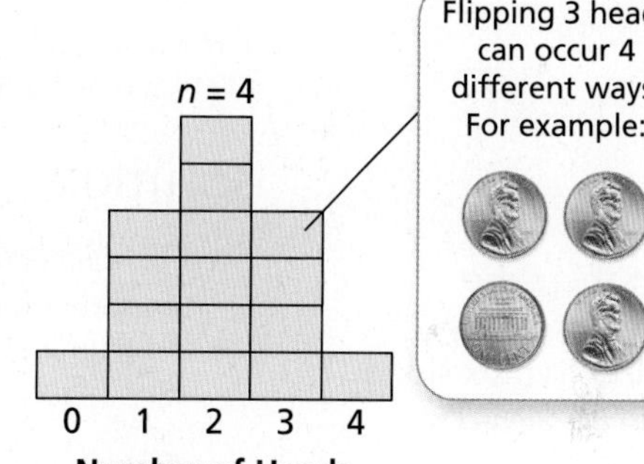

a. What is the probability of flipping 2 heads when 4 coins are flipped? Explain your reasoning.

b. Draw a similar diagram that represents the possible outcomes when flipping 5 coins. What is the probability of flipping 2 heads when 5 coins are flipped?

c. Complete the table showing the numbers of ways in which 2 heads can occur when n coins are flipped.

n	2	3	4	5	6
Occurrences of 2 heads					

d. Describe the pattern shown in part (c). Use the pattern to find the number of ways in which 2 heads can occur when 7 coins are flipped. Justify your answer.

Math Practice

Apply Mathematics

Finding the number of occurrences of 2 heads is the same as finding the number of ways that you can choose 2 out of n coins to show heads. What expression can you use to represent this number?

Probability Distributions

Vocabulary

random variable, *p. 450*
probability distribution, *p. 450*
binomial distribution, *p. 451*
binomial experiment, *p. 451*

A **random variable** is a variable whose value is determined by the outcomes of a probability experiment. For example, when you roll a six-sided die, you can define a random variable x that represents the number showing on the die. So, the possible values of x are 1, 2, 3, 4, 5, and 6. For every random variable, a *probability distribution* can be defined.

KEY IDEA

Probability Distributions

A **probability distribution** is a function that gives the probability of each possible value of a random variable. The sum of all the probabilities in a probability distribution must equal 1.

Probability Distribution for Rolling a Six-Sided Die

x	1	2	3	4	5	6
$P(x)$	$\frac{1}{6}$	$\frac{1}{6}$	$\frac{1}{6}$	$\frac{1}{6}$	$\frac{1}{6}$	$\frac{1}{6}$

EXAMPLE 1 Constructing a Probability Distribution

Let x be a random variable that represents the sum when two six-sided dice are rolled. Make a table and draw a histogram showing the probability distribution for x.

STUDY TIP

Recall that there are 36 possible outcomes when rolling two six-sided dice. These are listed in Example 3 on page 406.

SOLUTION

Step 1 Make a table. The possible values of x are the integers from 2 to 12. The table shows how many outcomes of rolling two dice produce each value of x. Divide the number of outcomes for x by 36 to find $P(x)$.

x (sum)	2	3	4	5	6	7	8	9	10	11	12
Number of Outcomes	1	2	3	4	5	6	5	4	3	2	1
$P(x)$	$\frac{1}{36}$	$\frac{1}{18}$	$\frac{1}{12}$	$\frac{1}{9}$	$\frac{5}{36}$	$\frac{1}{6}$	$\frac{5}{36}$	$\frac{1}{9}$	$\frac{1}{12}$	$\frac{1}{18}$	$\frac{1}{36}$

Step 2 Draw a histogram where the intervals are given by x and the relative frequencies are given by $P(x)$.

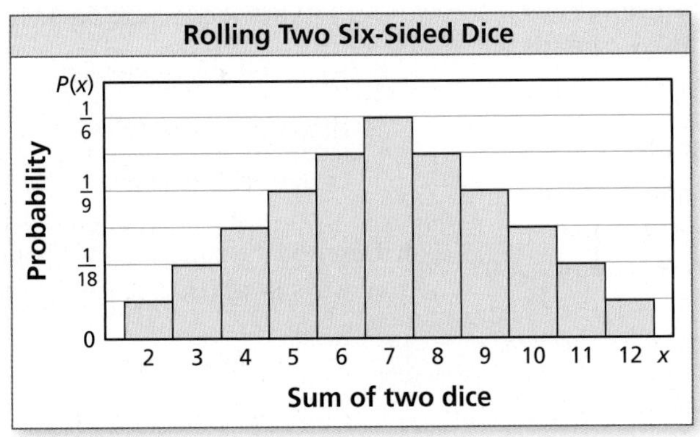

EXAMPLE 2 Interpreting a Probability Distribution

Use the probability distribution in Example 1 to answer each question.

a. What is the most likely sum when rolling two six-sided dice?

b. What is the probability that the sum of the two dice is at least 10?

SOLUTION

a. The most likely sum when rolling two six-sided dice is the value of x for which $P(x)$ is greatest. This probability is greatest for $x = 7$. So, when rolling the two dice, the most likely sum is 7.

b. The probability that the sum of the two dice is at least 10 is

$$\begin{aligned} P(x \geq 10) &= P(x = 10) + P(x = 11) + P(x = 12) \\ &= \frac{3}{36} + \frac{2}{36} + \frac{1}{36} \\ &= \frac{6}{36} \\ &= \frac{1}{6} \\ &\approx 0.167. \end{aligned}$$

▶ The probability is about 16.7%.

SELF-ASSESSMENT

1 I do not understand. 2 I can do it with help. 3 I can do it on my own. 4 I can teach someone else.

An octahedral die has eight sides numbered 1 through 8. Let x be a random variable that represents the sum when two such dice are rolled.

1. Make a table and draw a histogram showing the probability distribution for x.

2. What is the most likely sum when rolling the two dice?

3. What is the probability that the sum of the two dice is at most 3?

4. **WRITING** Explain why the sum of all the probabilities in a probability distribution must equal 1.

Binomial Distributions

One type of probability distribution is a **binomial distribution**. A binomial distribution shows the probabilities of the outcomes of a *binomial experiment*.

KEY IDEA

Binomial Experiments

A **binomial experiment** meets the following conditions.

- There are n independent trials.
- Each trial has only two possible outcomes: success and failure.
- The probability of success is the same for each trial. This probability is denoted by p. The probability of failure is $1 - p$.

For a binomial experiment, the probability of exactly k successes in n trials is

$$P(k \text{ successes}) = {}_nC_k p^k (1 - p)^{n-k}.$$

EXAMPLE 3 Constructing a Binomial Distribution

GO DIGITAL

According to a survey, about 60% of teenagers ages 13 to 17 in the U.S. say they spend time with friends online daily. You ask 6 randomly chosen teenagers (ages 13 to 17) whether they spend time with friends online daily. Draw a histogram of the binomial distribution for your survey.

SOLUTION

The probability that a randomly selected teenager says they spend time with friends online daily is $p = 0.6$. Because you survey 6 people, $n = 6$.

Math Practice

Calculate Accurately
When probabilities are rounded, the sum of the probabilities may differ slightly from 1.

$P(k = 0) = {}_6C_0(0.6)^0(0.4)^6 \approx 0.004$

$P(k = 1) = {}_6C_1(0.6)^1(0.4)^5 \approx 0.037$

$P(k = 2) = {}_6C_2(0.6)^2(0.4)^4 \approx 0.138$

$P(k = 3) = {}_6C_3(0.6)^3(0.4)^3 \approx 0.276$

$P(k = 4) = {}_6C_4(0.6)^4(0.4)^2 \approx 0.311$

$P(k = 5) = {}_6C_5(0.6)^5(0.4)^1 \approx 0.187$

$P(k = 6) = {}_6C_6(0.6)^6(0.4)^0 \approx 0.047$

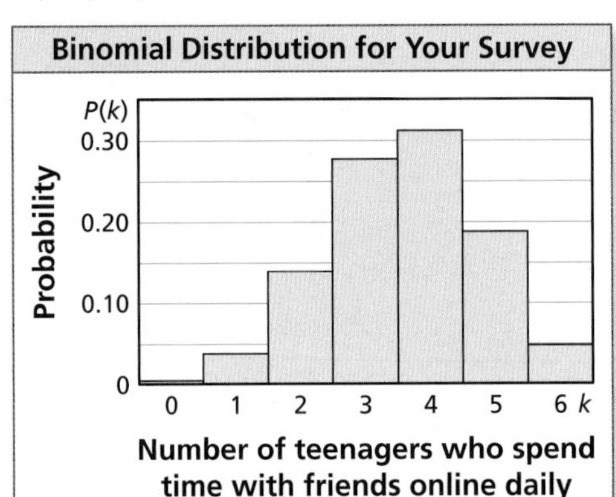

A histogram of the distribution is shown.

EXAMPLE 4 Interpreting a Binomial Distribution

Use the binomial distribution in Example 3 to answer each question.

a. What is the most likely outcome of the survey?

b. What is the probability that at most 2 teenagers spend time with friends online daily?

COMMON ERROR

Be sure you include $P(k = 0)$ when finding the probability that at most 2 teenagers spend time with friends online daily.

SOLUTION

a. The most likely outcome of the survey is the value of k for which $P(k)$ is greatest. This probability is greatest for $k = 4$. The most likely outcome is that 4 of the 6 teenagers spend time with friends online daily.

b. The probability that at most 2 teenagers spend time with friends online daily is

$$P(k \le 2) = P(k = 0) + P(k = 1) + P(k = 2)$$
$$\approx 0.004 + 0.037 + 0.138$$
$$= 0.179.$$

▶ The probability is about 17.9%.

SELF-ASSESSMENT

1 I do not understand. 2 I can do it with help. 3 I can do it on my own. 4 I can teach someone else.

According to a survey, about 26% of people ages 12 and older in the U.S. have listened to a podcast in the last month. You ask 4 randomly chosen people ages 12 and older whether they have listened to a podcast in the last month.

5. Draw a histogram of the binomial distribution for your survey.

6. What is the most likely outcome of your survey?

7. What is the probability that at most 2 people you survey have listened to a podcast in the last month?

8.7 Practice WITH CalcChat® AND CalcView®

In Exercises 1–4, make a table and draw a histogram showing the probability distribution for the random variable. *Example 1*

1. x = the number on a table tennis ball randomly chosen from a bag that contains 5 balls labeled "1," 3 balls labeled "2," and 2 balls labeled "3."

2. $c = 1$ when a randomly chosen card out of a standard deck of 52 playing cards is a heart, $c = 2$ when it is a diamond, and $c = 3$ otherwise.

3. $w = 1$ when a randomly chosen letter from the English alphabet is a vowel and $w = 2$ otherwise.

4. n = the number of digits in a random integer from 0 through 999.

In Exercises 5 and 6, use the probability distribution to determine (a) the number that is most likely to be spun on a spinner, and (b) the probability of spinning an even number. *Example 2*

5. 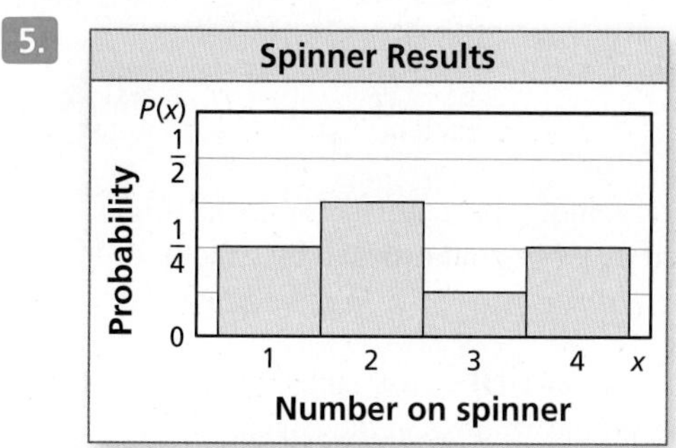

6. 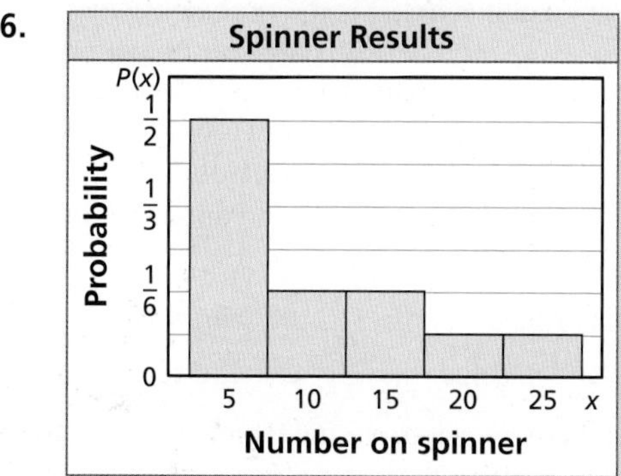

USING EQUATIONS In Exercises 7–10, calculate the probability of flipping a coin 20 times and getting the given number of heads.

7. 1

8. 4

9. 18

10. 20

11. **MODELING REAL LIFE** In your school, 30% of students plan to attend a movie night. You ask 5 randomly chosen students from your school whether they plan to attend the movie night. *Examples 3 and 4*

    a. Draw a histogram of the binomial distribution for your survey.

    b. What is the most likely outcome of your survey?

    c. What is the probability that at most 2 students plan to attend the movie night?

12. **MODELING REAL LIFE** In your school, 70% of students have completed a required service project. You ask 8 randomly chosen students in your school whether they have completed the service project.

    a. Draw a histogram of the binomial distribution for your survey.

    b. What is the most likely outcome of your survey?

    c. What is the probability that at most 3 students have completed the service project?

13. **ERROR ANALYSIS** Describe and correct the error in finding the probability of rolling a 1 exactly 3 times in 5 rolls of a six-sided die.

$$P(k = 3) = {}_5C_3\left(\frac{1}{6}\right)^{5-3}\left(\frac{5}{6}\right)^3$$
$$\approx 0.0161$$

14. **ERROR ANALYSIS** Describe and correct the error in finding the probability of rolling a 2 or 4 exactly 1 time in 6 rolls of a six-sided die.

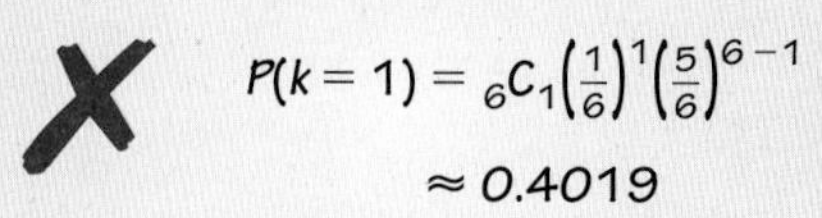
$$P(k = 1) = {}_6C_1\left(\frac{1}{6}\right)^1\left(\frac{5}{6}\right)^{6-1}$$
$$\approx 0.4019$$

15. **MP PROBLEM SOLVING** A sound system has n speakers. Each speaker functions with probability p, independent of the other speakers. The system will function when at least 50% of its speakers function. For what values of p is a 5-speaker system more likely to function than a 3-speaker system?

16. **HOW DO YOU SEE IT?**
The results of a binomial experiment with six trials are shown, where $P(x)$ represents the probability of x successes. What is the least likely outcome of the experiment? Explain.

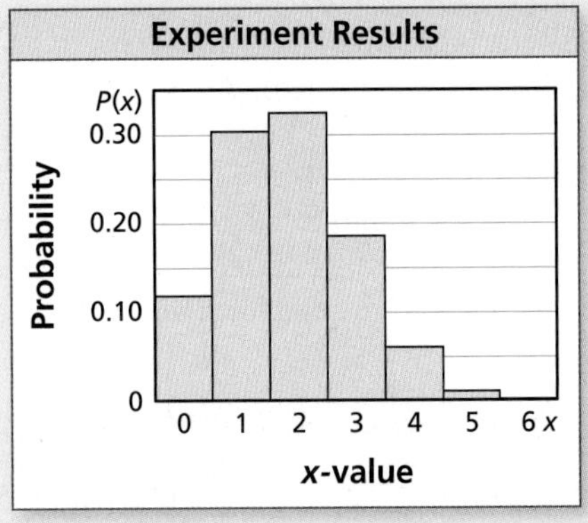

17. **MP REASONING** The probability of five successes in a binomial experiment with five trials is 1.024%. What is the probability of success for any individual trial?

GO DIGITAL

18. **THOUGHT PROVOKING**
How many successes might you expect from a binomial experiment with n trials and probability of success p? (*Hint*: Find the mean number of successes for n trials.)

19. **CONNECTING CONCEPTS** On the farm shown, 7 gopher holes appear each week. Assume that a gopher hole has an equal chance of appearing at any point on the farm. What is the probability that at least one gopher hole appears in the carrot patch?

REVIEW & REFRESH

20. Use the probability distribution below to determine the most likely number of weekdays with precipitation for one week.

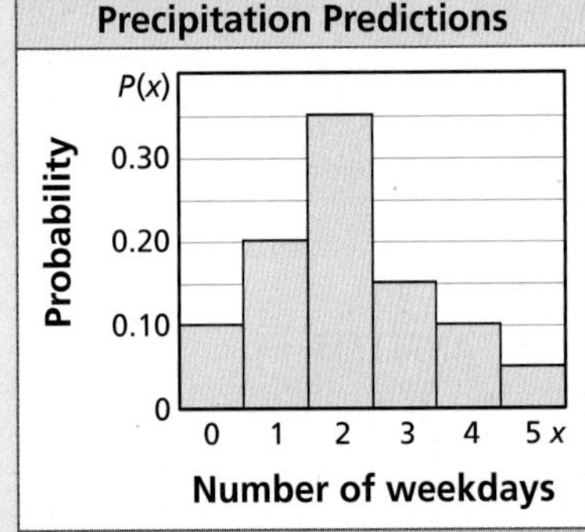

In Exercises 21 and 22, count the possible combinations of *r* letters chosen from the given list.

21. E, F, G, H; $r = 2$

22. L, M, N, O, P; $r = 3$

In Exercises 23 and 24, divide.

23. $(x^2 - 5x - 24) \div (x - 8)$

24. $(x^4 + 6x^3 + 3x^2 - 26x - 24) \div (x + 2)$

25. Let the graph of g be a translation 2 units right, followed by a horizontal shrink by a factor of $\frac{1}{2}$ of the graph of $f(x) = x^2 - x$. Write a rule for g.

26. **MODELING REAL LIFE** You collect data about a dog pageant. Of the 25 dogs in the pageant, 7 receive a ribbon, 18 receive a collar, and 5 receive both a ribbon and a collar. What is the probability that a dog in the pageant receives a ribbon *or* a collar?

27. A bag contains three \$10 gift cards, two \$20 gift cards, and a \$30 gift card. You randomly select a gift card and give it away. Then you randomly select another gift card.

Event *A*: You select the \$10 gift card first.

Event *B*: You select the \$20 gift card second.

Tell whether the events are independent or dependent. Explain your reasoning.

28. Determine whether the graph represents an *arithmetic sequence*, a *geometric sequence*, or *neither*. Explain your reasoning.

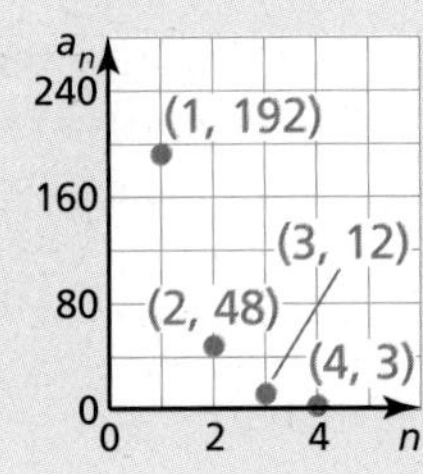

8 Chapter Review WITH CalcChat®

Chapter Learning Target Understand probability.

Chapter Success Criteria

- ◆ I can define theoretical and experimental probability.
- ◆ I can use two-way tables to find probabilities.
- ■ I can compare independent and dependent events.
- ■ I can construct and interpret probability and binomial distributions.

◆ Surface
■ Deep

SELF-ASSESSMENT 1 I do not understand. 2 I can do it with help. 3 I can do it on my own. 4 I can teach someone else.

8.1 Sample Spaces and Probability (pp. 403–410)

Learning Target: Find sample spaces and probabilities of events.

Vocabulary

probability experiment
outcome
event
sample space
probability of an event
theoretical probability
geometric probability
experimental probability

1. You flip a coin and draw a marble at random from a bag containing two blue marbles and two green marbles. Find the number of possible outcomes in the sample space. Then list the possible outcomes.

2. A bag contains 9 tiles, one for each letter in the word HAPPINESS. You choose a tile at random. What is the probability that you choose a tile with the letter S? What is the probability that you choose a tile with a letter other than P?

3. You throw a dart at the board shown. Your dart is equally likely to hit any point inside the square board. Are you most likely to get 5 points, 10 points, or 20 points?

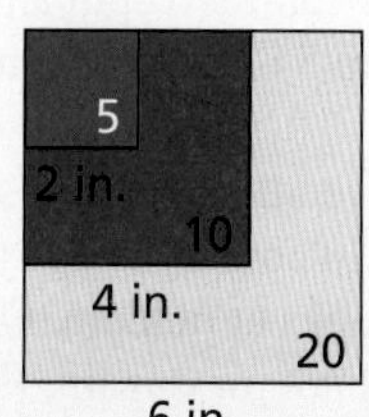

8.2 Two-Way Tables and Probability (pp. 411–416)

WATCH

Learning Target: Use two-way tables to represent data and find probabilities.

Vocabulary

two-way table
joint frequency
marginal frequency
joint relative frequency
marginal relative frequency
conditional relative frequency

4. A survey asks residents of the east and west sides of a city whether they support the construction of a mall. The results, given as joint relative frequencies, are shown in the two-way table. What is the probability that a randomly selected resident who responded no is from the west side?

		Location	
		East Side	West Side
Response	Yes	0.47	0.36
	No	0.08	0.09

5. After an assembly, 220 boys and 270 girls respond to a survey. Of those, 200 boys and 230 girls say the motivational speaker was impactful. Organize these results in a two-way table. Then find and interpret the marginal frequencies.

8.3 Conditional Probability (pp. 417–424)

Learning Target: Find and use conditional probabilities.

Vocabulary
conditional probability

6. You have two acrylic paintings and two oil paintings. You randomly select a painting to sell and then you randomly select a different painting to present at a gallery. Find the probability that you selected an acrylic painting to sell given that you randomly selected an oil painting to present at the gallery.

7. An inspector tests rotors of helicopter drones. The two-way table shows the joint and marginal relative frequencies. Find and compare $P(\text{single rotor} \mid \text{failed})$ and $P(\text{single rotor} \mid \text{passed})$.

		Result		
		Passed	Failed	Total
Type	Single Rotor	0.30	0.20	0.50
	Multi-Rotor	0.40	0.10	0.50
	Total	0.70	0.30	1

8. At a baseball game, 90% of guests receive a coupon code and 30% of guests receive a coupon code and a bobblehead. What is the probability that a guest who receives a coupon code also receives a bobblehead?

8.4 Independent and Dependent Events (pp. 425–432)

Learning Target: Understand and find probabilities of independent and dependent events.

Vocabulary
independent events
dependent events

9. As part of a board game, you need to spin the spinner, which is divided into equal parts. Find the probability that you get a 2 on your first spin and a number less than or equal to 5 on your second spin.

10. You are a DJ at a wedding. A playlist contains 10 pop songs and 20 country songs. You set the playlist to select songs at random. Once a song is played, the same song will not play again. Find the probability that the first two songs to play are both country songs.

8.5 Probability of Disjoint and Overlapping Events (pp. 433–438)

WATCH

Learning Target: Find probabilities of disjoint and overlapping events.

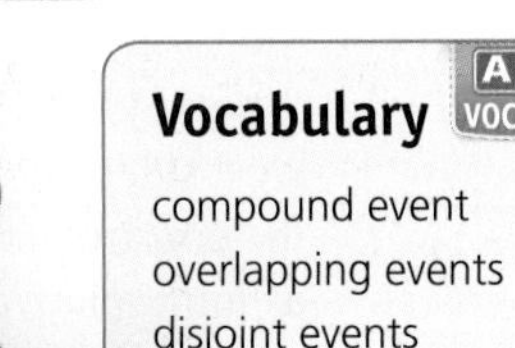

Vocabulary
compound event
overlapping events
disjoint events

11. Let A and B be events such that $P(A) = 0.32$, $P(B) = 0.48$, and $P(A \text{ and } B) = 0.12$. Find $P(A \text{ or } B)$.

12. Out of 100 employees in a restaurant, 92 either work part time or work 5 days each week. There are 14 employees who work part time and 80 employees who work 5 days each week. What is the probability that a randomly selected employee works both part time and 5 days each week?

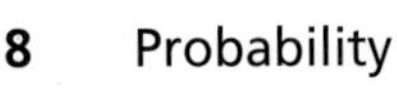

8.6 Permutations and Combinations (pp. 439–448) 

Learning Target: Count permutations and combinations.

Vocabulary
permutation
n factorial
combination
Binomial Theorem

Evaluate the expression.

13. ${}_{7}P_{6}$

14. ${}_{13}P_{10}$

15. ${}_{6}C_{2}$

16. ${}_{8}C_{4}$

17. You and your friend are two of the four winners of individual concert tickets. There is one VIP ticket, one superior ticket, one general admission ticket, and one value ticket. The tickets are given to the winners randomly. Find the probability that you get the superior ticket and your friend gets the value ticket.

18. You work in a food truck at a festival. Of the 11 food trucks, 2 are randomly selected to be placed at the entrance. What is the probability that your food truck is placed at the entrance?

Use the Binomial Theorem to write the expansion of the expression.

19. $(3x - 2y)^5$

20. $(2x + y^2)^4$

8.7 Binomial Distributions (pp. 449–454) 

Learning Target: Understand binomial distributions.

Vocabulary
random variable
probability distribution
binomial distribution
binomial experiment

21. Find the probability of flipping a coin 12 times and getting exactly 4 heads.

22. A basketball player makes a free throw 82.6% of the time. The player attempts 5 free throws. Draw a histogram of the binomial distribution of the number of successful free throws. What is the most likely outcome?

23. According to a survey, about 37% of Americans go online mostly using a smartphone. You ask 4 randomly chosen Americans about whether they go online mostly using a smartphone. Draw a histogram of the binomial distribution for your survey. What is the probability that two or more of the respondents go online mostly using a smartphone?

Mathematical Practices

Model with Mathematics

Mathematically proficient students apply the mathematics they know to solve problems arising in everyday life, society, and the workplace.

1. Describe a real-life situation that can be represented by a binomial distribution.
2. In Exercise 27 on page 410, explain how you used probability to determine the amount that you will charge and the amount that each winner will receive.
3. In Exercise 10 on page 422, what types of decisions can the owner of the gas station make using the given probabilities?

8 Practice Test WITH CalcChat®

1. You randomly choose one meat and one dressing for a salad. How many possible outcomes are in the sample space? List the possible outcomes.

• MEAT •	• DRESSING •
Chicken	Ranch
Steak	Italian
Salmon	French

Evaluate the expression.

2. ${}_7P_2$

3. ${}_6C_3$

4. Use the Binomial Theorem to write the binomial expansion of $(x + y^2)^5$.

5. According to a survey, about 54% of teenagers in the U.S. say they spend too much time on their cell phones. You ask 5 randomly chosen teenagers whether they think they spend too much time on their cell phones.

   a. Draw a histogram of the binomial distribution for the survey.

   b. What is the most likely outcome of the survey?

   c. What is the probability that at least 3 teenagers you survey say they spend too much time on their cell phones?

6. A bag contains the gift cards shown in the table.

   a. You randomly draw a gift card. Find the probability that you draw a $25 mall gift card.

   b. You randomly draw a gift card. Find the probability that you draw a $50 gift card or a restaurant gift card.

   c. You randomly draw a gift card, set it aside, and then draw a second gift card for your friend. Find the probability that you draw a mall gift card, then a gasoline gift card.

	Mall	Gasoline	Restaurant
$25	4	2	3
$50	1	3	2

7. Describe why it is necessary to subtract $P(A \text{ and } B)$ when finding $P(A \text{ or } B)$ for two overlapping events. Then describe why it is *not* necessary to subtract $P(A \text{ and } B)$ when finding $P(A \text{ or } B)$ for two disjoint events.

8. You roll a six-sided die twice. Find the probability that the first number is in the domain of $f(x) = \sqrt{x - 2}$ and the second number is in the domain of $g(x) = \sqrt{x - 5}$.

9. You are choosing a new cell phone carrier. The three plans you consider are equally priced. You ask several of your neighbors whether they are satisfied with their current cell phone carrier. The table shows the results. According to this survey, which carrier should you choose?

Carrier	Satisfied	Not Satisfied
A	IIII	II
B	IIII	III
C	~~IIII~~ I	~~IIII~~

10. Three volunteers are chosen at random from a group of 12 to help at a camp.

    a. What is the probability that you, your brother, and your friend are chosen?

    b. The first person chosen will be a counselor, the second will be a lifeguard, and the third will be a cook. What is the probability that you are the cook, your brother is the lifeguard, and your friend is the counselor?

8 Performance Task
Buried Treasures

Archaeologists study a wide variety of artifacts in order to learn about the past.

COINS
Coins are often made with words and images that provide valuable information about nations and rulers.

FOSSILS
Fossils provide information about plant and animal species from different time periods.

POTTERY
Pottery, one of the most common types of archaeological discovery, gives cultural insight into ancient societies.

INSCRIPTIONS
Inscriptions and manuscripts give insight into culture, language, chronology, and much more.

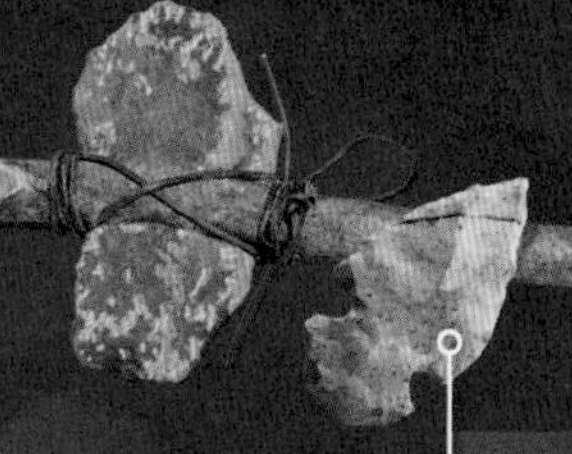

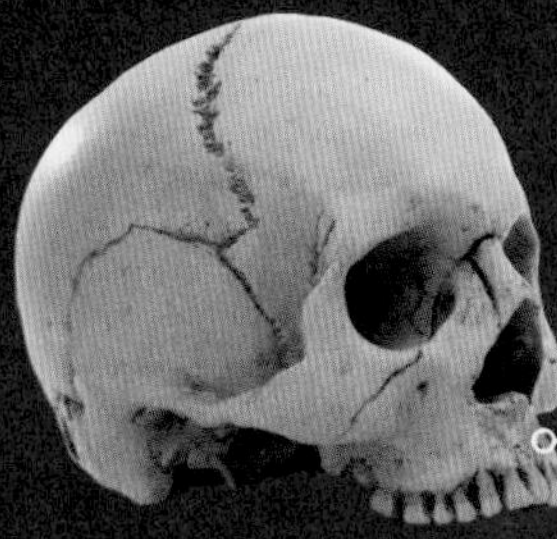

BONES
Bones provide information about topics such as lifestyle, health, and ages of civilizations.

TOOLS
Ancient tools demonstrate the technologies and behaviors of ancient peoples.

CHOOSING AN EXCAVATION SITE

Archaeologists will choose one of three sites to excavate. Multiple surveys are used to determine whether each site appears likely to contain a significant number of ancient artifacts. The conclusions of the surveys are shown. Which site should the archaeologists choose? Create a presentation to convince the archaeologists to choose this site.

Site	Likely	Unlikely
A	卌 卌 I	卌
B	卌 III	III
C	卌 IIII	IIII

The site is partitioned into 9 square-shaped regions. In any given region, the probability of finding an artifact is about 45%. Draw and interpret a histogram of a probability distribution for this situation.

8 College and Career Readiness WITH CalcChat®

Tutorial videos are available for each exercise.

1. Which statements describe the transformation of the graph of $f(x) = x^3 - x$ represented by $g(x) = 4(x - 2)^3 - 4(x - 2)$?

Ⓐ a vertical stretch by a factor of 4

Ⓑ a vertical shrink by a factor of $\frac{1}{4}$

Ⓒ a horizontal shrink by a factor of $\frac{1}{4}$

Ⓓ a horizontal stretch by a factor of 4

Ⓔ a horizontal translation 2 units right

Ⓕ a horizontal translation 2 units left

2. You randomly select a size and flavor for a shake from the menu shown. How many possible outcomes are in the sample space? List the possible outcomes. Then find the probability that the selected shake is *not* a peanut butter shake.

3. Which of the following is the condensed form of the logarithmic expression $3 \ln x - \ln 7$?

Ⓐ $\ln(x^3 - 7)$

Ⓑ $\ln(3x - 7)$

Ⓒ $\ln \frac{3x}{7}$

Ⓓ $\ln \frac{x^3}{7}$

4. The graphs of $f(x) = \frac{x + 1}{x + 2}$ and $g(x) = 2$ are shown. What is the solution of $f(x) = g(x)$?

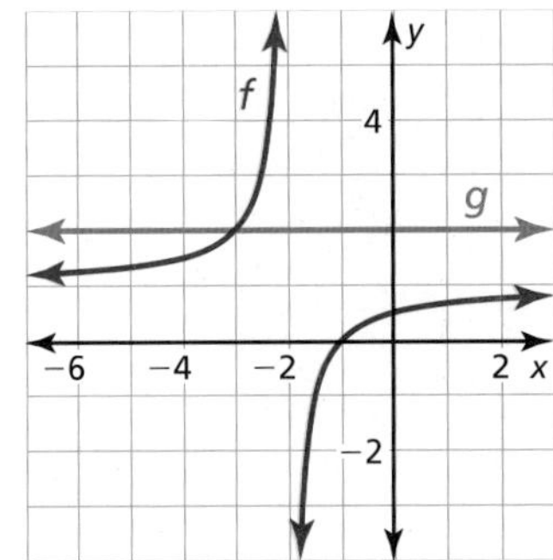

5. When you divide $2x^3 + x^2 - 5x + k$ by $x^2 - 3x + 1$, the remainder is $14x + 13$. What is the value of k?

6. A survey asked male and female students about whether they prefer to take gym class or choir. The table shows the results.

		Class		
		Gym	Choir	Total
Gender	Male			50
	Female	23		
	Total		49	106

a. Complete the two-way table.

b. What is the probability that a randomly selected student from the survey is female and prefers choir?

c. What is the probability that a randomly selected male student from the survey prefers gym class?

7. The graph of which system of inequalities is shown?

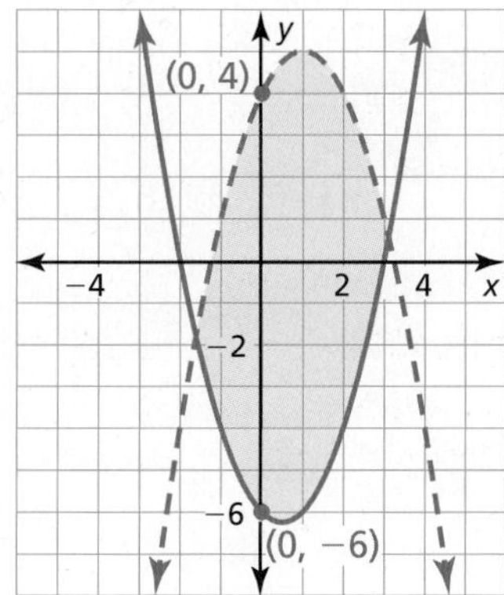

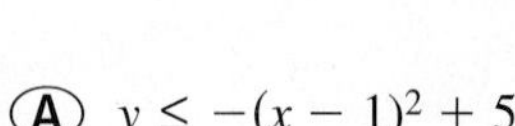

Ⓐ $y \leq -(x - 1)^2 + 5$
$y > (x + 2)(x - 3)$

Ⓑ $y > -(x - 1)^2 + 5$
$y \geq (x + 2)(x - 3)$

Ⓒ $y < -(x - 1)^2 + 5$
$y \geq (x + 2)(x - 3)$

Ⓓ $y < -(x - 1)^2 + 5$
$y \leq (x + 2)(x - 3)$

8. A card is randomly selected from a standard deck of 52 playing cards. What is the probability that it is a red card or a king?

Ⓐ $\frac{1}{26}$

Ⓑ $\frac{7}{13}$

Ⓒ $\frac{15}{26}$

Ⓓ $\frac{8}{13}$

9. Complete the equation.

$$(\square - 3i) + (4 + \square i) = 10 + 5i$$

9 Data Analysis and Statistics

NATIONAL GEOGRAPHIC EXPLORER

Arianna Soldati

Dr. Arianna Soldati is a volcanologist. She is especially interested in the interplay between the physical properties of lava, which can only be measured in the lab, and the appearance of lava in the field. Field observations are often the only data available to volcanologists, but it's the physical properties that determine the distance and speed of a lava flow.

- What does a volcanologist do?
- The United States has over 150 active volcanoes. Name some of the volcanoes in the United States. Have you ever visited a volcano?
- What is lava? What is the temperature of molten lava?
- What is the difference between lava and magma?

STEM

Volcanologists record cases of *new* and *ongoing* volcanic activity around the world. In the Performance Task, you will use data to write a report about worldwide volcanic activity.

Volcanology

Preparing for Chapter 9

Chapter Learning Target Understand data analysis and statistics.

Chapter Success Criteria
- ◆ I can find probabilities in normal distributions.
- ◆ I can identify populations and samples.
- ■ I can explain different methods for collecting data.
- ■ I can make inferences from sample surveys and experiments.

◆ Surface
■ Deep

Chapter Vocabulary

Work with a partner. Discuss each of the vocabulary terms.

hypothesis
random sample
convenience sample
unbiased sample
biased sample
survey
simulation
biased question

Mathematical Practices

Construct Viable Arguments and Critique the Reasoning of Others

Mathematically proficient students distinguish correct logic or reasoning from that which is flawed.

Work with a partner. Three researchers each use a different survey to determine whether people in the United States favor more government funding to monitor volcanic activity. The table shows the results.

Survey Question	Sample	"Yes"	"No"	Conclusion
Should the government spend more money to monitor volcanic activity?	1000 randomly selected people who live near a volcano	940	60	About 94% of people favor more funding.
Should the government spend more money to monitor volcanic activity?	1000 randomly selected people in Maryland	80	920	About 8% of people favor more funding.
Should the government spend more of our limited tax dollars to monitor volcanic activity?	1000 randomly selected people in the United States	190	810	About 19% of people favor more funding.

1. Are you confident in any of the conclusions drawn by the researchers? Explain.
2. Write a survey question and describe a sample that the researchers can use to draw a valid conclusion. Explain your reasoning.

9 Prepare WITH CalcChat®

Comparing Measures of Center

Example 1 Find the mean, median, and mode of the data set 4, 11, 16, 8, 9, 40, 4, 12, 13, 5, and 10. Then determine which measure of center best represents the data. Explain.

Mean $\bar{x} = \frac{4 + 11 + 16 + 8 + 9 + 40 + 4 + 12 + 13 + 5 + 10}{11} = 12$

Median 4, 4, 5, 8, 9, 10, 11, 12, 13, 16, 40 Order the data. The middle value is 10.

Mode 4, 4, 5, 8, 9, 10, 11, 12, 13, 16, 40 4 occurs most often.

▶ The mean is 12, the median is 10, and the mode is 4. The median best represents the data. The mode is less than most of the data, and the mean is greater than most of the data.

Find the mean, median, and mode of the data set. Then determine which measure of center best represents the data. Explain.

1. 36, 82, 94, 83, 86, 82

2. 74, 89, 71, 70, 68, 70

3. 1, 18, 12, 16, 11, 15, 17, 44, 44

Finding a Standard Deviation

Example 2 Find and interpret the standard deviation of the data set 10, 2, 6, 8, 12, 15, 18, and 25. Use a table to organize your work.

x	$\bar{x}$	$x - \bar{x}$	$(x - \bar{x})^2$
10	12	−2	4
2	12	−10	100
6	12	−6	36
8	12	−4	16
12	12	0	0
15	12	3	9
18	12	6	36
25	12	13	169

Step 1 Find the mean, $\bar{x}$.

$$\bar{x} = \frac{96}{8} = 12$$

Step 2 Find the deviation of each data value, $x - \bar{x}$.

Step 3 Square each deviation, $(x - \bar{x})^2$.

Step 4 Find the mean of the squared deviations, or variance.

$$\frac{(x_1 - \bar{x})^2 + (x_2 - \bar{x})^2 + \cdots + (x_n - \bar{x})^2}{n}$$

$$= \frac{4 + 100 + \cdots + 169}{8} = \frac{370}{8} = 46.25$$

Step 5 Use a calculator to take the square root of the variance.

$$\sqrt{46.25} \approx 6.80$$

▶ The standard deviation is about 6.80. This means that the typical data value differs from the mean by about 6.80 units.

Find and interpret the standard deviation of the data set.

4. 43, 48, 41, 51, 42

5. 28, 26, 21, 44, 29, 32

6. 65, 56, 49, 66, 62, 52, 53, 49

7. MP **STRUCTURE** Describe a data set that has a standard deviation of zero. Can a standard deviation be negative? Explain your reasoning.

9.1 Using Normal Distributions

Learning Target Understand normal distributions.

Success Criteria
- I can find probabilities in normal distributions.
- I can interpret normal distributions.
- I can find probabilities in standard normal distributions.

The *standard deviation* σ of a numerical data set is a measure of how much a typical value in the data set differs from the mean μ. It is given by

$$\sigma = \sqrt{\frac{(x_1 - \mu)^2 + (x_2 - \mu)^2 + \cdots + (x_n - \mu)^2}{n}}$$

where n is the number of values in the data set.

EXPLORE IT! Analyzing a Normal Distribution

Work with a partner. In many naturally occurring data sets, the histogram of the data is bell-shaped. In statistics, such data sets are said to have a *normal distribution*.

Math Practice

Find Entry Points
How can the number of shaded squares under the curve help you answer part (a)?

a. For the normal distribution shown below, estimate the percent of the data that lies within one, two, and three standard deviations of the mean.

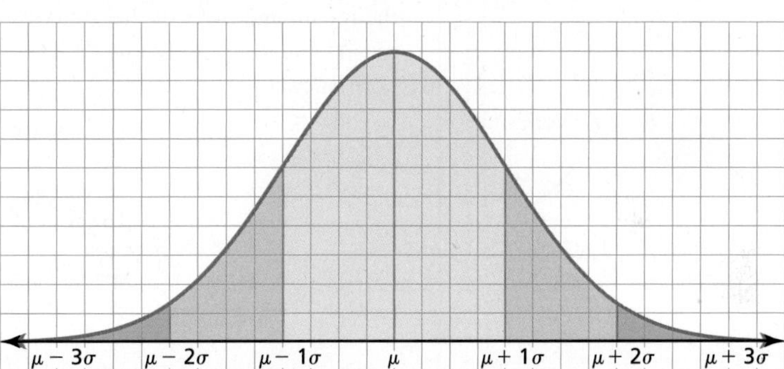

b. You randomly select a data value from a data set that has a normal distribution. Estimate the probability that the value you select is at least 1 standard deviation from the mean. Explain your reasoning.

c. A famous data set, collected in the mid-1800s, contains the chest sizes of 5738 men in the Scottish Militia. The distribution is approximately normal. Approximate the number of men with chest sizes of at least 44 inches. Explain your reasoning.

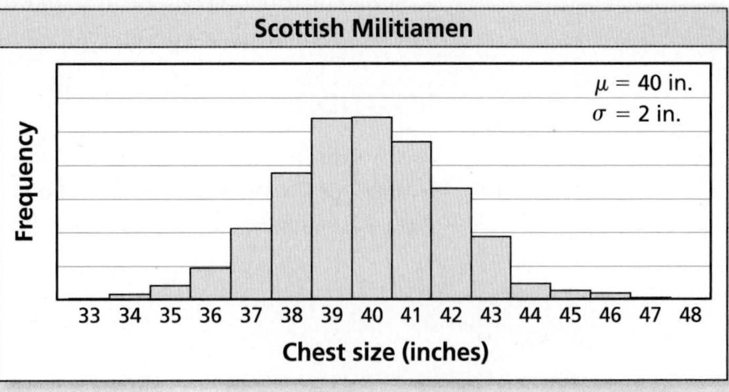

Normal Distributions

Vocabulary

normal distribution, *p. 466*
normal curve, *p. 466*
standard normal distribution, *p. 467*
z-score, *p. 467*

You have studied probability distributions. One type of probability distribution is a *normal distribution*. The graph of a **normal distribution** is a bell-shaped curve called a **normal curve** that is symmetric about the mean.

KEY IDEA

Areas Under a Normal Curve

A normal distribution with mean μ (the Greek letter *mu*) and standard deviation σ (the Greek letter *sigma*) has these properties.

- The total area under the related normal curve is 1.
- About 68% of the area lies within 1 standard deviation of the mean.
- About 95% of the area lies within 2 standard deviations of the mean.
- About 99.7% of the area lies within 3 standard deviations of the mean.

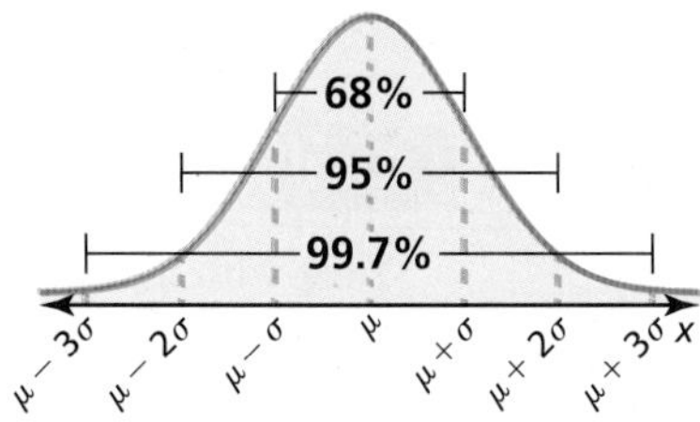

From the second bulleted statement above and the symmetry of a normal curve, you can deduce that 34% of the area lies within 1 standard deviation to the left of the mean, and 34% of the area lies within 1 standard deviation to the right of the mean. The diagram below shows other partial areas based on the properties of a normal curve.

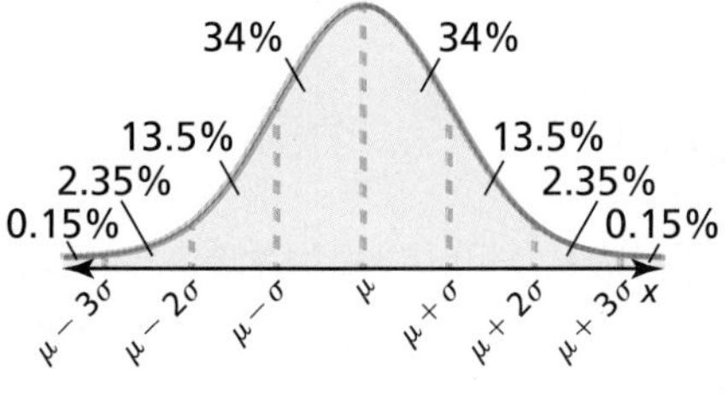

Math Practice

Use Technology

You can use technology to find areas under normal curves.

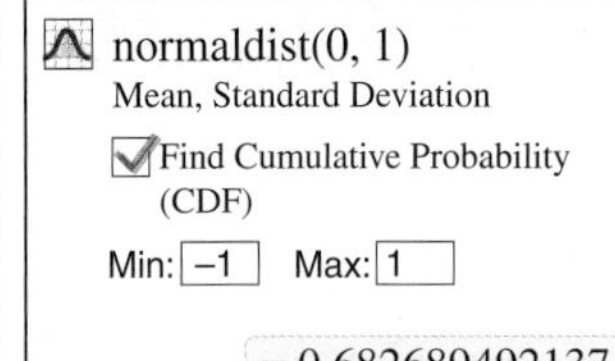

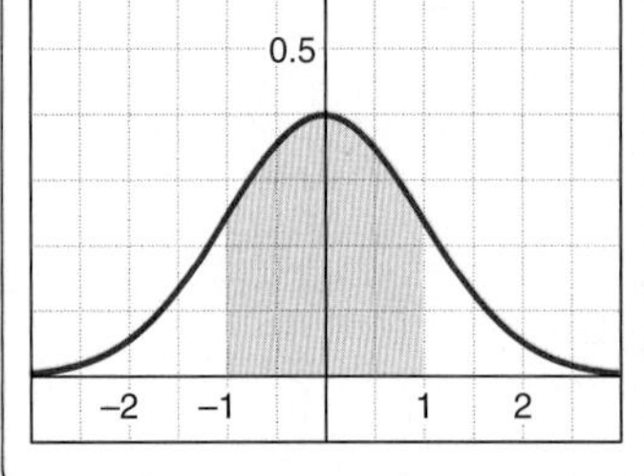

The areas under a normal curve can be interpreted as probabilities in a normal distribution. In a normal distribution, the probability that a randomly chosen x-value is between a and b is given by the area under the normal curve between a and b.

EXAMPLE 1 Finding a Normal Probability

A normal distribution has mean μ and standard deviation σ. An x-value is randomly selected from the distribution. Find $P(\mu - 2\sigma \le x \le \mu)$.

SOLUTION

The probability that a randomly selected x-value lies between $\mu - 2\sigma$ and μ is the shaded area under the normal curve shown.

$$P(\mu - 2\sigma \le x \le \mu) = 0.135 + 0.34$$
$$= 0.475$$

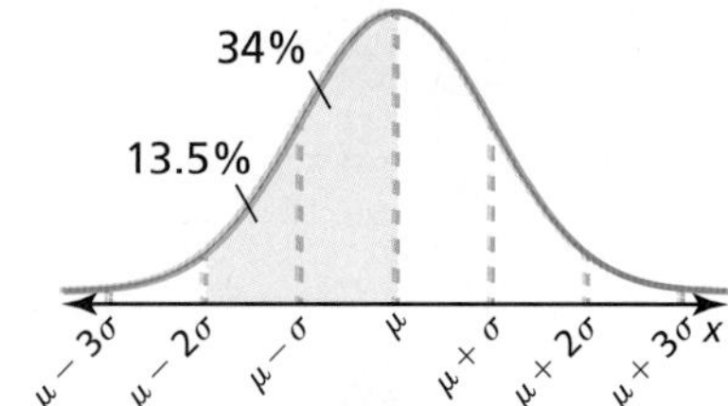

EXAMPLE 2 Interpreting Normally Distributed Data

The scores for a state's peace officer standards and training test are normally distributed with a mean of 55 and a standard deviation of 12. The test scores range from 0 to 100.

a. About what percent of the people taking the test have scores between 43 and 67?

b. An agency in the state will only hire applicants with test scores of 67 or greater. About what percent of the people have test scores that make them eligible to be hired by the agency?

SOLUTION

a. The scores of 43 and 67 represent one standard deviation on either side of the mean, as shown. So, about 68% of the people taking the test have scores between 43 and 67.

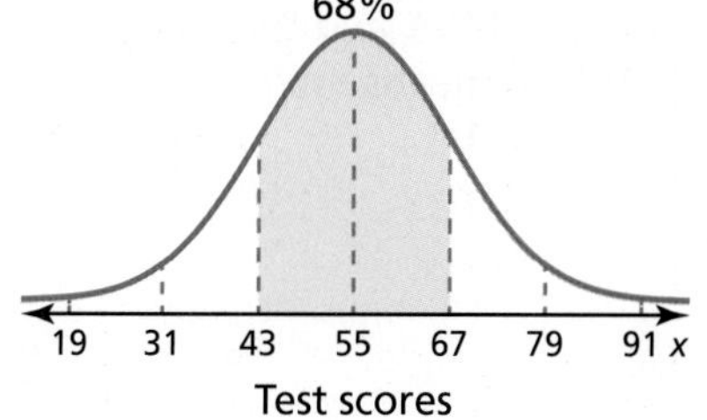

b. A score of 67 is one standard deviation to the right of the mean, as shown. So, the percent of the people who have test scores that make them eligible to be hired by the agency is about 13.5% + 2.35% + 0.15%, or 16%.

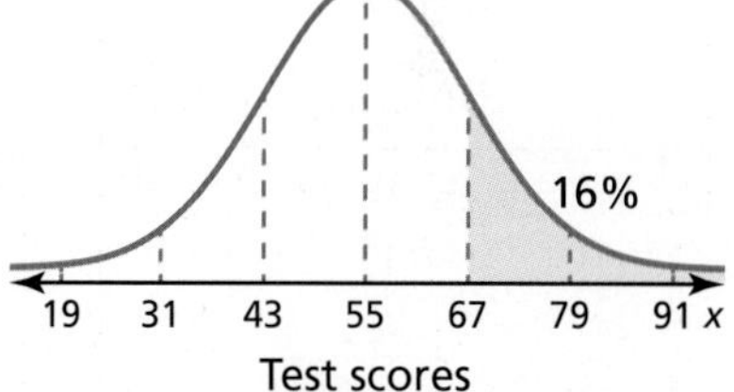

Check

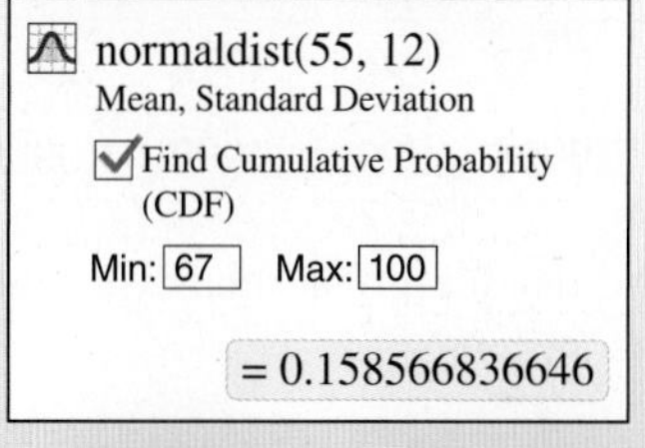

SELF-ASSESSMENT

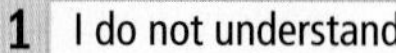

2 I can do it with help. 3 I can do it on my own. 4 I can teach someone else.

A normal distribution has mean μ and standard deviation σ. Find the indicated probability for a randomly selected x-value from the distribution.

1. $P(x \leq \mu)$
2. $P(x \geq \mu + \sigma)$
3. $P(\mu \leq x \leq \mu + 2\sigma)$
4. $P(\mu - \sigma \leq x \leq \mu)$
5. **WHAT IF?** In Example 2, about what percent of the people taking the test have scores between 43 and 79?
6. **MP REASONING** Explain why the total area under the normal curve is 1.

The Standard Normal Distribution

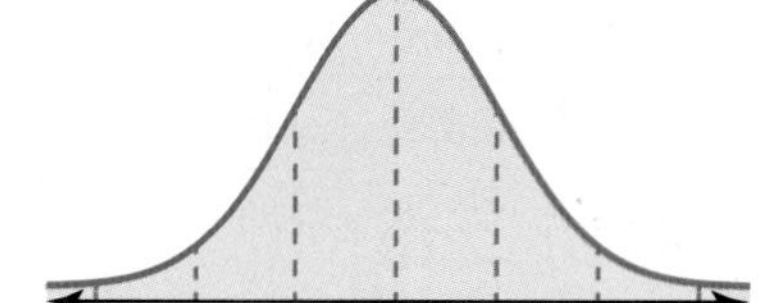

The **standard normal distribution** is the normal distribution with mean 0 and standard deviation 1. The formula below can be used to transform x-values from a normal distribution with mean μ and standard deviation σ into z-values having a standard normal distribution.

Formula $z = \dfrac{x - \mu}{\sigma}$ ← Subtract the mean from the given x-value, then divide by the standard deviation.

The z-value for a particular x-value is called the **z-score** for the x-value and is the number of standard deviations the x-value lies above or below the mean μ.

For a randomly selected z-value from a standard normal distribution, you can use the table below to find the probability that z is less than or equal to a given value. For example, the table shows that $P(z \leq -0.4) = 0.3446$. You can find the value of $P(z \leq -0.4)$ in the table by finding the value where row -0 and column .4 intersect.

READING

In the table, the value .0000+ means "slightly more than 0" and the value 1.0000− means "slightly less than 1."

Standard Normal Table

z	.0	.1	.2	.3	.4	.5	.6	.7	.8	.9
−3	.0013	.0010	.0007	.0005	.0003	.0002	.0002	.0001	.0001	.0000+
−2	.0228	.0179	.0139	.0107	.0082	.0062	.0047	.0035	.0026	.0019
−1	.1587	.1357	.1151	.0968	.0808	.0668	.0548	.0446	.0359	.0287
−0	.5000	.4602	.4207	.3821	.3446	.3085	.2743	.2420	.2119	.1841
0	.5000	.5398	.5793	.6179	.6554	.6915	.7257	.7580	.7881	.8159
1	.8413	.8643	.8849	.9032	.9192	.9332	.9452	.9554	.9641	.9713
2	.9772	.9821	.9861	.9893	.9918	.9938	.9953	.9965	.9974	.9981
3	.9987	.9990	.9993	.9995	.9997	.9998	.9998	.9999	.9999	1.0000−

You can use the standard normal table to find probabilities for any normal distribution by first converting values from the distribution to z-scores.

EXAMPLE 3 Using a z-Score and the Standard Normal Table

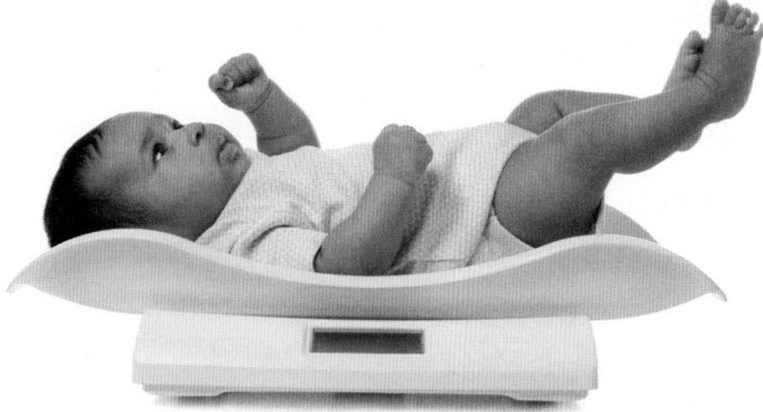

A study finds that the weights of infants at birth are normally distributed with a mean of 3270 grams and a standard deviation of 600 grams. An infant from the study is randomly chosen. What is the probability that the infant weighs 4170 grams or less?

SOLUTION

Step 1 Find the z-score corresponding to an x-value of 4170.

$$z = \frac{x - \mu}{\sigma} = \frac{4170 - 3270}{600} = 1.5$$

Step 2 Use the table to find $P(z \leq 1.5)$. The table shows that $P(z \leq 1.5) = 0.9332$.

Standard Normal Table

z	.0	.1	.2	.3	.4	.5	.6	.7	.8	.9
−3	.0013	.0010	.0007	.0005	.0003	.0002	.0002	.0001	.0001	.0000+
−2	.0228	.0179	.0139	.0107	.0082	.0062	.0047	.0035	.0026	.0019
−1	.1587	.1357	.1151	.0968	.0808	.0668	.0548	.0446	.0359	.0287
−0	.5000	.4602	.4207	.3821	.3446	.3085	.2743	.2420	.2119	.1841
0	.5000	.5398	.5793	.6179	.6554	.6915	.7257	.7580	.7881	.8159
1	.8413	.8643	.8849	.9032	.9192	.9332	.9452	.9554	.9641	.9713

Check

Use a spreadsheet to find the area.

	A	B
1	NORM.S.DIST(1.5, TRUE)	
2		0.9331928

▶ So, the probability that the infant weighs 4170 grams or less is about 0.9332.

Not all distributions are normal. For instance, consider the histograms shown below. The first histogram has a normal distribution. Notice that it is bell-shaped and symmetric. Another type of distribution is a skewed distribution. The second histogram is *skewed left* and the third histogram is *skewed right*. The second and third histograms do *not* have normal distributions.

COMMON ERROR

Be sure that you do not use a normal distribution to interpret skewed distributions. The areas under a normal curve do not correspond to the areas of a skewed distribution.

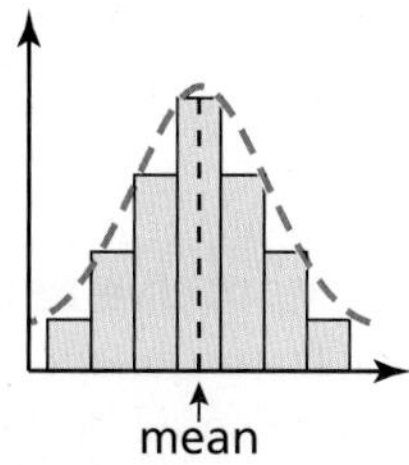

Bell-shaped and symmetric
- histogram has a normal distribution
- mean = median

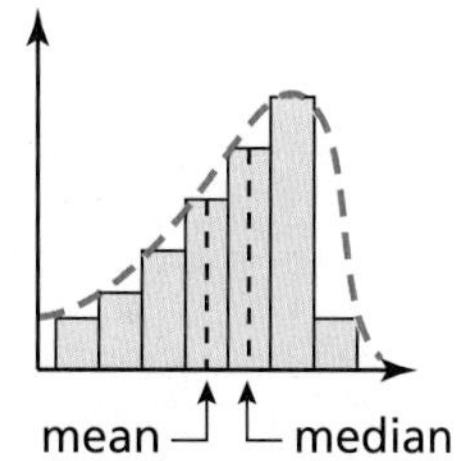

Skewed left
- histogram does not have a normal distribution
- mean < median

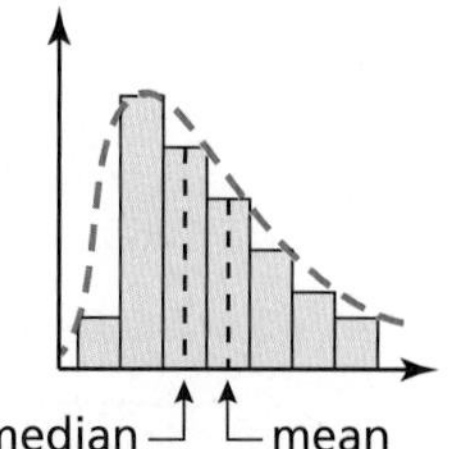

Skewed right
- histogram does not have a normal distribution
- mean > median

EXAMPLE 4 Recognizing Normal Distributions

Determine whether each histogram has a normal distribution.

a.

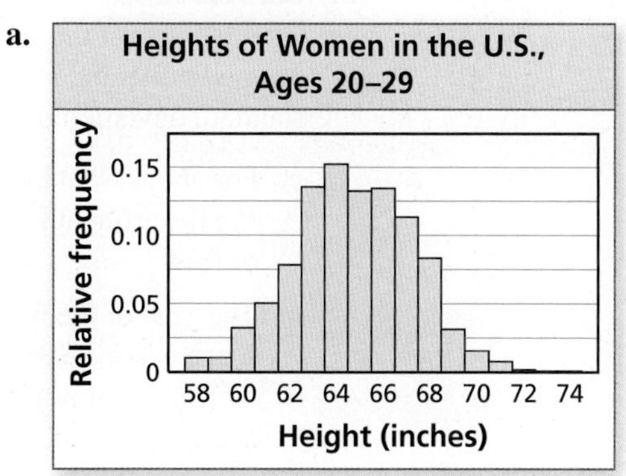

b.

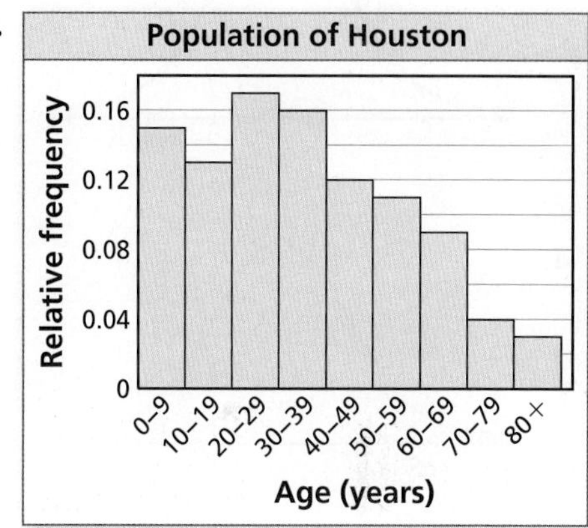

SOLUTION

a. The histogram is bell-shaped and fairly symmetric. So, the histogram has an approximately normal distribution.

b. The histogram is skewed right. So, the histogram does not have a normal distribution, and you cannot use a normal distribution to interpret the histogram.

SELF-ASSESSMENT

1 I do not understand. 2 I can do it with help. 3 I can do it on my own. 4 I can teach someone else.

7. **WHAT IF?** In Example 3, what is the probability that the infant weighs 3990 grams or more?

8. **MP REASONING** Explain why it makes sense that $P(z \leq 0) = 0.5$.

9. Determine whether the histogram has a normal distribution.

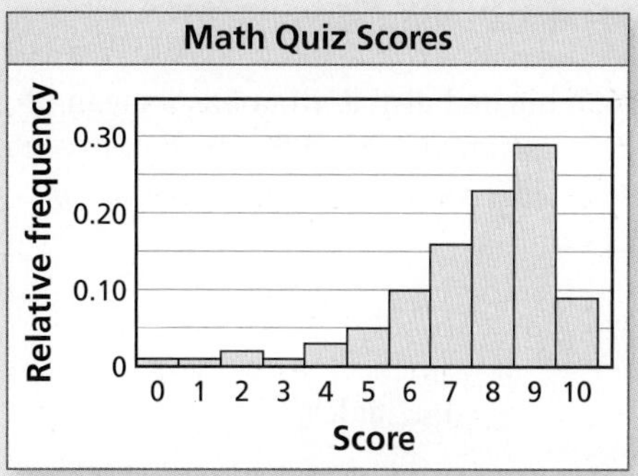

9.1 Practice WITH CalcChat® AND CalcView®

GO DIGITAL

In Exercises 1–4, give the percent of the area under the normal curve represented by the shaded region(s).

1.

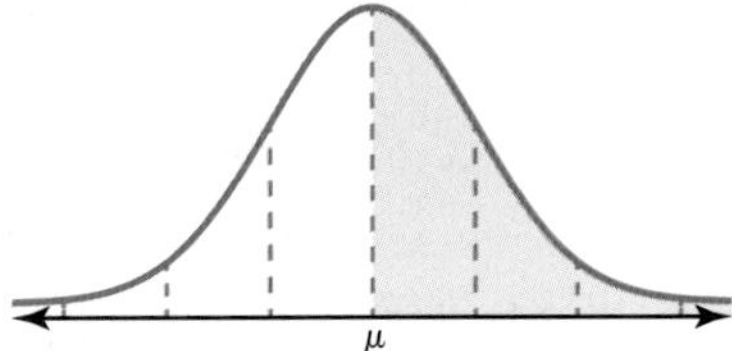

2.

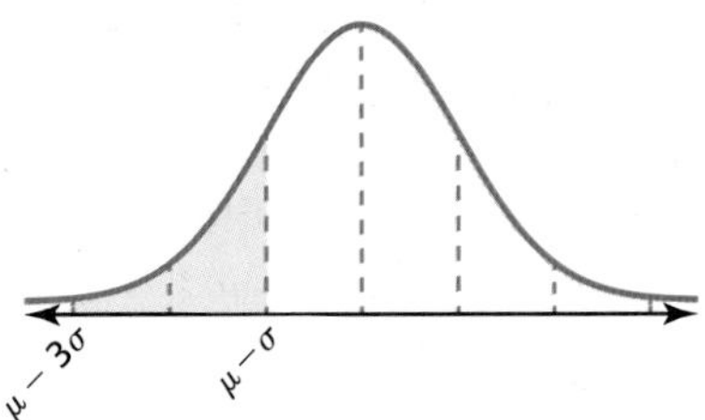

3.

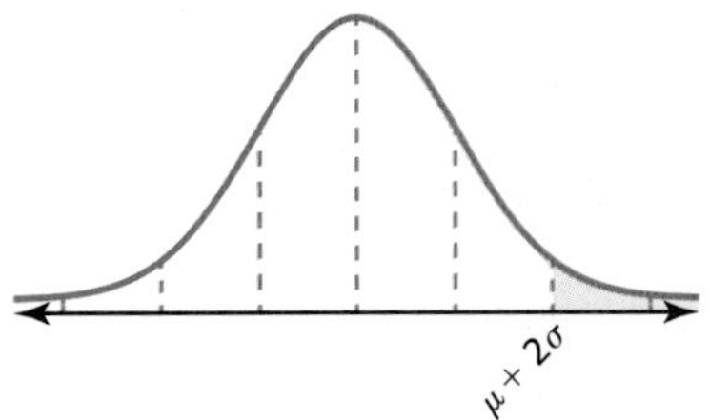

4.

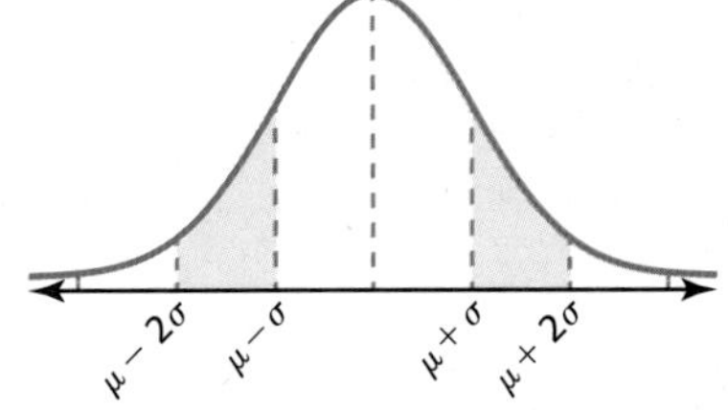

In Exercises 5–10, a normal distribution has mean μ and standard deviation σ. Find the indicated probability for a randomly selected x-value from the distribution. *Example 1*

5. $P(x \leq \mu - \sigma)$

6. $P(x \geq \mu - \sigma)$

7. $P(x \geq \mu + 2\sigma)$

8. $P(x \leq \mu + \sigma)$

9. $P(\mu - \sigma \leq x \leq \mu + \sigma)$

10. $P(\mu - 3\sigma \leq x \leq \mu)$

In Exercises 11–16, a normal distribution has a mean of 33 and a standard deviation of 4. Find the probability that a randomly selected x-value from the distribution is in the given interval.

11. between 29 and 37

12. between 33 and 45

13. at least 25

14. at least 29

15. at most 37

16. at most 21

17. **MODELING REAL LIFE** The daily amounts of time Internet users spend on social networking platforms are normally distributed with a mean of 142 minutes and a standard deviation of 32 minutes. *Example 2*

a. About what percent of Internet users spend between 78 minutes and 174 minutes on social networking platforms each day?

b. About what percent of Internet users spend more than 238 minutes on social networking platforms each day?

18. **MODELING REAL LIFE** The times a fire department take to arrive at the scene of an emergency are normally distributed with a mean of 6 minutes and a standard deviation of 1 minute.

a. For about what percent of emergencies does the fire department arrive at the scene in 8 minutes or less?

b. The goal of the fire department is to reach the scene of an emergency in 5 minutes or less. About what percent of the time does the fire department achieve its goal?

c. The fire department implements personnel changes that increase the standard deviation of the arrival times to 1.5 minutes. Discuss the advantages and disadvantages of these changes.

ERROR ANALYSIS **In Exercises 19 and 20, a normal distribution has a mean of 25 and a standard deviation of 2. Describe and correct the error in finding the probability that a randomly selected x-value is in the given interval.**

19. between 23 and 27

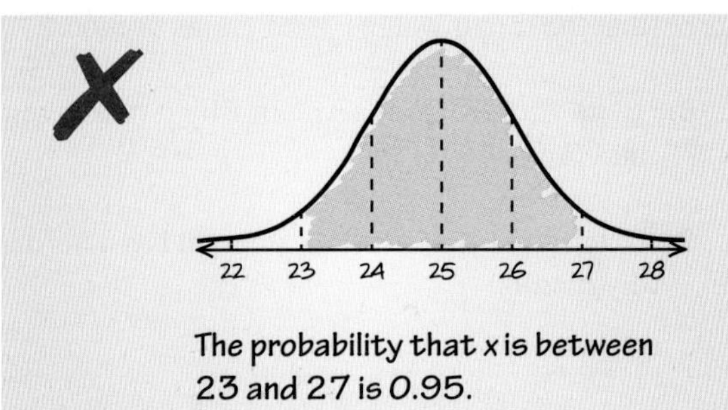

20. at least 21

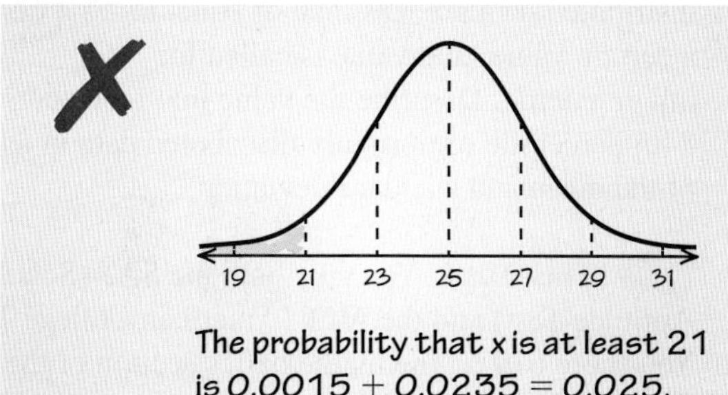

21. MP **PROBLEM SOLVING** The numbers of text messages U.S. teenagers send and receive daily are normally distributed with a mean of 67 messages and a standard deviation of 13 messages. What is the probability that a randomly chosen U.S. teenager sends and receives (a) at most 50 text messages and (b) between 75 and 100 text messages in a day? *Example 3*

22. MP **PROBLEM SOLVING** The wait times for a ride-sharing service are normally distributed with a mean of 5 minutes and a standard deviation of 1.25 minutes. It is currently 4:51 P.M. A movie begins at 5:10 P.M., and the estimated driving time from your location to the theater is 12 minutes. You want to request a ride to the theater only if it is unlikely that you will be late for the movie. Should you request a ride? Explain.

In Exercises 23 and 24, determine whether the histogram has a normal distribution. *Example 4*

23.

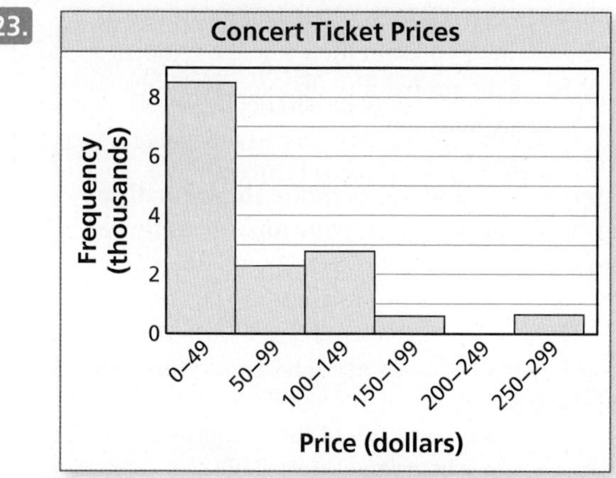

24.

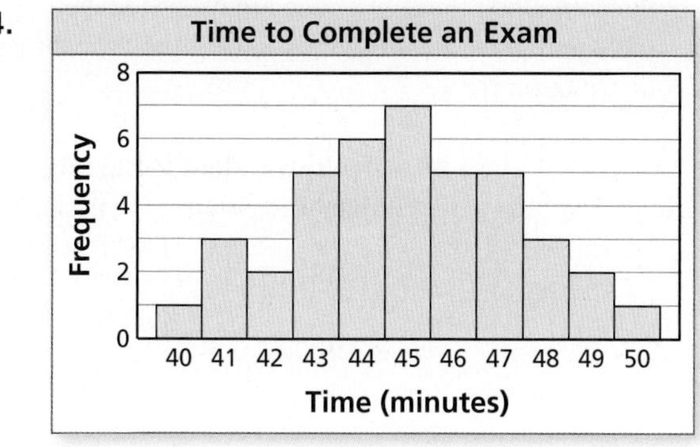

MP USING TOOLS In Exercises 25–28, a normal distribution has a mean of 86 and a standard deviation of 9. Use a spreadsheet to find the area under the normal curve for the given value(s) of x.

25. $P(x \leq 75)$

26. $P(x \geq 110)$

27. $P(90 \leq x \leq 100)$

28. $P(x \leq 70)$ or $P(x \geq 105)$

29. MP **REASONING** Boxes of cereal are filled by a machine. Tests show that the amount of cereal in each box varies. The weights are normally distributed with a mean of 20 ounces and a standard deviation of 0.25 ounce. Four boxes of cereal are randomly chosen.

   a. What is the probability that all four boxes contain no more than 19.4 ounces of cereal?

   b. Do you think the machine is functioning properly? Explain.

30. MP **PROBLEM SOLVING** An automobile manufacturer designs two different vehicles to accommodate different ranges of driver heights. In a survey of an equal number of men and women ages 20 and over, the women's heights are normally distributed with a mean of 63.5 inches and a standard deviation of 2.5 inches, and the men's heights are normally distributed with a mean of 69 inches and a standard deviation of 3 inches. Which automobile can accommodate more of the drivers surveyed? Explain your reasoning.

31. **MAKING AN ARGUMENT** A data set has a median of 80 and a mean of 90. Your friend claims that the distribution of the data is skewed left. Is your friend correct? Explain your reasoning.

32. MP **USING TOOLS** Use technology to graph the standard normal distribution function, given by

$$f(x) = \frac{1}{\sqrt{2\pi}}e^{-x^2/2}.$$

Estimate the area of the region bounded by the x-axis, the graph of f, and the vertical lines $x = -3$ and $x = 3$.

33. **COLLEGE PREP** A data set is normally distributed with a standard deviation of 34. The value 138 has a z-score of -1.5. What is the mean of the data set?

Ⓐ 87 Ⓑ about 106

Ⓒ about 136 Ⓓ 189

34. **HOW DO YOU SEE IT?**
In the figure, the shaded region represents 47.5% of the area under a normal curve. What are the mean and standard deviation of the normal distribution?

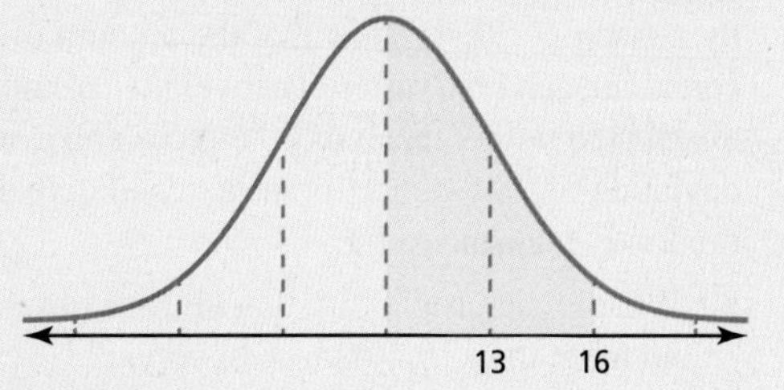

35. **DIG DEEPER** The scores on a history test are normally distributed with a mean of 75 and a standard deviation of 10. You randomly select a test score x. Find $P(|x - \mu| \geq 15)$.

GO DIGITAL

36. **MP REASONING** When n% of normally distributed data are less than or equal to a certain value, that value is called the nth *percentile*. Describe the value that represents the 84th percentile of normally distributed data in terms of the mean and standard deviation.

37. **MP STRUCTURE** You take both the SAT (Scholastic Aptitude Test) and the ACT (American College Test). You score 670 on the mathematics section of the SAT and 29 on the mathematics section of the ACT. The SAT test scores and the ACT test scores are each normally distributed. For the SAT, the mean is 531 and the standard deviation is 114. For the ACT, the mean is 20.5 and the standard deviation is 5.5.

a. In what percentile is your SAT math score?

b. In what percentile is your ACT math score?

c. On which test did you perform better? Explain your reasoning.

38. **THOUGHT PROVOKING**
Explain how you can convert ACT scores into corresponding SAT scores when you know the mean and standard deviation of each distribution.

REVIEW & REFRESH

In Exercises 39 and 40, graph the function. Identify the x-intercepts and the points where the local maximums and local minimums occur. Determine the intervals for which the function is increasing or decreasing.

39. $f(x) = x^3 - 4x^2 + 5$

40. $g(x) = \frac{1}{4}x^4 - 2x^2 - x - 3$

41. What percent of area under the normal curve is represented by the shaded region?

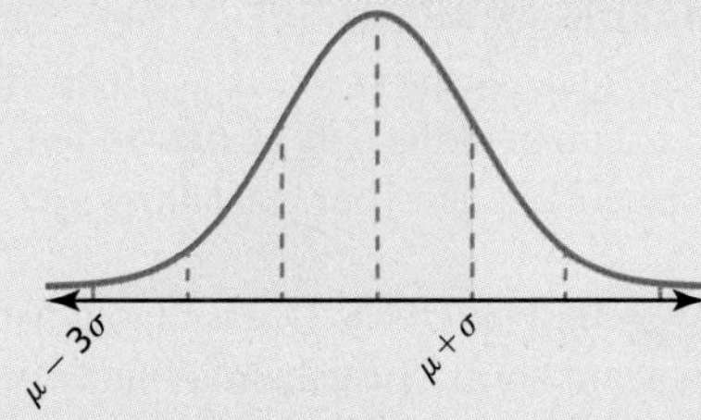

42. A card is randomly selected from a standard deck of 52 playing cards. What is the probability that it is an 8 *or* a spade?

43. **MODELING REAL LIFE** There are 25 students in your class. Your teacher randomly selects 2 students to present their science projects. What is the probability that you and your friend are selected?

In Exercises 44 and 45, evaluate the logarithm using technology. Round your answer to three decimal places.

44. log 7

45. ln 15

46. You roll a standard six-sided die and a six-sided die that displays each of the numbers 1 through 3 twice. Let x be a random variable that represents the sum when these two dice are rolled. Make a table and draw a histogram showing the probability distribution for x.

In Exercises 47 and 48, solve the system using any method. Explain your choice of method.

47. $y = x^2 - 1$
$y = -\frac{1}{2}x + 4$

48. $2x^2 - 3x + y = 8$
$-x^2 + 5x - y = -12$

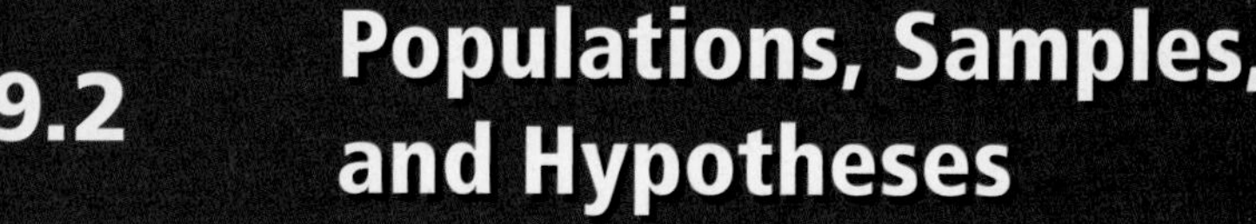

9.2 Populations, Samples, and Hypotheses

Learning Target Use random samples and simulations to make conclusions.

Success Criteria
- I can distinguish between populations and samples.
- I can find a sample proportion.
- I can use a simulation to test a hypothesis.

EXPLORE IT! Using a Simulation

Work with a partner. For a study, 10 babies are shown the same puppet scene.

A panda puppet rolls a ball to a "good" puppet, who rolls it back to the panda puppet. The panda puppet then rolls the ball to a "bad" puppet, who picks it up and runs away with it.

When given the opportunity to reach toward the good puppet or the bad puppet, 8 babies reach toward the good puppet.

a. If each of the 10 babies randomly select a puppet, how many babies do you expect to select the good puppet? Explain your reasoning.

b. How can you use a coin to *simulate* one trial of a baby randomly selecting a puppet? multiple trials?

c. Perform the simulation in part (b). Then extend the simulation to determine whether it is *unusual* for 8 out of 10 babies to randomly select the good puppet. Explain your reasoning.

Math Practice

Interpret Results
If the babies were not randomly selecting puppets, what does this imply about their behavior?

d. Is it *possible* that the babies were randomly selecting a puppet? Is it *likely*? Explain your reasoning.

e. Use the simulator at *BigIdeasMath.com* to simulate 200 trials of flipping a coin 10 times. Do the results support your answer in part (d)? Explain.

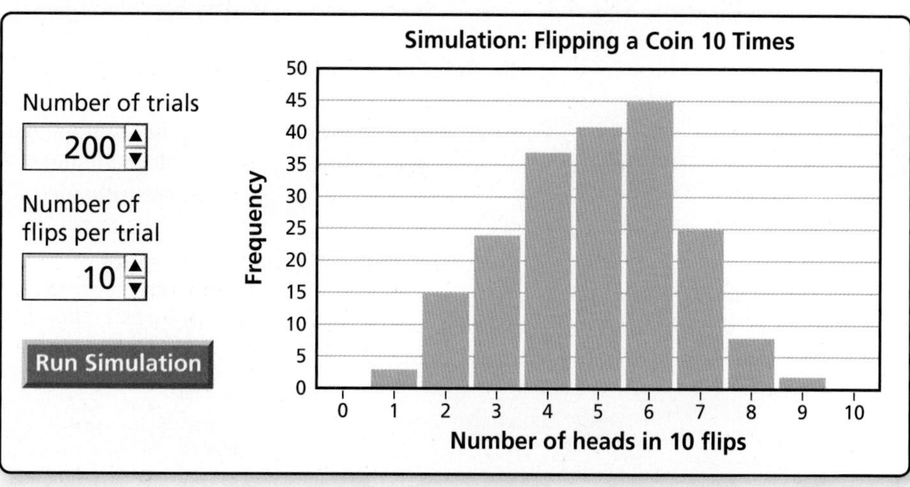

Simulator available at *BigIdeasMath.com*

Populations and Samples

GO DIGITAL

Vocabulary

population, *p. 474*
sample, *p. 474*
parameter, *p. 475*
statistic, *p. 475*
hypothesis, *p. 476*

A **population** is the collection of all data, such as responses, measurements, or counts, that are of interest. A **sample** is a subset of a population.

A *census* consists of data from an entire population. But, unless a population is small, it is usually impractical to obtain all the population data. In most studies, information is instead obtained from a *random sample*. (You will learn more about random sampling and data collection in the next section.)

It is important for a sample to be representative of a population so that sample data can be used to draw valid conclusions about the population. When the sample is not representative of the population, the conclusions may not be valid. Drawing conclusions about populations is an important use of *statistics*. Recall that statistics is the science of collecting, organizing, and interpreting data.

EXAMPLE 1 Distinguishing Between Populations and Samples

Identify the population and the sample. Describe the sample.

a. In the United States, a survey of 2184 adults ages 18 and over found that 1328 of them own at least one pet.

b. To estimate the gas mileage of new cars sold in the United States, a consumer advocacy group tests 845 new cars and finds they have an average gas mileage of 25.1 miles per gallon.

SOLUTION

a. The population consists of the responses of all adults ages 18 and over in the United States, and the sample consists of the responses of the 2184 adults in the survey. Notice in the diagram that the sample is a subset of the responses of all adults in the United States. The sample consists of 1328 adults who said they own at least one pet and 856 adults who said they do not own any pets.

Population: responses of all adults ages 18 and over in the U.S.

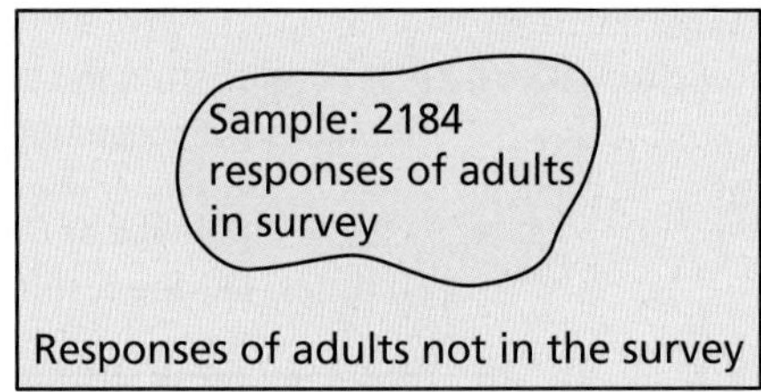

b. The population consists of the gas mileages of all new cars sold in the United States, and the sample consists of the gas mileages of the 845 new cars tested by the group. Notice in the diagram that the sample is a subset of the gas mileages of all new cars in the United States. The sample consists of 845 new cars with an average of 25.1 miles per gallon.

Population: gas mileages of all new cars sold in the U.S.

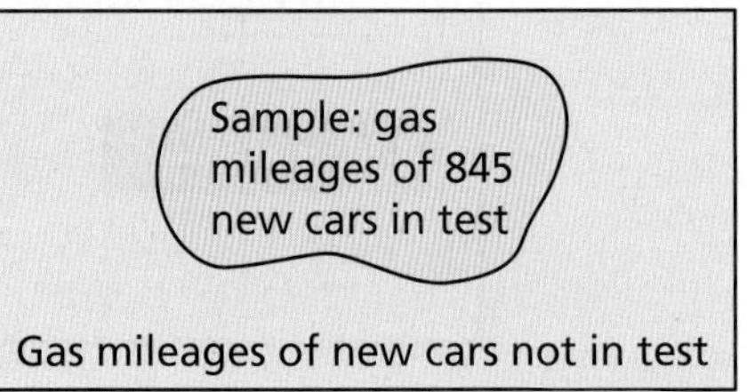

A numerical description of a population characteristic is called a **parameter**. A numerical description of a sample characteristic is called a **statistic**. Because some populations are too large to measure, a statistic, such as the sample mean, is used to estimate the parameter, such as the population mean. It is important that you are able to distinguish between a parameter and a statistic.

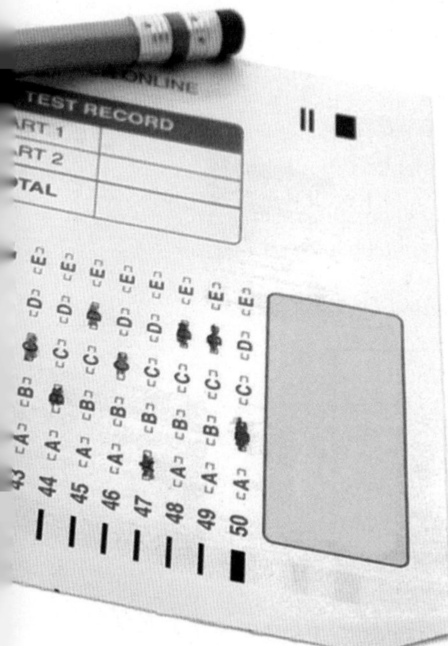

EXAMPLE 2 Distinguishing Between Parameters and Statistics

a. For all students taking the SAT in a recent year, the mean mathematics score was 531. Is the mean score a parameter or a statistic? Explain your reasoning.

b. A survey of 1060 women, ages 20–29 in the United States, found that the standard deviation of their heights is about 2.6 inches. Is the standard deviation of the heights a parameter or a statistic? Explain your reasoning.

SOLUTION

a. Because the mean score of 531 is based on all students who took the SAT in a recent year, it is a parameter.

b. Because there are more than 1060 women ages 20–29 in the United States, the survey is based on a subset of the population (all women ages 20–29 in the United States). So, the standard deviation of the heights is a statistic. Note that if the sample is representative of the population, then you can estimate that the standard deviation of the heights of all women ages 20–29 in the United States is about 2.6 inches.

SELF-ASSESSMENT

1 I do not understand. 2 I can do it with help. 3 I can do it on my own. 4 I can teach someone else.

In Exercises 1 and 2, identify the population and the sample.

1. To estimate the retail prices for three grades of gasoline sold in the United States, the Energy Information Association calls 800 retail gasoline outlets, records the prices, and then determines the average price for each grade.
2. A survey of 4464 shoppers in the United States found that they spent an average of $407.02 from Thursday through Sunday during a recent Thanksgiving holiday.
3. A survey found that the median salary of 1068 statisticians is about $87,800. Is the median salary a parameter or a statistic? Explain your reasoning.
4. What is the mean age of all Senators at the start of the 116th Congress? Is the mean age a parameter or a statistic? Explain your reasoning.

Mean age at the start of the Congress		
Congress	All Senators	Newly Elected Senators
116th	62.9 years	58.1 years
115th	61.8 years	54.8 years
114th	61.0 years	50.7 years
113th	62.0 years	53.0 years

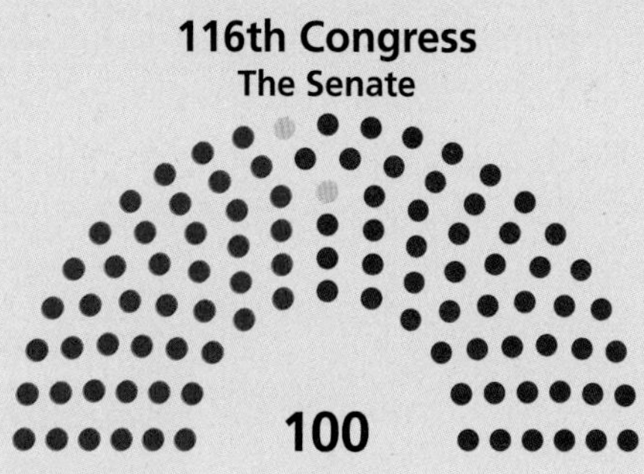

A *population proportion* is the ratio of members of a population with a particular characteristic to the total members of the population. A *sample proportion* is the ratio of members of a sample of the population with a particular characteristic to the total members of the sample.

EXAMPLE 3 Finding a Sample Proportion

Use technology to simulate rolling a die 50 times. What proportion of the 50 rolls result in an odd number?

SOLUTION

You can simulate the rolling of a die 50 times by randomly generating a set of 50 numbers from one through six and organizing the results in a bar graph.

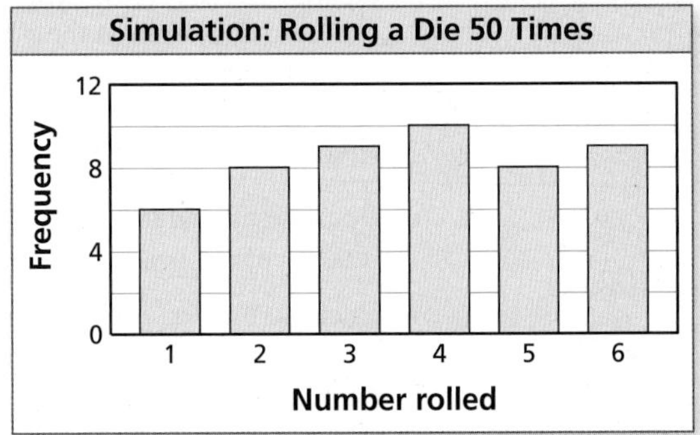

Simulator available at *BigIdeasMath.com*

From the bar graph, the odd numbers 1, 3, and 5 were rolled 6, 9, and 8 times, respectively. Getting $6 + 9 + 8 = 23$ odd numbers in 50 rolls corresponds to a proportion of $\frac{23}{50} = 0.46$.

▶ So, 46% of the rolls resulted in an odd number.

Analyzing Hypotheses

In statistics, a **hypothesis** is a claim about a characteristic of a population. For example:

A medical researcher claims that the proportion of U.S. adults living with one or more chronic conditions, such as high blood pressure, is 0.45, or 45%.

To analyze a hypothesis, you need to distinguish between results that can easily occur by chance and results that are highly unlikely to occur by chance. One way to analyze a hypothesis is to perform a simulation. When the results occur rarely in the simulation, the hypothesis is probably false.

Conclusions made about a hypothesis may or may not be correct. The table summarizes the incorrect and correct decisions that can be made about a hypothesis.

		Truth of Hypothesis	
		Hypothesis is true.	**Hypothesis is false.**
Decision	**You decide that the hypothesis is true.**	correct decision	incorrect decision
	You decide that the hypothesis is false.	incorrect decision	correct decision

EXAMPLE 4 Analyzing a Hypothesis

You roll a six-sided die 5 times and do not get an even number. The probability of this happening is $\left(\frac{1}{2}\right)^5 = 0.03125$, so you suspect this die favors odd numbers. The die maker claims the die does not favor odd numbers or even numbers. What should you conclude when you roll the actual die 50 times and get (a) 26 odd numbers and (b) 35 odd numbers?

SOLUTION

The maker's claim, or hypothesis, is "the die does not favor odd numbers or even numbers." This is the same as saying that the proportion of odd numbers rolled, in the long run, is 0.50. So, assume the probability of rolling an odd number is 0.50.

One way to test the hypothesis is to extend the simulation in Example 3 to 200 samples. For each sample, calculate the proportion of the 50 rolls that resulted in an odd number. Make a histogram of the distribution of the sample proportions. Then compare the results of rolling the actual die to the results of the simulation.

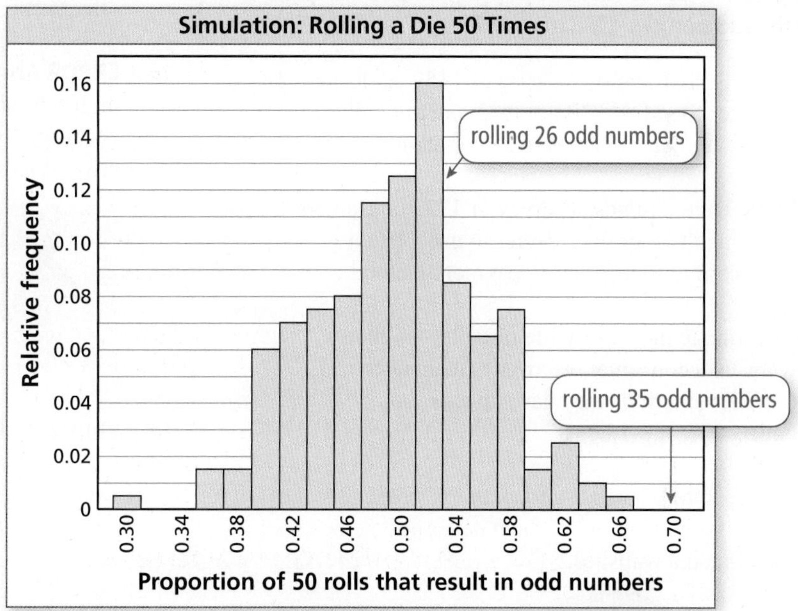

Simulator available at *BigIdeasMath.com*

Math Practice

Justifying Conclusions
What is the theoretical probability of getting 35 odd numbers in 50 rolls? Is it possible that your conclusion in part (b) is incorrect? Explain.

a. Getting 26 odd numbers in 50 rolls corresponds to a proportion of $\frac{26}{50} = 0.52$. In the simulation, this result had a relative frequency of 0.16. In fact, most of the results are close to 0.50. Because getting 26 odd numbers in 50 rolls can easily occur by chance, you can conclude that the maker's claim is most likely true.

b. Getting 35 odd numbers in 50 rolls corresponds to a proportion of $\frac{35}{50} = 0.70$. In the simulation, this result did not occur. Because getting 35 odd numbers is highly unlikely to occur by chance, you can conclude that the maker's claim is most likely false.

SELF-ASSESSMENT

1 I do not understand. 2 I can do it with help. 3 I can do it on my own. 4 I can teach someone else.

5. Use technology to simulate rolling a die 100 times. What proportion of the 100 rolls result in a multiple of 3?

6. **WHAT IF?** In Example 4, what should you conclude when you roll the actual die 50 times and get (a) 18 odd numbers and (b) 24 odd numbers?

9.2 Practice WITH CalcChat® AND CalcView®

In Exercises 1–4, determine whether the data are collected from a population or a sample. Explain your reasoning.

1. the number of high school students in the United States

2. the color of every third car in a parking lot

3. a survey of 100 spectators at a sporting event with 1800 spectators

4. the age of each dentist in the United States

In Exercises 5–8, identify the population and sample. Describe the sample. *Example 1*

5. In the United States, a survey of 1152 adults ages 18 and over found that 403 of them occasionally pretend to use their smartphones to avoid talking to someone.

6. In the United States, a survey of 1222 consumers found that 978 of them prefer to use a credit or debit card as their primary payment method.

7. To estimate the battery life of tablets sold on a website, a consumer electronics team tests 6 tablets and finds they have an average battery life of 9.1 hours.

8. In the United States, a survey of 743 teenagers ages 13–17 found that 193 of them never post selfies on social media websites.

In Exercises 9–12, determine whether the numerical value is a parameter or a statistic. Explain your reasoning. *Example 2*

9. The average cost of admission to some amusement parks in a state is $36.93.

10. In a recent year, 54% of the seats in the United States House of Representatives were held by Democrats.

11. Two percent of all active volcanoes in the United States have had a significant eruption in the past ten years.

12. In the United States, a survey of 2007 adults found that 8% have serious doubt about the safety and effectiveness of vaccines.

13. **ERROR ANALYSIS** A survey of 1270 students at a high school found that 965 students felt added stress because of their workload. Describe and correct the error in identifying the population and the sample.

The population consists of all the students in the high school. The sample consists of the 965 students who felt added stress.

14. **ERROR ANALYSIS** Each visitor to a website receives a survey via email. The mean age of all of the people who respond to the survey is 26 years. Describe and correct the error in determining whether the mean age represents a parameter or statistic.

Because the mean age of 26 is based on all of the people who respond to the survey, it is a parameter.

15. **WRITING** Describe the difference between a parameter and a statistic. Give an example of each.

16. **HOW DO YOU SEE IT?** Use the diagram to identify the population and sample. Explain your reasoning.

Majors of students at a university

Majors of students at a university who take chemistry

Majors of students at a university who do not take chemistry

17. **MODELING REAL LIFE** You use technology to simulate flipping a coin 25 times. The results are shown in the bar graph. What proportion of the 25 flips resulted in tails? *Example 3*

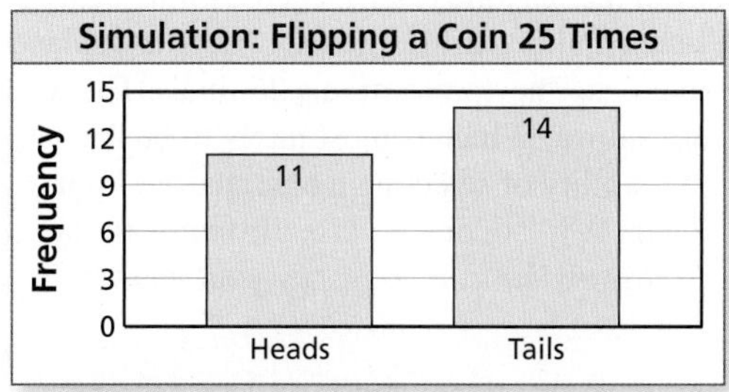

18. **MODELING REAL LIFE** You use technology to simulate rolling a die 50 times. The results are shown in the bar graph. What proportion of the 50 rolls resulted in a 6?

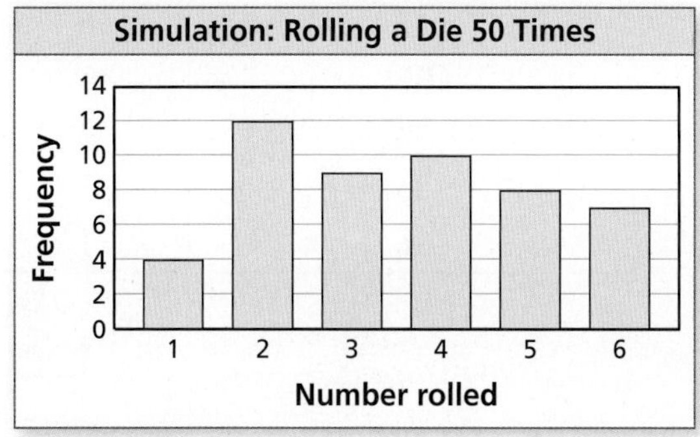

19. **MP USING TOOLS** Use technology to simulate rolling a die 50 times. What proportion of the 50 rolls result in a number less than 3?

20. **MP USING TOOLS** Use technology to simulate rolling a die 100 times. What proportion of the 100 rolls result in a prime number?

21. **MODELING REAL LIFE** You flip a coin 4 times and do not get a tails. You suspect this coin favors heads. The coin maker claims that the coin does not favor heads or tails. You use technology to simulate 200 random samples of flipping a coin 50 times. The histogram shows the results. What should you conclude when you flip the actual coin 50 times and get (a) 27 heads and (b) 33 heads? *Example 4*

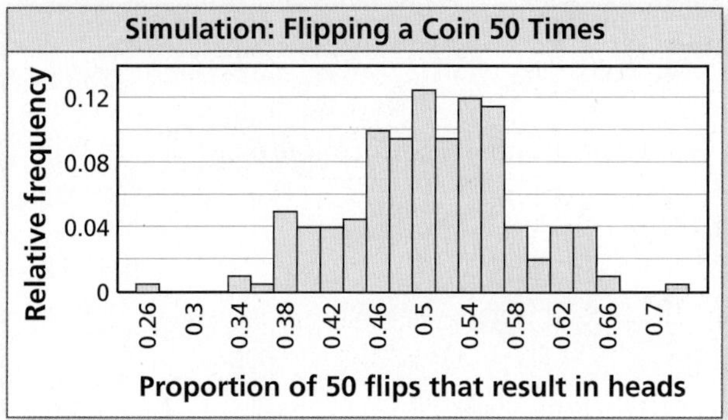

22. **MODELING REAL LIFE** You spin the spinner shown 6 times and get red 3 times. You suspect this spinner favors red. The maker claims that the spinner does not favor any color. You use technology to simulate 200 random samples of spinning the spinner 100 times. The histogram shows the results. What should you conclude when you spin the actual spinner 100 times and get red (a) 56 times and (b) 29 times?

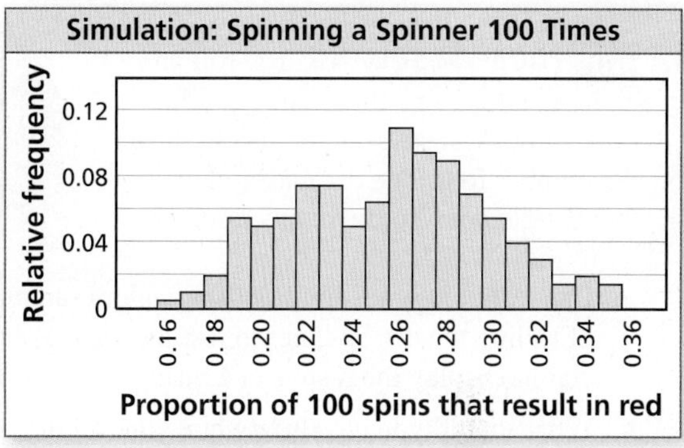

23. **MP USING TOOLS** Use the simulator available at *BigIdeasMath.com* to simulate 300 random samples of flipping a coin 100 times. What should you conclude about the actual coin in Exercise 21 when you flip it 100 times and get (a) 34 heads and (b) 46 heads?

24. **MP USING TOOLS** Use the simulator available at *BigIdeasMath.com* to simulate 500 random samples of spinning the spinner in Exercise 22 fifty times. What should you conclude about the actual spinner when you spin it 50 times and get red (a) 15 times and (b) 24 times?

25. **MAKING AN ARGUMENT** A random sample of five people at a movie theater from a population of 200 people gave the film 4 out of 4 stars. Can you conclude that everyone in the movie theater would give the film 4 stars? Explain your reasoning.

26. **MP REASONING** You use technology to perform two simulations of repeatedly drawing a card from a standard deck of cards with replacement. The first simulation uses 20 random samples of size 10, and the second uses 400 random samples of size 10. Which simulation should you use to accurately analyze a hypothesis? Explain.

27. **OPEN-ENDED** Find an article that describes a survey. Identify the population and sample. Describe the sample.

28. **THOUGHT PROVOKING**
You choose a random sample of 200 from a population of 2000. Each person in the sample is asked how many hours of sleep he or she gets each night. The mean of your sample is 5 hours. Is it possible that the mean of the entire population is 8 hours of sleep each night? Is it likely? Explain.

29. **MP PROBLEM SOLVING** You roll an eight-sided die five times and get a four every time. You suspect that the die favors the number four. The die maker claims that the die does not favor any number.

   a. Use technology to simulate 200 random samples of rolling the die 50 times to test the die maker's claim. Display the results in a histogram.

   b. What should you conclude when you roll the actual die 50 times and get 20 fours? 7 fours?

30. **DIG DEEPER** Each of 20 students has a bag that contains blue marbles and green marbles. The contents of each bag are identical. Each student randomly selects a marble from the bag, the teacher records how many students select a blue marble, then the students replace the marbles. They perform this 25 times. The results are shown. Which is most likely to be the actual probability of selecting a blue marble from a bag: 0.5, 0.6, or 0.7? Use the simulator at *BigIdeasMath.com* to justify your answer.

GO DIGITAL

Number of students out of 20 with a blue marble	Frequency
9	2
10	3
11	5
12	6
13	3
14	2
15	3
16	1

REVIEW & REFRESH

In Exercises 31 and 32, solve the equation using any method. Explain your choice of method.

31. $x^2 - 10x = 4$

32. $n^2 + 2n + 2 = 0$

33. Determine whether the histogram has a normal distribution.

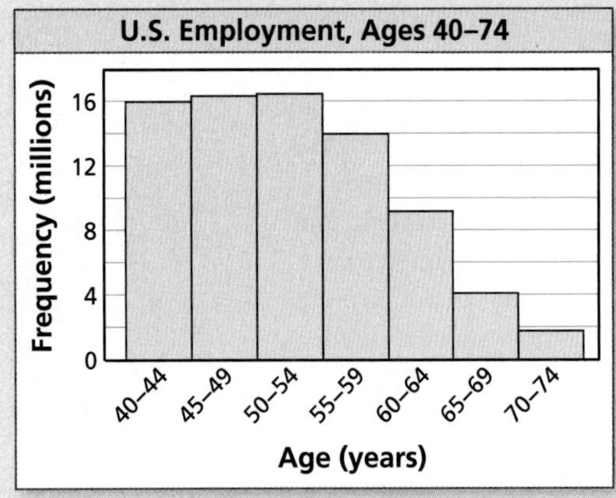

34. Identify the population and the sample. Describe the sample.

A survey of some U.S. teenagers ages 13–17 found that 90% play video games of some kind.

35. **MODELING REAL LIFE** The number y of duckweed fronds in a pond after t days is $y = a(1230.25)^{t/16}$, where a is the initial number of fronds. By what percent does the duckweed increase each day?

36. Find the probability of flipping a coin 50 times and getting 12 heads.

In Exercises 37 and 38, evaluate the expression.

37. $_{16}P_2$

38. $_6C_4$

39. The table shows the inputs and outputs of two functions. Use the table to find each value.

x	−2	−1	0	1	2	3
$f(x)$	−5	−3	−1	1	3	5
$g(x)$	1	0	1	2	3	4

   a. $f(g(-1))$

   b. $g(f(2))$

In Exercises 40 and 41, perform the operation.

40. $\frac{3xy^2}{x^3y} \cdot \frac{x}{9y}$

41. $\frac{6}{5x} - \frac{3}{4x}$

9.3 Collecting Data

Learning Target Describe sampling methods and recognize bias when collecting data.

Success Criteria
- I can identify types of sampling methods in statistical studies.
- I can analyze methods of collecting data.
- I can describe bias in sampling and in survey questions.

The goal of a statistical study is to collect data and use that data to draw a conclusion. A conclusion that you draw using the results of a statistical study is only as reliable as the process used to obtain the data. If the process is flawed, then the resulting decision is questionable.

EXPLORE IT! Conducting a Survey

Math Practice

Apply Mathematics Describe another method that is likely to result in a sample that is representative of the students in your school.

Work with a partner. For a class project, your class will survey 20 students about the use of technology in your school.

a. Your class proposes the following methods for selecting individuals to participate in the survey.

Method 1: Select the first 20 students who volunteer to participate in the survey.

Method 2: Assign each student a unique number. Then use a random number generator to select 20 of the numbers.

Method 3: Randomly select 20 students in a computer programming class.

i. Which method is most likely to result in a sample that will be representative of students in your school? Explain.

ii. Describe any disadvantages of the other two methods.

b. Students in your class propose two different ways to ask one of the questions in the survey. Analyze each question and explain how the wording can be improved. Then write a new question for the survey.

Would you rather use older methods in education, or have the school provide a tablet for each student?

Should the school spend money to provide a tablet for each student instead of using the money for more urgent needs?

GO DIGITAL

Identifying Sampling Methods in Statistical Studies

Vocabulary 

random sample, *p. 482*
self-selected sample, *p. 482*
systematic sample, *p. 482*
stratified sample, *p. 482*
cluster sample, *p. 482*
convenience sample, *p. 482*
bias, *p. 483*
unbiased sample, *p. 483*
biased sample, *p. 483*
experiment, *p. 484*
observational study, *p. 484*
survey, *p. 484*
simulation, *p. 484*
biased question, *p. 485*

The steps in a typical statistical study are shown below.

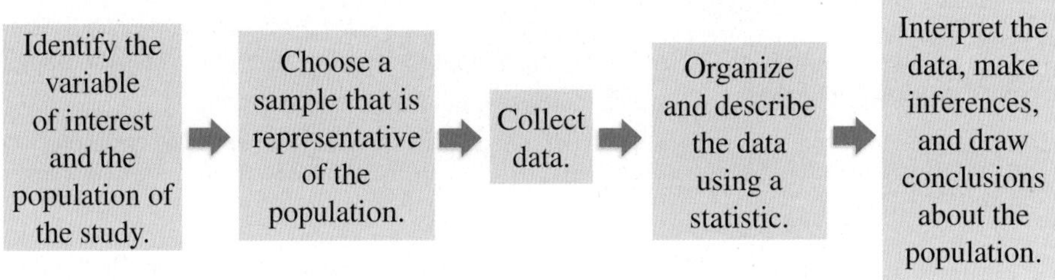

There are many different ways of sampling a population, but a *random sample* is preferred because it is most likely to be representative of a population. In a **random sample**, each member of a population has an equal chance of being selected.

The other types of samples given below are defined by the methods used to select members. Each sampling method has its advantages and disadvantages.

KEY IDEA

Types of Samples

For a **self-selected sample**, members of a population can volunteer to be in the sample.

For a **systematic sample**, a rule is used to select members of a population. For instance, selecting every other person.

For a **stratified sample**, a population is divided into smaller groups that share a similar characteristic. A sample is then randomly selected from each group.

STUDY TIP
A stratified sample ensures that every segment of a population is represented.

For a **cluster sample**, a population is divided into groups, called *clusters*. All of the members in one or more of the clusters are selected.

STUDY TIP
With cluster sampling, a member of a population cannot belong to more than one cluster.

For a **convenience sample**, only members of a population who are easy to reach are selected.

EXAMPLE 1 Identifying Types of Samples

You want to determine whether students in your school like the new design of the school's website. Identify the type of sample described.

a. You list all the students alphabetically and choose every sixth student.

b. You mail questionnaires and use only the questionnaires that are returned.

c. You ask all the students in your algebra class.

d. You randomly select two students from each classroom.

SOLUTION

a. You are using a rule to select students. So, the sample is a *systematic* sample.

b. The students can choose whether to respond. So, the sample is a *self-selected* sample.

c. You are selecting students who are readily available. So, the sample is a *convenience* sample.

d. The students are divided into similar groups by their classrooms, and two students are selected at random from each group. So, the sample is a *stratified* sample.

SELF-ASSESSMENT

1 I do not understand. 2 I can do it with help. 3 I can do it on my own. 4 I can teach someone else.

1. **WHAT IF?** In Example 1, you divide the students in your school according to their zip codes, then select all the students who live in one zip code. What type of sample are you using?

2. Describe another method you can use to obtain a stratified sample in Example 1.

Recognizing Bias in Sampling

A **bias** is an error that results in a misrepresentation of a population. In order to obtain reliable information and draw accurate conclusions about a population, it is important to select an *unbiased sample*. An **unbiased sample** is representative of a population. A sample that overrepresents or under-represents part of a population is a **biased sample**. When a sample is biased, conclusions based on the data may be invalid. A random sample can help reduce the possibility of a biased sample.

WORDS AND MATH

In everyday life, *bias* describes a person's tendency or inclination to believe particular things or behave in a particular way. A *biased sample* might not be representative of a population, in part, because of the biases of the individuals that compose it.

EXAMPLE 2 Identifying Biased Samples

Identify the type of sample and explain why the sample is biased.

a. A news organization asks its viewers to participate in an online poll about bullying.

b. A computer science teacher wants to know how students at a school most often access the Internet. The teacher asks students in one of the computer science classes.

SOLUTION

a. The viewers can choose whether to participate in the poll. So, the sample is a *self-selected* sample. The sample is biased because people who go online and respond to the poll most likely have a strong opinion on the subject of bullying.

b. The teacher selects students who are readily available. So, the sample is a *convenience* sample. The sample is biased because other students in the school do not have an opportunity to be chosen.

EXAMPLE 3 Selecting an Unbiased Sample

You are a member of your school's yearbook committee. You want to poll members of the senior class to find out what the theme of the yearbook should be. There are 246 students in the senior class. Describe a method for selecting a random sample of 50 seniors to poll.

STUDY TIP

When you obtain a duplicate integer, ignore it and generate a new, unique integer as a replacement.

SOLUTION

Step 1 Make a list of all 246 seniors. Assign each senior a different integer from 1 to 246.

Step 2 Use technology to generate 50 unique random integers from 1 to 246.

Step 3 Choose the 50 students who correspond to the 50 integers you generated in Step 2.

	A	B
1	RANDBETWEEN(1,246)	207
2		101
3		109
4		81
5		173
6		7

SELF-ASSESSMENT

1 I do not understand. 2 I can do it with help. 3 I can do it on my own. 4 I can teach someone else.

3. The manager of a concert hall wants to know how often people in the community attend concerts. The manager asks 45 people standing in line for a rock concert how many concerts they attend per year. Identify the type of sample the manager is using and explain why the sample is biased.

4. In Example 3, what is another method you can use to generate a random sample of 50 students? Explain why your sampling method is random.

Analyzing Methods of Data Collection

There are several ways to collect data for a statistical study. The objective of the study often dictates the best method for collecting the data.

KEY IDEA

Methods of Collecting Data

An **experiment** imposes a treatment on individuals in order to collect data on their response to the treatment. The treatment may be a medical treatment, or it can be any action that might affect a variable in the experiment, such as adding methanol to gasoline and then measuring its effect on fuel efficiency.

An **observational study** observes individuals and measures variables without controlling the individuals or their environment. This type of study is used when it is difficult to control or isolate the variable being studied, or when it may be unethical to subject people to a certain treatment or to withhold it from them.

A **survey** is an investigation of one or more characteristics of a population. In a survey, every member of a sample is asked one or more questions.

A **simulation** uses a model to reproduce the conditions of a situation or process so that the simulated outcomes closely match the real-world outcomes. Simulations allow you to study situations that are impractical or dangerous to create in real life.

READING

A *census* is a survey that obtains data from every member of a population. Often, a census is not practical because of its cost or the time required to gather the data. The U.S. population census is conducted every 10 years.

GO DIGITAL

EXAMPLE 4 Identifying Methods of Data Collection

Identify the method of data collection described in each situation.

a. A researcher records whether people at a gas station use hand sanitizer.

b. A landscaper fertilizes 20 lawns with a regular fertilizer mix and 20 lawns with a new organic fertilizer. The landscaper then compares the lawns after 10 weeks and determines which fertilizer is better.

SOLUTION

a. The researcher is gathering data without controlling the individuals or applying a treatment. So, this situation is an *observational study*.

b. A treatment (organic fertilizer) is being applied to some of the individuals (lawns) in the study. So, this situation is an *experiment*.

Recognizing Bias in Survey Questions

When designing a survey, it is important to word survey questions so they do not lead to biased results. Answers to poorly worded questions may not accurately reflect the opinions or actions of those being surveyed. Questions that are flawed in a way that leads to inaccurate results are called **biased questions**. Avoid questions that:

- encourage a particular response
- are too sensitive to answer truthfully
- do not provide enough information to give an accurate opinion
- address more than one issue

STUDY TIP

Bias may also be introduced in survey questioning in other ways, such as by the order in which questions are asked or by respondents giving answers they believe will please the questioner.

EXAMPLE 5 Identify and Correct Bias in Survey Questioning

A dentist surveys his patients by asking, "Do you brush your teeth at least twice per day and floss every day?" Explain why the question may be biased or otherwise introduce bias into the survey. Then describe a way to correct the flaw.

SOLUTION

Patients who brush less than twice per day or do not floss daily may be afraid to admit this because a dentist is asking the question. One improvement may be to have patients answer questions about dental hygiene on paper and then put the paper anonymously into a box.

SELF-ASSESSMENT

1 I do not understand. 2 I can do it with help. 3 I can do it on my own. 4 I can teach someone else.

In Exercises 5–7, identify the method of data collection the situation describes.

5. Members of a student council at your school ask every eighth student who enters the cafeteria whether they like the snacks in the school's vending machines.

6. A park ranger measures and records the heights of trees in a park as they grow.

7. A researcher uses a computer program to help determine how fast an influenza virus might spread within a city.

8. Explain why the survey question below may be biased or otherwise introduce bias into the survey. Then describe a way to correct the flaw.

"Should the school change its unhealthy cafeteria menu?"

GO DIGITAL

9.3 Practice WITH CalcChat® AND CalcView®

In Exercises 1–4, identify the type of sample described. *Example 1*

1. A local politician wants to know how people will vote in an upcoming election. The politician conducts telephone surveys and uses only the results from the people who agree to participate.

2. A ride-sharing company wants to know whether its customers are satisfied with the service. Drivers survey every tenth customer during the day.

3. Each employee in a company writes his or her name on a card and places it in a hat. The employees whose names are on the first two cards drawn each win a gift card.

4. The owner of a community pool wants to ask patrons whether they think the water should be colder. Patrons are divided into four age groups, and a sample is randomly surveyed from each age group.

In Exercises 5–8, identify the type of sample and explain why the sample is biased. *Example 2*

5. A town council wants to know whether residents support having an off-leash area for dogs in the town park. Eighty dog owners are surveyed at the park.

6. School officials want to gather feedback on teacher performance. They mail surveys to all parents and use the surveys that are returned.

7. You want to find out whether booth holders at a convention are pleased with their booth locations. You divide the convention center into six sections and survey every booth holder in the fifth section.

8. You want to determine whether students in your school support a renovation of the school auditorium. You ask all of the students in your homeroom.

In Exercises 9–12, determine whether the sample is biased. Explain your reasoning.

9. Your school principal randomly selects five students from each grade to complete a survey about classroom participation.

10. A governor wants to know whether voters in the state support building a highway that will pass through a state forest. Business owners in a town near the proposed highway are randomly surveyed.

11. To assess customers' experiences making purchases online, a rating company e-mails purchasers and asks that they click on a link and complete a survey.

12. Every third person who enters an athletic event is asked whether he or she supports the use of instant replay in officiating the event.

13. **ERROR ANALYSIS** Surveys are mailed to every other household in a neighborhood. Each survey that is returned is used. Describe and correct the error in identifying the type of sample that is used.

Because the surveys were mailed to every other household, the sample is a systematic sample.

14. **ERROR ANALYSIS** A researcher wants to know whether the U.S. workforce supports raising the minimum wage. Fifty high school students chosen at random are surveyed. Describe and correct the error in determining whether the sample is biased.

Because the students were chosen at random, the sample is not biased.

15. **WRITING** The staff of a student newsletter wants to conduct a survey about students' favorite television shows. There are 1225 students in the school. Describe a method for selecting a random sample of 250 students to survey. *Example 3*

16. **WRITING** A national collegiate athletic association wants to survey 15 of the 120 head football coaches in a division about a proposed rule change. Describe a method for selecting a random sample of coaches to survey.

In Exercises 17–20, identify the method of data collection described in the situation. *Example 4*

17. A researcher uses technology to estimate the damage that will be done if a volcano erupts.

STEM

18. An online seller asks 20 customers whether they are satisfied with their purchases.

19. A store manager records whether customers choose to use the regular checkout or the self-checkout.

20. A researcher places bacteria samples in two different climates. The researcher then measures the bacteria growth in each sample after 3 days.

In Exercises 21–24, explain why the survey question may be biased or otherwise introduce bias into the survey. Then describe a way to correct the flaw. *Example 5*

21. "Isn't it true that the budget of our city should be cut?"

22. "Would you rather watch the latest award-winning movie or just read some book?"

23. A child asks, "Do you support the construction of a new children's hospital?"

24. "Are you satisfied with the selection of colors and the quality of the clothing?"

In Exercises 25–28, determine whether the survey question may be biased or otherwise introduce bias into the survey. Explain your reasoning.

25. "Should the city build a skate park?"

26. "Do you support making necessary renovations to the old town hall?"

27. A police officer asks mall visitors, "Do you wear your seat belt regularly?"

GO DIGITAL

28. "Do you favor government funding to help prevent acid rain?"

29. **MP REASONING** A researcher studies the effect of fiber supplements on heart disease. The researcher identified 175 people who take fiber supplements and 175 people who do not take fiber supplements. The study found that those who took the supplements had 19.6% fewer heart attacks. The researcher concludes that taking fiber supplements reduces the chance of heart attacks.

   a. Explain why the researcher's conclusion may not be valid.

   b. Describe how the researcher could have conducted the study differently to produce valid results.

30. **HOW DO YOU SEE IT?**
A poll is conducted to predict the results of a statewide election in New Mexico before all the votes are counted. Fifty voters in each of the state's 33 counties are asked how they voted as they leave the polls.

   a. Identify the type of sample described.

   b. Explain how the diagram shows that the polling method could result in a biased sample.

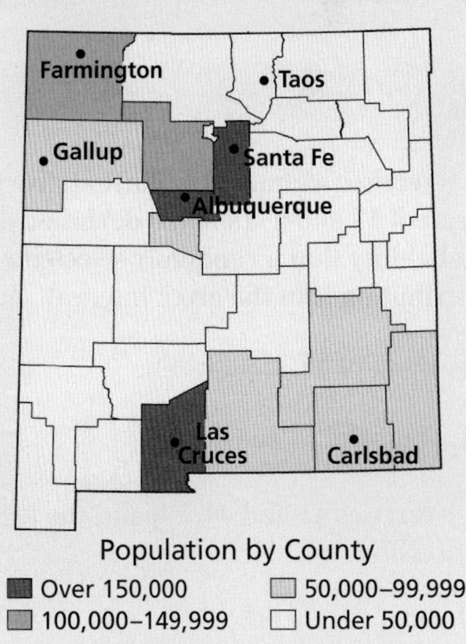

31. **WRITING** Consider each type of sample listed on page 482. Which of the sample types are most likely to introduce bias? Explain.

32. **OPEN-ENDED** An airline wants to know whether travelers have enough leg room on its planes.

a. Identify the population in this situation.

b. What method of data collection is appropriate for this situation?

c. Describe a sampling method that is likely to give biased results. Explain.

d. Describe a sampling method that is likely to give unbiased results. Explain.

e. Write one biased question and one unbiased question for this situation.

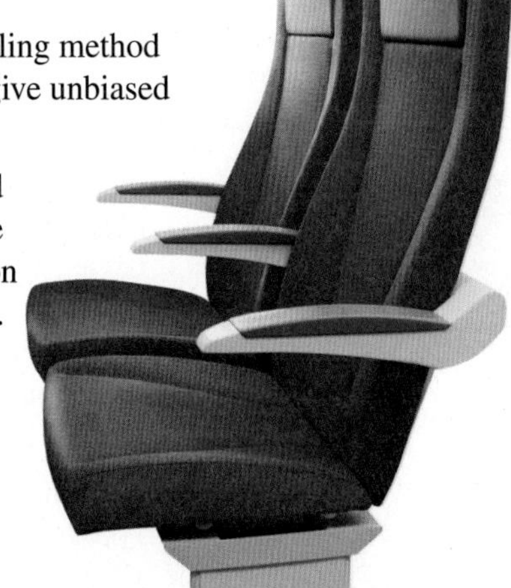

33. **MP REASONING** A website contains a link to a survey that asks how much time each person spends on the Internet each week.

a. What type of sampling method is used in this situation?

b. Which group of people is likely to respond to the survey? What can you conclude?

34. **THOUGHT PROVOKING**
What is the difference between a "blind experiment" and a "double-blind experiment?" Describe a possible advantage of the second type of experiment over the first.

35. **MP PRECISION** A company wants to survey its customers to assess the performance of its customer service team. You are in charge of designing the survey. Write three unbiased questions for the survey.

REVIEW & REFRESH

36. The median number of years of experience for teachers at a school is 8. Is the median number of years a parameter or a statistic? Explain your reasoning.

In Exercises 37–40, simplify the expression.

37. $(4^{3/2} \cdot 4^{1/4})^4$

38. $(6^{1/3} \cdot 3^{1/3})^{-2}$

39. $\sqrt[3]{4} \cdot \sqrt[3]{16}$

40. $\dfrac{\sqrt[4]{405}}{\sqrt[4]{5}}$

In Exercises 41 and 42, a normal distribution has a mean of 57 and a standard deviation of 3. Find the probability that a randomly selected *x*-value from the distribution is in the given interval.

41. at most 54

42. between 51 and 60

In Exercises 43 and 44, expand the logarithmic expression.

43. $\log_2 \dfrac{4x}{y}$

44. $\ln xy^6$

45. The owners of a chain of 260 retail stores want to assess employee job satisfaction. Employees from 12 stores near the headquarters are surveyed. What type of sample is being used?

46. Find the probability of rolling a 5 exactly 2 times in 8 rolls of a six-sided die.

47. Graph $f(x) = \dfrac{5}{x} - 1$. Find the domain and range.

In Exercises 48 and 49, evaluate the expression without using technology.

48. $-64^{1/2}$

49. $27^{2/3}$

50. **MODELING REAL LIFE** A class of 22 students takes a quiz. The letter grades that students earn are shown. What is the probability that a randomly selected student from the class earns an 'A' on the quiz?

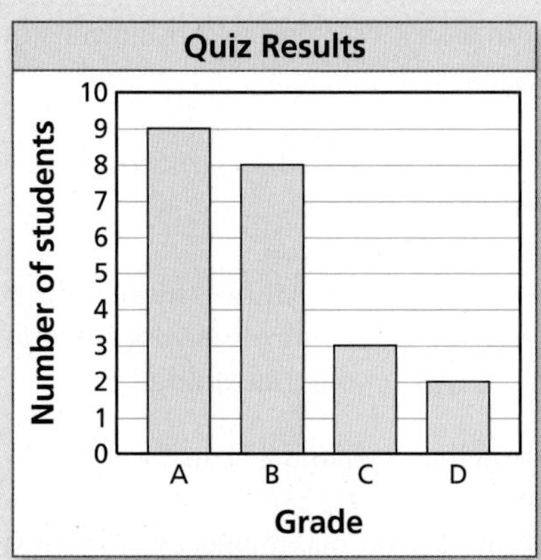

9.4 Experimental Design

Learning Target Describe and analyze experiments and their designs.

Success Criteria
- I can assess the validity of an experiment's results.
- I can design an experiment or observational study.
- I can analyze experimental designs.

EXPLORE IT! Designing Experiments

Work with a partner.

a. You want to study the following topic.

Can students create and send text messages faster using their dominant hand or non-dominant hand?

Describe an experiment to study this question. Be sure to include the following.

i. How should you select students? Why?

ii. How many students should you select? Why?

iii. Will your results be valid? How do you know?

iv. How can you improve your experiment?

b. You want to study the following topic.

Can students create and send text messages faster using a particular mobile device?

Repeat part (a) for this topic.

c. A researcher is studying the following topic.

Does texting while driving result in more accidents?

To gather data, the researcher plans an experiment in which one group of drivers text every time they drive, and another group do not text at all while they drive. The number of accidents for each driver will be monitored over time and the results will be compared between the two groups.

i. What ethical problems might this type of experiment pose?

ii. How else might the researcher study this topic?

iii. The researcher asks a group of drivers how often they text while driving and the number of vehicular accidents they have had in the last several years. The results show that the drivers who admitted to texting while driving have been involved in more accidents than those who did not admit to texting while driving. The researcher concludes that texting while driving causes more accidents. Is this conclusion valid? Explain your reasoning.

Math Practice

Use Other Resources
What are other examples of experiments where ethical problems may arise?

Describing Experiments

Vocabulary

controlled experiment, *p. 490*
control group, *p. 490*
treatment group, *p. 490*
randomization, *p. 490*
randomized comparative experiment, *p. 490*
placebo, *p. 490*

In a **controlled experiment**, groups are studied under the same conditions with the exception of one or more variables of interest. A group that is subjected to a treatment is the **treatment group**. A group that is not subjected to the treatment is the **control group**. Subjects in the control group are sometimes given a **placebo**, which is a harmless, fake treatment that is similar to the actual treatment.

Randomization randomly assigns subjects to different treatment groups. In a **randomized comparative experiment**, subjects are randomly assigned to the control group or the treatment group. Randomization reduces bias and produces groups of individuals who are very similar before the treatment is applied. Conclusions drawn from an experiment that is not a randomized comparative experiment may not be valid. Comparing the control group and the treatment group makes it possible to determine any effects of the treatment.

EXAMPLE 1 Evaluating Published Reports

Determine whether each study is a randomized comparative experiment. If it is, describe the treatment, the treatment group, and the control group. If it is not, explain why not and discuss whether the conclusions drawn from the study are valid.

a. **Health Watch**

Vitamin C Lowers Cholesterol

At a health clinic, patients were given the choice of whether to take a dietary supplement of 500 milligrams of vitamin C each day. Fifty patients who took the supplement were monitored for one year, as were fifty patients who did not take the supplement. At the end of one year, patients who took the supplement had 15% lower cholesterol levels than patients in the other group.

b. **Restaurant Ordering**

Now Order Even Faster

To test its new touch-screen kiosks, a restaurant randomly selected and divided 186 customers into two groups. One group used the new touch-screen kiosks and the other group ordered at the counter. Users of the new touch-screen kiosks received their food orders 25% faster.

STUDY TIP

The study in part (a) is an *observational study* because the treatment is not being imposed.

SOLUTION

a. The study is not a randomized comparative experiment because the individuals are not randomly assigned to a control group and a treatment group. The conclusion that vitamin C lowers cholesterol may or may not be valid. There may be other reasons why patients who took the supplement had lower cholesterol levels. For example, patients who voluntarily take the supplement may be more likely to have other healthy eating or lifestyle habits that can affect their cholesterol levels.

b. The study is a randomized comparative experiment. The treatment is the use of the new touch-screen kiosks. The treatment group is the individuals who use the new touch-screen kiosks. The control group is the individuals who order at the counter.

SELF-ASSESSMENT

1 I do not understand. 2 I can do it with help. 3 I can do it on my own. 4 I can teach someone else.

1. Repeat Example 1 for the study shown.

Motorist News

Early Birds Make Better Drivers

A recent study shows that adults who rise before 6:30 A.M. are better drivers than other adults. The study monitored the driving records of 140 drivers who always wake up before 6:30 A.M. and 140 drivers who never wake up before 6:30 A.M. The early risers had 12% fewer accidents.

Randomization in Experiments and Observational Studies

You have already studied random sampling and its usefulness in surveys. Randomization also applies to experiments and observational studies.

Experiment	Observational Study
Individuals are assigned at random to the treatment group or the control group.	When possible, random samples can be selected for the groups being studied.

Good experiments and observational studies are designed to compare data from two or more groups to identify relationships between variables. Only a well-designed experiment, however, can determine a *cause-and-effect* relationship.

KEY IDEA

Comparative Studies and Causality

A well-designed randomized comparative experiment, by eliminating sources of variation other than the controlled variable, can make it possible to draw valid cause-and-effect conclusions.

An observational study can identify *correlation* between variables, but not *causality*. Variables other than what is being measured may affect the results.

Designing an Experiment or Observational Study

Determine whether the following research topic is best investigated through an experiment or an observational study. Then describe the design of the experiment or observational study.

Does practicing yoga result in fewer falls for older people?

SOLUTION

The treatment, practicing yoga, may not be possible for those older people who are already unhealthy, so it is not ethical to assign individuals to a control or treatment group. Use an observational study. Randomly choose one group of older people who already practice yoga. Then randomly choose one group of older people who do not practice yoga. Monitor the numbers of falls the individuals in both groups have at regular intervals. Note that because you are using an observational study, you may be able to identify a *correlation* between practicing yoga in older people and number of falls, but not *causality*.

SELF-ASSESSMENT 1 I do not understand. 2 I can do it with help. 3 I can do it on my own. 4 I can teach someone else.

2. **WRITING** Explain how randomization can be used when conducting surveys, performing experiments, and conducting observational studies. Give an example of each.

3. Determine whether the following research topic is best investigated through an experiment or an observational study. Then describe the design of the experiment or observational study.

   You want to know whether flowers sprayed twice per day with a mist of water stay fresh longer than flowers that are not sprayed.

GO DIGITAL

Analyzing Experimental Designs

An important part of experimental design is *sample size*, or the number of subjects in the experiment. The validity of an experiment is dependent on proper randomization and sufficiently large sample sizes.

Math Practice

Understand Mathematical Terms

The *validity* of an experiment refers to the reliability of the results. The results of a valid experiment are more likely to be accepted.

EXAMPLE 3 Analyzing Experimental Designs

WATCH

A pharmaceutical company wants to test the effectiveness of a new chewing gum designed to help people lose weight. Identify a potential problem, if any, with each experimental design. Then describe how you can improve it.

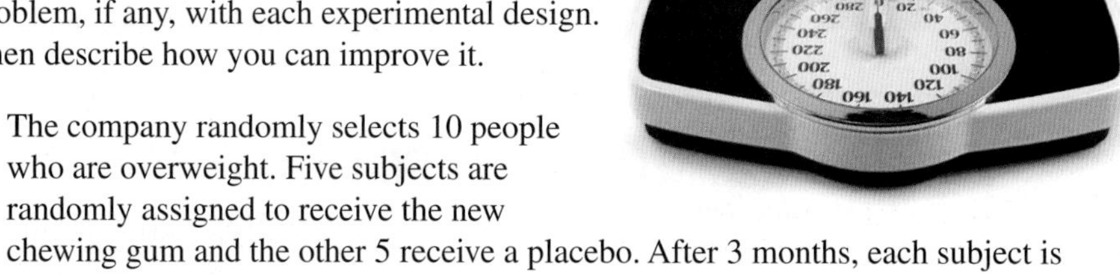

a. The company randomly selects 10 people who are overweight. Five subjects are randomly assigned to receive the new chewing gum and the other 5 receive a placebo. After 3 months, each subject is evaluated and it is determined that the 5 subjects who have been using the new chewing gum have lost weight.

b. The company randomly selects 10,000 people who are overweight. The subjects are divided into groups according to where they live. Subjects who live in a city receive the new chewing gum and subjects who live in rural areas receive the placebo. After 3 months, a significantly large number of the subjects who live in a city have lost weight.

c. The company randomly selects 10,000 people who are overweight. The subjects are divided into groups according to age. Within each age group, subjects are randomly assigned to receive the new chewing gum or the placebo. After 3 months, a significantly large number of the subjects who received the new chewing gum have lost weight.

STUDY TIP

The experimental design described in part (c) is an example of *randomized block design*.

SOLUTION

a. The sample size is not large enough to produce valid results. To improve the validity, the sample size must be larger.

b. Because the subjects are divided into groups according to where they live, the groups are not similar. The new chewing gum may have more of an effect on subjects who live in a city, or more of an effect on subjects who live in rural areas because of the lifestyle. It is not possible to see such an effect with the experiment the way it is designed. The subjects can be divided into groups according to where they live, but within each group, they must be randomly assigned to the treatment group or the control group.

c. The subjects are divided into groups according to a similar characteristic (age). Because subjects within each age group are randomly assigned to receive the new chewing gum or the placebo, the groups are similar. So, there appear to be no potential problems with the experimental design.

SELF-ASSESSMENT 1 I do not understand. 2 I can do it with help. 3 I can do it on my own. 4 I can teach someone else.

4. You design an experiment to test the effectiveness of a vaccine against a strain of influenza. In the experiment, 100,000 people under 40 years old are randomly assigned to receive the vaccine and another 100,000 people over 40 years old receive a placebo. Identify a potential problem with the experimental design. Then describe how you can improve it.

9.4 Practice WITH CalcChat® AND CalcView®

In Exercises 1 and 2, determine whether the study is a randomized comparative experiment. If it is, describe the treatment, the treatment group, and the control group. If it is not, explain why not and discuss whether the conclusions drawn from the study are valid.
 *Example 1*

1. **Insomnia**

   New Drug Improved Sleep

   To test a new drug for insomnia, a pharmaceutical company randomly selected and divided 200 adults into two groups. One group received the drug and one group received a placebo. After one month, the adults who took the drug slept 18% longer, while those who took the placebo experienced no significant change.

2. **Dental Health**

   Milk Fights Cavities

   At a high school, students can choose to drink milk or other beverages at lunch. Seventy-five students who chose milk were monitored for one year, as were 75 students who chose other beverages. At the end of the year, students in the "milk" group had 25% fewer cavities than students in the other group.

ERROR ANALYSIS In Exercises 3 and 4, describe and correct the error in describing the study.

A company's researchers want to study the effects of adding shea butter to their existing hair conditioner. They monitor the hair quality of 30 randomly selected people who were given the regular conditioner and 30 randomly selected people who were given the new shea butter conditioner.

3.  The control group is individuals who do not use either of the conditioners.

4.  The study is an observational study.

In Exercises 5–8, determine whether the research topic is best investigated through an experiment or an observational study. Then describe the design of the experiment or observational study. *Example 2*

5. A researcher wants to compare the body mass index of smokers and nonsmokers.

6. A researcher wants to know whether listening to jazz music improves a person's ability to memorize a list.

7. A farmer wants to know whether a new fertilizer affects the weight of the fruit produced by strawberry plants.

8. You want to know whether homes that are close to parks or schools have higher property values.

9. **DRAWING CONCLUSIONS** A company wants to test whether a nutritional supplement has an effect on an athlete's heart rate while exercising. Identify a potential problem, if any, with each experimental design. Then describe how you can improve it.
   Example 3

   a. The company randomly selects 250 athletes. Half of the athletes are randomly assigned to receive the supplement and their heart rates are monitored while they run on a treadmill. The other half of the athletes receive a placebo and their heart rates are monitored while they lift weights. The heart rates of the athletes who took the supplement significantly increased while exercising.

   b. The company randomly selects 1000 athletes. The athletes are divided into two groups based on age. Within each age group, the athletes are randomly assigned to receive the supplement or the placebo. The athletes' heart rates are monitored while they run on a treadmill. There was no significant difference in the increases in heart rates between the two groups.

10. **DRAWING CONCLUSIONS** A researcher wants to test the effectiveness of reading novels on raising intelligence quotient (IQ) scores. Identify a potential problem, if any, with each experimental design. Then describe how you can improve it.

    a. The researcher randomly selects and divides 500 adults into two groups. One group reads novels daily and one group does not read novels. At the end of 1 year, each adult is evaluated and it is determined that neither group had an increase in IQ scores.

    b. Fifty adults volunteer to spend time reading novels every day for 1 year. Fifty other adults volunteer to refrain from reading novels for 1 year. Each adult is evaluated and it is determined that the adults who read novels raised their IQ scores by 3 points more than the other group.

11. **MAKING AN ARGUMENT** Your friend wants to determine whether number of siblings has an effect on a student's grades. Your friend claims to be able to show causality between the number of siblings and grades. Is your friend correct? Explain.

12. **HOW DO YOU SEE IT?**
A fitness company claims that its workout program will increase vertical jump heights in 6 weeks. To test the workout program, 10 athletes are divided into two groups. The double bar graph shows the results of the experiment. Identify a potential problem with the experimental design.

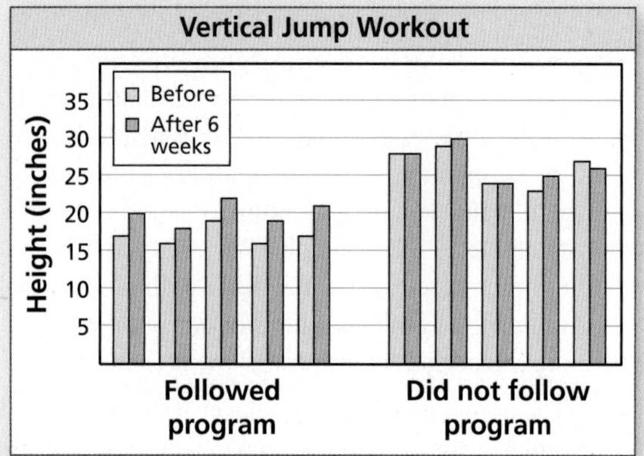

13. **COLLEGE PREP** To test the effect of political ads on voter preferences, a researcher randomly selects 8 voters. The voters are randomly assigned to watch 30 minutes of television with or without ads for candidate A. Voters then report which candidate they prefer. Which of the following are true?

    I. The study is a randomized comparative experiment.
    II. The treatment is watching television with ads for candidate A.
    III. There appear to be no potential problems with the experimental design.

    (A) I only
    (B) II only
    (C) III only
    (D) I and II only
    (E) I and III only
    (F) I, II, and III

14. **THOUGHT PROVOKING**
Describe the *placebo effect* and how it affects the results of an experiment.

15. **OPEN-ENDED** Choose a research topic that interests you. Design an experiment or observational study for the topic.

REVIEW & REFRESH

16. Explain why the survey question may be biased or otherwise introduce bias into the survey. Then describe a way to correct the flaw.

    "Should the manufacturer update its outdated cell phone model?"

17. Display the data in a dot plot. Describe the shape of the distribution.

Ages			
17	15	18	15
16	17	16	16
15	14	17	16

18. **MODELING REAL LIFE** A pitcher throws 16 strikes in the first 38 pitches. How many consecutive strikes must the pitcher throw to reach a strike percentage of 50%?

19. Determine whether the following research topic is best investigated through an experiment or an observational study. Then describe the design of the experiment or observational study.

    A researcher wants to know whether a new treatment reduces acne in teenagers.

20. A normal distribution has a mean of 15. The probability that a randomly selected x-value is between 13 and 17 is 0.68. What is the standard deviation of the distribution?

In Exercises 21 and 22, tell whether the function represents *exponential growth* or *exponential decay*. Then graph the function.

21. $y = \left(\frac{1}{5}\right)^x$

22. $y = (1.25)^x$

23. You use technology to simulate flipping a coin 20 times. The results are shown in the bar graph. What proportion of the 20 flips resulted in heads?

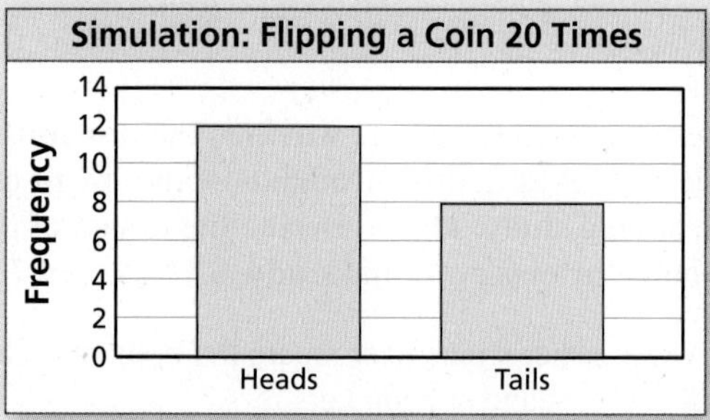

9.5 Making Inferences from Sample Surveys

Learning Target Use sample surveys to make conclusions about populations.

Success Criteria
- I can estimate population parameters.
- I can analyze the accuracy of a hypothesis using simulations.
- I can find margins of error for surveys.

EXPLORE IT! Observing Variability in Sample Surveys

Work with a partner. A poll says that 40% of dog owners let their dogs sleep on their beds. To test this, you survey 50 randomly chosen dog owners in your city and find that 16 of them let their dogs sleep on their beds.

a. Based on your sample survey, what percent of dog owners let their dogs sleep on their beds?

b. Is it still possible that 40% of all dog owners let their dogs sleep on their beds? Explain your reasoning.

c. You take a second random sample of 50 dog owners. Should you expect the sample proportion to be the same as the sample proportion in part (a)? Explain your reasoning.

d. Use the simulator at *BigIdeasMath.com* to simulate taking samples from the population of dog owners in your city. Assume that the population proportion is 40%. What do you notice as you adjust the number of samples and the sample size?

Math Practice

Analyze Givens
National polls often survey more than 1000 people. Why might so many people be surveyed?

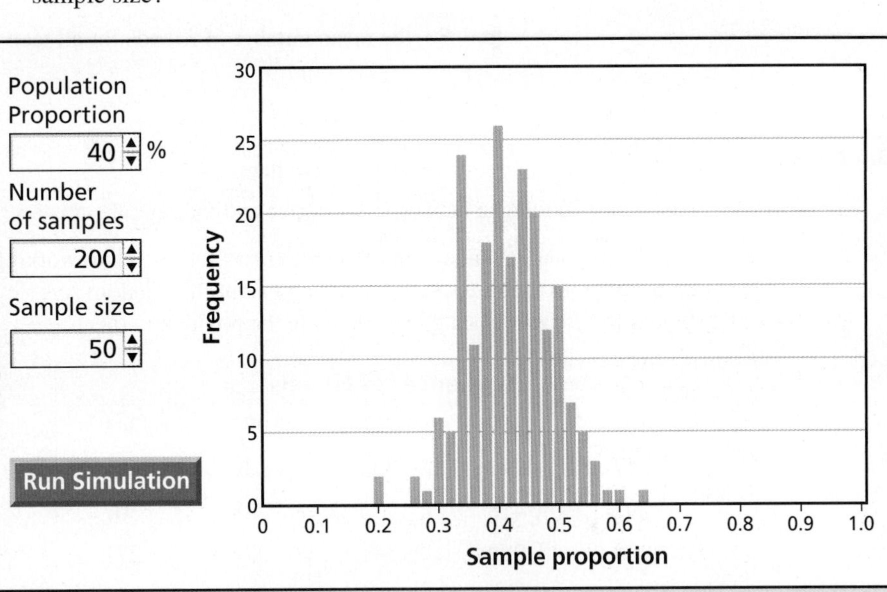

Simulator available at *BigIdeasMath.com*

Estimating Population Parameters

GO DIGITAL

Vocabulary AZ VOCAB

descriptive statistics, *p. 496*
inferential statistics, *p. 496*
margin of error, *p. 499*

The study of statistics has two major branches: *descriptive statistics* and *inferential statistics*. **Descriptive statistics** involves the organization, summarization, and display of data. **Inferential statistics** involves using a sample to draw conclusions about a population. You can use inferential statistics to make reasonable predictions, or *inferences*, about an entire population when the sample is representative of that population.

EXAMPLE 1 Estimating a Population Mean

The numbers of friends for a random sample of 40 teen users of a social networking website are shown in the table. Estimate the population mean μ.

Number of Friends				
281	342	229	384	320
247	298	248	312	445
385	286	314	260	186
287	342	225	308	343
262	220	320	310	150
274	291	300	410	255
279	351	370	257	350
369	215	325	338	278

REMEMBER
Recall that $\overline{x}$ denotes the sample mean. It is read as "*x* bar."

SOLUTION

To estimate the unknown population mean μ, find the sample mean $\overline{x}$.

$$\overline{x} = \frac{\Sigma x}{n} = \frac{11{,}966}{40} = 299.15$$

The probability that the population mean is exactly 299.15 is virtually 0, but the sample mean is a good estimate of the population mean μ.

▶ So, the mean number of friends for all teen users of the website is about 299.

SELF-ASSESSMENT

1 I do not understand. 2 I can do it with help. 3 I can do it on my own. 4 I can teach someone else.

1. **WRITING** What is the difference between descriptive and inferential statistics?

2. The data from another random sample of 30 teen users of the social networking website are shown in the table. Do you expect the sample mean of this random sample to be the same as in Example 1? Use this sample to estimate the population mean μ.

Number of Friends				
305	237	261	374	341
257	243	352	330	189
297	418	275	288	307
295	288	341	322	271
209	164	363	228	390
313	315	263	299	285

Not every random sample results in the same estimate of a population parameter; there will be some sampling variability. Larger sample sizes, however, tend to produce more accurate estimates.

EXAMPLE 2 Estimating Population Proportions

A website wants to predict the winner of a city's mayoral election. Two candidates, A and B, are running for office. Eight staff members conduct surveys of randomly selected residents. The residents are asked whether they will vote for Candidate A. The results are shown in the table.

Sample Size	Number of Votes for Candidate A in the Sample	Percent of Votes for Candidate A in the Sample
5	2	40%
12	4	33.3%
20	12	60%
30	17	56.7%
50	29	58%
125	73	58.4%
150	88	58.7%
200	118	59%

a. Based on the results of the first two sample surveys, do you think Candidate A will win the election? Explain.

b. Based on the results in the table, do you think Candidate A will win the election? Explain.

STUDY TIP

Statistics and probability provide information that you can use to weigh evidence and make decisions.

SOLUTION

a. The results of the first two surveys, with sample sizes 5 and 12, show that fewer than 50% of the residents will vote for Candidate A. Because there are only two candidates, one candidate needs more than 50% of the votes to win.

▶ Based on these surveys, you can predict Candidate A will not win the election.

b. As the sample sizes increase, the estimated percent of votes approaches 59%. You can predict that 59% of the city residents will vote for Candidate A.

▶ Because 59% of the votes are more than the 50% needed to win, you should feel confident that Candidate A will win the election.

SELF-ASSESSMENT

1 I do not understand. 2 I can do it with help. 3 I can do it on my own. 4 I can teach someone else.

3. Two candidates are running for class president. The table shows the results of four surveys of randomly selected students in the class. The students are asked whether they will vote for the incumbent. Do you think the incumbent will be reelected? Explain.

Sample Size	Number of "Yes" Responses	Percent of Votes for Incumbent
10	7	70%
20	11	55%
30	13	43.3%
40	17	42.5%

Analyzing Estimated Population Parameters

An estimated population parameter is an example of a hypothesis. You learned in Section 9.2 that one way to analyze a hypothesis is to perform a simulation.

EXAMPLE 3 Analyzing an Estimated Population Proportion

A national polling company claims 34% of U.S. adults say mathematics is the most valuable school subject. You survey a random sample of 50 adults.

a. What can you conclude about the accuracy of the claim that the population proportion is 0.34 when 15 adults in your survey say mathematics is the most valuable subject?

b. What can you conclude about the accuracy of the claim when 25 adults in your survey say mathematics is the most valuable subject?

c. Assume that the true population proportion is 0.34. Estimate the variation among sample proportions using samples of size 50.

SOLUTION

The polling company's claim (hypothesis) is that the population proportion of U.S. adults who say mathematics is the most valuable school subject is 0.34. To analyze this claim, simulate choosing 80 random samples of size 50 using a random number generator. Generate 50 random numbers from 1 to 100 for each sample. Let numbers 1 through 34 represent adults who say math. Find the sample proportions and make a dot plot showing the distribution of the sample proportions.

STUDY TIP

The dot plot shows the results of one simulation. Results of other simulations may give slightly different results, but the shape should be similar.

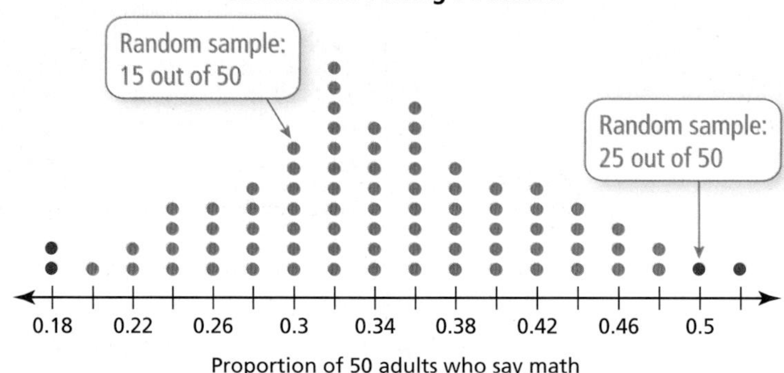

a. Note that 15 out of 50 corresponds to a sample proportion of $\frac{15}{50} = 0.3$. In the simulation, this result occurred in 7 of the 80 random samples. It is not unusual for 15 adults out of 50 to say that math is the most valuable subject when the true population percentage is 34%. So, you can conclude the company's claim is probably accurate.

b. Note that 25 out of 50 corresponds to a sample proportion of $\frac{25}{50} = 0.5$. In the simulation, this result occurred in only 1 of the 80 random samples. So, it is unusual for 25 adults out of 50 to say that math is the most valuable subject when the true population percentage is 34%. So, you can conclude the company's claim is probably *not* accurate.

c. Note that the dot plot is fairly bell-shaped and symmetric, so the distribution is approximately normal and about 95% of the possible sample proportions will lie within two standard deviations of 0.34. Excluding the two least and two greatest sample proportions, represented by red dots ● in the dot plot, leaves 76 of 80, or 95%, of the sample proportions. These 76 proportions range from 0.2 to 0.48. So, 95% of the time, a sample proportion should lie in the interval from 0.2 to 0.48.

Math Practice

Interpret Results

Note that the sample proportion 0.3 in part (a) lies in this interval, while the sample proportion 0.5 in part (b) falls outside this interval. What does this indicate?

SELF-ASSESSMENT

1 I do not understand. 2 I can do it with help. 3 I can do it on my own. 4 I can teach someone else.

4. **WHAT IF?** In Example 3, what can you conclude about the accuracy of the claim that the population proportion is 0.34 when 21 adults in your random sample say mathematics is the most valuable subject?

Finding Margins of Error for Surveys

When conducting a survey, make the sample size large enough so that it accurately represents the population. The **margin of error** is the maximum expected difference between a sample result and the population parameter it is estimating.

With data that is approximately normal, 95% of the data is within 2 standard deviations of the mean. You can use this two standard deviation distance as the margin of error.

EXAMPLE 4 Finding and Analyzing a Margin of Error

Use the simulation data from Example 3. The distribution has a standard deviation of about 0.07.

a. Find and interpret the margin of error.

b. Use the simulator at *BigIdeasMath.com* to determine what happens to the margin of error as the sample size increases.

SOLUTION

a. The margin of error is $2 \cdot 0.07 = 0.14$, so 95% of the sample proportions should be within 0.14 of the population proportion, 0.34.

b. Simulate choosing random samples of different sizes.

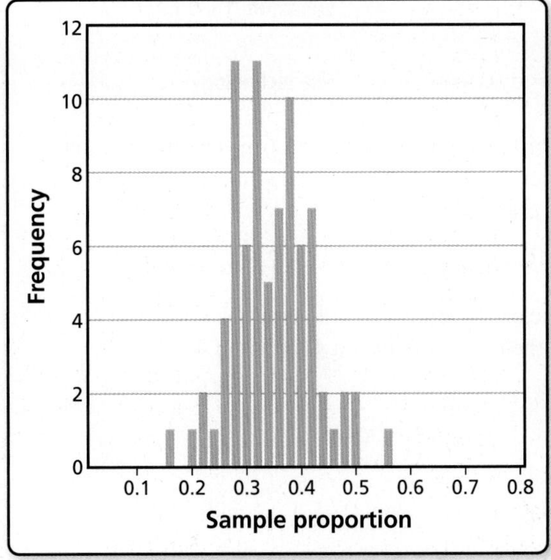

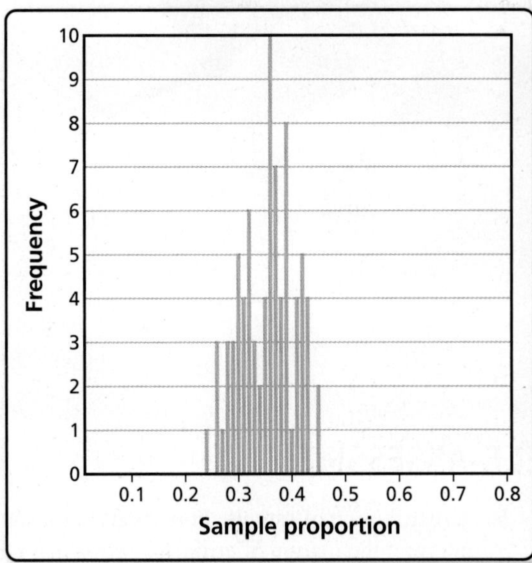

Simulator available at *BigIdeasMath.com*

As the sample size increases, the interval in which most of the data lie decreases.

▶ So, the margin of error decreases as the sample size increases.

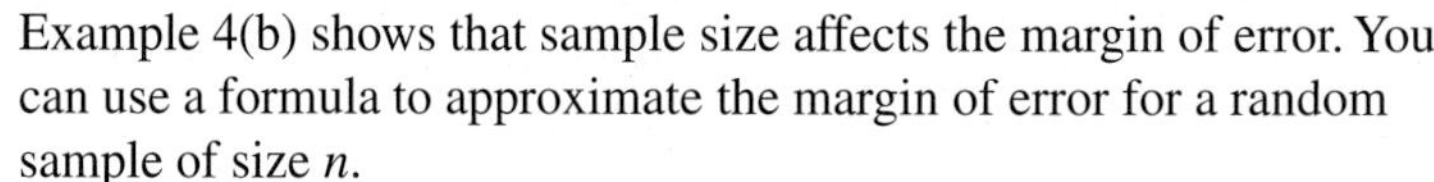

Example 4(b) shows that sample size affects the margin of error. You can use a formula to approximate the margin of error for a random sample of size n.

KEY IDEA

Margin of Error for a Population Proportion

When a random sample of size n is taken from a large population, the margin of error for a population proportion can be approximated by

$$\text{Margin of error} = \pm\frac{1}{\sqrt{n}}.$$

You can use the results of the sample and the margin of error to write an interval in which the population parameter likely lies (with 95% confidence). If the percent of the sample responding a certain way is p (expressed as a decimal), then the percent of the population who would respond the same way is likely to be between

$$p - \frac{1}{\sqrt{n}} \text{ and } p + \frac{1}{\sqrt{n}}.$$

Finding a Margin of Error Using a Formula

In a survey of 1509 U.S. adults, 47% said that they actively try to include organic foods in their diet. Give an interval that is likely to contain the exact percent of U.S. adults who actively try to include organic foods in their diet.

SOLUTION

Use the formula to approximate the margin of error.

$\text{Margin of error} = \pm\frac{1}{\sqrt{n}}$	Write formula.
$= \pm\frac{1}{\sqrt{1509}}$	Substitute 1509 for n.
$\approx \pm 0.026$	Use technology.

The margin of error for the survey is about $\pm$2.6%. To find the interval, subtract and add 2.6% to the percent of adults surveyed who said they actively try to include organic foods in their diet, 47%.

$47\% - 2.6\% = 44.4\%$ $\qquad$ $47\% + 2.6\% = 49.6\%$

▶ It is likely that the exact percent of U.S. adults who actively try to include organic foods in their diet is between 44.4% and 49.6%.

SELF-ASSESSMENT

1 I do not understand. 2 I can do it with help. 3 I can do it on my own. 4 I can teach someone else.

5. A distribution of sample proportions has a standard deviation of about 0.05. Find and interpret the margin of error.

6. In a survey of 654 U.S. teenagers, 55% said that bullying is a major problem among their peers. Give an interval that is likely to contain the exact percent of U.S. teenagers who think that bullying is a major problem among their peers.

9.5 Practice WITH CalcChat® AND CalcView®

1. MODELING REAL LIFE The numbers of text messages sent and received in one day by a random sample of 30 teen cell phone users are shown in the table. Estimate the population mean μ. *Example 1*

Number of Text Messages				
35	65	64	88	46
42	71	68	65	97
58	47	52	37	84
58	85	46	56	90
78	76	74	36	74
62	65	75	96	72

2. MODELING REAL LIFE The heart rates (in beats per minute) for a random sample of 36 blue whales are shown in the table. Estimate the population mean μ.

Blue Whale Heart Rates					
11	10	12	12	8	10
13	11	13	9	11	8
12	6	8	13	5	8
9	8	12	6	9	7
6	8	7	9	9	5
12	9	11	7	8	9

3. MP PROBLEM SOLVING Use the data in Exercise 1 to answer each question.

a. Estimate the population proportion p of teen cellphone users who send and receive more than 70 text messages each day.

b. Estimate the population proportion p of teen cellphone users who send and receive fewer than 50 text messages each day.

4. MP PROBLEM SOLVING Use the data in Exercise 2 to answer each question.

a. Estimate the population proportion p of blue whales that have a heart rate greater than 10 beats per minute.

b. Estimate the population proportion p of blue whales that have a heart rate less than 8 beats per minute.

5. DRAWING CONCLUSIONS When the President of the United States vetoes a bill, Congress can override the veto by a two-thirds majority vote in each House. Five news organizations conduct individual random surveys of U.S. Senators. The senators are asked whether they will vote to override the veto. The results are shown in the table. *Example 2*

Sample Size	Number of Votes to Override Veto	Percent of Votes to Override Veto
7	6	85.7%
22	16	72.7%
28	21	75%
31	17	54.8%
49	27	55.1%

a. Based on the results of the first two surveys, do you think the Senate will vote to override the veto? Explain.

b. Based on the results in the table, do you think the Senate will vote to override the veto? Explain.

6. DRAWING CONCLUSIONS Your teacher lets the students decide whether to have their test on Friday or Monday. The table shows the results from four surveys of randomly selected students in your grade who are taking the same class. The students are asked whether they want to have the test on Friday.

Sample Size	Number of "Yes" Responses	Percent of Votes
10	8	80%
20	12	60%
30	16	53.3%
40	18	45%

a. Based on the results of the first two surveys, do you think the test will be on Friday? Explain.

b. Based on the results in the table, do you think the test will be on Friday? Explain.

7. MP REASONING A senior class consisting of 292 students votes on whether they want their class trip to take place at an amusement park or a Broadway play. In a random sample of 50 seniors, 64% are in favor of an amusement park. How confident are you that the class trip will take place at an amusement park? Explain your reasoning.

8. **MP REASONING** A survey asks a random sample of U.S. teenagers how many hours of television they watch each night. The survey reveals that the sample mean is 3 hours per night. How confident are you that the average of all U.S. teenagers is exactly 3 hours per night? Explain your reasoning.

9. **MODELING REAL LIFE** A national polling company claims that 17% of U.S. public school teachers have a second job. You survey a random sample of 100 U.S. public school teachers. *Example 3*

   a. What can you conclude about the accuracy of the claim that the population proportion is 0.17 when 32 teachers in your survey have a second job?

   b. What can you conclude about the accuracy of the claim that the population proportion is 0.17 when 14 teachers in your survey have a second job?

   c. Assume that the true population proportion is 0.17. Estimate the variation among sample proportions for samples of size 100.

10. **MODELING REAL LIFE** A national polling company claims that 54% of U.S. adults are married. You survey a random sample of 40 adults.

    a. What can you conclude about the accuracy of the claim that the population proportion is 0.54 when 24 adults in your survey are married?

    b. What can you conclude about the accuracy of the claim that the population proportion is 0.54 when 15 adults in your survey are married?

    c. Assume that the true population proportion is 0.54. Estimate the variation among sample proportions for samples of size 40.

11. **MP NUMBER SENSE** A distribution of data simulated for Exercise 9c has a standard deviation of about 0.05. Find and interpret the margin of error. *Example 4*

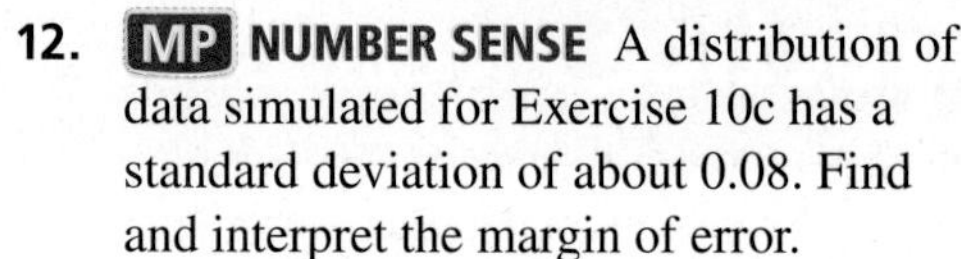

12. **MP NUMBER SENSE** A distribution of data simulated for Exercise 10c has a standard deviation of about 0.08. Find and interpret the margin of error.

In Exercises 13–18, find the margin of error for a survey that has the given sample size. Round your answer to the nearest tenth of a percent.

13. 260
14. 1000
15. 2024
16. 6400
17. 3275
18. 750

19. **MODELING REAL LIFE** In a survey of 920 U.S. teenagers, 81% said that helping others who are in need will be very important to them as adults. Give an interval that is likely to contain the exact percentage of all U.S. teenagers who think that helping others who are in need will be very important to them as adults. *Example 5*

20. **MODELING REAL LIFE** In a survey of 2000 U.S. adults, 70% said that they would support a national policy requiring rooftop solar panels to be installed on all new homes. Give an interval that is likely to contain the exact percent of all U.S. adults who would support this policy.

21. **MP REPEATED REASONING** What happens to the margin of error as a sample size increases? Use the margin of error formula to justify your answer.

22. **COLLEGE PREP** A survey claims that 32% of U.S. adults think that more emphasis should be placed on producing domestic energy from nuclear power. You simulate taking a large number of samples of size 500, and the distribution has a standard deviation of about 0.02. Which interval is likely to contain 95% of the data?

    Ⓐ 28%–36% Ⓑ 30%–34%
    Ⓒ 46%–54% Ⓓ 48%–52%

23. **MP STRUCTURE** A developer claims that the percent of city residents who favor building a splash pad at a local park is likely between 72.3% and 81.7%. About how many residents were surveyed?

24. HOW DO YOU SEE IT?
The figure shows the distribution of the sample proportions from three simulations using different sample sizes. Which simulation has the least margin of error? the greatest? Explain your reasoning.

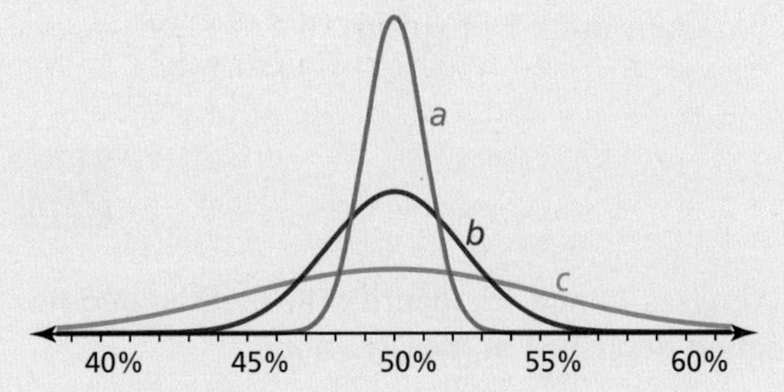

25. ERROR ANALYSIS In a random sample of 2500 consumers, 61% prefer Game A over Game B. Describe and correct the error in giving an interval that is likely to contain the exact percent of all consumers who prefer Game A over Game B.

✗

$$\text{Margin of error} = \pm\frac{1}{\sqrt{n}}$$
$$= \pm\frac{1}{\sqrt{2500}}$$
$$= \pm 0.02$$

It is likely that the exact percent of all consumers who prefer Game A over Game B is between 60.98% and 61.02%.

26. ERROR ANALYSIS In a survey, 8% of adult Internet users said they participate in sports fantasy leagues online. The margin of error is $\pm 4\%$. Describe and correct the error in approximating the sample size.

✗

$$\pm 0.08 = \pm\frac{1}{\sqrt{n}}$$
$$0.0064 = \frac{1}{n}$$
$$n \approx 156$$

27. MAKING AN ARGUMENT Your friend says that a margin of error can be any value between 0 and 100 percent, not including 0 or 100 percent. Is your friend correct? Explain your reasoning.

28. ABSTRACT REASONING Suppose a random sample of size n is required to produce a margin of error of $\pm E$. Write an expression in terms of n for the sample size needed to reduce the margin of error to $\pm\frac{1}{2}E$. How many times must the sample size be increased to cut the margin of error in half? Explain.

29. MP PROBLEM SOLVING A survey reports that 47% of the voters surveyed, or about 235 voters, said they voted for Candidate A and the remainder said they voted for Candidate B.

a. How many voters were surveyed?

b. What is the margin of error for the survey?

c. For each candidate, find an interval that is likely to contain the exact percent of all voters who voted for the candidate.

d. Based on your intervals in part (c), can you be confident that Candidate B won? If not, how many people in the sample would need to vote for Candidate B for you to be confident that Candidate B won?

30. THOUGHT PROVOKING
Consider a large population of which p percent (in decimal form) have a certain characteristic. To be reasonably sure that you are choosing a sample that is representative of a population, you should choose a random sample of n people where

$$n > 1500p(1 - p).$$

Find n for several values of p. How does the percent of a population that has the characteristic affect the size of the sample needed? Explain your reasoning.

31. MP PROBLEM SOLVING To estimate the margin of error for a population mean, you can use the formula

$$\text{Margin of error} = \pm\frac{2\sigma}{\sqrt{n}}$$

where σ is the standard deviation of the sample data and n is the sample size. To estimate the number of times cell phone users check their phone each day, a national polling company surveys a random sample of 2000 cell phone users. The sample has a mean of 52 checks per day and a standard deviation of 11 checks per day.

a. Find and interpret the margin of error.

b. Give an interval that is likely to contain the actual population mean.

32. **PERFORMANCE TASK** Write a statistical question about teenagers at your school. Use your question to survey a random sample of at least 50 teenagers at your school. Use the results of your survey to write a report. Your report should include any statistics found in your survey, the sample size, the margin of error, and any conclusions you can draw from the data.

33. **DIG DEEPER** In a survey, 52% of the respondents said they prefer sports drink X and 48% said they prefer sports drink Y. How many people do you have to survey to be confident that sports drink X is truly preferred to sports drink Y? Explain.

REVIEW & REFRESH

In Exercises 34–37, find the inverse of the function.

34. $y = 10^{x-3}$

35. $y = 2^x - 5$

36. $y = \ln(x + 5)$

37. $y = \log_6 x - 1$

In Exercises 38 and 39, determine whether the graph represents an arithmetic sequence or a geometric sequence. Then write a rule for the nth term.

38. 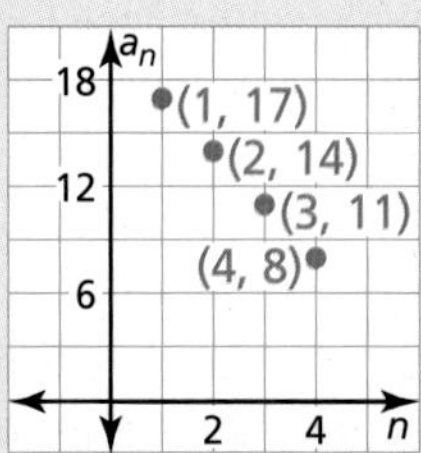

39. 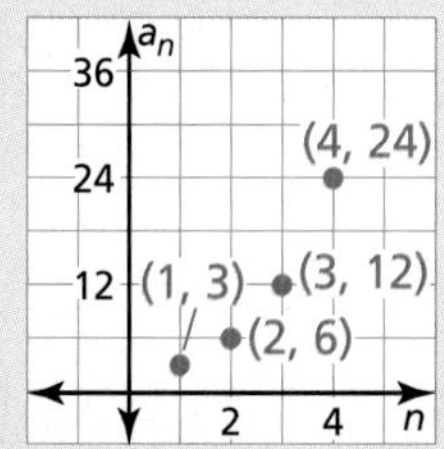

40. **MODELING REAL LIFE** In a survey of 900 U.S. adults, 41% said that their top priority for saving is retirement. Give an interval that is likely to contain the exact percent of all U.S. adults whose top priority for saving is retirement.

In Exercises 41 and 42, perform the operation.

41. $\dfrac{x^2 - 3x - 4}{x^2 - 8x + 12} \bullet \dfrac{2x^2 - 12x}{x^2 - 4x}$

42. $\dfrac{2x + 14}{x^2 - x - 20} - \dfrac{6}{x + 4}$

43. The two-way table shows the numbers of students who have been to a paintball park and the numbers of students who have been to a laser tag facility. Find each probability.

		Paintball	
		Yes	No
Laser Tag	Yes	71	58
	No	37	63

a. $P(\text{laser tag} \mid \text{paintball})$

b. $P(\text{no paintball} \mid \text{laser tag})$

In Exercises 44 and 45, identify the method of data collection described in the situation.

44. The driver of a ride-sharing service records whether each passenger wears a seat belt.

45. You ask 25 students in your class what method of transportation they use to get to school.

46. Find the surface area of the regular pyramid.

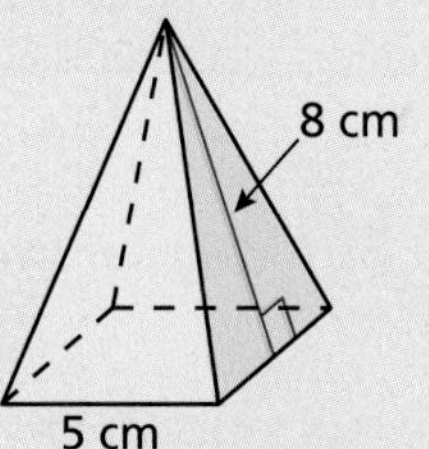

47. Determine whether the study is a randomized comparative experiment. If it is, describe the treatment, the treatment group, and the control group. If it is not, explain why not and discuss whether the conclusions drawn from the study are valid.

> **Mental Health**
>
> **Salt Rock Lamps Lower Stress**
>
> A recent study claims that using a Himalayan salt rock lamp for at least 1 hour each day reduces stress levels. One hundred twenty people who used a salt rock lamp for at least 1 hour each day were monitored for a month, as were one hundred twenty people who did not use a salt rock lamp at all. After a month, the stress levels of the people who used a salt rock lamp were 16% lower.

In Exercises 48–51, graph the function.

48. $y = \log_2 x + 1$

49. $f(x) = \sqrt[3]{-x} + 4$

50. $g(x) = 2|x - 3|$

51. $y = x^3 - 4x + 5$

52. In the United States, a survey of 1031 adults ages 18 and over found that 237 of them would trust a robot powered by artificial intelligence to perform surgery. Identify the population and the sample. Describe the sample.

9.6 Making Inferences from Experiments

Learning Target Understand how to make inferences from experiments.

Success Criteria
- I can analyze data from an experiment.
- I can explain how to resample data.
- I can use resampling to make inferences about a treatment.

EXPLORE IT! Analyzing Data

MP CHOOSE TOOLS **Work with a partner.** A randomized comparative experiment tests whether a new training program affects the 100-meter dash times of runners on track teams. The table shows the results.

Times (seconds)	
Control Group	**Treatment Group**
11.1	11.0
11.3	11.2
11.4	11.5
11.2	10.9
11.0	11.1
11.7	11.4
11.8	10.8
11.1	10.9
11.1	11.3
11.8	11.6

a. Find the mean dash time of the control group and the mean dash time of the treatment group. Then find and interpret the difference of the two means.

b. Write the dash times from the table on equal-sized pieces of paper. Place the pieces of paper in a bag and randomly draw 10 pieces. Call this the "control" group, and call the 10 pieces in the bag the "treatment" group. Then repeat part (a) and return the pieces to the bag. Perform this *resampling* experiment five times.

c. How does the difference in the means of the control and treatment groups compare with the differences resulting from chance?

d. Collect all the resampling differences of means found in part (b) for the whole class and display these values in a histogram. Compare the values in the histogram with the experimental difference of the means you found in part (a). Should your class *affirm* or *reject* the following hypothesis? Explain.

The new training program has no effect on the 100-meter dash times.

Math Practice

Maintain Oversight
Why is it useful to collect all of the resampling differences for the whole class?

Experiments with Two Samples

GO DIGITAL

In this lesson, you will compare data from two samples in an experiment to make inferences about a treatment using a method called *resampling*. Before learning about this method, consider the experiment described in Example 1.

EXAMPLE 1 Analyzing Data from an Experiment

A randomized comparative experiment tests whether a soil supplement affects the total yield (in kilograms) of cherry tomato plants. The control group has 10 plants and the treatment group, which receives the soil supplement, has 10 plants. The table shows the results.

	Total Yield of Cherry Tomato Plants (kilograms)									
Control Group	1.2	1.3	0.9	1.4	2.0	1.2	0.7	1.9	1.4	1.7
Treatment Group	1.4	0.9	1.5	1.8	1.6	1.8	2.4	1.9	1.9	1.7

a. Find the experimental difference of the mean yield of the treatment group, $\overline{x}_{\text{treatment}}$, and the mean yield of the control group, $\overline{x}_{\text{control}}$.

b. Display the data in a double dot plot.

c. What can you conclude from parts (a) and (b)?

The term "yield" in Example 1 refers to the amount or quantity of produce that a plant produces.

SOLUTION

a. $\overline{x}_{\text{control}} = \dfrac{1.2 + 1.3 + 0.9 + 1.4 + 2.0 + 1.2 + 0.7 + 1.9 + 1.4 + 1.7}{10} = \dfrac{13.7}{10} = 1.37$

$\overline{x}_{\text{treatment}} = \dfrac{1.4 + 0.9 + 1.5 + 1.8 + 1.6 + 1.8 + 2.4 + 1.9 + 1.9 + 1.7}{10} = \dfrac{16.9}{10} = 1.69$

$\overline{x}_{\text{treatment}} - \overline{x}_{\text{control}} = 1.69 - 1.37 = 0.32$

▶ The experimental difference of the means is 0.32 kilogram.

b.

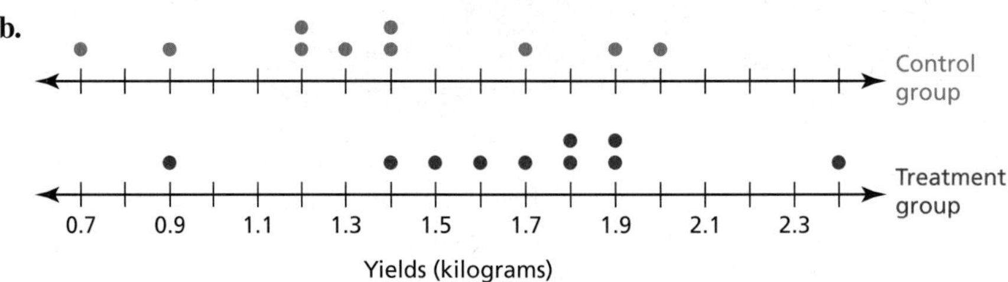

c. The plot of the data shows that the two data sets tend to be fairly symmetric, so the mean is a suitable measure of center. The mean yield of the treatment group is 0.32 kilogram more than the control group. It appears that the soil supplement might be slightly effective, but the sample size is small and the difference could be due to chance.

SELF-ASSESSMENT

1 I do not understand. 2 I can do it with help. 3 I can do it on my own. 4 I can teach someone else.

1. A randomized comparative experiment tests whether a supplement affects resting heart rate. Repeat Example 1 using the results of the experiment.

	Heart Rate (beats per minute)									
Control Group	88	72	72	63	66	74	81	76	71	74
Treatment Group	74	81	83	81	84	76	90	82	81	83

Resampling Data Using a Simulation

The samples in Example 1 are too small to make meaningful inferences about the treatment. Statisticians have developed a method called resampling to overcome this problem. You can resample data by combining the measurements from both groups and repeatedly creating new "control" and "treatment" groups at random from the measurements without repeats. Example 2 shows one resampling of the data in Example 1.

EXAMPLE 2 Resampling Data Using a Simulation

Resample the data in Example 1 using a simulation. Use the mean yields of the new control and treatment groups to calculate the difference of the means.

SOLUTION

Step 1 Combine the measurements from both groups and assign a number to each value. Let the numbers 1 through 10 represent the data in the original control group, and let the numbers 11 through 20 represent the data in the original treatment group, as shown.

original control group	1.2	1.3	0.9	1.4	2.0	1.2	0.7	1.9	1.4	1.7
assigned number	1	2	3	4	5	6	7	8	9	10
original treatment group	1.4	0.9	1.5	1.8	1.6	1.8	2.4	1.9	1.9	1.7
assigned number	11	12	13	14	15	16	17	18	19	20

Step 2 Use a random number generator. Randomly generate 20 numbers from 1 through 20 *without repeating a number*. The table shows the results.

14	19	4	3	18	9	5	15	2	7
1	17	20	16	6	8	13	12	11	10

Use the first 10 numbers to make the new control group, and the next 10 to make the new treatment group. The results are shown in the table.

	Resample of Cherry Tomato Plant Yields (kilograms)									
New Control Group	1.8	1.9	1.4	0.9	1.9	1.4	2.0	1.6	1.3	0.7
New Treatment Group	1.2	2.4	1.7	1.8	1.2	1.9	1.5	0.9	1.4	1.7

Step 3 Find the mean yields of the new control and treatment groups.

$$\bar{x}_{\text{new control}} = \frac{1.8 + 1.9 + 1.4 + 0.9 + 1.9 + 1.4 + 2.0 + 1.6 + 1.3 + 0.7}{10} = \frac{14.9}{10} = 1.49$$

$$\bar{x}_{\text{new treatment}} = \frac{1.2 + 2.4 + 1.7 + 1.8 + 1.2 + 1.9 + 1.5 + 0.9 + 1.4 + 1.7}{10} = \frac{15.7}{10} = 1.57$$

▶ So, $\bar{x}_{\text{new treatment}} - \bar{x}_{\text{new control}} = 1.57 - 1.49 = 0.08$. This is less than the experimental difference found in Example 1.

SELF-ASSESSMENT 1 I do not understand. 2 I can do it with help. 3 I can do it on my own. 4 I can teach someone else.

2. Resample the data in Exercise 1 using a simulation. Use the mean yields of the new control and treatment groups to calculate the difference of the means.

GO DIGITAL

Making Inferences About a Treatment

To perform an analysis of the data in Example 1, you will need to resample the data more than once. After resampling many times, you can see how often you get differences between the new groups that are at least as large as the one you measured.

EXAMPLE 3 Making Inferences About a Treatment

To conclude that the treatment in Example 1 is responsible for the difference in yield, analyze this hypothesis:

The soil nutrient has no effect on the yield of the cherry tomato plants.

Simulate 200 resamplings of the data in Example 1. Compare the experimental difference of 0.32 from Example 1 with the resampling differences. What can you conclude about the hypothesis? Does the soil nutrient have an effect on the yield?

SOLUTION

The histogram shows the results of the simulation. The histogram is approximately bell-shaped and fairly symmetric, so the differences have an approximately normal distribution.

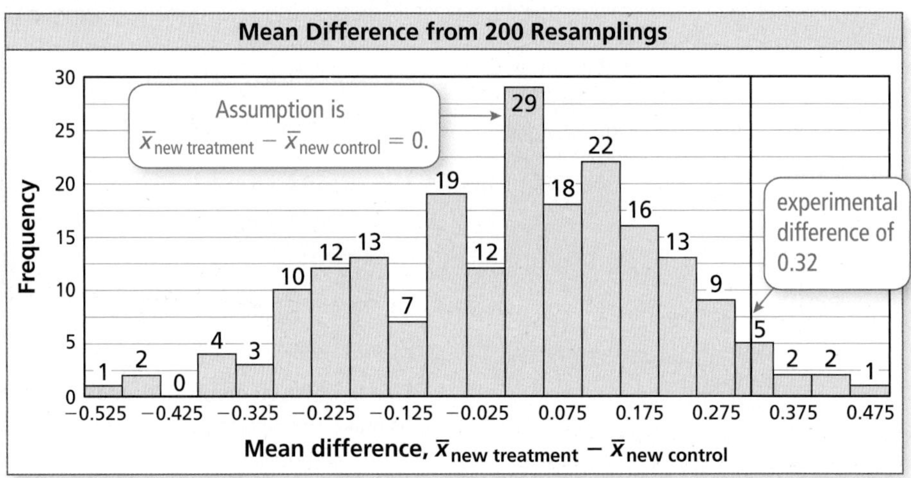

Note that the hypothesis assumes that the difference of the mean yields is 0. The experimental difference of 0.32, however, lies close to the right tail. From the graph, there are about 5 to 10 values out of 200 that are greater than 0.32, which is at most 5% of the values. Also, the experimental difference falls outside the middle 90% of the resampling differences. (The middle 90% is the area of the bars from −0.275 to 0.275, which contains 180 of the 200 values, or 90%.) This means it is unlikely to get a difference this large when you assume that the difference is 0, suggesting the control group and the treatment group differ.

▶ The experimental difference of 0.32 is significant in this situation. Because the experimental difference falls in the extreme values of the resampling distribution, you can conclude that the hypothesis is most likely false, and that the soil nutrient *does* have an effect on the yield of cherry tomato plants. Because the mean difference is positive, the treatment *increases* the yield.

Math Practice

Interpret Results
Explain why you can be 90% confident that the soil supplement does have an effect.

SELF-ASSESSMENT 1 I do not understand. 2 I can do it with help. 3 I can do it on my own. 4 I can teach someone else.

3. Explain how you can determine whether an experimental difference in measures of center is significant.

9.6 Practice WITH CalcChat® AND CalcView®

GO DIGITAL

In Exercises 1 and 2, analyze the data using the steps below. *Example 1*

a. **Find the experimental difference of the mean of the treatment group, $\overline{x}_{\text{treatment}}$, and the mean of the control group, $\overline{x}_{\text{control}}$.**

b. **Display the data in a double dot plot.**

c. **What can you conclude from parts (a) and (b)?**

1. A randomized comparative experiment tests whether music therapy affects the anxiety scores of high school students. Greater scores indicate greater anxiety. The control group has eight students and the treatment group, which receives the music therapy, has eight students. The tables show the results.

	Anxiety Score			
Control Group	49	45	43	47
Treatment Group	39	40	39	37

Control Group	46	45	47	46
Treatment Group	41	40	42	43

2. A randomized comparative experiment tests whether a software update affects the user satisfaction scores of teen cell phone users. Greater scores indicate greater satisfaction. The control group has eight teenagers and the treatment group, which receives the software update, has eight teenagers. The tables show the results.

	Satisfaction Score			
Control Group	8.1	8.5	7.9	6.7
Treatment Group	7.0	7.7	7.7	7.3

Control Group	7.1	7.3	7.6	7.6
Treatment Group	7.8	8.5	8.2	7.8

3. **MODELING REAL LIFE** Resample the data in Exercise 1 using a simulation. Use the means of the new control and treatment groups to calculate the difference of the means. *Example 2*

4. **MODELING REAL LIFE** Resample the data in Exercise 2 using a simulation. Use the means of the new control and treatment groups to calculate the difference of the means.

5. **DRAWING CONCLUSIONS** Analyze the hypothesis below. The histogram shows the results from 200 resamplings of the data in Exercise 1.

Music therapy has no effect on the anxiety score.

Compare the experimental difference in Exercise 1 with the resampling differences. What can you conclude about the hypothesis? Does the music therapy decrease anxiety? *Example 3*

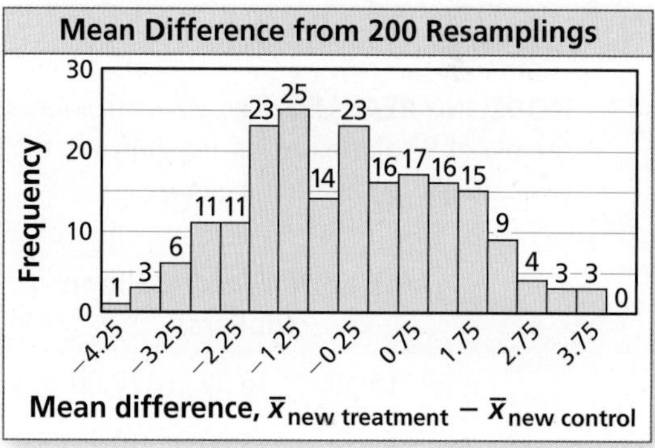

6. **DRAWING CONCLUSIONS** Analyze the hypothesis below. The histogram shows the results from 200 resamplings of the data in Exercise 2.

The software update has no effect on the satisfaction score.

Compare the experimental difference in Exercise 2 with the resampling differences. What can you conclude about the hypothesis? Does the software update improve teen user satisfaction?

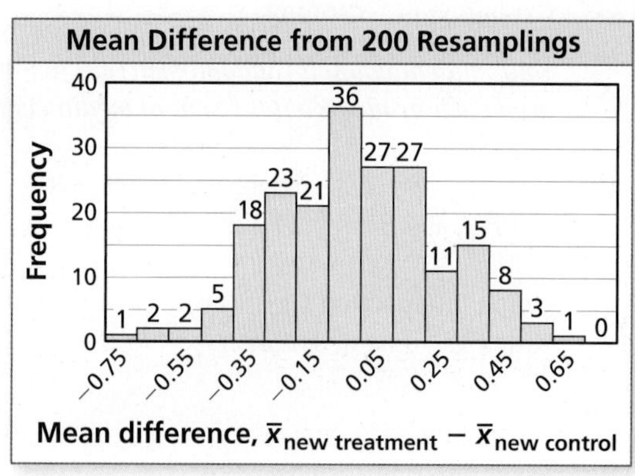

7. **MAKING AN ARGUMENT** Your friend states that the mean of the resampling differences should be close to 0 as the number of resamplings increases. Is your friend correct? Explain your reasoning.

8. **HOW DO YOU SEE IT?**
Without calculating, determine whether the experimental difference, $\bar{x}_{\text{treatment}} - \bar{x}_{\text{control}}$, is positive, negative, or zero. What can you conclude?

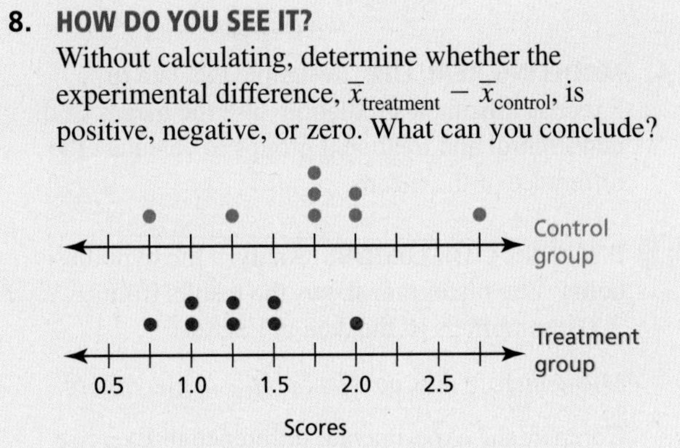

9. **CONNECTING CONCEPTS** In Exercise 1, how many resamplings of the treatment and control groups are theoretically possible? Explain.

10. **MP REASONING** You use a simulation to resample data from a randomized comparative experiment. When can you be 95% confident that the experimental difference $\bar{x}_{\text{treatment}} - \bar{x}_{\text{control}}$ is significant?

11. **OPEN-ENDED** The value of an experimental difference is k. Why is k significant for some situations but not for others?

12. **THOUGHT PROVOKING**
Describe an observation that you can make from an experiment. Then give possible inferences you can make from the observation.

REVIEW & REFRESH

13. **MODELING REAL LIFE** The prices from a random sample of 9 solar balloons are shown in the table. Estimate the population mean μ.

Prices of a Solar Balloon (dollars)		
15.50	16.35	17.00
13.53	15.00	12.77
15.85	12.55	18.25

14. Determine whether the research topic below is best investigated through an experiment or an observational study. Then describe the design of the experiment or observational study.

You want to know whether adults have better vision with larger or smaller smartphone screens.

15. Determine whether the sample below is biased. Explain your reasoning.

Your student council randomly surveys five students from each grade about the school media center.

16. Events A and B are independent. Let $P(B) = 0.3$ and $P(A \text{ and } B) = 0.24$. Find $P(A)$.

17. Graph the function $f(x) = (x - 1)^2$. Label the vertex and axis of symmetry.

18. **DRAWING CONCLUSIONS** A randomized comparative experiment tests whether a premium oil affects the lifespan of a particular engine. The control group involved six engines maintained using generic oil and the treatment group involved six engines maintained using premium oil. Analyze the hypothesis below. The histogram shows the results from 200 resamplings of the data.

The premium oil has no effect on lifespan.

Compare the experimental difference, $\bar{x}_{\text{treatment}} - \bar{x}_{\text{control}} = 9$ months, with the resampling differences. What can you conclude about the hypothesis? Does the premium oil increase the lifespan of the engine?

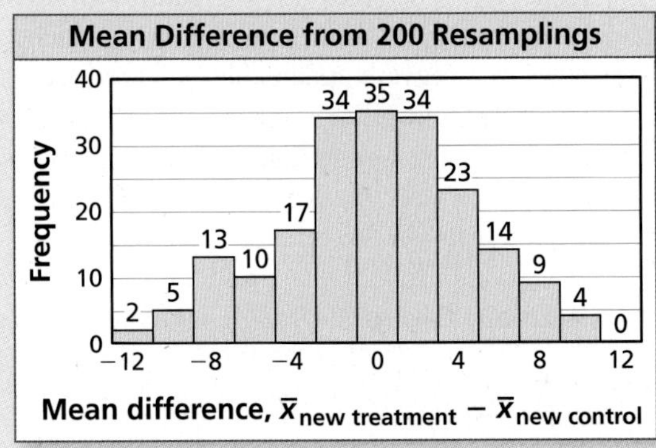

19. Simplify $(2z^2)^{-3}$. Write your answer as a power.

20. Solve $\sqrt{7x + 8} = 6$. Check your solution.

9 Chapter Review WITH CalcChat®

Chapter Learning Target Understand data analysis and statistics.

Chapter Success Criteria
- ◆ I can find probabilities in normal distributions.
- ◆ I can identify populations and samples.
- ■ I can explain different methods for collecting data.
- ■ I can make inferences from sample surveys and experiments.

◆ Surface
■ Deep

SELF-ASSESSMENT 1 I do not understand. 2 I can do it with help. 3 I can do it on my own. 4 I can teach someone else.

9.1 Using Normal Distributions (pp. 465–472)

Learning Target: Understand normal distributions.

Vocabulary

normal distribution
normal curve
standard normal distribution
z-score

1. A normal distribution has mean μ and standard deviation σ. An x-value is randomly selected from the distribution. Find $P(x \leq \mu - 3\sigma)$.

2. The times drivers spend waiting in a curbside pickup zone are normally distributed with a mean of 8 minutes and a standard deviation of 2 minutes. The goal of the curbside pickup service is for about 97.5% of drivers to spend no more than 10 minutes waiting. Is the service meeting the goal? Explain.

3. The weights of objects created in a welding class are normally distributed with a mean of 11.2 pounds and a standard deviation of 2 pounds. What is the probability that a randomly selected object is at least 14 pounds?

9.2 Populations, Samples, and Hypotheses (pp. 473–480)

Learning Target: Use random samples and simulations to make conclusions.

Vocabulary

population
sample
parameter
statistic
hypothesis

4. To estimate the average number of miles driven by U.S. motorists each year, a researcher conducts a survey of 1000 drivers, records the number of miles they drive in a year, and then determines the average. Identify the population and the sample.

5. A pitcher throws 40 fastballs in a baseball game. An analyst records the speeds of 10 of the fastballs and finds that the mean speed is 92.4 miles per hour. Is the mean speed a parameter or a statistic? Explain.

6. A social media activist features either a dog or a cat for adoption during several livestreams. You suspect that the activist features a dog more often. The activist claims that she does not favor either type of animal. What should you conclude when a dog is featured during 17 out of 28 livestreams?

9.3 Collecting Data (pp. 481–488)

Learning Target: Describe sampling methods and recognize bias when collecting data.

Vocabulary

random sample
self-selected sample
systematic sample
stratified sample
cluster sample
convenience sample
bias
unbiased sample
biased sample
experiment
observational study
survey
simulation
biased question

7. You want to determine whether students in your school are interested in a first responder class. Identify the type of sample described.

a. You list all the students alphabetically and choose every fifth student.

b. You email surveys and use only the surveys that are returned.

c. You ask all the students from your anatomy and physiology class.

d. You randomly select three students from each classroom.

8. An administrative assistant records whether students use the water bottle refilling station. Identify the method of data collection.

9. Explain why the question may be biased or otherwise introduce bias into the survey. Then describe a way to correct the flaw.

"Should the city replace the outdated police cars it is using?"

9.4 Experimental Design

(pp. 489–494)

Learning Target: Describe and analyze experiments and their designs.

Vocabulary

controlled experiment
control group
treatment group
randomization
randomized comparative experiment
placebo

10. Determine whether the study is a randomized comparative experiment. If it is, describe the treatment, the treatment group, and the control group. If it is not, explain why not and discuss whether the conclusions drawn from the study are valid.

Cleaner Cars in Less Time!

To test the new design of a car wash, an engineer randomly selected and divided 80 customers into two groups. One group used the old design to wash their cars and one group used the new design to wash their cars. Users of the new car wash design were able to wash their cars 30% faster.

11. A restaurant manager wants to know which type of sandwich bread attracts the most repeat customers. Is the topic best investigated through an experiment or an observational study? Describe the design of the experiment or observational study.

12. A researcher wants to test the effectiveness of a sleeping pill. Identify a potential problem, if any, with the experimental design below. Then describe how you can improve it.

The researcher selects 16 volunteers who have insomnia. Eight volunteers are given the sleeping pill and the other eight volunteers are given a placebo. Their sleep habits are recorded for 1 month.

9.5 Making Inferences from Sample Surveys *(pp. 495–504)*

Learning Target: Use sample surveys to make conclusions about populations.

Vocabulary VOCAB
descriptive statistics
inferential statistics
margin of error

13. There are two candidates for homecoming king. The table shows the results from four random surveys of the students in the school. The students were asked whether they will vote for Candidate A. Do you think Candidate A will be the homecoming king? Explain.

Sample Size	Number of "Yes" Responses	Percent of Votes
8	6	75%
22	14	63.6%
34	16	47.1%
62	29	46.8%

14. In a survey of 1000 U.S. teenagers, 41% consider entrepreneurship as a career option. Give an interval that is likely to contain the exact percent of U.S. teenagers who consider entrepreneurship as a career option.

9.6 Making Inferences from Experiments *(pp. 505–510)*

Learning Target: Understand how to make inferences from experiments.

15. A randomized comparative experiment tests whether a mentoring program affects number of absences from school. The control group has eight students and the treatment group, which participates in the mentoring program, has eight students. The table shows the results.

	Days Absent							
Control Group	6	8	8	8	7	9	12	4
Treatment Group	4	4	5	2	3	6	0	7

a. Find the experimental difference of the mean of the treatment group, $\bar{x}_{\text{treatment}}$, and the mean of the control group, $\bar{x}_{\text{control}}$.

b. Analyze the hypothesis below. The histogram shows the results from 200 resamplings of the data.

The mentoring program has no effect on the number of absences from school.

Compare the experimental difference in part (a) with the resampling differences. What can you conclude about the hypothesis?

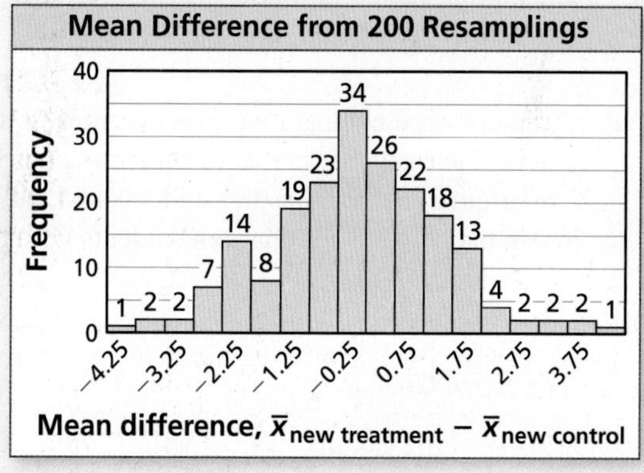

Mathematical Practices

Construct Viable Arguments and Critique the Reasoning of Others

Mathematically proficient students distinguish correct logic or reasoning from that which is flawed.

1. In Exercises 9 and 10 on page 493, how did you identify any problems with the experimental designs?

2. The values of weekly podcast giveaways form a skewed left distribution with a mean of \$25 and a standard deviation of \$5. Your friend claims that the probability that the next giveaway is worth more than \$15 is about 84%. Identify potential flaws with this conclusion.

9 Practice Test WITH CalcChat®

1. For all the students in a high school, the mean grade point average is 2.95. Is the mean grade point average a parameter or a statistic? Explain.

2. The principal asks 50 randomly selected students whether the student parking lot should be expanded. Identify the method of data collection.

A normal distribution has a mean of 72 and a standard deviation of 5. Find the probability that a randomly selected x-value from the distribution is in the given interval.

3. between 67 and 77

4. at least 75

5. A researcher wants to test the effectiveness of a new medication designed to lower blood pressure. Identify a potential problem, if any, with the experimental design. Then describe how you can improve it.

   The researcher randomly selects 30 people with high blood pressure. Fifteen people with the highest blood pressures are given the medication and the other 15 are given a placebo. After 1 month, the subjects are evaluated.

6. In a survey, 1600 randomly selected U.S. adults are asked whether they have purchased a product online. The results are shown in the circle graph.

   a. Identify the population and the sample. Describe the sample.

   b. Give an interval that is likely to contain the exact percent of U.S. adults who have purchased a product online.

Have You Purchased a Product Online?

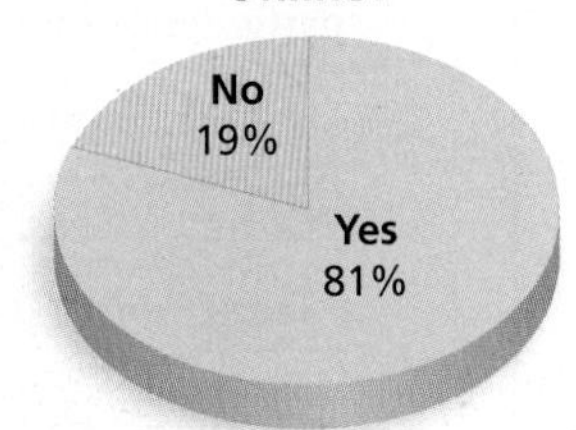

7. A normal distribution has mean μ and standard deviation σ. An x-value is randomly selected from the distribution. What is the probability that $x \geq \mu$ or $\mu - 2\sigma \leq x \leq \mu + 2\sigma$?

8. A randomized comparative experiment tests whether a new teaching method affects the math test scores of students. The control group, which is taught using the original method, has ten students and the treatment group, which is taught using the new method, has ten students. The table shows the results.

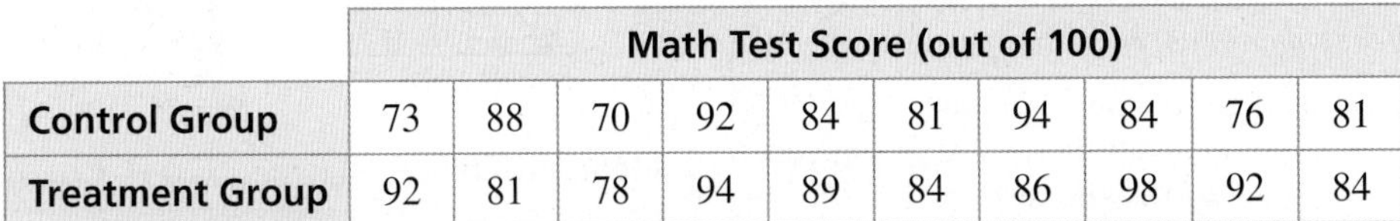

	Math Test Score (out of 100)									
Control Group	73	88	70	92	84	81	94	84	76	81
Treatment Group	92	81	78	94	89	84	86	98	92	84

   a. Find the experimental difference of the mean score of the treatment group, $\bar{x}_{\text{treatment}}$, and the mean score of the control group, $\bar{x}_{\text{control}}$.

   b. Analyze the hypothesis below. The histogram shows the results from 200 resamplings of the data.

   The new teaching method has no effect on the math test scores of students.

   Compare the experimental difference in part (a) with the resampling differences. What can you conclude about the hypothesis?

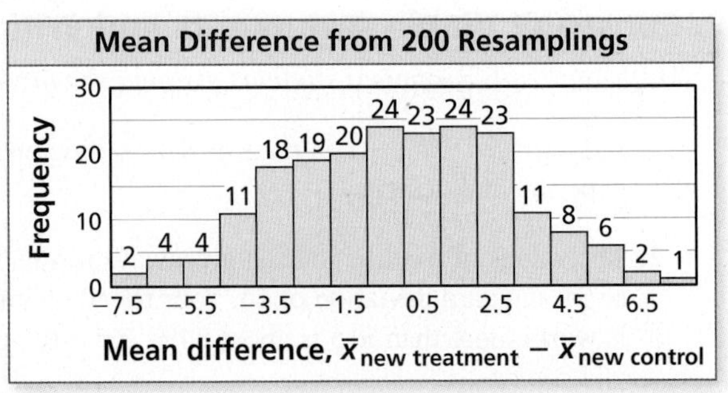

9 Performance Task The Ring of Fire

About 75% of the world's volcanoes are located in the "Ring of Fire."

10 Famous Volcanoes Around the World

- There are about 1500 potentially active volcanoes in the world.
- Over 80% of Earth's surface has been created by volcanoes.

MONITORING VOCANIC ACTIVITY

You work for an organization that monitors worldwide volcanic activity. The numbers of cases of volcanic activity each week in a recent year are normally distributed with a mean of 18.1 and a standard deviation of 2.9. Write a report that includes the following:

- a normal curve that represents the distribution
- several conclusions that can be made using the mean and standard deviation
- the probability that there are 25 or more cases of volcanic activity in a randomly selected week.

9 College and Career Readiness WITH CalcChat®

Tutorial videos are available for each exercise.

1. Which of the following samples are biased? Select all that apply.

Ⓐ A restaurant manager asks customers to participate in a survey about the food sold at the restaurant. The manager uses the surveys that are returned.

Ⓑ You want to know the favorite sport of students at your school. You randomly select athletes to survey at the winter sports banquet.

Ⓒ School district officials want to know whether students think school should start 30 minutes later. Eighty randomly selected students are surveyed.

Ⓓ The owner of a movie theater wants to know whether the volume of its movies is too loud. Patrons under the age of 18 are randomly surveyed.

2. What are the measures of angles A, B, and C?

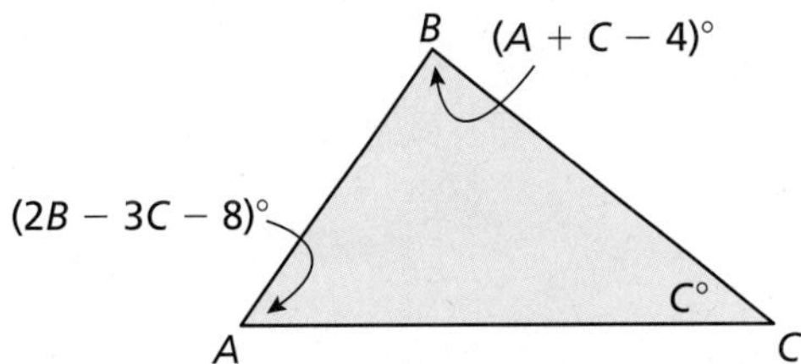

3. A survey asks 2100 randomly selected U.S. adults about their favorite way to eat ice cream. The results of the survey are displayed in the table. Give an interval that is likely to contain the exact percent of U.S. adults who prefer to eat ice cream in each way.

Survey Results	
Cup	45%
Cone	29%
Sundae	18%
Other	8%

4. Which of the following is a zero of $f(x) = (x - 7)(x + 3)(x^2 + 4)$? Select all that apply.

Ⓐ -7 Ⓑ -4

Ⓒ -3 Ⓓ 2

Ⓔ 3 Ⓕ 7

GO DIGITAL

5. Complete the table for the four functions.

Function	Is the inverse a function?	Inverse
$f(x) = 5x - 4$		
$f(x) = 3 \ln x + 2$		
$f(x) = \left(\frac{1}{x}\right)^2$		
$f(x) = \sqrt[3]{x - 2}$		

6. The amount y (in grams) of a sample of the radioactive isotope iodine-131 remaining after t days is $y = 5(0.5)^{t/8}$. About what percent of the iodine-131 decays each day?

Ⓐ 5%

Ⓑ 8.3%

Ⓒ 50%

Ⓓ 91.7%

7. The normal distribution shown has a mean of 63 and a standard deviation of 8. What percent of the area under the normal curve is represented by the shaded region?

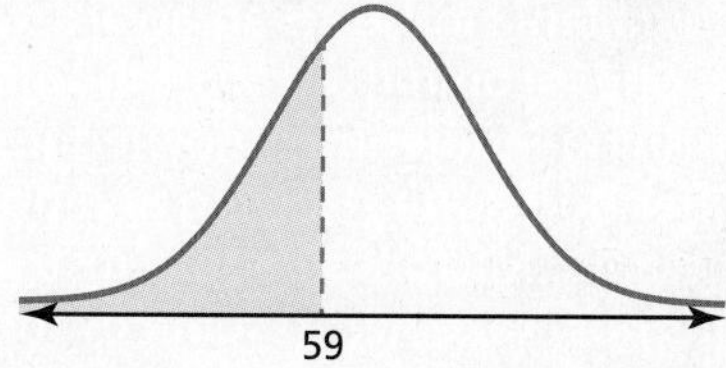

8. Which of the rational expressions *cannot* be simplified? Select all that apply.

Ⓐ $\dfrac{2x^2 + 5x - 3}{x^2 - 7x + 12}$

Ⓑ $\dfrac{3x^3 + 21x^2 + 30x}{x^2 - 25}$

Ⓒ $\dfrac{x^3 + 27}{x^2 - 3x + 9}$

Ⓓ $\dfrac{x^3 + 2x^2 - 8x - 16}{2x^2 - 21x + 55}$

9. A bag contains two purple marbles and two yellow marbles.

a. You randomly draw a marble, do *not* replace it, and then randomly draw a second marble. Determine whether randomly selecting a purple marble first and randomly selecting a yellow marble second are independent events.

b. You randomly draw a marble, replace it, and then randomly draw a second marble. Determine whether randomly selecting a purple marble first and randomly selecting a yellow marble second are independent events.

10 Trigonometric Ratios and Functions

NATIONAL GEOGRAPHIC EXPLORER

Elizabeth Kapu'uwailani Lindsey

Dr. Elizabeth Kapu'uwailani Lindsey is an award-winning filmmaker and anthropologist. She is committed to ethnographic rescue, the conservation of vanishing indigenous knowledge and tradition. Dr. Lindsey earned her doctorate studying and documenting the nearly lost traditions of the palu, Micronesian non-instrument navigators. Lindsey's expeditions now take her to some of the most remote regions of the world.

- Why is it important to document and conserve cultural traditions?
- What is ethnonavigation?
- Describe some ways to navigate without using modern instruments.

STEM

Most navigation today involves tools such as maps, compasses, and computers. In the Performance Task, you will learn how bearings are used in navigation.

Ethnographic Rescue

Preparing for Chapter 10

Chapter Learning Target Understand trigonometric ratios and functions.

Chapter Success Criteria
- ◆ I can define right triangle trigonometric functions.
- ◆ I can evaluate trigonometric functions of any angle.
- ■ I can graph trigonometric functions.
- ■ I can model using trigonometric functions.

◆ Surface
■ Deep

Chapter Vocabulary

Work with a partner. Discuss each of the vocabulary terms.

unit circle
quadrantal angle
amplitude
periodic function
frequency

Mathematical Practices

Attend to Precision

Mathematically proficient students try to communicate precisely to others.

Work with a partner. You are navigating a boat. The map shows one possible route that you can take to arrive at a port. Each grid line represents 1 mile.

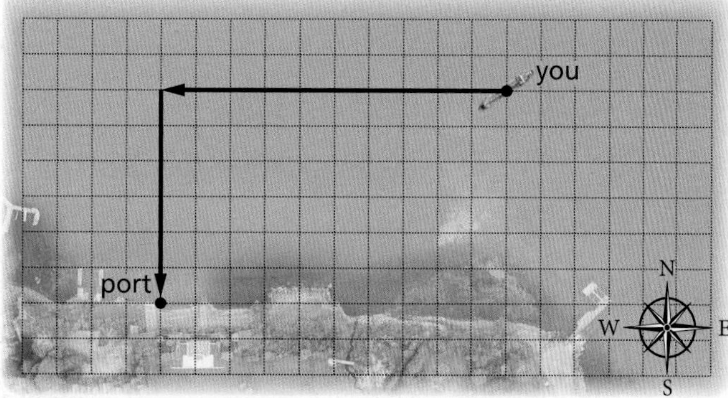

1. Write precise instructions for how you should travel to arrive at the port using this route.
2. You want to know how to arrive at the port using the shortest possible route.
   a. Draw the route. What information is needed to give precise instructions for the route?
   b. Describe the direction and the distance that you should travel. Explain how you found this information.

10 Prepare WITH CalcChat®

Solving Linear Equations

Example 1 **Solve $-3 = \dfrac{x + 8}{4}$.**

$-3 = \dfrac{x + 8}{4}$	Write the equation.
$4 \cdot (-3) = 4 \cdot \dfrac{x + 8}{4}$	Multiplication Property of Equality
$-12 = x + 8$	Simplify.
$\underline{-8} \quad \underline{-8}$	Subtraction Property of Equality
$-20 = x$	Simplify.

▶ The solution is $x = -20$.

Solve the equation.

1. $\dfrac{x}{4} = 6$

2. $\dfrac{5 + x}{3} = 2$

3. $3x - 7 = 11$

4. $-\dfrac{1}{2} = \dfrac{x - 6}{4}$

5. $3.5 = 2x + 5$

6. $-\dfrac{4}{3} = -10x + \dfrac{1}{3}$

Pythagorean Theorem

Example 2 **Find the missing side length of the triangle.**

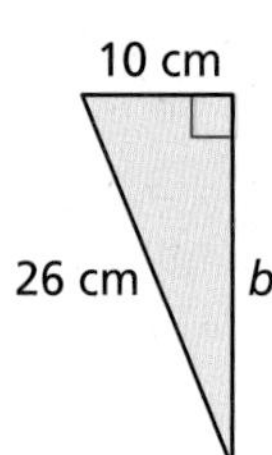

$a^2 + b^2 = c^2$	Write the Pythagorean Theorem.
$10^2 + b^2 = 26^2$	Substitute 10 for a and 26 for c.
$100 + b^2 = 676$	Evaluate powers.
$b^2 = 576$	Subtract 100 from each side.
$b = 24$	Take positive square root of each side.

▶ So, the missing side length is 24 centimeters.

Find the missing side length of the triangle.

7.

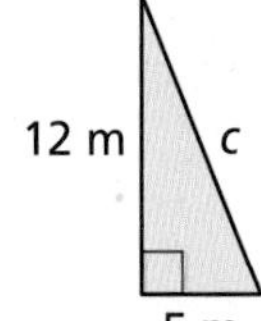

8.

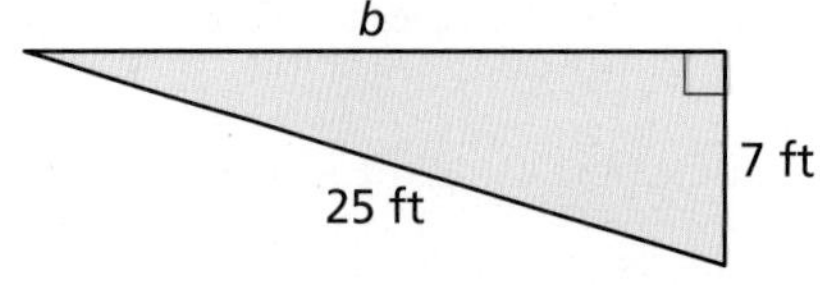

9.

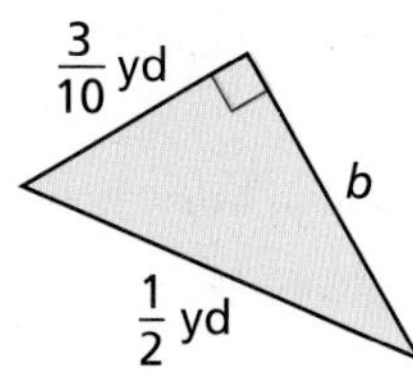

10. **MP REASONING** Show how you can use the Pythagorean Theorem to find the distance d between the points (x_1, y_1) and (x_2, y_2).

10.1 Right Triangle Trigonometry

Learning Target Understand the six trigonometric functions.

Success Criteria
- I can define the six trigonometric functions.
- I can evaluate trigonometric functions.
- I can use trigonometric functions to find side lengths of right triangles.

EXPLORE IT! Finding Ratios of Side Lengths of Right Triangles

Work with a partner. Consider a right triangle that has an acute angle θ (the Greek letter *theta*). The three sides of the triangle are the *hypotenuse*, the side *opposite* θ, and the side *adjacent* to θ.

a. Label the hypotenuse, opposite side, and adjacent side of the right triangle below.

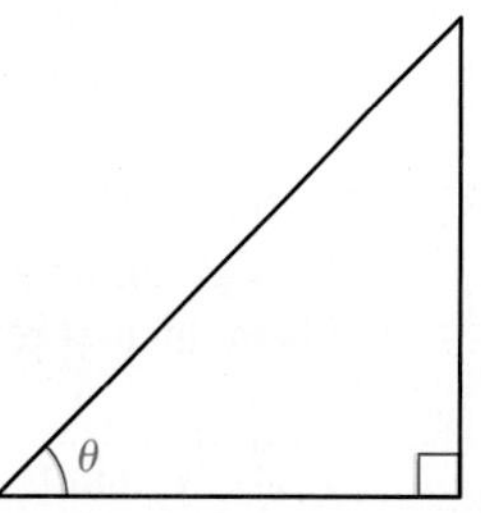

b. In each triangle shown, the measure of θ is 30°. Use a centimeter ruler to approximate the following ratios of side lengths. What do you notice?

$$\frac{\text{opposite}}{\text{hypotenuse}} \qquad \frac{\text{adjacent}}{\text{hypotenuse}} \qquad \frac{\text{opposite}}{\text{adjacent}}$$

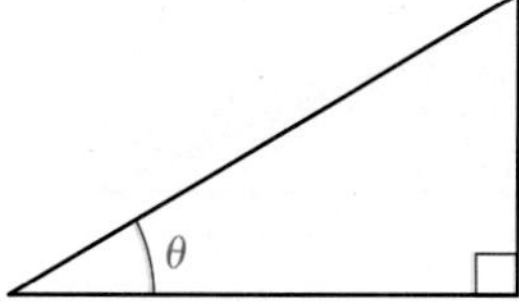

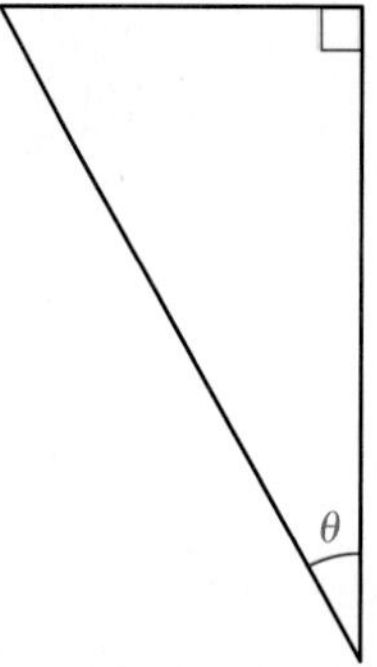

c. Are the relationships you found in part (b) true for any right triangle with a 30° angle? Explain your reasoning.

d. Construct right triangles with 45° angles. What do you notice about the ratios of the side lengths?

e. What do your results in parts (b)–(d) suggest about angles and ratios of side lengths in right triangles?

Math Practice

Choose Tools
What tools can you use to construct the triangles in part (d)?

The Six Trigonometric Functions

Vocabulary

sine, *p. 522*
cosine, *p. 522*
tangent, *p. 522*
cosecant, *p. 522*
secant, *p. 522*
cotangent, *p. 522*

Consider a right triangle that has an acute angle θ (the Greek letter *theta*). The three sides of the triangle are the *hypotenuse*, the side *opposite* θ, and the side *adjacent* to θ.

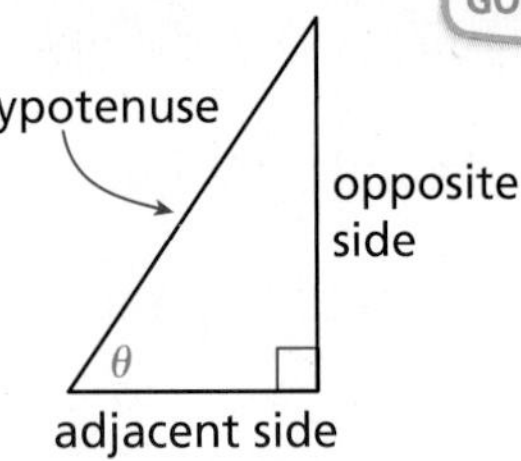

Ratios of a right triangle's side lengths are used to define the six trigonometric functions: **sine**, **cosine**, **tangent**, **cosecant**, **secant**, and **cotangent**. These six functions are abbreviated sin, cos, tan, csc, sec, and cot, respectively.

KEY IDEA

Right Triangle Definitions of Trigonometric Functions

Let θ be an acute angle of a right triangle. The six trigonometric functions of θ are defined as shown.

$$\sin\theta = \frac{\text{opposite}}{\text{hypotenuse}} \qquad \cos\theta = \frac{\text{adjacent}}{\text{hypotenuse}} \qquad \tan\theta = \frac{\text{opposite}}{\text{adjacent}}$$

$$\csc\theta = \frac{\text{hypotenuse}}{\text{opposite}} \qquad \sec\theta = \frac{\text{hypotenuse}}{\text{adjacent}} \qquad \cot\theta = \frac{\text{adjacent}}{\text{opposite}}$$

The abbreviations *opp*, *adj*, and *hyp* are often used to represent the side lengths of the right triangle. Note that the ratios in the second row are reciprocals of the ratios in the first row.

$$\csc\theta = \frac{1}{\sin\theta} \qquad \sec\theta = \frac{1}{\cos\theta} \qquad \cot\theta = \frac{1}{\tan\theta}$$

EXAMPLE 1 Evaluating Trigonometric Functions

Evaluate the six trigonometric functions of the angle θ.

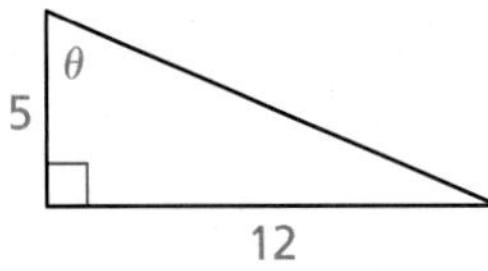

SOLUTION

From the Pythagorean Theorem, the length of the hypotenuse is

$$\begin{aligned} \text{hyp} &= \sqrt{5^2 + 12^2} \\ &= \sqrt{169} \\ &= 13. \end{aligned}$$

REMEMBER

The Pythagorean Theorem states that $a^2 + b^2 = c^2$ for a right triangle with hypotenuse of length c and legs of lengths a and b. So, $c = \sqrt{a^2 + b^2}$.

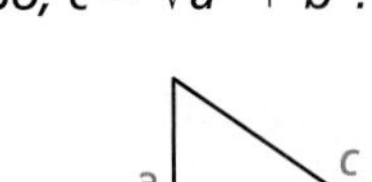

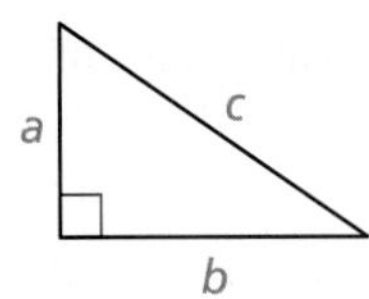

Using adj = 5, opp = 12, and hyp = 13, the values of the six trigonometric functions of θ are:

$$\sin\theta = \frac{\text{opp}}{\text{hyp}} = \frac{12}{13} \qquad \cos\theta = \frac{\text{adj}}{\text{hyp}} = \frac{5}{13} \qquad \tan\theta = \frac{\text{opp}}{\text{adj}} = \frac{12}{5}$$

$$\csc\theta = \frac{\text{hyp}}{\text{opp}} = \frac{13}{12} \qquad \sec\theta = \frac{\text{hyp}}{\text{adj}} = \frac{13}{5} \qquad \cot\theta = \frac{\text{adj}}{\text{opp}} = \frac{5}{12}$$

EXAMPLE 2 Evaluating Trigonometric Functions

In a right triangle, θ is an acute angle and $\sin\theta = \frac{4}{7}$. Evaluate the other five trigonometric functions of θ.

SOLUTION

Step 1 Draw a right triangle with acute angle θ such that the leg opposite θ has length 4 and the hypotenuse has length 7.

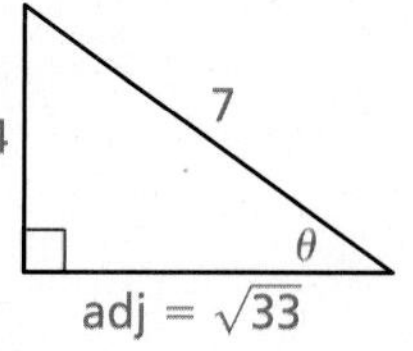

Step 2 Find the length of the adjacent side. By the Pythagorean Theorem, the length of the other leg is

$$\text{adj} = \sqrt{7^2 - 4^2} = \sqrt{33}.$$

Step 3 Find the values of the remaining five trigonometric functions.

Because $\sin\theta = \frac{4}{7}$, $\csc\theta = \frac{\text{hyp}}{\text{opp}} = \frac{7}{4}$. The other values are:

$$\cos\theta = \frac{\text{adj}}{\text{hyp}} = \frac{\sqrt{33}}{7} \qquad \tan\theta = \frac{\text{opp}}{\text{adj}} = \frac{4}{\sqrt{33}} = \frac{4\sqrt{33}}{33}$$

$$\sec\theta = \frac{\text{hyp}}{\text{adj}} = \frac{7}{\sqrt{33}} = \frac{7\sqrt{33}}{33} \qquad \cot\theta = \frac{\text{adj}}{\text{opp}} = \frac{\sqrt{33}}{4}$$

The angles 30°, 45°, and 60° occur frequently in trigonometry. You can use the trigonometric values for these angles to find unknown side lengths in special right triangles.

KEY IDEA

Trigonometric Values for Special Angles

The table gives the values of the six trigonometric functions for the angles 30°, 45°, and 60°. You can obtain these values from the triangles shown.

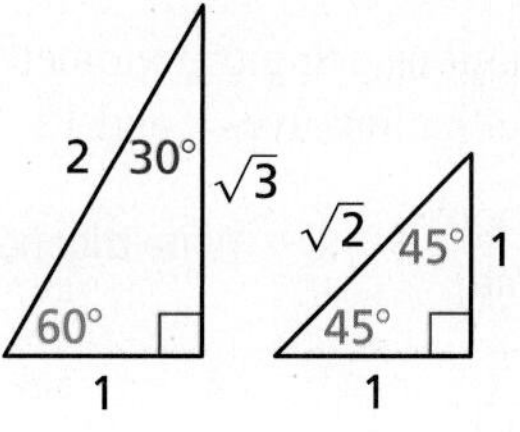

θ	$\sin\theta$	$\cos\theta$	$\tan\theta$	$\csc\theta$	$\sec\theta$	$\cot\theta$
30°	$\frac{1}{2}$	$\frac{\sqrt{3}}{2}$	$\frac{\sqrt{3}}{3}$	2	$\frac{2\sqrt{3}}{3}$	$\sqrt{3}$
45°	$\frac{\sqrt{2}}{2}$	$\frac{\sqrt{2}}{2}$	1	$\sqrt{2}$	$\sqrt{2}$	1
60°	$\frac{\sqrt{3}}{2}$	$\frac{1}{2}$	$\sqrt{3}$	$\frac{2\sqrt{3}}{3}$	2	$\frac{\sqrt{3}}{3}$

SELF-ASSESSMENT

1 I do not understand. 2 I can do it with help. 3 I can do it on my own. 4 I can teach someone else.

Evaluate the six trigonometric functions of the angle θ.

1.

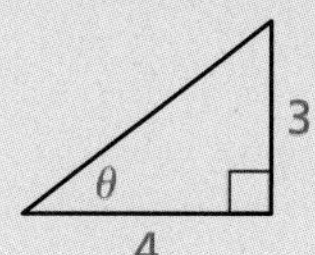

2.

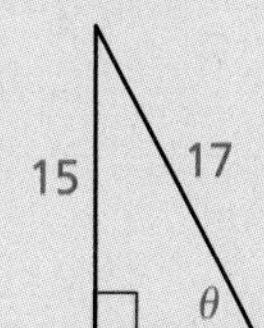

3.

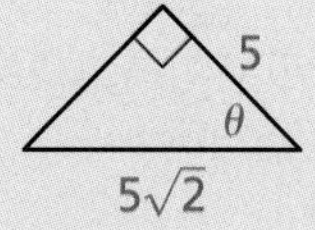

4. In a right triangle, θ is an acute angle and $\cos\theta = \frac{7}{10}$. Evaluate the other five trigonometric functions of θ.

Finding Side Lengths and Angle Measures

EXAMPLE 3 Finding an Unknown Side Length

Find the value of x for the right triangle.

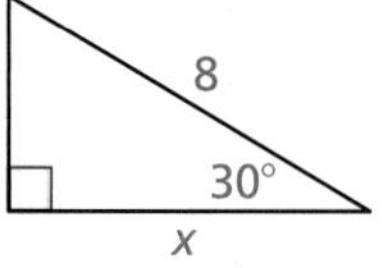

SOLUTION

Write an equation using a trigonometric function that involves the ratio of x and 8. Solve the equation for x.

$\cos 30° = \dfrac{\text{adj}}{\text{hyp}}$	Write trigonometric equation.
$\dfrac{\sqrt{3}}{2} = \dfrac{x}{8}$	Substitute.
$4\sqrt{3} = x$	Multiply each side by 8.

▶ The length of the side is $x = 4\sqrt{3}$.

Finding all unknown side lengths and angle measures of a triangle is called *solving the triangle*. Solving right triangles that have acute angles other than 30°, 45°, and 60° may require the use of technology. Be sure to use *degree* mode.

EXAMPLE 4 Using Technology to Solve a Right Triangle

Solve $\triangle ABC$. Round your answers to the nearest hundredth, if necessary.

B, c, a, 28°, A, $b = 15$, C

SOLUTION

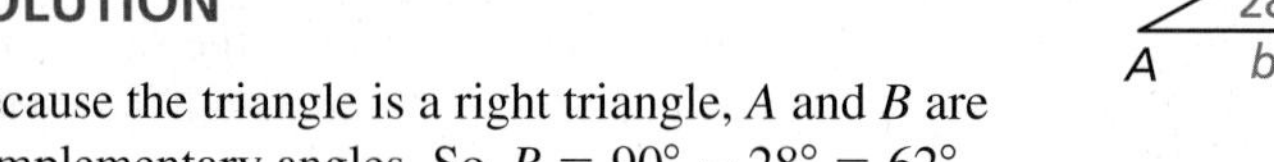

Because the triangle is a right triangle, A and B are complementary angles. So, $B = 90° - 28° = 62°$.

> **READING**
>
> Throughout this chapter, a capital letter is used to denote both an angle of a triangle and its measure. The same letter in lowercase is used to denote the length of the side opposite that angle.

Next, write two equations using trigonometric functions, one that involves the ratio of a and 15, and one that involves c and 15. Solve the equations for a and c.

$\tan 28° = \dfrac{\text{opp}}{\text{adj}}$	Write trigonometric equation.	$\sec 28° = \dfrac{\text{hyp}}{\text{adj}}$
$\tan 28° = \dfrac{a}{15}$	Substitute.	$\sec 28° = \dfrac{c}{15}$
$15(\tan 28°) = a$	Multiply each side by 15.	$15\left(\dfrac{1}{\cos 28°}\right) = c$
$7.98 \approx a$	Use technology.	$16.99 \approx c$

▶ So, $B = 62°$, $a \approx 7.98$, and $c \approx 16.99$.

SELF-ASSESSMENT 1 I do not understand. 2 I can do it with help. 3 I can do it on my own. 4 I can teach someone else.

5. Find the value of x for the right triangle shown.

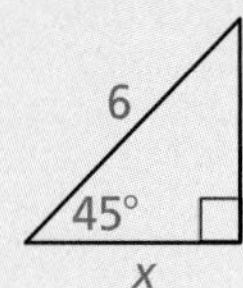

6. Solve $\triangle ABC$. Round your answers to the nearest hundredth, if necessary.

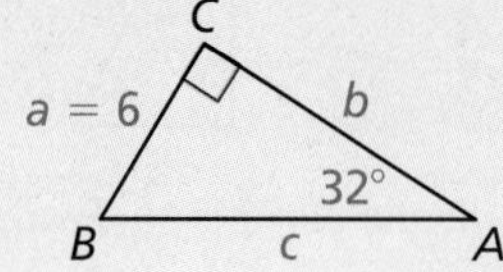

Solving Real-Life Problems

EXAMPLE 5 Using Indirect Measurement

You are hiking near a canyon. While standing at A, you measure an angle of 90° between B and C, as shown. You then walk to B and measure an angle of 76° between A and C. The distance between A and B is about 2 miles. About how wide is the canyon between A and C?

C
x
B 76° A
2 mi

Math Practice

Find Entry Points
How can you determine which trigonometric function to use when finding the unknown distance?

SOLUTION

$\tan 76° = \dfrac{x}{2}$	Write trigonometric equation.
$2(\tan 76°) = x$	Multiply each side by 2.
$8.0 \approx x$	Use technology.

▶ The width is about 8.0 miles.

An *angle of elevation* is an angle formed by a horizontal line and a line of sight *up* to an object.

An *angle of depression* is an angle formed by a horizontal line and a line of sight *down* to an object.

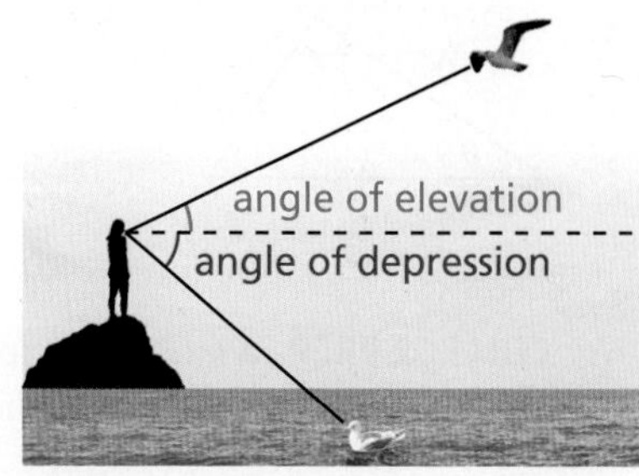

EXAMPLE 6 Using an Angle of Elevation

A parasailer is attached to a boat with a rope that is 72 feet long. The angle of elevation from the boat to the parasailer is 28°. Estimate the parasailer's height above the boat.

SOLUTION

Step 1 Draw a diagram that represents the situation.

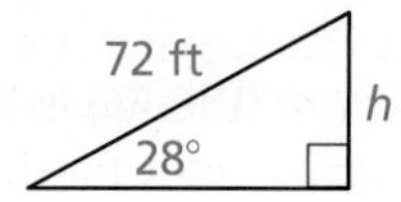

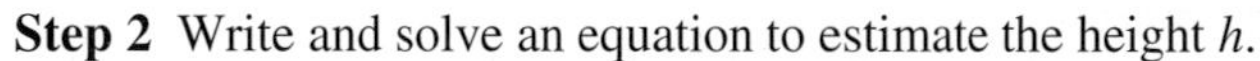

Step 2 Write and solve an equation to estimate the height h.

$\sin 28° = \dfrac{h}{72}$	Write trigonometric equation.
$72(\sin 28°) = h$	Multiply each side by 72.
$33.8 \approx h$	Use technology.

▶ The height of the parasailer above the boat is about 33.8 feet.

SELF-ASSESSMENT 1 I do not understand. 2 I can do it with help. 3 I can do it on my own. 4 I can teach someone else.

7. WHAT IF? In Example 5, about how wide is the canyon when the distance between A and B is 1.5 miles?

8. WHAT IF? In Example 6, estimate the height of the parasailer above the boat when the angle of elevation is 38°.

10.1 Practice WITH CalcChat® AND CalcView®

In Exercises 1–6, evaluate the six trigonometric functions of the angle θ. *Example 1*

1. 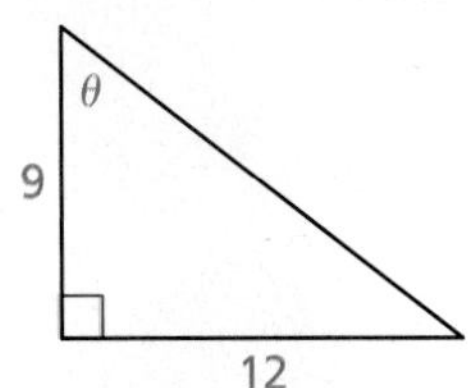

2. 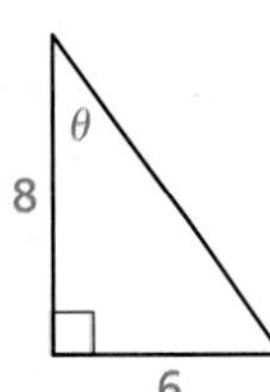

3. 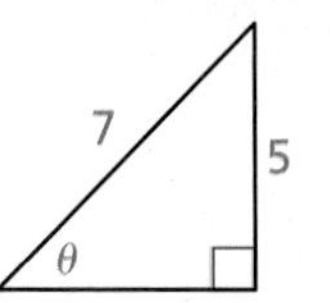

4. 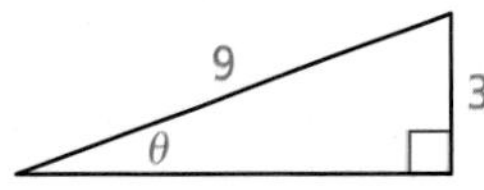

5. 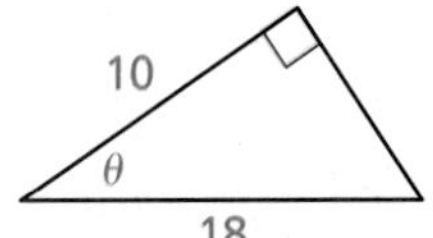

6. 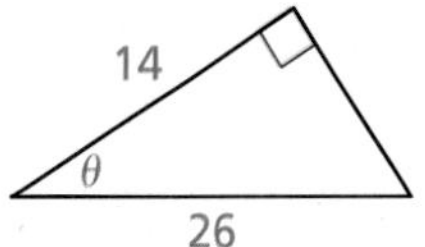

7. **COLLEGE PREP** Which of the following is *not* equal to the ratio of the hypotenuse to the side opposite θ?

   Ⓐ $\csc \theta$

   Ⓑ $\dfrac{1}{\sin \theta}$

   Ⓒ $\dfrac{2}{3}$

   Ⓓ $\dfrac{3}{2}$

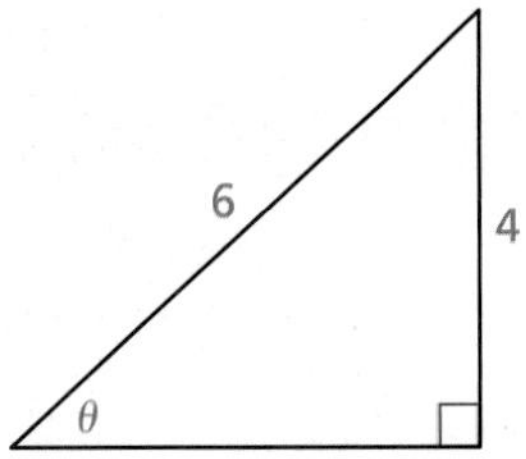

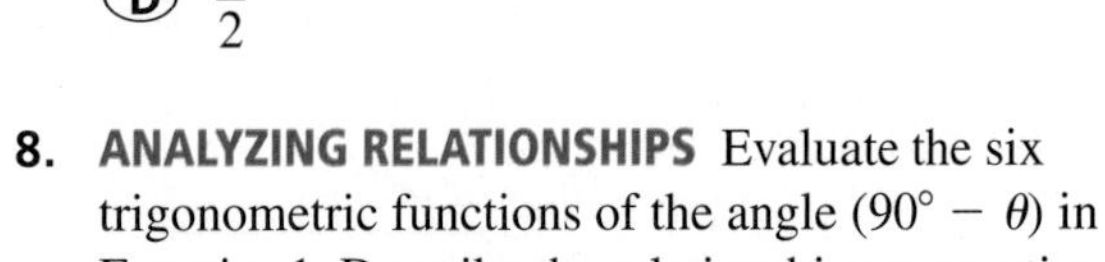

8. **ANALYZING RELATIONSHIPS** Evaluate the six trigonometric functions of the angle $(90° - \theta)$ in Exercise 1. Describe the relationships you notice.

In Exercises 9–14, let θ be an acute angle of a right triangle. Evaluate the other five trigonometric functions of θ. *Example 2*

9. $\sin \theta = \frac{7}{11}$

10. $\csc \theta = \frac{15}{8}$

11. $\cos \theta = \frac{5}{12}$

12. $\sec \theta = \frac{14}{9}$

13. $\tan \theta = \frac{7}{6}$

14. $\cot \theta = \frac{16}{11}$

15. **ERROR ANALYSIS** Describe and correct the error in finding $\sin \theta$.

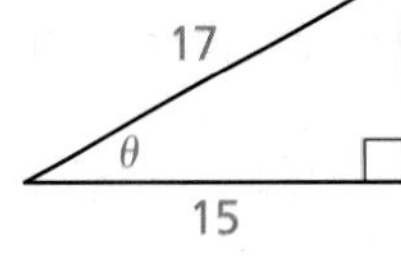

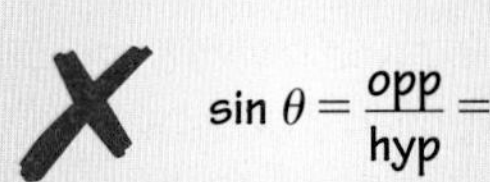

16. **ERROR ANALYSIS** Describe and correct the error in finding $\csc \theta$, given that θ is an acute angle of a right triangle and $\cos \theta = \frac{7}{11}$.

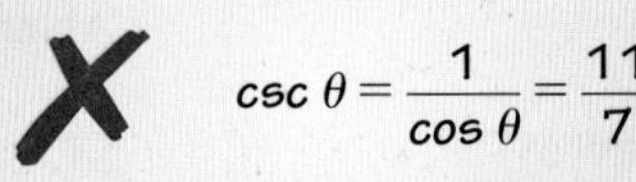

In Exercises 17–22, find the value of x for the right triangle. *Example 3*

17. 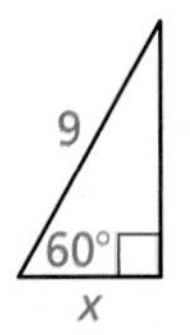

18. 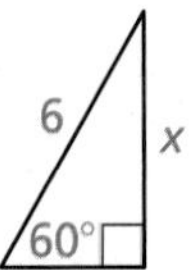

19. 30°, 12, x

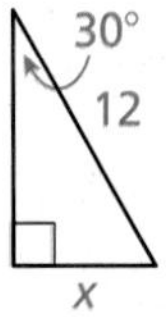

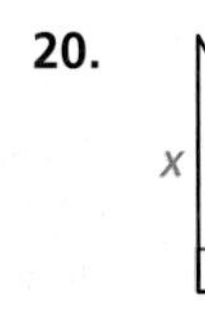

20. (see figure)

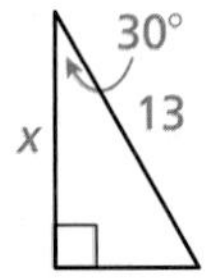

21. 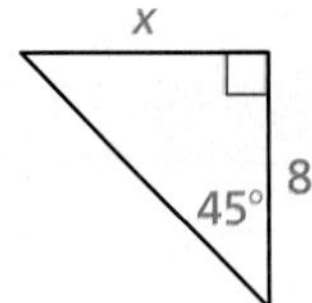

22. 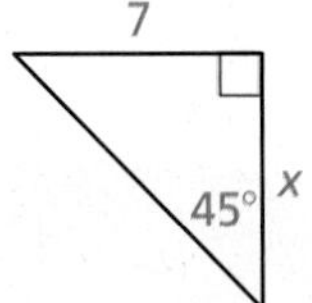

MP USING TOOLS In Exercises 23–28, evaluate the trigonometric function using technology. Round your answer to the nearest hundredth.

23. $\cos 14°$

24. $\tan 31°$

25. $\csc 59°$

26. $\sin 23°$

27. $\cot 6°$

28. $\sec 11°$

In Exercises 29–36, solve $\triangle ABC$ using the diagram and the given measurements. Round your answers to the nearest hundredth, if necessary. *Example 4*

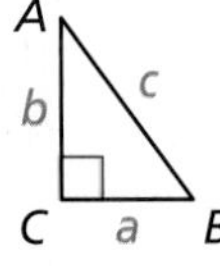

29. $B = 36°, a = 23$

30. $A = 27°, b = 9$

31. $A = 55°, a = 17$

32. $B = 16°, b = 14$

33. $A = 43°, b = 31$

34. $B = 31°, a = 23$

35. $B = 72°, c = 12.8$

36. $A = 64°, a = 7.4$

GO DIGITAL

37. MODELING REAL LIFE To measure the width of a river, you plant a stake on one side of the river, directly across from a boulder. You then walk 100 meters to the right of the stake and measure a 79° angle between the stake and the boulder. About how wide is the river? *Example 5*

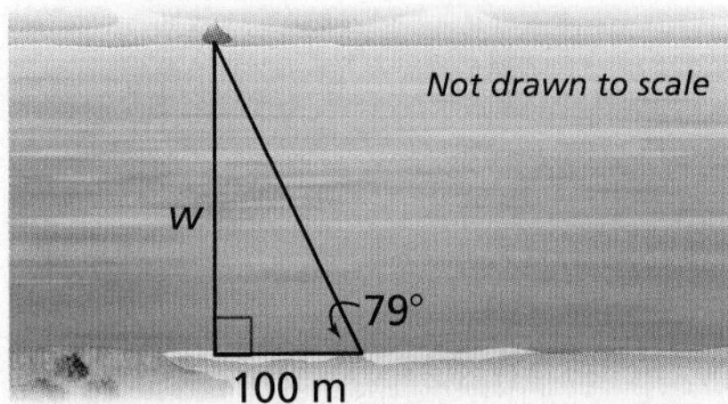

38. MODELING REAL LIFE Katoomba Scenic Railway in Australia is the steepest railway in the world. The railway makes an angle of about 52° with the ground. The railway covers about 458 feet of horizontal distance. About how tall is the railway at its highest point?

39. MODELING REAL LIFE A person whose eye level is 1.5 meters above the ground is standing 75 meters from the base of the Jin Mao Building in Shanghai, China. The person estimates the angle of elevation to the top of the building is about 80°. Estimate the height of the building. *Example 6*

40. MODELING REAL LIFE The Duquesne Incline in Pittsburgh, Pennsylvania, has an angle of elevation of 30°. The track has a length of about 800 feet. Estimate the height of the incline at its highest point.

41. MAKING AN ARGUMENT Is it possible to draw a right triangle in which the values of the cosine function of the acute angles are equal? Explain your reasoning.

42. HOW DO YOU SEE IT? Use the figure to answer each question.

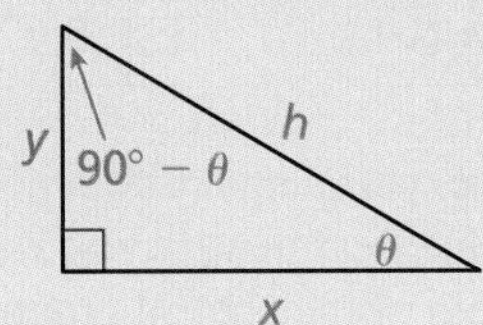

a. Which side is adjacent to θ?

b. Which side is opposite of θ?

c. Does $\cos\theta = \sin(90^\circ - \theta)$? Explain.

43. ANALYZING RELATIONSHIPS You are standing on the ground outside of your school. Your friend is standing in a window on the highest floor of your school. You look at each other along the same line of sight, as shown in the diagram. What must be true about the angle of depression and the angle of elevation in this situation?

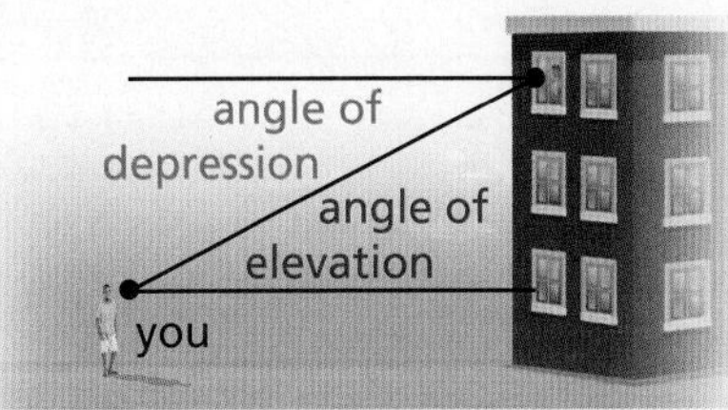

44. COLLEGE PREP Which of the following is *not* one of the values of the six trigonometric functions of the acute angles of an isosceles right triangle?

Ⓐ $\frac{1}{2}$ Ⓑ $\frac{\sqrt{2}}{2}$

Ⓒ 1 Ⓓ $\sqrt{2}$

45. MP PROBLEM SOLVING A tourist is standing on the Grand View Terrace viewing platform at Mount Rushmore, 1000 feet from the base of the monument. The elevation of the platform is 5280 feet. The tourist, whose eye level is 5.5 feet above the platform, looks up at the top of Mount Rushmore at an angle of 24°. Estimate the elevation of the top of Mount Rushmore.

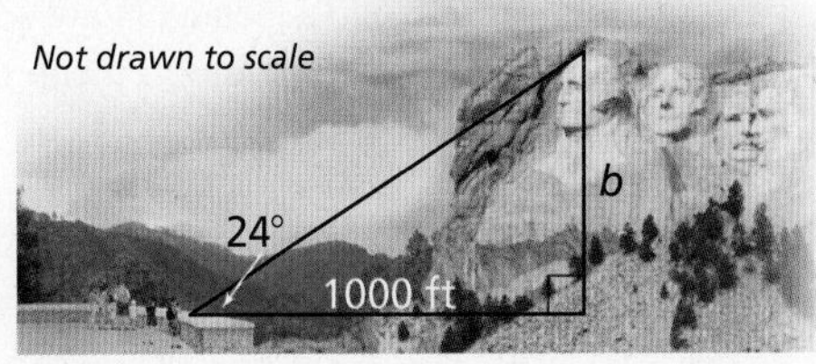

46. WRITING Write a real-life problem that can be solved using a right triangle. Then solve your problem.

47. CONNECTING CONCEPTS The Tropic of Cancer is the circle of latitude farthest north of the equator where the Sun can appear directly overhead. It lies 23.5° north of the equator, as shown.

North Pole
Tropic of Cancer
23.5°
equator
South Pole

a. Find the circumference of the Tropic of Cancer using 3960 miles as the approximate radius of Earth.

b. What is the distance between two points on the Tropic of Cancer that lie directly across from each other?

48. **THOUGHT PROVOKING** Consider a semicircle with a radius of 1 unit, as shown. Write the values of the six trigonometric functions of the angle θ. Explain your reasoning.

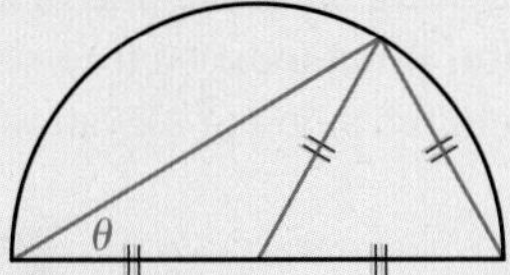

49. **MP PROBLEM SOLVING** A passenger in an airplane sees two towns directly to the left of the plane. What is the distance y between the two towns? Explain the process you used to find your answer.

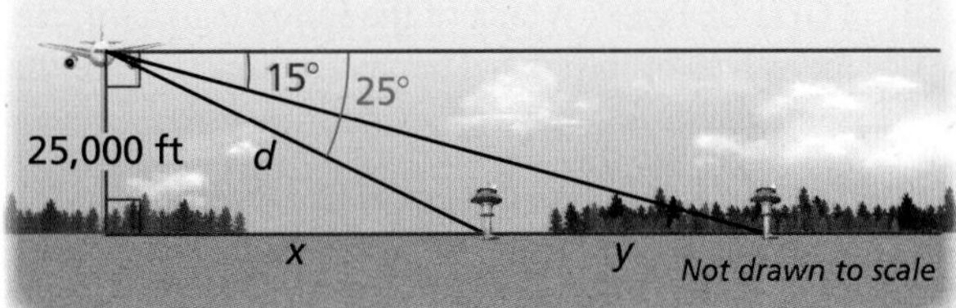

50. **DIG DEEPER** A procedure for approximating π based on the work of Archimedes is to inscribe a regular hexagon in a circle.

a. Use the diagram to solve for x. What is the perimeter of the hexagon?

b. Explain why a regular n-sided polygon inscribed in a circle of radius 1 has a perimeter of $2n \cdot \sin\left(\frac{180}{n}\right)^{\circ}$.

c. Use the expression from part (b) to find an expression in terms of n that approximates π. Then evaluate the expression when $n = 50$.

REVIEW & REFRESH

WATCH

In Exercises 51 and 52, find the circumference and area of the circle with the given radius.

51. $r = 6$ centimeters

52. $r = 11$ inches

53. The number of concerts attended in one year by a random sample of 32 teenagers are shown in the table. Estimate the population mean μ.

Number of Concerts Attended							
3	2	0	4	2	0	2	14
3	4	2	17	1	28	0	1
4	4	0	5	9	12	9	1
0	0	1	0	1	0	6	23

In Exercises 54–57, graph the function.

54. $g(x) = \frac{1}{2}(x + 1)^3$

55. $f(x) = e^{-x} + 8$

56. $y = -\sqrt{x} - 5$

57. $y = 2(x - 3)^2 + 6$

58. Determine whether the following research topic is best investigated through an experiment or an observational study. Then describe the design of the experiment or observational study.

You want to know whether eating cheese at night reduces the amount of time it takes a person to fall asleep.

59. Find the value of x for the right triangle.

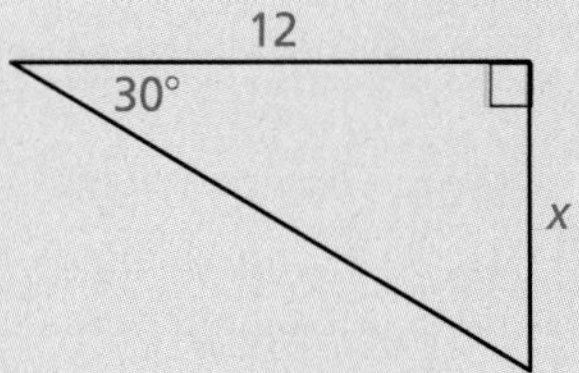

60. **MODELING REAL LIFE** A randomized comparative experiment tests whether a vitamin supplement increases human bone density (in grams per square centimeter). The control group has eight people and the treatment group, which receives the vitamin supplement, has eight people. The tables show the results.

	Bone Density (g/cm²)			
Control Group	0.9	1.2	1.0	0.8
Treatment Group	1.2	1.0	0.9	1.1

Control Group	1.3	1.1	0.9	1.0
Treatment Group	1.1	0.9	1.3	1.2

a. Find the experimental difference of the mean yield of the treatment group, $\bar{x}_{\text{treatment}}$, and the mean yield of the control group, $\bar{x}_{\text{control}}$.

b. Display the data in a double dot plot. What can you conclude?

10.2 Angles and Radian Measure

Learning Target Draw angles in standard position and understand radian measure.

Success Criteria
- I can draw angles in standard position.
- I can explain the meaning of radian measure.
- I can convert between degrees and radians.
- I can use radian measure to find arc lengths and the area of a sector.

EXPLORE IT! Using Radian Measure

Math Practice

Find General Methods How can you use the number of degrees in a circle and your answer in part (d) to convert between degrees and radians?

Work with a partner. Consider a circle with radius r centered at the origin. Let the vertex of an angle be at the origin, with one side of the angle on the positive x-axis. When the other side of the angle intercepts an arc of length r, the measure of the angle is one *radian*.

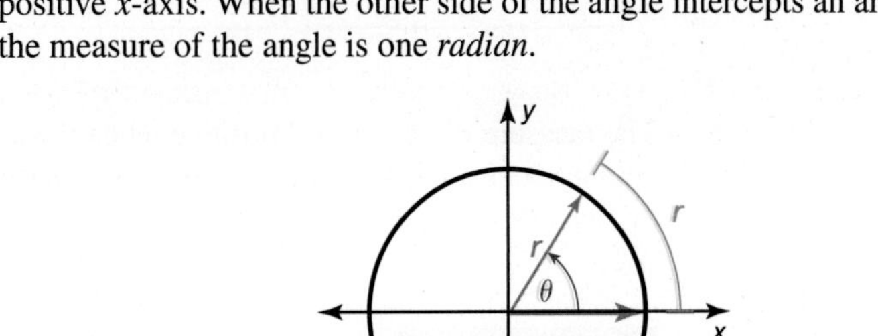

a. The circle below has a radius of 1 inch. The blue point corresponds to an angle of 1 radian. What is the length of the intercepted arc?

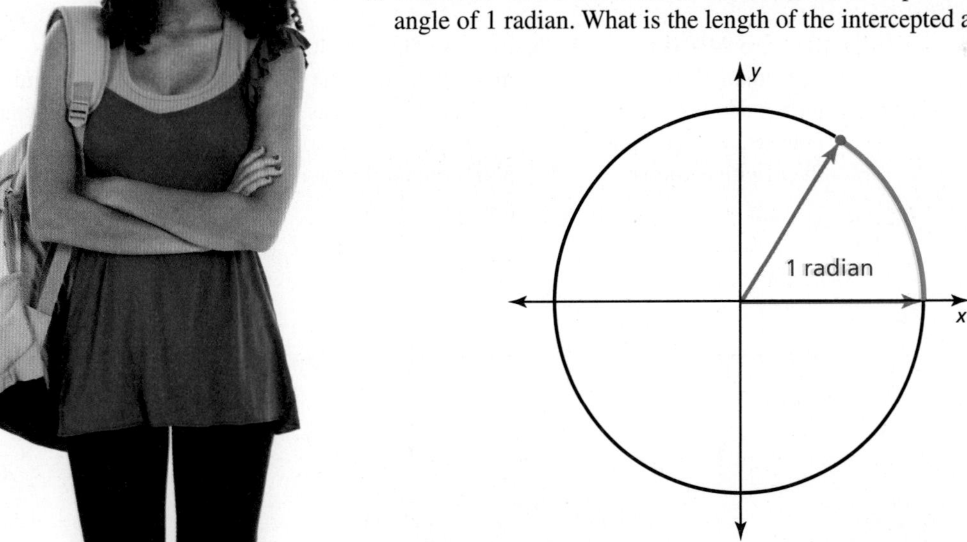

b. MP **CHOOSE TOOLS** Draw any circle. Plot points that correspond to angles of 1, 2, 3, 4, 5, and 6 radians.

c. Estimate the angle measures (in degrees) that correspond to the points you plotted in part (b).

d. The circumference of a circle with radius r is $2\pi r$. How many radians are in a circle?

Drawing Angles in Standard Position

GO DIGITAL

In this lesson, you will expand your study of angles to include angles with measures that can be any real numbers.

Vocabulary AZ VOCAB

initial side, *p. 530*
terminal side, *p. 530*
standard position, *p. 530*
coterminal, *p. 531*
radian, *p. 531*
sector, *p. 532*
central angle, *p. 532*

KEY IDEA

Angles in Standard Position

In a coordinate plane, an angle can be formed by fixing one ray, called the **initial side**, and rotating the other ray, called the **terminal side**, about the vertex.

An angle is in **standard position** when its vertex is at the origin and its initial side lies on the positive x-axis.

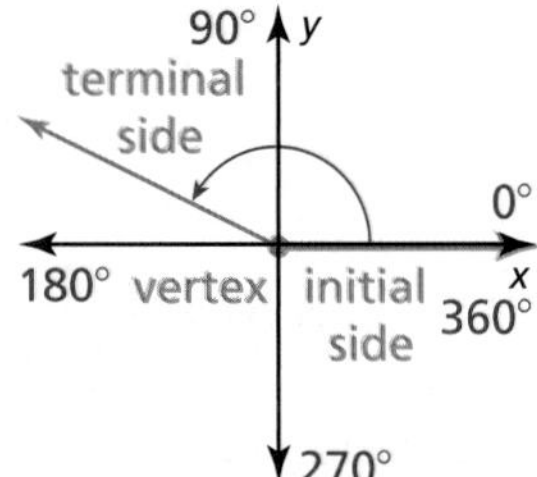

The measure of an angle is positive when the rotation of its terminal side is counterclockwise and negative when the rotation is clockwise. The terminal side of an angle can rotate more than 360°.

EXAMPLE 1 **Drawing Angles in Standard Position**

Draw an angle in standard position having the given measure.

a. 240° **b.** 500° **c.** −50°

SOLUTION

a. Because 240° is 60° more than 180°, the terminal side is 60° counterclockwise past the negative x-axis.

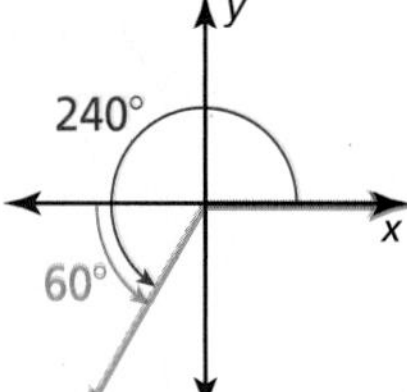

b. Because 500° is 140° more than 360°, the terminal side makes one complete rotation 360° counterclockwise plus 140° more.

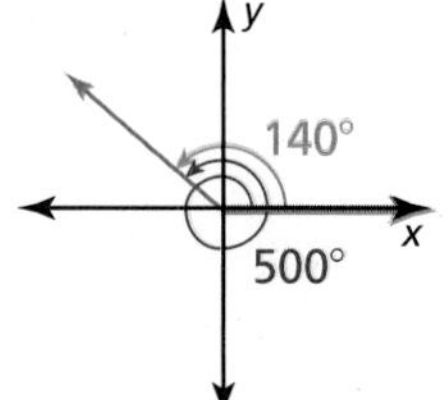

c. Because −50° is negative, the terminal side is 50° clockwise from the positive x-axis.

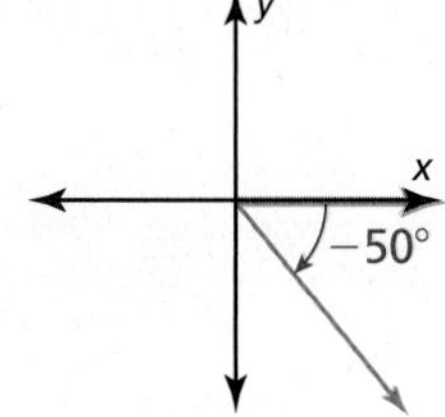

SELF-ASSESSMENT 1 I do not understand. 2 I can do it with help. 3 I can do it on my own. 4 I can teach someone else.

Draw an angle in standard position having the given measure.

1. 65° **2.** 300° **3.** −120° **4.** −450°

5. WRITING Explain how the sign of an angle measure determines its direction of rotation.

Finding Coterminal Angles

In Example 1(b), the angles 500° and 140° are **coterminal** because their terminal sides coincide. An angle coterminal with a given angle can be found by adding or subtracting multiples of 360°.

STUDY TIP

If two angles differ by a multiple of 360°, then the angles are coterminal.

GO DIGITAL

EXAMPLE 2 **Finding Coterminal Angles**

Find one positive angle and one negative angle that are coterminal with (a) −45° and (b) 395°.

SOLUTION

There are many such angles, depending on what multiple of 360° is added or subtracted.

a. $-45° + 360° = 315°$

$-45° - 360° = -405°$

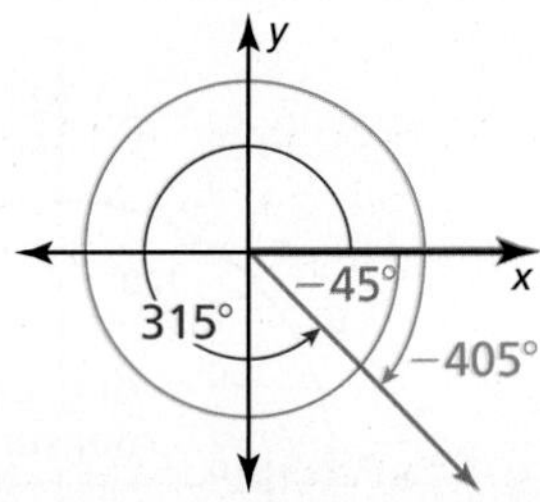

b. $395° - 360° = 35°$

$395° - 2(360°) = -325°$

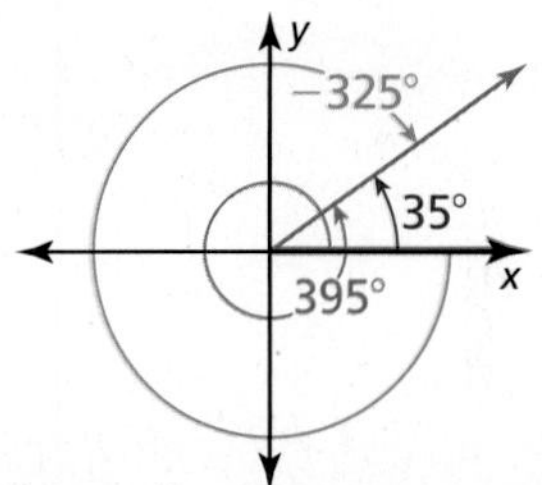

SELF-ASSESSMENT 1 I do not understand. 2 I can do it with help. 3 I can do it on my own. 4 I can teach someone else.

Find one positive angle and one negative angle that are coterminal with the given angle.

6. 80° **7.** 230° **8.** 740° **9.** −135°

Using Radian Measure

STUDY TIP

Notice that 1 radian is approximately equal to 57.3°.

$180° = \pi$ radians

$\frac{180°}{\pi} = 1$ radian

$57.3° \approx 1$ radian

Angles can also be measured in *radians*. To define a radian, consider a circle with radius r centered at the origin, as shown. One **radian** is the measure of an angle in standard position whose terminal side intercepts an arc of length r.

Because the circumference of a circle is $2\pi r$, there are 2π radians in a full circle. So, degree measure and radian measure are related by the equation $360° = 2\pi$ radians, or $180° = \pi$ radians.

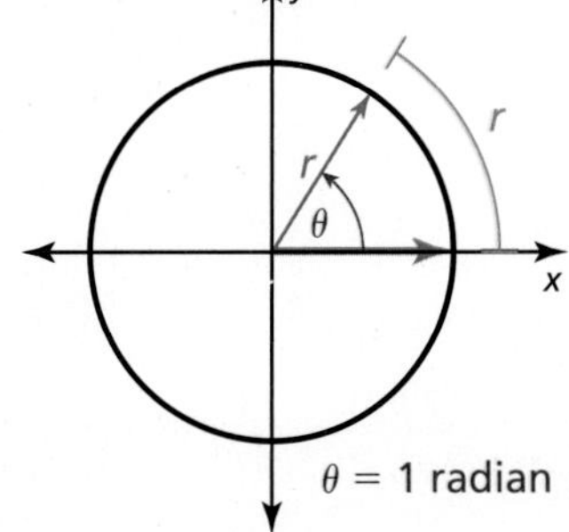

$\theta = 1$ radian

KEY IDEA

Converting Between Degrees and Radians

Degrees to radians

Multiply degree measure by

$$\frac{\pi \text{ radians}}{180°}.$$

Radians to degrees

Multiply radian measure by

$$\frac{180°}{\pi \text{ radians}}.$$

EXAMPLE 3 Converting Between Degrees and Radians

Convert the degree measure to radians or the radian measure to degrees.

a. $120°$ **b.** $-\frac{\pi}{12}$

> **READING**
> The unit "radians" is often omitted. For instance, the measure $-\frac{\pi}{12}$ radians may be written simply as $-\frac{\pi}{12}$.

SOLUTION

a. $120° = 120 \cancel{\text{degrees}}\left(\frac{\pi \text{ radians}}{180 \cancel{\text{degrees}}}\right)$

$= \frac{2\pi}{3}$

b. $-\frac{\pi}{12} = \left(-\frac{\pi}{12} \cancel{\text{radians}}\right)\left(\frac{180°}{\pi \cancel{\text{radians}}}\right)$

$= -15°$

CONCEPT SUMMARY

Degree and Radian Measures of Special Angles

The diagram shows equivalent degree and radian measures for special angles from $0°$ to $360°$ (0 radians to 2π radians).

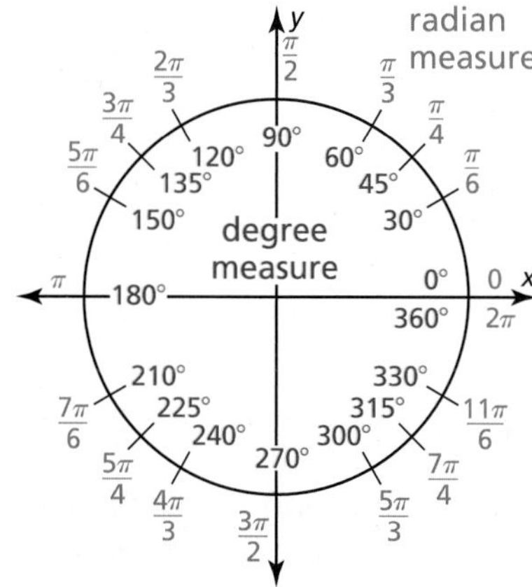

You may find it helpful to memorize the equivalent degree and radian measures for special angles from $0°$ to $90°$. All other special angles shown are multiples of these angles.

A **sector** is a region of a circle that is bounded by two radii and an arc of the circle. The **central angle** θ of a sector is the angle formed by the two radii. There are simple formulas for the arc length and area of a sector when the central angle is measured in radians.

KEY IDEAS

Arc Length and Area of a Sector

The arc length s and area A of a sector with radius r and central angle θ (measured in radians) are as follows.

Arc length: $s = r\theta$

Area: $A = \frac{1}{2}r^2\theta$

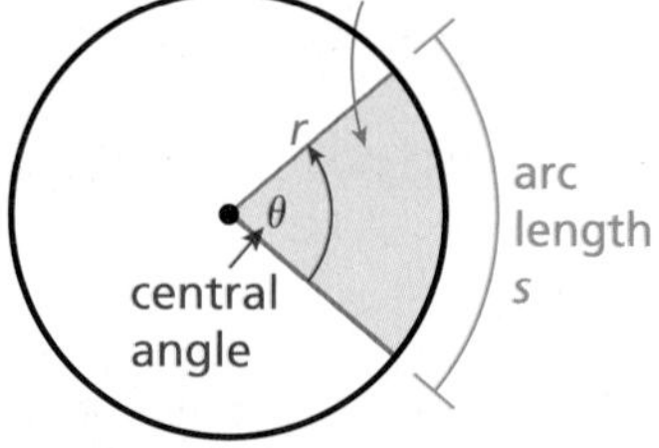

> **COMMON ERROR**
> You must write the measure of an angle in radians when using these formulas.

EXAMPLE 4 Modeling Real Life

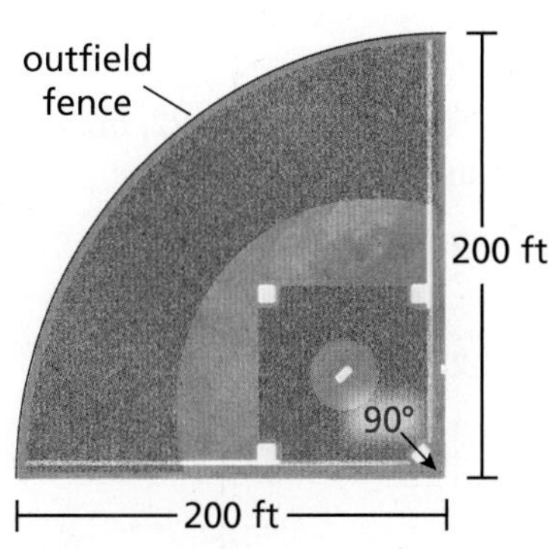

A softball field forms a sector with the dimensions shown. Find the length of the outfield fence and the area of the field.

SOLUTION

1. **Understand the Problem** You are given the dimensions of a softball field. You are asked to find the length of the outfield fence and the area of the field.
2. **Make a Plan** Find the measure of the central angle in radians. Then use the arc length and area of a sector formulas.
3. **Solve and Check**

Step 1 Convert the measure of the central angle to radians.

$$90° = 90 \text{ degrees}\left(\frac{\pi \text{ radians}}{180 \text{ degrees}}\right)$$
$$= \frac{\pi}{2} \text{ radians}$$

Step 2 Find the arc length and the area of the sector.

Arc length: $s = r\theta$ $= 200\left(\frac{\pi}{2}\right)$ $= 100\pi$

Area: $A = \frac{1}{2}r^2\theta$ $= \frac{1}{2}(200)^2\left(\frac{\pi}{2}\right)$ $= 10{,}000\pi$

▶ The length of the outfield fence is 100π, or about 314 feet. The area of the field is $10{,}000\pi$, or about 31,416 square feet.

ANOTHER WAY

Because the central angle is 90°, the sector represents $\frac{1}{4}$ of a circle with a radius of 200 feet. So,

$$s = \frac{1}{4} \cdot 2\pi r = \frac{1}{4} \cdot 2\pi(200) = 100\pi$$

and

$$A = \frac{1}{4} \cdot \pi r^2 = \frac{1}{4} \cdot \pi(200)^2 = 10{,}000\pi.$$

Check Reasonableness To check the area of the field, consider the square formed using the two 200-foot sides.

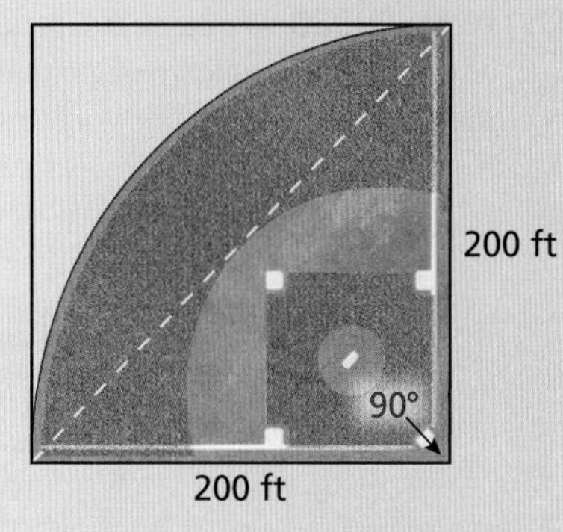

By drawing the diagonal, you can see that the area of the field is less than the area of the square but greater than one-half of the area of the square.

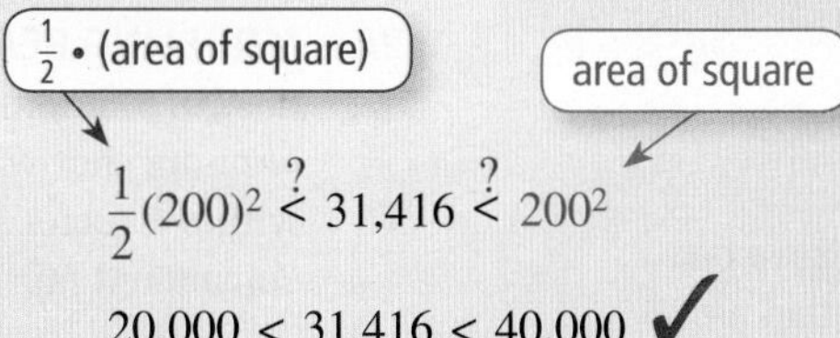

$$\frac{1}{2}(200)^2 \overset{?}{<} 31{,}416 \overset{?}{<} 200^2$$

$$20{,}000 < 31{,}416 < 40{,}000 \checkmark$$

SELF-ASSESSMENT 1 I do not understand. 2 I can do it with help. 3 I can do it on my own. 4 I can teach someone else.

Convert the degree measure to radians or the radian measure to degrees.

10. 135° **11.** −40° **12.** $\frac{5\pi}{4}$ **13.** −6.28

14. WHAT IF? In Example 4, the outfield fence is 220 feet from home plate. Estimate the length of the outfield fence and the area of the field.

10.2 Practice WITH CalcChat® AND CalcView®

GO DIGITAL

In Exercises 1–4, draw an angle in standard position having the given measure. *Example 1*

1. 110° 2. 450°

3. −900° 4. −10°

In Exercises 5–8, find one positive angle and one negative angle that are coterminal with the given angle. *Example 2*

5. 70° 6. 255°

7. −125° 8. −800°

In Exercises 9–16, convert the degree measure to radians or the radian measure to degrees. *Example 3*

9. 40° 10. 14°

11. −260° 12. −500°

13. $\frac{\pi}{9}$ 14. $\frac{3\pi}{4}$

15. −5 16. 12

17. **OPEN-ENDED** Using radian measure, give one positive angle and one negative angle that are coterminal with the angle shown. Justify your answers.

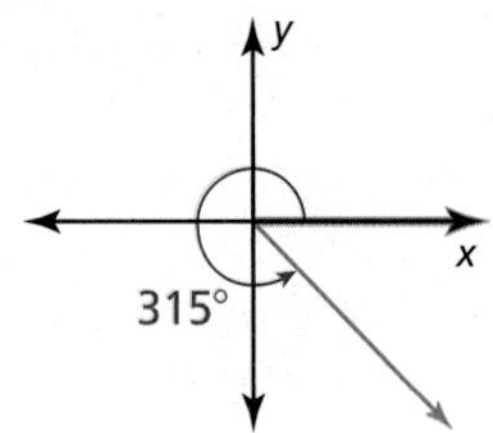

18. **OPEN-ENDED** Using degree measure, give one positive angle and one negative angle that are coterminal with the angle shown. Justify your answers.

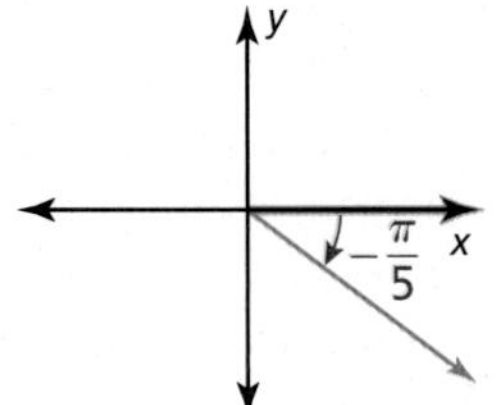

ANALYZING RELATIONSHIPS In Exercises 19–22, match the angle measure with the angle.

19. 600° 20. $-\frac{9\pi}{4}$

21. $\frac{5\pi}{6}$ 22. −240°

A.
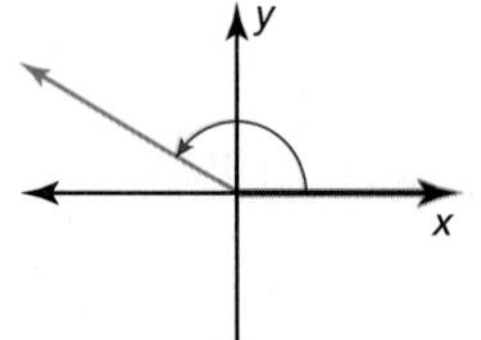

B.
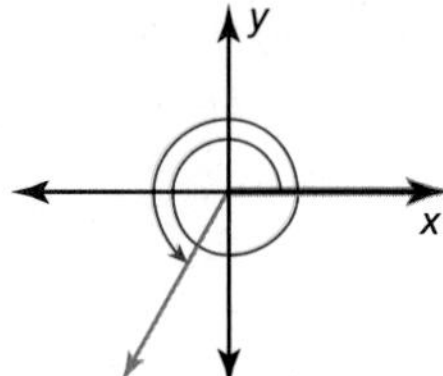

C.
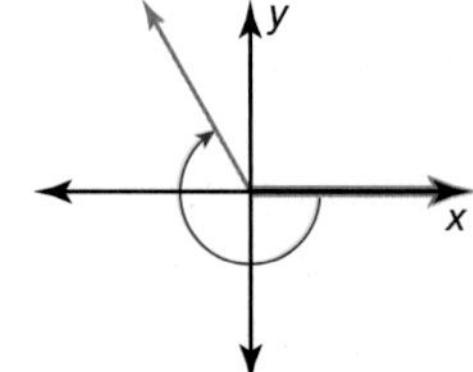

D.
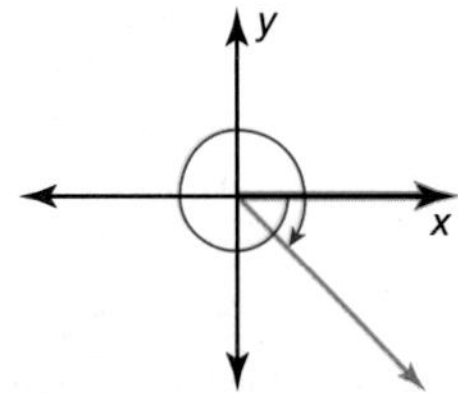

23. **MODELING REAL LIFE** The observation deck of a building forms a sector with the dimensions shown. Find the length of the safety rail and the area of the deck. *Example 4*

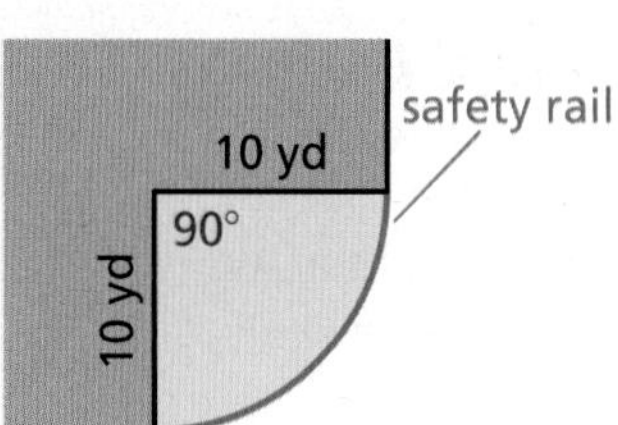

24. **MODELING REAL LIFE** In the men's shot put event at the 2016 Summer Olympic Games, the length of the winning shot was 22.52 meters. A shot put must land within a sector having a central angle of 34.92° to be considered fair.

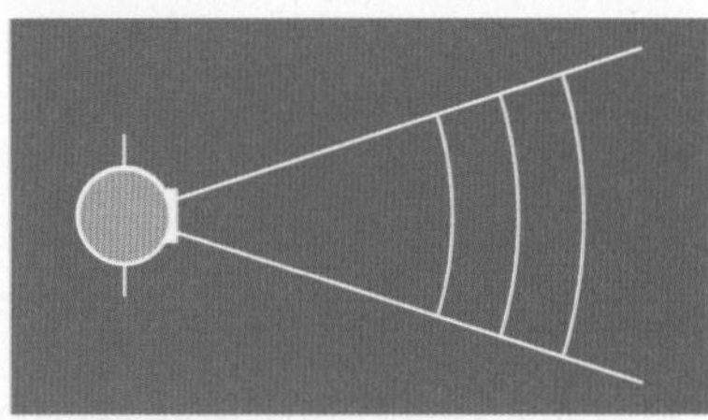

a. An arc across the fair landing area marks the farthest throw. Find the length of the arc.

b. All fair throws in the 2016 Olympics landed within a sector bounded by the arc in part (a). What is the area of this sector?

25. **ERROR ANALYSIS** Describe and correct the error in finding the length of an arc with a radius of 9 feet and a central angle of 60°.

✗ $s = 9\left(\frac{\pi}{3}\right) = 3\pi$ radians

26. **ERROR ANALYSIS** Describe and correct the error in finding the area of a sector with a radius of 6 centimeters and a central angle of 40°.

✗ $A = \frac{1}{2}(6)^2(40) = 720 \text{ cm}^2$

27. **MODELING REAL LIFE** A wind turbine rotates 15 times per minute. At that rate, through what angle does the tip of one of its blades rotate in one hour? Give your answer in both degrees and radians.

28. **MODELING REAL LIFE** Consider the analog clock shown. Through what angle does the tip of the minute hand rotate from 9:00 A.M. to 5:00 P.M.? Give your answer in both degrees and radians.

29. **MP REASONING** A scientist performed an experiment to study the effects of gravitational force on humans. In order for humans to experience twice Earth's gravity, they were placed in a centrifuge 58 feet long and spun at a rate of about 15 revolutions per minute. Through how many radians did the people rotate each second?

30. **MP REASONING** In astronomy, the *terminator* is the day-night line on a planet that divides the planet into daytime and nighttime regions. The terminator moves across the surface of a planet as the planet rotates. It takes about 4 hours for Earth's terminator to move across the continental United States. Through what angle does Earth rotate in this time?

GO DIGITAL

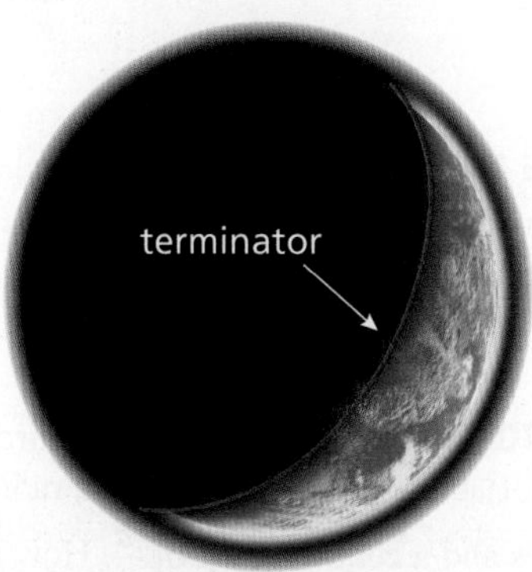

31. **MP PROBLEM SOLVING** A drone searches an area beyond the view of a lifeguard for a lost swimmer. Find the area searched by the drone.

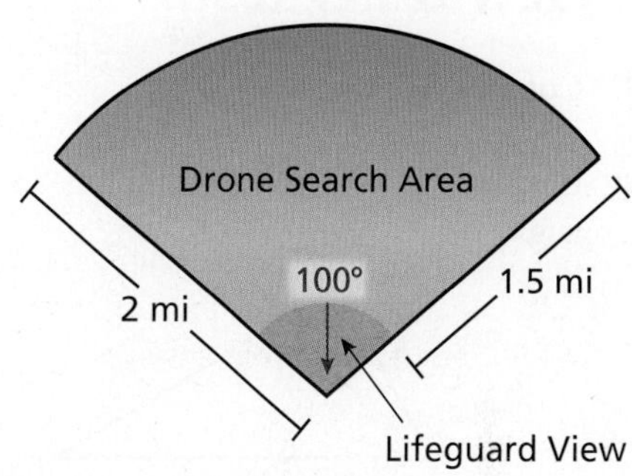

32. **MP PROBLEM SOLVING** A dartboard is divided into 20 sectors. Each sector is worth a point value from 1 to 20 and has shaded regions that double or triple this value. Find the area of the triple region for the entire dartboard.

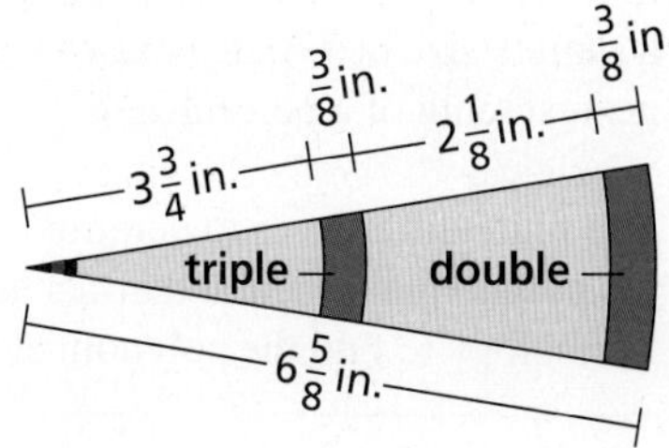

33. **MP PROBLEM SOLVING** You use a navigation system on your boat to avoid an algae bloom. Your original course involved traveling along an arc with a central angle of 150° and a radius of 1 mile. Your new course involves traveling along an arc with a central angle of 170° and a radius of 2 miles. How much longer is the new course?

34. **HOW DO YOU SEE IT?** Use the graph to find the measure of θ. Explain your reasoning.

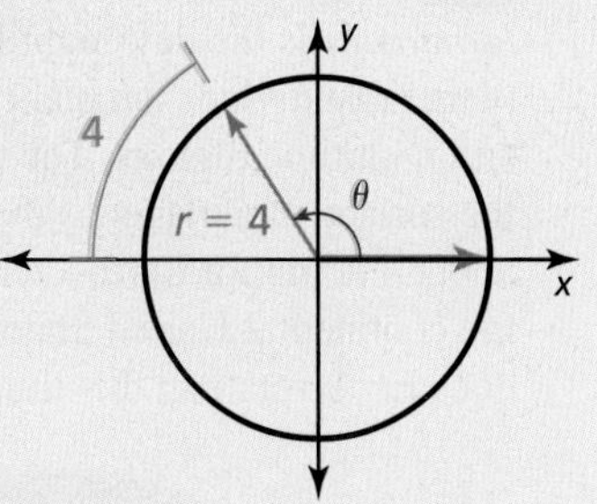

35. **MAKING AN ARGUMENT** Your friend claims that when the arc length of a sector equals the radius, the area of the sector can be given by $A = \frac{s^2}{2}$. Is your friend correct? Explain.

36. **MP PROBLEM SOLVING** A spiral staircase has 15 steps. Each step is a sector with a radius of 42 inches and a central angle of $\frac{\pi}{8}$. How many square inches of carpeting do you need to cover the 15 steps?

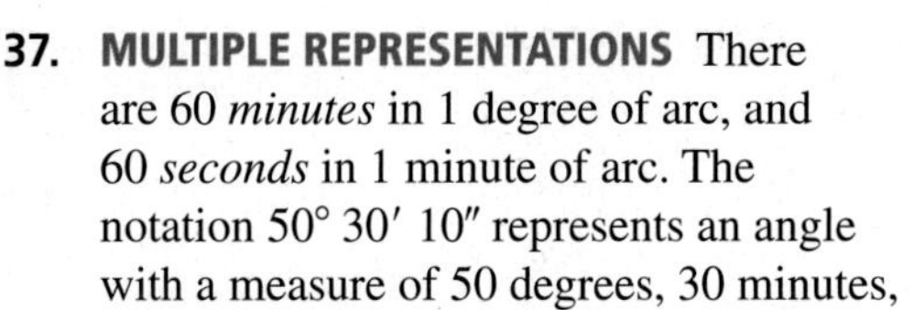

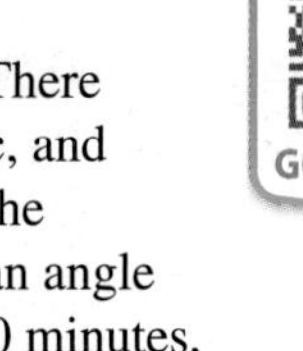

37. **MULTIPLE REPRESENTATIONS** There are 60 *minutes* in 1 degree of arc, and 60 *seconds* in 1 minute of arc. The notation $50° \, 30' \, 10''$ represents an angle with a measure of 50 degrees, 30 minutes, and 10 seconds.

  a. Write the angle measure $70.55°$ using the notation above.

  b. Write the angle measure $110° \, 45' \, 30''$ to the nearest hundredth of a degree.

  c. Write the angle measure $40° \, 15' \, 45''$ to the nearest tenth of a radian.

38. **THOUGHT PROVOKING** What happens to the length of an intercepted arc when the radius of a circle is doubled but the measure of the central angle remains the same? Explain.

REVIEW & REFRESH

39. Convert $200°$ to radians.

40. Evaluate the six trigonometric functions of the angle θ.

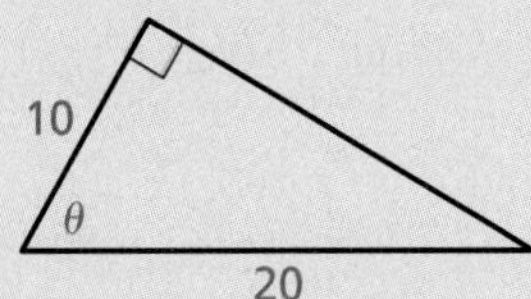

41. Complete the inequality $2 \; \_\_\_ \; |x + 1|$ with $<, \leq, >,$ or $\geq$ so that $x = 1$ and $x = -1$ are both solutions of the inequality.

42. Estimate the margin of error for a survey that has a sample size of 770. Round your answer to the nearest tenth of a percent.

43. Use finite differences to determine the degree of the polynomial function that fits the data. Then use technology to find the polynomial function.

x	1	2	3	4	5	6
$f(x)$	6	14	25	40	60	86

44. In the equation $\frac{y}{x} = 8$, tell whether x and y show *direct variation, inverse variation,* or *neither.*

45. Rewrite $5^0 = 1$ in logarithmic form.

46. **MODELING REAL LIFE** A repair shop receives 12 instruments from the music department of a school. The types of instruments are shown. An instrument is randomly selected to be repaired first. What is the probability that a brass instrument is selected?

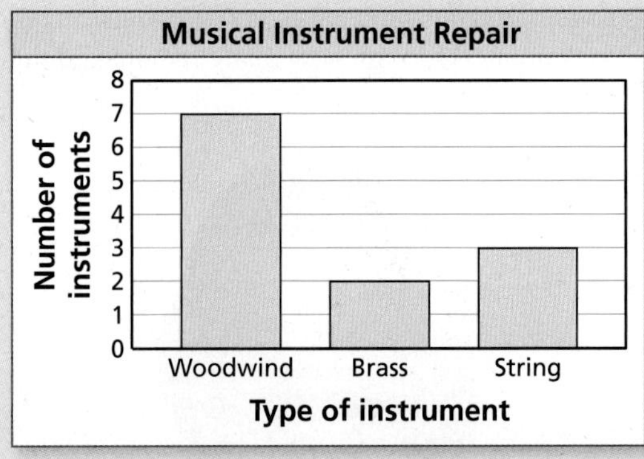

47. Write a polynomial function f of least degree that has rational coefficients, a leading coefficient of 1, and zeros of 3 and $\sqrt{2}$.

48. Multiply $5i$ and $(2 - i)$. Write the answer in standard form.

In Exercises 49 and 50, solve the equation. Check your solution.

49. $x^{3/4} - 8 = 0$

50. $7^{2x+3} = 7^{6-x}$

10.3 Trigonometric Functions of Any Angle

Learning Target Evaluate trigonometric functions of any angle.

Success Criteria

- I can evaluate trigonometric functions given a point on an angle.
- I can evaluate trigonometric functions using the unit circle.
- I can find and use reference angles to evaluate trigonometric functions.
- I can solve real-life problems involving projectiles.

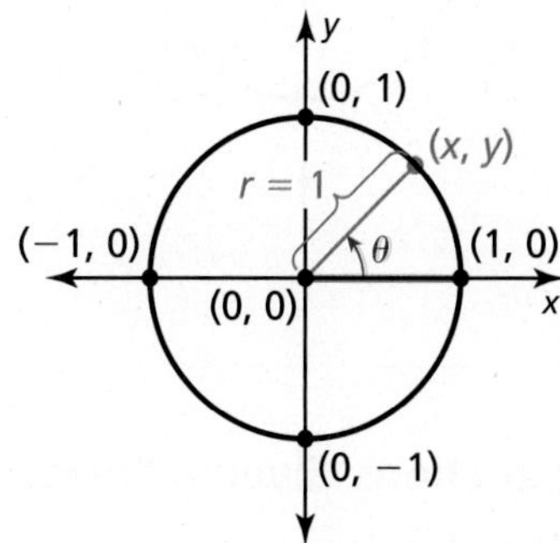

The *unit circle* is a circle in the coordinate plane with its center at the origin and a radius r of 1 unit. The equation of the unit circle is

$$x^2 + y^2 = 1. \qquad \text{Equation of unit circle}$$

As the point (x, y) starts at $(1, 0)$ and moves counterclockwise around the unit circle, the angle θ increases from 0° through 360°.

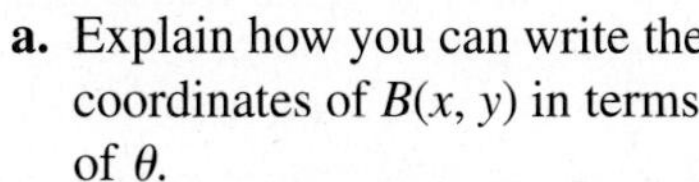

EXPLORE IT! Writing Trigonometric Functions

Work with a partner.
A right triangle with acute angle θ is inscribed inside the unit circle as shown.

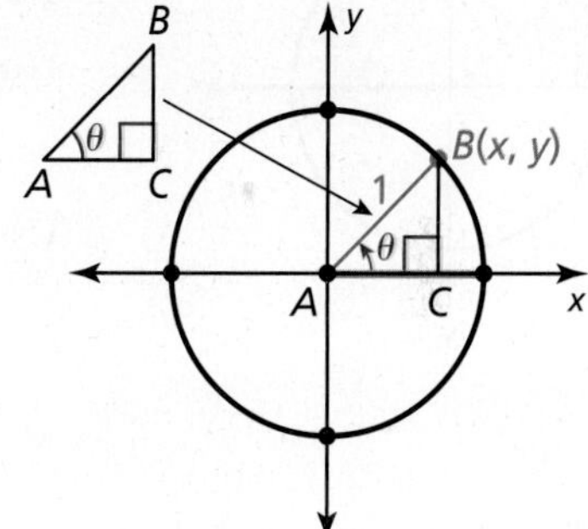

a. Explain how you can write the coordinates of $B(x, y)$ in terms of θ.

b. Find the exact coordinates of the point (x, y) on the unit circle when $\theta = 60°$. Then find the six trigonometric functions of θ.

c. Consider the supplement of $\theta = 60°$ as shown. What do you notice about the acute angle formed by the terminal side of the supplement and the x-axis? Explain how you can use this information to find the exact coordinates of the point (x, y). Then find the six trigonometric functions when $\theta = 120°$. What do you notice?

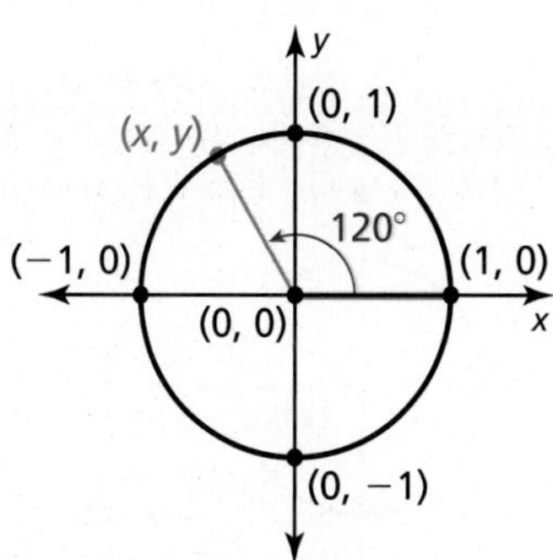

d. Explain how to use your results in parts (b) and (c) to find the exact coordinates of the point (x, y) when $\theta = 135°$.

Math Practice

Consider Similar Problems

How can you find the trigonometric functions of an angle between 180° and 360°?

Trigonometric Functions of Any Angle

Vocabulary

unit circle, *p. 539*
quadrantal angle, *p. 539*
reference angle, *p. 540*

You can generalize the right-triangle definitions of trigonometric functions so that they apply to any angle in standard position.

KEY IDEA

General Definitions of Trigonometric Functions

Let θ be an angle in standard position, and let (x, y) be the point where the terminal side of θ intersects the circle $x^2 + y^2 = r^2$. The six trigonometric functions of θ are defined as shown.

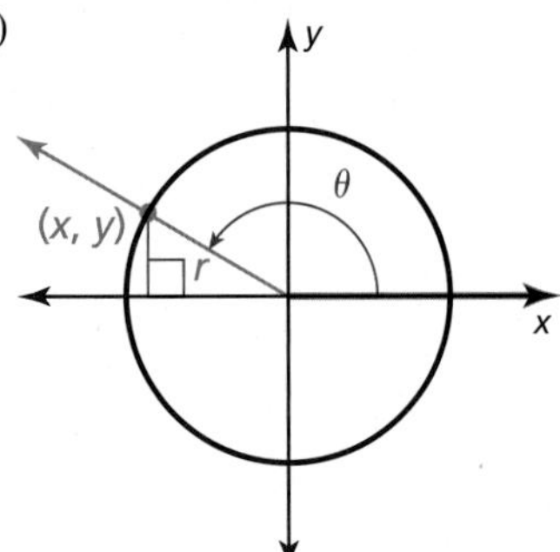

$\sin \theta = \dfrac{y}{r}$ $\qquad \csc \theta = \dfrac{r}{y}, y \neq 0$

$\cos \theta = \dfrac{x}{r}$ $\qquad \sec \theta = \dfrac{r}{x}, x \neq 0$

$\tan \theta = \dfrac{y}{x}, x \neq 0$ $\qquad \cot \theta = \dfrac{x}{y}, y \neq 0$

These functions are sometimes called *circular functions*.

EXAMPLE 1 Evaluating Trigonometric Functions Given a Point

Let $(-4, 3)$ be a point on the terminal side of an angle θ in standard position. Evaluate the six trigonometric functions of θ.

y
(−4, 3)
θ
r
x

SOLUTION

Use the Pythagorean Theorem to find the length of r.

$$r = \sqrt{x^2 + y^2} = \sqrt{(-4)^2 + 3^2} = \sqrt{25} = 5$$

Using $x = -4$, $y = 3$, and $r = 5$, the values of the six trigonometric functions of θ are:

$\sin \theta = \dfrac{y}{r} = \dfrac{3}{5}$ $\qquad \csc \theta = \dfrac{r}{y} = \dfrac{5}{3}$

$\cos \theta = \dfrac{x}{r} = -\dfrac{4}{5}$ $\qquad \sec \theta = \dfrac{r}{x} = -\dfrac{5}{4}$

$\tan \theta = \dfrac{y}{x} = -\dfrac{3}{4}$ $\qquad \cot \theta = \dfrac{x}{y} = -\dfrac{4}{3}$

SELF-ASSESSMENT 1 I do not understand. 2 I can do it with help. 3 I can do it on my own. 4 I can teach someone else.

Evaluate the six trigonometric functions of θ.

1.

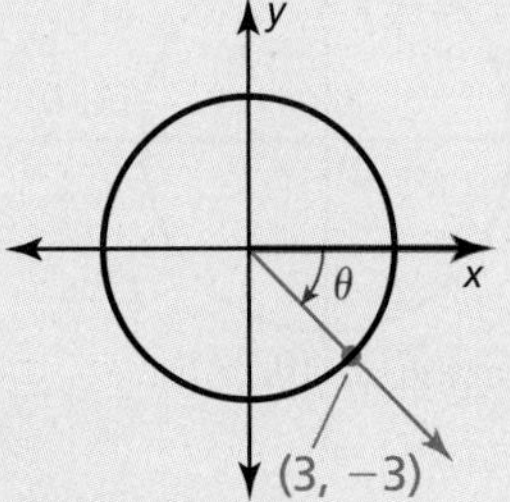

2.

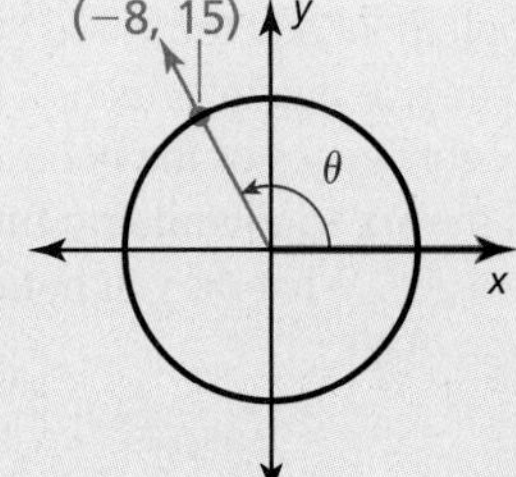

3.

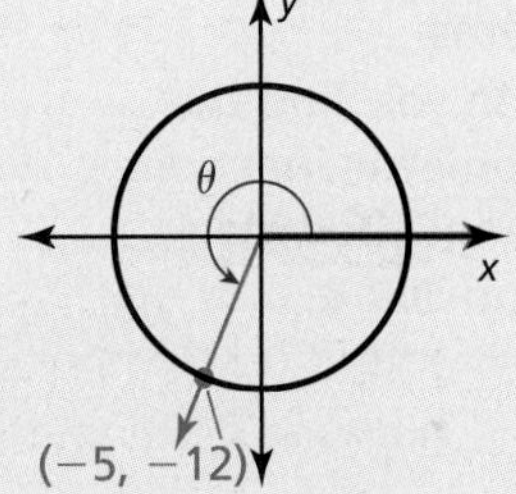

4. MP **REASONING** Explain why the sine and cosine functions are defined for any real value of θ.

KEY IDEA

The Unit Circle

The circle $x^2 + y^2 = 1$, which has center (0, 0) and radius 1, is called the **unit circle**. The values of sin θ and cos θ are the y-coordinate and x-coordinate, respectively, of the point where the terminal side of θ intersects the unit circle.

$$\sin \theta = \frac{y}{r} = \frac{y}{1} = y$$

$$\cos \theta = \frac{x}{r} = \frac{x}{1} = x$$

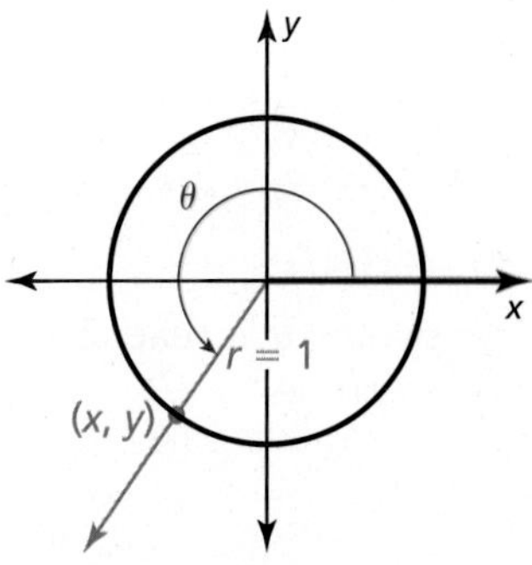

It is convenient to use the unit circle to find trigonometric functions of *quadrantal angles*. A **quadrantal angle** is an angle in standard position whose terminal side lies on an axis. The measure of a quadrantal angle is always a multiple of 90°, or $\frac{\pi}{2}$ radians.

EXAMPLE 2 Using the Unit Circle

Use the unit circle to evaluate the six trigonometric functions of $\theta = 270°$.

SOLUTION

Step 1 Draw a unit circle with the angle $\theta = 270°$ in standard position.

Step 2 Identify the point where the terminal side of θ intersects the unit circle. The terminal side of θ intersects the unit circle at $(0, -1)$.

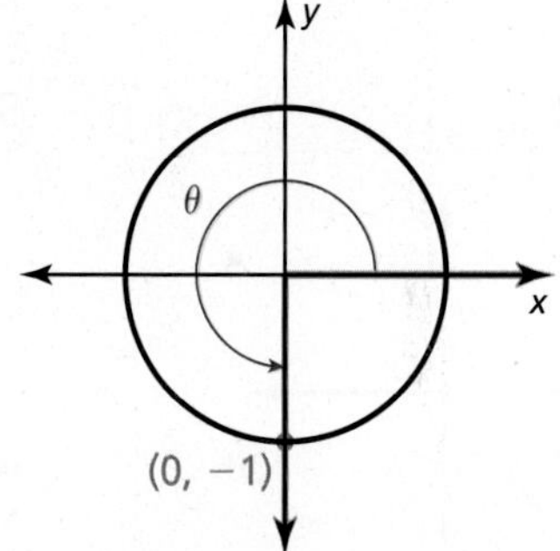

Step 3 Find the values of the six trigonometric functions. Let $x = 0$ and $y = -1$ to evaluate the trigonometric functions.

$$\sin \theta = \frac{y}{r} = \frac{-1}{1} = -1 \qquad \csc \theta = \frac{r}{y} = \frac{1}{-1} = -1$$

$$\cos \theta = \frac{x}{r} = \frac{0}{1} = 0 \qquad \sec \theta = \frac{r}{x} = \frac{1}{0} \text{ undefined}$$

$$\tan \theta = \frac{y}{x} = \frac{-1}{0} \text{ undefined} \qquad \cot \theta = \frac{x}{y} = \frac{0}{-1} = 0$$

ANOTHER WAY

The equation for the standard form of a circle, $x^2 + y^2 = r^2$, can also be used to find the six trigonometric functions of θ. The terminal side of θ intersects the circle at $(0, -r)$. So,

$$\sin \theta = \frac{y}{r} = \frac{-r}{r} = -1.$$

The other functions can be evaluated similarly.

SELF-ASSESSMENT

1 I do not understand. 2 I can do it with help. 3 I can do it on my own. 4 I can teach someone else.

5. **MP REASONING** Explain how the unit circle in the coordinate plane allows you to extend trigonometric functions to all real numbers.

Use the unit circle to evaluate the six trigonometric functions of θ.

6. $\theta = 90°$

7. $\theta = 180°$

8. $\theta = 2\pi$

Reference Angles

KEY IDEA

Reference Angle Relationships

Let θ be an angle in standard position. The **reference angle** for θ is the acute angle θ' formed by the terminal side of θ and the x-axis. The relationship between θ and θ' is shown below for nonquadrantal angles θ with terminal sides in Quadrants II, III, and IV, such that $90° < \theta < 360°$ or, in radians, $\frac{\pi}{2} < \theta < 2\pi$.

READING

The symbol θ' is read as "theta prime."

Quadrant II

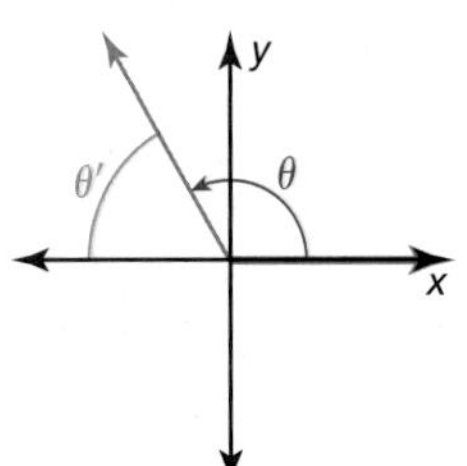

Degrees: $\theta' = 180° - \theta$
Radians: $\theta' = \pi - \theta$

Quadrant III

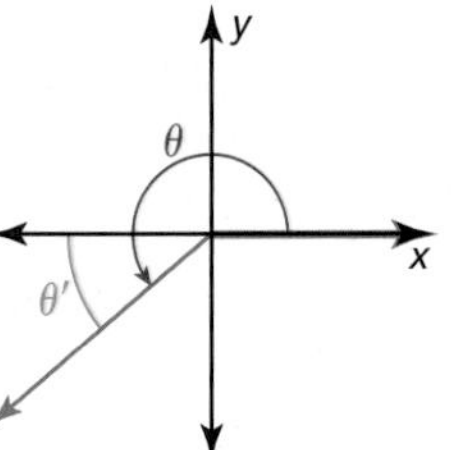

Degrees: $\theta' = \theta - 180°$
Radians: $\theta' = \theta - \pi$

Quadrant IV

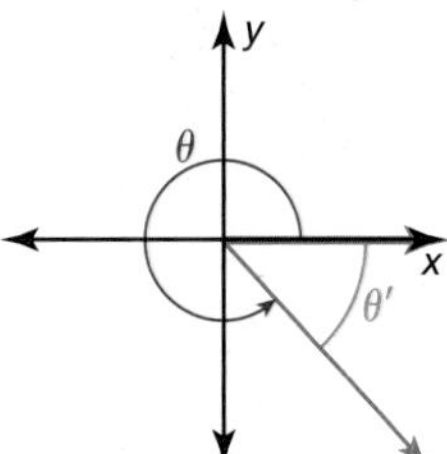

Degrees: $\theta' = 360° - \theta$
Radians: $\theta' = 2\pi - \theta$

EXAMPLE 3 Finding Reference Angles

Find the reference angle θ' for (a) $\theta = \frac{5\pi}{3}$ and (b) $\theta = -130°$.

SOLUTION

a. The terminal side of θ lies in Quadrant IV. So, $\theta' = 2\pi - \frac{5\pi}{3} = \frac{\pi}{3}$. The figure at the right shows $\theta = \frac{5\pi}{3}$ and $\theta' = \frac{\pi}{3}$.

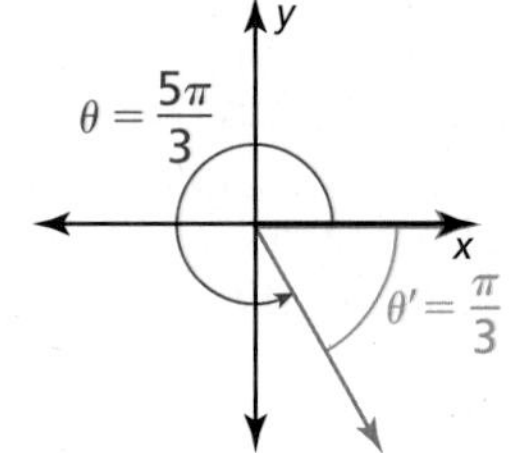

b. Note that θ is coterminal with 230°, whose terminal side lies in Quadrant III. So, $\theta' = 230° - 180° = 50°$. The figure at the left shows $\theta = -130°$ and $\theta' = 50°$.

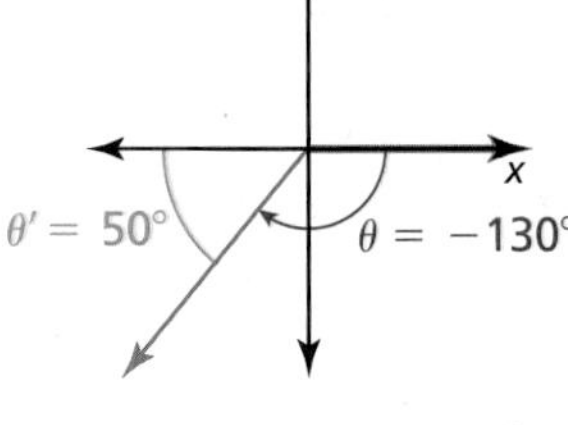

Reference angles allow you to evaluate a trigonometric function for any angle θ. The sign of the trigonometric function value depends on the quadrant in which θ lies.

KEY IDEA

Evaluating Trigonometric Functions

Use these steps to evaluate a trigonometric function for any angle θ:

Step 1 Find the reference angle θ'.

Step 2 Evaluate the trigonometric function for θ'.

Step 3 Determine the sign of the trigonometric function value from the quadrant in which θ lies.

Signs of Function Values

Quadrant II	Quadrant I
$\sin\theta, \csc\theta$: +	$\sin\theta, \csc\theta$: +
$\cos\theta, \sec\theta$: −	$\cos\theta, \sec\theta$: +
$\tan\theta, \cot\theta$: −	$\tan\theta, \cot\theta$: +
Quadrant III	**Quadrant IV**
$\sin\theta, \csc\theta$: −	$\sin\theta, \csc\theta$: −
$\cos\theta, \sec\theta$: −	$\cos\theta, \sec\theta$: +
$\tan\theta, \cot\theta$: +	$\tan\theta, \cot\theta$: −

EXAMPLE 4 Using Reference Angles to Evaluate Functions

Evaluate (a) $\tan(-240^\circ)$ and (b) $\csc \frac{17\pi}{6}$.

SOLUTION

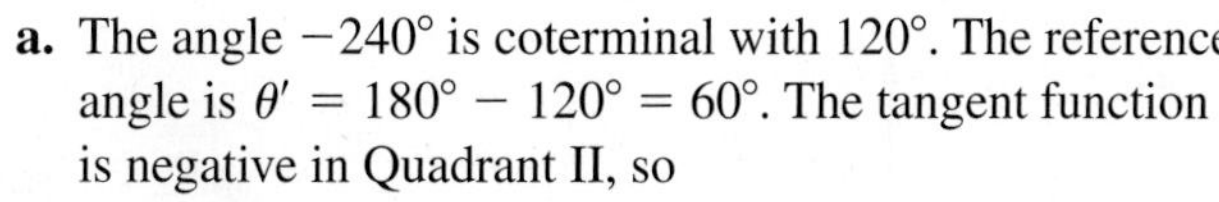

a. The angle -240° is coterminal with 120°. The reference angle is $\theta' = 180^\circ - 120^\circ = 60^\circ$. The tangent function is negative in Quadrant II, so

$$\tan(-240^\circ) = -\tan 60^\circ = -\sqrt{3}.$$

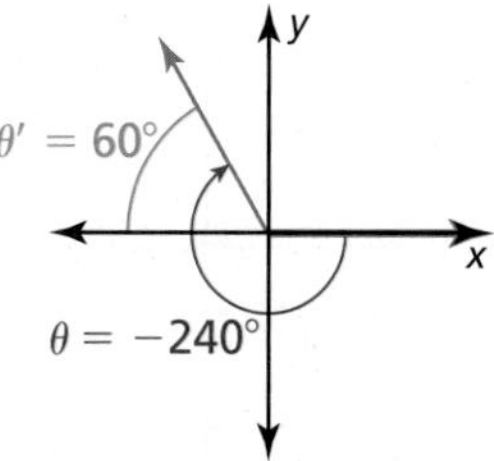

b. The angle $\frac{17\pi}{6}$ is coterminal with $\frac{5\pi}{6}$. The reference angle is

$$\theta' = \pi - \frac{5\pi}{6} = \frac{\pi}{6}.$$

The cosecant function is positive in Quadrant II, so

$$\csc \frac{17\pi}{6} = \csc \frac{\pi}{6} = 2.$$

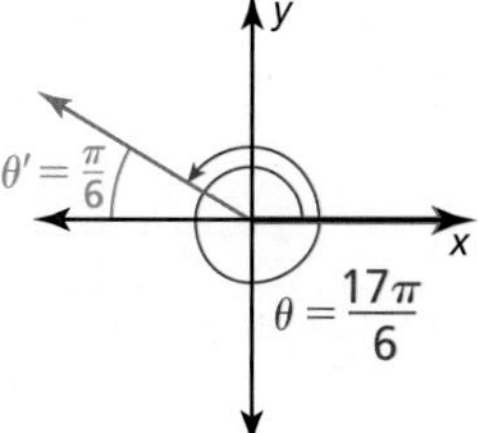

EXAMPLE 5 Modeling Real Life

The horizontal distance d (in feet) traveled by a projectile launched at an angle θ and with an initial speed v (in feet per second) is given by $d = \frac{v^2}{32} \sin 2\theta$. Estimate the horizontal distance traveled by a golf ball that is hit at an angle of 50° with an initial speed of 105 feet per second.

STUDY TIP
This model neglects air resistance and assumes that the projectile's starting and ending heights are the same.

SOLUTION

Note that the golf ball is launched at an angle of $\theta = 50^\circ$ with initial speed of $v = 105$ feet per second.

$d = \frac{v^2}{32} \sin 2\theta$	Write model for horizontal distance.
$= \frac{105^2}{32} \sin(2 \cdot 50^\circ)$	Substitute 105 for v and 50° for θ.
≈ 339	Use technology.

▶ The golf ball travels a horizontal distance of about 339 feet.

SELF-ASSESSMENT

1 I do not understand. 2 I can do it with help. 3 I can do it on my own. 4 I can teach someone else.

Sketch the angle. Then find its reference angle.

9. 210° **10.** -260° **11.** $\frac{-7\pi}{9}$ **12.** $\frac{15\pi}{4}$

Evaluate the function without using technology.

13. $\sin 315^\circ$ **14.** $\cos(-210^\circ)$ **15.** $\sec \frac{11\pi}{4}$ **16.** $\tan\left(-\frac{5\pi}{3}\right)$

17. Use the model in Example 5. A track and field long jumper jumps at an angle of 22° with an initial speed of 27 feet per second. Another jumper jumps at an angle of 20° with an initial speed of 9 meters per second. Which jumper travels farther horizontally? By how much?

10.3 Practice WITH CalcChat® AND CalcView®

In Exercises 1–6, evaluate the six trigonometric functions of θ. *Example 1*

1. 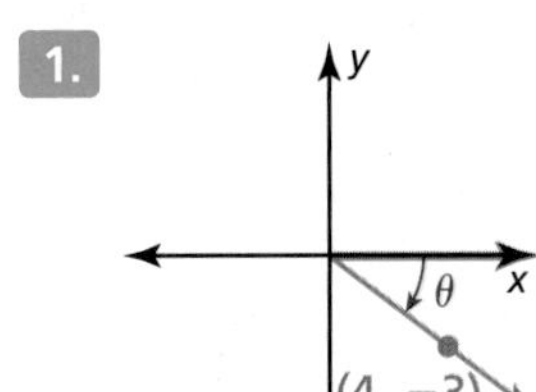

2. 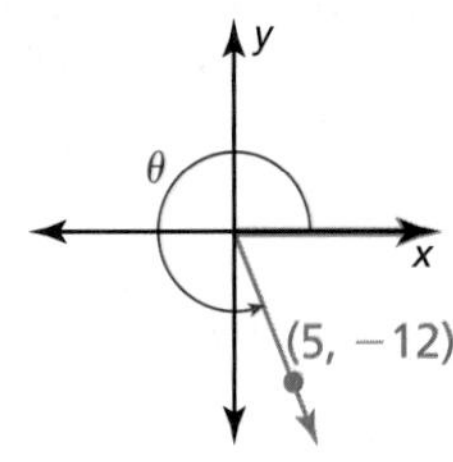

3. 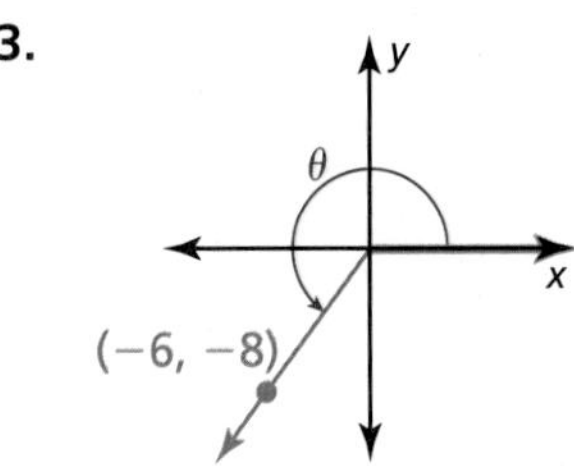

4. 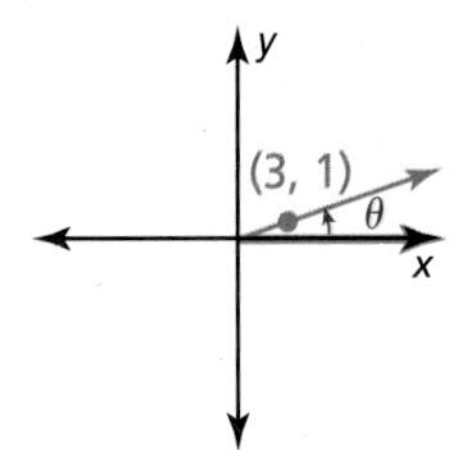

5. 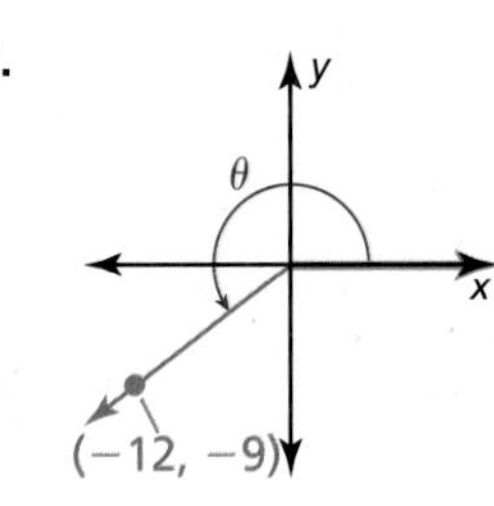

6. 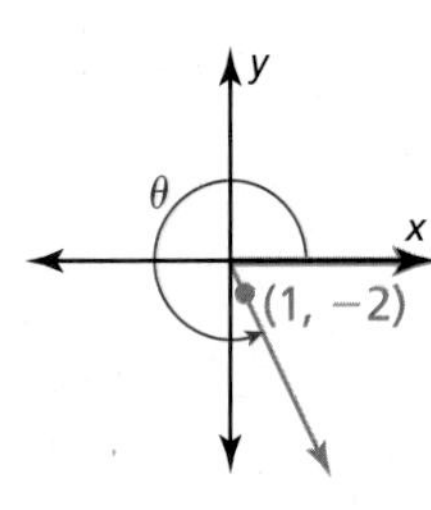

In Exercises 7–12, use the unit circle to evaluate the six trigonometric functions of θ. *Example 2*

7. $\theta = 0°$
8. $\theta = 540°$
9. $\theta = \frac{\pi}{2}$
10. $\theta = \frac{7\pi}{2}$
11. $\theta = -270°$
12. $\theta = -2\pi$

In Exercises 13–18, sketch the angle. Then find its reference angle. *Example 3*

13. $-100°$
14. $150°$
15. $\frac{23\pi}{4}$
16. $\frac{8\pi}{3}$
17. $-370°$
18. $-\frac{19\pi}{6}$

19. **ERROR ANALYSIS** Let $(-3, 2)$ be a point on the terminal side of an angle θ in standard position. Describe and correct the error in finding $\tan \theta$.

$$\tan \theta = \frac{x}{y} = -\frac{3}{2}$$

20. **ERROR ANALYSIS** Describe and correct the error in finding a reference angle θ' for $\theta = 650°$.

θ is coterminal with $290°$, whose terminal side lies in Quadrant IV.

So, $\theta' = 290° - 270° = 20°$.

In Exercises 21–32, evaluate the function without using technology. *Example 4*

21. $\sin 45°$
22. $\cot 60°$
23. $\sec 135°$
24. $\tan 240°$
25. $\sin(-150°)$
26. $\csc(-420°)$
27. $\cos \frac{\pi}{4}$
28. $\tan \frac{\pi}{6}$
29. $\tan\left(-\frac{3\pi}{4}\right)$
30. $\cot\left(\frac{-8\pi}{3}\right)$
31. $\cos \frac{7\pi}{4}$
32. $\sec \frac{11\pi}{6}$

In Exercises 33–36, use the model for horizontal distance given in Example 5. *Example 5*

33. You kick a football at an angle of 60° with an initial speed of 49 feet per second. Estimate the horizontal distance traveled by the football.

34. The "frogbot" is a robot designed for exploring rough terrain on other planets. It can jump at a 45° angle with an initial speed of 14 feet per second. Estimate the horizontal distance the frogbot can jump on Earth.

35. At what speed must the in-line skater launch himself off the ramp in order to land on the other side of the ramp?

36. To win a javelin throwing competition, your last throw must travel a horizontal distance of at least 100 feet. You release the javelin at a 40° angle with an initial speed of 71 feet per second. Do you win the competition? Justify your answer.

37. MODELING REAL LIFE A rock climber is using a rock climbing treadmill that is 10 feet long. The climber begins by lying horizontally on the treadmill, which is then rotated about its midpoint by 110° so that the rock climber is climbing toward the top. If the midpoint of the treadmill is 6 feet above the ground, how high above the ground is the top of the treadmill?

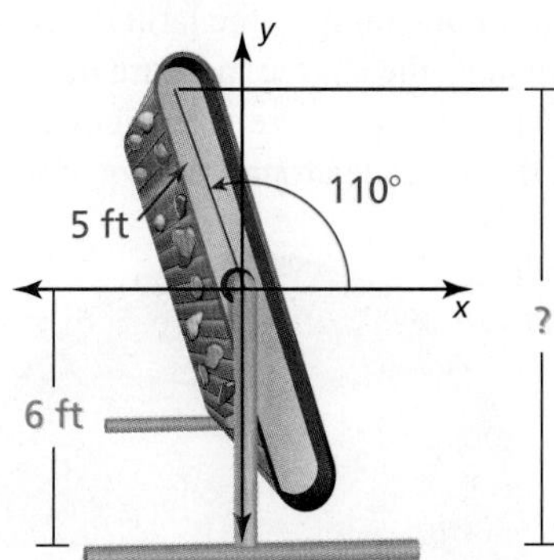

38. MODELING REAL LIFE A Ferris wheel has a radius of 75 feet. You board a car at the bottom of the Ferris wheel, which is 10 feet above the ground, and rotate 255° counterclockwise before the ride temporarily stops. How high above the ground are you when the ride stops? Explain your reasoning.

39. DRAWING CONCLUSIONS A sprinkler at ground level is used to water a garden. The water leaving the sprinkler has an initial speed of 25 feet per second.

a. Use the model for horizontal distance given in Example 5 to complete the table.

Angle of sprinkler, θ	Horizontal distance water travels, d
30°	
35°	
40°	
45°	
50°	
55°	
60°	

b. Which value of θ appears to maximize the horizontal distance traveled by the water? Use the model for horizontal distance and the unit circle to explain why your answer makes sense.

c. Compare the horizontal distance traveled by the water when $\theta = (45 - k)°$ with the distance when $\theta = (45 + k)°$, for $0 < k < 45$.

40. MODELING REAL LIFE Your school's marching band is performing at halftime during a football game. In the last formation, the band members form a circle 100 feet wide in the center of the field. You start at a point on the circle 100 feet from the goal line, march 300° around the circle, and then walk toward the goal line to exit the field. How far from the goal line are you at the point where you leave the circle?

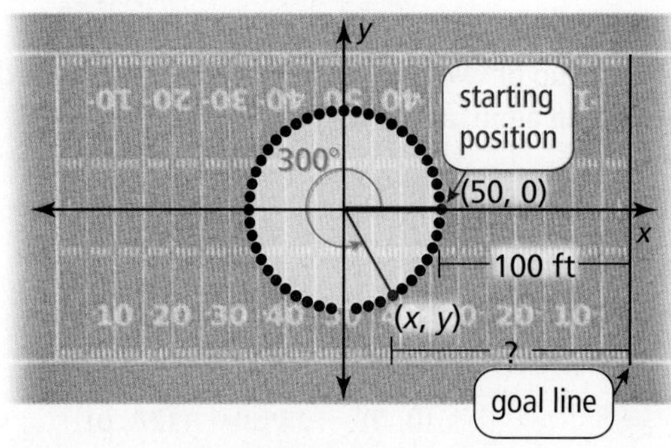

41. ANALYZING RELATIONSHIPS Use symmetry and the given information to label the coordinates of the other points corresponding to special angles on the unit circle.

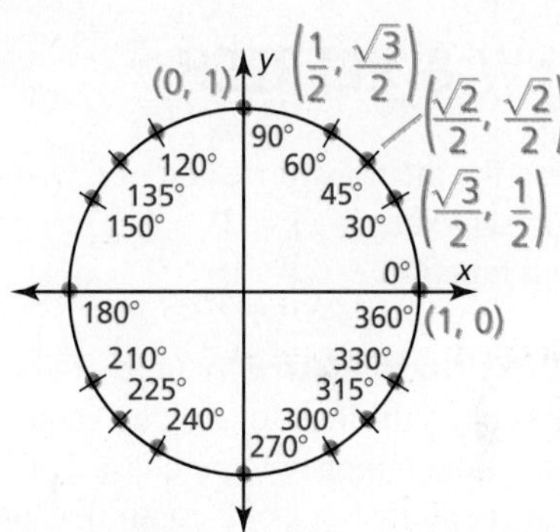

42. THOUGHT PROVOKING
Describe all values of θ that satisfy each set of conditions.

a. $\sin \theta > 0$, $\cos \theta < 0$, and $\tan \theta > 0$

b. $\sin \theta > 0$, $\cos \theta < 0$, and $\tan \theta < 0$

43. CRITICAL THINKING Write $\tan \theta$ as the ratio of two other trigonometric functions. Use this ratio to explain why $\tan 90°$ is undefined but $\cot 90° = 0$.

44. MAKING AN ARGUMENT Is $\theta = 60°$ the only solution of the equation $\tan \theta = \sqrt{3}$? Explain.

45. MP STRUCTURE A line with slope m passes through the origin. An angle θ in standard position has a terminal side that coincides with the line. Use a trigonometric function to relate the slope of the line to the angle.

46. HOW DO YOU SEE IT? Determine whether each of the six trigonometric functions of θ is *positive*, *negative*, or *zero*. Explain your reasoning.

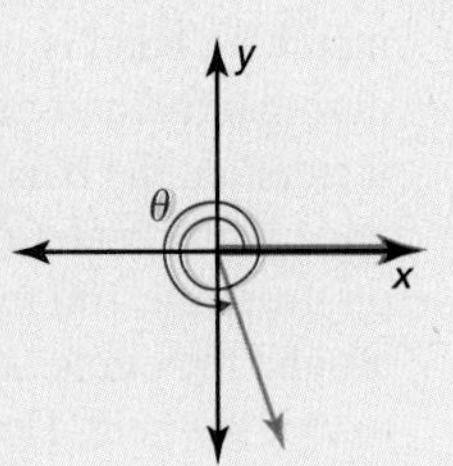

47. **MP PROBLEM SOLVING** An ozone molecule is made up of two oxygen atoms bonded to a third oxygen atom, as shown.

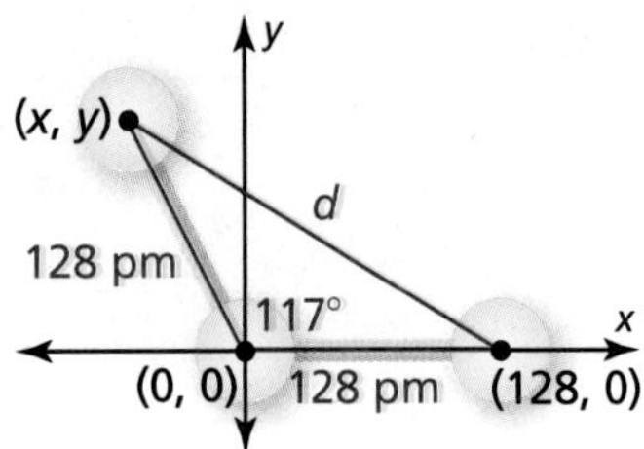

Find the distance d (in picometers) between the centers of the two unbonded oxygen atoms.

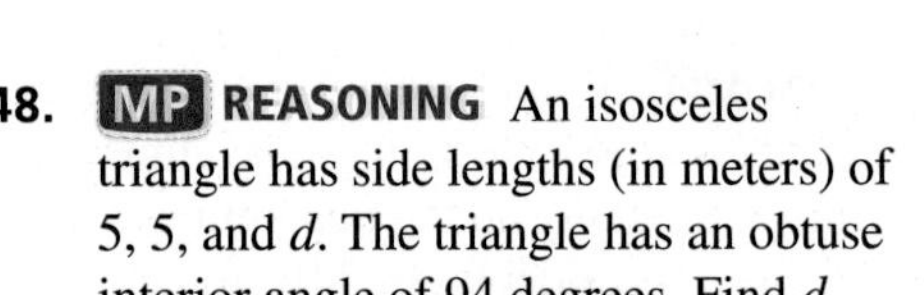

48. **MP REASONING** An isosceles triangle has side lengths (in meters) of 5, 5, and d. The triangle has an obtuse interior angle of 94 degrees. Find d.

49. **DIG DEEPER** The latitude of a point on Earth is the degree measure of the shortest arc from that point to the equator. For example, the latitude of point P in the diagram equals the degree measure of arc PE. At what latitude θ is the circumference of the circle of latitude at P half the distance around the equator?

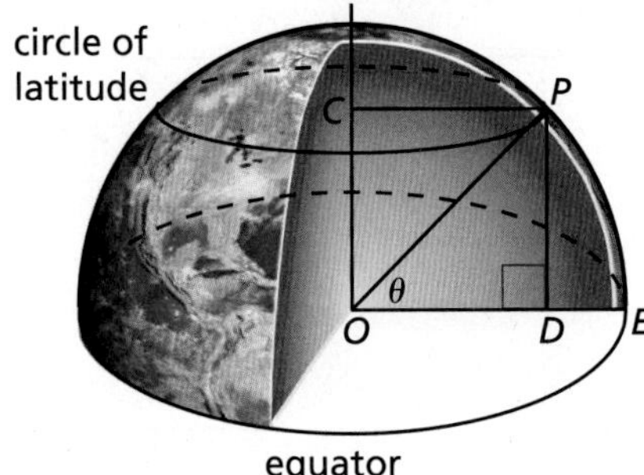

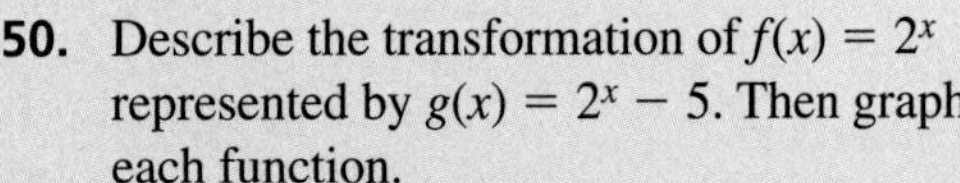

REVIEW & REFRESH

50. Describe the transformation of $f(x) = 2^x$ represented by $g(x) = 2^x - 5$. Then graph each function.

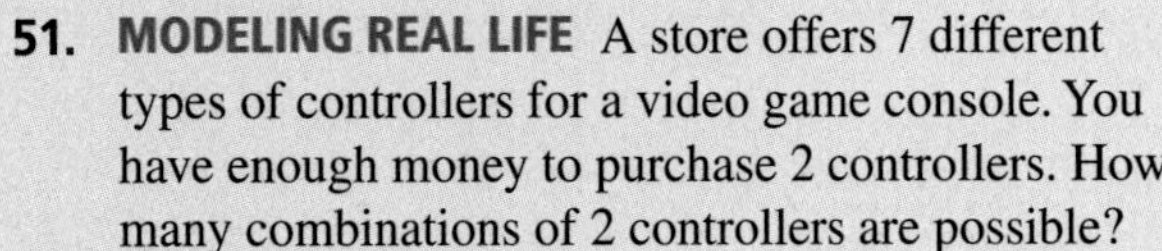

51. **MODELING REAL LIFE** A store offers 7 different types of controllers for a video game console. You have enough money to purchase 2 controllers. How many combinations of 2 controllers are possible?

52. Graph $f(x) = \sqrt{\frac{1}{2}x}$. Find the domain and range of the function.

53. Write an equation of the parabola in vertex form that passes through (0, 10) and has vertex (5, 25).

54. Find the value of x for the right triangle.

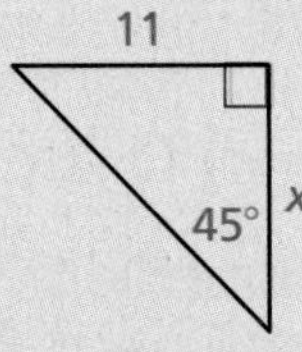

55. Sketch $-195°$. Then find its reference angle.

56. Let $f(x) = \sqrt{3x + 7}$ and $g(x) = x^2 - 1$. Find $f(g(2))$.

57. Write an equation of the parabola.

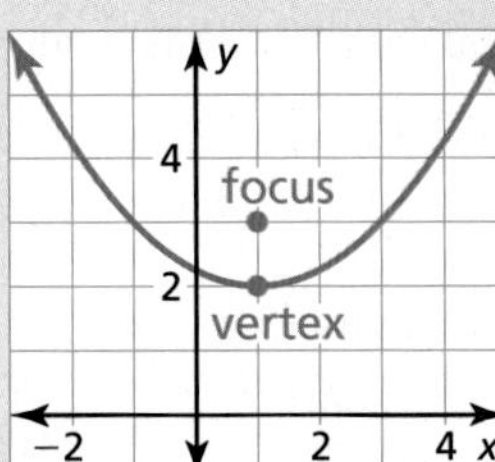

58. Using radian measure, give one positive angle and one negative angle that are coterminal with the angle shown. Justify your answers.

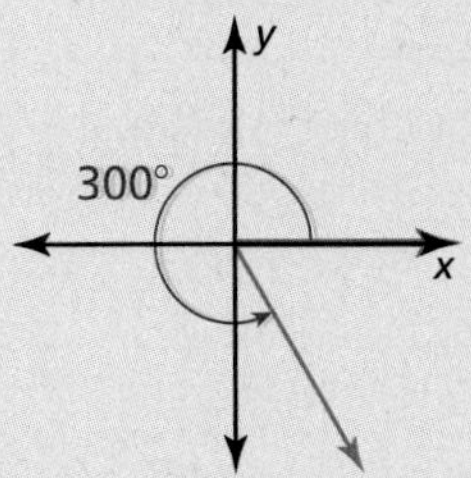

59. Find $(2x^2 - 11x - 6) \div (x - 6)$.

60. Find $\dfrac{3x}{x - 2} - \dfrac{6}{x - 2}$.

10.4 Graphing Sine and Cosine Functions

Learning Target Describe and graph sine and cosine functions.

Success Criteria
- I can identify characteristics of sine and cosine functions.
- I can graph transformations of sine and cosine functions.

EXPLORE IT! Graphing the Sine Function

Work with a partner.

a. Complete the table for $y = \sin x$, where x is an angle measure in radians.

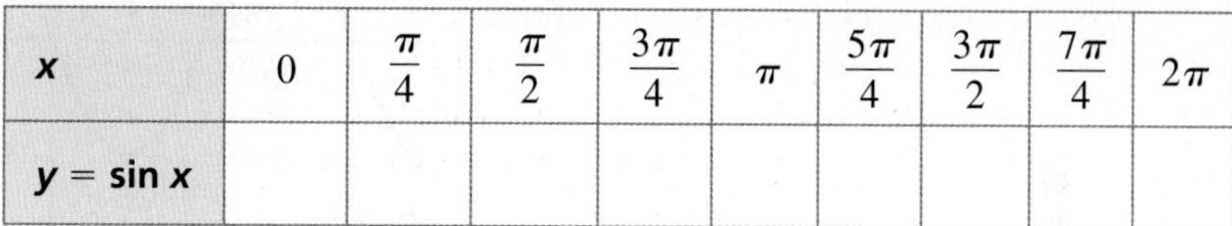

x	0	$\frac{\pi}{4}$	$\frac{\pi}{2}$	$\frac{3\pi}{4}$	π	$\frac{5\pi}{4}$	$\frac{3\pi}{2}$	$\frac{7\pi}{4}$	2π
$y = \sin x$									

b. Plot the points (x, y) from part (a). Draw a smooth curve through the points to sketch the graph of $y = \sin x$. Make several observations about the graph.

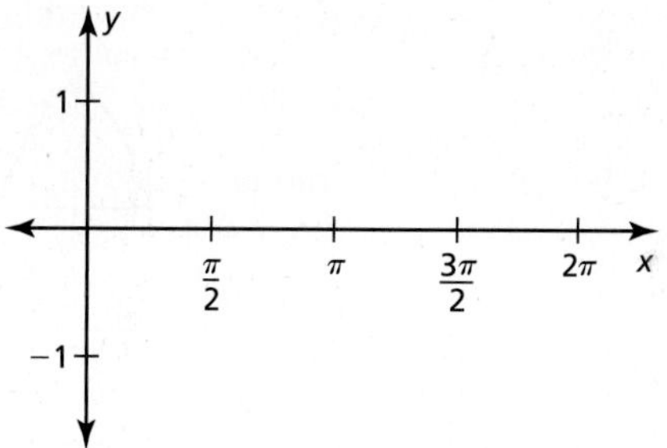

c. In the previous section, you learned how to use the unit circle in the coordinate plane to evaluate trigonometric functions of any angle. Use the graphing tool at *BigIdeasMath.com* to graph $y = \sin x$. Examine the graph when $x < 0$ and when $x > 2\pi$. What do you notice? Explain why the graph behaves this way.

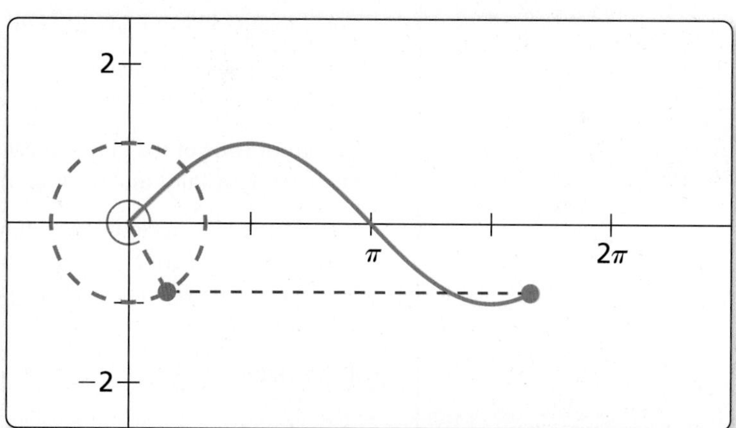

Available at *BigIdeasMath.com*

Math Practice

Use a Graph

How would you describe the end behavior of the graph of $y = \sin x$?

Exploring Characteristics of Sine and Cosine Functions

GO DIGITAL

Vocabulary

AZ VOCAB

amplitude, *p. 546*
periodic function, *p. 546*
cycle, *p. 546*
period, *p. 546*
phase shift, *p. 548*
midline, *p. 548*

The graphs of sine and cosine functions are related to the graphs of the parent functions $y = \sin x$ and $y = \cos x$, which are shown below.

x	-2π	$-\frac{3\pi}{2}$	$-\pi$	$-\frac{\pi}{2}$	0	$\frac{\pi}{2}$	π	$\frac{3\pi}{2}$	2π
$y = \sin x$	0	1	0	−1	0	1	0	−1	0
$y = \cos x$	1	0	−1	0	1	0	−1	0	1

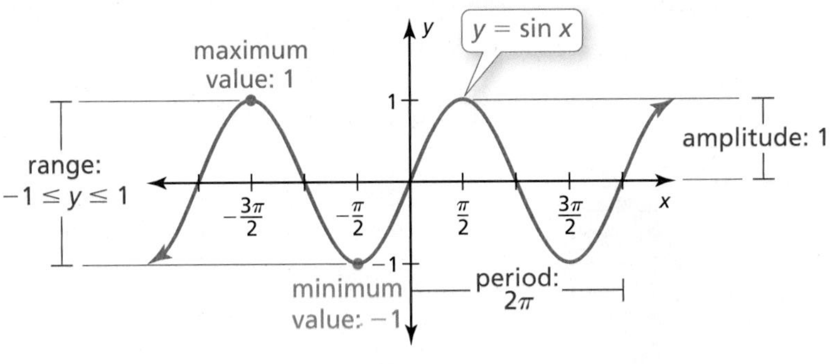

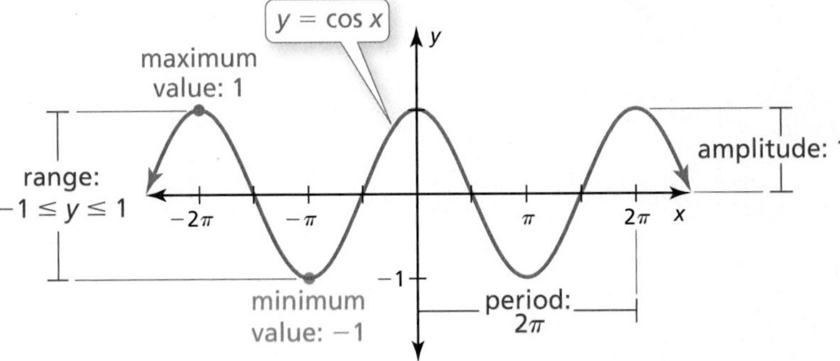

KEY IDEA

Characteristics of $y = \sin x$ and $y = \cos x$

- The domain of each function is all real numbers.
- The range of each function is $-1 \le y \le 1$. So, the minimum value of each function is -1 and the maximum value is 1.
- The **amplitude** of the graph of each function is one-half of the difference of the maximum value and the minimum value, or $\frac{1}{2}[1 - (-1)] = 1$.
- Each function is **periodic**, which means that its graph has a repeating pattern. The shortest repeating portion of the graph is called a **cycle**. The horizontal length of each cycle is called the **period**. The graph of each function has a period of 2π.
- The x-intercepts for $y = \sin x$ occur when $x = 0, \pm\pi, \pm 2\pi, \pm 3\pi, \ldots$.
- The x-intercepts for $y = \cos x$ occur when $x = \pm\frac{\pi}{2}, \pm\frac{3\pi}{2}, \pm\frac{5\pi}{2}, \pm\frac{7\pi}{2}, \ldots$.

Stretching and Shrinking Sine and Cosine Functions

$y = a \sin bx$

$y = a \cos bx$

vertical stretch or shrink by a factor of a

horizontal stretch or shrink by a factor of $\frac{1}{b}$

You can transform graphs of trigonometric functions in the same way you transformed graphs of functions previously. The graphs of $y = a \sin bx$ and $y = a \cos bx$ represent transformations of their parent functions. The value of a indicates a vertical stretch or shrink and changes the amplitude of the graph. The value of b indicates a horizontal stretch or shrink and changes the period of the graph.

KEY IDEAS

Amplitude and Period

The amplitude and period of the graphs of $y = a \sin bx$ and $y = a \cos bx$, where a and b are nonzero real numbers, are as follows:

Amplitude $= |a|$ Period $= \dfrac{2\pi}{|b|}$

Each graph below shows five key points that you can use to sketch the graphs of $y = a \sin bx$ and $y = a \cos bx$ for $a > 0$ and $b > 0$. These points partition the interval $0 \leq x \leq \frac{2\pi}{b}$ into four equal parts. The x-intercepts, maximum, and minimum occur at these points.

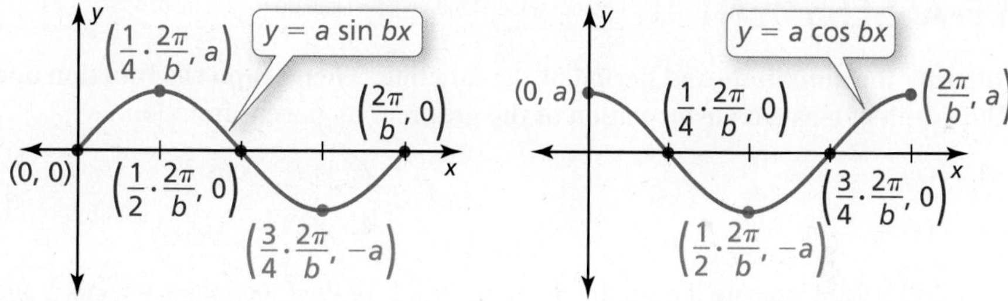

EXAMPLE 1 **Graphing a Sine Function**

Identify the amplitude and period of $g(x) = 4 \sin x$. Then graph the function and describe the graph of g as a transformation of the graph of $f(x) = \sin x$.

REMEMBER

A vertical stretch of a graph does not change its x-intercept(s). So, it makes sense that the x-intercepts of $g(x) = 4 \sin x$ and $f(x) = \sin x$ are the same.

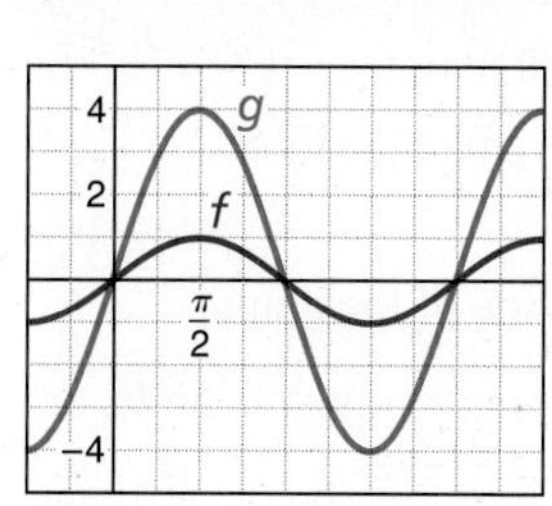

SOLUTION

The function is of the form $g(x) = a \sin bx$, where $a = 4$ and $b = 1$. So, the amplitude is $|a| = 4$ and the period is $\dfrac{2\pi}{|b|} = \dfrac{2\pi}{1} = 2\pi$.

x-Intercepts: $(0, 0)$; $\left(\frac{1}{2} \cdot 2\pi, 0\right) = (\pi, 0)$; $(2\pi, 0)$

Maximum: $\left(\frac{1}{4} \cdot 2\pi, 4\right) = \left(\frac{\pi}{2}, 4\right)$

Minimum: $\left(\frac{3}{4} \cdot 2\pi, -4\right) = \left(\frac{3\pi}{2}, -4\right)$

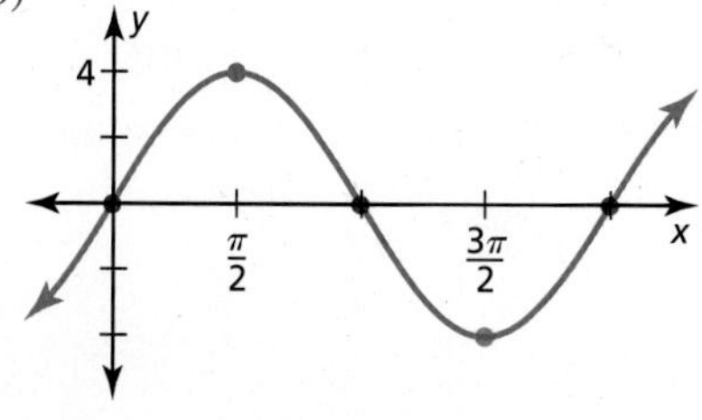

▶ The graph of g is a vertical stretch by a factor of 4 of the graph of f.

EXAMPLE 2 Graphing a Cosine Function 

Identify the amplitude and period of $g(x) = \frac{1}{2} \cos 2\pi x$. Then graph the function and describe the graph of g as a transformation of the graph of $f(x) = \cos x$.

SOLUTION

The function is of the form $g(x) = a \cos bx$, where $a = \frac{1}{2}$ and $b = 2\pi$. So, the amplitude is $|a| = \frac{1}{2}$ and the period is $\frac{2\pi}{|b|} = \frac{2\pi}{2\pi} = 1$.

STUDY TIP

After you have drawn one complete cycle of the graph in Example 2 on the interval $0 \le x \le 1$, you can extend the graph by repeating the cycle as many times as desired to the left and right of $0 \le x \le 1$.

x-Intercepts: $\left(\frac{1}{4} \bullet 1, 0\right) = \left(\frac{1}{4}, 0\right)$; $\left(\frac{3}{4} \bullet 1, 0\right) = \left(\frac{3}{4}, 0\right)$

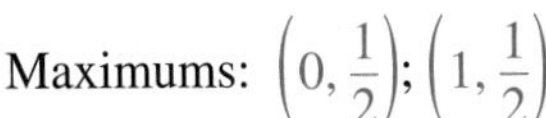

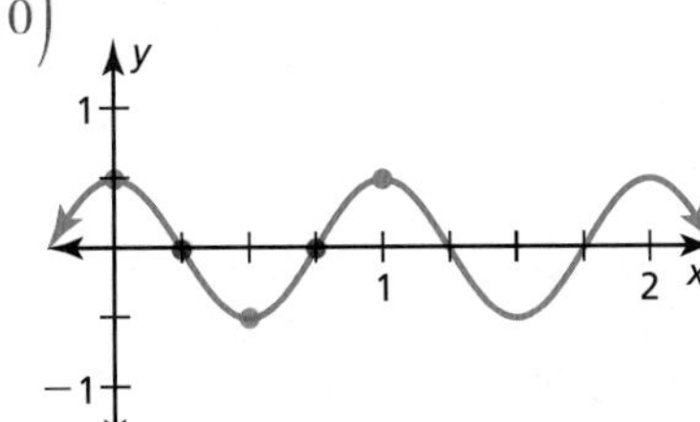

Maximums: $\left(0, \frac{1}{2}\right)$; $\left(1, \frac{1}{2}\right)$

Minimum: $\left(\frac{1}{2} \bullet 1, -\frac{1}{2}\right) = \left(\frac{1}{2}, -\frac{1}{2}\right)$

▶ The graph of g is a vertical shrink by a factor of $\frac{1}{2}$ and a horizontal shrink by a factor of $\frac{1}{2\pi}$ of the graph of f.

SELF-ASSESSMENT

1 I do not understand. 2 I can do it with help. 3 I can do it on my own. 4 I can teach someone else.

Identify the amplitude and period of the function. Then graph the function and describe the graph of g as a transformation of the graph of its parent function.

1. $g(x) = \frac{1}{4} \sin x$
2. $g(x) = \cos 2x$
3. $g(x) = 2 \sin \pi x$
4. $g(x) = \frac{1}{3} \cos \frac{1}{2}x$
5. **WRITING** Compare the amplitudes and periods of the functions $y = \frac{1}{2} \cos x$ and $y = 3 \cos 2x$.

Translating Sine and Cosine Functions

The graphs of $y = a \sin b(x - h) + k$ and $y = a \cos b(x - h) + k$ represent translations h units left or right and k units up or down of $y = a \sin bx$ and $y = a \cos bx$. A horizontal translation of a periodic function is called a **phase shift**.

KEY IDEA

Graphing $y = a \sin b(x - h) + k$ and $y = a \cos b(x - h) + k$

To graph $y = a \sin b(x - h) + k$ or $y = a \cos b(x - h) + k$, where $a > 0$ and $b > 0$, follow these steps:

Step 1 Identify the amplitude a, the period $\frac{2\pi}{b}$, the horizontal shift h, and the vertical shift k of the graph.

Step 2 Draw the horizontal line $y = k$, called the **midline** of the graph.

Step 3 Find the five key points by translating the key points of $y = a \sin bx$ or $y = a \cos bx$ horizontally h units and vertically k units.

Step 4 Draw the graph through the five translated key points.

EXAMPLE 3 Graphing a Vertical Translation

Graph $g(x) = 2 \sin 4x + 3$.

SOLUTION

Step 1 Identify the amplitude, period, horizontal shift, and vertical shift.

Amplitude: $a = 2$ Horizontal shift: $h = 0$

Period: $\frac{2\pi}{b} = \frac{2\pi}{4} = \frac{\pi}{2}$ Vertical shift: $k = 3$

Step 2 Draw the midline of the graph, $y = 3$.

Step 3 Find the five key points.

On $y = k$: $(0, 0 + 3) = (0, 3)$; $\left(\frac{\pi}{4}, 0 + 3\right) = \left(\frac{\pi}{4}, 3\right)$; $\left(\frac{\pi}{2}, 0 + 3\right) = \left(\frac{\pi}{2}, 3\right)$

Maximum: $\left(\frac{\pi}{8}, 2 + 3\right) = \left(\frac{\pi}{8}, 5\right)$

Minimum: $\left(\frac{3\pi}{8}, -2 + 3\right) = \left(\frac{3\pi}{8}, 1\right)$

Step 4 Draw the graph through the key points.

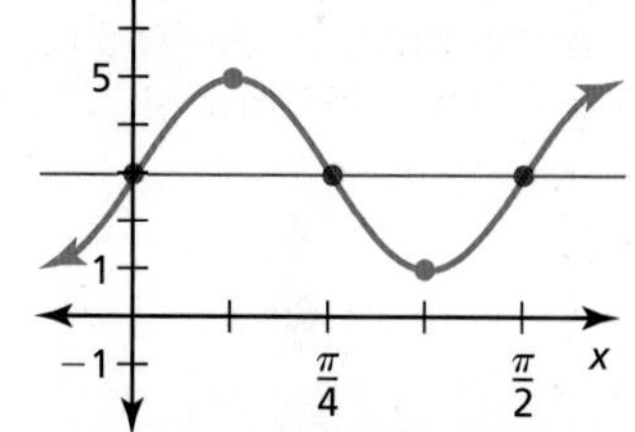

> **Math Practice**
> **Look for Structure**
> How are the five key points of g related to the five key points of $f(x) = 2 \sin 4x$? Explain.

EXAMPLE 4 Graphing a Horizontal Translation

Graph $g(x) = 5 \cos \frac{1}{2}(x - 3\pi)$.

SOLUTION

Step 1 Identify the amplitude, period, horizontal shift, and vertical shift.

Amplitude: $a = 5$ Horizontal shift: $h = 3\pi$

Period: $\frac{2\pi}{b} = \frac{2\pi}{\frac{1}{2}} = 4\pi$ Vertical shift: $k = 0$

Step 2 Draw the midline of the graph. Because $k = 0$, the midline is the x-axis.

Step 3 Find the five key points.

On $y = k$: $(\pi + 3\pi, 0) = (4\pi, 0)$; $(3\pi + 3\pi, 0) = (6\pi, 0)$

Maximums: $(0 + 3\pi, 5) = (3\pi, 5)$; $(4\pi + 3\pi, 5) = (7\pi, 5)$

Minimum: $(2\pi + 3\pi, -5) = (5\pi, -5)$

Step 4 Draw the graph through the key points.

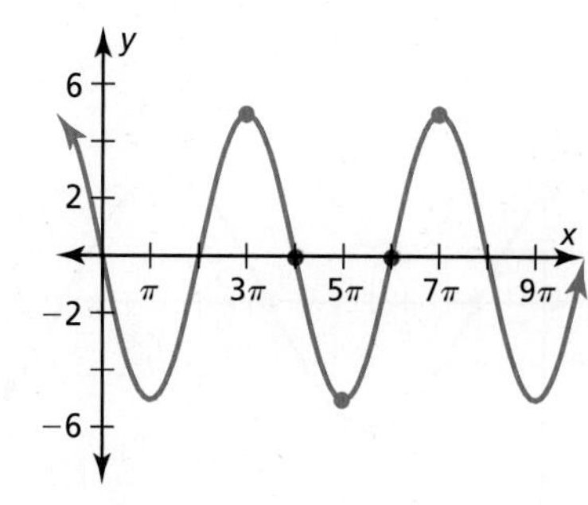

> **Math Practice**
> **Look for Structure**
> How are the five key points of g related to the five key points of $f(x) = 5 \cos \frac{1}{2}x$? Explain.

SELF-ASSESSMENT

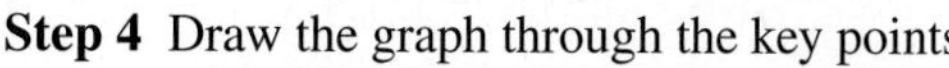

Graph the function.

6. $g(x) = \cos x + 4$
7. $g(x) = \frac{1}{2} \sin\left(x - \frac{\pi}{2}\right)$
8. $g(x) = \sin(x + \pi) - 1$

Reflecting Sine and Cosine Functions

You have graphed functions of the form $y = a \sin b(x - h) + k$ and $y = a \cos b(x - h) + k$, where $a > 0$ and $b > 0$. To see what happens when $a < 0$, consider the graphs of $y = -\sin x$ and $y = -\cos x$.

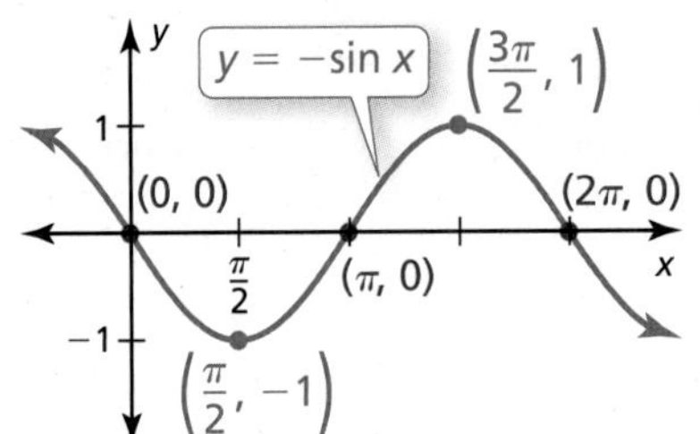

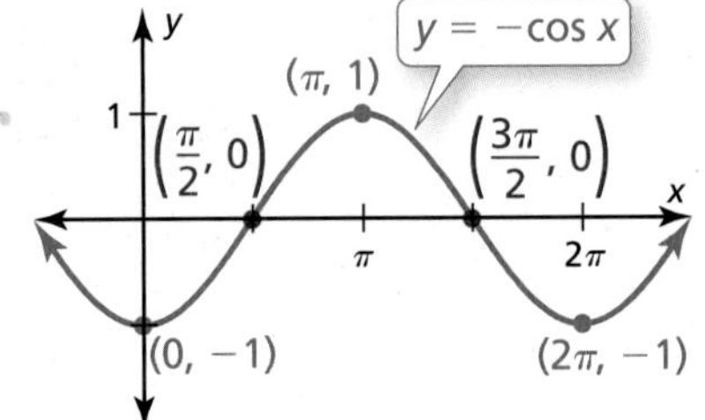

REMEMBER

This result makes sense because the graph of $y = -f(x)$ is a reflection in the x-axis of the graph of $y = f(x)$.

The graphs are reflections of the graphs of $y = \sin x$ and $y = \cos x$ in the x-axis. In general, when $a < 0$, the graphs of $y = a \sin b(x - h) + k$ and $y = a \cos b(x - h) + k$ are reflections of the graphs of $y = |a| \sin b(x - h) + k$ and $y = |a| \cos b(x - h) + k$, respectively, in the midline $y = k$.

EXAMPLE 5 Graphing a Reflection

Graph $g(x) = -2 \sin \frac{2}{3}\left(x - \frac{\pi}{2}\right)$.

SOLUTION

Step 1 Identify the amplitude, period, horizontal shift, and vertical shift.

Amplitude: $|a| = |-2| = 2$ Horizontal shift: $h = \frac{\pi}{2}$

Period: $\frac{2\pi}{b} = \frac{2\pi}{\frac{2}{3}} = 3\pi$ Vertical shift: $k = 0$

Step 2 Draw the midline of the graph. Because $k = 0$, the midline is the x-axis.

Step 3 Find the five key points of $f(x) = |-2| \sin \frac{2}{3}\left(x - \frac{\pi}{2}\right)$.

On $y = k$: $\left(0 + \frac{\pi}{2}, 0\right) = \left(\frac{\pi}{2}, 0\right)$; $\left(\frac{3\pi}{2} + \frac{\pi}{2}, 0\right) = (2\pi, 0)$;

$\left(3\pi + \frac{\pi}{2}, 0\right) = \left(\frac{7\pi}{2}, 0\right)$

Maximum: $\left(\frac{3\pi}{4} + \frac{\pi}{2}, 2\right) = \left(\frac{5\pi}{4}, 2\right)$

Minimum: $\left(\frac{9\pi}{4} + \frac{\pi}{2}, -2\right) = \left(\frac{11\pi}{4}, -2\right)$

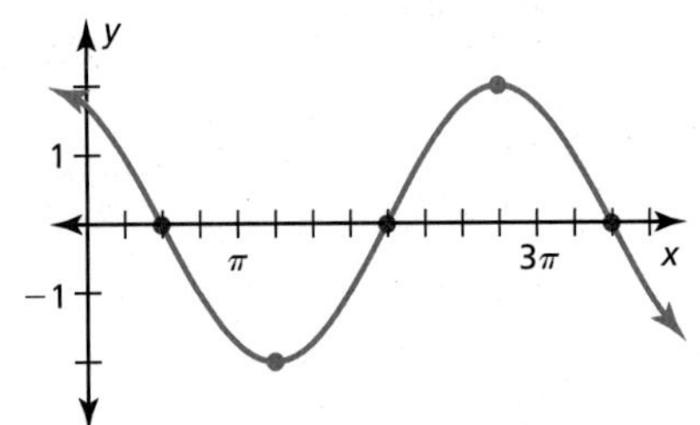

Step 4 Reflect the graph. Because $a < 0$, the graph is reflected in the midline $y = 0$. So, $\left(\frac{5\pi}{4}, 2\right)$ becomes $\left(\frac{5\pi}{4}, -2\right)$ and $\left(\frac{11\pi}{4}, -2\right)$ becomes $\left(\frac{11\pi}{4}, 2\right)$.

Step 5 Draw the graph through the key points.

SELF-ASSESSMENT

1 I do not understand. 2 I can do it with help. 3 I can do it on my own. 4 I can teach someone else.

Graph the function.

9. $g(x) = -\cos\left(x + \frac{\pi}{2}\right)$

10. $g(x) = -3 \sin \frac{1}{2}x + 2$

11. $g(x) = -2 \cos 4x - 1$

10.4 Practice WITH CalcChat® AND CalcView®

MP STRUCTURE In Exercises 1–4, determine whether the graph represents a periodic function. If so, identify the period.

1.
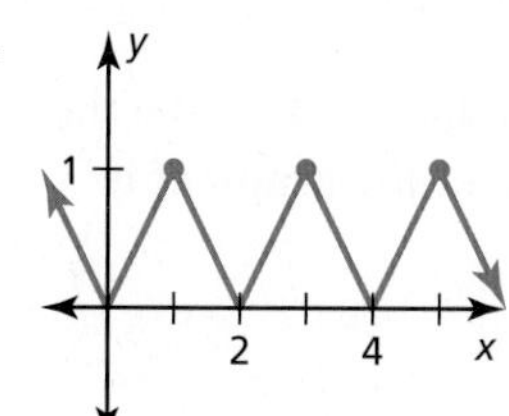

2.
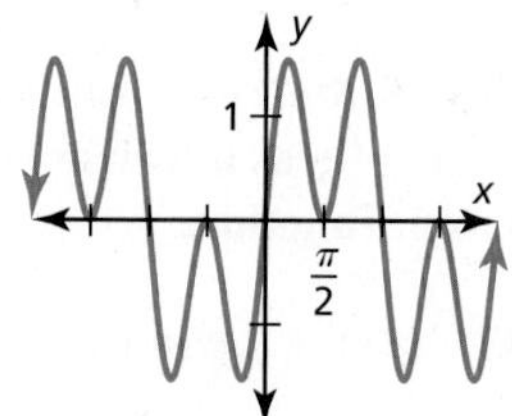

3.
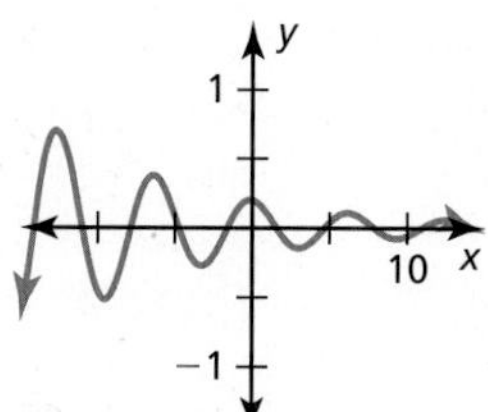

4.
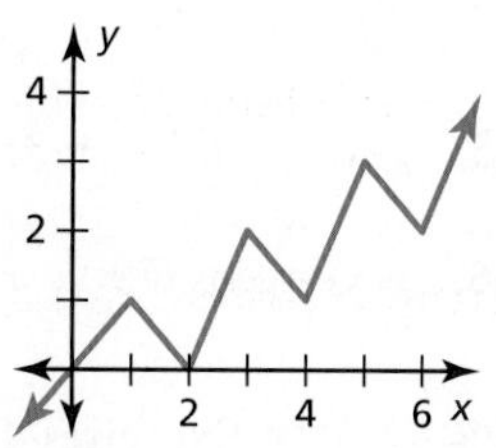

In Exercises 5–8, identify the amplitude and period of the graph of the function.

5.
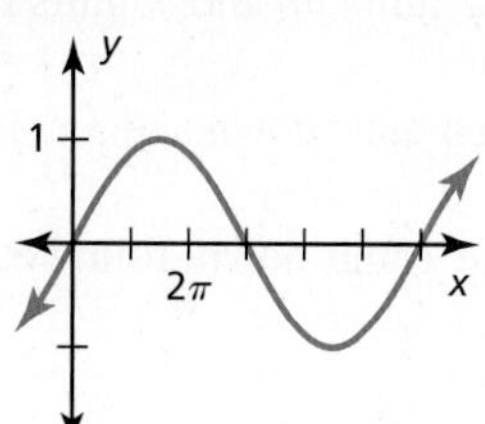

6.
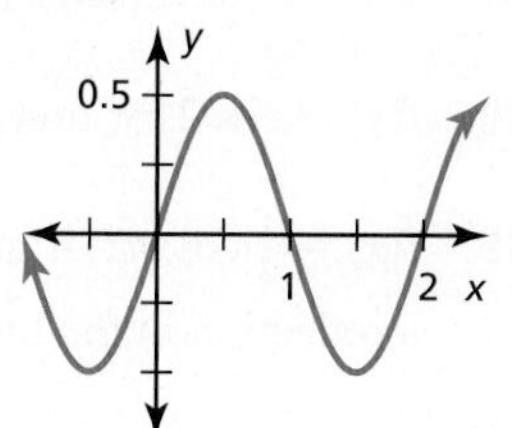

7.
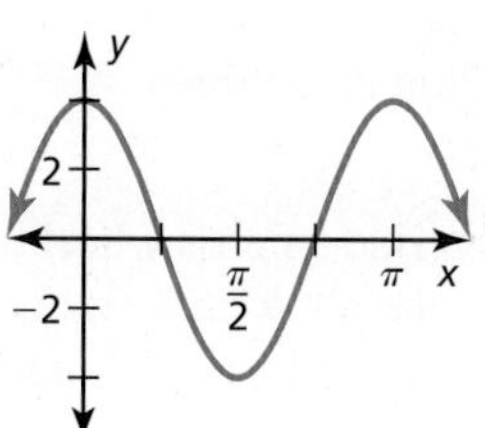

8.
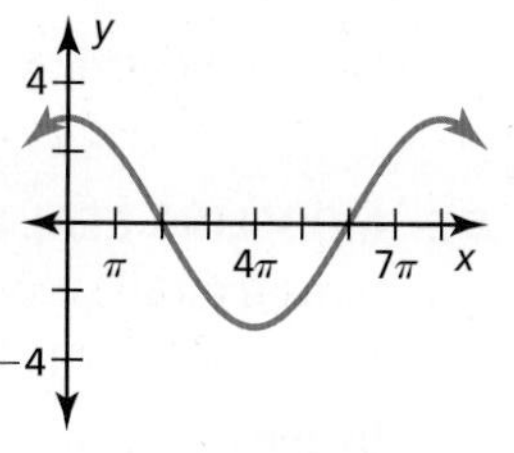

In Exercises 9–16, identify the amplitude and period of the function. Then graph the function and describe the graph of g as a transformation of the graph of its parent function. *Examples 1 and 2*

9. $g(x) = 3 \sin x$

10. $g(x) = 2 \sin x$

11. $g(x) = \cos 3x$

12. $g(x) = \cos 4x$

13. $g(x) = \sin 2\pi x$

14. $g(x) = 3 \sin 2x$

15. $g(x) = \frac{1}{3} \cos 4x$

16. $g(x) = \frac{1}{2} \cos 4\pi x$

17. **COLLEGE PREP** Which functions have an amplitude of 4 and a period of 2? Select all that apply.

(A) $y = 4 \cos 2x$

(B) $y = -4 \sin \pi x$

(C) $y = 2 \sin 4x$

(D) $y = 4 \cos \pi x$

18. **WRITING** Write an equation of the form $y = a \sin bx$ so that the graph has the given amplitude and period.

a. amplitude: 1
period: 5

b. amplitude: 10
period: 4

c. amplitude: 2
period: 2π

d. amplitude: $\frac{1}{2}$
period: 3π

19. **MODELING REAL LIFE** The motion of a pendulum can be modeled by the function $d = 4 \cos 8\pi t$, where d is the horizontal displacement (in inches) of the pendulum relative to its position at rest and t is the time (in seconds). Find and interpret the period and amplitude. Then graph the function.

20. **MODELING REAL LIFE** A buoy bobs up and down as waves go past. The vertical displacement y (in feet) of the buoy with respect to sea level can be modeled by $y = 1.75 \cos \frac{\pi}{3}t$, where t is the time (in seconds). Find and interpret the period and amplitude. Then graph the function.

In Exercises 21–30, graph the function. *Examples 3 and 4*

21. $g(x) = \sin x + 2$

22. $g(x) = \cos x - 4$

23. $g(x) = \cos\left(x - \frac{\pi}{2}\right)$

24. $g(x) = \sin\left(x + \frac{\pi}{4}\right)$

25. $g(x) = 2 \cos x - 1$

26. $g(x) = 3 \sin x + 1$

27. $g(x) = \sin 2(x + \pi)$

28. $g(x) = \cos 2(x - \pi)$

29. $g(x) = \sin \frac{1}{2}(x + 2\pi) + 3$

30. $g(x) = \cos \frac{1}{2}(x - 3\pi) - 5$

31. **ERROR ANALYSIS** Describe and correct the error in finding the period of the function $y = \frac{1}{2} \sin 4x$.

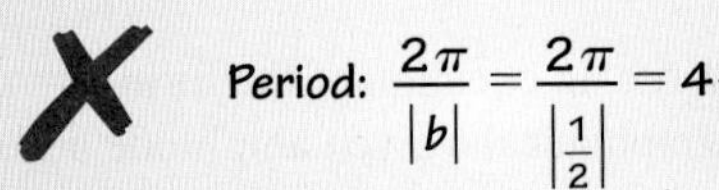

32. **ERROR ANALYSIS** Describe and correct the error in determining the point where the maximum value of the function $y = 2 \sin\left(x - \frac{\pi}{2}\right)$ occurs.

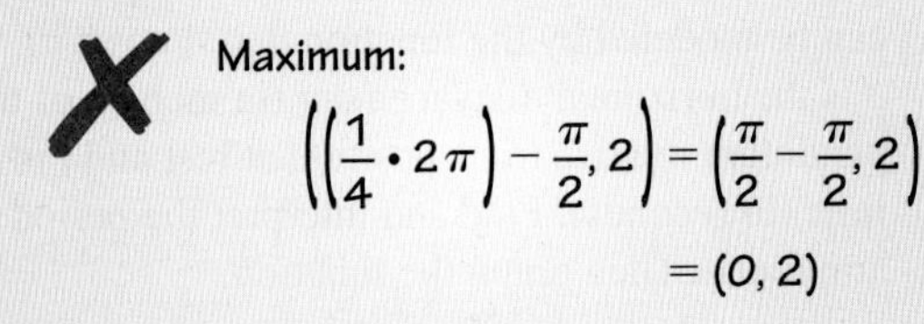

In Exercises 33–40, graph the function. *Example 5*

33. $g(x) = -\cos x + 3$
34. $g(x) = -\sin x - 5$
35. $g(x) = -\sin \frac{1}{2}x - 2$
36. $g(x) = -\cos 2x + 1$
37. $g(x) = -\sin(x - \pi) + 4$
38. $g(x) = -\cos(x + \pi) - 2$
39. $g(x) = -4 \cos\left(x + \frac{\pi}{4}\right) - 1$
40. $g(x) = -5 \sin\left(x - \frac{\pi}{2}\right) + 3$

41. **ANALYZING RELATIONSHIPS** Match each function with its graph. Explain your reasoning.

a. $y = 3 + \sin x$
b. $y = -3 + \cos x$
c. $y = \sin 2\left(x - \frac{\pi}{2}\right)$
d. $y = \cos 2\left(x - \frac{\pi}{2}\right)$

A.
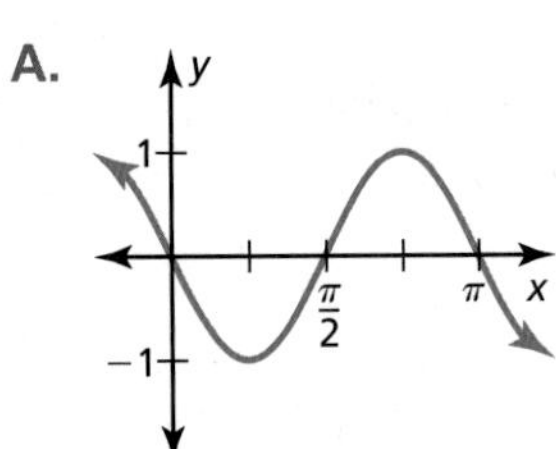

B.
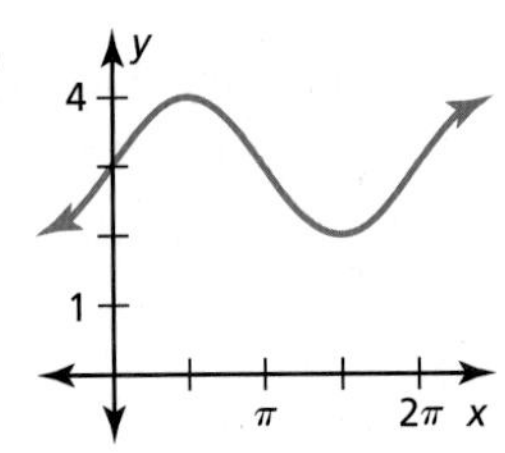

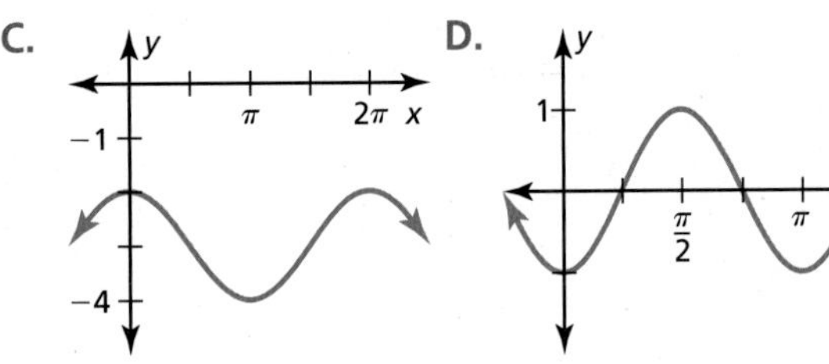

42. **COLLEGE PREP** Which of the following is a point where the maximum value of the graph of $y = -4 \cos\left(x - \frac{\pi}{2}\right)$ occurs?

Ⓐ $\left(-\frac{\pi}{2}, 4\right)$
Ⓑ $\left(\frac{\pi}{2}, 4\right)$
Ⓒ $(0, 4)$
Ⓓ $(\pi, 4)$

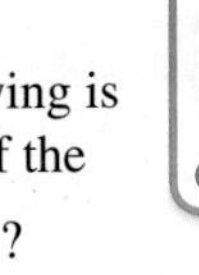

MP STRUCTURE In Exercises 43–46, describe the graph of *g* as a transformation of the graph of its parent function.

43. $g(x) = 2 \cos\left(x - \frac{\pi}{2}\right) + 1$
44. $g(x) = 3 \sin\left(x + \frac{\pi}{4}\right) - 2$
45. $g(x) = \sin 3(x + 3\pi) - 5$
46. $g(x) = \cos 6(x - \pi) + 9$

WRITING In Exercises 47–50, write a rule for *g* that represents the indicated transformations of the graph of *f*.

47. $f(x) = 3 \sin x$; translation 2 units up and π units right
48. $f(x) = \cos 2\pi x$; translation 4 units down and 3 units left
49. $f(x) = \frac{1}{3} \cos \pi x$; translation 1 unit down, followed by a reflection in the line $y = -1$
50. $f(x) = \frac{1}{2} \sin 6x$; translation $\frac{3}{2}$ units down and 1 unit right, followed by a reflection in the line $y = -\frac{3}{2}$

51. **MODELING REAL LIFE** You ride a Ferris wheel that turns for 180 seconds. Your height h (in feet) above the ground at any time t (in seconds) can be modeled by the equation $h = 85 \sin \frac{\pi}{20}(t - 10) + 90$.
    a. Graph the function.
    b. How many cycles does the Ferris wheel make in 180 seconds?
    c. What are your maximum and minimum heights?

52. **MP REASONING** Consider the functions $y = \sin(-x)$ and $y = \cos(-x)$.
    a. Construct a table of values for each function using the quadrantal angles in the interval $-2\pi \le x \le 2\pi$.
    b. Graph each function.
    c. Describe the transformations of the graphs of the parent functions.

53. MODELING REAL LIFE The height h (in feet) of a swing above the ground can be modeled by the function $h = -8 \cos \theta + 10$, where the pivot is 10 feet above the ground, the rope is 8 feet long, and θ is the angle (in degrees) that the rope makes with the vertical. Graph the function. Estimate the height of the swing when θ is 45°.

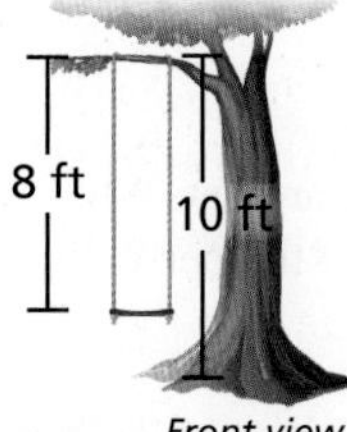

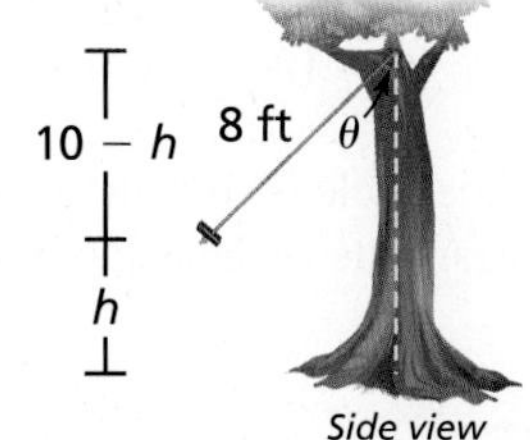

54. DRAWING CONCLUSIONS In a particular region, the population L (in thousands) of lynx (the predator) and the population H (in thousands) of hares (the prey) can be modeled by the equations

$$L = 11.5 + 6.5 \sin \frac{\pi}{5}t$$

$$H = 27.5 + 17.5 \cos \frac{\pi}{5}t$$

where t is the time in years.

a. Determine the ratio of hares to lynx when $t = 0$, 2.5, 5, and 7.5 years.

b. Use the figure to explain how the changes in the two populations appear to be related.

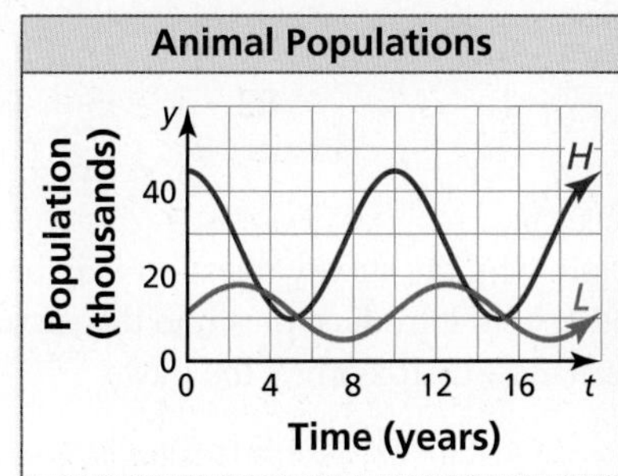

55. MULTIPLE REPRESENTATIONS Find the average rate of change of each function over the interval $0 < x < \pi$.

a.

x	0	$\frac{\pi}{2}$	π	$\frac{3\pi}{2}$	2π
$f(x) = -\cos x$	−1	0	1	0	−1

b.

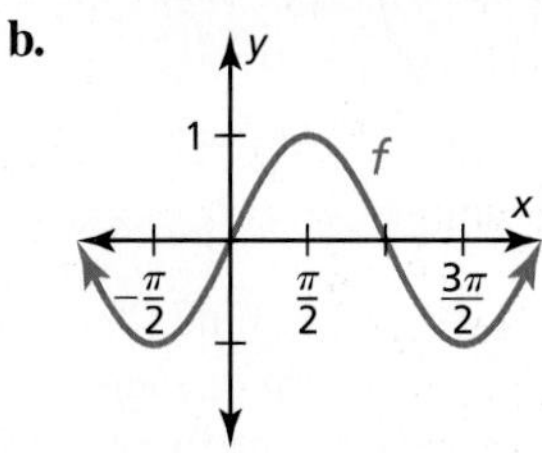

c. $y = 2 \cos x$

56. HOW DO YOU SEE IT?
Use the graph to answer each question.

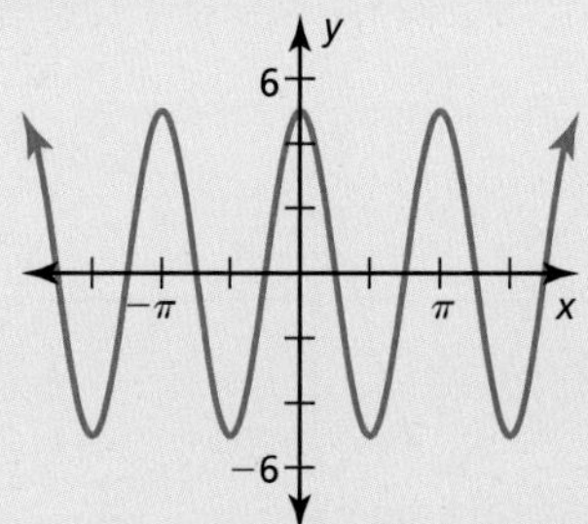

a. Does the graph represent a function of the form $f(x) = a \sin bx$ or $f(x) = a \cos bx$? Explain.

b. Identify the maximum value, minimum value, period, and amplitude of the function.

57. **MP** **USING TOOLS** The portion of the moon visible from Washington, D.C., can be approximated by

$$f(t) = 0.5 \sin \frac{4\pi}{59}(t - 1.3) + 0.5$$

where t is the number of days since January 1, 2020. Use technology to graph the function. On about which days of the year does a full moon occur? Explain.

58. **MP** **USING TOOLS** The water depth d (in feet) for the Bay of Fundy can be modeled by

$$d = 35 - 14 \cos \frac{\pi}{6.2}t$$

where t is the time in hours and $t = 0$ represents midnight. Use technology to graph the function. At what time(s) is the water depth 21 feet? Explain.

59. MAKING AN ARGUMENT Your friend states that for functions of the form $y = a \sin b(x - h) + k$, the values of a and b affect the x-intercepts of the graph of the function. Is your friend correct? Explain.

60. **MP** **PATTERNS** Write an expression in terms of the integer n that represents all the x-intercepts of the graph of the function $y = \cos 2x$. Justify your answer.

61. CRITICAL THINKING Describe a transformation of the graph of $f(x) = \sin x$ that results in the graph of $g(x) = \cos x$.

62. THOUGHT PROVOKING Use technology to find a function of the form $y = \sin b_1x + \cos b_2x$ whose graph matches the graph shown.

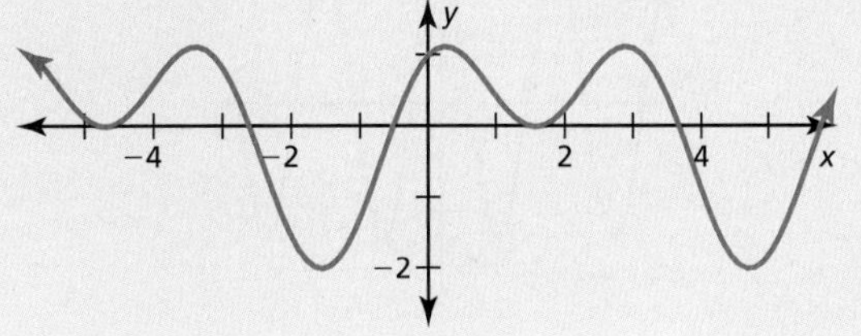

63.  **DIG DEEPER** For a person at rest, the blood pressure P (in millimeters of mercury) at time t (in seconds) is given by

$$P = 100 - 20 \cos \frac{8\pi}{3}t.$$

One cycle is equivalent to one heartbeat. What is the heart rate (in beats per minute) of the person? Explain.

REVIEW & REFRESH

WATCH

In Exercises 64–67, simplify the rational expression, if possible.

64. $\dfrac{x^2 + x - 6}{x + 3}$

65. $\dfrac{x^3 - 2x^2 - 24x}{x^2 - 2x - 24}$

66. $\dfrac{x^2 - 4x - 5}{x^2 + 4x - 5}$

67. $\dfrac{x^2 - 16}{x^2 + x - 20}$

68. Evaluate the six trigonometric functions of θ.

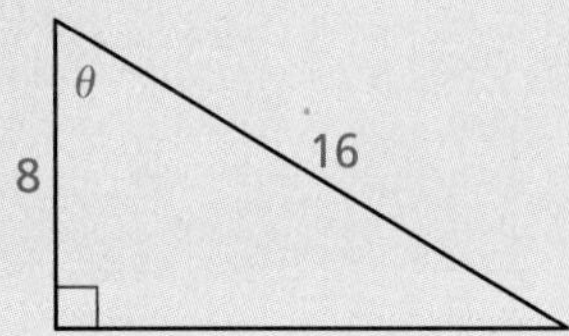

In Exercises 69–72, perform the operation.

69. $(-x^2 + 7x - 4)(2x^2 - x + 8)$

70. $(4x^3 - 9x^2 - 10) + (12x^2 - 8x - 5)$

71. $(x - 3)(x - 8)(3x + 1)$

72. $(5x^4 + 11x^3 - 10x + 4) - (8x^2 + 3 - 2x^3)$

73. MODELING REAL LIFE The table shows the numbers y (in thousands) of visitors to an amusement park x years after the park has been open. Write a function that models the data. Then use your model to predict the number of visitors after 10 years.

x	1	2	3	4	5	6	7
y	8	17	32	76	124	198	308

In Exercises 74 and 75, graph the function.

74. $g(x) = \sin x - 3$

75. $g(x) = -\cos 4x$

In Exercises 76–79, convert the degree measure to radians or the radian measure to degrees.

76. $-60°$

77. $72°$

78. $\dfrac{3\pi}{10}$

79. $-\dfrac{5\pi}{6}$

80. **MP NUMBER SENSE** Events A and B are independent. Let $P(A \text{ and } B) = 0.15$ and $P(A) = 0.5$. Find $P(B)$.

81. Solve $15x^2 - 8x + 1 = 0$.

In Exercises 82 and 83, graph the system of quadratic inequalities.

82. $y > x^2 - 1$
$y \leq -x^2 - x + 6$

83. $y \geq x^2 + 3x - 4$
$y < 2x^2 + 5x + 4$

84. Explain why the survey question may be biased or otherwise introduce bias into the survey. Then describe a way to correct the flaw.

A doctor asks, *"Do you favor government funding to build a new medical clinic?"*

85. Evaluate the six trigonometric functions of θ.

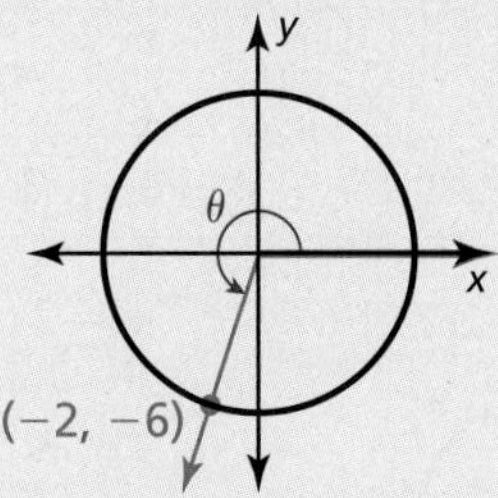

86. Let $f(x) = 5\sqrt{x}$ and $g(x) = -2x^{1/2}$. Find $(f + g)(x)$ and $(f - g)(x)$ and state the domain of each. Then evaluate $(f + g)(9)$ and $(f - g)(9)$.

10.5 Graphing Other Trigonometric Functions

Learning Target Describe and graph tangent, cotangent, secant, and cosecant functions.

Success Criteria
- I can identify characteristics of tangent, cotangent, secant, and cosecant functions.
- I can graph tangent and cotangent functions.
- I can graph secant and cosecant functions.

EXPLORE IT! Graphing the Tangent Function

Work with a partner.

a. Complete the table for $y = \tan x$, where x is an angle measure in radians. What do you notice? Why does this happen? How does this affect the graph of $y = \tan x$?

x	$-\frac{\pi}{6}$	0	$\frac{\pi}{6}$	$\frac{\pi}{4}$	$\frac{\pi}{3}$	$\frac{\pi}{2}$	$\frac{2\pi}{3}$	$\frac{3\pi}{4}$
$y = \tan x$								
x	$\frac{5\pi}{6}$	π	$\frac{7\pi}{6}$	$\frac{5\pi}{4}$	$\frac{4\pi}{3}$	$\frac{3\pi}{2}$	$\frac{5\pi}{3}$	2π
$y = \tan x$								

b. Plot the points (x, y) from part (a). Then sketch the graph of $y = \tan x$. Make several observations about the graph.

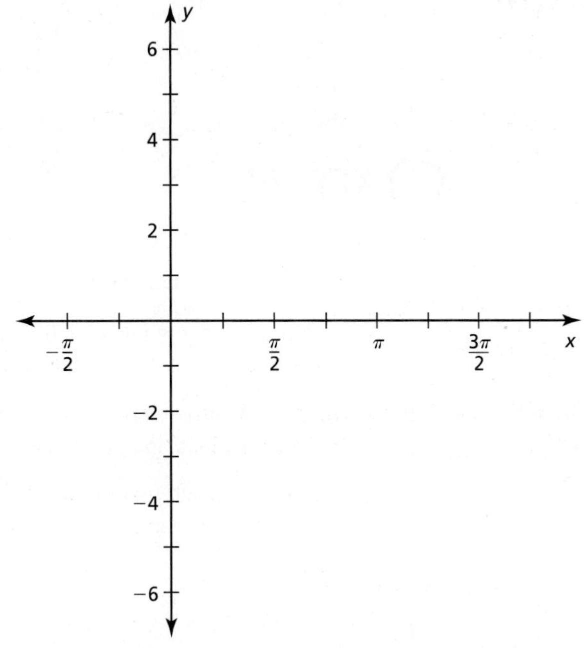

c. Use the graphing tool at *BigIdeasMath.com* to graph $y = \tan x$. How is the graph similar to the graphs of $y = \sin x$ and $y = \cos x$? How is it different? Explain.

Math Practice

Use a Graph

Are the graphs of the sine, cosine, and tangent functions *odd*, *even*, or *neither*?

Exploring Tangent and Cotangent Functions

The graphs of tangent and cotangent functions are related to the graphs of the parent functions $y = \tan x$ and $y = \cot x$, which are graphed below.

← x approaches $-\frac{\pi}{2}$ | x approaches $\frac{\pi}{2}$ →

x	$-\frac{\pi}{2}$	-1.57	-1.5	$-\frac{\pi}{4}$	0	$\frac{\pi}{4}$	1.5	1.57	$\frac{\pi}{2}$
$y = \tan x$	Undef.	-1256	-14.10	-1	0	1	14.10	1256	Undef.

← $\tan x$ approaches $-\infty$ | $\tan x$ approaches $+\infty$ →

STUDY TIP

Notice that

$$\sin x \div \cos x = \frac{\text{opp}}{\text{hyp}} \div \frac{\text{adj}}{\text{hyp}} = \frac{\text{opp}}{\text{hyp}} \cdot \frac{\text{hyp}}{\text{adj}} = \frac{\text{opp}}{\text{adj}} = \tan x.$$

So, $\tan x = \frac{\sin x}{\cos x}$.

Because $\tan x = \frac{\sin x}{\cos x}$, $\tan x$ is undefined for x-values at which $\cos x = 0$, such as $x = \pm\frac{\pi}{2}$. The table indicates that the graph has asymptotes at these values. The table represents one cycle of the graph, so the period is π.

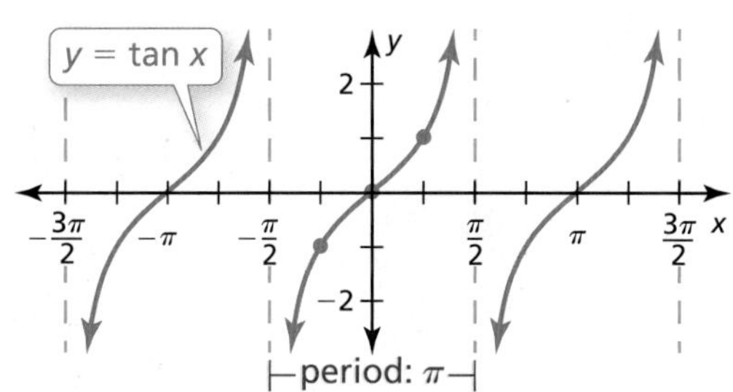

You can use a similar approach to graph $y = \cot x$. Because $\cot x = \frac{\cos x}{\sin x}$, $\cot x$ is undefined for x-values at which $\sin x = 0$, which are multiples of π. The graph has asymptotes at these values. The period of the graph is also π.

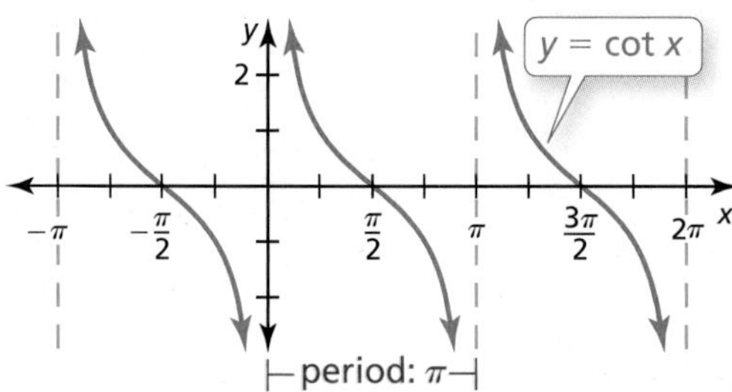

KEY IDEA

Characteristics of $y = \tan x$ and $y = \cot x$

The functions $y = \tan x$ and $y = \cot x$ have the following characteristics.

- The domain of $y = \tan x$ is all real numbers except odd multiples of $\frac{\pi}{2}$. At these x-values, the graph has vertical asymptotes.
- The domain of $y = \cot x$ is all real numbers except multiples of π. At these x-values, the graph has vertical asymptotes.
- The range of each function is all real numbers. So, the functions do not have maximum or minimum values, and the graphs do not have an amplitude.
- The period of each graph is π.
- The x-intercepts for $y = \tan x$ occur when $x = 0, \pm\pi, \pm 2\pi, \pm 3\pi, \ldots$.
- The x-intercepts for $y = \cot x$ occur when $x = \pm\frac{\pi}{2}, \pm\frac{3\pi}{2}, \pm\frac{5\pi}{2}, \pm\frac{7\pi}{2}, \ldots$.

STUDY TIP

Odd multiples of $\frac{\pi}{2}$ are values such as these:

$$\pm 1 \cdot \frac{\pi}{2} = \pm\frac{\pi}{2}$$

$$\pm 3 \cdot \frac{\pi}{2} = \pm\frac{3\pi}{2}$$

$$\pm 5 \cdot \frac{\pi}{2} = \pm\frac{5\pi}{2}$$

Graphing Tangent and Cotangent Functions

The graphs of $y = a \tan bx$ and $y = a \cot bx$ represent transformations of their parent functions. The value of a indicates a vertical stretch or shrink. The value of b indicates a horizontal stretch or shrink and changes the period of the graph.

KEY IDEAS

Period and Vertical Asymptotes of $y = a \tan bx$ and $y = a \cot bx$

The period and vertical asymptotes of the graphs of $y = a \tan bx$ and $y = a \cot bx$, where a and b are nonzero real numbers, are as follows.

- The period of the graph of each function is $\frac{\pi}{|b|}$.
- The vertical asymptotes for $y = a \tan bx$ occur at odd multiples of $\frac{\pi}{2|b|}$.
- The vertical asymptotes for $y = a \cot bx$ occur at multiples of $\frac{\pi}{|b|}$.

Each graph below shows five key x-values that you can use to sketch the graphs of $y = a \tan bx$ and $y = a \cot bx$ for $a > 0$ and $b > 0$. These are the x-intercept, the x-values where the asymptotes occur, and the x-values halfway between the x-intercept and the asymptotes. At each halfway point, the value of the function is either a or $-a$.

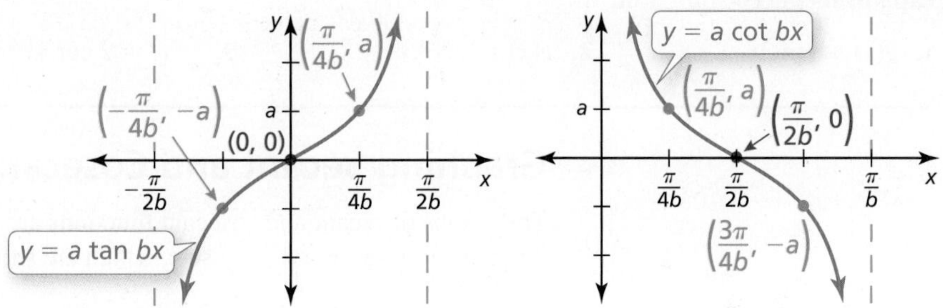

EXAMPLE 1 Graphing a Tangent Function

Graph one period of $g(x) = 2 \tan 3x$. Describe the graph of g as a transformation of the graph of $f(x) = \tan x$.

SOLUTION

The function is of the form $g(x) = a \tan bx$, where $a = 2$ and $b = 3$. So, the period is $\frac{\pi}{|b|} = \frac{\pi}{3}$.

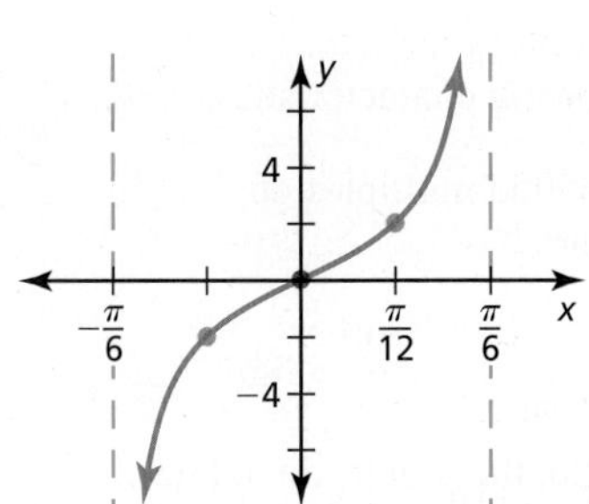

x-Intercept: $(0, 0)$

Asymptotes: $x = \frac{\pi}{2|b|} = \frac{\pi}{2(3)}$, or $x = \frac{\pi}{6}$; $\quad x = -\frac{\pi}{2|b|} = -\frac{\pi}{2(3)}$, or $x = -\frac{\pi}{6}$

Halfway points: $\left(\frac{\pi}{4b}, a\right) = \left(\frac{\pi}{4(3)}, 2\right) = \left(\frac{\pi}{12}, 2\right)$;

$$\left(-\frac{\pi}{4b}, -a\right) = \left(-\frac{\pi}{4(3)}, -2\right) = \left(-\frac{\pi}{12}, -2\right)$$

▶ The graph of g is a vertical stretch by a factor of 2 and a horizontal shrink by a factor of $\frac{1}{3}$ of the graph of f.

EXAMPLE 2 Graphing a Cotangent Function

Graph one period of $g(x) = \cot \frac{1}{2}x$. Describe the graph of g as a transformation of the graph of $f(x) = \cot x$.

SOLUTION

The function is of the form $g(x) = a \cot bx$, where $a = 1$ and $b = \frac{1}{2}$. So, the period is

$$\frac{\pi}{|b|} = \frac{\pi}{\frac{1}{2}} = 2\pi.$$

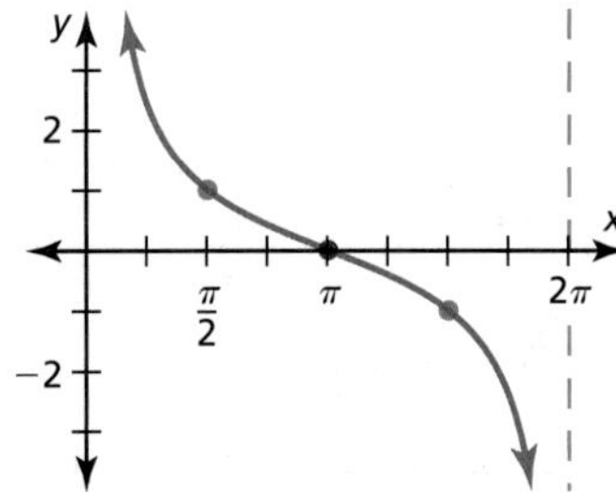

x-Intercept: $\left(\frac{\pi}{2b}, 0\right) = \left(\frac{\pi}{2\left(\frac{1}{2}\right)}, 0\right) = (\pi, 0)$

Asymptotes: $x = 0$; $x = \frac{\pi}{|b|} = \frac{\pi}{\frac{1}{2}}$, or $x = 2\pi$

Halfway points: $\left(\frac{\pi}{4b}, a\right) = \left(\frac{\pi}{4\left(\frac{1}{2}\right)}, 1\right) = \left(\frac{\pi}{2}, 1\right)$; $\left(\frac{3\pi}{4b}, -a\right) = \left(\frac{3\pi}{4\left(\frac{1}{2}\right)}, -1\right) = \left(\frac{3\pi}{2}, -1\right)$

▶ The graph of g is a horizontal stretch by a factor of 2 of the graph of f.

SELF-ASSESSMENT

1 I do not understand. 2 I can do it with help. 3 I can do it on my own. 4 I can teach someone else.

Graph one period of the function. Describe the graph of g as a transformation of the graph of its parent function.

1. $g(x) = \tan 2x$

2. $g(x) = \frac{1}{3}\cot x$

3. $g(x) = 2 \cot 4x$

4. $g(x) = 5 \tan \pi x$

Graphing Secant and Cosecant Functions

The graphs of secant and cosecant functions are related to the graphs of the parent functions $y = \sec x$ and $y = \csc x$, which are shown below.

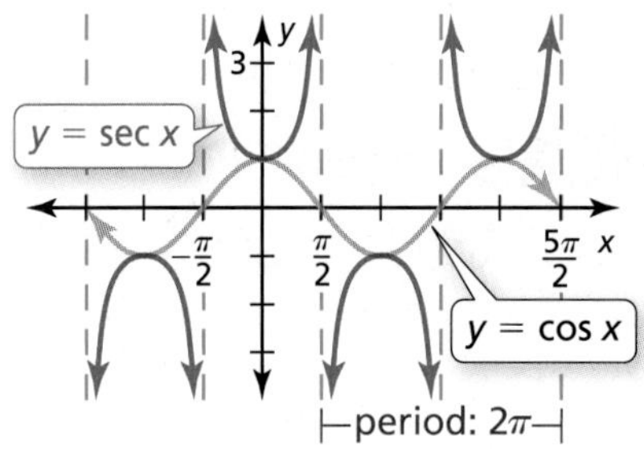

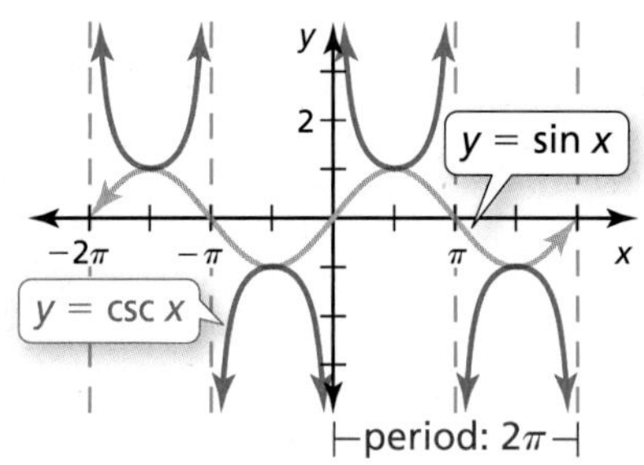

STUDY TIP

Because $\sec x = \frac{1}{\cos x}$, $\sec x$ is undefined for x-values at which $\cos x = 0$. The graph of $y = \sec x$ has vertical asymptotes at these x-values. You can use similar reasoning to understand the vertical asymptotes of the graph of $y = \csc x$.

KEY IDEA

Characteristics of $y = \sec x$ and $y = \csc x$

The functions $y = \sec x$ and $y = \csc x$ have the following characteristics.

- The domain of $y = \sec x$ is all real numbers except odd multiples of $\frac{\pi}{2}$. At these x-values, the graph has vertical asymptotes.
- The domain of $y = \csc x$ is all real numbers except multiples of π. At these x-values, the graph has vertical asymptotes.
- The range of each function is $y \leq -1$ and $y \geq 1$. So, the graphs do not have an amplitude.
- The period of each graph is 2π.

To graph $y = a \sec bx$ or $y = a \csc bx$, first graph the function $y = a \cos bx$ or $y = a \sin bx$, respectively. Then use the asymptotes and several points to sketch a graph of the function. Notice that the value of b represents a horizontal stretch or shrink by a factor of $\frac{1}{b}$, so the period of $y = a \sec bx$ and $y = a \csc bx$ is $\frac{2\pi}{|b|}$.

EXAMPLE 3 Graphing a Secant Function

Graph one period of $g(x) = 2 \sec x$. Describe the graph of g as a transformation of the graph of $f(x) = \sec x$.

SOLUTION

Step 1 Graph the function $y = 2 \cos x$.

The period is $\frac{2\pi}{1} = 2\pi$.

Step 2 Graph asymptotes of g. Because the asymptotes of g occur when $2 \cos x = 0$, graph $x = -\frac{\pi}{2}$, $x = \frac{\pi}{2}$, and $x = \frac{3\pi}{2}$.

Step 3 Plot points on g, such as $(0, 2)$ and $(\pi, -2)$. Then use the asymptotes to sketch the curve.

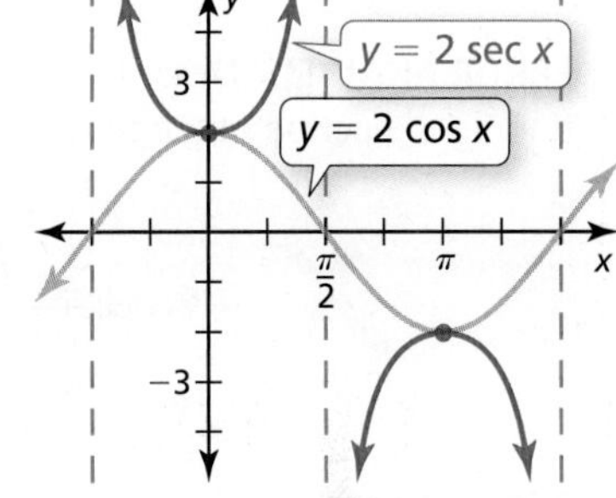

▶ The graph of g is a vertical stretch by a factor of 2 of the graph of f.

EXAMPLE 4 Graphing a Cosecant Function

Graph one period of $g(x) = \frac{1}{2} \csc \pi x$. Describe the graph of g as a transformation of the graph of $f(x) = \csc x$.

SOLUTION

Step 1 Graph the function $y = \frac{1}{2} \sin \pi x$. The period is $\frac{2\pi}{\pi} = 2$.

Step 2 Graph asymptotes of g. Because the asymptotes of g occur when $\frac{1}{2} \sin \pi x = 0$, graph $x = 0$, $x = 1$, and $x = 2$.

Step 3 Plot points on g, such as $\left(\frac{1}{2}, \frac{1}{2}\right)$ and $\left(\frac{3}{2}, -\frac{1}{2}\right)$. Then use the asymptotes to sketch the curve.

▶ The graph of g is a vertical shrink by a factor of $\frac{1}{2}$ and a horizontal shrink by a factor of $\frac{1}{\pi}$ of the graph of f.

Math Practice

Look for Patterns

In Examples 3 and 4, what is the relationship between the local maximums and minimums of each function?

SELF-ASSESSMENT

1 I do not understand. 2 I can do it with help. 3 I can do it on my own. 4 I can teach someone else.

Graph one period of the function. Describe the graph of g as a transformation of the graph of its parent function.

5. $g(x) = \csc 3x$

6. $g(x) = \frac{1}{2} \sec x$

7. $g(x) = 2 \csc 2x$

8. $g(x) = 2 \sec \pi x$

10.5 Practice WITH CalcChat® AND CalcView®

In Exercises 1–8, graph one period of the function. Describe the graph of g as a transformation of the graph of its parent function. *Examples 1 and 2*

1. $g(x) = 2 \tan x$
2. $g(x) = 3 \tan x$
3. $g(x) = \cot 3x$
4. $g(x) = \cot 2x$
5. $g(x) = 3 \cot \frac{1}{4}x$
6. $g(x) = 4 \cot \frac{1}{2}x$
7. $g(x) = \frac{1}{2} \tan \pi x$
8. $g(x) = \frac{1}{3} \tan 2\pi x$

9. **ERROR ANALYSIS** Describe and correct the error in finding the period of the function $y = \cot 3x$.

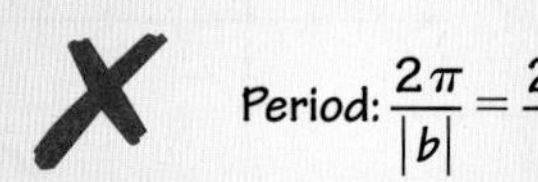

10. **ERROR ANALYSIS** Describe and correct the error in describing the transformation of $f(x) = \tan x$ represented by $g(x) = 2 \tan 5x$.

A vertical stretch by a factor of 5 and a horizontal shrink by a factor of $\frac{1}{2}$.

ANALYZING RELATIONSHIPS In Exercises 11 and 12, graph g using the graph of f as a guide.

11. $g(x) = 3 \sec 2x$
12. $g(x) = 4 \csc 3x$

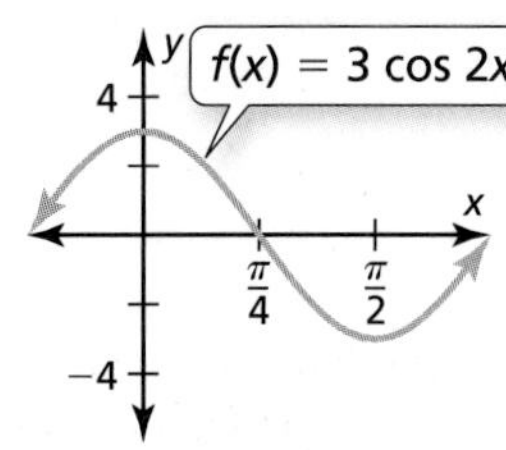

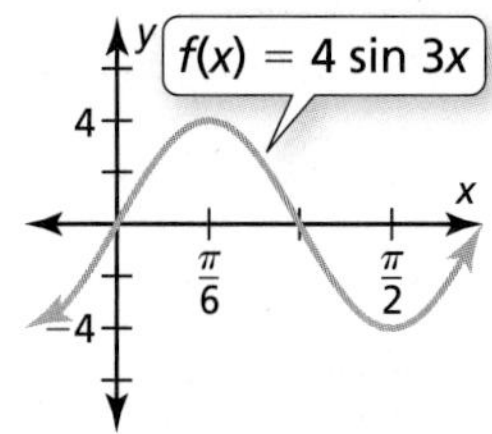

In Exercises 13–20, graph one period of the function. Describe the graph of g as a transformation of the graph of its parent function. *Examples 3 and 4*

13. $g(x) = 3 \csc x$
14. $g(x) = 2 \csc x$
15. $g(x) = \sec 4x$
16. $g(x) = \sec 3x$
17. $g(x) = \frac{1}{2} \sec \pi x$
18. $g(x) = \frac{1}{4} \sec 2\pi x$
19. $g(x) = 5 \csc \frac{1}{4}x$
20. $g(x) = 4 \csc \frac{1}{2}x$

ATTENDING TO PRECISION In Exercises 21–24, use the graph to write a function of the form $y = a \tan bx$.

21.
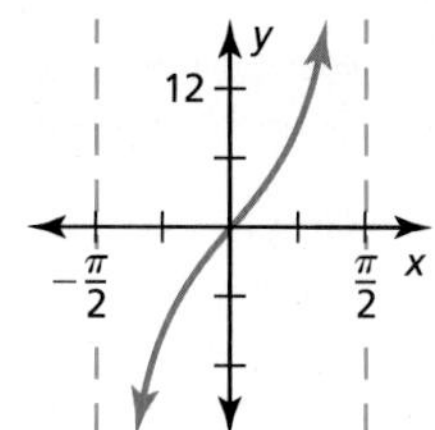

22.
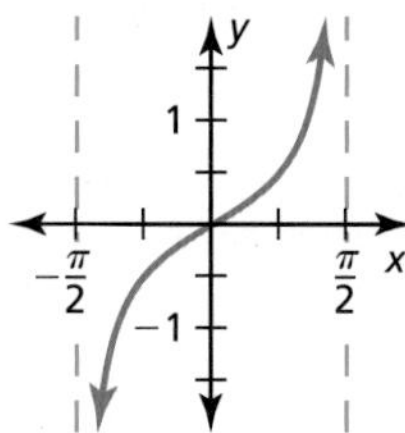

23.
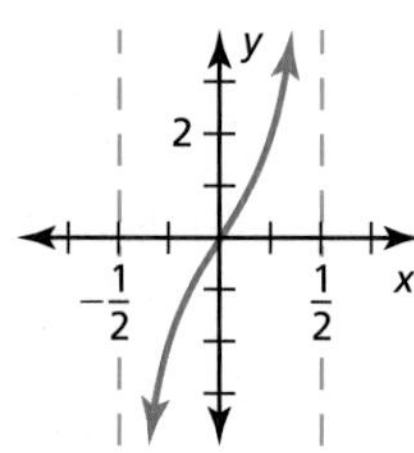

24.
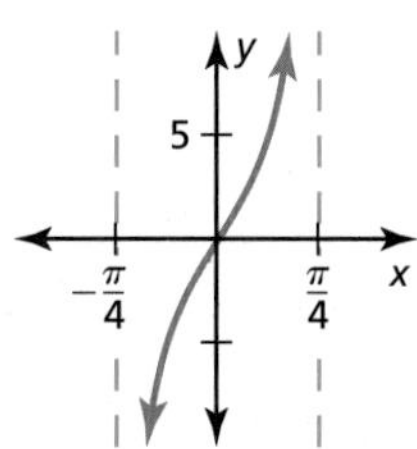

MP STRUCTURE In Exercises 25–30, match the equation with the correct graph. Explain your reasoning.

25. $g(x) = 4 \tan x$
26. $g(x) = 4 \cot x$
27. $g(x) = 4 \csc \pi x$
28. $g(x) = 4 \sec \pi x$
29. $g(x) = \sec 2x$
30. $g(x) = \csc 2x$

A.
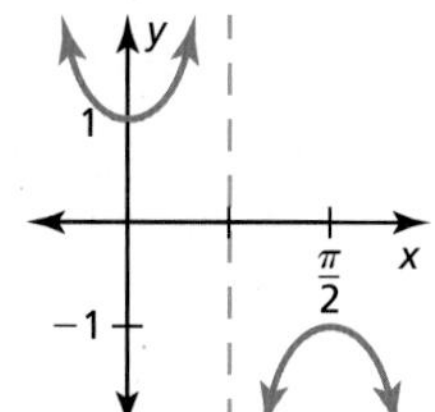

B.
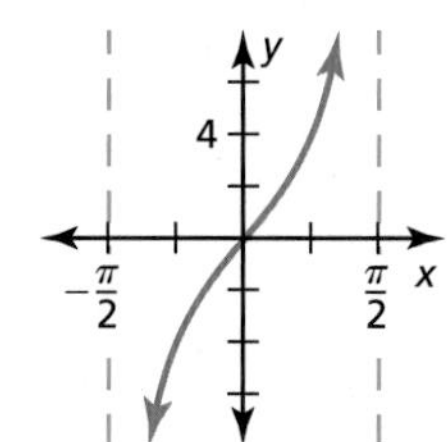

C.
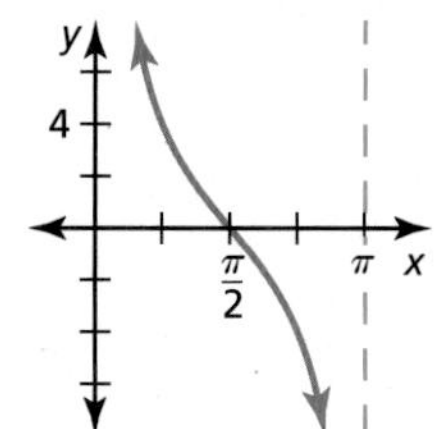

D.
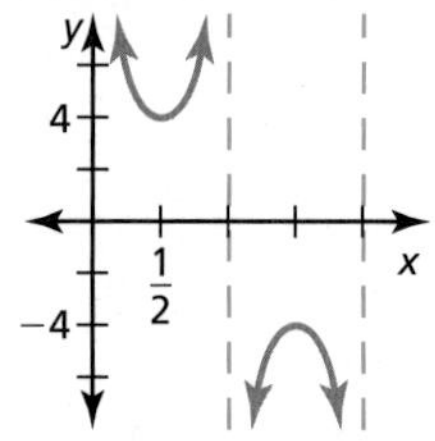

E.
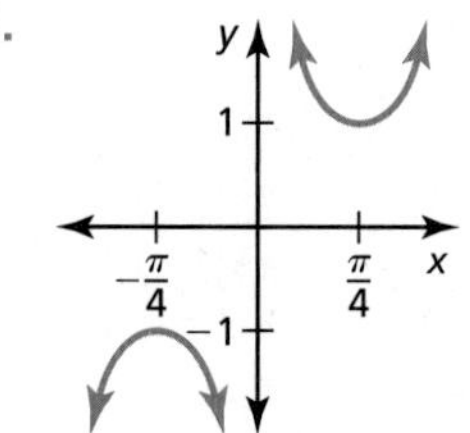

F.
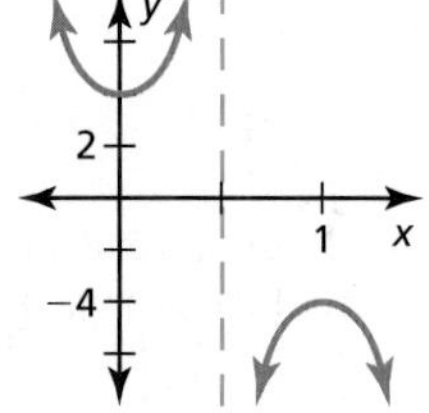

31. **MP REASONING** Explain why there is more than one tangent function whose graph passes through the origin and has asymptotes at $x = -\pi$ and $x = \pi$.

32. **USING EQUATIONS** Graph one period of each function. Describe the transformation of the graph of its parent function.

a. $g(x) = \sec x + 3$ **b.** $g(x) = \csc x - 2$

c. $g(x) = \cot(x - \pi)$ **d.** $g(x) = -\tan x$

WRITING EQUATIONS In Exercises 33–36, write a rule for *g* that represents the indicated transformation of the graph of *f*.

33. $f(x) = \cot 2x$; translation 3 units up and $\frac{\pi}{2}$ units left

34. $f(x) = 2 \tan x$; translation π units right, followed by a horizontal shrink by a factor of $\frac{1}{3}$

35. $f(x) = 5 \sec(x - \pi)$; translation 2 units down, followed by a reflection in the x-axis

36. $f(x) = 4 \csc x$; vertical stretch by a factor of 2 and a reflection in the x-axis

37. **MULTIPLE REPRESENTATIONS** Determine which function has a greater local maximum value and which function has a greater local minimum value.

A. $f(x) = \frac{1}{4} \csc \pi x$

B.

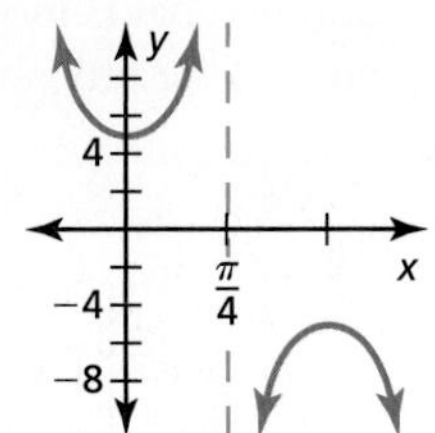

38. **ANALYZING RELATIONSHIPS** Order the functions from the least average rate of change to the greatest average rate of change over the interval $-\frac{\pi}{4} < x < \frac{\pi}{4}$.

A.

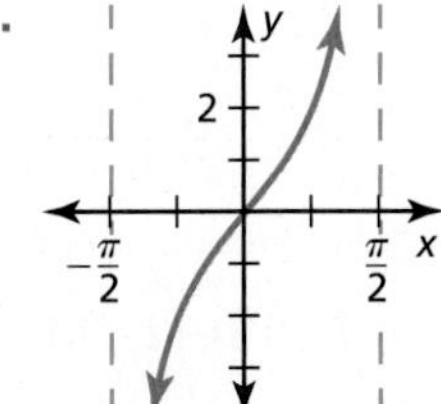

B.

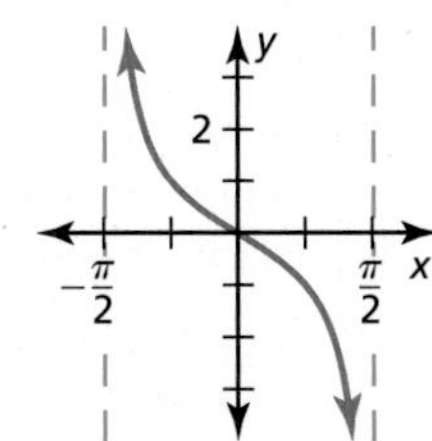

C.

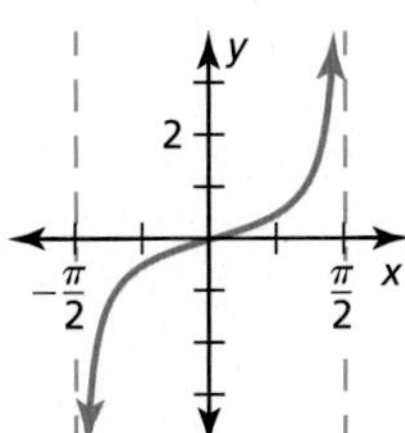

D.

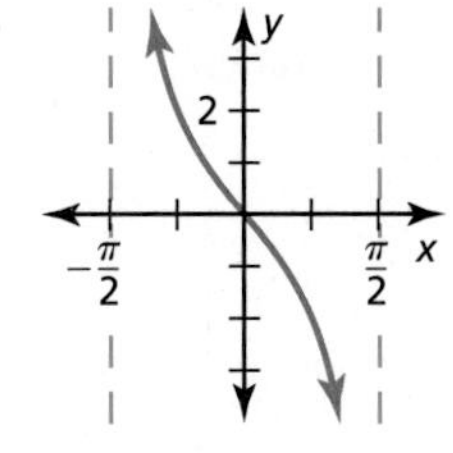

39. **MP USING TOOLS** You use the camera on your phone to pan up the Statue of Liberty. The height h (in feet) of the part of the Statue of Liberty that can be seen on the phone after t seconds can be modeled by $h = 100 \tan \frac{\pi}{36}t$. Graph the function using technology. Describe what happens to h as t increases.

GO DIGITAL

40. **MP USING TOOLS** You are standing on a bridge 140 feet above the ground. You look down at a car traveling away. The distance d (in feet) the car is from the base of the bridge can be modeled by $d = 140 \tan \theta$. Graph the function using technology. Describe what happens to θ as d increases.

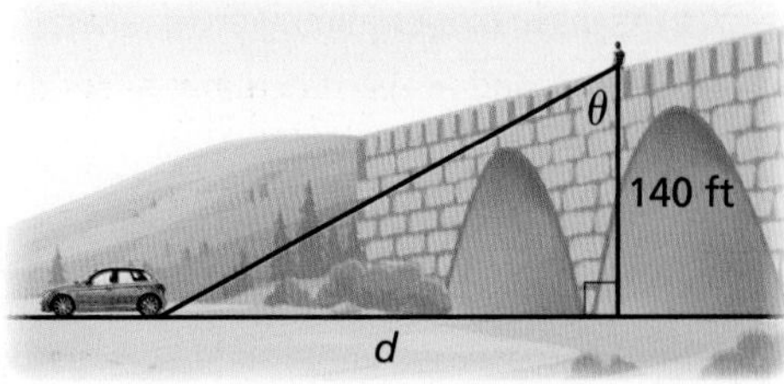

41. **MODELING REAL LIFE** You are standing 120 feet from the base of a 260-foot building. You watch your friend go down the side of the building in an elevator.

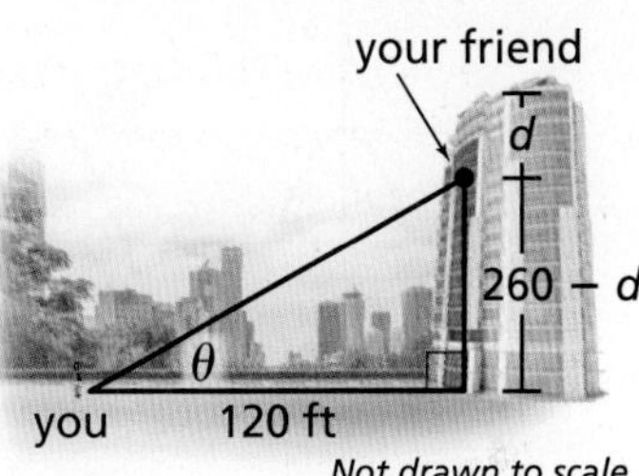

a. Write an equation that gives the distance d (in feet) your friend is from the top of the building as a function of the angle of elevation θ.

b. Graph the function found in part (a). Explain how the graph relates to this situation.

42. **MODELING REAL LIFE** You are standing 300 feet from the base of a 200-foot cliff. Your friend is rappelling down the cliff.

a. Write an equation that gives the distance d (in feet) your friend is from the top of the cliff as a function of the angle of elevation θ.

b. Graph the function found in part (a). Explain how the graph relates to the situation.

43. MAKING AN ARGUMENT Your friend states that it is not possible to write a cosecant function that has the same graph as $y = \sec x$. Is your friend correct? Explain your reasoning.

44. HOW DO YOU SEE IT?
Use the graph to answer each question.

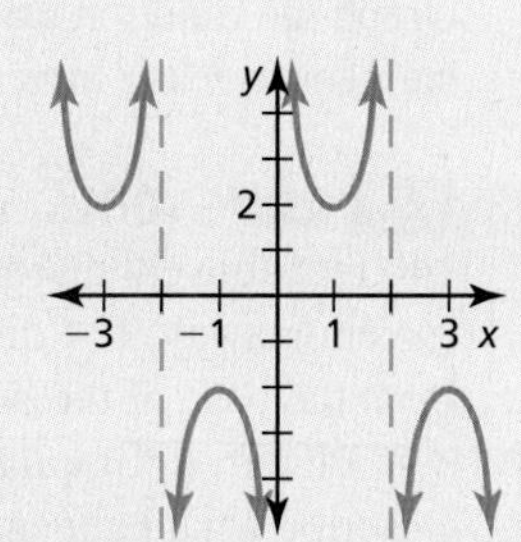

a. What is the period of the graph?

b. What is the range of the function?

c. Is the function of the form $f(x) = a \csc bx$ or $f(x) = a \sec bx$? Explain.

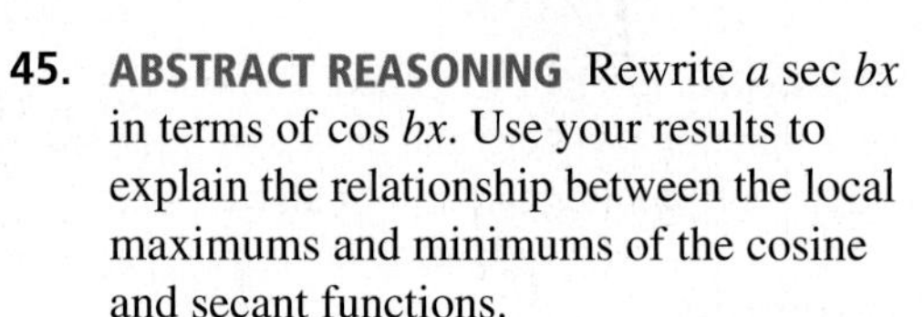

45. ABSTRACT REASONING Rewrite $a \sec bx$ in terms of $\cos bx$. Use your results to explain the relationship between the local maximums and minimums of the cosine and secant functions.

46. THOUGHT PROVOKING
A trigonometric equation that is true for all values of the variable for which both sides of the equation are defined is called a *trigonometric identity*. Use technology to graph the function

$$y = \frac{1}{2}\left(\tan \frac{x}{2} + \cot \frac{x}{2}\right).$$

Use your graph to write a trigonometric identity involving this function. Explain your reasoning.

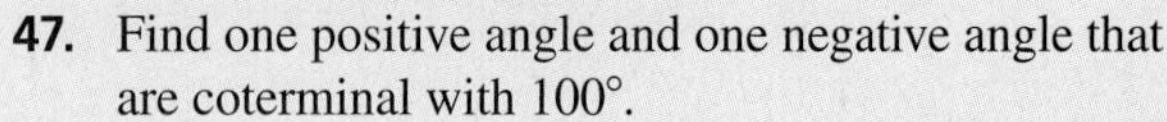

REVIEW & REFRESH

WATCH

47. Find one positive angle and one negative angle that are coterminal with 100°.

48. Find the amplitude and period of the graph of the function.

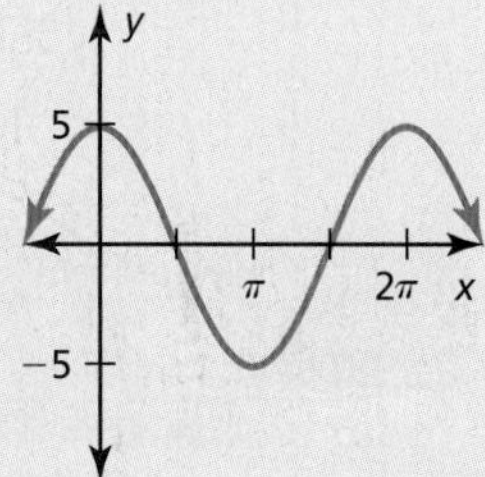
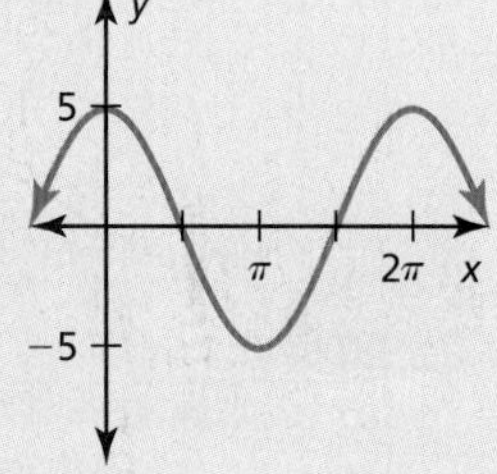

49. Evaluate sin 240° without using technology.

50. MODELING REAL LIFE An inflatable tube can safely support a weight W (in pounds) provided $W \leq 30x^2$, where x is the outer diameter (in feet) of the tube. Graph the inequality and interpret the solution.

51. Determine whether the data show an exponential relationship. Then write a function that models the data.

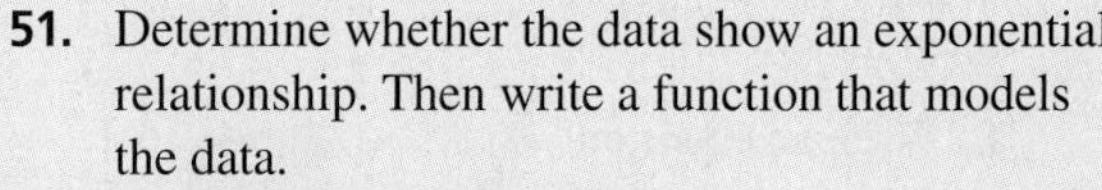

x	−2	−1	0	1	2	3
y	0.2	0.6	1.8	5.4	16.2	48.6

52. Simplify $e^{-4} \cdot e^{12}$.

53. Graph one period of the function $g(x) = \cot 4x$. Describe the graph of g as a transformation of the graph of its parent function.

54. Solve $\dfrac{9}{5x - 4} = \dfrac{2}{x - 1}$.

55. Use the probability distribution to determine (a) the number that is most likely to be spun on a spinner, and (b) the probability of spinning a 3.

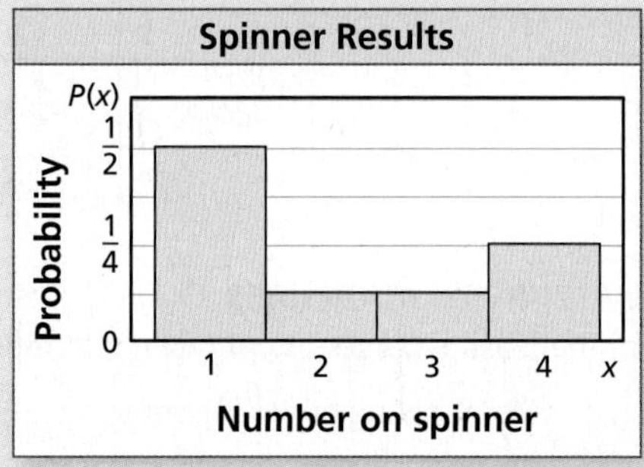

56. Use finite differences to determine the degree of the polynomial function that fits the data below. Then use technology to find the polynomial function.

$$(-2, -2), (-1, 0), (0, 4), (1, 10), (2, 18)$$

57. Graph the function $f(x) = \dfrac{x + 4}{x + 1}$. Find the domain and range.

58. Solve $x^2 + 3x - 10 = 0$.

10.6 Modeling with Trigonometric Functions

Learning Target Write trigonometric functions.

Success Criteria
- I can write and graph trigonometric functions using frequency.
- I can write trigonometric functions for a given graph.
- I can find a trigonometric model for a set of data using technology.

EXPLORE IT! Modeling a Ferris Wheel

Work with a partner. You board a car at the bottom of a Ferris wheel, which is 2 meters above the ground. At the highest point, you are 80 meters above the ground. The Ferris wheel rotates at a constant speed and it takes 48 seconds to complete one cycle.

a. Sketch the circle shown below. Moving in a counterclockwise direction, plot and label points on the circle that represent your location on the Ferris wheel every 12 seconds for one full cycle, starting at $t = 0$ as shown.

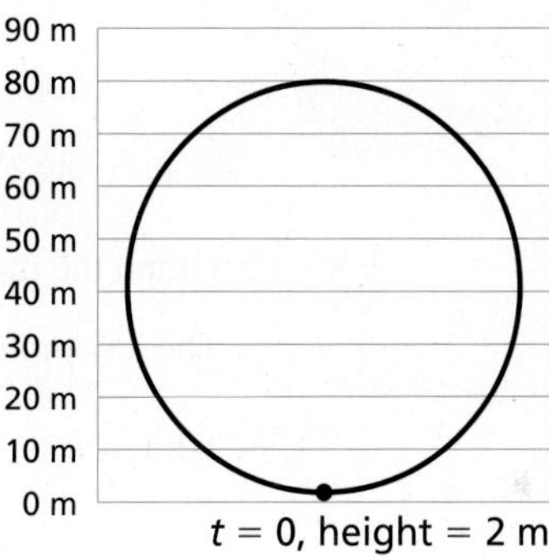

b. Complete the table of values that shows your heights h (in meters) above ground as a function of time t (in seconds).

t	0	6	12	18	24	30	36	42	48
h									

c. Sketch a graph that shows your heights above ground during two full cycles. Make several observations about the graph.

d. Write an equation for your graph using a trigonometric function. Explain the type of trigonometric function you chose. Compare your results with your classmates.

e. Describe another real-life situation that can be modeled using a trigonometric function.

Math Practice

Apply Mathematics
What methods did you use to complete the table?

Frequency

Vocabulary VOCAB
frequency, *p. 564*
sinusoid, *p. 565*

The periodic nature of trigonometric functions makes them useful for modeling *oscillating* motions or repeating patterns that occur in real life. Some examples are sound waves, the motion of a pendulum, and temperature during the year. In such applications, the reciprocal of the period is called the **frequency**, which gives the number of cycles per unit of time.

EXAMPLE 1 Using Frequency

A sound consisting of a single frequency is called a *pure tone*. An audiometer produces pure tones to test a person's auditory functions. An audiometer produces a pure tone with a frequency f of 2000 hertz (cycles per second). The maximum pressure P produced by the tone is 2 millipascals. Write and graph a sine model that gives the pressure P as a function of the time t (in seconds).

SOLUTION

Step 1 Find the values of a and b in the model $P = a \sin bt$. The maximum pressure is 2, so $a = 2$. Use the frequency f to find b.

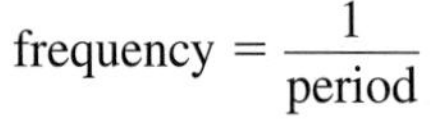

$$\text{frequency} = \frac{1}{\text{period}}$$ Write relationship involving frequency and period.

$$2000 = \frac{b}{2\pi}$$ Substitute.

$$4000\pi = b$$ Multiply each side by 2π.

The pressure P as a function of time t is given by $P = 2 \sin 4000\pi t$.

Step 2 Graph the model. The amplitude is $a = 2$ and the period is $\frac{1}{f} = \frac{1}{2000}$.

The key points are:

x-Intercepts: $(0, 0)$; $\left(\frac{1}{2} \cdot \frac{1}{2000}, 0\right) = \left(\frac{1}{4000}, 0\right)$; $\left(\frac{1}{2000}, 0\right)$

Maximum: $\left(\frac{1}{4} \cdot \frac{1}{2000}, 2\right) = \left(\frac{1}{8000}, 2\right)$

Minimum: $\left(\frac{3}{4} \cdot \frac{1}{2000}, -2\right) = \left(\frac{3}{8000}, -2\right)$

▶ The graph of $P = 2 \sin 4000\pi t$ is shown.

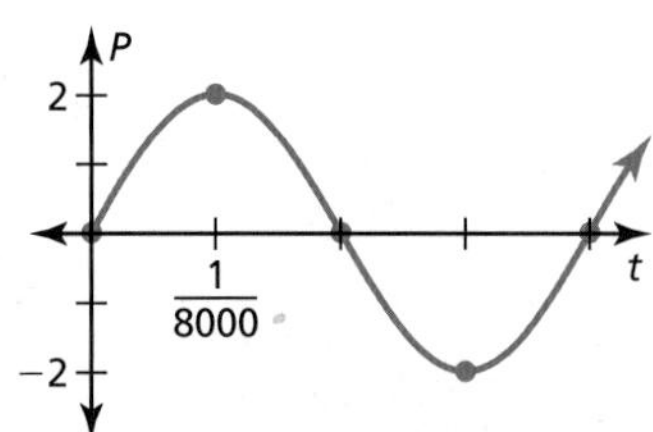

SELF-ASSESSMENT 1 I do not understand. 2 I can do it with help. 3 I can do it on my own. 4 I can teach someone else.

1. **WHAT IF?** In Example 1, how does the function change when the audiometer produces a pure tone with a frequency of 1000 hertz?

2. **WRITING** Describe how to find the frequency of the function whose graph is shown.

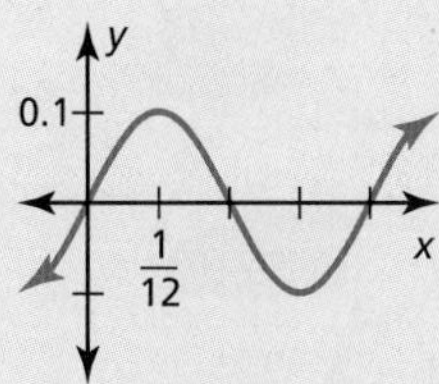

Writing Trigonometric Functions

Graphs of sine and cosine functions are called **sinusoids**. One method to write a sine or cosine function that models a sinusoid is to find the values of a, b, h, and k for

$$y = a \sin b(x - h) + k \quad \text{or} \quad y = a \cos b(x - h) + k$$

where $|a|$ is the amplitude, $\frac{2\pi}{b}$ is the period ($b > 0$), h is the horizontal shift, and k is the vertical shift.

EXAMPLE 2 Writing a Trigonometric Function

Write a function for the sinusoid shown.

SOLUTION

Step 1 Find the maximum and minimum values. From the graph, the maximum value is 5 and the minimum value is -1.

Step 2 Identify the vertical shift, k. The value of k is the mean of the maximum and minimum values.

$$k = \frac{(\text{maximum value}) + (\text{minimum value})}{2} = \frac{5 + (-1)}{2} = \frac{4}{2} = 2$$

Step 3 Decide whether the graph should be modeled by a sine or cosine function. Because the graph crosses the midline $y = 2$ on the y-axis, the graph is a sine curve with no horizontal shift. So, $h = 0$.

Step 4 Find the period and amplitude. The period is

$$\frac{\pi}{2} = \frac{2\pi}{b} \quad \Rightarrow \quad b = 4.$$

The amplitude is

$$|a| = \frac{(\text{maximum value}) - (\text{minimum value})}{2} = \frac{5 - (-1)}{2} = \frac{6}{2} = 3.$$

The graph is not a reflection, so $a > 0$. Therefore, $a = 3$.

▶ The function is $y = 3 \sin 4x + 2$.

Check

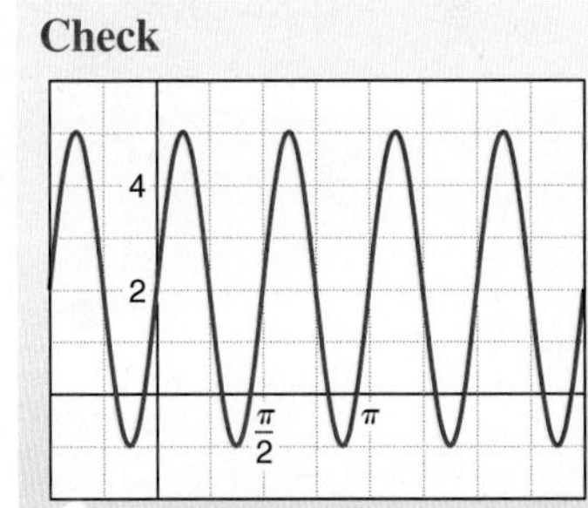

STUDY TIP

Because the graph repeats every $\frac{\pi}{2}$ units, the period is $\frac{\pi}{2}$.

SELF-ASSESSMENT 1 I do not understand. 2 I can do it with help. 3 I can do it on my own. 4 I can teach someone else.

Write a function for the sinusoid.

3.

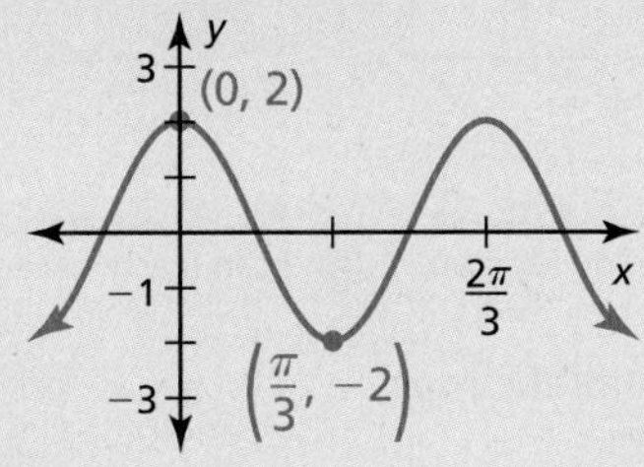

4.

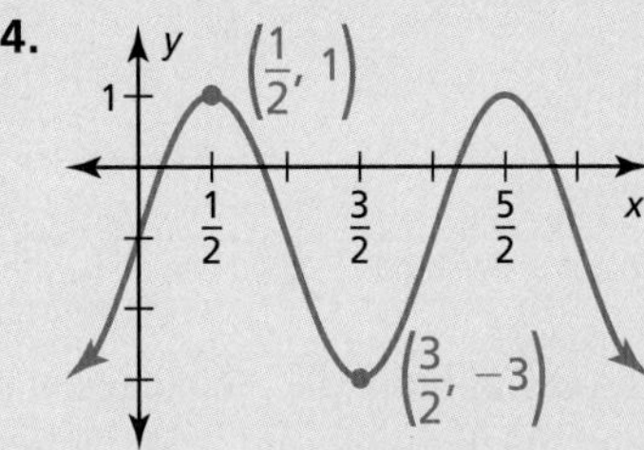

EXAMPLE 3 Modeling Circular Motion

Two people swing jump ropes. The highest and lowest points of the middle of each rope are shown. Each rope makes 2 revolutions per second. Write a model for the height h (in inches) of one of the ropes as a function of the time t (in seconds) given that the rope is at its lowest point when $t = 0$.

Not drawn to scale

SOLUTION

A rope oscillates between 3 inches and 75 inches above the ground. So, a sine or cosine function may be an appropriate model for the height over time.

Step 1 Identify the maximum and minimum values. The maximum height of a rope is 75 inches. The minimum height is 3 inches.

Step 2 Identify the vertical shift, k.

$$k = \frac{(\text{maximum value}) + (\text{minimum value})}{2} = \frac{75 + 3}{2} = 39$$

Step 3 Decide whether the height should be modeled by a sine or cosine function. When $t = 0$, the height is at its minimum. So, use a cosine function whose graph is a reflection in the x-axis with no horizontal shift ($h = 0$).

Step 4 Find the amplitude and period.

The amplitude is $|a| = \frac{(\text{maximum value}) - (\text{minimum value})}{2} = \frac{75 - 3}{2} = 36.$

Because the graph is a reflection in the x-axis, $a < 0$. So, $a = -36$. Because a rope is rotating at a rate of 2 revolutions per second, one revolution is completed in 0.5 second. So, the period is $\frac{2\pi}{b} = 0.5$, and $b = 4\pi$.

▶ A model for the height of a rope is $h(t) = -36 \cos 4\pi t + 39$.

Check

Create a table of values using technology to check your model.

t	$h(t)$
0	3
0.25	75
0.5	3
0.75	75
1	3
1.25	75

2 revolutions in 1 second

SELF-ASSESSMENT

1 I do not understand. 2 I can do it with help. 3 I can do it on my own. 4 I can teach someone else.

5. **WHAT IF?** Describe how the model in Example 3 changes when the lowest point of the rope is 5 inches above the ground and the highest point is 70 inches above the ground.

Using Technology to Find Trigonometric Models

Another way to model sinusoids is to use technology that has a sinusoidal regression feature.

EXAMPLE 4 Using Sinusoidal Regression

The table shows the numbers N of hours of daylight in Houston, Texas, on the 15th day of each month, where $t = 1$ represents January. Write a model that gives N as a function of t and interpret the period of its graph.

t	1	2	3	4	5	6	7	8	9	10	11	12
N	10.45	11.17	11.98	12.90	13.65	14.05	13.88	13.22	12.35	11.47	10.67	10.25

SOLUTION

Step 1 Enter the data from the table.

t_1	N_1
1	10.45
2	11.17
3	11.98
4	12.90
⋮	⋮
12	10.25

Step 2 Make a scatter plot. The data appears sinusoidal.

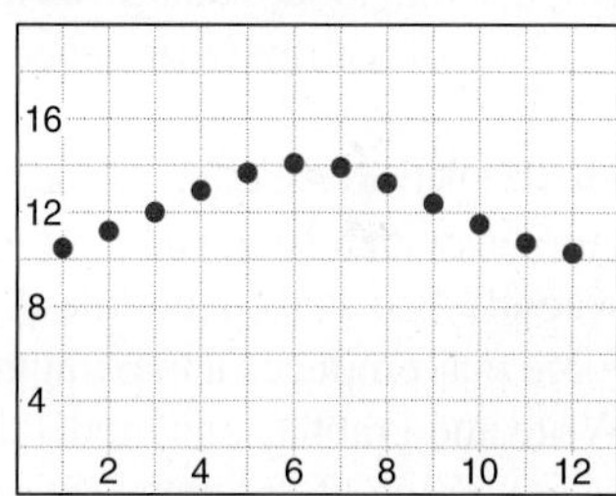

Step 3 Perform a sinusoidal regression.

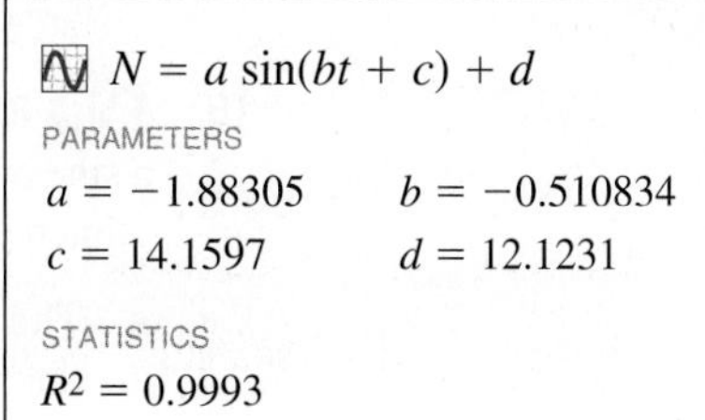

Step 4 Graph the regression equation with the data.

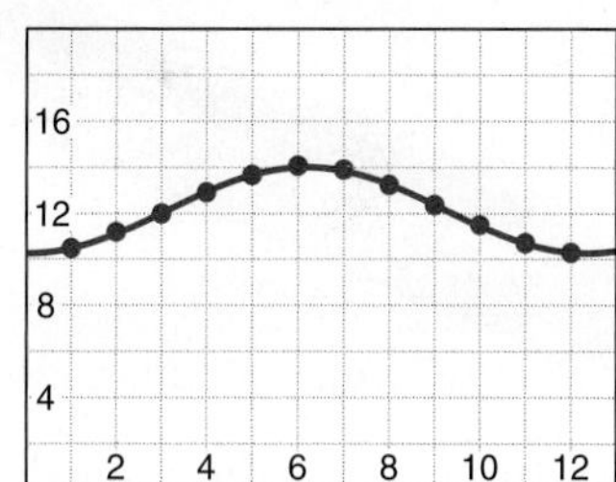

STUDY TIP

Notice that the *sinusoidal regression* feature finds a model of the form $y = a \sin(bx + c) + d$. This function has a period of $\frac{2\pi}{b}$ because it can be written as $y = a \sin b\left(x + \frac{c}{b}\right) + d$.

▶ The model appears to be a good fit. So, a model for the data is $N = -1.88 \sin(-0.511t + 14.16) + 12.1$. The period, $\frac{2\pi}{|-0.511|} \approx 12$, makes sense because there are 12 months in a year and you expect this pattern to continue in the years to follow.

SELF-ASSESSMENT

1 I do not understand. 2 I can do it with help. 3 I can do it on my own. 4 I can teach someone else.

6. The table shows the average daily temperature T (in degrees Fahrenheit) for a city each month, where $m = 1$ represents January. Write a model that gives T as a function of m and interpret the period of its graph.

m	1	2	3	4	5	6	7	8	9	10	11	12
T	29	32	39	48	59	68	74	72	65	54	45	35

10.6 Practice WITH CalcChat® AND CalcView®

GO DIGITAL

In Exercises 1–8, find the frequency of the function.

1. $y = \sin x$

2. $y = \sin 3x$

3. $y = \cos 4x + 2$

4. $y = -\cos 2x$

5. $y = \sin 3\pi x$

6. $y = \cos \dfrac{\pi x}{4}$

7. $y = \dfrac{1}{2}\cos 0.75x - 8$

8. $y = 3 \sin 0.2x + 6$

9. **MODELING REAL LIFE** Frequency is measured in *hertz*, or cycles per second. The lowest frequency of sounds that can be heard by humans is 20 hertz. The maximum pressure P produced from a sound with a frequency of 20 hertz is 0.02 millipascal. Write and graph a sine model that gives the pressure P as a function of the time t (in seconds). *Example 1*

10. **MODELING REAL LIFE** A middle-A tuning fork vibrates with a frequency f of 440 hertz (cycles per second). You strike a middle-A tuning fork with a force that produces a maximum pressure of 5 pascals. Write and graph a sine model that gives the pressure P as a function of the time t (in seconds).

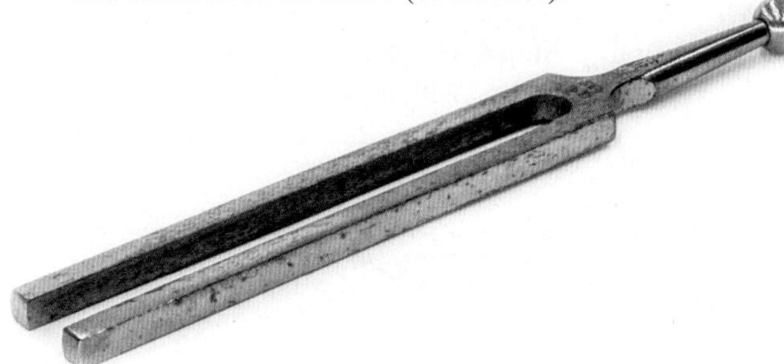

In Exercises 11–14, write a function for the sinusoid. *Example 2*

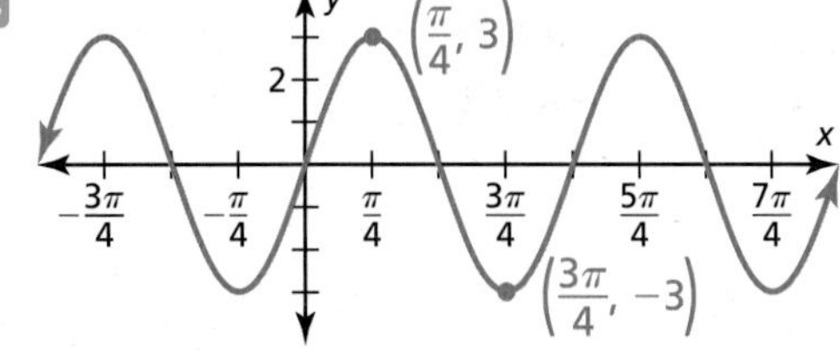

12.

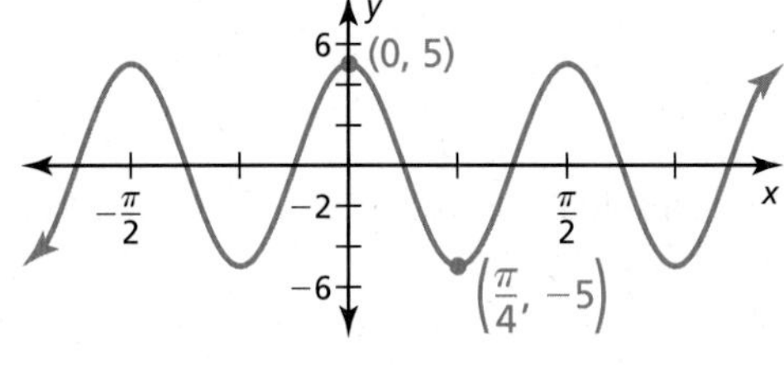

13.

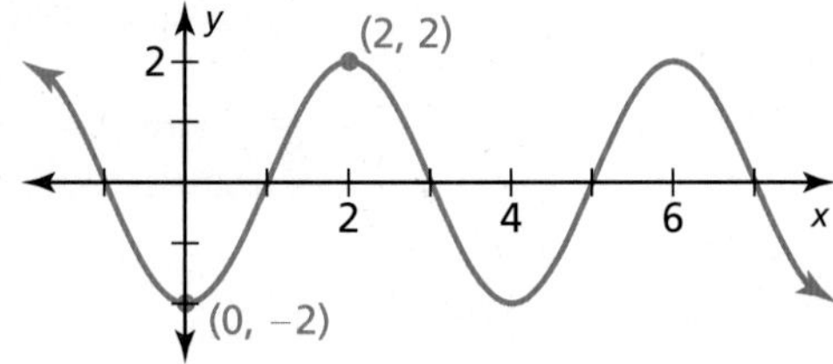

14.

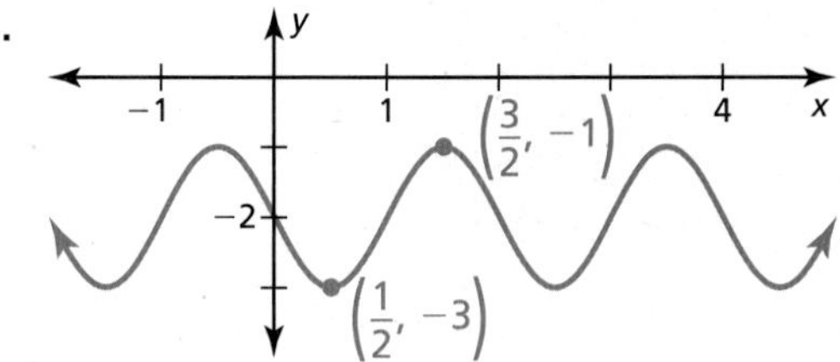

15. **ERROR ANALYSIS** Describe and correct the error in finding the amplitude of a sinusoid with a maximum point at (2, 10) and a minimum point at (4, −6).

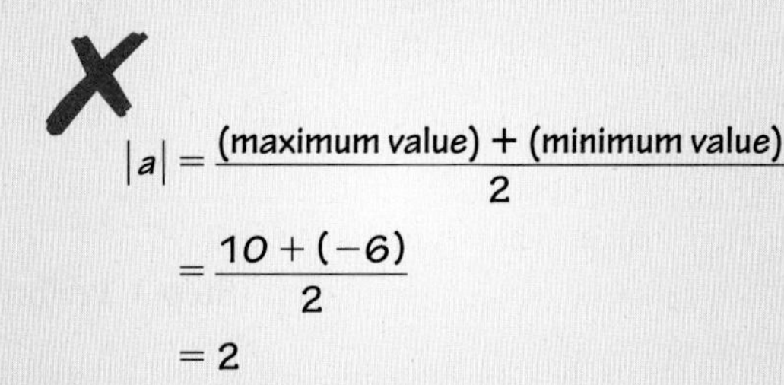

$$|a| = \frac{(\text{maximum value}) + (\text{minimum value})}{2}$$

$$= \frac{10 + (-6)}{2}$$

$$= 2$$

16. **MP REASONING** Determine whether you would use a sine or cosine function to model each sinusoid with the y-intercept described. Explain your reasoning.

a. The y-intercept occurs at the maximum value of the function.

b. The y-intercept occurs at the minimum value of the function.

c. The y-intercept occurs halfway between the maximum and minimum values of the function.

17. **MODELING REAL LIFE** You attach an LED light to the spokes of each of your bicycle wheels. On one wheel, the highest point of the light is 22 inches above the ground, and the lowest point is 4 inches. While riding your bike at a speed of 12 miles per hour, the wheel makes 2.5 revolutions per second. Write a model for the height h (in inches) of the light as a function of the time t (in seconds) given that the light is at its lowest point when $t = 0$. *Example 3*

18. MODELING REAL LIFE The Great Laxey Wheel, located on the Isle of Man, is the largest working water wheel in the world. The highest point of a bucket on the wheel is 70.5 feet above the viewing platform, and the lowest point is 2 feet below the viewing platform. The wheel makes a complete turn every 24 seconds. Write a model for the height h (in feet) of the bucket as a function of time t (in seconds) given that the bucket is at its lowest point when $t = 0$.

MP USING TOOLS In Exercises 19 and 20, the time t is measured in months, where $t = 1$ represents January. Write a model that gives the average monthly high temperature D as a function of t and interpret the period of the graph. *Example 4*

19. **Air Temperatures in Las Vegas, NV**

t	1	2	3	4	5	6
D	58	63	70	78	89	99

t	7	8	9	10	11	12
D	104	102	94	81	67	57

20. **Water Temperatures at Miami Beach, FL**

t	1	2	3	4	5	6
D	71	73	75	78	81	85

t	7	8	9	10	11	12
D	86	85	84	81	76	73

21. MODELING REAL LIFE A circuit has an alternating voltage of 100 volts that peaks every 0.5 second. Write a sinusoidal model for the voltage V as a function of the time t (in seconds).

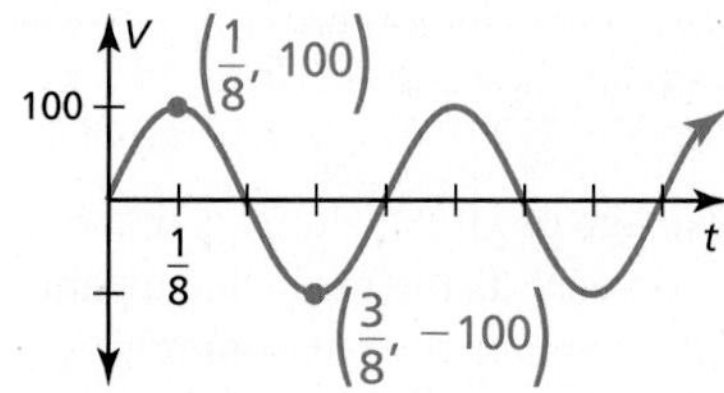

22. MULTIPLE REPRESENTATIONS The graph shows the average daily temperature of Lexington, Kentucky. The average daily temperature of Louisville, Kentucky, is modeled by $y = -22 \cos \frac{\pi}{6}t + 57$, where y is the temperature (in degrees Fahrenheit) and t is the number of months since January 1. Which city has the greater average daily temperature? Explain.

GO DIGITAL

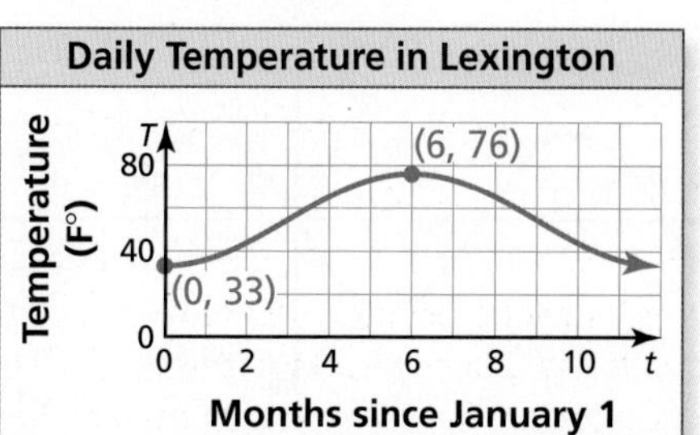

23. MP STRUCTURE During one cycle, a sinusoid has a minimum at $\left(\frac{\pi}{2}, 3\right)$ and a maximum at $\left(\frac{\pi}{4}, 8\right)$. Write a sine function *and* a cosine function for the sinusoid. Use technology to verify your answers.

24. HOW DO YOU SEE IT?

What is the frequency of the function whose graph is shown? Explain.

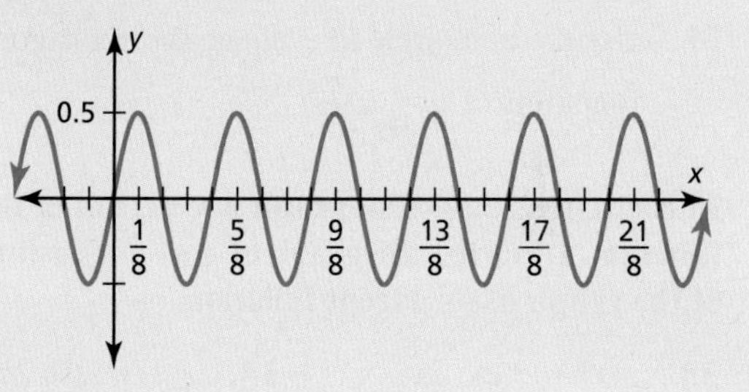

25. MP USING TOOLS The tables show the numbers of employees N (in thousands) at a retail store company each year for 11 years. The time t is measured in years, with $t = 1$ representing the first year.

t	1	2	3	4	5	6
N	20.8	22.7	24.6	23.2	20	17.5

t	7	8	9	10	11
N	16.7	17.8	21	22	24.1

a. Use sinusoidal regression to find a model that gives N as a function of t.

b. Predict the number of employees at the company in the 12th year.

26. THOUGHT PROVOKING
The *tangent line* to the graph of a function at a point is a line that best approximates the slope of the graph at that point. The figure shows a tangent line drawn to the graph of $y = \sin x$. At several points on the graph, draw a tangent line to the graph and estimate its slope. Then plot the points (x, m), where m is the slope of the tangent line. What can you conclude?

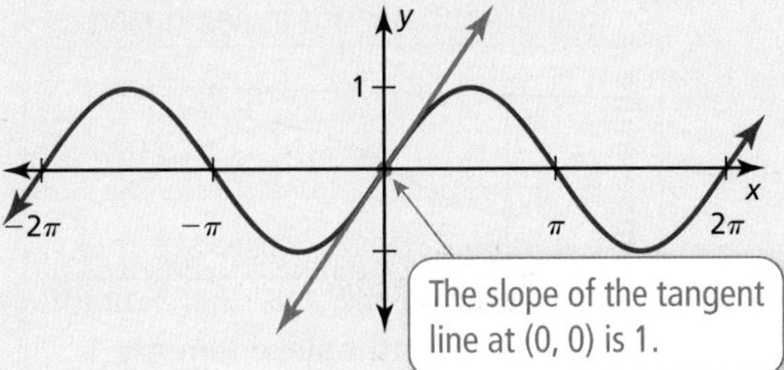

27. PERFORMANCE TASK You volunteer to clean a beach at a large body of water 3 days from now. The best time to do this is at low tide. Use the Internet or another resource to find the times and depths of the low and high tides in a location of your choice on a recent day.

GO DIGITAL

a. Use the data to write a sinusoidal model for the tide depth d (in feet) as a function of the time t (in hours).

b. Use your model to predict the optimal time(s) to clean the beach on the day that you volunteer. Write an itinerary for your day that includes when you will be at the beach and for how long.

REVIEW & REFRESH

WATCH

In Exercises 28–31, expand the logarithmic expression.

28. $\log_8 \frac{x}{7}$

29. $\ln 2x$

30. $\log_3 5x^3$

31. $\ln \frac{4x^6}{y}$

32. Use the unit circle to evaluate the six trigonometric functions of $\theta = -\frac{\pi}{2}$.

In Exercises 33 and 34, graph one period of the function. Describe the graph of g as a transformation of the graph of its parent function.

33. $g(x) = 3 \tan 2x$

34. $g(x) = \csc 2\pi x$

35. MODELING REAL LIFE The two-way table shows the ages and experience levels of several players of a video game. Find each probability.

		Age	
		Teenager	Adult
Level	Novice	72	59
	Intermediate	77	90
	Expert	64	41

a. $P(\text{novice} \mid \text{teenager})$ **b.** $P(\text{adult} \mid \text{expert})$

36. Solve $x^3 - 4x^2 - 9x + 36 = 0$.

In Exercises 37 and 38, graph the function.

37. $g(x) = \sin 2\left(x - \frac{\pi}{2}\right)$

38. $g(x) = 3 \cos x - 5$

39. Write a function for the sinusoid.

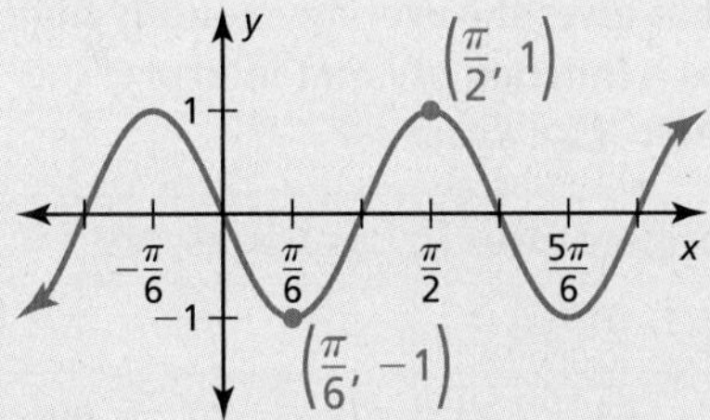

In Exercises 40–43, simplify the expression.

40. $\frac{17}{\sqrt{2}}$

41. $\frac{3}{\sqrt{6} - 2}$

42. $\frac{8}{\sqrt{10} + 3}$

43. $\frac{13}{\sqrt{3} + \sqrt{11}}$

In Exercises 44 and 45, a card is randomly selected from a standard deck of 52 playing cards. Find the probability of the event.

44. selecting a 2 *or* a 3

45. selecting an ace *or* a heart

46. Tell whether x and y show *direct variation, inverse variation,* or *neither.*

x	−2	−1	0	1	2
y	1	3	5	7	9

47. The mean age of all the students in a first aid class is 24 years. Is the mean age a parameter or a statistic? Explain your reasoning.

10.7 Using Trigonometric Identities

Learning Target Use trigonometric identities to evaluate trigonometric functions and simplify trigonometric expressions.

Success Criteria

- I can evaluate trigonometric functions using trigonometric identities.
- I can simplify trigonometric expressions using trigonometric identities.
- I can verify trigonometric identities.

EXPLORE IT! Writing a Trigonometric Identity

Work with a partner. In the diagram, the point (x, y) is on the unit circle. In Section 10.3, you wrote the coordinates of (x, y) in terms of θ, as shown.

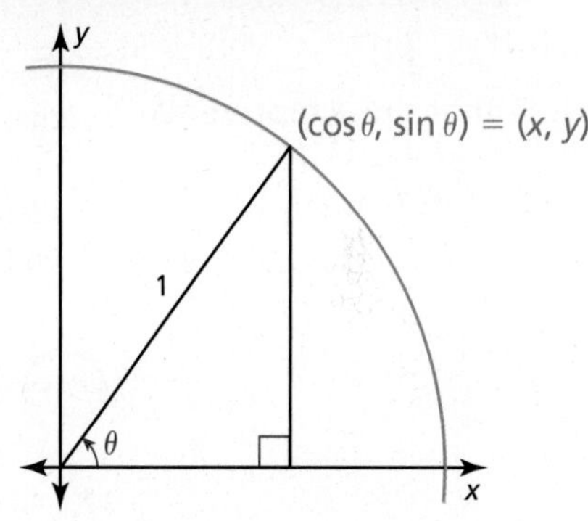

a. Write an equation in terms of θ that relates the side lengths of the inscribed triangle. Explain your reasoning.

b. Complete the table to verify that the equation you wrote in part (a) is valid for angles in each of the four quadrants.

	θ	$\sin^2\theta$	$\cos^2\theta$	$\sin^2\theta + \cos^2\theta$
QI				
QII				
QIII				
QIV				

c. The equation you wrote in part (a) is called a *Pythagorean identity*. Recall that an identity is an equation that is true for all values of the variable and has infinitely many solutions. There are two other equivalent Pythagorean identities that use different trigonometric functions. Explain how you can derive them from your results above.

d. Use the diagram above to sketch the angle $-\theta$. Explain how you can write the coordinates of $(\cos(-\theta), \sin(-\theta))$.

e. Use your results in part (d) to write trigonometric identities using each of the following.

i. $\cos(-\theta)$

ii. $\sin(-\theta)$

iii. $\tan(-\theta)$

Math Practice

Make a Plan
What steps can you take to verify a trigonometric identity?

Using Trigonometric Identities

Vocabulary 

trigonometric identity, *p. 572*

Recall that when an angle θ is in standard position with its terminal side intersecting the unit circle at (x, y), then $x = \cos\theta$ and $y = \sin\theta$.

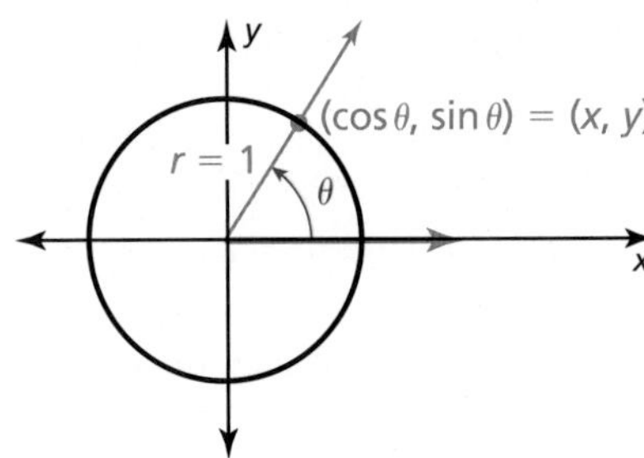

Because (x, y) is on a circle centered at the origin with radius 1, it follows that

$$x^2 + y^2 = 1 \qquad \text{and} \qquad \cos^2\theta + \sin^2\theta = 1.$$

STUDY TIP

Note that $\sin^2\theta$ represents $(\sin\theta)^2$ and $\cos^2\theta$ represents $(\cos\theta)^2$.

The equation $\cos^2\theta + \sin^2\theta = 1$ is true for any value of θ. A trigonometric equation that is true for all values of the variable for which both sides of the equation are defined is called a **trigonometric identity**. In Section 10.1, you used reciprocal identities to find the values of the cosecant, secant, and cotangent functions. These and other fundamental trigonometric identities are listed below.

KEY IDEA

Fundamental Trigonometric Identities

Reciprocal Identities

$$\sin\theta = \frac{1}{\csc\theta} \qquad \cos\theta = \frac{1}{\sec\theta} \qquad \tan\theta = \frac{1}{\cot\theta}$$

$$\csc\theta = \frac{1}{\sin\theta} \qquad \sec\theta = \frac{1}{\cos\theta} \qquad \cot\theta = \frac{1}{\tan\theta}$$

Tangent and Cotangent Identities

$$\tan\theta = \frac{\sin\theta}{\cos\theta} \qquad \cot\theta = \frac{\cos\theta}{\sin\theta}$$

Pythagorean Identities

$$\sin^2\theta + \cos^2\theta = 1 \qquad 1 + \tan^2\theta = \sec^2\theta \qquad 1 + \cot^2\theta = \csc^2\theta$$

Cofunction Identities

$$\sin\left(\frac{\pi}{2} - \theta\right) = \cos\theta \qquad \cos\left(\frac{\pi}{2} - \theta\right) = \sin\theta \qquad \tan\left(\frac{\pi}{2} - \theta\right) = \cot\theta$$

Negative Angle Identities

$$\sin(-\theta) = -\sin\theta \qquad \cos(-\theta) = \cos\theta \qquad \tan(-\theta) = -\tan\theta$$

You can use trigonometric identities to evaluate trigonometric functions, simplify trigonometric expressions, and verify other trigonometric identities.

EXAMPLE 1 Finding Trigonometric Values

Given that $\sin\theta = \frac{4}{5}$ and $\frac{\pi}{2} < \theta < \pi$, find the values of the other five trigonometric functions of θ.

SOLUTION

Step 1 Find $\cos\theta$.

$\sin^2\theta + \cos^2\theta = 1$	Write Pythagorean identity.
$\left(\frac{4}{5}\right)^2 + \cos^2\theta = 1$	Substitute $\frac{4}{5}$ for $\sin\theta$.
$\cos^2\theta = 1 - \left(\frac{4}{5}\right)^2$	Subtract $\left(\frac{4}{5}\right)^2$ from each side.
$\cos^2\theta = \frac{9}{25}$	Simplify.
$\cos\theta = \pm\frac{3}{5}$	Take square root of each side.
$\cos\theta = -\frac{3}{5}$	Because θ is in Quadrant II, $\cos\theta$ is negative.

Step 2 Find the values of the other four trigonometric functions of θ using the values of $\sin\theta$ and $\cos\theta$.

$$\tan\theta = \frac{\sin\theta}{\cos\theta} = \frac{\frac{4}{5}}{-\frac{3}{5}} = -\frac{4}{3} \qquad \cot\theta = \frac{\cos\theta}{\sin\theta} = \frac{-\frac{3}{5}}{\frac{4}{5}} = -\frac{3}{4}$$

$$\csc\theta = \frac{1}{\sin\theta} = \frac{1}{\frac{4}{5}} = \frac{5}{4} \qquad \sec\theta = \frac{1}{\cos\theta} = \frac{1}{-\frac{3}{5}} = -\frac{5}{3}$$

EXAMPLE 2 Simplifying Trigonometric Expressions

Simplify (a) $\tan\left(\frac{\pi}{2} - \theta\right)\sin\theta$ and (b) $\sec\theta\tan^2\theta + \sec\theta$.

SOLUTION

a.

$\tan\left(\frac{\pi}{2} - \theta\right)\sin\theta = \cot\theta\sin\theta$	Cofunction identity
$= \left(\frac{\cos\theta}{\sin\theta}\right)(\sin\theta)$	Cotangent identity
$= \cos\theta$	Simplify.

b.

$\sec\theta\tan^2\theta + \sec\theta = \sec\theta(\sec^2\theta - 1) + \sec\theta$	Pythagorean identity
$= \sec^3\theta - \sec\theta + \sec\theta$	Distributive Property
$= \sec^3\theta$	Simplify.

SELF-ASSESSMENT

1 I do not understand. 2 I can do it with help. 3 I can do it on my own. 4 I can teach someone else.

1. **WRITING** Describe the difference between a trigonometric identity and a trigonometric equation.

2. Given that $\cos\theta = \frac{1}{6}$ and $0 < \theta < \frac{\pi}{2}$, find the values of the other five trigonometric functions of θ.

Simplify the expression.

3. $\sin x\cot x\sec x$

4. $\cos\theta - \cos\theta\sin^2\theta$

5. $\frac{\tan x\csc x}{\sec x}$

Verifying Trigonometric Identities

GO DIGITAL

You can use the fundamental identities from this chapter to verify new trigonometric identities. When verifying an identity, begin with the expression on one side. Use algebra and trigonometric properties to manipulate the expression until it is identical to the other side.

EXAMPLE 3 Verifying a Trigonometric Identity

Verify the identity $\dfrac{\sec^2 \theta - 1}{\sec^2 \theta} = \sin^2 \theta$.

SOLUTION

$\dfrac{\sec^2 \theta - 1}{\sec^2 \theta} = \dfrac{\sec^2 \theta}{\sec^2 \theta} - \dfrac{1}{\sec^2 \theta}$	Write as separate fractions.
$= 1 - \left(\dfrac{1}{\sec \theta}\right)^2$	Simplify.
$= 1 - \cos^2 \theta$	Reciprocal identity
$= \sin^2 \theta$	Pythagorean identity

Notice that verifying an identity is not the same as solving an equation. When verifying an identity, you cannot assume that the two sides of the equation are equal because you are trying to verify that they are equal. So, you cannot use any properties of equality, such as adding the same quantity to each side of the equation.

EXAMPLE 4 Verifying a Trigonometric Identity

Verify the identity $\sec x + \tan x = \dfrac{\cos x}{1 - \sin x}$.

SOLUTION

$\sec x + \tan x = \dfrac{1}{\cos x} + \tan x$	Reciprocal identity
$= \dfrac{1}{\cos x} + \dfrac{\sin x}{\cos x}$	Tangent identity
$= \dfrac{1 + \sin x}{\cos x}$	Add fractions.
$= \dfrac{1 + \sin x}{\cos x} \cdot \dfrac{1 - \sin x}{1 - \sin x}$	Multiply by $\dfrac{1 - \sin x}{1 - \sin x}$.
$= \dfrac{1 - \sin^2 x}{\cos x(1 - \sin x)}$	Simplify numerator.
$= \dfrac{\cos^2 x}{\cos x(1 - \sin x)}$	Pythagorean identity
$= \dfrac{\cos x}{1 - \sin x}$	Simplify.

Math Practice

Look for Structure
Why is it reasonable to multiply the numerator and the denominator by the expression $1 - \sin x$?

SELF-ASSESSMENT

1 I do not understand. 2 I can do it with help. 3 I can do it on my own. 4 I can teach someone else.

Verify the identity.

6. $\cot(-\theta) = -\cot \theta$

7. $\csc^2 x(1 - \sin^2 x) = \cot^2 x$

8. $\cos x \csc x \tan x = 1$

9. $(\tan^2 x + 1)(\cos^2 x - 1) = -\tan^2 x$

10.7 Practice WITH CalcChat® AND CalcView®

In Exercises 1–8, find the values of the other five trigonometric functions of θ. *Example 1*

1. $\sin\theta = \frac{1}{3},\ 0 < \theta < \frac{\pi}{2}$
2. $\sin\theta = -\frac{7}{10},\ \pi < \theta < \frac{3\pi}{2}$
3. $\tan\theta = -\frac{3}{7},\ \frac{\pi}{2} < \theta < \pi$
4. $\cot\theta = -\frac{2}{5},\ \frac{\pi}{2} < \theta < \pi$
5. $\cos\theta = -\frac{5}{6},\ \pi < \theta < \frac{3\pi}{2}$
6. $\sec\theta = \frac{9}{4},\ \frac{3\pi}{2} < \theta < 2\pi$
7. $\cot\theta = -3,\ \frac{3\pi}{2} < \theta < 2\pi$
8. $\csc\theta = -\frac{5}{3},\ \pi < \theta < \frac{3\pi}{2}$

In Exercises 9–18, simplify the expression. *Example 2*

9. $\sin x \cot x$
10. $\cos\theta(1 + \tan^2\theta)$
11. $\dfrac{\sin(-\theta)}{\cos(-\theta)}$
12. $\dfrac{\cos^2 x}{\cot^2 x}$
13. $\dfrac{\cos\left(\frac{\pi}{2} - x\right)}{\csc x}$
14. $\sin\left(\frac{\pi}{2} - \theta\right)\sec\theta$
15. $\dfrac{\csc^2 x - \cot^2 x}{\sin(-x)\cot x}$
16. $\dfrac{\cos^2 x \tan^2(-x) - 1}{\cos^2 x}$
17. $\dfrac{\cos\left(\frac{\pi}{2} - \theta\right)}{\csc\theta} + \cos^2\theta$
18. $\dfrac{\sec x \sin x + \cos\left(\frac{\pi}{2} - x\right)}{1 + \sec x}$

ERROR ANALYSIS In Exercises 19 and 20, describe and correct the error in simplifying the expression.

19.

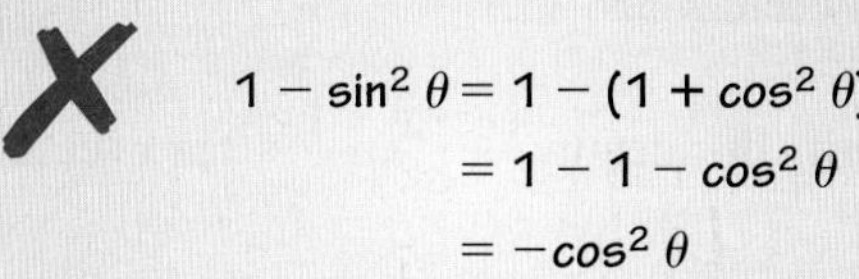

20.

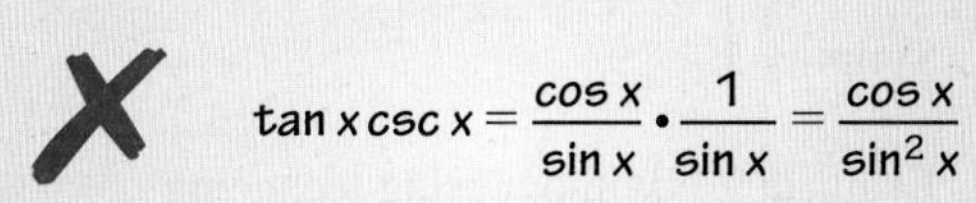

In Exercises 21–26, verify the identity. *Examples 3 and 4*

21. $\cos\left(\frac{\pi}{2} - x\right)\cot x = \cos x$
22. $\sin\left(\frac{\pi}{2} - x\right)\tan x = \sin x$
23. $\dfrac{\cos\left(\frac{\pi}{2} - \theta\right) + 1}{1 - \sin(-\theta)} = 1$
24. $\dfrac{\sin^2(-x)}{\tan^2 x} = \cos^2 x$
25. $\dfrac{1 + \cos x}{\sin x} + \dfrac{\sin x}{1 + \cos x} = 2\csc x$
26. $\dfrac{\sin x}{1 - \cos(-x)} = \csc x + \cot x$

In Exercises 27 and 28, use transformations to describe why the identity is valid.

27. $\cos(x + \pi) = \cos(x - \pi)$
28. $3 + \tan x = 3 + \tan(x + \pi)$

29. **MP LOGIC** The graph of g is a vertical translation of the graph of f. Is $f(x) = g(x)$ an identity? Explain.

30. **MAKING AN ARGUMENT** Your friend simplifies an expression and obtains $\sec x \tan x - \sin x$. You simplify the same expression and obtain $\sin x \tan^2 x$. Are your answers equivalent? Justify your answer.

31. **MP STRUCTURE** A function f is *odd* when $f(-x) = -f(x)$. A function f is *even* when $f(-x) = f(x)$. Which of the six trigonometric functions are odd? Which are even? Explain.

32. **HOW DO YOU SEE IT?**
The graphs of $f(x) = \csc(x + \pi)$ and $g(x) = -\csc x$ are shown. Write an identity based on the graphs. How can you be sure that your identity is valid?

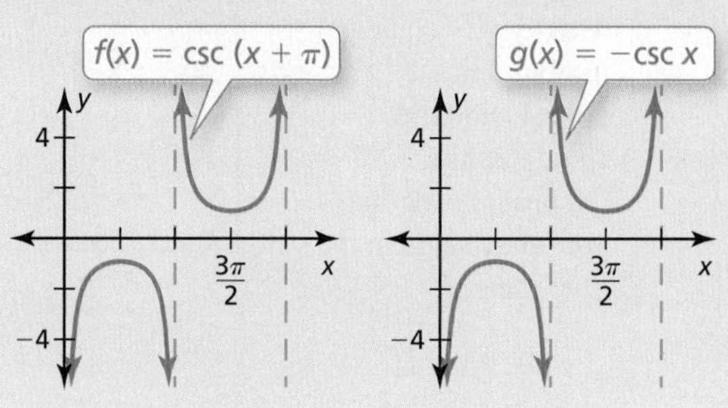

33. MODELING REAL LIFE A generator of a laser beam has height h. The length s of the laser beam measured from the generator to its target when the angle from the surface to the generator is θ can be modeled by the equation below. Show that the equation is equivalent to $s = h \csc \theta$.

$$s = \frac{h \cot \theta}{\sin(90° - \theta)}$$

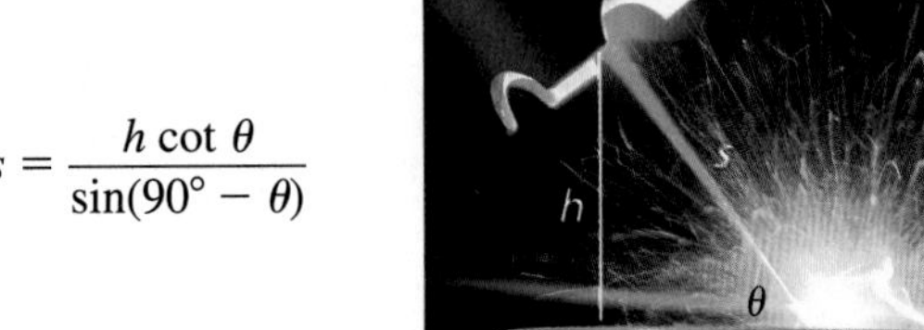

34. THOUGHT PROVOKING
Explain how you can use a trigonometric identity to find all the values of x for which $\sin x = \cos x$.

35. DRAWING CONCLUSIONS *Static friction* is the amount of force necessary to keep a stationary object on a flat surface from moving. A book weighing W pounds is set on a ramp inclined at an angle θ. The coefficient of static friction u for the book can be found using the equation $uW \cos \theta = W \sin \theta$. What happens to the value of u as θ increases?

36. MP PROBLEM SOLVING When light traveling in a medium (such as air) strikes the surface of a second medium (such as water) at an angle θ_1, the light begins to travel at a different angle θ_2. This change of direction is defined by Snell's law, $n_1 \sin \theta_1 = n_2 \sin \theta_2$, where n_1 and n_2 are the *indices of refraction* for the two mediums. Snell's law can be derived from the equation

$$\frac{n_1}{\sqrt{\cot^2 \theta_1 + 1}} = \frac{n_2}{\sqrt{\cot^2 \theta_2 + 1}}.$$

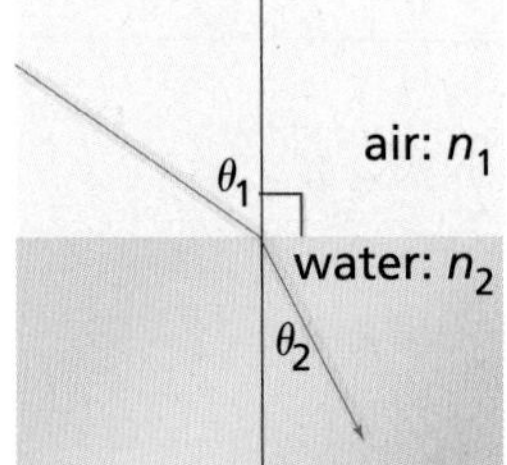

a. Simplify the equation to derive Snell's law.

b. If $\theta_1 = \theta_2$, then what must be true about the values of n_1 and n_2? When does this occur?

37. DIG DEEPER Verify each identity.

a. $\ln|\sec \theta| = -\ln|\cos \theta|$

b. $\ln|\tan \theta| = \ln|\sin \theta| - \ln|\cos \theta|$

REVIEW & REFRESH

WATCH

38. Graph one period of the function $g(x) = 5 \tan 2x$. Describe the graph of g as a transformation of the graph of its parent function.

39. MODELING REAL LIFE A buoy bobs up and down as waves go past. The vertical displacement y (in feet) of the buoy with respect to sea level can be modeled by $y = 11.5 \cos \frac{\pi}{4}t$, where t is the time (in seconds). Find and interpret the period and amplitude in the context of the problem. Then graph the function.

40. You throw a dart at the board shown. Your dart is equally likely to hit any point inside the square board. Find the probability that your dart lands in the blue region.

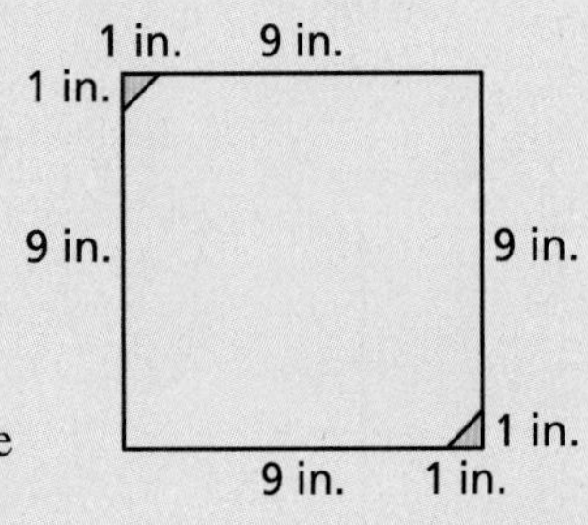

41. Write a function for the sinusoid.

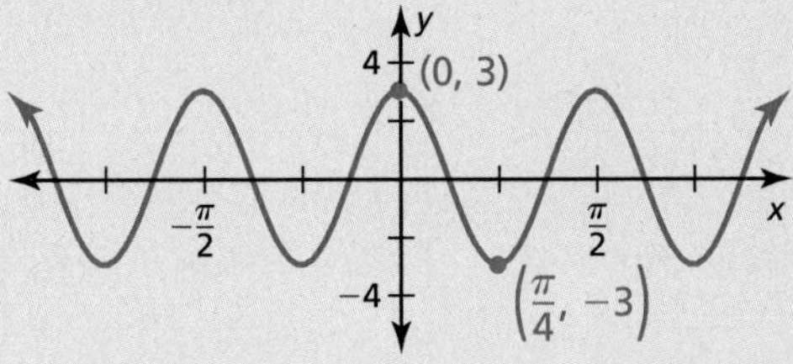

42. A normal distribution has a mean of 27 and a standard deviation of 3. Find the probability that a randomly selected x-value from the distribution is between 24 and 33.

43. Verify the identity $\dfrac{\sec^2 x - 1}{\sin x} = \tan x \sec x$.

44. Graph the function $f(x) = \dfrac{x + 2}{x - 1}$. Find the domain and range.

45. Simplify $10^{\log 4}$.

46. Evaluate $9^{5/2}$ without using technology.

10.8 Using Sum and Difference Formulas

Learning Target Use sum and difference formulas to evaluate and simplify trigonometric expressions.

Success Criteria

- I can evaluate trigonometric expressions using sum and difference formulas.
- I can simplify trigonometric expressions using sum and difference formulas.
- I can solve trigonometric equations using sum and difference formulas.

EXPLORE IT! Deriving Sum and Difference Formulas

Math Practice

Use Prior Results
What definitions and theorems did you use to help find your answers in parts (a)–(c)?

Work with a partner.

a. Use trigonometric ratios to help find the indicated missing angle measures and missing side lengths in terms of a and b in the diagram.

b. What can you conclude about $\sin(a + b)$ and $\cos(a + b)$? Explain your reasoning.

c. Use your results in part (b) to write formulas for $\sin(a - b)$ and $\cos(a - b)$. Explain your reasoning.

Using Sum and Difference Formulas

In this lesson, you will study formulas that allow you to evaluate trigonometric functions of the sum or difference of two angles.

KEY IDEA

Sum and Difference Formulas

Sum Formulas	Difference Formulas
$\sin(a+b) = \sin a \cos b + \cos a \sin b$	$\sin(a-b) = \sin a \cos b - \cos a \sin b$
$\cos(a+b) = \cos a \cos b - \sin a \sin b$	$\cos(a-b) = \cos a \cos b + \sin a \sin b$
$\tan(a+b) = \dfrac{\tan a + \tan b}{1 - \tan a \tan b}$	$\tan(a-b) = \dfrac{\tan a - \tan b}{1 + \tan a \tan b}$

In general, $\sin(a+b) \neq \sin a + \sin b$. Similar statements can be made for the other trigonometric functions of sums and differences.

EXAMPLE 1 Evaluating Trigonometric Expressions

Find the exact value of (a) $\sin 15°$ and (b) $\tan \dfrac{7\pi}{12}$.

SOLUTION

a. $\sin 15° = \sin(60° - 45°)$ — Substitute $60° - 45°$ for $15°$.

$= \sin 60° \cos 45° - \cos 60° \sin 45°$ — Difference formula for sine

$= \dfrac{\sqrt{3}}{2}\left(\dfrac{\sqrt{2}}{2}\right) - \dfrac{1}{2}\left(\dfrac{\sqrt{2}}{2}\right)$ — Evaluate.

$= \dfrac{\sqrt{6} - \sqrt{2}}{4}$ — Simplify.

▶ The exact value of $\sin 15°$ is $\dfrac{\sqrt{6} - \sqrt{2}}{4}$.

Check

sin(15)	= 0.2588190451
$\dfrac{\sqrt{6} - \sqrt{2}}{4}$	= 0.2588190451

b. $\tan \dfrac{7\pi}{12} = \tan\left(\dfrac{\pi}{3} + \dfrac{\pi}{4}\right)$ — Substitute $\dfrac{\pi}{3} + \dfrac{\pi}{4}$ for $\dfrac{7\pi}{12}$.

$= \dfrac{\tan \frac{\pi}{3} + \tan \frac{\pi}{4}}{1 - \tan \frac{\pi}{3} \tan \frac{\pi}{4}}$ — Sum formula for tangent

$= \dfrac{\sqrt{3} + 1}{1 - \sqrt{3} \cdot 1}$ — Evaluate.

$= -2 - \sqrt{3}$ — Simplify.

▶ The exact value of $\tan \dfrac{7\pi}{12}$ is $-2 - \sqrt{3}$.

Check

$\tan\left(\frac{7\pi}{12}\right)$	= −3.732050808
$-2 - \sqrt{3}$	= −3.732050808

SELF-ASSESSMENT 1 I do not understand. 2 I can do it with help. 3 I can do it on my own. 4 I can teach someone else.

Find the exact value of the expression.

1. $\sin 105°$

2. $\cos 15°$

3. $\tan \dfrac{5\pi}{12}$

4. $\cos \dfrac{7\pi}{12}$

EXAMPLE 2 Using a Difference Formula

Find $\cos(a - b)$ given that $\cos a = -\frac{4}{5}$ with $\pi < a < \frac{3\pi}{2}$ and $\sin b = \frac{5}{13}$ with $0 < b < \frac{\pi}{2}$.

SOLUTION

ANOTHER WAY

You can also use a Pythagorean identity and quadrant signs to find sin *a* and cos *b*.

Step 1 Find $\sin a$ and $\cos b$.

Because $\cos a = -\frac{4}{5}$ and a is in Quadrant III, $\sin a = -\frac{3}{5}$, as shown in the figure.

Because $\sin b = \frac{5}{13}$ and b is in Quadrant I, $\cos b = \frac{12}{13}$, as shown in the figure.

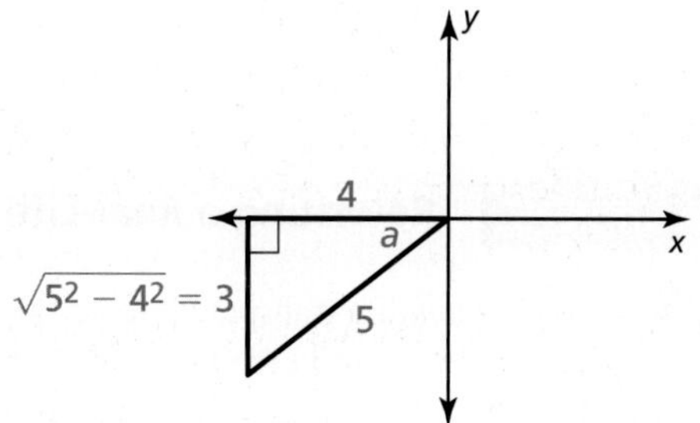

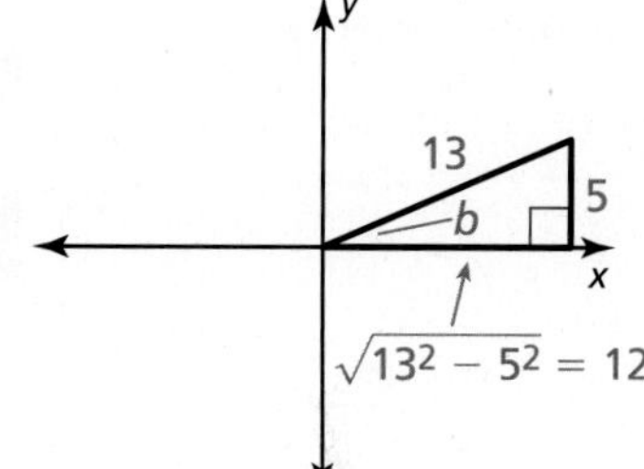

Step 2 Use the difference formula for cosine to find $\cos(a - b)$.

$$\cos(a - b) = \cos a \cos b + \sin a \sin b \quad \text{Difference formula for cosine}$$

$$= -\frac{4}{5}\left(\frac{12}{13}\right) + \left(-\frac{3}{5}\right)\left(\frac{5}{13}\right) \quad \text{Evaluate.}$$

$$= -\frac{63}{65} \quad \text{Simplify.}$$

▶ The value of $\cos(a - b)$ is $-\frac{63}{65}$.

EXAMPLE 3 Simplifying a Trigonometric Expression

Simplify the expression $\cos(x + \pi)$.

SOLUTION

$$\cos(x + \pi) = \cos x \cos \pi - \sin x \sin \pi \quad \text{Sum formula for cosine}$$

$$= (\cos x)(-1) - (\sin x)(0) \quad \text{Evaluate.}$$

$$= -\cos x \quad \text{Simplify.}$$

SELF-ASSESSMENT

1 I do not understand. 2 I can do it with help. 3 I can do it on my own. 4 I can teach someone else.

5. Find $\sin(a - b)$ given that $\sin a = \frac{8}{17}$ with $0 < a < \frac{\pi}{2}$ and $\cos b = -\frac{24}{25}$ with $\pi < b < \frac{3\pi}{2}$.

Simplify the expression.

6. $\sin(x + \pi)$

7. $\cos(x - 2\pi)$

8. $\tan(x - \pi)$

Solving Equations and Rewriting Formulas

EXAMPLE 4 Solving a Trigonometric Equation

Solve $\sin\left(x + \frac{\pi}{3}\right) + \sin\left(x - \frac{\pi}{3}\right) = 1$ for $0 \le x < 2\pi$.

ANOTHER WAY

You can also solve the equation using technology by graphing each side of the original equation and finding the *x*-value(s) of the intersection points in the given interval.

SOLUTION

$$\sin\left(x + \frac{\pi}{3}\right) + \sin\left(x - \frac{\pi}{3}\right) = 1 \qquad \text{Write equation.}$$

$$\sin x \cos\frac{\pi}{3} + \cos x \sin\frac{\pi}{3} + \sin x \cos\frac{\pi}{3} - \cos x \sin\frac{\pi}{3} = 1 \qquad \text{Use formulas.}$$

$$\frac{1}{2}\sin x + \frac{\sqrt{3}}{2}\cos x + \frac{1}{2}\sin x - \frac{\sqrt{3}}{2}\cos x = 1 \qquad \text{Evaluate.}$$

$$\sin x = 1 \qquad \text{Simplify.}$$

▶ In the interval $0 \le x < 2\pi$, the solution is $x = \frac{\pi}{2}$.

EXAMPLE 5 Rewriting a Real-Life Formula

The *index of refraction* of a transparent material is the ratio of the speed of light in a vacuum to the speed of light in the material. A triangular prism, like the one shown, can be used to measure the index of refraction using the formula

$$n = \frac{\sin\left(\frac{\theta}{2} + \frac{\alpha}{2}\right)}{\sin\frac{\theta}{2}}.$$

For $\alpha = 60°$, show that the formula can be rewritten as $n = \frac{\sqrt{3}}{2} + \frac{1}{2}\cot\frac{\theta}{2}$.

SOLUTION

$$n = \frac{\sin\left(\frac{\theta}{2} + 30°\right)}{\sin\frac{\theta}{2}} \qquad \text{Write formula with } \frac{\alpha}{2} = \frac{60°}{2} = 30°.$$

$$= \frac{\sin\frac{\theta}{2}\cos 30° + \cos\frac{\theta}{2}\sin 30°}{\sin\frac{\theta}{2}} \qquad \text{Sum formula for sine}$$

$$= \frac{\left(\sin\frac{\theta}{2}\right)\left(\frac{\sqrt{3}}{2}\right) + \left(\cos\frac{\theta}{2}\right)\left(\frac{1}{2}\right)}{\sin\frac{\theta}{2}} \qquad \text{Evaluate.}$$

$$= \frac{\frac{\sqrt{3}}{2}\sin\frac{\theta}{2}}{\sin\frac{\theta}{2}} + \frac{\frac{1}{2}\cos\frac{\theta}{2}}{\sin\frac{\theta}{2}} \qquad \text{Write as separate fractions.}$$

$$= \frac{\sqrt{3}}{2} + \frac{1}{2}\cot\frac{\theta}{2} \qquad \text{Simplify.}$$

SELF-ASSESSMENT 1 I do not understand. 2 I can do it with help. 3 I can do it on my own. 4 I can teach someone else.

9. Solve $\sin\left(\frac{\pi}{4} - x\right) - \sin\left(x + \frac{\pi}{4}\right) = 1$ for $0 \le x < 2\pi$.

10.8 Practice WITH CalcChat® AND CalcView®

In Exercises 1–8, find the exact value of the expression.
Example 1

1. $\tan(-15^\circ)$
2. $\tan 195^\circ$
3. $\sin \dfrac{23\pi}{12}$
4. $\sin(-165^\circ)$
5. $\cos 105^\circ$
6. $\cos \dfrac{11\pi}{12}$
7. $\tan \dfrac{17\pi}{12}$
8. $\sin\left(-\dfrac{7\pi}{12}\right)$

In Exercises 9–14, evaluate the expression given that $\cos a = \dfrac{4}{5}$ with $0 < a < \dfrac{\pi}{2}$ and $\sin b = -\dfrac{15}{17}$ with $\dfrac{3\pi}{2} < b < 2\pi$. *Example 2*

9. $\sin(a + b)$
10. $\sin(a - b)$
11. $\cos(a - b)$
12. $\cos(a + b)$
13. $\tan(a + b)$
14. $\tan(a - b)$

In Exercises 15–20, simplify the expression.
Example 3

15. $\tan(x + \pi)$
16. $\cos\left(x - \dfrac{\pi}{2}\right)$
17. $\cos(x + 2\pi)$
18. $\tan(x - 2\pi)$
19. $\sin\left(x - \dfrac{3\pi}{2}\right)$
20. $\tan\left(x + \dfrac{\pi}{2}\right)$

ERROR ANALYSIS In Exercises 21 and 22, describe and correct the error in simplifying the expression.

21.

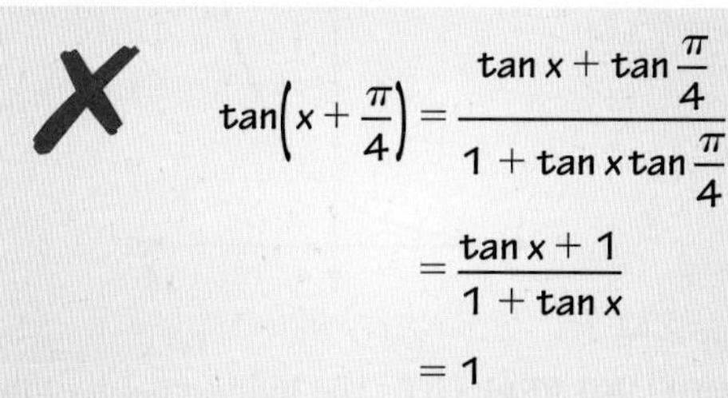

22.

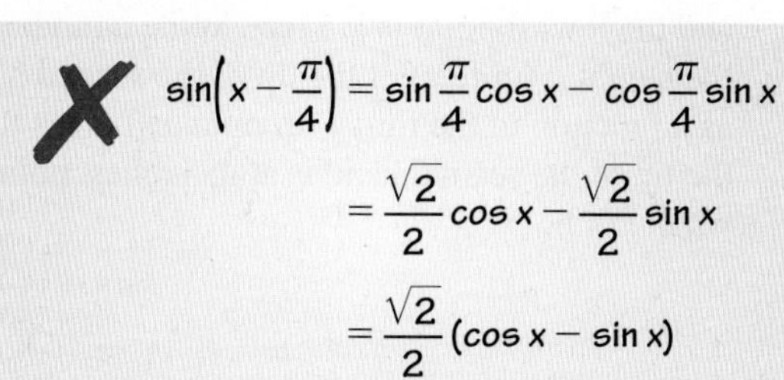

In Exercises 23–30, solve the equation for $0 \le x < 2\pi$.
Example 4

23. $2 \sin x - 1 = 0$
24. $\cos x + 1 = 0$
25. $\sin\left(x + \dfrac{\pi}{2}\right) = \dfrac{1}{2}$
26. $\tan\left(x - \dfrac{\pi}{4}\right) = 0$
27. $\cos\left(x + \dfrac{\pi}{6}\right) - \cos\left(x - \dfrac{\pi}{6}\right) = 1$
28. $\sin\left(x + \dfrac{3\pi}{2}\right) - \sin\left(x - \dfrac{3\pi}{2}\right) = \sqrt{3}$
29. $\tan(x + \pi) - \tan(\pi - x) = 0$
30. $\sin(x + \pi) + \cos(x + \pi) = 0$

31. **MODELING REAL LIFE** When a wave travels through a taut string, the displacement y of each point on the string depends on the time t and the point's position x. The equation of a *standing wave* can be obtained by adding the displacements of two waves traveling in opposite directions. A particular standing wave can be modeled by the formula
$$y = A \cos\left(\frac{2\pi t}{3} - \frac{2\pi x}{5}\right) + A \cos\left(\frac{2\pi t}{3} + \frac{2\pi x}{5}\right).$$
When $t = 1$, show that the formula can be rewritten as $y = -A \cos \dfrac{2\pi x}{5}$. *Example 5*

32. **MODELING REAL LIFE** A photographer is at a height h taking aerial photographs with a 35-millimeter camera. The ratio of the image length WQ to the length NA of the actual object is given by the formula
$$\frac{WQ}{NA} = \frac{35 \tan(\theta - t) + 35 \tan t}{h \tan \theta}$$
where θ is the angle between the vertical line perpendicular to the ground and the line from the camera to point A and t is the tilt angle of the film. When $t = 45^\circ$, show that the formula can be rewritten as $\dfrac{WQ}{NA} = \dfrac{70}{h(1 + \tan \theta)}$.

33. **USING EQUATIONS** Derive the cofunction identity $\sin\left(\dfrac{\pi}{2} - \theta\right) = \cos \theta$ using the difference formula for sine.

34. HOW DO YOU SEE IT?

Explain how to use the graph to solve the equation $\sin\left(x + \frac{\pi}{4}\right) - \sin\left(\frac{\pi}{4} - x\right) = 0$ for $0 \le x < 2\pi$.

Then find the solutions.

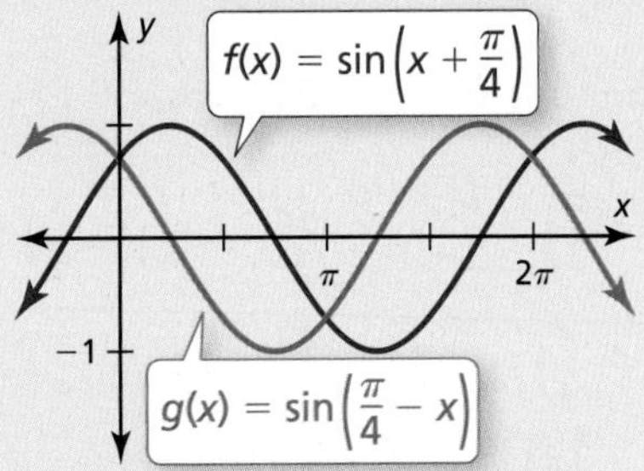

35. MAKING AN ARGUMENT Is it possible to use the difference formula for tangent to derive the cofunction identity $\tan\left(\frac{\pi}{2} - \theta\right) = \cot \theta$? Explain your reasoning.

36. DIG DEEPER Show how you can derive the formulas for $\tan(a + b)$ and $\tan(a - b)$.

37. CONNECTING CONCEPTS The figure shows the acute angle of intersection, $\theta_2 - \theta_1$, of two lines with slopes m_1 and m_2.

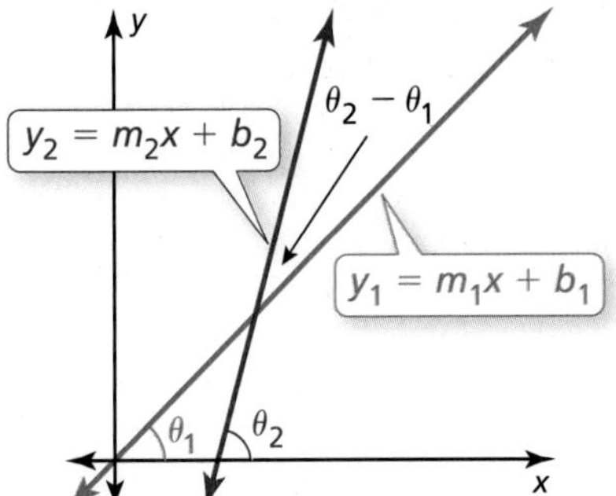

a. Use the difference formula for tangent to write an equation for $\tan(\theta_2 - \theta_1)$ in terms of m_1 and m_2.

b. Use the equation from part (a) to find the acute angle of intersection of the lines $y_1 = x$ and $y_2 = (2 + \sqrt{3})x - 8$.

38. THOUGHT PROVOKING

Write (a) $\sin 3x$ as a function of $\sin x$, (b) $\cos 3x$ as a function of $\cos x$, and (c) $\tan 3x$ as a function of $\tan x$.

REVIEW & REFRESH

In Exercises 39 and 40, solve the equation.

39. $1 - \frac{9}{x - 2} = -\frac{7}{2}$

40. $\frac{2x - 3}{x + 1} = \frac{10}{x^2 - 1} + 5$

In Exercises 41 and 42, find the exact value of the expression.

41. $\cos \frac{13\pi}{12}$

42. $\tan 165°$

43. Find the value of x for the right triangle.

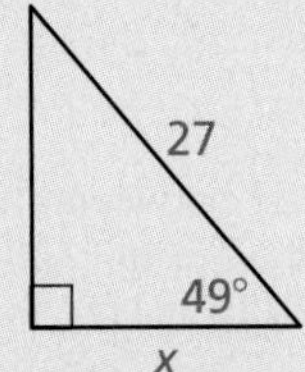

44. Simplify $(1 - \sin \theta)(1 + \sin \theta)$.

45. The owner of a restaurant asks 20 customers whether they are satisfied with the quality of their meals. Identify the method of data collection.

46. Graph one period of the function $g(x) = 4 \sec x$. Describe the graph of g as a transformation of the graph of $f(x) = \sec x$.

47. The graph of $f(x) = b^x$ is shown. Describe the possible values of b.

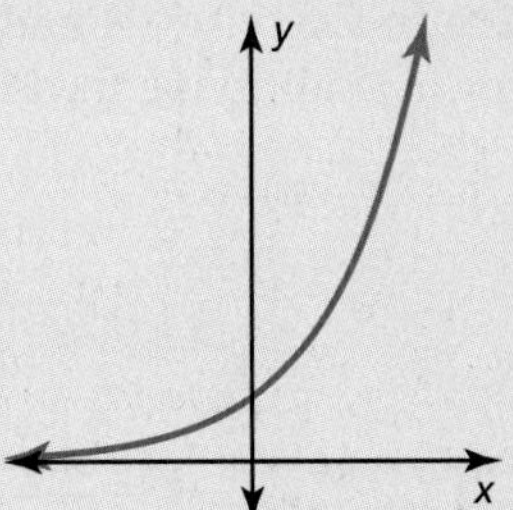

48. MODELING REAL LIFE The highest point of the tip of a clock's second hand is 8 feet above the floor, and the lowest point is 7.5 feet. Write a model for the height h (in feet) of the tip of the second hand as a function of the time t (in minutes) given that the tip of the second hand is at its highest point when $t = 0$.

10 Chapter Review WITH CalcChat®

Chapter Learning Target Understand trigonometric ratios and functions.

Chapter Success Criteria

- ◆ I can define right triangle trigonometric functions.
- ◆ I can evaluate trigonometric functions of any angle.
- ■ I can graph trigonometric functions.
- ■ I can model using trigonometric functions.

◆ Surface
■ Deep

SELF-ASSESSMENT 1 I do not understand. 2 I can do it with help. 3 I can do it on my own. 4 I can teach someone else.

10.1 Right Triangle Trigonometry (pp. 521–528)

Learning Target: Understand the six trigonometric functions.

Vocabulary
sine
cosine
tangent
cosecant
secant
cotangent

Evaluate the six trigonometric functions of the angle θ.

1. 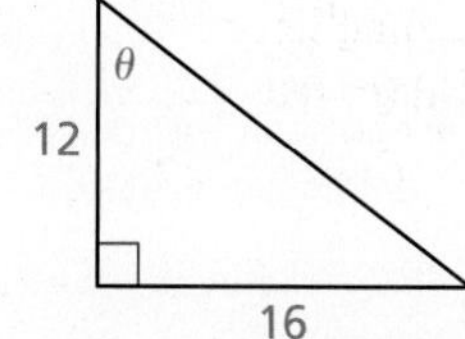

2. 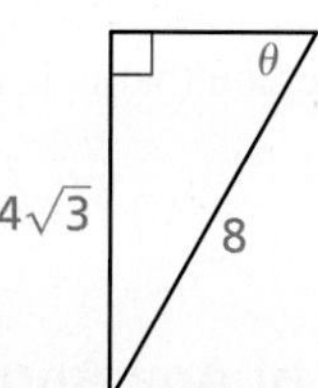

3. In a right triangle, θ is an acute angle and $\cos\theta = \frac{6}{11}$. Evaluate the other five trigonometric functions of θ.

Solve $\triangle ABC$. Round your answers to the nearest hundredth, if necessary.

4. 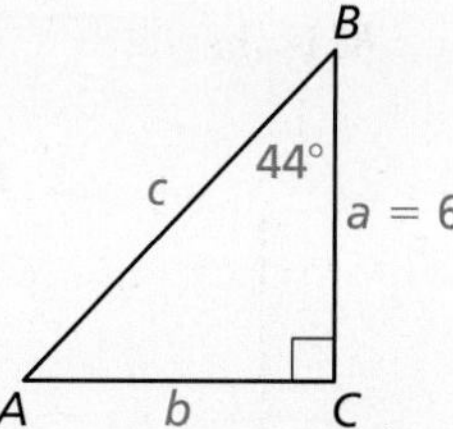

5. 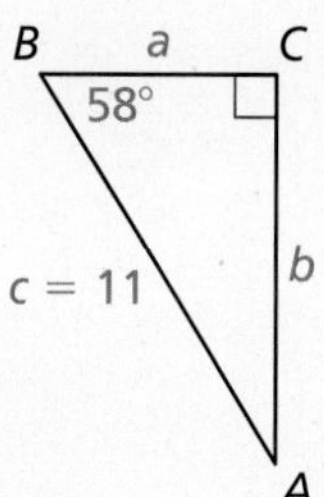

6. For a given angle θ, explain why $\sec\theta$ and $\csc\theta$ must both be greater than or equal to 1.

7. You fly a kite at an angle of 70°. The length of the string is 400 feet, and you hold the reel 4 feet above the ground.

   a. How high above the ground is the kite?

   b. A friend watching the kite estimates that the angle of elevation to the kite is 85°. How far from your friend are you standing?

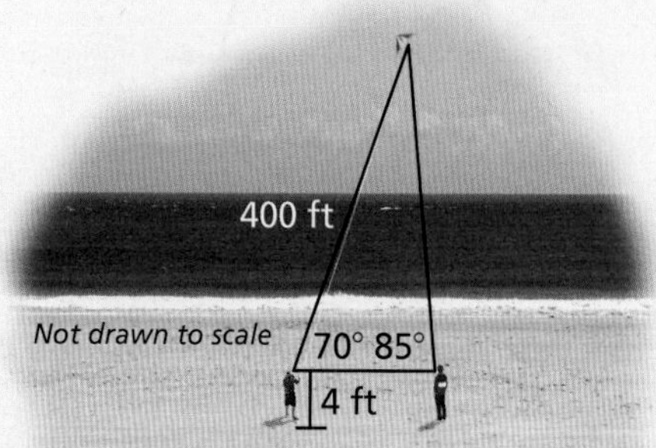

10.2 Angles and Radian Measure (pp. 529–536)

Learning Target: Draw angles in standard position and understand radian measure.

Vocabulary

initial side
terminal side
standard position
coterminal
radian
sector
central angle

Convert the degree measure to radians or the radian measure to degrees.

8. $30°$ **9.** $225°$ **10.** $\frac{3\pi}{4}$ **11.** $\frac{5\pi}{3}$

12. Using radian measure, write one positive angle and one negative angle that are coterminal with 380°.

13. Find the value of θ. Then draw the angle in standard position.

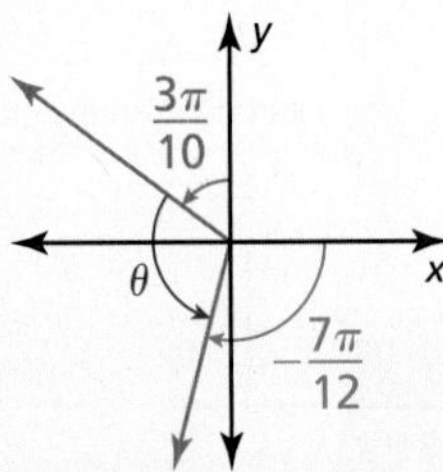

14. Find the arc length and area of a sector with a radius of 7 inches and a central angle of $\frac{\pi}{6}$.

15. A sprinkler system on a farm rotates 140° and sprays water up to 35 meters. Draw a diagram that shows the region that is irrigated by the sprinkler. Then find the area of the region.

10.3 Trigonometric Functions of Any Angle (pp. 537–544)

Learning Target: Evaluate trigonometric functions of any angle.

Vocabulary

unit circle
quadrantal angle
reference angle

Evaluate the six trigonometric functions of θ.

16.

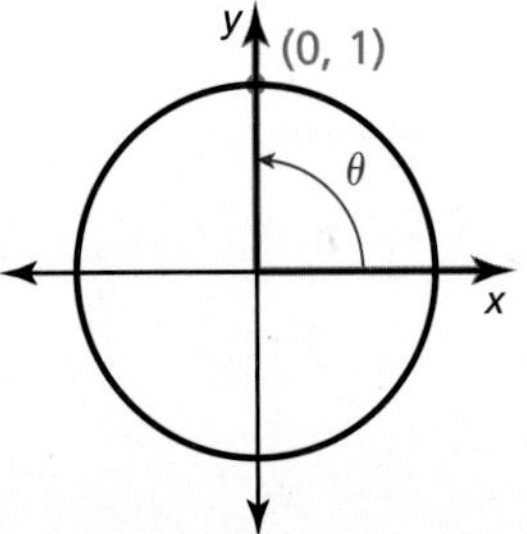

17.

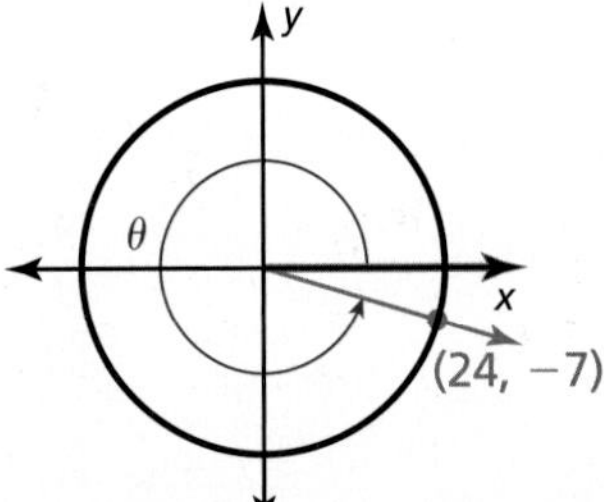

18.

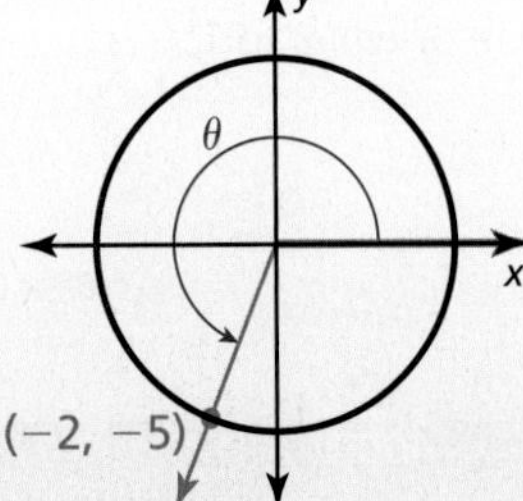

19.

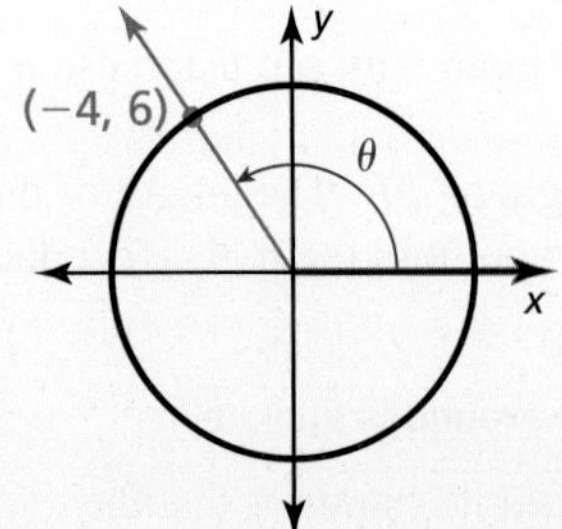

Evaluate the function without using a calculator.

20. $\tan 330°$ **21.** $\sec(-405°)$ **22.** $\sin \frac{13\pi}{6}$ **23.** $\sec \frac{11\pi}{3}$

10.4 Graphing Sine and Cosine Functions (pp. 545–554)

Learning Target: Describe and graph sine and cosine functions.

Vocabulary
amplitude
periodic function
cycle
period
phase shift
midline

Identify the amplitude and period of the function. Then graph the function and describe the graph of g as a transformation of the graph of its parent function.

24. $g(x) = 3 \sin x$

25. $g(x) = 8 \cos x$

26. $g(x) = 6 \sin \pi x$

27. $g(x) = \frac{1}{4} \cos 4x$

Use the graph to write a function of the form $y = a \sin bx$. Explain your reasoning.

28.

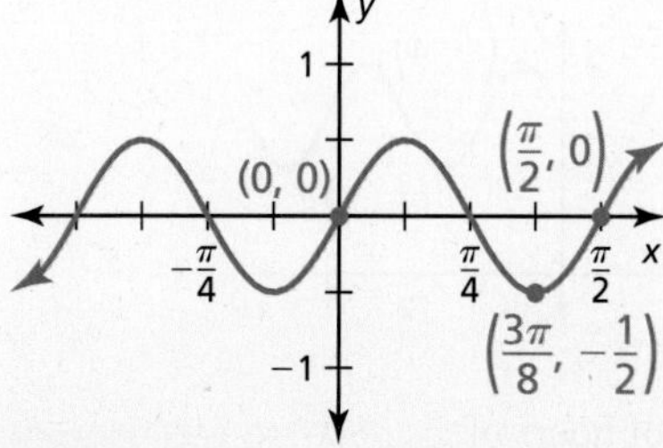

29.

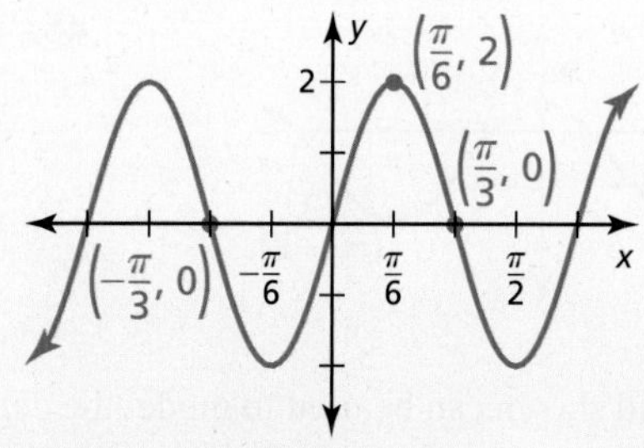

Graph the function.

30. $g(x) = \cos(x + \pi) + 2$

31. $g(x) = -\sin x - 4$

32. $g(x) = 2 \sin\left(x + \frac{\pi}{2}\right)$

33. $g(x) = \frac{1}{2} \cos\left(x - \frac{3\pi}{2}\right) + 1$

10.5 Graphing Other Trigonometric Functions (pp. 555–562)

Learning Target: Describe and graph tangent, cotangent, secant, and cosecant functions.

Graph one period of the function. Describe the graph of g as a transformation of the graph of its parent function.

34. $g(x) = \tan \frac{1}{2}x$

35. $g(x) = 2 \cot x$

36. $g(x) = 4 \tan 3\pi x$

37. $g(x) = 5 \csc x$

38. $g(x) = \sec \frac{1}{2}x$

39. $g(x) = \frac{1}{2} \csc \frac{\pi}{4}x$

40. The graph of $y = \sec bx$ has a period of $\frac{\pi}{3}$. Describe the asymptotes of the graph. Explain your reasoning.

41. In 2017, Alex Honnold completed the first *free solo* climb of El Capitan in Yosemite National Park. Suppose a spectator stood 1500 feet from the base of the 3000-foot-tall rock wall. Write and graph an equation that represents the distance d (in feet) of Alex from the top of the wall as a function of the angle of elevation θ.

10.6 Modeling with Trigonometric Functions (pp. 563–570)

Learning Target: Write trigonometric functions.

Vocabulary
frequency
sinusoid

Write a function for the sinusoid.

42.

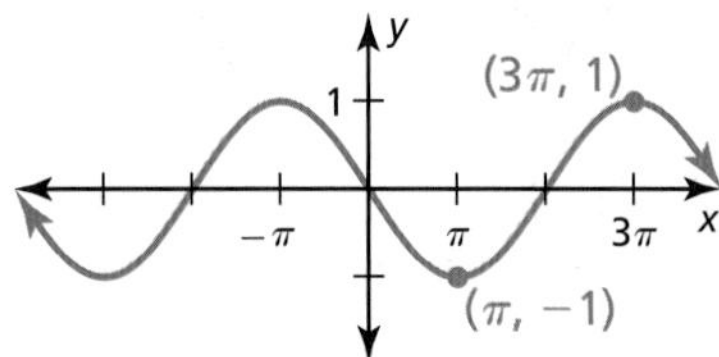

43.

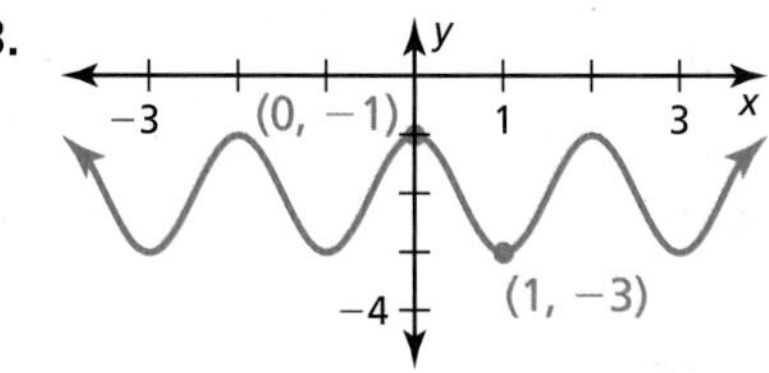

44.

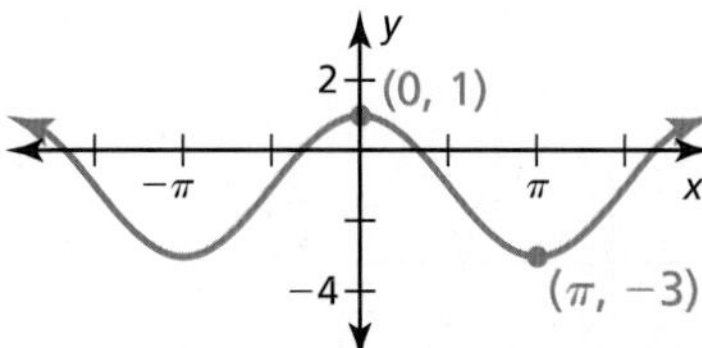

45.

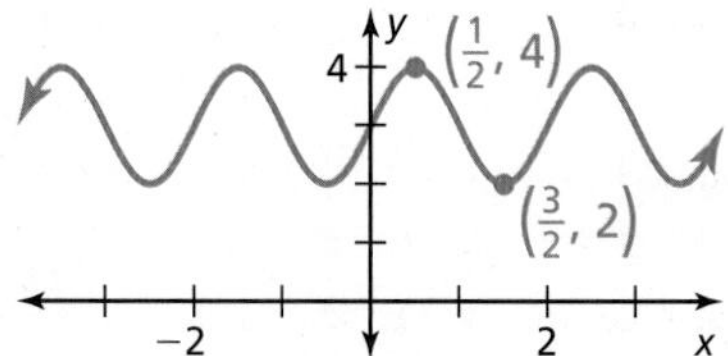

46. The sinusoid shown can be used to model the daily numbers of hours of daylight in Bozeman, Montana. Write a function for the model.

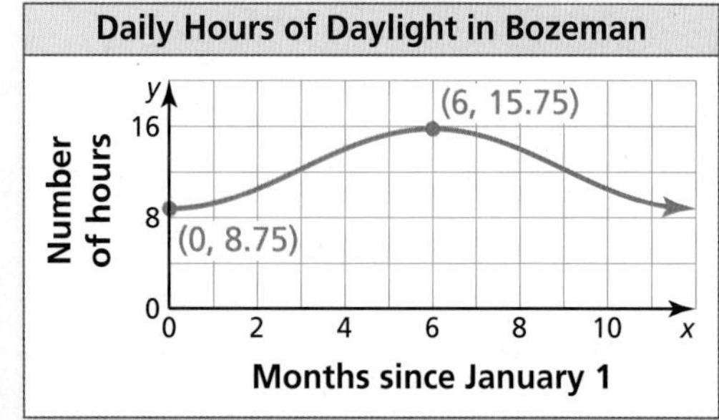

47. One of the largest sewing machines in the world has a *flywheel* (which turns as the machine sews) that is 5 feet in diameter. The highest point of the handle at the edge of the flywheel is 9 feet above the ground, and the lowest point is 4 feet. The wheel makes a complete turn every 2 seconds. Write a model for the height h (in feet) of the handle as a function of the time t (in seconds) given that the handle is at its lowest point when $t = 0$.

48. The table shows the monthly precipitation P (in inches) for Minneapolis, Minnesota, where the time t is measured in months and $t = 1$ represents January. Write a model that gives P as a function of t and interpret the period of its graph.

Time, t	Precipitation, P
1	0.87
2	0.75
3	1.89
4	2.64
5	3.35
6	4.25
7	4.02
8	4.29
9	3.07
10	2.40
11	1.73
12	1.14

10.7 Using Trigonometric Identities (pp. 571–576)

Learning Target: Use trigonometric identities to evaluate and simplify trigonometric expressions.

Vocabulary

trigonometric identity

Find the values of the other five trigonometric functions of θ.

49. $\cos \theta = \frac{3}{5}, 0 < \theta < \frac{\pi}{2}$

50. $\sin \theta = -\frac{5}{13}, \frac{3\pi}{2} < \theta < 2\pi$

51. $\sin \theta = \frac{1}{4}, \frac{\pi}{2} < \theta < \pi$

52. $\tan \theta = \frac{7}{2}, \pi < \theta < \frac{3\pi}{2}$

Simplify the expression.

53. $\cot^2 x - \cot^2 x \cos^2 x$

54. $\frac{(\sec x + 1)(\sec x - 1)}{\tan x}$

55. $\sin\left(\frac{\pi}{2} - x\right) \tan x$

56. $\frac{\sin x - \csc x}{\csc x}$

Verify the identity.

57. $\frac{\cos x \sec x}{1 + \tan^2 x} = \cos^2 x$

58. $\tan\left(\frac{\pi}{2} - x\right) \cot x = \csc^2 x - 1$

10.8 Using Sum and Difference Formulas (pp. 577–582)

Learning Target: Use sum and difference formulas to evaluate and simplify trigonometric expressions.

Find the exact value of the expression.

59. $\sin 75°$

60. $\tan(-45°)$

61. $\sin \frac{\pi}{12}$

62. Find $\tan(a + b)$, given that $\tan a = \frac{1}{4}$ with $\pi < a < \frac{3\pi}{2}$ and $\tan b = \frac{3}{7}$ with $0 < b < \frac{\pi}{2}$.

Simplify the expression.

63. $\sin\left(x - \frac{\pi}{2}\right)$

64. $\cos\left(x + \frac{\pi}{2}\right)$

65. $\tan\left(x - \frac{\pi}{2}\right)$

Solve the equation for $0 \le x < 2\pi$.

66. $\cos\left(x + \frac{3\pi}{4}\right) + \cos\left(x - \frac{3\pi}{4}\right) = 1$

67. $\tan(x + \pi) + \cos\left(x + \frac{\pi}{2}\right) = 0$

Mathematical Practices

Attend to Precision

Mathematically proficient students try to communicate precisely to others.

1. In your own words, describe the meaning of the terms *angle of depression* and *angle of elevation*.

2. In the two similar triangles shown, $\theta_1 = \theta_2$. Explain why the values of the trigonometric ratios of θ_1 and θ_2 are equal.

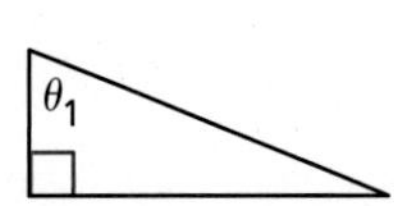

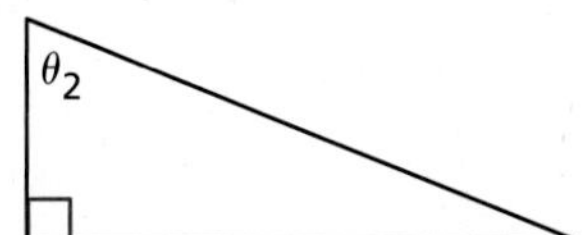

10 Practice Test WITH CalcChat®

Verify the identity.

1. $\dfrac{\cos^2 x + \sin^2 x}{1 + \tan^2 x} = \cos^2 x$

2. $\dfrac{1 + \sin x}{\cos x} + \dfrac{\cos x}{1 + \sin x} = 2 \sec x$

3. $\cos\left(x + \dfrac{3\pi}{2}\right) = \sin x$

Write a function for the sinusoid.

4.

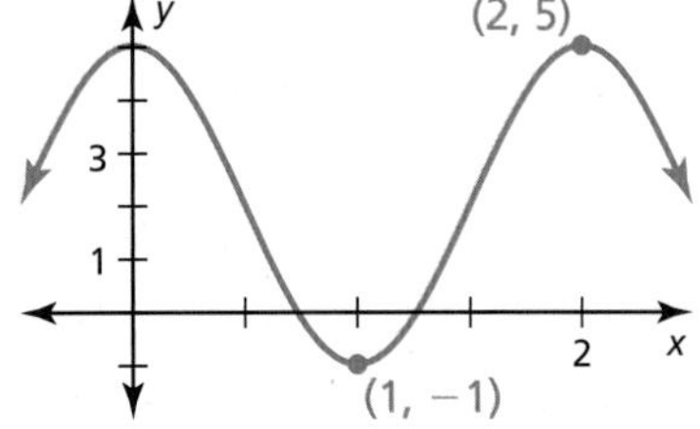

5.

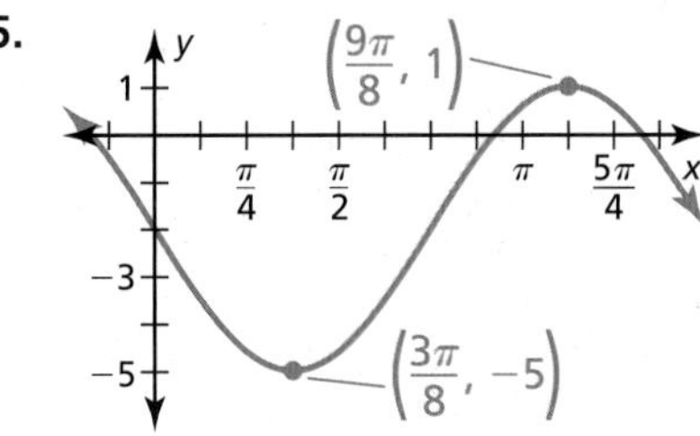

Graph the function. Then describe the graph of g as a transformation of the graph of its parent function.

6. $g(x) = -4 \tan 2x$

7. $g(x) = -2 \cos \frac{1}{3}x + 3$

8. $g(x) = 3 \csc \pi x$

Convert the degree measure to radians or the radian measure to degrees. Then find one positive angle and one negative angle that are coterminal with the given angle.

9. $-50°$

10. $\dfrac{4\pi}{5}$

11. $\dfrac{8\pi}{3}$

12. Find the arc length and area of a sector with radius $r = 13$ inches and central angle $\theta = \dfrac{3\pi}{4}$.

Evaluate the six trigonometric functions of the angle θ.

13.

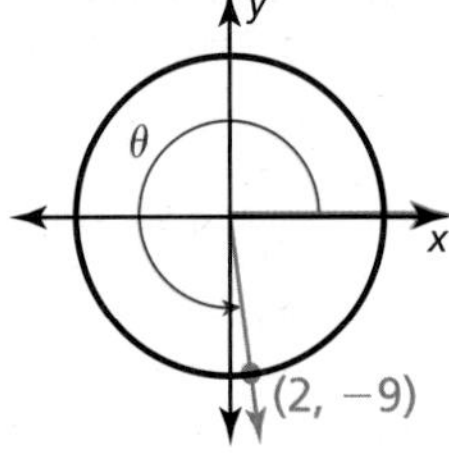

14.

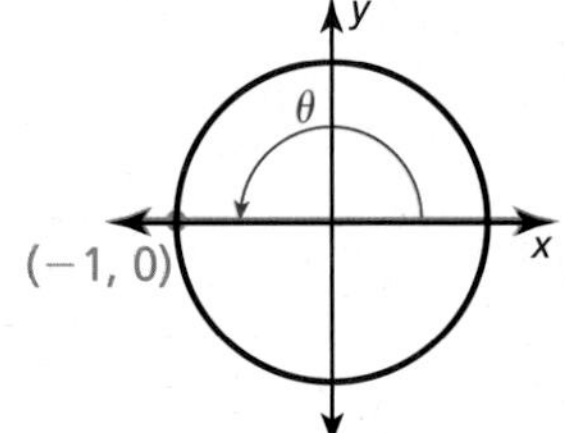

15. How tall is the building shown? Justify your answer.

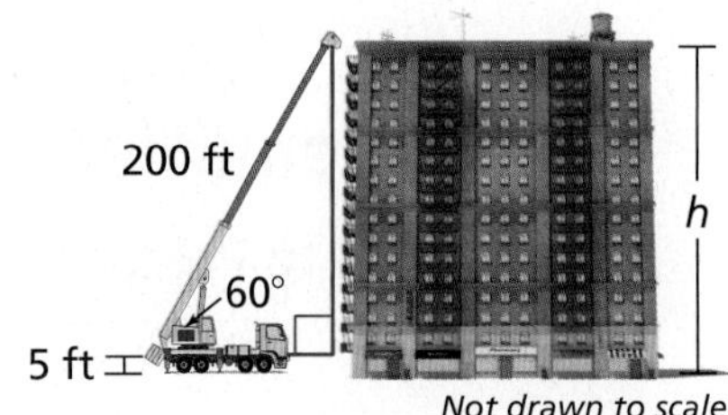

Not drawn to scale

16. Write and graph a function that represents the area A (in square feet) of a sector with a central angle of 60° and a radius of r feet.

17. The table shows the average daily high temperatures T (in degrees Fahrenheit) in Baltimore, Maryland, where $m = 1$ represents January. Write a model that gives T as a function of m and interpret the period of its graph.

m	1	2	3	4	5	6	7	8	9	10	11	12
T	42	46	54	65	75	85	89	87	80	68	58	46

10 Performance Task
Smooth Sailing

In navigation, *bearings* are used to indicate direction.

The bearing of a line indicates the measure of the angle formed by the line and either the north or the south direction.

Bearings are written as either a north or a south direction, followed by a number of degrees in either the east or west direction.

Bearings are never greater than 90°. Navigators often use the terms *due north*, *due south*, *due east*, and *due west* to indicate a bearing of 0° or 90°.

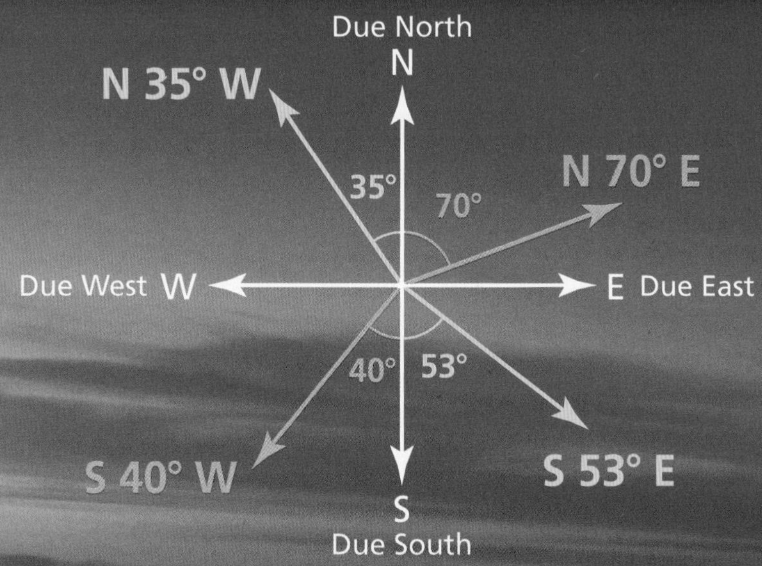

Sailors use *nautical miles* to measure distances and *knots* to measure speeds.

NAUTICAL MILE:

A unit for distance based on the circumference of Earth

1 nautical mile ≈ 1.15 miles

KNOT:

A knot is one nautical mile per hour.

1 knot ≈ 1.15 miles per hour

GET YOUR BEARINGS

You are navigating a boat to Port A, which is 5.2 nautical miles due east of Port B. You determine that the bearing from your current location to Port A is S 60° E and your bearing to Port B is S 30° W. You travel at an average speed of 24 knots. How long will it take you to reach your destination if you can take a direct route?

To avoid an island directly between your location and Port A, you travel due east until your new bearing to Port A is S 40° E. How does this affect your travel time? Justify your answer.

10 College and Career Readiness WITH CalcChat®

WATCH Tutorial videos are available for each exercise.

1. Given that $\sin \theta = \frac{3}{5}$ and $\frac{\pi}{2} < \theta < \pi$, which of the following is *not* a trigonometric function of θ?

Ⓐ $\cos \theta = -\frac{4}{5}$

Ⓑ $\csc \theta = \frac{5}{3}$

Ⓒ $\tan \theta = \frac{3}{4}$

Ⓓ $\sec \theta = -\frac{5}{4}$

2. Order the values from least to greatest. Use $\log_2 5 \approx 2.322$ and $\log_2 3 \approx 1.585$, if necessary.

$\log 1000$	$\log_2 15$	$\ln e$
$\log_2 9$	$\log_2 \frac{5}{3}$	$\log_2 1$

3. The tables show the average monthly temperatures (in degrees Fahrenheit) in a city and the amounts of natural gas (in cubic feet) used in a residence for 12 months.

January	February	March	April	May	June
34°F	35°F	44°F	56°F	67°F	76°F
20,000 ft^3	17,000 ft^3	11,000 ft^3	9,000 ft^3	7,000 ft^3	5,000 ft^3

July	August	September	October	November	December
80°F	79°F	72°F	61°F	50°F	38°F
4,000 ft^3	4,000 ft^3	7,000 ft^3	14,000 ft^3	17,000 ft^3	19,000 ft^3

a. Use technology to find trigonometric models for the average monthly temperatures y_1 as a function of time and the amounts of natural gas y_2 (in thousands of cubic feet) as a function of time. Let $t = 1$ represent January.

b. Use technology to graph the two regression equations in the same coordinate plane. Describe the relationship between the graphs.

4. Use the Rational Root Theorem and the graph to find all the real zeros of the function $f(x) = 2x^3 - x^2 - 13x - 6$.

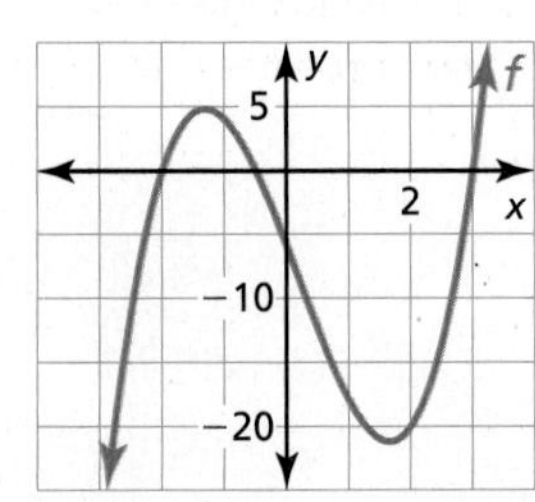

5. The mean score on a test is 79 and the standard deviation is 6. About what percent of the scores are greater than 73?

Ⓐ 2.5% Ⓑ 16%

Ⓒ 84% Ⓓ 97.5%

6. Which graph represents $y = \frac{1}{2}(4)^{x-2} - 2$?

Ⓐ
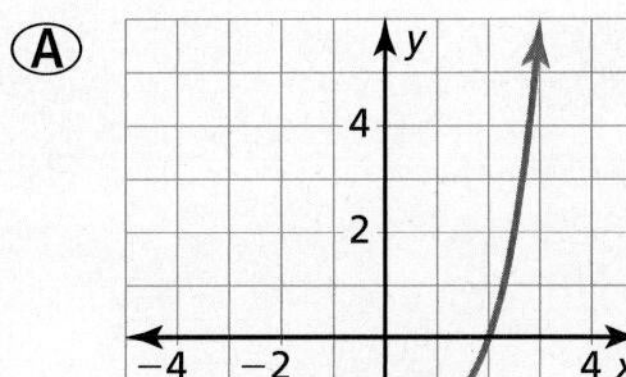

Ⓑ
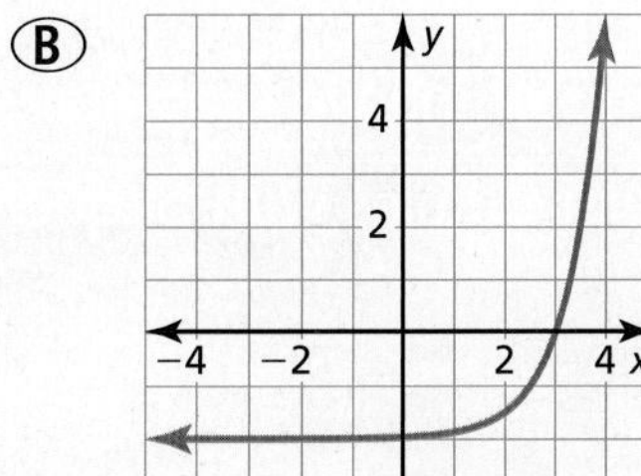

Ⓒ
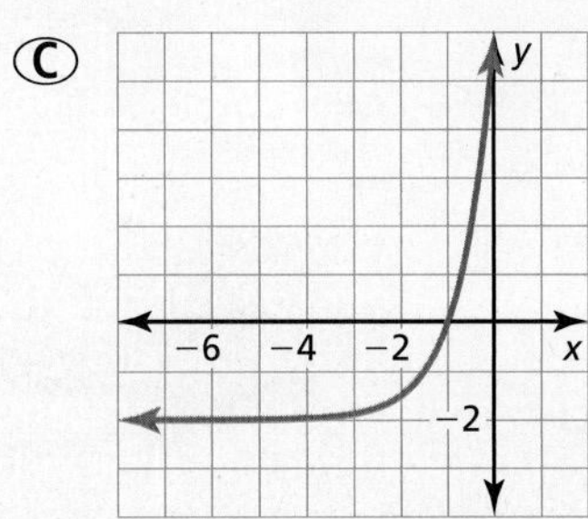

Ⓓ
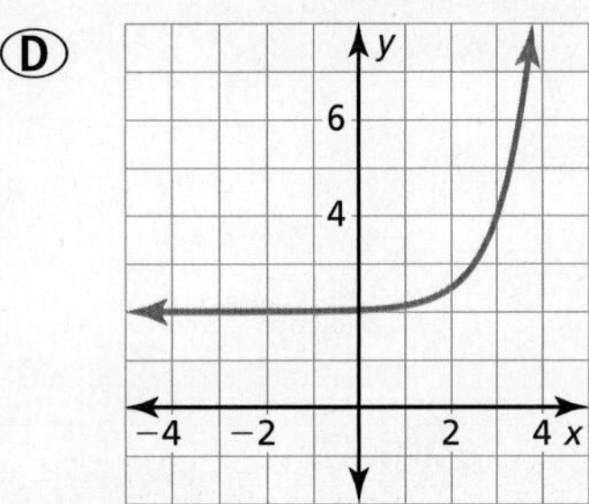

7. Complete each statement with < or > so that each statement is true.

a. θ ▭ 3 radians

b. $\tan\theta$ ▭ 0

c. θ' ▭ 45°

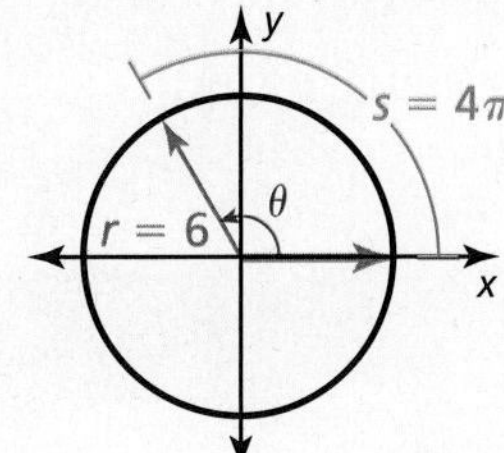

8. Which of the following are solutions of $2 + 3x = 2x^2 - 3$? Select all that apply.

Ⓐ $x = -\frac{5}{2}$ Ⓑ $x = -1$

Ⓒ $x = 1$ Ⓓ $x = \frac{5}{2}$

9. The table shows that the force F (in pounds) needed to loosen a certain bolt with a wrench depends on the length ℓ (in inches) of the wrench's handle. Write an equation that relates ℓ and F. Describe the relationship.

Length, ℓ	4	6	10	12
Force, F	375	250	150	125

11 Sequences and Series

NATIONAL GEOGRAPHIC EXPLORER

Barton Seaver

Barton Seaver is a chef who has dedicated his career to restoring the relationship we have with our ocean. It is his belief that the choices we make for dinner directly impact the ocean and its fragile ecosystems. He is the author of *For Cod and Country*, a book of recipes that inspires ocean conservation.

- Some of the most popular fish in the United States are salmon, tuna, tilapia, pollock, and pangasius. Are any of these endangered?
- What does it mean to "farm raise" fish?
- What percent of the meat eaten by Americans is fish? beef? chicken? pork?

STEM

Conservationists frequently monitor fish populations. In the Performance Task, you will analyze a plan to stabilize a fish population.

Ocean Conservation

Preparing for Chapter 11

Chapter Learning Target Understand sequences and series.

Chapter Success Criteria

- I can define and use sequences and series.
- I can describe how to find sums of infinite geometric series.
- I can analyze arithmetic and geometric sequences and series.
- I can explain how to write recursive rules for sequences.

◆ Surface
■ Deep

Chapter Vocabulary

Work with a partner. Discuss each of the vocabulary terms.

sequence
arithmetic sequence
common difference
geometric sequence
common ratio
partial sum
explicit rule
recursive rule

Mathematical Practices

Look for and Express Regularity in Repeated Reasoning

Mathematically proficient students notice if calculations are repeated, and look both for general methods and for shortcuts.

Work with a partner. A conservationist estimates the number of salmon in a region each year for t years. The results are shown in the table.

Time, t (years)	Number of salmon, a_t (thousands)
1	800
2	823
3	846
4	869
5	892
6	915

1. Assuming the population continues to grow at this rate, estimate the number of salmon after 7 years, 8 years, and 9 years. Explain your reasoning.

2. Write and graph an equation that relates t and a_t.

3. Write an equation that relates a_t and a_{t-1}. Can you graph the relationship using only this equation? Explain.

11 Prepare WITH CalcChat®

Evaluating Functions

WATCH

Example 1 **Evaluate the function $y = 2x^2 - 10$ for the values $x = 0, 1, 2, 3,$ and 4.**

Input, x	$2x^2 - 10$	Output, y
0	$2(0)^2 - 10$	-10
1	$2(1)^2 - 10$	-8
2	$2(2)^2 - 10$	-2
3	$2(3)^2 - 10$	8
4	$2(4)^2 - 10$	22

Complete the table to evaluate the function.

1. $y = 3 - 2^x$

x	y
1	
2	
3	

2. $y = 5x^2 + 1$

x	y
2	
3	
4	

3. $y = -4x + 24$

x	y
5	
10	
15	

Solving Equations

WATCH

Example 2 **Solve the equation $45 = 5(3)^x$.**

$45 = 5(3)^x$ Write original equation.

$\frac{45}{5} = \frac{5(3)^x}{5}$ Division Property of Equality

$9 = 3^x$ Simplify.

$\log_3 9 = \log_3 3^x$ Take $\log_3$ of each side.

$2 = x$ Simplify.

Solve the equation. Check your solution.

4. $7x + 3 = 31$

5. $\frac{1}{16} = 4\left(\frac{1}{2}\right)^x$

6. $216 = 3(x + 6)$

7. $2^x + 16 = 144$

8. $\frac{1}{4}x - 8 = 17$

9. $8\left(\frac{3}{4}\right)^x = \frac{27}{8}$

10. **MP STRUCTURE** Find three consecutive odd numbers that have a sum of 165. Justify your answer.

11.1 Defining and Using Sequences and Series

Learning Target Understand sequences and series.

Success Criteria

- I can use rules to write terms of sequences.
- I can write rules for sequences.
- I can write and find sums of series.

EXPLORE IT! Finding Terms of Sequences

Work with a partner.

a. For each pattern, find the number of objects in each figure. Then find the number of objects in the next figure. Explain your reasoning.

i.

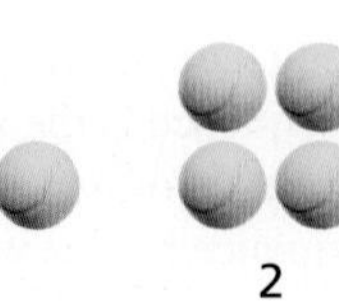

1 2 3 4 5

ii.

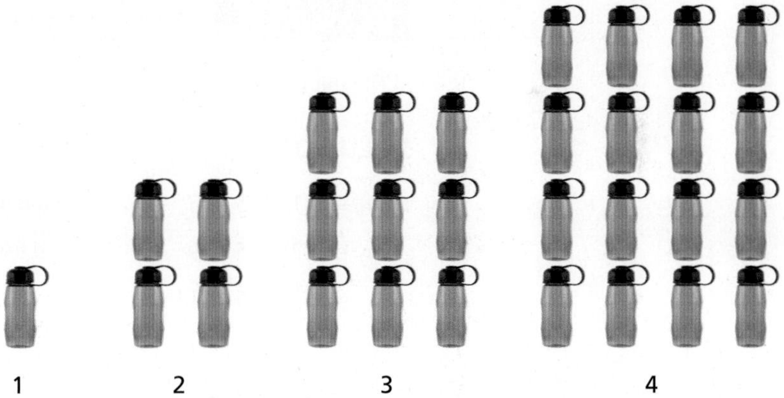

1 2 3 4

iii.

1 2 3

b. For each pattern in part (a), find the number of objects in the 10th figure. Explain your reasoning.

Math Practice

Use Equations
How can you use an equation to find the number a_n of objects in the nth figure?

Writing Terms of Sequences

Vocabulary 

sequence, *p. 596*
terms of a sequence, *p. 596*
series, *p. 598*
summation notation, *p. 598*
sigma notation, *p. 598*

KEY IDEA

Sequences

A **sequence** is an ordered list of numbers. A *finite sequence* is a function that has a limited number of terms and whose domain is the finite set $\{1, 2, 3, \ldots, n\}$. The values in the range are called the **terms** of the sequence.

Domain:	1	2	3	4	...	n	Relative position of each term
	↓	↓	↓	↓		↓	
Range:	a_1	a_2	a_3	a_4	...	a_n	Terms of the sequence

An *infinite sequence* is a function that continues without stopping and whose domain is the set of positive integers. Here are examples of a finite sequence and an infinite sequence.

Finite sequence: 2, 4, 6, 8

Infinite sequence: 2, 4, 6, 8, . . .

A sequence can be specified by an equation, or *rule*. For example, both sequences above can be described by the rule $a_n = 2n$ or $f(n) = 2n$.

The domain of a sequence may begin with 0 instead of 1. When this is the case, the domain of a finite sequence is the set $\{0, 1, 2, 3, \ldots, n\}$ and the domain of an infinite sequence becomes the set of nonnegative integers. Unless otherwise indicated, assume the domain of a sequence begins with 1.

EXAMPLE 1 Writing the Terms of Sequences

Write the first six terms of (a) $a_n = 2n + 5$ and (b) $f(n) = (-3)^{n-1}$.

SOLUTION

a.

$a_1 = 2(1) + 5 = 7$	1st term
$a_2 = 2(2) + 5 = 9$	2nd term
$a_3 = 2(3) + 5 = 11$	3rd term
$a_4 = 2(4) + 5 = 13$	4th term
$a_5 = 2(5) + 5 = 15$	5th term
$a_6 = 2(6) + 5 = 17$	6th term

▶ The first six terms are 7, 9, 11, 13, 15, 17.

b.

$f(1) = (-3)^{1-1} = 1$

$f(2) = (-3)^{2-1} = -3$

$f(3) = (-3)^{3-1} = 9$

$f(4) = (-3)^{4-1} = -27$

$f(5) = (-3)^{5-1} = 81$

$f(6) = (-3)^{6-1} = -243$

▶ The first six terms are 1, −3, 9, −27, 81, −243.

SELF-ASSESSMENT 1 I do not understand. 2 I can do it with help. 3 I can do it on my own. 4 I can teach someone else.

Write the first six terms of the sequence.

1. $a_n = n + 4$

2. $f(n) = (-2)^{n-1}$

3. $a_n = \dfrac{n}{n+1}$

Writing Rules for Sequences

STUDY TIP

When you are given only the first several terms of a sequence, there may be more than one rule for the nth term. For instance, the sequence 2, 4, 8, . . . can be given by $a_n = 2^n$ or $a_n = n^2 - n + 2$.

When the terms of a sequence have a recognizable pattern, you may be able to write a rule for the nth term of the sequence.

EXAMPLE 2 **Writing Rules for Sequences**

Describe the pattern, write the next term, and write a rule for the nth term of the sequence (a) $-1, -8, -27, -64, \ldots$ and (b) $0, 2, 6, 12, \ldots$.

SOLUTION

a. You can write the terms as $(-1)^3, (-2)^3, (-3)^3, (-4)^3, \ldots$. The next term is $a_5 = (-5)^3 = -125$. A rule for the nth term is $a_n = (-n)^3$.

b. You can write the terms as $0(1), 1(2), 2(3), 3(4), \ldots$. The next term is $f(5) = 4(5) = 20$. A rule for the nth term is $f(n) = (n - 1)n$.

To graph a sequence, let the horizontal axis represent the position numbers (the domain) and let the vertical axis represent the terms (the range).

EXAMPLE 3 **Modeling Real Life**

You work in a grocery store and stack apples in the shape of a square pyramid with seven layers. Write a rule for the number of apples in each layer. Then graph the sequence.

SOLUTION

Step 1 Make a table showing the numbers of apples in the first three layers. Let a_n represent the number of apples in layer n.

Layer, n	1	2	3
Number of apples, a_n	$1 = 1^2$	$4 = 2^2$	$9 = 3^2$

COMMON ERROR

Although the plotted points in Example 3 follow a curve, do not draw the curve because the sequence is defined only for integer values of n, specifically $n = 1, 2, 3, 4, 5, 6,$ and 7.

Step 2 Write a rule for the number of apples in each layer. From the table, you can see that $a_n = n^2$.

Step 3 Plot the points (1, 1), (2, 4), (3, 9), (4, 16), (5, 25), (6, 36), and (7, 49).

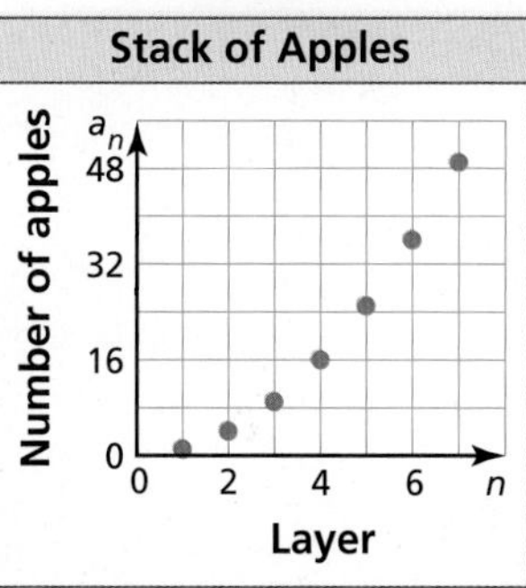

SELF-ASSESSMENT 1 I do not understand. 2 I can do it with help. 3 I can do it on my own. 4 I can teach someone else.

Describe the pattern, write the next term, graph the first five terms, and write a rule for the nth term of the sequence.

4. 3, 5, 7, 9, . . .

5. 1, −2, 4, −8, . . .

6. 2, 5, 10, 17, . . .

7. **WHAT IF?** In Example 3, there are nine layers of apples. How many apples are in the ninth layer?

Writing Rules for Series

KEY IDEAS

Series and Summation Notation

When the terms of a sequence are added together, the resulting expression is a **series**. A series can be finite or infinite.

Finite series: $2 + 4 + 6 + 8$

Infinite series: $2 + 4 + 6 + 8 + \cdots$

You can use **summation notation** to write a series. For example, the two series above can be written in summation notation as follows.

Finite series: $2 + 4 + 6 + 8 = \sum_{i=1}^{4} 2i$

Infinite series: $2 + 4 + 6 + 8 + \cdots = \sum_{i=1}^{\infty} 2i$

For both series, the *index of summation* is i and the *lower limit of summation* is 1. The *upper limit of summation* is 4 for the finite series and ∞ (infinity) for the infinite series. Summation notation is also called **sigma notation** because it uses the uppercase Greek letter *sigma*, written Σ.

READING

When written in summation notation, this series is read as "the sum of $2i$ for values of i from 1 to 4."

EXAMPLE 4 **Writing Series Using Summation Notation**

Write each series using summation notation.

a. $25 + 50 + 75 + \cdots + 250$

b. $\frac{1}{2} + \frac{2}{3} + \frac{3}{4} + \frac{4}{5} + \cdots$

SOLUTION

a. Notice that the first term is 25(1), the second is 25(2), the third is 25(3), and the last is 25(10). So, the terms of the series can be written as

$a_i = 25i$, where $i = 1, 2, 3, \ldots, 10$.

The lower limit of summation is 1 and the upper limit of summation is 10.

▶ The summation notation for the series is $\sum_{i=1}^{10} 25i$.

b. Notice that for each term, the denominator of the fraction is 1 more than the numerator. So, the terms of the series can be written as

$a_i = \frac{i}{i+1}$, where $i = 1, 2, 3, 4, \ldots$.

The lower limit of summation is 1 and the upper limit of summation is infinity.

▶ The summation notation for the series is $\sum_{i=1}^{\infty} \frac{i}{i+1}$.

SELF-ASSESSMENT 1 I do not understand. 2 I can do it with help. 3 I can do it on my own. 4 I can teach someone else.

Write the series using summation notation.

8. $5 + 10 + 15 + \cdots + 100$

9. $\frac{1}{2} + \frac{4}{5} + \frac{9}{10} + \frac{16}{17} + \cdots$

10. $6 + 36 + 216 + 1296 + \cdots$

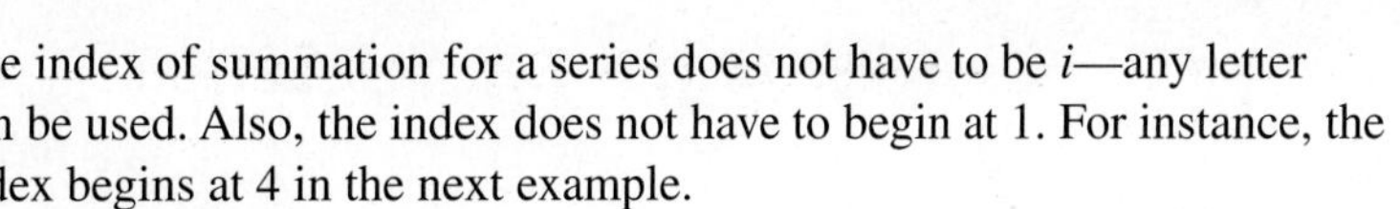

GO DIGITAL

The index of summation for a series does not have to be i—any letter can be used. Also, the index does not have to begin at 1. For instance, the index begins at 4 in the next example.

EXAMPLE 5 Finding the Sum of a Series

WATCH

COMMON ERROR
Be sure to use the correct lower and upper limits of summation when finding the sum of a series.

Find the sum $\sum_{k=4}^{8}(3 + k^2)$.

SOLUTION

$$\begin{aligned}\sum_{k=4}^{8}(3 + k^2) &= (3 + 4^2) + (3 + 5^2) + (3 + 6^2) + (3 + 7^2) + (3 + 8^2)\\ &= 19 + 28 + 39 + 52 + 67\\ &= 205\end{aligned}$$

For series with many terms, finding the sum by adding the terms can be tedious. Below are formulas you can use to find the sums of three special types of series.

KEY IDEA

Formulas for Special Series

Sum of n terms of 1: $\sum_{i=1}^{n} 1 = n$

Sum of first n positive integers: $\sum_{i=1}^{n} i = \frac{n(n + 1)}{2}$

Sum of squares of first n positive integers: $\sum_{i=1}^{n} i^2 = \frac{n(n + 1)(2n + 1)}{6}$

EXAMPLE 6 Using a Formula for a Sum

WATCH

How many apples are in the stack in Example 3?

SOLUTION

From Example 3, you know that the ith term of the series is given by $a_i = i^2$, where $i = 1, 2, 3, \ldots, 7$. Using summation notation and the third formula listed above, you can find the total number of apples as follows:

$$1^2 + 2^2 + \cdots + 7^2 = \sum_{i=1}^{7} i^2 = \frac{7(7 + 1)(2 \cdot 7 + 1)}{6} = \frac{7(8)(15)}{6} = 140$$

▶ There are 140 apples in the stack.

SELF-ASSESSMENT

1 I do not understand. 2 I can do it with help. 3 I can do it on my own. 4 I can teach someone else.

Find the sum.

11. $\sum_{i=1}^{5} 8i$ **12.** $\sum_{k=3}^{7}(k^2 - 1)$ **13.** $\sum_{i=1}^{34} 1$ **14.** $\sum_{k=1}^{6} k$

15. WHAT IF? There are nine layers in the apple stack in Example 3. How many apples are in the stack?

16. You begin to make a display of baseballs in the shape of a square pyramid, similar to the pyramid in Example 3. The pyramid will have 10 layers. You run out of baseballs after making the bottom 6 layers. How many baseballs did you use?

11.1 Practice WITH CalcChat® AND CalcView®

GO DIGITAL

In Exercises 1–10, write the first six terms of the sequence. *Example 1*

1. $a_n = n + 2$
2. $a_n = 6 - n$
3. $a_n = n^2$
4. $f(n) = n^3 + 2$
5. $f(n) = 4^{n-1}$
6. $a_n = -n^2$
7. $a_n = n^2 - 5$
8. $a_n = (n + 3)^2$
9. $f(n) = \dfrac{2n}{n + 2}$
10. $f(n) = \dfrac{n}{2n - 1}$

In Exercises 11–22, describe the pattern, write the next term, and write a rule for the *n*th term of the sequence. *Example 2*

11. 1, 6, 11, 16, . . .
12. 1, 2, 4, 8, . . .
13. 3.1, 3.8, 4.5, 5.2, . . .
14. 9, 16.8, 24.6, 32.4, . . .
15. −4, 8, −12, 16, . . .
16. 4.2, 2.6, 1, −0.6, . . .
17. $\frac{1}{4}, \frac{2}{4}, \frac{3}{4}, \frac{4}{4}, \ldots$
18. $\frac{1}{10}, \frac{3}{20}, \frac{5}{30}, \frac{7}{40}, \ldots$
19. $\frac{2}{3}, \frac{2}{6}, \frac{2}{9}, \frac{2}{12}, \ldots$
20. $\frac{2}{3}, \frac{4}{4}, \frac{6}{5}, \frac{8}{6}, \ldots$
21. 2, 9, 28, 65, . . .
22. 1.2, 4.2, 9.2, 16.2, . . .

23. **MODELING REAL LIFE** Rectangular tables are placed together along their short edges, as shown in the diagram. Write a rule for the number of people who can be seated around *n* tables arranged in this manner. Then graph the sequence. *Example 3*

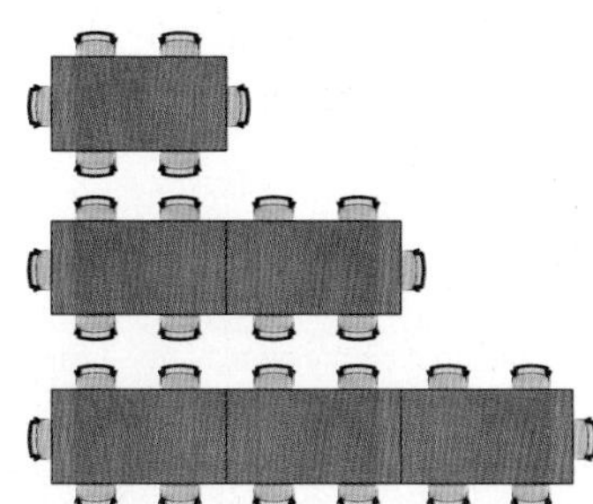

24. **MODELING REAL LIFE** An employee at a construction company earns $33,000 for the first year of employment. Employees at the company receive raises of $2400 each year. Write a rule for the salary of the employee each year. Then graph the sequence.

In Exercises 25–32, write the series using summation notation. *Example 4*

25. $7 + 10 + 13 + 16 + 19$
26. $5 + 11 + 17 + 23 + 29$
27. $4 + 7 + 12 + 19 + \cdots$
28. $-1 + 2 + 7 + 14 + \cdots$
29. $\frac{1}{3} + \frac{1}{9} + \frac{1}{27} + \frac{1}{81} + \cdots$
30. $\frac{1}{4} + \frac{2}{5} + \frac{3}{6} + \frac{4}{7} + \cdots$
31. $-3 + 4 - 5 + 6 - 7$
32. $-2 + 4 - 8 + 16 - 32$

In Exercises 33–44, find the sum. *Examples 5 and 6*

33. $\sum_{i=1}^{6} 2i$
34. $\sum_{i=1}^{5} 7i$
35. $\sum_{n=0}^{4} n^3$
36. $\sum_{k=1}^{4} 3k^2$
37. $\sum_{k=3}^{6} (5k - 2)$
38. $\sum_{n=1}^{5} (n^2 - 1)$
39. $\sum_{i=2}^{8} \dfrac{2}{i}$
40. $\sum_{k=4}^{6} \dfrac{k}{k + 1}$
41. $\sum_{i=1}^{35} 1$
42. $\sum_{n=1}^{16} n$
43. $\sum_{i=10}^{25} i$
44. $\sum_{n=1}^{18} n^2$

45. **COLLEGE PREP** Which rule gives the total number of small squares in the *n*th figure of the pattern shown? Justify your answer.

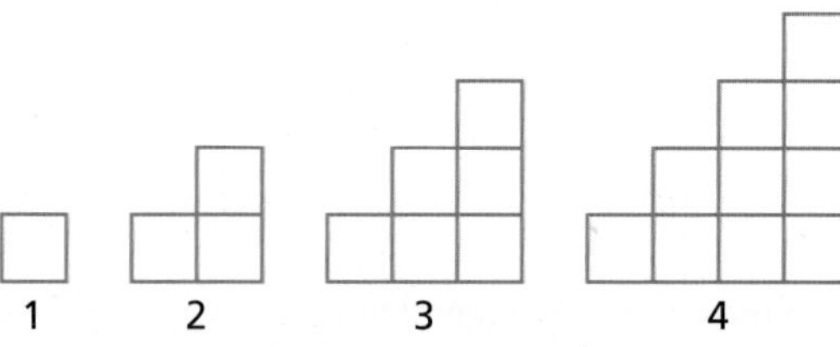

Ⓐ $a_n = 3n - 3$

Ⓑ $a_n = 4n - 5$

Ⓒ $a_n = n$

Ⓓ $a_n = \dfrac{n(n + 1)}{2}$

46. **COLLEGE PREP** Which rule gives the total number of green squares in the nth figure of the pattern shown? Justify your answer.

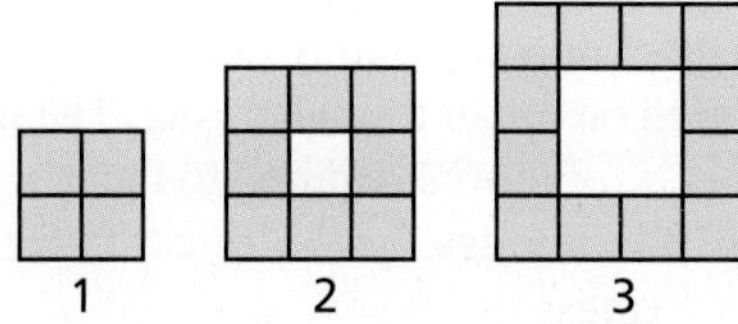

Ⓐ $a_n = n^2 - 1$ Ⓑ $a_n = \frac{n^2}{2}$

Ⓒ $a_n = 4n$ Ⓓ $a_n = 2n + 1$

ERROR ANALYSIS In Exercises 47 and 48, describe and correct the error in finding the sum of the series.

47.

$$\sum_{n=1}^{10} (3n - 5) = -2 + 1 + 4 + 7 + 10$$
$$= 20$$

48.

$$\sum_{i=2}^{4} i^2 = \frac{4(4+1)(2 \cdot 4 + 1)}{6}$$
$$= \frac{180}{6}$$
$$= 30$$

49. **MODELING REAL LIFE** For an exercise program, you do 25 push-ups the first week. Each week, you do 10 more push-ups than the previous week. How many push-ups will you do in the ninth week? Justify your answer.

50. **MODELING REAL LIFE** For a display at a sports store, you stack soccer balls in a pyramid with five layers whose base is an equilateral triangle. Write a rule for the number of soccer balls in each layer. Then graph the sequence.

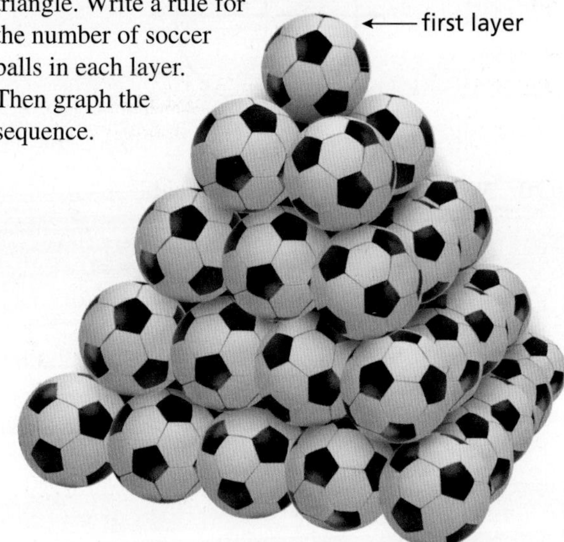

51. **MP PROBLEM SOLVING** You want to save \$500 for a new tablet. You begin by saving a penny on the first day. You save an additional penny each day after that.

   a. How much money will you have saved after 100 days?

   b. Use a series to determine how many days it takes you to save \$500.

52. **HOW DO YOU SEE IT?**
Use the diagram to determine the sum of the series.
Explain your reasoning.

$1 + 3 + 5 + 7 + 9 + \cdots + (2n - 1) = ?$

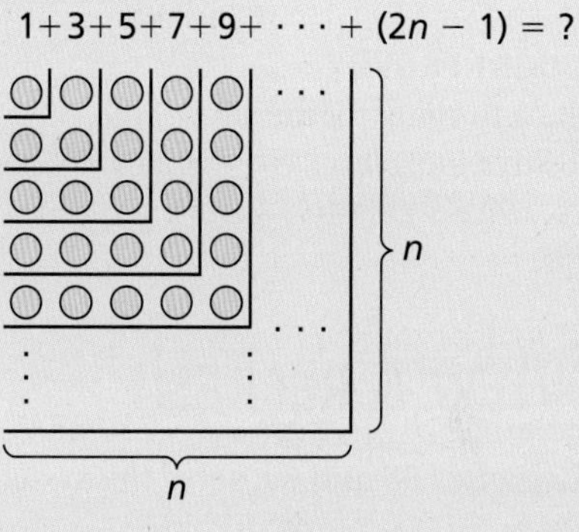

53. **MAKING AN ARGUMENT** Is there a way to use the formula for the sum of the first n positive integers to evaluate $\sum_{i=3}^{1659} i$? If so, explain how to use it. If not, explain why not.

54. **CONNECTING CONCEPTS** A *regular* polygon has equal angle measures and equal side lengths. For a regular n-sided polygon ($n \geq 3$), the measure a_n of an interior angle is given by $a_n = \frac{180(n-2)}{n}$.

   a. Write the first five terms of the sequence.

   b. Write a rule for the sequence giving the sum T_n of the measures of the interior angles of a regular n-sided polygon.

   c. Use your rule in part (b) to find the sum of the interior angle measures of the Guggenheim Museum skylight, which is a regular dodecagon.

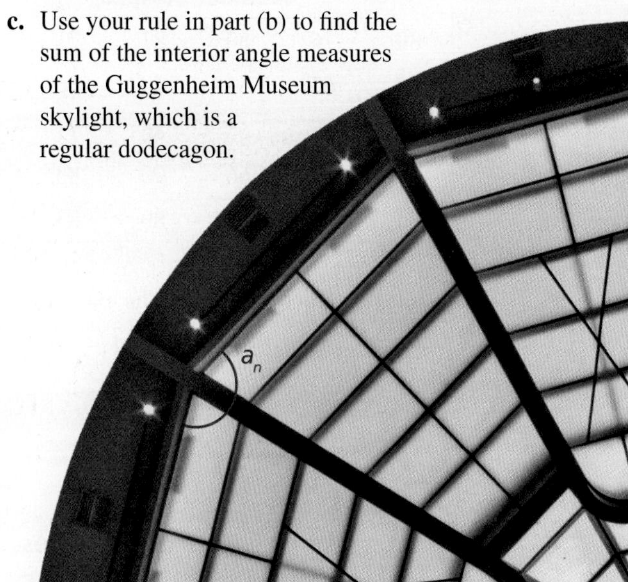

55. **DIG DEEPER** Determine whether each statement is true. If so, show that it is true. If not, provide a counterexample.

a. $\sum_{i=1}^{n} ca_i = c\sum_{i=1}^{n} a_i$

b. $\sum_{i=1}^{n}(a_i + b_i) = \sum_{i=1}^{n} a_i + \sum_{i=1}^{n} b_i$

c. $\sum_{i=1}^{n} a_i b_i = \sum_{i=1}^{n} a_i \sum_{i=1}^{n} b_i$

d. $\sum_{i=1}^{n}(a_i)^c = \left(\sum_{i=1}^{n} a_i\right)^c$

56. **THOUGHT PROVOKING**
Write a formula for the sum of the cubes of the first n positive integers.

57. **CRITICAL THINKING** In the puzzle called the Tower of Hanoi, the object is to use a series of moves to move the rings from one peg and stack them in order on another peg. A move consists of moving exactly one ring, and no ring may be placed on top of a smaller ring. The minimum number a_n of moves required to move n rings is 1 for 1 ring, 3 for 2 rings, 7 for 3 rings, 15 for 4 rings, and 31 for 5 rings.

GO DIGITAL

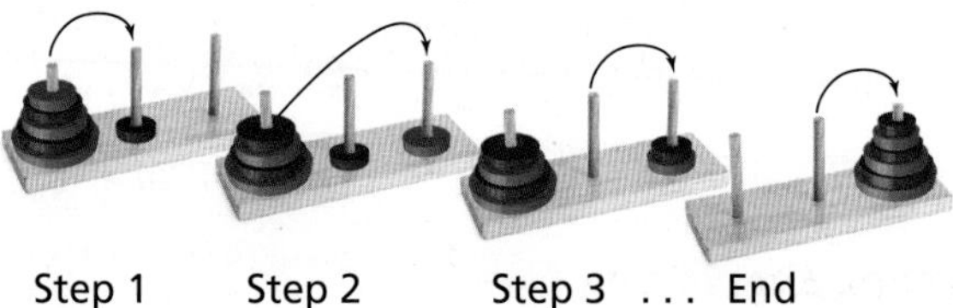

a. Write a rule for the sequence.

b. What is the minimum number of moves required to move 6 rings? 7 rings? 8 rings?

REVIEW & REFRESH

WATCH

In Exercises 58 and 59, solve the system.

58. $2x - y - 3z = 6$
$x + y + 4z = -1$
$3x - 2z = 8$

59. $2x - 3y + z = 4$
$x - 2z = 1$
$y + z = 2$

In Exercises 60 and 61, write the series using summation notation. Then find the sum of the series.

60. $0 + \frac{1}{2} + \frac{2}{3} + \frac{3}{4} + \cdots + \frac{7}{8}$

61. $9 + 16 + 25 + \cdots + 100$

62. **MODELING REAL LIFE** The numbers of apps installed on the cell phones of a random sample of 30 cell phone users are shown in the table. Estimate the population mean μ.

Number of Apps					
89	76	80	87	71	90
78	63	81	79	66	92
67	78	65	86	71	56
86	74	66	90	83	88
84	71	81	80	83	70

In Exercises 63 and 64, simplify the expression.

63. $\dfrac{\sin(-\theta)}{\csc\theta}$

64. $\tan\left(x - \dfrac{3\pi}{2}\right)$

65. A screen-printing website offers 20 different colors for T-shirt logos. How many combinations of 3 colors are possible?

In Exercises 66 and 67, find the sum or difference.

66. $\dfrac{5}{8x} + \dfrac{3}{8x}$

67. $\dfrac{6}{x+2} - \dfrac{2}{x-2}$

68. Complete the square for $x^2 - 16x$. Then factor the trinomial.

69. Evaluate the six trigonometric functions of θ.

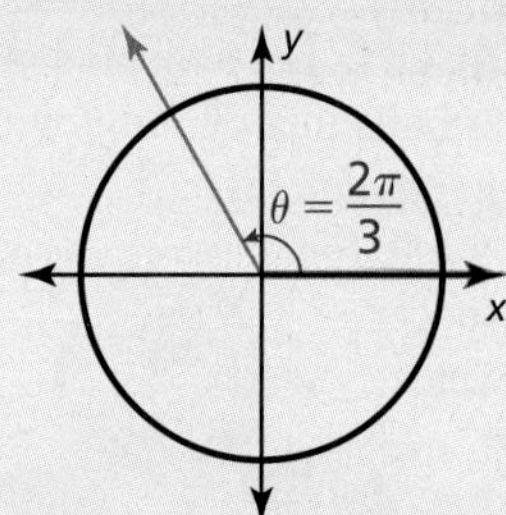

70. Write a function for the sinusoid.

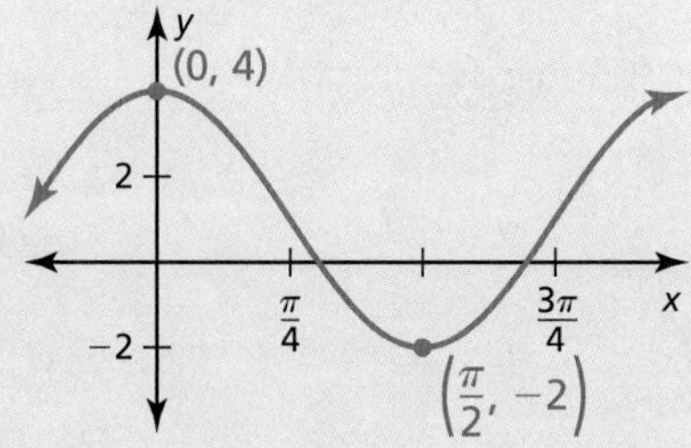

11.2 Analyzing Arithmetic Sequences and Series

GO DIGITAL

Learning Target Analyze arithmetic sequences and series.

Success Criteria

- I can identify arithmetic sequences.
- I can write rules for arithmetic sequences.
- I can find sums of finite arithmetic series.

In an **arithmetic sequence**, the difference of consecutive terms, called the *common difference*, is constant. For example, in the arithmetic sequence 1, 4, 7, 10, . . . , the common difference is 3.

EXPLORE IT! Finding the Sum of an Arithmetic Sequence

Work with a partner. When German mathematician Carl Friedrich Gauss (1777–1855) was young, one of his teachers asked him to find the sum of the whole numbers from 1 through 100. To the astonishment of his teacher, Gauss came up with the answer after only a few moments. Here is what Gauss did:

$$\begin{array}{rcrcrcccr} 1 & + & 2 & + & 3 & + & \cdots & + & 100 \\ 100 & + & 99 & + & 98 & + & \cdots & + & 1 \\ \hline 101 & + & 101 & + & 101 & + & \cdots & + & 101 \end{array}$$

$$\frac{100 \times 101}{2} = 5050$$

Math Practice

Construct Arguments
Explain why Gauss's method works for *any* arithmetic sequence.

a. Explain Gauss's thought process. Then write a formula for the sum S_n of the first n terms of an arithmetic sequence.

b. Show that the numbers of shoes in the figures below form an arithmetic sequence. Then find the total number of shoes in the first 8 figures by (i) writing the number of shoes in each figure and adding, and (ii) using the formula you found in part (a).

1

2

3

4

Identifying Arithmetic Sequences

Vocabulary

arithmetic sequence, *p. 604*
common difference, *p. 604*
arithmetic series, *p. 606*

In an **arithmetic sequence**, the difference of consecutive terms is constant. This constant difference is called the **common difference** and is denoted by d.

EXAMPLE 1 Identifying Arithmetic Sequences

Determine whether each sequence is arithmetic. Explain your reasoning.

a. $-9, -2, 5, 12, 19, \ldots$

b. $23, 15, 9, 5, 3, \ldots$

SOLUTION

Find the differences of consecutive terms.

a. $a_2 - a_1 = -2 - (-9) = 7$

$a_3 - a_2 = 5 - (-2) = 7$

$a_4 - a_3 = 12 - 5 = 7$

$a_5 - a_4 = 19 - 12 = 7$

Position	1	2	3	4	5
Term	−9	−2	5	12	19

+7 +7 +7 +7

Each term is 7 greater than the previous term.

▶ The differences are constant, so the sequence is arithmetic.

b. $a_2 - a_1 = 15 - 23 = -8$

$a_3 - a_2 = 9 - 15 = -6$

$a_4 - a_3 = 5 - 9 = -4$

$a_5 - a_4 = 3 - 5 = -2$

Position	1	2	3	4	5
Term	23	15	9	5	3

+(−8) +(−6) +(−4) +(−2)

▶ The differences are not constant, so the sequence is not arithmetic.

SELF-ASSESSMENT 1 I do not understand. 2 I can do it with help. 3 I can do it on my own. 4 I can teach someone else.

Determine whether the sequence is arithmetic. Explain your reasoning.

1. $2, 5, 8, 11, 14, \ldots$

2. $15, 9, 3, -3, -9, \ldots$

3. $8, 4, 2, 1, \frac{1}{2}, \ldots$

Writing Rules for Arithmetic Sequences

KEY IDEA

Rule for an Arithmetic Sequence

Algebra The nth term of an arithmetic sequence with first term a_1 and common difference d is given by

$$a_n = a_1 + (n - 1)d.$$

Example The nth term of an arithmetic sequence with a first term of 3 and a common difference of 2 is given by

$$a_n = 3 + (n - 1)2, \text{ or } a_n = 2n + 1.$$

EXAMPLE 2 Writing a Rule for the *n*th Term

Write a rule for the *n*th term of each sequence. Then find a_{15}.

a. 3, 8, 13, 18, . . .

b. 55, 47, 39, 31, . . .

SOLUTION

a. The sequence is arithmetic with first term $a_1 = 3$, and common difference $d = 8 - 3 = 5$. So, a rule for the *n*th term is

$a_n = a_1 + (n - 1)d$ — Write general rule.

$= 3 + (n - 1)5$ — Substitute 3 for a_1 and 5 for d.

$= 5n - 2.$ — Simplify.

▶ A rule is $a_n = 5n - 2$, and the 15th term is $a_{15} = 5(15) - 2 = 73$.

COMMON ERROR

In the general rule for an arithmetic sequence, note that the common difference *d* is multiplied by *n* − 1, not *n*.

b. The sequence is arithmetic with first term $a_1 = 55$, and common difference $d = 47 - 55 = -8$. So, a rule for the *n*th term is

$a_n = a_1 + (n - 1)d$ — Write general rule.

$= 55 + (n - 1)(-8)$ — Substitute 55 for a_1 and −8 for d.

$= -8n + 63.$ — Simplify.

▶ A rule is $a_n = -8n + 63$, and the 15th term is $a_{15} = -8(15) + 63 = -57$.

EXAMPLE 3 Writing a Rule Given a Term and Common Difference

One term of an arithmetic sequence is $a_{19} = -45$. The common difference is $d = -3$. Write a rule for the *n*th term. Then graph the first six terms of the sequence.

SOLUTION

Step 1 Use the general rule to find the first term.

$a_n = a_1 + (n - 1)d$ — Write general rule.

$a_{19} = a_1 + (19 - 1)d$ — Substitute 19 for n.

$-45 = a_1 + 18(-3)$ — Substitute −45 for a_{19} and −3 for d.

$9 = a_1$ — Solve for a_1.

Step 2 Write a rule for the *n*th term.

$a_n = a_1 + (n - 1)d$ — Write general rule.

$= 9 + (n - 1)(-3)$ — Substitute 9 for a_1 and −3 for d.

$= -3n + 12$ — Simplify.

Step 3 Use the rule to create a table of values for the sequence. Then plot the points.

n	1	2	3	4	5	6
a_n	9	6	3	0	−3	−6

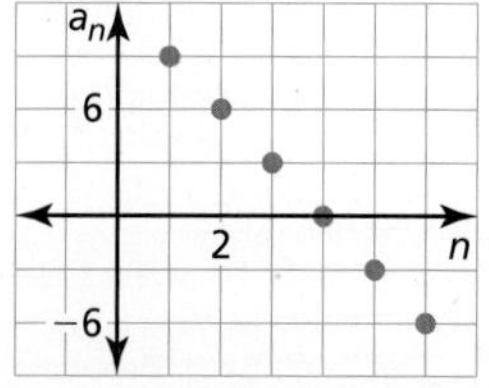

Math Practice

Analyze Relationships

Notice that the points lie on a line. This is true for any arithmetic sequence. So, an arithmetic sequence is a linear function whose domain is a subset of the integers. Can you use function notation to write sequences?

EXAMPLE 4 Writing a Rule Given Two Terms

Two terms of an arithmetic sequence are $a_7 = 17$ and $a_{26} = 93$. Write a rule for the nth term.

SOLUTION

Step 1 Write a system of equations using $a_n = a_1 + (n - 1)d$. Substitute 26 for n to write Equation 1. Substitute 7 for n to write Equation 2.

$a_{26} = a_1 + (26 - 1)d$ ➡ $93 = a_1 + 25d$ Equation 1

$a_7 = a_1 + (7 - 1)d$ ➡ $17 = a_1 + 6d$ Equation 2

Step 2 Solve the system. $76 = 19d$ Subtract.

$4 = d$ Solve for d.

$93 = a_1 + 25(4)$ Substitute for d in Equation 1.

$-7 = a_1$ Solve for a_1.

Step 3 Write a rule for a_n. $a_n = a_1 + (n - 1)d$ Write general rule.

$= -7 + (n - 1)4$ Substitute for a_1 and d.

$= 4n - 11$ Simplify.

▶ A rule is $a_n = 4n - 11$.

Check
Use the rule to verify that the 7th term is 17 and the 26th term is 93.

$a_7 = 4(7) - 11 = 17$ ✓

$a_{26} = 4(26) - 11 = 93$ ✓

SELF-ASSESSMENT

1 I do not understand. 2 I can do it with help. 3 I can do it on my own. 4 I can teach someone else.

Write a rule for the nth term of the sequence. Then find a_{15} and graph the first six terms of the sequence.

4. 7, 11, 15, 19, . . .
5. $a_{11} = 50, d = 7$
6. $a_7 = 71, a_{16} = 26$

Finding Sums of Finite Arithmetic Series

The expression formed by adding the terms of an arithmetic sequence is called an **arithmetic series**. The sum of the first n terms of an arithmetic series is denoted by S_n. To find a rule for S_n, you can write S_n in two different ways and add the results.

$$S_n = a_1 + (a_1 + d) + (a_1 + 2d) + \cdots + a_n$$

$$S_n = a_n + (a_n - d) + (a_n - 2d) + \cdots + a_1$$

$$2S_n = \underbrace{(a_1 + a_n) + (a_1 + a_n) + (a_1 + a_n) + \cdots + (a_1 + a_n)}_{(a_1 + a_n) \text{ is added } n \text{ times.}}$$

You can conclude that $2S_n = n(a_1 + a_n)$, which leads to the following result.

KEY IDEA

The Sum of a Finite Arithmetic Series

The sum of the first n terms of an arithmetic series is

$$S_n = n\left(\frac{a_1 + a_n}{2}\right).$$

In words, S_n is the mean of the first and nth terms, multiplied by the number of terms.

EXAMPLE 5 Finding the Sum of an Arithmetic Series

Find the sum $\sum_{i=1}^{20}(3i + 7)$.

SOLUTION

Step 1 Find the first and last terms.

$a_1 = 3(1) + 7 = 10$ — Find first term.

$a_{20} = 3(20) + 7 = 67$ — Find last term.

Step 2 Find the sum.

$S_{20} = 20\left(\dfrac{a_1 + a_{20}}{2}\right)$ — Write rule for S_{20}.

$= 20\left(\dfrac{10 + 67}{2}\right)$ — Substitute 10 for a_1 and 67 for a_{20}.

$= 770$ — Evaluate.

EXAMPLE 6 Modeling Real Life

You are making a house of cards similar to the one shown.

a. Write a rule for the number of cards in the *n*th row when the top row is Row 1.

b. How many cards do you need to make a house of cards with 12 rows?

SOLUTION

a. Starting with the top row, the numbers of cards in the rows are 3, 6, 9, 12, ... These numbers form an arithmetic sequence with a first term of 3 and a common difference of 3. So, a rule for the sequence is

$a_n = a_1 + (n - 1)d$ — Write general rule.

$= 3 + (n - 1)3$ — Substitute 3 for a_1 and 3 for *d*.

$= 3n.$ — Simplify.

b. Find the sum of an arithmetic series with first term $a_1 = 3$ and last term $a_{12} = 3(12) = 36$.

$$S_{12} = 12\left(\frac{a_1 + a_{12}}{2}\right) = 12\left(\frac{3 + 36}{2}\right) = 234$$

▶ So, you need 234 cards to make a house of cards with 12 rows.

Check

$\sum_{n=1}^{12} 3n = 234$

SELF-ASSESSMENT

1 I do not understand. 2 I can do it with help. 3 I can do it on my own. 4 I can teach someone else.

Find the sum.

7. $\sum_{i=1}^{10} 9i$

8. $\sum_{k=1}^{12}(7k + 2)$

9. $\sum_{n=1}^{20}(-4n + 6)$

10. WHAT IF? In Example 6, how many cards do you need to make a house of cards with eight rows?

11.2 Practice WITH CalcChat® AND CalcView®

In Exercises 1–8, determine whether the sequence is arithmetic. Explain your reasoning. ▶ *Example 1*

1. $1, -1, -3, -5, -7, \ldots$ **2.** $12, 6, 0, -6, -12, \ldots$

3. $5, 8, 13, 20, 29, \ldots$ **4.** $3, 5, 9, 15, 23, \ldots$

5. $36, 18, 9, \frac{9}{2}, \frac{9}{4}, \ldots$ **6.** $81, 27, 9, 3, 1, \ldots$

7. $\frac{1}{2}, \frac{3}{4}, 1, \frac{5}{4}, \frac{3}{2}, \ldots$ **8.** $\frac{1}{6}, \frac{1}{2}, \frac{5}{6}, \frac{7}{6}, \frac{3}{2}, \ldots$

9. WRITING EQUATIONS Write a rule for the sequence with the given description.

a. The first term is -3, and each subsequent term is 6 less than the previous term.

b. The first term is 7, and each subsequent term is 5 more than the previous term.

10. ANALYZING RELATIONSHIPS What can you conclude about the terms of an arithmetic sequence when $d > 0$? $d < 0$?

In Exercises 11–18, write a rule for the nth term of the sequence. Then find a_{20}. ▶ *Example 2*

11. $12, 20, 28, 36, \ldots$ **12.** $7, 12, 17, 22, \ldots$

13. $51, 48, 45, 42, \ldots$ **14.** $86, 79, 72, 65, \ldots$

15. $-1, -\frac{1}{3}, \frac{1}{3}, 1, \ldots$ **16.** $-2, -\frac{5}{4}, -\frac{1}{2}, \frac{1}{4}, \ldots$

17. $2.3, 1.5, 0.7, -0.1, \ldots$ **18.** $11.7, 10.8, 9.9, 9, \ldots$

ERROR ANALYSIS In Exercises 19 and 20, describe and correct the error in writing a rule for the nth term of the arithmetic sequence $22, 9, -4, -17, -30, \ldots$.

19.

The first term is 22 and the common difference is -13.

$a_n = a_1 + nd$

$a_n = 22 + n(-13)$

$a_n = 22 - 13n$

20.

The first term is 22 and the common difference is -13.

$a_n = -13 + (n - 1)(22)$

$a_n = -35 + 22n$

In Exercises 21–26, write a rule for the nth term of the sequence. Then graph the first six terms of the sequence. ▶ *Example 3*

21. $a_{11} = 43, d = 5$ **22.** $a_{13} = 42, d = 4$

23. $a_{20} = -27, d = -2$ **24.** $a_{15} = -35, d = -3$

25. $a_{17} = -5, d = -\frac{1}{2}$ **26.** $a_{21} = -25, d = -\frac{3}{2}$

In Exercises 27–34, write a rule for the nth term of the arithmetic sequence. ▶ *Example 4*

27. $a_5 = 41, a_{10} = 96$ **28.** $a_7 = 58, a_{11} = 94$

29. $a_6 = -8, a_{15} = -62$ **30.** $a_8 = -15, a_{17} = -78$

31. $a_{18} = -59, a_{21} = -71$

32. $a_{12} = -38, a_{19} = -73$

33. $a_8 = 12, a_{16} = 22$

34. $a_{12} = 9, a_{27} = 15$

In Exercises 35–40, write a rule for the sequence with the given terms.

35.

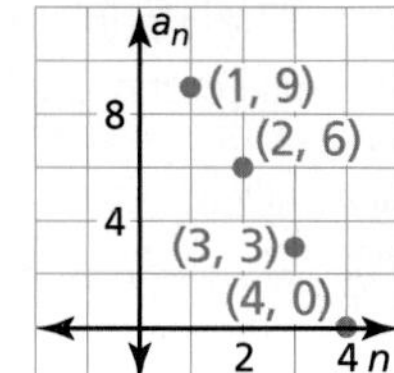

36.

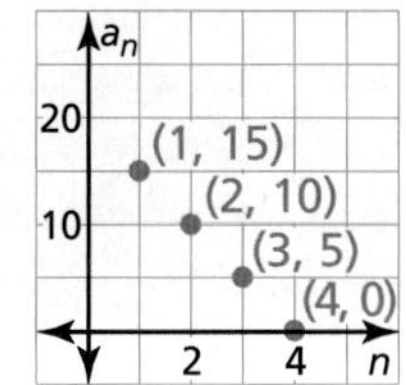

37.

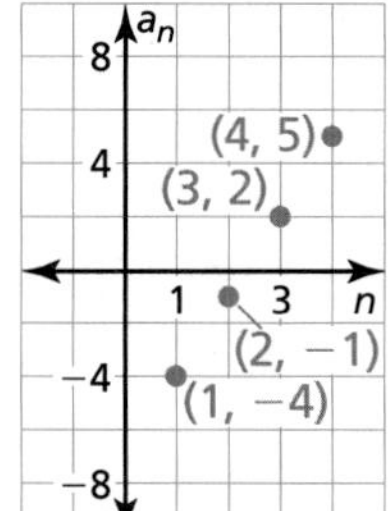

38.

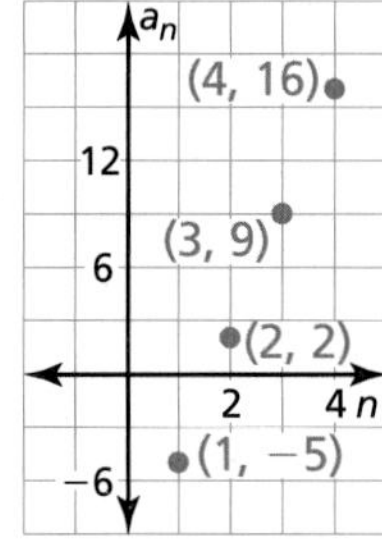

39.

n	4	5	6	7	8
a_n	25	29	33	37	41

40.

n	4	5	6	7	8
a_n	31	39	47	55	63

In Exercises 41–46, find the sum. *Example 5*

41. $\sum_{i=1}^{20}(2i - 3)$

42. $\sum_{i=1}^{26}(4i + 7)$

43. $\sum_{i=1}^{33}(6 - 2i)$

44. $\sum_{i=1}^{31}(-3 - 4i)$

45. $\sum_{i=1}^{41}(-2.3 + 0.1i)$

46. $\sum_{i=1}^{39}(-4.1 + 0.4i)$

MP NUMBER SENSE In Exercises 47 and 48, find the indicated sum.

47. The sum of the first 19 terms of the sequence 9, 2, −5, −12, . . .

48. The sum of the first 22 terms of the sequence 17, 9, 1, −7, . . .

49. MODELING REAL LIFE A marching band is arranged in rows. The first row has three band members, and each subsequent row has two more band members than the previous row. *Example 6*

a. Write a rule for the number of band members in the *n*th row.

b. How many band members are in a formation with seven rows?

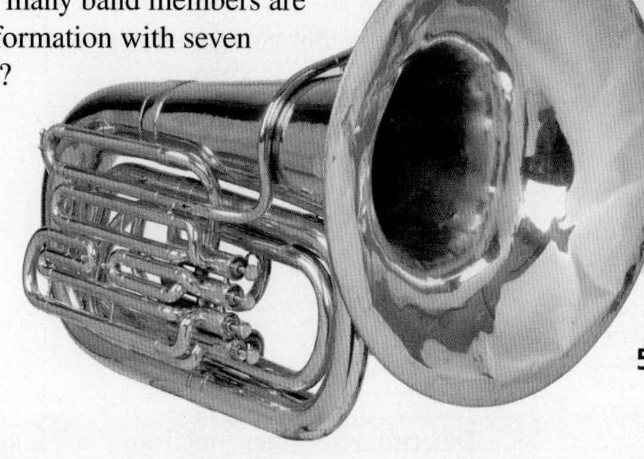

50. MODELING REAL LIFE Domestic bees make their honeycomb by starting with a single hexagonal cell, then forming ring after ring of hexagonal cells around the initial cell, as shown. The numbers of cells in successive rings forms an arithmetic sequence.

Initial cell

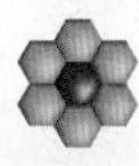
1 ring

2 rings

a. Write a rule for the number of cells in the *n*th ring.

b. How many cells are in the honeycomb after the ninth ring is formed?

51. WRITING Compare the graph of $a_n = 3n + 1$, where *n* is a positive integer, with the graph of $f(x) = 3x + 1$, where *x* is a real number.

52. COLLEGE PREP One term of an arithmetic sequence is $a_{12} = 43$. The common difference is 6. What is another term of the sequence?

Ⓐ $a_3 = -11$ Ⓑ $a_4 = -53$

Ⓒ $a_5 = 13$ Ⓓ $a_6 = -47$

53. DRAWING CONCLUSIONS Describe how doubling each term of an arithmetic sequence changes the common difference. Justify your answer.

54. HOW DO YOU SEE IT?
Which graph(s) represents an arithmetic sequence? Explain your reasoning.

a. 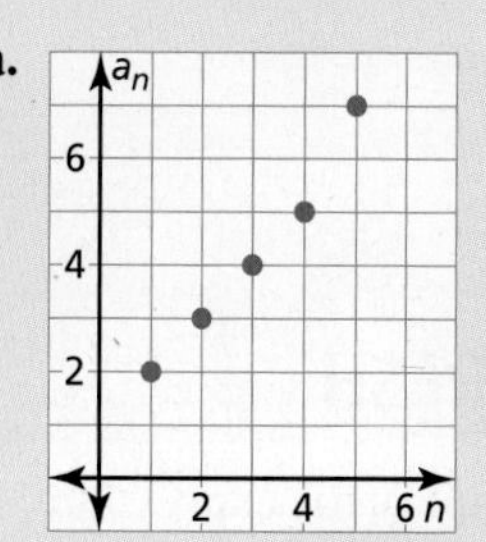

b. 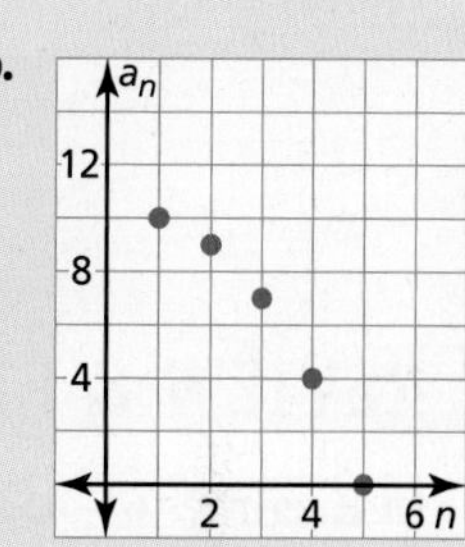

c. 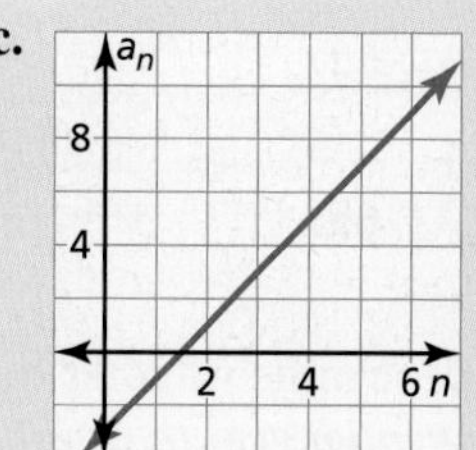

d. 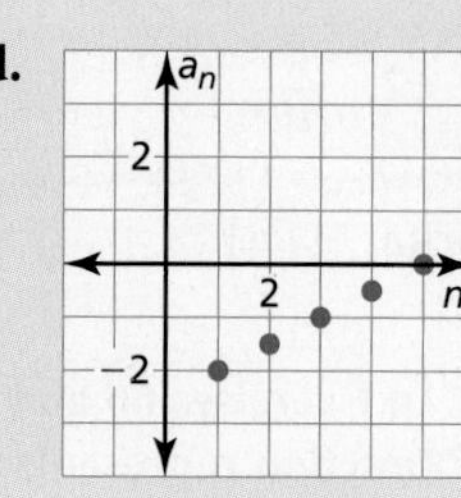

55. MAKING AN ARGUMENT Does the sum of a series double when the common difference is doubled, and the first term and number of terms remain unchanged? Explain your reasoning.

56. CONNECTING CONCEPTS A quilt is made up of strips of cloth, starting with an inner square surrounded by rectangles to form successively larger squares. The inner square and the rectangles have a width of 1 foot. Write an expression using summation notation that gives the sum of the areas of the strips of cloth used to make the quilt shown. Then evaluate the expression.

57. **MP REASONING** Find the sum of the positive odd integers less than 300. Explain your reasoning.

58. **USING EQUATIONS** Find the value of n.

a. $\sum_{i=1}^{n}(3i + 5) = 544$ **b.** $\sum_{i=1}^{n}(-4i - 1) = -1127$

c. $\sum_{i=5}^{n}(7 + 12i) = 455$ **d.** $\sum_{i=3}^{n}(-3 - 4i) = -507$

59. **ABSTRACT REASONING** A theater has n rows of seats, and each row has d more seats than the row in front of it. There are x seats in the last (nth) row and a total of y seats in the theater. How many seats are in the front row of the theater? Write your answer in terms of n, x, and y.

60. **THOUGHT PROVOKING** One of the major sources of our knowledge of Egyptian mathematics is the Ahmes papyrus, which is a scroll copied in 1650 B.C. by an Egyptian scribe. The following problem is from the Ahmes papyrus.

Divide 10 hekats of barley among 10 men so that the common difference is $\frac{1}{8}$ of a hekat of barley.

Use what you know about arithmetic sequences and series to determine what portion of a hekat each man should receive.

GO DIGITAL

61. **CRITICAL THINKING** The expressions $3 - x$, x, and $1 - 3x$ are the first three terms of an arithmetic sequence. Find the value of x and the next term of the sequence.

REVIEW & REFRESH

In Exercises 62–65, simplify the expression.

62. $\dfrac{7}{7^{1/3}}$

63. $(3^{-1/3})^9$

64. $\left(\dfrac{9}{49}\right)^{1/2}$

65. $5^{1/2} \cdot 5^{1/4}$

In Exercises 66 and 67, determine whether the function represents *exponential growth* or *exponential decay*. Then graph the function.

66. $y = 3e^{-x}$

67. $y = e^{0.25x}$

68. The graph of a polynomial function is shown. Is the degree of the function *odd* or *even*? Is the leading coefficient of the function *positive* or *negative*?

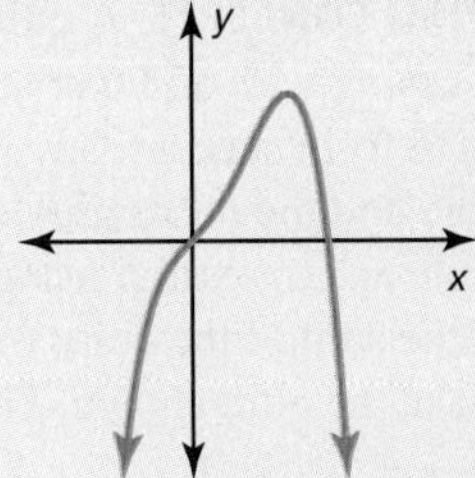

69. One term of an arithmetic sequence is $a_{12} = 19$. The common difference is $d = 7$.

a. Write a rule for the nth term. Then graph the first six terms of the sequence.

b. Find the sum of the first 12 terms.

70. **MODELING REAL LIFE** You and your friend enter a drawing to win tickets to a play. From 35 entries, 2 winners are randomly selected. What is the probability that you and your friend win?

71. Simplify $\cos\left(x - \dfrac{3\pi}{2}\right)$.

72. Solve the system using any method. Explain your choice of method.

$$-2x + y = -1$$
$$y = x^2 - 4$$

73. Determine whether functions f and g are inverses. Explain your reasoning.

x	-1	0	1	2	3
$f(x)$	2	4	6	8	10

x	-1	0	1	2	3
$g(x)$	$\frac{1}{2}$	$\frac{1}{4}$	$\frac{1}{6}$	$\frac{1}{8}$	$\frac{1}{10}$

74. Given that $\cos\theta = \dfrac{15}{17}$ and $\dfrac{3\pi}{2} < \theta < 2\pi$, find the values of the other five trigonometric functions of θ.

75. Find the sum $\sum_{k=1}^{4}(k^2 + 2)$.

11.3 Analyzing Geometric Sequences and Series

Learning Target Analyze geometric sequences and series.

Success Criteria
- I can identify geometric sequences.
- I can write rules for geometric sequences.
- I can find sums of finite geometric series.

EXPLORE IT! Finding the Sum of a Geometric Sequence

Work with a partner. In a *geometric sequence*, the ratio of any term to the previous term, called the *common ratio*, is constant. You can write the nth term of a geometric sequence with first term a_1 and common ratio r as

$$a_n = a_1r^{n-1}.$$

So, you can write the sum S_n of the first n terms of a geometric sequence as

$$S_n = a_1 + a_1r + a_1r^2 + a_1r^3 + \cdots + a_1r^{n-1}.$$

This sum may have many terms that can be tedious to add.

a. A student wants to find a way to write S_n concisely by doing something Gauss may have tried. A portion of the student's work is shown below. What did the student do? Explain.

Math Practice

Look for Structure
Why does the student multiply by r in part (a)?

$$S_n = a_1 + a_1r + a_1r^2 + a_1r^3 + \cdots + a_1r^{n-1}$$
$$-rS_n = \quad - a_1r - a_1r^2 - a_1r^3 - \cdots - a_1r^{n-1} - a_1r^n$$

b. Continue the student's work by completing the statement.

$$S_n - rS_n = \underline{\qquad\qquad}$$

c. Show how you can solve for S_n in part (b). Explain your reasoning.

d. Show that the numbers of fish in the figures below form a geometric sequence. Then find the total number of fish in the first 10 figures by (i) writing the number of fish in each figure and adding, and (ii) using the formula you wrote in part (c).

1

2

3

4

Identifying and Writing Rules for Geometric Sequences

Vocabulary AZ VOCAB

geometric sequence, *p. 612*
common ratio, *p. 612*
geometric series, *p. 614*

In a **geometric sequence**, the ratio of any term to the previous term is constant. This constant ratio is called the **common ratio** and is denoted by r.

EXAMPLE 1 Identifying Geometric Sequences

Determine whether each sequence is geometric. Explain your reasoning.

a. 6, 12, 20, 30, 42, . . .

b. 256, 64, 16, 4, 1, . . .

SOLUTION

Find the ratios of consecutive terms.

a. $\frac{a_2}{a_1} = \frac{12}{6} = 2$ $\quad \frac{a_3}{a_2} = \frac{20}{12} = \frac{5}{3}$ $\quad \frac{a_4}{a_3} = \frac{30}{20} = \frac{3}{2}$ $\quad \frac{a_5}{a_4} = \frac{42}{30} = \frac{7}{5}$

▶ The ratios are not constant, so the sequence is not geometric.

b. $\frac{a_2}{a_1} = \frac{64}{256} = \frac{1}{4}$ $\quad \frac{a_3}{a_2} = \frac{16}{64} = \frac{1}{4}$ $\quad \frac{a_4}{a_3} = \frac{4}{16} = \frac{1}{4}$ $\quad \frac{a_5}{a_4} = \frac{1}{4}$

▶ The ratios are constant, so the sequence is geometric.

KEY IDEA

Rule for a Geometric Sequence

Algebra The nth term of a geometric sequence with first term a_1 and common ratio r is given by

$$a_n = a_1 r^{n-1}.$$

Example The nth term of a geometric sequence with a first term of 2 and a common ratio of 3 is given by

$$a_n = 2(3)^{n-1}.$$

EXAMPLE 2 Writing a Rule for the nth Term

Write a rule for the nth term of each sequence. Then find a_8.

a. 5, 15, 45, 135, . . .

b. 88, −44, 22, −11, . . .

SOLUTION

a. The sequence is geometric with first term $a_1 = 5$, and common ratio $r = \frac{15}{5} = 3$. So, a rule for the nth term is

$a_n = a_1 r^{n-1}$ Write general rule.

$= 5(3)^{n-1}$. Substitute values.

▶ A rule is $a_n = 5(3)^{n-1}$, and the 8th term is

$a_8 = 5(3)^{8-1} = 10{,}935$.

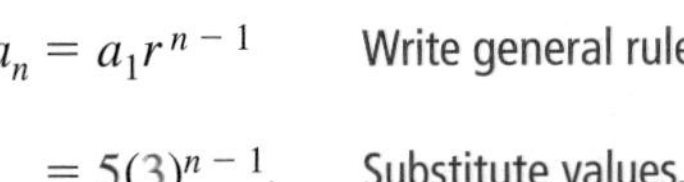

COMMON ERROR

In the general rule for a geometric sequence, note that the exponent is $n - 1$, not n.

b. The sequence is geometric with first term $a_1 = 88$, and common ratio $r = \frac{-44}{88} = -\frac{1}{2}$. So, a rule for the nth term is

$a_n = a_1 r^{n-1}$ Write general rule.

$= 88\left(-\frac{1}{2}\right)^{n-1}$. Substitute values.

▶ A rule is $a_n = 88\left(-\frac{1}{2}\right)^{n-1}$, and the 8th term is

$a_8 = 88\left(-\frac{1}{2}\right)^{8-1} = -\frac{11}{16}$.

EXAMPLE 3 Writing a Rule Given a Term and Common Ratio

One term of a geometric sequence is $a_4 = 12$. The common ratio is $r = 2$. Write a rule for the nth term. Then graph the first six terms of the sequence.

SOLUTION

Step 1 Use the general rule to find the first term.

$a_n = a_1 r^{n-1}$ — Write general rule.

$a_4 = a_1 r^{4-1}$ — Substitute 4 for n.

$12 = a_1(2)^3$ — Substitute 12 for a_4 and 2 for r.

$1.5 = a_1$ — Solve for a_1.

Step 2 Write a rule for the nth term.

$a_n = a_1 r^{n-1}$ — Write general rule.

$= 1.5(2)^{n-1}$ — Substitute 1.5 for a_1 and 2 for r.

Step 3 Use the rule to create a table of values for the sequence. Then plot the points.

n	1	2	3	4	5	6
a_n	1.5	3	6	12	24	48

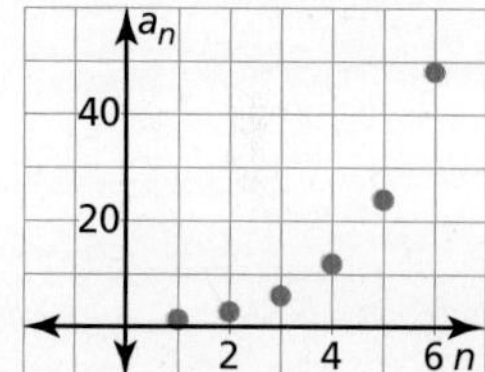

Math Practice

Analyze Relationships
Explain why a geometric sequence in which $r > 0$ and $r \neq 1$ is an exponential function whose domain is a subset of the integers.

EXAMPLE 4 Writing a Rule Given Two Terms

Two terms of a geometric sequence are $a_2 = 12$ and $a_5 = -768$. Write a rule for the nth term.

SOLUTION

Step 1 Write a system of equations using $a_n = a_1 r^{n-1}$. Substitute 2 for n to write Equation 1. Substitute 5 for n to write Equation 2.

$a_2 = a_1 r^{2-1}$ ➡ $12 = a_1 r$ — Equation 1

$a_5 = a_1 r^{5-1}$ ➡ $-768 = a_1 r^4$ — Equation 2

Step 2 Solve the system.

$\frac{12}{r} = a_1$ — Solve Equation 1 for a_1.

$-768 = \frac{12}{r}(r^4)$ — Substitute for a_1 in Equation 2.

$-768 = 12r^3$ — Simplify.

$-4 = r$ — Solve for r.

$12 = a_1(-4)$ — Substitute for r in Equation 1.

$-3 = a_1$ — Solve for a_1.

Step 3 Write a rule for a_n.

$a_n = a_1 r^{n-1}$ — Write general rule.

$= -3(-4)^{n-1}$ — Substitute for a_1 and r.

▶ A rule is $a_n = -3(-4)^{n-1}$.

Check
Use the rule to verify that the 2nd term is 12 and the 5th term is −768.

$a_2 = -3(-4)^{2-1}$
$= -3(-4)$
$= 12$ ✓

$a_5 = -3(-4)^{5-1}$
$= -3(256)$
$= -768$ ✓

SELF-ASSESSMENT

1 I do not understand. 2 I can do it with help. 3 I can do it on my own. 4 I can teach someone else.

Determine whether the sequence is geometric. Explain your reasoning.

1. $27, 9, 3, 1, \frac{1}{3}, \ldots$

2. $2, 6, 24, 120, 720, \ldots$

3. $-1, 2, -4, 8, -16, \ldots$

4. Write a rule for the nth term of the sequence 3, 15, 75, 375, ... Then find a_9.

5. WRITING How can you determine whether a sequence is geometric from its graph?

Write a rule for the *n*th term of the sequence. Then graph the first six terms of the sequence.

6. $a_6 = -96, r = -2$

7. $a_2 = 12, a_4 = 3$

8. $a_1 = -4, a_5 = -2500$

Finding Sums of Finite Geometric Series

The expression formed by adding the terms of a geometric sequence is called a **geometric series**. The sum of the first n terms of a geometric series is denoted by S_n. You can develop a rule for S_n as follows.

$$\begin{aligned} S_n &= a_1 + a_1r + a_1r^2 + a_1r^3 + \cdots + a_1r^{n-1} \\ -rS_n &= \quad - a_1r - a_1r^2 - a_1r^3 - \cdots - a_1r^{n-1} - a_1r^n \\ \hline S_n - rS_n &= a_1 + 0 + 0 + 0 + \cdots + 0 \quad - a_1r^n \\ S_n(1 - r) &= a_1(1 - r^n) \end{aligned}$$

When $r \neq 1$, you can divide each side of this equation by $1 - r$ to obtain the following rule for S_n.

KEY IDEA

The Sum of a Finite Geometric Series

The sum of the first n terms of a geometric series with common ratio $r \neq 1$ is

$$S_n = a_1\left(\frac{1 - r^n}{1 - r}\right).$$

EXAMPLE 5 Finding the Sum of a Geometric Series

Find the sum $\sum_{k=1}^{10} 4(3)^{k-1}$.

SOLUTION

Step 1 Find the first term and identify the common ratio.

$a_1 = 4(3)^{1-1} = 4$ Find first term.

$r = 3$ Identify common ratio.

Step 2 Find the sum.

$S_{10} = a_1\left(\frac{1 - r^{10}}{1 - r}\right)$ Write rule for S_{10}.

$= 4\left(\frac{1 - 3^{10}}{1 - 3}\right)$ Substitute 4 for a_1 and 3 for r.

$= 118{,}096$ Evaluate.

Check

$\sum_{k=1}^{10} 4(3)^{k-1} = 118{,}096$

EXAMPLE 6 Modeling Real Life

You post a meme on your social network page. Six of your friends repost the meme, then six of each of their friends repost the meme, and so on. Find the total number of people who reposted the meme after the seventh round.

SOLUTION

After the first round, 6 people reposted the meme. There are 7 rounds. So, use $a_1 = 6$, $r = 6$, and $n = 7$ to find the sum.

$$S_7 = a_1\left(\frac{1 - r^7}{1 - r}\right) \qquad \text{Write rule for } S_7.$$

$$= 6\left(\frac{1 - 6^7}{1 - 6}\right) \qquad \text{Substitute 6 for } a_1 \text{ and 6 for } r.$$

$$= 335{,}922 \qquad \text{Evaluate.}$$

▶ So, 335,922 people reposted the meme after the seventh round.

EXAMPLE 7 Modeling Real Life

You can calculate the monthly payment M (in dollars) for a loan using the formula

$$M = \frac{L}{\sum_{k=1}^{t}\left(\frac{1}{1+i}\right)^k}$$

where L is the loan amount (in dollars), i is the monthly interest rate (in decimal form), and t is the term (in months). Calculate the monthly payment on a 5-year loan for \$20,000 with an annual interest rate of 6%.

SOLUTION

Step 1 Substitute for L, i, and t. The loan amount is $L = 20{,}000$, the monthly interest rate is $i = \frac{0.06}{12} = 0.005$, and the term is $t = 5(12) = 60$.

$$M = \frac{20{,}000}{\sum_{k=1}^{60}\left(\frac{1}{1+0.005}\right)^k}$$

Step 2 Notice that the denominator is a geometric series with first term $\frac{1}{1.005}$ and common ratio $\frac{1}{1.005}$. Use technology to find the monthly payment.

$$\frac{20{,}000}{\left(\sum_{k=1}^{60}\left(\frac{1}{1+0.005}\right)^k\right)} = 386.656030589$$

▶ So, the monthly payment is \$386.66.

SELF-ASSESSMENT

1 I do not understand. 2 I can do it with help. 3 I can do it on my own. 4 I can teach someone else.

Find the sum.

9. $\sum_{k=1}^{8} 5^{k-1}$

10. $\sum_{i=1}^{12} 6(-2)^{i-1}$

11. $\sum_{t=1}^{7} -16(0.5)^{t-1}$

12. You post a link for a video game trailer on your social network page. Four of your friends repost the link, then four of each of their friends repost the link, and so on. Find the total number of people who reposted the link after the sixth round.

13. WHAT IF? In Example 7, how does the monthly payment change when the annual interest rate is 5%? By how much does it change?

11.3 Practice WITH CalcChat® AND CalcView®

In Exercises 1–8, determine whether the sequence is geometric. Explain your reasoning. *Example 1*

1. 96, 48, 24, 12, 6, . . .
2. 729, 243, 81, 27, 9, . . .
3. 2, 4, 6, 8, 10, . . .
4. 5, 20, 35, 50, 65, . . .
5. 0.2, 3.2, −12.8, 51.2, −204.8, . . .
6. 0.3, −1.5, 7.5, −37.5, 187.5, . . .
7. $\frac{1}{2}, \frac{1}{6}, \frac{1}{18}, \frac{1}{54}, \frac{1}{162}, \ldots$
8. $\frac{1}{4}, \frac{1}{16}, \frac{1}{64}, \frac{1}{256}, \frac{1}{1024}, \ldots$

9. **WRITING EQUATIONS** Write a rule for the geometric sequence with the given description.
   a. The first term is −3, and each subsequent term is 5 times the previous term.
   b. The first term is 72, and each subsequent term is $\frac{1}{3}$ times the previous term.

10. **ANALYZING RELATIONSHIPS** What can you conclude about the terms of a geometric sequence when $r > 1$? $0 < r < 1$?

In Exercises 11–18, write a rule for the *n*th term of the sequence. Then find a_7. *Example 2*

11. 4, 20, 100, 500, . . .
12. 6, 24, 96, 384, . . .
13. 112, 56, 28, 14, . . .
14. 375, 75, 15, 3, . . .
15. $4, 6, 9, \frac{27}{2}, \ldots$
16. $2, \frac{3}{2}, \frac{9}{8}, \frac{27}{32}, \ldots$
17. 1.3, −3.9, 11.7, −35.1, . . .
18. 1.5, −7.5, 37.5, −187.5, . . .

In Exercises 19–26, write a rule for the *n*th term of the sequence. Then graph the first six terms of the sequence. *Example 3*

19. $a_3 = 4, r = 2$
20. $a_3 = 27, r = 3$
21. $a_2 = 30, r = \frac{1}{2}$
22. $a_2 = 64, r = \frac{1}{4}$
23. $a_4 = -192, r = 4$
24. $a_4 = -500, r = 5$
25. $a_5 = 3, r = -\frac{1}{3}$
26. $a_5 = 1, r = -\frac{1}{5}$

27. **ERROR ANALYSIS** Describe and correct the error in writing a rule for the *n*th term of the geometric sequence 4, 12, 36, 108, ...

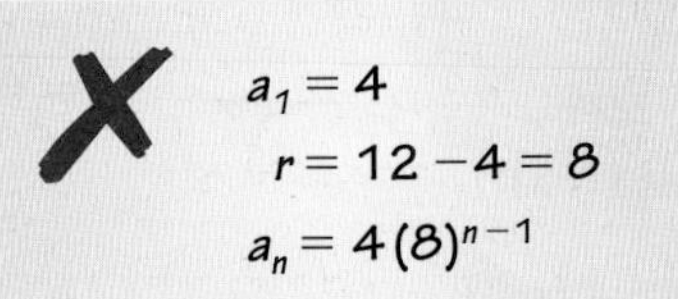

28. **ERROR ANALYSIS** Describe and correct the error in writing a rule for the *n*th term of the geometric sequence for which $a_2 = 48$ and $r = 6$.

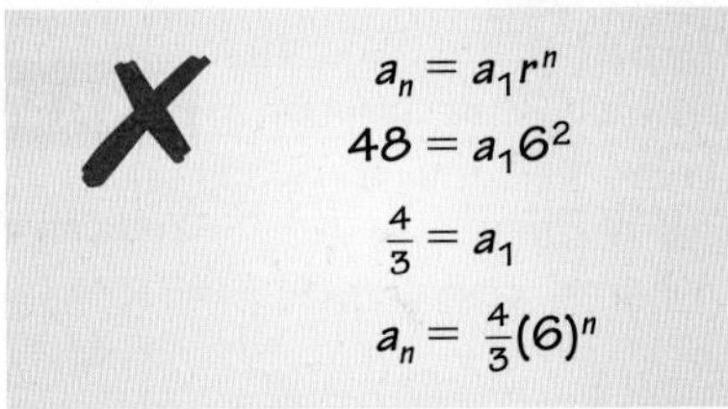

In Exercises 29–36, write a rule for the *n*th term of the geometric sequence. *Example 4*

29. $a_2 = 28, a_5 = 1792$
30. $a_1 = 11, a_4 = 88$
31. $a_1 = -6, a_5 = -486$
32. $a_2 = -10, a_6 = -6250$
33. $a_2 = 64, a_4 = 1$
34. $a_1 = 1, a_2 = 49$
35. $a_2 = -72, a_6 = -\frac{1}{18}$
36. $a_2 = -48, a_5 = \frac{3}{4}$

In Exercises 37–40, write a rule for the sequence with the given terms.

37.

38.
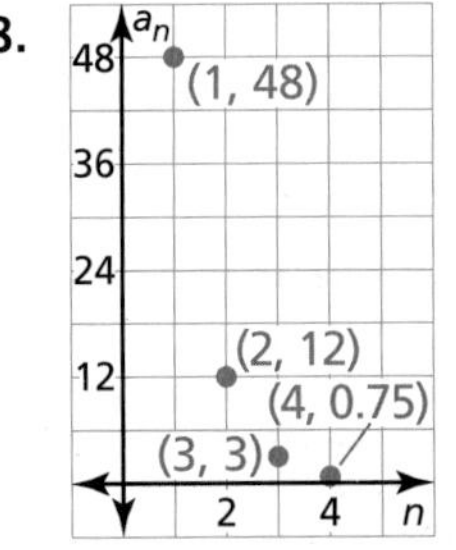

39.

n	2	3	4	5	6
a_n	−12	24	−48	96	−192

40.

n	2	3	4	5	6
a_n	−21	63	−189	567	−1701

In Exercises 41–46, find the sum. *Example 5*

41. $\sum_{i=1}^{9} 6(7)^{i-1}$

42. $\sum_{i=1}^{10} 7(4)^{i-1}$

43. $\sum_{i=1}^{10} 4\left(\frac{3}{4}\right)^{i-1}$

44. $\sum_{i=1}^{8} 5\left(\frac{1}{3}\right)^{i-1}$

45. $\sum_{i=0}^{8} 8\left(-\frac{2}{3}\right)^{i}$

46. $\sum_{i=0}^{9} 9\left(-\frac{3}{4}\right)^{i}$

MP NUMBER SENSE In Exercises 47 and 48, find the indicated sum.

47. The sum of the first 8 terms of the geometric sequence $-12, -48, -192, -768, \ldots$

48. The sum of the first 9 terms of the geometric sequence $-14, -42, -126, -378, \ldots$

49. **MODELING REAL LIFE** You share a link for a movie trailer in a chat. Three of your friends repost the link, then three of each of their friends repost the link, and so on. Find the total number of people who reposted the link after the sixth round. *Example 6*

50. **MODELING REAL LIFE** An electronics repair store offers a five-dollar kickback reward per referral. You refer two of your friends (earning you \$10), then each of them refers two of their friends, and so on. What is the total amount (in dollars) of the kickback rewards distributed after four rounds of referrals?

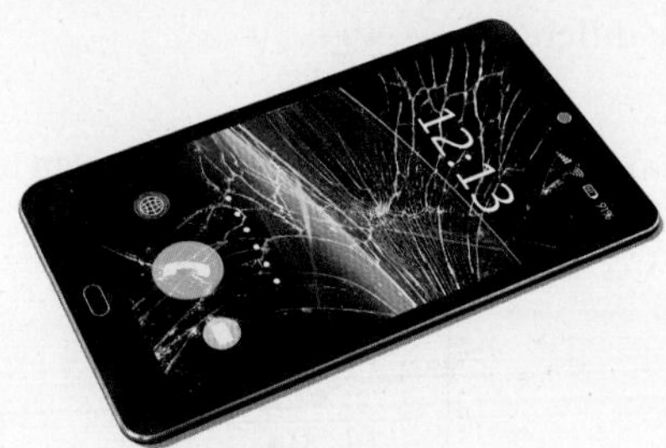

MODELING REAL LIFE In Exercises 51 and 52, use the monthly payment formula given in Example 7. *Example 7*

51. You are buying a used car. You take out a 5-year loan for \$15,000. The annual interest rate of the loan is 4%. Calculate the monthly payment.

52. You take out a 3-year personal loan for \$1300 to pay for a training trip with your swim team. The annual interest rate of the loan is 4.5%. Calculate the monthly payment.

53. **MP PROBLEM SOLVING** A hatchery raises trout for creek restocking. There are 6400 unhatched eggs at first. Each day, this number decreases by 25% as the eggs hatch. How long will it be until only 2025 unhatched eggs remain?

GO DIGITAL

54. **MP PROBLEM SOLVING** In a skydiving formation with R rings, each ring after the first has twice as many skydivers as the preceding ring. The formation for $R = 2$ is shown. Find the total number of skydivers when there are four rings.

55. **CONNECTING CONCEPTS** The *Sierpinski carpet* is a fractal created using squares. The process involves removing smaller squares from larger squares. First, divide a large square into nine congruent squares. Then remove the center square. Repeat these steps for each smaller square, as shown below. Assume that each side of the initial square is 1 unit long.

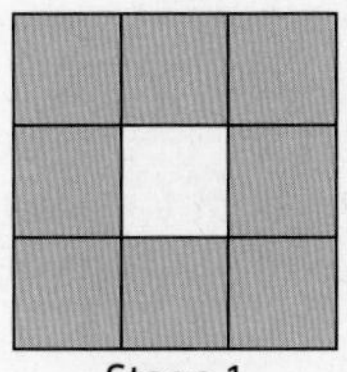
Stage 1

Stage 2

Stage 3

a. Let a_n be the number of squares removed at the nth stage. Write a rule for a_n. Then find the total number of squares removed through Stage 8.

b. Let b_n be the remaining area of the original square after the nth stage. Write a rule for b_n. Then find the remaining area of the original square after Stage 12.

56. **HOW DO YOU SEE IT?**
Match each sequence with its graph. Explain your reasoning.

a. $a_n = 10\left(\frac{1}{2}\right)^{n-1}$

b. $a_n = 10(2)^{n-1}$

A.
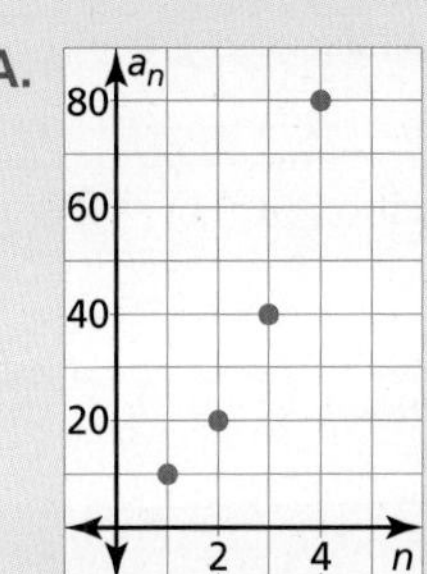

B.
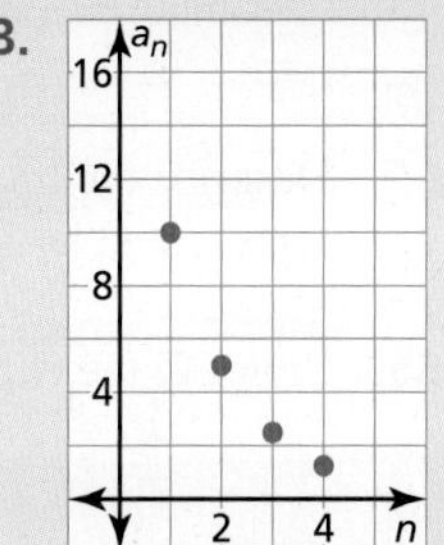

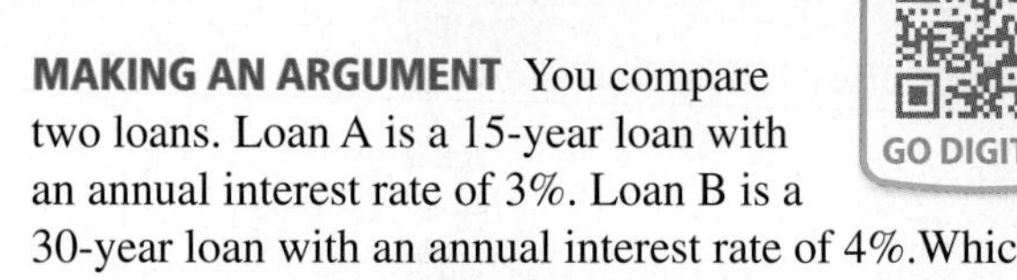

57. **PERFORMANCE TASK** **Brainstorm an idea for a small business that you could own and operate. Describe the goods or services your business would provide.**

    a. How much money would you need to start?

    b. Research loans for covering the startup costs. Which option do you prefer? Explain.

    c. Show a sample repayment plan.

58. **THOUGHT PROVOKING**
The first four iterations of the fractal called the *Koch snowflake* are shown below. Find the perimeter and area of each iteration. Do the perimeters and areas form geometric sequences? Explain your reasoning.

59. **MAKING AN ARGUMENT** You compare two loans. Loan A is a 15-year loan with an annual interest rate of 3%. Loan B is a 30-year loan with an annual interest rate of 4%. Which loan do you prefer for paying back \$16,500? Explain.

60. **CRITICAL THINKING** Let L be the amount of a loan (in dollars), i be the monthly interest rate (in decimal form), t be the term (in months), and M be the monthly payment (in dollars).

    a. When making monthly payments, you are paying on the loan amount plus the interest the loan gathers each month. For a 1-month loan ($t = 1$), the equation for repayment is $L(1 + i) - M = 0$. For a 2-month loan ($t = 2$), the equation is $[L(1 + i) - M](1 + i) - M = 0$. Solve both of these repayment equations for L.

    b. Write a repayment equation for a t-month loan. (*Hint*: L is equal to M times a geometric series.) Then solve the equation for M.

61. **MP REASONING** Use the rule for the sum of a finite geometric series to write $3x + 6x^3 + 12x^5 + 24x^7$ as a rational expression.

REVIEW & REFRESH

62. Find the discriminant of $x^2 - 4x + 1 = 0$ and describe the number and type of solutions of the equation.

63. Determine whether the study is a randomized comparative experiment. If it is, describe the treatment, the treatment group, and the control group. If it is not, explain why not and discuss whether the conclusions drawn from the study are valid.

Physical Health

Bananas Improve Flexibility

On a cross country team, students can choose a banana or another snack after each practice. Fifty-five athletes who chose a banana were monitored for the season, as were 55 athletes who chose other snacks. At the end of the season, students in the "banana" group had 5% greater flexibility than students in the other group.

64. Describe the transformation of $f(x) = 2^x$ represented by $g(x) = 2^x + 3$.

65. Simplify the expression $\tan(x - 6\pi)$.

66. Find the sum $\sum_{k=2}^{6}(3k - 1)$.

67. Find the difference $\frac{5}{2x} - \frac{3}{5x}$.

68. Write a rule for the sequence with the given terms.

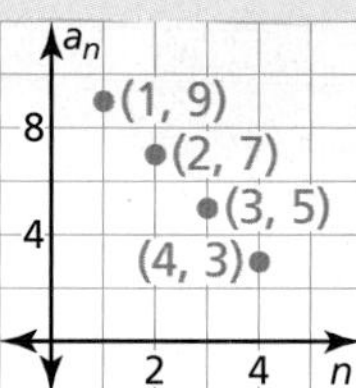

69. Write a rule for the nth term of the sequence with $a_4 = -400$ and $r = 2$. Then graph the first six terms of the sequence.

70. Each section of the spinner has the same area. What is the probability of spinning yellow *or* an 11?

11.4 Finding Sums of Infinite Geometric Series

Learning Target Find partial sums and sums of infinite geometric series.

Success Criteria
- I can find partial sums of infinite geometric series.
- I can find sums of infinite geometric series.
- I can solve real-life problems using infinite geometric series.

EXPLORE IT! Finding Sums of Infinite Geometric Series

Work with a partner. Use the grid shown that represents 1 square unit.

a. Shade one half of the grid. Then shade one half of the grid that remains. Record how much area of the original grid you shade at each step. Explain why these areas form a geometric sequence. Repeat this until you find it too difficult to shade one half of the grid that remains.

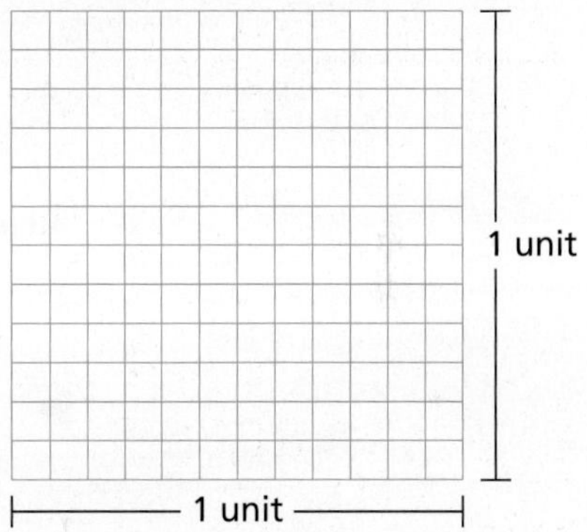

b. Complete the table.

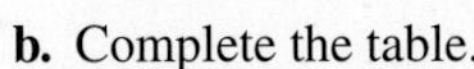

Number of shaded regions	1	2	3	4	5	6	...
Combined area of shaded regions	$\frac{1}{2}$	$\frac{3}{4}$					...

What number is the combined area of the shaded regions approaching?

c. In the previous lesson, you learned that the sum of the first n terms of a finite geometric series with first term a_1 and common ratio $r \neq 1$ is

$$S_n = a_1\left(\frac{1 - r^n}{1 - r}\right).$$

Write a rule for the combined area in part (a) after n regions are shaded. Explain what happens when n approaches infinity. What does this mean?

d. Use your results in part (c) to write a formula for the sum of an infinite geometric series when $-1 < r < 1$. Explain your reasoning.

e. In part (a), each successive region you shaded is *one half* the area of the previous shaded region. Suppose you begin with the entire square unit shaded, and you continuously shade a region that is *twice* the area of the previous shaded region. Can you determine what the combined area might be? Explain.

Math Practice

Make Conjectures
What do you think happens to the sum of an infinite geometric series when $|r| \geq 1$?

Partial Sums of Infinite Geometric Series

GO DIGITAL

Vocabulary AZ VOCAB

partial sum, *p. 620*

The sum S_n of the first n terms of an infinite series is called a **partial sum**. The partial sums of an infinite geometric series may approach a limiting value.

EXAMPLE 1 **Finding Partial Sums**

Consider the infinite geometric series

$$\frac{1}{2}+\frac{1}{8}+\frac{1}{32}+\frac{1}{128}+\frac{1}{512}+\cdots.$$

Find and graph the partial sums S_n for $n = 1, 2, 3, 4$, and 5. Then describe what happens to S_n as n increases.

SOLUTION

Step 1 Find the partial sums.

$$S_1 = \frac{1}{2} = 0.5 \qquad S_2 = \frac{1}{2}+\frac{1}{8} = 0.625$$

$$S_3 = \frac{1}{2}+\frac{1}{8}+\frac{1}{32} \approx 0.656 \qquad S_4 = \frac{1}{2}+\frac{1}{8}+\frac{1}{32}+\frac{1}{128} \approx 0.664$$

$$S_5 = \frac{1}{2}+\frac{1}{8}+\frac{1}{32}+\frac{1}{128}+\frac{1}{512} \approx 0.666$$

Step 2 Plot the points (1, 0.5), (2, 0.625), (3, 0.656), (4, 0.664), and (5, 0.666). The graph is shown at the right.

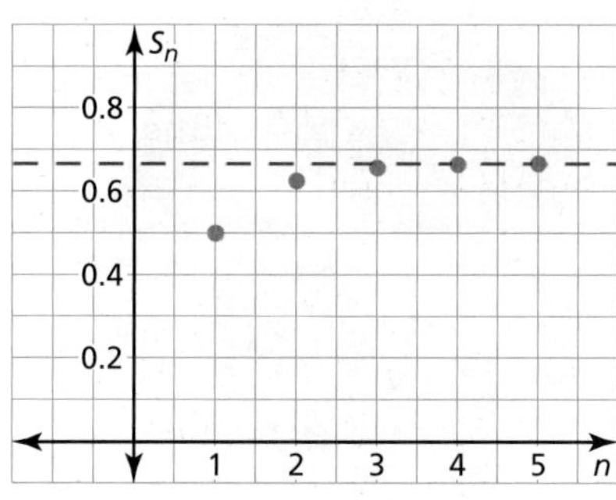

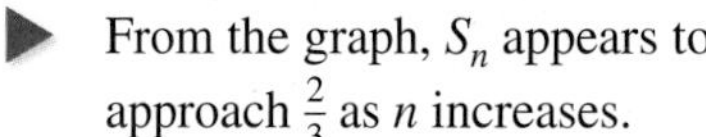

▶ From the graph, S_n appears to approach $\frac{2}{3}$ as n increases.

Sums of Infinite Geometric Series

In Example 1, you can understand why S_n approaches $\frac{2}{3}$ as n increases by considering the rule for the sum of a finite geometric series.

$$S_n = a_1\left(\frac{1-r^n}{1-r}\right) = \frac{1}{2}\left(\frac{1-\left(\frac{1}{4}\right)^n}{1-\frac{1}{4}}\right) = \frac{1}{2}\left(\frac{1-\left(\frac{1}{4}\right)^n}{\frac{3}{4}}\right) = \frac{2}{3}\left[1-\left(\frac{1}{4}\right)^n\right]$$

As n increases, $\left(\frac{1}{4}\right)^n$ approaches 0, so S_n approaches $\frac{2}{3}$. Therefore, $\frac{2}{3}$ is defined to be the sum of the infinite geometric series in Example 1. Generally, as n increases for *any* infinite geometric series with common ratio r between -1 and 1, the value of S_n approaches

$$S_n = a_1\left(\frac{1-r^n}{1-r}\right) \approx a_1\left(\frac{1-0}{1-r}\right) = \frac{a_1}{1-r}.$$

KEY IDEA

The Sum of an Infinite Geometric Series

The sum of an infinite geometric series with first term a_1 and common ratio r is given by

$$S = \frac{a_1}{1-r}$$

provided $|r| < 1$. If $|r| \geq 1$, then the sum does not exist.

Math Practice

Understand Quantities

Even though a geometric series with a common ratio of $|r| < 1$ has *infinitely* many terms, the series has a *finite* sum.

EXAMPLE 2 Finding Sums of Infinite Geometric Series

WATCH

Find the sum of each infinite geometric series, if it exists.

a. $\sum_{i=1}^{\infty} 3(0.7)^{i-1}$

b. $1 + 3 + 9 + 27 + \cdots$

c. $1 - \frac{3}{4} + \frac{9}{16} - \frac{27}{64} + \cdots$

SOLUTION

a. For this series, $a_1 = 3(0.7)^{1-1} = 3$ and $r = 0.7$. The sum of the series is

$S = \frac{a_1}{1-r}$ — Formula for sum of an infinite geometric series

$= \frac{3}{1-0.7}$ — Substitute 3 for a_1 and 0.7 for r.

$= 10.$ — Simplify.

b. For this series, $a_1 = 1$ and $a_2 = 3$. So, the common ratio is $r = \frac{3}{1} = 3$. Because $|3| \geq 1$, the sum does not exist.

STUDY TIP

For the geometric series in part (b), the graph of the partial sums S_n for $n = 1, 2, 3, 4, 5$, and 6 are shown. From the graph, it appears that as n increases, the partial sums do not approach a fixed number.

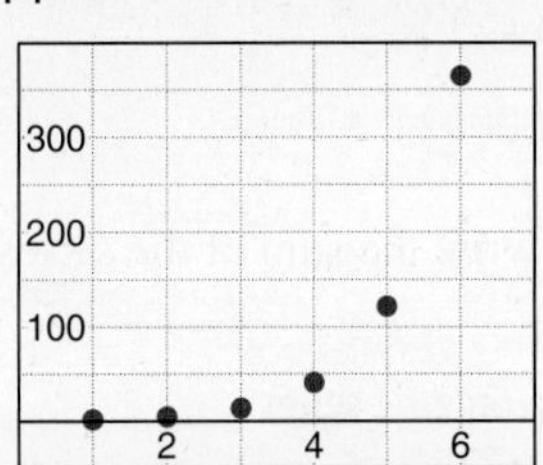

c. For this series, $a_1 = 1$ and $a_2 = -\frac{3}{4}$. So, the common ratio is

$$r = \frac{-\frac{3}{4}}{1} = -\frac{3}{4}.$$

The sum of the series is

$S = \frac{a_1}{1-r}$ — Formula for sum of an infinite geometric series

$= \frac{1}{1-\left(-\frac{3}{4}\right)}$ — Substitute 1 for a_1 and $-\frac{3}{4}$ for r.

$= \frac{4}{7}.$ — Simplify.

SELF-ASSESSMENT

1 I do not understand. 2 I can do it with help. 3 I can do it on my own. 4 I can teach someone else.

1. Consider the infinite geometric series

$$\frac{2}{5} + \frac{4}{25} + \frac{8}{125} + \frac{16}{625} + \frac{32}{3125} + \cdots.$$

Find and graph the partial sums S_n for $n = 1, 2, 3, 4$, and 5. Then describe what happens to S_n as n increases.

2. WRITING Explain how to tell whether the series $\sum_{i=1}^{\infty} a_1 r^{i-1}$ has a sum.

Find the sum of the infinite geometric series, if it exists.

3. $\sum_{n=1}^{\infty} \left(-\frac{1}{2}\right)^{n-1}$

4. $\sum_{n=1}^{\infty} 3\left(\frac{5}{4}\right)^{n-1}$

5. $3 + \frac{3}{4} + \frac{3}{16} + \frac{3}{64} + \cdots$

EXAMPLE 3 Modeling Real Life

GO DIGITAL

A pendulum that is released and swings freely travels 18 inches on the first swing. On each successive swing, the pendulum travels 80% of the distance of the previous swing. What is the total distance the pendulum travels?

SOLUTION

Write an infinite geometric series to represent the problem. The pendulum travels 18 inches on the first swing, so the first term is 18. On successive swings, it travels 18(0.8) inches, [18(0.8)](0.8) inches, [18(0.8²)](0.8) inches, and so on. So, the total distance traveled by the pendulum is given by

$$18 + 18(0.8) + 18(0.8)^2 + 18(0.8)^3 + \cdots.$$

For this series, $a_1 = 18$ and $r = 0.8$. The sum of the series is

$S = \dfrac{a_1}{1 - r}$ Formula for sum of an infinite geometric series

$= \dfrac{18}{1 - 0.8}$ Substitute 18 for a_1 and 0.8 for r.

$= 90.$ Simplify.

▶ The pendulum travels a total distance of 90 inches, or 7.5 feet.

EXAMPLE 4 Writing a Repeating Decimal as a Fraction

REMEMBER

Because a repeating decimal is a rational number, it can be written as $\frac{a}{b}$, where a and b are integers and $b \neq 0$.

Write 0.242424 . . . as a fraction in simplest form.

SOLUTION

Write the repeating decimal as an infinite geometric series.

$$0.242424\ldots = 0.24 + 0.0024 + 0.000024 + 0.00000024 + \cdots$$

For this series, $a_1 = 0.24$ and $r = \dfrac{0.0024}{0.24} = 0.01$. Next, write the sum of the series.

$S = \dfrac{a_1}{1 - r}$ Formula for sum of an infinite geometric series

$= \dfrac{0.24}{1 - 0.01}$ Substitute 0.24 for a_1 and 0.01 for r.

$= \dfrac{0.24}{0.99}$ Simplify.

$= \dfrac{24}{99}$ Write as a quotient of integers.

$= \dfrac{8}{33}$ Simplify.

SELF-ASSESSMENT

1 I do not understand. 2 I can do it with help. 3 I can do it on my own. 4 I can teach someone else.

6. A pendulum that is released and swings freely travels 10 inches on its first swing. On each successive swing, the pendulum travels 90% of the distance of the previous swing. What is the total distance the pendulum travels?

Write the repeating decimal as a fraction in simplest form.

7. 0.555 . . . **8.** 0.727272 . . . **9.** 0.131313 . . .

11.4 Practice WITH CalcChat® AND CalcView®

In Exercises 1–4, consider the infinite geometric series. Find and graph the partial sums S_n for $n = 1, 2, 3, 4$, and 5. Then describe what happens to S_n as n increases. *Example 1*

1. $\frac{1}{2} + \frac{1}{6} + \frac{1}{18} + \frac{1}{54} + \frac{1}{162} + \cdots$

2. $\frac{2}{3} + \frac{1}{3} + \frac{1}{6} + \frac{1}{12} + \frac{1}{24} + \cdots$

3. $4 + \frac{12}{5} + \frac{36}{25} + \frac{108}{125} + \frac{324}{625} + \cdots$

4. $2 + \frac{2}{6} + \frac{2}{36} + \frac{2}{216} + \frac{2}{1296} + \cdots$

In Exercises 5–12, find the sum of the infinite geometric series, if it exists. *Example 2*

5. $\sum_{n=1}^{\infty} 8\left(\frac{1}{5}\right)^{n-1}$

6. $\sum_{k=1}^{\infty} -6\left(\frac{3}{2}\right)^{k-1}$

7. $\sum_{i=1}^{\infty} \frac{2}{5}\left(\frac{5}{3}\right)^{i-1}$

8. $\sum_{k=1}^{\infty} \frac{11}{3}\left(\frac{3}{8}\right)^{k-1}$

9. $2 + \frac{6}{4} + \frac{18}{16} + \frac{54}{64} + \cdots$

10. $-5 - 2 - \frac{4}{5} - \frac{8}{25} - \cdots$

11. $3 + \frac{5}{2} + \frac{25}{12} + \frac{125}{72} + \cdots$

12. $\frac{1}{2} - \frac{5}{3} + \frac{50}{9} - \frac{500}{27} + \cdots$

ERROR ANALYSIS In Exercises 13 and 14, describe and correct the error in finding the sum of the infinite geometric series.

13. $\sum_{n=1}^{\infty} \left(\frac{7}{2}\right)^{n-1}$

For this series, $a_1 = 1$ and $r = \frac{7}{2}$.

$$S = \frac{a_1}{1 - r} = \frac{1}{1 - \frac{7}{2}} = \frac{1}{-\frac{5}{2}} = -\frac{2}{5}$$

14. $4 + \frac{8}{3} + \frac{16}{9} + \frac{32}{27} + \cdots$

For this series, $a_1 = 4$ and $r = \frac{4}{\frac{8}{3}} = \frac{3}{2}$.

Because $\left|\frac{3}{2}\right| \geq 1$, the sum does not exist.

15. **MODELING REAL LIFE** You push a tire swing one time and then allow it to swing freely. On the first swing, the tire travels a distance of 14 feet. On each successive swing, the tire travels 75% of the distance of the previous swing. What is the total distance the tire travels? *Example 3*

16. **MODELING REAL LIFE** A ball that is allowed to bounce freely reaches a height of 3 feet on its first bounce. On each successive bounce, the ball bounces to 60% of its previous height. Starting with the first bounce, what is the total vertical distance the ball travels? (*Hint*: Be sure to consider the distance the ball travels up *and* down on each bounce.)

In Exercises 17–22, write the repeating decimal as a fraction in simplest form. *Example 4*

17. 0.222 . . .

18. 0.444 . . .

19. 0.161616 . . .

20. 0.625625625 . . .

21. 32.323232 . . .

22. 130.130130130 . . .

23. **OPEN-ENDED** Write two infinite geometric series that each have a sum of 6. Justify your answers.

24. **HOW DO YOU SEE IT?**
The graph shows the partial sums of the geometric series $a_1 + a_2 + a_3 + a_4 + \cdots$.
What is the value of $\sum_{n=1}^{\infty} a_n$? Explain.

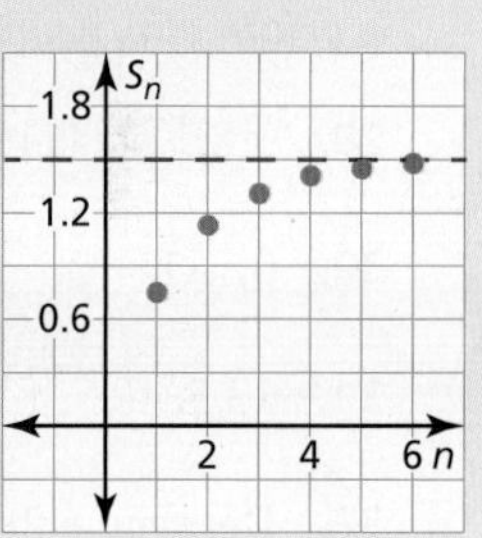

25. **CONNECTING CONCEPTS** The *Sierpinski triangle* is a fractal created using equilateral triangles. The process involves removing smaller triangles from larger triangles by joining the midpoints of the sides of the larger triangles as shown. Assume that the initial triangle has an area of 1 square foot.

Stage 1

Stage 2

Stage 3

a. Let a_n be the total area of the triangles that are removed at Stage n. Write a rule for a_n.

b. Find $\sum_{n=1}^{\infty} a_n$. Interpret your answer in the context of this situation.

26. **DIG DEEPER** Can a person running at 20 feet per second ever catch up to a tortoise traveling at 10 feet per second when the tortoise has a 20-foot head start? The Greek mathematician Zeno said no. He reasoned that the person will keep halving the distance but will never catch up to the tortoise. Looking at the race as Zeno did, the distances and the times it takes the person to run the distances both form infinite geometric series. Using the table, show that both series have finite sums. Does the person catch up to the tortoise? Justify your answer.

Distance (ft)	20	10	5	2.5	...
Time (sec)	1	0.5	0.25	0.125	...

27. **MAKING AN ARGUMENT** Is 0.999 . . . equal to 1? Justify your answer.

28. **THOUGHT PROVOKING**
Archimedes used the sum of an infinite geometric series to compute the area enclosed by a parabola and a straight line. In "Quadrature of the Parabola," he proved that the area of the region is $\frac{4}{3}$ the area of the inscribed triangle. The first term of the series for the parabola below is represented by the area of the blue triangle, and the second term is represented by the total area of the red triangles. Use Archimedes' result to find the area of the region. Then write the area as the sum of an infinite geometric series.

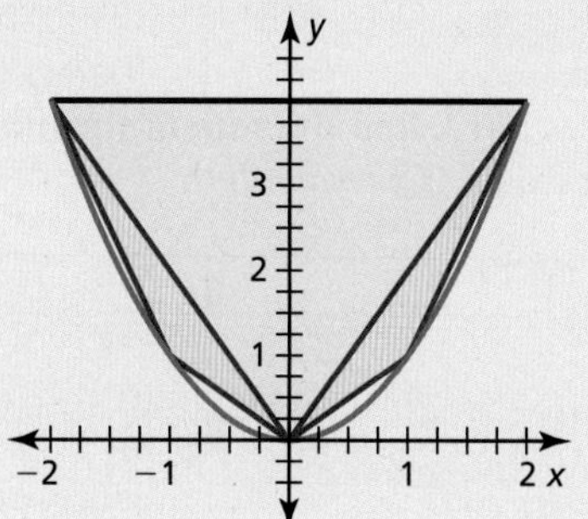

REVIEW & REFRESH

In Exercises 29–31, determine whether the sequence is *arithmetic*, *geometric*, or *neither*.

29. $-8, -2, 4, 10, 16, \ldots$

30. $0, -1, -3, -7, -15, \ldots$

31. $13.5, 40.5, 121.5, 364.5, \ldots$

32. Determine the type of function represented by the table.

x	0	4	8	12	16
y	−7	−1	2	2	−1

33. **MODELING REAL LIFE** A group of students is arranged in rows for a yearbook photograph. The first row has five students, and each subsequent row has two more students than the previous row.

  a. Write a rule for the number of students in the nth row.

  b. There are a total of eight rows. How many students are in the group?

In Exercises 34–37, solve the equation.

34. $\frac{1}{2}x^2 + 5 = -3$

35. $-5x^3 + 45x^2 = 90x$

36. $4^x = 12$

37. $\frac{10}{x+3} - 6 = \frac{1}{x}$

In Exercises 38 and 39, find the sum.

38. $\sum_{i=2}^{6} \frac{3}{i}$

39. $\sum_{n=1}^{\infty} 2\left(\frac{5}{6}\right)^{n-1}$

40. Divide $x^3 + 3x^2 - 1$ by $x + 4$.

41. The graph of g is a transformation of the graph of $f(x) = 0.5^x$. Write a rule for g.

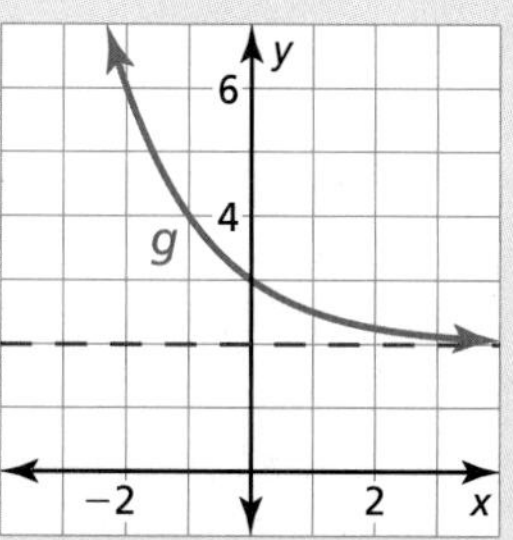

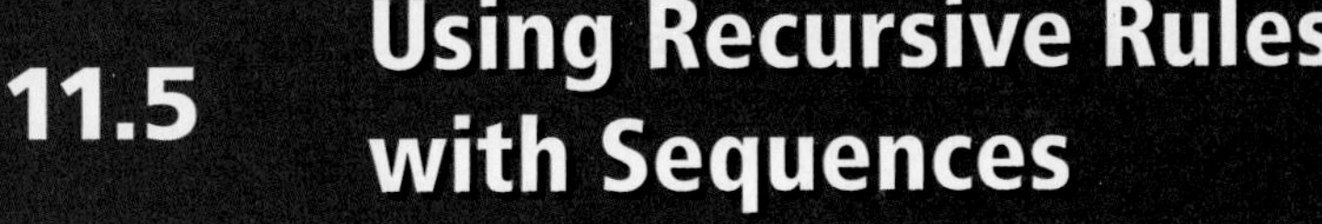

11.5 Using Recursive Rules with Sequences

Learning Target Write and use recursively defined sequences.

Success Criteria
- I can write terms of recursively defined sequences.
- I can write recursive rules for sequences.
- I can translate between recursive rules and explicit rules.
- I can use recursive rules to solve real-life problems.

EXPLORE IT! Writing a Recursive Equation

Work with a partner. You use a ride-sharing service to visit friends. You enter your destination and obtain the fare estimate shown.

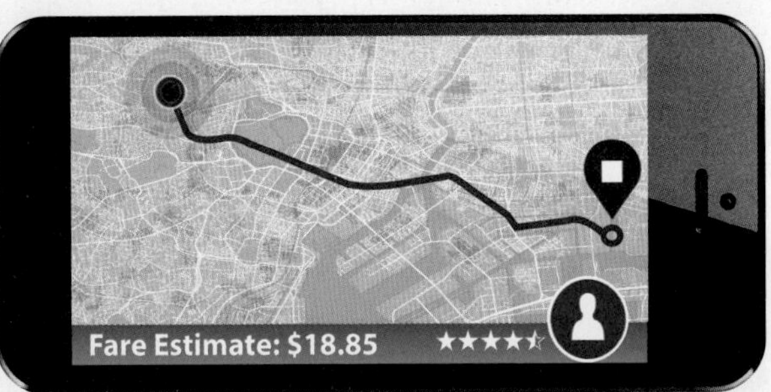

a. The actual fare depends on how long the ride takes. Your fare is \$12.20 plus \$0.35 per minute. Use a spreadsheet to repeatedly add \$0.35 to the cost. How much time was used for the fare estimate?

	A	B
1	Minutes	Cost (dollars)
2	0	12.20
3	1	12.55 ← B2+0.35
4	2	
5	3	
6	4	
7	5	

b. A *recursive equation* tells how a term of a sequence is related to one or more preceding terms. Write a recursive equation for the sequence in part (a) that relates a term a_n to the preceding term a_{n-1}.

c. Find and interpret a_{15}.

d. The actual ride takes 23 minutes. What is your total fare?

Math Practice

Reason Abstractly

Given a recursive equation, can you find a_1? What does this imply about expressing sequences *recursively*?

Evaluating Recursive Rules

Vocabulary 

explicit rule, *p. 626*
recursive rule, *p. 626*

So far in this chapter, you have worked with explicit rules for the *n*th term of a sequence, such as $a_n = 3n - 2$ and $a_n = 7(0.5)^n$. An **explicit rule** gives a_n as a function of the term's position number *n* in the sequence.

In this section, you will learn another way to define a sequence—by a *recursive rule*. A **recursive rule** gives the beginning term(s) of a sequence and a *recursive equation* that tells how a_n is related to one or more preceding terms.

EXAMPLE 1 Evaluating Recursive Rules

Write the first six terms of each sequence.

a. $a_0 = 1, a_n = a_{n-1} + 4$ **b.** $f(1) = 1, f(n) = 3 \cdot f(n-1)$

SOLUTION

a.		b.
$a_0 = 1$	1st term	$f(1) = 1$
$a_1 = a_0 + 4 = 1 + 4 = 5$	2nd term	$f(2) = 3 \cdot f(1) = 3(1) = 3$
$a_2 = a_1 + 4 = 5 + 4 = 9$	3rd term	$f(3) = 3 \cdot f(2) = 3(3) = 9$
$a_3 = a_2 + 4 = 9 + 4 = 13$	4th term	$f(4) = 3 \cdot f(3) = 3(9) = 27$
$a_4 = a_3 + 4 = 13 + 4 = 17$	5th term	$f(5) = 3 \cdot f(4) = 3(27) = 81$
$a_5 = a_4 + 4 = 17 + 4 = 21$	6th term	$f(6) = 3 \cdot f(5) = 3(81) = 243$

SELF-ASSESSMENT 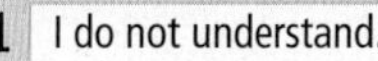 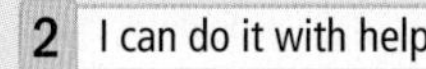 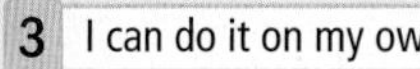 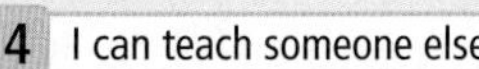

Write the first six terms of the sequence.

1. $a_1 = 3, a_n = a_{n-1} - 7$

2. $a_0 = 162, a_n = 0.5a_{n-1}$

3. $f(0) = 1, f(n) = f(n-1) + n$

4. $a_1 = 4, a_n = 2a_{n-1} - 1$

5. MP **PRECISION** Explain the difference between an explicit rule and a recursive rule for a sequence.

Writing Recursive Rules

In part (a) of Example 1, the *differences* of consecutive terms of the sequence are constant, so the sequence is arithmetic. In part (b), the *ratios* of consecutive terms are constant, so the sequence is geometric. In general, rules for arithmetic and geometric sequences can be written recursively as follows.

KEY IDEA

Recursive Equations for Arithmetic and Geometric Sequences

Arithmetic Sequence

$a_n = a_{n-1} + d$, where *d* is the common difference

Geometric Sequence

$a_n = r \cdot a_{n-1}$, where *r* is the common ratio

EXAMPLE 2 Writing Recursive Rules

WATCH

GO DIGITAL

Write a recursive rule for (a) 3, 13, 23, 33, 43, . . . and (b) 16, 40, 100, 250, 625, ...

SOLUTION

Use a table to organize the terms and find the pattern.

a.

n	1	2	3	4	5
a_n	3	13	23	33	43

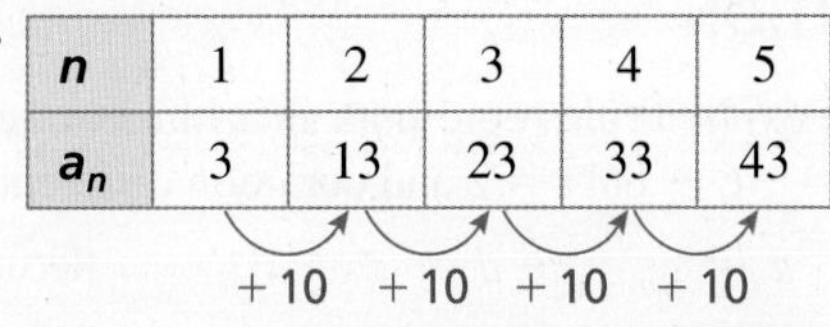

The sequence is arithmetic with first term $a_1 = 3$ and common difference $d = 10$.

$a_n = a_{n-1} + d$ Recursive equation for arithmetic sequence

$= a_{n-1} + 10$ Substitute 10 for *d*.

▶ A recursive rule for the sequence is $a_1 = 3$, $a_n = a_{n-1} + 10$.

> **COMMON ERROR**
> A recursive *equation* for a sequence does not include the initial term. To write a recursive *rule* for a sequence, the initial term(s) must be included.

b.

n	1	2	3	4	5
a_n	16	40	100	250	625

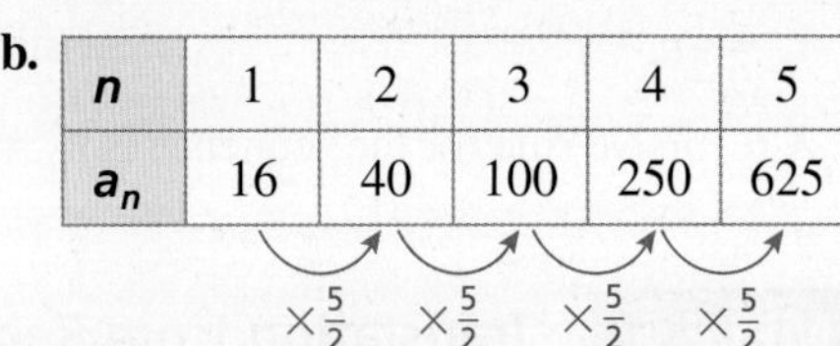

The sequence is geometric with first term $a_1 = 16$ and common ratio $r = \frac{5}{2}$.

$a_n = r \cdot a_{n-1}$ Recursive equation for geometric sequence

$= \frac{5}{2}a_{n-1}$ Substitute $\frac{5}{2}$ for *r*.

▶ A recursive rule for the sequence is $a_1 = 16$, $a_n = \frac{5}{2}a_{n-1}$.

EXAMPLE 3 Writing Recursive Rules

Write a recursive rule for each sequence.

a. 1, 1, 2, 3, 5, . . .

b. 1, 1, 2, 6, 24, . . .

> **STUDY TIP**
> The sequence in part (a) of Example 3 is called the *Fibonacci sequence*. The sequence in part (b) lists *factorial numbers*.
> $0! = 1$ $1! = 1$ $2! = 2$
> $3! = 6$ $4! = 24$

SOLUTION

a. The terms have neither a common difference nor a common ratio. Beginning with the third term of the sequence, each term is the sum of the two previous terms.

▶ A recursive rule for the sequence is $a_1 = 1$, $a_2 = 1$, $a_n = a_{n-2} + a_{n-1}$.

b. The terms have neither a common difference nor a common ratio. Denote the first term by $a_0 = 1$. Note that $a_1 = 1 = 1 \cdot a_0$, $a_2 = 2 = 2 \cdot a_1$, $a_3 = 6 = 3 \cdot a_2$, and so on.

▶ A recursive rule for the sequence is $a_0 = 1$, $a_n = n \cdot a_{n-1}$.

SELF-ASSESSMENT

1 I do not understand. 2 I can do it with help. 3 I can do it on my own. 4 I can teach someone else.

Write a recursive rule for the sequence.

6. 2, 14, 98, 686, 4802, . . .

7. 11, 22, 33, 44, 55, . . .

8. 1, 2, 2, 4, 8, 32, . . .

GO DIGITAL

Translating Between Recursive and Explicit Rules

EXAMPLE 4 Translating from Explicit Rules to Recursive Rules

Write a recursive rule for (a) $a_n = -6 + 8n$ and (b) $a_n = -3\left(\frac{1}{2}\right)^{n-1}$.

SOLUTION

a. The explicit rule represents an arithmetic sequence with first term $a_1 = -6 + 8(1) = 2$ and common difference $d = 8$.

$a_n = a_{n-1} + d$ — Recursive equation for arithmetic sequence

$a_n = a_{n-1} + 8$ — Substitute 8 for d.

▶ A recursive rule for the sequence is $a_1 = 2$, $a_n = a_{n-1} + 8$.

b. The explicit rule represents a geometric sequence with first term $a_1 = -3\left(\frac{1}{2}\right)^0 = -3$ and common ratio $r = \frac{1}{2}$.

$a_n = r \cdot a_{n-1}$ — Recursive equation for geometric sequence

$a_n = \frac{1}{2}a_{n-1}$ — Substitute $\frac{1}{2}$ for r.

▶ A recursive rule for the sequence is $a_1 = -3$, $a_n = \frac{1}{2}a_{n-1}$.

EXAMPLE 5 Translating from Recursive Rules to Explicit Rules

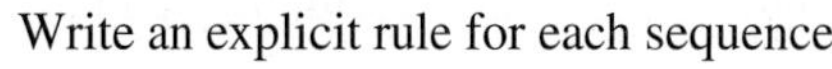

Write an explicit rule for each sequence.

a. $a_1 = -5$, $a_n = a_{n-1} - 2$ **b.** $a_1 = 10$, $a_n = 2a_{n-1}$

SOLUTION

a. The recursive rule represents an arithmetic sequence with first term $a_1 = -5$ and common difference $d = -2$.

$a_n = a_1 + (n - 1)d$ — Explicit rule for arithmetic sequence

$a_n = -5 + (n - 1)(-2)$ — Substitute -5 for a_1 and -2 for d.

$a_n = -3 - 2n$ — Simplify.

▶ An explicit rule for the sequence is $a_n = -3 - 2n$.

b. The recursive rule represents a geometric sequence with first term $a_1 = 10$ and common ratio $r = 2$.

$a_n = a_1r^{n-1}$ — Explicit rule for geometric sequence

$a_n = 10(2)^{n-1}$ — Substitute 10 for a_1 and 2 for r.

▶ An explicit rule for the sequence is $a_n = 10(2)^{n-1}$.

SELF-ASSESSMENT

1 I do not understand. 2 I can do it with help. 3 I can do it on my own. 4 I can teach someone else.

Write a recursive rule for the sequence.

9. $a_n = 17 - 4n$

10. $a_n = 16(3)^{n-1}$

Write an explicit rule for the sequence.

11. $a_1 = -12$, $a_n = a_{n-1} + 16$

12. $a_1 = 2$, $a_n = -6a_{n-1}$

Solving Real-Life Problems

EXAMPLE 6 Modeling Real Life

A lake initially contains 5200 fish. Each year, the population declines 30% due to fishing and other causes, so the lake is restocked with 400 fish.

a. Write a recursive rule for the number a_n of fish at the start of the nth year.

b. Find the number of fish at the start of the fifth year.

c. Describe what happens to the population of fish over time.

SOLUTION

a. The initial value is 5200. Because the population declines 30% each year, 70% of the fish remain in the lake from one year to the next. Also, 400 fish are added each year. Use a verbal model to write a recursive equation.

Fish at start of year n	$= 0.7 \cdot$	Fish at start of year $n-1$	$+$	New fish added
↓		↓		↓
a_n	$= 0.7 \cdot$	a_{n-1}	$+$	400

▶ A recursive rule is $a_1 = 5200$, $a_n = 0.7a_{n-1} + 400$.

b. To find the number of fish at the start of the fifth year, use technology to enter 5200 (the value of a_1). Then enter the rule

$.7 \times \text{ans} + 400$

to find a_2. Press enter three more times to find $a_5 \approx 2262$.

5200	
.7· 5200 (ans) + 400	= 4040
.7· 4040 (ans) + 400	= 3228
.7· 3228 (ans) + 400	= 2659.6
.7· 2659.6 (ans) + 400	= 2261.72

▶ There are about 2262 fish in the lake at the start of the fifth year.

c. Continue pressing enter to determine what happens to the population of fish over time. The screen at the right shows the fish populations for Years 46 to 50. The population of fish appears to approach 1333.

.7· 1333.33... (ans) + 400	= 1333.333747
.7· 1333.33... (ans) + 400	= 1333.333623
.7· 1333.33... (ans) + 400	= 1333.333536
.7· 1333.33... (ans) + 400	= 1333.333475
.7· 1333.33... (ans) + 400	= 1333.333433

▶ Over time, the population of fish in the lake stabilizes at about 1333 fish.

SELF-ASSESSMENT 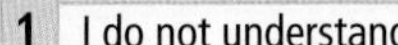 1 I do not understand. 2 I can do it with help. 3 I can do it on my own. 4 I can teach someone else.

13. WHAT IF? In Example 6, 75% of the fish remain each year. What happens to the population of fish over time?

EXAMPLE 7 Modeling Real Life

A homebuyer borrows $150,000 at 6% annual interest compounded monthly for 30 years. The monthly payment is $899.33.

- Find the balance after the third payment.
- Due to rounding in the calculations, the last payment is often different from the original payment. Find the amount of the last payment.

REMEMBER

In Section 11.3, you used a formula involving a geometric series to calculate the monthly payment for a similar loan.

SOLUTION

1. **Understand the Problem** You are given the conditions of a loan. You are asked to find the balance after the third payment and the amount of the last payment.

2. **Make a Plan** Because the balance after each payment depends on the balance after the previous payment, write a recursive equation that gives the balance after each payment. Then use a spreadsheet to find the balance after each payment, rounded to the nearest cent.

3. **Solve and Check** Because the monthly interest rate is $\frac{0.06}{12} = 0.005$, the balance increases by a factor of 1.005 each month, and then the payment of $899.33 is subtracted.

Balance after payment = 1.005 • Balance before payment − Payment

$$a_n = 1.005 \cdot a_{n-1} - 899.33$$

Use a spreadsheet and the recursive equation to find the balance after the third payment and after the 359th payment.

	A	B
1	Payment number	Balance after payment
2	1	149850.67
3	2	149700.59
4	3	149549.76
⋮	⋮	⋮
358	357	2667.38
359	358	1781.39
360	359	890.97

B2 =Round(1.005*150000−899.33, 2)

B3 =Round(1.005*B2−899.33, 2)

B360 =Round(1.005*B359−899.33, 2)

▶ The balance after the third payment is $149,549.76. The balance after the 359th payment is $890.97, so the final payment is 1.005(890.97) = $895.42.

Check Reasonableness By continuing the spreadsheet for the 360th payment using the original monthly payment of $899.33, the balance is −3.91.

361	360	−3.91

B361 =Round(1.005*B360−899.33, 2)

This shows an overpayment of $3.91. So, it is reasonable that the last payment is $899.33 − $3.91 = $895.42.

SELF-ASSESSMENT

1 I do not understand. 2 I can do it with help. 3 I can do it on my own. 4 I can teach someone else.

14. WHAT IF? How do the answers in Example 7 change when the annual interest rate is 7.5% and the monthly payment is $1048.82?

In Exercises 1–8, write the first six terms of the sequence. *Example 1*

1. $a_1 = 1$
$a_n = a_{n-1} + 3$

2. $a_1 = 1$
$a_n = a_{n-1} - 5$

3. $f(0) = 4$
$f(n) = 2 \cdot f(n-1)$

4. $f(0) = 10$
$f(n) = \frac{1}{2} \cdot f(n-1)$

5. $a_1 = 2$
$a_n = (a_{n-1})^2 + 1$

6. $a_1 = 1$
$a_n = (a_{n-1})^2 - 10$

7. $f(0) = 2, f(1) = 4$
$f(n) = f(n-1) - f(n-2)$

8. $f(1) = 2, f(2) = 3$
$f(n) = f(n-1) \cdot f(n-2)$

In Exercises 9–20, write a recursive rule for the sequence. *Examples 2 and 3*

9. 21, 14, 7, 0, −7, . . .

10. 54, 43, 32, 21, 10, . . .

11. 3, 12, 48, 192, 768, . . .

12. 4, −12, 36, −108, . . .

13. $44, 11, \frac{11}{4}, \frac{11}{16}, \frac{11}{64}, \ldots$

14. 1, 8, 15, 22, 29, . . .

15. 2, 5, 10, 50, 500, . . .

16. 3, 5, 15, 75, 1125, . . .

17. 1, 4, 5, 9, 14, . . .

18. 16, 9, 7, 2, 5, . . .

19. 6, 12, 36, 144, 720, . . .

20. −3, −1, 2, 6, 11, . . .

In Exercises 21 and 22, write a recursive rule for the sequence shown in the graph.

21.
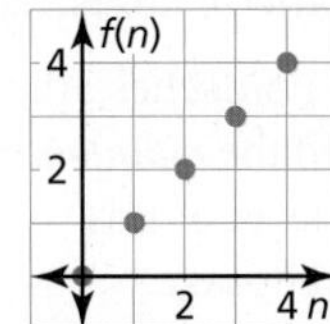

22.
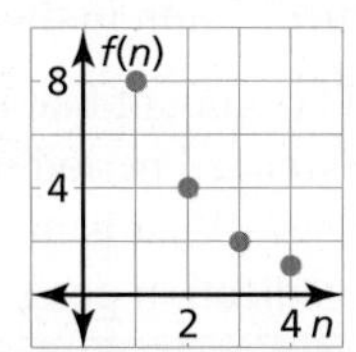

ERROR ANALYSIS In Exercises 23 and 24, describe and correct the error in writing a recursive rule for the sequence 5, 2, 3, −1, 4, ...

23.

Beginning with the third term of the sequence, each term a_n equals $a_{n-2} - a_{n-1}$. So, a recursive rule is given by

$a_n = a_{n-2} - a_{n-1}$.

24.

Beginning with the second term of the sequence, each term a_n equals $a_{n-1} - 3$. So, a recursive rule is given by

$a_1 = 5, a_n = a_{n-1} - 3$.

In Exercises 25–34, write a recursive rule for the sequence. *Example 4*

25. $a_n = 3 + 4n$

26. $a_n = -2 - 8n$

27. $a_n = 12 - 10n$

28. $a_n = 9 - 5n$

29. $a_n = 12(11)^{n-1}$

30. $a_n = -7(6)^{n-1}$

31. $a_n = 2.5 - 0.6n$

32. $a_n = -1.4 + 0.5n$

33. $a_n = -\frac{1}{2}\left(\frac{1}{4}\right)^{n-1}$

34. $a_n = \frac{1}{4}(5)^{n-1}$

35. MODELING REAL LIFE You have saved \$82 to buy a video game console. You save an additional \$30 each month. The explicit rule $a_n = 30n + 82$ gives the amount saved after n months. Write a recursive rule for the amount you have saved n months from now.

36. MODELING REAL LIFE An employee's salary is given by the explicit rule $a_n = 35{,}000(1.04)^{n-1}$, where n is the number of years the employee has worked. Write a recursive rule for the employee's salary.

In Exercises 37–44, write an explicit rule for the sequence. *Example 5*

37. $a_1 = 3, a_n = a_{n-1} - 6$

38. $a_1 = 16, a_n = a_{n-1} + 7$

39. $a_1 = -2, a_n = 3a_{n-1}$

40. $a_1 = 13, a_n = 4a_{n-1}$

41. $a_1 = -12, a_n = a_{n-1} + 9.1$

42. $a_1 = -4, a_n = 0.65a_{n-1}$

43. $a_1 = 5, a_n = a_{n-1} - \frac{1}{3}$

44. $a_1 = -5, a_n = \frac{1}{4}a_{n-1}$

45. MODELING REAL LIFE A grocer arranges cans in a pyramid-shaped display with 20 cans in the bottom row and two fewer cans in each subsequent row going up. The number of cans in each row is represented by the recursive rule $a_1 = 20$, $a_n = a_{n-1} - 2$. Write an explicit rule for the number of cans in row n.

46. MODELING REAL LIFE The value of a car is given by the recursive rule $a_1 = 25{,}600$, $a_n = 0.86a_{n-1}$, where n is the number of years since the car was new. Write an explicit rule for the value of the car after n years.

47. COLLEGE PREP What is the 1000th term of the sequence whose first term is $a_1 = 4$ and whose nth term is $a_n = a_{n-1} + 6$? Justify your answer.

Ⓐ 4006 Ⓑ 5998

Ⓒ 1010 Ⓓ 10,000

48. COLLEGE PREP What is the 873rd term of the sequence whose first term is $a_1 = 0.01$ and whose nth term is $a_n = 1.01a_{n-1}$? Justify your answer.

Ⓐ 58.65 Ⓑ 8.73

Ⓒ 1.08 Ⓓ 586,459.38

49. MP PROBLEM SOLVING A music streaming service initially has 50,000 members. Each year, the company loses 20% of its current members and gains 5000 new members. *Example 6*

a. Write a recursive rule for the number a_n of members at the start of the nth year.

b. Find the number of members at the start of the fifth year.

c. Describe what happens to the number of members over time.

50. MP PROBLEM SOLVING You add chlorine to a swimming pool. You add 34 ounces of chlorine the first week and 16 ounces every week thereafter. Each week, 40% of the chlorine in the pool evaporates.

a. Write a recursive rule for the amount a_n of chlorine in the pool at the start of the nth week.

b. Find the amount of chlorine in the pool at the start of the third week.

c. Describe what happens to the amount of chlorine in the pool over time.

51. OPEN-ENDED Give an example of a real-life situation that you can represent with a recursive rule. Then write the rule.

52. OPEN-ENDED Give an example of a sequence in which each term after the third term is a function of the three preceding terms. Write a recursive rule for the sequence and find its first eight terms.

53. MODELING REAL LIFE You borrow \$2000 to travel. The loan has a 9% annual interest rate that is compounded monthly for 2 years. The monthly payment is \$91.37. *Example 7*

a. Find the balance after the fifth payment.

b. Find the amount of the last payment.

54. MODELING REAL LIFE You borrow \$10,000 to take some college courses. The loan is secured for 7 years at an annual interest rate of 11.5%. The monthly payment is \$173.86.

a. Find the balance after the fourth payment.

b. Find the amount of the last payment.

55. DRAWING CONCLUSIONS A tree farm initially has 9000 trees. Each year, 10% of the trees are harvested and 800 seedlings are planted.

a. Write a recursive rule for the number a_n of trees on the tree farm at the beginning of the nth year.

b. What happens to the number of trees after an extended period of time?

56. DRAWING CONCLUSIONS You sprain your ankle and your doctor prescribes 325 milligrams of an anti-inflammatory medication every 8 hours for 10 days. Sixty percent of the medication is removed from the bloodstream every 8 hours.

a. Write a recursive rule for the amount a_n of the medication in the bloodstream after n doses.

b. The amount that a medication approaches after an extended period of time is called the *maintenance level*. What is the maintenance level of this medication given the prescribed dosage?

c. How does doubling the dosage affect the maintenance level of the medication? Justify your answer.

57. COMPARING METHODS In 1202, the mathematician Leonardo Fibonacci wrote *Liber Abaci,* in which he proposed the following rabbit problem.

Begin with a pair of newborn rabbits. When a pair of rabbits is two months old, the rabbits begin producing a new pair of rabbits each month. Assume none of the rabbits die.

Month	1	2	3	4	5	6
Pairs at start of month	1	1	2	3	5	8

This problem produces a sequence called the Fibonacci sequence, which has both a recursive rule and an explicit rule as follows.

Recursive: $a_1 = 1, a_2 = 1, a_n = a_{n-2} + a_{n-1}$

Explicit: $f_n = \frac{1}{\sqrt{5}}\left(\frac{1+\sqrt{5}}{2}\right)^n - \frac{1}{\sqrt{5}}\left(\frac{1-\sqrt{5}}{2}\right)^n, n \geq 1$

Use each formula to determine how many rabbits there will be after one year. Justify your answers.

58. MP USING TOOLS A town library initially has 54,000 books in its collection. Each year, 2% of the books are lost or discarded. The library can afford to purchase 1150 new books each year.

a. Write a recursive rule for the number a_n of books in the library at the beginning of the nth year.

b. Use technology to graph the sequence. What happens to the number of books in the library over time? Explain.

59. MP PATTERNS A fractal tree starts with a single branch (the trunk). At each stage, each new branch from the previous stage grows two more branches, as shown.

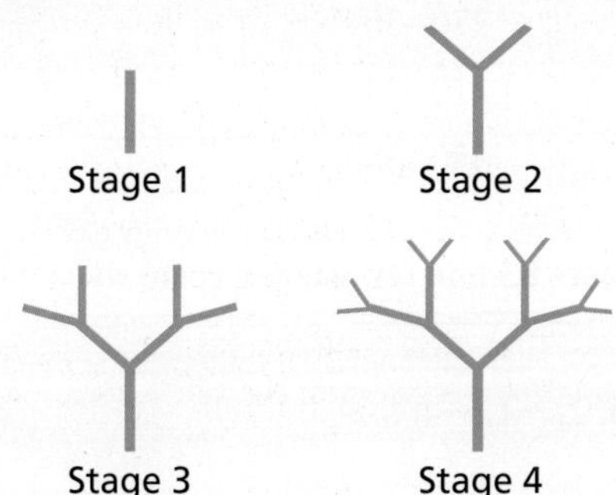

a. List the number of new branches in each of the first seven stages. What type of sequence do these numbers form?

b. Write an explicit rule and a recursive rule for the sequence in part (a).

60. HOW DO YOU SEE IT?
The graph shows the first six terms of the sequence $a_1 = p, a_n = ra_{n-1}$.

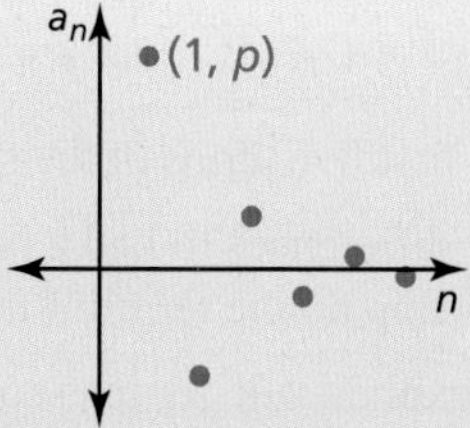

a. Describe what happens to the terms of the sequence as n increases.

b. Describe the set of possible values of r. Explain your reasoning.

GO DIGITAL

61. MODELING REAL LIFE You make a $500 down payment on a $3500 telephoto lens for your camera. You borrow the remaining balance at 10% annual interest compounded monthly. The monthly payment is $213.59. How long does it take to pay back the loan? What is the amount of the last payment? Justify your answers.

62. THOUGHT PROVOKING
Let $a_1 = 34$. Write the terms of the sequence until you discover a pattern.

$$a_{n+1} = \begin{cases} \frac{1}{2}a_n, & \text{if } a_n \text{ is even} \\ 3a_n + 1, & \text{if } a_n \text{ is odd} \end{cases}$$

Do the same for $a_1 = 25$. What can you conclude?

63. CRITICAL THINKING The first four triangular numbers T_n and the first four square numbers S_n are represented by the numbers of points in the diagrams.

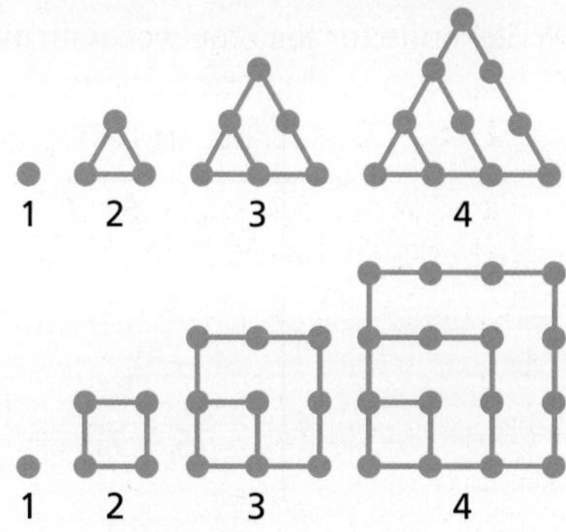

a. Write an explicit rule for each sequence.

b. Write a recursive rule for each sequence.

c. Write a rule for the square numbers in terms of the triangular numbers. Draw diagrams to support the rule.

64. **MP REASONING** The recursive rule for a sequence is as follows.

$f(1) = 3, f(2) = 10$

$f(n) = 4 + 2 \cdot f(n-1) - f(n-2)$

a. Write the first five terms of the sequence.

b. Use finite differences to find a pattern. What type of relationship do the terms of the sequence show?

c. Write an explicit rule for the sequence.

65. **MAKING AN ARGUMENT** Is it possible that a recursive equation for a sequence is the same as an explicit rule for the sequence? Explain.

66. **DIG DEEPER** You are saving money for retirement. You plan to withdraw \$30,000 at the beginning of each year for 20 years after you retire. Based on the type of investment you are making, you can expect to earn an annual return of 8% on your savings after you retire.

GO DIGITAL

a. Let a_n be your balance n years after retiring. Write a recursive equation that shows how a_n is related to a_{n-1}.

b. Solve the equation from part (a) for a_{n-1}. Find a_0, the minimum amount of money you should have in your account when you retire. (*Hint*: Let $a_{20} = 0$.)

REVIEW & REFRESH

In Exercises 67 and 68, solve the equation.

67. $\sqrt{x} + 2 = 7$

68. $2\sqrt[3]{x} - 13 = -5$

69. Find the value of x for the right triangle.

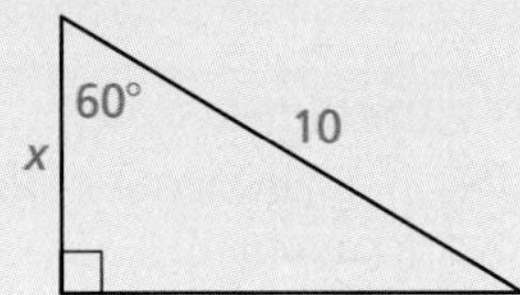

70. Two terms of a geometric sequence are $a_6 = -50$ and $a_9 = -6250$. Write a rule for the nth term.

In Exercises 71 and 72, the variables x and y vary inversely. Use the given values to write an equation relating x and y. Then find y when x = 4.

71. $x = 2, y = 9$

72. $x = -4, y = \frac{1}{2}$

73. Write a rule for the sequence with the given terms.

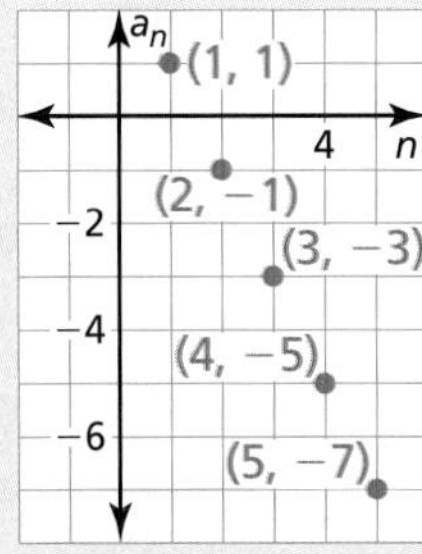

In Exercises 74 and 75, find the sum of the infinite geometric series, if it exists.

74. $\sum_{i=1}^{\infty} 6(0.5)^{i-1}$

75. $1, -\frac{3}{2}, \frac{9}{4}, -\frac{27}{8}, \frac{81}{16}, \ldots$

In Exercises 76–81, graph the function.

76. $g(x) = \frac{6}{x}$

77. $f(x) = \left(\frac{5}{2}\right)^x$

78. $f(x) = 2 \log_3 x - 3$

79. $y = -\sqrt{x-1} + 5$

80. $y = -\frac{1}{2}(x+1)^2 - 2$

81. $g(x) = (2x)^4 - 4$

82. **MODELING REAL LIFE** The table shows the numbers of tickets sold for various baseball games in a league over a season. Display the data in a histogram. Do the data fit a normal distribution? Explain.

Tickets sold	Frequency
150–189	1
190–229	2
230–269	4
270–309	8
310–349	8
350–389	7

In Exercises 83 and 84, write a recursive rule for the sequence.

83. $8, 5, 2, -1, -4, \ldots$

84. $-5, -10, -20, -40, -80, \ldots$

In Exercises 85 and 86, solve the system using any method. Explain your choice of method.

85. $y = -x + 1$
$y = (x-2)^2 - 3$

86. $x^2 + 3x = 4 - y$
$y = 4$

11 Chapter Review WITH CalcChat®

Chapter Learning Target Understand sequences and series.

Chapter Success Criteria
- ◆ I can define and use sequences and series.
- ◆ I can describe how to find sums of infinite geometric series.
- ■ I can analyze arithmetic and geometric sequences and series.
- ■ I can explain how to write recursive rules for sequences.

◆ Surface
■ Deep

SELF-ASSESSMENT 1 I do not understand. 2 I can do it with help. 3 I can do it on my own. 4 I can teach someone else.

11.1 Defining and Using Sequences and Series (pp. 595–602)

Learning Target: Understand sequences and series.

Vocabulary
sequence
terms of a sequence
series
summation notation
sigma notation

Write the first six terms of the sequence.

1. $a_n = 3n - 1$
2. $f(n) = (-2)^{n+1}$
3. Describe the pattern shown in the figure. Then write a rule for the nth layer of the figure, where $n = 1$ represents the top layer.

Write the series using summation notation.

4. $7 + 10 + 13 + \cdots + 40$
5. $0 + 2 + 6 + 12 + \cdots$

Find the sum.

6. $\sum_{i=2}^{7}(9 - i^3)$
7. $\sum_{i=1}^{46} i$
8. $\sum_{i=1}^{12} i^2$

11.2 Analyzing Arithmetic Sequences and Series (pp. 603–610)

Learning Target: Analyze arithmetic sequences and series.

Vocabulary
arithmetic sequence
common difference
arithmetic series

9. Determine whether the sequence 12, 4, −4, −12, −20, . . . is arithmetic. Explain your reasoning.

Write a rule for the nth term of the sequence. Then find a_{15} and graph the first six terms of the sequence.

10. 2, 8, 14, 20, . . .
11. $a_{14} = 42, d = 3$
12. $a_6 = -12, a_{12} = -36$
13. Find the sum $\sum_{i=1}^{36}(2 + 3i)$.
14. Pieces of chalk are stacked in a pile. Part of the pile is shown. The bottom row has 15 pieces of chalk, and the top row has 6 pieces of chalk. Each row has one less piece of chalk than the row below. Use an arithmetic series to find the number of pieces of chalk in the pile. Justify your answer.

11.3 Analyzing Geometric Sequences and Series (pp. 611–618)

Learning Target: Analyze geometric sequences and series.

Vocabulary
geometric sequence
common ratio
geometric series

15. Determine whether the sequence 7, 14, 28, 56, 112, . . . is geometric. Explain your reasoning.

Write a rule for the *n*th term of the geometric sequence. Then graph the first six terms of the sequence.

16. 25, 10, 4, $\frac{8}{5}$, . . . **17.** $a_5 = 162, r = -3$ **18.** $a_3 = 16, a_5 = 256$

Write a rule for the sequence with the given terms.

19.

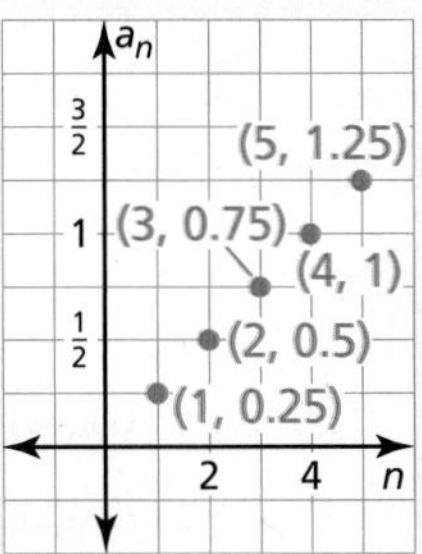

20.

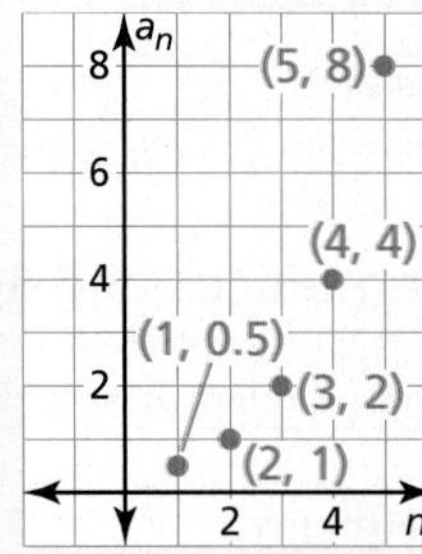

Find the sum.

21. $\sum_{i=1}^{9} 5(-2)^{i-1}$ **22.** $\sum_{k=1}^{5} 11(-3)^{k-2}$ **23.** $\sum_{i=1}^{12} -4\left(\frac{1}{2}\right)^{i+3}$

24. A job as an environmental engineer pays a salary of $65,000 the first year. After the first year, the salary increases by 3.5% per year.

a. Write a rule giving the salary a_n during the nth year of employment.

b. What is the salary during the fifth year of employment?

c. An employee works 10 years for the company. What are the total earnings? Justify your answer.

11.4 Finding Sums of Infinite Geometric Series (pp. 619–624)

Learning Target: Find partial sums and sums of infinite geometric series.

Vocabulary
partial sum

25. Consider the infinite geometric series $1 + \left(-\frac{1}{4}\right) + \frac{1}{16} + \left(-\frac{1}{64}\right) + \frac{1}{256} + \cdots$. Find and graph the partial sums S_n for $n = 1, 2, 3, 4$, and 5. Then describe what happens to S_n as n increases.

Find the sum of the infinite geometric series, if it exists.

26. $\sum_{n=1}^{\infty} 3\left(\frac{1}{5}\right)^{n-1}$ **27.** $\sum_{n=1}^{\infty} \frac{1}{2}\left(\frac{5}{3}\right)^{n-1}$ **28.** $-2 + \frac{1}{2} - \frac{1}{8} + \frac{1}{32} + \cdots$

29. Write the repeating decimal 0.1212 . . . as a fraction in simplest form.

30. On an amusement park ride, you swing back and forth from a harness. You travel 250 feet on the first swing. On each subsequent swing, you travel 70% of the distance of the previous swing. What is the total distance that you travel?

11.5 Using Recursive Rules with Sequences (pp. 625–634) 

Learning Target: Write and use recursively defined sequences.

Vocabulary
explicit rule
recursive rule

Write the first six terms of the sequence.

31. $a_1 = 7, a_n = a_{n-1} + 11$

32. $a_1 = 6, a_n = 4a_{n-1}$

33. $f(0) = -2, f(n) = -f(n-1) + 5$

34. $f(0) = 4, f(n) = f(n-1) + 2n$

Write a recursive rule for the sequence.

35. $9, 6, 4, \frac{8}{3}, \frac{16}{9}, \ldots$

36. $2, 2, 4, 12, 48, \ldots$

37. $7, 3, 4, -1, 5, \ldots$

38. Write a recursive rule for $a_n = 105\left(\frac{3}{5}\right)^{n-1}$.

Write an explicit rule for the sequence.

39. $a_1 = -4, a_n = a_{n-1} + 26$

40. $a_1 = 8, a_n = -5a_{n-1}$

41. $a_1 = 26, a_n = \frac{2}{5}a_{n-1}$

42. The graph shows the expected population of a city n years after 2020. Write a recursive rule for the population P_n of the city.

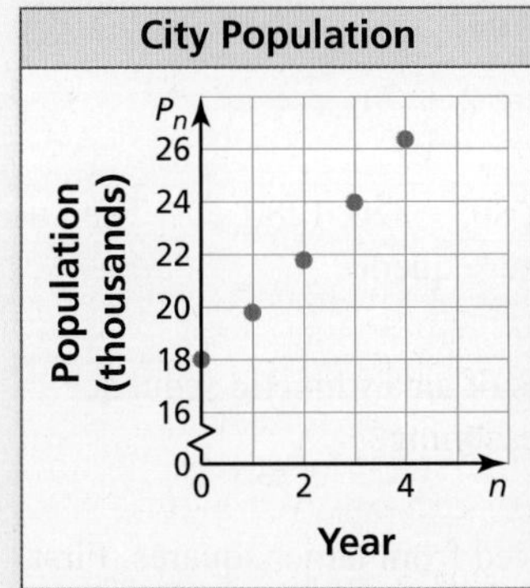

43. The first four hexagonal numbers are represented by the numbers of points in the diagrams. Write a recursive rule for the nth hexagonal number.

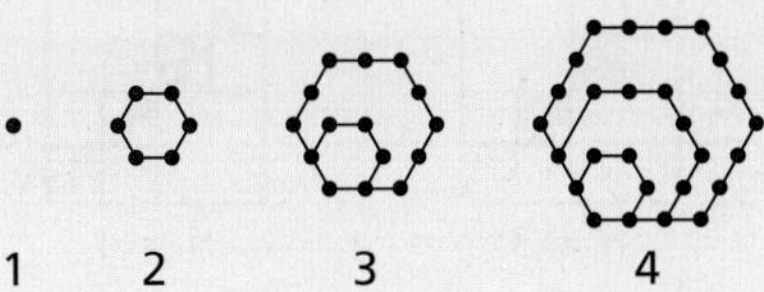

Mathematical Practices

Look for and Express Regularity in Repeated Reasoning

Mathematically proficient students notice if calculations are repeated, and look both for general methods and for shortcuts.

1. You borrow money at an annual interest rate of $r\%$. The monthly payment is p dollars. Explain how you can use repeated calculations to find the balance after the nth payment.

2. Write 0.253125312531. . . using summation notation. Explain your reasoning.

11 Practice Test WITH CalcChat®

Find the sum.

1. $\sum_{i=1}^{24}(6i - 13)$

2. $\sum_{n=1}^{16} n^2$

3. $\sum_{k=1}^{\infty} 2(0.8)^{k-1}$

4. $\sum_{i=1}^{6} 4(-3)^{i-1}$

Determine whether the graph represents an *arithmetic sequence*, a *geometric sequence*, or *neither*. Explain your reasoning. Then write a rule for the *n*th term.

5.

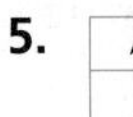

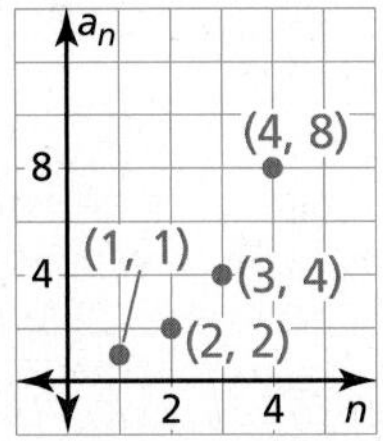

6.

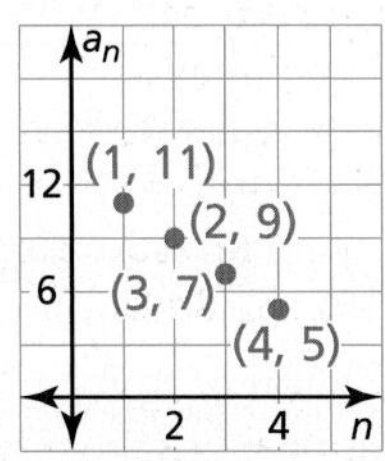

7.

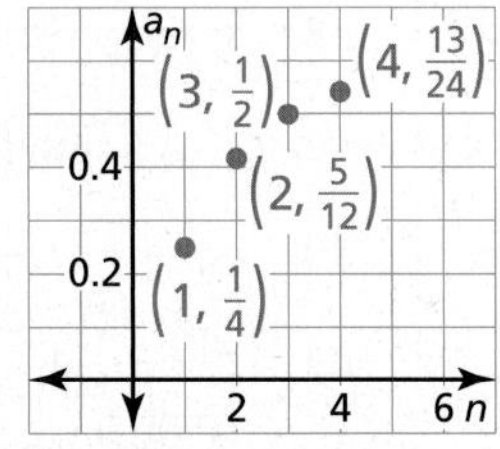

Write a recursive rule for the sequence. Then find a_9.

8. $a_1 = 32, r = \frac{1}{2}$

9. $a_n = 2 + 7n$

10. 2, 0, −3, −7, −12, . . .

11. Write a recursive rule for the sequence 5, −20, 80, −320, 1280, ... Then use the recursive rule to write an explicit rule for the sequence.

12. The numbers *a*, *b*, and *c* are the first three terms of an arithmetic sequence. Is *b* half of the sum of *a* and *c*? Explain your reasoning.

13. In the figures shown, smaller squares are removed from larger squares. First, divide each shaded square into four congruent squares. Then remove two of the squares. Repeat these steps for each smaller square, as shown. The area of the first square is 1 square foot.

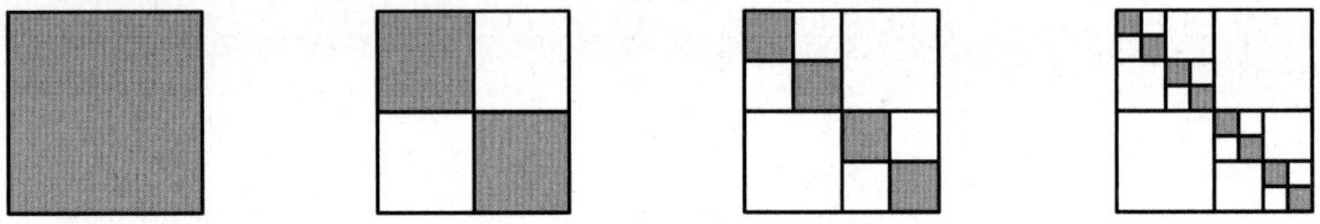

$n = 1$

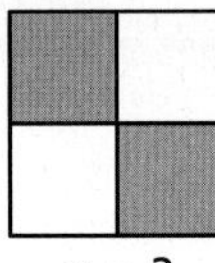

$n = 2$

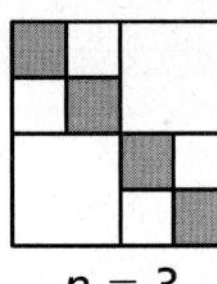

$n = 3$

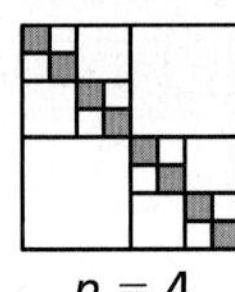

$n = 4$

a. Write a rule that represents the shaded area a_n of the *n*th figure.

b. Find and interpret $\sum_{n=1}^{\infty} a_n$.

14. Consider the sequence shown. Find *n* such that $a_n = 795$. Justify your answer.

18, 55, 92, 129, 166, 203, . . .

15. The length ℓ_1 of the first loop of a spring is 16 inches. The length ℓ_2 of the second loop is 0.9 times the length of the first loop. The length ℓ_3 of the third loop is 0.9 times the length of the second loop, and so on. Suppose the spring has infinitely many loops. Find the length of the spring, if possible. Explain your reasoning.

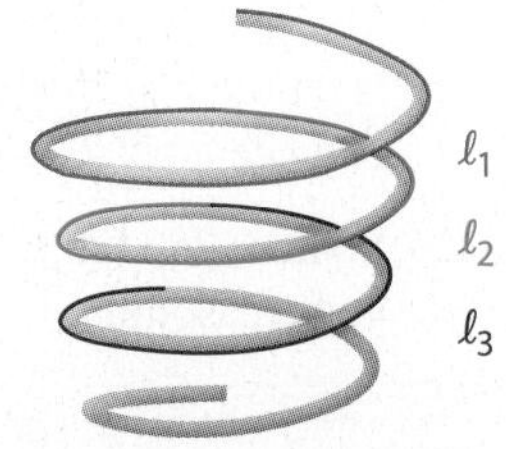

11 Performance Task
Walleye Stocking

Walleye is the state fish of:

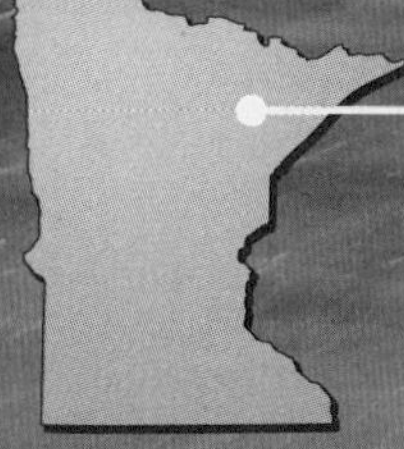

Walleye occupy about 1700 lakes and 100 streams in Minnesota. About 900 of these lakes are stocked by the Minnesota Department of Natural Resources.

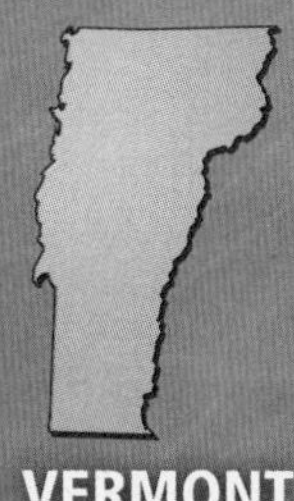

LIFE CYCLE OF FISH

adult fish

eggs

embryos

larvae

fry

fingerlings

In Minnesota, lakes that are stocked with walleye receive about 1000 fry per littoral acre or 1 pound of fingerlings per littoral acre.

A littoral acre is a measure of the surface area of a lake where the depth of the water is less than 15 feet.

CONSERVATION PLAN

A lake in Minnesota covers about 10,000 littoral acres and contains about 700,000 walleye that are at least 14 inches long. Researchers estimate that this population declines about 15% each year. Starting this year, the Department of Natural Resources (DNR) plans to stock the lake with fry every year. About 1% of the fry are expected to survive to reach a length of 14 inches, which takes about 4 years.

The DNR wants to stabilize this population at a minimum of 650,000 walleye. Analyze the DNR's plan to determine whether this goal will be achieved. Justify your answer.

11 College and Career Readiness WITH CalcChat®

WATCH Tutorial videos are available for each exercise.

1. The frequencies (in hertz) of the notes on a piano form a geometric sequence. The frequencies of G (labeled 8) and A (labeled 10) are shown in the diagram. Use a geometric sequence to find the approximate frequency of E flat (labeled 4).

Ⓐ 200 Hz

Ⓑ 247 Hz

Ⓒ 296 Hz

Ⓓ 311 Hz

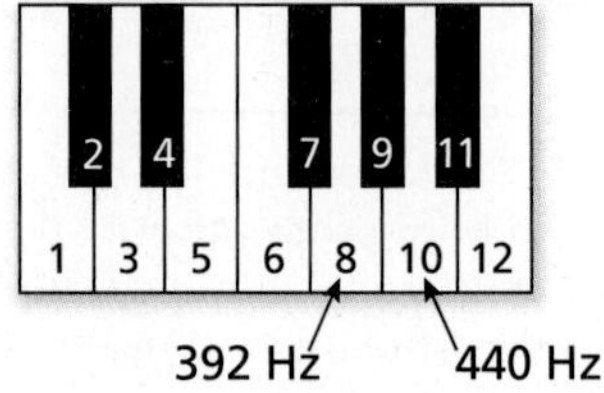

2. Find the arc length of the sector.

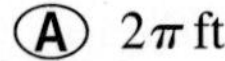

Ⓐ 2π ft

Ⓑ 4π ft

Ⓒ 360 ft

Ⓓ 720 ft

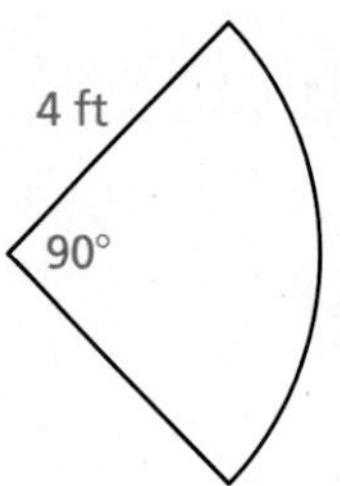

3. Order the functions from the least average rate of change to the greatest average rate of change on the interval $1 \leq x \leq 4$. Justify your answers.

A. $f(x) = 4\sqrt{x + 2}$

B. x and y vary inversely, and $y = 2$ when $x = 5$.

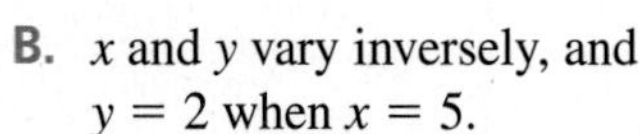

C.

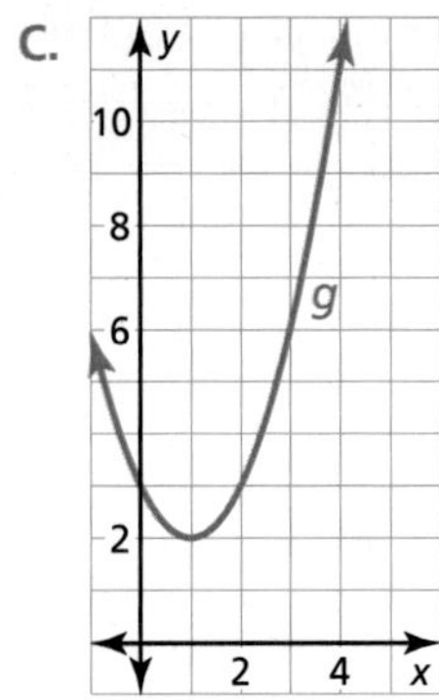

D.

x	y
1	−4
2	−1
3	2
4	5

4. Company A and Company B offer the same annual starting salary of \$40,000. Company A gives a \$2000 raise each year. Company B gives a 4% raise each year.

a. Write rules giving the salaries a_n and b_n for your nth year of employment at Company A and Company B, respectively. Determine whether the sequence represented by each rule is *arithmetic*, *geometric*, or *neither*.

b. Graph each sequence in the same coordinate plane.

c. Under what conditions would you choose to work for Company B?

d. After 20 years of employment, compare your total earnings with each company.

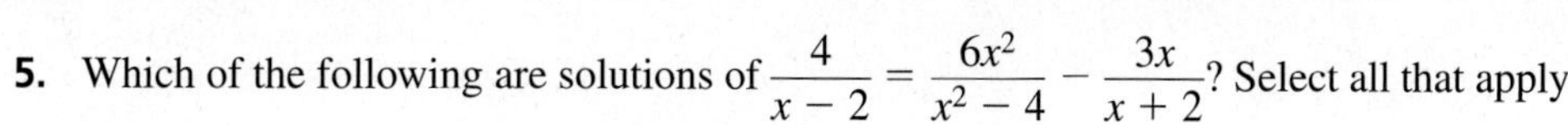

5. Which of the following are solutions of $\frac{4}{x-2} = \frac{6x^2}{x^2-4} - \frac{3x}{x+2}$? Select all that apply.

Ⓐ $x = -\frac{4}{3}$

Ⓑ $x = \frac{4}{3}$

Ⓒ $x = 2$

Ⓓ $x = -2$

6. A running track is shaped like a rectangle with two semicircular ends. The track has 8 lanes that are each 1.22 meters wide. The lanes are numbered from 1 to 8 starting from the inside lane. The distance from the center of a semicircle to the inside of a lane is called the curve radius of that lane. The curve radius of lane 1 is 36.5 meters, as shown in the figure.

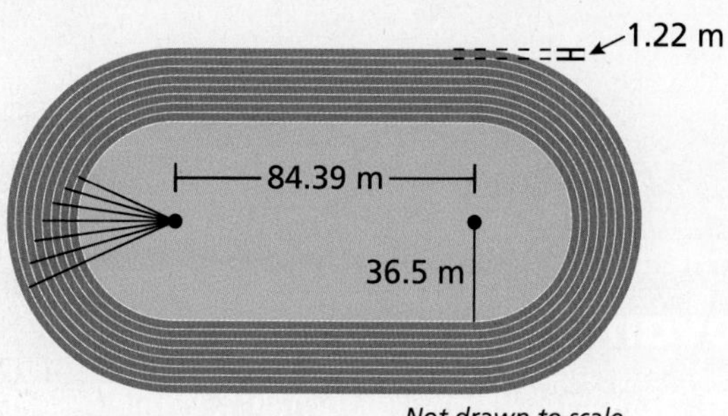

Not drawn to scale

a. Is the sequence formed by the curve radii *arithmetic*, *geometric*, or *neither*? Explain.

b. Write a rule for the sequence formed by the curve radii.

c. World records must be set on tracks that have a curve radius of at most 50 meters in the outside lane. Does the track shown meet the requirement? Explain.

7. The diagram shows the bounce heights of a basketball and baseball dropped from a height of 10 feet. On each bounce, the basketball bounces to 55% of its previous height, and the baseball bounces to 30% of its previous height. About how much greater is the total vertical distance traveled by the basketball than the total vertical distance traveled by the baseball?

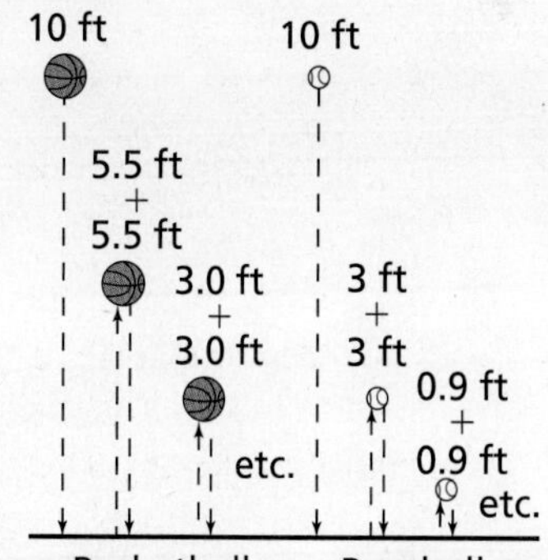

Ⓐ 7.9 feet

Ⓑ 15.9 feet

Ⓒ 18.6 feet

Ⓓ 34.4 feet

8. A card is randomly selected from a standard deck of 52 playing cards. What is the probability that it is a 6 *or* a black card?

Ⓐ $\frac{1}{26}$

Ⓑ $\frac{6}{13}$

Ⓒ $\frac{7}{13}$

Ⓓ $\frac{15}{26}$

12 Matrices

GO DIGITAL

NATIONAL GEOGRAPHIC EXPLORER

Ronan M. Donovan

Ronan M. Donovan is a photojournalist. While researching chimpanzees in Uganda's Kibale National Park, he captured the images that helped him establish a career in conservation photography, using images to advocate for conservation outcomes. Part of his work involved climbing fig trees to create a series of photographs of the primates from above.

- If you were a conservation photographer, what species of endangered animals would be of interest to you?
- There are 4 types of great apes: gorillas, orangutans, bonobos, and chimpanzees. Find an interesting fact about each type of great ape.

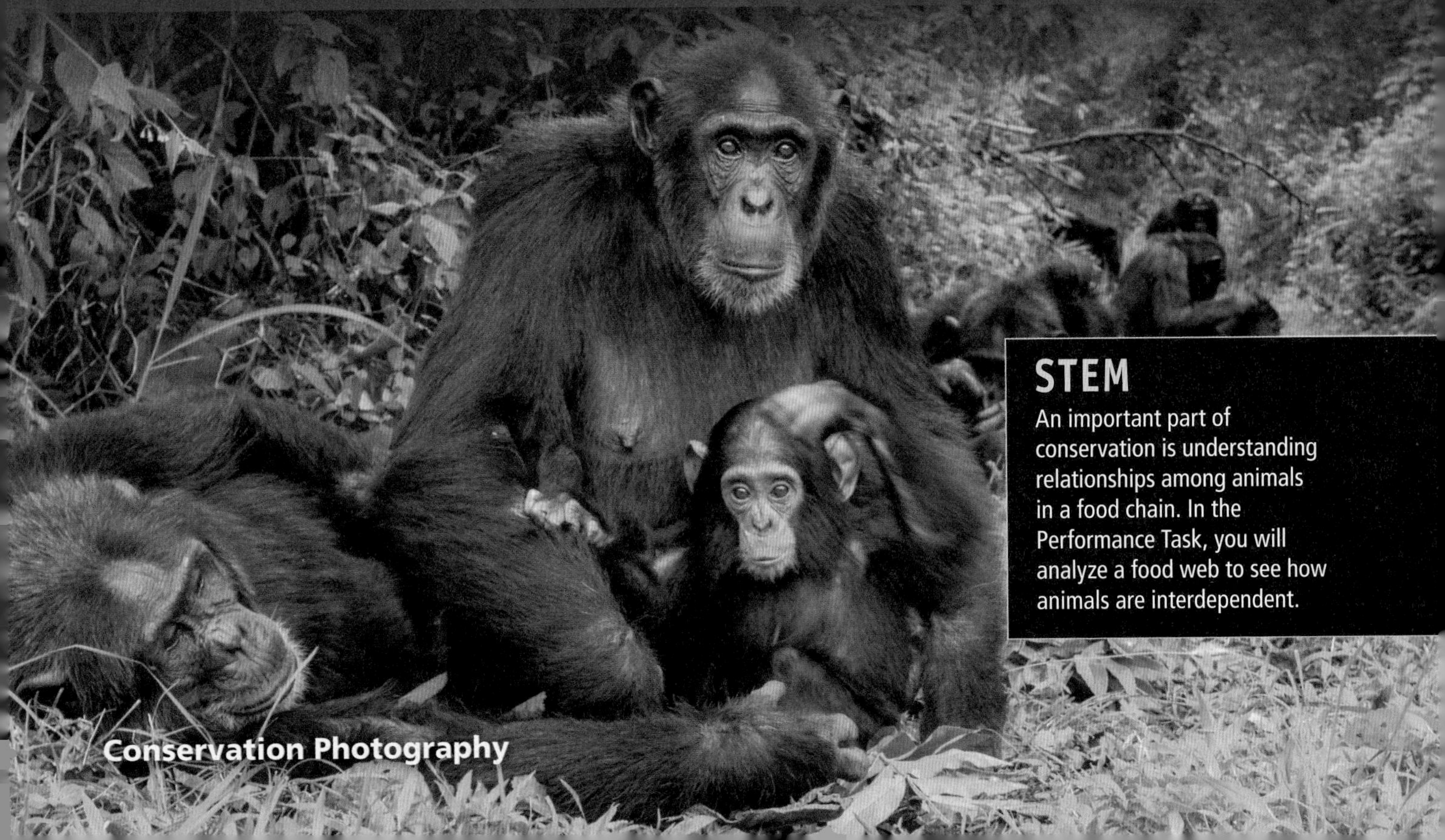

STEM

An important part of conservation is understanding relationships among animals in a food chain. In the Performance Task, you will analyze a food web to see how animals are interdependent.

Conservation Photography

Preparing for Chapter 12

Chapter Learning Target Understand matrices.

Chapter Success Criteria

- ◆ I can perform operations with matrices.
- ◆ I can determine when a product of matrices is defined.
- ■ I can evaluate determinants of matrices.
- ■ I can use inverse matrices to solve problems.

◆ Surface
■ Deep

Chapter Vocabulary

Work with a partner. Discuss each of the vocabulary terms.

matrix

scalar

Mathematical Practices

Use Appropriate Tools Strategically

Mathematically proficient students use technological tools to explore and deepen their understanding of concepts.

Work with a partner. The table shows the numbers of gorillas, bonobos, and orangutans at three zoos.

	Zoo A	Zoo B	Zoo C
Gorillas	6	10	20
Bonobos	5	7	9
Orangutans	4	6	5

1. For each zoo, the number of each type of primate can be represented by a *matrix*, as shown. Use technology to perform each of the following operations. Then interpret the results.

$$A = \begin{bmatrix} 6 \\ 5 \\ 4 \end{bmatrix} \qquad B = \begin{bmatrix} 10 \\ 7 \\ 6 \end{bmatrix} \qquad C = \begin{bmatrix} 20 \\ 9 \\ 5 \end{bmatrix}$$

a. $A + B$

b. $A + B + C$

c. $C - A$

d. $\frac{1}{3}(A + B + C)$

2. Explain how to perform each of the operations in Exercise 1 without using technology.

3. Describe when it is helpful to use technology to perform operations with matrices.

12 Prepare WITH CalcChat®

Solving Linear Equations

Example 1 **Solve $2x = 6x - 14$.**

$$2x = 6x - 14 \quad \text{Write original equation.}$$

$$\begin{aligned} 2x &= 6x - 14 \\ -6x & \quad -6x \end{aligned} \quad \text{Subtraction Property of Equality}$$

$$-4x = -14 \quad \text{Simplify.}$$

$$\frac{-4x}{-4} = \frac{-14}{-4} \quad \text{Division Property of Equality}$$

$$x = \frac{7}{2} \quad \text{Simplify.}$$

▶ The solution is $x = \frac{7}{2}$.

Solve the equation. Check your solution.

1. $4x - 3 = 10x$

2. $-2x = 5x - 5$

3. $\frac{2}{3}(x - 9) = x + 1$

Solving Linear Systems

Example 2 **Solve the system.** $5x - 2y = -5$ Equation 1
$x + 2y = 11$ Equation 2

Step 1 Because the coefficients of the y-terms are the same, you can solve by elimination without multiplying either equation by a constant.

Step 2 Add the equations to eliminate the y-terms.

$$\begin{aligned} 5x - 2y &= -5 && \text{Equation 1} \\ x + 2y &= 11 && \text{Equation 2} \\ 6x &= 6 && \text{Add the equations.} \end{aligned}$$

Step 3 Solve for x.

$$\begin{aligned} 6x &= 6 && \text{Resulting equation from Step 2} \\ x &= 1 && \text{Divide each side by 6.} \end{aligned}$$

Step 4 Substitute 1 for x in one of the original equations and solve for y.

$$\begin{aligned} x + 2y &= 11 && \text{Equation 2} \\ 1 + 2y &= 11 && \text{Substitute 1 for } x. \\ y &= 5 && \text{Simplify.} \end{aligned}$$

▶ The solution is $(1, 5)$.

Solve the system. Check your solution.

4. $-x + 3y = 12$
$x - 7y = -20$

5. $4x - y = 7$
$y = 3x - 3$

6. $\frac{1}{2}x - 6y = -1$
$3x - 8y = 8$

7. **MP STRUCTURE** Complete the linear system so that there are infinitely many solutions. Justify your answer.

$-8x + 2y = 12$
$y = 2(\square x + \square)$

12.1 Basic Matrix Operations

Learning Target Perform basic operations involving matrices.

Success Criteria

- I can add and subtract matrices.
- I can multiply matrices by scalars.
- I can solve matrix equations.
- I can represent data in a matrix to solve real-life problems.

EXPLORE IT! Analyzing Matrices

Work with a partner. A *matrix* is a rectangular array of numbers. The plural of matrix is *matrices*. The matrices below represent the T-shirt inventories at four stores.

Store A (columns: Short Sleeve, Long Sleeve; rows: Small, Medium, Large)

$$A = \begin{bmatrix} 65 & 40 \\ 52 & 60 \\ 46 & 46 \end{bmatrix}$$

Store B (columns: Sleeveless, Short Sleeve, Long Sleeve; rows: Small, Medium, Large)

$$B = \begin{bmatrix} 38 & 44 & 58 \\ 34 & 28 & 30 \\ 48 & 40 & 52 \end{bmatrix}$$

Store C (columns: Short Sleeve, Long Sleeve; rows: Small, Medium, Large)

$$C = \begin{bmatrix} 55 & 39 \\ 50 & 40 \\ 32 & 36 \end{bmatrix}$$

Store D (columns: Sleeveless, Short Sleeve, Long Sleeve; rows: Small, Medium, Large)

$$D = \begin{bmatrix} 25 & 24 & 27 \\ 30 & 28 & 21 \\ 15 & 18 & 20 \end{bmatrix}$$

a. Describe the matrices. How are they similar? How are they different?

b. How can you describe the *dimensions* of each matrix?

c. MP **CHOOSE TOOLS** Find and interpret each of the following, if possible.

i. $A + C$ ii. $B - D$

iii. $A + B$ iv. $C - B$

v. $2A$ vi. $\frac{1}{2}B$

d. Use your results in part (c) to describe how to add and subtract matrices, and multiply a matrix by a real number.

e. Find $C + A$. Compare your result with $A + C$ in part (c). What do you notice?

Math Practice

Make Conjectures
What are some other properties of real numbers that can be used to perform operations with matrices?

Adding and Subtracting Matrices

Vocabulary

matrix, p. 646
dimensions of a matrix, p. 646
elements of a matrix, p. 646
equal matrices, p. 646
scalar, p. 647
scalar multiplication, p. 647

A **matrix** is a rectangular array of numbers. The **dimensions** of a matrix with *m* rows and *n* columns are $m \times n$ (read "*m* by *n*"). So, the dimensions of matrix *A* are 2×3. The numbers in the matrix are its **elements**.

$$A = \begin{bmatrix} -1 & 0 & 3 \\ 6 & 5 & 2 \end{bmatrix}$$

2 rows; 3 columns. The element in the first row and third column is 3.

Two matrices are **equal** when their dimensions are the same *and* the elements in corresponding positions are equal.

KEY IDEA

Adding and Subtracting Matrices

To add or subtract two matrices, add or subtract their corresponding elements. You can add or subtract matrices only when they have the same dimensions.

Adding Matrices $\begin{bmatrix} a & b \\ c & d \end{bmatrix} + \begin{bmatrix} e & f \\ g & h \end{bmatrix} = \begin{bmatrix} a+e & b+f \\ c+g & d+h \end{bmatrix}$

Subtracting Matrices $\begin{bmatrix} a & b \\ c & d \end{bmatrix} - \begin{bmatrix} e & f \\ g & h \end{bmatrix} = \begin{bmatrix} a-e & b-f \\ c-g & d-h \end{bmatrix}$

EXAMPLE 1 Adding and Subtracting Matrices

Perform the indicated operation, if possible. If not possible, explain why not.

a. $\begin{bmatrix} 2 & -1 \\ 3 & 0 \end{bmatrix} + \begin{bmatrix} 1 & 2 \\ 4 & -2 \end{bmatrix}$

b. $\begin{bmatrix} 2 & -3 \\ 5 & 4 \\ -2 & 8 \end{bmatrix} - \begin{bmatrix} -1 & 2 \\ 7 & 8 \\ -5 & 6 \end{bmatrix}$

c. $\begin{bmatrix} -8 & 1 & 3 \\ 5 & -4 & 9 \end{bmatrix} + \begin{bmatrix} 6 & -1 \\ 2 & 7 \end{bmatrix}$

SOLUTION

a. $\begin{bmatrix} 2 & -1 \\ 3 & 0 \end{bmatrix} + \begin{bmatrix} 1 & 2 \\ 4 & -2 \end{bmatrix} = \begin{bmatrix} 2+1 & -1+2 \\ 3+4 & 0+(-2) \end{bmatrix} = \begin{bmatrix} 3 & 1 \\ 7 & -2 \end{bmatrix}$

b. $\begin{bmatrix} 2 & -3 \\ 5 & 4 \\ -2 & 8 \end{bmatrix} - \begin{bmatrix} -1 & 2 \\ 7 & 8 \\ -5 & 6 \end{bmatrix} = \begin{bmatrix} 2-(-1) & -3-2 \\ 5-7 & 4-8 \\ -2-(-5) & 8-6 \end{bmatrix} = \begin{bmatrix} 3 & -5 \\ -2 & -4 \\ 3 & 2 \end{bmatrix}$

c. The dimensions of the first matrix are 2×3, and the dimensions of the second matrix are 2×2. Because the matrices have different dimensions, the sum is undefined.

SELF-ASSESSMENT 1 I do not understand. 2 I can do it with help. 3 I can do it on my own. 4 I can teach someone else.

Perform the indicated operation, if possible. If not possible, explain why not.

1. $\begin{bmatrix} -3 & 4 \\ 9 & 6 \end{bmatrix} + \begin{bmatrix} 4 & 0 \\ -5 & 7 \end{bmatrix}$

2. $\begin{bmatrix} -5 & 1 \end{bmatrix} + \begin{bmatrix} 0 \\ -3 \end{bmatrix}$

3. $\begin{bmatrix} 6 & 5 & 3 \\ 8 & 7 & 8 \end{bmatrix} - \begin{bmatrix} 5 & 5 & 5 \\ 4 & -6 & -3 \end{bmatrix}$

Scalar Multiplication and Properties of Matrices

KEY IDEAS

Scalar Multiplication and Properties of Matrix Operations

In operations with matrices, numbers are usually referred to as **scalars**. In this text, scalars will always be real numbers. To multiply a matrix by a scalar, multiply each element in the matrix by the scalar. This process is called **scalar multiplication**.

Multiplying a Matrix by a Scalar, k $\quad k\begin{bmatrix} a & b \\ c & d \end{bmatrix} = \begin{bmatrix} ka & kb \\ kc & kd \end{bmatrix}$

Let A, B, and C be matrices with the same dimensions, and let k be a scalar.

Associative Property of Addition $\quad (A + B) + C = A + (B + C)$

Commutative Property of Addition $\quad A + B = B + A$

Distributive Property $\quad k(A + B) = kA + kB$

$k(A - B) = kA - kB$

STUDY TIP

Many of the properties you use to perform operations with real numbers can be used to perform operations with matrices.

EXAMPLE 2 Multiplying Matrices by Scalars

Perform the indicated operation(s).

a. $2\begin{bmatrix} 3 & -2 \\ 1 & 5 \\ 2 & 0 \end{bmatrix}$ **b.** $-3\begin{bmatrix} 5 & 0 \\ -2 & 4 \end{bmatrix} + \begin{bmatrix} -1 & 7 \\ 3 & 2 \end{bmatrix}$

SOLUTION

a. $2\begin{bmatrix} 3 & -2 \\ 1 & 5 \\ 2 & 0 \end{bmatrix} = \begin{bmatrix} 2(3) & 2(-2) \\ 2(1) & 2(5) \\ 2(2) & 2(0) \end{bmatrix} = \begin{bmatrix} 6 & -4 \\ 2 & 10 \\ 4 & 0 \end{bmatrix}$

b. $-3\begin{bmatrix} 5 & 0 \\ -2 & 4 \end{bmatrix} + \begin{bmatrix} -1 & 7 \\ 3 & 2 \end{bmatrix} = \begin{bmatrix} -3(5) & -3(0) \\ -3(-2) & -3(4) \end{bmatrix} + \begin{bmatrix} -1 & 7 \\ 3 & 2 \end{bmatrix}$

$= \begin{bmatrix} -15 & 0 \\ 6 & -12 \end{bmatrix} + \begin{bmatrix} -1 & 7 \\ 3 & 2 \end{bmatrix}$

$= \begin{bmatrix} -15 + (-1) & 0 + 7 \\ 6 + 3 & -12 + 2 \end{bmatrix}$

$= \begin{bmatrix} -16 & 7 \\ 9 & -10 \end{bmatrix}$

STUDY TIP

The order of operations for matrix expressions is similar to that for real numbers. In Example 2(b), perform scalar multiplication before matrix addition.

SELF-ASSESSMENT 1 I do not understand. 2 I can do it with help. 3 I can do it on my own. 4 I can teach someone else.

Perform the indicated operation(s).

4. $-7\begin{bmatrix} 2 & 3 & -2 \\ -7 & 4 & 7 \\ -2 & 5 & -6 \end{bmatrix}$

5. $4\begin{bmatrix} 3 & 5 \\ 4 & 2 \\ 0 & -2 \end{bmatrix} - \begin{bmatrix} 9 & 7 \\ -6 & 5 \\ 2 & -3 \end{bmatrix}$

6. $-4\left(\begin{bmatrix} 1 & 4 \\ -3 & 1 \end{bmatrix} - \begin{bmatrix} 6 & 3 \\ 9 & 3 \end{bmatrix}\right)$

Solving Matrix Equations

You can use what you know about matrix operations and matrix equality to solve equations involving matrices.

EXAMPLE 3 Using Equality of Matrices

Solve the matrix equation for a, b, c, and d.

$$\begin{bmatrix} a & b \\ 2c & d+4 \end{bmatrix} = \begin{bmatrix} 4 & -7 \\ 8 & 6 \end{bmatrix}$$

SOLUTION

Equate corresponding elements and solve the resulting equations, if necessary.

$a = 4$ $\quad$ $b = -7$ $\quad$ $2c = 8$ $\quad$ $d + 4 = 6$

$c = 4$ $\quad$ $d = 2$

▶ The solution is $a = 4$, $b = -7$, $c = 4$, and $d = 2$.

EXAMPLE 4 Solving a Matrix Equation

Solve the matrix equation for a, b, c, and d.

$$4\left(\begin{bmatrix} -2a & 5 \\ -4 & 2 \end{bmatrix} + \begin{bmatrix} 3 & -6 \\ 7c & 1 \end{bmatrix}\right) = \begin{bmatrix} -28 & b \\ 40 & d \end{bmatrix}$$

SOLUTION

Simplify the left side of the equation.

$$4\left(\begin{bmatrix} -2a & 5 \\ -4 & 2 \end{bmatrix} + \begin{bmatrix} 3 & -6 \\ 7c & 1 \end{bmatrix}\right) = \begin{bmatrix} -28 & b \\ 40 & d \end{bmatrix}$$ Write original equation.

$$4\begin{bmatrix} -2a+3 & -1 \\ 7c-4 & 3 \end{bmatrix} = \begin{bmatrix} -28 & b \\ 40 & d \end{bmatrix}$$ Add matrices inside parentheses.

$$\begin{bmatrix} -8a+12 & -4 \\ 28c-16 & 12 \end{bmatrix} = \begin{bmatrix} -28 & b \\ 40 & d \end{bmatrix}$$ Perform scalar multiplication.

ANOTHER WAY

You can simplify the left side of the equation by first using the Distributive Property to multiply each matrix in parentheses by 4 and then adding the resulting matrices.

Equate corresponding elements and solve the resulting equations, if necessary.

$-8a + 12 = -28$ $\quad$ $-4 = b$ $\quad$ $28c - 16 = 40$ $\quad$ $12 = d$

$-8a = -40$ $\quad$ $28c = 56$

$a = 5$ $\quad$ $c = 2$

▶ The solution is $a = 5$, $b = -4$, $c = 2$, and $d = 12$.

SELF-ASSESSMENT

1 I do not understand. 2 I can do it with help. 3 I can do it on my own. 4 I can teach someone else.

Solve the matrix equation for a, b, c, and d.

7. $\begin{bmatrix} a & b \\ c-2 & 4d \end{bmatrix} = \begin{bmatrix} -5 & 4 \\ 3 & 8 \end{bmatrix}$

8. $3\left(\begin{bmatrix} 2 & 4 \\ 2c & 2d \end{bmatrix} - \begin{bmatrix} 8 & 0 \\ c & 5 \end{bmatrix}\right) = \begin{bmatrix} a & b \\ 9 & 9 \end{bmatrix}$

Solving Real-Life Problems

Matrices are useful for organizing data and for performing the same operations on multiple data values simultaneously.

EXAMPLE 5 Modeling Real Life

A high school district track and field organization used the same standard qualifying times for its district championships in two consecutive years. The tables show the numbers of boys and girls in three class levels who qualified in the 100-meter run in those years.

Organize the data using two matrices, one for each year. Then find and interpret a matrix that gives the average numbers of boys and girls who qualified in each class.

Qualifiers: 100-Meter Run

	Class	2019	2020
Boys	1	18	16
	2	23	25
	3	16	12

	Class	2019	2020
Girls	1	21	15
	2	22	18
	3	24	18

SOLUTION

Step 1 Organize the data using two 3×2 matrices.

$$\begin{array}{c} \textbf{2019} \\ \begin{array}{cc} \textbf{Boys} & \textbf{Girls} \end{array} \\ A = \begin{bmatrix} 18 & 21 \\ 23 & 22 \\ 16 & 24 \end{bmatrix} \begin{array}{l} \textbf{Class 1} \\ \textbf{Class 2} \\ \textbf{Class 3} \end{array} \end{array} \qquad \begin{array}{c} \textbf{2020} \\ \begin{array}{cc} \textbf{Boys} & \textbf{Girls} \end{array} \\ B = \begin{bmatrix} 16 & 15 \\ 25 & 18 \\ 12 & 18 \end{bmatrix} \begin{array}{l} \textbf{Class 1} \\ \textbf{Class 2} \\ \textbf{Class 3} \end{array} \end{array}$$

Step 2 To find the average numbers of boys and girls who qualified in each class, add matrix A and matrix B, and then multiply the result by $\frac{1}{2}$.

$$\frac{1}{2}(A + B) = \frac{1}{2}\left(\begin{bmatrix} 18 & 21 \\ 23 & 22 \\ 16 & 24 \end{bmatrix} + \begin{bmatrix} 16 & 15 \\ 25 & 18 \\ 12 & 18 \end{bmatrix}\right)$$

$$= \frac{1}{2}\begin{bmatrix} 34 & 36 \\ 48 & 40 \\ 28 & 42 \end{bmatrix}$$

$$= \begin{bmatrix} 17 & 18 \\ 24 & 20 \\ 14 & 21 \end{bmatrix}$$

▶ Over both years, the average numbers of boys and girls who qualified were 17 boys and 18 girls in Class 1, 24 boys and 20 girls in Class 2, and 14 boys and 21 girls in Class 3.

SELF-ASSESSMENT

1 I do not understand. 2 I can do it with help. 3 I can do it on my own. 4 I can teach someone else.

9. Repeat Example 5 using two 2×3 matrices. Compare the results.

10. **MP REASONING** In Example 5, what does $A + B$ represent?

11. **MP PROBLEM SOLVING** Find and interpret a matrix that gives the change in the number of boys and girls who qualified in each class from 2019 to 2020.

12.1 Practice WITH CalcChat® AND CalcView®

In Exercises 1–6, perform the indicated operation, if possible. If not possible, explain why not. *Example 1*

1. $\begin{bmatrix} 4 & -1 \\ 3 & -2 \end{bmatrix} + \begin{bmatrix} 6 & -7 \\ 3 & -5 \end{bmatrix}$

2. $\begin{bmatrix} 4 & -3 \\ 7 & -2 \end{bmatrix} - \begin{bmatrix} 1 & -2 \\ 3 & -6 \end{bmatrix}$

3. $\begin{bmatrix} 14 \\ 13 \\ -5 \end{bmatrix} - \begin{bmatrix} 12 \\ -17 \\ 9 \end{bmatrix}$

4. $\begin{bmatrix} 2 & 3 \\ 5 & 3 \\ 8 & 6 \end{bmatrix} + \begin{bmatrix} 1 \\ -1 \\ 6 \end{bmatrix}$

5. $\begin{bmatrix} 1 & 9 \\ 3 & -4 \\ -7 & 2 \end{bmatrix} - \begin{bmatrix} -1 & 1 & 12 \\ 7 & -3 & 10 \end{bmatrix}$

6. $\begin{bmatrix} -5 & 3 & 1 \\ -4 & 6 & 0 \\ 10 & -2 & 7 \end{bmatrix} + \begin{bmatrix} 9 & 7 & 12 \\ -1 & 5 & -3 \\ -6 & 11 & -8 \end{bmatrix}$

ERROR ANALYSIS In Exercises 7 and 8, describe and correct the error in adding the matrices.

7.

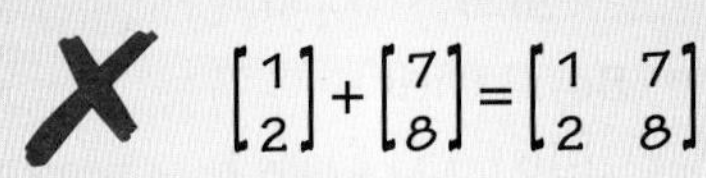

8. ✗ $\begin{bmatrix} 3 \\ 5 \end{bmatrix} + \begin{bmatrix} 4 \\ 1 \end{bmatrix} = \begin{bmatrix} 7 & 6 \end{bmatrix}$

In Exercises 9–16, perform the indicated operation(s). *Example 2*

9. $3\begin{bmatrix} 3 & 1 \\ 1 & 4 \end{bmatrix}$

10. $-4\begin{bmatrix} -2 & 1 \\ 12 & 9 \end{bmatrix}$

11. $\frac{1}{2}\begin{bmatrix} 4 & -6 \\ 8 & 12 \\ 2 & 22 \end{bmatrix}$

12. $\frac{3}{2}\begin{bmatrix} 4 & -6 & 10 \\ 2 & 8 & -4 \\ 9 & -7 & 18 \end{bmatrix}$

13. $6\begin{bmatrix} 1 & 3 & 2 \\ -2 & 4 & -1 \end{bmatrix} + \begin{bmatrix} 5 & 7 & -1 \\ 6 & -4 & 7 \end{bmatrix}$

14. $\begin{bmatrix} -7 & 8 & 11 \\ 12 & -5 & 16 \end{bmatrix} - 3\begin{bmatrix} -4 & 4 & 6 \\ 5 & -2 & 7 \end{bmatrix}$

15. $7\left(\begin{bmatrix} -1 & 0 \\ 8 & -4 \\ -3 & 5 \end{bmatrix} - \begin{bmatrix} 4 & 3 \\ 6 & 0 \\ 5 & 1 \end{bmatrix}\right)$

16. $-2\left(\begin{bmatrix} 3 & -6 \\ 5 & -7 \\ 12 & 8 \end{bmatrix} + \begin{bmatrix} 6 & 9 \\ -8 & 1 \\ 10 & -3 \end{bmatrix}\right)$

In Exercises 17–22, use the given matrices to evaluate the expression.

$$A = \begin{bmatrix} 9 & -6 \\ 7 & 5 \end{bmatrix}, B = \begin{bmatrix} 4 & 3 \\ -7 & -6 \end{bmatrix}, C = \begin{bmatrix} 0.5 & 3.6 \\ 2.4 & -3.2 \end{bmatrix}$$

17. $A + B$

18. $B - A$

19. $2B - C$

20. $C + 2A$

21. $A + B + 10C$

22. $2B - 10C + A$

In Exercises 23–30, solve the matrix equation for *a*, *b*, *c*, and *d*. *Examples 3 and 4*

23. $\begin{bmatrix} a & b \\ 3 & -4 \end{bmatrix} = \begin{bmatrix} 6 & 2 \\ c & d \end{bmatrix}$

24. $\begin{bmatrix} 7 & d \\ 5 & b \end{bmatrix} = \begin{bmatrix} c & 4 \\ a & 17 \end{bmatrix}$

25. $\begin{bmatrix} 30 & b \\ a + 6 & -9 \\ c & 4d \end{bmatrix} = \begin{bmatrix} 30 & 21 \\ 16 & -9 \\ -5 & 44 \end{bmatrix}$

26. $\begin{bmatrix} 18 - a & -2 & 5b \\ 14 & -d & c \end{bmatrix} = \begin{bmatrix} 5 & -2 & 500 \\ 14 & 64 & 112 \end{bmatrix}$

27. $2\left(\begin{bmatrix} 3a & 11 \\ 4 & 6 \end{bmatrix} + \begin{bmatrix} -7 & -6 \\ 11 & 5d \end{bmatrix}\right) = \begin{bmatrix} 22 & b \\ c & 52 \end{bmatrix}$

28. $-3\left(\begin{bmatrix} 7 & 2b \\ 8c & 8 \end{bmatrix} - \begin{bmatrix} 4 & 4b \\ 5 & d \end{bmatrix}\right) = \begin{bmatrix} a & 54 \\ 63 & d \end{bmatrix}$

29. $\begin{bmatrix} 8 & 2a & 3 \\ 13 & 20 & 7 \end{bmatrix} - 5\begin{bmatrix} b & -2 & -6 \\ 1 & 4 & 3c \end{bmatrix} = \begin{bmatrix} -2 & 3 & 33 \\ d & 0 & -8 \end{bmatrix}$

30. $\frac{1}{2}\begin{bmatrix} -6a & -2 \\ 3 & 14 \\ -10 & -8 \end{bmatrix} + \begin{bmatrix} 5 & 3 \\ -\frac{5}{2} & b - 3 \\ 6 & -1 \end{bmatrix} = \begin{bmatrix} 9 & 4d \\ -1 & 11 \\ c + 4 & -5 \end{bmatrix}$

31. MODELING REAL LIFE The table shows the numbers of dogs and cats at a shelter by age group adopted in May and June. Organize the data using two matrices, one for each month. Then find and interpret a matrix that gives the average numbers of dogs and cats adopted in each age group. *Example 5*

Adoptions

	Dogs		Cats	
Age Group	May	June	May	June
< 1 year	6	12	13	7
1–6 years	7	9	5	3
> 6 years	4	2	1	3

32. **MODELING REAL LIFE** The table shows the amount (in inches) of snow that each of three cities received in January and February of 2018 and 2019. Organize the data using two matrices, one for each year. Then find and interpret a matrix that gives the change in the amount (in feet) of snow from 2018 to 2019 by month for each city.

Amount of Snow

	January		February	
City	**2018**	**2019**	**2018**	**2019**
City A	23	47	13	12
City B	5	11	7	11
City C	18	2	9	12

33. **MODELING REAL LIFE** The table shows the numbers of species from five groups in the United States and in the world listed as endangered or threatened under the Endangered Species Act in 2019. Organize the data using two matrices, one for the United States and one for the world. Then find and interpret a matrix that gives the numbers of species in each group listed as endangered or threatened that are not in the United States.

Endangered and Threatened Species

	Endangered		Threatened	
Group	**U.S.**	**World**	**U.S.**	**World**
Mammals	66	326	28	51
Birds	80	298	21	41
Reptiles	17	88	29	53
Amphibians	21	29	15	16
Fishes	93	115	74	80

34. **MODELING REAL LIFE** For regular admission to an amusement park, the park charges \$70.95 for a 1-Day pass, \$89.00 for a 2-Day pass, \$134.00 for a 3-Day pass, and \$33.95 for an Evening pass. For children, the park charges \$48.95 for a 1-Day pass, \$72.00 for a 2-Day pass, \$106.75 for a 3-Day pass, and \$29.95 for an Evening pass. Organize the data using a matrix. Then find and interpret a matrix that gives the prices of each type of pass when the park offers a 10% discount on all passes.

35. **COLLEGE PREP** What is the value of $3x - 2y$?

$$\begin{bmatrix} 2x & 0 \\ 0.5 & -0.75 \end{bmatrix} = \begin{bmatrix} 6.4 & 0 \\ 0.5 & 3y \end{bmatrix}$$

Ⓐ −7.15 Ⓑ 9.1 Ⓒ 10.1 Ⓓ 20.7

36. **MAKING AN ARGUMENT** Is the matrix $\begin{bmatrix} -\frac{1}{3} & 0 \\ 1 & 0 \end{bmatrix}$ equivalent to the matrix $\begin{bmatrix} -\frac{1}{3} \\ 1 \end{bmatrix}$? Explain.

MP REASONING In Exercises 37–40, find the matrix X that makes the equation true.

37. $X + \begin{bmatrix} 5 & 0 \\ -2 & 3 \end{bmatrix} = \begin{bmatrix} 6 & 3 \\ 1 & 0 \end{bmatrix}$

38. $X - \begin{bmatrix} 3 & 1 \\ 4 & 5 \end{bmatrix} = \begin{bmatrix} 2 & 5 \\ -1 & 3 \end{bmatrix}$

39. $-X + \begin{bmatrix} 9 & 6 \\ -5 & 1 \end{bmatrix} = \begin{bmatrix} 6 & -1 \\ 4 & -2 \end{bmatrix}$

40. $2X + \begin{bmatrix} 5 & 0 \\ 8 & -2 \end{bmatrix} = \begin{bmatrix} 9 & -8 \\ 4 & 4 \end{bmatrix}$

41. **MP NUMBER SENSE** One important property of addition of real numbers is that the number 0 is the additive identity. That is, $a + 0 = a$ for any real number a. For any $m \times n$ matrix A, is there a matrix O such that $A + O = A$? If so, describe matrix O. If not, explain why not.

42. **HOW DO YOU SEE IT?**
The prices (in dollars) of different types and sizes of subs at a sub shop are represented by matrix A.

Subs

	Ham	Turkey	Roast Beef	
$A =$	4.29	4.79	5.29	**6-inch**
	5.89	6.99	8.19	**12-inch**

a. Interpret the element in the second row and first column.

b. How can you find the prices after a 6% sales tax is applied?

43. **CONNECTING CONCEPTS** The vertices of a triangle are $(-4, 3)$, $(-2, 5)$, and $(-1, 3)$.

a. Write a 2×3 matrix A where the columns represent the vertices of the triangle and the first row represents the x-coordinates.

b. Let matrix $B = \begin{bmatrix} 2 & 2 & 2 \\ -1 & -1 & -1 \end{bmatrix}$. Add matrices A and B. Then draw the triangles represented by the matrices A and $A + B$ in the same coordinate plane. How are the triangles related?

c. Let matrix $B = \begin{bmatrix} c & c & c \\ d & d & d \end{bmatrix}$, where c and d are any real numbers. How are the triangles represented by the matrices A and $A + B$ related?

44. CONNECTING CONCEPTS The vertices of a rectangle are (1, 1), (1, 4), (5, 1), and (5, 4).

a. Write a 2×4 matrix A where the columns represent the vertices of the rectangle and the first row represents the x-coordinates.

b. Multiply matrix A by 3. Then draw the rectangles represented by the matrices A and $3A$ in the same coordinate plane. How are the rectangles related?

c. Multiply matrix A by -0.5. Then draw the rectangles represented by the matrices A and $-0.5A$ in the same coordinate plane. How are the rectangles related?

d. Let k be any real number. How are the rectangles represented by matrices A and kA related?

45. OPEN-ENDED Write two matrices A and B such that $2A - 3B = \begin{bmatrix} 5 & 0 \\ -1 & 2 \end{bmatrix}$.

GO DIGITAL

46. THOUGHT PROVOKING Use matrices A, B, and C, defined as shown, to show that each property is true for 2×2 matrices.

$$A = \begin{bmatrix} a & b \\ c & d \end{bmatrix} \quad B = \begin{bmatrix} e & f \\ g & h \end{bmatrix} \quad C = \begin{bmatrix} p & q \\ r & s \end{bmatrix}$$

a. Commutative Property of Addition

b. Associative Property of Addition

c. Distributive Property

47. DIG DEEPER Write two matrices A and B such that

$$A + B = \begin{bmatrix} 2 & 6 & 5 \\ -5 & -7 & -8 \\ 3 & 14 & 4 \end{bmatrix} \text{ and}$$

$$A - B = \begin{bmatrix} -6 & -8 & 11 \\ -1 & -5 & 10 \\ -3 & 4 & -12 \end{bmatrix}.$$

REVIEW & REFRESH

48. Write the first six terms of the sequence.

$$a_1 = 15, a_n = a_{n-1} - 3$$

In Exercises 49–51, find the product.

49. $(x + 2)(3x^2 - 2x - 5)$

50. $(4t - 1)^3$

51. $\dfrac{x^2 - 2x - 15}{2x} \cdot \dfrac{2x^2 - 14x}{x^2 - 10x + 21}$

In Exercises 52 and 53, let $P(A) = 0.26$, $P(B) = 0.4$, and $P(A \text{ and } B) = 0.12$. Find the indicated probability.

52. $P(A \text{ or } B)$

53. $P(A|B)$

54. Write a rule for the sequence with the given terms.

n	2	3	4	5	6
a_n	−2	6	−18	54	−162

55. When can two matrices be added? Give an example of two matrices that *cannot* be added.

56. A city official records whether people litter in a park before and after more garbage cans are added. Identify the method of data collection.

57. MODELING REAL LIFE The rear windshield wiper of a car rotates 120°, as shown. Find the area cleared by the wiper.

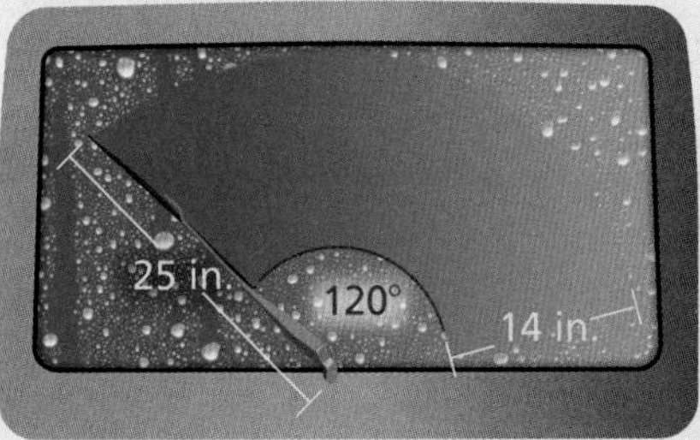

58. Find the sum of the infinite geometric series.

$$16 + 4 + 1 + \tfrac{1}{4} + \cdots$$

In Exercises 59–62, perform the indicated operation(s).

59. $\begin{bmatrix} 3 & -7 & 9 \end{bmatrix} - \begin{bmatrix} -2 & 11 & 1 \end{bmatrix}$

60. $\begin{bmatrix} 5 & 8 \\ -2 & 7 \end{bmatrix} + \begin{bmatrix} -3 & -11 \\ -4 & 9 \end{bmatrix}$

61. $-4\begin{bmatrix} 3 & -5 & 6 \\ -1 & 10 & 2 \\ 8 & 12 & -3 \end{bmatrix}$

62. $\begin{bmatrix} 7 & 0 & 4 \\ 9 & -1 & -2 \end{bmatrix} + 3\begin{bmatrix} 15 & 5 & 8 \\ -1 & -3 & -10 \end{bmatrix}$

12.2 Multiplying Matrices

Learning Target Understand how to multiply matrices.

Success Criteria
- I can determine whether a product of matrices is defined.
- I can multiply matrices.
- I can use matrix multiplication to solve real-life problems.

EXPLORE IT! Multiplying Matrices

Work with a partner. In 12.1 Explore It!, you used matrices to represent the T-shirt inventories at several stores.

Store A

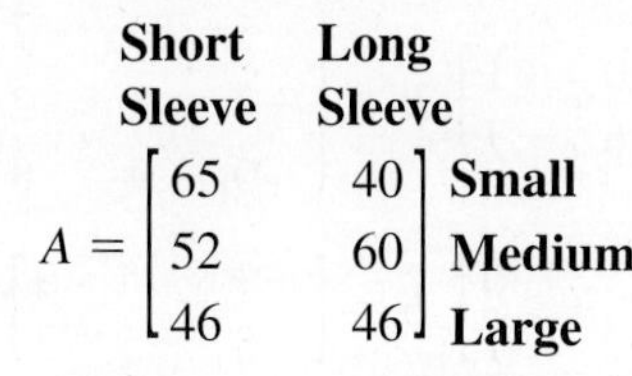

$$A = \begin{array}{c} \textbf{Short Sleeve} \quad \textbf{Long Sleeve} \\ \begin{bmatrix} 65 & 40 \\ 52 & 60 \\ 46 & 46 \end{bmatrix} \end{array} \begin{array}{l} \textbf{Small} \\ \textbf{Medium} \\ \textbf{Large} \end{array}$$

Store B

$$B = \begin{array}{c} \textbf{Sleeveless} \quad \textbf{Short Sleeve} \quad \textbf{Long Sleeve} \\ \begin{bmatrix} 38 & 44 & 58 \\ 34 & 28 & 30 \\ 48 & 40 & 52 \end{bmatrix} \end{array} \begin{array}{l} \textbf{Small} \\ \textbf{Medium} \\ \textbf{Large} \end{array}$$

a. Store A charges $10 for each short-sleeve shirt and $15 for each long-sleeve shirt. What is the total value of the inventory for each size? Explain your reasoning.

b. Matrix P represents the cost per shirt at Store A.

Store A
Dollars

$$P = \begin{bmatrix} 10 \\ 15 \end{bmatrix} \begin{array}{l} \textbf{Short Sleeve} \\ \textbf{Long Sleeve} \end{array}$$

Use technology to find $A \times P$. Interpret the results. Then explain how to find $A \times P$ without using technology.

c. Matrix Q represents the cost per shirt at Store B.

Store B
Dollars

$$Q = \begin{bmatrix} 8 \\ 12 \\ 20 \end{bmatrix} \begin{array}{l} \textbf{Sleeveless} \\ \textbf{Short Sleeve} \\ \textbf{Long Sleeve} \end{array}$$

Find and interpret $B \times Q$ without using technology. Explain your method.

Math Practice

Use Technology to Explore
Can you multiply a matrix by any other matrix? Explain your reasoning.

Multiplying Matrices

The product of two matrices A and B is defined provided the number of columns in A is equal to the number of rows in B.

If A is an $m \times n$ matrix and B is an $n \times p$ matrix, then the product AB is an $m \times p$ matrix.

$$\underset{m \times n}{A} \quad \bullet \quad \underset{n \times p}{B} \quad = \quad \underset{m \times p}{AB}$$

equal

dimensions of AB

EXAMPLE 1 **Describing Matrix Products** 

Determine whether each product AB is defined. If so, state the dimensions of AB.

a. $A = \begin{bmatrix} 5 & 0 & -1 \\ 3 & -6 & 7 \end{bmatrix}, B = \begin{bmatrix} 5 & 10 & -7 & -3 \\ -2 & 3 & 2 & 6 \\ 0 & 9 & 8 & 1 \end{bmatrix}$

b. $A = \begin{bmatrix} 6 & -5 & 0 \\ 1 & 2 & -1 \end{bmatrix}, B = \begin{bmatrix} -3 & 11 & 9 \\ 8 & -1 & 2 \end{bmatrix}$

SOLUTION

a. Because A is a 2×3 matrix and B is a 3×4 matrix, the number of columns in A is equal to the number of rows in B. So, the product AB is defined and is a 2×4 matrix.

b. Because A and B are 2×3 matrices, the number of columns in A does not equal the number of rows in B. So, the product AB is not defined.

SELF-ASSESSMENT

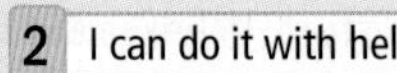

1 I do not understand. 2 I can do it with help. 3 I can do it on my own. 4 I can teach someone else.

Determine whether the product AB is defined. If so, state the dimensions of AB.

1. $A = \begin{bmatrix} 3 \\ -1 \\ 1 \end{bmatrix}, B = \begin{bmatrix} -7 & 8 \end{bmatrix}$

2. $A = \begin{bmatrix} 1 & 0 \\ -2 & 8 \\ 6 & 10 \end{bmatrix}, B = \begin{bmatrix} 12 & -2 & 5 \end{bmatrix}$

KEY IDEA

Multiplying Matrices

Words To find the element in the ith row and jth column of the product matrix AB, multiply each element in the ith row of A by the corresponding element in the jth column of B, then add the products.

Algebra
$$\underset{A}{\begin{bmatrix} a & b \\ c & d \end{bmatrix}} \bullet \underset{B}{\begin{bmatrix} e & f \\ g & h \end{bmatrix}} = \underset{AB}{\begin{bmatrix} ae + bg & af + bh \\ ce + dg & cf + dh \end{bmatrix}}$$

EXAMPLE 2 **Finding the Product of Two Matrices** 

Find AB when $A = \begin{bmatrix} 3 & 2 \\ -7 & 8 \end{bmatrix}$ and $B = \begin{bmatrix} -1 & 4 \\ 6 & 5 \end{bmatrix}$.

SOLUTION

Because A is a 2×2 matrix and B is a 2×2 matrix, the product AB is defined and is a 2×2 matrix.

Step 1 Multiply the numbers in the first row of A by the numbers in the first column of B, add the products, and put the result in the first row, first column of AB.

$$\begin{bmatrix} 3 & 2 \\ -7 & 8 \end{bmatrix}\begin{bmatrix} -1 & 4 \\ 6 & 5 \end{bmatrix} = \begin{bmatrix} 3(-1) + 2(6) & \\ & \end{bmatrix}$$

COMMON ERROR

Order is important when multiplying matrices. To find AB, write matrix A on the left and matrix B on the right.

Step 2 Multiply the numbers in the first row of A by the numbers in the second column of B, add the products, and put the result in the first row, second column of AB.

$$\begin{bmatrix} 3 & 2 \\ -7 & 8 \end{bmatrix}\begin{bmatrix} -1 & 4 \\ 6 & 5 \end{bmatrix} = \begin{bmatrix} 3(-1) + 2(6) & 3(4) + 2(5) \\ & \end{bmatrix}$$

Step 3 Multiply the numbers in the second row of A by the numbers in the first column of B, add the products, and put the result in the second row, first column of AB.

$$\begin{bmatrix} 3 & 2 \\ -7 & 8 \end{bmatrix}\begin{bmatrix} -1 & 4 \\ 6 & 5 \end{bmatrix} = \begin{bmatrix} 3(-1) + 2(6) & 3(4) + 2(5) \\ -7(-1) + 8(6) & \end{bmatrix}$$

Step 4 Multiply the numbers in the second row of A by the numbers in the second column of B, add the products, and put the result in the second row, second column of AB.

$$\begin{bmatrix} 3 & 2 \\ -7 & 8 \end{bmatrix}\begin{bmatrix} -1 & 4 \\ 6 & 5 \end{bmatrix} = \begin{bmatrix} 3(-1) + 2(6) & 3(4) + 2(5) \\ -7(-1) + 8(6) & -7(4) + 8(5) \end{bmatrix}$$

Step 5 Simplify the product matrix.

$$\begin{bmatrix} 3(-1) + 2(6) & 3(4) + 2(5) \\ -7(-1) + 8(6) & -7(4) + 8(5) \end{bmatrix} = \begin{bmatrix} 9 & 22 \\ 55 & 12 \end{bmatrix}$$

In Example 2, notice that the product BA is not the same as the product AB.

$$BA = \begin{bmatrix} -1 & 4 \\ 6 & 5 \end{bmatrix}\begin{bmatrix} 3 & 2 \\ -7 & 8 \end{bmatrix} = \begin{bmatrix} -31 & 30 \\ -17 & 52 \end{bmatrix} \neq AB$$

In general, matrix multiplication is *not* commutative.

SELF-ASSESSMENT

1 I do not understand. 2 I can do it with help. 3 I can do it on my own. 4 I can teach someone else.

Find the product.

3. $\begin{bmatrix} 5 & -2 \end{bmatrix}\begin{bmatrix} 4 \\ 9 \end{bmatrix}$

4. $\begin{bmatrix} 6 & 4 \\ 0 & -5 \end{bmatrix}\begin{bmatrix} 0 & 2 \\ -3 & 1 \end{bmatrix}$

5. $\begin{bmatrix} 3 & -4 \\ 6 & 5 \\ 1 & 0 \end{bmatrix}\begin{bmatrix} -1 & 7 & -2 \\ -6 & 2 & 4 \end{bmatrix}$

6. MP **REASONING** Show that matrix multiplication is not commutative for 2×2 matrices.

EXAMPLE 3 Using Matrix Operations

Use the given matrices to evaluate (a) $A(B + C)$ and (b) $AB + AC$.

$$A = \begin{bmatrix} 5 & 7 \\ 3 & 1 \\ -4 & 2 \end{bmatrix}, B = \begin{bmatrix} 0 & 1 \\ 3 & -6 \end{bmatrix}, C = \begin{bmatrix} 2 & -3 \\ -1 & 5 \end{bmatrix}$$

SOLUTION

a. $A(B + C) = \begin{bmatrix} 5 & 7 \\ 3 & 1 \\ -4 & 2 \end{bmatrix}\left(\begin{bmatrix} 0 & 1 \\ 3 & -6 \end{bmatrix} + \begin{bmatrix} 2 & -3 \\ -1 & 5 \end{bmatrix}\right)$

$$= \begin{bmatrix} 5 & 7 \\ 3 & 1 \\ -4 & 2 \end{bmatrix}\begin{bmatrix} 2 & -2 \\ 2 & -1 \end{bmatrix}$$

$$= \begin{bmatrix} 24 & -17 \\ 8 & -7 \\ -4 & 6 \end{bmatrix}$$

b. $AB + AC = \begin{bmatrix} 5 & 7 \\ 3 & 1 \\ -4 & 2 \end{bmatrix}\begin{bmatrix} 0 & 1 \\ 3 & -6 \end{bmatrix} + \begin{bmatrix} 5 & 7 \\ 3 & 1 \\ -4 & 2 \end{bmatrix}\begin{bmatrix} 2 & -3 \\ -1 & 5 \end{bmatrix}$

$$= \begin{bmatrix} 21 & -37 \\ 3 & -3 \\ 6 & -16 \end{bmatrix} + \begin{bmatrix} 3 & 20 \\ 5 & -4 \\ -10 & 22 \end{bmatrix}$$

$$= \begin{bmatrix} 24 & -17 \\ 8 & -7 \\ -4 & 6 \end{bmatrix}$$

SELF-ASSESSMENT

1 I do not understand. 2 I can do it with help. 3 I can do it on my own. 4 I can teach someone else.

Use the matrices in Example 3 to evaluate the expression.

7. $A(B - C)$ **8.** $A(BC)$ **9.** $2(AB)$

Notice in Example 3 that $A(B + C) = AB + AC$, which is true in general. This and other properties of matrix multiplication are summarized below.

KEY IDEA

Properties of Matrix Multiplication

Let A, B, and C be matrices and let k be a scalar.

Associative Property of Matrix Multiplication	$A(BC) = (AB)C$
Left Distributive Property	$A(B + C) = AB + AC$
Right Distributive Property	$(A + B)C = AC + BC$
Associative Property of Scalar Multiplication	$k(AB) = (kA)B = A(kB)$

Solving Real-Life Problems

Matrix multiplication is useful in business applications because an *inventory* matrix, when multiplied by a *cost per item* matrix, results in a *total cost* matrix.

$$\begin{bmatrix} \text{Inventory} \\ \text{matrix} \end{bmatrix} \cdot \begin{bmatrix} \text{Cost per item} \\ \text{matrix} \end{bmatrix} = \begin{bmatrix} \text{Total cost} \\ \text{matrix} \end{bmatrix}$$

$m \times n \qquad n \times p \qquad m \times p$

The column labels for the inventory matrix must match the row labels for the cost per item matrix for the total cost matrix to be meaningful.

Meal Selections

CLASS A
10 Chicken Meals
12 Beef Meals
8 Vegetarian Meals

CLASS B
11 Chicken Meals
14 Beef Meals
7 Vegetarian Meals

EXAMPLE 4 **Modeling Real Life**

The students in two classes submit meal choices for an upcoming banquet as shown. Each chicken meal costs $6, each beef meal costs $8, and each vegetarian meal costs $4. Use matrix multiplication to find the total cost of the meals for each class.

SOLUTION

To begin, write the meal selections and the costs per meal in matrix form. To use matrix multiplication, set up the matrices so that the columns of the meal selection matrix match the rows of the cost matrix.

Meal Selection

	Chicken	Beef	Vegetarian
Class A	10	12	8
Class B	11	14	7

Cost

	Dollars
Chicken	6
Beef	8
Vegetarian	4

The total cost of the meals for each class can be found by multiplying the meal selection matrix by the cost matrix. The meal selection matrix is 2×3 and the cost matrix is 3×1. So, their product is a 2×1 matrix.

$$\begin{bmatrix} 10 & 12 & 8 \\ 11 & 14 & 7 \end{bmatrix} \begin{bmatrix} 6 \\ 8 \\ 4 \end{bmatrix} = \begin{bmatrix} 10(6) + 12(8) + 8(4) \\ 11(6) + 14(8) + 7(4) \end{bmatrix}$$

$$= \begin{bmatrix} 188 \\ 206 \end{bmatrix}$$

The labels for the product matrix are shown below.

Total Cost

	Dollars
Class A	188
Class B	206

▶ The total cost of the meals for Class A is $188, and the total cost for Class B is $206.

SELF-ASSESSMENT 1 I do not understand. 2 I can do it with help. 3 I can do it on my own. 4 I can teach someone else.

10. WHAT IF? What is the total cost for each class in Example 4 when a chicken meal costs $5, a beef meal costs $6, and a vegetarian meal costs $3?

12.2 Practice WITH CalcChat® AND CalcView®

In Exercises 1–8, determine whether the product AB is defined. If so, state the dimensions of AB. ▶ *Example 1*

1. $A: 2 \times 3, B: 3 \times 2$
2. $A: 4 \times 2, B: 2 \times 3$
3. $A: 3 \times 2, B: 3 \times 1$
4. $A: 2 \times 1, B: 3 \times 1$
5. $A = \begin{bmatrix} 6 & 8 & 7 \end{bmatrix}, B = \begin{bmatrix} 8 \\ -1 \\ -5 \end{bmatrix}$
6. $A = \begin{bmatrix} -1 & 3 & -7 \\ 4 & 2 & -2 \end{bmatrix}, B = \begin{bmatrix} 1 & -5 \\ -6 & 2 \end{bmatrix}$
7. $A = \begin{bmatrix} 5 & -8 & 10 \\ -6 & 3 & -2 \end{bmatrix}, B = \begin{bmatrix} 1 \\ -7 \end{bmatrix}$
8. $A = \begin{bmatrix} 5 & 8 & -3 & 2 \\ 3 & 0 & -9 & 6 \end{bmatrix}, B = \begin{bmatrix} -1 & 0 \\ 8 & 3 \\ -5 & 4 \\ 7 & 2 \end{bmatrix}$

In Exercises 9–22, find the product, if possible. If not possible, explain why not. ▶ *Example 2*

9. $\begin{bmatrix} 6 & -1 \end{bmatrix}\begin{bmatrix} 3 \\ 2 \end{bmatrix}$
10. $\begin{bmatrix} 5 \\ 1 \end{bmatrix}\begin{bmatrix} -3 & 2 \end{bmatrix}$
11. $\begin{bmatrix} 3 & 0 \\ 1 & 5 \end{bmatrix}\begin{bmatrix} 2 & -4 \end{bmatrix}$
12. $\begin{bmatrix} -2 & 3 \end{bmatrix}\begin{bmatrix} 4 & 0 \\ 2 & 1 \end{bmatrix}$
13. $\begin{bmatrix} 6 & 1 \\ -4 & 3 \end{bmatrix}\begin{bmatrix} 2 & -5 \\ 0 & 4 \end{bmatrix}$
14. $\begin{bmatrix} 2 & 7 \\ 0 & -2 \end{bmatrix}\begin{bmatrix} 5 & -1 \\ 1 & 3 \end{bmatrix}$
15. $\begin{bmatrix} 3 & -1 \\ -2 & 6 \\ 2 & -3 \end{bmatrix}\begin{bmatrix} 1 & 0 \\ 4 & -4 \end{bmatrix}$
16. $\begin{bmatrix} 1 & 6 \\ -2 & -3 \\ 7 & 2 \end{bmatrix}\begin{bmatrix} 4 & -5 \\ 0 & -1 \\ 8 & 3 \end{bmatrix}$
17. $\begin{bmatrix} 2 & 3 \\ 0 & -1 \end{bmatrix}\begin{bmatrix} 4 & 2 \\ -6 & 0 \\ 5 & 1 \end{bmatrix}$
18. $\begin{bmatrix} -8 & 3 \\ 1 & -2 \end{bmatrix}\begin{bmatrix} -5 & -9 \\ -4 & 9 \\ 3 & -4 \\ -8 & 3 \end{bmatrix}$
19. $\begin{bmatrix} 2 & 0 & -3 \\ 4 & 1 & 5 \end{bmatrix}\begin{bmatrix} -2 & 7 \\ 3 & -1 \\ -6 & -4 \end{bmatrix}$
20. $\begin{bmatrix} -4 & 7 \\ 1 & 2 \\ 10 & 0 \end{bmatrix}\begin{bmatrix} 6 & -2 & 3 \\ -1 & -3 & 4 \end{bmatrix}$
21. $\begin{bmatrix} 5 & 7 & 0 \\ -2 & -4 & 1 \end{bmatrix}\begin{bmatrix} 1 & -1 & 4 \\ 5 & 2 & 0 \\ 8 & 0 & -3 \end{bmatrix}$
22. $\begin{bmatrix} 9 & -2 & 3 \\ 0 & 5 & -1 \\ 4 & 1 & 6 \end{bmatrix}\begin{bmatrix} -6 & 4 & 5 \\ 1 & -5 & 2 \\ 0 & 9 & 7 \end{bmatrix}$

ERROR ANALYSIS In Exercises 23 and 24, describe and correct the error in finding the element in the first row and first column of the product matrix.

23. ✗ $\begin{bmatrix} -2 & 3 \\ 5 & 1 \end{bmatrix}\begin{bmatrix} 4 & 2 \\ 7 & 0 \end{bmatrix} = \begin{bmatrix} -2(4) + 3(2) & \end{bmatrix} = \begin{bmatrix} -2 & \end{bmatrix}$

24. ✗ $\begin{bmatrix} 3 & 0 \\ 1 & 6 \end{bmatrix}\begin{bmatrix} -3 & 5 \\ 2 & 4 \end{bmatrix} = \begin{bmatrix} 3(-3) + 1(5) & \end{bmatrix} = \begin{bmatrix} -4 & \end{bmatrix}$

In Exercises 25–30, use the given matrices to evaluate the expression. ▶ *Example 3*

$$A = \begin{bmatrix} 4 & 1 \\ -3 & 0 \end{bmatrix}, B = \begin{bmatrix} 5 & -2 \\ 6 & -1 \end{bmatrix}, C = \begin{bmatrix} 3 & 0 \\ -1 & 8 \end{bmatrix}$$

25. $A(B - C)$
26. $AC + BC$
27. $(AB)C$
28. $C(AB)$
29. $3(AC)$
30. $\frac{1}{2}(AB)$

MP STRUCTURE In Exercises 31 and 32, solve for x and y.

31. $\begin{bmatrix} 3 & -1 & 4 \\ 2 & 0 & 1 \\ -4 & -2 & 0 \end{bmatrix}\begin{bmatrix} x \\ 1 \\ 5 \end{bmatrix} = \begin{bmatrix} 25 \\ y \\ -10 \end{bmatrix}$
32. $\begin{bmatrix} 2 & x & 1 \\ 3 & -1 & 4 \end{bmatrix}\begin{bmatrix} -3 & 8 \\ 1 & 4 \\ 5 & 2 \end{bmatrix} = \begin{bmatrix} -7 & -6 \\ y & 28 \end{bmatrix}$

In Exercises 33 and 34, use the given matrix to find $A^2 = AA$ and $A^3 = AAA$.

33. $A = \begin{bmatrix} -2 & 1 \\ 3 & 0 \end{bmatrix}$
34. $A = \begin{bmatrix} 1 & 3 & 0 \\ -1 & 0 & 5 \\ 4 & 2 & -3 \end{bmatrix}$

MP USING TOOLS In Exercises 35 and 36, use technology to find AB and BA, if possible.

35. $A = \begin{bmatrix} 3 & -4 & 10 \\ -1 & 4 & -5 \\ 10 & -3 & -6 \end{bmatrix}, B = \begin{bmatrix} 9 & -5 & 7 \\ 4 & 3 & -4 \\ 5 & -8 & 2 \end{bmatrix}$
36. $A = \begin{bmatrix} -14 & -8 & 2 \\ 10 & 3 & -12 \\ 5 & 2 & -1 \end{bmatrix}, B = \begin{bmatrix} 5 & 13 \\ -7 & 4 \\ -10 & -6 \end{bmatrix}$

37. MODELING REAL LIFE A softball coach buys equipment for two teams. The coach buys 4 bats, 36 softballs, and 12 uniforms for Team A and 6 bats, 45 softballs, and 15 uniforms for Team B. Each bat costs \$80, each softball costs \$4, and each uniform costs \$20. Use matrix multiplication to find the total cost of the equipment for each team. *Example 4*

38. MODELING REAL LIFE A business buys supplies for two floors of a building. The business buys 20 chairs, 14 desks, and 16 trash bins for the first floor and 10 chairs, 8 desks, and 12 trash bins for the second floor. Each chair costs \$60, each desk costs \$200, and each trash bin costs \$20. Use matrix multiplication to find the total cost of the supplies for each floor.

39. MODELING REAL LIFE A conservation photographer wants to print several photographs of different animals in different sizes. The table shows the numbers of each photograph size needed. Each 5×7 costs \$2.25, each 8×10 costs \$4.50, and each 11×14 costs \$11.00. Use matrix multiplication to find the total cost of the photographs for each animal.

	5 × 7	8 × 10	11 × 14
Bonobos	8	4	1
Elephants	6	5	3
Sea lions	10	4	1

40. HOW DO YOU SEE IT?
Matrix A is shown. How many rows must matrix B have for AB to be defined?

$$A = \begin{bmatrix} 7 & -4 & 4 \\ 2 & 6 & -2 \end{bmatrix}$$

41. COLLEGE PREP Given matrices A, B, and C, which products are *not* defined? Select all that apply.

$$A = \begin{bmatrix} -6 & 1 \\ 3 & 3 \end{bmatrix}, B = \begin{bmatrix} 4 & -5 & 0 \\ 2 & -1 & -9 \end{bmatrix}, C = \begin{bmatrix} 4 & -2 \\ -8 & 3 \\ 0 & 10 \end{bmatrix}$$

Ⓐ AB Ⓑ AC
Ⓒ BA Ⓓ BC
Ⓔ CA Ⓕ CB

42. CONNECTING CONCEPTS Use the graph of the triangle shown and matrices $A = \begin{bmatrix} 1 & 0 \\ 0 & -1 \end{bmatrix}$ and $B = \begin{bmatrix} 0 & -1 \\ 1 & 0 \end{bmatrix}$.

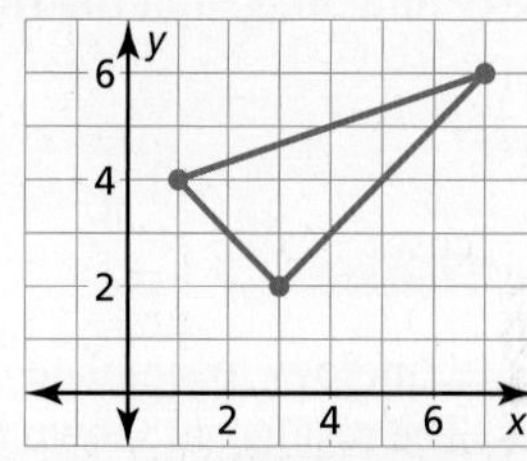

a. Write a 2×3 matrix C whose columns represent the vertices of the triangle.

b. Find AC and draw the resulting triangle. How are the triangles related?

c. Find BC and draw the resulting triangle. How are the triangles related?

d. Make a hypothesis about matrices A and B.

43. PERFORMANCE TASK As a teacher, you assign your students' total grades using a weighted system of four components: homework, quizzes, tests, and projects.

Student	Homework	Quizzes	Tests	Projects
A	82	90	84	85
B	71	77	94	89
C	90	88	93	90
D	92	84	86	88
E	83	85	72	78

a. Assign a weight to each component. Use matrix multiplication to find the total grades of the students shown in the table.

b. Analyze the total grades of each student. Then write a letter to the parents/guardians of each student explaining the student's total grade in your class.

44. THOUGHT PROVOKING
A *diagonal matrix* is a square matrix in which each element not on the main diagonal (from top left to bottom right) is zero. Consider two diagonal matrices A and B with the same dimensions where $A \neq B$. Write a rule that can be used to find AB without using traditional matrix multiplication. Justify your answer.

45. MAKING AN ARGUMENT Your friend says that because matrix multiplication is not commutative, it is also not associative. Is your friend correct? Explain.

46. OPEN-ENDED Find two matrices A and B such that $A \neq B$ and $AB = BA$.

47. CRITICAL THINKING Let $A = \begin{bmatrix} a & b \\ c & d \end{bmatrix}$ and $B = \begin{bmatrix} e & f \\ g & h \end{bmatrix}$, and let k be a scalar. Show that the Associative Property of Scalar Multiplication is true for 2×2 matrices.

48. DIG DEEPER Let $A = \begin{bmatrix} 1 & 3 \\ 2 & -3 \end{bmatrix}$ and $B = \begin{bmatrix} 0 & -3 \\ -1 & 2 \end{bmatrix}$. Show that $(A + B)^2 = A^2 + AB + BA + B^2$.

REVIEW & REFRESH

WATCH

In Exercises 49 and 50, graph the function.

49. $g(x) = \frac{1}{2}\sin 2\pi x$

50. $h(x) = -\cos(x - \pi) + 4$

51. You use technology to simulate rolling a die 50 times. The results are shown in the bar graph. What proportion of the 50 rolls resulted in a number greater than 4?

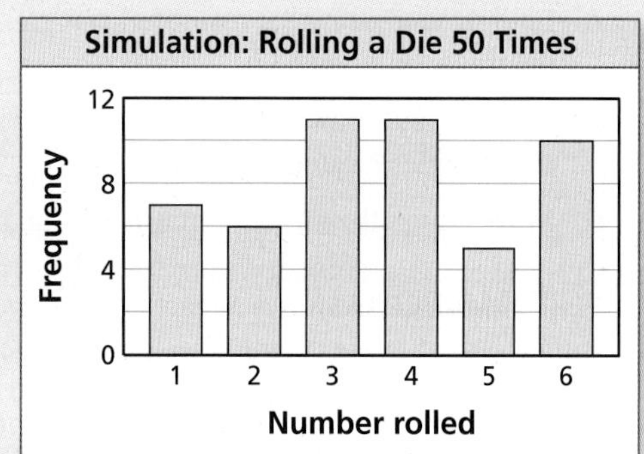

In Exercises 52 and 53, graph one period of the function. Describe the graph of *g* as a transformation of the graph of its parent function.

52. $g(x) = \csc 4x$

53. $g(x) = \frac{1}{2}\tan x$

54. MODELING REAL LIFE You borrow $8000 to buy a car. The loan has a 4.5% annual interest rate that is compounded monthly for 5 years. The monthly payment is $149.14.

a. Find the balance after the sixth payment.

b. Find the amount of the last payment.

In Exercises 55 and 56, solve the equation.

55. $x^2 + 9 = 5$

56. $2x^2 - 6 = -24$

57. Consider the infinite geometric series $\frac{1}{4} + \frac{1}{8} + \frac{1}{16} + \frac{1}{32} + \frac{1}{64} + \cdots$. Find and graph the partial sums S_n for $n = 1, 2, 3, 4$, and 5. Then describe what happens to S_n as n increases.

In Exercises 58–63, perform the indicated operation(s), if possible. If not possible, explain why not.

58. $2\begin{bmatrix} 3 & -8 \\ 1 & 0 \\ -1 & 4 \end{bmatrix}$

59. $\begin{bmatrix} -2 & 7 \end{bmatrix} + \begin{bmatrix} 4 \\ -6 \end{bmatrix}$

60. $\begin{bmatrix} 1 & 6 \\ 2 & -5 \end{bmatrix}\begin{bmatrix} 8 & -1 \\ -3 & 2 \end{bmatrix}$

61. $\begin{bmatrix} 3 & -4 \\ 6 & 5 \\ 1 & 0 \end{bmatrix}\begin{bmatrix} -1 & 2 \\ -6 & -2 \\ 7 & 4 \end{bmatrix}$

62. $-4\begin{bmatrix} 0 & 6 \\ -4 & -1 \end{bmatrix} + \begin{bmatrix} -9 & 3 \\ 4 & -2 \end{bmatrix}$

63. $\begin{bmatrix} 4 & 0 & -2 \\ -7 & 9 & 6 \end{bmatrix} - \begin{bmatrix} -6 & 8 & -2 \\ -1 & 5 & 1 \end{bmatrix}$

64. Each section of the spinner shown has the same area. You spin the spinner 40 times. It stops on orange 7 times. Compare the experimental probability of stopping on orange with the theoretical probability.

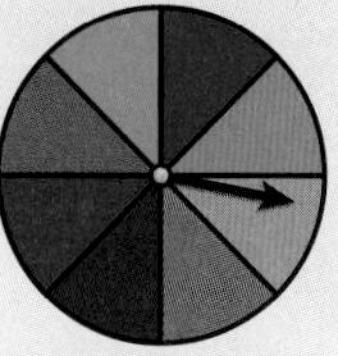

In Exercises 65 and 66, let $f(x) = \sqrt{x - 2}$ and $g(x) = x^2 - 5$. Find the indicated value.

65. $f(g(4))$

66. $g(f(6))$

12.3 Determinants and Cramer's Rule

Learning Target Find and use determinants of matrices.

Success Criteria

- I can find the determinant of a square matrix.
- I can use determinants to find areas of triangles.
- I can use determinants to solve systems of equations.

EXPLORE IT! Finding the Determinant

Work with a partner. Consider the unit square shown.

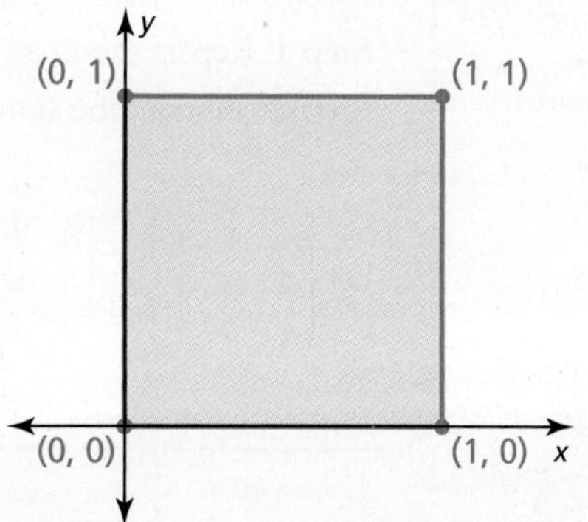

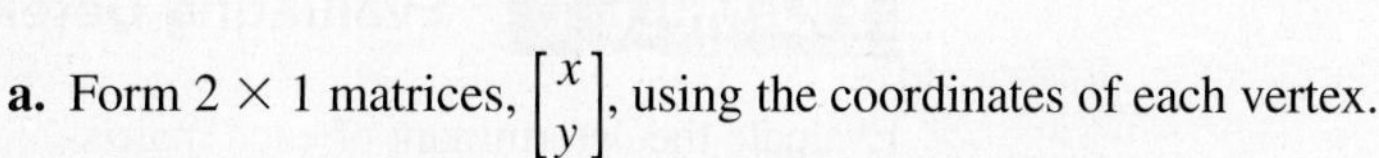

a. Form 2×1 matrices, $\begin{bmatrix} x \\ y \end{bmatrix}$, using the coordinates of each vertex.

b. Multiply $\begin{bmatrix} a & b \\ c & d \end{bmatrix}$ by each matrix in part (a). How does the diagram below correspond to your products?

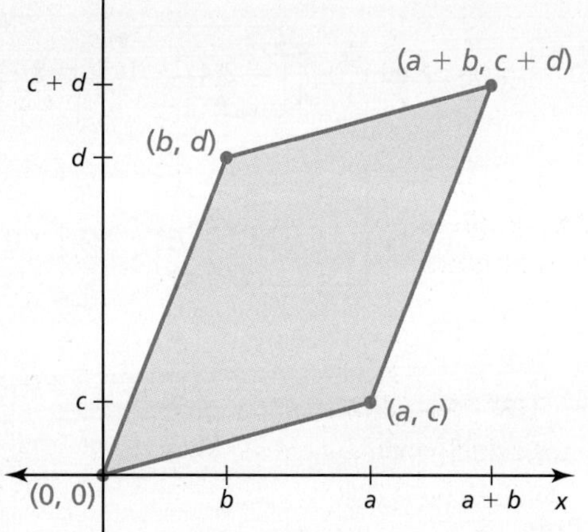

c. The area of the shaded parallelogram in part (b) is called the *determinant* of $\begin{bmatrix} a & b \\ c & d \end{bmatrix}$. Find the determinant of $\begin{bmatrix} a & b \\ c & d \end{bmatrix}$.

Math Practice

Find Entry Points

How can drawing a rectangle around the parallelogram help you find the determinant?

Evaluating Determinants

Associated with each square ($n \times n$) matrix is a real number called its **determinant**. The determinant of a square matrix A is denoted by det A or by $|A|$.

Vocabulary

determinant, *p. 662*
Cramer's Rule, *p. 664*
coefficient matrix, *p. 664*

STUDY TIP

In the Explore It!, you viewed the determinant as the area of a transformed figure. In this lesson, you will use determinants to find areas of triangles and solutions of linear systems.

KEY IDEA

The Determinant of a Matrix

Determinant of a 2 × 2 Matrix

$$\det\begin{bmatrix} a & b \\ c & d \end{bmatrix} = \begin{vmatrix} a & b \\ c & d \end{vmatrix} = ad - cb$$

The determinant of a 2 × 2 matrix is the difference of the products of the elements on the diagonals in the order shown.

Determinant of a 3 × 3 Matrix

Step 1 Repeat the first two columns to the right of the determinant.

Step 2 Subtract the sum of the red products from the sum of the blue products.

$$\det\begin{bmatrix} a & b & c \\ d & e & f \\ g & h & i \end{bmatrix} = \begin{vmatrix} a & b & c \\ d & e & f \\ g & h & i \end{vmatrix}\begin{matrix} a & b \\ d & e \\ g & h \end{matrix} = (aei + bfg + cdh) - (gec + hfa + idb)$$

EXAMPLE 1 Evaluating Determinants

Evaluate the determinant of each matrix.

a. $\begin{bmatrix} 2 & 5 \\ 1 & 4 \end{bmatrix}$

b. $\begin{bmatrix} 3 & 4 & -1 \\ 2 & 0 & 6 \\ -2 & -3 & 1 \end{bmatrix}$

SOLUTION

a. $\begin{vmatrix} 2 & 5 \\ 1 & 4 \end{vmatrix} = 2(4) - 1(5) = 8 - 5 = 3$

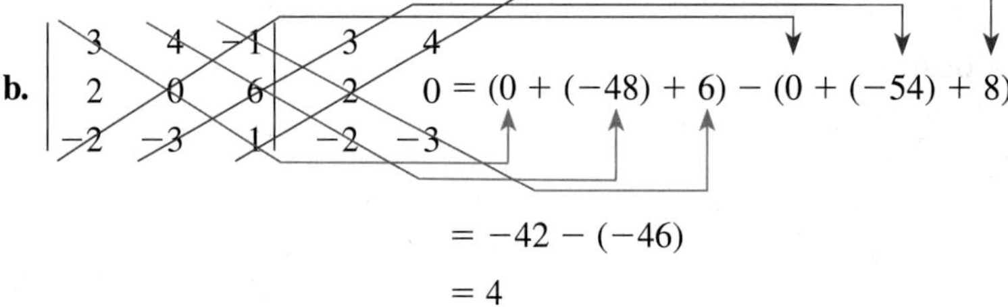

b. $\begin{vmatrix} 3 & 4 & -1 \\ 2 & 0 & 6 \\ -2 & -3 & 1 \end{vmatrix}\begin{matrix} 3 & 4 \\ 2 & 0 \\ -2 & -3 \end{matrix} = (0 + (-48) + 6) - (0 + (-54) + 8)$

$= -42 - (-46)$

$= 4$

SELF-ASSESSMENT

1 I do not understand. 2 I can do it with help. 3 I can do it on my own. 4 I can teach someone else.

Evaluate the determinant of the matrix.

1. $\begin{bmatrix} 6 & -2 \\ 3 & 5 \end{bmatrix}$

2. $\begin{bmatrix} 2 & -3 & 4 \\ 1 & 6 & 0 \\ 3 & -1 & 5 \end{bmatrix}$

3. $\begin{bmatrix} 5 & -1 & 6 \\ 1 & 2 & 4 \\ -3 & 0 & 2 \end{bmatrix}$

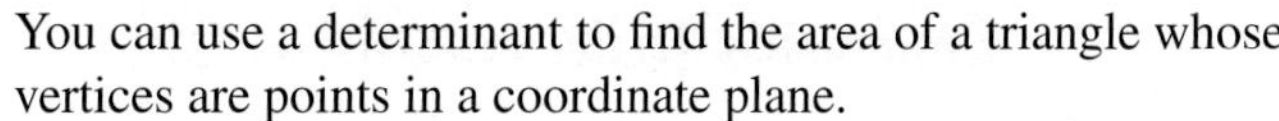

You can use a determinant to find the area of a triangle whose vertices are points in a coordinate plane.

KEY IDEA

Area of a Triangle

The area of a triangle with vertices (x_1, y_1), (x_2, y_2), and (x_3, y_3) is given by

$$\text{Area} = \pm\frac{1}{2}\begin{vmatrix} x_1 & y_1 & 1 \\ x_2 & y_2 & 1 \\ x_3 & y_3 & 1 \end{vmatrix}$$

where the symbol $\pm$ indicates that the appropriate sign should be chosen to yield a positive value.

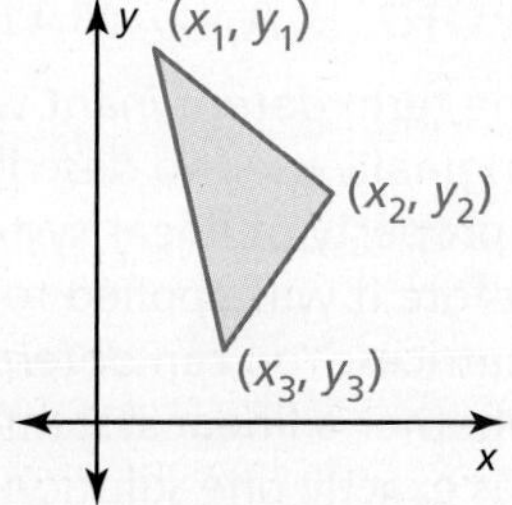

EXAMPLE 2 **Finding the Area of a Triangle**

Find the area of the triangle.

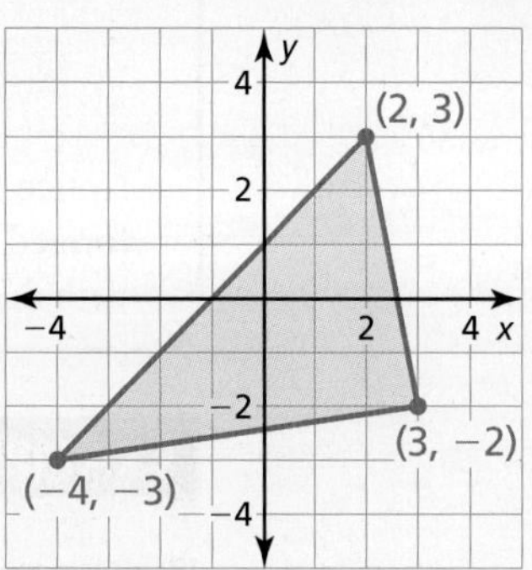

SOLUTION

$$\text{Area} = \pm\frac{1}{2}\begin{vmatrix} 2 & 3 & 1 \\ 3 & -2 & 1 \\ -4 & -3 & 1 \end{vmatrix}$$

$$= \pm\frac{1}{2}\begin{vmatrix} 2 & 3 & 1 & 2 & 3 \\ 3 & -2 & 1 & 3 & -2 \\ -4 & -3 & 1 & -4 & -3 \end{vmatrix}$$

$$= \pm\tfrac{1}{2}[(-4 - 12 - 9) - (8 - 6 + 9)]$$

$$= \pm\tfrac{1}{2}(-25 - 11)$$

$$= \pm(-18)$$

STUDY TIP
As stated in the Key Idea above, choose the sign that yields a positive value. Choose the negative sign because $-(-18) = 18$.

▶ So, the area of the triangle is 18 square units.

SELF-ASSESSMENT 1 I do not understand. 2 I can do it with help. 3 I can do it on my own. 4 I can teach someone else.

4. Find the area of the triangle with vertices (3, 6), (8, −1), and (−4, 5).

Cramer's Rule

You can use determinants to solve a system of linear equations. The method, called **Cramer's Rule** and named after Swiss mathematician Gabriel Cramer (1704–1752), uses the **coefficient matrix** of the linear system.

Linear System	Coefficient Matrix
$ax + by = e$ $cx + dy = f$	$\begin{bmatrix} a & b \\ c & d \end{bmatrix}$

WORDS AND MATH

The term *determinant* was originally used to describe a property of linear systems before it was applied to matrices. You can *determine* whether a linear system has exactly one solution by calculating the determinant of its coefficient matrix.

KEY IDEA

Cramer's Rule for a 2 × 2 System

Let A be the coefficient matrix of the linear system

$$\begin{aligned} ax + by &= e \\ cx + dy &= f \end{aligned}.$$

If $\det A \neq 0$, then the system has exactly one solution. The solution is

$$x = \frac{\begin{vmatrix} e & b \\ f & d \end{vmatrix}}{\det A} \quad \text{and} \quad y = \frac{\begin{vmatrix} a & e \\ c & f \end{vmatrix}}{\det A}.$$

Notice that the numerators for x and y are the determinants of the matrices formed by replacing the values of the x and y coefficient columns, respectively, with the column of the constant values.

EXAMPLE 3 Using Cramer's Rule for a 2 × 2 System

Use Cramer's Rule to solve the system $\begin{aligned} 3x - 2y &= 7 \\ 5x + 4y &= -3 \end{aligned}$.

ANOTHER WAY

You can also solve the system in Example 3 using the elimination method.

SOLUTION

Step 1 Evaluate the determinant of the coefficient matrix.

$$\begin{vmatrix} 3 & -2 \\ 5 & 4 \end{vmatrix} = 12 - (-10) = 22$$

Step 2 Apply Cramer's Rule because the determinant is not 0.

$$x = \frac{\begin{vmatrix} 7 & -2 \\ -3 & 4 \end{vmatrix}}{22} = \frac{28 - 6}{22} = \frac{22}{22} = 1$$

$$y = \frac{\begin{vmatrix} 3 & 7 \\ 5 & -3 \end{vmatrix}}{22} = \frac{-9 - 35}{22} = \frac{-44}{22} = -2$$

▶ The solution is $(1, -2)$.

Check

$3x - 2y = 7$	Original equation	$5x + 4y = -3$
$3(1) - 2(-2) \stackrel{?}{=} 7$	Substitute.	$5(1) + 4(-2) \stackrel{?}{=} -3$
$3 + 4 \stackrel{?}{=} 7$	Simplify.	$5 - 8 \stackrel{?}{=} -3$
$7 = 7$ ✓	Simplify.	$-3 = -3$ ✓

KEY IDEA

Cramer's Rule for a 3 × 3 System

Let A be the coefficient matrix of the linear system shown below.

Linear System

$$ax + by + cz = j$$
$$dx + ey + fz = k$$
$$gx + hy + iz = l$$

Coefficient Matrix

$$A = \begin{bmatrix} a & b & c \\ d & e & f \\ g & h & i \end{bmatrix}$$

If $\det A \neq 0$, then the system has exactly one solution. The solution is

$$x = \frac{\begin{vmatrix} j & b & c \\ k & e & f \\ l & h & i \end{vmatrix}}{\det A}, \quad y = \frac{\begin{vmatrix} a & j & c \\ d & k & f \\ g & l & i \end{vmatrix}}{\det A}, \quad \text{and} \quad z = \frac{\begin{vmatrix} a & b & j \\ d & e & k \\ g & h & l \end{vmatrix}}{\det A}.$$

STUDY TIP

The numerators for x, y, and z are the determinants of the matrices formed by replacing the values of the x, y, and z coefficient columns, respectively, with the column of the constant values.

EXAMPLE 4 Using Cramer's Rule for a 3 × 3 System

Use Cramer's Rule to solve the system.

$$2x - 3y + 5z = 12$$
$$x + 4y - 3z = -5$$
$$3x - 2y - z = -23$$

SOLUTION

Step 1 Evaluate the determinant of the coefficient matrix.

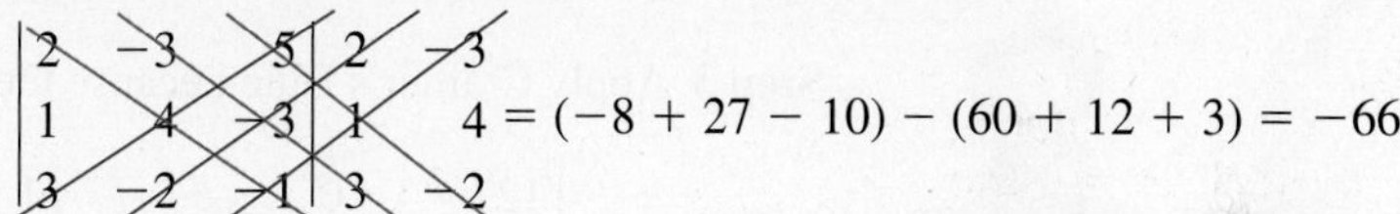

$$\begin{vmatrix} 2 & -3 & 5 \\ 1 & 4 & -3 \\ 3 & -2 & -1 \end{vmatrix} \begin{matrix} 2 & -3 \\ 1 & 4 \\ 3 & -2 \end{matrix} = (-8 + 27 - 10) - (60 + 12 + 3) = -66$$

Step 2 Apply Cramer's Rule because the determinant is not 0.

$$x = \frac{\begin{vmatrix} 12 & -3 & 5 \\ -5 & 4 & -3 \\ -23 & -2 & -1 \end{vmatrix}}{-66} \qquad y = \frac{\begin{vmatrix} 2 & 12 & 5 \\ 1 & -5 & -3 \\ 3 & -23 & -1 \end{vmatrix}}{-66} \qquad z = \frac{\begin{vmatrix} 2 & -3 & 12 \\ 1 & 4 & -5 \\ 3 & -2 & -23 \end{vmatrix}}{-66}$$

$$= \frac{198}{-66} \qquad = \frac{-264}{-66} \qquad = \frac{-396}{-66}$$

$$= -3 \qquad = 4 \qquad = 6$$

▶ The solution is $(-3, 4, 6)$.

SELF-ASSESSMENT

1 I do not understand. 2 I can do it with help. 3 I can do it on my own. 4 I can teach someone else.

Use Cramer's Rule to solve the linear system.

5. $7x - 2y = 20$
$3x + 4y = -6$

6. $5x + 6y = 14$
$-2x - 3y = -8$

7. $5x - 2y + 3z = -2$
$4x + 7y - z = 0$
$2x - 6y + 5z = -7$

Solving Real-Life Problems

EXAMPLE 5 **Modeling Real Life** 

The molecular mass of a compound is the sum of the atomic masses of the atoms it contains. The table shows the molecular masses (in atomic mass units) of three compounds. Use a linear system and Cramer's Rule to find the atomic masses of bromine (Br), nitrogen (N), and fluorine (F).

Compound	Formula	Molecular Mass
Bromine azide	BrN_3	122
Bromine trifluoride	BrF_3	137
Nitrogen trifluoride	NF_3	71

READING

Subscripts in a chemical formula indicate the number of atoms of each element in one molecule of the compound. No subscript indicates there is 1 atom in the molecule.

SOLUTION

Step 1 Write a linear system using the formula for each compound. Let B, N, and F represent the atomic masses of bromine, nitrogen, and fluorine.

$$B + 3N = 122 \qquad BrN_3\text{: 1 bromine atom and 3 nitrogen atoms}$$
$$B + 3F = 137 \qquad BrF_3\text{: 1 bromine atom and 3 fluorine atoms}$$
$$N + 3F = 71 \qquad NF_3\text{: 1 nitrogen atom and 3 fluorine atoms}$$

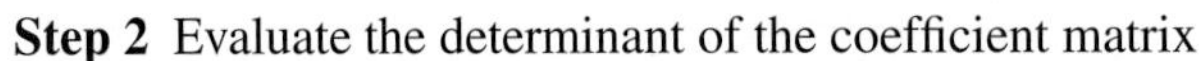
Step 2 Evaluate the determinant of the coefficient matrix.

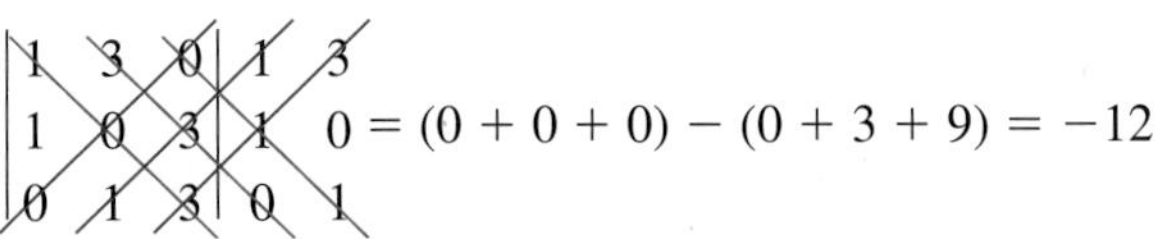

$$\begin{vmatrix} 1 & 3 & 0 \\ 1 & 0 & 3 \\ 0 & 1 & 3 \end{vmatrix} \begin{matrix} 1 & 3 \\ 1 & 0 \\ 0 & 1 \end{matrix} = (0 + 0 + 0) - (0 + 3 + 9) = -12$$

Step 3 Apply Cramer's Rule because the determinant is not 0.

$$B = \frac{\begin{vmatrix} 122 & 3 & 0 \\ 137 & 0 & 3 \\ 71 & 1 & 3 \end{vmatrix}}{-12} = \frac{-960}{-12} = 80 \qquad N = \frac{\begin{vmatrix} 1 & 122 & 0 \\ 1 & 137 & 3 \\ 0 & 71 & 3 \end{vmatrix}}{-12} = \frac{-168}{-12} = 14 \qquad F = \frac{\begin{vmatrix} 1 & 3 & 122 \\ 1 & 0 & 137 \\ 0 & 1 & 71 \end{vmatrix}}{-12} = \frac{-228}{-12} = 19$$

▶ The atomic masses (in atomic mass units) of bromine, nitrogen, and fluorine are 80, 14, and 19, respectively.

SELF-ASSESSMENT

1 I do not understand. 2 I can do it with help. 3 I can do it on my own. 4 I can teach someone else.

8. The table shows the molecular masses (in atomic mass units) of three compounds. Use a linear system and Cramer's Rule to find the atomic masses of carbon (C), hydrogen (H), and oxygen (O).

Compound	Formula	Molecular Mass
Acetone	C_3H_6O	58
Butanoic acid	$C_4H_8O_2$	88
Citric acid	$C_6H_8O_7$	192

12.3 Practice WITH CalcChat® AND CalcView®

In Exercises 1–16, evaluate the determinant of the matrix. *Example 1*

1. $\begin{bmatrix} 3 & 1 \\ 2 & 4 \end{bmatrix}$

2. $\begin{bmatrix} 5 & 2 \\ 7 & 3 \end{bmatrix}$

3. $\begin{bmatrix} -1 & 3 \\ 2 & 6 \end{bmatrix}$

4. $\begin{bmatrix} 2 & 5 \\ 8 & -4 \end{bmatrix}$

5. $\begin{bmatrix} 1 & -2 \\ -3 & 4 \end{bmatrix}$

6. $\begin{bmatrix} -5 & 9 \\ 7 & -2 \end{bmatrix}$

7. $\begin{bmatrix} -2 & 4 \\ -8 & 10 \end{bmatrix}$

8. $\begin{bmatrix} -8 & -9 \\ 14 & 12 \end{bmatrix}$

9. $\begin{bmatrix} 1 & 0 & 5 \\ 6 & 2 & 0 \\ 3 & 8 & 9 \end{bmatrix}$

10. $\begin{bmatrix} 6 & 1 & 2 \\ 5 & 0 & 4 \\ 9 & 3 & 0 \end{bmatrix}$

11. $\begin{bmatrix} -2 & 7 & 0 \\ -3 & 1 & 4 \\ 5 & 0 & -6 \end{bmatrix}$

12. $\begin{bmatrix} 2 & -1 & 3 \\ 5 & 0 & 7 \\ 0 & -6 & -4 \end{bmatrix}$

13. $\begin{bmatrix} -9 & 0 & 1 \\ 2 & 4 & 8 \\ -3 & -4 & -6 \end{bmatrix}$

14. $\begin{bmatrix} -1 & 7 & 5 \\ 2 & -9 & -2 \\ 1 & 4 & 0 \end{bmatrix}$

15. $\begin{bmatrix} 4 & -1 & 7 \\ 2 & 8 & 5 \\ -3 & 1 & -7 \end{bmatrix}$

16. $\begin{bmatrix} 9 & 1 & 4 \\ -1 & -6 & -2 \\ -3 & 7 & 8 \end{bmatrix}$

ERROR ANALYSIS In Exercises 17 and 18, describe and correct the error in evaluating the determinant of the matrix.

17.

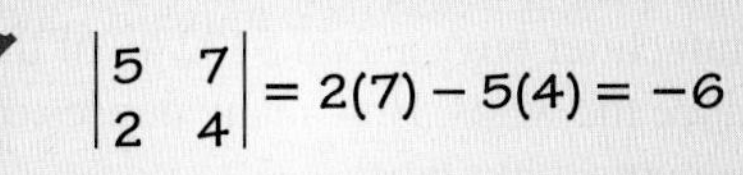

18.

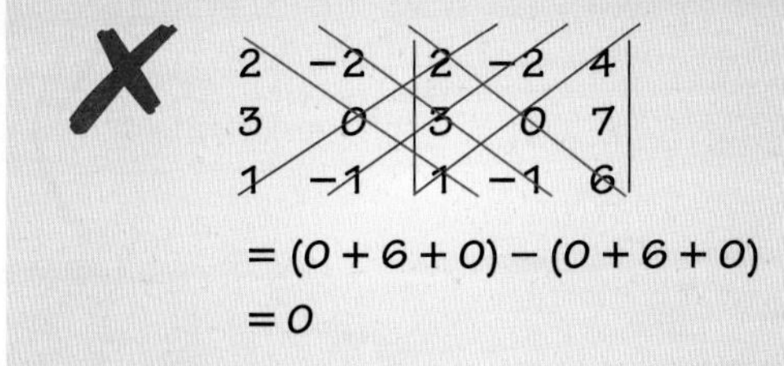

19. **MP NUMBER SENSE** Order the determinants from least to greatest.

A. $\begin{vmatrix} 5 & -2 \\ 1 & 5 \end{vmatrix}$ B. $\begin{vmatrix} 1 & 6 \\ 3 & 8 \end{vmatrix}$

C. $\begin{vmatrix} 5 & -3 \\ 7 & -1 \end{vmatrix}$ D. $\begin{vmatrix} -4 & 1 \\ 6 & 3 \end{vmatrix}$

20. **COLLEGE PREP** For what value of k is the determinant of the matrix below equal to 0?

$$\begin{bmatrix} 0 & 2 & 0 \\ k & 9 & 2 \\ 5 & 4 & 2 \end{bmatrix}$$

Ⓐ $k = -10$ Ⓑ $k = -5$

Ⓒ $k = 5$ Ⓓ $k = 10$

In Exercises 21–24, find the area of the triangle. *Example 2*

21.

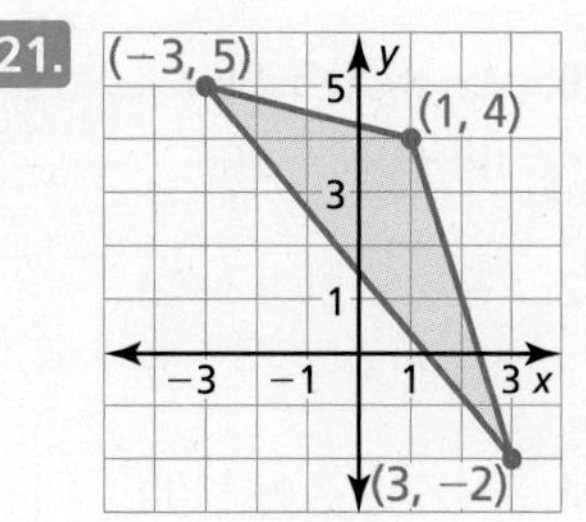

22.

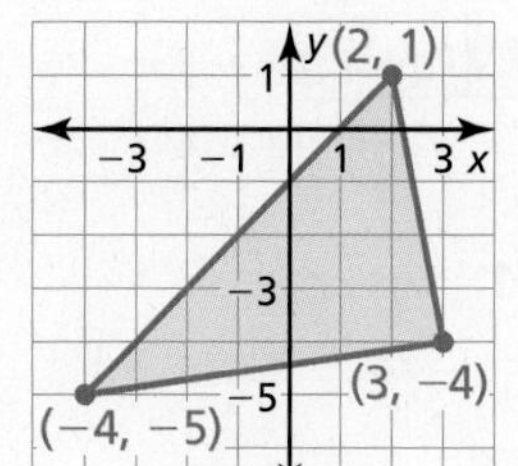

23.

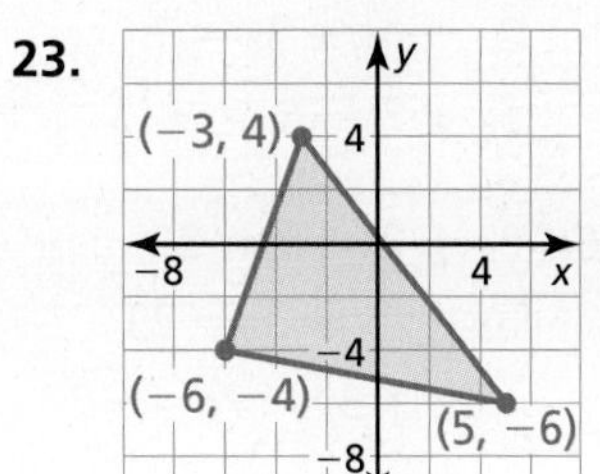

24.

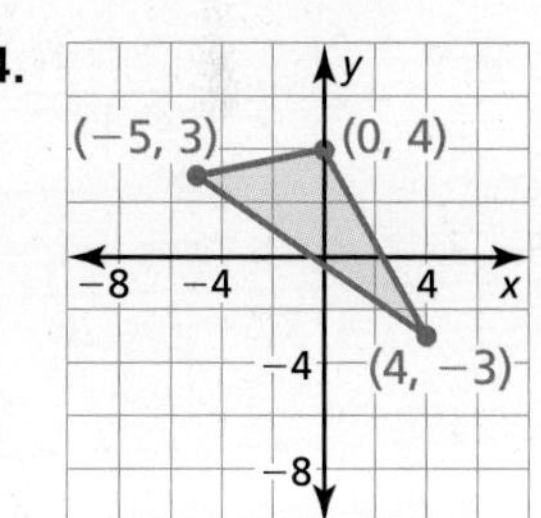

25. **MODELING REAL LIFE** A researcher of *Lyme disease* tests ticks from the triangular region shown below. Find the area of the triangular region.

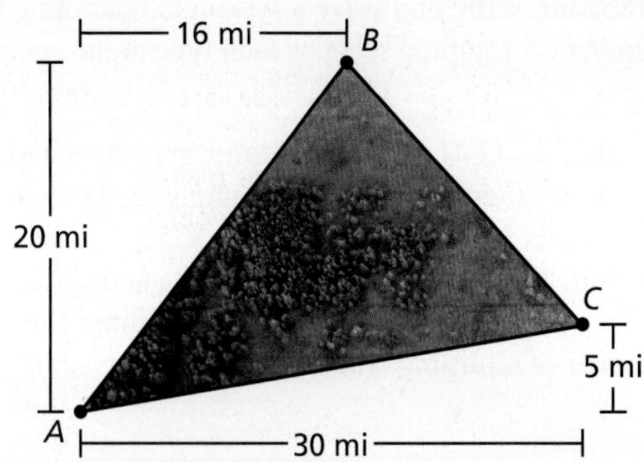

26. **MODELING REAL LIFE** A school resource officer uses three cameras to observe the lobby shown below. Find the area of the lobby.

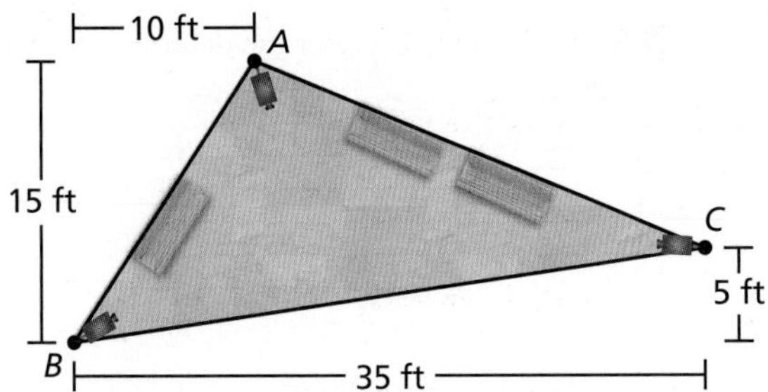

MP STRUCTURE In Exercises 27 and 28, find a positive value of y such that a triangle with the given vertices has an area of 5 square units.

27. $(-4, 3), (0, 1), (1, y)$

28. $(-3, -3), (0, -2), (-1, y)$

In Exercises 29–36, use Cramer's Rule to solve the linear system. *Examples 3 and 4*

29. $4x + 3y = 5$
$3x + 2y = 4$

30. $2x + 5y = 11$
$4x + 8y = 20$

31. $5x - y = 12$
$-x + 6y = -14$

32. $-7x + 2y = -13$
$8x + 3y = -1$

33. $-x + y - 4z = -7$
$3x + 5y - 6z = -5$
$2x - 3y + 5z = 12$

34. $x + 3y + 2z = 11$
$2x - 4y + 3z = 7$
$5x + 2y - z = -13$

35. $2x - 4y + 7z = -1$
$-3x + 5y - z = 26$
$x - 6y + z = -24$

36. $3x + 2y + z = 2$
$6x - 2y - 3z = 23$
$-2x + 3y - 2z = -20$

37. **MODELING REAL LIFE** There are x occupied floor seats and y occupied balcony seats at a concert with 6700 total attendees. The tickets cost \$40 per floor seat and \$25 per balcony seat. The total revenue is \$185,500. Write and solve a system to determine the number of occupied seats of each type at the concert.

38. **MODELING REAL LIFE** There are x beginners and y returning students in a coding camp with 31 students. The cost is \$200 per beginner and \$350 per returning student. The total cost is \$8000. Write and solve a system to determine the number of beginners and the number of returning students at the coding camp.

In Exercises 39 and 40, the table shows the molecular masses (in atomic mass units) of three compounds. Use a linear system and Cramer's Rule to find the atomic masses of the indicated elements. *Example 5*

39. sulfur (S), chlorine (Cl), calcium (Ca)

Compound	Formula	Molecular Mass
Sulfur dichloride	SCl_2	103
Calcium chloride	$CaCl_2$	111
Calcium sulfide	CaS	72

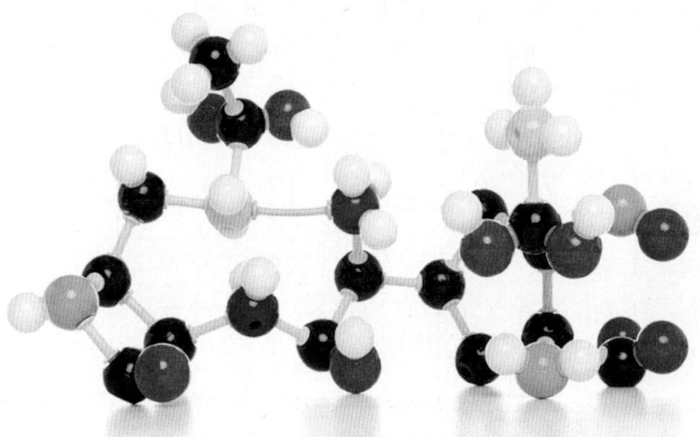

40. phosphorus (P), selenium (Se), iodine (I)

Compound	Formula	Molecular Mass
Diphosphorus pentaselenide	P_2Se_5	457
Phosphorus triiodide	PI_3	412
Selenium diiodide	SeI_2	333

41. **MODELING REAL LIFE** The metal wire of a particular dental retainer is constructed using 40% nickel and 60% titanium. The price per ounce of nickel is \$0.50 and the price per ounce of titanium is \$1.80. A manufacturer buys a total \$102.40 of the metals to produce the wires. How many ounces of nickel does the manufacturer buy?

42. **MODELING REAL LIFE** Tin is usually found as an oxide called Cassiterite, shown above. When tin is melted down, it can be combined with other metals. An artist creates bronze jewelry using aluminum, copper, and tin. The costs of each metal are shown in the table. The artist orders a total of 10 pounds of metals for a cost of \$32.70. The artist orders seven times as much copper as tin. How many pounds of tin does the artist order?

STEM

Metal	Price Per Pound
Aluminum	\$0.75
Copper	\$2.75
Tin	\$7.75

43. **MODELING REAL LIFE** A system of pulleys is loaded with 128-pound and 32-pound weights, as shown.

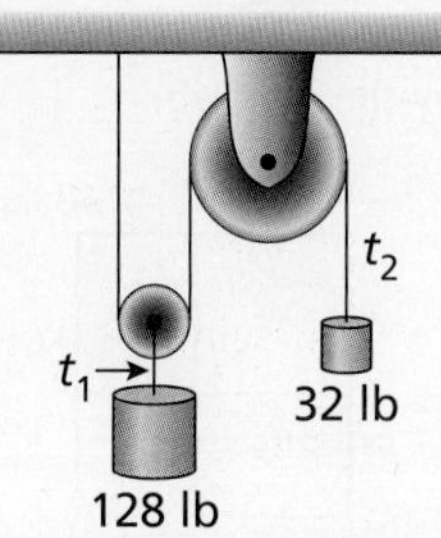

The tensions t_1 and t_2 (in pounds) in the ropes and the acceleration a (in feet per second squared) of the 32-pound weight are represented by the system

$$\begin{aligned} t_1 - 2t_2 \quad &= 0 \\ t_1 \quad - 2a &= 128. \\ t_2 + a &= 32 \end{aligned}$$

Find t_1, t_2, and a.

44. **MODELING REAL LIFE** Solar flares are classified based on their strength. In a study, the average intensities (in watts per square meter) of solar flares of class C, M, and X are solutions of the system

$$\begin{aligned} 37C + M + X &= 0.000705 \\ 15C + 14M + 4X &= 0.002775. \\ 5C + 9M + 4X &= 0.002475 \end{aligned}$$

Find the three intensities.

In Exercises 45 and 46, (x_1, y_1), (x_2, y_2), and (x_3, y_3) lie on the same line only when

$$\begin{vmatrix} x_1 & y_1 & 1 \\ x_2 & y_2 & 1 \\ x_3 & y_3 & 1 \end{vmatrix} = 0.$$

Determine whether the points lie on the same line.

45. (0, 1), (2, 4), (3, 6)

46. (−5, −4), (−2, −1), (3, 4)

47. **OPEN ENDED** Compare the area of the red triangle to the area of the blue triangle using two methods. Which method do you prefer? Explain.

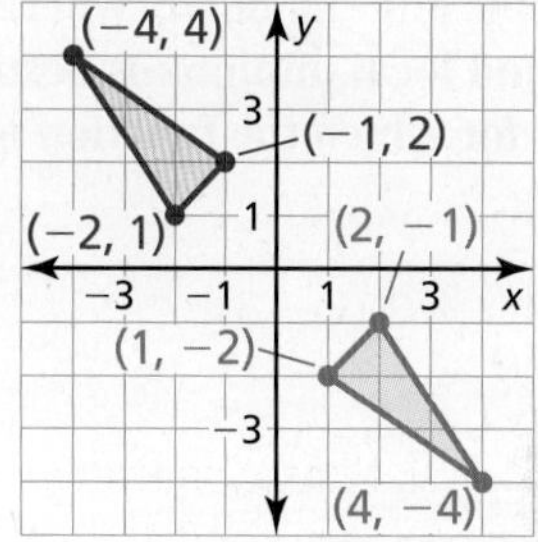

48. MP **STRUCTURE** Solve the equation

$$\begin{vmatrix} x+3 & x \\ 4 & x-1 \end{vmatrix} = 5.$$

49. MP **STRUCTURE** A community organizer requests a triangular plot of land with an area of 5000 square feet for an urban garden. On a blueprint, one vertex is at (0, 0) and another is at (100, 50). The y-coordinate of the final vertex is 120. Find the possible locations of the final vertex.

50. **HOW DO YOU SEE IT?**
Without calculating, explain why the determinant of the matrix below is 0.

$$\begin{bmatrix} 6 & -2 & 8 \\ 0 & 0 & 0 \\ 1 & 7 & 3 \end{bmatrix}$$

51. MP **REPEATED REASONING** Consider 3×3 square matrices in which the elements are consecutive integers. An example is shown below.

$$\begin{bmatrix} 2 & 3 & 4 \\ 5 & 6 & 7 \\ 8 & 9 & 10 \end{bmatrix}$$

Find the determinants of four matrices of this type. Make a conjecture based on the results.

52. THOUGHT PROVOKING
Consider the equation for the determinant of a 3×3 matrix,

$$\begin{vmatrix} a & b & c \\ d & e & f \\ g & h & i \end{vmatrix} = (aei + bfg + cdh) - (gec + hfa + idb).$$

How can you rewrite the determinant of a 3×3 matrix using determinants of 2×2 matrices? Show that your equation is equivalent to the equation above.

53. **DIG DEEPER** Consider the system

$$ax + by = e$$
$$cx + dy = f.$$

a. Solve the system by finding rational expressions for x and y.

b. What is the relationship between determinants and your answers in part (a)? Explain.

REVIEW & REFRESH

In Exercises 54 and 55, graph the function. Identify the x-intercepts and the points where the local maximums and local minimums occur. Determine the intervals for which the function is increasing or decreasing.

54. $g(x) = \frac{1}{2}(x + 2)(x - 3)$

55. $f(x) = x^3 - 2x^2 - x + 2$

56. Solve the equation for a, b, c, and d.

$$\begin{bmatrix} 8 - a & 5b \\ c & -2d \end{bmatrix} = \begin{bmatrix} 4 & 20 \\ 22 & 14 \end{bmatrix}$$

57. Find the product $\begin{bmatrix} 0 & 2 \\ -1 & 3 \end{bmatrix}\begin{bmatrix} 0 & -9 \\ 7 & 1 \end{bmatrix}$.

58. Write a recursive rule for the sequence.

5, 10, 30, 120. . .

59. Find the value of x for the right triangle.

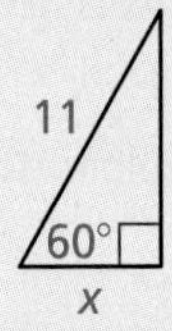

60. Use Cramer's Rule to solve the system.

$$8x + y = 21$$
$$x + 5y = 27$$

61. Describe the pattern, write the next term, and write a rule for the nth term of the sequence.

2.5, 6.5, 11.5, 17.5, . . .

62. Find all the real zeros of $f(x) = 4x^3 - 10x^2 - 8x + 6$.

63. Verify the identity $\sin\left(\frac{3\pi}{2} - x\right)\tan x = -\sin x$.

64. You are considering six full and three rimless frames for prescription glasses. You randomly select a frame, set it aside, and then randomly select another frame. Determine whether randomly selecting a full frame first and a rimless frame second are independent events.

65. Find the zeros of the function $h(x) = -2x^3 - 2x^2 + 18x + 18$. Then sketch a graph of the function.

66. Find the inverse of the function $f(x) = 9x^2, x \leq 0$. Then graph the function and its inverse.

67. Find the value of c. Then write an expression represented by the diagram.

	x	3
x	x^2	$3x$
3	$3x$	c

68. Graph the function $y = e^{x+4}$. Then find the domain and range.

69. Make a table and draw a histogram showing the probability distribution for the random variable.

x = the number on a table tennis ball randomly chosen from a bag that contains 3 balls labeled "1," 2 balls labeled "2," and 1 ball labeled "3."

70. Find the sum.

$$\frac{3}{x + 1} + \frac{2x}{x + 2}$$

71. Graph the system of quadratic inequalities.

$$y \geq x^2$$
$$y < x^2 + 4x - 5$$

12.4 Inverse Matrices

Learning Target Understand the relationship between a matrix and its inverse.

Success Criteria
- I can find the inverse of a matrix.
- I can solve linear systems using inverse matrices.
- I can solve real-life problems using inverse matrices.

EXPLORE IT! Describing Matrices and Their Inverses

Work with a partner.

a. Each matrix shown below has an *inverse*. Find the determinant of each matrix. Then use technology to find the inverse of each matrix. How is each matrix related to its inverse?

$$A = \begin{bmatrix} 3 & 7 \\ 2 & 5 \end{bmatrix} \qquad B = \begin{bmatrix} 2 & 1 \\ 5 & 2 \end{bmatrix}$$

$$C = \begin{bmatrix} -4 & 2 \\ 2 & -2 \end{bmatrix} \qquad D = \begin{bmatrix} -4 & -2 \\ -2 & -2 \end{bmatrix}$$

READING
The notation for the inverse of a matrix is similar to the notation for inverse functions. The inverse of matrix A can be written as A^{-1}.

b. Use technology to find the inverse of each matrix. What do you notice? Why does this happen?

$$E = \begin{bmatrix} 6 & 3 \\ 4 & 2 \end{bmatrix} \qquad F = \begin{bmatrix} -4 & -2 \\ -10 & -5 \end{bmatrix}$$

c. Use your results in parts (a) and (b) to describe how you can find the inverse of a 2×2 matrix.

d. Find the product of each matrix in part (a) and its inverse. What do you notice?

e. The matrix below is called the 2×2 *identity matrix I*.

$$I = \begin{bmatrix} 1 & 0 \\ 0 & 1 \end{bmatrix} \qquad 2 \times 2 \text{ identity matrix}$$

Explore the relationship between a matrix, its inverse, and the identity matrix. Make several observations.

Math Practice

Make Conjectures
What do you think happens when you multiply a 3×3 matrix or a 4×4 matrix by its inverse? Use technology to verify your conjecture.

Finding Inverse Matrices

Vocabulary

identity matrix, *p. 672*
inverse matrices, *p. 672*
matrix of variables, *p. 674*
matrix of constants, *p. 674*

The $n \times n$ **identity matrix** is a matrix that consists of 1's on its main diagonal (from top left to bottom right) and 0's for all other elements. If A is any $n \times n$ matrix and I is the $n \times n$ identity matrix, then $AI = A$ and $IA = A$.

2 × 2 Identity Matrix

$$I = \begin{bmatrix} 1 & 0 \\ 0 & 1 \end{bmatrix}$$

3 × 3 Identity Matrix

$$I = \begin{bmatrix} 1 & 0 & 0 \\ 0 & 1 & 0 \\ 0 & 0 & 1 \end{bmatrix}$$

Two $n \times n$ matrices A and B are **inverses** of each other when their products are the $n \times n$ identity matrix. That is, $AB = I$ and $BA = I$. An $n \times n$ matrix A has an inverse if and only if $\det A \neq 0$. The inverse of A is denoted by A^{-1}.

KEY IDEA

The Inverse of a 2 × 2 Matrix

The inverse of the matrix $A = \begin{bmatrix} a & b \\ c & d \end{bmatrix}$ is

$$A^{-1} = \frac{1}{\det A}\begin{bmatrix} d & -b \\ -c & a \end{bmatrix} = \frac{1}{ad - cb}\begin{bmatrix} d & -b \\ -c & a \end{bmatrix} \text{ when } \det A \neq 0.$$

EXAMPLE 1 Finding the Inverse of a 2 × 2 Matrix

Find the inverse of each matrix, if possible.

a. $A = \begin{bmatrix} 4 & 7 \\ 3 & 5 \end{bmatrix}$ **b.** $B = \begin{bmatrix} 5 & 3 \\ 4 & 2 \end{bmatrix}$ **c.** $C = \begin{bmatrix} -6 & 9 \\ 2 & -3 \end{bmatrix}$

SOLUTION

a. $A^{-1} = \frac{1}{20 - 21}\begin{bmatrix} 5 & -7 \\ -3 & 4 \end{bmatrix} = -1\begin{bmatrix} 5 & -7 \\ -3 & 4 \end{bmatrix} = \begin{bmatrix} -5 & 7 \\ 3 & -4 \end{bmatrix}$

b. $B^{-1} = \frac{1}{10 - 12}\begin{bmatrix} 2 & -3 \\ -4 & 5 \end{bmatrix} = -\frac{1}{2}\begin{bmatrix} 2 & -3 \\ -4 & 5 \end{bmatrix} = \begin{bmatrix} -1 & \frac{3}{2} \\ 2 & -\frac{5}{2} \end{bmatrix}$

c. $C^{-1} = \frac{1}{18 - 18}\begin{bmatrix} -3 & -9 \\ -2 & -6 \end{bmatrix} = \frac{1}{0}\begin{bmatrix} -3 & -9 \\ -2 & -6 \end{bmatrix}$

Because the determinant of matrix C is 0, C does not have an inverse.

STUDY TIP

In Example 1, you can check the inverse by showing that $AA^{-1} = I = A^{-1}A$.

SELF-ASSESSMENT 1 I do not understand. 2 I can do it with help. 3 I can do it on my own. 4 I can teach someone else.

Find the inverse of the matrix, if possible.

1. $\begin{bmatrix} 2 & 9 \\ 1 & 5 \end{bmatrix}$ **2.** $\begin{bmatrix} 1 & 4 \\ 2 & 7 \end{bmatrix}$ **3.** $\begin{bmatrix} 6 & 8 \\ 2 & 3 \end{bmatrix}$

4. MP **REASONING** Give another example of a 2 × 2 matrix that does not have an inverse.

EXAMPLE 2 Solving a Matrix Equation

Solve the matrix equation $AX = B$ for the 2×2 matrix X.

$$\overbrace{\begin{bmatrix} 2 & 7 \\ 1 & 4 \end{bmatrix}}^{A} X = \overbrace{\begin{bmatrix} 2 & 8 \\ 1 & 5 \end{bmatrix}}^{B}$$

SOLUTION

Begin by finding the inverse of A: $A^{-1} = \dfrac{1}{8-7}\begin{bmatrix} 4 & -7 \\ -1 & 2 \end{bmatrix} = \begin{bmatrix} 4 & -7 \\ -1 & 2 \end{bmatrix}$

To solve the equation for X, multiply both sides of $AX = B$ by A^{-1} on the left.

$$\begin{bmatrix} 4 & -7 \\ -1 & 2 \end{bmatrix}\begin{bmatrix} 2 & 7 \\ 1 & 4 \end{bmatrix} X = \begin{bmatrix} 4 & -7 \\ -1 & 2 \end{bmatrix}\begin{bmatrix} 2 & 8 \\ 1 & 5 \end{bmatrix} \qquad A^{-1}AX = A^{-1}B$$

$$\begin{bmatrix} 1 & 0 \\ 0 & 1 \end{bmatrix} X = \begin{bmatrix} 1 & -3 \\ 0 & 2 \end{bmatrix} \qquad IX = A^{-1}B$$

$$X = \begin{bmatrix} 1 & -3 \\ 0 & 2 \end{bmatrix} \qquad X = A^{-1}B$$

EXAMPLE 3 Finding the Inverse of a 3 × 3 Matrix Using Technology

Use technology to find the inverse of A. Then use technology to verify your result.

$$A = \begin{bmatrix} 2 & 1 & -2 \\ -1 & -1 & 2 \\ -3 & -1 & 3 \end{bmatrix}$$

SOLUTION

Enter matrix A and calculate A^{-1}.

$A =$	$\begin{bmatrix} 2 & 1 & -2 \\ -1 & -1 & 2 \\ -3 & -1 & 3 \end{bmatrix}$
A^{-1}	$= \begin{bmatrix} 1 & 1 & 0 \\ 3 & 0 & 2 \\ 2 & 1 & 1 \end{bmatrix}$

Check Calculate AA^{-1} and $A^{-1}A$ to verify that you obtain the 3×3 identity matrix.

AA^{-1}	$= \begin{bmatrix} 1 & 0 & 0 \\ 0 & 1 & 0 \\ 0 & 0 & 1 \end{bmatrix}$ ✓
$A^{-1}A$	$= \begin{bmatrix} 1 & 0 & 0 \\ 0 & 1 & 0 \\ 0 & 0 & 1 \end{bmatrix}$ ✓

SELF-ASSESSMENT

1 I do not understand. **2** I can do it with help. **3** I can do it on my own. **4** I can teach someone else.

Solve the matrix equation.

5. $\begin{bmatrix} 2 & 3 \\ 5 & 0 \end{bmatrix} X = \begin{bmatrix} 3 & 12 \\ 0 & 15 \end{bmatrix}$

6. $\begin{bmatrix} 4 & -1 \\ 2 & 6 \end{bmatrix} X = \begin{bmatrix} 11 & -10 \\ 12 & 8 \end{bmatrix}$

Use technology to find the inverse of A. Then use technology to verify your result.

7. $A = \begin{bmatrix} 2 & -2 & 5 \\ 0 & -1 & 1 \\ 1 & -1 & 2 \end{bmatrix}$

8. $A = \begin{bmatrix} -1 & 3 & -3 \\ 1 & 0 & 1 \\ 3 & 4 & 0 \end{bmatrix}$

9. $A = \begin{bmatrix} 1 & -1 & 4 \\ 1 & 0 & -2 \\ 6 & -2 & -1 \end{bmatrix}$

Using Inverse Matrices to Solve Linear Systems

KEY IDEA

Using an Inverse Matrix to Solve a Linear System

Step 1 Write the system as a matrix equation $AX = B$. The matrix A is the coefficient matrix, X is the **matrix of variables**, and B is the **matrix of constants**.

Step 2 Find the inverse of matrix A.

Step 3 Multiply each side of $AX = B$ by A^{-1} on the left to find the solution $X = A^{-1}B$.

EXAMPLE 4 Solving a Linear System 

Use an inverse matrix to solve the linear system.

$2x + 5y = 3$ Equation 1

$x + 3y = 2$ Equation 2

STUDY TIP

You can use the method shown in Example 4 when A has an inverse. If A does not have an inverse, then the system has either no solution or infinitely many solutions.

SOLUTION

Step 1 Write the linear system as a matrix equation $AX = B$.

coefficient matrix (A) · matrix of variables (X) = matrix of constants (B)

$$\begin{bmatrix} 2 & 5 \\ 1 & 3 \end{bmatrix} \cdot \begin{bmatrix} x \\ y \end{bmatrix} = \begin{bmatrix} 3 \\ 2 \end{bmatrix}$$

Step 2 Find the inverse of matrix A.

$$A^{-1} = \frac{1}{6-5}\begin{bmatrix} 3 & -5 \\ -1 & 2 \end{bmatrix} = \begin{bmatrix} 3 & -5 \\ -1 & 2 \end{bmatrix}$$

Step 3 Multiply each side of $AX = B$ by A^{-1} on the left.

$$\begin{bmatrix} 3 & -5 \\ -1 & 2 \end{bmatrix}\begin{bmatrix} 2 & 5 \\ 1 & 3 \end{bmatrix}X = \begin{bmatrix} 3 & -5 \\ -1 & 2 \end{bmatrix}\begin{bmatrix} 3 \\ 2 \end{bmatrix} \qquad A^{-1}AX = A^{-1}B$$

$$\begin{bmatrix} 1 & 0 \\ 0 & 1 \end{bmatrix}X = \begin{bmatrix} -1 \\ 1 \end{bmatrix} \qquad IX = A^{-1}B$$

$$X = \begin{bmatrix} -1 \\ 1 \end{bmatrix} \qquad X = A^{-1}B$$

▶ The solution of the system is $(-1, 1)$.

Check

Equation 1

$2(-1) + 5(1) \stackrel{?}{=} 3$

$3 = 3$ ✓

Equation 2

$-1 + 3(1) \stackrel{?}{=} 2$

$2 = 2$ ✓

SELF-ASSESSMENT 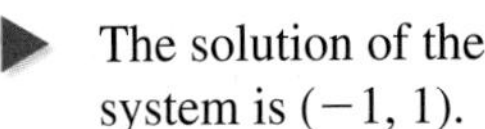 **1** I do not understand. **2** I can do it with help. **3** I can do it on my own. **4** I can teach someone else.

Use an inverse matrix to solve the linear system.

10. $6x + 7y = 5$
$7x + 8y = 6$

11. $2x - 3y = 1$
$-4x + 5y = 1$

12. $7x - 6y = 11$
$4x - 3y = 8$

EXAMPLE 5 Modeling Real Life

A company sells three sizes of fruit baskets as shown. What is the cost of each type of fruit?

SOLUTION

1. **Understand the Problem** You know how many of each type of fruit each basket contains and the total cost for each basket. You are asked to find the cost of each type of fruit.
2. **Make a Plan** Use a verbal model to write a system of linear equations that represents the problem. Then solve the system.
3. **Solve and Check**

Words 2 • [Cost of apple] + 2 • [Cost of grapefruit] + [Cost of peach] = $5.99

3 • [Cost of apple] + 2 • [Cost of grapefruit] + 3 • [Cost of peach] = $9.27

5 • [Cost of apple] + 3 • [Cost of grapefruit] + 4 • [Cost of peach] = $13.76

Variables Let x be the cost (in dollars) of an apple, let y be the cost (in dollars) of a grapefruit, and let z be the cost (in dollars) of a peach.

System

$2x + 2y + z = 5.99$ Equation 1

$3x + 2y + 3z = 9.27$ Equation 2

$5x + 3y + 4z = 13.76$ Equation 3

Step 1 Rewrite the system as a matrix equation.

$$\begin{bmatrix} 2 & 2 & 1 \\ 3 & 2 & 3 \\ 5 & 3 & 4 \end{bmatrix} \begin{bmatrix} x \\ y \\ z \end{bmatrix} = \begin{bmatrix} 5.99 \\ 9.27 \\ 13.76 \end{bmatrix}$$

Step 2 Use technology to enter the coefficient matrix A and the matrix of constants B. Then find the solution $X = A^{-1}B$.

$$A = \begin{bmatrix} 2 & 2 & 1 \\ 3 & 2 & 3 \\ 5 & 3 & 4 \end{bmatrix}$$

$$B = \begin{bmatrix} 5.99 \\ 9.27 \\ 13.76 \end{bmatrix}$$

$$A^{-1}B = \begin{bmatrix} 0.9 \\ 1.5 \\ 1.19 \end{bmatrix}$$

▶ The solution is (0.9, 1.5, 1.19). So, an apple costs $0.90, a grapefruit costs $1.50, and a peach costs $1.19.

Check Small basket: $2(0.90) + 2(1.50) + 1.19 = \$5.99$ ✓

Medium basket: $3(0.90) + 2(1.50) + 3(1.19) = \$9.27$ ✓

Large basket: $5(0.90) + 3(1.50) + 4(1.19) = \$13.76$ ✓

SELF-ASSESSMENT

1 I do not understand. 2 I can do it with help. 3 I can do it on my own. 4 I can teach someone else.

13. The company in Example 5 introduces three new fruit baskets. A small basket that costs $5.20 contains 2 oranges and 3 pears. A medium basket that costs $7.55 contains 3 oranges, 2 pears, and 2 plums. A large basket that costs $11.70 contains 4 oranges, 3 pears, and 4 plums. What is the cost of each type of fruit?

12.4 Practice WITH CalcChat® AND CalcView®

In Exercises 1–10, find the inverse of the matrix, if it exists. ▶ *Example 1*

1. $\begin{bmatrix} 4 & 3 \\ 9 & 7 \end{bmatrix}$
2. $\begin{bmatrix} 3 & 5 \\ 4 & 7 \end{bmatrix}$
3. $\begin{bmatrix} 9 & 8 \\ 8 & 7 \end{bmatrix}$
4. $\begin{bmatrix} 17 & 13 \\ 4 & 3 \end{bmatrix}$
5. $\begin{bmatrix} 6 & -3 \\ 4 & -2 \end{bmatrix}$
6. $\begin{bmatrix} 3 & 9 \\ 5 & 15 \end{bmatrix}$
7. $\begin{bmatrix} 5 & -3 \\ -11 & 7 \end{bmatrix}$
8. $\begin{bmatrix} -2 & 3 \\ 3 & -6 \end{bmatrix}$
9. $\begin{bmatrix} -6 & 2 \\ -14 & 5 \end{bmatrix}$
10. $\begin{bmatrix} -8 & -5 \\ 12 & 8 \end{bmatrix}$

ERROR ANALYSIS In Exercises 11 and 12, describe and correct the error in finding the inverse of the matrix.

11. ✗ $\begin{bmatrix} 4 & 1 \\ 6 & 2 \end{bmatrix}^{-1} = 2\begin{bmatrix} 2 & -1 \\ -6 & 4 \end{bmatrix} = \begin{bmatrix} 4 & -2 \\ -12 & 8 \end{bmatrix}$

12. ✗ $\begin{bmatrix} 2 & 3 \\ 5 & 7 \end{bmatrix}^{-1} = -1\begin{bmatrix} -7 & 3 \\ 5 & -2 \end{bmatrix} = \begin{bmatrix} 7 & -3 \\ -5 & 2 \end{bmatrix}$

In Exercises 13–20, solve the matrix equation.
▶ *Example 2*

13. $\begin{bmatrix} 2 & 5 \\ 7 & 3 \end{bmatrix}X = \begin{bmatrix} 12 & 9 \\ 13 & 17 \end{bmatrix}$
14. $\begin{bmatrix} 3 & 4 \\ 5 & 1 \end{bmatrix}X = \begin{bmatrix} 2 & 25 \\ 9 & 19 \end{bmatrix}$
15. $\begin{bmatrix} -1 & 4 \\ 6 & 3 \end{bmatrix}X = \begin{bmatrix} -8 & 17 \\ 21 & -21 \end{bmatrix}$
16. $\begin{bmatrix} 3 & -2 \\ 5 & 4 \end{bmatrix}X = \begin{bmatrix} 14 & 3 \\ 16 & 5 \end{bmatrix}$
17. $\begin{bmatrix} -10 & 5 \\ 2 & -8 \end{bmatrix}X = \begin{bmatrix} -85 & 30 \\ 38 & 50 \end{bmatrix}$
18. $\begin{bmatrix} -4 & -8 \\ -12 & 5 \end{bmatrix}X = \begin{bmatrix} 4 & 12 \\ -17 & 94 \end{bmatrix}$
19. $\begin{bmatrix} -1 & 5 \\ 0 & -2 \end{bmatrix}X = \begin{bmatrix} 3 & -1 & 0 \\ 6 & 8 & 4 \end{bmatrix}$
20. $\begin{bmatrix} -5 & 2 \\ -9 & 3 \end{bmatrix}X = \begin{bmatrix} 4 & 5 & 0 \\ 3 & 1 & 6 \end{bmatrix}$

MP USING TOOLS In Exercises 21–26, use technology to find the inverse of A. Then use technology to verify your result. ▶ *Example 3*

21. $A = \begin{bmatrix} 1 & -1 & -2 \\ 0 & 1 & 2 \\ 3 & 0 & 1 \end{bmatrix}$
22. $A = \begin{bmatrix} 2 & 1 & 1 \\ 1 & 0 & 2 \\ -2 & 1 & -6 \end{bmatrix}$
23. $A = \begin{bmatrix} 2 & -2 & 1 \\ -1 & 1 & 0 \\ 2 & 0 & 2 \end{bmatrix}$
24. $A = \begin{bmatrix} 2 & 1 & 0 \\ -3 & 4 & 7 \\ 5 & 0 & -3 \end{bmatrix}$
25. $A = \begin{bmatrix} 1 & 5 & -2 \\ 2 & 3 & -6 \\ -1 & 4 & 4 \end{bmatrix}$
26. $A = \begin{bmatrix} 3 & 1 & -7 \\ 1 & -1 & 0 \\ 2 & -2 & 1 \end{bmatrix}$

In Exercises 27–34, use an inverse matrix to solve the linear system. ▶ *Example 4*

27. $x + 2y = 1$
$3x + 7y = 2$
28. $5x - 7y = -1$
$-3x + 5y = 3$
29. $-9x + 8y = 1$
$5x - 6y = -13$
30. $-2x - 5y = 17$
$-3x + y = 0$
31. $4x + 9y = 14$
$6x + 7y = 8$
32. $2x - 8y = -28$
$3x + 7y = 15$
33. $-7x + 2y = 29$
$5x - 3y = -27$
34. $-x - 7y = 37$
$4x - 2y = 32$

MP USING TOOLS In Exercises 35–38, use an inverse matrix and technology to solve the linear system.

35. $x - y - 3z = 2$
$5x + 2y + z = -17$
$-3x - y = 8$
36. $-3x + y - 8z = 18$
$x - 2y + z = -11$
$2x - 2y + 5z = -17$
37. $2x + 4y + 5z = 5$
$x + 2y + 3z = 4$
$5x - 4y - 2z = -3$
38. $4x - y - z = -20$
$6x - z = -27$
$-x + 4y + 5z = 23$

39. **MODELING REAL LIFE** A bouquet of 2 roses, 6 carnations, and 2 tulips costs \$23. A bouquet of 4 roses, 4 carnations, and 2 tulips costs \$30. A bouquet of 3 roses, 2 carnations, and 5 tulips costs \$28. What is the cost of each type of flower? ▶ *Example 5*

40. **MODELING REAL LIFE** A bag that contains 6 ounces of walnuts, 4 ounces of pecans, and 6 ounces of cashews costs \$13.98. A bag that contains 7 ounces of walnuts, 3 ounces of pecans, and 6 ounces of cashews costs \$13.79. A bag that contains 5 ounces of walnuts, 4 ounces of pecans, and 7 ounces of cashews costs \$13.81. What is the cost per ounce of each type of nut?

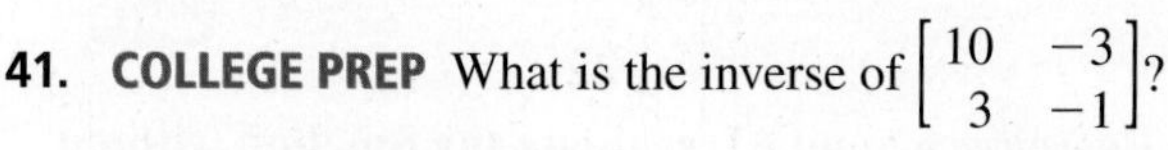

41. **COLLEGE PREP** What is the inverse of $\begin{bmatrix} 10 & -3 \\ 3 & -1 \end{bmatrix}$?

Ⓐ $\begin{bmatrix} -10 & 3 \\ -3 & 1 \end{bmatrix}$ Ⓑ $\begin{bmatrix} -1 & 3 \\ -3 & 10 \end{bmatrix}$

Ⓒ $\begin{bmatrix} 1 & -3 \\ 3 & -10 \end{bmatrix}$ Ⓓ $\begin{bmatrix} 10 & -3 \\ 3 & -1 \end{bmatrix}$

42. **COLLEGE PREP** For what value of x does $A = A^{-1}$?

$$A = \begin{bmatrix} -4 & 3 \\ x & 4 \end{bmatrix}$$

Ⓐ -5 Ⓑ -3

Ⓒ 3 Ⓓ 5

MP LOGIC In Exercises 43 and 44, determine whether the statement is *always*, *sometimes*, or *never* true. Explain your reasoning.

43. Multiplication of a matrix and its inverse is commutative.

44. If the product of two matrices is an identity matrix, then the matrices are inverses.

45. **MAKING AN ARGUMENT** Is it possible for a 3×2 matrix to have an inverse? Explain your reasoning.

46. **HOW DO YOU SEE IT?**
Find the product without performing any calculations.

$$\begin{bmatrix} -5 & 9 & -1 \\ 2 & 8 & -7 \\ 4 & 7 & 6 \end{bmatrix}\begin{bmatrix} 1 & 0 & 0 \\ 0 & 1 & 0 \\ 0 & 0 & 1 \end{bmatrix}$$

47. **MP PRECISION** Explain how multiplying an $n \times n$ matrix by the $n \times n$ identity matrix is similar to multiplying a real number a by 1.

48. **MP NUMBER SENSE** The *zero matrix*, denoted O, is an $m \times n$ matrix consisting entirely of 0's. Find the products of several $k \times m$ matrices and $m \times n$ zero matrices. What do you notice? How is multiplying a matrix A by O similar to multiplying a real number a by 0?

49. **ANALYZING RELATIONSHIPS** You write the matrix equation shown to represent a linear system. Explain how p and q are related in each situation.

$$\begin{bmatrix} 2m & 2n \\ m & n \end{bmatrix} \cdot \begin{bmatrix} x \\ y \end{bmatrix} = \begin{bmatrix} p \\ q \end{bmatrix}$$

a. The system has infinitely many solutions.

b. The system has no solution.

50. **MP USING TOOLS** Use an inverse matrix and technology to solve the linear system.

$$2w + 5x - 4y + 6z = 0$$
$$2x + y - 7z = 52$$
$$4w + 8x - 7y + 14z = -25$$
$$3w + 6x - 5y + 10z = -16$$

51. **MP PROBLEM SOLVING** You can use matrix multiplication and inverses to encode and decode words.

a. Let the numbers 1 to 26 represent the corresponding letters in the alphabet, where 1 = A and 26 = Z. Convert each letter in the word "CAT" to a number and write the result as a 1×3 matrix.

b. You can produce a coded matrix by multiplying the 1×3 matrix from part (a) by a 3×3 matrix that has an inverse, called the encoding matrix. Let matrix A be the encoding matrix. Find the coded matrix.

$$A = \begin{bmatrix} -4 & -1 & 1 \\ 3 & 1 & -1 \\ 2 & -2 & 1 \end{bmatrix}$$

c. A different three-letter word is encoded using matrix A from part (b). The coded matrix is $[19 \quad -25 \quad 11]$. Find the decoded matrix by multiplying the coded matrix by A^{-1}. What is the word?

d. Repeat parts (a) and (b) using a different three-letter word. Then exchange coded matrices with a partner and find your partner's word.

52. THOUGHT PROVOKING

Let $A = \begin{bmatrix} x & 0 \\ y & z \end{bmatrix}$. For what values of x, y, and z does $A = A^{-1}$? Justify your answer.

53. **DIG DEEPER** Let $A = \begin{bmatrix} a & b \\ c & d \end{bmatrix}$ where $\det A \neq 0$. Verify that

$$A^{-1} = \frac{1}{ad - bc}\begin{bmatrix} d & -b \\ -c & a \end{bmatrix}.$$

GO DIGITAL

REVIEW & REFRESH

In Exercises 54–57, factor the polynomial completely.

54. $2x^5 + 11x^4 + 5x^3$

55. $9t^4 - 100$

56. $y^3 + 216$

57. $n^3 + 3n^2 - 16n - 48$

58. Find the domain and range of the function.

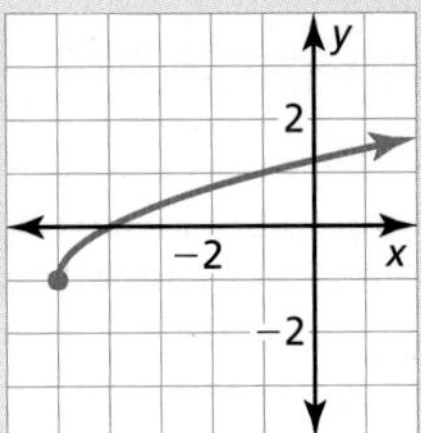

59. MODELING REAL LIFE The table shows the male and female populations (in thousands) of a city by age group for 2010 and 2020. Organize the information using two matrices, one for 2010 and one for 2020. Then find and interpret a matrix that gives the change in the male and female population for each age group from 2010 to 2020.

Populations

	Male		Female	
Age Group	**2010**	**2020**	**2010**	**2020**
0–19	13	15	12	14
20–59	26	27	27	29
60+	7	8	9	10

60. Let $f(x) = 5x^{1/2}$ and $g(x) = -3x^{1/2}$. Find $(f + g)(x)$ and $(f - g)(x)$ and state the domain of each. Then evaluate $(f + g)(16)$ and $(f - g)(16)$.

61. Evaluate the determinant of the matrix.

$$\begin{bmatrix} 3 & 1 & -1 \\ -2 & -4 & 0 \\ 4 & 7 & 5 \end{bmatrix}$$

In Exercises 62 and 63, evaluate the function without using technology.

62. $\sec \dfrac{7\pi}{3}$

63. $\tan(-210^\circ)$

64. Determine the type of function represented by the table.

x	−3	−2	−1	0	1
y	0.5	1.5	4.5	13.5	40.5

65. Use the given matrices to evaluate $B(A + C)$.

$$A = \begin{bmatrix} 2 & -6 \\ 5 & 8 \end{bmatrix}, B = \begin{bmatrix} 4 & 3 \\ -6 & -2 \\ -1 & 2 \end{bmatrix}, C = \begin{bmatrix} 1 & 10 \\ -7 & 3 \end{bmatrix}$$

66. Rewrite $g(x) = \dfrac{3x + 4}{x - 2}$ in the form $g(x) = \dfrac{a}{x - h} + k$. Graph the function. Describe the graph of g as a transformation of the graph of $f(x) = \dfrac{a}{x}$.

67. Use an inverse matrix to solve the linear system.

$$-x + 4y = 12$$
$$3x - 2y = -16$$

68. The shaded region represents 68% of the area under a normal curve. What are the mean and standard deviation of the normal distribution?

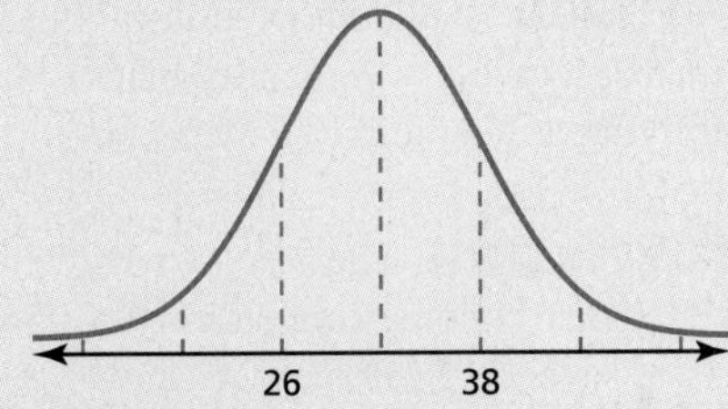

69. Solve $\frac{2}{3}(x - 4)^2 = 24$.

12 Chapter Review WITH CalcChat®

Chapter Learning Target Understand matrices.

Chapter Success Criteria
- ◆ I can perform operations with matrices.
- ◆ I can determine when a product of matrices is defined.
- ■ I can evaluate determinants of matrices.
- ■ I can use inverse matrices to solve problems.

◆ Surface
■ Deep

SELF-ASSESSMENT 1 I do not understand. 2 I can do it with help. 3 I can do it on my own. 4 I can teach someone else.

12.1 Basic Matrix Operations *(pp. 645–652)*

Learning Target: Perform basic operations involving matrices.

Vocabulary
- matrix
- dimensions of a matrix
- elements of a matrix
- equal matrices
- scalar
- scalar multiplication

Perform the indicated operation(s).

1. $\begin{bmatrix} 4 & -5 \\ 2 & 3 \end{bmatrix} + \begin{bmatrix} -1 & 3 \\ -7 & 4 \end{bmatrix}$

2. $\begin{bmatrix} -2 & 3 & 5 \\ -1 & 6 & -2 \end{bmatrix} - \begin{bmatrix} -4 & 7 & 5 \\ -8 & 0 & -9 \end{bmatrix}$

3. $-3\begin{bmatrix} 5 & -2 \\ 3 & 6 \end{bmatrix}$

4. $8\begin{bmatrix} 8 & 4 & 5 \\ -1 & 6 & -2 \end{bmatrix}$

5. $2\begin{bmatrix} 4 & 2 \\ 1 & -3 \\ 0 & -3 \end{bmatrix} + \begin{bmatrix} -1 & 2 \\ 6 & 5 \\ 3 & 7 \end{bmatrix}$

6. $\frac{1}{3}\begin{bmatrix} 0 & 12 \\ 3 & -9 \\ 6 & 0 \end{bmatrix} - \frac{3}{4}\begin{bmatrix} -4 & -8 \\ -12 & 0 \\ 4 & -8 \end{bmatrix}$

Solve the matrix equation for *a*, *b*, *c*, and *d*.

7. $\begin{bmatrix} -a+3 & 2b \\ c-1 & d \end{bmatrix} = \begin{bmatrix} 9 & 6 \\ 7 & -3 \end{bmatrix}$

8. $\begin{bmatrix} 6 & b+4 \\ -c & 12 \end{bmatrix} = \begin{bmatrix} a-4 & 1 \\ 1 & 4d \end{bmatrix}$

9. $\begin{bmatrix} 2 & b \\ c-5 & d+1 \end{bmatrix} + \begin{bmatrix} -3 & 7 \\ 4 & -2 \end{bmatrix} = \begin{bmatrix} a & 9 \\ -6 & -3 \end{bmatrix}$

10. An orchard sells apples and peaches. The tables show the numbers of pounds of fruit sold during July, August, and September for two years. Organize the data using two matrices, one for each year. Then find and interpret a matrix that gives the average numbers of pounds of apples and peaches sold in each month.

Apples

Month	Year 1	Year 2
July	450	510
August	530	650
September	1050	990

Peaches

Month	Year 1	Year 2
July	960	930
August	1130	1260
September	720	580

12.2 Multiplying Matrices (pp. 653–660)

Learning Target: Understand how to multiply matrices.

Find the product, if possible. If not possible, explain why not.

11. $\begin{bmatrix} -1 & -1 \end{bmatrix}\begin{bmatrix} 8 & 2 \\ -6 & -9 \end{bmatrix}$

12. $\begin{bmatrix} 11 & 7 \\ 1 & -5 \end{bmatrix}\begin{bmatrix} 0 & -5 \\ 4 & -3 \end{bmatrix}$

13. $\begin{bmatrix} 4 & -1 \\ 1 & 7 \end{bmatrix}\begin{bmatrix} 5 & -2 & 4 \\ 3 & 12 & 6 \end{bmatrix}$

14. $\begin{bmatrix} -2 & 5 \\ 0 & 3 \end{bmatrix}\begin{bmatrix} 6 & -3 & 5 \\ 2 & 0 & -1 \end{bmatrix}$

15. $\begin{bmatrix} -2 & 3 \\ 3 & 1 \end{bmatrix}\begin{bmatrix} 2 & -3 \\ -1 & 0 \\ 4 & 5 \end{bmatrix}$

16. $\begin{bmatrix} 4 & -2 & 3 \\ -1 & 0 & 5 \end{bmatrix}\begin{bmatrix} 2 & -6 \\ 0 & 5 \\ -3 & 1 \end{bmatrix}$

Use the given matrices to evaluate the expression.

$$A = \begin{bmatrix} 4 & -1 \\ 2 & -3 \end{bmatrix}, B = \begin{bmatrix} -5 & 0 \\ 6 & -4 \end{bmatrix}, C = \begin{bmatrix} -8 & 4 \\ 6 & 0 \\ 0 & 2 \end{bmatrix}, D = \begin{bmatrix} -6 & -3 & 9 \\ 12 & -9 & 6 \end{bmatrix}$$

17. $AB + B$

18. $\frac{1}{3}DC$

19. $C(A + B)$

20. A company manufactures three models of virtual reality headsets. The headsets are shipped to two warehouses. The matrices show the numbers of units shipped to each warehouse and the prices of the models. Write a matrix that gives the total value of the headsets in each warehouse.

Shipping Location

	Model A	Model B	Model C
Warehouse 1	5,000	6,000	8,000
Warehouse 2	4,000	10,000	5,000

	Cost Dollars
Model A	199
Model B	399
Model C	499

12.3 Determinants and Cramer's Rule (pp. 661–670)

Learning Target: Find and use determinants of matrices.

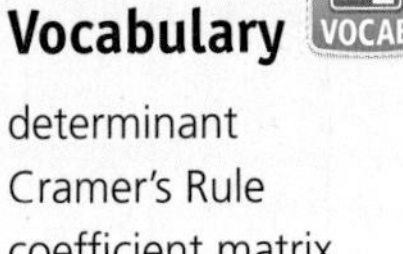

Vocabulary
- determinant
- Cramer's Rule
- coefficient matrix

Evaluate the determinant of the matrix.

21. $\begin{bmatrix} -4 & 2 \\ 5 & 8 \end{bmatrix}$

22. $\begin{bmatrix} 3 & -5 \\ 2 & 6 \end{bmatrix}$

23. $\begin{bmatrix} 3 & 0 & 2 \\ 1 & -6 & 3 \\ 2 & 4 & -1 \end{bmatrix}$

24. Find two ways to complete the matrix so that the determinant is 1. Justify your answer.

$$\begin{bmatrix} 1 & \blacksquare & \blacksquare \\ -2 & 0 & -5 \\ 1 & 1 & 3 \end{bmatrix}$$

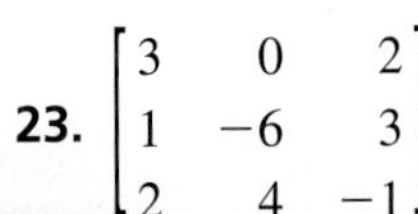

25. You sketch a large triangular pennant for your school football team. In a coordinate plane, the vertices of the triangle are (0, 0), (0, 50), and (70, 20) where the coordinates are measured in inches. How many square *feet* of material do you need to make the pennant?

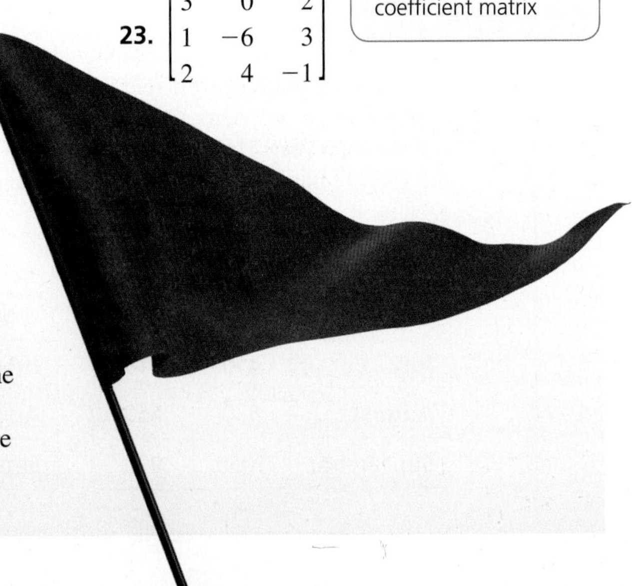

12.4 Inverse Matrices (pp. 671–678)

Learning Target: Understand the relationship between a matrix and its inverse.

Vocabulary
identity matrix
inverse matrices
matrix of variables
matrix of constants

Find the inverse of the matrix, if possible.

26. $\begin{bmatrix} 1 & 2 \\ 4 & 5 \end{bmatrix}$ **27.** $\begin{bmatrix} -3 & -2 \\ 5 & -2 \end{bmatrix}$ **28.** $\begin{bmatrix} 4 & -8 \\ -3 & -6 \end{bmatrix}$

Solve the matrix equation.

29. $\begin{bmatrix} -3 & 2 \\ -7 & 5 \end{bmatrix} X = \begin{bmatrix} 6 & 3 \\ -4 & 1 \end{bmatrix}$ **30.** $\begin{bmatrix} 6 & 4 \\ 4 & 3 \end{bmatrix} X = \begin{bmatrix} 1 & 1 \\ 2 & 3 \end{bmatrix}$ **31.** $\begin{bmatrix} -8 & 2 \\ 2 & -1 \end{bmatrix} X = \begin{bmatrix} 4 & -8 \\ 2 & 16 \end{bmatrix}$

Use an inverse matrix to solve the linear system.

32. $x + 4y = 11$
$2x - 5y = 9$

33. $3x + y = -1$
$-x + 2y = 12$

34. $3x + 2y = -11$
$4x - 3y = 8$

35. Find the inverse of matrix A, where $n \neq 0$. Justify your answer.

$$A = \begin{bmatrix} n & 0 & 0 \\ 0 & n & 0 \\ 0 & 0 & n \end{bmatrix}$$

36. A diner sells three different breakfast platters as shown. Find the cost of one pancake, the cost of one egg, and the cost of one sausage link.

Mathematical Practices

Use Appropriate Tools Strategically

Mathematically proficient students use technological tools to explore and deepen their understanding of concepts.

1. Write any 3×3 matrices A, B, and C with nonzero elements. Then use your matrices and technology to verify each property of matrix multiplication on page 656.

2. Use technology to find D^{-1}. What does the result tell you about a linear system with coefficient matrix D? Justify your answer.

$$D = \begin{bmatrix} -2 & 6 \\ -1 & 3 \end{bmatrix}$$

12 Practice Test WITH CalcChat®

Use the given matrices to evaluate the expression, if possible.

$$A = \begin{bmatrix} 1 & -2 \\ 4 & -3 \end{bmatrix}, B = \begin{bmatrix} 3 & 5 \\ -1 & 0 \end{bmatrix}, C = \begin{bmatrix} -6 & 8 \\ 10 & 14 \end{bmatrix}, D = \begin{bmatrix} -1 & 3 & -2 \\ 2 & 0 & -1 \end{bmatrix}$$

1. $C - B$

2. $A - 2D$

3. $\frac{1}{2}C + B$

4. AD

Evaluate the determinant of the matrix.

5. $\begin{bmatrix} 3 & -2 \\ 4 & 1 \end{bmatrix}$

6. $\begin{bmatrix} -1 & 3 & 1 \\ 0 & 2 & -3 \\ 5 & 1 & -2 \end{bmatrix}$

7. Find the area of the triangle.

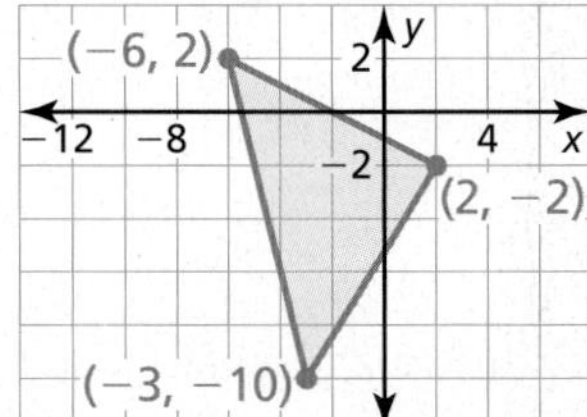

8. Use Cramer's rule to solve the linear system.

$$5x + 3y - 3z = -2$$
$$-9x - 6y + 2z = 10$$
$$9x - 4y + 7z = 31$$

9. Use an inverse matrix to solve the linear system.

$$3x + 4y = 6$$
$$4x + 5y = 7$$

10. Solve the matrix equation.

$$\begin{bmatrix} 1 & 1 \\ 4 & 5 \end{bmatrix} X = \begin{bmatrix} 2 & 3 \\ -1 & 6 \end{bmatrix}$$

11. The tables show the types and numbers of medals earned by Norway, Germany, and Canada at the 2014 and 2018 Winter Olympics. Organize the data using two matrices, one for each year. Then find and interpret a matrix that gives the average numbers of bronze, silver, and gold medals won by each of the countries.

Norway

Medal	2014	2018
Gold	11	14
Silver	5	14
Bronze	10	11

Germany

Medal	2014	2018
Gold	8	14
Silver	6	10
Bronze	5	7

Canada

Medal	2014	2018
Gold	10	11
Silver	10	8
Bronze	5	10

12. Use a system of three equations and an inverse matrix to write an equation of the parabola. Justify your answer.

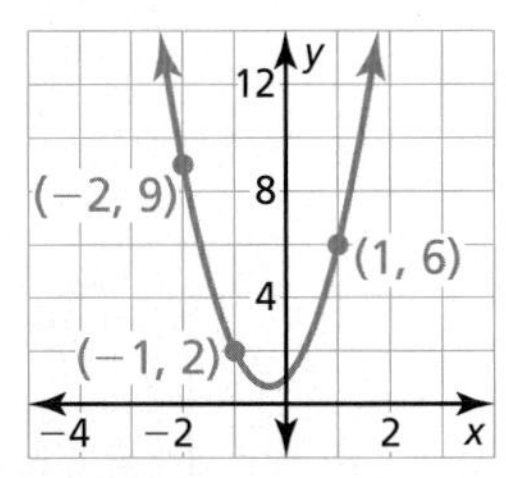

13. On the opening day of a carnival, 800 admission tickets were sold for a total of \$3775. Tickets for children cost \$3 each, tickets for adults cost \$8 each, and tickets for senior citizens cost \$5 each. There were twice as many children's tickets sold as adult tickets. How many of each type of ticket were sold?

12 Performance Task
Food Webs

A food web is a visual representation of the food chains in an ecosystem. A partial food web for an ecosystem is shown.

Arrows represent the flow of energy.

- *Monkeys eat insects, so an arrow indicates that energy flows from insects to monkeys.*

A food web shows ***direct*** and ***indirect*** food sources.

- *Eagles eat parrots. So, parrots are a direct food source for eagles.*
- *Pythons eat chimpanzees, and chimpanzees eat insects. So, insects are an indirect food source (through one intermediary) for pythons.*

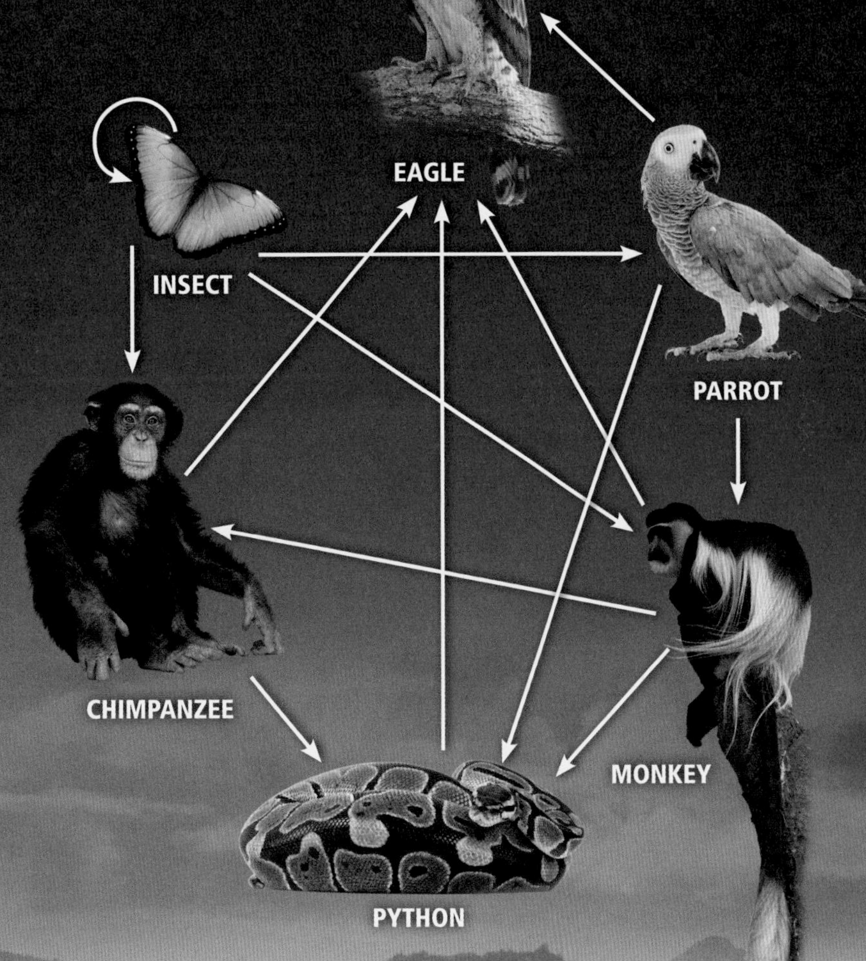

IDENTIFYING FOOD SOURCES

INFO

The food web shown at the right represents the relationships among chimpanzees, insects, and monkeys in the region described above. These relationships are also represented in matrix A. Explain how the matrix is related to the food web. Then find and interpret A^2.

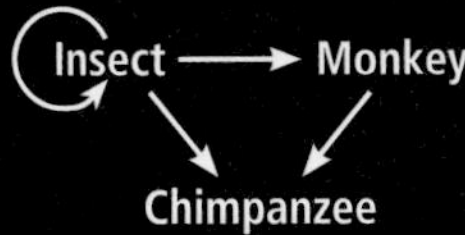

Local government officials plan to use an insecticide to drastically reduce the insect population. Create a matrix B to represent the entire food web above. Then find and interpret B^2 and B^3. Use the matrices to explain the potential impact of this plan. (*Hint*: Make sure the animal represented by each row of your matrix matches the animal represented by the corresponding column.)

$$A = \begin{array}{c} \\ C \\ I \\ M \end{array} \begin{array}{c} \begin{array}{ccc} C & I & M \end{array} \\ \begin{bmatrix} 0 & 1 & 1 \\ 0 & 1 & 0 \\ 0 & 1 & 0 \end{bmatrix} \end{array}$$

12 College and Career Readiness WITH CalcChat®

WATCH Tutorial videos are available for each exercise.

1. Which matrix has no inverse?

Ⓐ $\begin{bmatrix} 1 & 0 \\ 0 & 1 \end{bmatrix}$ Ⓑ $\begin{bmatrix} 4 & 6 \\ -6 & -9 \end{bmatrix}$

Ⓒ $\begin{bmatrix} -2 & 4 \\ 3 & 6 \end{bmatrix}$ Ⓓ $\begin{bmatrix} 0 & 1 \\ 1 & 0 \end{bmatrix}$

2. A triangle has an area of 100 square units. Its vertices are (0, 0), (20, 0), and (x, y). Write and solve an equation involving a determinant that you can use to find possible coordinates of the unknown vertex.

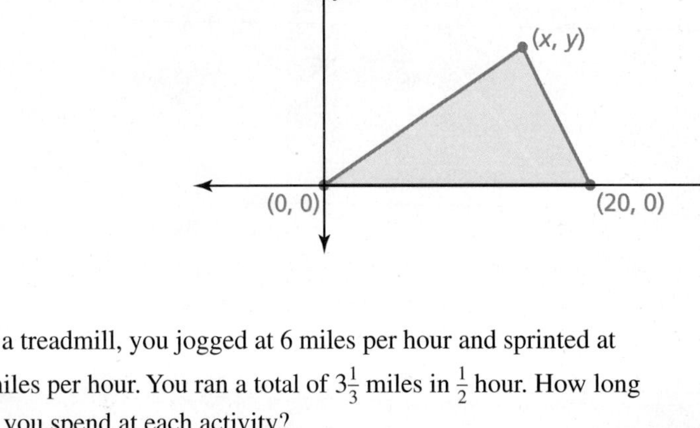

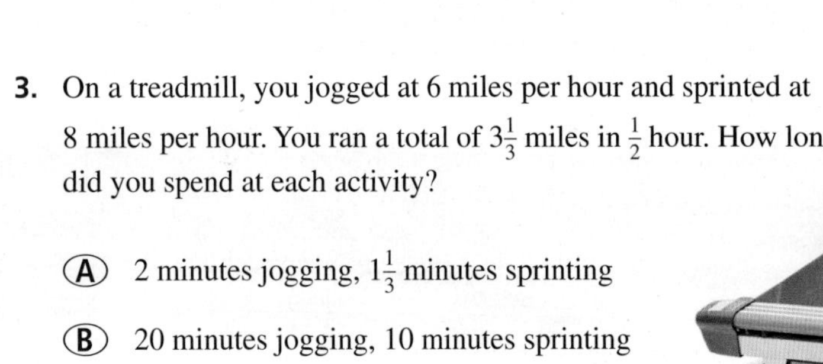

3. On a treadmill, you jogged at 6 miles per hour and sprinted at 8 miles per hour. You ran a total of $3\frac{1}{3}$ miles in $\frac{1}{2}$ hour. How long did you spend at each activity?

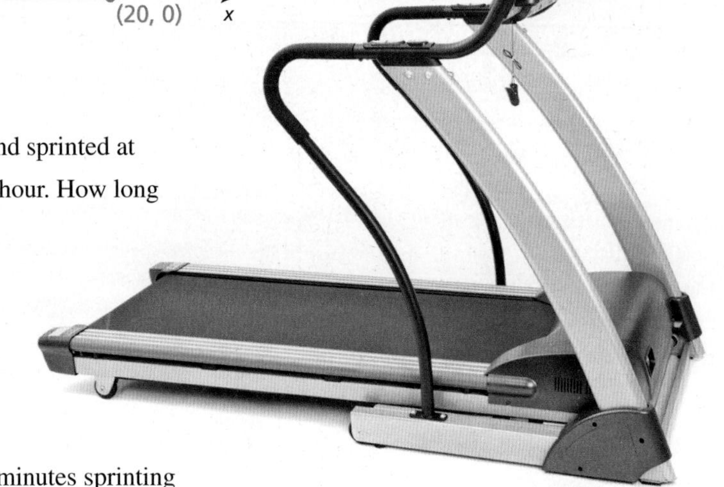

Ⓐ 2 minutes jogging, $1\frac{1}{3}$ minutes sprinting

Ⓑ 20 minutes jogging, 10 minutes sprinting

Ⓒ 10 minutes jogging, 20 minutes sprinting

Ⓓ about 11.25 minutes jogging, about 18.75 minutes sprinting

4. The area of the shaded region is 21.5 square inches. What is the radius of the circle?

Ⓐ about 3.2 inches

Ⓑ about 5 inches

Ⓒ about 10 inches

Ⓓ about 25 inches

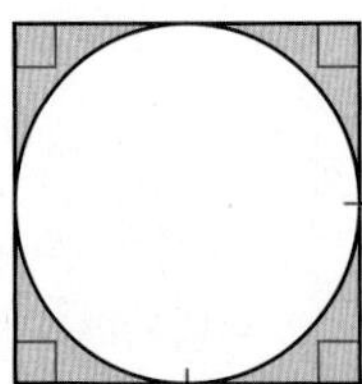

5. Which is the graph of an arithmetic sequence with $a_1 = 1$ and $d = -2$?

Ⓐ 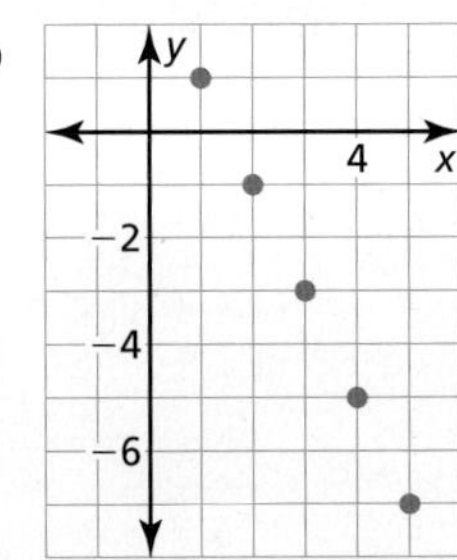

Ⓑ 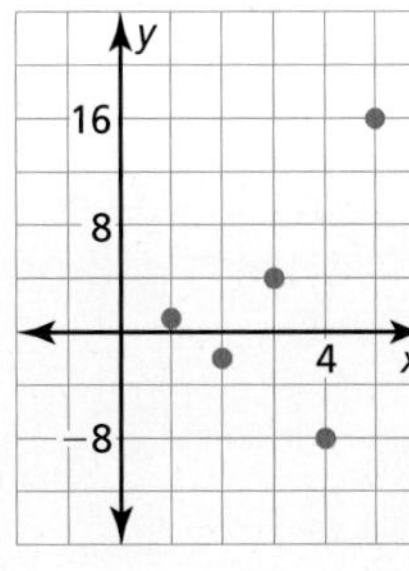

Ⓒ 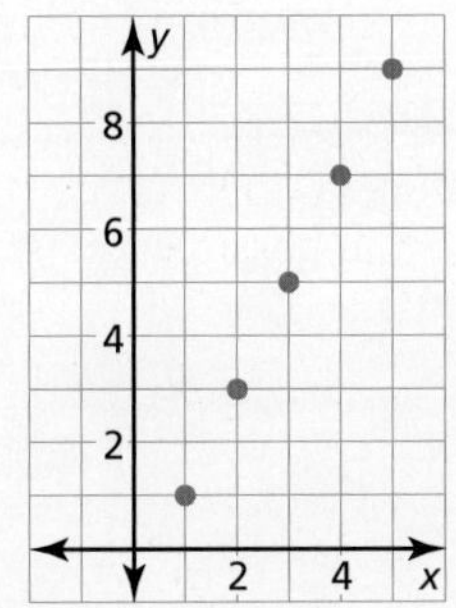

Ⓓ 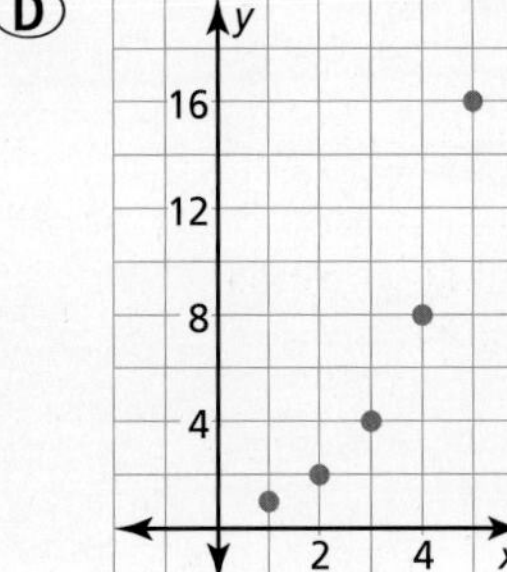

6. What is the solution of the matrix equation?

$$\begin{bmatrix} 2 & -3 \\ -5 & 7 \end{bmatrix} X = \begin{bmatrix} 4 & 6 \\ 0 & -1 \end{bmatrix}$$

Ⓐ $\begin{bmatrix} -58 & -24 \\ 5 & 2 \end{bmatrix}$

Ⓑ $\begin{bmatrix} -7 & -3 \\ -5 & -2 \end{bmatrix}$

Ⓒ $\begin{bmatrix} 8 & 15 \\ -20 & -37 \end{bmatrix}$

Ⓓ $\begin{bmatrix} -28 & -39 \\ -20 & -28 \end{bmatrix}$

7. Which function is a translation 3 units left of the graph of $y = \log_3 (x + 2) - 4$?

Ⓐ $y = \log_3(x + 2) - 7$

Ⓑ $y = \log_3(x + 2) - 1$

Ⓒ $y = \log_3(x + 5) - 4$

Ⓓ $y = \log_3(x - 1) - 4$

8. For the matrix equation, what is the value of $x + 4y$?

$$2\begin{bmatrix} 5x & 0 \\ -2 & 3 \end{bmatrix} - \begin{bmatrix} 3 & -1 \\ 4y & -2 \end{bmatrix} = \begin{bmatrix} 17 & 1 \\ -10 & 8 \end{bmatrix}$$

Selected Answers

Chapter 1

Chapter 1 Prepare

1. 47
2. −46
3. $3\frac{3}{5}$
4. 4
5. 13
6. 0
7. 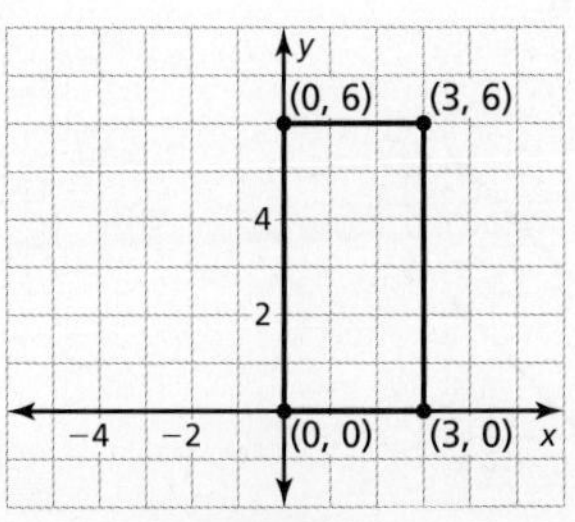

8. 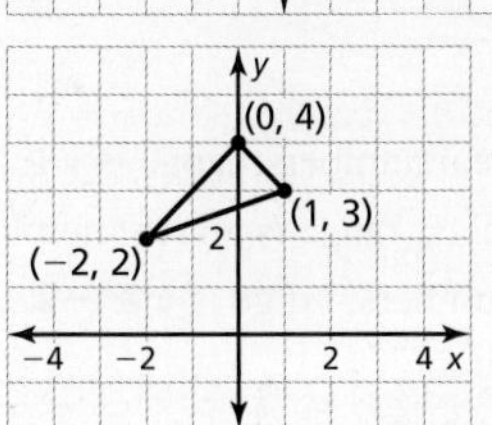

9. 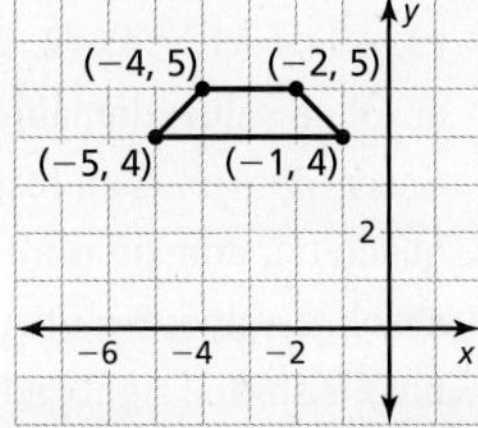

10. Because performing the wrong operation first may result in a different answer; 12 + 18 ÷ 3 equals 18 when division is performed first and 10 when addition is performed first; yes; If the point (3, 2) is translated up 3 units then reflected in the x-axis, the new coordinate is (3, −5). If it is reflected in the x-axis first then translated up 3, the new coordinate is (3, 1).

1.1 Practice

1. absolute value; The graph is a vertical stretch with a translation 2 units left and 8 units down; The domain of each function is all real numbers, but the range of f is $y \geq -8$, and the range of the parent function is $y \geq 0$.
3. linear; The graph is a vertical stretch and a translation 2 units down; The domain and range of each function is all real numbers.
5. quadratic
7. 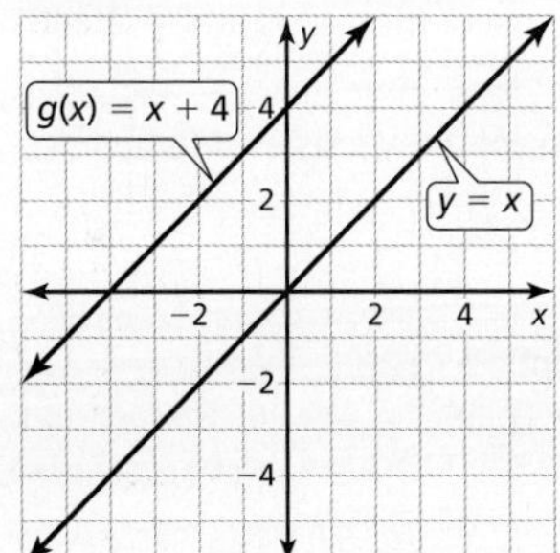

The graph of g is a vertical translation 4 units up of the parent linear function.

9. 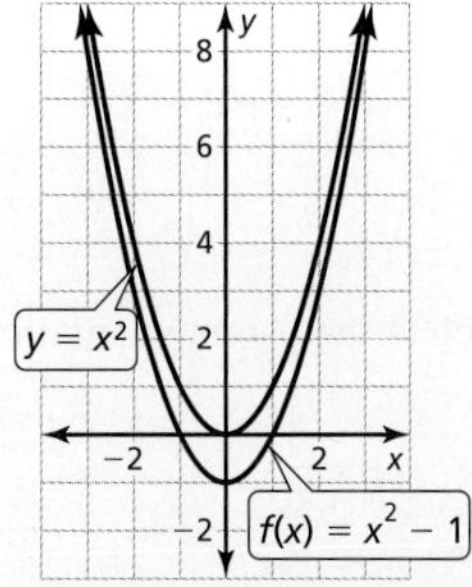

The graph of f is a vertical translation 1 unit down of the parent quadratic function.

11. 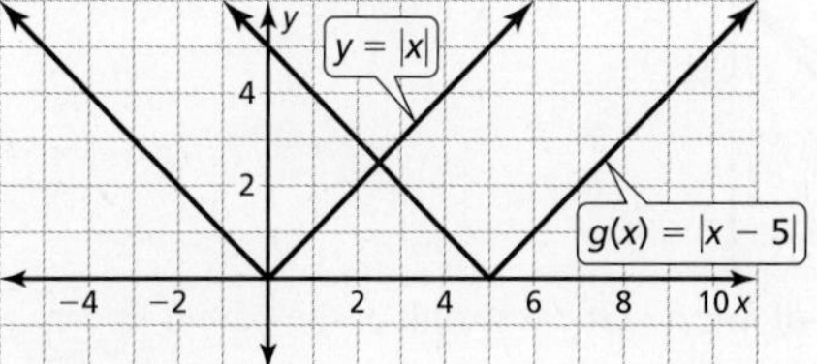

The graph of g is a horizontal translation 5 units right of the parent absolute value function.

13. 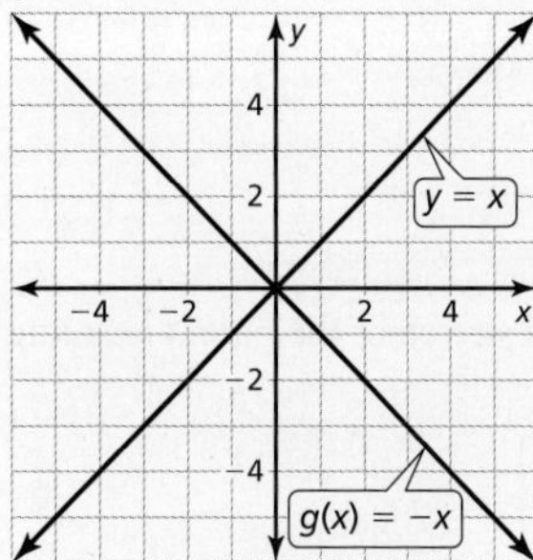

The graph of g is a vertical translation 4 units up of the parent absolute value function.

15. 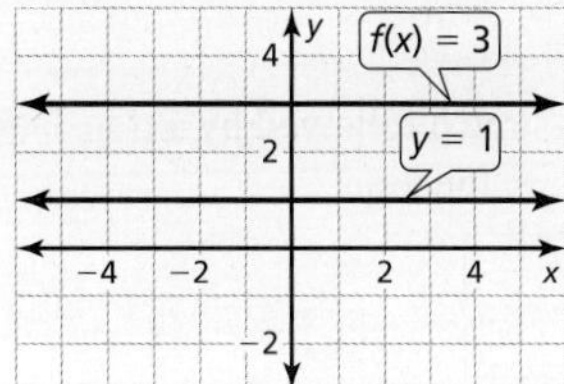

The graph of f is a vertical translation 2 units up of the parent constant function.

17. 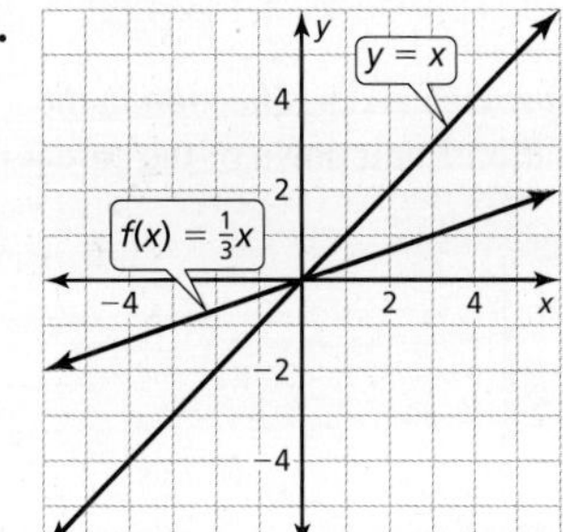

The graph of f is a vertical shrink of the parent linear function.

19. 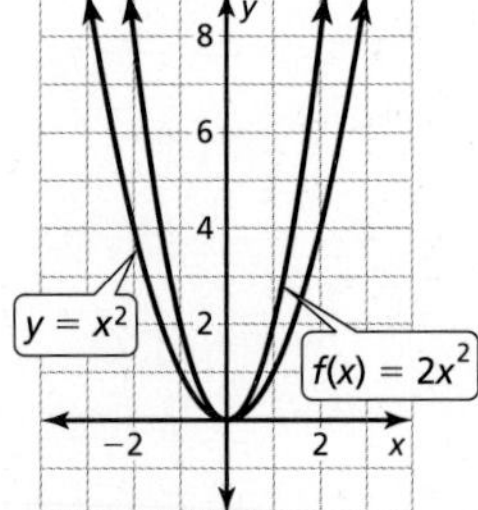

The graph of f is a vertical stretch of the parent quadratic function.

21. 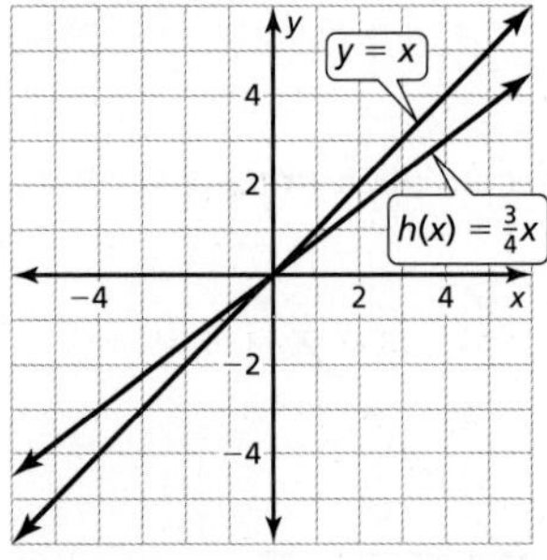

The graph of h is a vertical shrink of the parent linear function.

23. 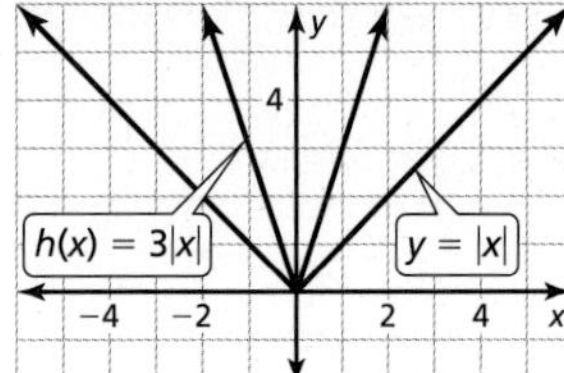

The graph of h is a vertical stretch of the parent absolute value function.

25. 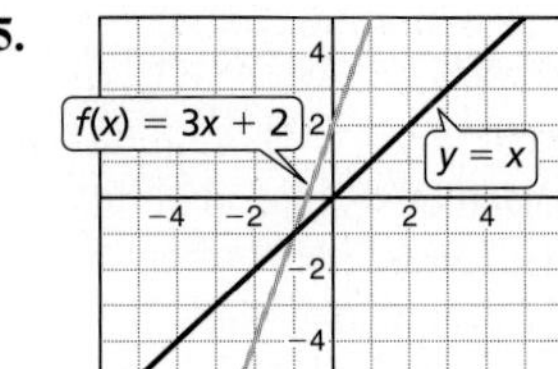

The graph of f is a vertical stretch followed by a translation 2 units up of the parent linear function.

27. 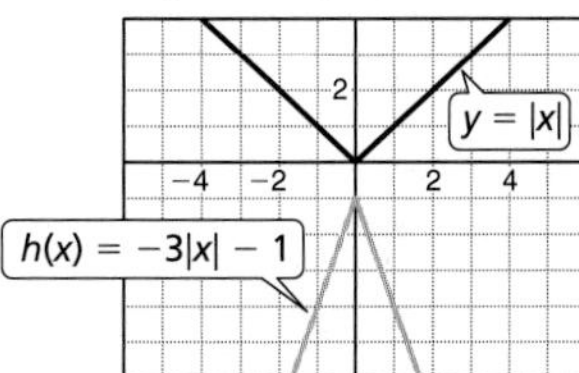

The graph of h is a vertical stretch and a reflection in the x-axis followed by a translation 1 unit down of the parent absolute value function.

29. 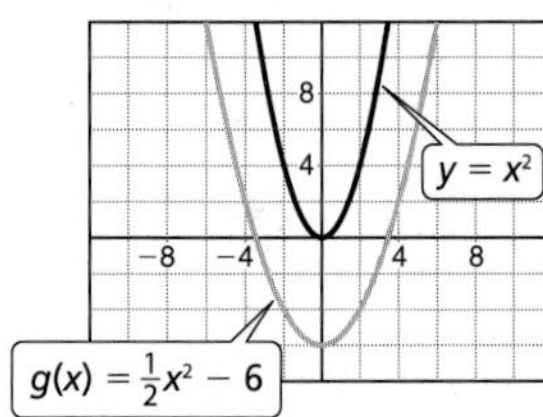

The graph of g is a vertical shrink followed by a translation 6 units down of the parent quadratic function.

31. 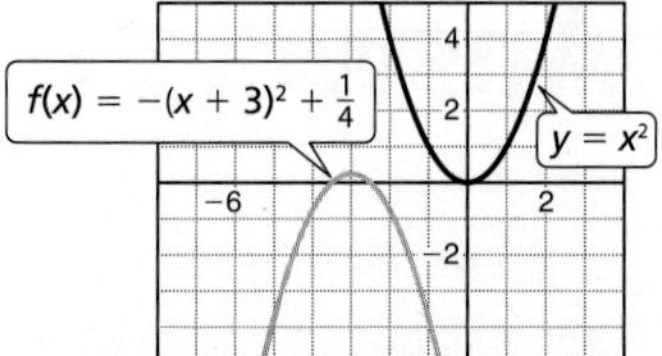

The graph of f is a reflection in the x-axis followed by a translation 3 units left and $\frac{1}{4}$ unit up of the parent quadratic function.

33. The graph of g is a horizontal translation 3 units left of the graph of f, not 3 units right.

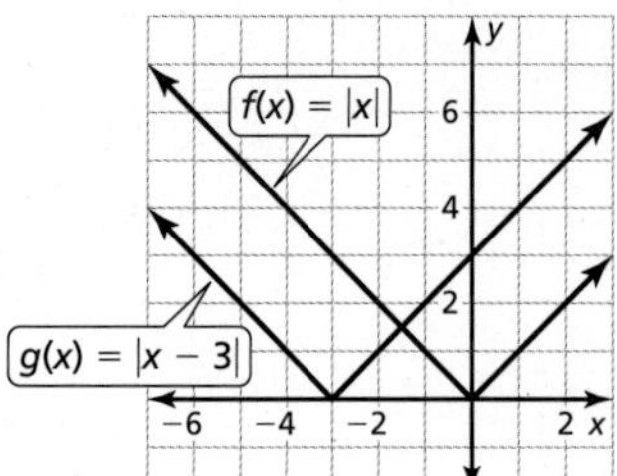

35. $(2, -1), (-1, -4), (2, -5)$

37. absolute value; domain is all real numbers; range is $y \geq -1$

39. linear; domain is all real numbers; range is all real numbers

41. quadratic; domain is all real numbers; range is $y \geq -2$

43. absolute value; 8 mi/h

45. no; f is shifted right and g is shifted down.

47. linear; vertical translation; The graph will be shifted up 10 units to represent the head start.

49. **a.** quadratic
    b. 0; At the moment the ball is released, 0 seconds have passed.
    c. 6.5; Because $f(t)$ represents the height of the ball, find $f(0)$.

51. **a.** neither; The graph has a vertical stretch.
    b. horizontal translation; The graph will be shifted 8 units right.
    c. both; The graph will be shifted 2 units left and 4 units up.
    d. neither; The graph will have a vertical stretch.

53. **a.** 1; The graph will intersect the x-axis at $x = -\frac{1}{3}$.
    b. 2; The graph will intersect the x-axis at $x = 2$ and $x = 4$.
    c. -1; The graph will intersect the x-axis at $x = 1$ and $x = -1$.
    d. 0; The graph will intersect the x-axis everywhere.

1.1 Review & Refresh

54. yes

55. x-intercept: -2; y-intercept: 2

56. x-intercept: $\frac{1}{3}$; y-intercept: 1

57. 6

58. 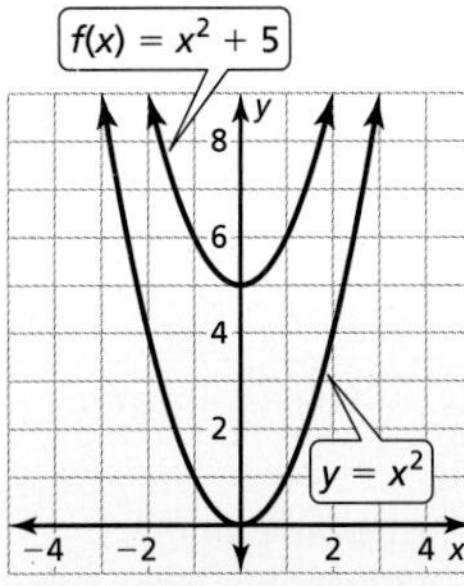

The graph of f is a vertical translation 5 units up of the parent quadratic function.

59. 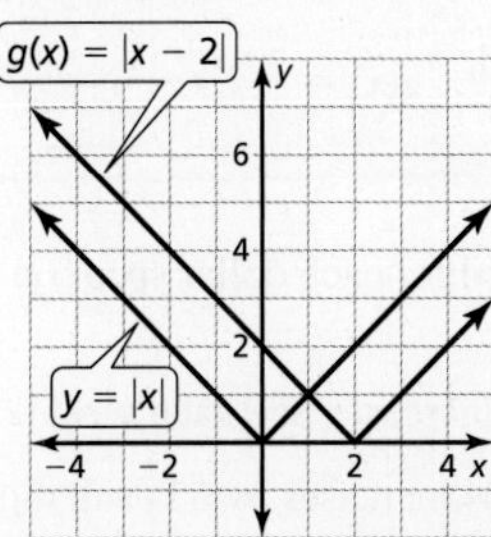

The graph of g is a horizontal translation 2 units right of the parent absolute value function.

60. 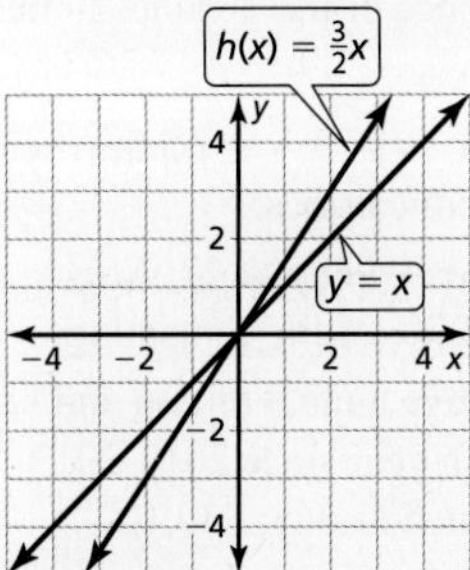

The graph of h is a vertical stretch by a factor of $\frac{3}{2}$ of the graph of the parent linear function.

61. 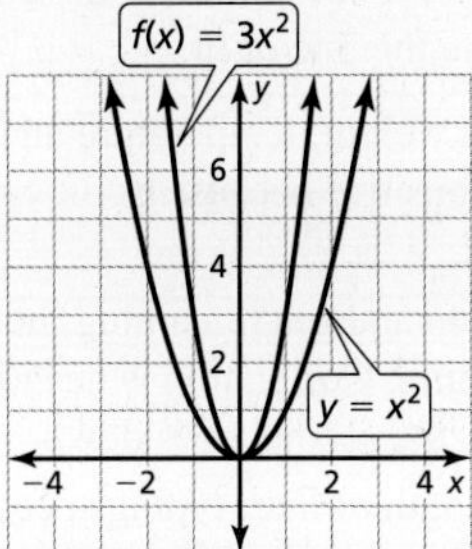

The graph of f is a vertical stretch by a factor of 3 of the graph of the parent quadratic function.

62. no; The graph does not pass the Vertical Line Test.

63. $x = 9$ **64.** $x = 4$

65. $x = -8, x = 8$ **66.** $x = \dfrac{5 \pm \sqrt{97}}{4}$

67. exponential **68.** 502.7 in.^{3}

69. 56.5 cm^3

70. Lines a and b are perpendicular.

71. about 649 bacteria

72.

		Use Social Media: Yes	No	Total
Own a Cell Phone	Yes	0.41	0.18	0.59
	No	0.27	0.14	0.41
	Total	0.68	0.32	1

73. $(x - 6)(x + 5)$ **74.** $3(x + 1)(x + 4)$

75. $(x - 9)^2$ **76.** $2x(x - 1)(x + 1)$

1.2 Practice

1. $g(x) = x - 1$ **3.** $g(x) = |4x + 3|$

5. $g(x) = 4 - |x - 2|$

7. f could be translated 3 units up or 3 units right.

9. $g(x) = 5x - 2$ **11.** $g(x) = |6x| - 2$

13. $g(x) = -3 + |x + 11|$ **15.** $g(x) = 5x + 10$

17. $g(x) = |4x| + 4$ **19.** $g(x) = \frac{1}{2}x - 3$

21. $g(x) = -|x - 4| + 1$

23. C; The graph has been translated left.

25. D; The graph has been translated up.

27. $g(x) = 2x + 1$ **29.** $g(x) = \left|\frac{1}{2}x - 2\right|$

31. $g(x) = -|x| - 8$

33. Translating a graph to the right requires subtraction, not addition; $g(x) = |x - 3| + 2$

35. \$21.56

37. The graph has been translated 6 units left; $A = 9$

39. The graph of g is a vertical stretch by a factor of 4, a reflection in the x-axis, and a vertical translation 2 units up of the graph of the parent absolute function; Because $a = -4$ and $-4 < 0$, the graph reflects in the x-axis and $|-4| > 1$, so the graph is a vertical stretch. Because $k = 2$, and $2 > 0$, the graph is a vertical shift up.

41. $-2, 1, 0$; $g(x) = -f(x + 1) + 1$
$= -\left[2|(x + 1) - 2| + 1\right] + 1$
$= -2|x - 1| - 1 + 1 = -2|x - 1|$

43. $f\left(x + \dfrac{c - b}{m}\right)$

1.2 Review & Refresh

44. 7 **45.** 0

46. 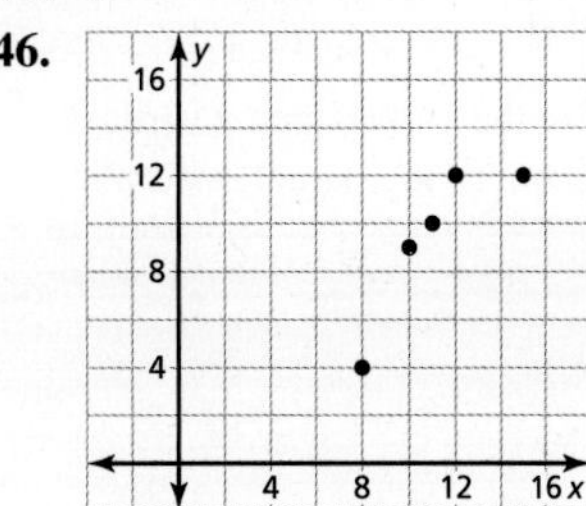

positive linear correlation

47. 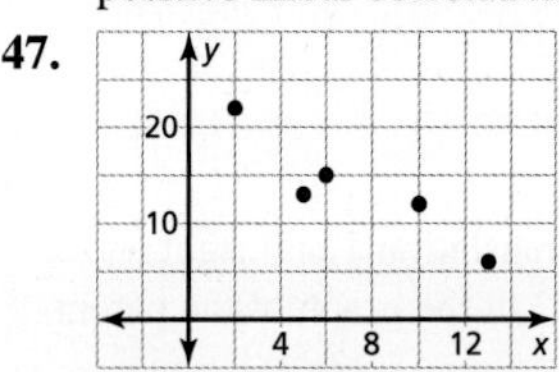

negative linear correlation

48. quadratic; The graph is a vertical stretch by a factor of 2 followed by a translation 1 unit left of the parent quadratic function.

49. $(-1, 6)$; Explanations will vary.

50. $(-9, -10)$; Explanations will vary.

51. $\left(\frac{25}{7}, \frac{6}{7}\right)$; Explanations will vary.

52. no solution; Explanations will vary.

53. a.

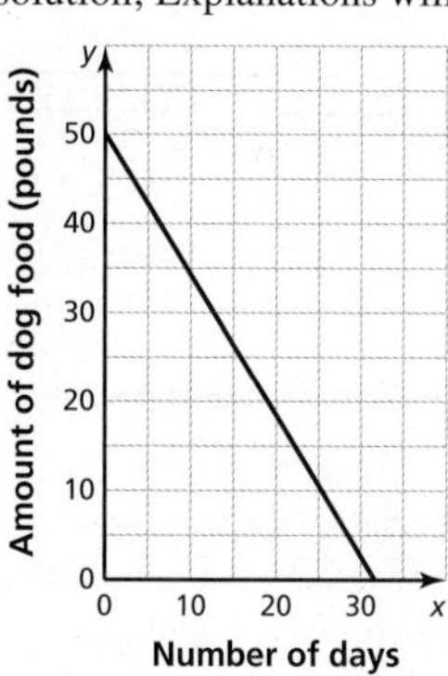

domain: $0 \le x \le 33\frac{1}{3}$, range: $0 \le y \le 50$

b. The slope of -1.5 represents a decrease of 1.5 pounds of dog food each day. The y-intercept of 50 means that the initial amount of dog food in the bag is 50 pounds, and the x-intercept of $33\frac{1}{3}$ means after $33\frac{1}{3}$ days the bag is empty.

54.

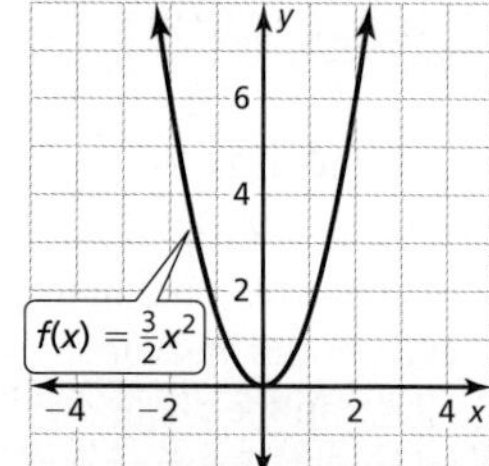

The graph of f is a vertical stretch by a factor of $\frac{3}{2}$ of the graph of the parent quadratic function.

55.

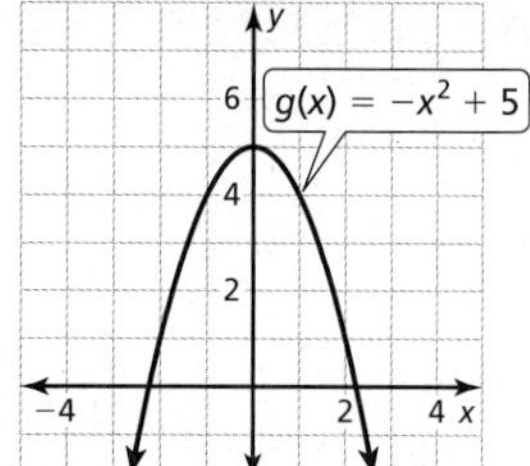

The graph of g is a reflection in the x-axis, then a vertical translation 5 units up of the graph of the parent quadratic function.

56.

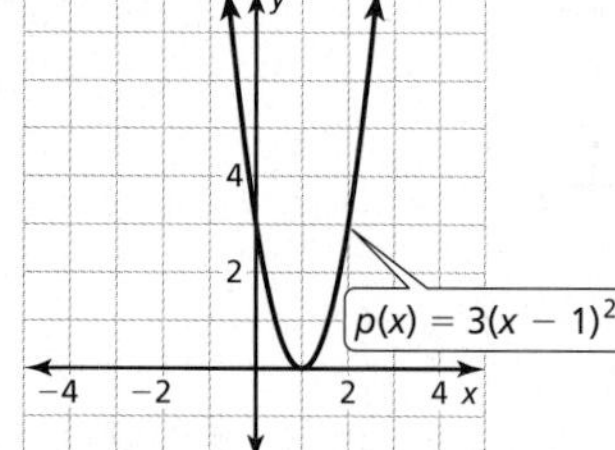

The graph of p is a horizontal translation 1 unit right and a vertical stretch by a factor of 3 of the graph of the parent quadratic function.

57.

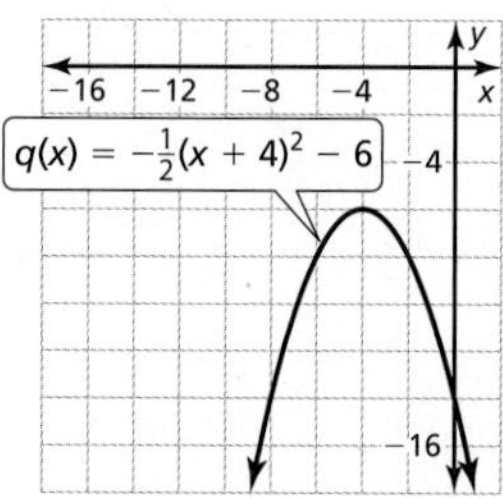

The graph of q is a horizontal translation 4 units left and a vertical shrink by a factor of $\frac{1}{2}$, a reflection in the x-axis, and a translation 6 units down of the graph of the parent quadratic function.

58. $g(x) = \frac{3}{2}x - 2$

59. $g(x) = -4|x - 1| - 7.$

1.3 Practice

1. $y = \frac{1}{5}x$; The tip increases \$0.20 for each dollar spent on the meal.

3. $y = 50x + 100$; The balance increases \$50 each week.

5. $y = 55x$; The number of words increases by 55 each minute.

7. Carrier A; 10 months

9. The slope equation should have the difference of the y-values in the numerator and the difference of the x-values in the denominator; $y = \frac{3}{4}x + 8$

11. yes; *Sample answer:* $y = 4.25x + 1.75$; $y = 65.5$; After 15 minutes, you have burned 65.5 calories.

13. yes; *Sample answer:* $y = -4.6x + 96$; $y = 27$; After 15 hours, the battery will have 27% of life remaining.

15. $y = 723.2x + 31{,}868$; The average annual tuition and fees is increasing by about \$723 each year since 2012-2013 academic year when it was about \$31,868; \$39,100

17. $y = 0.42x + 1.44$; $r = 0.61$; weak positive correlation

19. $y = -1.04x + 5.68$; $r = -0.93$; strong negative correlation

21. *Sample answer:* $y = -6.2x + 549$; no; The value 85 is not close to the values used to create the line of fit.

23. a. *Sample answer:* height and weight; temperature and ice cream sales; Correlation is positive because as the first goes up, so does the second.

b. *Sample answer:* miles driven and gas remaining; hours used and battery life remaining; Correlation is negative because as the first goes up, the second goes down.

c. *Sample answer:* age and length of hair; typing speed and shoe size; There is no relationship between the first and second.

25. D

27. There is a strong negative correlation; As x increases, y increases, so z decreases.

29. a–b. Answers will vary. Check students' work.

1.3 Review & Refresh

30. $(16, -41)$; Explanations will vary.

31. infinitely many solutions; Explanations will vary.

32. $\left(1, \frac{1}{2}\right)$; Explanations will vary.

33. $(2, -2)$; Explanations will vary.

34. $y < -2x + 1$ and $y \ge \frac{1}{3}x - 2$

35. $x = \frac{1}{2}z - 2y - 4$

36. 56%

37.
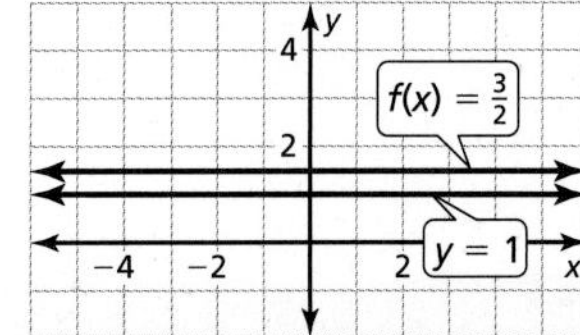

The graph of f is a translation $\frac{1}{2}$ unit up of the parent constant function.

38.
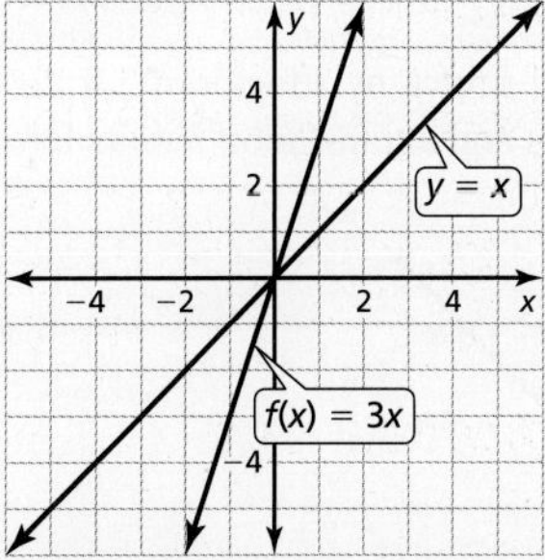

The graph of f is a vertical stretch by a factor of 3 of the parent linear function.

39.
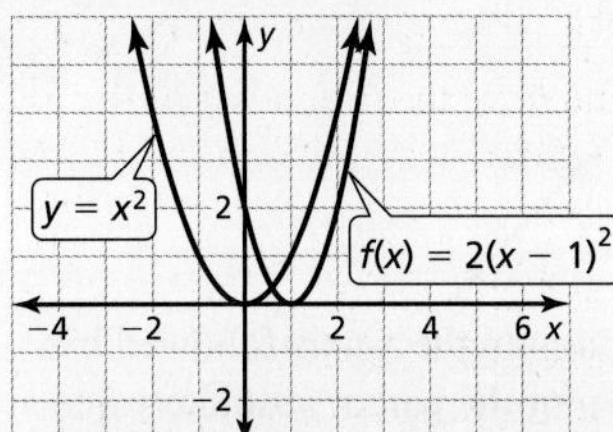

The graph of f is a vertical stretch by a factor of 2 followed by a translation 1 unit right of the parent quadratic function.

40.
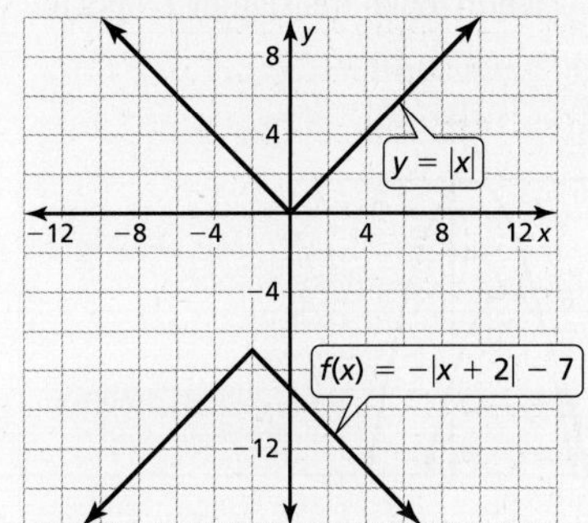

The graph of f is a reflection in the x-axis followed by a translation 2 units left and 7 units down of the parent absolute value function.

41. $5x^2 - 5x - 2$

42. $-5n^3 - 5n^2 - 16n + 13$

43. Company A; 10 months

44. 17

45. $g(x) = 2x + 4$

46. $g(x) = -\frac{3}{2}|x - 4|$

1.4 Practice

1. $(1, 2, -1)$

3. no solution

5. $(3, -1, -4)$

7. $(z - 1, 1, z)$

9. $\left(\frac{9}{4}, 2, -\frac{1}{2}\right)$

11. no solution

13. The entire second equation should be multiplied by 4, not just the x-term.

$$\begin{aligned} 4x - y + 2z &= -18 \\ -4x + 8y + 4z &= 44 \\ \hline 7y + 6z &= 26 \end{aligned}$$

15. A small pizza costs \$5, a liter of soda costs \$1, and a salad costs \$3.

17. $(7, 3, 5)$

19. $(4, -3, 2)$

21. no solution

23. $(3, 2, 1)$

25. $\left(\frac{-3z + 3}{5}, \frac{-13z + 13}{5}, z\right)$

27. 7 first-place finishers, 10 second-place finishers, 3 third-place finishers

29. *Sample answer:* When one variable has the same coefficient or its opposite in each equation. The system

$$3x + 2y - 4z = -5$$
$$2x + 2y + 3z = 8$$
$$5x - 2y - 7z = -9$$

31. $\ell + m + n = 65$, $n = \ell + m - 15$, $\ell = \frac{1}{3}m$; $\ell = 10$ ft, $m = 30$ ft, $n = 25$ ft

33. *Sample answer:* Eliminate one variable in three of the equations and solve for the remaining variables. Then substitute the values into one of the original equations to find the value of the fourth variable.

35. no; It is possible for a point (x, y, z) to satisfy two equations but not the third.

37. a. *Sample answer:* $a = -1, b = -1, c = -1$; Use elimination on equations 1 and 2.

b. *Sample answer:* $a = 4, b = 4, c = 5$; The solution is $\left(\frac{2}{3}, -\frac{2}{3}, 2\right)$.

c. *Sample answer:* $a = 5, b = 5, c = 5$; Use elimination on equations 1 and 2.

39. $3x + 2y + (-5)z = -30$ or $2x + (-5)y + 3z = -30$; The solutions are $(-3, 2, 5)$ and $(-699, -288, -24)$, respectively.

41. 5 tangerines;

$$t + a = g,$$
$$t + b = a,$$
$$2g = 3b$$

1.4 Review & Refresh

42. $g(x) = |x + 2| - 5$

43. $g(x) = -|x| + 5$

44. $g(x) = |x| - 1$

45. $g(x) = 3|x| - 15$

46. $x^2 - 4x + 4$

47. $9m^2 + 6m + 1$

48. $w > -21$

−23 −22 −21 −20 −19 −18

49. $y \le 6$

3 4 5 6 7 8

50. $n \ge -19.5$

−19.5

−22 −21 −20 −19 −18 −17

51. $x < 2$

−2 −1 0 1 2 3

52. $-\frac{5}{2} < h < -\frac{1}{2}$

$-\frac{5}{2}$ $-\frac{1}{2}$

−4 −3 −2 −1 0 1

53. $t < -7$ or $t \geq -4$

-7

$-10 \quad -8 \quad -6 \quad -4 \quad -2$

54. linear; 13,800 mi

55. $x = 2.5$

56. *Sample answer:* red, red, blue, blue, yellow

57. $y = 25x + 100$; A gym membership costs \$25 per month.

58. k^8

59. $\frac{1}{b^3}$

60. $64c^6$

61. $\frac{81}{z^{28}}$

62. 39

63. no solution

64. $(5, -1, 2)$

65. Because $100 > 0$, the equation has two real solutions.

Chapter 1 Review

1.

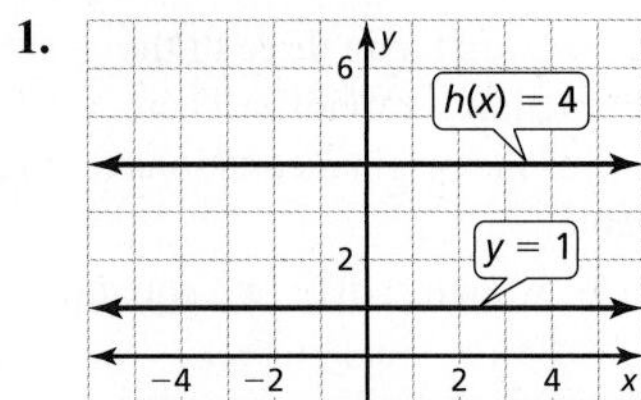

The graph of h is a translation 3 units up of the parent constant function.

2.

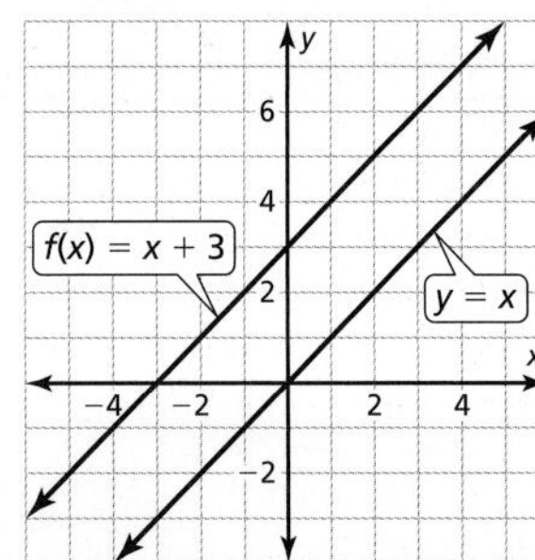

The graph of f is a translation 3 units up of the parent linear function.

3.

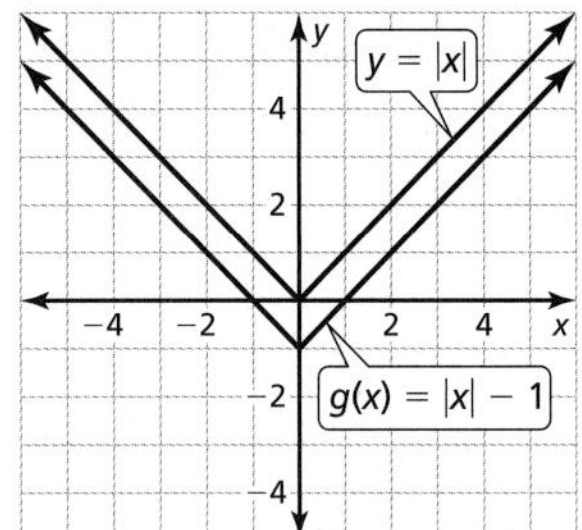

The graph of g is a translation 1 unit down of the parent absolute value function.

4.

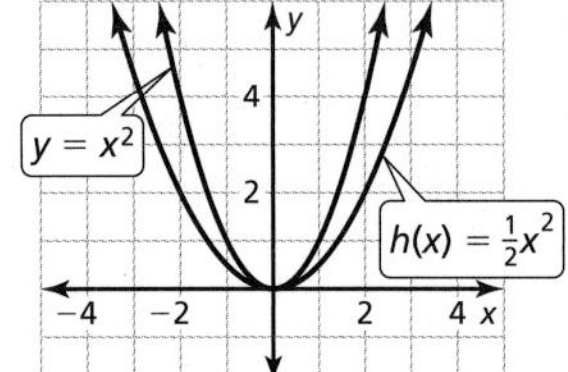

The graph of h is a vertical shrink by a factor of $\frac{1}{2}$ of the parent quadratic function.

5.

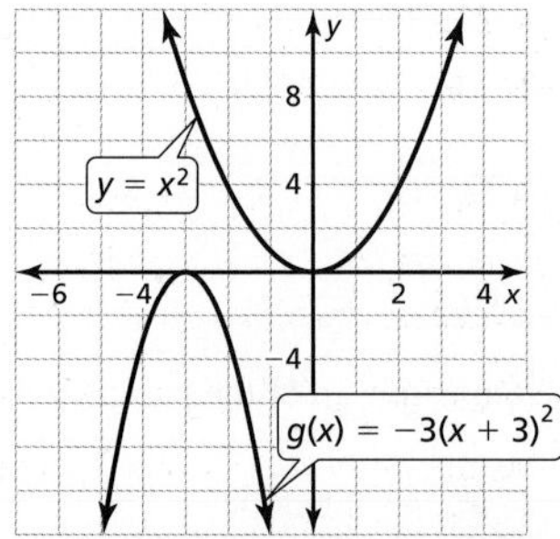

The graph of g is a vertical stretch by a factor of 3 followed by a reflection in the x-axis and a translation 3 units left of the parent quadratic function.

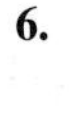

6.

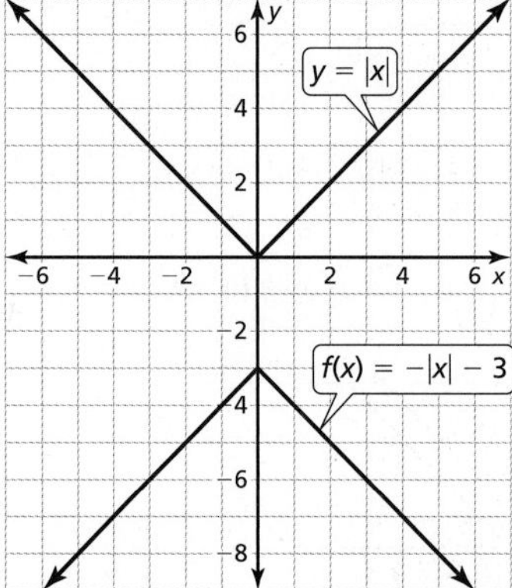

The graph of f is a reflection in the x-axis followed by a translation 3 units down of the parent absolute value function.

7. The graph of g is a vertical translation 4 units up of the graph of f. The graph of f is a horizontal translation 2 units left of the graph of f.

8.

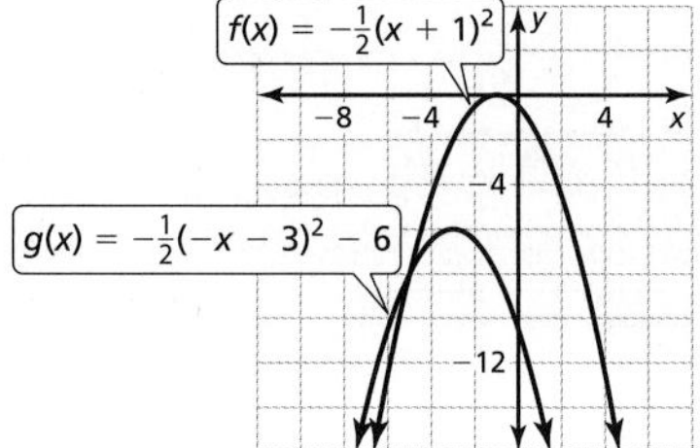

9. The graph of g is a horizontal translation 2 units left and a vertical translation 1 unit down of the graph of f.

10. The graph of g is a horizontal translation 1 unit left, a reflection in the x-axis, and a vertical translation 4 units down of the graph of f.

11. linear; about 570 mi

12. $g(x) = 3x$

13. $g(x) = -|x + 4|$

14. $g(x) = 3x + 1$

15. $g(x) = \frac{1}{2}|x + 1| + 1$

16. \$50

17. $y = 55x$; The distance is increasing at a rate of 55 miles per hour.

18. $y = -20x + 700$; the hot air balloon is descending at a rate of 20 meters per minute.

19. $y = 0.35x$; 15.75 mi

20. yes; 102 ice cream cones

21. $y = 46.3x + 175$; The number of tickets sold at a movie theater increases by 46,300 each year and 175,000 tickets were sold initially; 730,600 tickets

22. $(4, -2, 1)$

23. $\left(-\frac{4}{3}, -\frac{17}{3}, \frac{26}{3}\right)$

24. $(9 + 4y, y, -7 - 5y)$

25. no solution

26. $(-11, -8, 3)$ **27.** $(-16, 12, 10)$

28. 200 student tickets, 350 adult tickets, and 50 children under 12 tickets

29. *Sample answer:* $-2, -1, 1, 4, -4, 2$; $(x, 4x + z, 6x)$

30. Party A candidate: 50 million votes, Party B candidate: 40 million votes, Other candidates: 10 million votes

Chapter 1 Mathematical Practices (Chapter Review)

1. The numbers are large, so using approximated data instead of exact data makes the calculations easier.

2. *Sample answer:* $y = 5x$; about 1.67 mi; Assuming you jog at a constant speed of 5 miles per hour

Chapter 1 Practice Test

1. $y = 120x$; The height increases by 120 feet each minute, and the initial height is 0 feet.

2. $y = -\frac{1}{2}x + 50$; The price decreases \$0.50 for each 1% of discount, and the initial price is \$50.

3. $(26, -3, 15)$ **4.** $\left(3, -\frac{1}{12}, -\frac{1}{6}\right)$

5. $\left(-\frac{14}{5}z + \frac{11}{5}, \frac{11}{5}z - \frac{4}{5}, z\right)$

6.

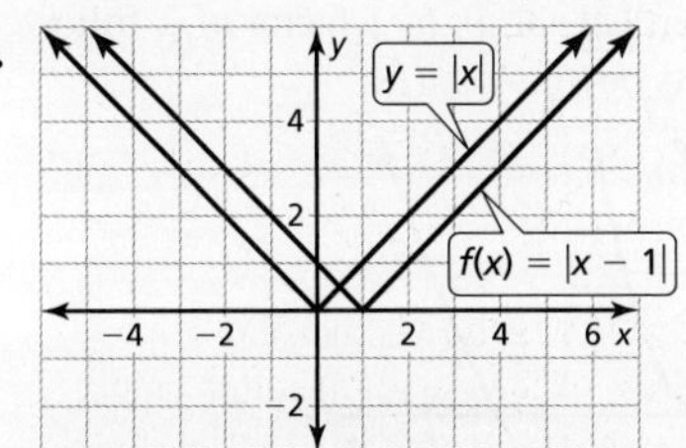

The graph of f is a translation 1 unit right of the parent absolute value function.

7.

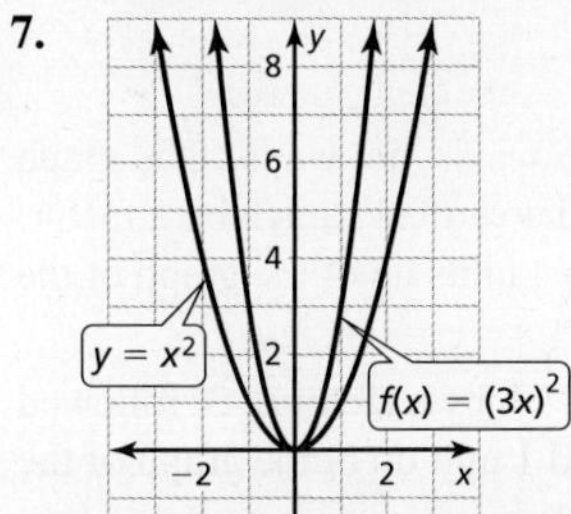

The graph of f is a horizontal shrink by a factor of $\frac{1}{3}$ of the parent quadratic function.

8.

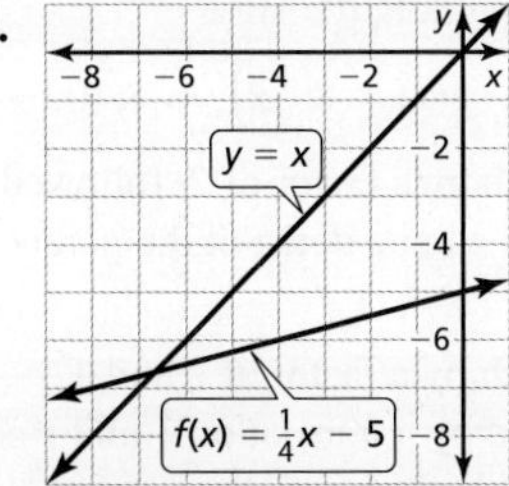

The graph of f is a vertical shrink by a factor of $\frac{1}{4}$ and a translation 5 units down of the parent linear function.

9. B; $g(x) = 2x + 3$ **10.** C; $g(x) = 3x - 2$

11. A; $g(x) = -2x - 3$

12. 75 doughnuts, 30 muffins, and 25 bagels; The situation is modeled by the system:

$d = 3b$

$d + m + b = 130$

$1d + 1.5m + 1.2b = 150$

13. horizontally shrink by a factor of $\frac{1}{2}$ to yield $g(t) = \frac{1}{4}|2t - 20|$; 0 min and $13\frac{1}{3}$ min; When $f(t) = g(t)$, $\frac{1}{4}|t - 20| = \frac{1}{4}|2t - 20|$ and $t = 0, \frac{40}{3}$.

Chapter 1 College and Career Readiness

1. D **2.** one solution

3. A

4. $<$; $f(22) = 58$ and $g(22) = 78$

5. B **6.** D

7. C

8. a. $y = 1462.60x + 36{,}183.60$

b. The tuition increased about \$1462.60 per year and the cost of tuition the year the school was opened was about \$36,183.60.

c. \$43,496.60

9. B

10. first round: 12, second round: 5, third round: 7

Chapter 2

Chapter 2 Prepare

1. $-\frac{7}{2}$ **2.** $\frac{4}{3}$

3. -3.6 **4.** 5

5. -10 **6.** 8

7. $\sqrt{40}$ **8.** $\sqrt{65}$

9. $\sqrt{5}$ **10.** $\sqrt{160}$

11. 10 **12.** $\sqrt{234}$

13. $\sqrt{(q - s)^2 + (p - r)^2}$; yes; yes; When the x-coordinates are equal, find the absolute value of the difference of the y-coordinates. When the y-coordinates are equal, find the absolute value of the difference of the x-coordinates.

2.1 Practice

1. The graph of g is a translation 3 units down of the graph of f.

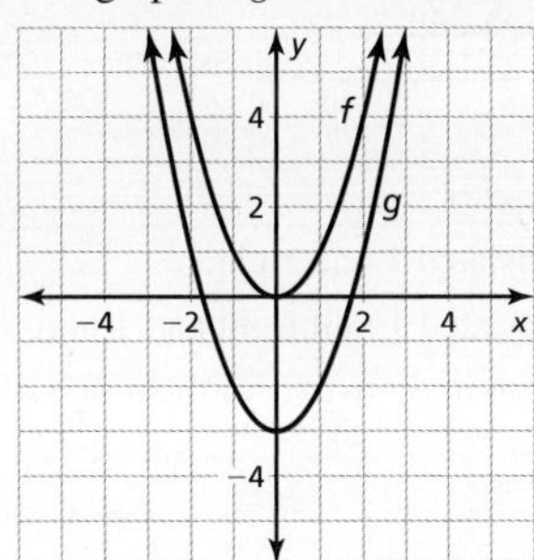

3. The graph of g is a translation 2 units left of the graph of f.

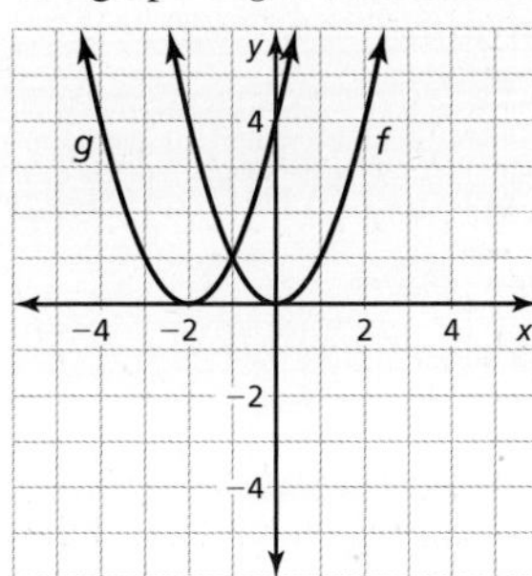

5. The graph of g is a translation 1 unit right of the graph of f.

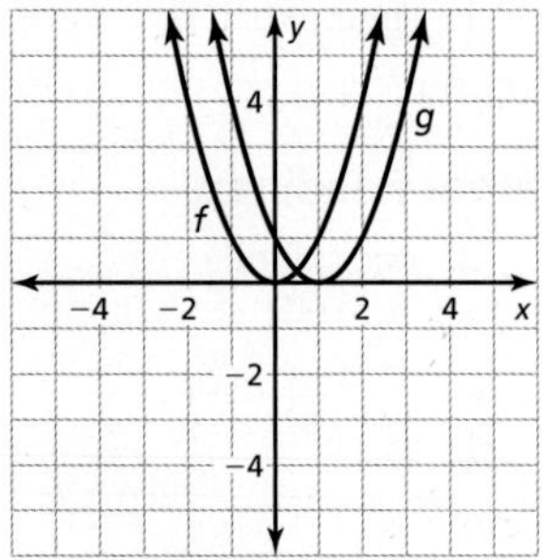

7. The graph of g is a translation 6 units left and 2 units down of the graph of f.

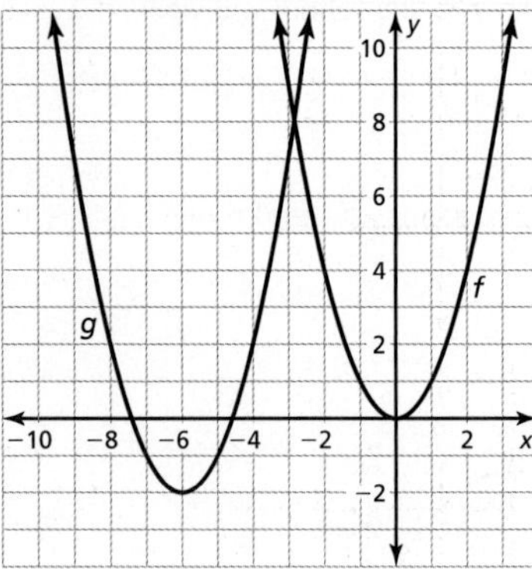

9. The graph of g is a translation 7 units right and 1 unit up of the graph of f.

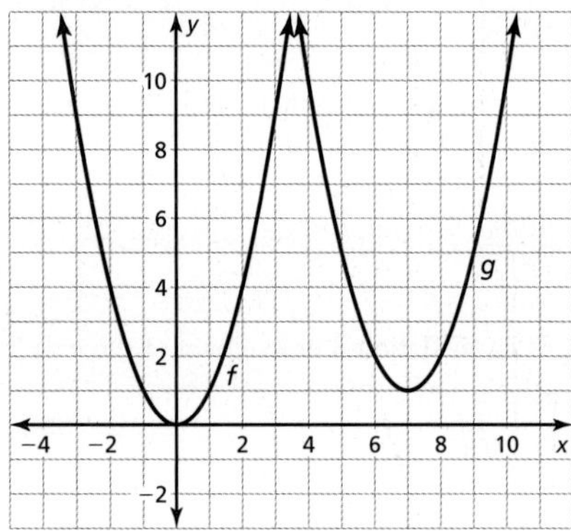

11. A; The graph has been translated 1 unit right.

13. C; The graph has been translated 1 unit right and 1 unit up.

15. The graph of g is a reflection in the x-axis of the graph of f.

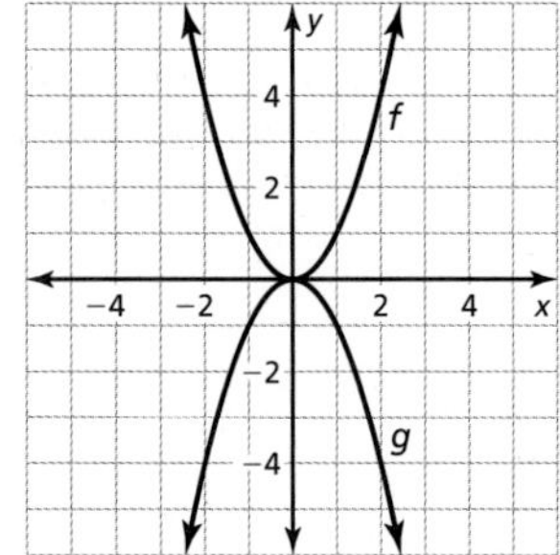

17. The graph of g is a vertical stretch by a factor of 3 of the graph of f.

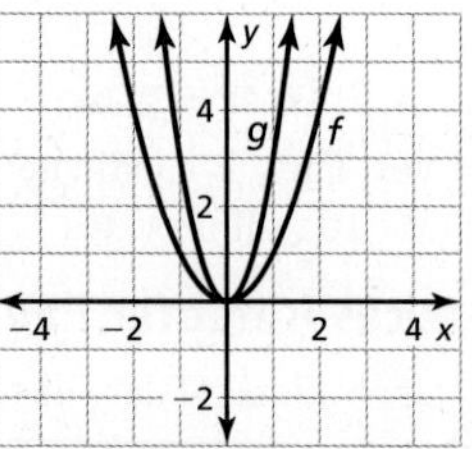

19. The graph of g is a horizontal shrink by a factor of $\frac{1}{2}$ of the graph of f.

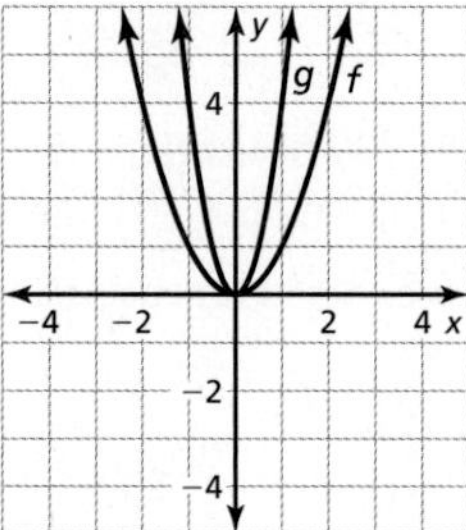

21. The graph of g is a vertical shrink by a factor of $\frac{1}{5}$, followed by a translation 4 units down.

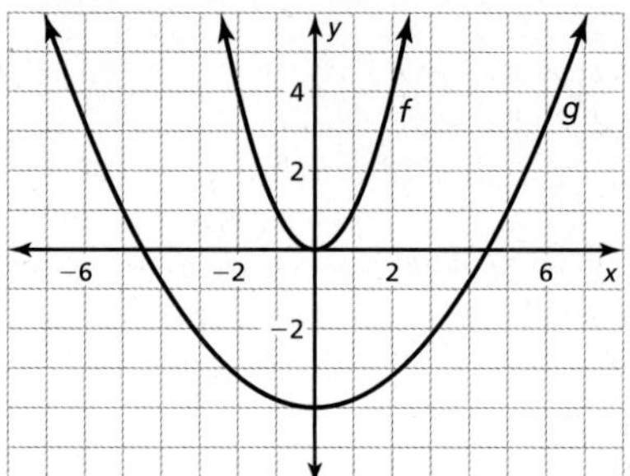

23. The graph is a reflection in the x-axis, not y-axis; The graph is a reflection in the x-axis and a vertical stretch by a factor of 6, followed by a translation 4 units up of the graph of the parent quadratic function.

25. The graph of f is a vertical stretch by a factor of 3, followed by a translation 2 units left and 1 unit up of the graph of the parent quadratic function; $(-2, 1)$

27. The graph of f is a vertical stretch by a factor of 2, followed by a reflection in the x-axis and a translation 5 units up of the graph of the parent quadratic function; $(0, 5)$

29. $g(x) = -4x^2 + 2$; $(0, 2)$ **31.** $g(x) = 8\left(\frac{1}{2}x\right)^2 - 4$; $(0, -4)$

33. C; The graph is a vertical stretch by a factor of 2, followed by a translation 1 unit right and 2 units down of the parent quadratic function.

35. D; The graph is a vertical stretch by a factor of 2 and a reflection in the x-axis, followed by a translation 1 unit right and 2 units up of the parent quadratic function.

37. F; The graph is a vertical stretch by a factor of 2 and a reflection in the x-axis, followed by a translation 1 unit left and 2 units down of the parent quadratic function.

39. Subtract 6 from the output; Substitute $2x^2 + 6x$ for $f(x)$; Multiply the output by -1; Substitute $2x^2 + 6x - 6$ for $h(x)$; Simplify.

41. $f(x) = -\frac{1}{20}x^2 + x + \frac{11}{5}$

43. The graph of g is a horizontal stretch by a factor of $\sqrt{6}$ of the graph of f; about 1.67 ft

45. a. $y = -\frac{5}{1089}(x - 33)^2 + 5$

b. The domain is $0 \leq x \leq 66$ and the range is $0 \leq y \leq 5$; The domain represents the horizontal distance and the range represents the height of the fish.

c. yes; The value changes to $-\frac{1}{225}$.

47. a vertical shrink by a factor of $\frac{7}{16}$

2.1 Review & Refresh

48. $(-6, 3, -5)$

49. $(2, 3z - 4, z)$

50. $\left(\frac{1}{3}, -2, 4\right)$

51. no solution

52. $g(x) = \frac{3}{2}(x + 3)^2 - 3$; $(-3, -3)$

53. $x > -7$

54. $x \leq 4.5$

55. $8x^2(x - 5)$

56.

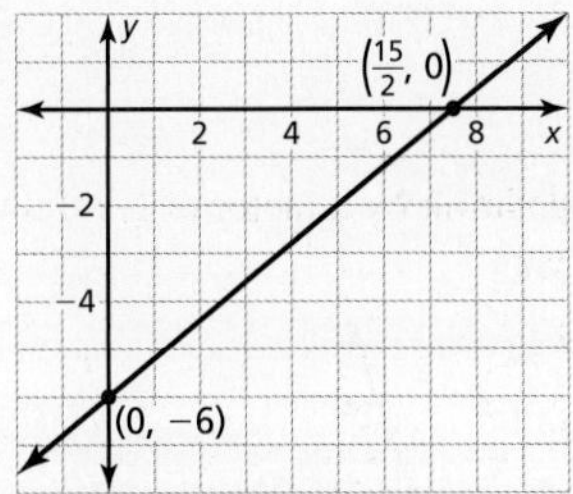

57. The slope is positive.

58. The graph is a reflection in the x-axis, followed by a translation 1 unit right.

59. $-27, -39, -51$

60. 6, 10, 14

61.

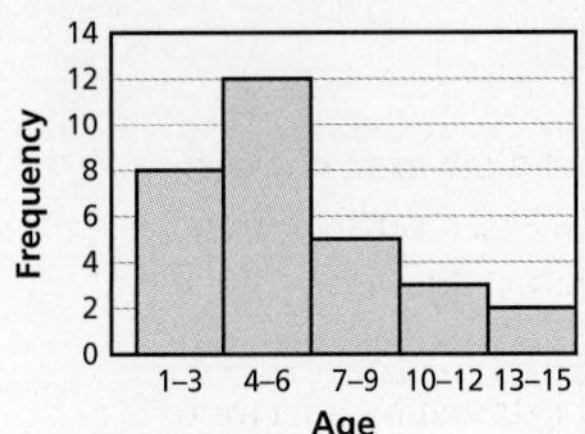

skewed right

62. \$97

63. $4\sqrt{3}$

64. $\frac{5\sqrt{7}}{7}$

2.2 Practice

1.

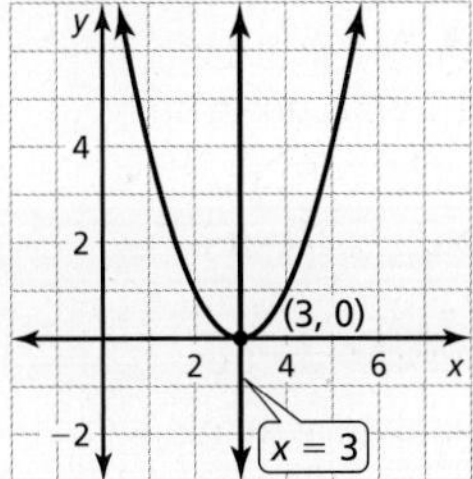

3.

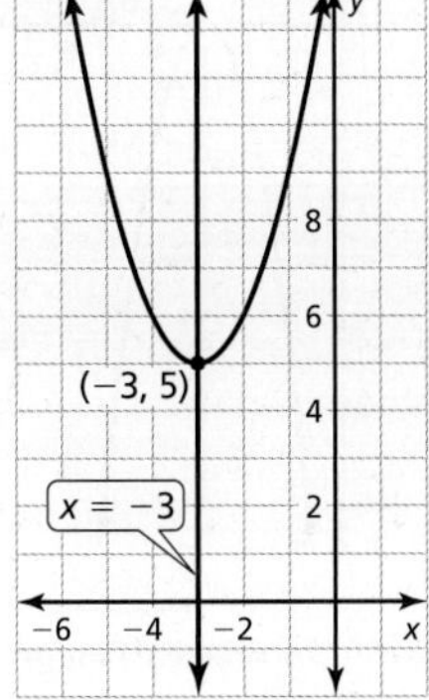

5.

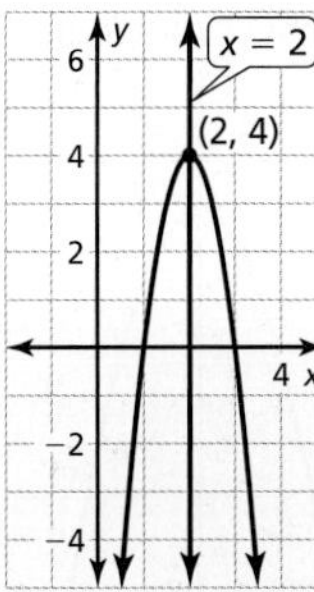

7.

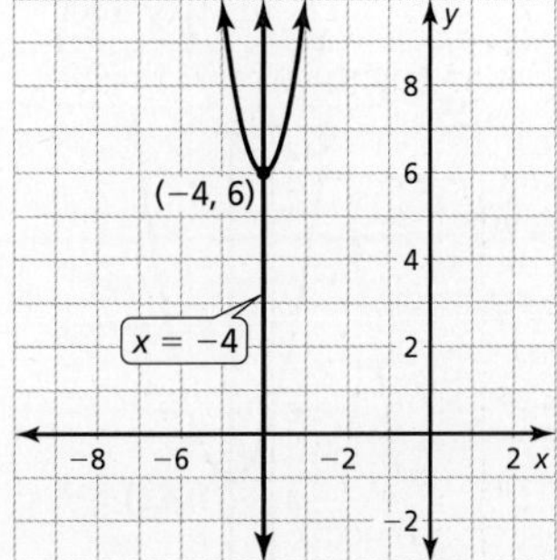

9.

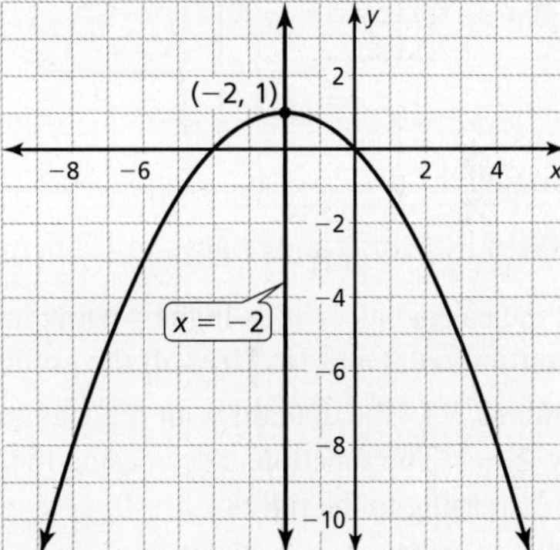

11.

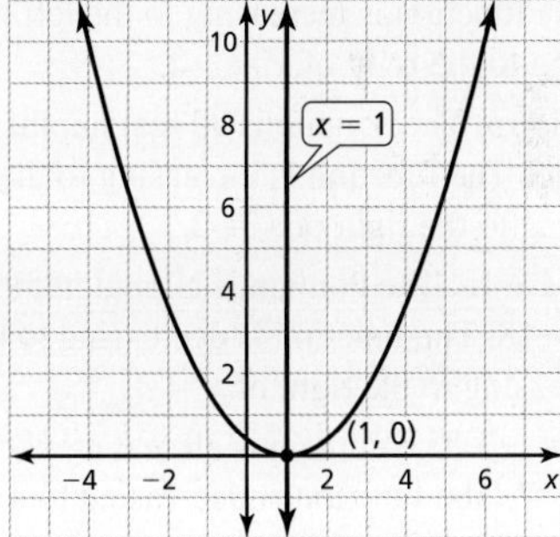

13. C

15. B

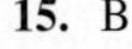

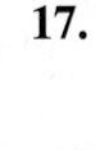

17.

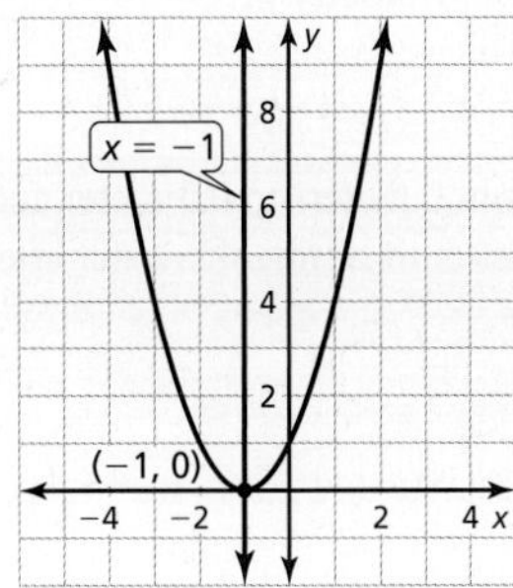

19. 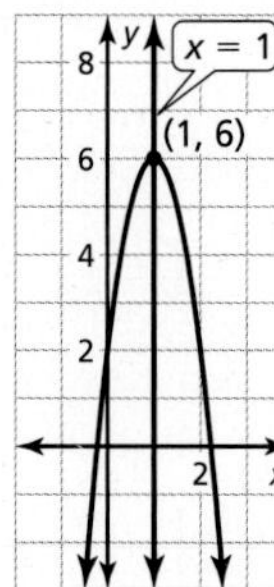

21. 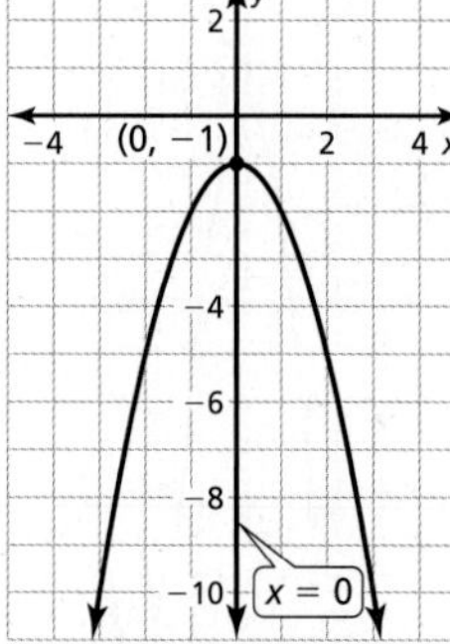

23. 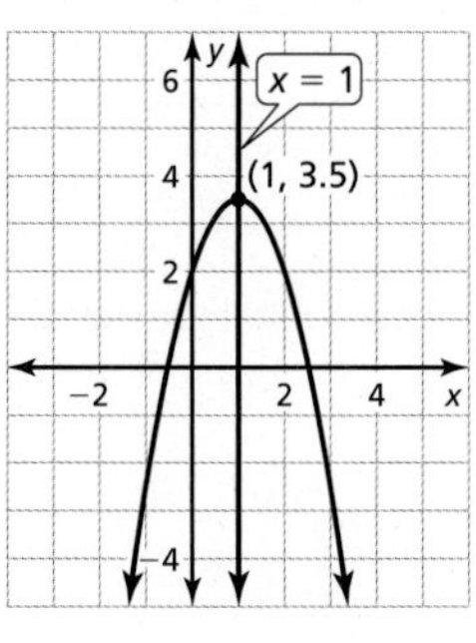

25. 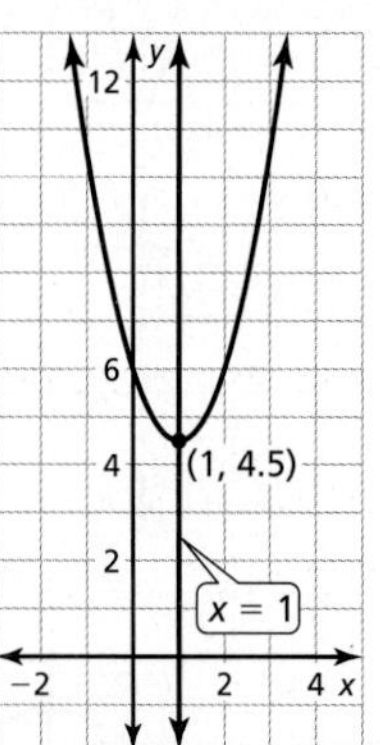

27. The formula is missing the negative sign; The x-coordinate of the vertex is $x = -\frac{b}{2a} = -\frac{24}{2(4)} = -3$.

29. (25, 18.5); When the basketball is at its highest point, it is 25 feet from its starting point and 18.5 feet off the ground.

31. The minimum value is -1. The domain is all real numbers and the range is $y \geq -1$. The function is decreasing to the left of $x = 0$ and increasing to the right of $x = 0$.

33. The maximum value is 2. The domain is all real numbers and the range is $y \leq 2$. The function is increasing to the left of $x = -2$ and decreasing to the right of $x = -2$.

35. The maximum value is 15. The domain is all real numbers and the range is $y \leq 15$. The function is increasing to the left of $x = 2$ and decreasing to the right of $x = 2$.

37. The minimum value is -18. The domain is all real numbers and the range is $y \geq -18$. The function is decreasing to the left of $x = 3$ and increasing to the right of $x = 3$.

39. The minimum value is -7. The domain is all real numbers and the range is $y \geq -7$. The function is decreasing to the left of $x = 6$ and increasing to the right of $x = 6$.

41. Both functions have an axis of symmetry of $x = 2$.

43. **a.** 1 m

b. 3.25 m

c. The diver is ascending from 0 meters to 0.5 meter and descending from 0.5 meter until hitting the water after approximately 1.1 meters.

45. 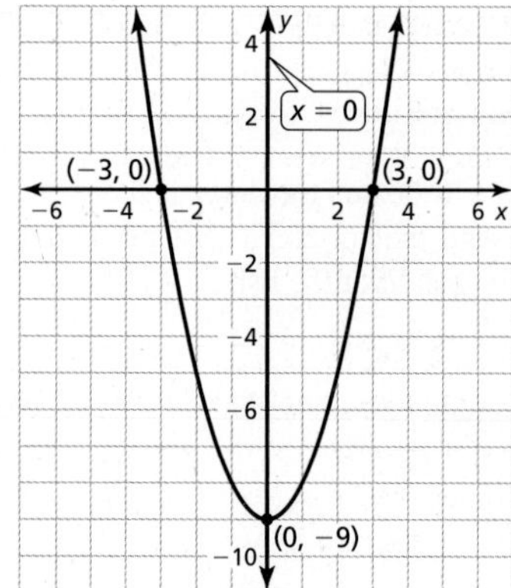

47. 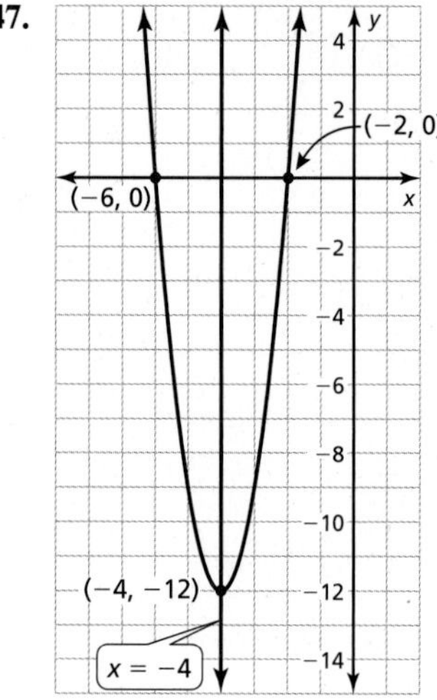

49. 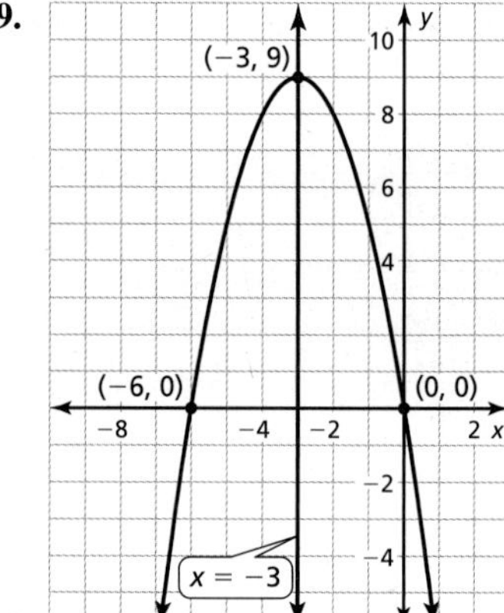

51. 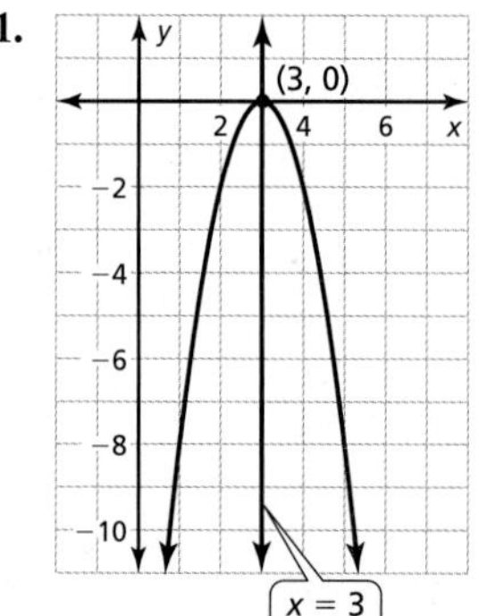

53. $p = 2$, $q = -6$; The graph is decreasing to the left of $x = -2$ and increasing to the right of $x = -2$.

55. $p = 4$, $q = 2$; The graph is increasing to the left of $x = 3$ and decreasing to the right of $x = 3$.

57. first flare; first flare; Its vertex is higher than the second flare's vertex, which means it traveled higher. Its t-intercept is 8, which means it was in the air for 8 seconds, which is longer than the 7 seconds that the second flare was in the air.

59. B

61. $A = w(20 - w) = -w^2 + 20w$; The maximum area is 100 square units.

63. no; Either of the points could be the axis of symmetry, or neither of the points could be the axis of symmetry. You can only determine the axis of symmetry if the y-coordinates of the two points are the same, because the axis of symmetry would lie halfway between the two points.

65. 160 ft; about 1.5 ft

67. All three graphs are the same; $f(x) = x^2 + 4x + 3$, $g(x) = x^2 + 4x + 3$

69.

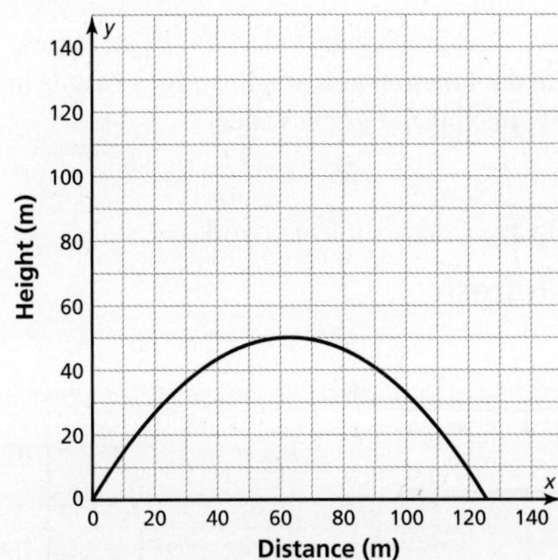

The x-axis is labeled Distance (m) and the y-axis is labeled Height (m). The domain is $0 \le x \le 126$ and the range is $0 \le y \le 50$; The domain represents the distance from the start of the bridge on one side of the river, and the range represents the height of the arch.

71. **a.** about 14.1%; about 55.5 cm³/g

b. about 13.6%; about 44.1 cm³/g

c.

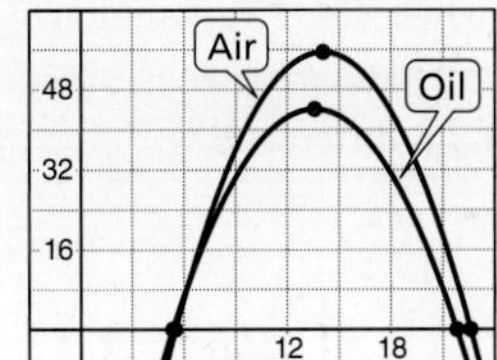

The domain for hot-air popping is $5.52 \le x \le 22.6$, and the range is $0 \le y \le 55.5$. The domain for hot-oil popping is $5.35 \le x \le 21.8$, and the range is $0 \le y \le 44.1$. This means that the moisture content for the kernels can range from 5.52% to 22.6% and 5.35% to 21.8%, while the popping volume can range from 0 to 55.5 cubic centimeters per gram and 0 to 44.11 cubic centimeters per gram.

73. no; (1, 5) and (0, 5) have the same y-coordinate, so the vertex is between the points.

75. The x-coordinate of the vertex does not change, and the y-coordinate moves further from the x-axis; The x-coordinate of the vertex does not change, and the y-coordinate moves closer to the x-axis.

2.2 Review & Refresh

76. $x = 8$

77. no solution

78. $x = -2$

79. $x = 6$

80. $x = 6$

81. $x = -8$

82. The graph is a vertical shrink by a factor of $\frac{1}{4}$, followed by a translation 2 units up of the parent quadratic function.

83. no solution

84. (1.32, −1.72, 8.24)

85. yes; *Sample answer:* $y = 26.6x - 6$; about 313 posts

86. $x = -25, x = 3$

87.

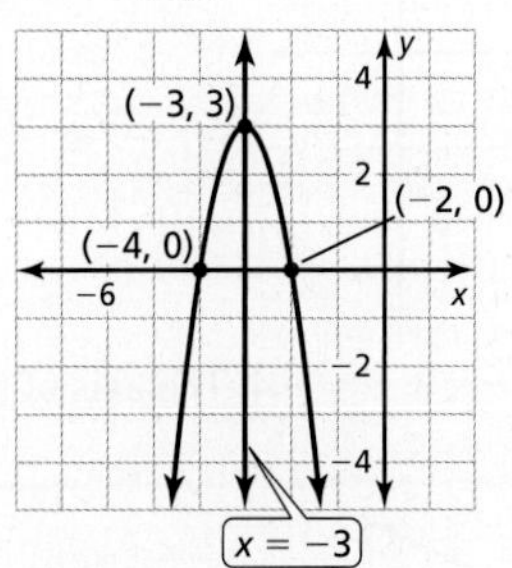

88.

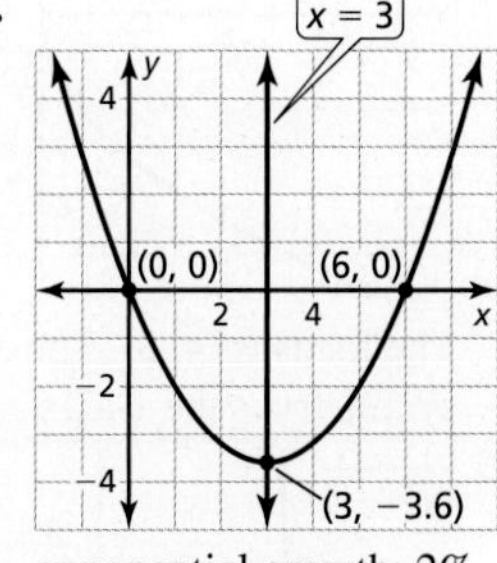

89. 168 ft³

90. exponential growth; 2%

91. exponential decay; 14%

92. *Sample answer:*

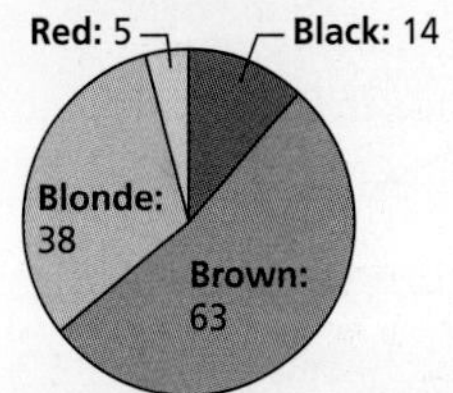

The circle graph shows the different hair colors as parts to a whole.

93. $-2 < n \le 10$

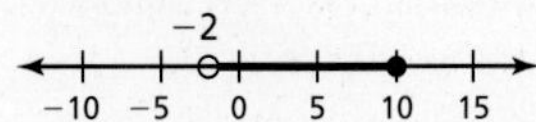

94. $d < -6$ *or* $d \ge 20$

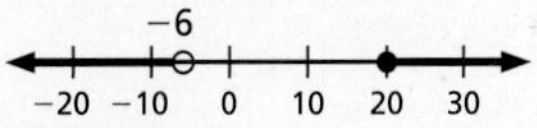

2.3 Practice

1. $y = \frac{1}{4}x^2$

3. $y = -\frac{1}{8}x^2$

5. $y = \frac{1}{24}x^2$

7. $y = -\frac{1}{40}x^2$

9. The focus is (0, 2). The directrix is $y = -2$. The axis of symmetry is the y-axis.

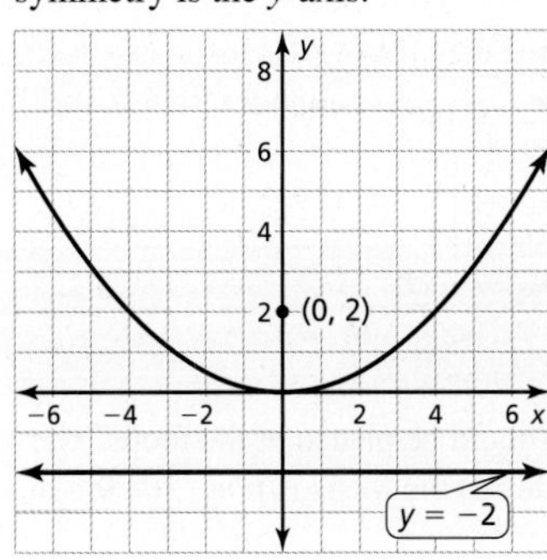

11. The focus is $(-5, 0)$. The directrix is $x = 5$. The axis of symmetry is the x-axis.

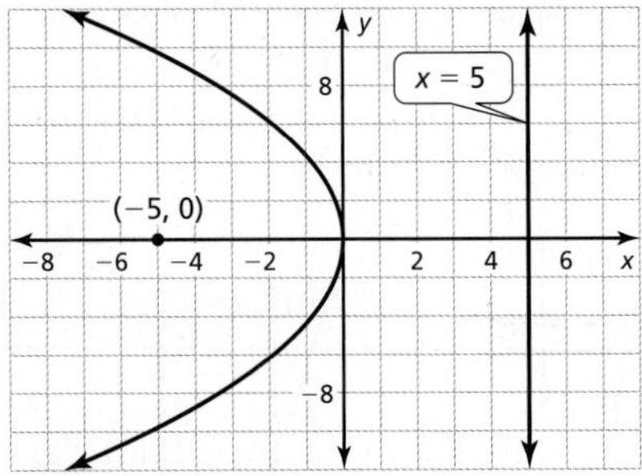

13. The focus is $(4, 0)$. The directrix is $x = -4$. The axis of symmetry is the x-axis.

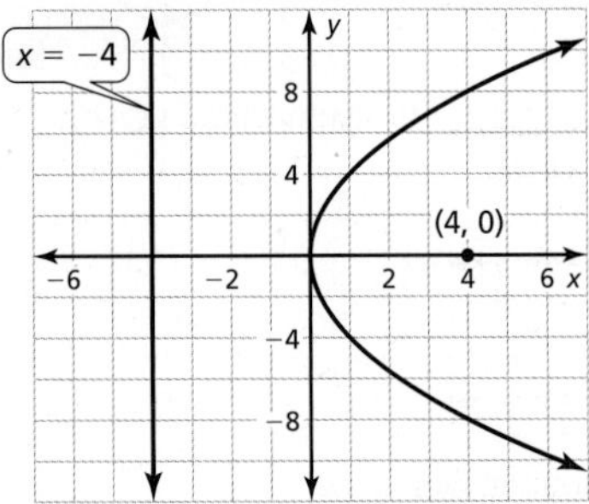

15. The focus is $\left(0, -\frac{1}{8}\right)$. The directrix is $y = \frac{1}{8}$. The axis of symmetry is the y-axis.

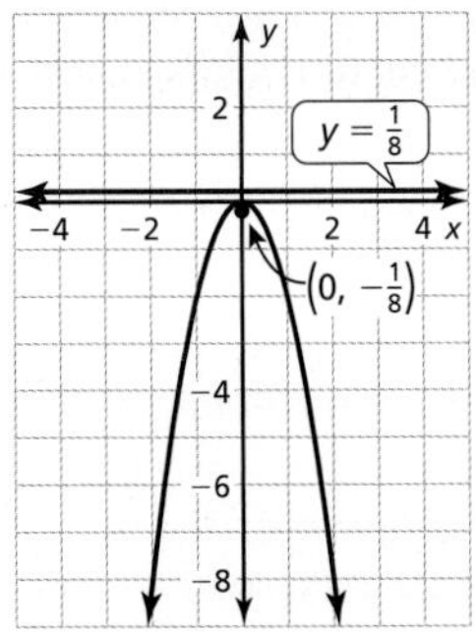

17. Instead of a vertical axis of symmetry, the graph should have a horizontal axis of symmetry.

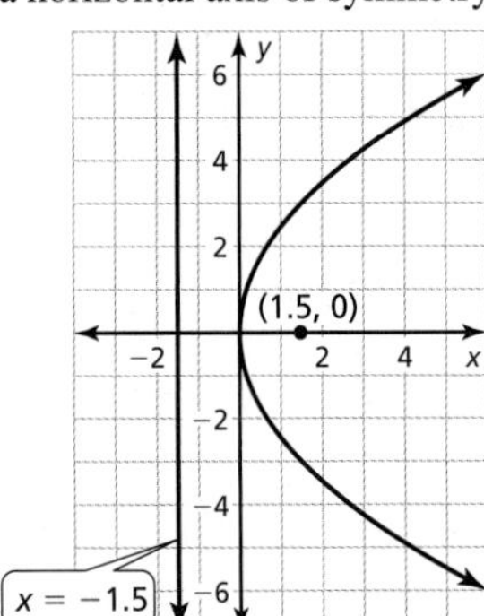

19. 9.5 in.; The receiver should be placed at the focus. The distance from the vertex to the focus is $p = \frac{38}{4} = 9.5$ in.

21. $y = \frac{1}{32}x^2$

23. $x = -\frac{1}{10}y^2$

25. $x = -\frac{1}{28}y^2$

27. $x = \frac{1}{40}y^2$

29. $y = -\frac{3}{20}x^2$

31. $y = \frac{7}{24}x^2$

33. $x = -\frac{1}{16}y^2 - 4$

35. $y = \frac{1}{6}x^2 + 1$

37. $y = -\frac{1}{36}(x - 2)^2 + 3$

39. $x = (y + 1)^2 + 1$

41. The vertex is $(3, 2)$. The focus is $(3, 4)$. The directrix is $y = 0$. The axis of symmetry is $x = 3$. The graph is a vertical shrink by a factor of $\frac{1}{2}$, followed by a translation 3 units right and 2 units up.

43. The vertex is $(1, 3)$. The focus is $(5, 3)$. The directrix is $x = -3$. The axis of symmetry is $y = 3$. The graph is a horizontal shrink by a factor of $\frac{1}{4}$, followed by a translation 1 unit right and 3 units up.

45. The vertex is $(2, -4)$. The focus is $\left(\frac{23}{12}, -4\right)$. The directrix is $x = \frac{25}{12}$. The axis of symmetry is $y = -4$. The graph is a horizontal stretch by a factor of 12, followed by a reflection in the y-axis and a translation 2 units right and 4 units down.

47. $x = \frac{1}{5.2}y^2$; about 3.08 in.

49. A, B, D

51. As $|p|$ increases, the graph gets wider; As $|p|$ increases, the constant in the function gets smaller which results in a vertical shrink, making the graph wider.

53. $y = \frac{1}{4}x^2$

55. $x = \frac{1}{4p}y^2$

57. Answers will vary. Check students' work.

2.3 Review & Refresh

58. $y = 3x - 7$

59. $y = -2x + 6$

60.

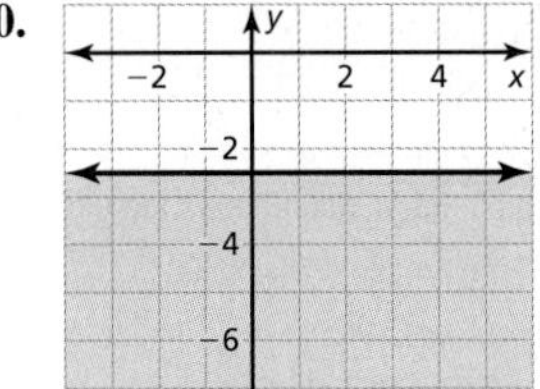

61.

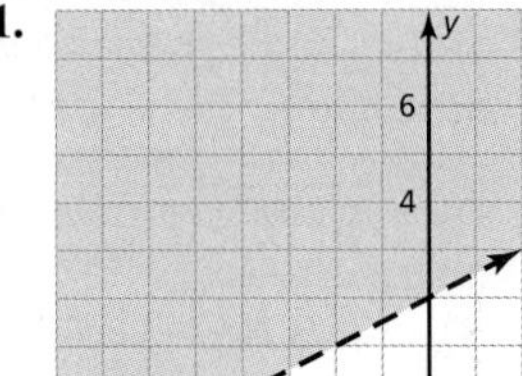

62. $1 \div \frac{\sqrt[3]{9/2}}{3} \approx 1.8$ times greater

63. $y = \frac{1}{20}(x + 2)^2 - 6$

64. $y = 4.0x + 1$

65. The function is decreasing when $x < -3$, and increasing when $x > -3$.

66. nonlinear; There is no common difference.

67. $g(x) = -6x^2 - 12$; $(0, -12)$

68. $n = -25$

69. $h = \frac{5}{2}$

70. $x = 7$

71. no solution

72. 3 one-point free throws, 5 two-point shots, and 3 three-point shots

73. The focus is $\left(-\frac{3}{4}, 0\right)$, the directrix is $x = \frac{3}{4}$, and the axis of symmetry is the x-axis.

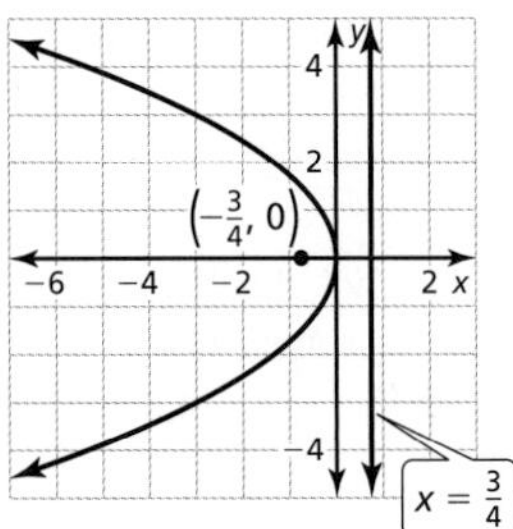

2.4 Practice

1. $y = -3(x + 2)^2 + 6$

3. $y = 0.06(x - 3)^2 + 2$

5. $y = -\frac{1}{3}(x + 6)^2 - 12$ **7.** $y = -4(x - 2)(x - 4)$

9. $y = \frac{1}{10}(x - 12)(x + 6)$ **11.** $y = 2.25(x + 16)(x + 2)$

13. If given the x-intercepts, it is easier to write the equation in intercept form. If given the vertex, it is easier to write the equation in vertex form.

15. $y = -16(x - 3)^2 + 150$ **17.** $y = -0.75x(x - 4)$

19. The x-intercepts were substituted incorrectly.
$y = a(x - p)(x - q)$
$4 = a(3 + 1)(3 - 2)$
$a = 1$
$y = (x + 1)(x - 2)$

21. $S(C) = 180C^2$; 18,000 lb

23. $y = 0.026x^2 - 0.02x + 1.6$; about 27,600 users

25. using intercept form; You are given the x-intercepts and a point.

27. **a.** linear; x and y change at a constant rate.
b. $y = 45x$; 270 mi

29. quadratic; The second differences are constant; $y = -2x^2 + 42x + 470$

31. neither; The first and second differences are not constant.

33. *Sample answer*: The surfaces of some roads are shaped like parabolas so rain water can run off each side. The height of the road can be modeled by a quadratic equation.

35. 155 tiles

2.4 Review & Refresh

37. $(x + 3)(x + 1)$ **38.** $(x - 2)(x - 1)$

39. $3(x - 4)(x - 1)$ **40.** $(x + 3)(x - 2)$

41. $y = -16x^2 + 128x$; 256 ft

42. yes; No vertical line can be drawn through more than one point on the graph.

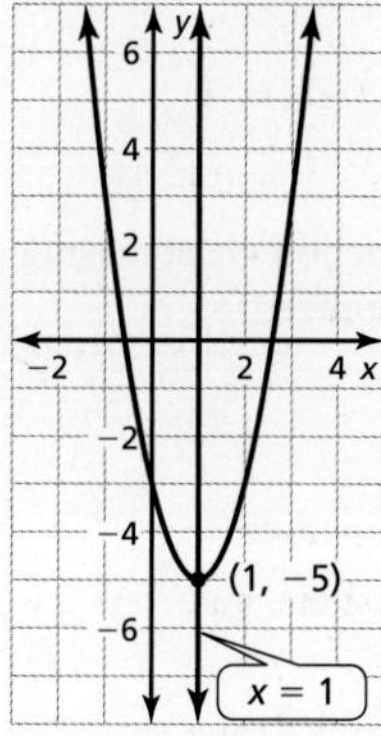

44.

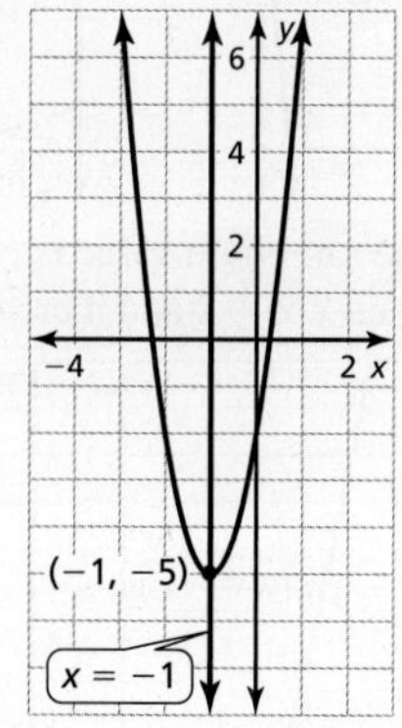

45. The focus is $(-3, 0)$, the directrix is $x = 3$, and the axis of symmetry is the x-axis.

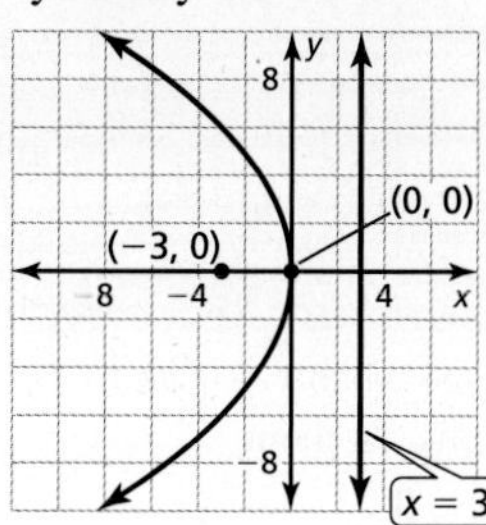

46. The focus is $(4, 0)$, the directrix is $y = -4$, and the axis of symmetry is the y-axis.

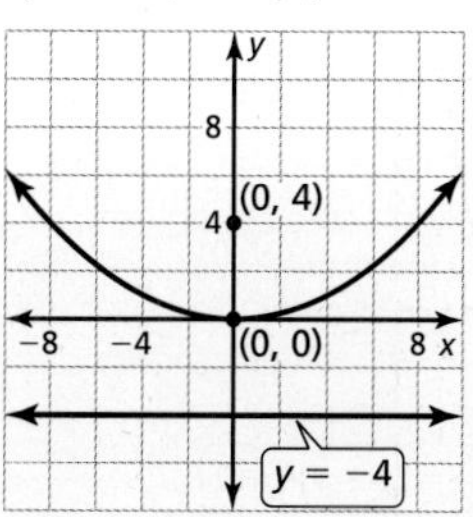

47. $g(x) = (8x - 23)^2 - 10$; $\left(\frac{23}{8}, -10\right)$

48. $m \geq 4$

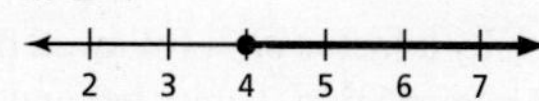

49. $n > 21$

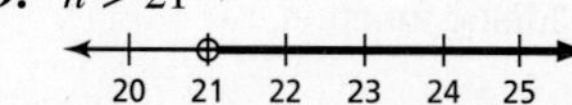

50. $p > 2$

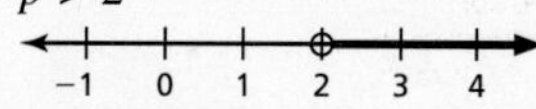

51. $q \geq -12$

−13 −12 −11 −10 −9 −8

52. exponential; The common factor is 4.

53. $y = -x + 3$ **54.** $y = \frac{3}{2}x + \frac{5}{2}$

Chapter 2 Review

1. The graph is a translation 4 units left of the parent quadratic function.

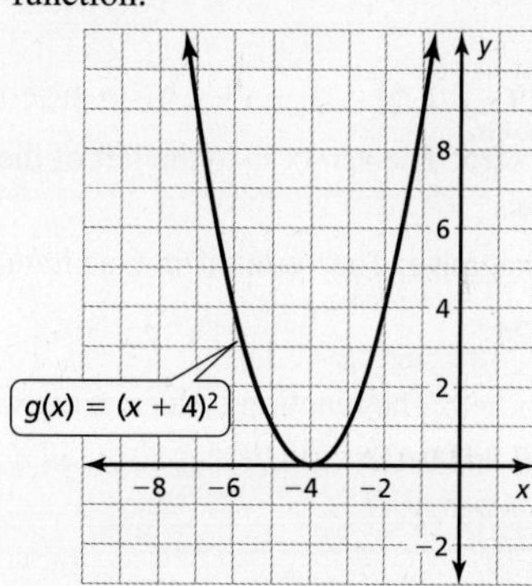

2. The graph is a vertical shrink by a factor of $\frac{1}{5}$ and a reflection in the x-axis of the graph of f.

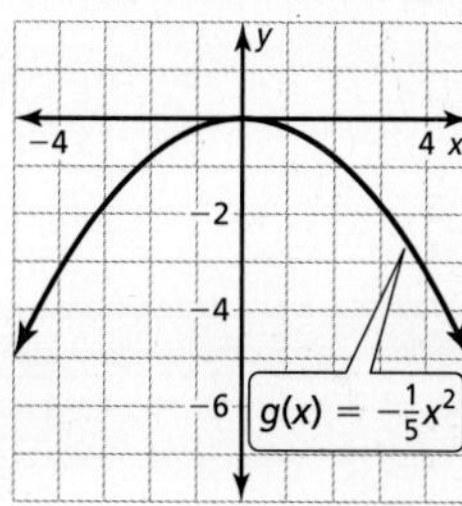

3. The graph is a translation 7 units right and 2 units up of the parent quadratic function.

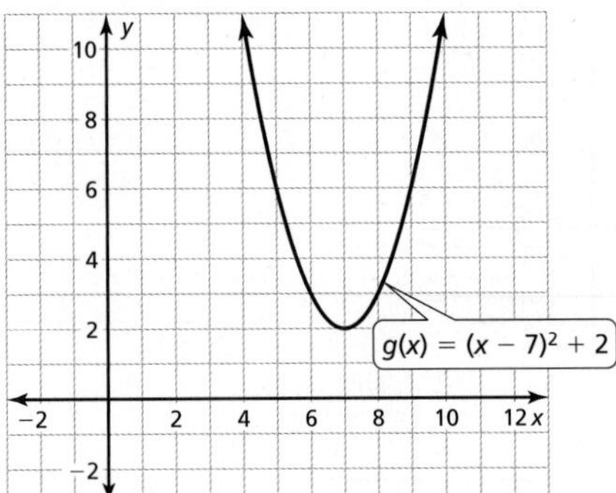

4. The graph is a vertical stretch by a factor of 3, followed by a reflection in the x-axis and a translation 2 units left and 1 unit down of the parent quadratic function.

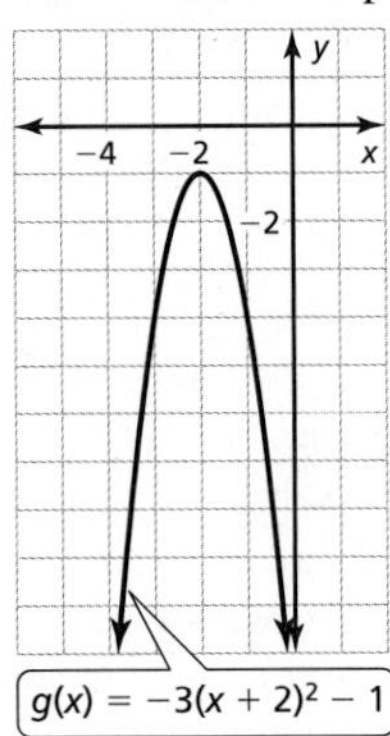

5. $g(x) = \frac{9}{4}(x + 5)^2 - 2$

6. $g(x) = (-x + 2)^2 - 2(-x + 2) + 3 = x^2 - 2x + 3$

7. **a.** h is negative, k is zero; The vertex is to the left of the origin, on the x-axis.

b. h is positive, k is negative; The vertex is in Quadrant IV.

8. $y = -\frac{2}{75}(x - 30)^2 + 24$

9. The minimum value is -8; The function is decreasing when $x < -5$ and increasing when $x > -5$.

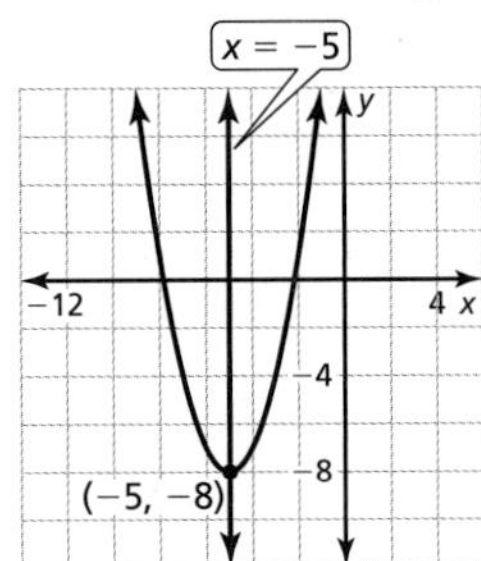

10. The minimum value is -4; The function is decreasing when $x < 1$ and increasing when $x > 1$.

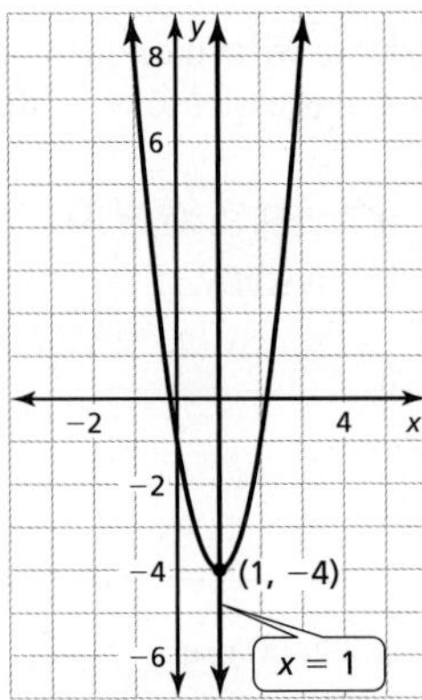

11. The maximum value is 35; The function is increasing when $x < 4$ and decreasing when $x > 4$.

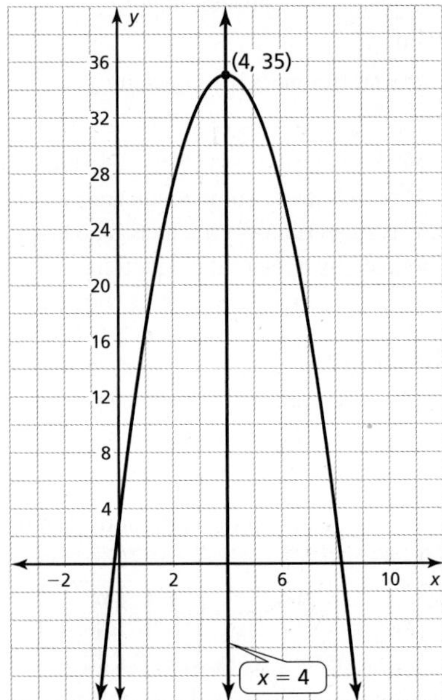

12. The minimum value is -25; The function is decreasing when $x < -2$ and increasing when $x > -2$.

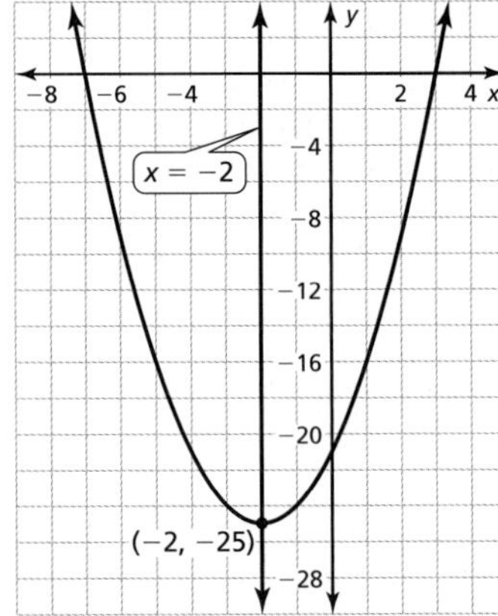

13. (4, 13); The y-values are the same when $x = 1$ and $x = 7$, so the vertex is located halfway between them.

14. *Sample answer:* $y = x^2 + 10x + 3$

15. the first kick; the second kick

16. $x = -\frac{1}{8}y^2$

17. $y = -\frac{1}{16}(x - 2)^2 + 6$

18. The focus is (0, 9), the directrix is $y = -9$, and the axis of symmetry is $x = 0$.

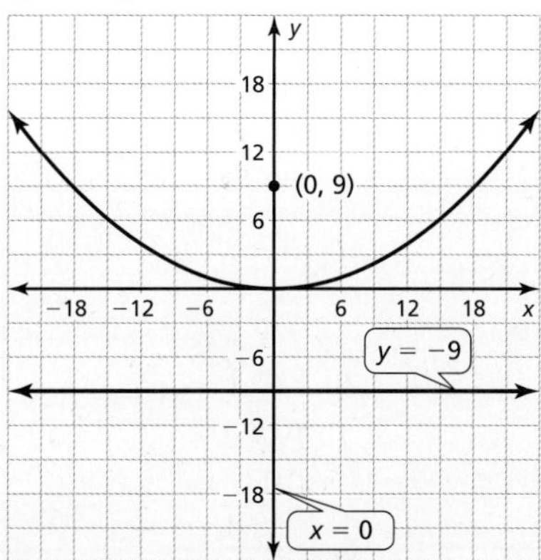

19. The focus is $(-2, 0)$, the directrix is $x = 2$, and the axis of symmetry is $y = 0$.

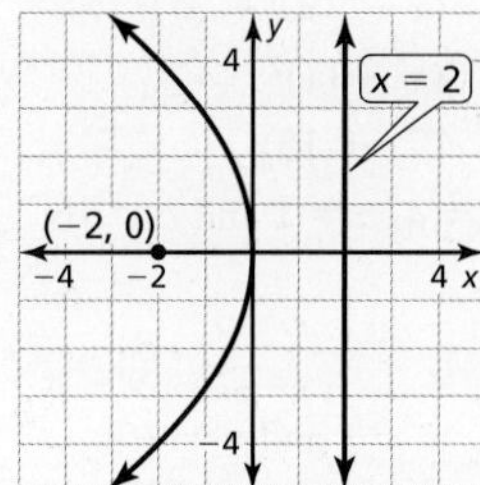

20. $y = \frac{1}{4}(x - 2)^2 - 4$

21. $x = \frac{1}{8}(y - 1)^2 + 3$

22. The microphone is about 1.8 inches below the opening of the parabolic dish.

23. $y = \frac{16}{81}(x - 10)^2 - 4$

24. $y = -\frac{3}{5}(x + 1)(x - 5)$

25. $y = 4x^2 + 5x + 1$

26. $y = -\frac{1}{640}(x - 80)^2 + 30$; 20 ft

27. $y = -16x^2 + 150$; about 3.06 sec

28. **a.** $0.05x^2 + 2.4x + 1$

b. about 210 ft

Chapter 2 Mathematical Practices (Chapter Review)

1. Transformations of quadratic functions have similar effects on the graph as transformations of linear functions.
2. There are an infinite number of linear functions that have a y-intercept of (0, 2). You need to know another point or the slope to distinguish between two linear functions.
3. $(-1, -3)$; The points are the vertices of the corresponding graphs.

Chapter 2 Practice Test

1. The graph of g is a vertical translation 6 units down of the graph of f.

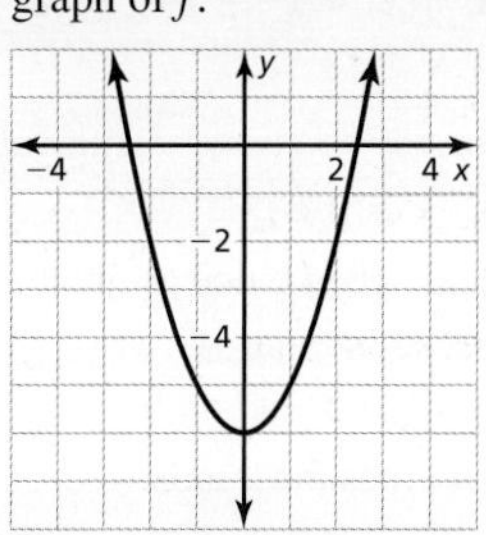

2. The graph of g is a horizontal translation 1 unit left of the graph of f.

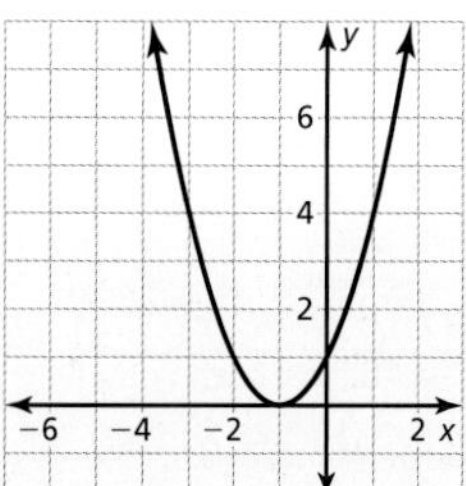

3. The graph of g is a vertical shrink by a factor of $\frac{1}{4}$ of the graph of f.

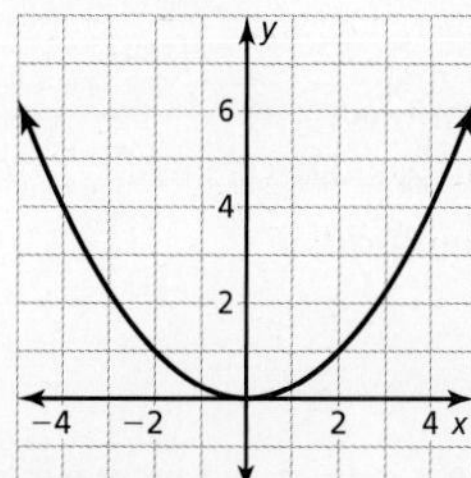

4. The graph of g is a horizontal shrink by a factor of $\frac{1}{3}$ of the graph of f.

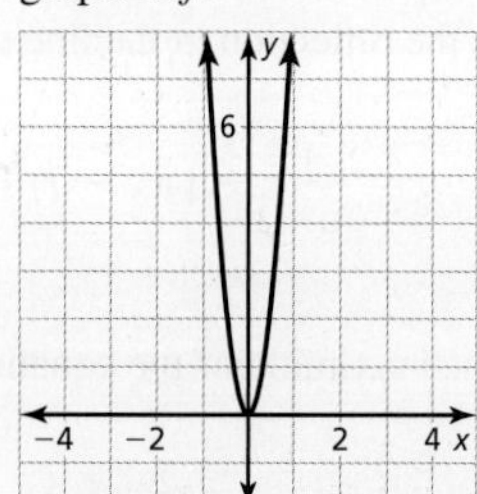

5. The graph of g is a reflection in the x-axis and a vertical translation 3 units up of the graph of f.

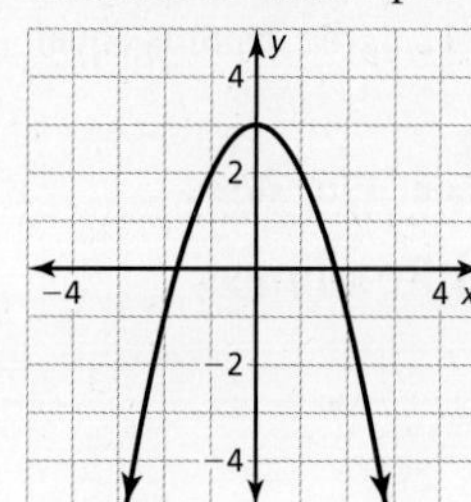

6. The graph of g is a horizontal translation 1 unit left, horizontal stretch by a factor of $\frac{1}{2}$, then a vertical translation 4 units down of the graph of f.

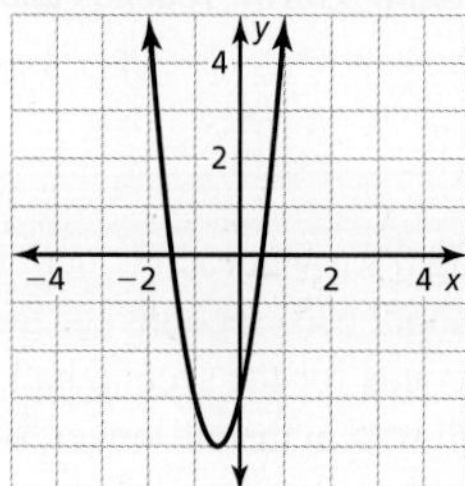

7. The focus is $\left(\frac{1}{8}, 0\right)$, the directrix is $x = -\frac{1}{8}$, and the axis of symmetry is $y = 0$.

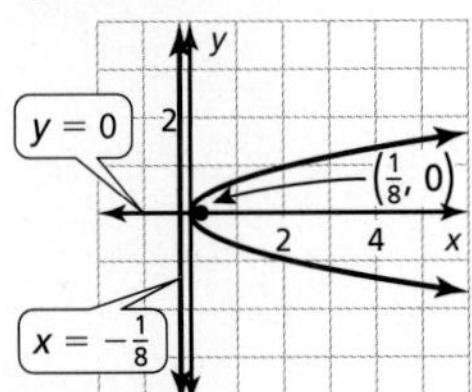

8.

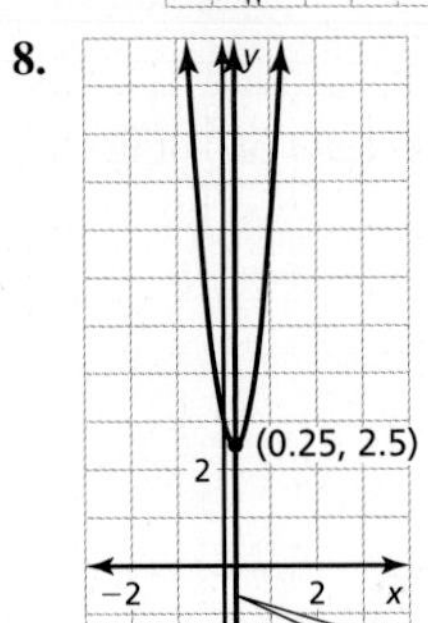

The function is decreasing when $x < 0.25$ and increasing when $x > 0.25$.

9. (2, 5); If the point (2, 1) is on the parabola, (2, 5) must also be on the parabola because it is the reflection in the line of symmetry.

10. $y = -\frac{1}{28}(x + 4)^2 + 2$

11. $y = -\frac{1}{4}(x + 1)(x - 7)$

12. $x = \frac{1}{16}y^2 + 2$

13. \$450; \$20,250; (5, 20,250) is the maximum of the equation $P = (40 + x)(500 - 10x)$.

14. The second differences are constant; $f(x) = -x^2 - 0.5x + 5$

15. **a.** $y = \frac{1}{53.6}x^2$

b. 2.9 m; When $x = 25 \div 2 = 12.5$, the depth is equal to $\frac{1}{53.6}(12.5)^2 \approx 2.9$.

16. $y = -0.03x^2 + 9.2x + 4347$; about 4967 ft/sec

Chapter 2 College and Career Readiness

1. A, C, D
2. **a.** \$5

   b. \$4.75
3. D
4. <; Your throw reaches a maximum height of about 71 feet, but the graph shows that your friend's throw reaches about 80 feet.
5. A
6. **a.** $y = -5(x - 3)^2 + 51.5$

   b. no; the first ball; Substituting 0 for y in each equation and solving gives times of about 6.14 seconds for the first ball, and about 6.21 seconds for the second ball, which means the second ball was in the air longer, so it hit the ground later.
7. B, D, F
8. B, C

9. **a.** Gym A: $y = 10x + 100$, Gym B: $y = 30x$

   b. If the membership is expected to be longer than 5 months

   c. The graph for Gym A is translated down 75 units. This change would mean that it is more economical to join Gym A if the membership is expected to be at least 2 months.

Chapter 3

Chapter 3 Prepare

1. $3\sqrt{3}$
2. $-4\sqrt{7}$
3. $\frac{\sqrt{11}}{8}$
4. $\frac{7\sqrt{3}}{10}$
5. $\frac{3\sqrt{2}}{7}$
6. $-\frac{\sqrt{65}}{11}$
7. $-4\sqrt{5}$
8. $4\sqrt{2}$
9. $(x - 6)(x + 6)$
10. $(x - 3)(x + 3)$
11. $(2x - 5)(2x + 5)$
12. $(x - 11)^2$
13. $(x + 14)^2$
14. $(7x + 15)^2$
15. $a = 16$ and $c = 1$, $a = 4$ and $c = 4$, $a = 1$ and $c = 16$; $2\sqrt{ac} = 8$

3.1 Practice

1. $x = -1$ and $x = -2$
3. $x = 3$ and $x = -3$
5. $x = -1$
7. no real solution
9. no real solution
11. $s = \pm 12$
13. $z = 1$ and $z = 11$
15. $x = 1 \pm \sqrt{2}$
17. no real solution
19. The $\pm$ was not used when taking the square root; $2(x + 1)^2 + 3 = 21$; $2(x + 1)^2 = 18$; $(x + 1)^2 = 9$; $x + 1 = \pm 3$; $x = 2$ and $x = -4$
21. $x = -3$
23. $x = 6$ and $x = 2$
25. $n = 0$ and $n = 6$
27. $p = -4$ and $p = \frac{1}{3}$
29. $w = 12$ and $w = 2$
31. $u = 0$ and $u = -9$; Explanations will vary.
33. no real solution; Explanations will vary.
35. $x = 6$ and $x = 2$; Explanations will vary.
37. $x = -0.5$ and $x = -2.5$; Explanations will vary.
39. $x = -2$ and $x = -4$
41. $x = 3$ and $x = -10$
43. $x = -11$
45. $x = 3$ and $x = -2$
47. $x = \frac{3}{8}$ and $x = 2$
49. \$5.75; \$1983.75
51. **a.** $h(t) = -16t^2 + 40$; The acceleration due to gravity is $-16t^2$ feet and the initial height is 40 feet; about 1.6 sec

    b. The seashell fell 12 feet between 0.5 second and 1 second.
53. A, B, and E
55. $f(x) = x^2 - 19x + 88$
57. **a.** *Sample answer:* $x^2 = 0$

    b. *Sample answer:* $x^2 = -9$
59. $x = 4$
61. $x = 3$
63. The 20-foot wave requires a wind speed twice as great as the wind speed required for a 5-foot wave.
65. $x(x + 2) = 143$; 11 and 13 or -13 and -11
67. **a.** positive; The graph does not cross the x-axis.

    b. yes; The graph opens up towards the x-axis.
69. 7 ft

71. you; The function does not cross the x-axis.

73. $k = -5$ and $k = 5$

75. a. $mn = a^2$ and $m + n = 0$

b. $m = \sqrt{-a^2} = a\sqrt{-1}$, $n = -\sqrt{-a^2} = -a\sqrt{-1}$; m and n are not real numbers.

77. yes; Figure 20

3.1 Review & Refresh

79. $3x^2 - x + 2$ **80.** $3x^2 - 3x + 1$

81. $x^3 + 4x^2 + 6$ **82.** $-3x^3 + 7x^2 - 15x + 9$

83. $y = \frac{3}{5}(x + 8)(x - 4)$ **84.** $y = -\frac{1}{3}(x + 3)^2 - 2$

85. $-44x^3 + 33x^2 + 88x$ **86.** $-x^2 + 8x - 7$

87. $x^2 - 4$ **88.** $9x^2 + 30x + 25$

89. $x = \pm\frac{\sqrt{30}}{2}$; Explanations will vary.

90. $x = 1$ and $x = -\frac{2}{3}$; Explanations will vary.

91. $|n - 3| > 9$; $n < -6$ *or* $n > 12$

92. a.

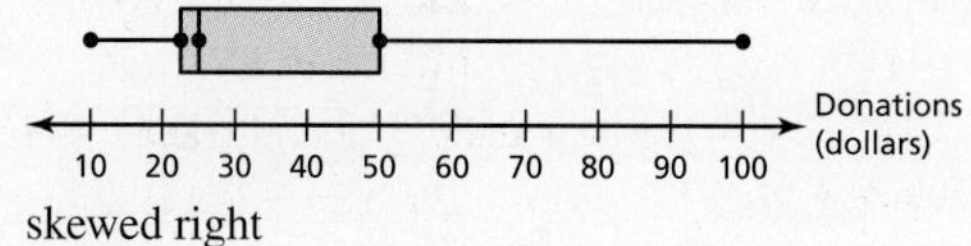

skewed right

b. yes, 100

93. The maximum is 10; domain: all real numbers, range: $y \le 10$; The function is increasing when $x < -2$ and decreasing when $x > -2$.

94. The minimum is -6.5; domain: all real numbers, range: $y \ge -6.5$; The function is decreasing when $x < 3$ and increasing when $x > 3$.

95. $\frac{1}{4}$ or 25% **96.** $p < 0$

3.2 Practice

1. $6i$ **3.** $3i\sqrt{2}$

5. $8i$ **7.** $-16i\sqrt{2}$

9. $x = 2$ and $y = 2$ **11.** $x = -2$ and $y = 4$

13. $x = 7$ and $y = -12$ **15.** $x = 6$ and $y = 28$

17. $13 + 2i$ **19.** $9 + 11i$

21. 19 **23.** $4 + 2i$

25. $-4 - 14i$

27. a. $-4 + 5i$

b. $2\sqrt{2} + 10i$

29. $-3 - 15i$ **31.** $14 - 5i$

33. $-16 - 11i$ **35.** $-27 - 36i$

37. i^2 can be simplified; $15 - 3i + 10i - 2i^2 = 15 + 7i + 2 = 17 + 7i$

39. 2 **41.** 20

43. 8 **45.** 34

47. $(6 - 7i) - (4 - 3i) = 2 - 4i$

49. $(12 + 2i)$ ohms **51.** $(8 + i)$ ohms

53. Distributive Property; Simplify; Definition of complex addition; Write in standard form.

55. $x = \pm 3i$ **57.** $x = \pm i\sqrt{7}$

59. $x = \pm 2i\sqrt{5}$ **61.** $x = \pm i\sqrt{2}$

63. $x = \pm 6i$ **65.** $x = \pm 3i\sqrt{3}$

67. $x = \pm 4i\sqrt{3}$ **69.** $a^2 - b^2 - 2abi$

71. $1 + \sqrt{-12}$; 13

73. a. D

b. F

c. B

d. E

e. A

f. C

75. $-28 + 27i$ **77.** $-15 - 25i$

79. $9 + 5i$

81.

Powers of i	i^1	i^2	i^3	i^4	i^5	i^6	i^7	i^8	i^{25}	i^{50}	i^{75}	i^{100}
Simplified form	i	-1	$-i$	1	i	-1	$-i$	1	i	-1	$-i$	1

The results of i^n alternate in the pattern i, -1, $-i$, and 1.

83. a. $-46 - 9i$

b. $28 + 96i$

85. B

87. Definition of i; Evaluate the power using inverse operations.

89. a. $-\frac{i - 3}{2}$

b. $1 - 3i$

91. a. false; *Sample answer:* $(3 - 5i) + (4 + 5i) = 7$

b. true; *Sample answer:* $(3i)(2i) = 6i^2 = -6$

c. true; *Sample answer:* $3i = 0 + 3i$

d. false; *Sample answer:* $1 + 8i$

93. $\frac{\sqrt{2}}{2} + \frac{\sqrt{2}}{2}i$

3.2 Review & Refresh

95.

The graph of f is a vertical shrink by a factor of $\frac{1}{4}$, followed by a translation 1 unit up of the parent quadratic function.

96.

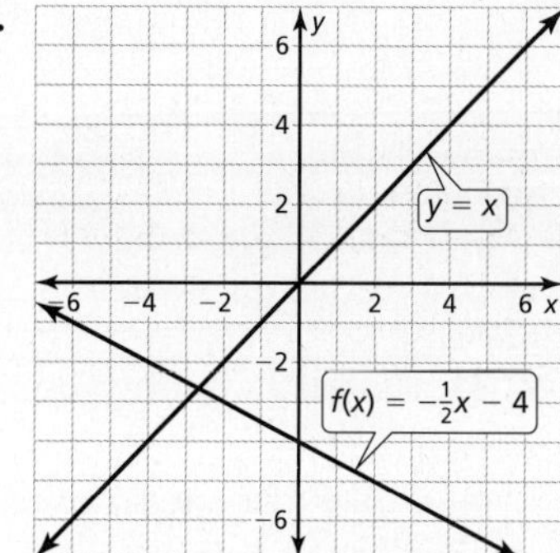

The graph of f is a reflection in the x-axis, followed by a vertical shrink by a factor of $\frac{1}{2}$ and a translation 4 units down of the parent linear function.

97. $\frac{c^8}{4d^{18}}$

98. $432m^{11}n^{21}$

99. $y = -(x - 2)^2 - 1$

100. $\pm i\frac{\sqrt{2}}{3}$; no; The zeros are imaginary, so the graph of the function does not intersect the x-axis.

101. $y = -\frac{1}{8}x^2$

102. $x = \frac{1}{12}(y + 4)^2 + 5$

103.

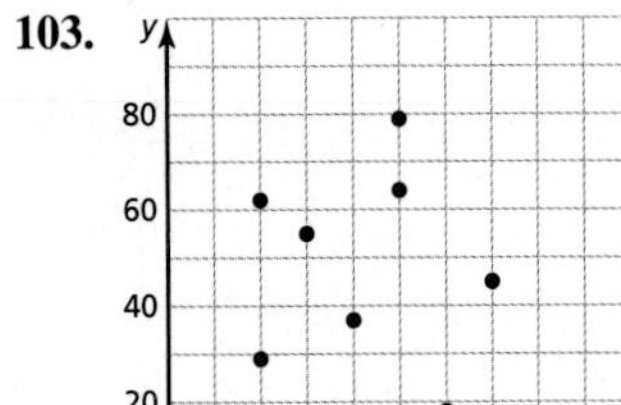

no correlation

104. about 7.9 cm

105. long-sleeved shirts: \$15, short-sleeved shirts: \$10

106. $-12 - 27i$

107. $11 - i$

108. $-19 - 62i$

109. $-9 + 2i$

110. $x > -2$

111. $x \leq 9$

112. $g(x) = -\frac{1}{3}x + 2$

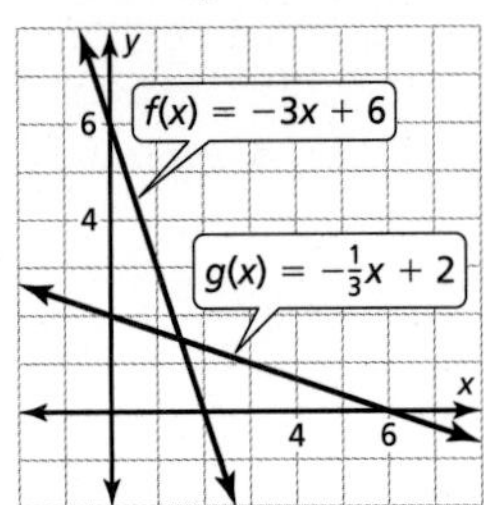

113. $g(x) = \sqrt{\frac{1}{2}x + 9}$

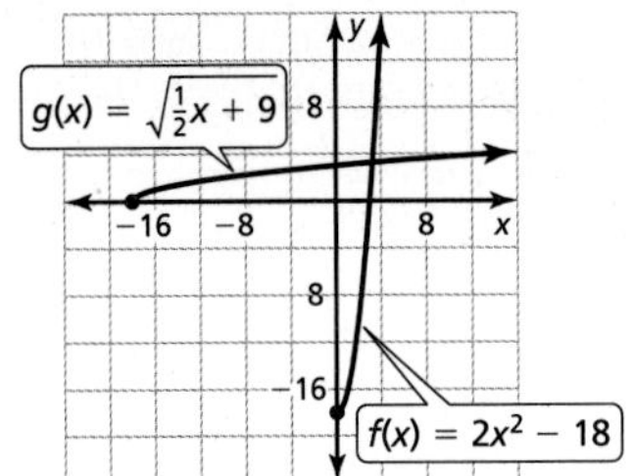

114. $x = 5$

115.

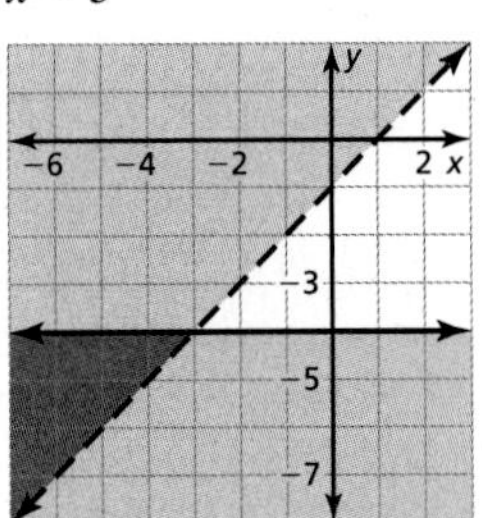

Sample answer: $(-5, -5)$

116.

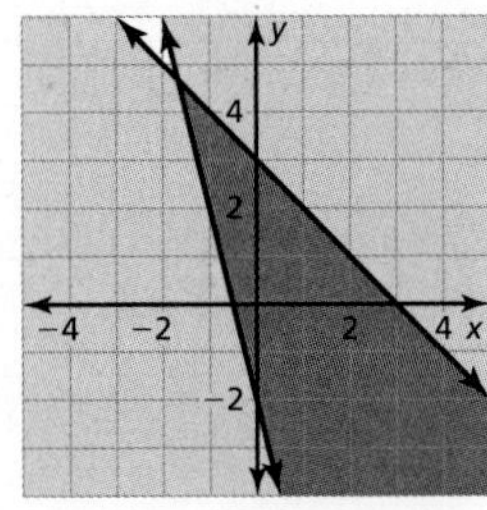

Sample answer: $(0, 0)$

3.3 Practice

1. $x = 9$ and $x = -1$

3. $x = 9 \pm \sqrt{5}$

5. $y = 12 \pm 10i$

7. $w = \frac{-1 \pm 5\sqrt{3}}{2}$

9. $x^2 + 10x + 25$; $(x + 5)^2$

11. $y^2 - 12y + 36$; $(y - 6)^2$

13. $x^2 - 6x + 9$; $(x - 3)^2$

15. $z^2 - 5z + \frac{25}{4}$; $\left(z - \frac{5}{2}\right)^2$

17. $w^2 + 13w + \frac{169}{4}$; $\left(w + \frac{13}{2}\right)^2$

19. 4; $x^2 + 4x + 4$

21. $x = -3 \pm \sqrt{6}$

23. $x = -2 \pm \sqrt{6}$

25. $z = \frac{-9 \pm \sqrt{85}}{2}$

27. $t = -2 \pm 2i$

29. $x = -3 \pm i$

31. $x = 5 \pm 2\sqrt{7}$

33. factoring; The equation can be factored; $x = 7$ and $x = -3$

35. square roots; The equation can be written in the form $u^2 = d$; $x = -8$ and $x = 0$

37. completing the square; The equation cannot be factored or written in the form $u^2 = d$; $x = -6 \pm i\sqrt{14}$

39. completing the square; The equation cannot be factored or written in the form $u^2 = d$; $x = -1 \pm \frac{\sqrt{10}}{2}$

41. square roots; The equation can be written in the form $u^2 = d$; $x = \pm 11i$

43. $y = (x - 4)^2 + 3$; $(4, 3)$

45. $g(x) = (x + 6)^2 + 1$; $(-6, 1)$

47. $f(x) = \left(x - \frac{3}{2}\right)^2 + \frac{7}{4}$; $\left(\frac{3}{2}, \frac{7}{4}\right)$

49. $y = -(x + 1)^2 - 8$; $(-1, -8)$

51. $f(x) = 2(x - 2)^2 - 21$; $(2, -21)$

53. The value of c was not squared before being introduced into the expression; $x^2 + 30x + \left(\frac{30}{2}\right)^2$; $x^2 + 30x + 225$

55. **a.** 20 ft

b. about 2.12 sec

57. $x = -5 + 5\sqrt{3}$

59. $x = -2 + 2\sqrt{21}$

61. **a.** \$3600

b. *Sample answer:* vertex form; The y-coordinate of the vertex of the graph gives the maximum value.

63. no; The problem cannot be solved by factoring because the answers are not rational.

65. E and F

67. *Sample answer:* $g(x) = x^2 + 4x + 1$; $x = -2 \pm \sqrt{3}$;

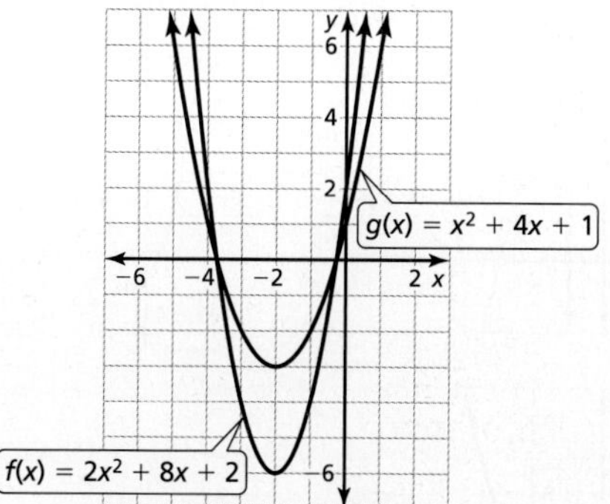

69. $x = \dfrac{-b \pm \sqrt{b^2 - 4c}}{2}$; The Quadratic Formula when $a = 1$

71. a. *Sample answer:* Let the left and right borders be 0.25 centimeter and the top and bottom borders be 0.5 centimeter;
$f(x) = [x + 2(0.25)][2x + 2(0.5)] = 2(x + 0.5)^2$
When $f(x) = 120$, $x \approx 7.25$. So, the dimensions of the screen are about 7.25 centimeters by about $2(7.25) = 14.5$ centimeters.

b. 

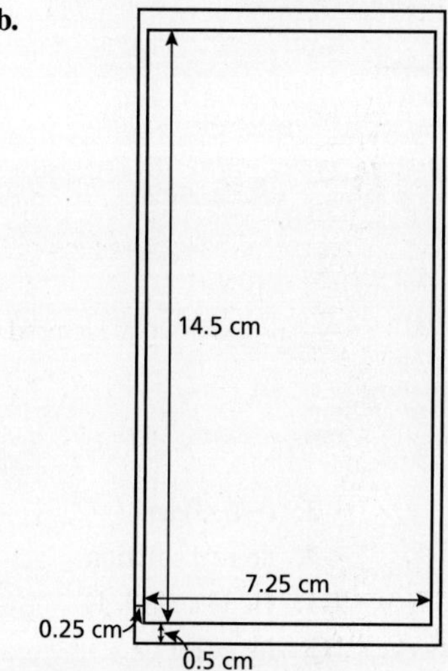

3.3 Review & Refresh

72.

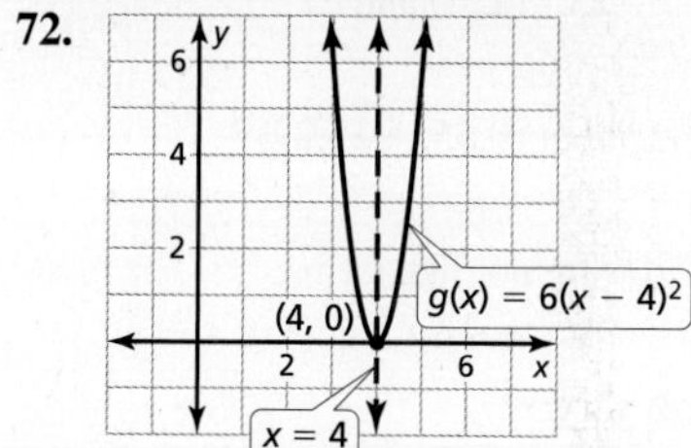

73.

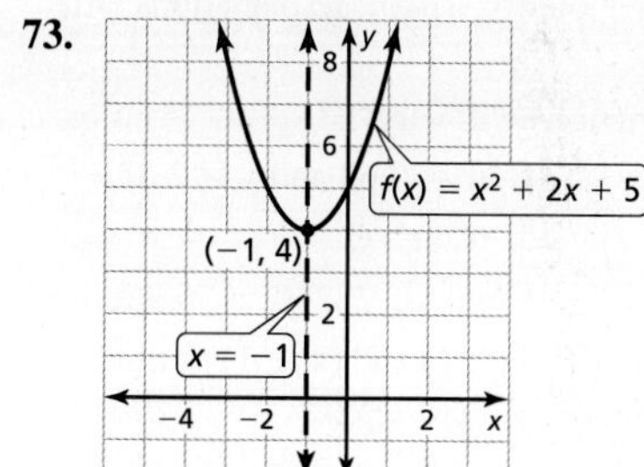

74.

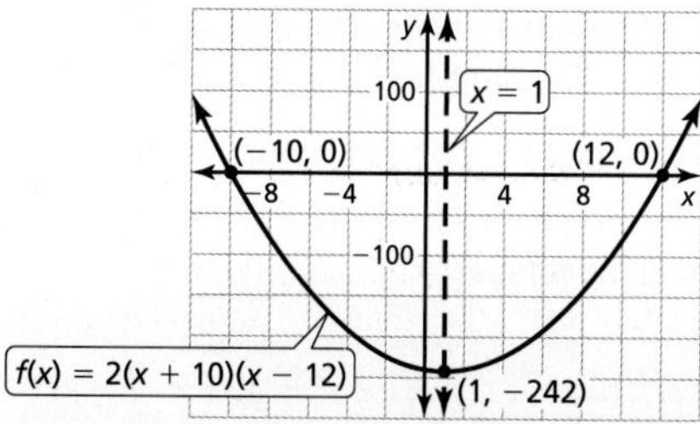

75. $x < 4$

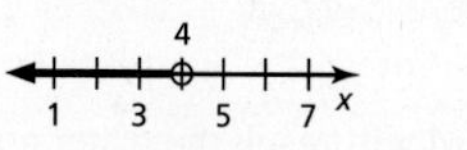

76. $y \leq -1$

77. $n > -15$

78. $s \geq -20$

79. $-2 + 8i$

80. $2 + 16i$

81. $14 - 22i$

82. $77 - 36i$

83. absolute value; The graph is a translation 1 unit left and 2 units down of the parent absolute value function.

84. $y = (x + 1)^2 - 49$; $(-1, -49)$

85. $m = -\frac{3}{2}$; $m = \frac{2}{3}$

86. $g(x) = -3|x + 5|$

87. $g(x) = \frac{1}{3}(x + 4) - \frac{2}{3}$

88. $y = 5x^2 - 2x + 6$

89. $t = 2 \pm i\sqrt{5}$

90. 8 ft

3.4 Practice

1. $x = 3$ and $x = 1$

3. $x = -3 \pm i\sqrt{6}$

5. $x = 7$

7. $x = \dfrac{-1 \pm i\sqrt{14}}{3}$

9. $x = 5$

11. $x = \dfrac{3 \pm \sqrt{89}}{8}$

13. $z = 6 \pm \sqrt{30}$

15. 0; one real: $x = -6$

17. 400; two real: $n = 3$ and $n = -2$

19. -135; two imaginary: $x = \dfrac{5 \pm 3i\sqrt{15}}{8}$

21. 0; one real: $x = -4$

23. C; The discriminant is negative, so the graph has no x-intercepts.

25. A; The discriminant is positive, so the graph has two x-intercepts. The y-intercept is -9.

27. The i was left out after taking the square root;
$x = \dfrac{-10 \pm \sqrt{-196}}{2} = \dfrac{-10 \pm 14i}{2}$
$= -5 \pm 7i$

29. *Sample answer:* $a = 1$ and $c = 5$; $x^2 + 4x + 5 = 0$

31. *Sample answer:* $a = 2$ and $c = 4$; $2x^2 - 8x + 4 = 0$

33. *Sample answer:* $a = 5$ and $c = -5$; $5x^2 + 10x + 5 = 0$

35. A

37. $h = -16t^2 - 55t + 10$

39. yes; no; *Sample answer:* When $h = 26$, $t = 1$ and $t \approx 1.19$. When $h = 30$, the equation has two imaginary solutions.

41. $-5x^2 + 8x - 12 = 0$

43. $-7x^2 + 4x - 5 = 0$

45. $3x^2 + 4x + 1 = 0$

47. $x = \pm 2\sqrt{2}$; *Sample answer:* square roots; The equation can be written in the form $u^2 = d$.

49. $x = 9$ and $x = -3$; *Sample answer:* factoring; The equation can be factored.

51. $x = -4 \pm \sqrt{29}$; *Sample answer:* completing the square; $a = 1$ and b is an even number.

53. $x = \frac{-1 \pm 3i}{4}$; *Sample answer:* Quadratic Formula; $a \neq 1$, the equation cannot be factored, and it cannot be easily written in the form $u^2 = d$.

55. $x = 6$

57. *Sample answer:* $a = \frac{13}{2}, c = \frac{13}{2}; \frac{13}{2}x^2 - 13x + \frac{13}{2} = 0$

59. *Sample answer:* $a = \frac{1}{4}, c = \frac{1}{4}; \frac{1}{4}x^2 + \frac{1}{2}x + \frac{1}{4} = 0$

61. **a.** about 0.97 sec

 b. the first bird; The second bird will reach the water after about 0.98 second.

63. *Sample answer:* A basketball is pushed downward from a height of 3 feet at a speed of 6 feet per second; $h = -16t^2 - 6t + 3$; about 0.28 second

65. using the Quadratic Formula; Completing the square will require factoring out a 4 from the first two terms, resulting in a decimal coefficient with the linear term.

67. Add the solutions to get $\frac{-b}{a}$, then divide the result by 2 to get $-\frac{b}{2a}$; Because it is symmetric, the vertex of a parabola is halfway between the two x-intercepts and the x-coordinate of the vertex is $-\frac{b}{2a}$.

69. $n = \frac{1}{4}$; $b^2 - 4ac = 0$, so $(-3)^2 - 4(1)(n + 2) = 0$, $9 - 4n - 8 = 0$, $-4n = -1$, and $n = \frac{1}{4}$.

71. *Sample answer:* Using the Quadratic Formula, the solutions are $x = \frac{-b \pm \sqrt{b^2 - 4ac}}{2a} = \frac{-b}{2a} \pm \frac{\sqrt{b^2 - 4ac}}{2a}$, so when $b^2 - 4ac < 0$, the solutions are complex conjugates; If $x = 3i$ and $x = -2i$ are solutions, then the equation can be written as $a(x - 3i)(x + 2i) = ax^2 - aix + 6a$. a and ai cannot both be real numbers.

73. yes; $1 \pm i\frac{\sqrt{2}}{2}$

3.4 Review & Refresh

74. (4, 5); Explanations will vary.

75. (2, 3); Explanations will vary.

76. no solution; Explanations will vary.

77. (0, 2); Explanations will vary.

78. $x = 2$ and $x = -4$

79. $x = 3 \pm i$

80. $x = -2 \pm 2i$

81. $y = (x - 5)^2 - 21$; $(5, -21)$

82. $x = 2$ and $y = -6$

83. 100

84. 104

85. $x = 3$

86. $x = 2, x = 3$

87. $x = \frac{-9 \pm \sqrt{33}}{8}$

88. $x = \frac{-1 \pm \sqrt{5}}{2}$

89. $-1.5 < x \leq 2.5$

90. $g(x) = -x - 9$

91. $g(x) = \frac{1}{2}|x + 2| - \frac{1}{2}$

92. 20%

93.

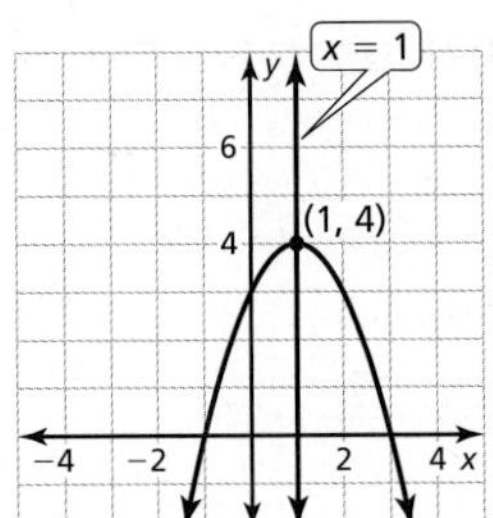

94.

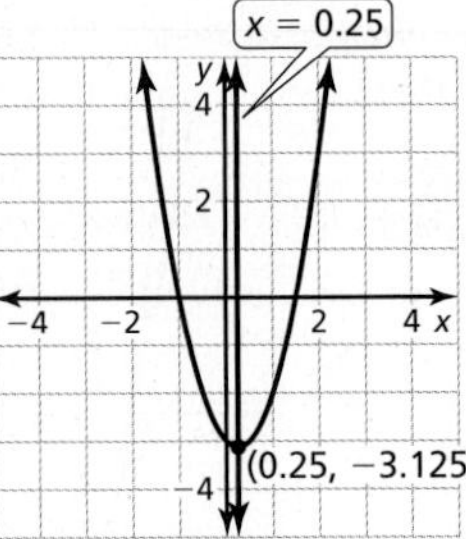

95.

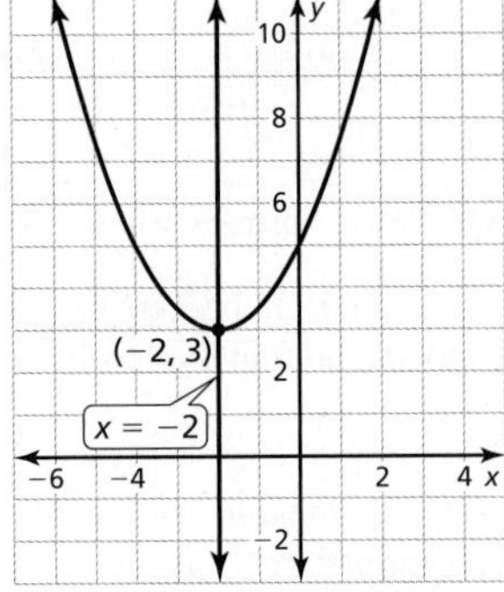

96.

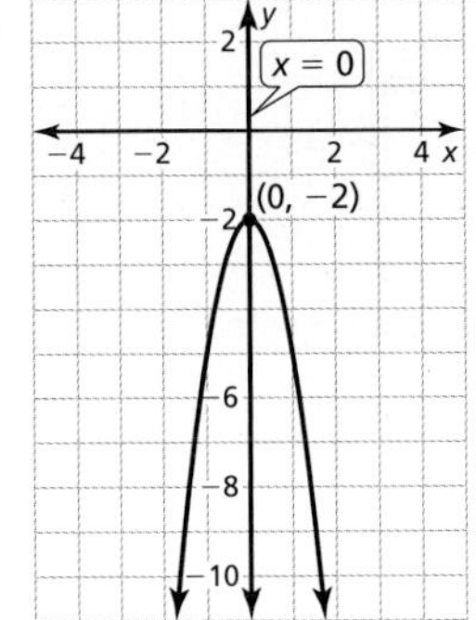

3.5 Practice

1. no real solution

3. (−6, 3) and (−2, 3)

5. (0, 2) and (−2, 0)

7. no real solution

9. (−4, 2)

11. (1, 1) and (3, 1)

13. (3, 8) and (−1, 4)

15. (4, −2)

17. no real solution

19. (2, 3) and (−2, 3)

21. no real solution

23. (2, 7) and (0, 5)

25. no real solution

27. about (−4.65, −4.71) and about (0.65, −15.29)

29. (−4, −4) and (−6, −4)

31. The terms that were added were not like terms; $0 = 2x^2 - x - 36 = (2x - 9)(x + 4)$; $x = -4$ or $x = \frac{9}{2}$

33. (0, −1); Explanations will vary.

35. about (−11.31, 10) and about (5.31, 10); Explanations will vary.

37. (3, 3) and (5, 3); Explanations will vary.

39. $x = 0$

41. $x \approx 0.63$ and $x \approx 2.37$

43. $x = 2$ and $x = 3$

45. A and C

47. from (−18, 36) to (36, 18), a length of $\sqrt{3240} \approx 56.9$ miles

49. *Sample answer:* Graph to find (3, 1) and (4, −1) as the points of intersection. Solve by factoring $0 = 4x^2 + 28x + 48 = 4(x - 3)(x - 4)$ where $x = 3$ and $x = 4$; Explanations will vary.

51. your friend; $(3, -3)$ and $(-3, 3)$ are solutions to Equation 1, but not Equation 2.

53. If (x, y) is a solution, then $(-x, -y)$ must be a solution. The solutions will always be reflections in the origin.

55. a. no solution, one solution, two solutions, three solutions, or four solutions

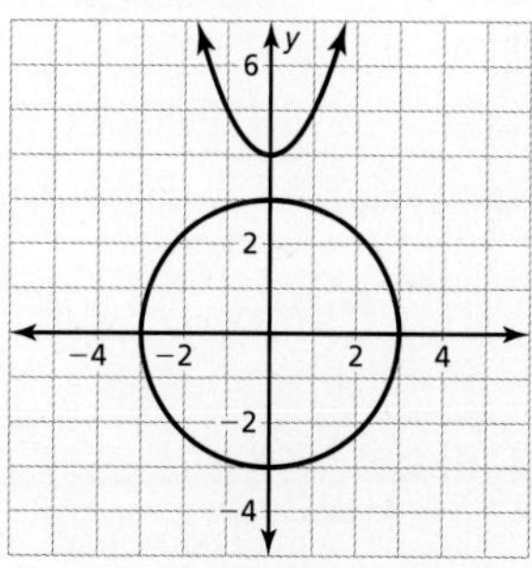

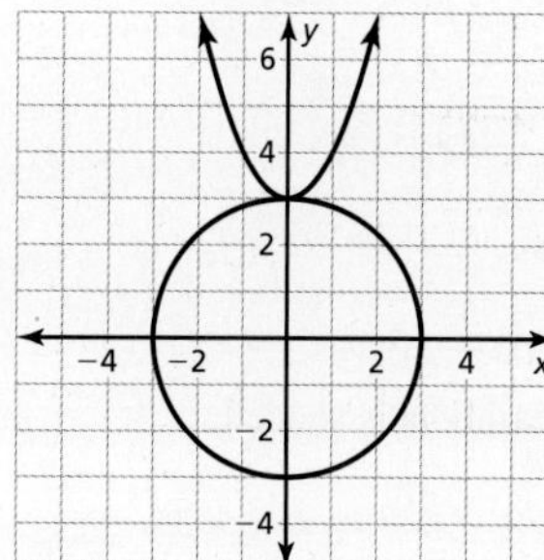

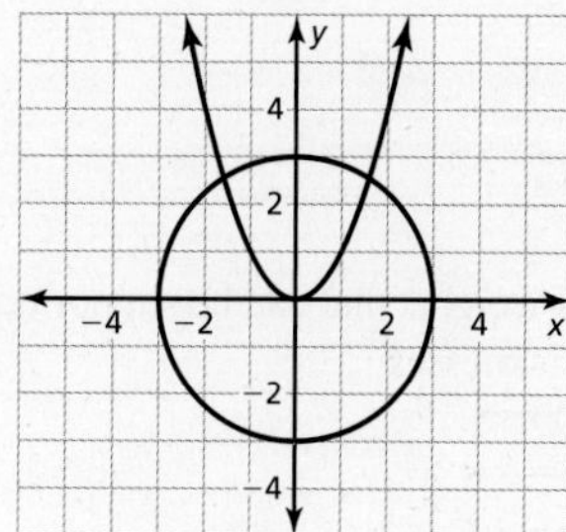

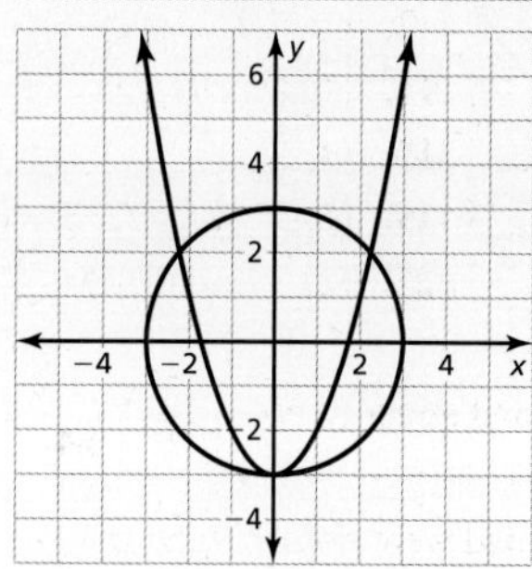

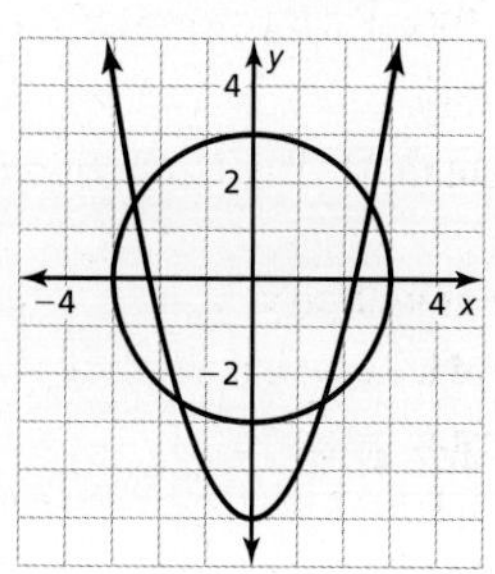

b. no solution, one solution, or two solutions

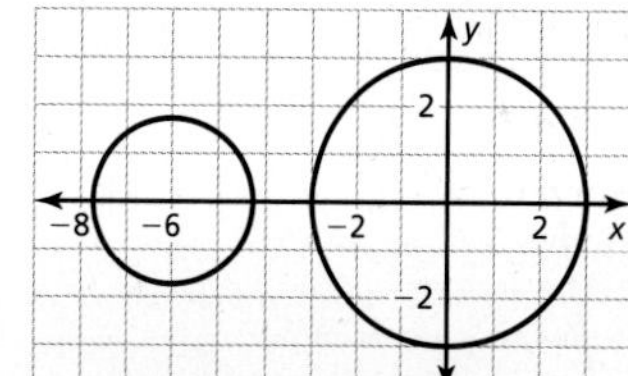

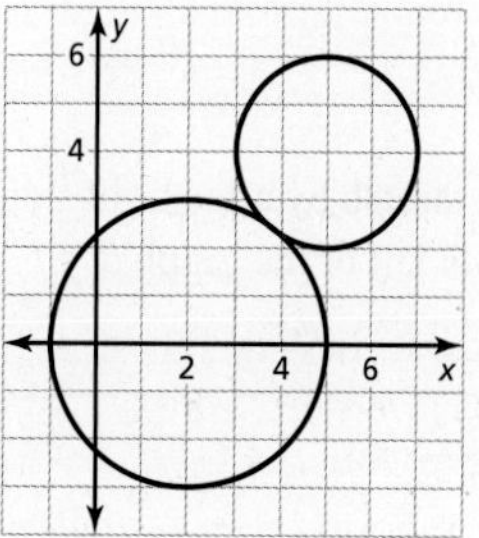

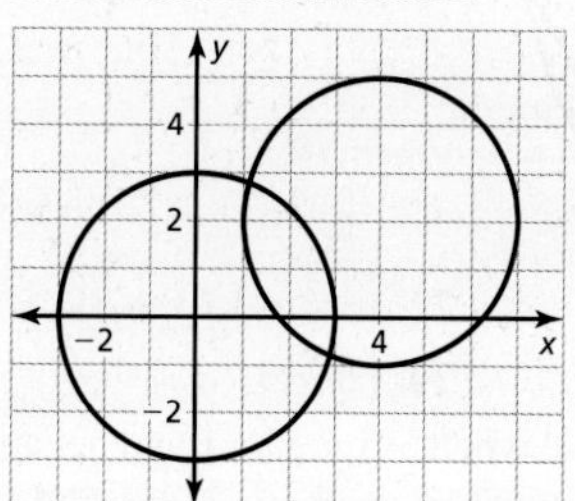

57. $(0, 2)$

3.5 Review & Refresh

59. $x > 3$

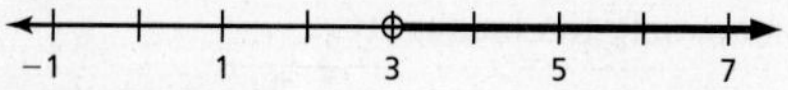

60. $x \leq -3$

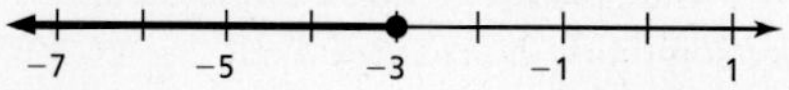

61. $x \leq -4$

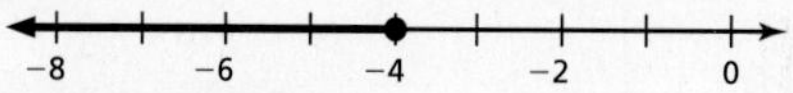

62. all real numbers

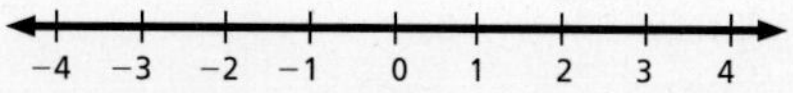

63. $y \geq -x + 1$

64. $y < x - 2$

65. $(-1, -4)$; Explanations will vary.

66. $(-3, -4)$ and $(4, 3)$; Explanations will vary.

67.

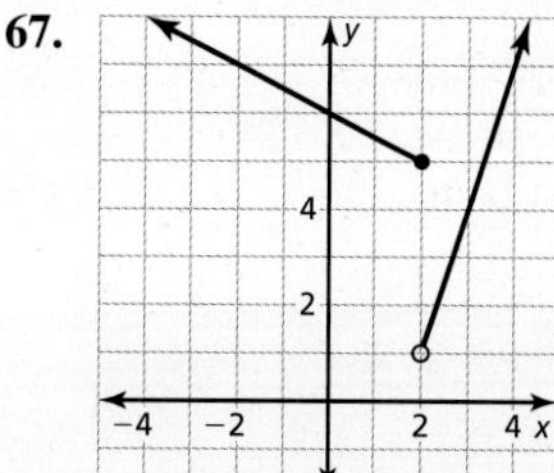

domain: all real numbers, range: $y > 1$

68. no; The ball reaches a maximum height of about 33.6 feet.

69. The graph of g is a horizontal translation 5 units right and 3 units down of the graph of f.

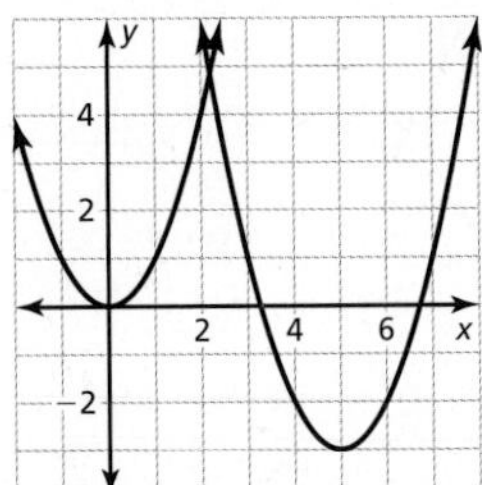

70. The graph of g is a vertical stretch by a factor of $\frac{1}{4}$ and a horizontal translation 2 units left of the graph of f.

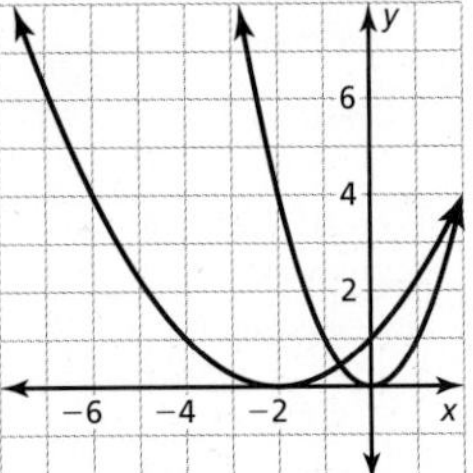

71. ± 18

72. $y = -1.0x + 19$

73. $12i$

74. $2i\sqrt{13}$

75. The function is positive when $-5 < x < 1$ and negative when $x < -5$ and $x > 1$. The function is increasing when $x < -2$ and decreasing when $x > -2$.

3.6 Practice

1. C; The x-intercepts are $x = -1$ and $x = -3$. The test point $(-2, 5)$ does not satisfy the inequality.

3. B; The x-intercepts are $x = 1$ and $x = 3$. The test point $(2, 5)$ does not satisfy the inequality.

5\.

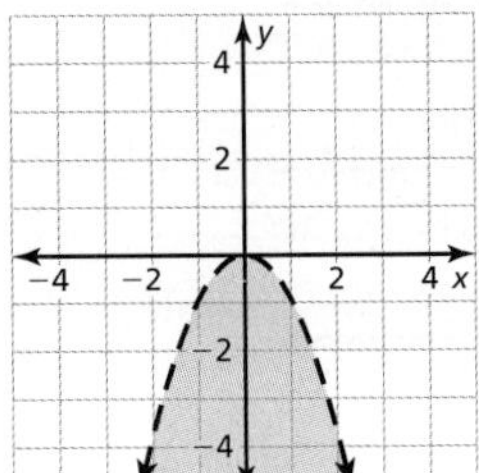

7\.

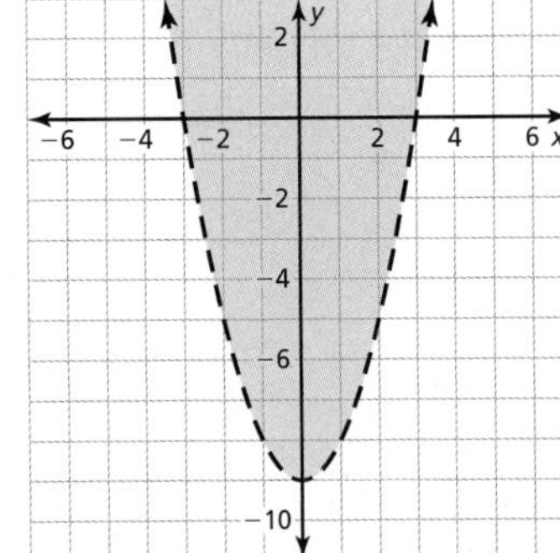

9\.

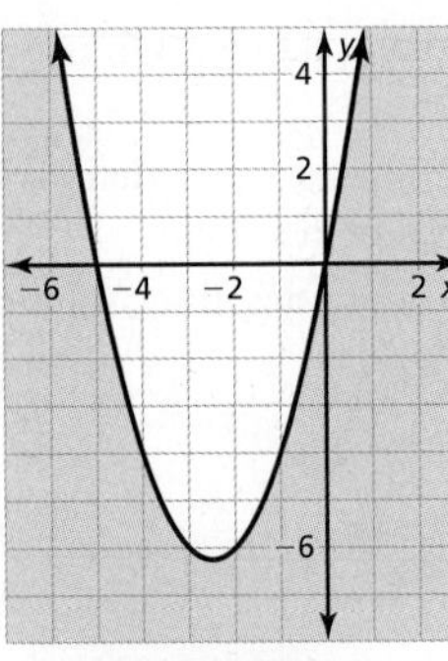

11\.

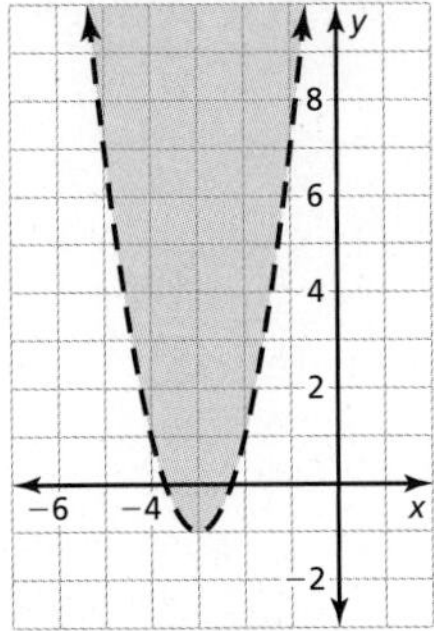

13. *Sample answer:* $y < -(x - 2)^2$

15. The wrong side of the parabola is shaded.

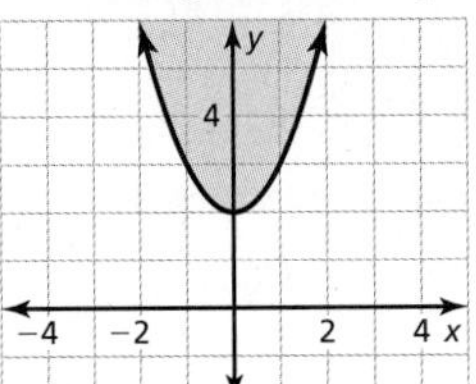

17. The solution represents weights that can be supported by shelves with various thicknesses.

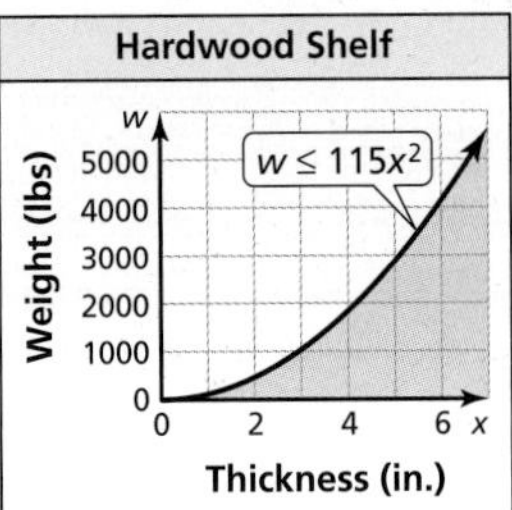

19\.

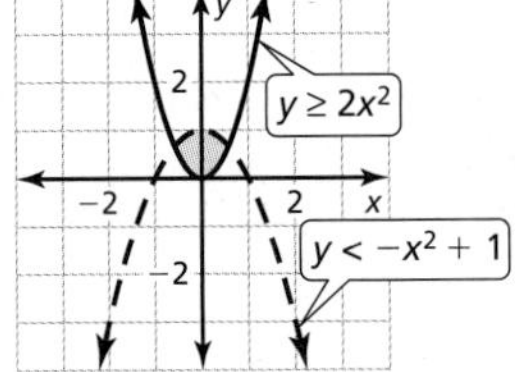

21\.

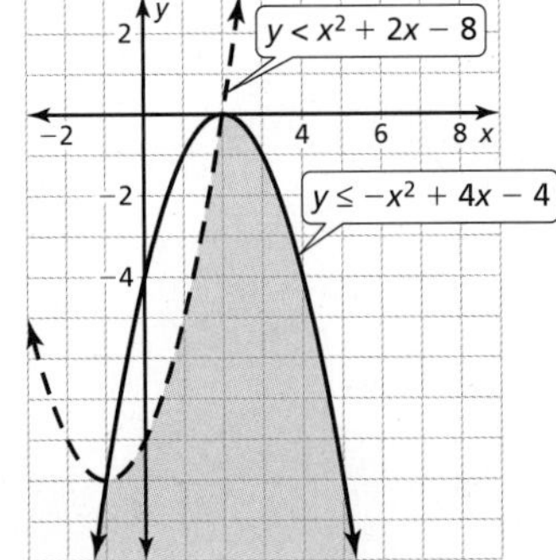

23.

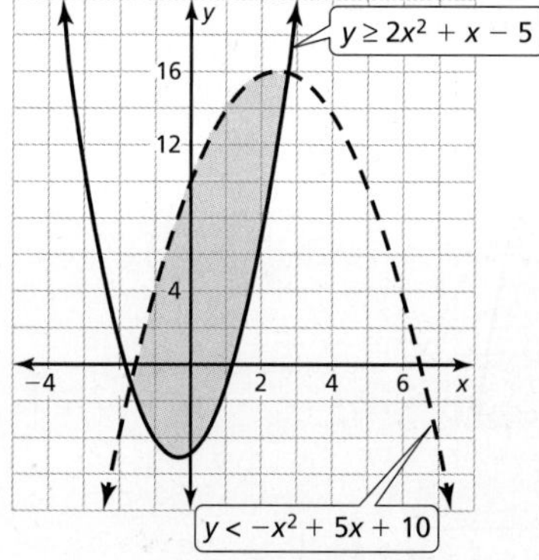

25.

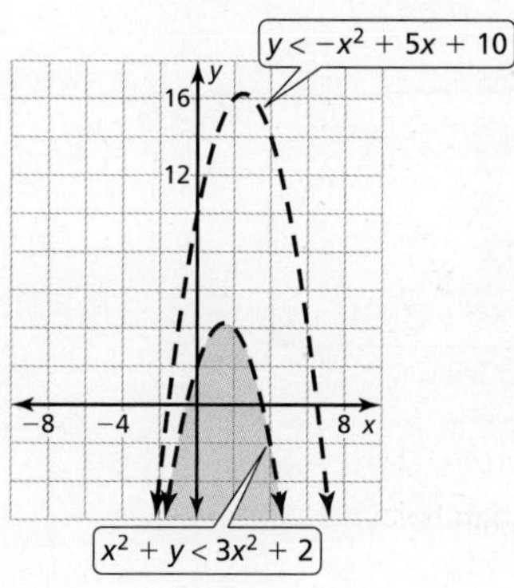

27. $-\frac{5}{2} < x < \frac{5}{2}$

29. $x \leq 4$ or $x \geq 7$

31. $-0.5 \leq x \leq 3$

33. $x < -2$ or $x > 4$

35. $\frac{3}{2} - \frac{\sqrt{5}}{2} < x < \frac{3}{2} + \frac{\sqrt{5}}{2}$

37. $x < -7$ or $x > -1$

39. $-2 \leq x \leq \frac{4}{3}$

41. $x \leq -3\sqrt{15}$ or $x \geq -3 + \sqrt{15}$

43. at least 70 ft and at most 130 ft

45. **a.** $x_1 < x < x_2$

b. $x < x_1$ or $x > x_2$

c. $x_1 < x < x_2$

47. 4; $T(x) > 1000$ when $x > 3.1$.

49. after about 23 days through 44 days; Because the domain is $0 \leq x \leq 44$, only the positive solution for x is used.

51. **a.** $\frac{32}{3} \approx 10.67$ square units

b. $\frac{256}{3} \approx 85.33$ square units

53. **a.** yes; The points on the parabola that are exactly 11 feet high are (6, 11) and (14, 11). Because these points are 8 feet apart, there is enough room for a 7-foot wide truck.

b. 8 ft

c. about 11.2 ft

3.6 Review & Refresh

55.

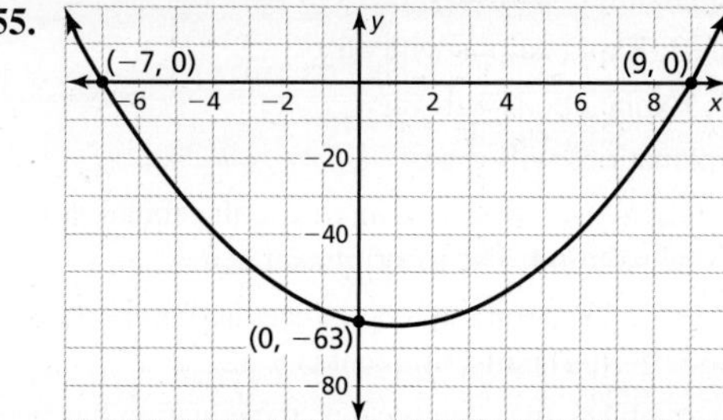

56.

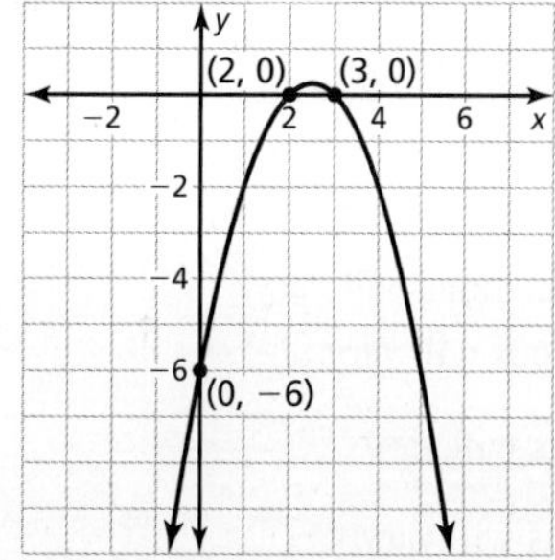

57. The maximum value is -1; The function is increasing when $x < -3$ and decreasing when $x > -3$.

58. The minimum value is -1; The function is decreasing when $x < -2$ and increasing when $x > -2$.

59.

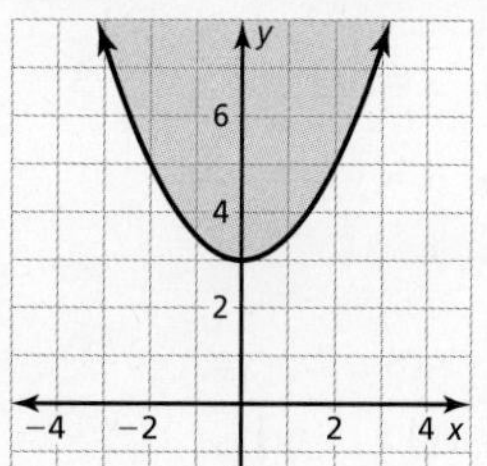

60.

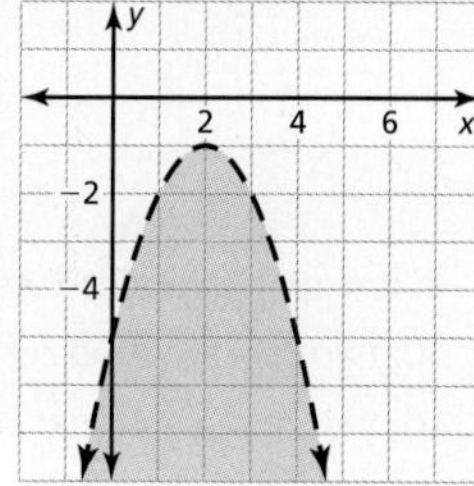

61. $(-1, -2)$ and $(1, 2)$

62. -55; two imaginary solutions: $\pm i\sqrt{55}$

63. 216; two real solutions: $\pm 6\sqrt{6}$

64. $x = -6 \pm 4\sqrt{2}$

65. $x = -3 \pm i$

66. $a_n = 2(3)^n$; $a_8 = 13{,}122$

67. **a.** The cost of renting the pavilion is \$30 per hour with an initial fee of \$50.

b. $0 < x \leq 24$; The domain is discrete because the pavilion cannot be rented for part of an hour.

c.

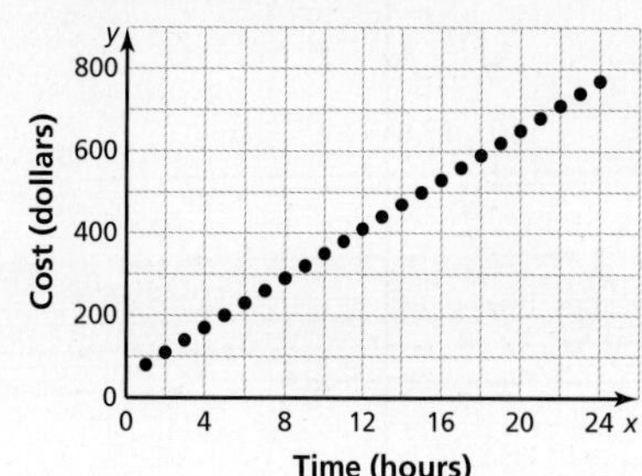

68. $\left(\frac{114}{89}, -\frac{286}{89}, \frac{398}{89}\right)$

69. no real solution

70. $y = -3x + 4$

Chapter 3 Review

1. $x = \pm 5$; Explanations will vary.

2. $x = \pm 2$; Explanations will vary.

3. $x = 2$ and $x = -8$; Explanations will vary.

4. $x = 6$ and $x = 2.5$; Explanations will vary.

5. $h(t) = -16t^2 + 3$; about 0.43 sec

6. **a.** yes; Because a and c are both positive, $b^2 - 4ac$ could be negative.

b. no; If $a > 0$ and $c < 0$, then $b^2 - 4ac > 0$.

c. no; If $a < 0$ and $c > 0$, then $b^2 - 4ac > 0$.

d. yes; Because a and c are both negative, $b^2 - 4ac$ could be negative.

7. $(x + 18)(x + 35) = 1260$; $x = 10$; 28 ft by 45 ft

8. $x = 9$ and $y = -3$

9. $5 - 3i$

10. $11 + 10i$

11. $-62 + 11i$

12. 68

13. $(7 + 3i)$ ohms

14. $x = \pm i\sqrt{3}$

15. $x = \pm 4i$

16. $x = -10$ and $x = 4$; Explanations will vary.

17. $x = -8 \pm \sqrt{47}$; Explanations will vary.

18. $x = \dfrac{-4 \pm 3i}{2}$; Explanations will vary.

19. $x = 3 \pm 3\sqrt{2}$; Explanations will vary.

20. $y = (x - 1)^2 + 19$; $(1, 19)$

21. 94 ft

22. $10 + 2\sqrt{15} \approx 17.7$ ft by $20 - 4\sqrt{15} = 4.5$ ft or $10 - 2\sqrt{15} \approx 2.3$ ft by $20 + 4\sqrt{15} \approx 35.5$ ft

23. $x = \dfrac{5 \pm \sqrt{17}}{2}$

24. $x = 0.5$ and $x = -3$

25. $x = \frac{3}{2}$

26. $x = \dfrac{6 \pm i\sqrt{3}}{3}$

27. 0; one real solution: $x = -3$

28. 40; two real solutions: $x = 1 \pm \sqrt{10}$

29. 16; two real solutions: $x = -5$ and $x = -1$

30. *Sample answer:* $a = 6$, $c = 6$; $6x^2 + 12x + 6 = 0$

31. $5x^2 - 3x + 7 = 0$

32. about 929.462 m and about 2045.538 m

33. $(-2, 6)$ and $(1, 0)$; Explanations will vary.

34. $(4, 5)$; Explanations will vary.

35. about $(-0.32, 1.97)$ and $(0.92, -1.77)$; Explanations will vary.

36. $x \approx -0.14$ and $x \approx 1.77$

37. $x = 0$ and $x = \frac{9}{2}$

38.

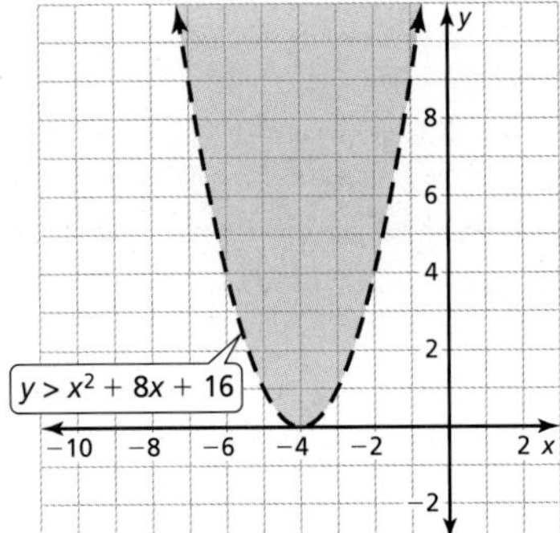

39.

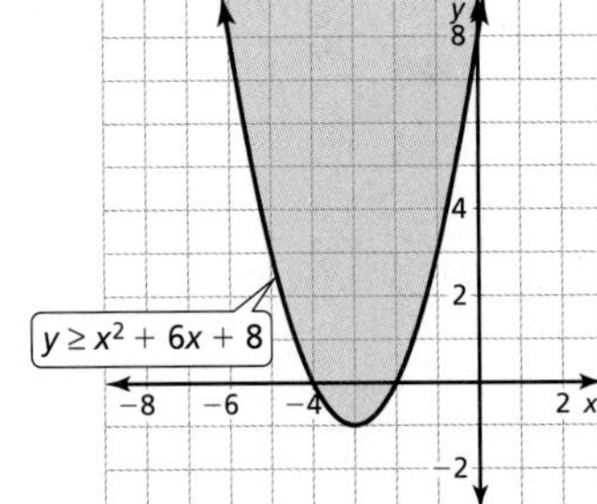

40.

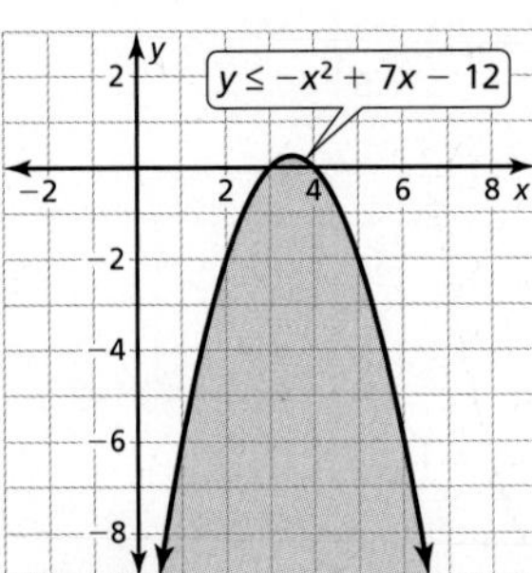

41.

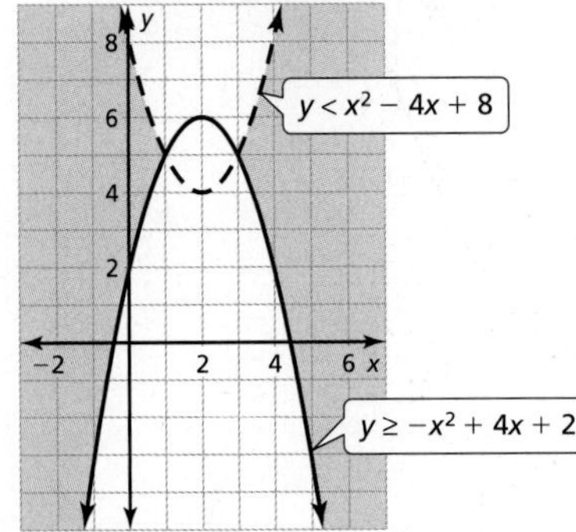

42.

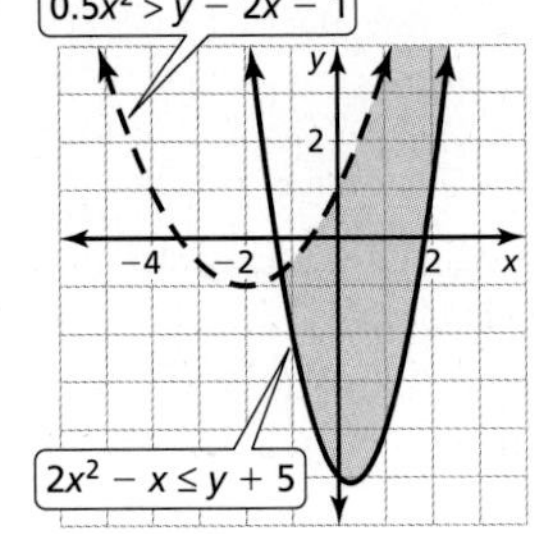

43. $x \le -5$ or $x \ge 4$

44. $x < -7$ or $x > -3$

45. $\frac{2}{3} \le x \le 1$

46. a. $>$ or $\ge$; $4(-1)^2 - 3(-1) > (-1) + 6$, $7 > 5$

b. $<$ or $\le$; $4(1)^2 - 3(1) < (-4) + 6$, $1 < 2$

c. *Sample answer:* $\ge$ or $\le$; $4(2)^2 - 3(2) \ge (4) + 6$, $10 \ge 10$

Chapter 3 Mathematical Practices (Chapter Review)

1. To ensure that you are currently writing a quadratic equation that models the situation; An equation for area can be written to solve the problem using the length and width of the quilt and total area of the fabric to find the width of the border.

2. Set up an equation for perimeter, $2\ell + 2w = 400$, and an inequality for the area $\ell w > 9100$. Solve the perimeter equation for ℓ and substitute the result into the inequality for the area. Solve the resulting inequality.

Chapter 3 Practice Test

1. $x = \pm 6$; Explanations will vary.

2. $x = -1 \pm i\sqrt{2}$; Explanations will vary.

3. $x = 3 \pm \sqrt{2}$; Explanations will vary.

4. $x = \pm 2$; Explanations will vary.

5. Because the graph has only one x-intercept, the equation has exactly one real solution; The discriminant is 0.

6. Because the graph has no x-intercept, the equation has two imaginary solutions; The discriminant is -32.

7. Because the graph has two x-intercepts, the equation has two real solutions; The discriminant is 6.25.

8. (6, −6) and (8, −2) **9.** (−6, −2) and (2, 6)

10.

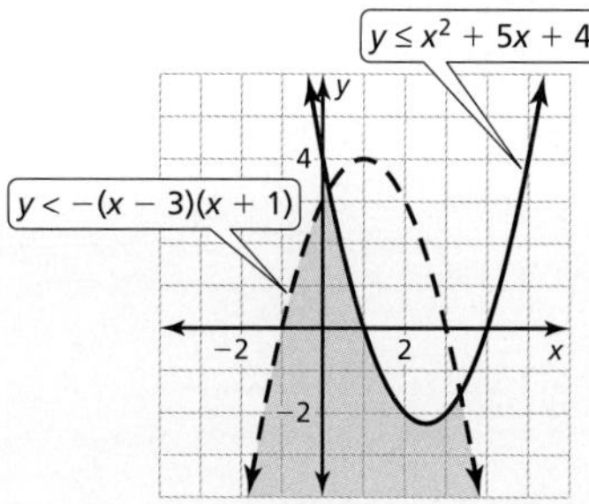

11.

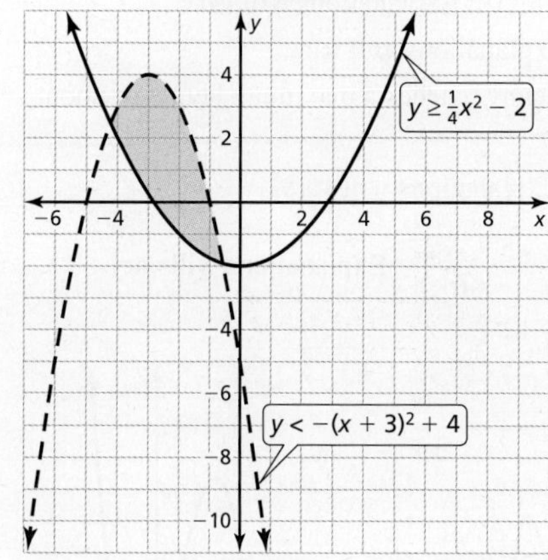

12. $36 - 2i$

13. 4.25 ft; about 35.6 ft; The y-coordinate of the vertex is 4.25 and the x-intercept of the graph is about 35.6.

14. about 55 ft to about 580 ft; Graph $y = -0.0063x^2 + 4x$ and $y = 200$ and determine the points of intersection. The graph is above 200 feet between these points.

15. The width is about 27.9 inches and the height is about 15.7 inches; Solving $32^2 = (9x)^2 + (16x)^2$ for x gives $x \approx 1.743$.

Chapter 3 College and Career Readiness

1. B **2.** C

3. B

4. a. about 196.5 ft

b. about 423 ft

5. B, C **6.** $-\frac{3}{5}$; 12

7. B

8. a. *Sample answer:* $h = -5$; $k = 2$

b. *Sample answer:* $h = 2$; $k = 1$

c. *Sample answer:* $h = -4$; $k = -6$

9. C

Chapter 4

Chapter 4 Prepare

1. $7y + 6$ **2.** $x + 4$

3. $z - 4$ **4.** $5x$

5. $6x^2 + 4x + 5$ **6.** $2x^2 + 5$

7. 64 in.^{3} **8.** $\frac{32\pi}{3}$ ft^3 $\approx$ 33.51 ft^3

9. 48 ft^3 **10.** 45π cm^3 $\approx$ 141.37 cm^3

11. by a factor of k^3

4.1 Practice

1. polynomial function; $f(x) = 5x^3 - 6x^2 - 3x + 2$; degree: 3 (cubic), leading coefficient: 5

3. not a polynomial function

5. polynomial function; $h(x) = -\sqrt{7}x^4 + 8x^3 + \frac{5}{3}x^2 + x - \frac{1}{2}$; degree 4: (quartic), leading coefficient: $-\sqrt{7}$

7. The function is not in standard form so the wrong term was used to classify the function; f is a polynomial function. The degree is 4 and f is a quartic function. The leading coefficient is −7.

9. $f(-4) = -192$ **11.** $h(-2) = -46$

13. $g(8) = -43$ **15.** $p\left(\frac{1}{2}\right) = \frac{45}{4}$

17. The function f has degree 0 (constant) because it can also be written as $f(x) = 13x^0$. The leading coefficient is 13; $f(x) \to 13$ as $x \to -\infty$ and $f(x) \to 13$ as $x \to +\infty$ because the y-values are always 13.

19. $h(x) \to -\infty$ as $x \to -\infty$ and $h(x) \to -\infty$ as $x \to +\infty$

21. $f(x) \to +\infty$ as $x \to -\infty$ and $f(x) \to +\infty$ as $x \to +\infty$

23. The degree of the function is odd and the leading coefficient is negative.

25.

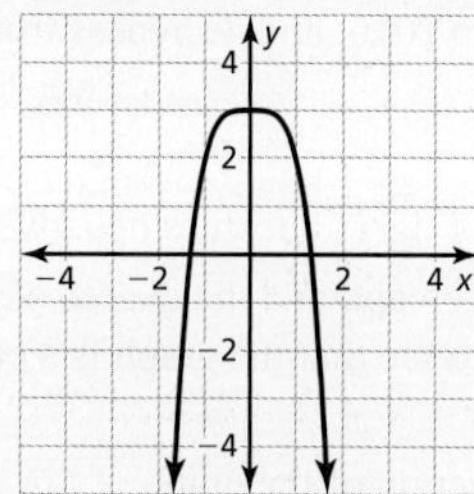

27.

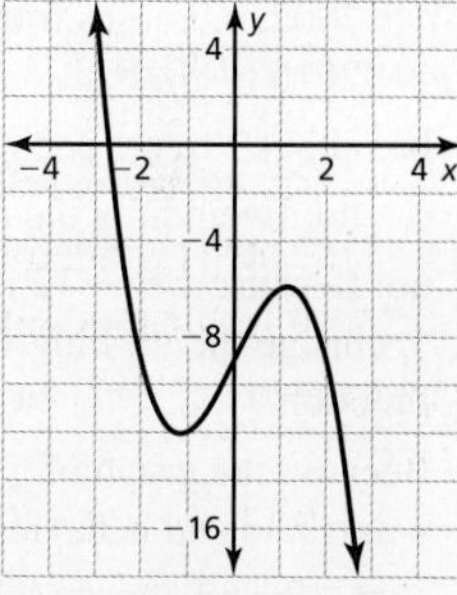

29.

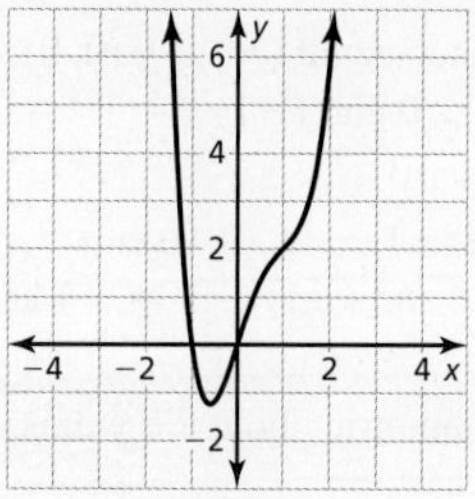

31.

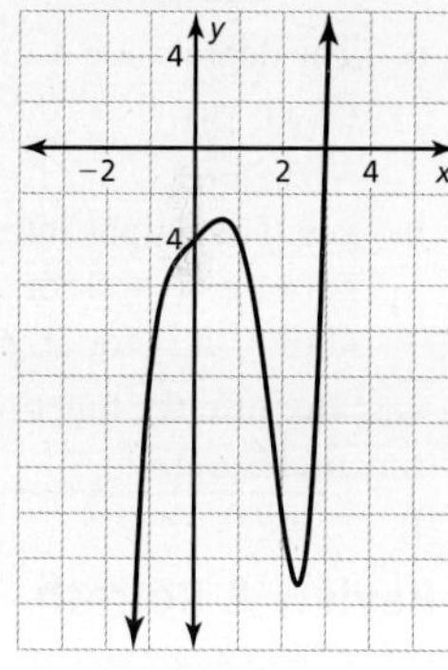

33. a. $x > 4$

b. $x < 4$

c. $x < 3$ and $x > 5$

d. $3 < x < 5$

35. The degree is even and the leading coefficient is positive.

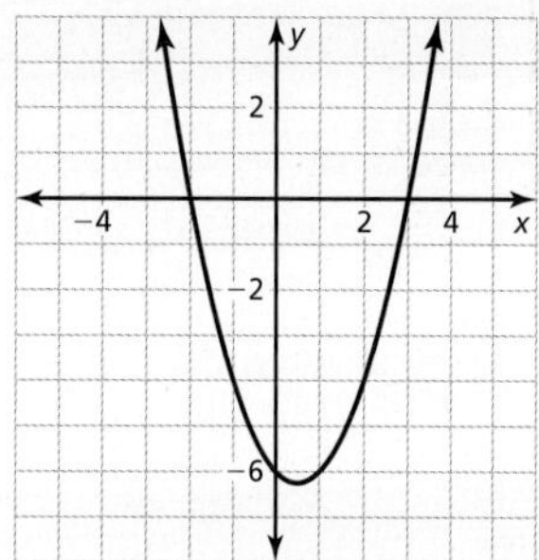

37. The degree is even and the leading coefficient is positive.

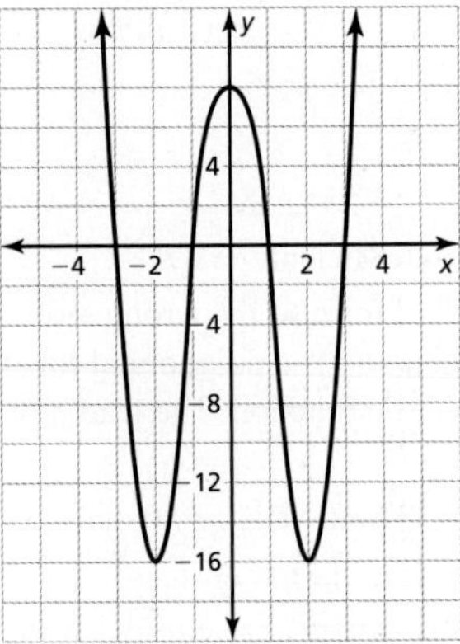

39. a. 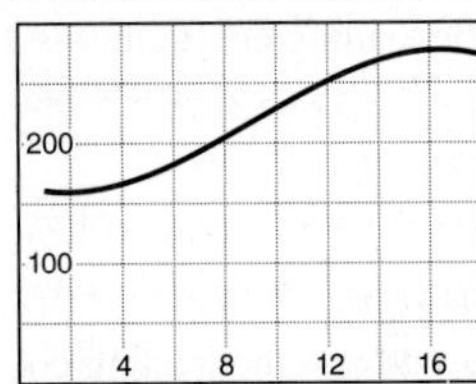

The number of tigers decreases slightly from 2001 to 2002, increases from 2002 to 2016, and decreases from 2016 to 2018.

b. about 7 tigers per year

c. no; Eventually the number of tigers becomes negative.

41. no; Because $x = -12$ is an x-intercept, and the degree of f is 3, change the viewing window to see that the graph is a cubic function.

43. Because the graph of g is a reflection of the graph of f in the y-axis, the end behavior would be opposite; $g(x) \to -\infty$ as $x \to -\infty$ and $g(x) \to +\infty$ as $x \to +\infty$.

45. a. The degrees are even and intersect at $(-1, 1)$, $(0, 0)$, and $(1, 1)$; yes; $0^n = 0$ for all $n > 0$ and $(-1)^{2n} = 1^{2n} = 1$ for all $n > 0$.

b. yes; The graphs intersect at $(-1, -1)$, $(0, 0)$ and $(1, 1)$ because $0^n = 0$ for all $n > 0$ and $(-1)^{2n+1} = -1$ and $(1)^{2n+1} = 1$ for all $n > 0$.

47. yes; Because the function is symmetric about the y-axis, the function is even.

49. B

4.1 Review & Refresh

51. $12kz - 4kw$

52. $-7a^5 + 10m$

53. $g(x) = -|x - 2| - 1$

54. The graph of g is a horizontal translation 5 units left of the graph of f.

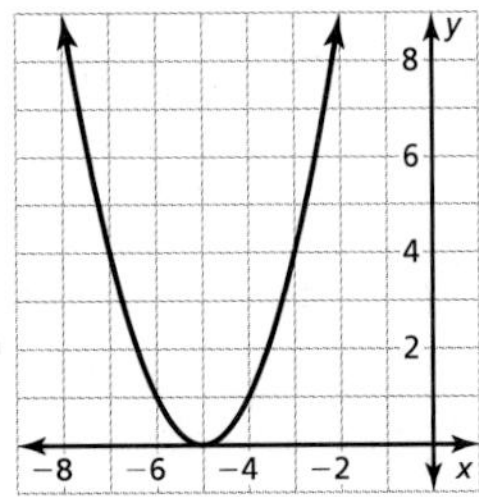

55. The graph of g is a vertical stretch by a factor of $\frac{3}{2}$ and a reflection in the x-axis of the graph of f.

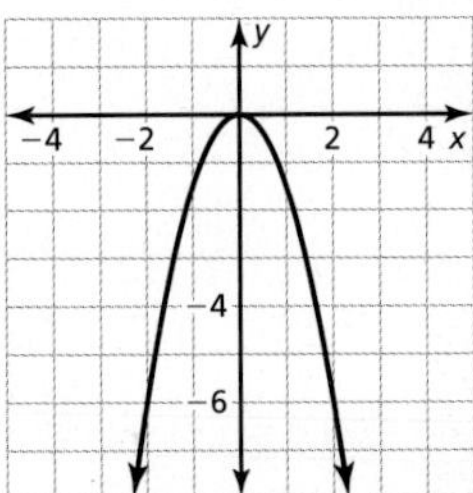

56. $(-2, -4)$ and $(2, 0)$; Explanations will vary.

57. no solution; Explanations will vary.

58. yes; no; The penny reaches a maximum height of about 13.8 feet.

59. $-\frac{1}{2} \le x \le 4$; Explanations will vary.

60. $\frac{5 - \sqrt{37}}{6} < x < \frac{5 + \sqrt{37}}{6}$; Explanations will vary.

61. $x < -3$ or $x > 12$

62. 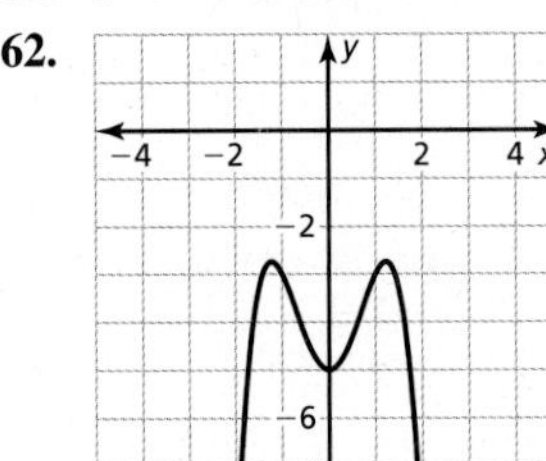

63. 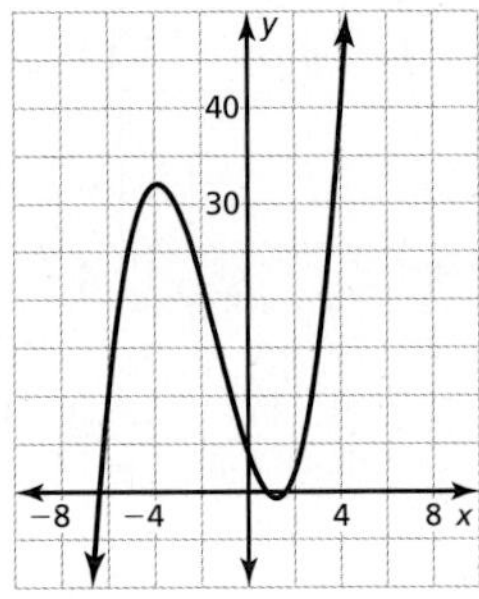

64. polynomial function; $f(x) = -4x^4 + \frac{5}{2}x^3 + \sqrt{2}x^2 + 4x - 6$; degree: 4 (quartic), leading coefficient: -4

4.2 Practice

1. $x^2 + x + 1$

3. $12x^5 + 5x^4 - 3x^3 + 6x - 4$

5. $7x^6 + 7x^5 + 8x^3 - 9x^2 + 11x - 5$

7. $-2x^3 - 14x^2 + 7x - 4$

9. $5x^6 - 7x^5 + 6x^4 + 9x^3 + 7$

11. $-x^5 + 7x^3 + 11x^2 + 10x - 4$

13. $35x^5 + 21x^4 + 7x^3$

15. $-10x^3 + 23x^2 - 24x + 18$

17. $x^4 - 5x^3 - 3x^2 + 22x + 20$

19. $3x^5 - 6x^4 - 6x^3 + 25x^2 - 23x + 7$

21. $x^3 + 3x^2 - 10x - 24$

23. $12x^3 - 29x^2 + 7x + 6$

25. $-24x^3 + 86x^2 - 57x - 20$

27. $(a + b)(a - b) = a^2 - ab + ab - b^2 = a^2 - b^2$;
Sample answer: $24 \cdot 16 = (20 + 4)(20 - 4)$
$= 20^2 - 4^2$
$= 400 - 16$
$= 384$

29. $x^2 - 81$

31. $9c^2 - 30c + 25$

33. $49h^2 + 56h + 16$

35. $8k^3 + 72k^2 + 216k + 216$

37. $p^3q^3 - 6p^2q^2 + 12pq - 8$

39. The negative was not distributed through the entire second set of parenthesis;
$(x^2 - 3x + 4) - (x^3 + 7x - 2) = x^2 - 3x + 4 - x^3 - 7x + 2$
$= -x^3 + x^2 - 10x + 6$

41. $36m^2 + 24m + 4$

43. $16q^4 - 96q^3 + 216q^2 - 216q + 81$

45. $y^5z^5 + 5y^4z^4 + 10y^3z^3 + 10y^2z^2 + 5yz + 1$

47. $23.19t^2 - 343.6t + 20{,}991$; 20,991,000 people attend degree-granting institutions during the year when $t = 0$.

49. $2x^3 + 10x^2 + 14x + 6$

51. no; The set of polynomials is closed under addition, subtraction, and multiplication and $x^2 + 3x + 2x^{-1}$ is not a polynomial.

53. $x^3 + 94.9x^2 + 549.7x + 966.5$

55. a. $5000(1 + r)^3 + 1000(1 + r)^2 + 4000(1 + r)$

b. $7000r^3 + 25{,}000r^2 + 34{,}000r + 16{,}000$; 7000 is the total amount of money that gained interest for three years, 25,000 is the total amount of money that gained interest for two years, 34,000 is the total amount of money that gained interest for one year, and 16,000 is the total amount of money invested.

c. about \$16,342.51

57.

1
1 1
1 2 1
1 3 3 1
1 4 6 4 1
1 5 10 10 5 1
1 6 15 20 15 6 1
1 7 21 35 35 21 7 1
1 8 28 56 70 56 28 8 1
1 9 36 84 126 126 84 36 9 1
1 10 45 120 210 252 210 120 45 10 1

$(x + 3)^7 = x^7 + 21x^6 + 189x^5 + 945x^4 + 2835x^3 + 5103x^2 + 5103x + 2187$;

$(x - 5)^9 = x^9 - 45x^8 + 900x^7 - 10{,}500x^6 + 78{,}750x^5 - 393{,}750x^4 + 1{,}312{,}500x^3 - 2{,}812{,}500x^2 + 3{,}515{,}625x - 1{,}953{,}125$

59. a. 5; 5; 9

b. m; m; $m + n$

61. $1 + 5i + 10i^2 + 10i^3 + 5i^4 + i^5$; $-4 - 4i$

63. a. $(x^2 - y^2)^2 + (2xy)^2 = (x^2 + y^2)^2$

$(x^4 - 2x^2y^2 + y^4) + (4x^2y^2) = x^4 + 2x^2y^2 + y^4x^4 + 2x^2y^2 + y^4 = x^4 + 2x^2y^2 + y^4$

b. The Pythagorean triple is 11, 60, and 61;

$(11)^2 + (60)^2 = (61)^2$

$121 + 3600 = 3721$

$3721 = 3721$

4.2 Review & Refresh

65. $x \approx 0.745$ and $x \approx 4.922$

66. $4x^2 + 5x - 5$

67. $-x^4 - 9x^3 + 2x^2 + x - 15$

68. $3x^3 - 10x^2 + 9x - 2$

69. $x^3 - 12x^2 + 48x - 64$

70. $x = -\frac{1}{24}y^2$

71. $f(x) \to +\infty$ as $x \to -\infty$ and $f(x) \to -\infty$ as $x \to +\infty$

72. $g(x) \to +\infty$ as $x \to -\infty$ and $g(x) \to +\infty$ as $x \to +\infty$

73. -8; The axis of symmetry is $x = -3$, so the other x-intercept is 5 units left of $(-3, 0)$.

74.

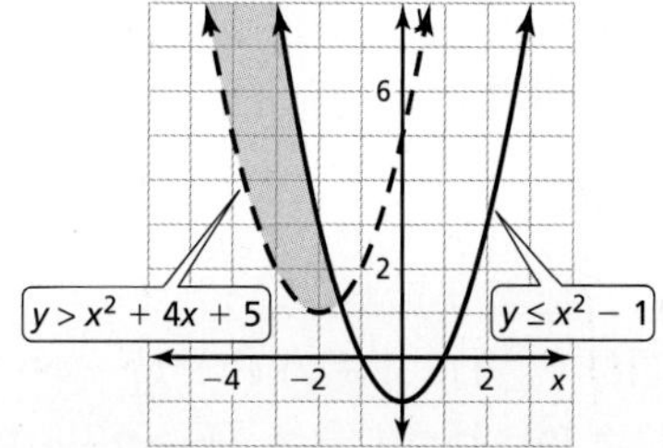

75. $y = 0.25$

76. $y = -3$

77. $8 + 7i$

78. $5 + 11i$

79. 21

80. $9 - 2i$

81. 350 ft²

4.3 Practice

1. $x + 5 + \dfrac{3}{x - 4}$

3. $x + 1 + \dfrac{2x + 3}{x^2 - 1}$

5. $2 + \dfrac{-2x^2 + x + 7}{4x^3 + x^2 - 2x - 3}$

7. $5x^2 - 12x + 37 + \dfrac{-122x + 109}{x^2 + 2x - 4}$

9. $x + 12 + \dfrac{49}{x - 4}$

11. $2x - 11 + \dfrac{62}{x + 5}$

13. $x^2 - 3x + 5 - \dfrac{9}{x + 3}$

15. $x^3 + x^2 - 2x + 1 - \dfrac{6}{x - 6}$

17. D; $(2)^2 + (2) - 3 = 3$ so the remainder must be 3.

19. C; $(2)^2 - (2) + 3 = 5$ so the remainder must be 5.

21. The quotient should be one degree less than the dividend.

$$\frac{x^3 - 5x + 3}{x - 2} = x^2 + 2x - 1 + \frac{1}{x - 2}$$

23. $f(-1) = 37$

25. $f(2) = 11$

27. $f(6) = 181$

29. $f(3) = 115$

31. 48 in.

33. no; The Remainder Theorem states that $f(a) = 25$.

35. A

37. $5x^3 - 3x^2 + 21x - 8$; *Sample answer:* Multiply by $x + 2$.

4.3 Review & Refresh

39. $x = 3$

40. $x = -6$ and $x = 2$

41. $x = -9$ and $x = -5$

42. $x = \pm 3i$

43. $f(-5) = -98$

44. $y = -\frac{1}{4}(x + 6)^2 - 3$

45. $k = 6$

46.

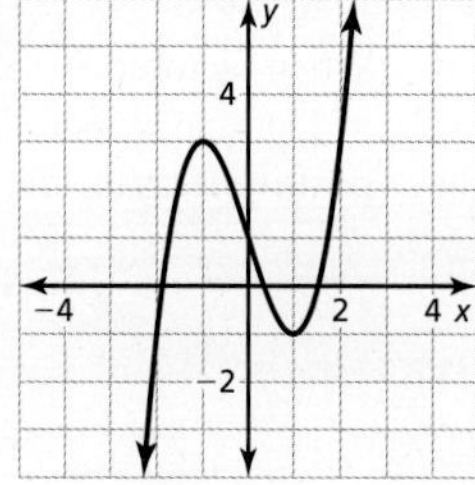

47. $4x^2 + 6x + 17 + \dfrac{35x + 25}{x^2 - 2x - 1}$

48. $x = 4$

49. $x = 7$

50. $\frac{23}{50}$, or 46%

51. $10x\sqrt{3x}$

52. $\dfrac{\sqrt{10}}{7}$

53. $9\sqrt{3} - 6\sqrt{5}$

54. $3\sqrt{2}$

55. at least 5 ft and at most 20 ft

4.4 Practice

1. $x(x - 6)(x + 4)$ **3.** $3p^3(p - 8)(p + 8)$

5. $q^2(2q - 3)(q + 6)$ **7.** $w^8(5w - 2)(2w - 3)$

9. $(x + 4)(x^2 - 4x + 16)$ **11.** $(g - 7)(g^2 + 7g + 49)$

13. $4h^6(h - 4)(h^2 + 4h + 16)$ **15.** $2t^4(2t + 5)(4t^2 - 10t + 25)$

17. $x^2 + 9$ is not a factorable binomial because it is not the difference of two squares; $3x^3 + 27x = 3x(x^2 + 9)$

19. $(y^2 + 6)(y - 5)$ **21.** $(3a^2 + 8)(a + 6)$

23. $(x - 2)(x + 2)(x - 8)$ **25.** $(2q + 3)(2q - 3)(q - 4)$

27. $(7k^2 + 3)(7k^2 - 3)$ **29.** $(c^2 + 5)(c^2 + 4)$

31. $(2z - 5)(2z + 5)(4z^2 + 25)$

33. $3r^2(r^3 + 5)(r^3 - 4)$ **35.** factor

37. not a factor **39.** factor

41.

−4	1	−1	−20	0
		−4	20	0
	1	−5	0	0

$g(x) = x(x + 4)(x - 5)$

43.

6	1	−6	0	−8	48
		6	0	0	−48
	1	0	0	−8	0

$f(x) = (x - 6)(x - 2)(x^2 + 2x + 4)$

45.

−7	1	0	−37	84
		−7	49	−84
	1	−7	12	0

$r(x) = (x + 7)(x - 3)(x - 4)$

47. $a^4(a + 6)(a - 5)$; A common monomial can be factored out to obtain a factorable trinomial in quadratic form.

49. $(z - 3)(z + 3)(z - 7)$; Factoring by grouping can be used because the expression contains pairs of monomials that have a common factor. Difference of two squares can be used to factor one of the resulting binomials.

51. $(4r + 9)(16r^2 - 36r + 81)$; The sum of two cubes pattern can be used because the expression is of the form $a^3 + b^3$.

53. $(4n^2 + 1)(2n - 1)(2n + 1)$; The difference of two squares pattern can be used to factor the original expression and one of the resulting binomials.

55. D; The x-intercepts of the graph are 2, 3, and −1.

57. A; The x-intercepts of the graph are −2, −3, and 1.

59. The model makes sense for $x > 6.5$; When factored completely, the volume is $V = x(2x - 13)(x - 3)$. For all three dimensions of the box to have positive lengths, the value of x must be greater than 6.5.

61. **a.** no; $7z^4(2z + 3)(z - 2)$

b. no; $n(2 - n)(n + 6)(3n - 11)$

c. yes

63. no; $f(x)$ may be factorable by factors other than $x - a$.

65. **a.** $(c - d)(c + d)(7a + b)$

b. $(x^n - 1)(x^n - 1)$

c. $(a^3 - b^2)(ab + 1)^2$

67. $k = 22$

7	2	−13	−22	105
		14	7	−105
	2	1	−15	0

69. **a.** If the volume of the missing block is included, the volume of the diagram is a^3 because the length, width, and height are all a. Because the length, width, and height of the missing piece are b, the volume of the missing block is b^3. Subtracting the volume of the missing block from the entire volume gives $a^3 - b^3$.

b. I: $a^2(a - b)$, II: $ab(a - b)$, III: $b^2(a - b)$

c. $a^3 - b^3 = a^2(a - b) + ab(a - b) + b^2(a - b)$
$= (a - b)(a^2 + ab + b^2)$

4.4 Review & Refresh

71. $x = 6$ and $x = -5$; Explanations will vary.

72. $x = \frac{1}{9}$ and $x = 3$; Explanations will vary.

73. $x = 4 \pm 3\sqrt{3}$; Explanations will vary.

74. $x = \dfrac{-9 \pm \sqrt{85}}{2}$; Explanations will vary.

75. $-x^2 + 3x - 8$

76. The area is $3x^2 + 7x + 3$ and the perimeter is $8x + 8$.

77. polynomial function; $f(x) = -3x^4 - x^3 + 2x^2 - 2x + 5$; degree: 4 (quartic), leading coefficient: −3

78. $(z - 2)(z + 2)(z + 1)$ **79.** $(7b^2 - 8)(7b^2 + 8)$

80. exponential decay function; The common factor is $\frac{1}{4}$.

81.

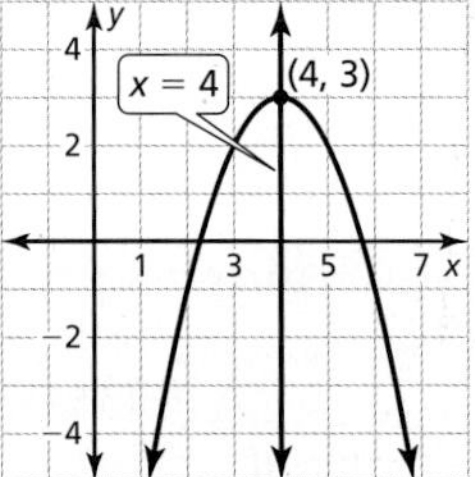

82.

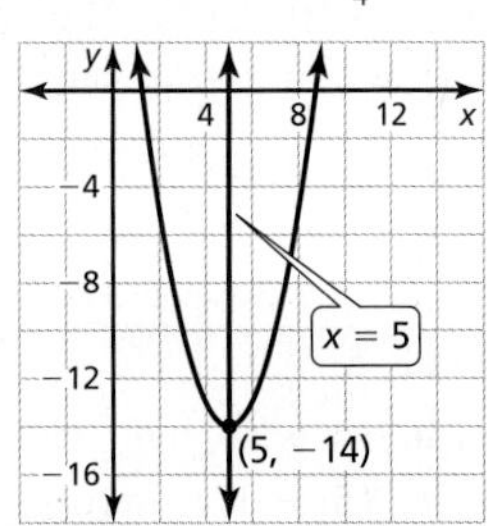

83.

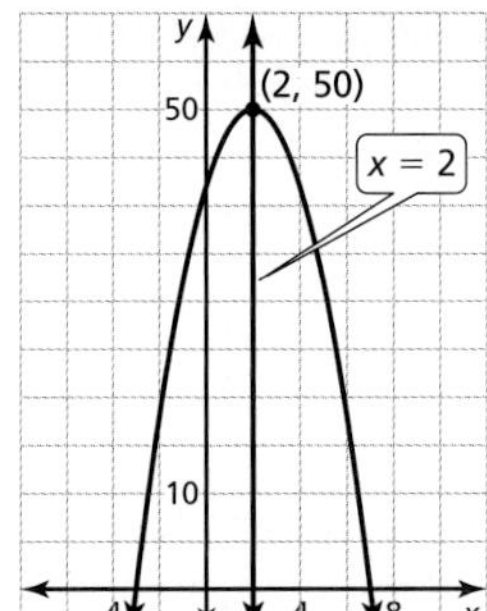

84.

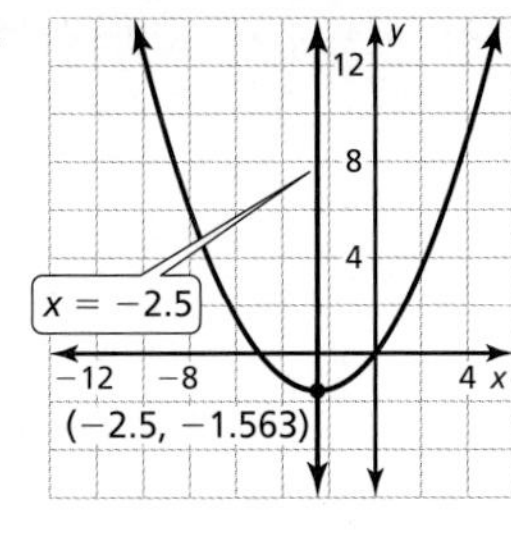

85. yes; $y = 0.18x + 0.4$; You skate about 11.2 miles after 60 minutes.

86. $n + 8.5 \leq 17$

4.5 Practice

1. $z = -3, z = 0$, and $z = 4$ **3.** $x = 0$ and $x = 1$

5. $w = 0$ and $w = \pm\sqrt{10}$ **7.** $c = 0, c = 3$, and $c = \pm\sqrt{6}$

9. $n = -4$

11. $x = -3, x = 0$, and $x = 2$

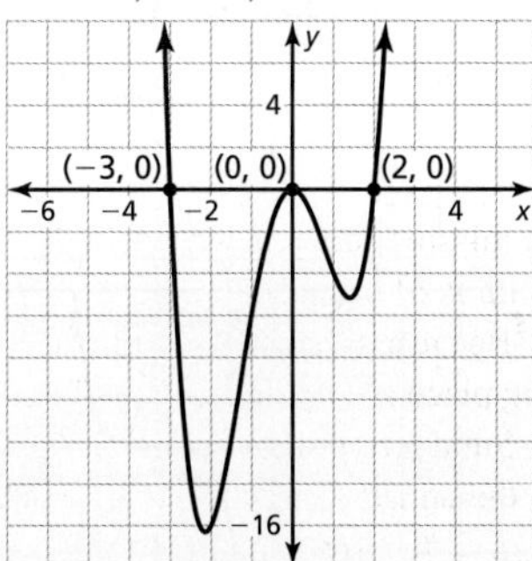

13. $x = 0, x = 5$, and $x = 6$

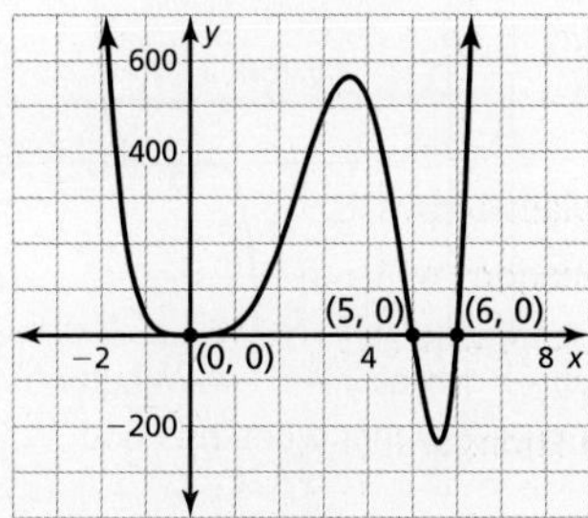

15. $x = -3, x = 0$, and $x = 5$

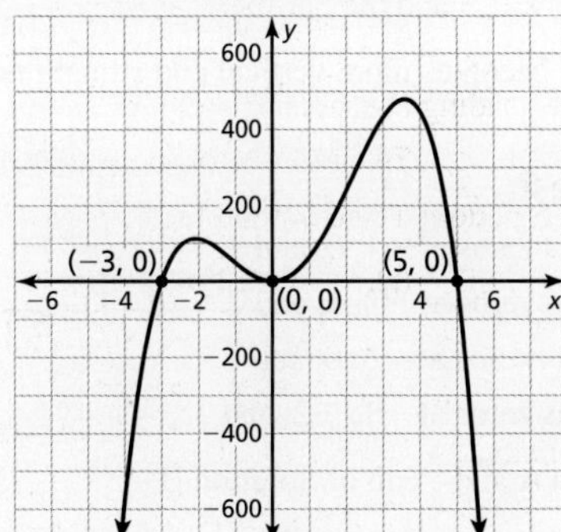

17. $x = -3, x = -1$, and $x = 3$

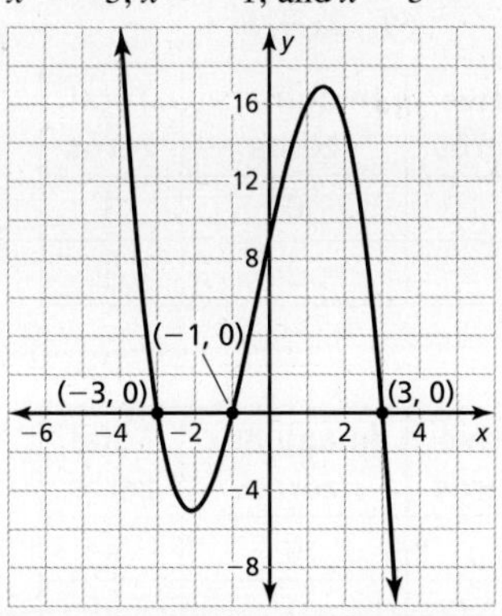

19. no; The graph crosses through the x-axis at each x-intercept.

21. $x = -5, x = 1$, and $x = 3$ **23.** $x = -1, x = 5$, and $x = 6$

25. $x = -3, x = 4$, and $x = 5$

27. $x = -4, x = -0.5$, and $x = 6$

29. C

31. The $\pm$ was not included with each factor; $\pm1, \pm3, \pm5, \pm9, \pm15, \pm45$

33. -1 and 2 **35.** -4, 1.5, and 3

37. $1, \dfrac{-1+\sqrt{17}}{2}$, and $\dfrac{-1-\sqrt{17}}{2}$

39. $-\frac{3}{4}$ and $\frac{1}{2}$

41. $f(x) = x^3 - 7x^2 + 36$ **43.** $f(x) = x^2 - 12x - 29$

45. $f(x) = x^3 - 10x - 12$ **47.** $f(x) = x^4 - 32x^2 + 24x$

49. no; The Rational Root Theorem lists all possible rational zeros, so the zeros could be either irrational or imaginary.

51. $x = 4$

53. no; The number of zeros for a function is always equal to its degree. A cubic function can have three real zeros.

55. 5 years and 10 years **57.** $x = 1$

59. $x = 2$ and $x = 4$

61. **a.** $k = 60$
b. $k = 33$
c. $k = 6$

63. Each side of the base is 2 feet and the height is 3 feet.

4.5 Review & Refresh

65. $4b^2 - 9$ **66.** $25x^2 + 80x + 64$

67. $64p^3 - 96p^2 + 48p - 8$

68. $m^3n^3 + 18m^2n^2 + 108mn + 216$

69. $x^2 - 3x - 4$ **70.** $x^3 + 7x^2 + 11x + 5$

71. linear function; The graph of f is a vertical translation 2 units up of the parent linear function.

72. absolute value function; The graph of f is a vertical stretch by a factor of 3 of the parent absolute value function.

73. $y = -\frac{1}{2}x^2 + 3x + 8$

74. $f(x) = \left(x + \frac{7}{2}\right)^2 + \frac{3}{4}$; vertex: $\left(-\frac{7}{2}, \frac{3}{4}\right)$

75. -2, 1, and 4 **76.** $\frac{1}{5}$ and $\frac{2}{3}$

77. $x = \pm\dfrac{\sqrt{2}}{4}$ **78.** $x = \pm i\sqrt{6}$

79. $x = \pm 2i$ **80.** $x = 4 \pm \sqrt{30}$

81. 30 million grips **82.** $y = \frac{1}{8}x^2 + 3$

83. $x = \frac{1}{4}(y - 2)^2 - 1$

4.6 Practice

1. 3; -5, -2, and 3 **3.** 5; 0, $1 \pm \dfrac{i\sqrt{2}}{2}$

5. 4; -1, 2, $\dfrac{1}{2} - \dfrac{i\sqrt{3}}{2}$, and $\dfrac{1}{2} + \dfrac{i\sqrt{3}}{2}$

7. -1, 1, 2, and 4 **9.** -2, -2, 1, and 3

11. -3, -1, $2i$, and $-2i$ **13.** -4, -1, 2, $i\sqrt{2}$, and $-i\sqrt{2}$

15. 2; The graph shows 2 real zeros, so the remaining zeros must be imaginary.

17. 2; The graph shows no real zeros, so all of the zeros must be imaginary.

19. $f(x) = x^3 + 4x^2 - 7x - 10$

21. $f(x) = x^3 - 11x^2 + 41x - 51$

23. $f(x) = x^3 - 4x^2 - 5x + 20$

25. $f(x) = x^5 - 8x^4 + 23x^3 - 32x^2 + 22x - 4$

27. The conjugate of the given imaginary zeros was not included.

$$\begin{aligned} f(x) &= (x-2)[x-(1+i)][x-(1-i)] \\ &= (x-2)[(x-1)-i][(x-1)+i] \\ &= (x-2)[(x-1)^2-i^2] \\ &= (x-2)[(x^2-2x+1)-(-1)] \\ &= (x-2)(x^2-2x+2) \\ &= x^3-2x^2+2x-2x^2+4x-4 \\ &= x^3-4x^2+6x-4 \end{aligned}$$

29.

Positive real zeros	Negative real zeros	Imaginary zeros	Total zeros
1	1	2	4

31.

Positive real zeros	Negative real zeros	Imaginary zeros	Total zeros
2	1	0	3
0	1	2	3

33.

Positive real zeros	Negative real zeros	Imaginary zeros	Total zeros
3	2	0	5
3	0	2	5
1	2	2	5
1	0	4	5

35.

Positive real zeros	Negative real zeros	Imaginary zeros	Total zeros
3	3	0	6
3	1	2	6
1	3	2	6
1	1	4	6

37. 2014

39. in the 3rd year and in the 9th year

41. 2; $(x-4i)(x+4i)=x^2+16$

43. C; There are two sign changes in the coefficients of $f(-x)$. So, the number of negative real zeros is two or zero, not four.

45. real; The function has degree 3, so it must have three solutions. Because the imaginary solutions come in conjugate pairs, there must be an even number of imaginary solutions. Given that the first two are real, the third must also be real.

47. no; The Fundamental Theorem of Algebra applies to functions of degree greater than zero. Because the function $f(x)=2$ is equivalent to $f(x)=2x^0$, it has degree 0, and does not fall under the Fundamental Theorem of Algebra.

49.

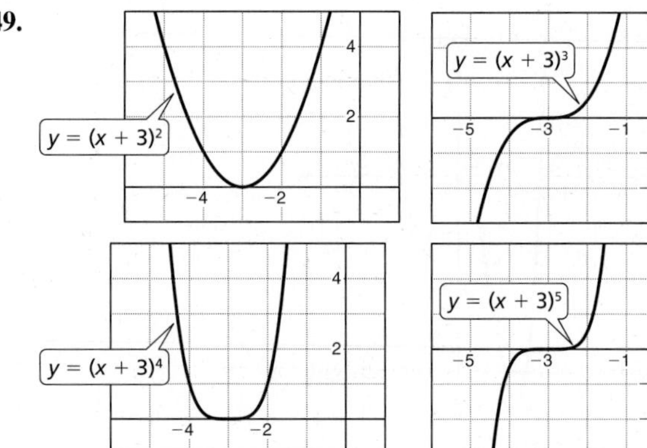

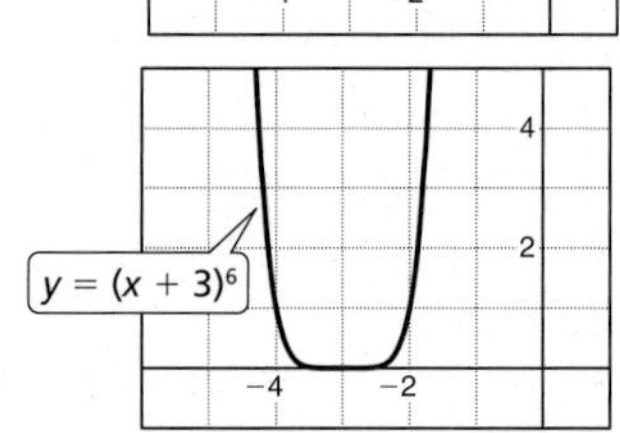

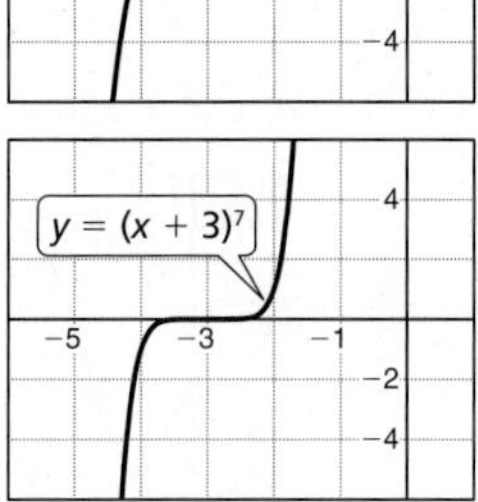

$y=(x+3)^6$

$y=(x+3)^7$

a. For all functions, $f(x)\to+\infty$ as $x\to+\infty$. When n is even, $f(x)\to+\infty$ as $x\to-\infty$, but when n is odd, $f(x)\to-\infty$ as $x\to-\infty$.

b. As n increases, the graph becomes more flat near the zero $x=-3$.

c. The graph of g becomes more vertical and straight near $x=4$.

4.6 Review & Refresh

51. B; The function has zeros at -1, 0, and 3.

52. C; The function has zeros at -3, 1, and 2.

53. D; The function has zeros at -3, 0, and 1.

54. A; The function has zeros at -1, -2, and 3.

55. $1\frac{3}{5}$ cups of Solution A and $\frac{2}{5}$ cup of Solution B

56. $g(x)=-\frac{1}{3}x$

57. $g(x)=\left|\frac{1}{9}x+1\right|-3$

58. $g(x)=-(x-2)^2+7$

59. $2x+5$

60.

Positive real zeros	Negative real zeros	Imaginary zeros	Total zeros
2	1	0	3
0	1	2	3

$-1, \frac{3}{2}$, and 2

61.

Positive real zeros	Negative real zeros	Imaginary zeros	Total zeros
2	2	0	4
2	0	2	4
0	2	2	4
0	0	4	4

-3 and 3

62.

Positive real zeros	Negative real zeros	Imaginary zeros	Total zeros
0	3	1	4
0	1	3	4

-1, 0, $-2i$, and $2i$

4.7 Practice

1. The graph of g is a translation 3 units up of the graph of f.

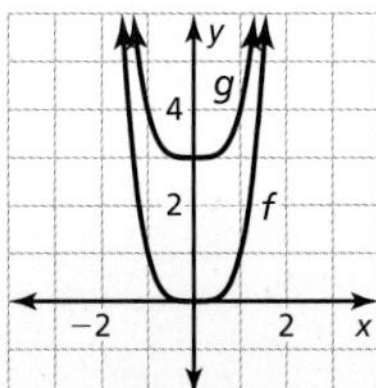

3. The graph of g is a translation 2 units right and 1 unit down of the graph of f.

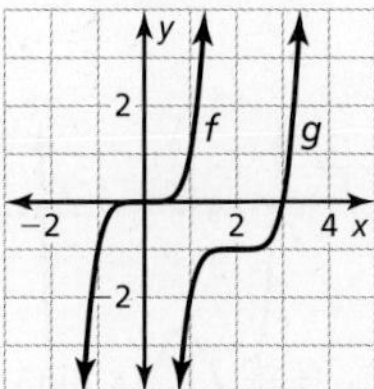

5. B; The graph has been translated 2 units right.
7. D; The graph has been translated 2 units right and 2 units up.
9. The graph of g is a vertical stretch by a factor of 2, followed by a reflection in the x-axis of the graph of f.

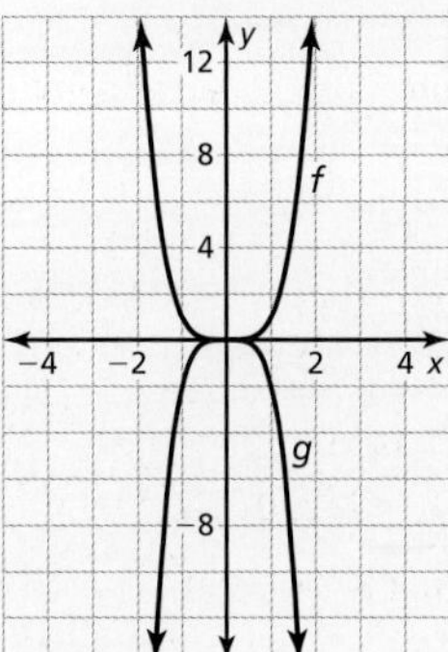

11. The graph of g is a vertical stretch by a factor of 5, followed by a translation 1 unit up of the graph of f.

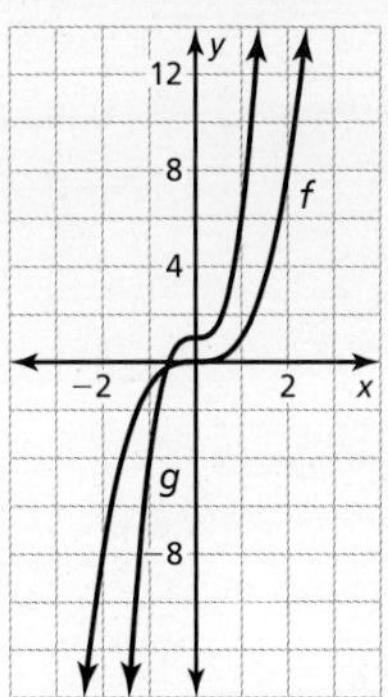

13. The graph of g is a vertical shrink by a factor of $\frac{3}{4}$, followed by a translation 4 units left of the graph of f.

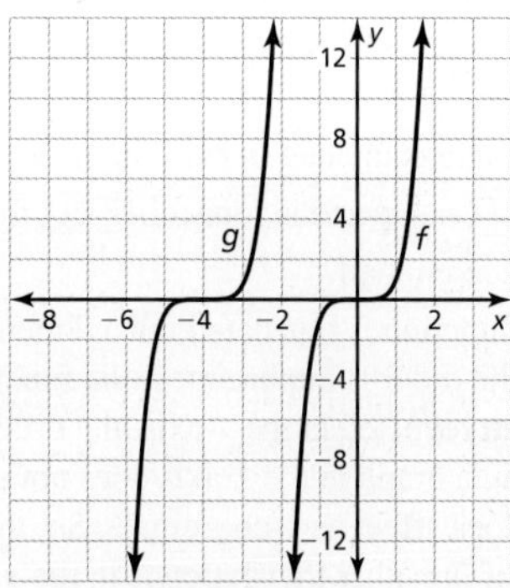

15. $g(x) = (x + 2)^4 + 1$

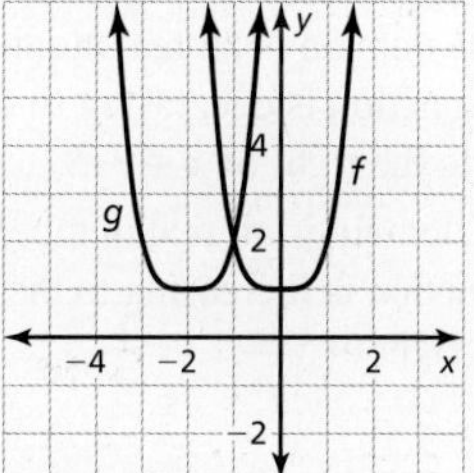

The graph of g is a translation 2 units left of the graph of f.

17. $g(x) = 3x^5 - 6x + 9$

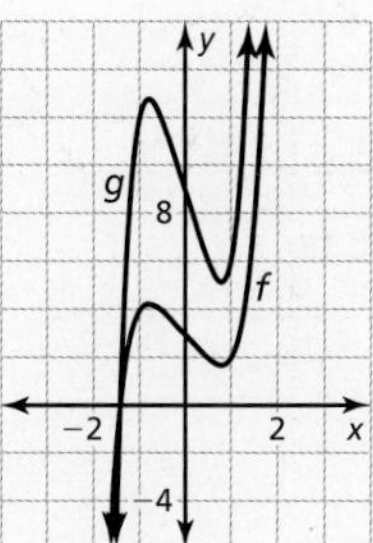

The graph of g is a vertical stretch by a factor of 3 of the graph of f.

19. $g(x) = x^4 - x^3 - 6$

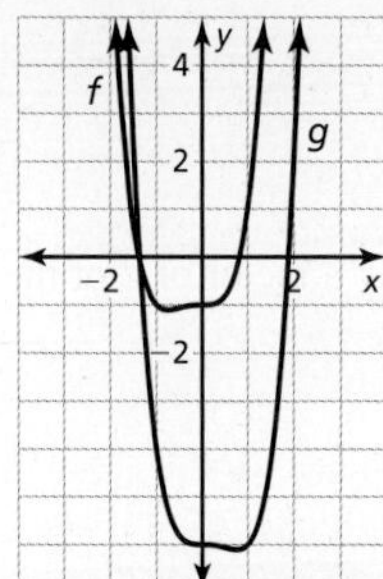

The graph of g is a reflection in the y-axis, followed by a translation 5 units down of the graph of f.

21. The graph has been translated horizontally to the right 2 units instead of to the left 2 units.

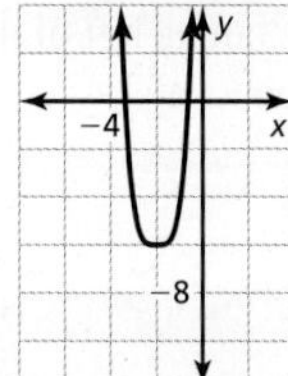

23. $g(x) = -x^3 + 9x^2 - 27x + 21$

25. $g(x) = -27x^3 - 18x^2 + 7$

27. $W(x) = 27x^3 - 12x$; $W(5) = 3315$; When x is 5 yards, the volume of the pyramid is 3315 cubic feet.

29. side length; When each side is divided in half, the new volume is $V\left(\frac{1}{2}x\right) = \left(\frac{1}{2}x\right)^3 = \frac{1}{8}x^3$ and is four times less than when the volume is divided in half.

31. *Sample answer:* If the function is translated up and then reflected in the x-axis, the order is important; If the function is translated left and then reflected in the x-axis, the order is not important; Reflecting a graph in the x-axis does not affect its x-coordinate, but it does affect its y-coordinate. So, the order is only important if the other translation is in the y.

4.7 Review & Refresh

33. The minimum value is -7; The domain is all real numbers, and the range is $y \geq -7$. The function is decreasing to the left of $x = -5$ and increasing to the right of $x = -5$.

34. The maximum value is 1; The domain is all real numbers, and the range is $y \leq 1$. The function is increasing to the left of $x = 1$ and decreasing to the right of $x = 1$.

35. $-\frac{3}{2}$; $6 + 2\sqrt{3}$, and $6 - 2\sqrt{3}$

36. The model makes sense for $x > 3$; When factored completely, the volume is $V = (x - 1)(x - 3)(3x - 5)$. For all three dimensions of the cage to have positive lengths, the value of x must be greater than 3.

37. $y = -2(x + 11)(x + 5)$

38. 4; $x = -1$, $x = 1$, $x = 3i$, and $x = -3i$

39. $13 - 5i$

40. $9 + 6i$

41. $21 + 35i$

42. $26 + 58i$

43. $y \geq x^2 - x - 2$

44. $g(x) = -2x^4 + 4x^2 - 6$

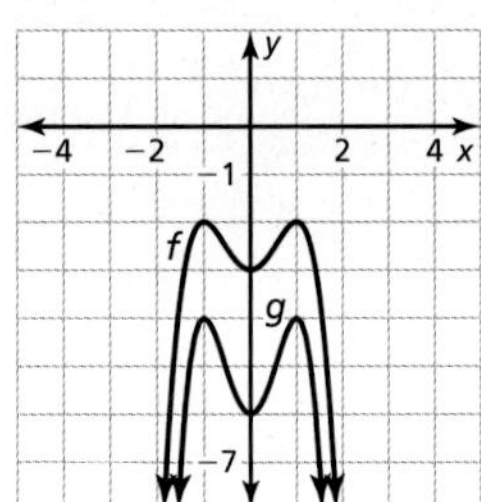

The graph of g is a vertical stretch by a factor of 2 of the graph of f.

45.

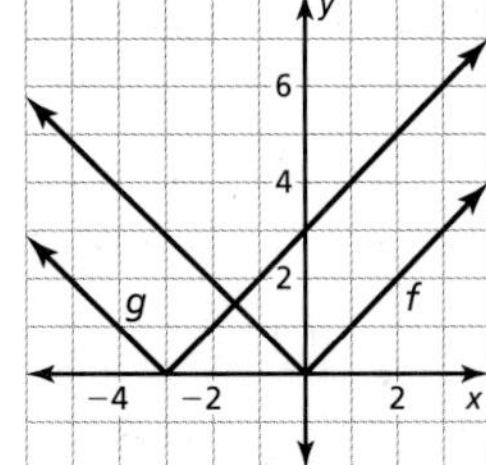

The graph of g is a horizontal translation 3 units left of the graph of the parent absolute value function.

46.

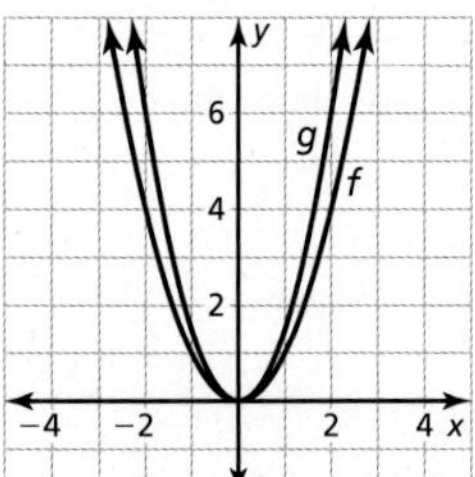

The graph of h is a vertical stretch by a factor of $\frac{3}{2}$ of the graph of the parent quadratic function.

4.8 Practice

1. D

3. A

5.

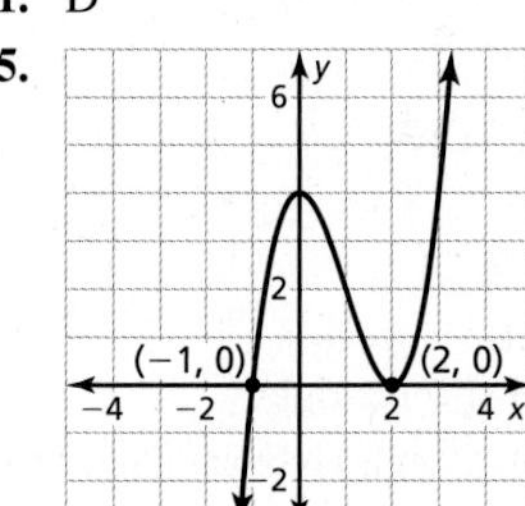

7.

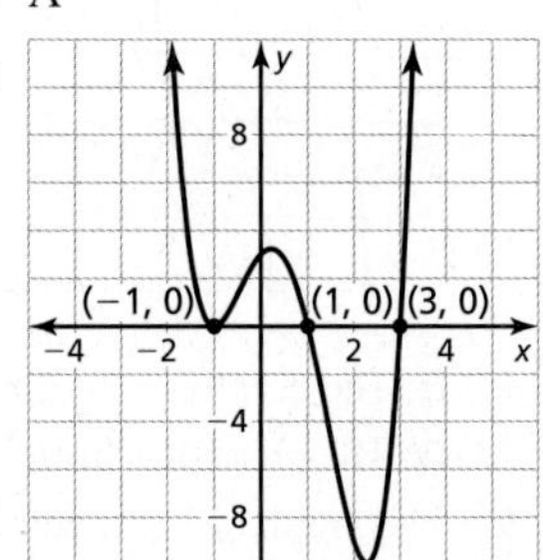

9.

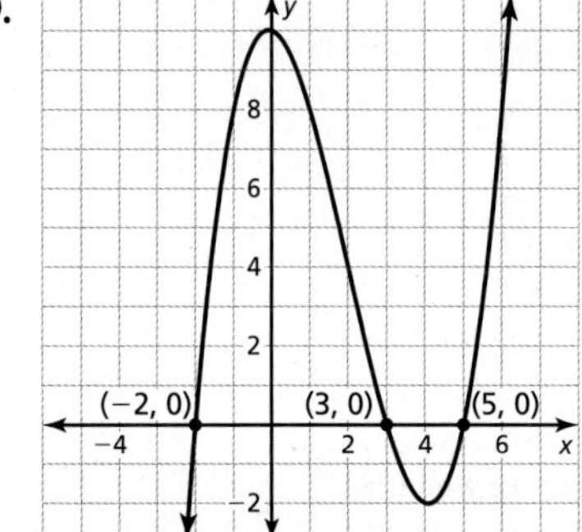

11.

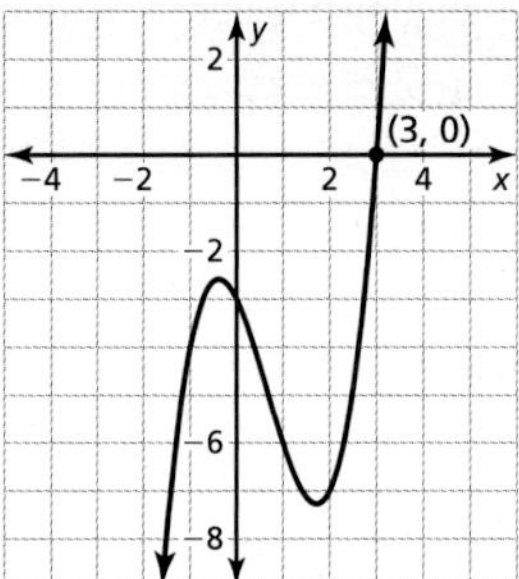

13. The x-intercepts should be -2 and 1.

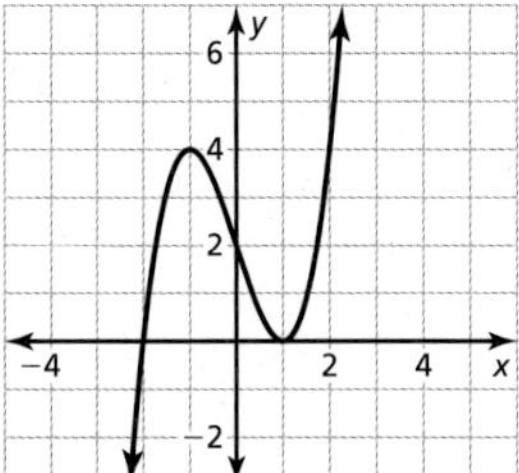

15. -1, 1, and 4

17. -4, $-\frac{1}{2}$, and 1

19. -4, $\frac{3}{4}$, and 3

21. -2 and $\frac{7}{2}$

23. 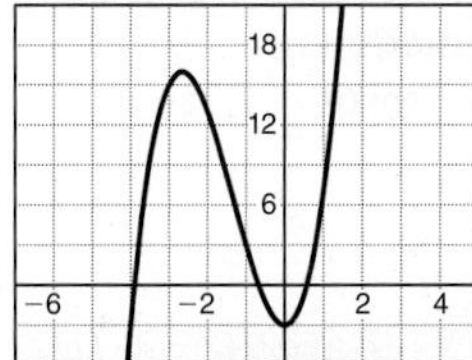

The x-intercepts of the graph are $x \approx -3.90$, $x \approx -0.67$, and $x \approx 0.57$. The function has a local maximum at $(-2.67, 15.96)$ and a local minimum at $(0, -3)$; The function is increasing when $x < -2.67$ and $x > 0$ and is decreasing when $-2.67 < x < 0$.

25. 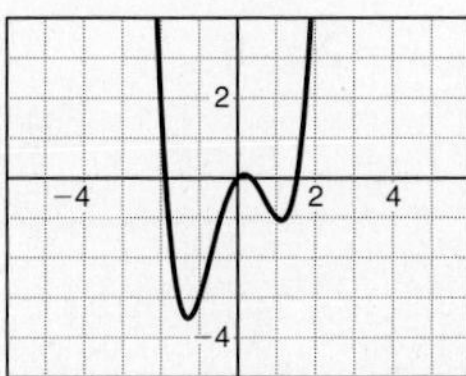

The x-intercepts of the graph are $x \approx -1.88$, $x = 0$, $x \approx 0.35$, and $x \approx 1.53$. The function has a local maximum at $(0.17, 0.08)$ and local minimums at $(-1.30, -3.51)$ and $(1.13, -1.07)$; The function is increasing when $-1.30 < x < 0.17$ and $x > 1.13$ and is decreasing when $x < -1.30$ and $0.17 < x < 1.13$.

27. 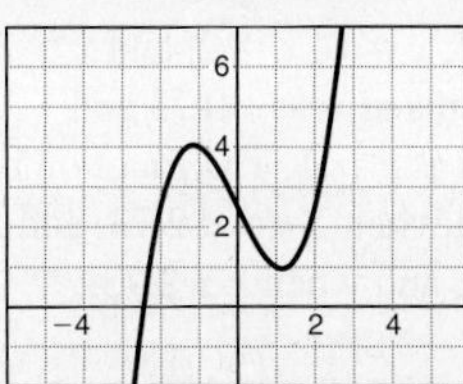

The x-intercept of the graph is $x \approx -2.46$. The function has a local maximum at $(-1.15, 4.04)$ and a local minimum at $(1.15, 0.96)$; The function is increasing when $x < -1.15$ and $x > 1.15$ and is decreasing when $-1.15 < x < 1.15$.

29. 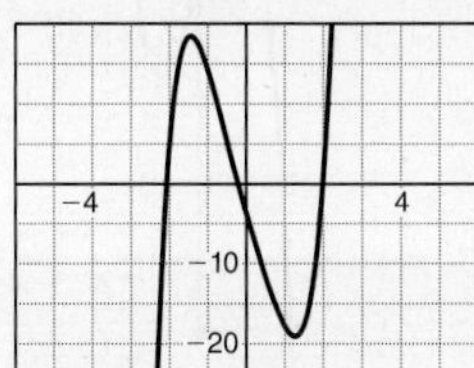

The x-intercepts of the graph are $x \approx -2.10$, $x = -0.23$, and $x \approx 1.97$. The function has a local maximum at $(-1.46, 18.45)$ and a local minimum at $(1.25, -19.07)$; The function is increasing when $x < -1.46$ and $x > 1.25$ and is decreasing when $-1.46 < x < 1.25$.

31. 3

33. 4

35. 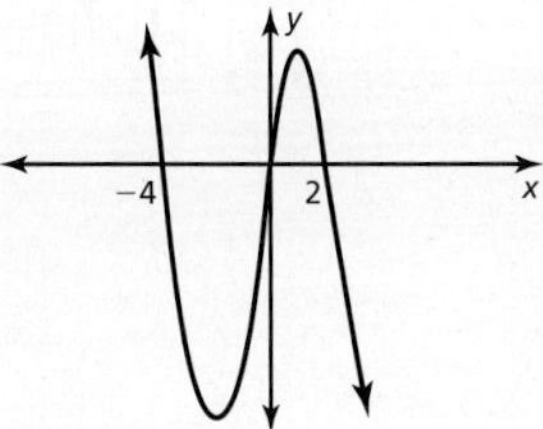

37. odd

39. even

41. neither

43. even

45. 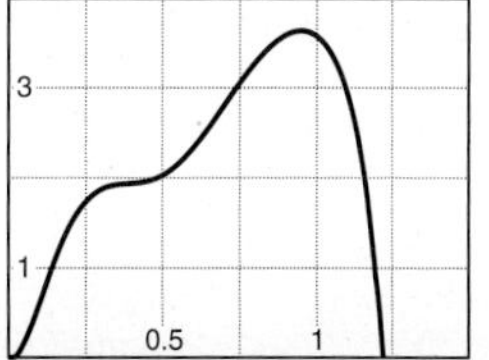

about 1 sec into the stroke

47. A quadratic function only has one turning point, and it is always the maximum or minimum value of the function.

49. yes; $f(x) = x^3$ has no turning points because its graph is always increasing.

51. *Sample answer:* Choose an 8.5 inches by 11 inches piece of paper. The length of the box is $11 - 2x$ inches and the width is $8.5 - 2x$ inches. The height of the box is x inches.
$V = x(11 - 2x)(8.5 - 2x)$
Use technology to graph the function. The maximum volume of about 66.148 cubic inches occurs when x is about 1.585 inches.

53. no; Let $f(x)$ and $g(x)$ be odd functions.
$$f(x) \cdot g(x) = f(-x) \cdot g(-x) = [f(x)] \cdot [-g(x)] = f(x) \cdot g(x).$$
So, the product of two odd functions is an even function.

55. Answers will vary. Check students' work.

4.8 Review & Refresh

56. $n = -3, n = 0, n = 2$

57. $m = -5$, $m = 0$, $m = \sqrt{2}$, and $m = -\sqrt{2}$

58. linear; The first differences are constant.

59. quadratic; The second differences are constant.

60. **a.** 14 ft

b. 1.5 sec

61. The graph of g is a translation 2 units left and 5 units down of the graph of f.

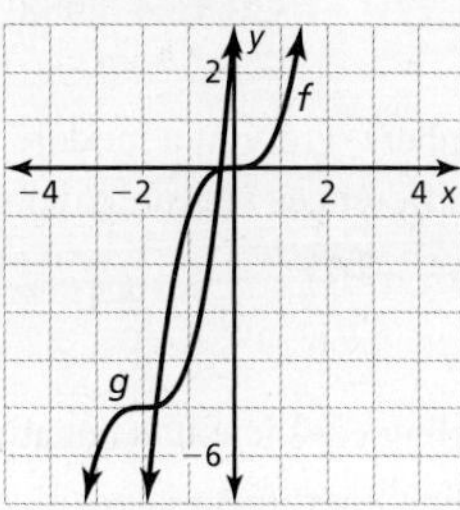

62. The graph of g is a vertical shrink by a factor of $\frac{1}{2}$, followed by a reflection in the x-axis of the graph of f.

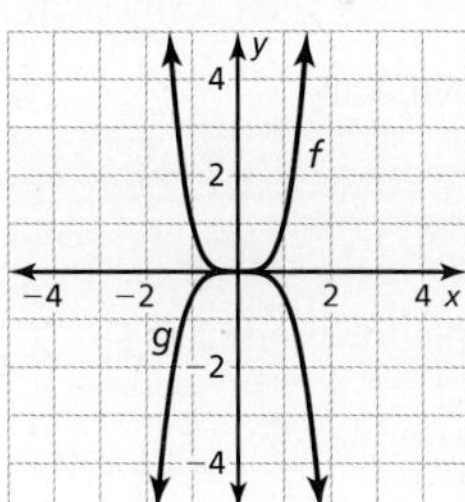

63. $2x + 3 + \frac{-14}{x + 3}$ **64.** $7x + 5 + \frac{-5x - 4}{x^2 - x + 2}$

65. The graph of g is a horizontal translation 2 units right of the graph of f; $g(x) = f(x - 2) = (x - 2) - 3 = x - 5$

66. $-2, -2, 1, -3i, 3i$ **67.** $x = 4$ and $x = 2$

68.

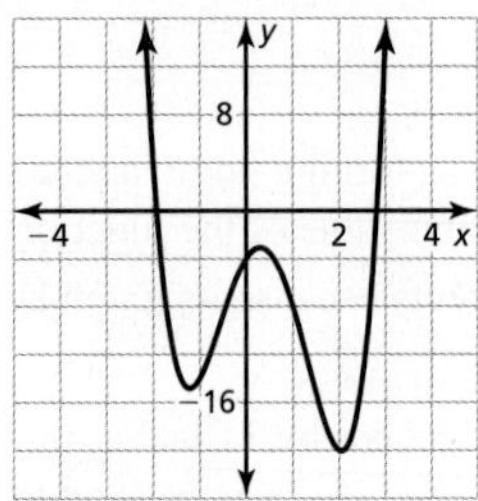

The x-intercepts are $x \approx -1.93$ and $x \approx 2.81$. Local minimums occur at $x \approx -1.22$ and $x \approx 2.05$, and a local maximum occurs at $x = 0.3$. The function is decreasing when $x < -1.93$ and when $0.3 < x < 2.05$, and increasing when $-122 < x < 0.3$, and when $x > 2.05$.

69. $9z^2 - 16$ **70.** $36y^2 - 120y + 100$

4.9 Practice

1. $f(x) = (x + 1)(x - 1)(x - 2)$

3. $f(x) = \frac{1}{7}(x + 5)(x - 1)(x - 4)$

5. $3; f(x) = \frac{2}{3}x^3 + 4x^2 - \frac{1}{3}x - 4$

7. $4; f(x) = -3x^4 - 5x^3 + 9x^2 + 3x - 1$

9. $4; f(x) = x^4 - 15x^3 + 81x^2 - 183x + 142$

11. The sign in each parentheses is wrong. The x-intercepts should have been subtracted from zero, not added.

$(-6, 0), (1, 0), (3, 0), (0, 54)$

$54 = a(0 + 6)(0 - 1)(0 - 3)$

$54 = 18a$

$a = 3$

$f(x) = 3(x + 6)(x - 1)(x - 3)$

13. $y = 0.1860x^4 - 8.135x^3 + 111.22x^2 - 330.4x + 2958$; about 5051 trillion Btus

15. With real-life data sets, the numbers rarely fit a model perfectly. Because of this, the differences are rarely constant.

17. $d = \frac{1}{2}n^2 - \frac{3}{2}n$; 35 **19.** 2; 145

4.9 Review & Refresh

21. The degree is even, and the leading coefficient is negative.

22. The degree is odd, and the leading coefficient is positive.

23. $g(x) = -(x + 3)^3 + 2$

24. (2, 1); Explanations will vary.

25. $\left(\frac{1}{2}, \frac{7}{4}\right)$ and (2, 1); Explanations will vary.

26. $y = x(x + 2)(x - 2)$

27. $y = (x - 1)(x - 2)(x - 4)$

28. The focus is $\left(0, c + \frac{1}{4a}\right)$ and the directrix is $y = c - \frac{1}{4a}$.

29.

Positive real zeros	Negative real zeros	Imaginary zeros	Total zeros
3	2	0	5
3	0	2	5
1	2	2	5
1	0	4	5

30. $y = 54.4x + 39$; About 54 species are added each year to the Endangered Species Act that had about 39 species in 2010.

31. $x = \pm 6$ **32.** $x = \pm 3\sqrt{5}$

33. $x = \frac{-3 \pm \sqrt{29}}{10}$ **34.** $x = 2 \pm 4i$

35. $4x^3 + 2x^2 - 4x - 2$

36.

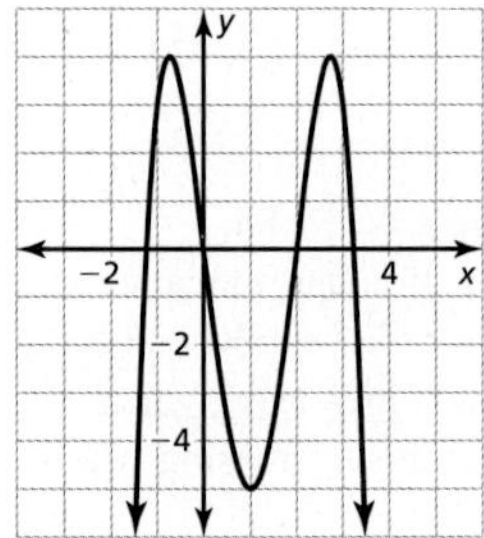

The x-intercepts are $x \approx -1.24$, $x = 0$, $x = 2$, and $x \approx 3.24$. The function has local maximums at $x \approx -0.73$ and $x \approx 2.73$, and a local minimum at $x = 1$. The function is increasing when $x < -0.73$ and when $1 < x < 2.73$, and decreasing when $-0.73 < x < 1$ and when $x > 2.73$.

Chapter 4 Review

1.

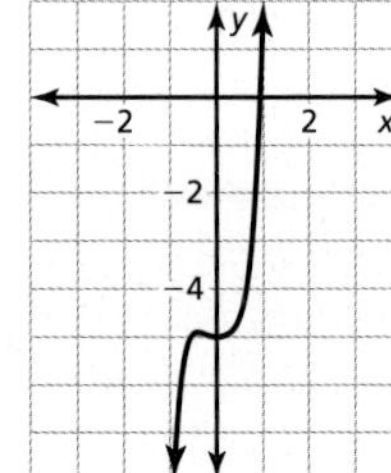

2.

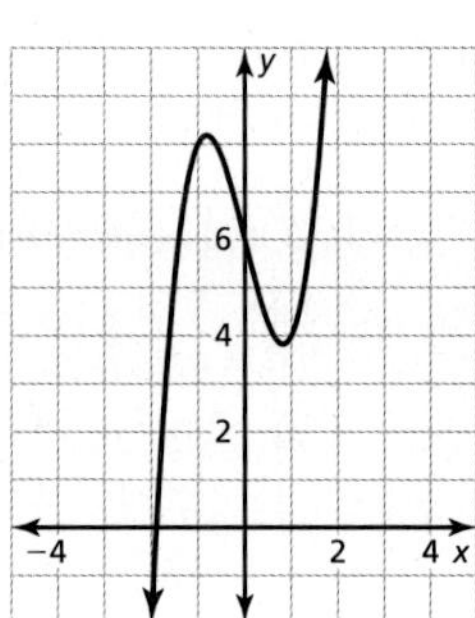

3.

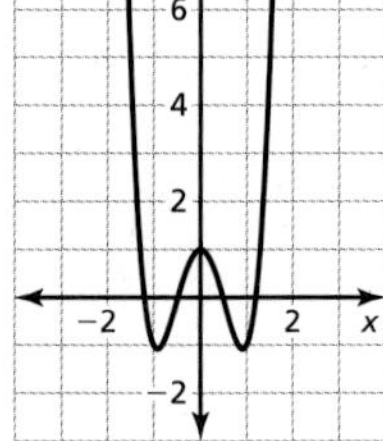

4.

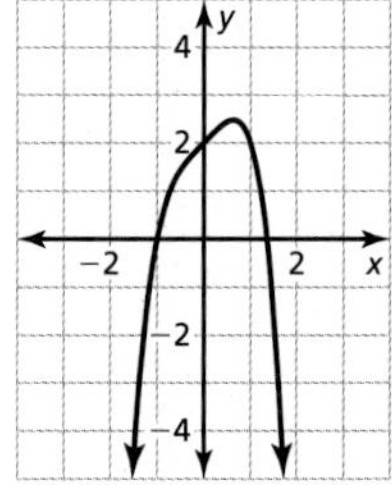

5. a.

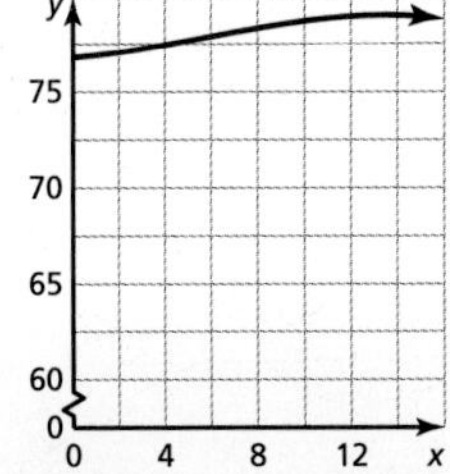

The graph is increasing.

b. 0.1252

c. no; After 2016 the model decreases for all future years, which is not likely.

6. $4x^3 - 4x^2 - 4x - 8$

7. $3x^4 + 3x^3 - x^2 - 3x + 15$

8. $2x^2 + 11x + 1$

9. $2y^3 + 10y^2 + 5y - 21$

10. $8m^3 + 12m^2n + 6mn^2 + n^3$

11. $s^3 + 3s^2 - 10s - 24$

12. $m^4 + 16m^3 + 96m^2 + 256m + 256$

13. $243s^5 + 810s^4 + 1080s^3 + 720s^2 + 240s + 32$

14. $z^6 + 6z^5 + 15z^4 + 20z^3 + 15z^2 + 6z + 1$

15. $x - 1 + \dfrac{4x - 3}{x^2 + 2x + 1}$

16. $x^2 + 2x - 10 + \dfrac{7x + 43}{x^2 + x + 4}$

17. $-2x^2 - 4x - 5 + \dfrac{-15}{x - 2}$

18. $x^3 - 4x^2 + 15x - 60 + \dfrac{233}{x + 4}$

19. $f(5) = 546$

20. $f(-3) = -18$

21. $-3, 2, -2, -39$; $2x^3 + x^2 - 2x + 4$, $x + 3$, $2x^2 - 5x + 13 + \dfrac{-35}{x + 3}$

22. about 337 overnight stays;

18	−0.032	0.73	2.2	248
		−0.576	2.772	89.496
	−0.032	0.154	4.972	337.496

23. $8(2x - 1)(4x^2 + 2x + 1)$

24. $y^3(5y + 2)(25y^2 - 10y + 4)$

25. $2z(z^2 - 5)(z - 1)(z + 1)$

26. $(a - 2)(a + 2)(2a - 7)$

27.

−2	1	2	0	−27	−54
		−2	0	0	54
	1	0	0	−27	0

$f(x) = (x + 2)(x - 3)(x^2 + 3x + 9)$

28. *Sample answer:*
$(x + 8)$ inches by $(x + 6)$ inches by $(x - 1)$ inches;
$(x + 8)(x + 6)(x - 1) = (x^2 + 14x + 48)(x - 1)$
$= x^3 + 13x^2 + 34x - 48$

29. about 2,732,000 copies

30. $x = -4$, $x = -2$, and $x = 3$

31. $x = -4$, $x = -3$, and $x = 2$

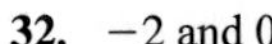

32. −2 and 0

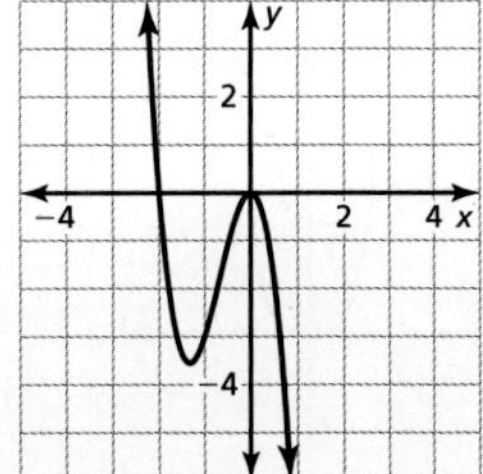

33. −3 and 3

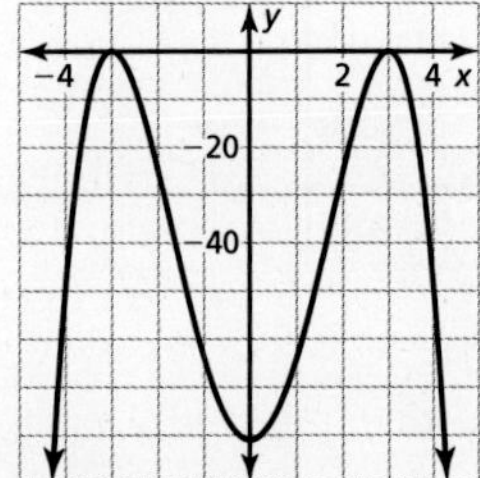

34. $f(x) = x^3 - 5x^2 + 5x - 1$

35. $f(x) = x^4 - 5x^3 + x^2 + 25x - 30$

36. $f(x) = x^4 - 9x^3 + 11x^2 + 51x - 30$

37. The length is 6 inches, the width is 2 inches, and the height is 20 inches; When $\ell(\ell - 4)(3\ell + 2) = 240$, $\ell = 6$.

38. a. The length is 3 inches, the width is 3 inches, and the height is 58 inches.

b. 8,156,250 ft^3

39. $-1, 5$, and $\pm 2i$

40. $-3, -1, -1, -i$, and i

41. $f(x) = x^3 - 5x^2 + 11x - 15$

42. $f(x) = x^4 - x^3 + 14x^2 - 16x - 32$

43. $f(x) = x^4 + 7x^3 + 6x^2 - 4x + 80$

44.

Positive real zeros	Negative real zeros	Imaginary zeros	Total zeros
2	0	2	4
0	0	4	4

45.

Positive real zeros	Negative real zeros	Imaginary zeros	Total zeros
1	3	0	4
1	1	2	4

46. May and September

47. The graph of g is a reflection in the y-axis, followed by a translation 2 units up of the graph of f.

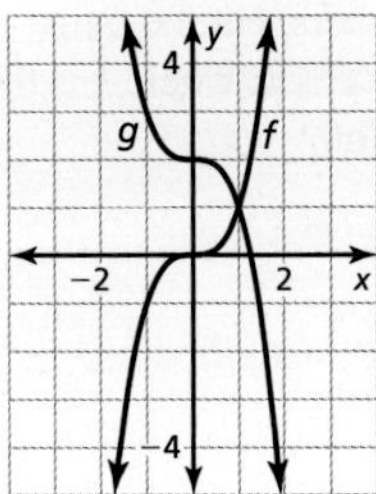

48. The graph of g is a reflection in the x-axis, followed by a translation 9 units left of the graph of f.

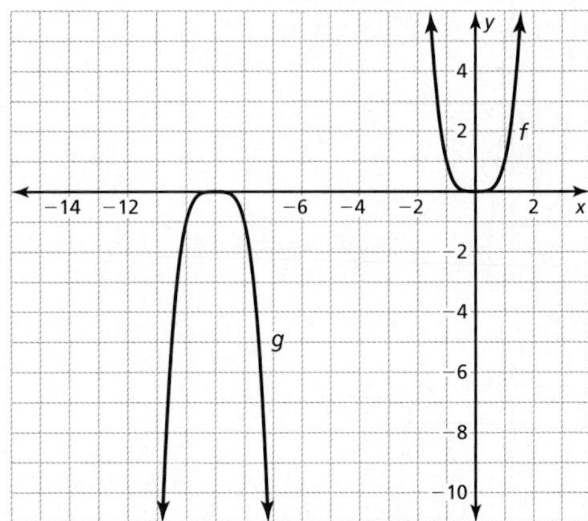

49. $g(x) = \frac{1}{1024}(x - 3)^5 + \frac{3}{4}(x - 3) - 5$

50. $g(x) = x^4 + 2x^3 - 7$

51. C

52. B

53. A

54. D

55.

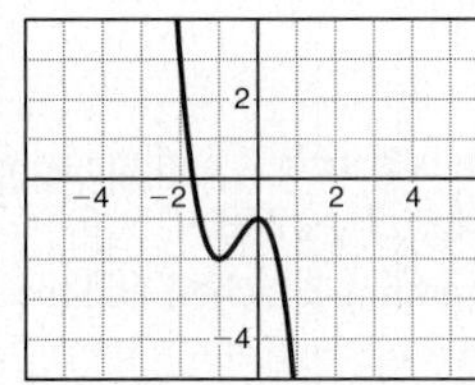

The x-intercept of the graph is $x \approx -1.68$. The function has a local maximum at $(0, -1)$ and a local minimum at $(-1, -2)$; The function is increasing when $-1 < x < 0$ and decreasing when $x < -1$ and $x > 0$.

56.

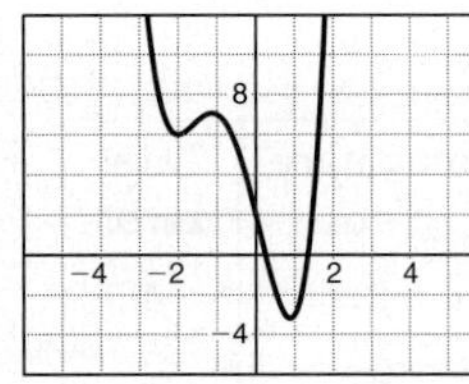

The x-intercepts of the graph are $x \approx 0.25$ and $x \approx 1.34$. The function has a local maximum at $(-1.13, 7.06)$ and local minimums at $(-2, 6)$ and $(0.88, -3.17)$; The function is increasing when $-2 < x < -1.13$ and $x > 0.88$ and is decreasing when $x < -2$ and $-1.13 < x < 0.88$.

57. odd

58. even

59. neither

60. The domains of both odd-degree and even-degree polynomial functions is all real numbers. The range of odd-degree functions is all real numbers, but the range of even-degree functions is $y \geq k$ or $y \leq k$, where k is the minimum or maximum of the function.

61. *Sample answer:*

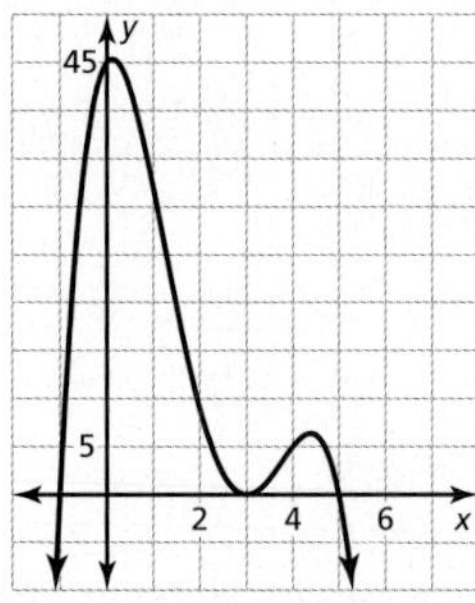

62. $y = x(x - 2)(x - 5)$

63. $f(x) = \frac{3}{16}(x + 4)(x - 4)(x - 2)$

64. $3; f(x) = 2x^3 - 7x^2 - 6x$

65. $4; f(x) = -0.125x^4 + x^3 - 8x + 4$

66. $y = -2.828x^3 + 29.46x^2 + 76.6x + 483$; about 1497 moose

Chapter 4 Mathematical Practices (Chapter Review)

1. *Sample answers:* The diagonals in both directions are equal. Starting from the top, the first diagonals are all 1. Starting from the top, the second diagonals are the natural numbers.
2. Order the terms with powers of a from greatest to least. Then factor out a^3 from the three terms with the highest powers of a, and $-b^2$ from the three terms with the highest powers of b. This leaves the factor $a^2b^2 + 2ab + 1$ in each term. Using the square of a binomial pattern, $a^2b^2 + 2ab + 1 = (ab + 1)^2$. Then factor out $(ab + 1)^2$ from each term to find the simplified expression $(a^3 - b^2)(ab + 1)^2$.
3. Write a fourth degree polynomial function because the fourth differences are constant. Then find the fourth differences. Multiply the fourth differences by a number so that the fourth differences are equal to -2. Then multiply the polynomial by the same number. The first, second, and third differences remain the same except divided by that number.

Chapter 4 Practice Test

1. not a polynomial function
2. polynomial function; $g(x) = 3x^4 - 2x^3 - \frac{1}{2}x$; degree: 4, leading coefficient: 3
3. The graph does not have any x-intercepts. The local maximum occurs at $x = 0$, and there are no local minimums. The function is increasing when $x < 0$ and decreasing when $x > 0$.
4. $f(x) = x^3 - 5x^2 + 5x + 3$
5. $f(x) = x^4 - 2x^3 + x^2 - 18x - 72$
6. $x^8 - 7x^7 + 5x^6 - 4x^2 + 28x - 20$
7. $8x^3 + 36x^2 + 54x + 27$
8. $2x^2 - 7x + 19 - \dfrac{39}{x + 2}$
9. $3x^2 + 4x + 5 + \dfrac{5x - 6}{x^2 - 2x + 1}$
10. $(3x + 4)(9x^2 - 12x + 16)$
11. $-x^2(5x - 2)(25x^2 - 10x + 4)$
12. $(2x - 1)(2x + 1)(4x^2 + 1)$
13. $2x(x^4 + 2)(x^2 + 2)(x^2 - 2)$
14. **a.** Each function has one zero repeated four times; The zero for f is 0 and the zero for g is 3.

    b. The graph of g is a translation 3 units right of the graph of f.

    c. g is increasing when $x > 3$ and decreasing when $x < 3$.

15. $(-4, -77)$, $(1, -7)$, and $(4, -37)$; Explanations will vary.

16. $T = 20t^4 - 374t^3 + 2277t^2 - 3918t + 8449$; 8,710,000 cars

17. 3; $p = t^3 + 5t^2 - t + 60$; \$641

Chapter 4 College and Career Readiness

1. -1;

4	1	−3	−1	3
		4	4	12
	1	1	3	15

2. positive; 5; 5; There are 5 real zeros because the graph crosses the x-axis 5 times. The function has degree 5 because there are 5 real zeros. Because the function has an odd degree and the end behavior of the graph is $f(x) \to -\infty$ as $x \to -\infty$ and $f(x) \to +\infty$ as $x \to +\infty$, the function's leading coefficient must be positive.

3. C

4. $(-4, 1)$ and $(-5, 1)$; $(1, 1)$, $(0, 1)$, and $(-2, 1)$; Because the axis of symmetry can be found by using the mean of two symmetrical points, the mean of the x-coordinates must be negative when the axis of symmetry is $x = -a$, and positive when it is $x = a$.

5. **a.** 1; −3; 2 **b.** 1; 2; −3 **c.** 2; 0; 2 **d.** $\frac{1}{2}$; 3; −4

6. D

7. *Sample answer:* $y = 13.899x + 40.587$; about 3515 mm

8. C

9. $t \approx 2.4$; The number of retirees receiving Social Security benefits was decreasing until about the middle of 2012, where it started to increase.

Chapter 5

Chapter 5 Prepare

1. y^7
2. n
3. $\dfrac{1}{x^3}$
4. $3x^3$
5. $\dfrac{8w^9}{z^6}$
6. $\dfrac{m^{10}}{z^4}$
7. $y = 2 - 4x$
8. $y = 3 + 3x$
9. $y = \dfrac{13}{2}x + \dfrac{9}{2}$
10. $y = \dfrac{5}{x + 3}$
11. $y = \dfrac{8x - 3}{4x}$
12. $y = \dfrac{15 - 6x}{7x}$
13. yes; *Sample answer:* When simplifying $x^3 \cdot (x^2)^2$, you must first apply the Power of a Power Property and then apply the Product of Powers Property.

5.1 Practice

1. 2
3. 0
5. −2
7. 2
9. 125
11. −3
13. $\frac{1}{4}$
15. The negative cube root of 27 is −3; $-27^{5/3} = (-27^{1/3})^5 = -3^5 = -243$
17. B; The denominator of the exponent is 3 and the numerator is 4.
19. A; The denominator of the exponent is 4 and the exponent is negative.
21. 8
23. 0.34
25. 2840.40
27. 50.57
29. $x = 5$
31. $x \approx -7.66$
33. $x \approx -2.17$
35. $x = \pm 2$
37. $x = \pm 3$
39. potatoes: 0.019 or 1.9%, oranges: 0.035 or 3.5%, ground beef: 0.053 or 5.3%
41. 3, 4; $\sqrt[4]{81} = 3$ and $\sqrt[4]{256} = 4$
43. $r \approx 3.72$ ft
45. 1.12 m/sec; 1.47 m/sec; 2.15 m/sec

5.1 Review & Refresh

47.

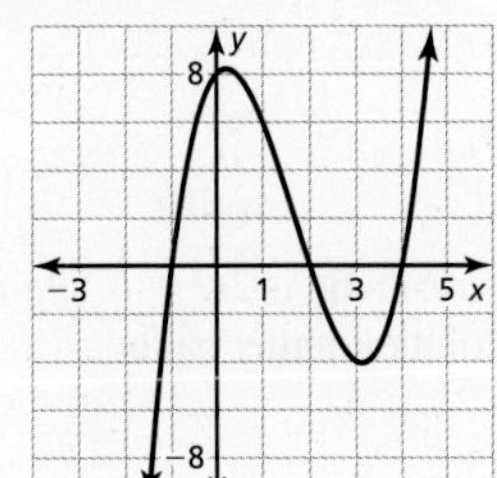

48.

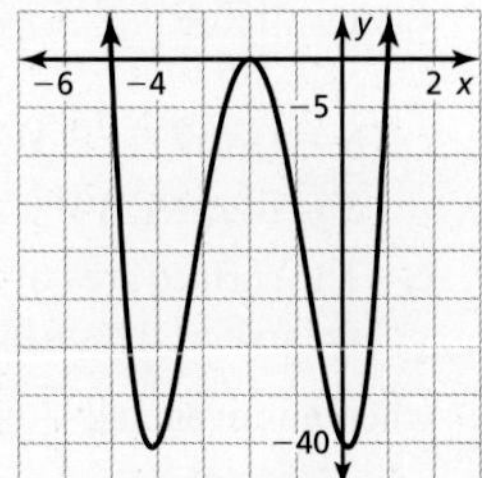

49. 4; $f(x) = -x^4 + 2x^3 + 5x^2 - 6x + 1$
50. 3, 6, and $\pm i$
51. $x = -5$ and $x = 5$
52. $x \approx 13.24$
53. $g(x) = \frac{1}{2}(x + 3)^3 - 2(x + 3)$
54. $y = \frac{1}{4}(x - 8)^2 + 5$
55. $38 - i$
56. linear; 3.0 mi

5.2 Practice

1. $9^{2/3}$
3. $6^{3/4}$
5. $\frac{5}{4}$
7. $3^{1/3}$
9. 4
11. 12
13. 5
15. 3
17. 6
19. $3\sqrt[4]{7}$
21. $\dfrac{\sqrt[3]{10}}{2}$
23. $\dfrac{\sqrt{6}}{4}$
25. $\dfrac{4\sqrt[3]{7}}{7}$
27. $\dfrac{1 - \sqrt{3}}{-2}$
29. $\dfrac{15 + 5\sqrt{2}}{7}$
31. $\dfrac{9\sqrt{3} - 9\sqrt{7}}{-4}$
33. $\dfrac{3\sqrt{2} + \sqrt{30}}{-2}$
35. $12\sqrt[3]{11}$
37. $12(14^{1/4})$
39. $-9\sqrt{3}$
41. $5\sqrt[5]{7}$
43. $6(3^{1/3})$
45. $3y^2$
47. $\dfrac{m^2}{n}$
49. $\dfrac{|g|}{|h|}$
51. The radicand should not change when the expression is factored; $3\sqrt[3]{12} + 5\sqrt[3]{12} = (3 + 5)\sqrt[3]{12} = 8\sqrt[3]{12}$
53. *Sample answer:* $\sqrt[6]{x^6} = |x|$ requires absolute value because x could be negative; $\sqrt[6]{x^{12}} = x^2$ does not require absolute value because x is being squared.
55. $9a^3b^6c^4\sqrt{ac}$
57. $\dfrac{c^3\sqrt[4]{d}}{d^2}$

59. $\frac{2m\sqrt[5]{5mn^3}}{n^2}$

61. $\frac{2v^{3/4}}{3w}$

63. $21\sqrt[3]{y}$

65. $-2x^{7/2}$

67. $4w^2\sqrt{w}$

69. $P = 2x^3 + 4x^{2/3}$
$A = 2x^{11/3}$

71. about 0.45 mm

73. no; The second radical can be simplified to $18\sqrt{11}$. The difference is $-11\sqrt{11}$.

75. $10 + 6\sqrt{5}$; yes

77. a. $r = \sqrt[3]{\frac{3V}{4\pi}}$

b. $S = 4\pi\left(\sqrt[3]{\frac{3V}{4\pi}}\right)^2$

$S = \frac{4\pi(3V)^{2/3}}{(4\pi)^{2/3}}$

$S = (4\pi)^{3/3\,-\,2/3}(3V)^{2/3}$

$S = (4\pi)^{1/3}(3V)^{2/3}$

c. The surface area of the larger balloon is $2^{2/3} \approx 1.59$ times as large as the surface area of the smaller balloon.

79. when n is even and $\frac{m}{n}$ is odd

5.2 Review & Refresh

80. $g(x) = -x^4 + 3x^2 + 2x$; The graph of g is a reflection in the x-axis of the graph of f.

81. $g(x) = x^3 - x - 3$; The graph of g is a translation 3 units down of the graph of f.

82. $g(x) = (x - 2)^3 - 4$; The graph of g is a translation 2 units right of the graph of f.

83. $g(x) = 16x^4 + 16x^3 - 16x^2$; The graph of g is a horizontal shrink by a factor of $\frac{1}{2}$ of the graph of f.

84. The focus is $\left(0, \frac{1}{8}\right)$. The directrix is $y = -\frac{1}{8}$. The axis of symmetry is $x = 0$.

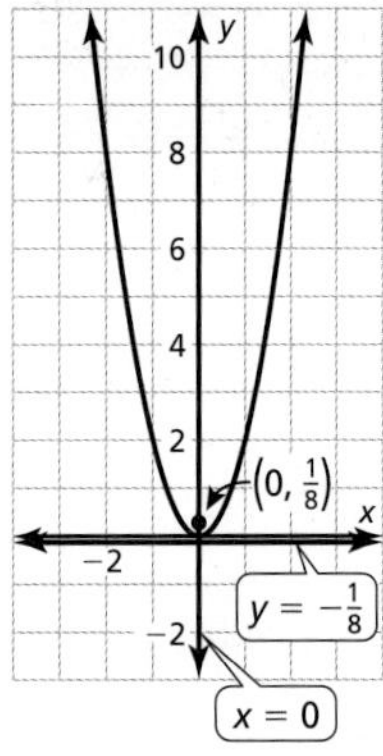

85. The focus is $\left(-\frac{1}{4}, 0\right)$. The directrix is $x = \frac{1}{4}$. The axis of symmetry is $y = 0$.

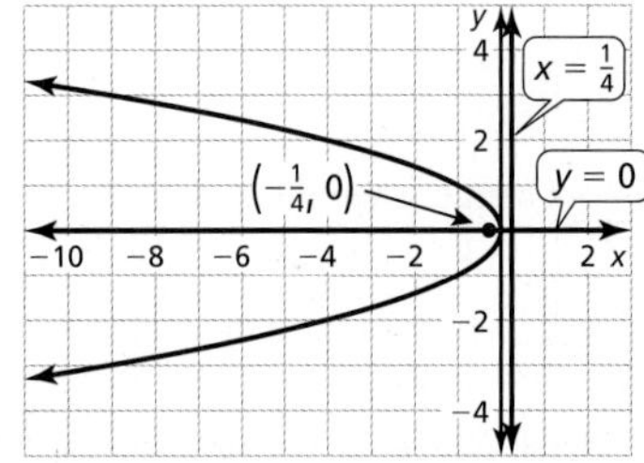

86. $y = \frac{1}{4}(x - 2)(x + 3)(x - 4)$

87. no; Polynomials cannot have terms with variable exponents.

88. geometric; The common ratio is 3.

89. $16 \cdot 2^{1/2}$

90. 6

91. $\frac{3 - \sqrt{2}}{7}$

92. $-3\sqrt[3]{2}$

93. even

94. neither

95. 8

96. 25

97. a. $h(t) = -16t^2 + 25$; about 1.6 sec

b. The sunglasses fell 15 feet between 0.25 second and 1 second.

5.3 Practice

1.

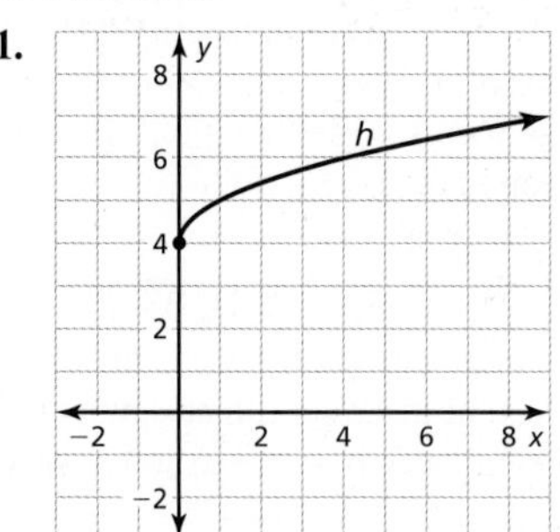

The domain is $x \geq 0$. The range is $y \geq 4$.

3.

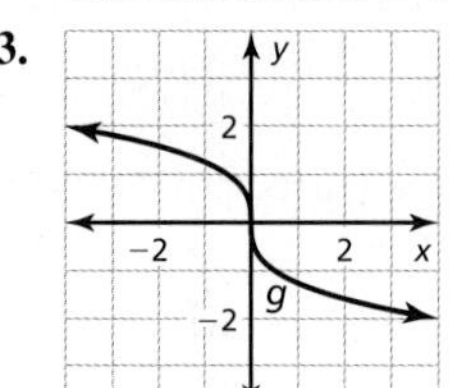

The domain and range are all real numbers.

5.

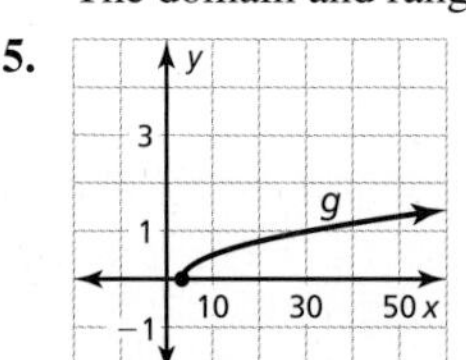

The domain is $x \geq 3$. The range is $y \geq 0$.

7.

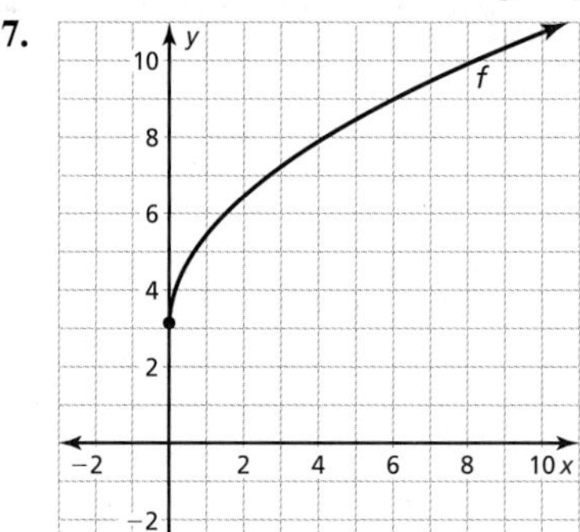

The domain is $x \geq 0$. The range is $y \geq 3$.

9.

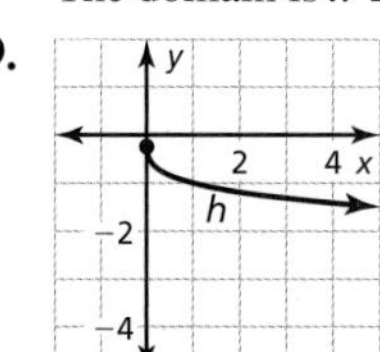

The domain is $x \geq 0$. The range is $y \leq 0$.

11. B

13. F

15. E

17. The graph of g is a translation 1 unit left and 8 units up of the graph of f.

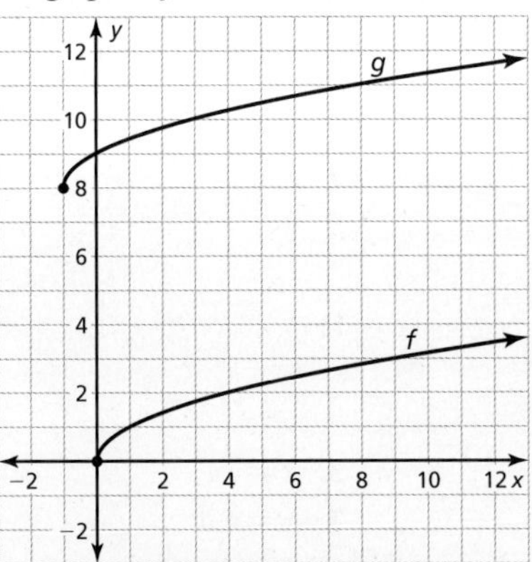

19. The graph of g is a reflection in the x-axis, followed by a translation 1 unit down of the graph of f.

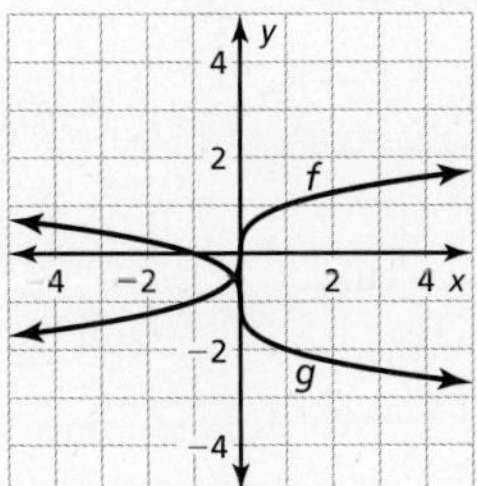

21. The graph of g is a vertical shrink by a factor of $\frac{1}{4}$, followed by a reflection in the y-axis of the graph of f.

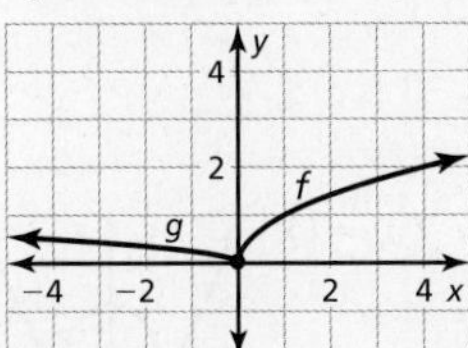

23. The graph of g is a vertical stretch by a factor of 2, followed by a translation 5 units left and 4 units down of the graph of f.

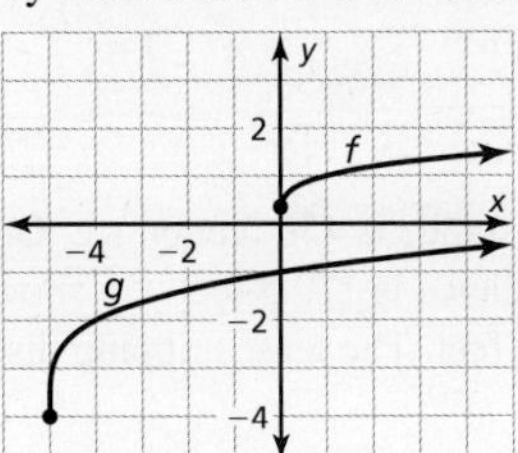

25. The graph was translated 2 units left but it should be translated 2 units right.

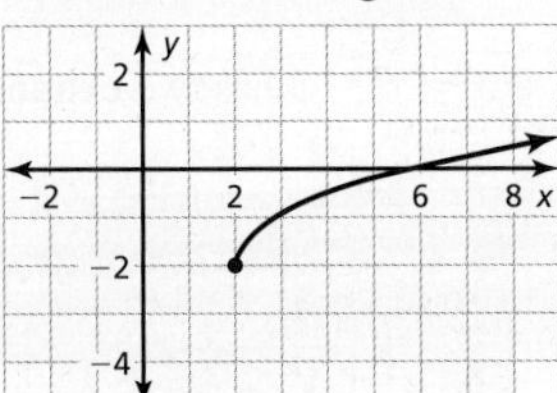

27.

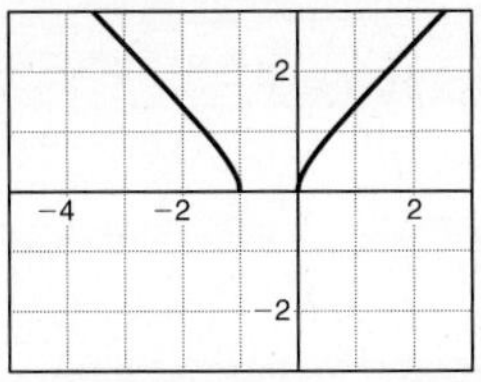

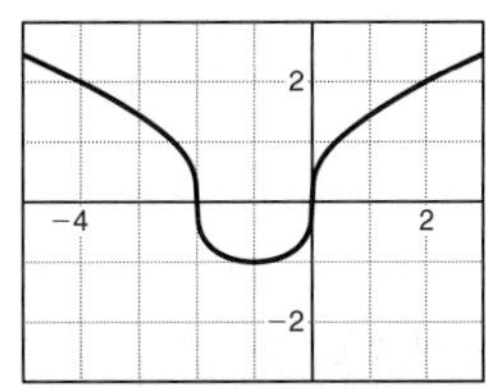

The domain is $x \leq -1$ and $x \geq 0$. The range is $y \geq 0$.

29.

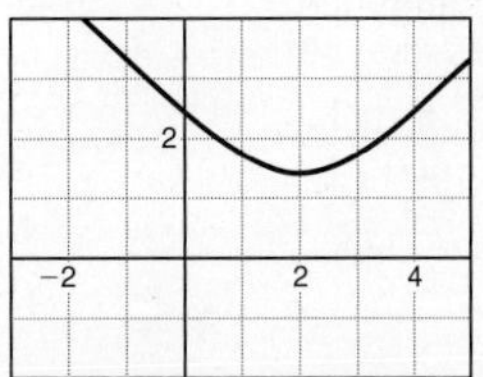

The domain is all real numbers. The range is $y \geq -1$.

31.

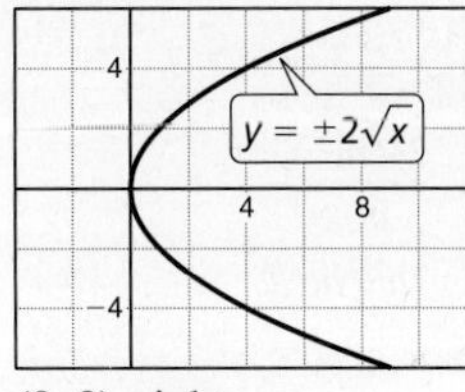

The domain is all real numbers. The range is $y \geq \sqrt{2}$.

33. 24 ft per sec

35. $g(x) = 2\sqrt{x} + 8$

37. $g(x) = \sqrt{9x + 36}$

39. $g(x) = 2\sqrt{x + 1}$

41. $g(x) = 2\sqrt{x + 3}$

43. $g(x) = 2\sqrt{(x + 5)^2} - 2$

45.

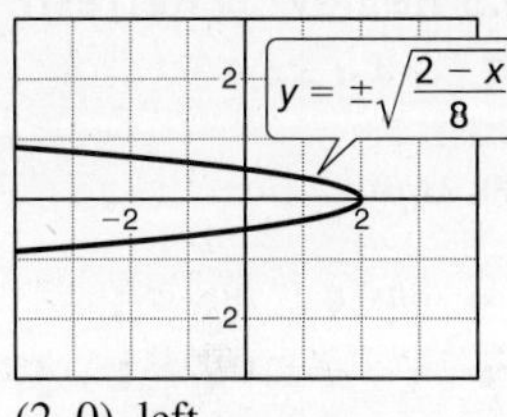

(0, 0), right

47.

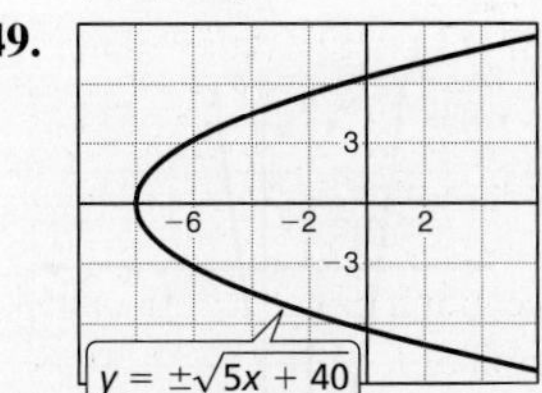

(2, 0), left

49.

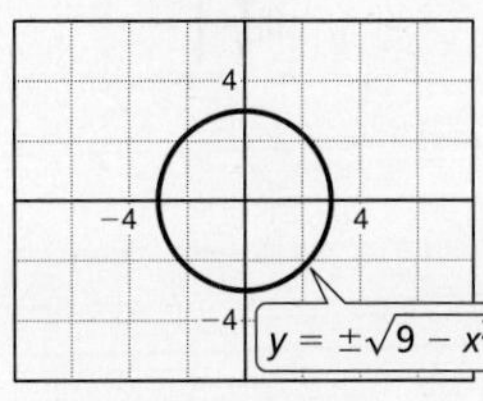

(−8, 0), right

51.

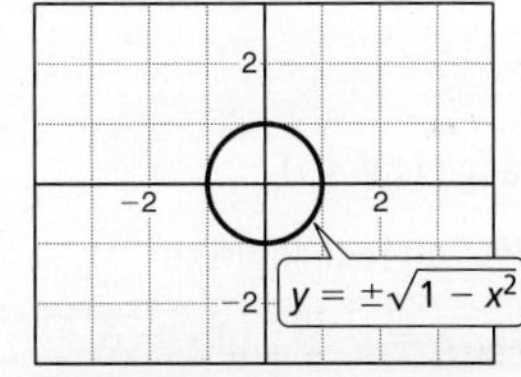

The radius is 3 units. The x-intercepts are ± 3. The y-intercepts are ± 3.

53.

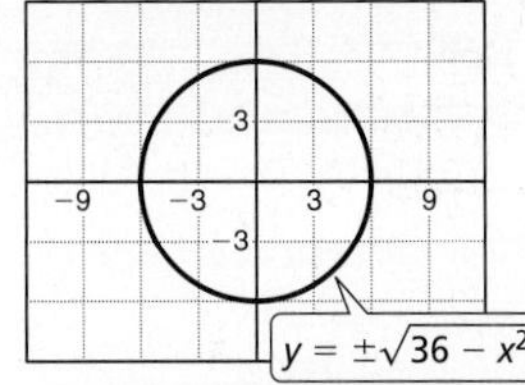

The radius is 1 unit. The x-intercepts are ± 1. The y-intercepts are ± 1.

55.

The radius is 6 units. The x-intercepts are ± 6. The y-intercepts are ± 6.

57. always

59. always

61. about 3 ft

63. a. about 2468 hp

b. about 0.04 mph/hp

65. a. $\pi\left(r^2 + r + \frac{1}{4}\right) = S + \frac{\pi}{4}$

$$\left(r + \frac{1}{2}\right)^2 = \frac{1}{\pi}\left(S + \frac{\pi}{4}\right)$$

$$r = \frac{1}{\sqrt{\pi}}\sqrt{S + \frac{\pi}{4}} - \frac{1}{2}$$

b. 0.5 unit

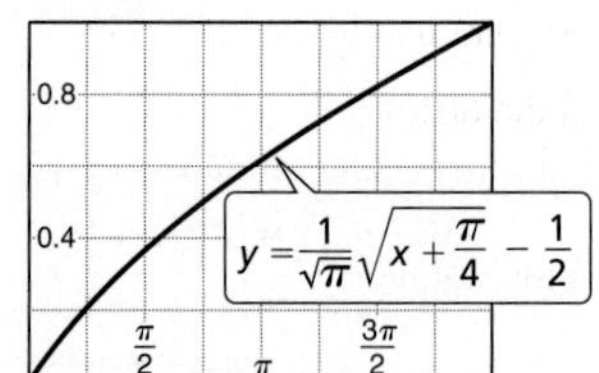

5.3 Review & Refresh

67. $-4 < x < -3$

68. $x \leq 3$ or $x \geq 7$

69. $6p^3$

70. $\frac{2\sqrt[5]{m^2}}{m}$

71. $8n\sqrt[4]{q}$

72. $7a^{2/3}bc^{1/4}$

73. $3; y = \frac{1}{2}x^3 + \frac{3}{2}x^2 + 2x - 1$

74.

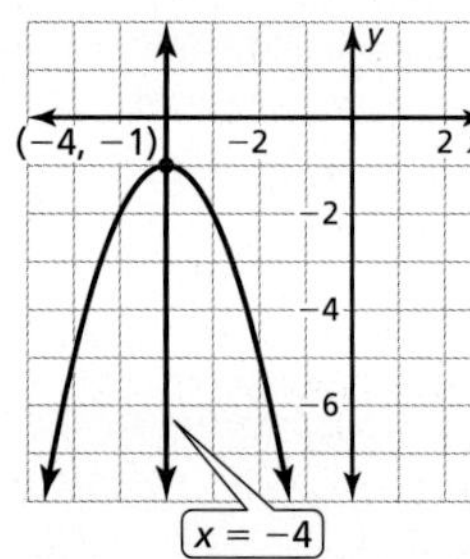

75.

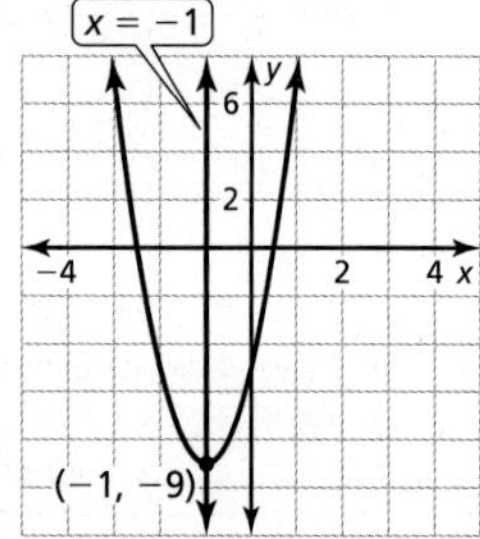

76. 4.64

77.

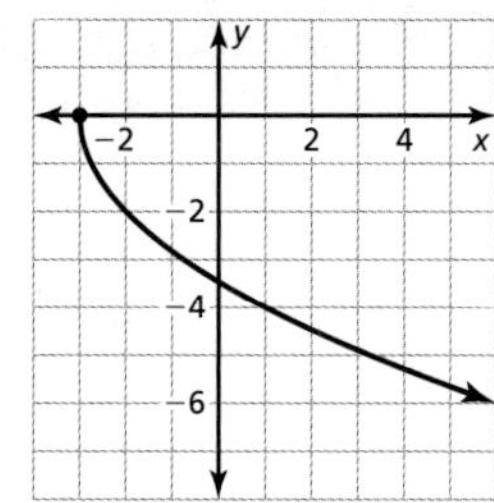

The domain is $x \geq -3$. The range is $y \leq 0$.

78. $x = 1$ and $x = -\frac{7}{3}$

79. no real solution

80. $x = 3$

81. $x = -\frac{10}{3}$ and $x = 6$

82. $y = \begin{cases} \frac{1}{2}x - 1, & \text{if } x \leq -2 \\ x + 2, & \text{if } x > -2 \end{cases}$

83. decrease by \$5; decrease by 15%

84. $(-3, 1, 4)$

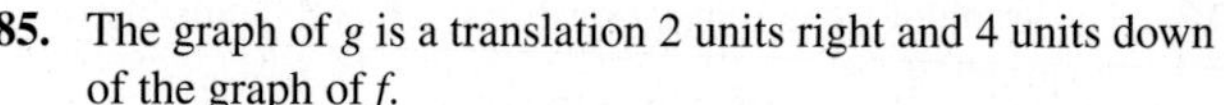

85. The graph of g is a translation 2 units right and 4 units down of the graph of f.

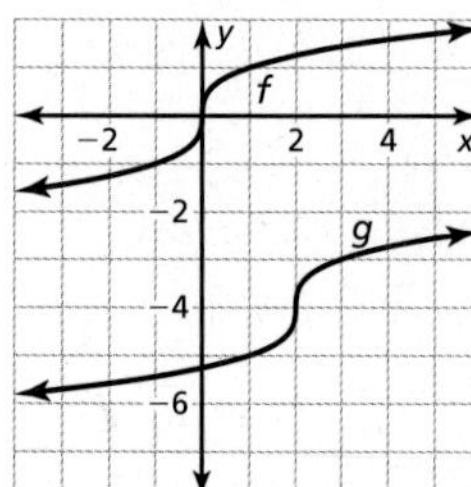

5.4 Practice

1. $x = 7$

3. $x = 24$

5. $x = 6$

7. $x = 6.4$

9. $x = 1024$

11. 2.5 m

13. $x = 12$

15. $x = 14$

17. $x = 1$

19. $x = 3$

21. $x = -1$

23. $x = \pm 8$

25. no real solution

27. $x = 3$

29. $x = 5$

31. Only one side of the equation was cubed;

$$\sqrt[3]{3x - 8} = 4$$
$$\left(\sqrt[3]{3x - 8}\right)^3 = 4^3$$
$$3x - 8 = 64$$
$$x = 24$$

33. $x > 25$

35. $x \geq 32$

37. $x \geq 1$

39. $0 \leq x \leq \frac{25}{4}$

41. 207.4464 N

43. (3, 0) and (4, 1);

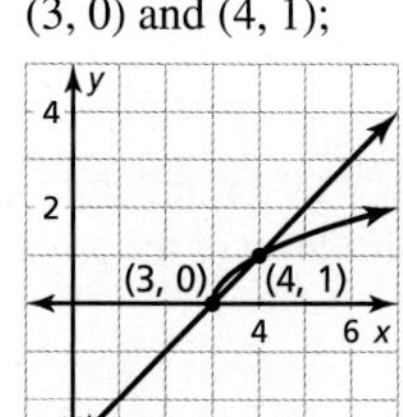

45. (0, −1);

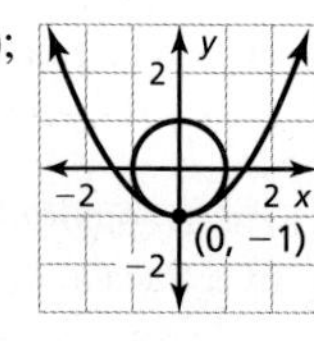

47. a. The greatest stopping distance is 450 feet on ice. On wet asphalt, the stopping distance is 112.5 feet. On snow, the stopping distance is 225 feet. The least stopping distance is 90 feet on dry asphalt.

b. about 272.2 ft; When $s = 35$ and $f = 0.15$, $d \approx 272.2$.

49. The square root of a real number cannot be negative.

51. $36\pi \approx 113.1$ ft²

53. yes; *Sample answer:* $\sqrt{x^2 + 3} = x^2 - 3$ has two extraneous solutions, $x = \pm 1$.

55. $2\sqrt{6} \approx 4.9$ units

5.4 Review & Refresh

57. $x^4 + x^3 - 2x^2 - 4x + 1$

58. $x^5 + x^4 - 4x^2 + 3$

59. $x^5 + 2x^4 + 5x^3 + 11x^2 + 5$

60. $x^3 + 11x - 8$

61. $g(x) = \sqrt{-x}$

62. $g(x) = \sqrt{x - 3} - 2$

63. $4p^3$

64. $3|m|n^2$

65. $\frac{y^4}{|z|}$

66. gk^2

67. $x = -7$ and $x = 1$; The point $(-7, 12)$ is located 4 units to the left of the axis of symmetry, so the second solution is located 4 units right of the axis of symmetry at the point $(1, 12)$.

68. $g(x) = -x^3 - 4x^2 + 10$; The graph of g is a reflection in the y-axis and a translation 4 units up of the graph of f.

69. $g(x) = \frac{1}{2}x^3 - 2x^2$; The graph of g is a vertical shrink by a factor of $\frac{1}{2}$, followed by a translation 3 units down of the graph of f.

70. $g(x) = -x^3 + 7x^2 - 11x - 1$; The graph of g is a reflection in the x-axis and a translation 1 unit right of the graph of f.

71. $g(x) = \frac{1}{64}x^3 - \frac{1}{4}x^2 + 11$; The graph of g is a horizontal stretch by a factor of 4 and a translation 5 units up of the graph of f.

72. $1 \le x \le 10$ **73.** $x > 64$

74. $x > -125$ **75.** $1 \le x \le \frac{25}{16}$

76. F3 **77.** $x = 4 \pm \sqrt{22}$

78. $x = -4$ and $x = 2$ **79.** $x = -2 \pm i\sqrt{7}$

80. $x = \frac{3}{2} \pm \frac{i\sqrt{3}}{2}$

81. $(-6, 4, 9)$; Explanations will vary.

5.5 Practice

1. $(f + g)(x) = 14\sqrt[4]{x}$ and the domain is $x \ge 0$; $(f - g)(x) = -24\sqrt[4]{x}$ and the domain is $x \ge 0$; $(f + g)(16) = 28$; $(f - g)(16) = -48$

3. $(f + g)(x) = -7x^3 + 5x^2 + x$ and the domain is all real numbers; $(f - g)(x) = -7x^3 - 13x^2 + 11x$ and the domain is all real numbers; $(f + g)(-1) = 11$; $(f - g)(-1) = -17$

5. $(fg)(x) = 2x^{10/3}$ and the domain is all real numbers; $\left(\frac{f}{g}\right)(x) = 2x^{8/3}$ and the domain is $x \ne 0$; $(fg)(-27) = 118{,}098$; $\left(\frac{f}{g}\right)(-27) = 13{,}122$

7. $(fg)(x) = 36x^{3/2}$ and the domain is $x \ge 0$; $\left(\frac{f}{g}\right)(x) = \frac{4}{9}x^{1/2}$ and the domain is $x > 0$; $(fg)(9) = 972$; $\left(\frac{f}{g}\right)(9) = \frac{4}{3}$

9. $(fg)(x) = -98x^{11/6}$ and the domain is $x \ge 0$; $\left(\frac{f}{g}\right)(x) = -\frac{1}{2}x^{7/6}$; and the domain is $x > 0$; $(fg)(64) = -200{,}704$; $\left(\frac{f}{g}\right)(64) = -64$

11. 2541.04; 2458.96; 102,598.56; 60.92

13. 7.76; −14.60; −38.24; −0.31

15. The domain is incorrect; The domain of $\left(\frac{f}{g}\right)(x)$ is all real numbers except $x = 2$ and $x = -2$.

17. **a.** $(F + M)(t) = 0.0227t^3 - 0.238t^2 + 1.56t + 155.2$

b. the total number of employees in the United States over the age of 16

19. yes; yes; When adding or multiplying functions, the order in which the terms appear does not matter.

21. **a.** −21

b. −1

c. 0

d. 2

23. *Sample answer:* $f(-1) = 12$ and $g(-1) = -8$

5.5 Review & Refresh

25. $x = 7$ **26.** $x = -4$

27. $n = \frac{2y + 3}{x}$ **28.** $n = \frac{3}{7b - 4}$

29. yes; Every input has exactly one output.

30. no; The input, 2 has two outputs, 5 and −3.

31. $(fg)(x) = -16x^{9/2}$ and the domain is $x \ge 0$; $(fg)(4) = -8192$; $\left(\frac{f}{g}\right)(x) = -4(x)^{3/2}$ and the domain is $x > 0$; $\left(\frac{f}{g}\right)(4) = -32$

32. $3z\sqrt[5]{z^3}$ **33.** $\frac{|y|}{5}$

34. $-4\sqrt[3]{9}$ **35.** $13\sqrt{5}$

36. The graph of g is a reflection in the x-axis, followed by a translation 2 units left of the graph of f.

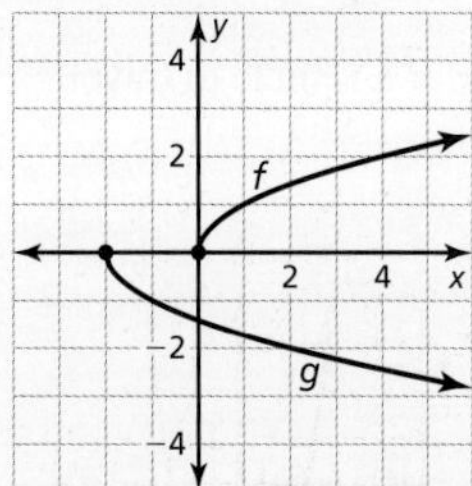

37. The graph of g is a vertical stretch by a factor of 4 and a translation 6 units down of the graph of f.

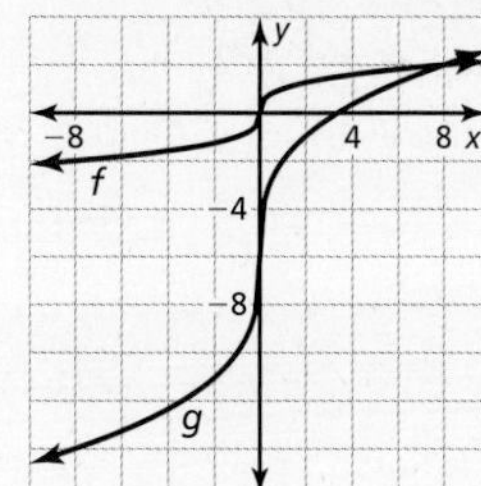

38. linear; As x decreases by 3, y increases by 1, so the differences are constant.

39. **a.** 2017

b. The number of commercial drones sold increased by 68,000 each year from 2016 to 2018.

c. no; This model shows that the number of drones sold continues to increase for all future years, which is not likely.

5.6 Practice

1. 2 **3.** 13

5. 30 **7.** −25

9. **a.** $f(g(x)) = -5x - 30$; all real numbers

b. $g(f(x)) = -5x + 6$; all real numbers

c. $f(f(x)) = 25x$; all real numbers

11. a. $f(g(x)) = 2x^2 - 4x + 2$; all real numbers

b. $g(f(x)) = 2x^2 - 1$; all real numbers

c. $f(f(x)) = 8x^4$; all real numbers

13. a. $f(g(x)) = \dfrac{3}{4x + 8}$; all real numbers except $x = -2$

b. $g(f(x)) = \dfrac{12}{x} + 8$; all real numbers except $x = 0$

c. $f(f(x)) = x$; all real numbers

15. a. $f(g(x)) = 3\sqrt{x + 7} - 7$; $x \geq -7$

b. $g(f(x)) = \sqrt{3x}$; $x \geq 0$

c. $f(f(x)) = 9x - 28$; all real numbers

17. a. $f(g(x)) = -\sqrt[3]{x - 3} + 11$; all real numbers

b. $g(f(x)) = \sqrt[3]{8 - x}$; all real numbers

c. $f(f(x)) = x$; all real numbers

19. a. $f(g(x)) = 2x^2 + 12x - 19$; all real numbers

b. $g(f(x)) = 4x^2 + 16x - 3$; all real numbers

c. $f(f(x)) = 4x + 3$; all real numbers

21. The functions were multiplied instead of performing the composition; $f(g(x)) = f(4x) = (4x)^2 - 3 = 16x^2 - 3$

23. a. $C(g(m)) = 0.11m$; The cost of gasoline is \$0.11 for each mile a vehicle drives.

b. 11; It costs \$11 in gasoline for a vehicle to travel 100 miles.

25. a. 7

b. −1

c. −2

d. 5

27. (8, 11), (5, −4), (0, 9), (−3, 3)(−10, −5)

29. $A = 4\pi t^2$

31. *Sample answer:* $f(x) = x + 6$ and $g(x) = \frac{1}{2}x$

33. *Sample answer:* $f(x) = \sqrt[3]{x}$ and $g(x) = x + 2$

35.

x	f(x)	g(x)
1	3.5	7
2	4	3
4	5	−5
7	6.5	−17

37. $12x^2 + 12x + 8$

39. $27x + 65$

41. $g(p(q(h(x)))) = g(p(q(x - 2))) = g\left(p\left(\sqrt{x - 2}\right)\right)$
$= g\left(\sqrt{x - 2} + 9\right) = \frac{1}{3}\left(\sqrt{x - 2} + 9\right) = \frac{1}{3}\sqrt{x - 2} + 3$

5.6 Review & Refresh

42. $0 \leq x < 16$

43. $x \geq -217$

44. a. The function is increasing when $x < 2$ and decreasing when $x > 2$.

b. $1 < x < 3$

c. $x < 1$ and $x > 3$

45. 1

46. 5

47. $g(x) = \sqrt{2x} + 3$

48. (−2, 5), (−1, 3); Explanations will vary.

49. $\left(\frac{7}{2}, -\frac{9}{4}\right)$; Explanations will vary.

50. $(P - S)(t) = 0.0208t^4 - 0.2067t^3 + 0.602t^2 + 1.02t + 229.6$; The number of people in the United States who speak English at home.

51. 25.1 cm^3

5.7 Practice

1. $x = \dfrac{y - 5}{3}$; $-\dfrac{8}{3}$

3. $x = 2y + 6$; 0

5. $x = \sqrt[3]{\dfrac{y}{3}}$; −1

7. $x = 2 \pm \sqrt{y + 7}$; 0, 4

9. $f^{-1}(x) = \frac{1}{6}x$

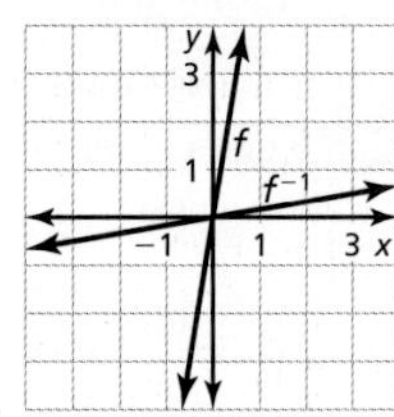

11. $f^{-1}(x) = \dfrac{x - 5}{-2}$

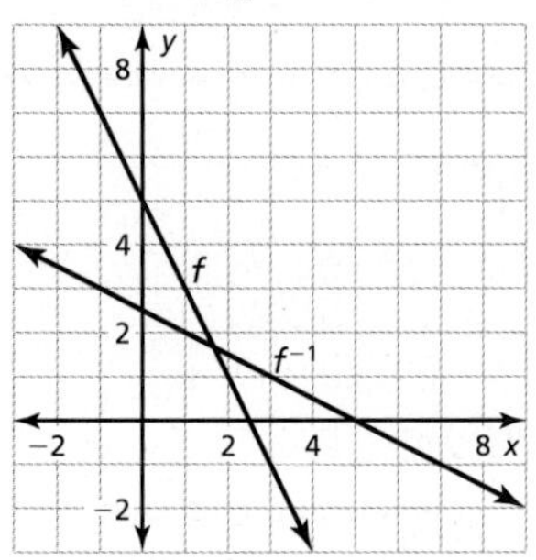

13. $f^{-1}(x) = -2x + 8$

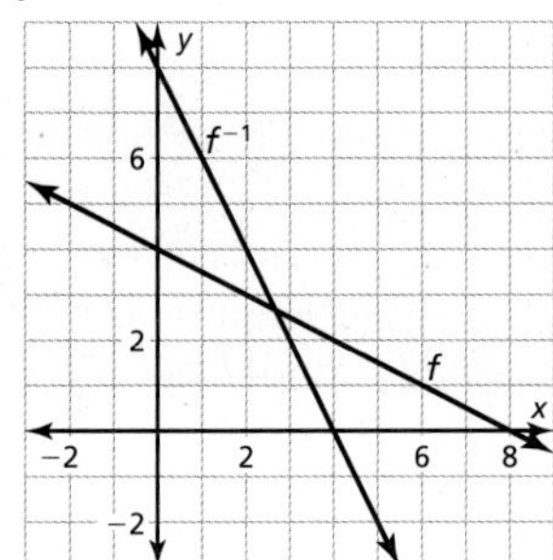

15. $f^{-1}(x) = \dfrac{3x + 1}{2}$

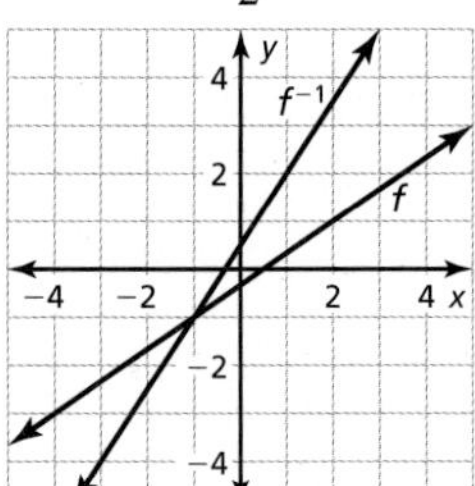

17. yes; The x- and y-coordinates are switched.

19. $f^{-1}(x) = -\frac{\sqrt{x}}{2}$

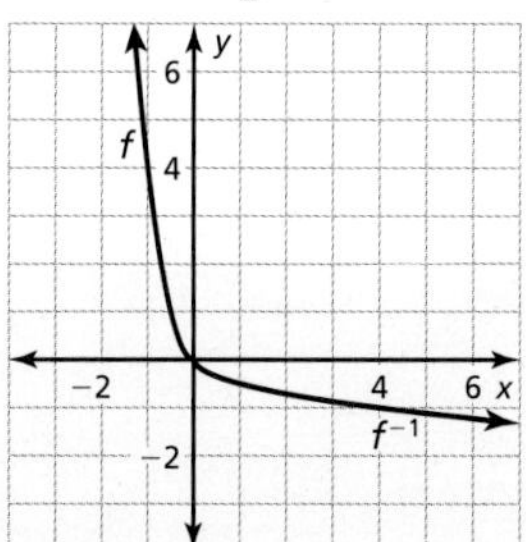

21. $f^{-1}(x) = \sqrt{x} + 3$

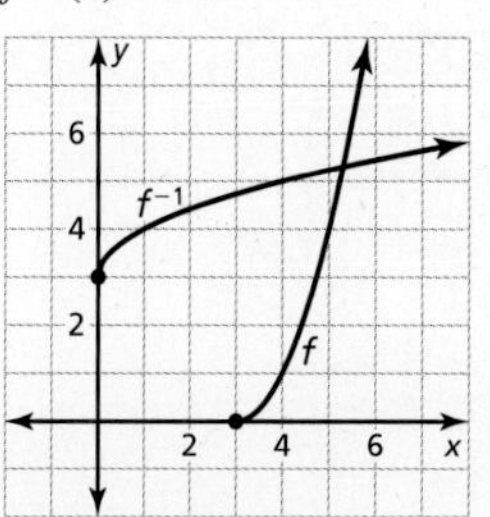

23. $f^{-1}(x) = \sqrt{6 - x} + 1$

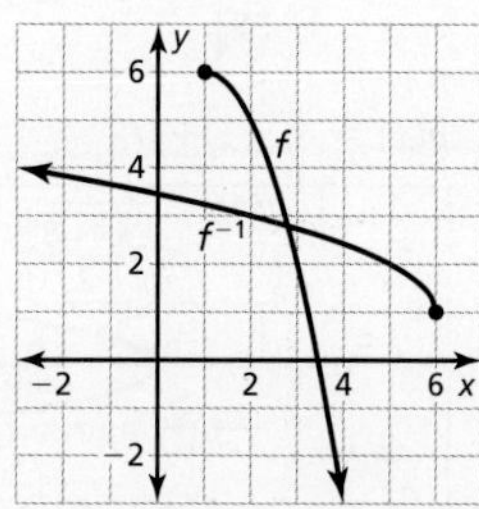

25. When switching x and y, the negative should not be switched with the variables;

$y = -x + 3$
$x = -y + 3$
$-x + 3 = y$
So, $f^{-1}(x) = -x + 3$.

27. no; The function does not pass the horizontal line test.

29. $f^{-1}(x) = \sqrt[3]{x + 1}$

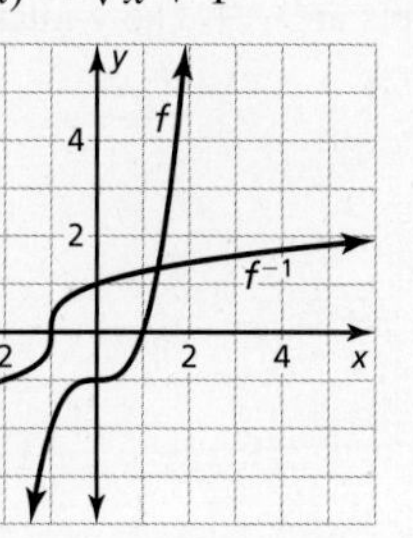

31. $f^{-1}(x) = \sqrt[3]{-x + 2}$

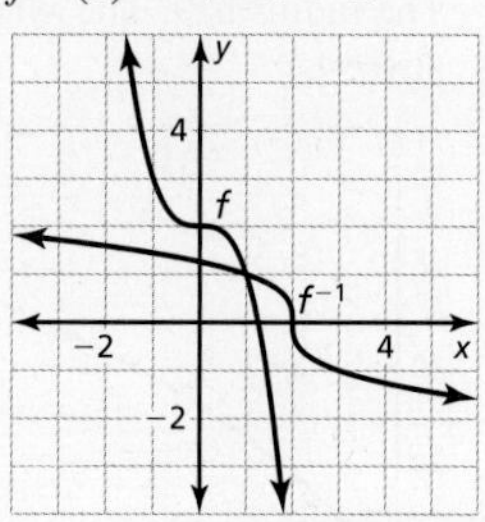

33. $f^{-1}(x) = x^2 - 4, x \geq 0$

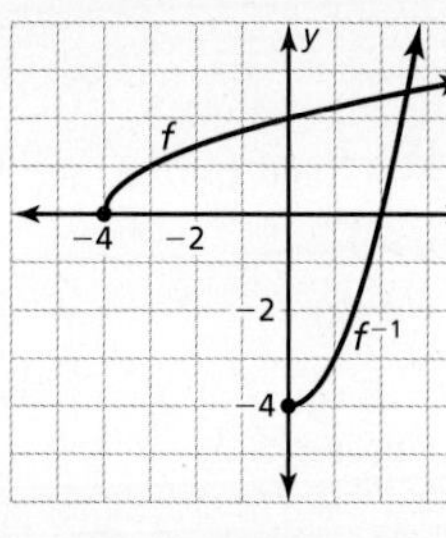

35. $f^{-1}(x) = \frac{x^3}{8} + 5$

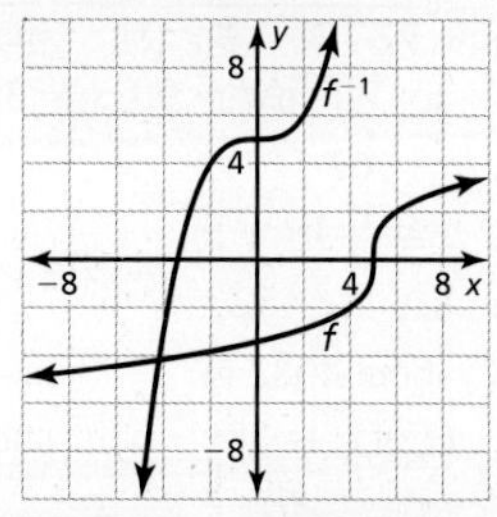

37. $f^{-1}(x) = \sqrt[3]{\frac{3}{2}x - 12} - 1$

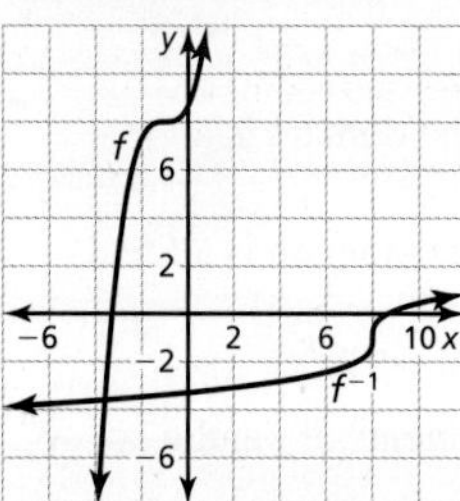

39. $f^{-1}(x) = \frac{-3x^3 - 4}{2}$

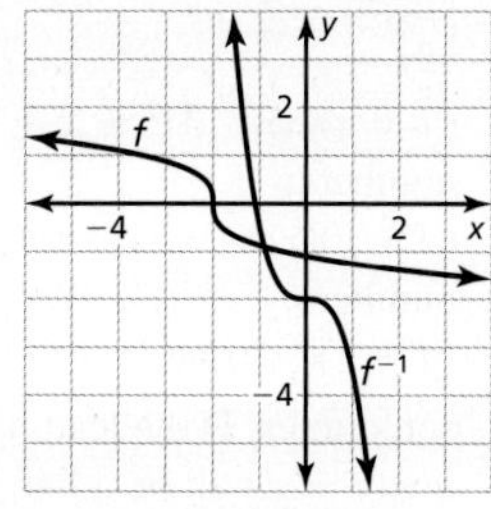

41. C **43.** no

45. yes

47. $f^{-1}(7.5) \approx 31.3$; To achieve a maximum speed of 7.5 knots, the waterline length of a boat needs to be about 31.3 feet.

49. B **51.** A

53. $f^{-1}(-2) = -1$; $f(-1) = -2$, so $f^{-1}(-2) = -1$.

55. $f^{-1}(x) = \frac{x - 4}{-3}$; *Sample answer:* switching x and y; You can graph the inverse to check your answer.

57. B **59.** A

61. a. $h^{-1}(x) = 2x - 6$; the weight of an object on a stretched spring of length x

b. 5 lb

c. $0.5(2x - 6) + 3 = x$; $2(0.5x + 3) - 6 = x$

63. a. $C^{-1}(x) = \frac{9}{5}x + 32$; The equation converts temperatures in Celsius to Fahrenheit.

b. start: 41°F; end: 14°F

65. no; *Sample answer:* $y = (x - 1)^2, x \geq 0$ does not have an inverse function.

67. The inverse of $y = mx + b$ has slope $\frac{1}{m}$ and y-intercept $-\frac{b}{m}$; no; The inverse of a horizontal line is a vertical line, which is not a function.

69. a. false; All functions of the form $f(x) = x^n$, where n is an even integer, fail the horizontal line test.

b. true; All functions of the form $f(x) = x^n$, where n is an odd integer, pass the horizontal line test.

c. true; All functions of the form $f(x) = x^n$, where $x \leq 0$ and n is a positive even integer, pass the horizontal line test.

5.7 Review & Refresh

70. The function is increasing when $x > 1$ and decreasing when $x < 1$. The function is positive when $x < 0$ and when $x > 2$, and negative when $0 < x < 2$.

71. The function is increasing when $x < -1.15$ and $x > 1.15$ and decreasing when $-1.15 < x < 1.15$. The function is positive when $-2 < x < 0$ and $x > 2$ and negative when $x < -2$ and $0 < x < 2$.

72. $f^{-1}(x) = -\frac{x - 7}{4}$

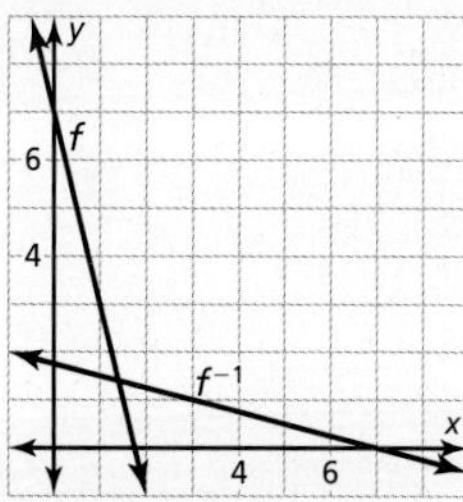

73. $f^{-1}(x) = \sqrt{-\frac{x + 9}{3}}$

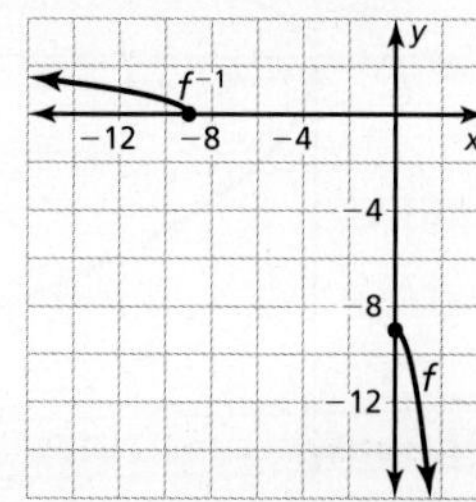

74. $f^{-1}(x) = \sqrt[3]{\frac{x + 10}{2}}$

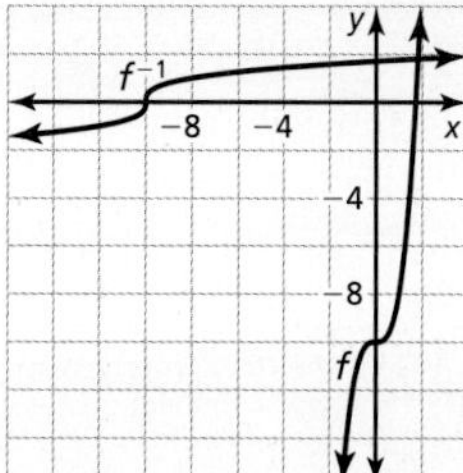

75. $f^{-1}(x) = \frac{1}{25}x^2 - 3, x \geq 0$

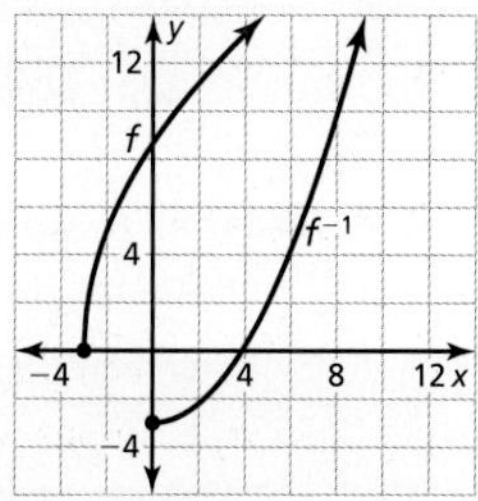

76. $x = 7$

77. $x = 2$

78. $x = 33$

79. $x = -9$ and $x = 9$

80. $y = -4x^2 + 10x + 6$

81. $0 = 2x^2 + 5x - 8$

82. $x = \frac{1}{6}$ and $y = 2$

83. $(f + g)(x) = -9\sqrt[3]{x}$, all real numbers; $(f - g)(x) = 15\sqrt[3]{x}$, all real numbers; $(f + g)(64) = -36$, $(f - g)(64) = 60$

84. $(f + g)(x) = 6x^2 + 7x + 8$, all real numbers; $(f - g)(x) = -2x^2 + 7x - 14$, all real numbers; $(f + g)(3) = 83$, $(f - g)(3) = -11$

85. $V = 12x^3 + 86x^2 + 182x + 120$

86. $y = \frac{1}{12}(x - 3)^2 + 1$

87. $f(h(x)) = 9x + 16$; all real numbers

88. $h(f(x)) = 9x$; all real numbers

89. $g(f(x)) = \dfrac{2}{6x - 2}$; all real numbers except $x = \dfrac{1}{3}$

90. $f(g(x)) = \dfrac{12}{x} - 2$; all real numbers except $x = 0$

91. 3

92. 4

Chapter 5 Review

1. ± 6

2. -4

3. 128

4. 243

5. $\frac{1}{9}$

6. $x \approx 1.78$

7. $x = 3$

8. $x = -10$ and $x = -6$

9. $3^{1.45} < 3^{1.5}$ and $3^{3/2} = \sqrt{3^3} = \sqrt{27} < \sqrt{36} = 6$. So, $3^{1.45} < 6$.

10. about 7.0 mm

11. $6^{3/5}$

12. 4

13. $-\dfrac{2 + \sqrt{7}}{3}$

14. $7\sqrt[5]{8}$

15. $7\sqrt{3}$

16. $5^{1/3} \cdot 2^{3/4}$

17. $5z^3$

18. $\dfrac{(2z)^{1/4}}{6}$

19. $-z^2\sqrt{10z}$

20. The graph of g is a vertical stretch by a factor of 2, followed by a reflection in the x-axis of the graph of f.

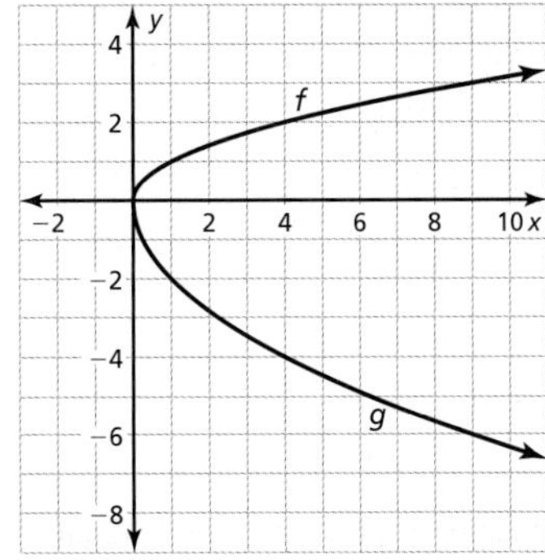

21. The graph of g is a reflection in the y-axis, followed by a translation 6 units down of the graph of f.

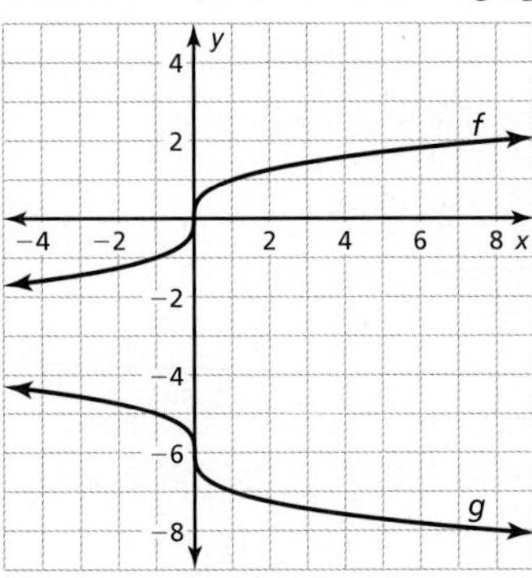

22. $g(x) = \sqrt[3]{-x + 7}$

23.

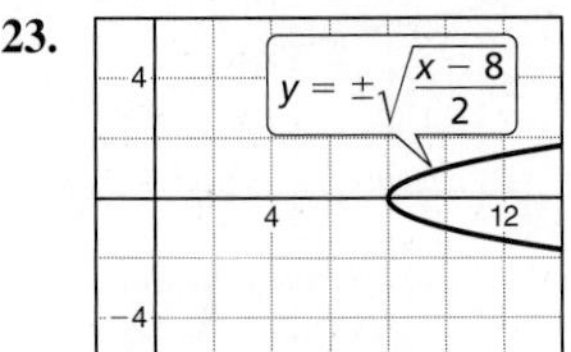

(8, 0); right

24.

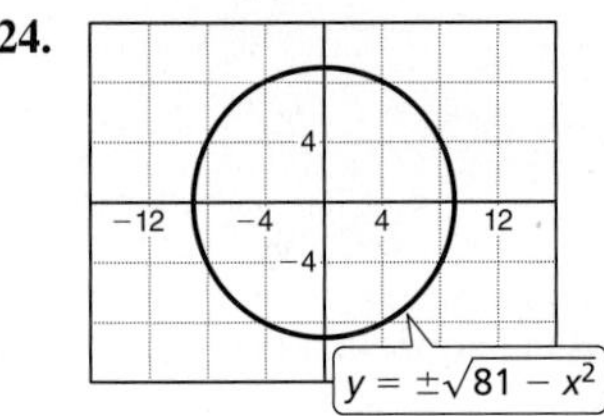

The radius is 9. The x-intercepts are ± 9. The y-intercepts are ± 9.

25.

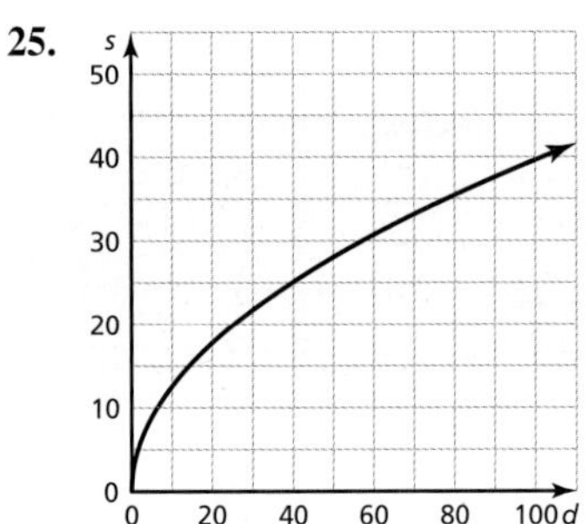

no; When $d = 90$, $s \approx 38$.

26. $x = 62$

27. $x = 2$ and $x = 10$

28. $x = \pm 36$

29. $x > 9$

30. $8 \le x < 152$

31. $x \ge 30$

32. about 4082 m

33. $(fg)(x) = 8(3 - x)^{5/6}$ and the domain is $x \le 3$; $\left(\dfrac{f}{g}\right)(x) = \dfrac{1}{2}(3 - x)^{1/6}$ and the domain is $x < 3$; $(fg)(2) = 8$; $\left(\dfrac{f}{g}\right)(2) = \dfrac{1}{2}$

34. $(f + g)(x) = 3x^2 + x + 5$ and the domain is all real numbers; $(f - g)(x) = 3x^2 - x - 3$ and the domain is all real numbers; $(f + g)(-5) = 75$; $(f - g)(-5) = 77$

35. sometimes; If the leading coefficients of f and g are opposites then $f + g$ will be a linear function.

36. always; $f(a) \cdot g(a) = (fg)(a)$.

37. 5

38. 100

39. 3

40. $f(g(x)) = \frac{2}{x^2} - 5$; all real numbers except $x = 0$

41. $h(f(x)) = 6x + 11$; all real numbers

42. $g(h(x)) = \frac{1}{(3x + 4)^2}$; all real numbers except $x = -\frac{4}{3}$

43. radical function

44. the 10% coupon; Let $f(x) = x - 15$ and $g(x) = (1 - 0.10)x = 0.9x$. $f(g(x)) = 0.9x - 15$ and $g(f(x)) = 0.9x - 13.5$, so $f(g(x)) < g(f(x))$.

45. $f^{-1}(x) = -2x + 20$

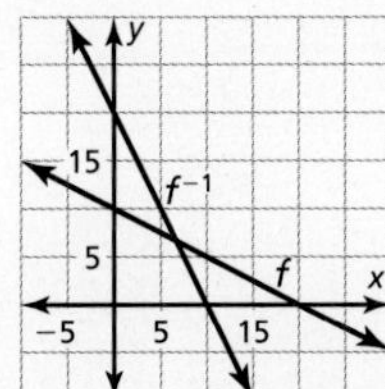

46. $f^{-1}(x) = \sqrt{x - 8}$

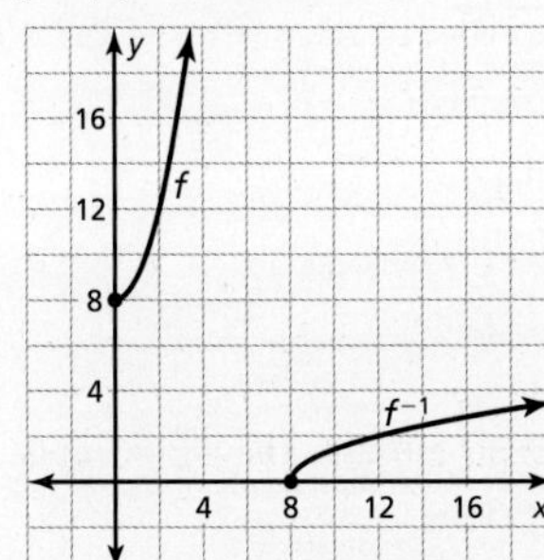

47. $f^{-1}(x) = \sqrt[3]{-x - 9}$

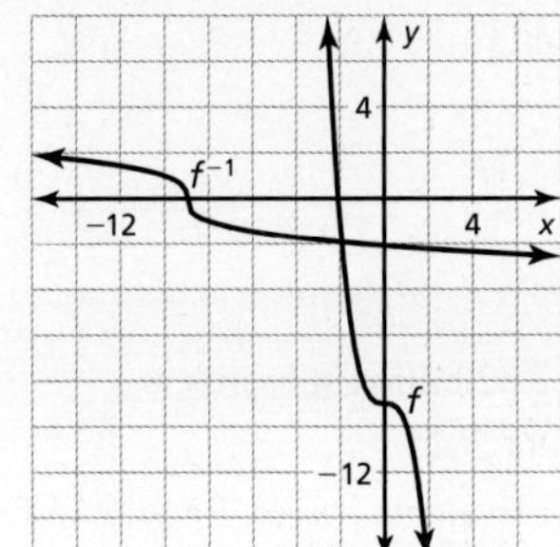

48. $f^{-1}(x) = \frac{1}{9}(x - 5)^2, x \geq 5$

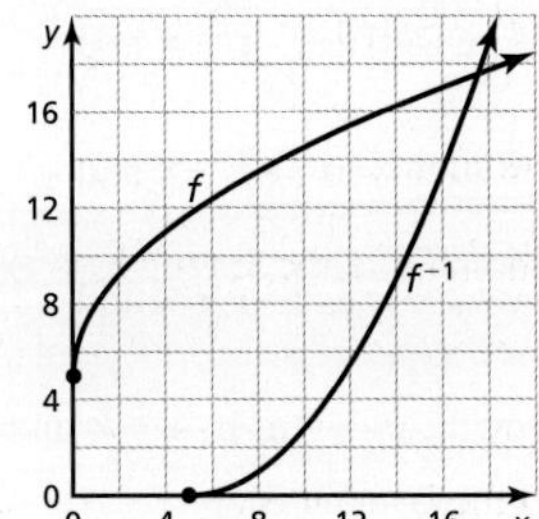

49. no

50. yes

51. $d^{-1}(100) = 128.7$; 100 U.S. dollars is equal to 128.7 British pounds.

Chapter 5 Mathematical Practices (Chapter Review)

1. The equation shows a proportional relationship between the mass of the particles and the speed of the river.

2. *Sample answer:*

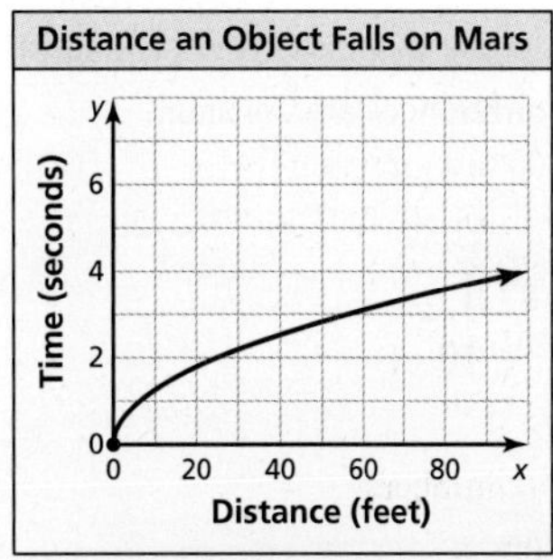

Distance an object falls on Mars	
Distance (feet)	Time (seconds)
1	0.4
4	0.8
9	1.2
16	1.6
25	2

Chapter 5 Practice Test

1. $3 \leq x \leq 12$; $x = 12$; In each process, the same operations are used but when solving the inequality you must check the domain for values that make the radicand negative.

2. The graph of g is a translation 3 units right of the graph of f; $g(x) = \sqrt{x - 3}$

3. The graph of g is a vertical stretch by a factor of 2, followed by a reflection in the x-axis of the graph of f; $g(x) = -2\sqrt[3]{x}$

4. The graph of g is a vertical stretch by a factor of 2, followed by a translation 2 units up of the graph of f; $g(x) = 2\sqrt[5]{x} + 2$

5. 16; The cube root of 64 is 4 and 4^2 is 16.

6. -243; The cube root of -27 is -3 and $(-3)^5$ is -243.

7. $2y^2\sqrt[4]{3xy^3z^3}$; The fourth root of 16 and y^8 can be simplified.

8. 2; The radical can be simplified to $\sqrt[3]{8}$.

9. $f(h(x)) = x + 9$; all real numbers

10. $h(g(x)) = \frac{12}{x} + 12$; all real numbers except $x = 0$

11. $g(f(x)) = \frac{3}{\frac{1}{4}x + 6}$; all real numbers except $x = -24$

12. $f(f(x)) = \frac{1}{16}x + \frac{15}{2}$; all real numbers

13. $(-7, -2)$; $x = -1$

14. rabbit: about 145.7 kilocalories per day; sheep: about 1378 kilocalories per day; human: about 1774 kilocalories per day; lion: about 4044 kilocalories per day

15. $(f + g)(x) = 5x^{3/5}$ and the domain is all real numbers; $(f - g)(x) = 7x^{3/5}$ and the domain is all real numbers; $(f + g)(32) = 40$; $(f - g)(32) = 56$

16. $(fg)(x) = 4x^{7/4}$ and the domain is $x \geq 0$; $\left(\frac{f}{g}\right)(x) = \frac{1}{16x^{1/4}}$ and the domain is $x > 0$; $(fg)(16) = 512$; $\left(\frac{f}{g}\right)(16) = \frac{1}{32}$

17. $r^{-1} = \frac{t - 1.13}{0.83}$; about 300 cm

Chapter 5 College and Career Readiness

1. $(\sqrt{a})^n = \sqrt{a^n}$, $a^{1/n} = \sqrt[n]{a}$, $\sqrt[n]{a^n} = a$; Use properties of exponents and radicals to rewrite the expressions.

2. $-3; 2$

3. B, E, F

4. $-80, -261$; The fourth differences are constant.

5. B

6. C

7. C

8. $h = \sqrt{d^2 - 2500}$; about 87 ft

9. $x = 6$

10. D

Chapter 6

Chapter 6 Prepare

1. 6

2. $-32n^5$

3. $\frac{81w^4}{16x^4}$

4. $48g$

5. domain: $-5 \leq x \leq 5$, range: $0 \leq y \leq 5$

6. domain: $-2, -1, 0, 1$, range: $3, 1, -1, -3$

7. domain: all real numbers, range: $y \leq 0$

8. all values, odd values; no values, even values; The exponent of $-a^n$ is evaluated first, then the result is multiplied by -1, so the value will always remain negative. The product of an odd number of negative values is negative. After the exponent of $-a^n$ is evaluated, the result is multiplied by -1, so it will never be positive. The product of an even number of negative values is positive.

6.1 Practice

1. a. $\frac{1}{4}$

b. 8

3. a. $\frac{8}{9}$

b. 216

5. a. about 4.71

b. about 5.46

7. exponential growth

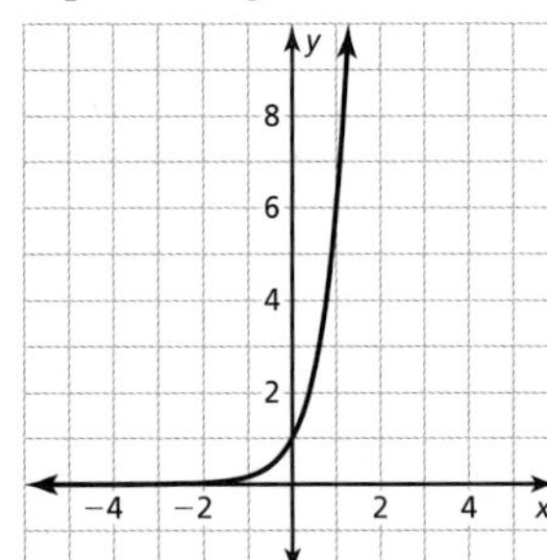

9. exponential decay

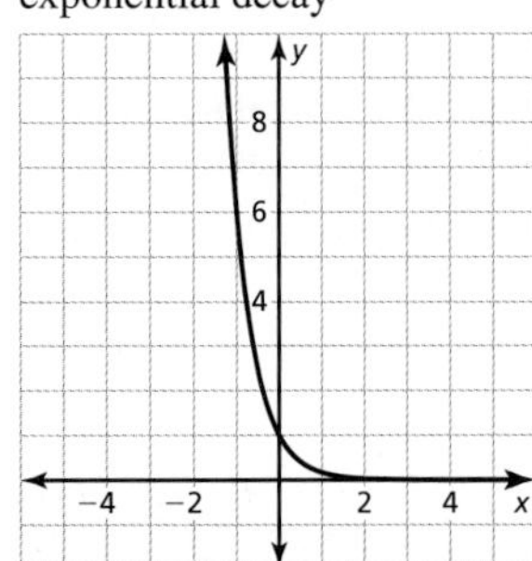

11. exponential growth

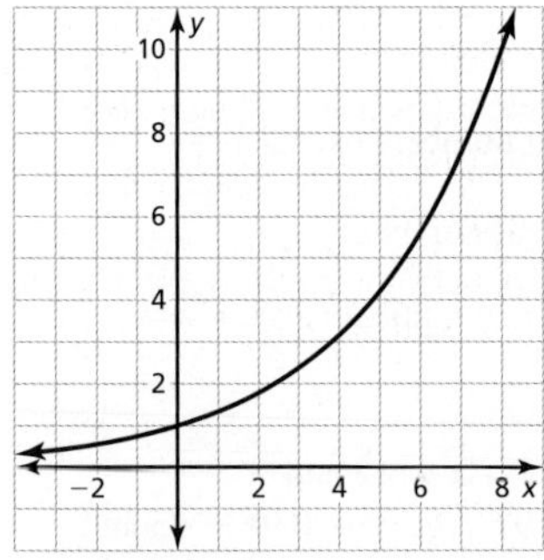

13. exponential growth

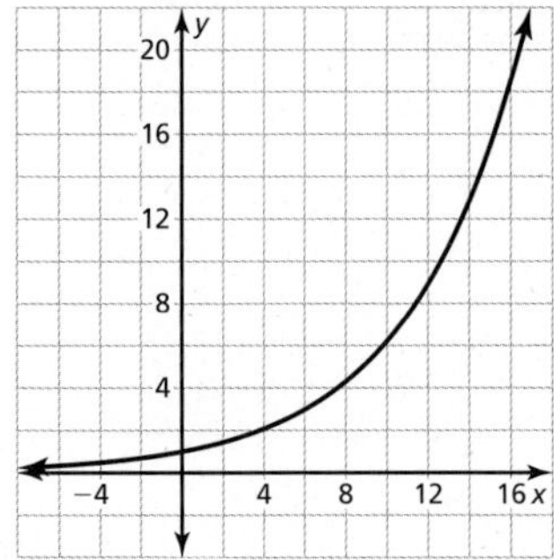

15. exponential decay

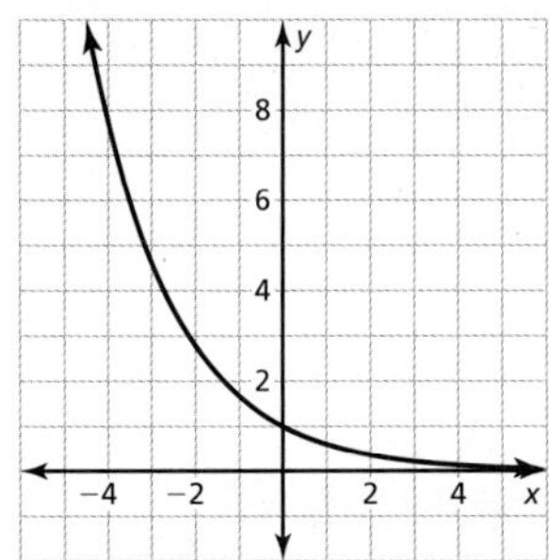

17. $b = 3$

19. a. exponential decay

b. 35% decrease

c. in about 3.2 years

21. a. $y = 6.26(1.04)^t$; about 7.32 billion subscribers

b. in the year 2014, or about 2015

23. Power of a Power Property; Evaluate power; Rewrite in form $y = a(1 + r)^t$.

25. about 0.01%

27. $y = a(1 + 0.26)^t$; 26% growth; $y \to 0$ as $t \to -\infty$ and $y \to +\infty$ as $t \to +\infty$

29. $y = a(1 - 0.06)^t$; 6% decay; $y \to +\infty$ as $t \to -\infty$ and $y \to 0$ as $t \to +\infty$

31. $y = a(1 - 0.04)^t$; 4% decay; $y \to +\infty$ as $t \to -\infty$ and $y \to 0$ as $t \to +\infty$

33. $y = a(1 + 255)^t$; 25,500% growth; $y \to 0$ as $t \to -\infty$ and $y \to +\infty$ as $t \to +\infty$

35. $5593.60

37. The percent decrease needs to be subtracted from 1 to produce the decay factor;

$y = \begin{pmatrix}\text{Initial}\\\text{amount}\end{pmatrix}\begin{pmatrix}\text{Decay}\\\text{factor}\end{pmatrix}^t$;

$y = 500(1 - 0.02)^t$; $y = 500(0.98)^t$

39. $3982.92

41. $3774.71

43. The initial principal deposited in the account; the interest; no; no; Both quantities are independent of each other.

45. f; g; Because $f(0) > g(0)$ and $f(3) < g(3)$, f has a greater y-intercept and g is increasing at a faster rate than f.

47. about 221.5; The curve contains the points (0, 6850) and (6, 8179.26) and $\frac{8179.26 - 6850}{6 - 0} \approx 221.5$.

49. C

51. a. The decay factor is 0.9978. The percent decrease is 0.22%.

b. 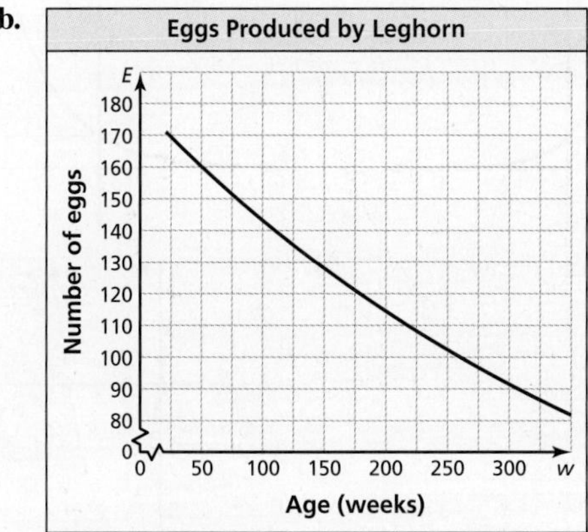

c. about 134 eggs per year

d. Replace $\frac{w}{52}$ with y, where y represents the age of the chicken in years.

6.1 Review & Refresh

53. x^{11}

54. $216x^{18}$

55. $16x^8$

56. $3 + 5x$

57. The initial amount is 2.4, the growth factor is 1.5, and the percent increase is 0.5 or 50%.

58. yes

59. no

60. $(fg)(x) = -4x^{7/2}, x \geq 0$; $\left(\frac{f}{g}\right)(x) = -\frac{x^{5/2}}{4}, x > 0$; $(fg)(4) = -512$, $\left(\frac{f}{g}\right)(4) = -8$

61. $g(h(x)) = -\frac{2}{x} + 5$; all real numbers except $x = 0$

62. $f(g(x)) = \frac{1}{4}x^2 - 5x + 19$; all real numbers

63. $g(g(x)) = \frac{1}{4}x + \frac{5}{2}$; all real numbers

64. $h(f(x)) = \frac{4}{x^2 - 6}$; all real numbers except $x = \pm\sqrt{6}$

65. exponential growth

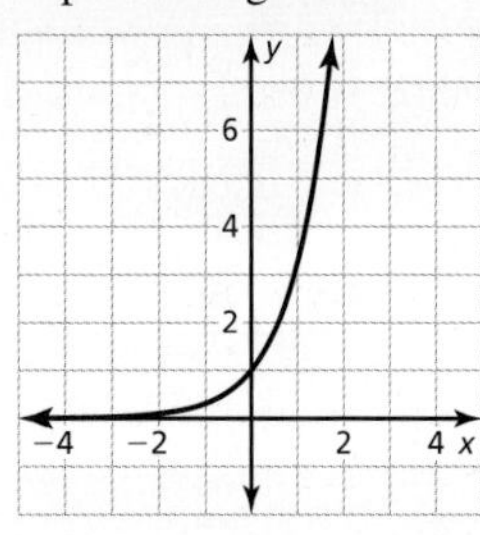

66. exponential decay

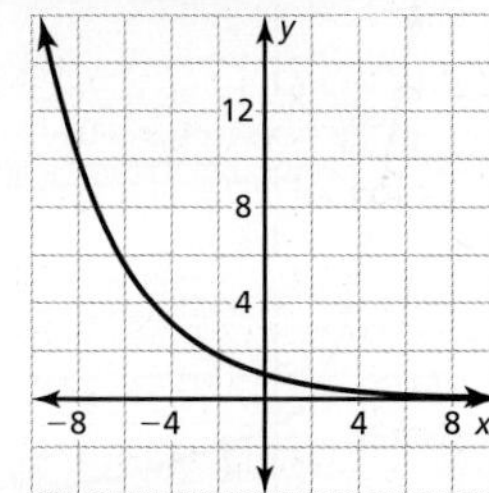

67. a. when $x < -2$ and $x > 0$

b. when $-2 < x < 0$

c. when $x > 1$

d. when $x < -2$ and $-2 < x < 1$

68. a. Distance traveled (miles): 1 3 5 7 9 11 13

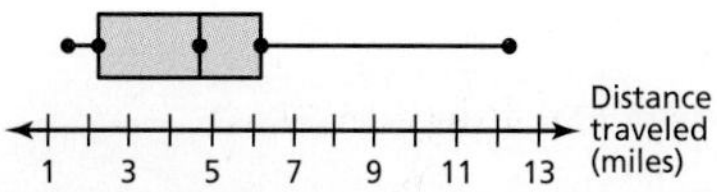

skewed right

b. yes; The outlier increases the mean and increases the range.

6.2 Practice

1. e^8

3. $\frac{1}{2e}$

5. $625e^{28x}$

7. $3e^{3x}$

9. e^{-5x+8}

11. The 4 was not squared; $(4e^{3x})^2 = 4^2e^{(3x)(2)} = 16e^{6x}$

13. D; The graph shows growth and has a y-intercept of 1.

15. B; The graph shows decay and has a y-intercept of 4.

17. exponential growth

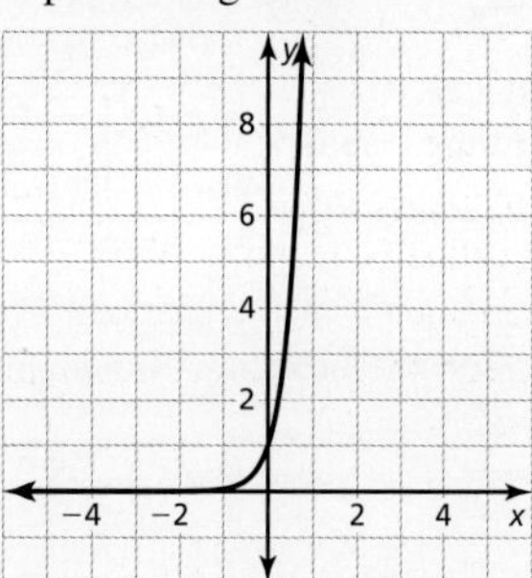

19. exponential decay

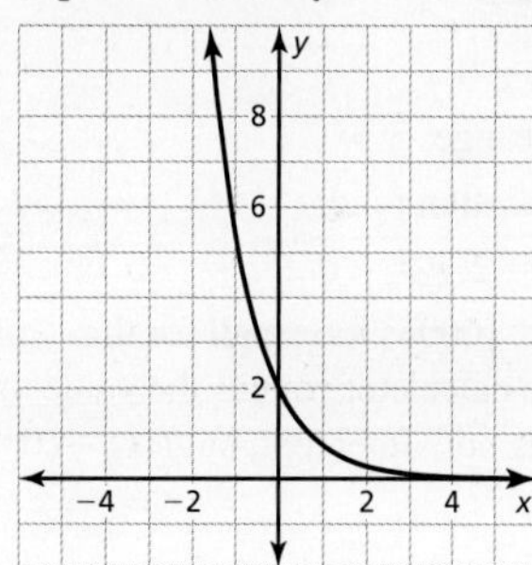

21. exponential growth

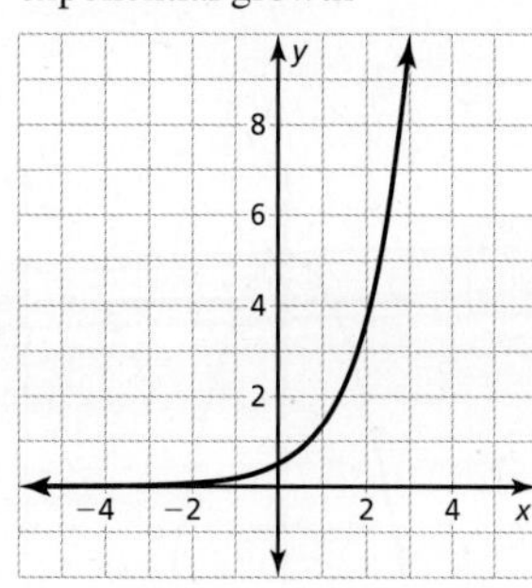

23. exponential decay

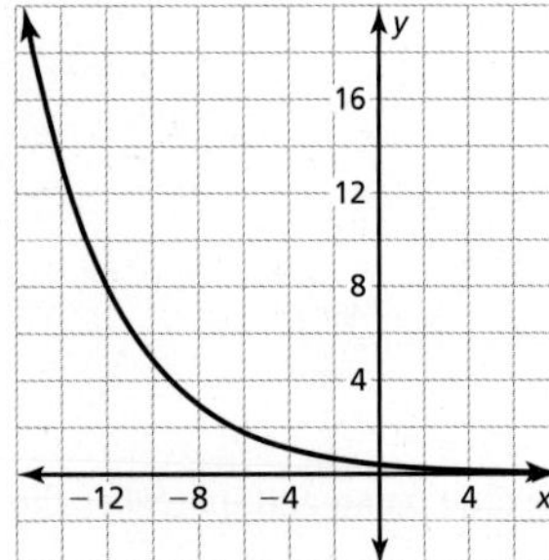

25. $y \approx (1 - 0.528)^t$; about 52.8% decay

27. $y \approx 2(1 + 0.492)^t$; about 49.2% growth

29.

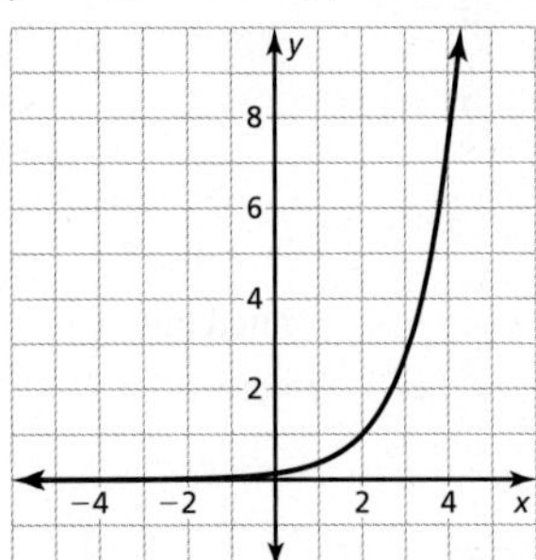

domain: all real numbers, range: $y > 0$

31.

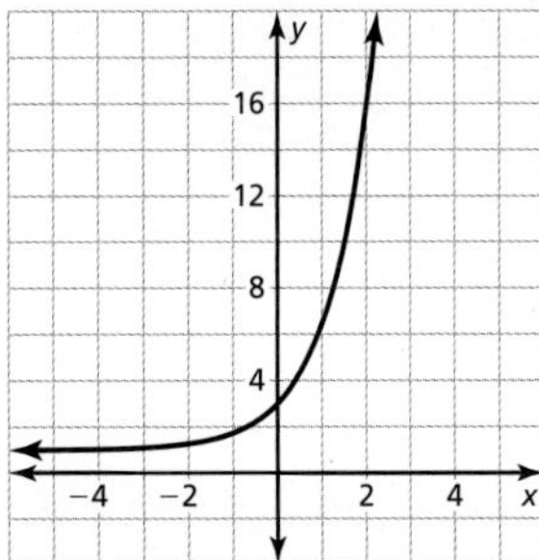

domain: all real numbers, range: $y > 1$

33. the education fund; the education fund

35. *Sample answer:* $a = 6, b = 2, r = -0.2, q = -0.7$

37. no; The value of $f(x)$ at $x = 1000$ is too small for the calculator to display, so the calculator rounds the value to 0. The function $f(x) = e^{-x}$ has no x-intercept, but $f(x) \to 0$ as $x \to +\infty$.

39. about 47 bacteria

6.2 Review & Refresh

41. 2.6×10^7

42. 4.7×10^{-8}

43.

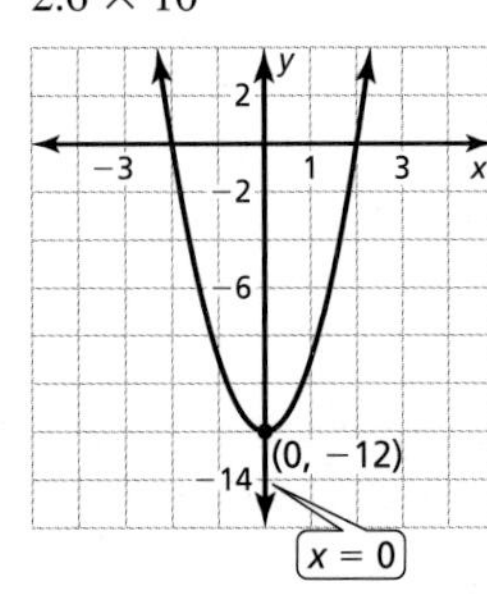

44.

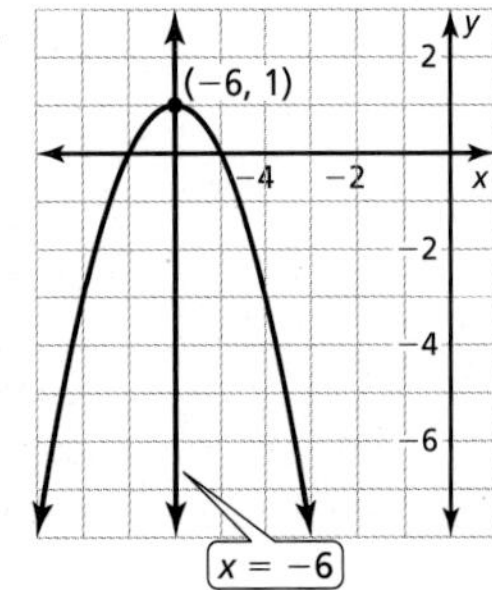

45. $y = -\frac{1}{5}(x - 1)(x + 5)(x - 4)$

46. *Sample answer:* $(2, -11)$

47. exponential growth

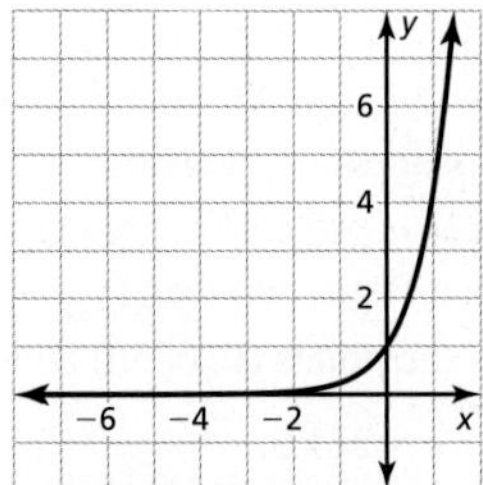

48. exponential decay

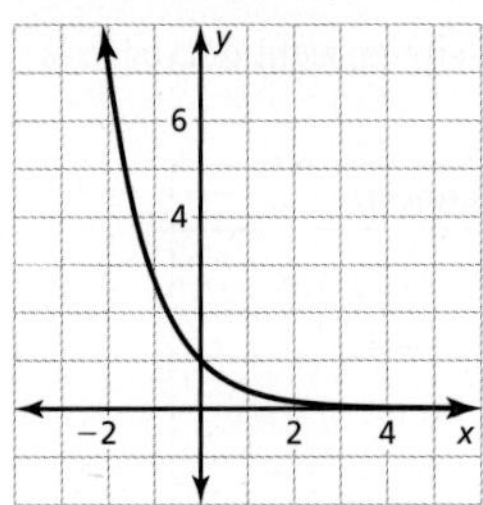

49. exponential growth

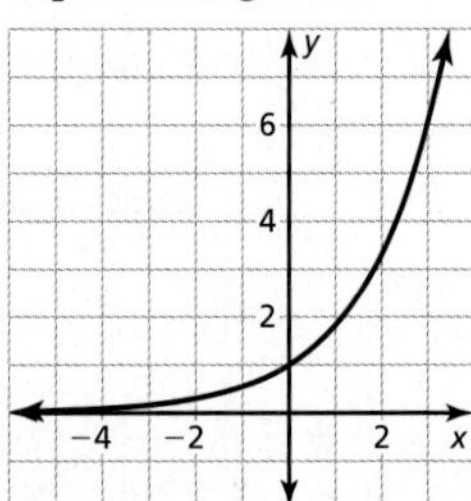

50. exponential decay

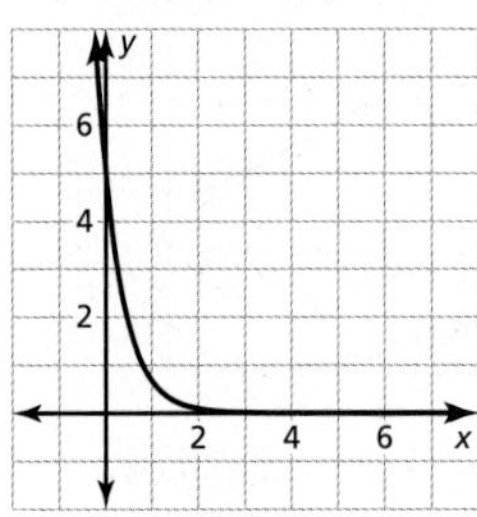

51.

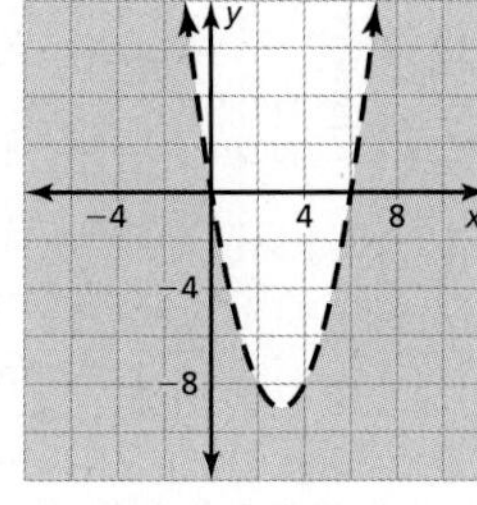

52.

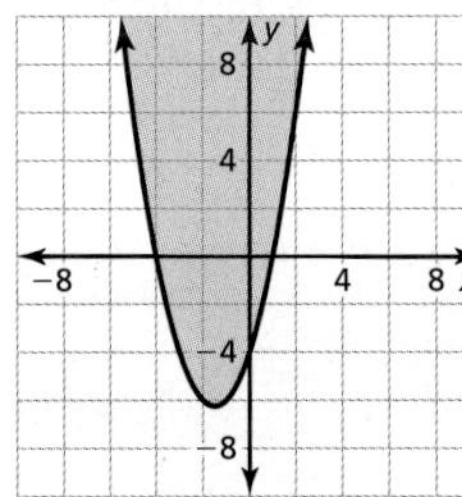

53. $y = \frac{x - 5}{3}$

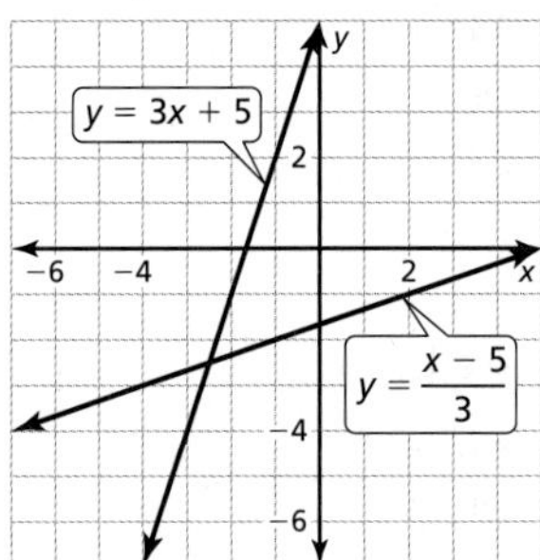

54. $y = -\sqrt{x + 1}$

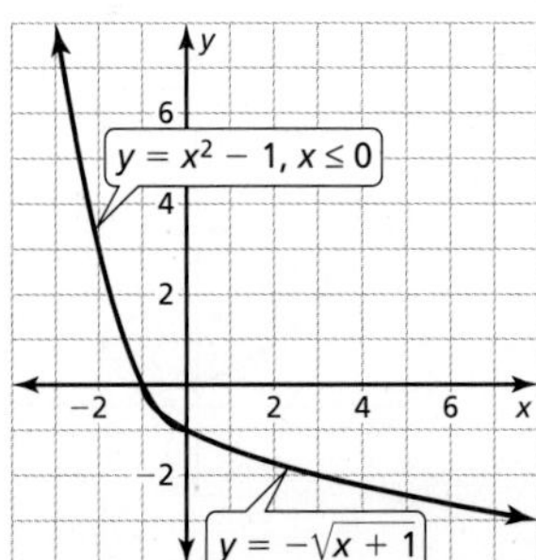

55. $y = x^2 - 6, x \geq 0$

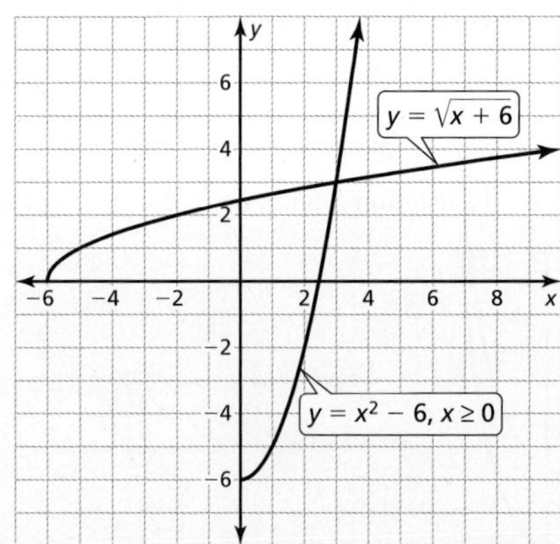

56. $y = \sqrt[3]{x + 2}$

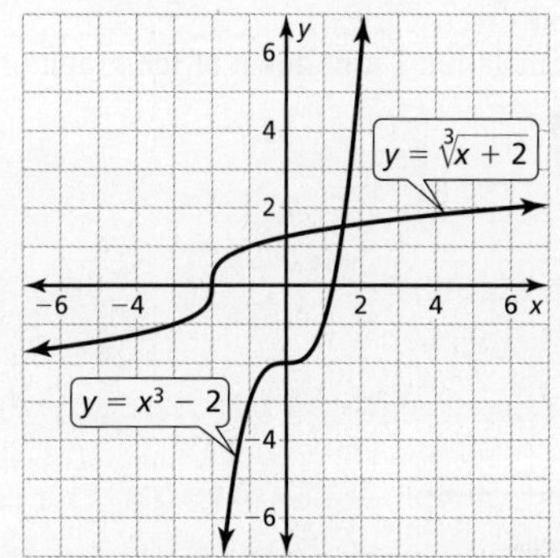

57. a. $f(t(x)) = 146.25x$; You earn \$146.25 each week.

b. $f(t(12)) = 1755$; After 12 weeks you earn \$1755.

6.3 Practice

1. $3^2 = 9$ | **3.** $6^0 = 1$

5. $\left(\frac{1}{2}\right)^{-4} = 16$ | **7.** $\log_6 36 = 2$

9. $\log_{16} \frac{1}{16} = -1$ | **11.** $\log_{125} 25 = \frac{2}{3}$

13. 4 | **15.** 1

17. -4 | **19.** -1

21. $\log_7 8, \log_5 23, \log_6 38, \log_2 10$

23. 0.778 | **25.** -1.099

27. -2.079 | **29.** 3

31. x | **33.** 4

35. $2x$ | **37.** $-x$

39. They are inverse equations.

41. -3 and $\frac{1}{64}$ are in the wrong position; $\log_4 \frac{1}{64} = -3$

43. $f(x) = \log_{0.3} x$ | **45.** $y = 2^x$

47. $y = e^x + 1$ | **49.** $f(x) = \frac{1}{3} \ln x$

51. $y = \log_5(x + 9)$

53. a. about 93.99 mi/h

b. $f^{-1}(x) = 10^{(x - 65)/93}$; The distance (in miles) the tornado travels when the wind speed near the center of the tornado is x miles per hour.

55.

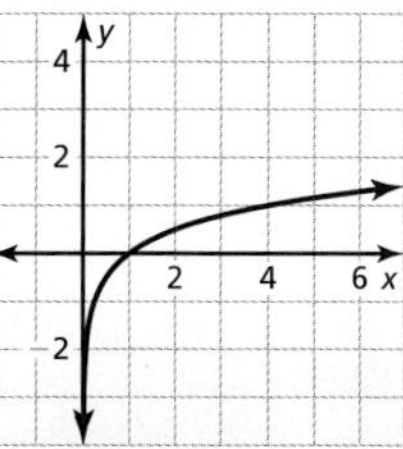

57.

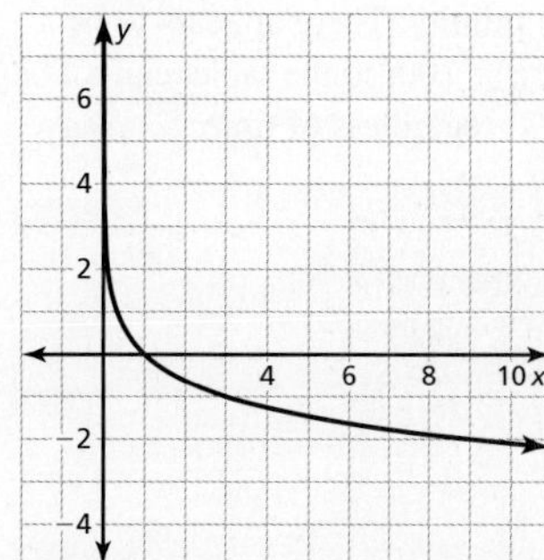

59.

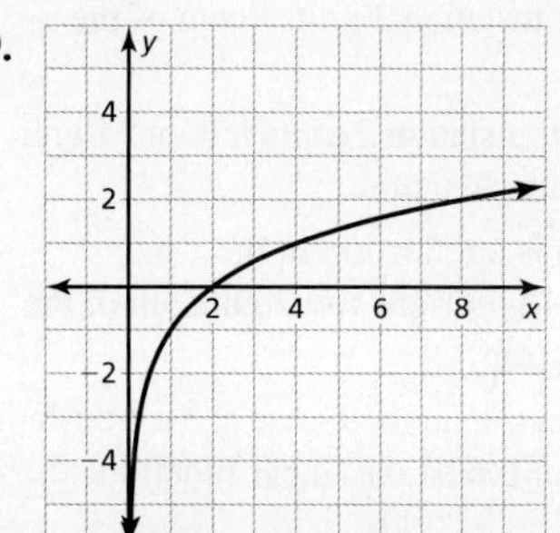

61.

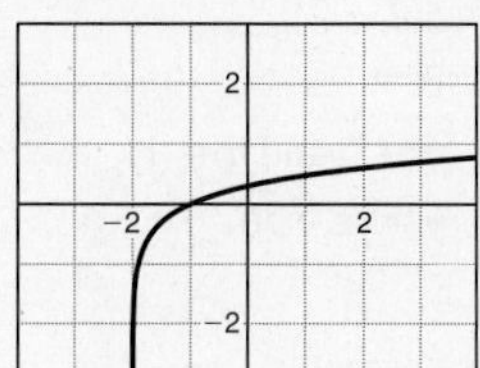

domain: $x > -2$, range: all real numbers, asymptote: $x = -2$

63.

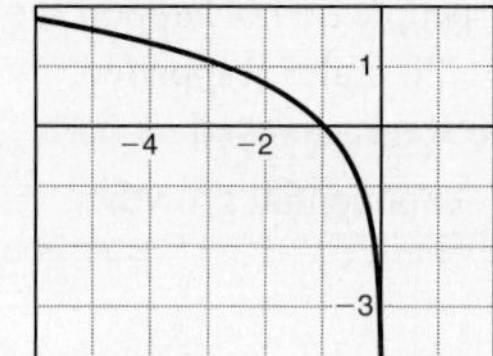

domain: $x < 0$, range: all real numbers, asymptote: $x = 0$

65. yes; Every base with an exponent of 0 equals 1.

67. a.

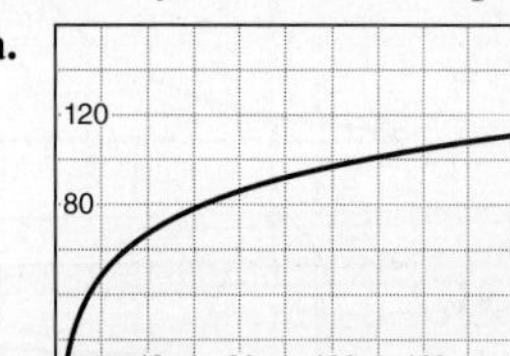

b. about 281 lb

c. (3.4, 0); no; The x-intercept shows that an alligator with a weight of 3.4 pounds has no length. If an object has weight, it must have length.

69. a. 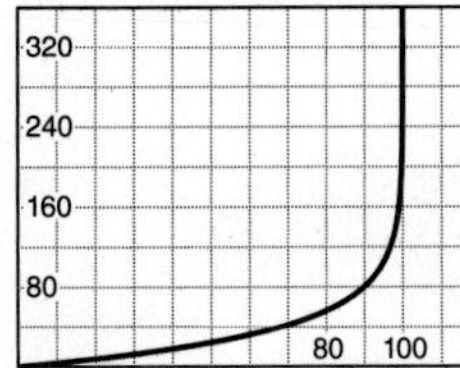

b. about 18 min

c. t approaches positive infinity; There appears to be a vertical asymptote at $r = 100$, so the tablet cannot be charged beyond 100%, regardless of time.

71. a. $\frac{2}{3}$

b. $\frac{5}{3}$

c. $\frac{4}{3}$

d. $\frac{7}{2}$

6.3 Review & Refresh

73. constant; The graph is a translation 3 units down of the parent constant function.

74. quadratic; The graph is a translation 2 units left and 1 unit down of the parent quadratic function.

75. absolute value; The graph is a reflection in the x-axis, followed by a translation 1 unit right and 2 units up of the parent absolute value function.

76. linear; The graph is a reflection in the x-axis and a translation 1 unit down of the graph of the parent linear function.

77. $-e^{11}$

78. $\frac{1}{5e^2}$

79. $16e^{4x}$

80. $2e^{4x}$

81. $x = -11$ and $x = -1$

82. $n = 0$ and $n = 1$

83. $x = -7$

84. $y = \pm\sqrt[6]{70}$

85. function; $f^{-1}(x) = \sqrt[3]{\frac{x-2}{3}}$

86. function; $f^{-1}(x) = x^2 - 1, x \geq 0$

87. 22 people support the contest, 8 people do not support the contest, 10 people are undecided, 20 males responded, 20 females responded, 40 people were surveyed

88. exponential decay

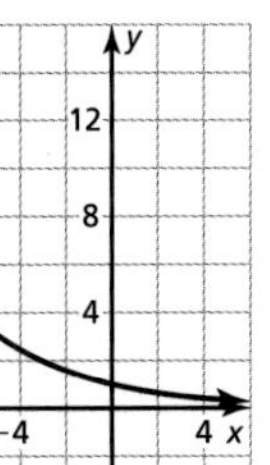

89. exponential growth

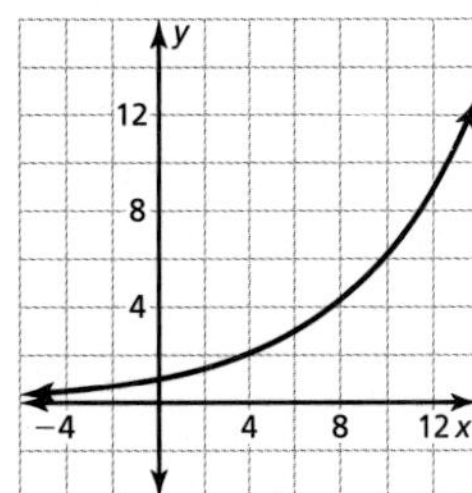

90.

91.

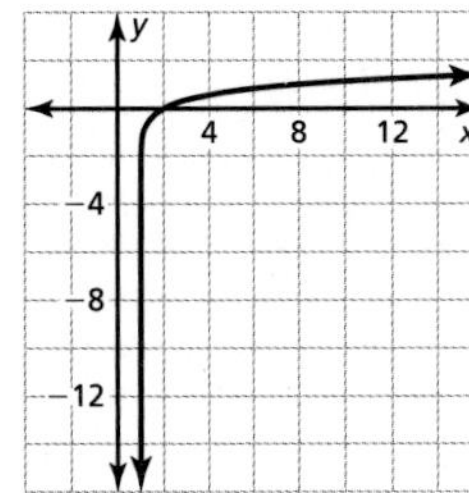

92. 60 ft

6.4 Practice

1. C; The graph is a translation 2 units left and 2 units down of the graph of the parent function $y = 2^x$.

3. A; The graph is a translation 2 units right and 2 units down of the graph of the parent function $y = 2^x$.

5. The graph of g is a translation 5 units up of the graph of f.

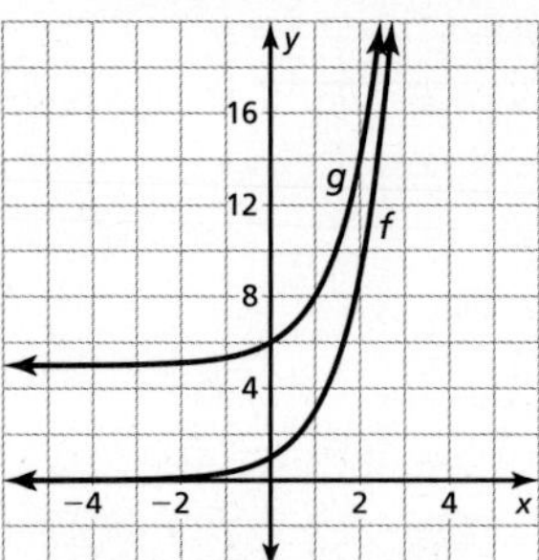

7. The graph of g is a translation 1 unit down of the graph of f.

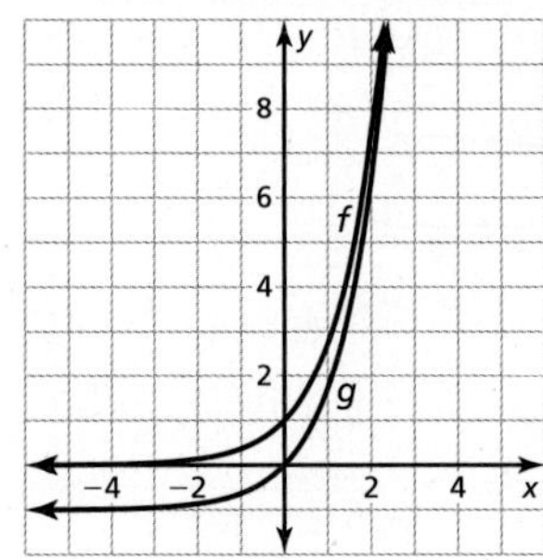

9. The graph of g is a translation 7 units right of the graph of f.

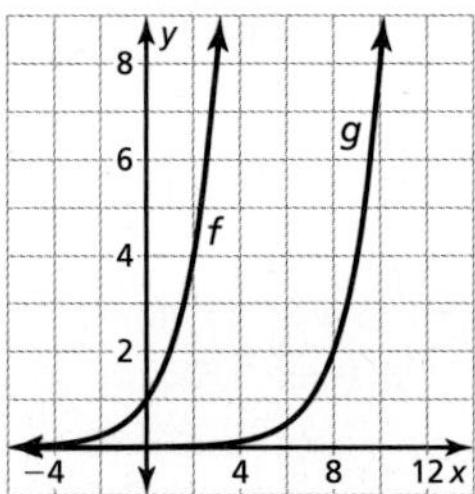

11. The graph of g is a translation 6 units up of the graph of f.

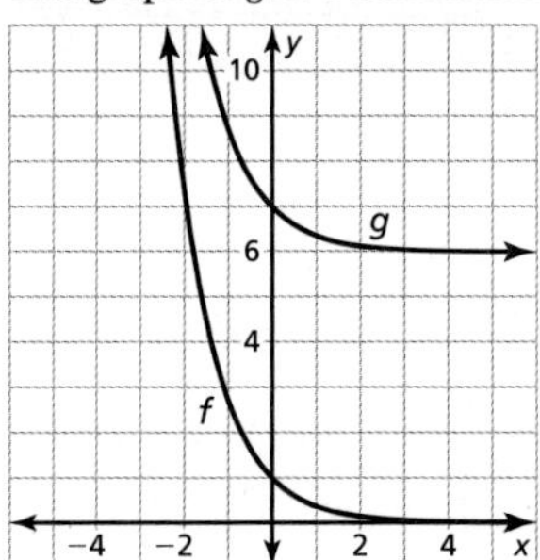

13. The graph of g is a translation 3 units right and 12 units up of the graph of f.

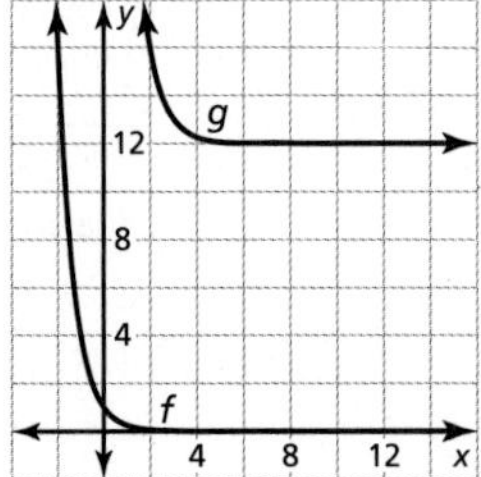

15. The graph of g is a horizontal shrink by a factor of $\frac{1}{2}$ of the graph of f.

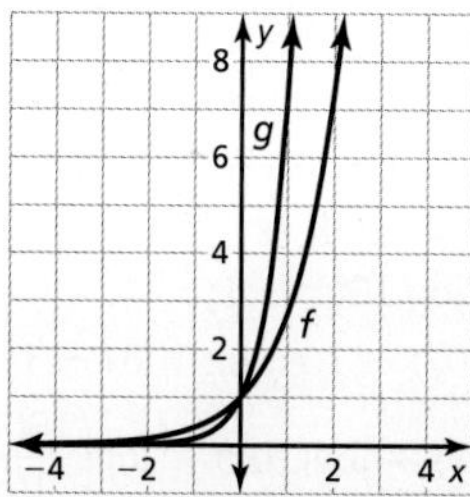

17. The graph of g is a reflection in the x-axis, followed by a translation 3 units right of the graph of f.

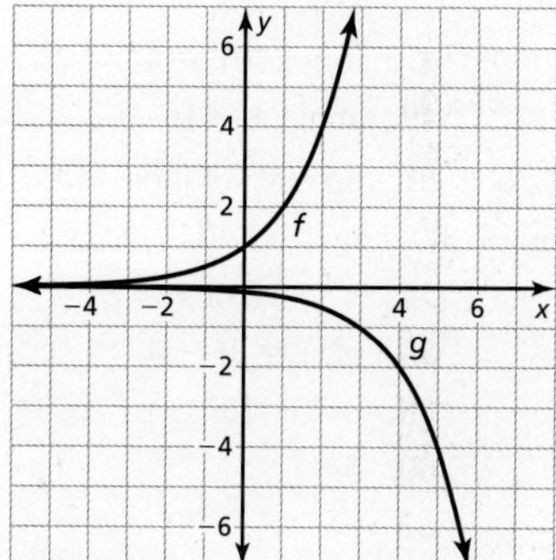

19. The graph of g is a horizontal shrink by a factor of $\frac{1}{6}$, followed by a vertical stretch by a factor of 3 of the graph of f.

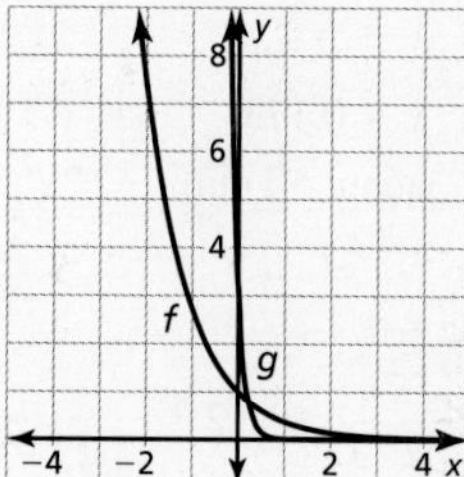

21. The graph of g is a vertical stretch by a factor of 6, followed by a translation 5 units left and 2 units down of the graph of f.

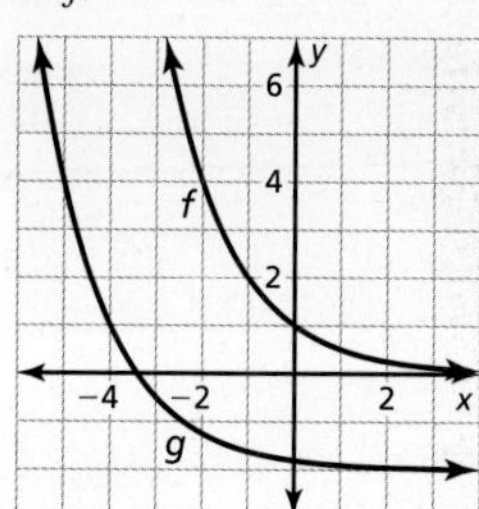

23. The graph of the parent function $f(x) = 2^x$ was translated 3 units left instead of up.

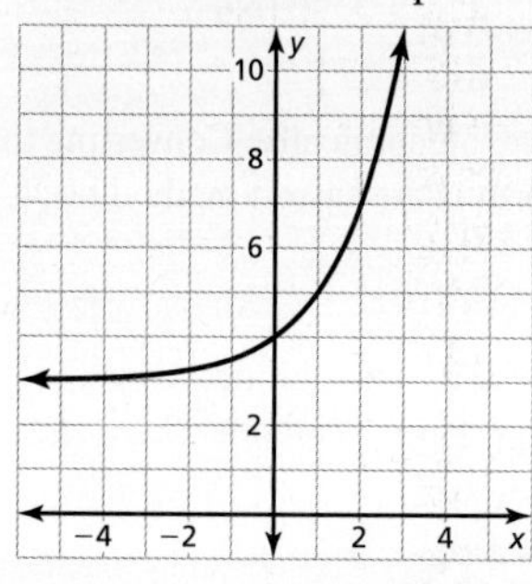

25. The graph of g is a vertical stretch by a factor of 3, followed by a translation 5 units down of the graph of f.

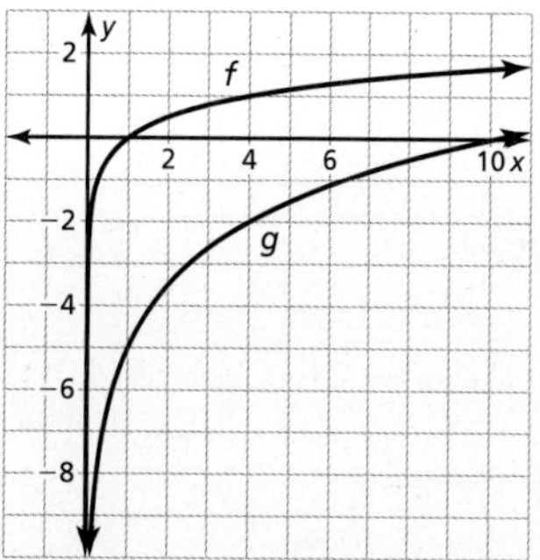

27. The graph of g is a reflection in the x-axis, followed by a translation 7 units right of the graph of f.

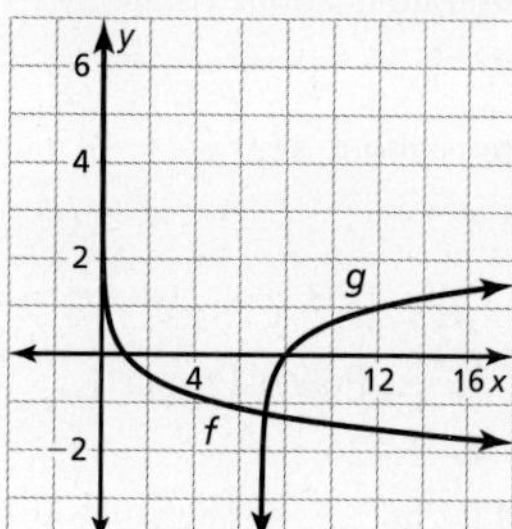

29. A

31. C

33. Multiply the output by -1; Substitute $\log_7 x$ for $f(x)$. Subtract 6 from the output; Substitute $-\log_7 x$ for $h(x)$.

35. $g(x) = 5^{-x} - 2$

37. $g(x) = e^{2x} + 5$

39. $g(x) = 6 \log_6 x - 5$

41. $g(x) = \log_{1/2}(-x + 3) + 2$

43. The graph of g is a translation 9 units right of the graph of f; $y = 0$

45. Greater values of a make the graph steeper; As a increases, the time it takes the hoverboard to reach a given speed decreases, and as a decreases, the time it takes the hoverboard to reach given speeds increases.

47. no; $g(x) = \log_4\left(\frac{1}{4}x\right)$ represents a horizontal stretch by a factor of 4, and $h(x) = \frac{1}{4} \log_4 x$ represents a vertical shrink by a factor of $\frac{1}{4}$, and $g(x) \neq h(x)$

49. The graph of h is a translation 2 units left of the graph of f; The graph of h is a reflection in the y-axis, followed by a translation 2 units left of the graph of g; x has been replaced with $x + 2$. x has been replaced with $-(x + 2)$.

51. **a.** 69.77 g

b. The graph would be a vertical stretch by a factor of 5.5 of the graph of P.

c. The translation does not affect the domain but it does affect the range; It changes the range to $0 < P \leq 550$ because the initial amount is 550, but in both cases there can never be 0 grams remaining.

6.4 Review & Refresh

53. x

54. 9

55. $2x$

56. $x - 3$

57. linear; $y = 8x$; 160; 160 calories are burned after 20 minutes of gliding.

58. linear; $y = \frac{1}{30}x + 1.9$; After 20 months, the attendance is about 2567.

59. $g(x) = e^{3x} - 1$

60. $g(x) = \log_2(-x + 3)$

61. $x = -4, x = 0, x = 3$

62. $x = 7$

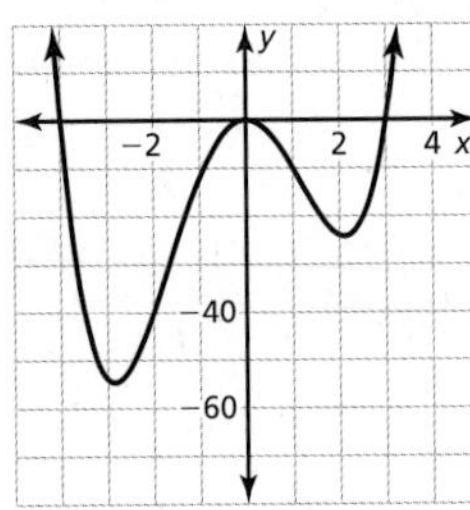

63. ride sharing rewards; social media advertisement revenue

64. $y = a(1 + 0.189)^t$; The growth rate is about 18.9%; $y \to 0$ as $x \to -\infty$ and $y \to +\infty$ as $x \to +\infty$

65. $y = a\left(1 - \frac{8}{9}\right)^t$; The decay rate is about 88.9%; $y \to +\infty$ as $x \to -\infty$ and $y \to 0$ as $x \to +\infty$

6.5 Practice

1. B; Quotient Property
3. A; Power Property
5. 0.565
7. 1.424
9. −0.712
11. $\log_3 2 + \log_3 x$
13. $1 + 5 \log x$
15. $\ln x - \ln 3 - \ln y$
17. $\log_7 5 + \frac{1}{2}\log_7 x$
19. The two expressions should be added, not multiplied; $\log_2 5x = \log_2 5 + \log_2 x$
21. $\log_4 \frac{7}{10}$
23. $\ln x^6y^4$
25. $\log_5 4\sqrt[3]{x}$
27. $\ln 32x^7y^4$
29. about 1.404
31. about 1.232
33. about 1.581
35. about −0.860
37. 10 decibels
39. B
41. a. $2 \ln 2 \approx 1.39$ knots

b.
$$\begin{aligned} s(h) &= 2 \ln 100h \\ s(h) &= \ln(100h)^2 \\ e^{s(h)} &= e^{\ln(100h)^2} \\ e^{s(h)} &= (100h)^2 \\ \log e^{s(h)} &= \log(100h)^2 \\ s(h) \log e &= 2 \log(100h) \\ s(h) \log e &= 2(\log 100 + \log h) \\ s(h) \log e &= 2(2 + \log h) \\ s(h) &= \frac{2}{\log e}(\log h + 2) \end{aligned}$$

43. It is not true; By the Product Property, $\log_b M + \log_b N = \log_b(MN)$. If $\log_b(M + N) = \log_b(MN)$, then $M + N = M \bullet N$ which is not always true.

45. *Sample answer:* The graph of g could be a translation 1 unit up of the graph of f. The graph of g could be a horizontal shrink by a factor of $\frac{1}{100}$, followed by a translation 1 unit down of the graph of f. The graph of g could be a horizontal shrink by a factor of $\frac{1}{10}$ of the graph of f; Transformation 1: $g(x) = f(x) + 1 = \log x + 1 = 2 + \log x - 1$
$= \log 100 + \log x - 1 = \log 100x - 1$;
Transformation 2: $g(x) = f(100x) - 1 = \log 100x - 1$;
Transformation 3: $g(x) = f(10x) = \log(10x) = \log\left(\frac{100x}{10}\right)$
$= \log 100x - \log 10 = \log 100x - 1$

6.5 Review & Refresh

46. $4^5 = 1024$
47. $\log_7 2401 = 4$
48. $y = \frac{3}{4}(x + 1)^2 - 2$
49. about 1.861
50. $x \approx -0.76$ and $x \approx 2.36$
51. no real solution
52. small: \$2.50, medium: \$2.80, large: \$3.40
53. $-7 < x < -6$
54. $x \leq -6$ or $x \geq 2$
55. $3 \log y - 5 \log x$
56. $g(x) = 3^x - 4$
57. $26 - 2i$
58. $-7 + 15i$
59. e^{12}
60. $5e^2$
61. $125e^{12x}$
62. e^6

6.6 Practice

1. $x = -1$
3. $x = 7$
5. $x \approx 1.771$
7. $x = -\frac{5}{3}$
9. $x \approx 0.255$
11. $x \approx 0.173$
13. about 17.6 years old
15. about 50 min
17. $x = 4$
19. $x = 3$
21. $x = 6$
23. $x = 1$
25. $x = \frac{1 + \sqrt{41}}{2} \approx 3.7$ and $x = \frac{1 - \sqrt{41}}{2} \approx -2.7$
27. $x = 4$
29. $x \approx 6.04$
31. $x = \pm 1$
33. $x \approx 10.24$
35. 3 should be the base on both sides of the equation;
$$\begin{aligned} \log_3(5x - 1) &= 4 \\ 3^{\log_3(5x - 1)} &= 3^4 \\ 5x - 1 &= 81 \\ 5x &= 82 \\ x &= 16.4 \end{aligned}$$
37. 38.66 years; 38.38 years
39. a. $x \approx 3.57$

b. $x = 0.8$
41. $x < 3$
43. $x > 2.050$
45. $x > 3$
47. $x \geq 20.086$
49. $x < 1.723$
51. $x \geq \frac{1}{5}$
53. $0 < x < 25$; *Sample answer:* algebraically; Converting the equation to exponential form is the easiest method because it isolates the variable.
55. $r > 0.0718$ or $r > 7.18\%$
57. $x \approx 1.78$
59. no solution
61. 36 cm footprint: 11.7 years old;
32 cm footprint: 7.6 years old;
28 cm footprint: 4.6 years old;
24 cm footprint: 2.2 years old

63. *Sample answer:* $2^x = 16$ **65.** $x \approx 0.89$

67. $x \approx 10.61$ **69.** $x = 0$ and $x \approx 2.58$

71. To solve exponential equations with different bases, take a logarithm of each side. Then use the Power Property to move the exponent to the front of the logarithm, and solve for x. To solve logarithmic equations of different bases, find a common multiple of the bases, and exponentiate each side with this common multiple as the base. Rewrite the base as a power that will cancel out the given logarithm and solve the resulting equation.

73. A lead apron does not need to be as thick as aluminum or copper to result in the same intensity.

6.6 Review & Refresh

74. about 6.99 decibels

75. The graph of g is a vertical translation 7 units up of the graph of f.

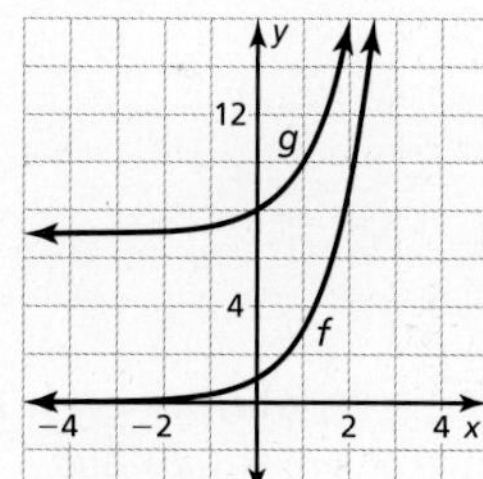

76. The graph of g is a horizontal translation 2 units left of the graph of f.

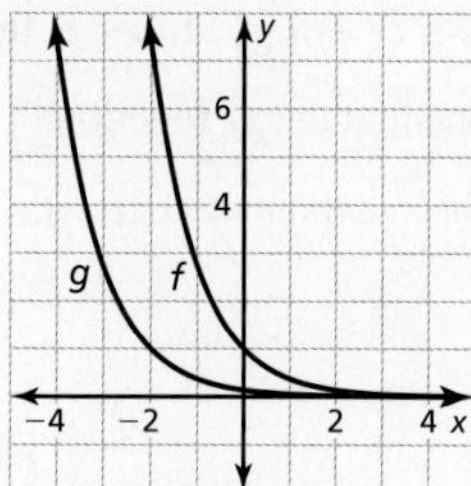

77. $x = -1$ and $x = 3$

78. The graph of g is a translation 1 unit left, followed by a vertical stretch by a factor of 2 of the graph of f.

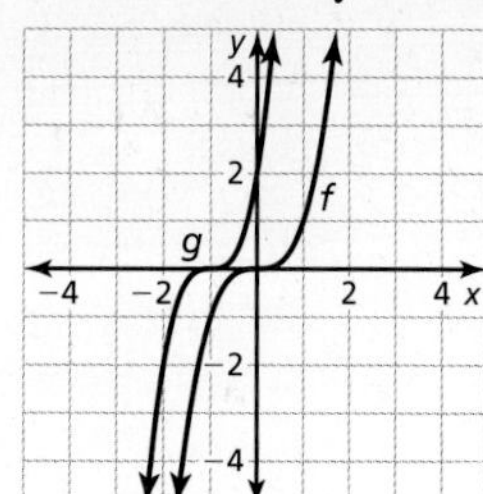

79. $7\sqrt[3]{17}$ **80.** $\frac{m^5}{n}$

81. $f(2) = 8$ and $g(2) = 4$ **82.** $x = \pm\sqrt{7}$

83. $x = \frac{-3 \pm \sqrt{53}}{2}$ **84.** $x \approx 4.531$

85. $x \approx \pm 8.839$ **86.** 6

87. -3 **88.** $(3, -1, 2)$

89. $(1, 4, 1)$ **90.** $6x^3 - 5x^2 + 3x - 1$

6.7 Practice

1. exponential; The data have a common ratio of 4.

3. quadratic; The second differences are constant.

5. $y = 0.75(4)^x$ **7.** $y = 2\left(\frac{1}{2}\right)^x$

9. $y = \frac{2}{5}(5)^x$ **11.** $y = 5(0.5)^x$

13. $y = 0.25(2)^x$

15. Data are linear when the first differences are constant; The outputs have a common ratio of 3, so the data represents an exponential function.

17. *Sample answer:* $y = 7.20(1.39)^x$

19. yes; *Sample answer:* $y = 8.88(1.21)^x$

21. no; *Sample answer:* $y = -0.8x + 66$

23.

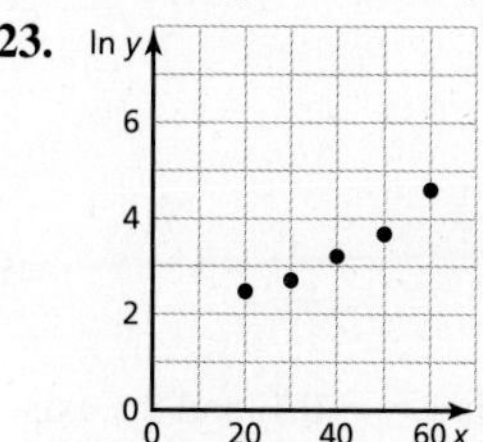

Sample answer: $y = 3.25(1.052)^x$

25.

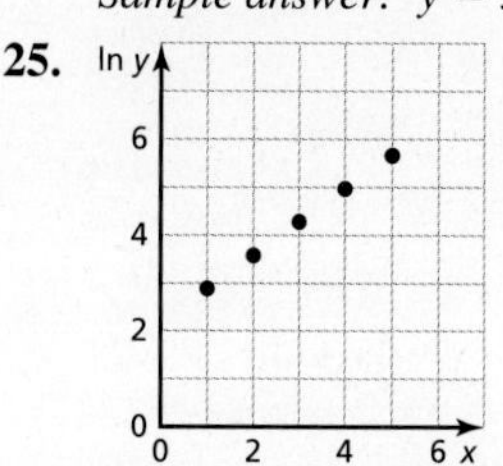

yes; $y = 9.14(1.99)^x$

27.

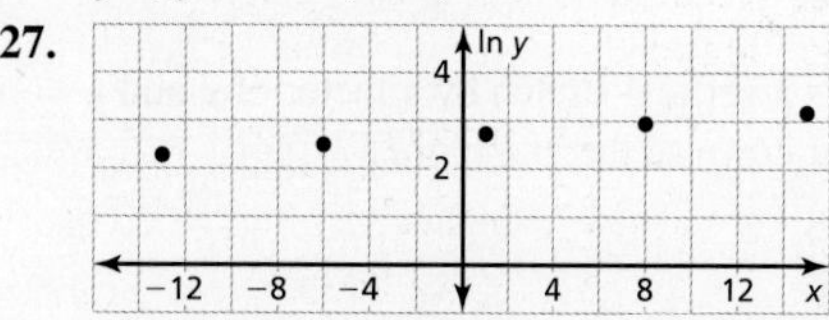

yes; $y = 14.73(1.03)^x$

29. $y = 6.70(1.41)^x$; about 208 electric scooters

31. $t = 12.59 - 2.55 \ln d$; 2.6 h

33. no; When d is the independent variable and t is the dependent variable, the data can be modeled with a logarithmic function. When the variables are switched, the data can be modeled with an exponential function.

35. **a.** 5.9 weeks

b.

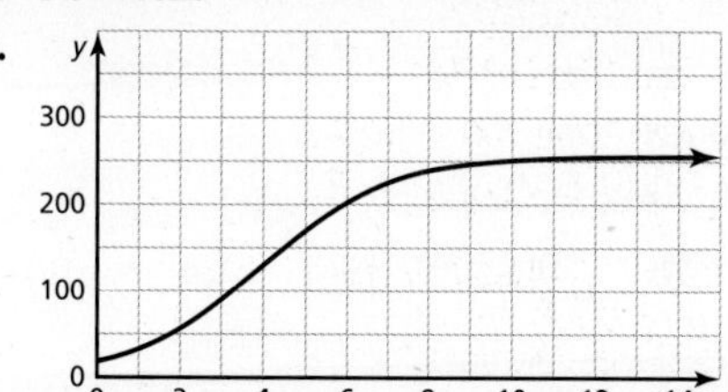

The asymptote is the line $y = 256$ and represents the maximum height of the sunflower.

6.7 Review & Refresh

37. yes; When one variable is increased by a factor, the other variable increases by the same factor.

38. no; When one variable is increased by a factor, the other variable does not increase by the same factor.

39. about 20 min

40. yes; The x-values of $f(x)$ are the y-values for $g(x)$, and the x-values of $g(x)$ are the y-values for $f(x)$.

41. about 2.727

42. about -0.632

43. $y = \frac{1}{8}(2)^x$

44. $y = 3(0.75)^x$

45. The focus is (2, 0), the directrix is $x = -2$, and the axis of symmetry is $y = 0$.

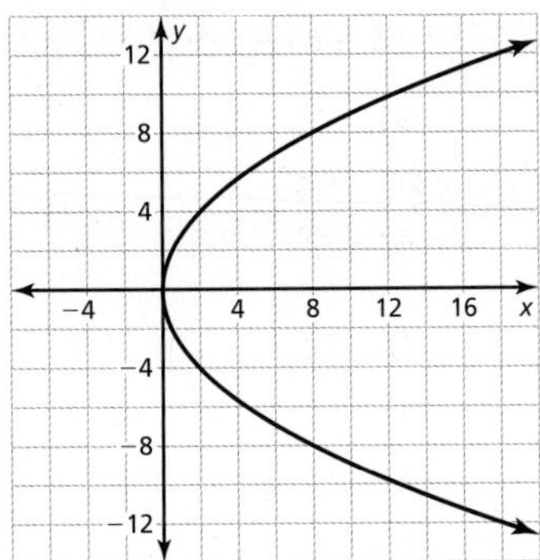

46. The focus is (0.1, 0), the directrix is $x = -0.1$, and the axis of symmetry is $y = 0$.

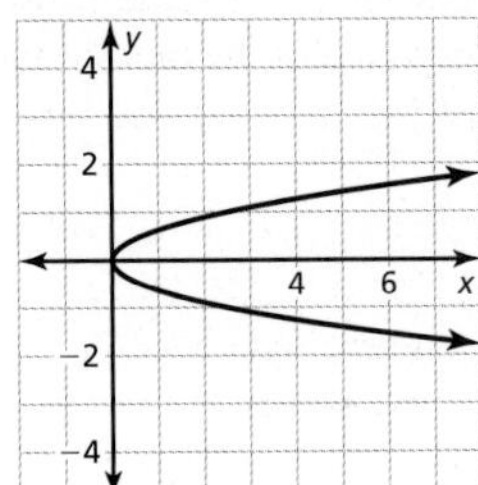

47. $g(x) = \log_3(x - 2) + 1$

48. The graph of g is a vertical stretch by a factor of 2 and a translation 1 unit down of the graph of f.

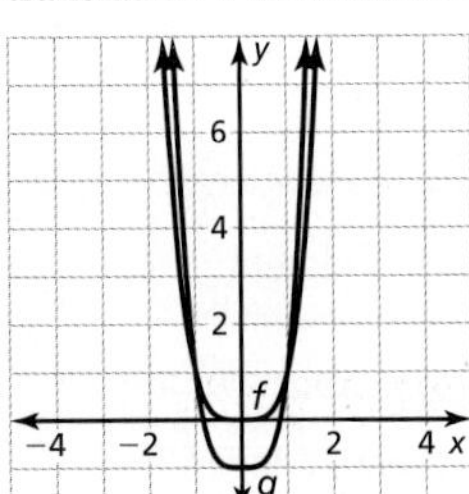

49. $x \approx 1.585$

50. $x = 3$

51. $x = \frac{1}{2}$

52. $x = 11$

53.

−5	1	−2	−23	60
		−5	35	−60
	1	−7	12	0

$f(x) = (x + 5)(x - 3)(x - 4)$

54. $x^2 - 4x + 4$; $(x - 2)^2$

Chapter 6 Review

1. exponential decay

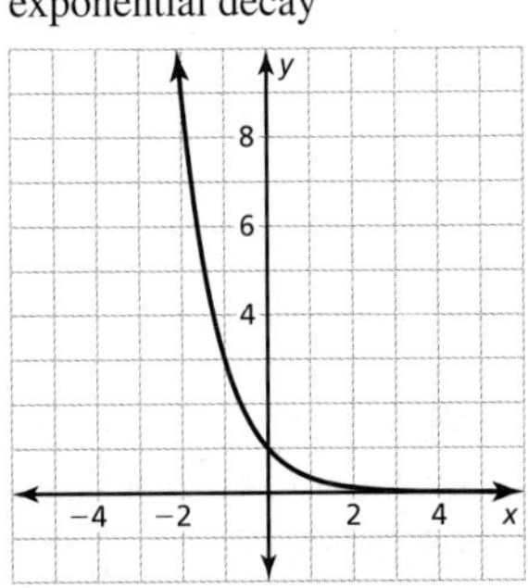

2. exponential growth

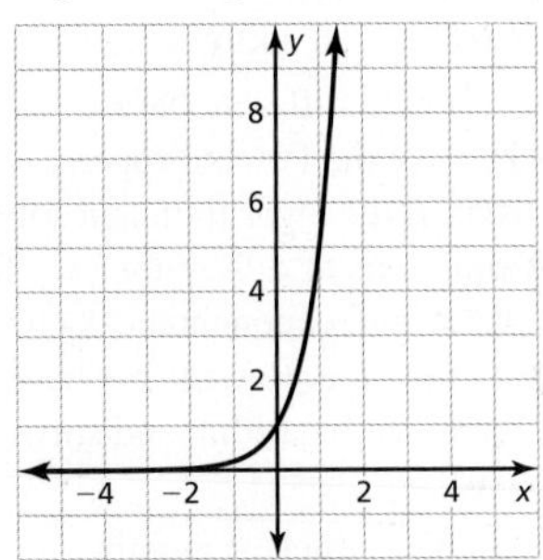

3. exponential decay

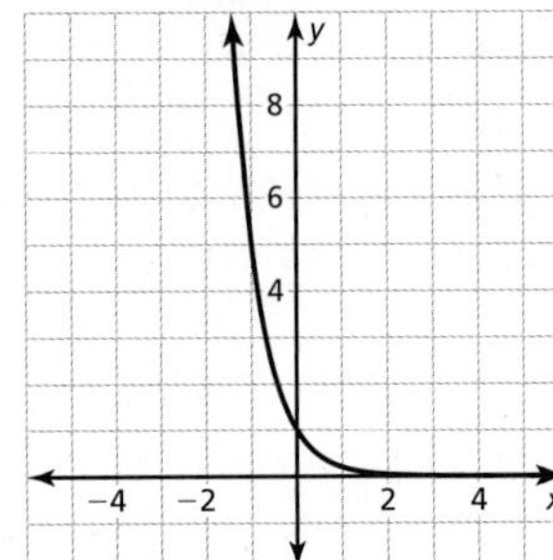

4. \$1725.39

5. **a.** always; Let $f(x) = a^x$ and $g(x) = b^x$, where $0 < a < 1$ and $0 < b < 1$. Then $(fg)(x) = a^x \cdot b^x = (ab)^x$ and $0 < ab < 1$.

b. sometimes; Let $f(x) = a^x$ and $g(x) = b^x$, where $0 < a < 1$ and $0 < b < 1$. Then $\left(\frac{f}{g}\right)(x) = \frac{a^x}{b^x} = \left(\frac{a}{b}\right)^x$. If $a < b$, then $0 < \frac{a}{b} < 1$ and $\frac{f}{g}$ is an exponential decay function. If $a > b$, then $\frac{a}{b} > 1$ and $\frac{f}{g}$ is an exponential growth function.

6. about 15 g

7. e^{15}

8. $\frac{2}{e^3}$

9. $\frac{9}{e^{10x}}$

10. exponential growth

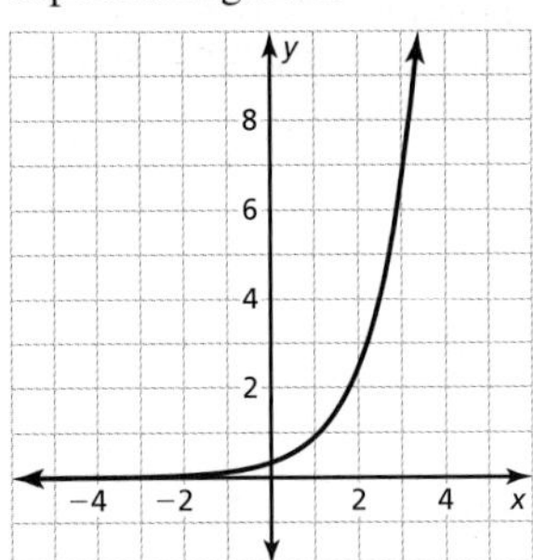

11. exponential decay

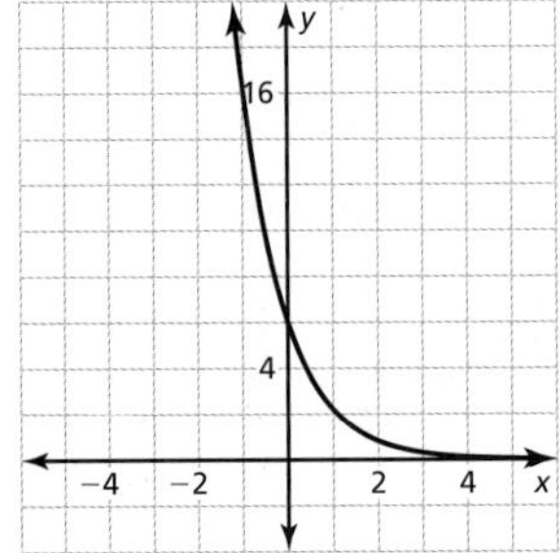

12. exponential decay

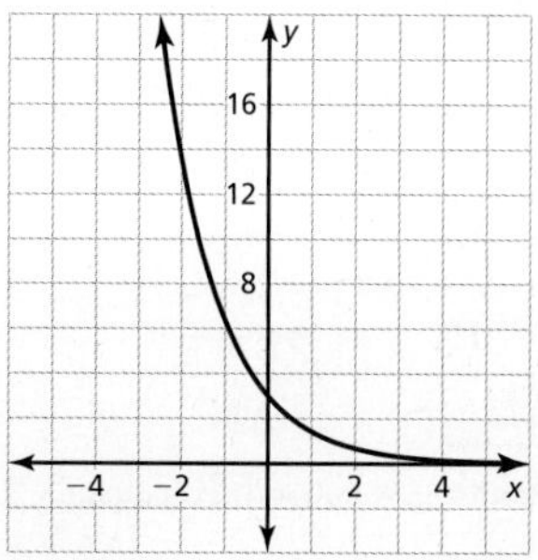

13. \$74.08

14. 3

15. −2

16. 0

17. $g(x) = \log_8 x$

18. $y = e^x + 4$

19. $y = 10^x - 9$

20.

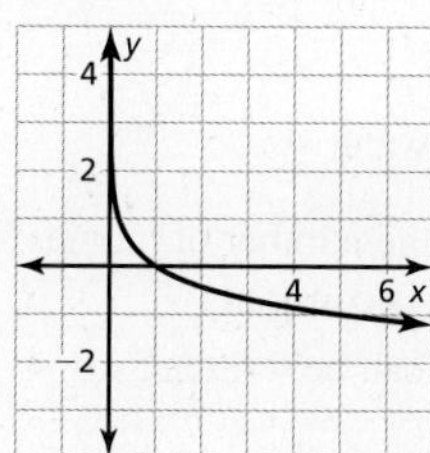

21.

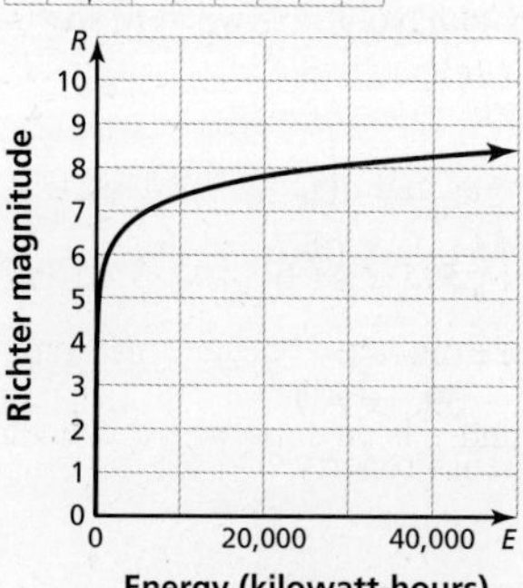

The Richter magnitude is about 7.9.

22. The graph of g is a horizontal shrink by a factor of $\frac{1}{5}$, followed by a translation 8 units down of the graph of f.

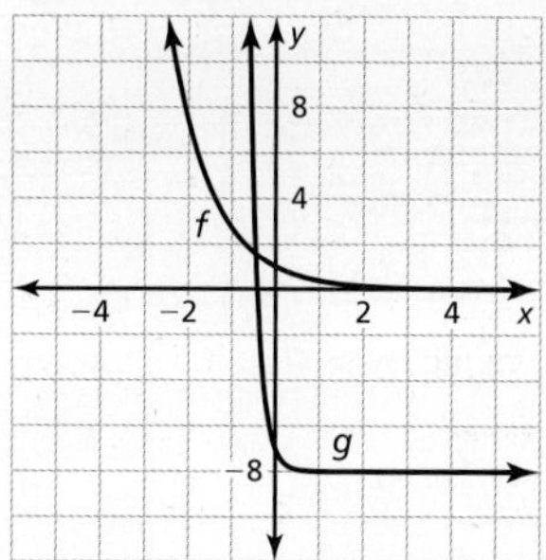

23. The graph of g is a vertical shrink by a factor of $\frac{1}{2}$, followed by a translation 5 units left of the graph of f.

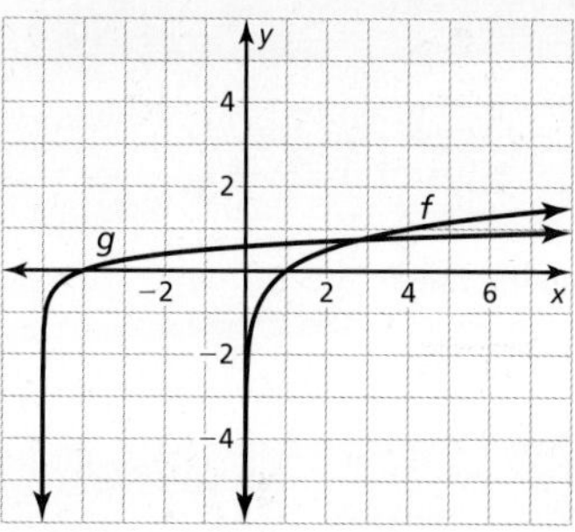

24. domain: all real numbers, range: $y < -ak$

25. $g(x) = 3e^{x+6} + 3$

26. $g(x) = \log(-x) - 2$

27. $\log_8 3 + \log_8 x + \log_8 y$

28. $1 + 3 \log x + \log y$

29. $\ln 3 + \ln y - 5 \ln x$

30. $\log_7 384$

31. $\log_2 \frac{12}{x^2}$

32. $\ln 4x^2$

33. about 3.32

34. about 1.13

35. about 1.19

36. $x \approx 1.29$

37. $x = 7$

38. $x \approx 3.59$

39. $x > 1.39$

40. $0 < x \leq 8103.08$

41. $x \geq 1.19$

42. 27

43. about 43 min

44. $y = 64\left(\frac{1}{2}\right)^x$

45. $y = \frac{1}{2}(6)^x$

46. $y = 12(0.75)^x$

47. $s = 3.95 + 27.48 \ln t$; 53 pairs

Chapter 6 Mathematical Practices (Chapter Review)

1. When x and b are rewritten as powers of the same base, the value of the expression is the value of the ratio of the exponent of b to the exponent of x; Let $x = n^p$ and $b = n^q$. Then $\log_b x = \log_{n^q} n^p = \frac{p}{q}$.

2. Data of a linear function have a common difference, data of a quadratic function have a common second difference, and data of an exponential function have a common ratio.

Chapter 6 Practice Test

1.

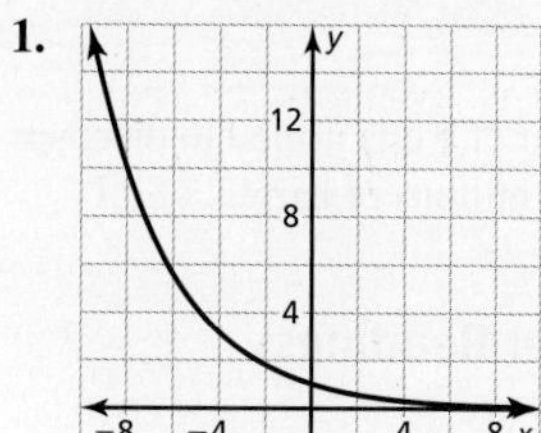

domain: all real numbers, range: $y > 0$, asymptote: $y = 0$

2.

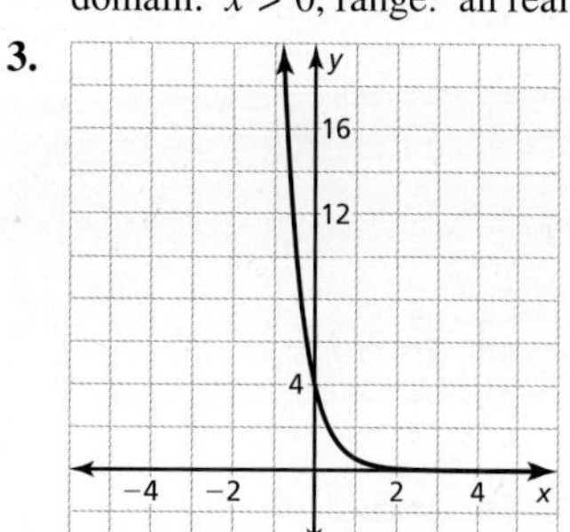

domain: $x > 0$, range: all real numbers, asymptote: $x = 0$

3.

domain: all real numbers, range: $y > 0$, asymptote: $y = 0$

4. The graph of g is a reflection in the x-axis, followed by a translation 4 units right of the graph of f; $g(x) = -\log(x - 4)$

5. The graph of g is a reflection in the y-axis, followed by a translation 2 units up of the graph of f; $g(x) = e^{-x} + 2$

6. The graph of g is a vertical stretch by a factor of 2 of the graph of f; $g(x) = 2\left(\frac{1}{4}\right)^x$

7. 3.597
8. 0.335
9. 2.524
10. 1.262

11. a. exponential decay; Natural base functions of the form $y = ae^{rx}$ show decay when r is negative.
    b. about 1.8%

12. The expressions are all equivalent; change-of-base formula

13. *Sample answer:* To find an exponential equation in the form $y = ab^x$, the common ratio, b, can be found by dividing consecutive terms and a is the y-value when x is 0. Two points can be used to create a system of equations in the form $y = ab^x$ which can be solved for a and b. Or, use the *regression* feature of a graphing calculator to find an exponential model which fits the data; $y = 250(0.9)^x$; in the 4th year

14. $x \approx 0.421$

$$f(g(x)) = g(f(x))$$
$$2(3)^{4x} = 4[2(3)^x]$$
$$(3)^{4x} = 4(3)^x$$
$$(3)^{3x} = 4$$
$$27^x = 4$$
$$x = \log_{27} 4 \approx 0.421$$

15. a. about 9 billion barrels
    b. $y = e^{(x+14.3)/3.4}$; the number of wells drilled to discover x amount of oil and gas (in billions of barrels of oil equivalent)

Chapter 6 College and Career Readiness

1. 0.94 and $e^{-1/2}$
2. D
3. B
4. C, A, D, B
5. B
6. $y = 5 \cdot 2^x$
   $y = 0.5 \cdot 3^x$
   The equation represented by the graph has a larger y-intercept and grows at a rate of 100%. The equation represented by the table has a smaller y-intercept but grows at a faster rate of 200% and will become larger than the equation represented by the graph for $x > 5.7$.
7. C
8. D
9. quadratic; $y = -0.261x^2 + 22.59x + 23.0$; 36.5° and 50.0°

Chapter 7

Chapter 7 Prepare

1. $\frac{1}{3}$
2. $\frac{19}{15}$, or $1\frac{4}{15}$
3. $-\frac{17}{42}$
4. $\frac{11}{12}$
5. $-\frac{3}{7}$
6. $-\frac{1}{20}$
7. The common denominator is the product of a and b.

7.1 Practice

1. inverse variation
3. direct variation
5. neither
7. direct variation
9. direct variation
11. inverse variation
13. $y = -\frac{20}{x}$; $y = -\frac{20}{3}$
15. $y = -\frac{24}{x}$; $y = -8$
17. $y = \frac{21}{x}$; $y = 7$
19. $y = \frac{2}{x}$; $y = \frac{2}{3}$
21. B
23. The equation for direct variation was used; Because $5 = \frac{a}{8}$, $a = 40$. So, $y = \frac{40}{x}$.
25. a.

Size (MB)	20	25	30	50
Number of apps	280	224	186	112

    b. The number of apps decreases.
27. $A = \frac{26{,}000}{c}$; about 321 chips per wafer
29. inverse variation; The product of the number of movies and the price per movie is \$40, which is constant.
31. inverse variation; V; The formula can be written as $B = \frac{V}{h}$.
33. x varies directly with z; $xy = a$, so $y = \frac{a}{x}$; $yz = b$, so $y = \frac{b}{z}$; $\frac{a}{x} = \frac{b}{z}$, $az = bx$, $x = \frac{a}{b}z$

7.1 Review & Refresh

35. $x - 9$
36. $x^2 - 6$
37. quadratic function; about 15 in.
38. $x = -3$
39. $x = 1$
40. Power Property and Quotient Property
41. direct variation
42.

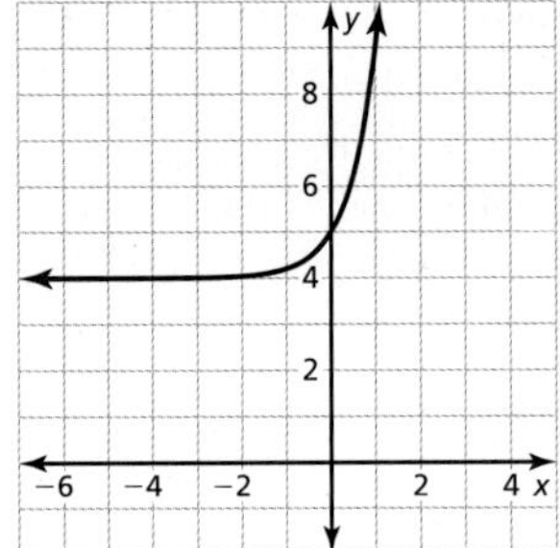

domain: all real numbers, range: $y > 4$

43.

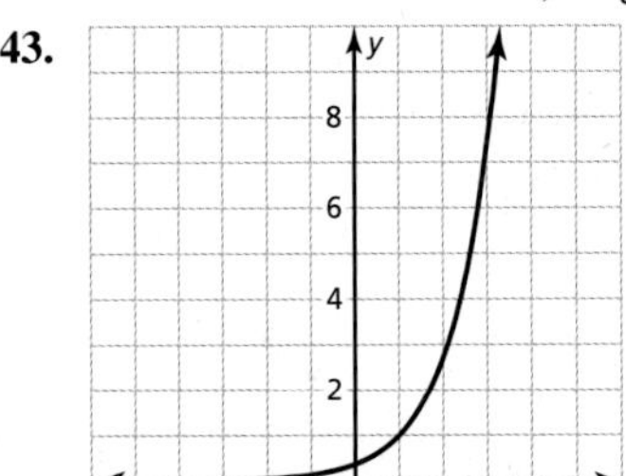

domain: all real numbers, range: $y > 0$

44. 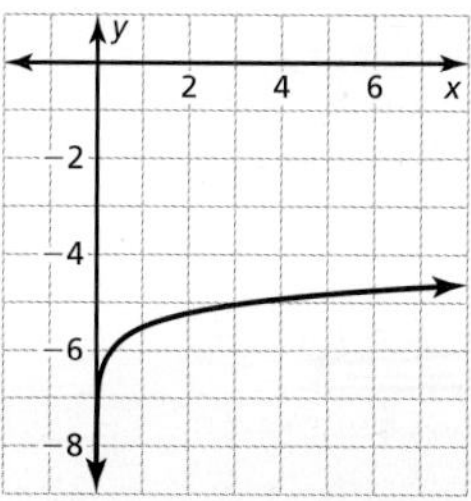

domain: $x > 0$, range: all real numbers

45. 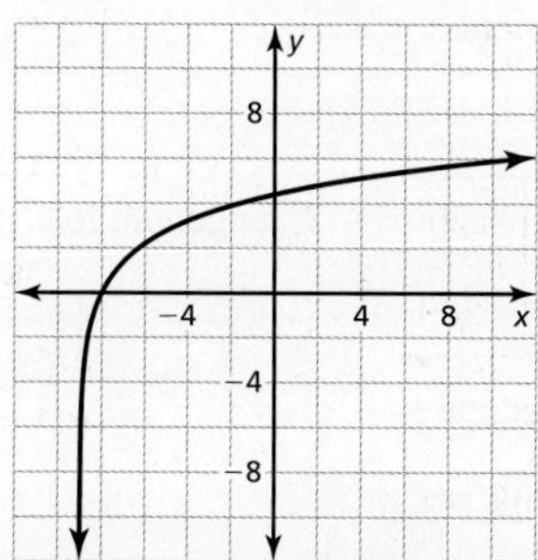

domain: $x > -9$, range: all real numbers

46. yes

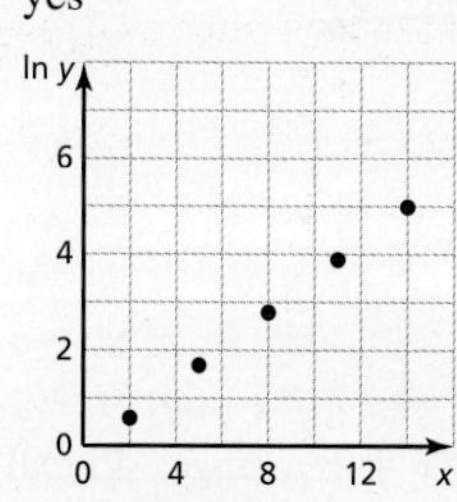

$y = 0.87(1.44)^x$

47. $8^{7/4}$ **48.** $11\sqrt{3}$

49. 3 **50.** $\dfrac{|a^3|}{3b^4}$

7.2 Practice

1. 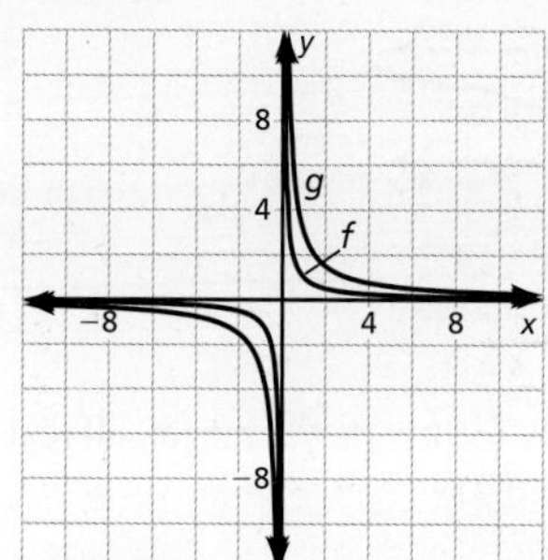

The graph of g lies farther from the axes. Both graphs lie in the first and third quadrants and have the same asymptotes, domain, and range.

3. 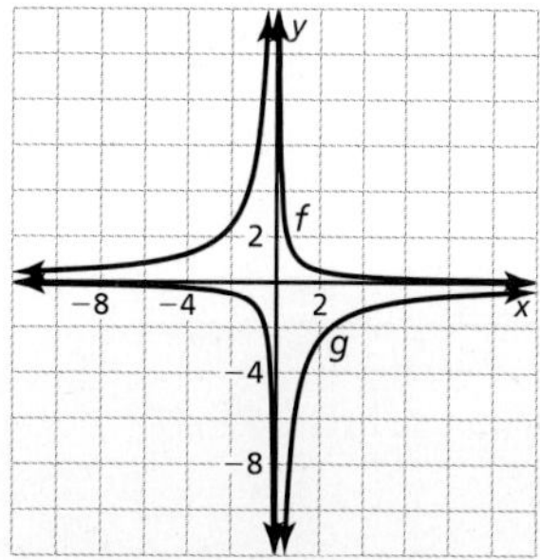

The graph of g lies farther from the axes and is reflected over the x-axis. Both graphs have the same asymptotes, domain, and range.

5. 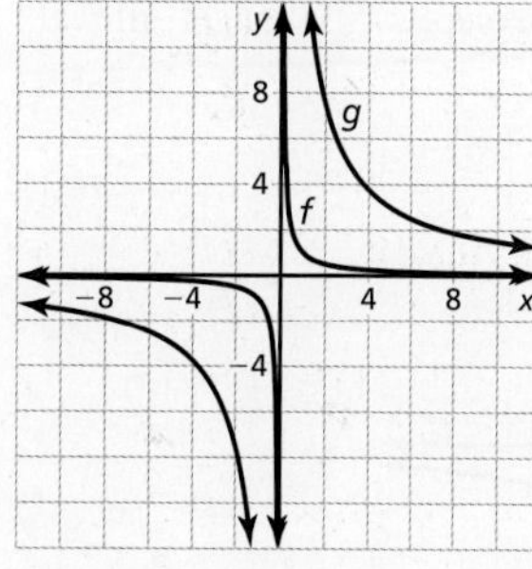

The graph of g lies farther from the axes. Both graphs lie in the first and third quadrants and have the same asymptotes, domain, and range.

7. 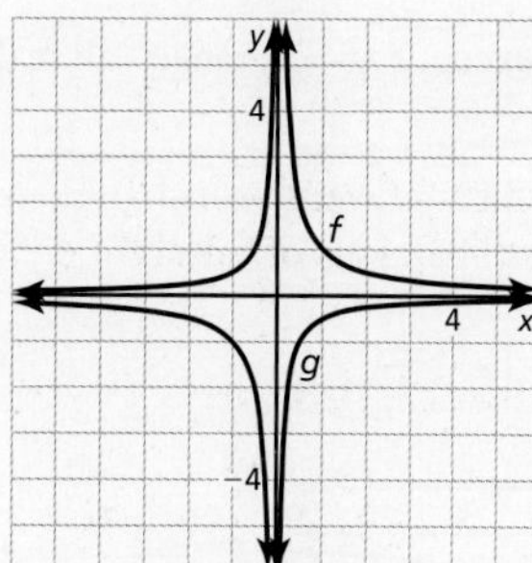

The graph of g lies closer to the axes and is reflected over the x-axis. Both graphs have the same asymptotes, domain, and range.

9. 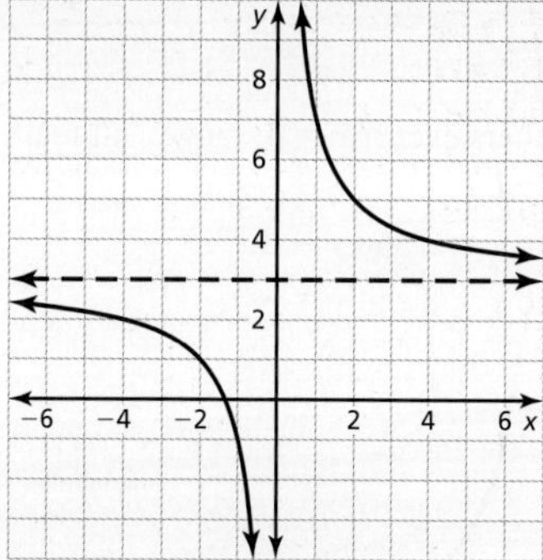

domain: all real numbers except $x = 0$; range: all real numbers except $y = 3$

11. 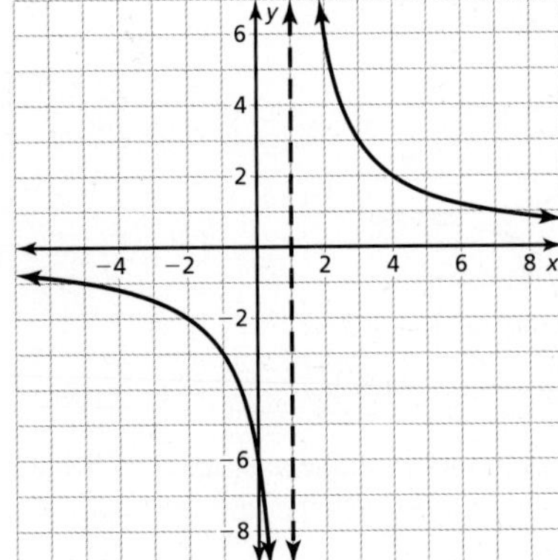

domain: all real numbers except $x = 1$; range: all real numbers except $y = 0$

13. 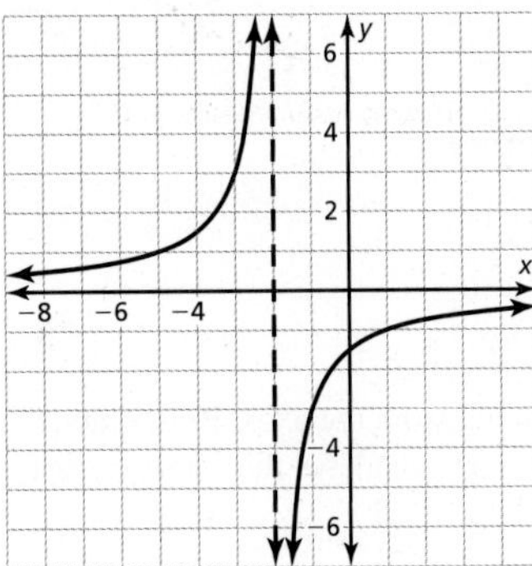

domain: all real numbers except $x = -2$; range: all real numbers except $y = 0$

15. 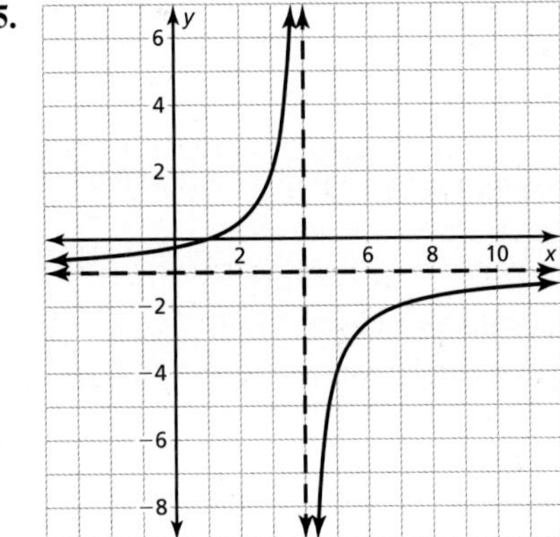

domain: all real numbers except $x = 4$; range: all real numbers except $y = -1$

17. A; The asymptotes are $x = 3$ and $y = 1$.

19. B; The asymptotes are $x = 3$ and $y = -1$.

21. 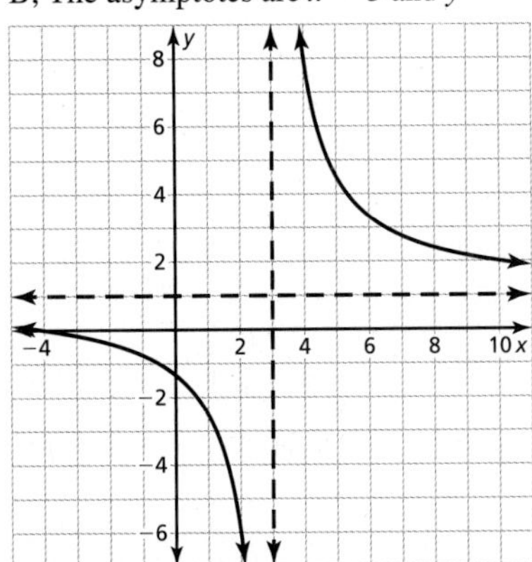

domain: all real numbers except $x = 3$; range: all real numbers except $y = 1$

23. 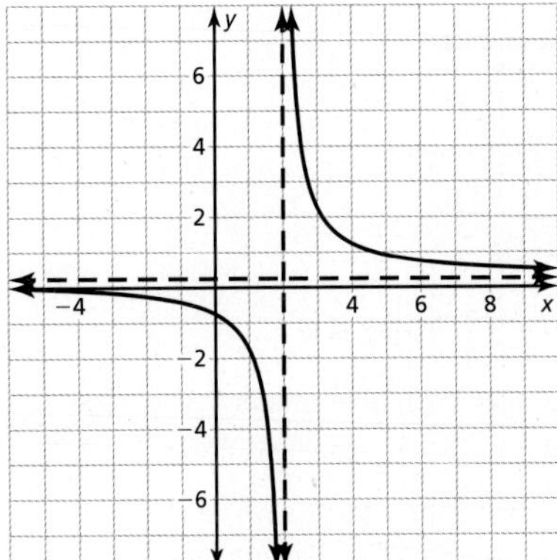

domain: all real numbers except $x = 2$; range: all real numbers except $y = \frac{1}{4}$

25. 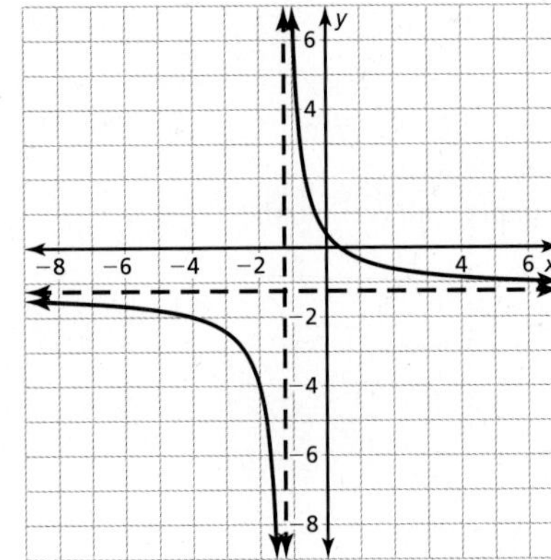

domain: all real numbers except $x = -\frac{5}{4}$; range: all real numbers except $y = -\frac{5}{4}$

27. 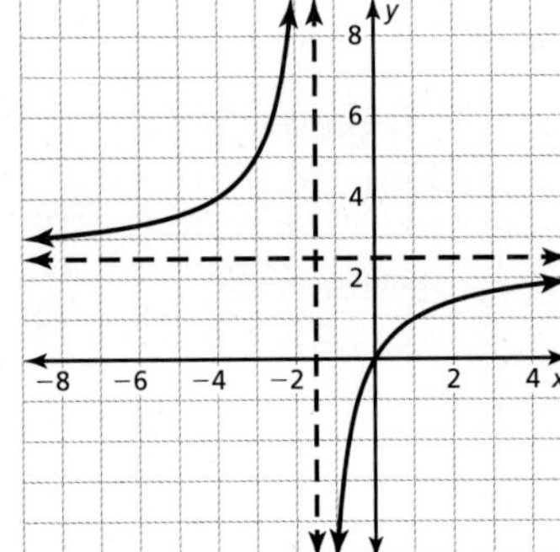

domain: all real numbers except $x = -\frac{3}{2}$; range: all real numbers except $y = \frac{5}{2}$

29. The vertical asymptote is the value for x that makes the denominator 0; The vertical asymptote is $x = -6$.

31. $g(x) = \dfrac{1}{x + 1} + 5$

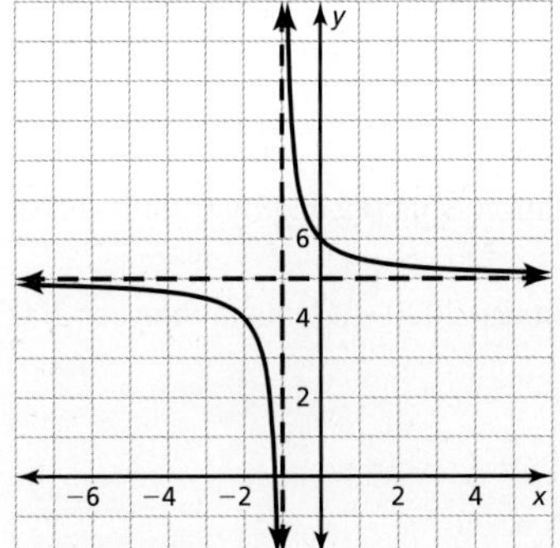

The graph of g is a translation 1 unit left and 5 units up of the graph of f.

33. $g(x) = \dfrac{6}{x - 5} + 2$

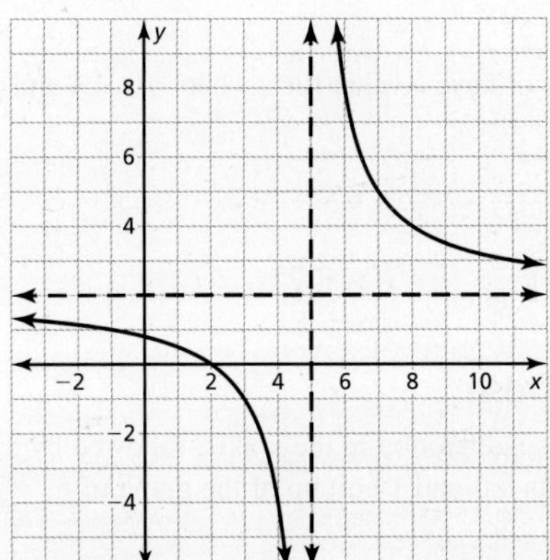

The graph of g is a translation 5 units right and 2 units up of the graph of f.

35. $g(x) = \dfrac{24}{x - 6} + 1$

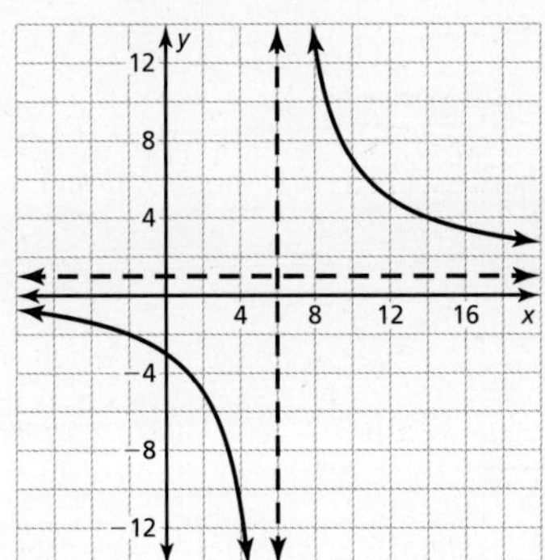

The graph of g is a translation 6 units right and 1 unit up of the graph of f.

37. $g(x) = \dfrac{-111}{x + 13} + 7$

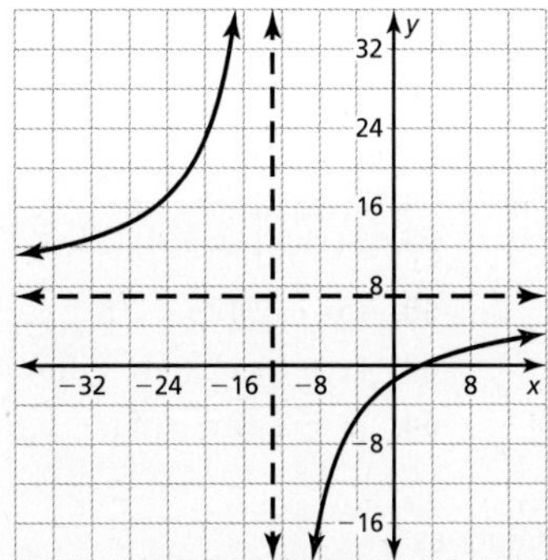

The graph of g is a translation 13 units left and 7 units up of the graph of f.

39. a. 50 students

b. The average cost per student approaches \$20.

41. D

43. a.

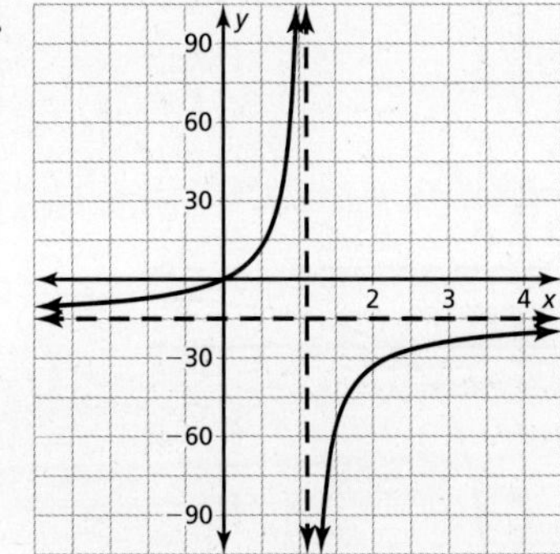

Sample answer: domain: $0 < x < 1$; range: $0 < y < 150$

b. about \$3333; about \$8571; \$40,000; no; Doubling the percentage does not double the cost because this is not a linear function.

45.

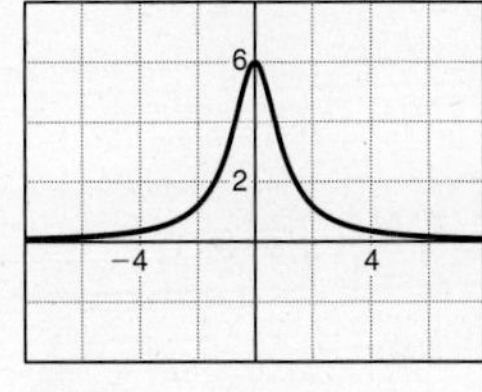

even

47.

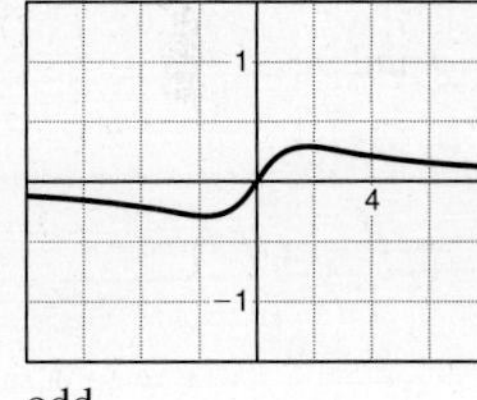

odd

49. provider B; provider A; provider A

51.

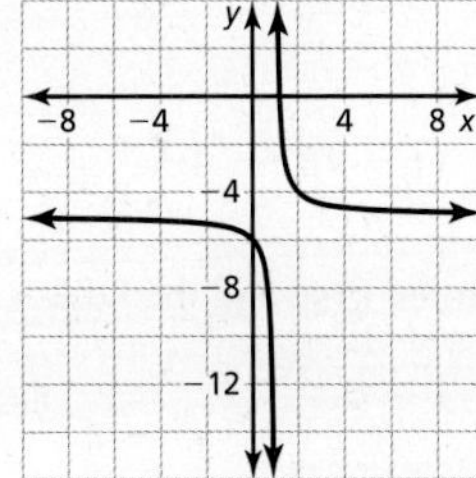

53. *Sample answer:* $\left(1, \frac{3}{2}\right)$, (4, 3), $\left(5, \frac{5}{2}\right)$; Because the asymptotes intersect at (3, 2), $h = 3$ and $k = 2$. Because (2, 1) is a point on the graph, $a = 1$. So, $f(x) = \dfrac{1}{x - 3} + 2$.

55. a. decreasing: $(-\infty, 0)$, $(0, \infty)$: The graph falls from left to right.
b. increasing: $(-\infty, 0)$, $(0, \infty)$; The graph rises from left to right.

7.2 Review & Refresh

57. $g(x) = -x + 6$
58. $g(x) = \left|\frac{1}{3}x + 4\right|$
59. $4(x - 5)(x + 4)$
60. $(5x - 2)(2x + 7)$
61. $(x + 10)^2$
62. $(x - 6)(x^2 + 6x + 36)$
63. $x(x + 7)(x + 4)$
64. $(x - 7)(2x^2 + 5)$
65. 28, 25
66. -12; two imaginary solutions
67. $x \approx 2.196$
68. $x = 16$
69. $2^{11/10}$
70. $6^{2/3}$
71. $g(x) = \dfrac{-7}{x + 8} + 2$

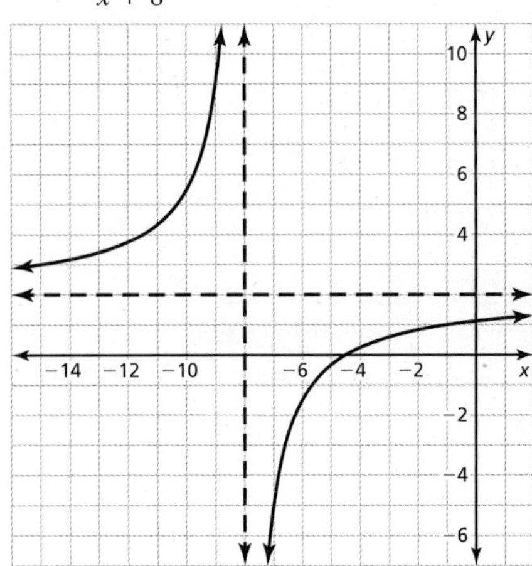

The graph of g is a translation 8 units left and 2 units up of the graph of f.

72. exponential; The common ratio is $\frac{1}{4}$.
73. g and p

7.3 Practice

1. $\dfrac{2x}{3x - 4}$, $x \neq 0$
3. $\dfrac{x + 3}{x - 1}$, $x \neq 6$
5. $\dfrac{x + 9}{x^2 - 2x + 4}$, $x \neq -2$
7. $\dfrac{2(4x^2 + 5)}{x - 3}$, $x \neq \pm\dfrac{\sqrt{5}}{2}$
9. $\dfrac{y^3}{2x^2}$, $y \neq 0$
11. $\dfrac{(x - 4)(x + 6)}{x}$, $x \neq 3$
13. $(x - 3)(x + 3)$, $x \neq 0$, $x \neq 2$
15. $\dfrac{2x(x + 4)}{(x + 2)(x - 3)}$, $x \neq 1$
17. $\dfrac{(x + 9)(x - 4)^2}{(x + 7)}$, $x \neq 7$
19. The polynomials need to be factored first, and then the common factors can divide out; $\dfrac{x + 12}{x + 4}$
21. $\dfrac{y^5}{x^3}$; Explanations will vary.
23. $\dfrac{256x^7}{y^{14}}$, $x \neq 0$
25. 2, $x \neq -2$, $x \neq 0$, $x \neq 3$
27. $\dfrac{(x + 2)}{(x + 4)(x - 3)}$
29. $\dfrac{(x + 6)(x - 2)}{(x + 2)(x - 6)}$, $x \neq -4$, $x \neq -3$
31. a. $\dfrac{2(r + h)}{rh}$
b. soup: about 0.784, coffee: about 0.382, paint: about 0.341; from most efficient to least efficient: paint can, coffee can, soup can
33. about \$439
35. a. The school population is increasing by 6 students each year.
b. The school system has 2090 students in the year 2000.
37.

x	y
−3.5	−0.1333
−3.8	−0.1282
−3.9	−0.1266
−4.1	−0.1235
−4.2	−0.1220

The graph does not have a value for y when $x = -4$ and approaches $y = -0.125$.

39. $\dfrac{4}{7x}$
41. $f(x) = \dfrac{x(x - 1)}{x + 2}$, $g(x) = \dfrac{x(x + 2)}{x - 1}$

7.3 Review & Refresh

43. The graph of g is a reflection in the x-axis, followed by a translation 2 units left and 1 unit up of the graph of f.
44.

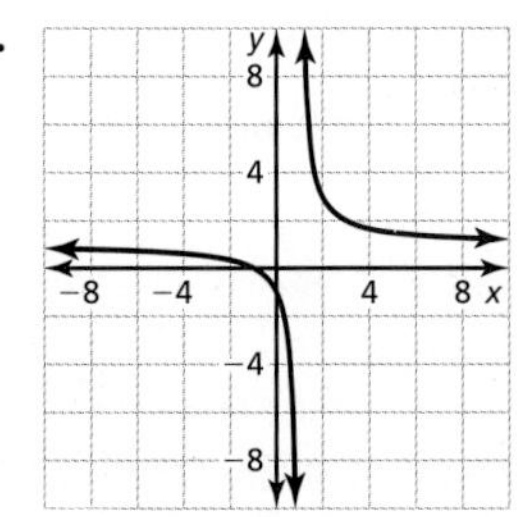

domain: all real numbers except $x = 1$; range: all real numbers except $y = 1$

45.

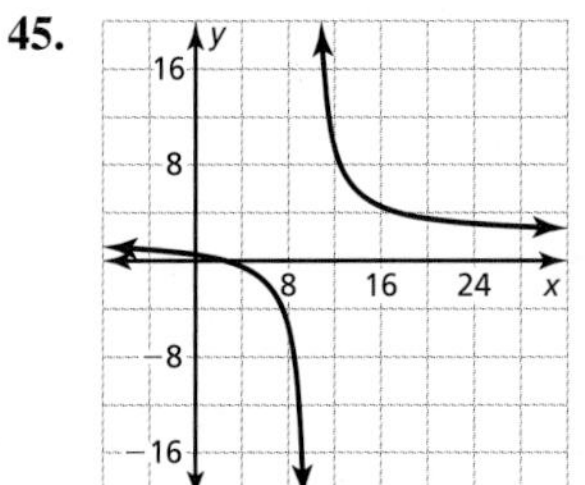

domain: all real numbers except $x = 10$; range: all real numbers except $y = 2$

46. $y = -\dfrac{4}{x}$; $y = -\dfrac{2}{3}$
47. $y = \dfrac{12}{x}$; $y = 2$
48. exponential function; The common ratio is $\sqrt{2}$.
49. linear function; The common difference is -5.
50. $\dfrac{1}{2xy}$
51. $\dfrac{2z}{x^2y}$, $z \neq 0$
52. 5th year
53. $(2x + 3)(4x^2 - 6x + 9)$
54. $3y^2(y^2 - 3)(y^2 - 2)$
55. $y = 4^x$

7.4 Practice

1. $\frac{5}{x}$

3. $\frac{9 - 2x}{x + 1}$

5. $5, x \neq -3$

7. $3x(x - 2)$

9. $5x(x - 2)$

11. $2(x - 3)(x + 3)(x + 4)$

13. $(x - 5)(x + 8)(x - 8)$

15. $\frac{37}{30x}$

17. $\frac{2(x + 7)}{(x + 4)(x + 6)}$

19. $\frac{3(x + 12)}{(x + 8)(x - 3)}$

21. $\frac{8x^3 - 9x^2 - 28x + 8}{x(x - 4)(3x - 1)}$

23. The LCM of $5x$ and x^2 is $5x^2$, so multiply the first term by $\frac{x}{x}$ and the second term by $\frac{5}{5}$ before adding the numerators; $\frac{2(x + 10)}{5x^2}$

25. **a.** sometimes; When the denominators have no common factors, the product of the denominators is the LCD. When the denominators have common factors, use the LCM to find the LCD.

    b. always; The LCD is the product of the highest power of each factor that appears in any of the denominators.

27. $g(x) = \frac{-2}{x - 1} + 5$

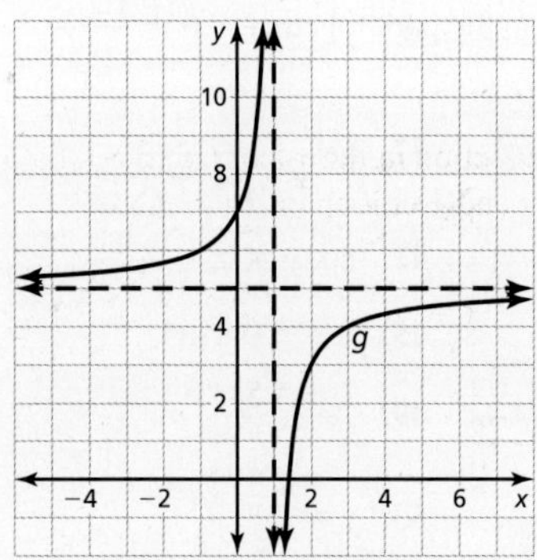

The graph of g is a translation 1 unit right and 5 units up of the graph of $f(x) = \frac{-2}{x}$.

29. $g(x) = \frac{60}{x - 5} + 12$

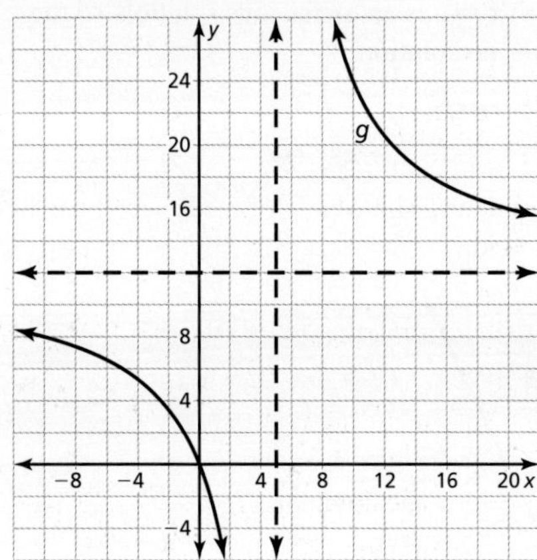

The graph of g is a translation 5 units right and 12 units up of the graph of $f(x) = \frac{60}{x}$.

31. $g(x) = \frac{3}{x} + 2$

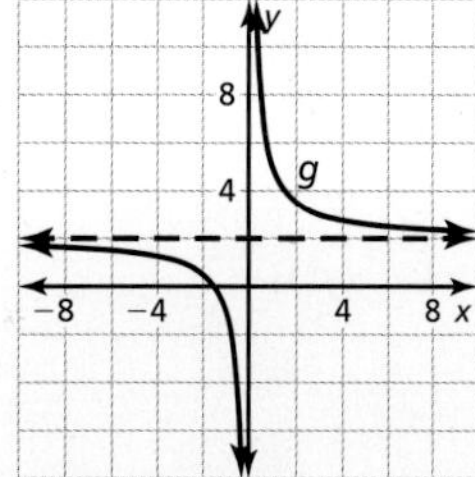

The graph of g is a translation 2 units up of the graph of $f(x) = \frac{3}{x}$.

33. $g(x) = \frac{20}{x - 3} + 3$

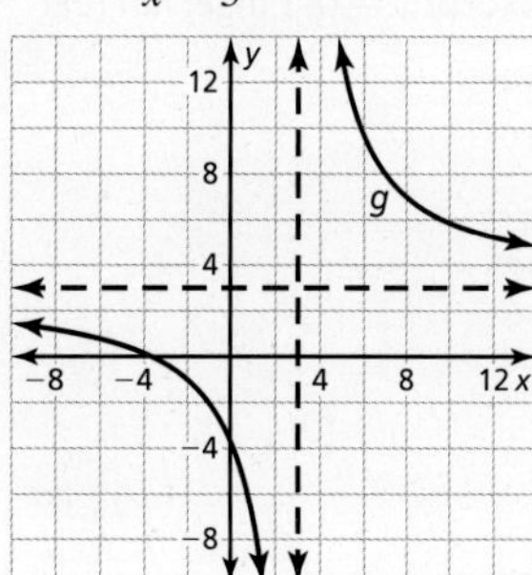

The graph of g is a translation 3 units right and 3 units up of the graph of $f(x) = \frac{20}{x}$.

35. $\frac{x(x - 18)}{6(5x + 2)}, x \neq 0$

37. $-\frac{3}{4x}, x \neq \frac{5}{2}$

39. $\frac{x - 4}{12(x - 6)(x - 1)}, x \neq -1, x \neq 4$

41. $T = \frac{2ad}{(a + j)(a - j)}$; about 10.2 h

43. **a.** $t = \frac{44.8r + 84.5}{9r(r + 5)}$

    b. about 1 h and 23 min

45. no; If one expression is a factor of the other expression, then the least common multiple is equal to the second expression.

47. **a.** $M = \frac{Pi}{1 - \left(\frac{1}{1 + i}\right)^{12t}}$

    $= \frac{Pi}{1 - \frac{1}{(1 + i)^{12t}}} \bullet \frac{(1 + i)^{12t}}{(1 + i)^{12t}}$

    $= \frac{Pi(1 + i)^{12t}}{(1 + i)^{12t} - 1}$

    b. \$117.43

49. *Sample answer:* $\frac{\frac{5}{(x + 3)(x - 1)}}{3}$

51. $6 + \frac{60}{x}$

53. $A = \dfrac{391t^2 + 0.112}{0.218t^4 + 0.991t^2 + 1} + \dfrac{391(t-1)^2 + 0.112}{0.218(t-1)^4 + 0.991(t-1)^2 + 1}$

7.4 Review & Refresh

55. 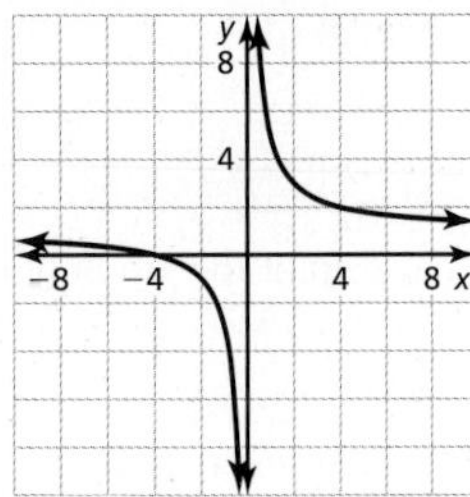

domain: all real numbers except $x = 0$; range: all real numbers except $y = 1$

56. 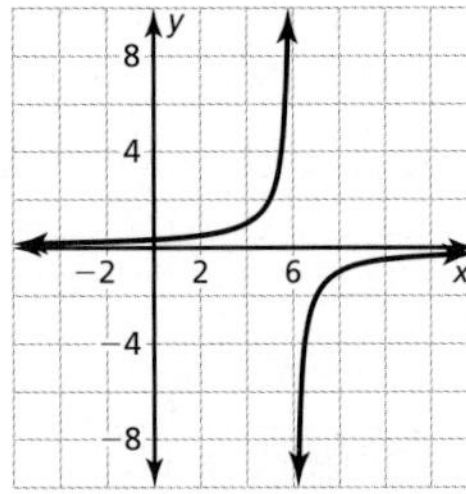

domain: all real numbers except $x = 6$; range: all real numbers except $y = 0$

57. direct variation

58. $\frac{1}{6y}, x \neq 0$

59. $\frac{x^2}{y}, x \neq 0$

60. \$5.50

61. $m = -2$

62. $x = -9$ and $x = 9$

63. $y = \frac{1}{8}x^2$

64. 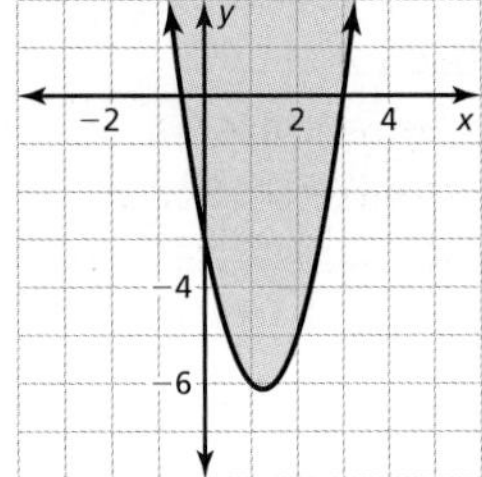

65. The graph of g is a translation 1 unit up of the graph of f.

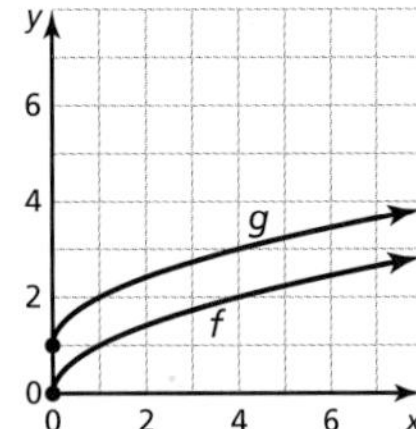

66. The graph of g is a vertical stretch by a factor of 2, followed by a translation 3 units right of the graph of f.

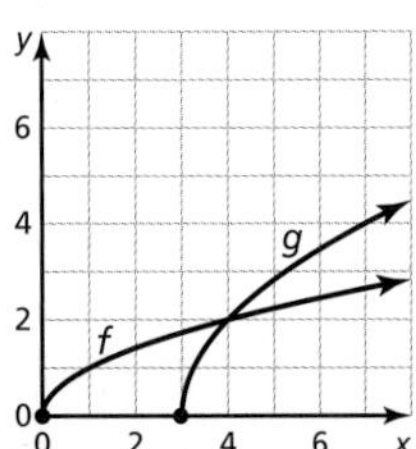

67. $\frac{9}{4x}$

68. $\frac{5x^2 + 4}{4x^3}$

7.5 Practice

1. $x = 4$

3. $x = 5$

5. $x = -5, x = 7$

7. $x = -1, x = 0$

9. 26 questions

11. 20.5 oz

13. $x(x + 3)$

15. $2(x + 1)(x + 4)$

17. $x = 2$

19. $x = 2$

21. $x = -\frac{3}{2}, x = 2$

23. no solution

25. $x = -2, x = 3$

27. $x = \frac{-3 \pm \sqrt{129}}{4}$

29. Both terms of the expression on the left side of the equation should be multiplied by $3x^2$; $3x^2 \cdot \frac{5}{3x} + 3x^2 \cdot \frac{2}{x^2} = 1 \cdot 3x^2$

31. B and D

33. a.

	Work rate	Time	Work done
You	$\frac{1 \text{ park}}{2 \text{ hours}}$	1.2 hours	0.6 park
Friend	$\frac{1 \text{ park}}{t \text{ hours}}$	1.2 hours	$\frac{1.2}{t}$ park

b. The sum is the amount of time it would take for you and your friend to clean the park together; $0.6 + \frac{1.2}{t} = 1$, $t = 3$ h

35. yes; $y = \frac{2}{x} + 4$

37. yes; $y = \frac{3}{x + 2}$

39. yes; $y = \frac{-2}{x} + \frac{11}{2}$

41. no; $y = \pm\sqrt{\frac{1}{x - 4}}$

43. about 190.6 ft

45. $x \approx \pm 0.8165$

47. $x \approx 1.3247$

49. $\frac{1 + \sqrt{5}}{2}$

51. $f^{-1}(x) = \frac{4x + 1}{x - 3}$

53. $y = \frac{b - xd}{cx - a}$

55. a. always true; When $x = a$, the denominators of the fractions are both zero.

b. sometimes true; The equation will have exactly one solution except when $a = 3$.

c. always true; $x = a$ is an extraneous solution, so the equation has no solution.

7.5 Review & Refresh

57. 3

58. 28

59. a. $p > 0$; continuous; The weight of the broccoli can be any part of a pound.

b. 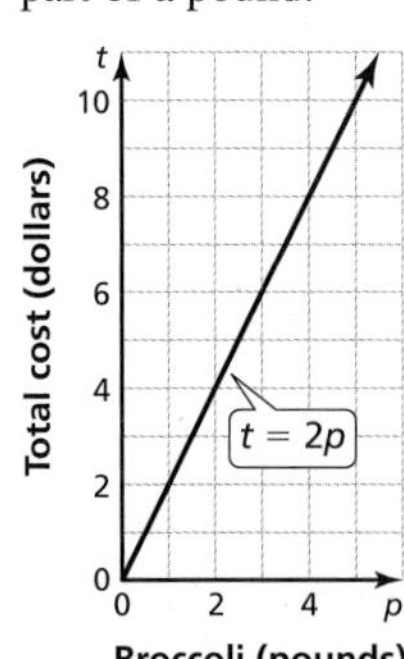

60. $x - 2, x \neq -2$

61. $-\frac{x + 4}{2(x + 6)}, x \neq 3$

62. $\frac{x}{2}, x \neq -7, x \neq 0, x \neq 2$

63. $x - 3, x \neq -2, x \neq 0, x \neq 5$

64. $f(g(8)) = 13, g(f(-2)) = 3$

65. D; The vertical asymptote is $x = 0$ and the horizontal asymptote is $y = 0$.

66. C; The vertical asymptote is $x = 0$ and the horizontal asymptote is $y = 2$.

67. A; The vertical asymptote is $x = -3$ and the horizontal asymptote is $y = -2$.

68. B; The vertical asymptote is $x = -\frac{1}{3}$ and the horizontal asymptote is $y = \frac{2}{3}$.

69. $x = -\frac{2}{3}$

70. $x = 1, x = 8$

Chapter 7 Review

1. inverse variation

2. direct variation

3. direct variation

4. neither

5. direct variation

6. inverse variation

7. $y = \frac{5}{x}; y = -\frac{5}{3}$

8. $y = \frac{24}{x}; y = -8$

9. $y = \frac{45}{x}; y = -15$

10. $y = \frac{-8}{x}; y = \frac{8}{3}$

11.

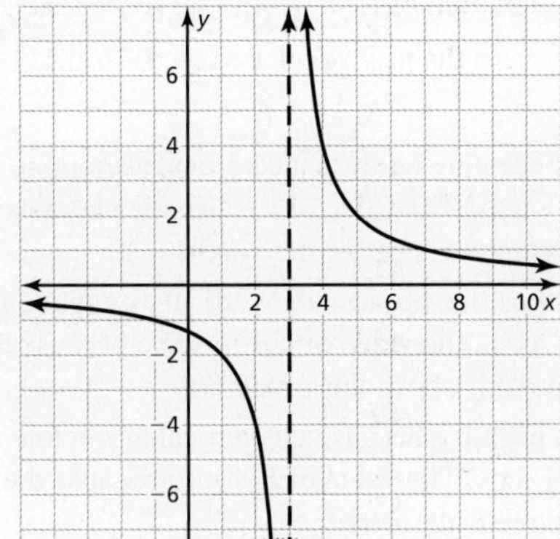

domain: all real numbers except $x = 3$, range: all real numbers except $y = 0$

12.

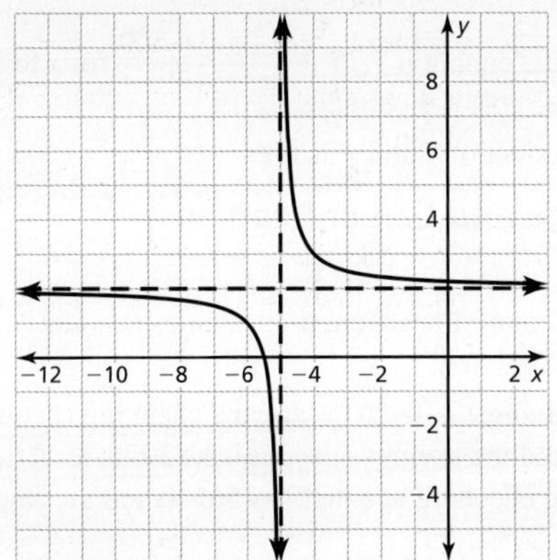

domain: all real numbers except $x = -5$, range: all real numbers except $y = 2$

13.

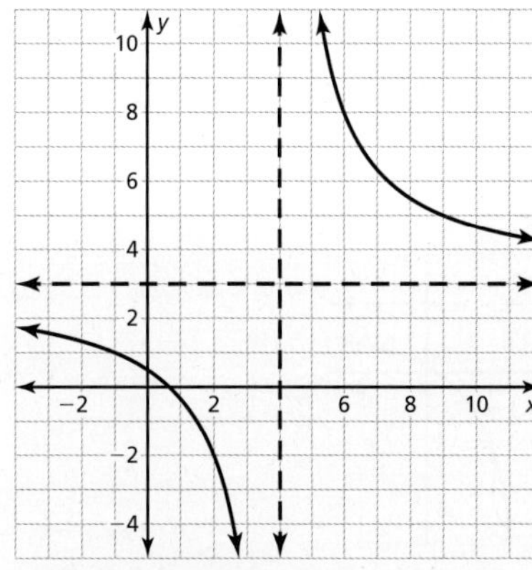

domain: all real numbers except $x = 4$, range: all real numbers except $y = 3$

14.

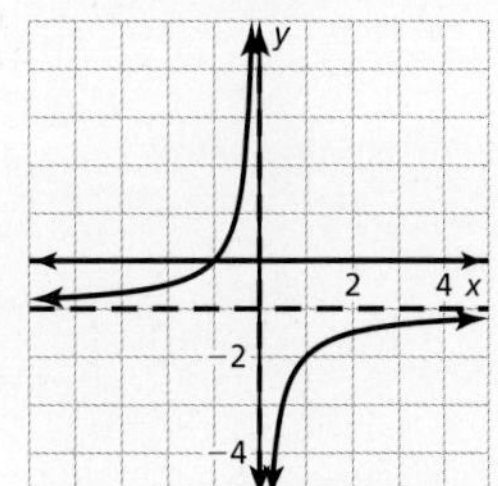

domain: all real numbers except $x = 0$, range: all real numbers except $y = -1$

15. 20 stands

16. $\frac{16x^3}{y^2}, x \neq 0$

17. $\frac{3(x + 4)}{x + 3}, x \neq 3, x \neq 4$

18. $\frac{3x(4x - 1)}{(x - 4)(x - 3)}, x \neq 0, x \neq \frac{1}{4}$

19. $\frac{1}{(x + 3)^2}, x \neq 5, x \neq 8$

20. -1

21. all real numbers except $x = -2$ and $x = 2$

22. $\frac{3x^2 + 26x + 36}{6x(x + 3)}$

23. $\frac{5x^2 - 11x - 9}{(x + 8)(x - 3)}$

24. $\frac{-2(2x^2 + 3x + 3)}{(x - 3)(x + 3)(x + 1)}$

25. $\frac{2x^2 + x + 6}{2(x - 2)}$

26. $g(x) = \frac{16}{x - 3} + 5$

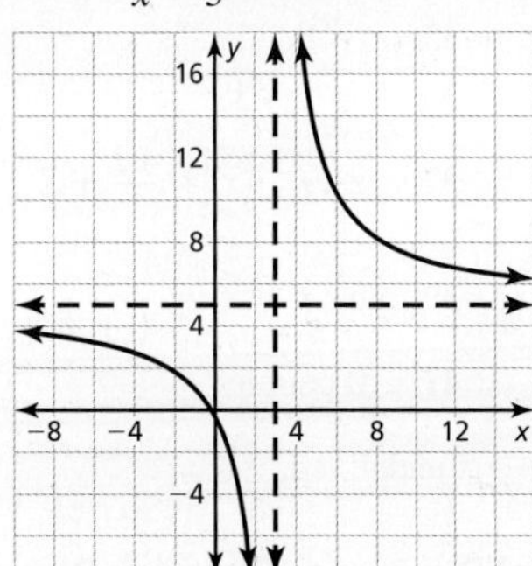

The graph of g is a translation 3 units right and 5 units up of the graph of f.

27. $g(x) = \frac{-26}{x+7} + 4$

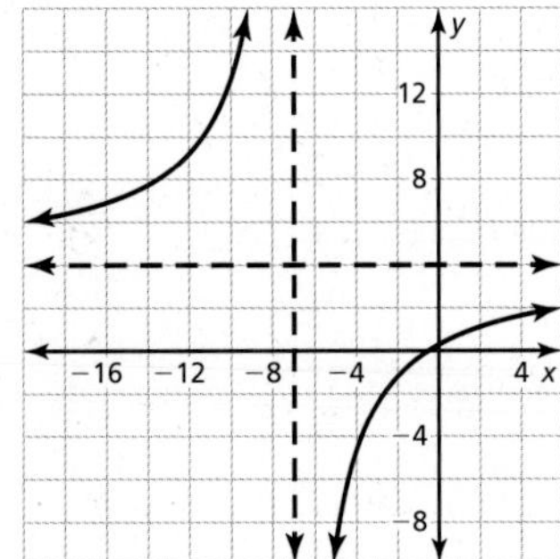

The graph of g is a translation 7 units left and 4 units up of the graph of f.

28. $g(x) = \frac{-1}{x-1} + 9$

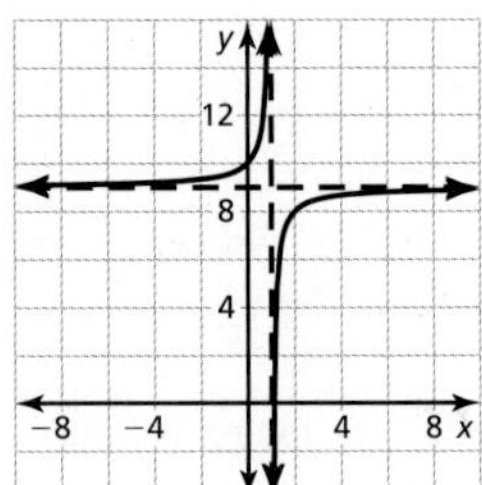

The graph of g is a translation 1 unit right and 9 units up of the graph of f.

29. $g(x) = \frac{-1}{x+2}$

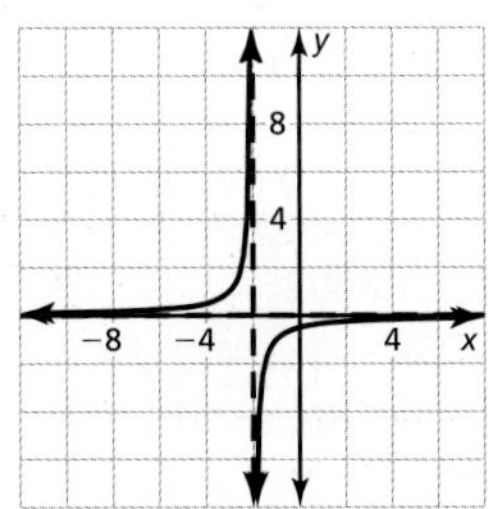

The graph of g is a translation 2 units left of the graph of f.

30. $\frac{pq}{p+q}, p \neq 0, q \neq 0$

31. $\frac{140x^2 - 600x - 500}{x(x-10)(x+5)}$

32. $x = 5$

33. $x = 0$

34. no solution

35. $x = \pm\sqrt{3}$

36. yes; $f^{-1}(x) = \frac{3}{x} - 6$

37. yes; $f^{-1}(x) = \frac{10}{x} + 7$

38. yes; $f^{-1}(x) = \frac{1}{x-8}$

39. yes; $f^{-1}(x) = \frac{x}{1+x}$

40. 8 expert ratings

41. 10 people

42. $x = 6$; When $x = 6$, $\frac{1}{x-6}$ is undefined.

Chapter 7 Mathematical Practices (Chapter Review)

1. The value of M doubles; $M = \frac{Pi(1+i)^{12t}}{(1+i)^{12t} - 1}$, when P is doubled, then

$$M = \frac{(2P)i(1+i)^{12t}}{(1+i)^{12t} - 1} = 2\left(\frac{Pi(1+i)^{12t}}{(1+i)^{12t} - 1}\right) = 2M.$$

2. The model is divided by 1000, which would yield $E = \frac{111.082t + 1422.329}{1 - 0.002t}$.

3. *Sample answer:* $c(x) = \frac{20x + 1200}{x}$; As x increases, the average cost per item decreases. As $x \to +\infty$, $c(x) \to a$ and b affects the model less.

Chapter 7 Practice Test

1. $y = \frac{10}{x}$; $y = \frac{5}{2}$

2.

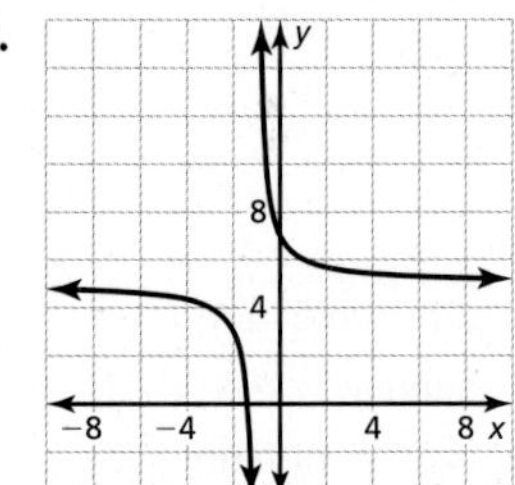

domain: all real numbers except $x = -1$; range: all real numbers except $y = 5$

3. $\frac{1}{4y^3}, x \neq 0$

4. $\frac{-3(x-6)}{(x+4)(x-3)}$

5. $\frac{x-4}{x+3}, x \neq -1, x \neq 6$

6. $\frac{2(3x-10)}{(x+5)(x-5)}$

7. $x = -2, x = -1$

8. $x = 6$

9. The value of h is negative because the vertical asymptote is to the left of the y-axis. The value of k is negative because the horizontal asymptote is below the x-axis.

10. The value of h is positive because the vertical asymptote is to the right of the y-axis. The value of k is positive because the horizontal asymptote is above the x-axis.

11. The value of h is negative because the vertical asymptote is to the left of the y-axis. The value of k is zero because the horizontal asymptote is the x-axis.

12. $g(x) = x - 2, x \neq -3$; yes; They are the same everywhere except at $x = -3$ where $g(x)$ is undefined.

13. $a = 8$

14. 1000 lb; Solve the equation $1.75 = \frac{1.25x + 500}{x}$ for x to find when the average cost per pound is \$1.75.

15. 40 ft-lb; The product of d and F is 600.

Chapter 7 College and Career Readiness

1. A, D

2. C

3. a. checking account: linear function; savings account: exponential function

   b. checking; savings; After 10 years, the checking account has \$5990 and the savings account has \$5975.46. After 15 years, the checking account has \$6540 and the savings account has \$6597.39.

4. B

5. $25^{1/2}, (\sqrt{5})^3, (\sqrt[3]{125})^2, 125^{3/2}$

6. C

7. $p = \frac{-36}{q-r}$; $-6, 1, 5$

8. 8 free throws; $\frac{13+x}{20+x} = \frac{75}{100}, x = 8$

9. g

Chapter 8

Chapter 8 Prepare

1. $\frac{6}{30} = \frac{p}{100}$, 20%   2. $\frac{a}{25} = \frac{68}{100}$, 17

3. $\frac{34.4}{86} = \frac{p}{100}$, 40%

4. Movies Watched per Week

Frequency: 0, 5, 10, 15, 20, 25, 30, 35
Movies: 0–1, 2–3, 4–5

5. no; The sofa will cost 80% of the retail price and the arm chair will cost 81% of the retail price.

8.1 Practice

1. 6; HP, HP, HW, TP, TP, TW
3. 18; A1, A2, A3, B1, B2, B3, C1, C2, C3, D1, D2, D3, E1, E2, E3, F1, F2, F3
5. $\frac{5}{16}$, or 31.25%
7. a. $\frac{11}{12}$, or about 92%
   b. $\frac{13}{18}$, or about 72%
9. There are 4 outcomes, not 3; The probability is $\frac{1}{4}$.
11. about 0.56, or about 56%   13. 4
15. $\frac{7}{26}$, or about 27%
17. no; Your friend calculated the experimental probability. The theoretical probability of the coin landing heads up is $\frac{1}{2}$.
19. C, A, D, B
21. a. 2, 3, 4, 5, 6, 7, 8, 9, 10, 11, 12
    b. 2: $\frac{1}{36}$, 3: $\frac{1}{18}$, 4: $\frac{1}{12}$, 5: $\frac{1}{9}$, 6: $\frac{5}{36}$, 7: $\frac{1}{6}$, 8: $\frac{5}{36}$, 9: $\frac{1}{9}$, 10: $\frac{1}{12}$; 11: $\frac{1}{18}$, 12: $\frac{1}{36}$
    c. *Sample answer:* The probabilities are similar.
23. $\frac{\pi}{6}$, or about 52%
25. about 113; $\left(\frac{9}{1200}\right)15{,}000 = 112.5$
27. *Sample answer:* Each person pays $1 to play. From a standard deck of 52 cards, if the player can correctly guess the suit, they win back twice their money. There is a $\frac{1}{4}$ chance of winning $2 and a $\frac{3}{4}$ chance of not winning. So, if 200 people play the game, you can expect to earn $200 - 200\left(\frac{1}{4}\right)(2) = 200 - 100 = \$100$.

8.1 Review & Refresh

28. 9   29. $-8x$

30. The graph of g is a vertical shrink by a factor of 0.5 and a reflection in the x-axis of the graph of f.

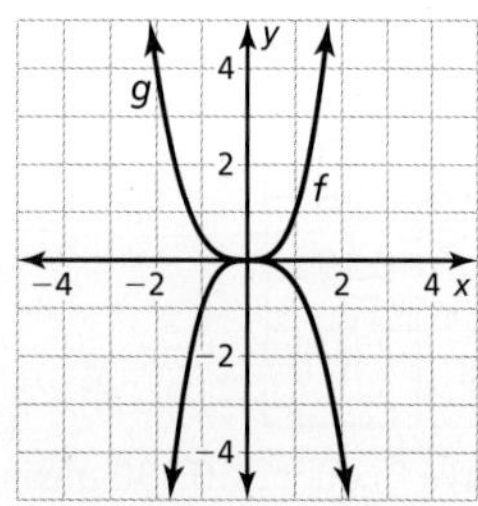

31. The graph of g is a translation 1 unit left and 2 units down of the graph of f.

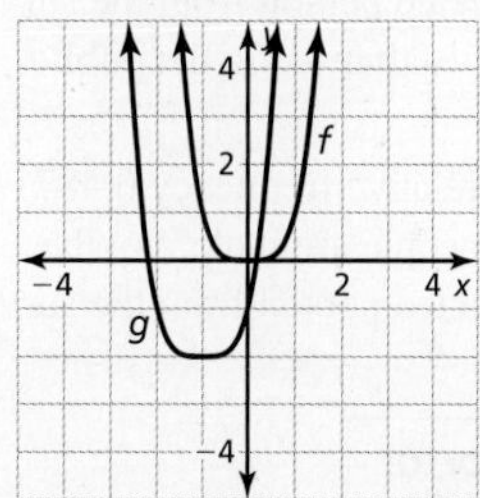

32. The experimental probability, 80%, is less than the theoretical probability, 90%.
33. $x = 4$ and $x = 12$ 34. 5
35. $\frac{x^7}{3}$, $x \neq 0, y \neq 0$ 36. $\frac{12}{5}$, $x \neq 0, y \neq 0$
37. $\frac{3x^2 + x + 7}{(x-2)(x+1)}$ 38. $\frac{x + 20}{3x^2(x+5)}$
39. $\frac{x^2 + 7x - 8}{x + 5}$, $x \neq 6$ 40. $\frac{5x + 10}{x - 3}$, $x \neq -3, x \neq -7$
41. Shop A; 4 toppings   42. 125

8.2 Practice

1. 34; 40; 4; 6; 12
3.

		Gender		
		Male	Female	Total
Response	Yes	132	151	283
	No	39	29	68
	Total	171	180	351

351 people were surveyed, 171 males were surveyed, 180 females were surveyed, 283 people said yes, 68 people said no.

5.

		Gender		
		Male	Female	Total
Response	Yes	0.376	0.430	0.806
	No	0.111	0.083	0.194
	Total	0.487	0.513	1

Sample answer: The joint relative frequency 0.430 means that about 43.0% of the people in the survey are female and wash their hands after using the public restrooms. So, the probability that a randomly selected person from the survey is a female who washes her hands after using the public restroom is 43.0%.

Sample answer: The marginal relative frequency 0.487 means that about 48.7% of the people are male. So, the probability that a randomly selected person from the survey is male is about 48.7%.

7. a.

		Like Horror Movies	
		Yes	No
Visited Haunted House	Yes	0.534	0.483
	No	0.466	0.517

Sample answer: The conditional relative frequency 0.483 means that of the people in the survey who do not like horror movies, about 48.3% have visited a haunted house. So, given that a randomly selected person in the survey who does not like horror movies, the probability that the person has visited a haunted house is about 48.3%.

b.

		Like Horror Movies	
		Yes	No
Visited Haunted House	Yes	0.481	0.519
	No	0.431	0.569

Sample answer: The conditional relative frequency 0.431 means that of the people in the survey who have not visited a haunted house, about 43.1% like horror movies. So, given that a randomly selected person in the survey has not visited a haunted house, the probability that the person likes horror movies is about 43.1%.

9. The table entries are conditional relative frequencies based on the row totals, not the column totals; 0.271 means that about 27.1% of the students surveyed who are upperclassmen dislike roller coasters.

11. $\frac{6}{31}$, or about 19.4%

13.

		Preference		
		Math	Science	Total
Gender	Male	93	57	150
	Female	148	52	200
	Total	241	109	350

15. a. $\frac{44}{481}$, or about 9.1%

b. $\frac{79}{155}$, or about 51.0%

17. Answers will vary.

8.2 Review & Refresh

18. yes; $f^{-1}(x) = -\frac{6}{x} + 13$ 19. no; $y = \pm\sqrt{\frac{1}{x-5}}$

20.

		Breakfast	
		Ate	Did Not Eat
Feeling	Tired	0.091	0.333
	Not Tired	0.909	0.667

Sample answer: The conditional relative frequency 0.333 means that of the people in the survey who did not eat breakfast, about 33.3% felt tired. So, given that a randomly selected person in the survey ate breakfast, the probability that the person felt tired is about 33.3%.

21. $\frac{2x}{5x-12}$, $x \neq 0, x \neq 3$ 22. $\frac{5}{6}$, or about 83.3%

23. $g(x) = \sqrt{x-2} + 2$

24. exponential decay

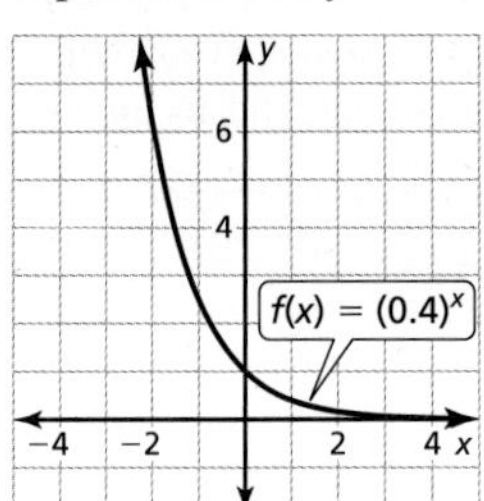

25. exponential growth

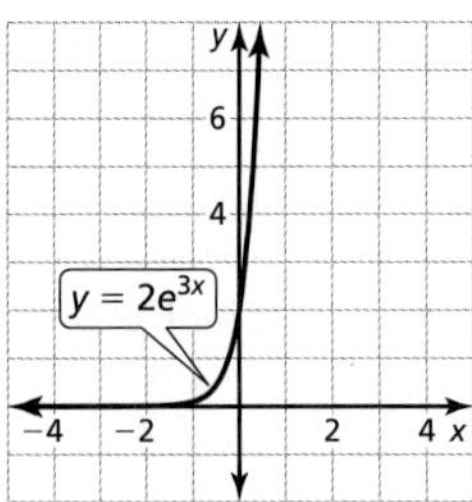

26. $2\log_4 3 + 3\log_4 x$ 27. $(a-2)(a-3)(a+3)$

28. $x = 2$ and $x = 2.5$; Explanations will vary.

29. $x = -\frac{7}{3} + \frac{2\sqrt{13}}{3}$ and $x = -\frac{7}{3} - \frac{2\sqrt{13}}{3}$; Explanations will vary.

8.3 Practice

1. 50%
3. a. 87.5%
   b. 48%
5. 87.5%
7. The value for P(yes) was used in the denominator instead of the value for P(Tokyo); $\frac{0.049}{0.39} \approx 0.126$
9. a. $\frac{23}{43}$, or about 53.5%
   b. $\frac{23}{48}$, or about 47.9%
11. Route B; It has the best probability of getting to school on time.
13. A
15. a. about 0.438
    b. about 0.387
17. no; Routine B is the best choice because there is a 66.7% chance of meeting the time limit, which is higher than the chances of Routine A (62.5%) and Routine C (63.6%).
19. a. 31.96%
    b. about 60.3%
21. false; $P(X \mid Y) = \frac{P(X \text{ and } Y)}{P(Y)}$ and $P(Y \mid X) = \frac{P(X \text{ and } Y)}{P(X)}$; The expressions for both probabilities have the same numerator, but the expression for $P(X \mid Y)$ is divided by $P(Y)$ and the expression for $P(Y \mid X)$ is divided by $P(X)$. Because the area of the region representing Y is much larger than the area representing X, $P(Y) > P(X)$. So, $P(X \mid Y) < P(Y \mid X)$.

8.3 Review & Refresh

23. $x = 0.2$
24. $x = 2$
25. focus: (3, 0); directrix: $x = -3$; axis of symmetry: $y = 0$

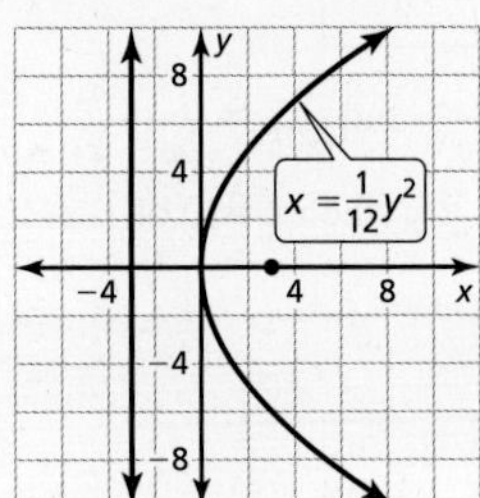

26. focus: $(-3, -1)$; directrix: $y = -3$; axis of symmetry: $x = -3$

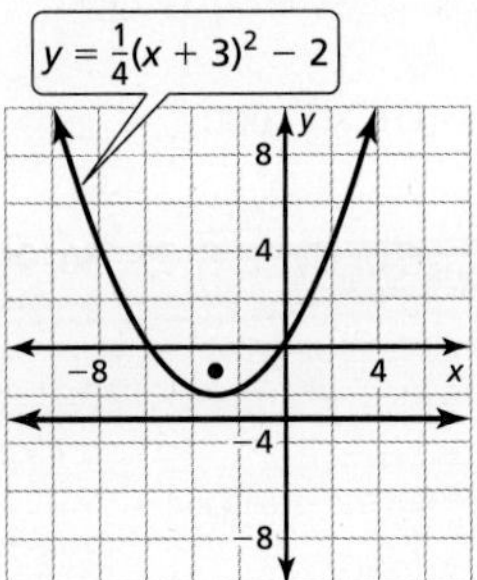

27.

		Dominant Hand		
		Left	Right	Total
Gender	Female	0.048	0.450	0.498
	Male	0.104	0.398	0.502
	Total	0.152	0.848	1

28. $x = -\frac{1}{2} - \frac{\sqrt{33}}{2}$ and $x = -\frac{1}{2} + \frac{\sqrt{33}}{2}$
29. $(f + g)(x) = -6\sqrt[3]{4x}$, domain: all real numbers; $(f - g)(x) = 18\sqrt[3]{4x}$, domain: all real numbers; $(f + g)(-16) = 24$; $(f - g)(-16) = -72$
30. $(f + g)(x) = 6x^2 + 4x + 8$, domain: all real numbers; $(f - g)(x) = 12x^2 + 4x - 12$, domain: all real numbers; $(f + g)(1) = 18$; $(f - g)(1) = 4$
31. $10x^5 - 5x^4 + 65x^2$
32. $4x^2 - 49$
33. $x^4 - 6x^3 - 12x^2 + 38x - 21$
34. $2x^3 - 3x^2 - 17x - 12$
35. $\frac{1}{6}, \frac{4}{15}$
36. $x = -5, x = 0, x = \frac{1}{2}$

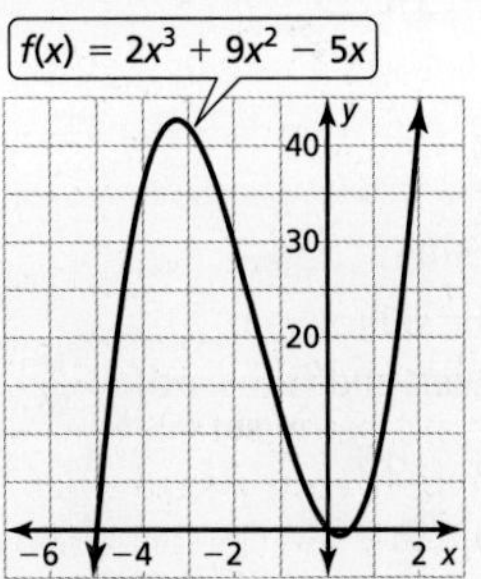

37. a. $\frac{19}{34}$, or about 55.9%
    b. $\frac{41}{86}$, or about 47.7%

8.4 Practice

1. independent
3. independent
5. not independent
7. independent
9. not independent
11. independent
13. about 2.8%
15. about 14.7%
17. $P(B \mid A) = \frac{4}{6}$ not $\frac{4}{7}$; $P(A \text{ and } B) = \frac{3}{7} \cdot \frac{4}{6} = \frac{2}{7} \approx 0.286$
19. 0.325
21. dependent; The first water balloon chosen affects the occurrence of the second water balloon.
23. independent; P(grand prize) • P(door prize) = (0.05)(0.2) = 0.01 and P(grand prize and door prize) = 0.01.
25. yes; The chance that it will be rescheduled is (0.7)(0.75) = 0.525, or 52.5%, which is greater than 50%.
27. a. The occurrence of one event does not affect the occurrence of the other, so the probability of each event is the same whether or not the other event has occurred.
    b. yes; $P(A \text{ and } B) = P(A) \cdot P(B)$ and $P(A) = P(A \mid B)$.

8.4 Review & Refresh

29. $x = \pm 3\sqrt{3}$
30. $x = \frac{1}{5}$
31. $x = 16$
32. $x = 0.15$
33. $\frac{1}{12}$, or about 8.3%

34.

		Escape Room		
		Yes	No	Total
Gender	Male	35	33	68
	Female	29	28	57
	Total	64	61	125

There are 68 males, 57 females, 64 who responded yes, 61 who responded no, and 125 total people in the survey.

35. 5

36. $18\sqrt{2}$

37. inverse variation

38.

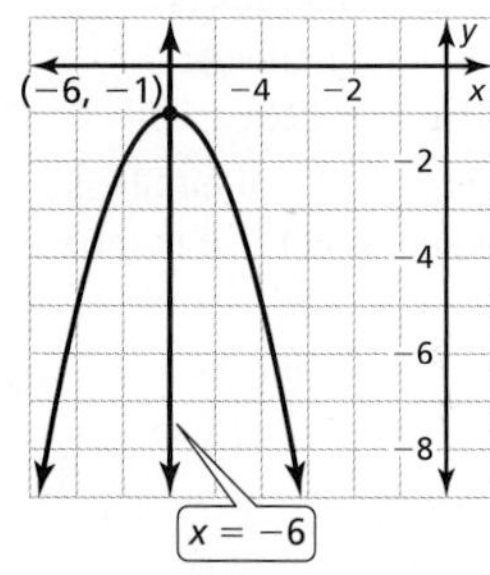

39.

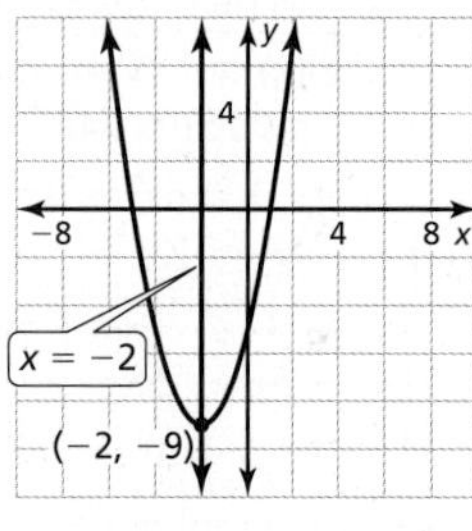

40. 55%; 25%

41. $\frac{11}{17}$, or about 64.7%

8.5 Practice

1. 0.4

3. $\frac{1}{3}$

5. $\frac{2}{3}$

7. $\frac{7}{12}$

9. P(heart and face card) should be subtracted;
$P(\text{heart}) + P(\text{face card}) - P(\text{heart and face card}) = \frac{11}{26}$

11. $\frac{7}{10}$, or 70%

13. 10%

15. 0.4742, or 47.42%

17. $\frac{13}{18}$

19. $\frac{13}{20}$

8.5 Review & Refresh

21. $y = (x + 3)^2 - 13$; $(-3, -13)$

22. $y = 3(x - 2)^2 - 1$; $(2, -1)$

23. $\frac{1}{17}$, or about 5.9%

24. $x = 3$

25. $24

26. 0.2

27. 0.64

28. $f^{-1}(x) = 4x + 12$

29. $f^{-1}(x) = x^2 - 7, x \geq 0$

30.

		Vote		
		Friday	Monday	Total
Gender	Male	0.269	0.308	0.577
	Female	0.192	0.231	0.423
	Total	0.461	0.539	1

Sample answer: The joint relative frequency 0.269 means that about 26.9% of the students who voted are males who voted for Friday. So, the probability that a randomly selected student who voted is a male who voted for Friday is about 26.9%.

Sample answer: The marginal relative frequency 0.423 means that about 42.3% of the students who voted are female. So, the probability that a randomly selected student who voted is female is about 42.3%.

8.6 Practice

1. a. 2
b. 2

3. a. 24
b. 12

5. a. 720
b. 30

7. 20

9. 9

11. 20, 160

13. 990

15. $\frac{1}{56}$

17. 4

19. 20

21. 5

23. 1

25. 220

27. 53,130

29. The factorial in the denominator was left out;
$${}_{11}P_7 = \frac{11!}{(11-7)!} = 1{,}663{,}200$$

31. A

33. combinations; The order is not important; 45

35. permutations; The order is important; 132,600

37. $\frac{1}{44{,}850}$

39. *Sample answer:* There is only one way to arrange a data set with zero elements.

41. *Sample answer:* Two candidates are chosen from a group of 5 to be the president and vice president; Two candidates are chosen from a group of 5 to be on a committee.

43.

	$r = 0$	$r = 1$	$r = 2$	$r = 3$
${}_3P_r$	1	3	6	6
${}_3C_r$	1	3	3	1

${}_nP_r \geq {}_nC_r$; Because ${}_nP_r = \frac{n!}{(n-r)!}$ and ${}_nC_r = \frac{n!}{(n-r)! \bullet r!}$, ${}_nP_r > {}_nC_r$ when $r > 1$ and ${}_nP_r = {}_nC_r$ when $r = 0$ or $r = 1$.

45. $\frac{1}{15{,}890{,}700}$

47. $x^3 + 6x^2 + 12x + 8$

49. $a^4 + 12a^3b + 54a^2b^2 + 108ab^3 + 81b^4$

51. $w^{12} - 12w^9 + 54w^6 - 108w^3 + 81$

53. $729u^6 + 1458u^5v^2 + 1215u^4v^4 + 540u^3v^6 + 135u^2v^8 + 18uv^{10} + v^{12}$

55. −8064

57. 316,800,000

59. −337,920

61. ${}_8C_0, {}_8C_1, {}_8C_2, {}_8C_3, {}_8C_4, {}_8C_5, {}_8C_6, {}_8C_7, {}_8C_8$; 1, 8, 28, 56, 70, 56, 28, 8, 1

63. a. ${}_nC_{n-2} - n$
b. $\frac{n(n-3)}{2}$

65. 18

67. $\frac{1061}{1250}$

69. a. $\frac{1}{90}$
b. $\frac{9}{10}$

71. 5148

73. 10

8.6 Review & Refresh

75. $s = 7$ cm

76.

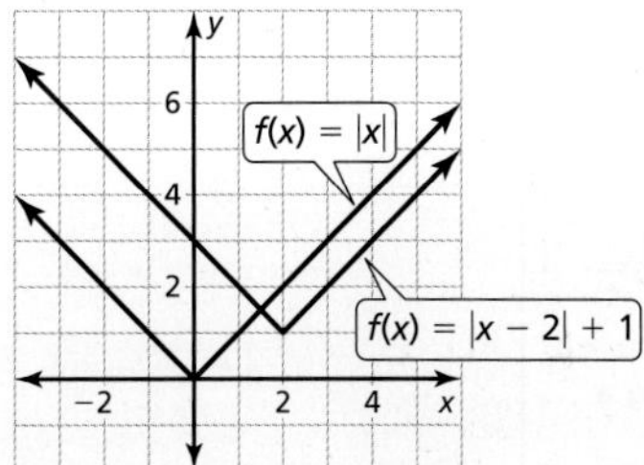

The graph of $f(x) = |x - 2| + 1$ is a translation 2 units right and 1 unit up of the graph of $f(x) = |x|$.

77. $x^3 + 18x^2 + 108x + 216$

78. $8x^3 - 36x^2y + 54xy^2 - 27y^3$

79. independent **80.** 0.25

81.

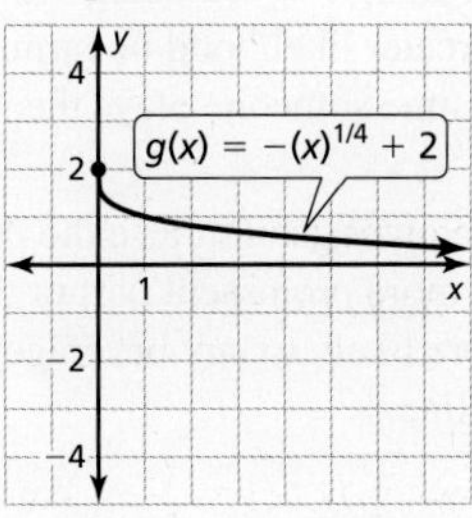

domain: $x \geq 0$, range: $y \leq 2$

82.

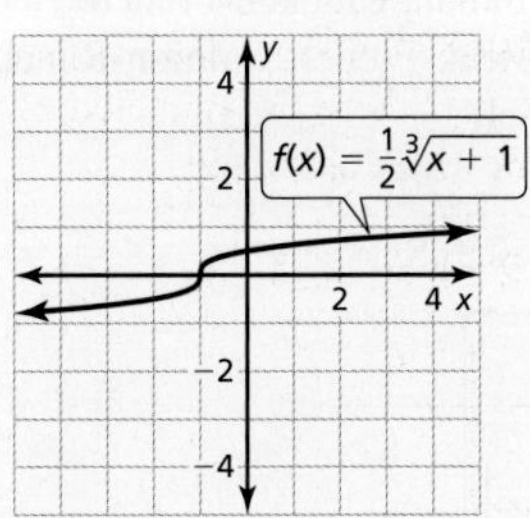

domain: all real numbers, range: all real numbers

83. exponential; As the x-values increase by 1, the y-values increase by a factor of 2.

84. The graph of r is a vertical shrink by a factor of $\frac{1}{2}$ and a vertical translation 1 unit up of the graph of f.

85. $x = 0$ and $x = \frac{1}{4}$ **86.** 1

87. exponential growth

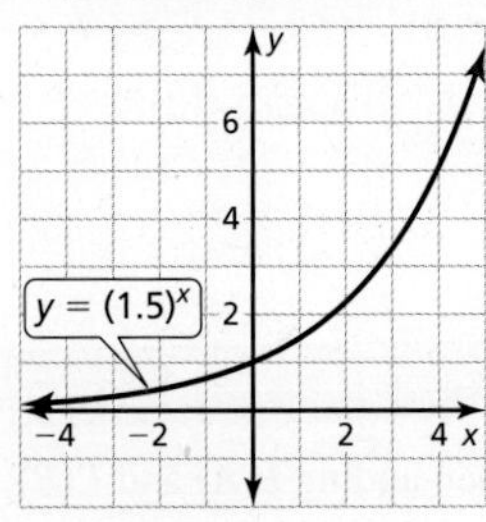

8.7 Practice

1.

x (value)	1	2	3
Outcomes	5	3	2
$P(x)$	$\frac{1}{2}$	$\frac{3}{10}$	$\frac{1}{5}$

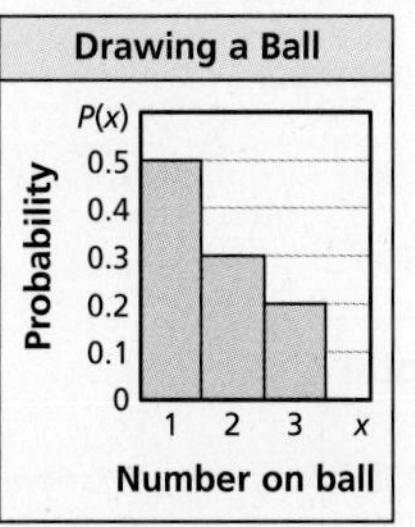

3.

w (value)	1	2
Outcomes	5	21
$P(w)$	$\frac{5}{26}$	$\frac{21}{26}$

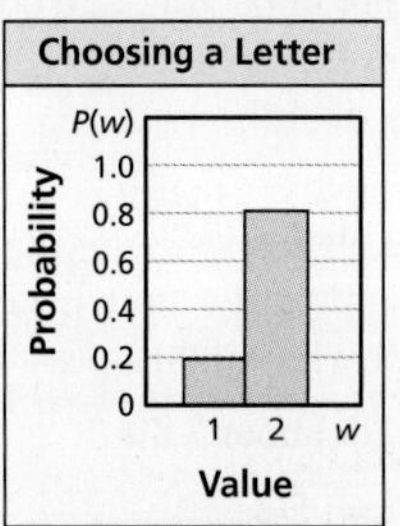

5. **a.** 2

b. $\frac{5}{8}$

7. about 0.00002 **9.** about 0.00018

11. **a.**

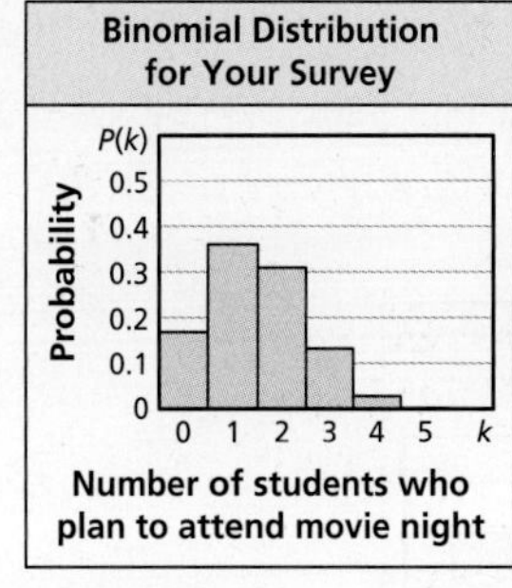

b. 1 student plans to attend movie night.

c. about 83.7%

13. The exponents are switched; $P(k = 3) = {}_5C_3\left(\frac{1}{6}\right)^3\left(\frac{5}{6}\right)^{5-3} \approx 0.032$

15. $p > 0.5$ **17.** 40%

19. about 90.1%

8.7 Review & Refresh

20. 2 **21.** 6

22. 10 **23.** $x + 3$

24. $x^3 + 4x^2 - 5x - 16 + \dfrac{8}{x + 2}$

25. $g(x) = (2x - 2)^2 - (2x - 2)$

26. $\frac{4}{5}$, or 80%

27. dependent; The gift card that is drawn first affects the probability of drawing a certain type of gift card second.

28. geometric sequence; As the x-values increase by 1, the y-values decrease by a constant factor of $\frac{1}{4}$.

Chapter 8 Review

1. 8; H–B, H–B, H–G, H–G, T–B, T–B, T–G, T–G

2. $\frac{2}{9}$; $\frac{7}{9}$

3. 20 points

4. about 0.529

5.

		Gender		
		Boy	Girl	Total
Response	Yes	200	230	430
	No	20	40	60
	Total	220	270	490

490 students were surveyed, 430 said the speaker was impactful, 60 said the speaker was not impactful, 220 boys were surveyed, 270 girls were surveyed.

6. $\frac{2}{3}$

7. $\frac{2}{3}$; $\frac{3}{7}$; P(single rotor | failed) is higher than P(single rotor | passed), which means that it's more likely that a randomly selected single rotor will fail than pass.

8. $\frac{1}{3}$

9. $\frac{5}{64}$, or about 7.8%

10. $\frac{38}{87}$, or about 43.7%

11. 0.68

12. 0.02

13. 5040

14. 1,037,836,800

15. 15

16. 70

17. $\frac{1}{12}$

18. $\frac{2}{11}$

19. $243x^5 - 810x^4y + 1080x^3y^2 - 720x^2y^3 + 240xy^4 - 32y^5$

20. $16x^4 + 32x^3y^2 + 24x^2y^4 + 8xy^6 + y^8$

21. about 0.12

22.

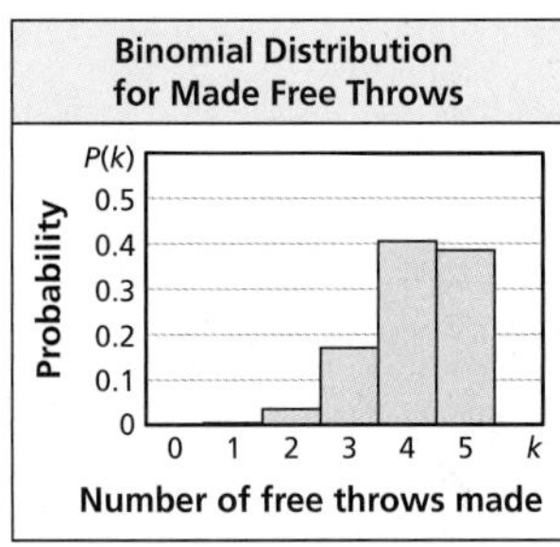

The most likely outcome is that 4 of the 5 free throw shots will be made.

23.

Binomial Distribution for Your Survey

P(k)

Probability

0 1 2 3 4 k

Number of people who go online mostly using a smartphone

about 47.3%

Chapter 8 Mathematical Practices (Chapter Review)

1. *Sample answer:* the probability of making k sales of a product when 40% of customers buy the product

2. *Sample answer:* The fundraiser was designed using probabilities so that there is a greater likelihood of earning money than losing money each time someone plays the game.

3. *Sample answer:* The gas station owner could raise the price of beverages or place them in a more prominent part of the store because customers are more likely to buy beverages than snacks when they get gasoline.

Chapter 8 Practice Test

1. 9; Chicken-Ranch, Chicken-Italian, Chicken-French, Steak-Ranch, Steak-Italian, Steak-French, Salmon-Ranch, Salmon-Italian, Salmon-French

2. 42

3. 20

4. $x^5 + 5x^4y^2 + 10x^3y^4 + 10x^2y^6 + 5xy^8 + y^{10}$

5. a.

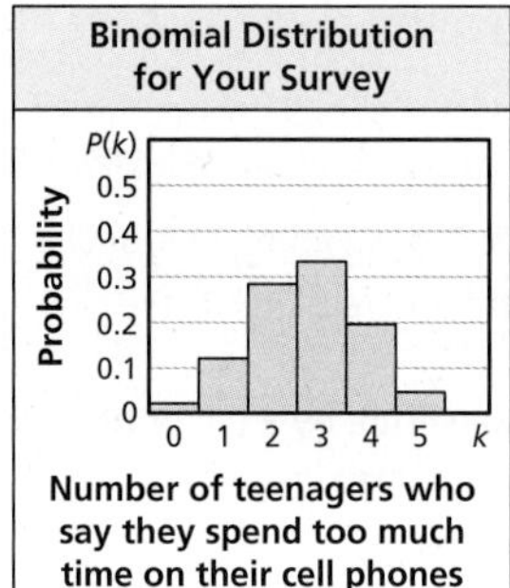

b. 3 teenagers say they spend too much time on their cell phones.

c. about 57.5%

6. a. $\frac{4}{15}$, or about 26.7%

b. $\frac{3}{5}$, or 60%

c. $\frac{5}{42}$, or about 11.9%

7. $P(A$ and $B)$ is counted twice when adding $P(A)$ and $P(B)$; When events A and B are disjoint, $P(A$ and $B) = 0$.

8. $\frac{5}{18}$, or about 27.8%

9. Carrier A

10. a. $\frac{1}{220}$

b. $\frac{1}{1320}$

Chapter 8 College and Career Readiness

1. A, E
2. 15; S-Choc, S-Van, S-Straw, S-Ban, S-PB, M-Choc, M-Van, M-Straw, M-Ban, M-PB, L-Choc, L-Van, L-Straw, L-Ban, L-PB; $\frac{4}{5}$, or 80%
3. D
4. $x = -3$
5. $k = 20$
6. a. 34; 16; 33; 56; 57
   b. about 0.3113
   c. 0.68
7. C
8. B
9. 6; 8

Chapter 9

Chapter 9 Prepare

1. about 77.2, 82.5, 82; median or mode; The mean is less than most of the data.
2. about 73.7, 70.5, 70; median or mode; The mean is greater than most of the data.
3. about 19.8, 16, 44; median; The mean and mode are both greater than most of the data.
4. about 3.85; The typical data value differs from the mean by about 3.85 units.
5. about 7.09; The typical data value differs from the mean by about 7.09 units.
6. 6.5; The typical data value differs from the mean by 6.5 units.
7. All the data values are the same; no; The formula for standard deviation includes taking only the positive square root.

9.1 Practice

1. 50%
3. 2.5%
5. 0.16
7. 0.025
9. 0.68
11. 0.68
13. 0.975
15. 0.84
17. a. 81.5%
    b. 0.15%
19. The values on the horizontal axis show a standard deviation of 1 instead of 2.

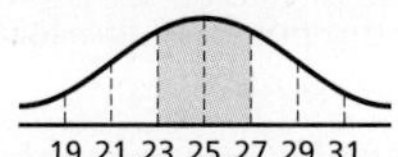

The probability that x is between 23 and 27 is 0.68.

21. a. 0.0968
    b. 0.2681
23. no
25. 0.1151
27. 0.2898
29. a. about 4.52×10^{-9}
    b. yes; The probability that a box contains an amount of cereal significantly less than the mean is very small.
31. no; When the mean is greater than the median, the distribution is skewed right.
33. D
35. 0.1336
37. a. 88th percentile
    b. 93rd percentile
    c. ACT; Your percentile on the ACT was higher than your percentile on the SAT.

9.1 Review & Refresh

39.

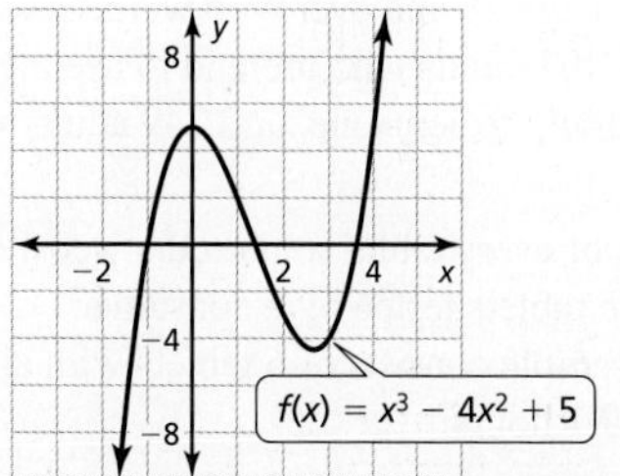

x-intercepts: -1, about 1.4, and about 3.6; local maximum: (0, 5); local minimum: (2.67, -4.48); increasing when $x < 0$ and $x > 2.67$; decreasing when $0 < x < 2.67$

40.

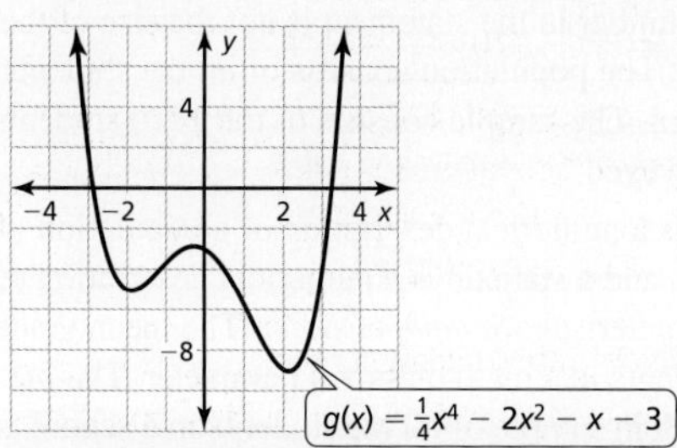

x-intercepts: about -2.8 and about 3.2; local maximum: (-0.25, -2.87); local minimums: (-1.86, -5.07) and (2.11, -9.06); increasing when $-1.86 < x < -0.25$ and $x > 2.11$; decreasing when $x < -1.86$ and $-0.25 < x < 2.11$

41. 83.85%
42. $\frac{4}{13}$, or about 30.8%
43. $\frac{1}{300}$, or about 0.3%
44. 0.845
45. 2.708
46.

	Second die					
First die	**1**	**1**	**2**	**2**	**3**	**3**
1	2	2	3	3	4	4
2	3	3	4	4	5	5
3	4	4	5	5	6	6
4	5	5	6	6	7	7
5	6	6	7	7	8	8
6	7	7	8	8	9	9

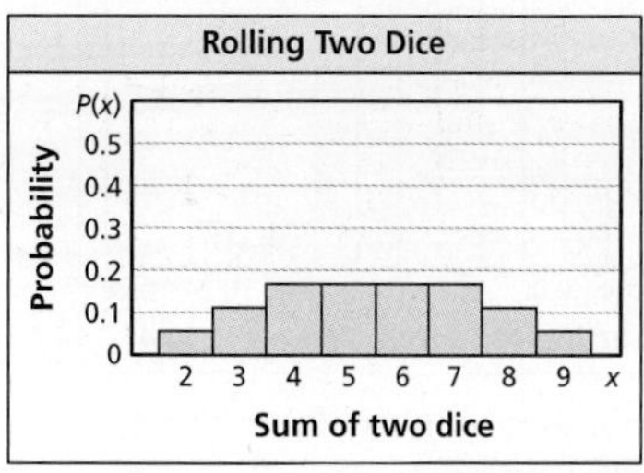

47. $\left(-\frac{5}{2}, \frac{21}{4}\right)$ and (2, 3); Explanations will vary.
48. no solution; Explanations will vary.

9.2 Practice

1. population; Every high school student is counted.
3. sample; The survey is given to a subset of the population of spectators.
5. population: every adult age 18 and over in the United States, sample: the 1152 adults age 18 and over who were surveyed; The sample consists of 403 adults who pretend to use their smartphone to avoid talking to someone, and 749 adults who do not.
7. population; battery life of every tablet sold on the website; sample; battery life of 6 tablets tested by a consumer electronics team; The sample consists of 6 tablets with an average battery life of 9.1 hours.
9. statistic; The average cost of admission of a subset of the population of amusement parks was calculated.
11. parameter; The percentage of every active volcano in the United States was calculated.
13. The sample number in the statement is not the size of the entire sample; The population consists of all the students in the high school. The sample consists of the 1270 students who were surveyed.
15. A parameter is a numerical description of a population characteristic, and a statistic is a numerical description of a sample characteristic; *Sample answer:* The mean grade of all the students in a math class is a parameter. The mean GPA of a random sample of all the students in a school is a statistic.
17. 56%
19. *Sample answer:* 30%
21. a. The maker's claim is most likely true.
    b. The maker's claim is most likely false.
23. a. The maker's claim is most likely false.
    b. The maker's claim is most likely true.
25. The sample size of the population is too small to make such a conclusion.
27. *Sample answer:* population: all American adults, sample: the 801 American adults surveyed; The sample consists of 606 American adults who say the world's temperature will go up over the next 100 years, 174 American adults who say it will go down, and 21 American adults who have no opinion.
29. a. *Sample answer:*

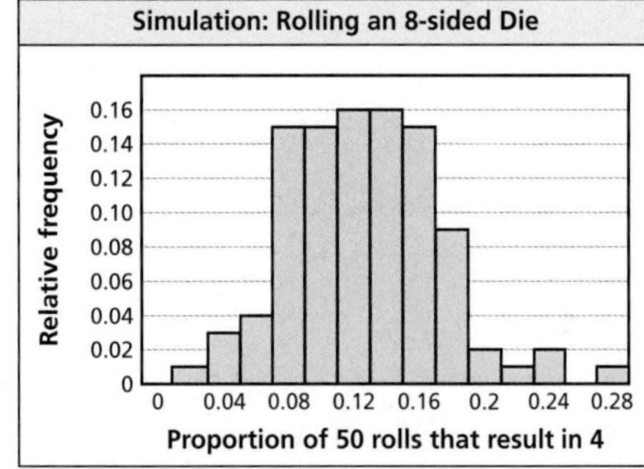

    b. The maker's claim is most likely false; The maker's claim is most likely true.

9.2 Review & Refresh

31. $x = 5 \pm \sqrt{29}$; Explanations will vary.
32. $n = -1 \pm i$; Explanations will vary.
33. no
34. population; every teenager ages 13–17 in the United States; sample; some teenagers ages 13–17 who were surveyed; The sample consists of some teenagers ages 13–17 of whom 90% play video games of some kind.
35. about 56%
36. about 0.011%
37. 240
38. 15
39. a. -1
    b. 4
40. $\frac{1}{3x}, y \neq 0$
41. $\frac{9}{20x}$

9.3 Practice

1. self-selected sample
3. random sample
5. convenience sample; Dog owners probably have a strong opinion about an off-leash area for dogs.
7. cluster sample; Booth holders in section 5 are likely to have a different opinion than booth holders in other sections about the location of their booth.
9. no; The sample represents the population.
11. yes; Only customers with a strong opinion about their experience are likely to complete the survey.
13. Not every survey that was mailed out will be returned, so it is not a systematic sample; Because households in the neighborhood can choose whether or not to return the survey, the sample is a self-selected sample.
15. *Sample answer:* Assign each student in the school a different integer from 1 to 1225. Generate 250 unique random integers from 1 to 1225 using the random number function in a spreadsheet program. Choose the 250 students who correspond to the 250 integers generated.
17. simulation
19. observational study
21. encourages a yes response; *Sample answer:* Reword the question, for example: Should the budget of our city be cut?
23. Respondents may be unwilling to answer truthfully when this question is asked by a child; *Sample answer:* Provide a method for the respondents to answer anonymously.
25. no; Responses to the question will accurately reflect the opinions of those being surveyed.
27. yes; Visitors are unlikely to admit to a police officer that they do not wear their seatbelt.
29. a. *Sample answer:* The researcher did not take into account previous heart conditions.
    b. *Sample answer:* Divide the population into groups based on past heart conditions and whether or not they take fiber supplements. Select a random sample from each group.
31. self-selected sample and convenience sample; In a self-selected sample, only people with strong opinions are likely to respond. In a convenience sample, parts of the population have no chance of being selected for the survey.
33. a. self-selected sample
    b. people who spend a lot of time on the Internet and visit that particular site; The survey is probably biased.
35. *Sample answer:* Was the customer service team member knowledgeable? Was the customer service team member friendly? Did the customer service team member address your problem?

9.3 Review & Refresh

36. parameter; The median number of years of experience of every teacher at the school was calculated.

37. 4^7 or 16,384

38. $\frac{\sqrt[3]{18}}{18}$

39. 4

40. 3

41. 0.1587

42. 0.8185

43. $\log_2 4 + \log_2 x - \log_2 y$

44. $\ln x + 6 \ln y$

45. convenience sample

46. about 26.0%

47.

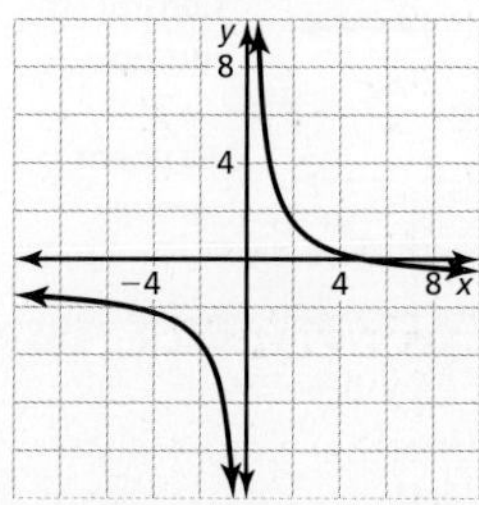

domain: all real numbers except $x = 0$; range: all real numbers except $y = -1$

48. -8

49. 9

50. $\frac{9}{22}$, or about 40.9%

9.4 Practice

1. The study is a randomized comparative experiment; The treatment is the drug for insomnia. The treatment group is the individuals who received the drug. The control group is the individuals who received the placebo.

3. The individuals who do not use either of the conditioners were not monitored; The control group is the individuals who use the regular conditioner.

5. observational study; *Sample answer:* Randomly choose one group of individuals who smoke. Then randomly choose one group of individuals who do not smoke. Find the body mass index of the individuals in each group.

7. experiment; *Sample answer:* Randomly select the same number of strawberry plants to be put in each of two groups. Use the new fertilizer on the plants in one group, and use the regular fertilizer on plants in the other group. Keep all other variables constant and record the weight of the fruit produced by each plant.

9. **a.** *Sample answer:* Because the heart rates are monitored for two different types of exercise, the groups cannot be compared. Running on a treadmill may have a different effect on heart rate than lifting weights; Check the heart rates of all the athletes after the same type of exercise.

b. There appear to be no potential problems.

11. no; Your friend would have to perform an observational study, and an observational study can show correlation, but not causality.

13. D

15. *Sample answer:* Randomly select 50 students and ask if they play video games for an average of at least one hour per day and ask for their current school year grade point average. This is an observational study intended to find out if there is a correlation between the time spent playing video games and grades.

9.4 Review & Refresh

16. It encourages a yes response; *Sample answer:* Reword the question, for example: Should the manufacturer update its cell phone model?

17.

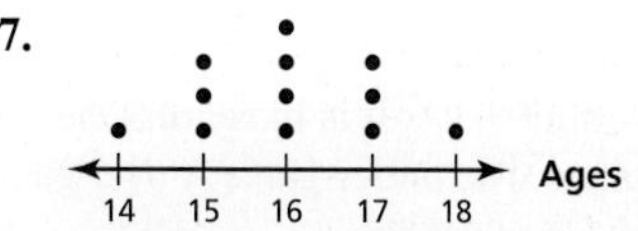

bell-shaped and symmetric

18. 6 strikes

19. experiment; *Sample answer:* Randomly select and divide teenagers with acne into two groups. One group receives the acne treatment and one group receives the placebo. After 6 months, check whether the acne has improved in each group.

20. 2

21. exponential decay

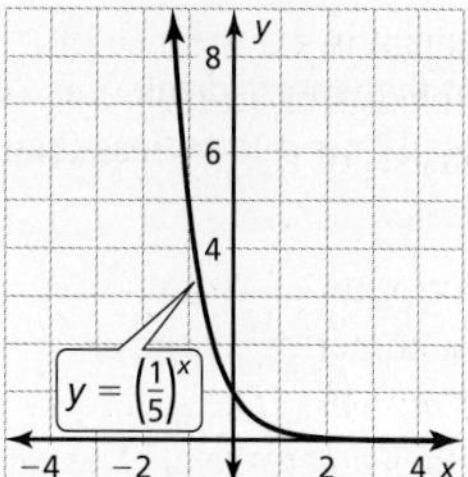

22. exponential growth

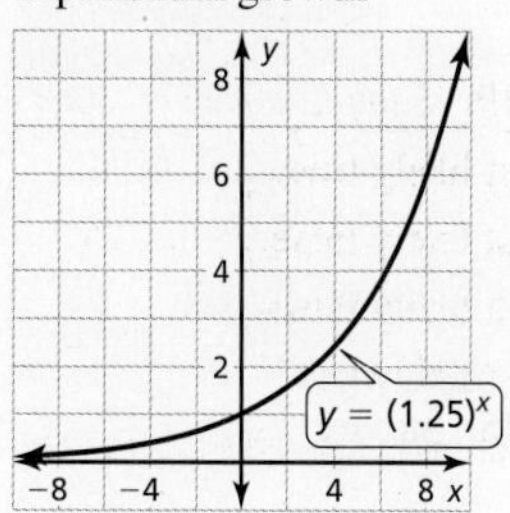

23. $\frac{3}{5}$, or 60%

9.5 Practice

1. about 65.4

3. **a.** about 0.43

b. about 0.23

5. **a.** yes; The first 2 surveys show more than the 66.7% of votes needed to override the veto.

b. no; As the sample size increases, the percent of votes approaches 55.1%, which is not enough to override the veto.

7. *Sample answer:* very confident; The margin of error for the survey is about 0.141, so it is likely that the exact percent of students who want their class trip to take place at an amusement park is between 0.499 and 0.781.

9. **a.** The claim is probably not accurate.

b. The claim is probably accurate.

c. *Sample answer:* 0.11 to 0.25

11. 0.16; 95% of the sample proportions should be within 0.16 of the population proportion, 0.17.

13. about $\pm 6.2\%$

15. about $\pm 2.2\%$

17. about $\pm 1.7\%$

19. between 77.7% and 84.3%

21. decreases; As n increases, the denominator of the formula, Margin of error $= \pm\frac{1}{\sqrt{n}}$, increases, so the expression decreases.

23. about 453 residents

25. The margin of error is 2%, not 0.02%; It is likely that the exact percent of all consumers who prefer game A over game B is between 59% and 63%.

27. no; A sample size of 1 would have a margin of error of 100%.

29. **a.** 500 voters

b. about $\pm 4.5\%$

c. candidate A: between 42.5% and 51.5%, candidate B: between 48.5% and 57.5%

d. no; 273 voters

31. **a.** about ± 0.492; It is likely that the population mean is within 0.492 of the sample mean, 52.

b. between 51.508 and 52.492

33. more than 2500; To be confident that sports drink X is preferred, the margin of error would need to be less than 2%.

9.5 Review & Refresh

34. $y = \log x + 3$

35. $y = \log_2(x + 5)$

36. $y = e^x - 5$

37. $y = 6^{x+1}$

38. arithmetic; $a_n = -3n + 20$

39. geometric; $a_n = 3(2)^{n-1}$

40. between 37.7% and 44.3%

41. $\frac{2x + 2}{x - 2}$, $x \neq 0, x \neq 4, x \neq 6$

42. $\frac{-4x + 44}{x^2 - x - 20}$

43. **a.** about 65.7%

b. about 45.0%

44. observational study

45. survey

46. 105 cm^2

47. The study is not a randomized comparative experiment. The people were not randomly assigned to a control group and a treatment group. The conclusion that using a Himalayan salt rock lamp for at least 1 hour each day reduced stress levels may not be valid.

48.

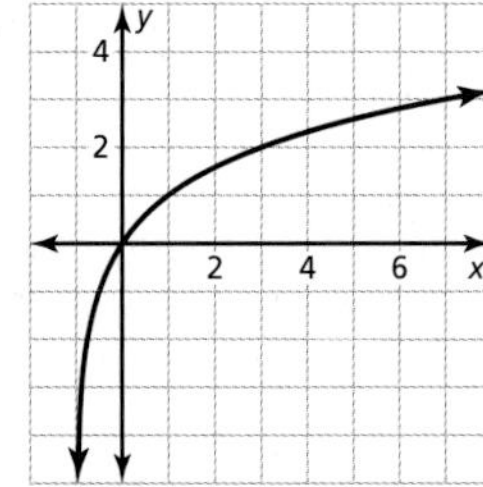

49.

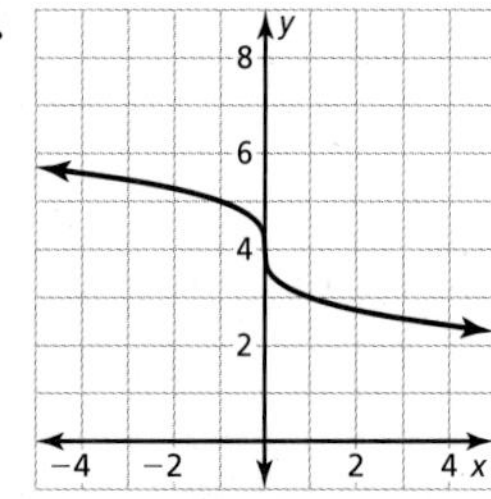

50.

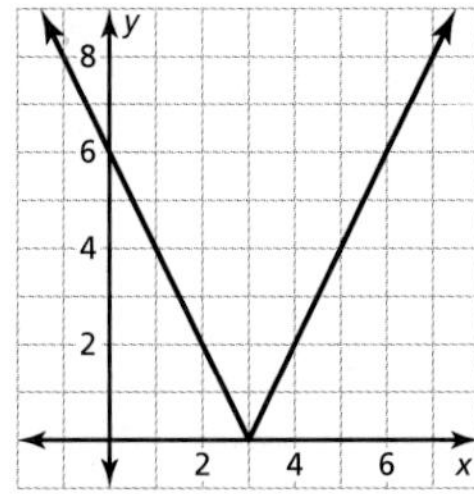

51.

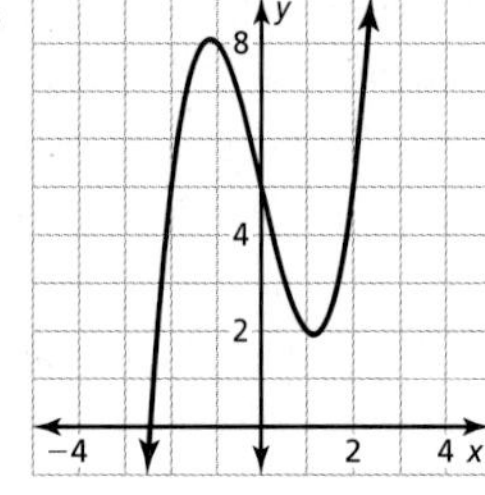

52. population: every adult in the United States ages 18 and over; sample: 1031 adults in the United States ages 18 and over; The sample consists of 237 adults in the United States ages 18 and over who would trust a robot powered by artificial intelligence to perform surgery and 794 who would not.

9.6 Practice

1. **a.** -5.875

b.

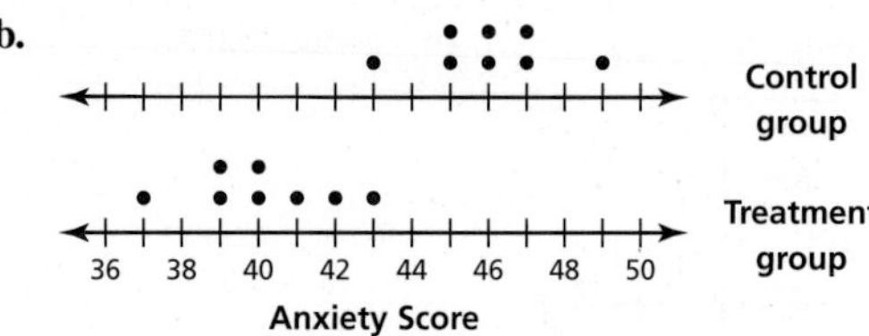

c. The music therapy may be effective in reducing anxiety scores of college students.

3. *Sample answer:* -1.75

5. The experimental difference -5.875 lies on the left tail, beyond all the resampling differences. So, the experimental difference is significant and the hypothesis is most likely false. Yes, music therapy decreases anxiety scores.

7. yes; As the number of samplings increase, the individual values should end up in each group approximately the same number of times, so the positive and negative differences in the means should balance out to 0.

9. 12,870; The number of combinations of 16 items in groups of 8 amounts to 12,870.

11. *Sample answer:* An experimental difference k could fall outside the range of probable sampling differences, for instance, outside the middle 90%, which makes it significant, or it could fall inside that range for a different experiment and be insignificant.

9.6 Review & Refresh

13. 15.2

14. observational study; Randomly choose one group of adults who have used smartphones with larger screens for the past year and one group who have used smartphones with smaller screens. Perform vision tests on each group.

15. no; The sample represents the population.

16. 0.8

17.

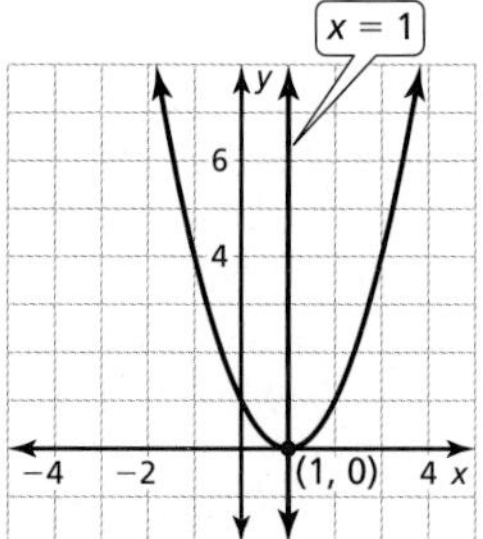

18. The experimental difference 9 lies on the right tail, inside the middle 90% of the resampling differences. So, the experimental difference is significant and the hypothesis is most likely false. Yes, the premium oil increases the lifespan of the engine.

19. $\frac{1}{8z^6}$

20. $x = 4$

Chapter 9 Review

1. 0.0015
2. no; Only 84% of drivers spend 10 minutes or less waiting.
3. 0.0808
4. population: all U.S. motorists, sample: the 1000 drivers surveyed
5. statistic; The mean was calculated from a sample.
6. The activist's claim is most likely true.
7. **a.** systematic sample
   b. self-selected sample
   c. convenience sample
   d. stratified sample
8. observational study
9. It encourages a yes response; *Sample answer:* Reword the question, for example: Should the city replace the police cars it is currently using?
10. The study is a randomized comparative experiment; The treatment is using the new design of the car wash. The treatment group is the individuals who use the new design of the car wash. The control group is the individuals who use the old design of the car wash.
11. experiment; *Sample answer:* Randomly select the same number of customers to give each type of bread to. Record how many customers from each group return.
12. *Sample answer:* The volunteers may not be representative of the population; Randomly select from members of the population for the study.
13. no; As the sample size increases, the percent of votes approaches 46.8%, which is not enough to win.
14. between 37.8% and 44.2%
15. **a.** -3.875
    b. The experimental difference -3.875 lies on the left tail, beyond the middle 99% of the resampling differences. So, the experimental difference is significant and the hypothesis is most likely false.

Chapter 9 Mathematical Practices (Chapter Review)

1. *Sample answer:* The experiments described should fit the definition of a randomized comparative experiment.
2. *Sample answer:* The probability was calculated using assumptions that are only true for a normal distribution.

Chapter 9 Practice Test

1. parameter; The mean is based on all the students in high school.
2. survey
3. 0.6826
4. 0.2743
5. The subjects were not randomly divided into the treatment group and the control group; Randomly assign 15 subjects to each group.
6. **a.** population: all U.S. adults, sample: the 1600 adults surveyed; The sample includes 1296 adults who said they purchased a product online and 304 adults who said they did not.
   b. between 78.5% and 83.5%
7. 97.5%
8. **a.** 5.5
   b. The experimental difference 5.5 lies on the right tail, beyond the middle 90% of the resampling differences. So, the experimental difference is significant and the hypothesis is most likely false.

Chapter 9 College and Career Readiness

1. A, B, D
2. $m\angle A = 54°, m\angle B = 88°, m\angle C = 38°$
3. 42.8% and 47.2%; 26.8% and 31.2%; 15.8% and 20.2%; 5.8% and 10.2%
4. C, F
5.

Function	Is the inverse a function?	Inverse
$f(x) = 5x - 4$	yes	$f^{-1}(x) = \frac{x+4}{5}$
$f(x) = 3 \ln x + 2$	yes	$f^{-1}(x) = e^{(x-2)/3}$
$f(x) = \left(\frac{1}{x}\right)^2$	no	$f^{-1}(x) = \pm\frac{\sqrt{x}}{x}$
$f(x) = \sqrt[3]{x-2}$	yes	$f^{-1}(x) = x^3 + 2$

6. B
7. 0.3085, or 30.85%
8. A, D
9. **a.** no
   b. yes

Chapter 10

Chapter 10 Prepare

1. $x = 24$
2. $x = 1$
3. $x = 6$
4. $x = 4$
5. $x = -0.75$
6. $x = \frac{1}{6}$
7. 13 m
8. 24 ft
9. $\frac{2}{5}$ yd
10. $c^2 = a^2 + b^2$
    $d^2 = (x_2 - x_1)^2 + (y_2 - y_1)^2$
    $d = \pm\sqrt{(x_2 - x_1)^2 + (y_2 - y_1)^2}$
    Because $d \geq 0$, $d = \sqrt{(x_2 - x_1)^2 + (y_2 - y_1)^2}$.

10.1 Practice

1. $\sin \theta = \frac{4}{5}, \cos \theta = \frac{3}{5}, \tan \theta = \frac{4}{3},$
   $\csc \theta = \frac{5}{4}, \sec \theta = \frac{5}{3}, \cot \theta = \frac{3}{4}$
3. $\sin \theta = \frac{5}{7}, \cos \theta = \frac{2\sqrt{6}}{7},$
   $\tan \theta = \frac{5\sqrt{6}}{12}, \csc \theta = \frac{7}{5},$
   $\sec \theta = \frac{7\sqrt{6}}{12}, \cot \theta = \frac{2\sqrt{6}}{5}$

5. $\sin\theta = \frac{2\sqrt{14}}{9}$, $\cos\theta = \frac{5}{9}$, $\tan\theta = \frac{2\sqrt{14}}{5}$, $\csc\theta = \frac{9\sqrt{14}}{28}$, $\sec\theta = \frac{9}{5}$, $\cot\theta = \frac{5\sqrt{14}}{28}$

7. C

9. $\cos\theta = \frac{6\sqrt{2}}{11}$, $\tan\theta = \frac{7\sqrt{2}}{12}$, $\csc\theta = \frac{11}{7}$, $\sec\theta = \frac{11\sqrt{2}}{12}$, $\cot\theta = \frac{6\sqrt{2}}{7}$

11. $\sin\theta = \frac{\sqrt{119}}{12}$, $\tan\theta = \frac{\sqrt{119}}{5}$, $\csc\theta = \frac{12\sqrt{119}}{119}$, $\sec\theta = \frac{12}{5}$, $\cot\theta = \frac{5\sqrt{119}}{119}$

13. $\sin\theta = \frac{7\sqrt{85}}{85}$, $\cos\theta = \frac{6\sqrt{85}}{85}$, $\csc\theta = \frac{\sqrt{85}}{7}$, $\sec\theta = \frac{\sqrt{85}}{6}$, $\cot\theta = \frac{6}{7}$

15. The adjacent side was used instead of the opposite; $\sin\theta = \frac{\text{opp}}{\text{hyp}} = \frac{8}{17}$

17. $x = 4.5$
19. $x = 6$
21. $x = 8$
23. 0.97
25. 1.17
27. 9.51
29. $A = 54°, b \approx 16.71, c \approx 28.43$
31. $B = 35°, b \approx 11.90, c \approx 20.75$
33. $B = 47°, a \approx 28.91, c \approx 42.39$
35. $A = 18°, a \approx 3.96, b \approx 12.17$
37. about 514 m
39. about 427 m
41. yes; The triangle must be a 45-45-90 triangle because both acute angles would be the same and have the same cosine value.
43. The angles are equal.
45. about 5731 ft
47. a. about 22,818 mi
    b. about 7263 mi
49. about 39,688 ft; Use the tangent function to find the horizontal distance, $x + y$, from the airplane to the second town to be about 93,301 feet. Use the tangent function to find the horizontal distance x from the airplane to the first town to be about 53,613 feet. Subtract 53,613 feet to find the distance between the two towns.

10.1 Review & Refresh

51. $C \approx 37.7$ cm, $A \approx 113.1$ cm^2
52. $C \approx 69.1$ in., $A \approx 380.1$ in.^{2}
53. about 5
54.
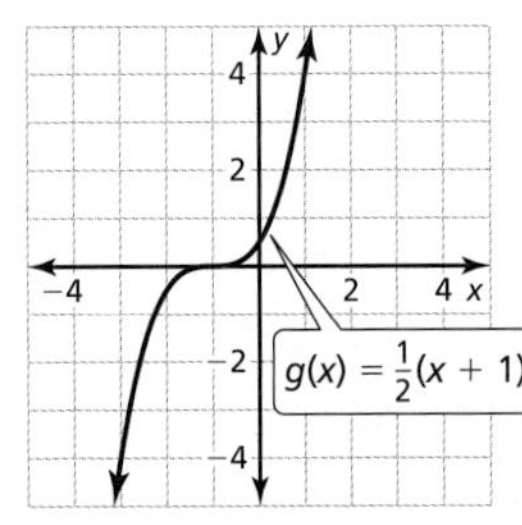

55.
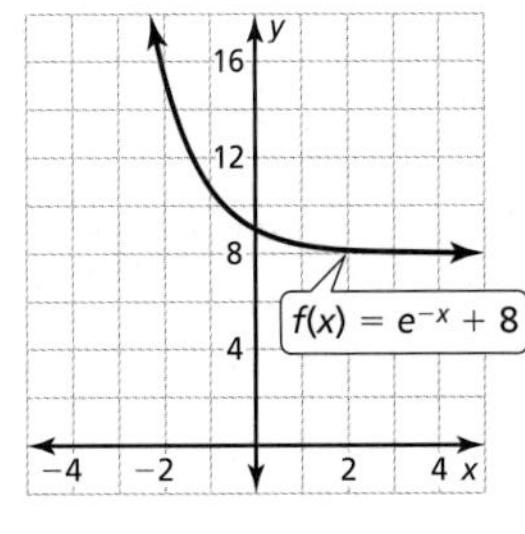

56.
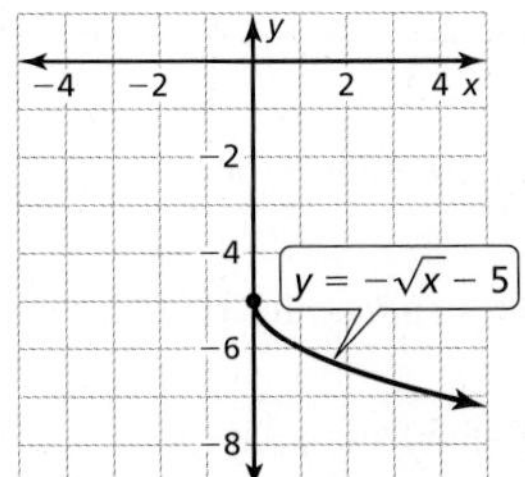

57.
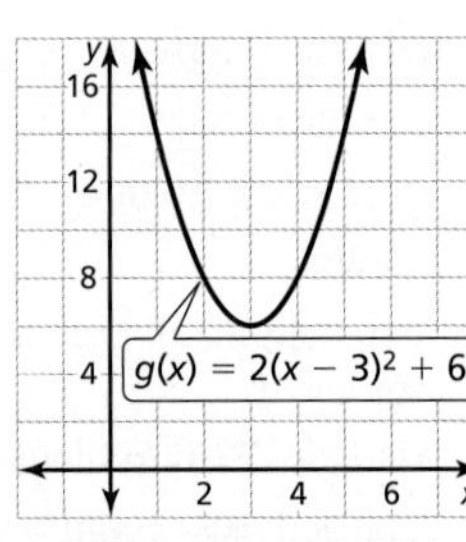

58. experiment; *Sample answer:* Randomly select and divide people into two groups. Ask all of the people in one group to eat the same amount of cheese right before bed. In the morning, ask each person in both groups to estimate the amount of time it took them to fall asleep. Make sure other variables such as the amount of sleep the previous night and bedtime are the same in both groups.
59. $x = 4\sqrt{3}$
60. a. 0.0625
    b.
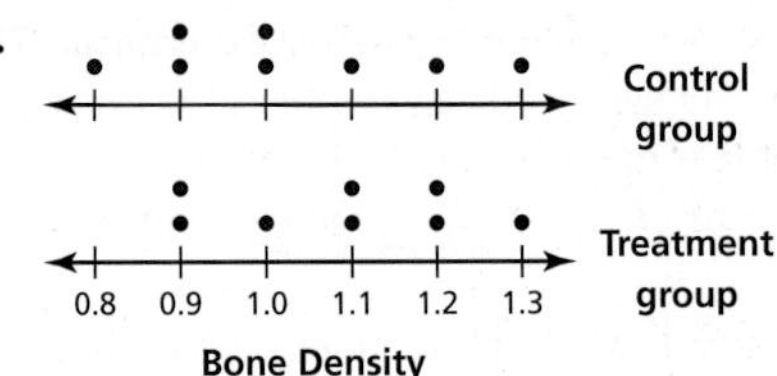

The vitamin supplement has no effect on bone density.

10.2 Practice

1.

110°

3.
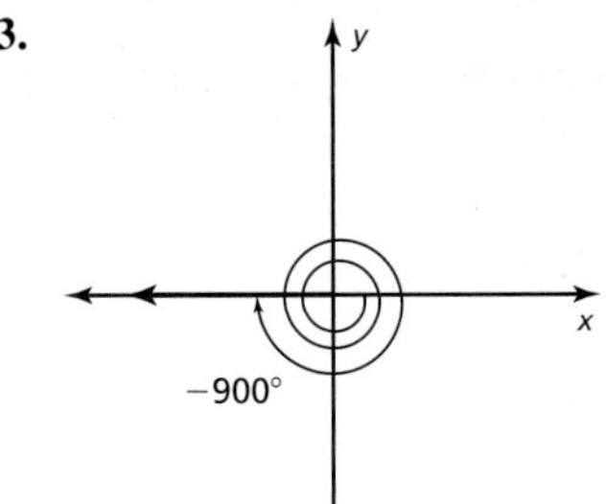

5. *Sample answer:* 430°, −290°
7. *Sample answer:* 235°, −485°
9. $\frac{2\pi}{9}$
11. $-\frac{13\pi}{9}$
13. 20°
15. about −286.5°
17. $\frac{15\pi}{4}$; $-\frac{\pi}{4}$; *Sample answer:* 315° is equivalent to $\frac{7\pi}{4}$ radians, and $\frac{7\pi}{4} + 2\pi = \frac{15\pi}{4}$ and $\frac{7\pi}{4} - 2\pi = -\frac{\pi}{4}$.
19. B
21. A
23. about 15.7 yd, about 78.5 yd^2

25. The arc length should have π in the simplified answers and the units are feet; $s = 9\left(\frac{\pi}{3}\right) = 3\pi$ ft

27. 324,000°, or 1800π **29.** $\frac{\pi}{2}$

31. $\frac{75\pi}{72}$ mi^2 **33.** $\frac{19\pi}{18}$ mi

35. yes; When the arc length is equal to the radius, the equation $s = r\theta$ shows that $\theta = 1$ and $A = \frac{1}{2}r^2\theta$ is equivalent to $A = \frac{s^2}{2}$ for $r = s$ and $\theta = 1$.

37. a. 70° 33′

b. 110.76°

c. 0.7 rad

10.2 Review & Refresh

39. $\frac{10\pi}{9}$

40. $\sin\theta = \frac{\sqrt{3}}{2}$, $\cos\theta = \frac{1}{2}$, $\tan\theta = \sqrt{3}$, $\csc\theta = \frac{2\sqrt{3}}{3}$, $\sec\theta = 2$, $\cot\theta = \frac{\sqrt{3}}{3}$

41. $\geq$ **42.** $\pm 3.6\%$

43. cubic; $f(x) = \frac{1}{6}x^3 + \frac{1}{2}x^2 + \frac{16}{3}x$

44. direct variation **45.** $\log_5 1 = 0$

46. $\frac{1}{6}$, or about 16.7%

47. *Sample answer:* $f(x) = x^3 - 3x^2 - 2x + 6$

48. $5 + 10i$ **49.** $x = 16$

50. $x = 1$

10.3 Practice

1. $\sin\theta = -\frac{3}{5}$, $\cos\theta = \frac{4}{5}$, $\tan\theta = -\frac{3}{4}$, $\csc\theta = -\frac{5}{3}$, $\sec\theta = \frac{5}{4}$, $\cot\theta = -\frac{4}{3}$

3. $\sin\theta = -\frac{4}{5}$, $\cos\theta = -\frac{3}{5}$, $\tan\theta = \frac{4}{3}$, $\csc\theta = -\frac{5}{4}$, $\sec\theta = -\frac{5}{3}$, $\cot\theta = \frac{3}{4}$

5. $\sin\theta = -\frac{3}{5}$, $\cos\theta = -\frac{4}{5}$, $\tan\theta = \frac{3}{4}$, $\csc\theta = -\frac{5}{3}$, $\sec\theta = -\frac{5}{4}$, $\cot\theta = \frac{4}{3}$

7. $\sin\theta = 0$, $\cos\theta = 1$, $\tan\theta = 0$, $\csc\theta =$ undefined, $\sec\theta = 1$, $\cot\theta =$ undefined

9. $\sin\theta = 1$, $\cos\theta = 0$, $\tan\theta =$ undefined, $\csc\theta = 1$, $\sec\theta =$ undefined, $\cot\theta = 0$

11. $\sin\theta = 1$, $\cos\theta = 0$, $\tan\theta =$ undefined, $\csc\theta = 1$, $\sec\theta =$ undefined, $\cot\theta = 0$

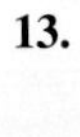
13. 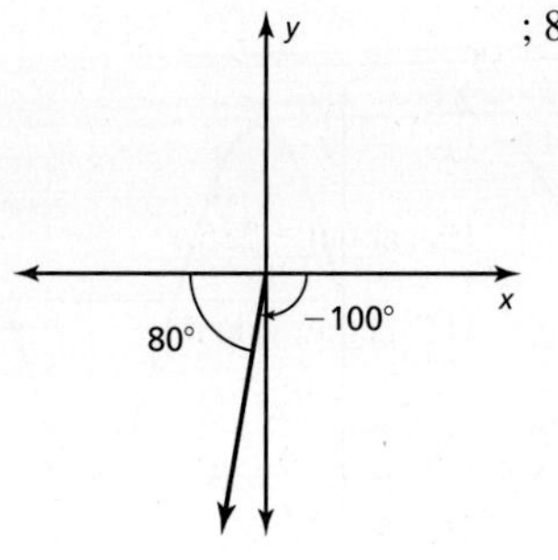

; 80°

15. 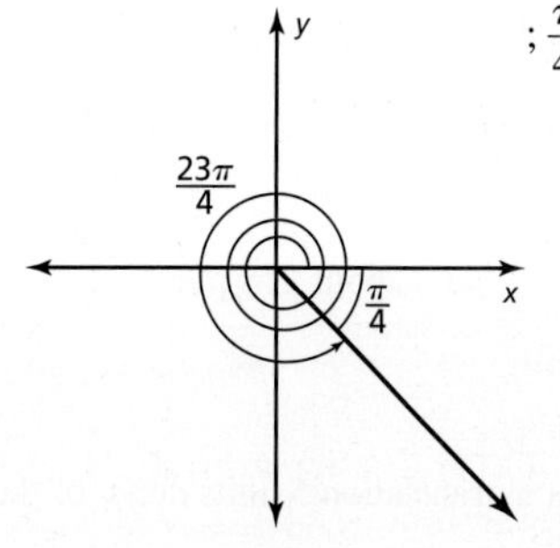

; $\frac{\pi}{4}$

17. 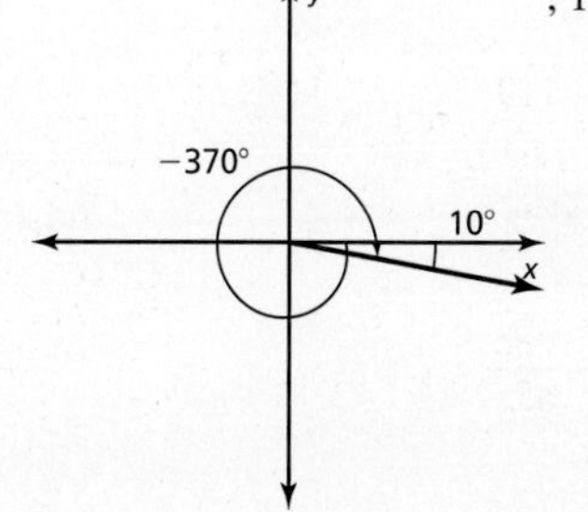

; 10°

19. The equation for tangent is $\tan\theta = \frac{y}{x}$; $\tan\theta = \frac{y}{x} = -\frac{2}{3}$

21. $\frac{\sqrt{2}}{2}$ **23.** $-\sqrt{2}$

25. $-\frac{1}{2}$ **27.** $\frac{\sqrt{2}}{2}$

29. 1 **31.** $\frac{\sqrt{2}}{2}$

33. 65 ft **35.** about 16.5 ft/sec

37. about 10.7 ft

39. a.

Angle of sprinkler, θ	Horizontal distance water travels, d
30°	16.9
35°	18.4
40°	19.2
45°	19.5
50°	19.2
55°	18.4
60°	16.9

b. 45°; Because $\frac{v^2}{32}$ is constant in this situation, the maximum distance traveled will occur when $\sin 2\theta$ is as large as possible. The maximum value of $\sin 2\theta$ occurs when $2\theta = 90°$, that is, when $\theta = 45°$.

c. The distances are the same.

41. 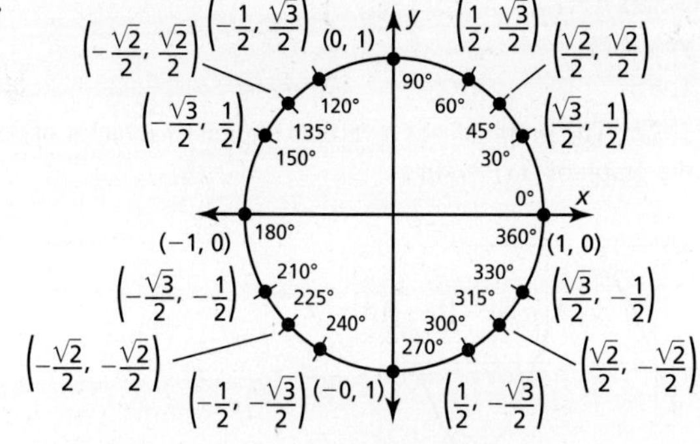

43. $\tan\theta = \dfrac{\sin\theta}{\cos\theta}$; $\sin 90° = 1$ and $\cos 90° = 0$, so $\tan 90°$ is undefined because you cannot divide by 0, but $\cot 90° = \dfrac{0}{1} = 0$.

45. $m = \tan\theta$

47. about 218 pm

49. 60°

10.3 Review & Refresh

50. The graph of g is a vertical translation 5 units down of the graph of f.

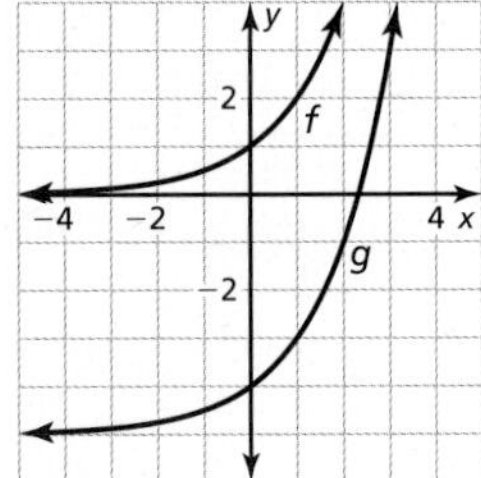

51. 21

52.

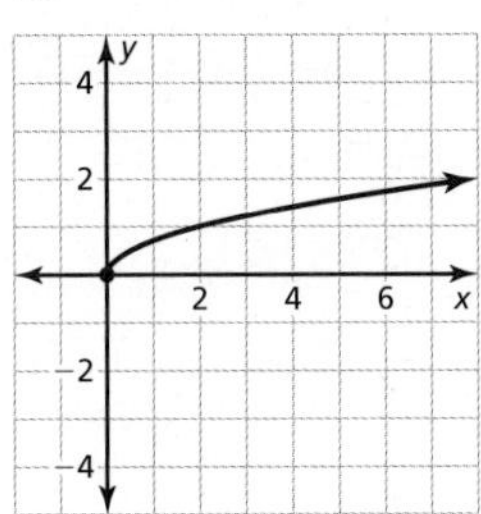

domain: $x \geq 0$; range: $y \geq 0$

53. $y = -\frac{3}{5}(x-5)^2 + 25$

54. $x = 11$

55.

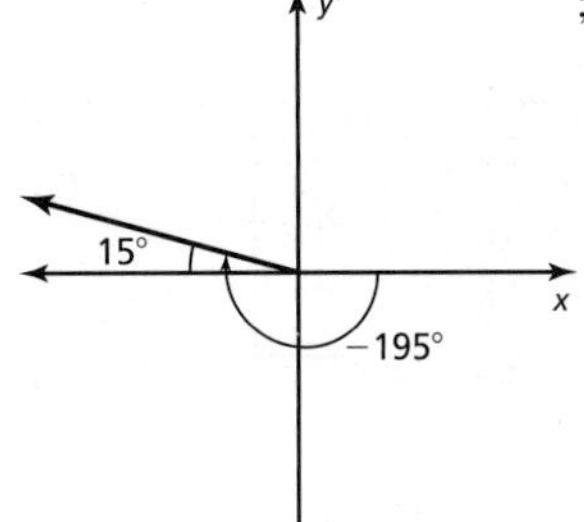

; 15°

56. $f((g(2)) = 4$

57. $y = \frac{1}{4}(x-1)^2 + 2$

58. $\dfrac{11\pi}{3}$; $-\dfrac{\pi}{3}$; *Sample answer:* 300° is equivalent to $\dfrac{5\pi}{3}$, and $\dfrac{5\pi}{3} + 2\pi = \dfrac{11\pi}{3}$ and $\dfrac{5\pi}{3} - 2\pi = -\dfrac{\pi}{3}$.

59. $2x + 1$

60. $3, x \neq 2$

10.4 Practice

1. yes; 2

3. no

5. $1, 6\pi$

7. $4, \pi$

9. $3, 2\pi$; The graph of g is a vertical stretch by a factor of 3 of the graph of $f(x) = \sin x$.

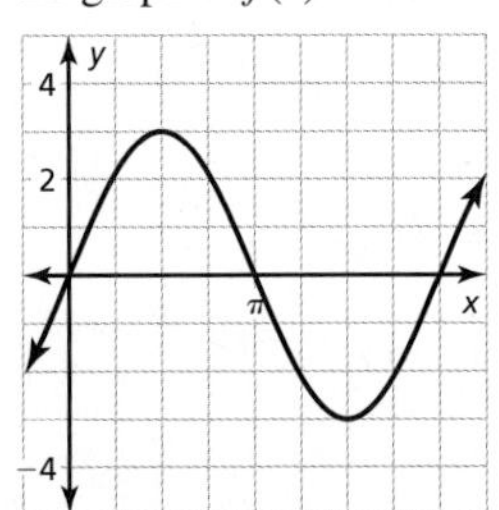

11. $1, \dfrac{2\pi}{3}$; The graph of g is a horizontal shrink by a factor of $\dfrac{1}{3}$ of the graph of $f(x) = \cos x$.

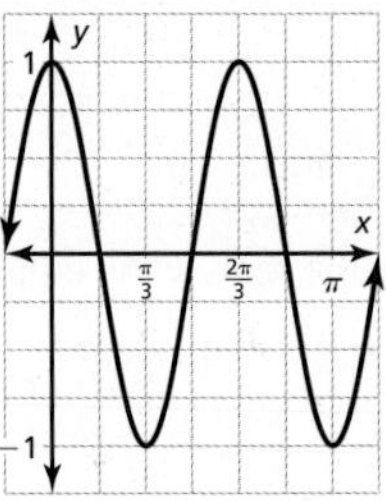

13. 1, 1; The graph of g is a horizontal shrink by a factor of $\dfrac{1}{2\pi}$ of the graph of $f(x) = \sin x$.

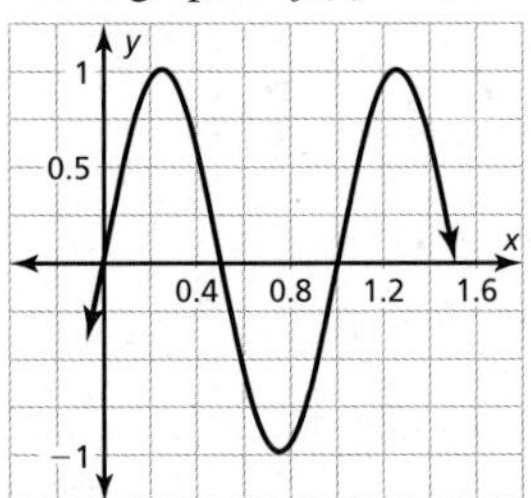

15. $\dfrac{1}{3}, \dfrac{\pi}{2}$; The graph of g is a horizontal shrink by a factor of $\dfrac{1}{4}$ and a vertical shrink by a factor of $\dfrac{1}{3}$ of the graph of $f(x) = \cos x$.

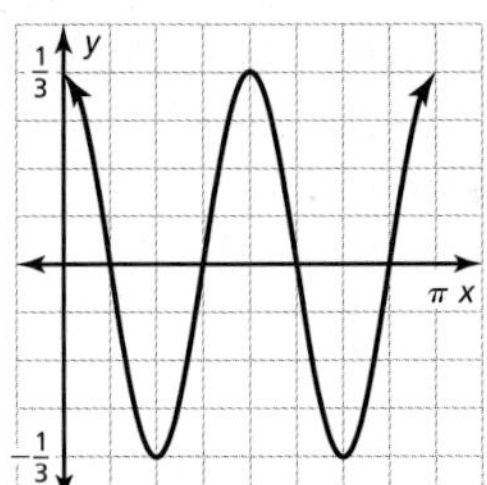

17. B, D

19. The period is $\frac{1}{4}$ and represents the amount of time, in seconds, that it takes for the pendulum to go back and forth and return to the same position. The amplitude is 4 and represents the maximum distance, in inches, the pendulum will be from its resting position.

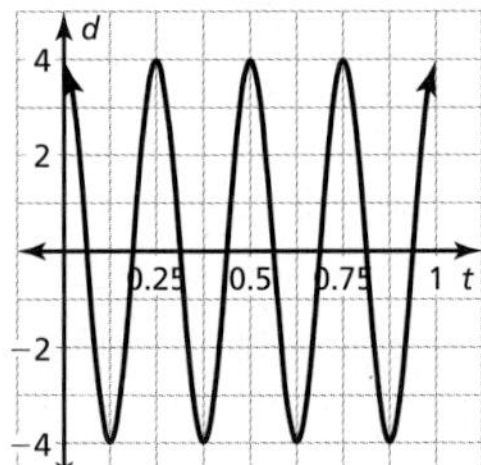

21.

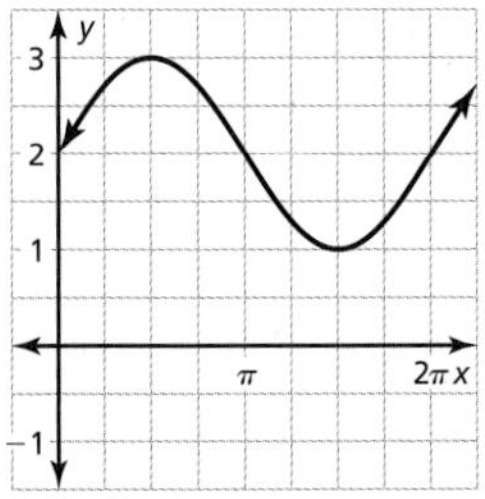

23.

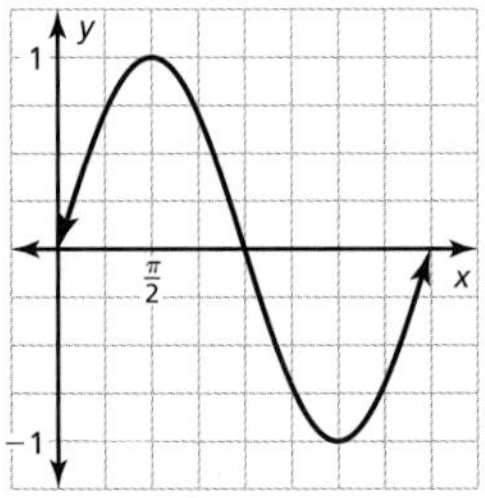

25. 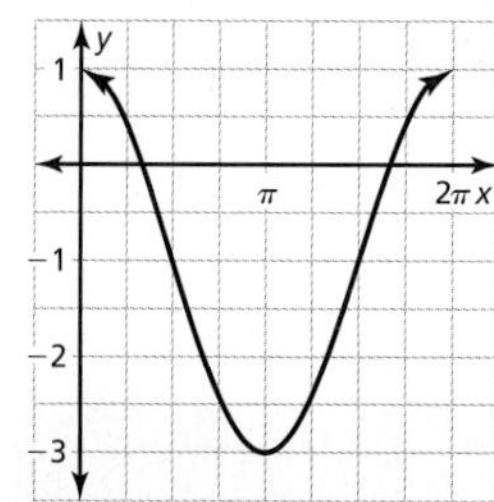

27. 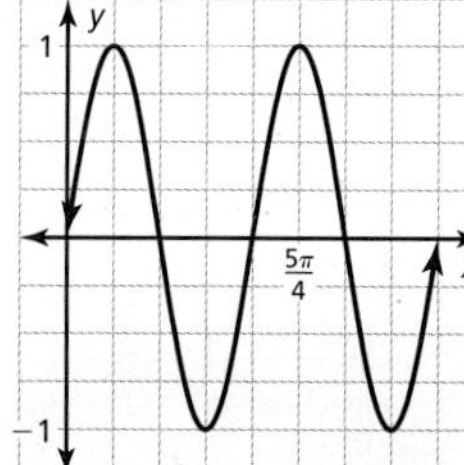

29. 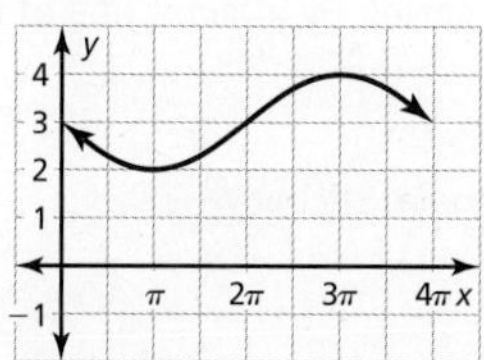

31. The value of a was substituted instead of the value of b; $\dfrac{2\pi}{|b|} = \dfrac{2\pi}{|4|} = \dfrac{\pi}{2}$

33. 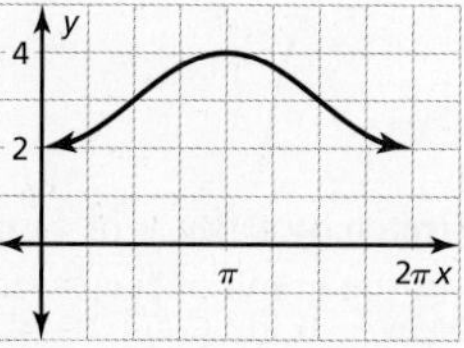

35. 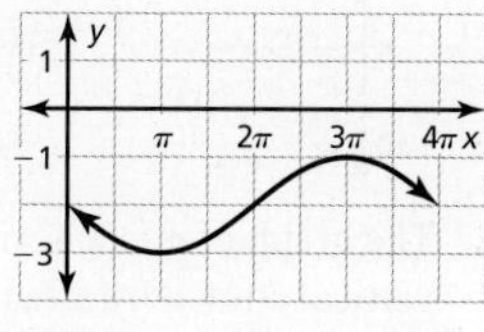

37. 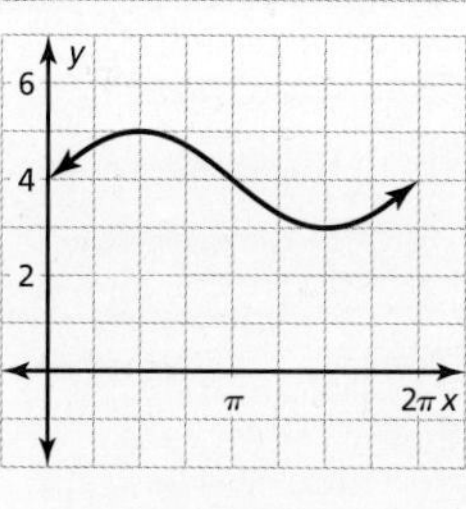

39. 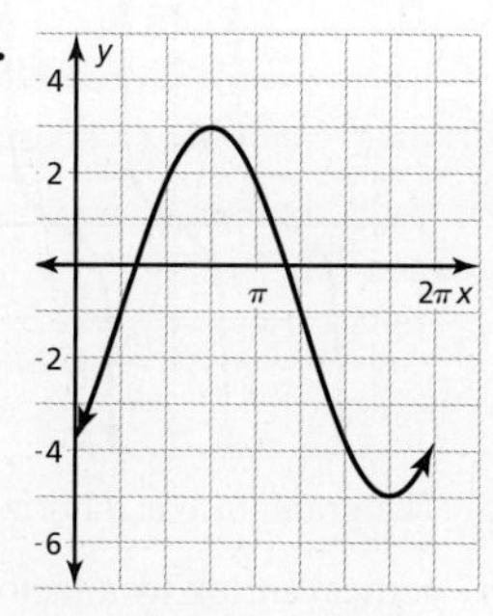

41. **a.** B; The graph of sine has been translated 3 units up.
b. C; The graph of cosine has been translated 3 units down.
c. A; The graph of sine has been shrunk horizontally by a factor of $\frac{1}{2}$ then translated $\frac{\pi}{2}$ units right.
d. D; The graph of cosine has been shrunk horizontally by a factor of $\frac{1}{2}$ then translated $\frac{\pi}{2}$ units right.

43. The graph of g is a vertical stretch by a factor of 2, followed by a translation $\frac{\pi}{2}$ units right and 1 unit up of the graph of f.

45. The graph of g is a horizontal shrink by a factor of $\frac{1}{3}$, followed by a translation 3π units left and 5 units down of the graph of f.

47. $g(x) = 3 \sin(x - \pi) + 2$

49. $g(x) = -\frac{1}{3} \cos \pi x - 1$

51. **a.** 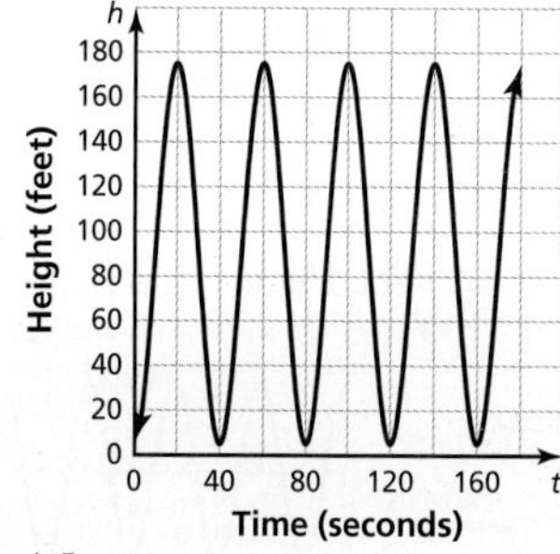

b. 4.5
c. 175 ft, 5 ft

53. 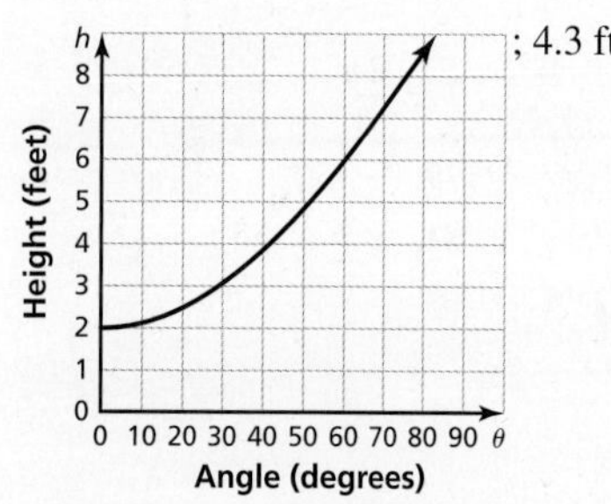

; 4.3 ft

55. **a.** $\dfrac{2}{\pi}$
b. 0
c. $-\dfrac{4}{\pi}$

57. 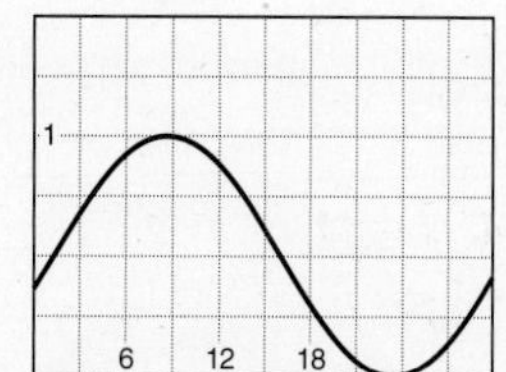

Days 9, 39, 68, 98, 127, 157, 186, 216, 245, 275, 304, 334, 363; $f(t) = 1$ when $t = 8.675, 38.175, 97.175, 126.675, 156.175, 185.675, 215.175, 244.675, 274.175, 303.675, 333.175$, and 362.675.

59. no; The value of a indicates a vertical stretch or a vertical shrink and changes the amplitude of the graph. It does not affect the x-intercepts of the function. The value of b indicates a horizontal stretch of a horizontal shrink and changes the period of the graph, which is the horizontal length of each cycle. So, the value of b affects the x-intercepts of the function.

61. *Sample answer:* The graph of $g(x) = \cos x$ is a translation $\frac{\pi}{2}$ units to the right of the graph of $f(x) = \sin x$.

63. 80 beats per minute; The period is $\frac{3}{4}$, so there is one heartbeat every $\frac{3}{4}$ second and $\dfrac{1 \text{ beat}}{\frac{3}{4} \cancel{\text{sec}}} \cdot \dfrac{60 \cancel{\text{sec}}}{1 \text{ min}} = 80$ beats/min.

10.4 Review & Refresh

64. $x - 2, x \neq -3$

65. $x, x \neq -4, 6$

66. $\dfrac{(x-5)(x+1)}{(x+5)(x-1)}$

67. $\dfrac{x+4}{x+5}, x \neq 4$

68. $\sin \theta = \dfrac{\sqrt{3}}{2}, \cos \theta = \dfrac{1}{2}, \tan \theta = \sqrt{3}, \csc \theta = \dfrac{2\sqrt{3}}{3},$
$\sec \theta = 2, \cot \theta = \dfrac{\sqrt{3}}{3}$

69. $-2x^4 + 15x^3 - 23x^2 + 60x - 32$

70. $4x^3 + 3x^2 - 8x - 15$ **71.** $3x^3 - 32x^2 + 61x + 24$

72. $5x^4 + 13x^3 - 8x^2 - 10x + 1$

73. $y = 5(1.8)^x$; about 1,785,000 visitors

74.

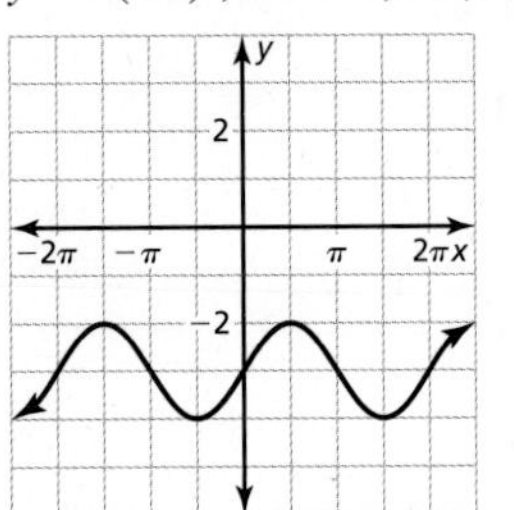

75.

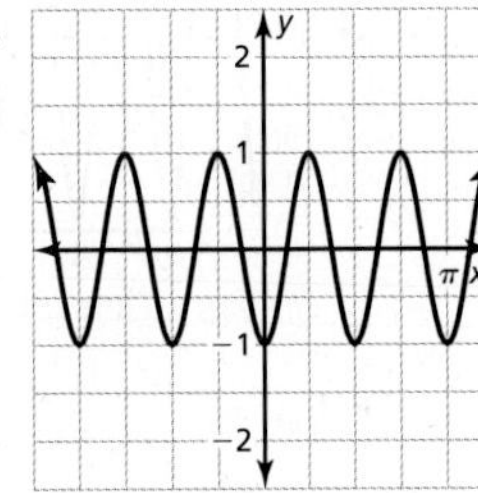

76. $-\frac{\pi}{3}$ **77.** $\frac{2\pi}{5}$

78. 54° **79.** −150°

80. 0.3 **81.** $x = \frac{1}{5}$ and $x = \frac{1}{3}$

82.

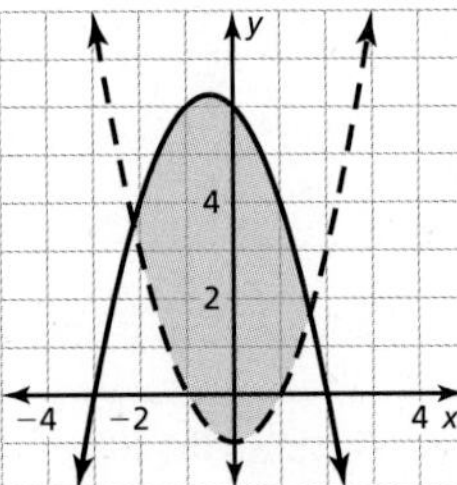

83.

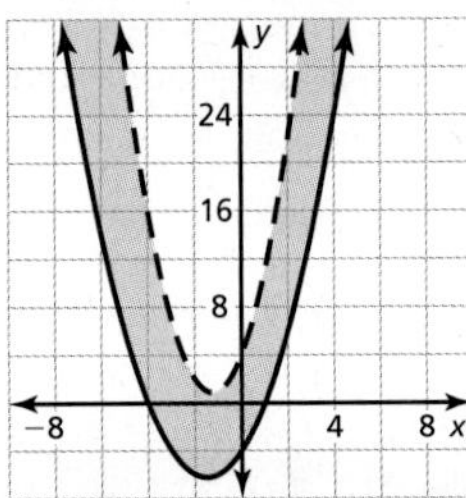

84. The question encourages a yes response because the question is asked by a doctor; *Sample answer:* Have an unaffiliated organization conduct the survey.

85. $\sin\theta = -\frac{3\sqrt{10}}{10}$, $\cos\theta = -\frac{\sqrt{10}}{10}$,

$\tan\theta = 3$, $\csc\theta = -\frac{\sqrt{10}}{3}$,

$\sec\theta = -\sqrt{10}$, $\cot\theta = \frac{1}{3}$

86. $(f + g)(x) = 3\sqrt{x}$, domain: $x \geq 0$; $(f - g)(x) = 7\sqrt{x}$, domain: $x \geq 0$; 9; 21

10.5 Practice

1.

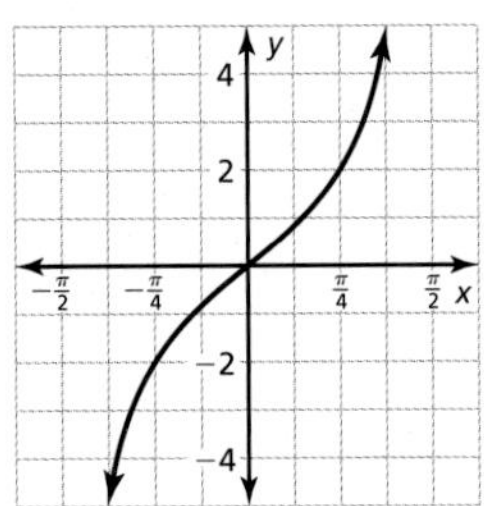

The graph of g is a vertical stretch by a factor of 2 of the graph of $f(x) = \tan x$.

3.

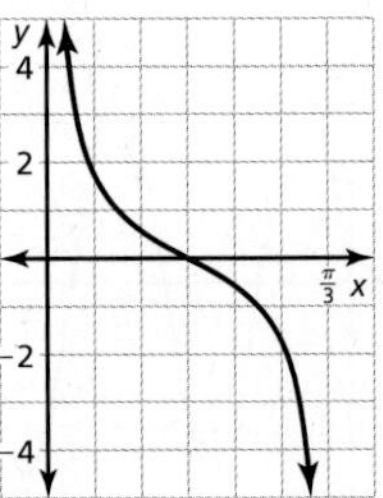

The graph of g is a horizontal shrink by a factor of $\frac{1}{3}$ of the graph of $f(x) = \cot x$.

5.

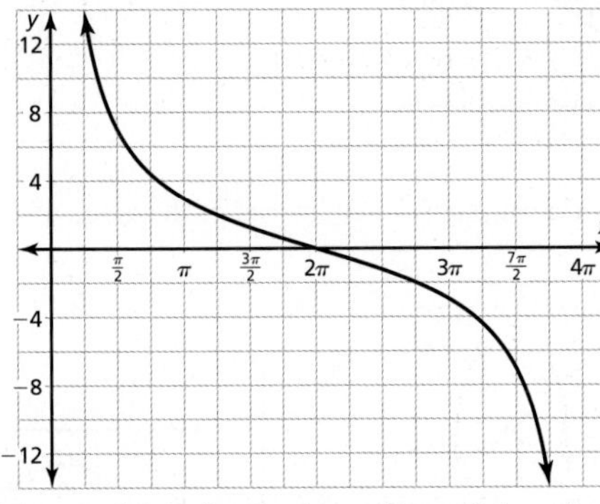

The graph of g is a horizontal stretch by a factor of 4 and a vertical stretch by a factor of 3 of the graph of $f(x) = \cot x$.

7.

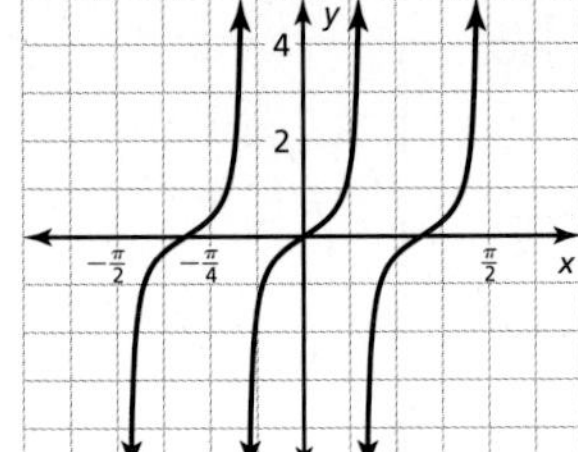

The graph of g is a horizontal shrink by a factor of $\frac{1}{\pi}$ and a vertical shrink by a factor of $\frac{1}{2}$ of the graph of $f(x) = \tan x$.

9. To find the period, use the expression $\frac{\pi}{|b|}$;

Period: $\frac{\pi}{|b|} = \frac{\pi}{3}$

11.

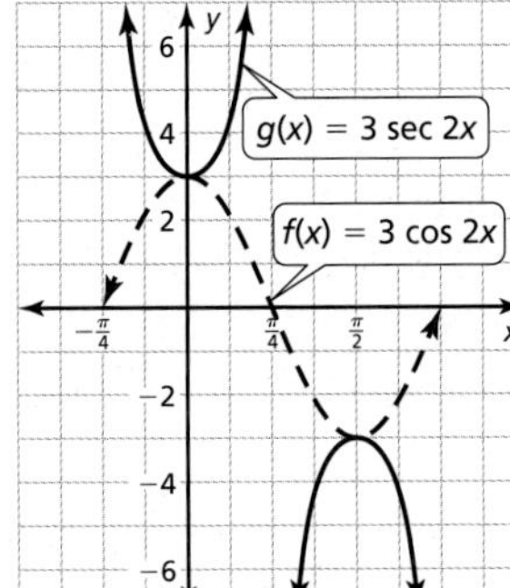

13. 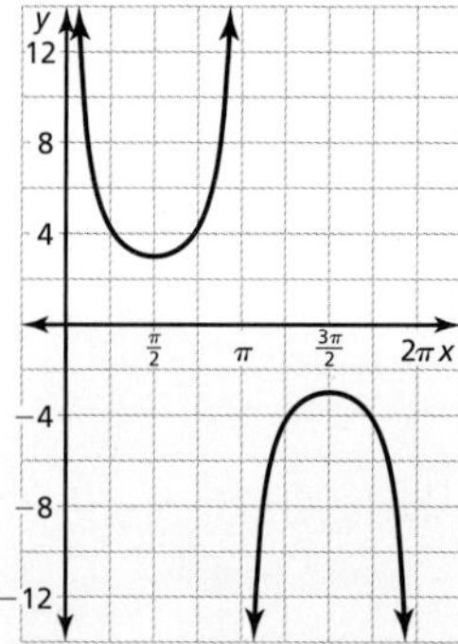

The graph of g is a vertical stretch by a factor of 3 of the graph of $f(x) = \csc x$.

15. 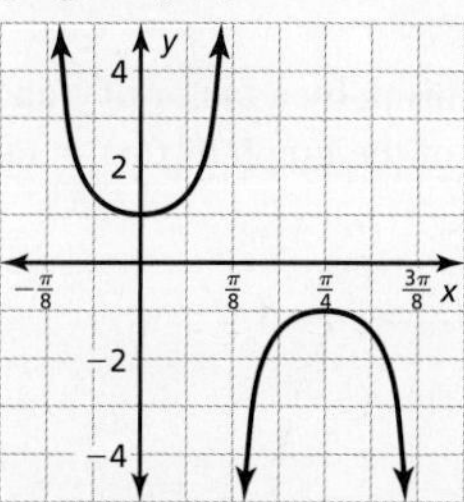

The graph of g is a horizontal shrink by a factor of $\frac{1}{4}$ of the graph of $f(x) = \sec x$.

17. 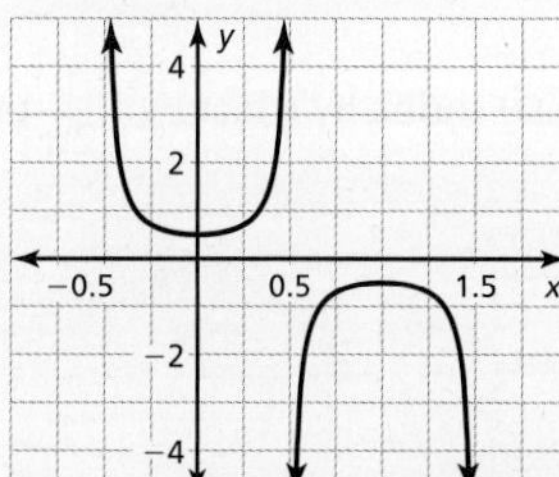

The graph of g is a horizontal shrink by a factor of $\frac{1}{\pi}$ and a vertical shrink by a factor of $\frac{1}{2}$ of the graph of $f(x) = \sec x$.

19. 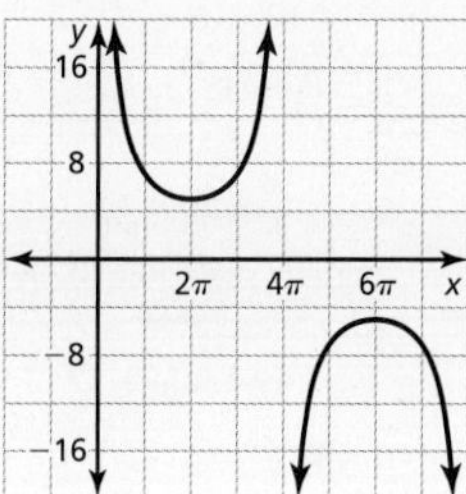

The graph of g is a horizontal stretch by a factor of 4 and a vertical stretch by a factor of 5 of the graph of $f(x) = \csc x$.

21. $y = 6 \tan x$

23. $y = 2 \tan \pi x$

25. B; The parent function is the tangent function and the graph has an asymptote at $x = \frac{\pi}{2}$.

27. D; The parent function is the cosecant function and the graph has an asymptote at $x = 1$.

29. A; The parent function is the secant function and the graph has an asymptote at $x = \frac{\pi}{4}$.

31. The tangent function that passes through the origin and has asymptotes at $x = \pi$ and $x = -\pi$ can be stretched or shrunk vertically to create more tangent functions with the same characteristics.

33. $g(x) = \cot\left(2x + \frac{\pi}{2}\right) + 3$

35. $g(x) = -5 \sec(x - \pi) + 2$

37. Function B has a local maximum value of -5 so Function A's local maximum value of $-\frac{1}{4}$ is greater. Function A has a local minimum of $\frac{1}{4}$ so Function B's local minimum value of 5 is greater.

39. 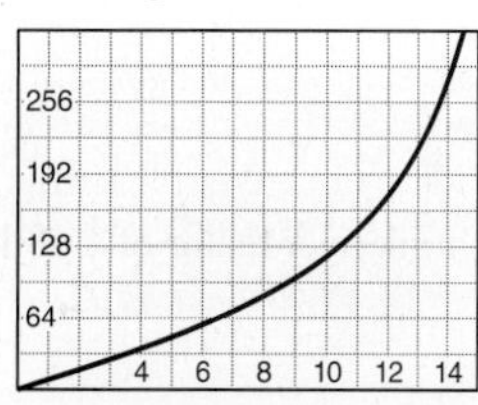

$0 < t < 15$ and $0 < h < 320$; As t increases, h increases.

41. a. $d = 260 - 120 \tan \theta$

b. 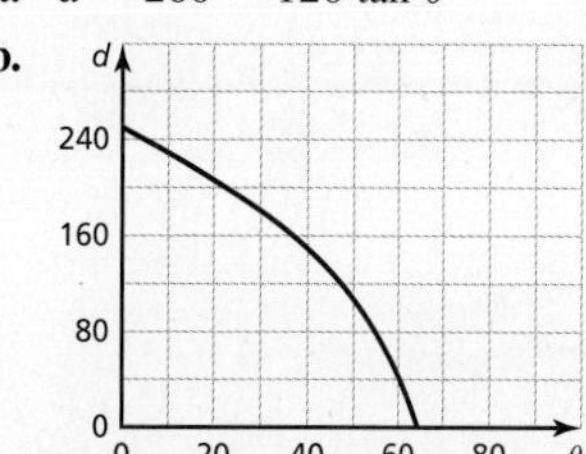

The graph shows a negative correlation meaning that as the angle gets larger, the distance from your friend to the top of the building gets smaller. As the angle gets smaller, the distance from your friend to the top of the building gets larger.

43. no; The graph of cosecant can be translated $\frac{\pi}{2}$ units right to create the same graph as $y = \sec x$.

45. $a \sec bx = \dfrac{a}{\cos bx}$

Because the cosine function is at most 1, $y = a \cos bx$ will produce a maximum when $\cos bx = 1$ and $y = a \sec bx$ will produce a minimum. When $\cos bx = -1$, $y = a \cos bx$ will produce a minimum and $y = a \sec bx$ will produce a maximum.

10.5 Review & Refresh

47. *Sample answer:* 460°; −260°

48. 5; 2π

49. 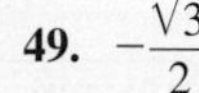 $-\frac{\sqrt{3}}{2}$

50. 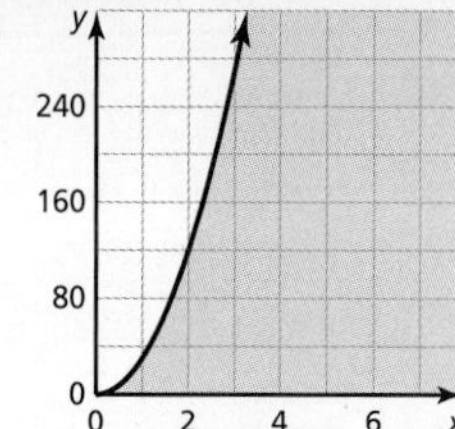

As the diameter of the tube increases, the amount of possible weights it can safely support increases.

51. yes; $y = 1.8(3)^x$

52. e^8

53. 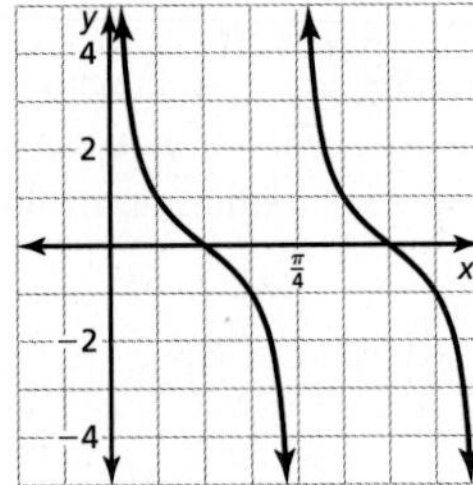

The graph of g is a horizontal shrink by a factor of $\frac{1}{4}$ of the graph of $f(x) = \cot x$.

54. $x = -1$

55. a. 1

b. $\frac{1}{8}$

56. 2nd degree; $y = x^2 + 5x + 4$

57. 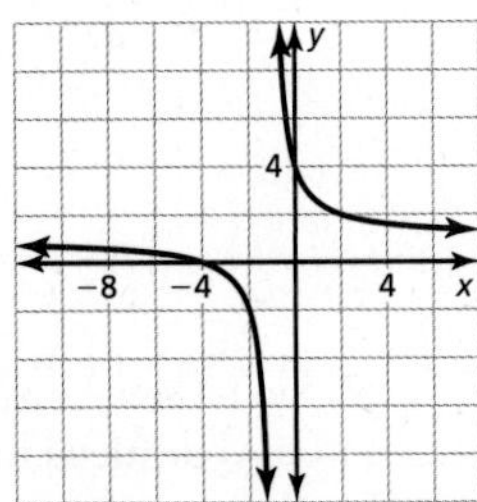

domain: all real numbers except $x = -1$; range: all real numbers except $y = 1$

58. $x = -5$ and $x = 2$

10.6 Practice

1. $\dfrac{1}{2\pi}$

3. $\dfrac{2}{\pi}$

5. $\dfrac{3}{2}$

7. $\dfrac{3}{8\pi}$

9. *Sample answer:* $P = 0.02 \sin 40\pi t$

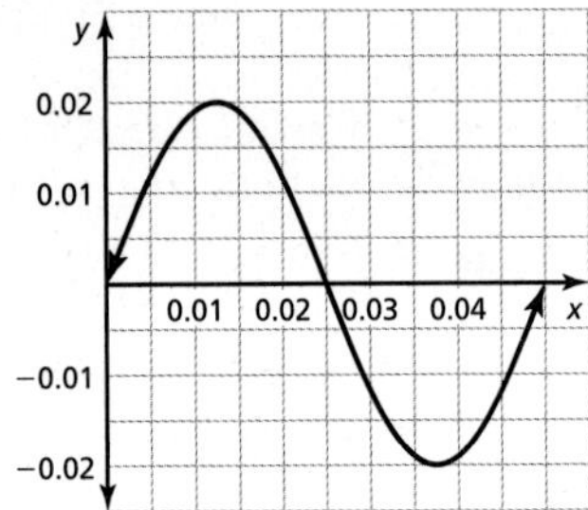

11. *Sample answer:* $y = 3 \sin 2x$

13. *Sample answer:* $y = -2 \cos \frac{\pi}{2}(x + 4)$

15. To find the amplitude, take half of the difference between the maximum and the minimum; $\dfrac{10 - (-6)}{2} = 8$

17. $h = -9 \cos 5\pi t + 13$

19. $D = 22.90 \sin(0.542t - 2.25) + 80.9$; The period of the graph represents the amount of time it takes for the weather to repeat its cycle, which is about 11.6 months.

21. *Sample answer:* $V = 100 \sin 4\pi t$

23. $y = 2.5 \sin 4\left(x - \frac{\pi}{8}\right) + 5.5$, $y = -2.5 \cos 4x + 5.5$

25. a. *Sample answer:* $N = 3.68 \sin(0.776t - 0.70) + 20.4$

b. about 23,100 employees

27. Answers will vary. Check students' work.

10.6 Review & Refresh

28. $\log_8 x - \log_8 7$

29. $\ln 2 + \ln x$

30. $\log_3 5 + 3 \log_3 x$

31. $\ln 4 + 6 \ln x - \ln y$

32. $\sin \theta = -1$, $\cos \theta = 0$, $\tan \theta =$ undefined, $\csc \theta = -1$, $\sec \theta =$ undefined, $\cot \theta = 0$

33. 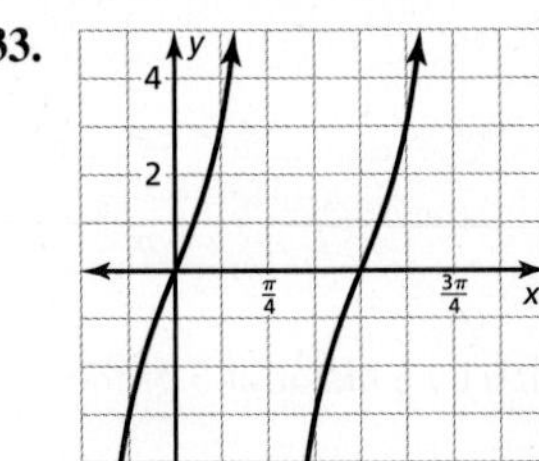

The graph of g is a horizontal shrink by a factor of $\frac{1}{2}$ and a vertical stretch by a factor of 3 of the graph of $f(x) = \tan x$.

34. 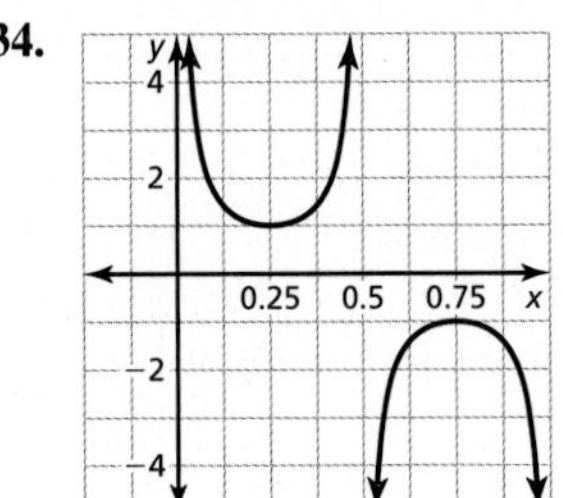

The graph of g is a horizontal shrink by a factor of $\dfrac{1}{2\pi}$ of the graph of $f(x) = \csc x$.

35. a. $\frac{24}{71}$, or about 33.8%

b. $\frac{41}{105}$, or about 39.0%

36. $x = -3$, $x = 3$, and $x = 4$

37.

38.

39. *Sample answer:* $y = \sin 3x$

40. $\dfrac{17\sqrt{2}}{2}$

41. $\dfrac{6 + 3\sqrt{6}}{2}$

42. $-24 + 8\sqrt{10}$

43. $\dfrac{13\sqrt{11} - 13\sqrt{3}}{8}$

44. $\frac{2}{13}$, or about 15.3%

45. $\frac{4}{13}$, or about 30.8%

46. neither

47. parameter; The mean is based on all the students in the first aid class.

10.7 Practice

1. $\cos\theta = \frac{2\sqrt{2}}{3}$, $\tan\theta = \frac{\sqrt{2}}{4}$, $\csc\theta = 3$, $\sec\theta = \frac{3\sqrt{2}}{4}$, $\cot\theta = 2\sqrt{2}$

3. $\sin\theta = \frac{3\sqrt{58}}{58}$, $\cos\theta = -\frac{7\sqrt{58}}{58}$, $\csc\theta = \frac{\sqrt{58}}{3}$, $\sec\theta = -\frac{\sqrt{58}}{7}$, $\cot\theta = -\frac{7}{3}$

5. $\sin\theta = -\frac{\sqrt{11}}{6}$, $\tan\theta = \frac{\sqrt{11}}{5}$, $\csc\theta = -\frac{6\sqrt{11}}{11}$, $\sec\theta = -\frac{6}{5}$, $\cot\theta = \frac{5\sqrt{11}}{11}$

7. $\sin\theta = -\frac{\sqrt{10}}{10}$, $\cos\theta = \frac{3\sqrt{10}}{10}$, $\tan\theta = -\frac{1}{3}$, $\csc\theta = -\sqrt{10}$, $\sec\theta = \frac{\sqrt{10}}{3}$

9. $\cos x$

11. $-\tan\theta$

13. $\sin^2 x$

15. $-\sec x$

17. 1

19. $\sin^2\theta = 1 - \cos^2\theta$;
$1 - \sin^2\theta = 1 - (1 - \cos^2\theta) = 1 - 1 + \cos^2\theta = \cos^2\theta$

21. $$\cos\left(\frac{\pi}{2} - x\right)\cot x = \sin x \cdot \frac{\cos x}{\sin x} = \cos x$$

23. $$\frac{\cos\left(\frac{\pi}{2} - \theta\right) + 1}{1 - \sin(-\theta)} = \frac{\sin\theta + 1}{1 - \sin(-\theta)} = \frac{\sin\theta + 1}{1 - (-\sin\theta)} = \frac{\sin\theta + 1}{1 + \sin\theta} = 1$$

25. $$\frac{1 + \cos x}{\sin x} + \frac{\sin x}{1 + \cos x} = \frac{1 + \cos x}{\sin x} + \frac{\sin x(1 - \cos x)}{(1 + \cos x)(1 - \cos x)}$$
$$= \frac{1 + \cos x}{\sin x} + \frac{\sin x(1 - \cos x)}{1 - \cos^2 x}$$
$$= \frac{1 + \cos x}{\sin x} + \frac{\sin x(1 - \cos x)}{\sin^2 x}$$
$$= \frac{\sin x(1 + \cos x)}{\sin^2 x} + \frac{\sin x(1 - \cos x)}{\sin^2 x}$$
$$= \frac{\sin x(1 + \cos x) + \sin x(1 - \cos x)}{\sin^2 x}$$
$$= \frac{\sin x(1 + \cos x + 1 - \cos x)}{\sin^2 x}$$
$$= \frac{\sin x(2)}{\sin^2 x}$$
$$= \frac{2}{\sin x}$$
$$= 2\csc x$$

27. The cosine function has a period of 2π and $y = \cos(x - \pi)$ is a horizontal translation 2π units right of the graph of $y = \cos(x + \pi)$.

29. no; $f(x)$ does not equal $g(x)$ for all values of x.

31. $\sin x$, $\csc x$, $\tan x$, $\cot x$; $\cos x$, $\sec x$;
$\sin(-\theta) = -\sin\theta$
$\csc(-\theta) = \frac{1}{\sin(-\theta)} = -\frac{1}{\sin\theta} = -\csc\theta$
$\tan(-\theta) = -\tan\theta$
$\cot(-\theta) = \frac{1}{\tan(-\theta)} = -\frac{1}{\tan\theta} = -\cot\theta$

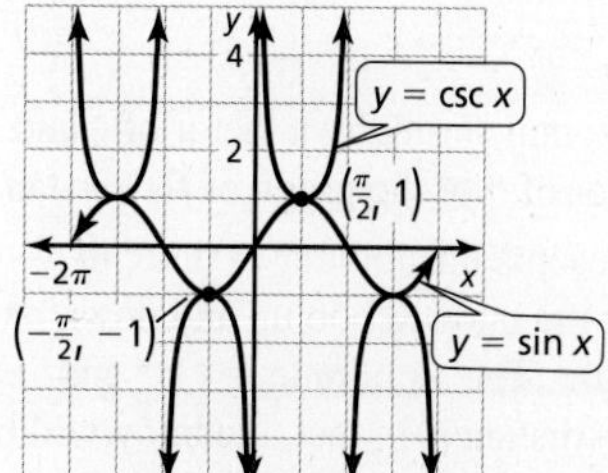

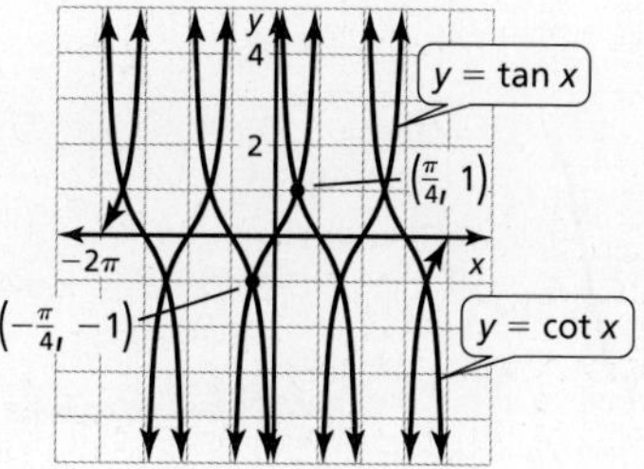

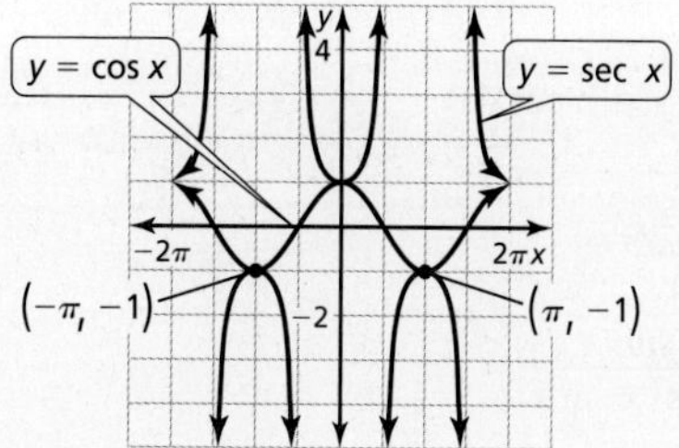

33. $$s = \frac{h\cot\theta}{\sin(90° - \theta)} = \frac{h\cot\theta}{\cos\theta} = \frac{h\cos\theta}{\sin\theta\cos\theta} = \frac{h}{\sin\theta} = h\csc\theta$$

35. u starts at 0 and increases without bound.

37. a. $\ln|\sec\theta| = \ln\frac{1}{|\cos\theta|} = \ln|(\cos\theta)^{-1}| = -\ln|\cos\theta|$

b. $\ln|\tan\theta| = \ln\frac{|\sin\theta|}{|\cos\theta|} = \ln|\sin\theta| - \ln|\cos\theta|$

10.7 Review & Refresh

38. 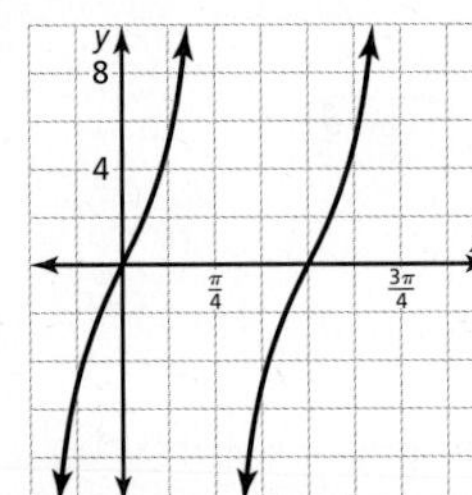

The graph of g is a horizontal shrink by a factor of $\frac{1}{2}$ and a vertical stretch by a factor of 5 of the graph of $f(x) = \tan x$.

39. The period is 8 and represents the amount of time, in seconds, that it takes for the buoy to bob up and down and return to the same position. The amplitude is 11.5 and represents the maximum distance, in feet, the buoy will be from its midline.

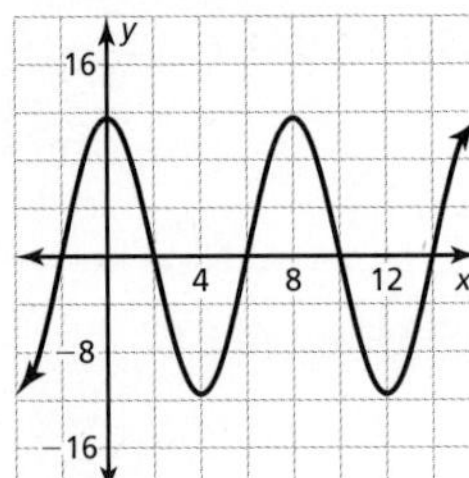

40. 99%

41. *Sample answer:* $y = 3 \cos 4x$

42. 81.85%

43. $\frac{\sec^2 x - 1}{\sin x} = \frac{\tan^2 x}{\sin x}$

$= \frac{\sin^2 x}{\cos^2 x \sin x}$

$= \frac{\sin x}{\cos^2 x}$

$= \frac{\sin x}{\cos x} \bullet \frac{1}{\cos x}$

$= \tan x \sec x$

44. 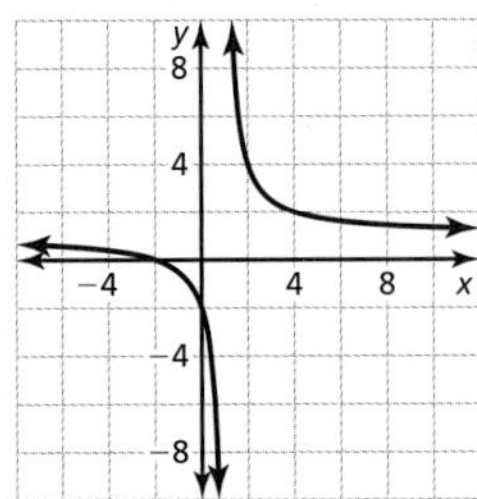

domain: all real numbers except $x = 1$; range: all real numbers except $y = 1$

45. 4 **46.** 243

10.8 Practice

1. $\sqrt{3} - 2$ **3.** $\frac{\sqrt{2} - \sqrt{6}}{4}$

5. $\frac{\sqrt{2} - \sqrt{6}}{4}$ **7.** $\sqrt{3} + 2$

9. $-\frac{36}{85}$ **11.** $-\frac{13}{85}$

13. $-\frac{36}{77}$ **15.** $\tan x$

17. $\cos x$ **19.** $\cos x$

21. The sign in the denominator should be negative when using the sum formula;

$$\frac{\tan x + \tan \frac{\pi}{4}}{1 - \tan x \tan \frac{\pi}{4}} = \frac{\tan x + 1}{1 - \tan x}$$

23. $x = \frac{\pi}{6}, \frac{5\pi}{6}$ **25.** $x = \frac{\pi}{3}, \frac{5\pi}{3}$

27. $x = \frac{3\pi}{2}$ **29.** $x = 0, \pi$

31. $A \cos\left(\frac{2\pi}{3} - \frac{2\pi x}{5}\right) + A \cos\left(\frac{2\pi}{3} + \frac{2\pi x}{5}\right)$

$= A \cos \frac{2\pi}{3} \cos \frac{2\pi x}{5} + A \sin \frac{2\pi}{3} \sin \frac{2\pi x}{5} + A \cos \frac{2\pi}{3}$
$\cos \frac{2\pi x}{5} - A \sin \frac{2\pi}{3} \sin \frac{2\pi x}{5}$

$= A \cos \frac{2\pi}{3} \cos \frac{2\pi x}{5} + A \cos \frac{2\pi}{3} \cos \frac{2\pi x}{5}$

$= 2A \cos \frac{2\pi}{3} \cos \frac{2\pi x}{5}$

$= 2A\left(-\frac{1}{2}\right) \cos \frac{2\pi x}{5}$

$= -A \cos \frac{2\pi x}{5}$

33. $\sin\left(\frac{\pi}{2} - \theta\right) = \sin \frac{\pi}{2} \cos \theta - \cos \frac{\pi}{2} \sin \theta$

$= (1) \cos \theta - (0) \sin \theta$

$= \cos \theta$

35. no; The difference formula for $\tan\left(\frac{\pi}{2} - \theta\right)$ would require finding $\tan \frac{\pi}{2}$, which is undefined.

37. a. $\tan(\theta_2 - \theta_1) = \frac{m_2 - m_1}{1 + m_2 m_1}$

b. 30°

10.8 Review & Refresh

39. $x = 4$ **40.** $x = -\frac{2}{3}$

41. $-\frac{\sqrt{2} + \sqrt{6}}{4}$ **42.** $\sqrt{3} - 2$

43. $x \approx 17.7$ **44.** $\cos^2 \theta$

45. survey

46. 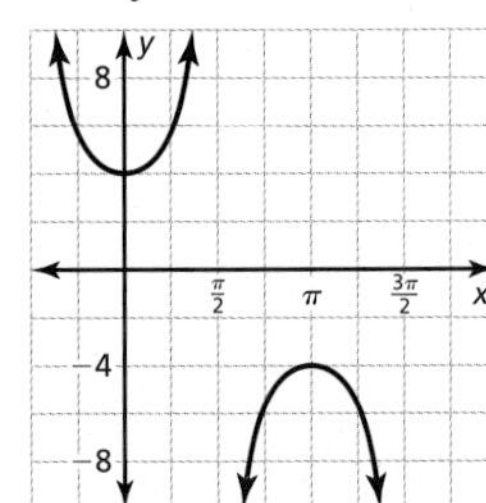

The graph of g is a vertical stretch by a factor of 4 of the graph of f.

47. $b > 1$ **48.** $h(t) = \frac{1}{4} \cos 2\pi t + 7.75$

Chapter 10 Review

1. $\sin \theta = \frac{4}{5}$, $\cos \theta = \frac{3}{5}$, $\tan \theta = \frac{4}{3}$, $\csc \theta = \frac{5}{4}$, $\sec \theta = \frac{5}{3}$, $\cot \theta = \frac{3}{4}$

2. $\sin\theta = \frac{\sqrt{3}}{2}$, $\cos\theta = \frac{1}{2}$, $\tan\theta = \sqrt{3}$, $\csc\theta = \frac{2\sqrt{3}}{3}$, $\sec\theta = 2$, $\cot\theta = \frac{\sqrt{3}}{3}$

3. $\sin\theta = \frac{\sqrt{85}}{11}$, $\tan\theta = \frac{\sqrt{85}}{6}$, $\csc\theta = \frac{11\sqrt{85}}{85}$, $\sec\theta = \frac{11}{6}$, $\cot\theta = \frac{6\sqrt{85}}{85}$

4. $A = 46°$, $b \approx 5.79$, $c = 8.34$

5. $A = 32°$, $a \approx 5.83$, $b = 9.33$

6. $\cos\theta$ and $\sin\theta$ are always less than or equal to 1, so their inverses must be at least 1.

7. **a.** about 380 ft
   b. about 170 ft

8. $\frac{\pi}{6}$

9. $\frac{5\pi}{4}$

10. 135°

11. 300°

12. *Sample answer:* $\frac{\pi}{9}, -\frac{17\pi}{9}$

13. $\frac{37\pi}{60}$

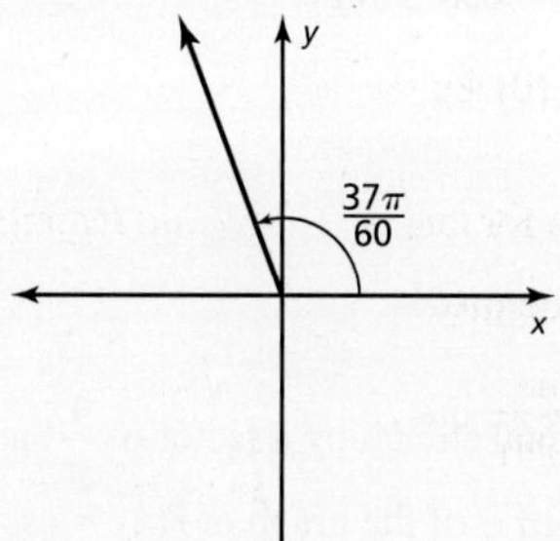

14. $\frac{7\pi}{6}$ in.; $\frac{49\pi}{12}$ in.^{2}

15. 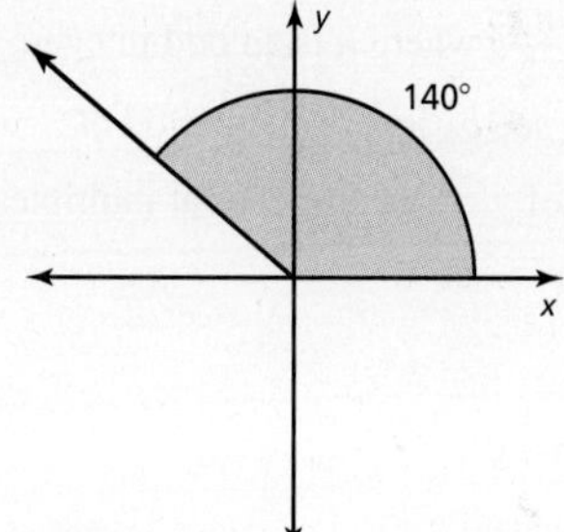

about 1497 m^2

16. $\sin\theta = 1$, $\cos\theta = 0$, $\tan\theta =$ undefined, $\csc\theta = 1$, $\sec\theta =$ undefined, $\cot\theta = 0$

17. $\sin\theta = -\frac{7}{25}$, $\cos\theta = \frac{24}{25}$, $\tan\theta = -\frac{7}{24}$, $\csc\theta = -\frac{25}{7}$, $\sec\theta = \frac{25}{24}$, $\cot\theta = -\frac{24}{7}$

18. $\sin\theta = -\frac{5\sqrt{29}}{29}$, $\cos\theta = -\frac{2\sqrt{29}}{29}$, $\tan\theta = \frac{5}{2}$, $\csc\theta = -\frac{\sqrt{29}}{5}$, $\sec\theta = -\frac{\sqrt{29}}{2}$, $\cot\theta = \frac{2}{5}$

19. $\sin\theta = \frac{3\sqrt{13}}{13}$, $\cos\theta = -\frac{2\sqrt{13}}{13}$, $\tan\theta = -\frac{3}{2}$, $\csc\theta = \frac{\sqrt{13}}{3}$, $\sec\theta = -\frac{\sqrt{13}}{2}$, $\cot\theta = -\frac{2}{3}$

20. $-\frac{\sqrt{3}}{3}$

21. $\sqrt{2}$

22. $\frac{1}{2}$

23. 2

24. 3, 2π; The graph of g is a vertical stretch by a factor of 3 of the graph of $f(x) = \sin x$;

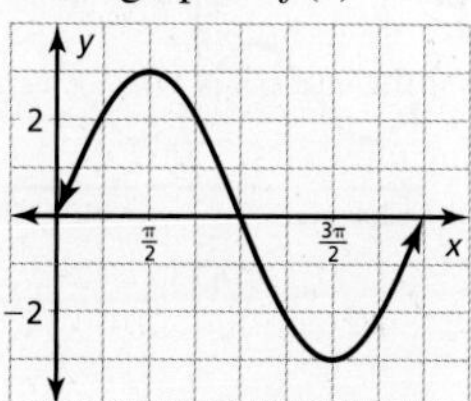

25. 8, 2π; The graph of g is a vertical stretch by a factor of 8 of the graph of $f(x) = \cos x$;

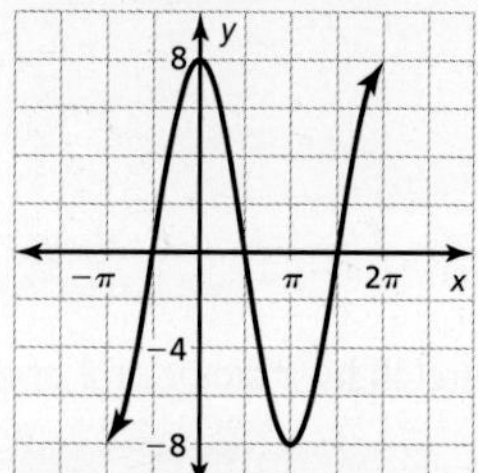

26. 6, 2; The graph of g is a horizontal shrink by a factor of $\frac{1}{\pi}$ and a vertical stretch by a factor of 6 of the graph of $f(x) = \sin x$;

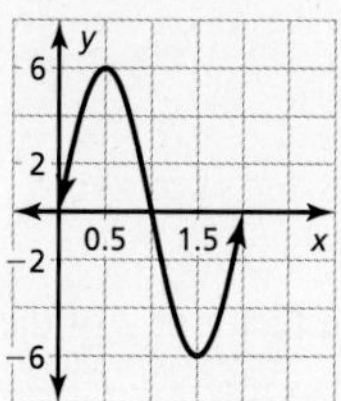

27. $\frac{1}{4}, \frac{\pi}{2}$; The graph of g is a horizontal shrink by a factor of $\frac{1}{4}$ and a vertical shrink by a factor of $\frac{1}{4}$ of the graph of $f(x) = \cos x$;

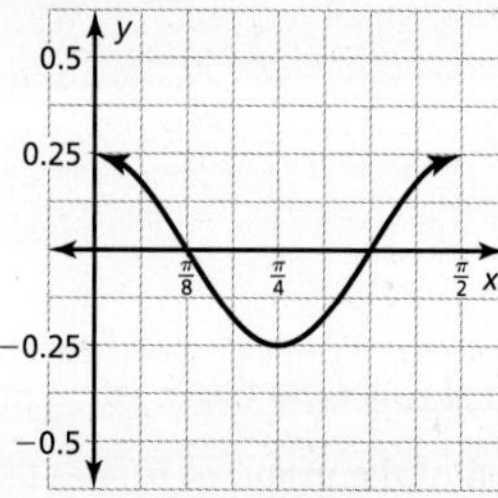

28. $y = \frac{1}{2}\sin 4x$; The function has a period of $\frac{\pi}{2}$ and an amplitude of $\frac{1}{2}$, so $b = 2\pi \div \frac{\pi}{2} = 4$ and $a = \frac{1}{2}$.

29. $y = 2\sin 3x$; The function has a period of $\frac{2\pi}{3}$ and an amplitude of 2, so $b = 2\pi \div \frac{2\pi}{3} = 3$ and $a = 2$.

30. 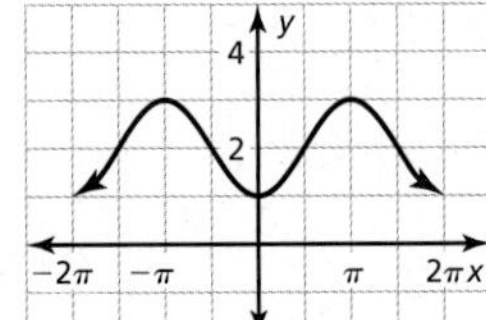

31. 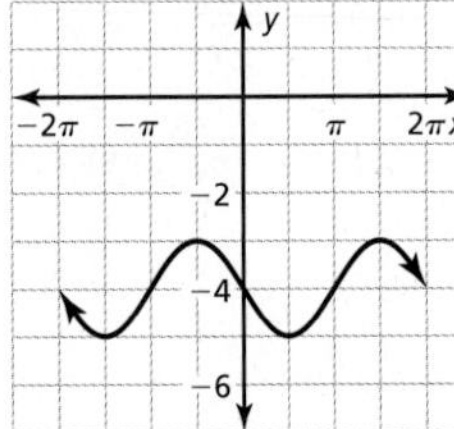

32. 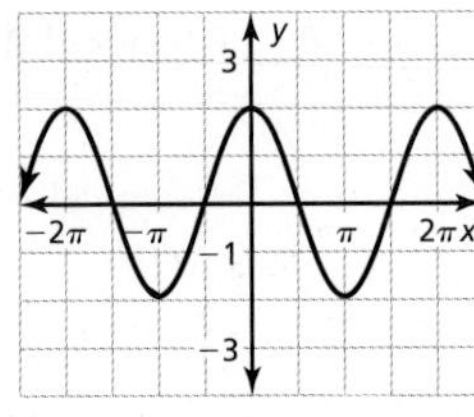

33. 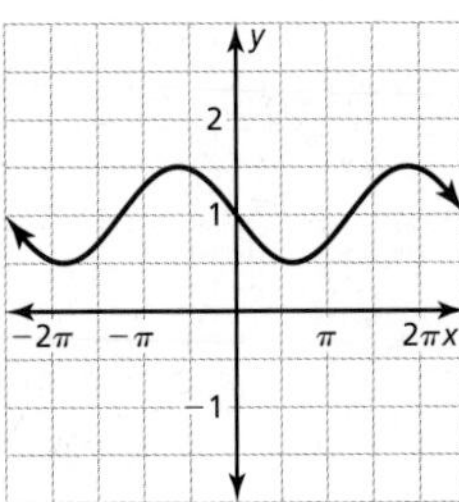

34. 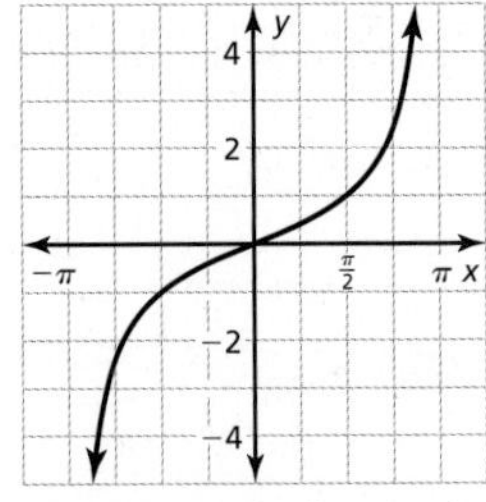

The graph of g is a horizontal stretch by a factor of 2 of the graph of $f(x) = \tan x$.

35. 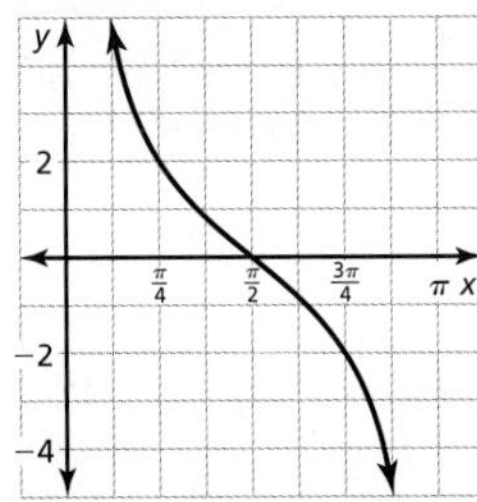

The graph of g is a vertical stretch by a factor of 2 of the graph of $f(x) = \cot x$.

36. 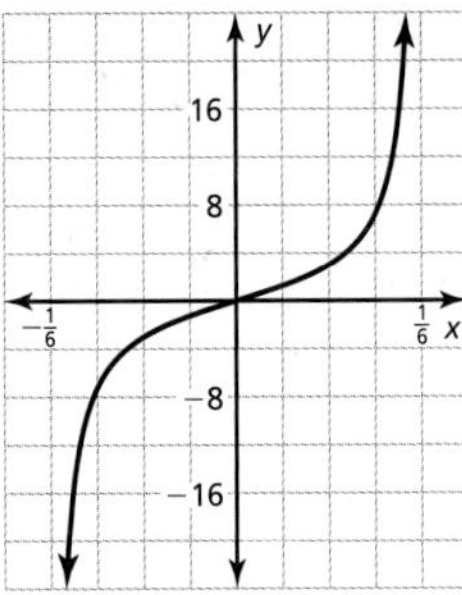

The graph of g is a horizontal shrink by a factor of $\frac{1}{3\pi}$ and a vertical stretch by a factor of 4 of the graph of $f(x) = \tan x$.

37. 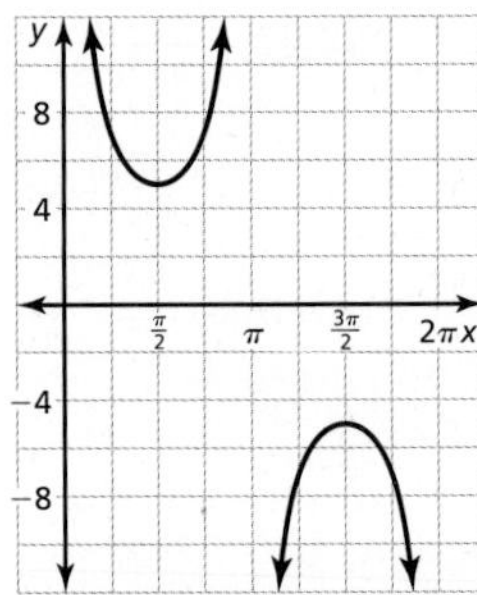

The graph of g is a vertical stretch by a factor of 5 of the graph of $f(x) = \csc x$.

38. 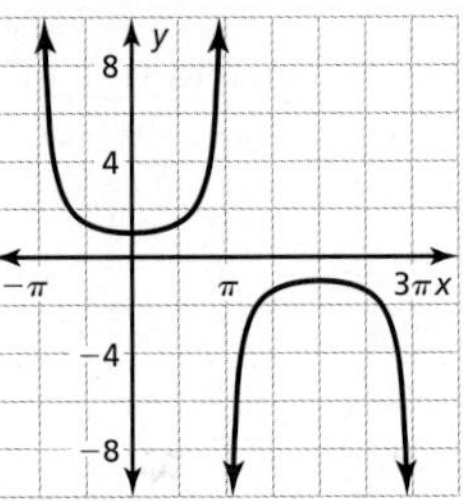

The graph of g is a horizontal stretch by a factor of 2 of the graph of $f(x) = \sec x$.

39. 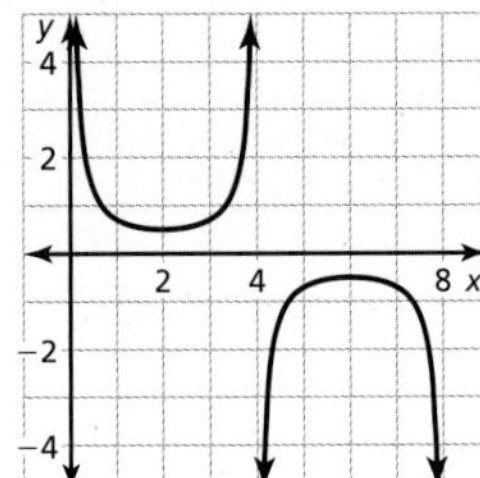

The graph of g is a horizontal stretch by a factor of $\frac{4}{\pi}$ and a vertical shrink by a factor of $\frac{1}{2}$ of the graph of $f(x) = \csc x$.

40. The asymptotes are at $x = \frac{n\pi}{12}$, where n is an odd integer; *Sample answer:* The graph of $y = \sec x$ has a period of 2π and asymptotes at $x = \frac{n\pi}{2}$, where n is an odd integer. Because the period of $y = \sec bx$ is $\frac{1}{6}$ of the period of $y = \sec x$, the asymptotes of $y = \sec bx$ occur at multiples of $\frac{1}{6}$ of the asymptotes of $y = \sec x$.

41. $d = 3000 - 1500 \tan \theta$

42. *Sample answer:* $y = -\sin \frac{1}{2}x$

43. *Sample answer:* $y = \cos \pi x - 2$

44. *Sample answer:* $y = 2 \cos x - 1$

45. *Sample answer:* $y = \sin \pi x + 3$

46. *Sample answer:* $y = -3.5 \cos \frac{\pi}{6}x + 12.25$

47. $h = -2.5 \cos \pi t + 6.5$

48. *Sample answer:* $P = 1.71 \sin(0.527t - 2.08) + 2.55$; 11.9 months

49. $\sin \theta = \frac{4}{5}$, $\tan \theta = \frac{4}{3}$, $\csc \theta = \frac{5}{4}$, $\sec \theta = \frac{5}{3}$, $\cot \theta = \frac{3}{4}$

50. $\cos \theta = \frac{12}{13}$, $\tan \theta = -\frac{5}{12}$, $\csc \theta = -\frac{13}{5}$, $\sec \theta = \frac{13}{12}$, $\cot \theta = -\frac{12}{5}$

51. $\cos\theta = -\frac{\sqrt{15}}{4}$, $\tan\theta = -\frac{\sqrt{15}}{15}$, $\csc\theta = 4$, $\sec\theta = -\frac{4\sqrt{15}}{15}$, $\cot\theta = -\sqrt{15}$

52. $\sin\theta = -\frac{7\sqrt{53}}{53}$, $\cos\theta = -\frac{2\sqrt{53}}{53}$, $\csc\theta = -\frac{\sqrt{53}}{7}$, $\sec\theta = -\frac{\sqrt{53}}{2}$, $\cot\theta = \frac{2}{7}$

53. $\cos^2 x$

54. $\tan x$

55. $\sin x$

56. $\cos^2 x$

57. $\frac{\cos x \sec x}{1 + \tan^2 x} = \frac{\cos x \sec x}{\sec^2 x}$
$= \frac{\cos x}{\sec x}$
$= \cos x \cos x$
$= \cos^2 x$

58. $\tan\left(\frac{\pi}{2} - x\right)\cot x = \cot x \cot x$
$= \cot^2 x$
$= \csc^2 x - 1$

59. $\frac{\sqrt{2} + \sqrt{6}}{4}$

60. -1

61. $\frac{\sqrt{6} - \sqrt{2}}{4}$

62. $\frac{19}{25}$

63. $-\cos x$

64. $-\sin x$

65. $-\cot x$

66. $x = \frac{3\pi}{4}$ and $x = \frac{5\pi}{4}$

67. $x = 0$ and $x = \pi$

Chapter 10 Mathematical Practices (Chapter Review)

1. *Sample answer:* An angle of elevation is an angle between a horizontal line and a line extending upward from the horizontal line. An angle of depression is an angle between a horizontal line and a line extending downward from the horizontal line.

2. *Sample answer:* The values of the trigonometric ratios are defined by the ratios of sides of the triangles. Because the triangles are similar and θ_1 and θ_2 are corresponding angles, the trigonometric ratios of the angles are equal.

Chapter 10 Practice Test

1. $\frac{\cos^2 x + \sin^2 x}{1 + \tan^2 x} = \frac{1}{\sec^2 x}$
$= \cos^2 x$

2. $\frac{1 + \sin x}{\cos x} + \frac{\cos x}{1 + \sin x} = \frac{(1 + \sin x)(1 + \sin x) + \cos^2 x}{\cos x(1 + \sin x)}$
$= \frac{1 + 2\sin x + \sin^2 x + \cos^2 x}{\cos x(1 + \sin x)}$
$= \frac{2 + 2\sin x}{\cos x(1 + \sin x)}$
$= \frac{2(1 + \sin x)}{\cos x(1 + \sin x)}$
$= \frac{2}{\cos x}$
$= 2\sec x$

3. $\cos\left(x + \frac{3\pi}{2}\right) = \cos x \cos\frac{3\pi}{2} - \sin x \sin\frac{3\pi}{2}$
$= (\cos x)(0) - (\sin x)(-1)$
$= \sin x$

4. *Sample answer:* $y = 3\cos\pi x + 2$

5. *Sample answer:* $y = -3\sin\frac{4}{3}x - 2$

6. 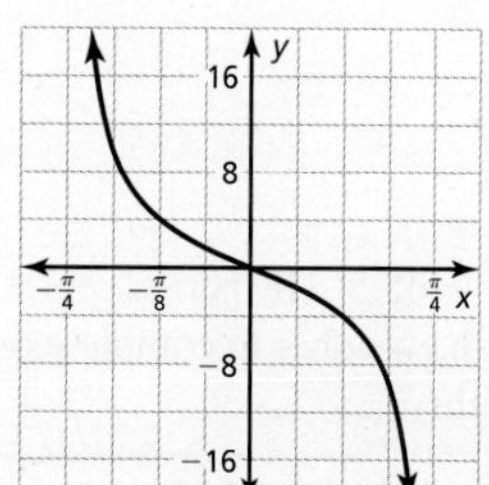

The graph of g is a horizontal shrink by a factor of $\frac{1}{2}$ and a vertical stretch by a factor of 4, followed by a reflection across the x-axis of the graph of $f(x) = \tan x$.

7. 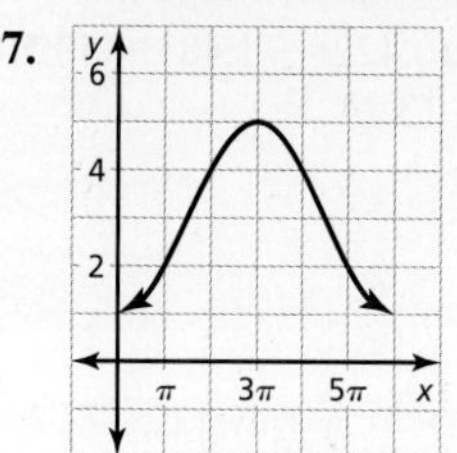

The graph of g is a horizontal stretch by a factor of 3 and a vertical stretch by a factor of 2, followed by a reflection across the x-axis and a translation 3 units up of the graph of $f(x) = \cos x$.

8. 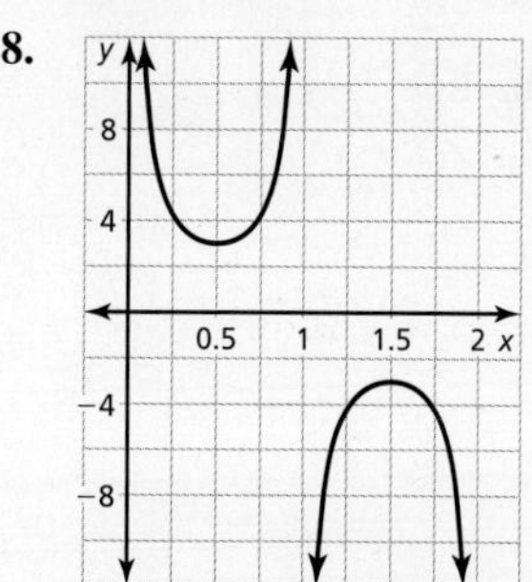

The graph of g is a horizontal shrink by a factor of $\frac{1}{\pi}$ and a vertical stretch by a factor of 3 of the graph of $f(x) = \csc x$.

9. $-\frac{5\pi}{18}$; $310°$, $-410°$

10. $144°$; $\frac{14\pi}{5}$, $-\frac{6\pi}{5}$

11. $480°$; $\frac{2\pi}{3}$, $-\frac{4\pi}{3}$

12. $\frac{39\pi}{4}$ in.; $\frac{507\pi}{8}$ in.^{2}

13. $\sin\theta = -\frac{9\sqrt{85}}{85}$, $\cos\theta = \frac{2\sqrt{85}}{85}$, $\tan\theta = -\frac{9}{2}$, $\csc\theta = -\frac{\sqrt{85}}{9}$, $\sec\theta = \frac{\sqrt{85}}{2}$, $\cot\theta = -\frac{2}{9}$

14. $\sin\theta = 0$, $\cos\theta = -1$, $\tan\theta = 0$, $\csc\theta =$ undefined, $\sec\theta = -1$, $\cot\theta =$ undefined

15. about 178 ft; $h = 200\sin 60° + 5$

16. $A(r) = \frac{\pi r^2}{6}, r \geq 0$

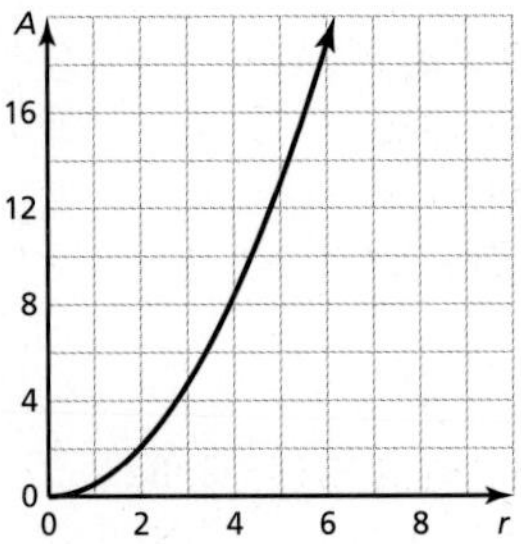

17. $T = 23.43 \sin(0.506m - 2.05) + 65.5$; The period represents the amount of time it takes for the weather to complete one cycle, which is about 12.4 months.

Chapter 10 College and Career Readiness

1. C

2. $\log_2 1, \log_2 \frac{5}{3}, \ln e, \log 1000, \log_2 9, \log_2 15$

3. **a.** *Sample answer:* $y_1 = 29.27 \sin(0.422t - 1.48) + 50.50$; $y_2 = 9.34 \sin(0.429t + 1.90) + 13.14$

b.

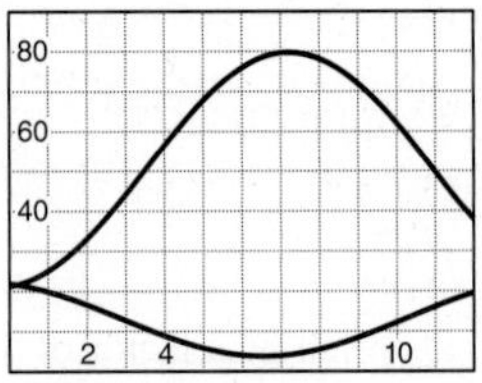

Sample answer: They increase and decrease in about the same intervals.

4. $x = -2, x = -\frac{1}{2}$, and $x = 3$

5. C

6. B

7. **a.** <

b. <

c. >

8. B, D

9. $F = \frac{1500}{\ell}$; inverse variation

Chapter 11

Chapter 11 Prepare

1.

x	y
1	1
2	−1
3	−5

2.

x	y
2	21
3	46
4	81

3.

x	y
5	4
10	−16
15	−36

4. $x = 4$

5. $x = 6$

6. $x = 66$

7. $x = 7$

8. $x = 100$

9. $x = 3$

10. 53, 55, 57; 53 + 55 + 57 = 165

11.1 Practice

1. 3, 4, 5, 6, 7, 8

3. 1, 4, 9, 16, 25, 36

5. 1, 4, 16, 64, 256, 1024

7. −4, −1, 4, 11, 20, 31

9. $\frac{2}{3}, 1, \frac{6}{5}, \frac{4}{3}, \frac{10}{7}, \frac{3}{2}$

11. The terms can be written as $5(1) - 4, 5(2) - 4, 5(3) - 4, 5(4) - 4$; $a_5 = 5(5) - 4 = 21$; $a_n = 5n - 4$

13. The terms can be written as $0.7(1) + 2.4, 0.7(2) + 2.4, 0.7(3) + 2.4, 0.7(4) + 2.4$; $a_5 = 0.7(5) + 2.4 = 5.9$; $a_n = 0.7n + 2.4$

15. The terms can be written as $-4(1), 4(2), -4(3), 4(4)$; $a_5 = -4(5) = -20$; $a_n = (-1)^n 4n$

17. The terms can be written as $\frac{1}{4}(1), \frac{1}{4}(2), \frac{1}{4}(3), \frac{1}{4}(4)$; $a_5 = \frac{1}{4}(5) = \frac{5}{4}$; $a_n = \frac{n}{4}$

19. The terms can be written as $\frac{2}{3(1)}, \frac{2}{3(2)}, \frac{2}{3(3)}, \frac{2}{3(4)}$; $a_5 = \frac{2}{3(5)} = \frac{2}{15}$; $a_n = \frac{2}{3n}$

21. The terms can be written as $(1)^3 + 1, (2)^3 + 1, (3)^3 + 1, (4)^3 + 1$;$a_5 = 5^3 + 1 = 126$; $a_n = n^3 + 1$

23. $a_n = 4n + 2$

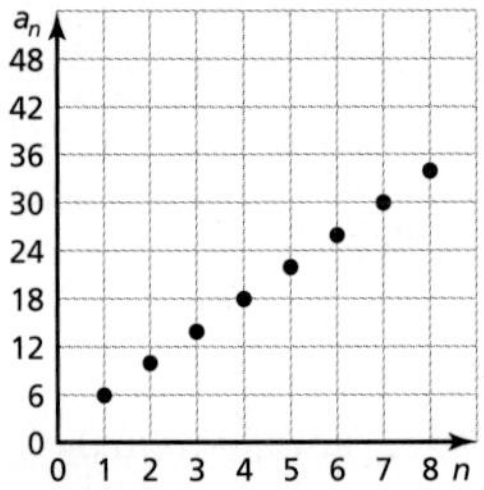

25. $\sum_{i=1}^{5} (3i + 4)$

27. $\sum_{i=1}^{\infty} (i^2 + 3)$

29. $\sum_{i=1}^{\infty} \frac{1}{3^i}$

31. $\sum_{i=1}^{5} (-1)^i(i + 2)$

33. 42

35. 100

37. 82

39. $\frac{481}{140}$

41. 35

43. 280

45. D; The number of squares in the nth figure is equal to the sum of the first positive n integers which is equal to the equation shown in D.

47. There should be ten terms in the series;

$$\sum_{n=1}^{10} (3n - 5) = -2 + 1 + 4 + 7 + 10 + 13 + 16 + 19 + 22 + 25 = 115$$

49. 105 push-ups; The nth term of the series is $a_n = 10n + 15$.

51. **a.** \$50.50

b. 316 days

53. yes; Subtract 1 + 2 = 3 from the sum.

55. **a.** true;

$$\sum_{i=1}^{n} ca_i = ca_1 + ca_2 + ca_3 + \cdots + ca_n$$
$$= c(a_1 + a_2 + a_3 + \cdots + a_n)$$
$$= c\sum_{i=1}^{n} a_i$$

b. true;

$$\sum_{i=1}^{n}(a_i + b_i) = (a_1 + b_1) + (a_2 + b_2) + \cdots + (a_n + b_n)$$
$$= a_1 + a_2 + \cdots + a_n + b_1 + b_2 + \cdots + b_n$$
$$= \sum_{i=1}^{n} a_i + \sum_{i=1}^{n} b_i$$

c. false; $\sum_{i=1}^{2}(2i)(3i) = 30, \left(\sum_{i=1}^{2} 2i\right)\left(\sum_{i=1}^{2} 3i\right) = 54$

d. false; $\sum_{i=1}^{2}(2i)^2 = 20, \left(\sum_{i=1}^{2} 2i\right)^2 = 36$

57. a. $a_n = 2^n - 1$

b. 63; 127; 255

11.1 Review & Refresh

58. (2, 1, −1)

59. (3, 1, 1)

60. $\sum_{i=1}^{8} \frac{i-1}{i} = \frac{1479}{280}$

61. $\sum_{i=3}^{10} i^2 = 380$

62. 77.7, or about 78 apps

63. $-\sin^2\theta$

64. $-\cot x$

65. 1140

66. $\frac{1}{x}$

67. $\frac{4x - 16}{(x + 2)(x - 2)}$

68. $x^2 - 16x + 64$; $(x - 8)^2$

69. $\sin\theta = \frac{\sqrt{3}}{2}$, $\cos\theta = -\frac{1}{2}$, $\tan\theta = -\sqrt{3}$, $\csc\theta = \frac{2\sqrt{3}}{3}$, $\sec\theta = -2$, $\cot\theta = \frac{-\sqrt{3}}{3}$

70. *Sample answer:* $y = 3\cos 2x + 1$

11.2 Practice

1. arithmetic; The common difference is −2.

3. not arithmetic; The differences are not constant.

5. not arithmetic; The differences are not constant.

7. arithmetic; The common difference is $\frac{1}{4}$.

9. a. $a_n = -6n + 3$

b. $a_n = 5n + 2$

11. $a_n = 8n + 4$; 164

13. $a_n = -3n + 54$; −6

15. $a_n = \frac{2}{3}n - \frac{5}{3}$; $\frac{35}{3}$

17. $a_n = -0.8n + 3.1$; −12.9

19. The formula should be $a_n = a_1 + (n - 1)d$; $a_n = 35 - 13n$

21. $a_n = 5n - 12$

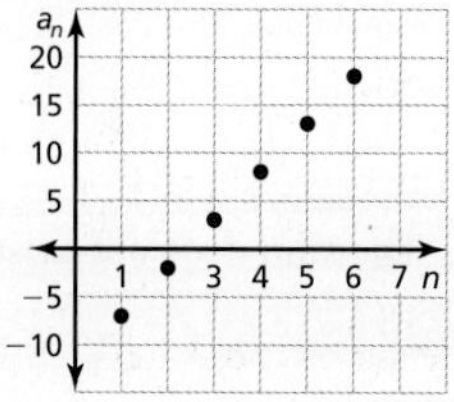

23. $a_n = -2n + 13$

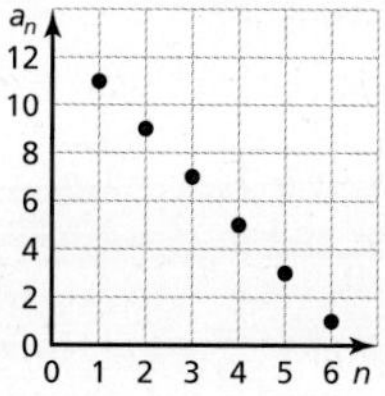

25. $a_n = -\frac{1}{2}n + \frac{7}{2}$

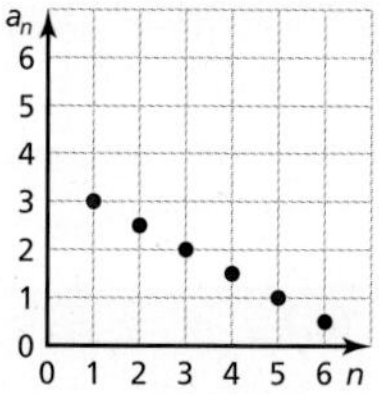

27. $a_n = 11n - 14$

29. $a_n = -6n + 28$

31. $a_n = -4n + 13$

33. $a_n = \frac{5}{4}n + 2$

35. $a_n = -3n + 12$

37. $a_n = 3n - 7$

39. $a_n = 4n + 9$

41. 360

43. −924

45. −8.2

47. −1026

49. a. $a_n = 2n + 1$

b. 63 band members

51. The graph of a_n consists of discrete points and the graph of f consists of a continuous line.

53. The common difference doubles; Doubling two numbers doubles the difference.

55. no; Doubling the difference does not necessarily double the terms.

57. 22,500; $\sum_{i=1}^{150}(2i - 1) = 150\left(\frac{1 + 299}{2}\right)$

59. $\left(\frac{2y}{n} - x\right)$ seats

61. $x = \frac{2}{3}; -\frac{8}{3}$

11.2 Review & Refresh

62. $7^{2/3}$

63. $\frac{1}{27}$

64. $\frac{3}{7}$

65. $5^{3/4}$

66. exponential decay

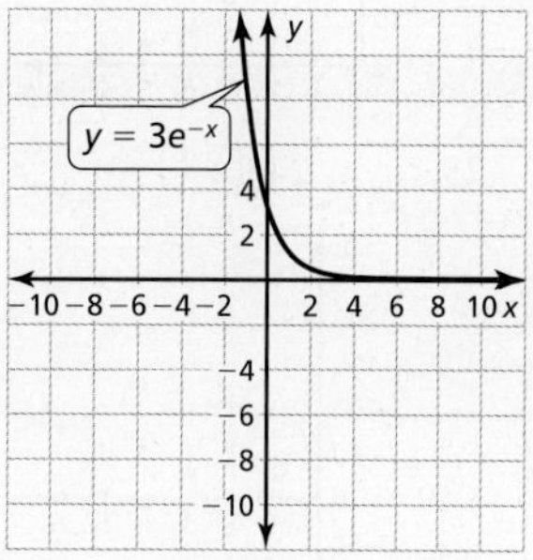

67. exponential growth

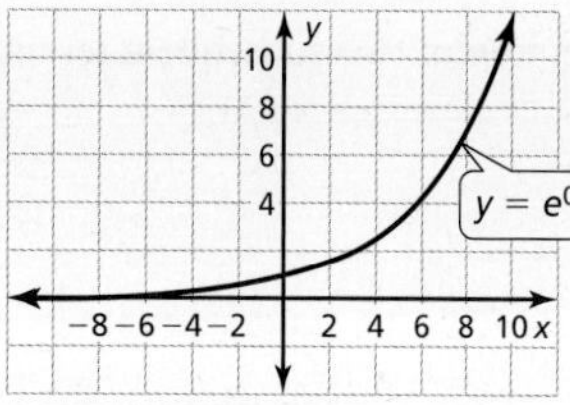

68. even; negative

69. a. $a_n = 7n - 65$

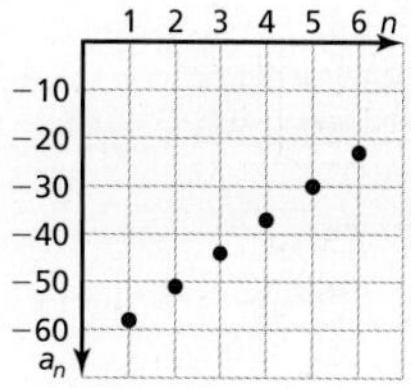

b. −234

70. $\frac{1}{595}$, or about 0.17%

71. $-\sin x$

72. (−1, −3) and (3, 5); Explanations will vary.

73. no; $f(-1) = 2$, so $f^{-1}(2) = -1$, but $g(2) \neq -1$.

74. $\sin\theta = -\frac{8}{17}$, $\tan\theta = -\frac{8}{15}$, $\csc\theta = -\frac{17}{8}$, $\sec\theta = \frac{17}{15}$, $\cot\theta = -\frac{15}{8}$

75. 38

11.3 Practice

1. geometric; The common ratio is $\frac{1}{2}$.
3. not geometric; The ratios are not constant.
5. not geometric; The ratios are not constant.
7. geometric; The common ratio is $\frac{1}{3}$.
9. **a.** $a_n = -3(5)^{n-1}$
   b. $a_n = 72\left(\frac{1}{3}\right)^{n-1}$
11. $a_n = 4(5)^{n-1}$; $a_7 = 62{,}500$
13. $a_n = 112\left(\frac{1}{2}\right)^{n-1}$; $a_7 = \frac{7}{4}$
15. $a_n = 4\left(\frac{3}{2}\right)^{n-1}$; $a_7 = \frac{729}{16}$
17. $a_n = 1.3(-3)^{n-1}$; $a_7 = 947.7$
19. $a_n = 2^{n-1}$
21. $a_n = 60\left(\frac{1}{2}\right)^{n-1}$

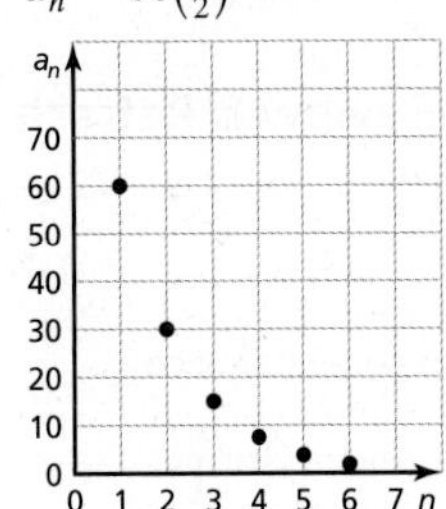

23. $a_n = -3(4)^{n-1}$

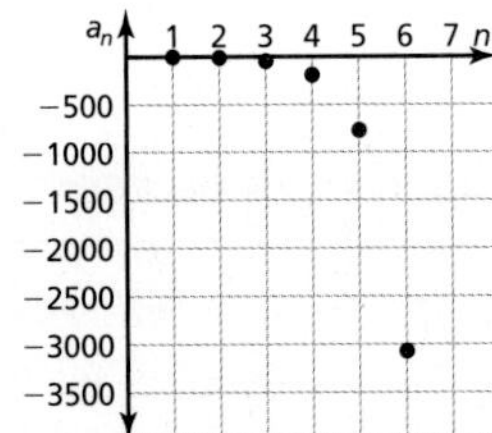

25. $a_n = 243\left(-\frac{1}{3}\right)^{n-1}$

27. The common ratio r is the ratio of two subsequent terms, not the difference.

$a_1 = 4$

$r = \frac{12}{4} = 3$

$a_n = 4(3)^{n-1}$

29. $a_n = 7(4)^{n-1}$
31. $a_n = -6(3)^{n-1}$ or $a_n = -6(-3)^{n-1}$
33. $a_n = 512\left(\frac{1}{8}\right)^{n-1}$ or $a_n = -512\left(-\frac{1}{8}\right)^{n-1}$
35. $a_n = -432\left(\frac{1}{6}\right)^{n-1}$ or $a_n = 432\left(-\frac{1}{6}\right)^{n-1}$
37. $a_n = 5(3)^{n-1}$
39. $a_n = 6(-2)^{n-1}$
41. 40,353,606
43. $\frac{989{,}527}{65{,}536}$
45. $\frac{32{,}312}{6561}$
47. $-262{,}140$
49. 1092 people
51. $276.25
53. 5 days
55. **a.** $a_n = 8^{n-1}$; 2,396,745 squares
    b. $b_n = \left(\frac{8}{9}\right)^n$; about 0.243 square units
57. Answers will vary. Check students' work.
59. *Sample answer:* Loan A; The total amount repaid for Loan A is about $20,510 and the total amount repaid for Loan B is about $28,358.
61. $\dfrac{3x - 48x^9}{1 - 2x^2}$

11.3 Review & Refresh

62. 12; 2 real solutions
63. no; Subjects are not randomly assigned to control groups and treatment groups. The conclusion may or may not be valid.
64. The graph of g is a vertical translation 3 units up of the graph of f.
65. $\tan x$
66. 55
67. $\dfrac{19}{10x}$
68. $a_n = -2n + 11$
69. $a_n = -50(2)^{n-1}$

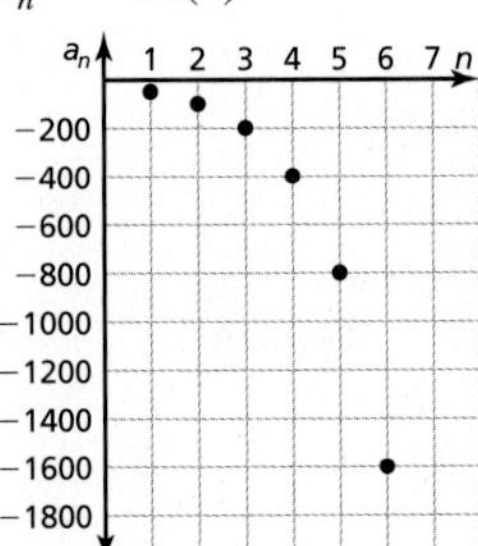

70. $\frac{1}{3}$

11.4 Practice

1. $S_1 = 0.5$, $S_2 = 0.67$, $S_3 \approx 0.72$, $S_4 \approx 0.74$, $S_5 \approx 0.75$; S_n appears to approach 0.75.

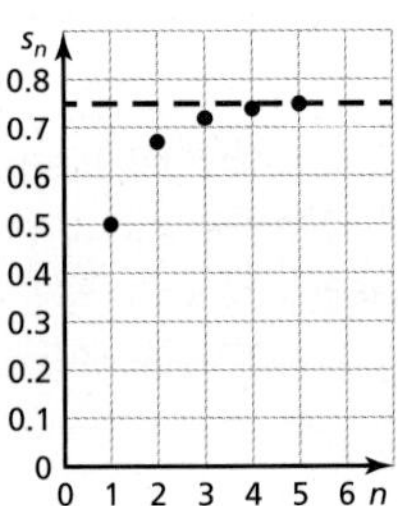

3. $S_1 = 4$, $S_2 = 6.4$, $S_3 = 7.84$, $S_4 \approx 8.70$, $S_5 \approx 9.22$; S_n appears to approach 10.

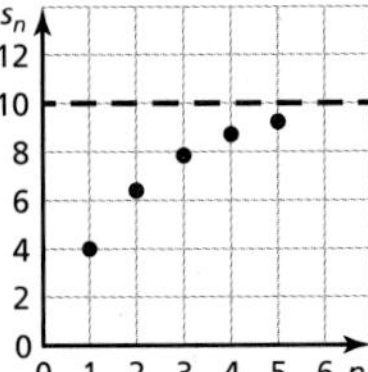

5. 10
7. The sum does not exist.
9. 8
11. 18
13. Because $\left|\frac{7}{2}\right| > 1$, the sum does not exist.
15. 56 ft
17. $\frac{2}{9}$
19. $\frac{16}{99}$
21. $\frac{3200}{99} = 32\frac{32}{99}$
23. *Sample answer:* $\sum_{i=1}^{\infty} 3\left(\frac{1}{2}\right)^{i-1}$; $\sum_{i=1}^{\infty} 2\left(\frac{2}{3}\right)^{i-1}$; $\dfrac{3}{1-\frac{1}{2}} = 6$ and $\dfrac{2}{1-\frac{2}{3}} = 6$

25. a. $a_n = \frac{1}{4}\left(\frac{3}{4}\right)^{n-1}$

b. 1 ft²; As n increases, the area of the removed triangles gets closer to the area of the original triangle.

27. yes; $\sum_{i=1}^{\infty} 9(0.1)^i = 1$

11.4 Review & Refresh

29. arithmetic **30.** neither

31. geometric **32.** exponential

33. a. $a_n = 2n + 3$

b. 96 students

34. $x = \pm 4i$ **35.** $x = 0, x = 3$, and $x = 6$

36. $x = \frac{\ln 12}{\ln 4} \approx 1.79$ **37.** $x = -1$ and $x = -\frac{1}{2}$

38. $4\frac{7}{20}$ **39.** 12

40. $x^2 - x + 4 - \frac{17}{x + 4}$ **41.** $g(x) = 0.5^x + 2$

11.5 Practice

1. $a_1 = 1, a_2 = 4, a_3 = 7, a_4 = 10, a_5 = 13, a_6 = 16$

3. $f(0) = 4, f(1) = 8, f(2) = 16, f(3) = 32, f(4) = 64, f(5) = 128$

5. $a_1 = 2, a_2 = 5, a_3 = 26, a_4 = 677, a_5 = 458{,}330, a_6 = 210{,}066{,}388{,}901$

7. $f(0) = 2, f(1) = 4, f(2) = 2, f(3) = -2, f(4) = -4, f(5) = -2$

9. $a_1 = 21, a_n = a_{n-1} - 7$ **11.** $a_1 = 3, a_n = 4a_{n-1}$

13. $a_1 = 44, a_n = \frac{a_{n-1}}{4}$

15. $a_1 = 2, a_2 = 5, a_n = a_{n-2} \cdot a_{n-1}$

17. $a_1 = 1, a_2 = 4, a_n = a_{n-2} + a_{n-1}$

19. $a_1 = 6, a_n = n \cdot a_{n-1}$

21. $f(1) = 1, f(n) = f(n-1) + 1$

23. A recursive rule needs to include the values of the first terms; $a_1 = 5, a_2 = 2, a_n = a_{n-2} - a_{n-1}$

25. $a_1 = 7, a_n = a_{n-1} + 4$ **27.** $a_1 = 2, a_n = a_{n-1} - 10$

29. $a_1 = 12, a_n = 11a_{n-1}$ **31.** $a_1 = 1.9, a_n = a_{n-1} - 0.6$

33. $a_1 = -\frac{1}{2}, a_n = \frac{1}{4}a_{n-1}$ **35.** $a_1 = 112, a_n = a_{n-1} + 30$

37. $a_n = -6n + 9$ **39.** $a_n = -2(3)^{n-1}$

41. $a_n = 9.1n - 21.1$ **43.** $a_n = -\frac{1}{3}n + \frac{16}{3}$

45. $a_n = -2n + 22$

47. B; An explicit rule is $a_n = 6n - 2$.

49. a. $a_1 = 50{,}000, a_n = 0.8a_{n-1} + 5000$

b. 35,240 members

c. The number stabilizes at about 25,000 people.

51. *Sample answer:* You have saved \$100 for a vacation. Each week, you save \$5 more. $a_1 = 100, a_n = a_{n-1} + 5$

53. a. \$1612.38

b. \$91.39

55. a. $a_1 = 9000, a_n = 0.9a_{n-1} + 800$

b. The number stabilizes at 8000 trees.

57. 144 rabbits; When $n = 12$, each formula produces 144.

59. a. 1, 2, 4, 8, 16, 32, 64; geometric

b. $a_n = 2^{n-1}; a_1 = 1, a_n = 2a_{n-1}$

61. 15 months; \$213.60; $a_1 = 3000$, $a_n = \left(1 + \frac{0.1}{12}\right)a_{n-1} - 213.59$

63. a. $T_n = \frac{1}{2}n^2 + \frac{1}{2}n; S_n = n^2$

b. $T_1 = 1, T_n = T_{n-1} + n; S_1 = 1, S_n = S_{n-1} + 2n - 1$

c. $S_n = T_{n-1} + T_n$

65. no; A recursive rule tells how a_n is related to one or more preceding terms so a recursive equation must contain a previous term such as a_{n-1}. An explicit rule gives a_n as a function of only n.

11.5 Review & Refresh

67. $x = 25$ **68.** $x = 64$

69. $x = 5$ **70.** $a_n = -\frac{2}{125}(5)^{n-1}$

71. $y = \frac{18}{x}; y = \frac{9}{2}$ **72.** $y = -\frac{2}{x}; y = -\frac{1}{2}$

73. $a_n = -2n + 3$ **74.** 12

75. The sum does not exist.

76.

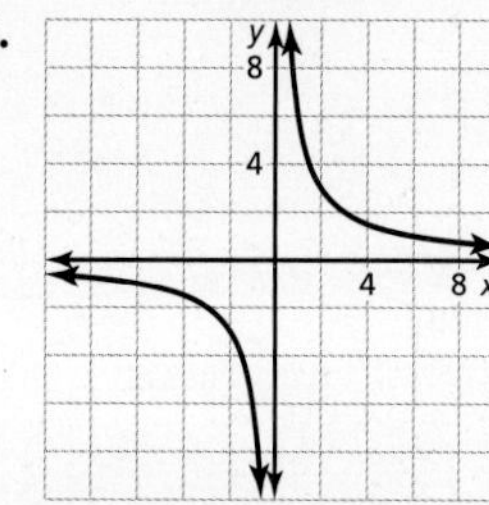

77.

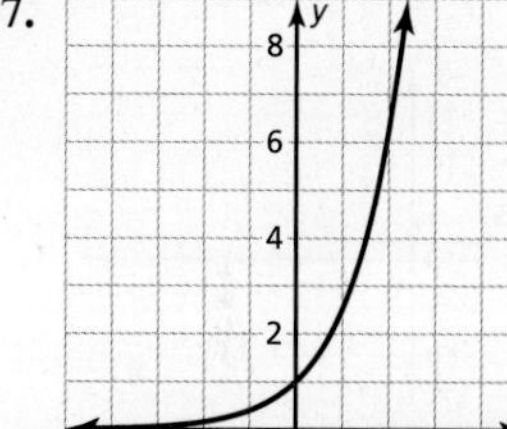

78.

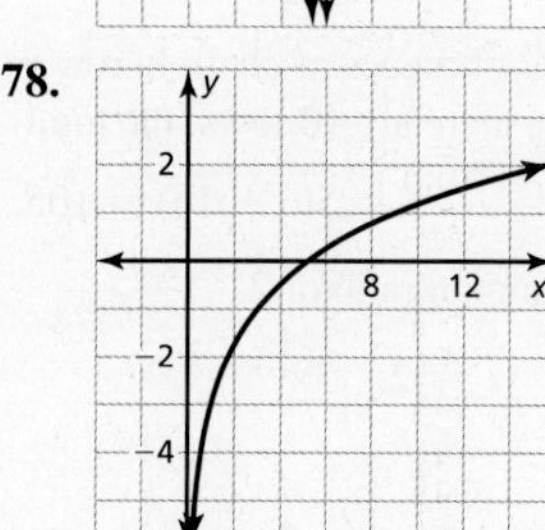

79.

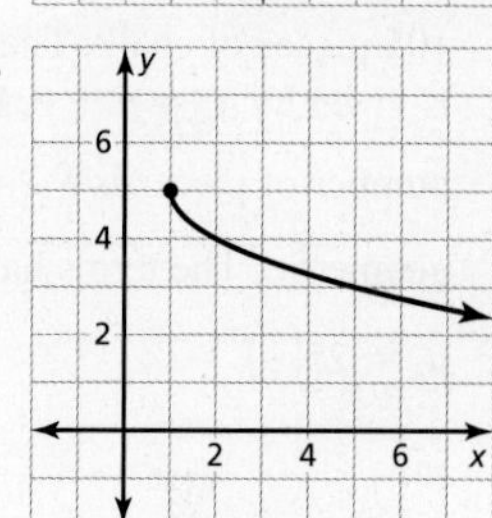

80.

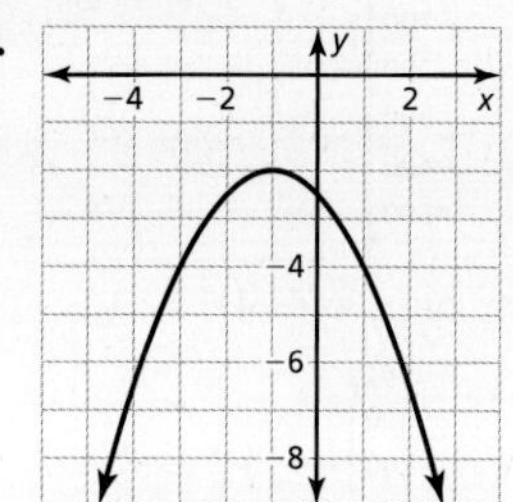

81.

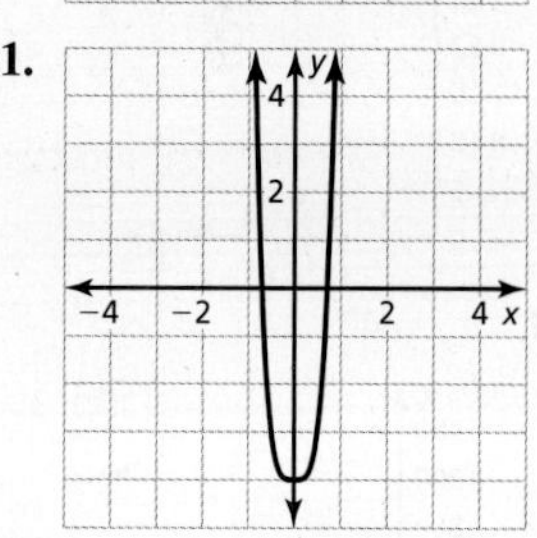

82.

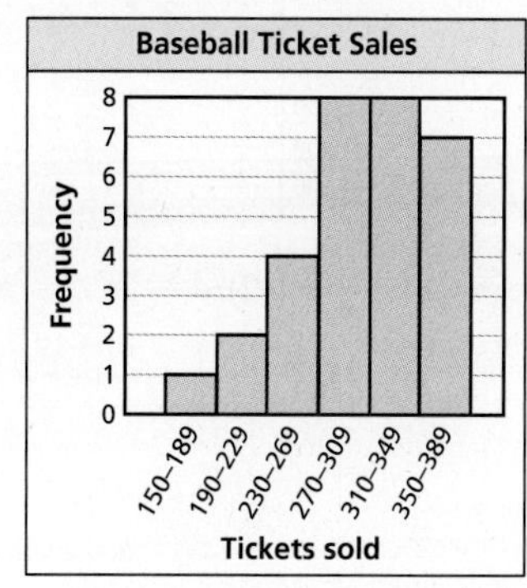

no; The histogram is skewed left, not bell-shaped.

83. $a_1 = 8, a_n = a_{n-1} - 3$ **84.** $a_1 = -5, a_n = 2a_{n-1}$

85. (0, 1), (3, −2); Explanations will vary.

86. $(-3, 4), (0, 4)$; Explanations will vary.

Chapter 11 Review

1. 2, 5, 8, 11, 14, 17

2. 4, −8, 16, −32, 64, −128

3. $a_n = n^2 + n$

4. $\sum_{i=1}^{12} (3i + 4)$

5. $\sum_{i=0}^{\infty} (i^2 + i)$

6. −729

7. 1081

8. 650

9. arithmetic; The terms have a common difference of −8.

10. $a_n = 6n - 4$; $a_{15} = 86$

11. $a_n = 3n$; $a_{15} = 45$

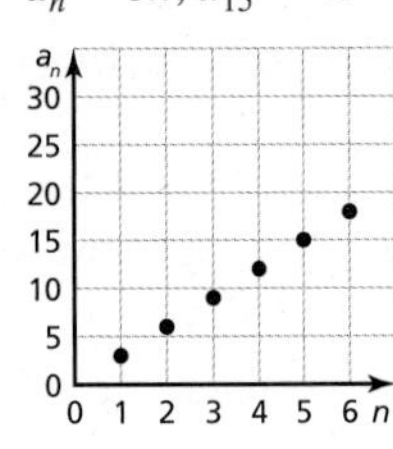

12. $a_n = -4n + 12$; $a_{15} = -48$

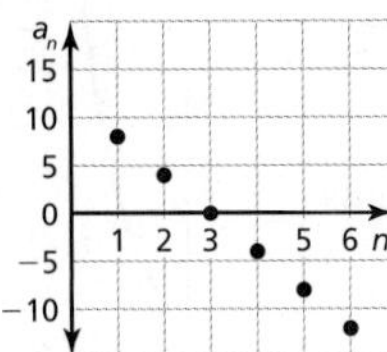

13. 2070

14. 105 pieces of chalk; The number of pieces of chalk in row n is given by $a_n = n + 5$. Because there are 10 rows, the total number of pieces is $S_{10} = \frac{10(a_1 + a_{10})}{2} = 5(6 + 15) = 105$.

15. geometric; The terms have a common ratio of 2.

16. $a_n = 25\left(\frac{2}{5}\right)^{n-1}$

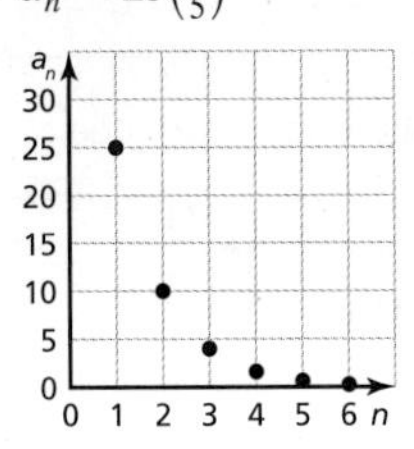

17. $a_n = 2(-3)^{n-1}$

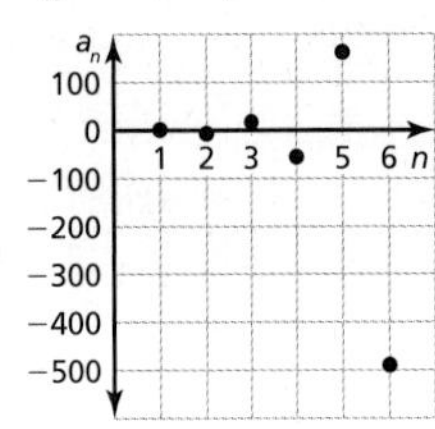

18. $a_n = 4^{n-1}$

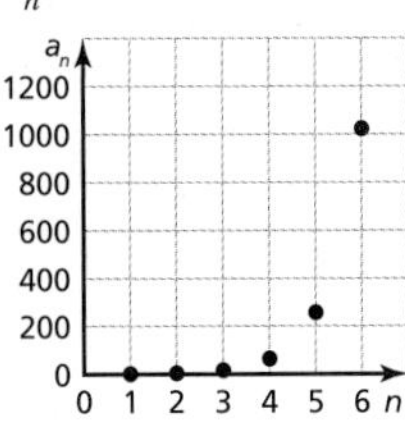

or $a_n = (-4)^{n-1}$

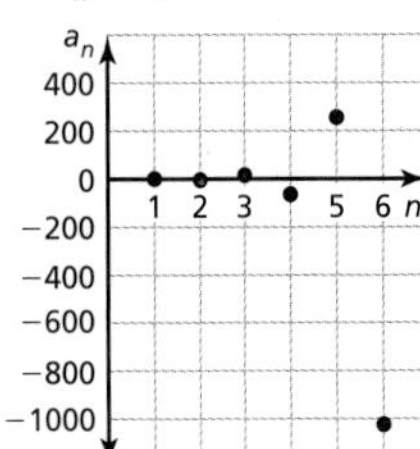

19. $a_n = \frac{1}{4}n$

20. $a_n = \frac{1}{2}(2)^{n-1}$

21. 855

22. $-223\frac{2}{3}$

23. $-\frac{4095}{8192}$

24. a. $a_n = 65{,}000(1.035)^{n-1}$

b. \$74,589

c. \$762,541; The sum $\sum_{n=1}^{10} 65{,}000(1.035)^{n-1}$ is $S_{10} = 65{,}000\left(\frac{1 - 1.035^{10}}{1 - 1.035}\right)$.

25. $S_1 = 1, S_2 = 0.75, S_3 \approx 0.81, S_4 \approx 0.80, S_5 \approx 0.80$; S_n approaches 0.80.

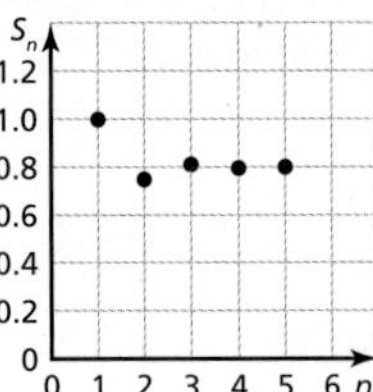

26. $\frac{15}{4}$

27. The sum does not exist.

28. −1.6

29. $\frac{4}{33}$

30. $833\frac{1}{3}$ ft

31. $a_1 = 7, a_2 = 18, a_3 = 29, a_4 = 40, a_5 = 51, a_6 = 62$

32. $a_1 = 6, a_2 = 24, a_3 = 96, a_4 = 384, a_5 = 1536, a_6 = 6144$

33. $f(0) = -2, f(1) = 7, f(2) = -2, f(3) = 7, f(4) = -2, f(5) = 7$

34. $f(0) = 4, f(1) = 6, f(2) = 10, f(3) = 16, f(4) = 24, f(5) = 34$

35. $a_1 = 9, a_n = \frac{2}{3}a_{n-1}$

36. $a_1 = 2, a_n = a_{n-1}(n - 1)$

37. $a_1 = 7, a_2 = 3, a_n = a_{n-2} - a_{n-1}$

38. $a_1 = 105, a_n = \frac{3}{5}a_{n-1}$

39. $a_n = 26n - 30$

40. $a_n = 8(-5)^{n-1}$

41. $a_n = 26\left(\frac{2}{5}\right)^{n-1}$

42. $P_0 = 18, P_n = 1.1P_{n-1}$

43. $a_1 = 1, a_n = a_{n-1} + 4n - 3$

Chapter 11 Mathematical Practices (Chapter Review)

1. *Sample answer:* Write a rule for a recursive sequence that describes the balance after each payment. Then use a spreadsheet to repeat the calculation until you find the balance after the nth payment.

2. $\sum_{n=1}^{\infty} 0.2531(0.0001)^n$; The sum of the series is

$$S = \frac{a_1}{1 - r} = \frac{0.2531}{1 - 0.0001} = \frac{0.2531}{0.9999} = 0.25312531\ldots$$

Chapter 11 Practice Test

1. 1488

2. 1496

3. 10

4. −728

5. geometric; The points appear to follow an exponential curve; $a_n = 2^{n-1}$

6. arithmetic; The points lie on a line; $a_n = -2n + 13$

7. neither; The points do not lie on a line nor follow an exponential curve; $a_n = a_{n-1} + \frac{1}{3 \cdot 2^{n-1}}$.

8. $a_1 = 32, a_n = \frac{1}{2}a_{n-1}, a_9 = \frac{1}{8}$

9. $a_1 = 9, a_n = a_{n-1} + 7, a_9 = 65$

10. $a_1 = 2, a_n = a_{n-1} - n, a_9 = -42$

11. $a_1 = 5, a_n = -4a_{n-1}$; $a_n = 5(-4)^{n-1}$

12. yes; *Sample answer:* $b - a$ and $c - b$ are the same, so b is halfway between a and c.

13. a. $a_n = \left(\frac{1}{2}\right)^{n-1}$

b. 2; As n increases, the sum of the areas of all the shaded squares starting with $n = 2$ approaches the area of the original large square and $1 \text{ ft}^2 + 1 \text{ ft}^2 = 2 \text{ ft}^2$.

14. 22; $a_n = 37n - 19$ and $a_{22} = 37(22) - 19 = 795$

15. 160 in.; The length of each loop of the spring can be represented by a geometric sequence with a common ratio $r = 0.9$. Because $r < 1$, the sum of the infinite geometric sequence of loops is $S = \frac{16}{1 - 0.9} = 160$.

Chapter 11 College and Career Readiness

1. D **2.** A

3. B, A, C, and D; The average rates are −2.5, about 0.96, 3, and 3, respectively.

4. a. $a_n = 38{,}000 + 2000n$, arithmetic; $b_n = 40{,}000(1.04)^{n-1}$, geometric

b.

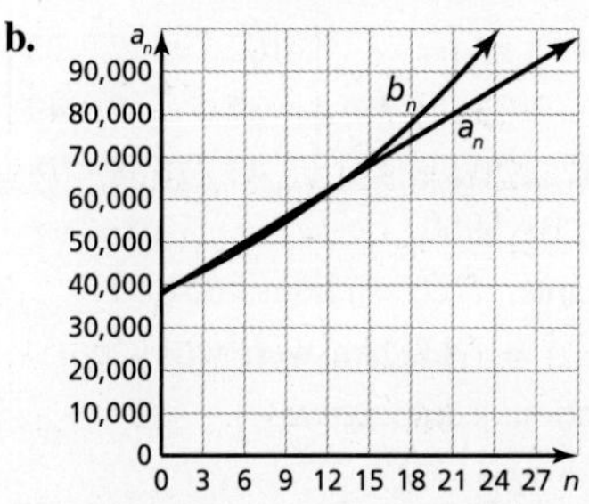

c. Company B is a better choice when you know you will work for 13 years or more.

d. Company A: $1,180,000; Company B: about $1,191,123; The total earnings at Company B are about $11,123 more.

5. B

6. a. arithmetic; The common difference is 1.22 meters.

b. $a_n = 1.22n + 35.28$

c. yes; The curve radius in the outside lane is 45.04 meters.

7. B **8.** C

Chapter 12

Chapter 12 Prepare

1. $x = -\frac{1}{2}$ **2.** $x = \frac{5}{7}$

3. $x = -21$ **4.** $(-6, 2)$

5. $(4, 9)$ **6.** $\left(4, \frac{1}{2}\right)$

7. $y = 2(2x + 3)$; The equations are equivalent.

12.1 Practice

1. $\begin{bmatrix} 10 & -8 \\ 6 & -7 \end{bmatrix}$ **3.** $\begin{bmatrix} 2 \\ 30 \\ -14 \end{bmatrix}$

5. not possible; The matrices have different dimensions.

7. Corresponding elements were not added together;

$\begin{bmatrix} 1 \\ 2 \end{bmatrix} + \begin{bmatrix} 7 \\ 8 \end{bmatrix} = \begin{bmatrix} 8 \\ 10 \end{bmatrix}$

9. $\begin{bmatrix} 9 & 3 \\ 3 & 12 \end{bmatrix}$ **11.** $\begin{bmatrix} 2 & -3 \\ 4 & 6 \\ 1 & 11 \end{bmatrix}$

13. $\begin{bmatrix} 11 & 25 & 11 \\ -6 & 20 & 1 \end{bmatrix}$ **15.** $\begin{bmatrix} -35 & -21 \\ 14 & -28 \\ -56 & 28 \end{bmatrix}$

17. $\begin{bmatrix} 13 & -3 \\ 0 & -1 \end{bmatrix}$ **19.** $\begin{bmatrix} 7.5 & 2.4 \\ -16.4 & -8.8 \end{bmatrix}$

21. $\begin{bmatrix} 18 & 33 \\ 24 & -33 \end{bmatrix}$

23. $a = 6, b = 2, c = 3, d = -4$

25. $a = 10, b = 21, c = -5, d = 11$

27. $a = 6, b = 10, c = 30, d = 4$

29. $a = -\frac{7}{2}, b = 2, c = 1, d = 8$

31.

	May Dogs	May Cats	June Dogs	June Cats	Average Dogs	Average Cats
< 1 yr	6	13	12	7	9	10
1–6 yr	7	5	9	3	8	4
> 6 yr	4	1	2	3	3	2

Over the two months, the monthly average number of adoptions were 9 dogs under 1 year old, 10 cats under 1 year old, 8 dogs between 1 and 6 years old, 4 cats between 1 and 6 years old, 3 dogs over 6 years old, and 2 cats over 6 years old.

33.

U.S.

	Endangered	Threatened
Mammals	66	28
Birds	80	21
Reptiles	17	29
Amphibians	21	15
Fishes	93	74

World

	Endangered	Threatened
Mammals	326	51
Birds	298	41
Reptiles	88	53
Amphibians	29	16
Fishes	115	80

Non-U.S.

	Endangered	Threatened
Mammals	260	23
Birds	218	20
Reptiles	71	24
Amphibians	8	1
Fishes	22	6

The numbers of endangered species not in the United States are 260 mammals, 218 birds, 71 reptiles, 8 amphibians, and 22 fishes. The numbers of threatened species not in the United States are 23 mammals, 20 birds, 24 reptiles, 1 amphibian, and 6 fishes.

35. C **37.** $X = \begin{bmatrix} 1 & 3 \\ 3 & -3 \end{bmatrix}$

39. $X = \begin{bmatrix} 3 & 7 \\ -9 & 3 \end{bmatrix}$

41. yes; The dimension of matrix O is $m \times n$ and every element in it is 0.

43. **a.** $A = \begin{bmatrix} -4 & -2 & -1 \\ 3 & 5 & 3 \end{bmatrix}$

b. $\begin{bmatrix} -2 & 0 & 1 \\ 2 & 4 & 2 \end{bmatrix}$

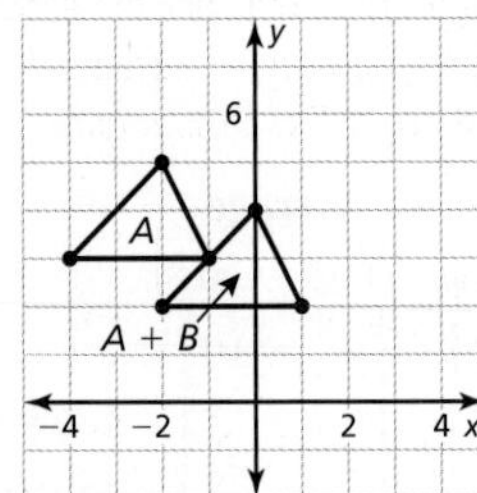

The triangles have the same shape and size and triangle $A + B$ is a translation 2 units right and 1 unit down of triangle A.

c. The triangle represented by $A + B$ is a translation $|c|$ units left or right and $|d|$ units up or down of the triangle represented by A.

45. *Sample answer:* $A = \begin{bmatrix} 4 & 3 \\ 1 & 1 \end{bmatrix}, B = \begin{bmatrix} 1 & 2 \\ 1 & 0 \end{bmatrix}$

47. $A = \begin{bmatrix} -2 & -1 & 8 \\ -3 & -6 & 1 \\ 0 & 9 & -4 \end{bmatrix}$,

$B = \begin{bmatrix} 4 & 7 & -3 \\ -2 & -1 & -9 \\ 3 & 5 & 8 \end{bmatrix}$

12.1 Review & Refresh

48. 15, 12, 9, 6, 3, 0

49. $3x^3 + 4x^2 - 9x - 10$

50. $64t^3 - 48t^2 + 12t - 1$

51. $\dfrac{x^2 - 2x - 15}{x - 3}, x \neq 0, x \neq 7$

52. 0.54

53. 0.3

54. $a_n = \frac{2}{3}(-3)^{n-1}$

55. when the matrices have the same dimensions; *Sample answer:* $[1 \quad 0], [1 \quad 2 \quad 3]$

56. observational study

57. 528 in.^{2}

58. $\frac{64}{3}$

59. $[5 \quad -18 \quad 8]$

60. $\begin{bmatrix} 2 & -3 \\ -6 & 16 \end{bmatrix}$

61. $\begin{bmatrix} -12 & 20 & -24 \\ 4 & -40 & -8 \\ -32 & -48 & 12 \end{bmatrix}$

62. $\begin{bmatrix} 52 & 15 & 28 \\ 6 & -10 & -32 \end{bmatrix}$

12.2 Practice

1. defined; 2×2

3. not defined

5. defined; 1×1

7. not defined

9. [16]

11. not possible; The product is not defined.

13. $\begin{bmatrix} 12 & -26 \\ -8 & 32 \end{bmatrix}$

15. $\begin{bmatrix} -1 & 4 \\ 22 & -24 \\ -10 & 12 \end{bmatrix}$

17. not possible; The product is not defined.

19. $\begin{bmatrix} 14 & 26 \\ -35 & 7 \end{bmatrix}$

21. $\begin{bmatrix} 40 & 9 & 20 \\ -14 & -6 & -11 \end{bmatrix}$

23. Each element in the first row of the first matrix is multiplied by the corresponding element in the first row of the second matrix instead of the first column of the second matrix; $\begin{bmatrix} -2(4) + 3(7) & \\ & \end{bmatrix} = \begin{bmatrix} 13 & \\ & \end{bmatrix}$

25. $\begin{bmatrix} 15 & -17 \\ -6 & 6 \end{bmatrix}$

27. $\begin{bmatrix} 87 & -72 \\ -51 & 48 \end{bmatrix}$

29. $\begin{bmatrix} 33 & 24 \\ -27 & 0 \end{bmatrix}$

31. $x = 2, y = 9$

33. $A^2 = \begin{bmatrix} 7 & -2 \\ -6 & 3 \end{bmatrix}; A^3 = \begin{bmatrix} -20 & 7 \\ 21 & -6 \end{bmatrix}$

35. $AB = \begin{bmatrix} 61 & -107 & 57 \\ -18 & 57 & -33 \\ 48 & -11 & 70 \end{bmatrix}; BA = \begin{bmatrix} 102 & -77 & 73 \\ -31 & 8 & 49 \\ 43 & -58 & 78 \end{bmatrix}$

37. Team A: \$704, Team B: \$960

39. bonobos: \$47; elephants: \$69; sea lions: \$51.50

41. B, C

43. Answers will vary.

45. no; Matrix multiplication is associative.

47. $k(AB) = k\left(\begin{bmatrix} a & b \\ c & d \end{bmatrix}\begin{bmatrix} e & f \\ g & h \end{bmatrix}\right)$

$= k\begin{bmatrix} ae + bg & af + bh \\ ce + dg & cf + dh \end{bmatrix}$

$= \begin{bmatrix} k(ae + bg) & k(af + bh) \\ k(ce + dg) & k(cf + dh) \end{bmatrix}$

$= \begin{bmatrix} kae + kbg & kaf + kbh \\ kce + kdg & kcf + kdh \end{bmatrix}$

$= \begin{bmatrix} (ka)e + (kb)g & (ka)f + (kb)h \\ (kc)e + (kd)g & (kc)f + (kd)h \end{bmatrix}$

$= \begin{bmatrix} ka & kb \\ kc & kd \end{bmatrix}\begin{bmatrix} e & f \\ g & h \end{bmatrix}$

$= \left(k\begin{bmatrix} a & b \\ c & d \end{bmatrix}\right)\begin{bmatrix} e & f \\ g & h \end{bmatrix}$

$= (kA)B$

Similarly, $k(AB) = A(kB)$.

12.2 Review & Refresh

49.

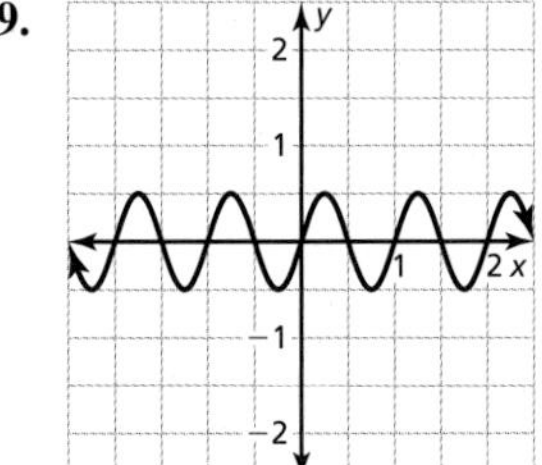

50.

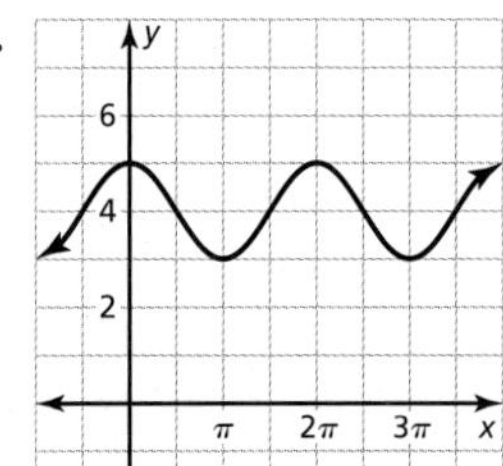

51. $\frac{3}{10}$

52.

The graph of g is a horizontal shrink by a factor of $\frac{1}{4}$ of the graph of $f(x) = \csc x$.

53. 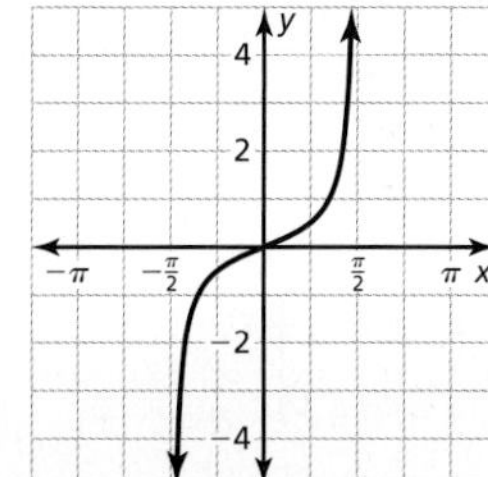

The graph of g is a vertical shrink by a factor of $\frac{1}{2}$ of the graph of $f(x) = \tan x$.

54. **a.** \$7278.42

b. \$149.42

55. $x = \pm 2i$ **56.** $x = \pm 3i$

57. 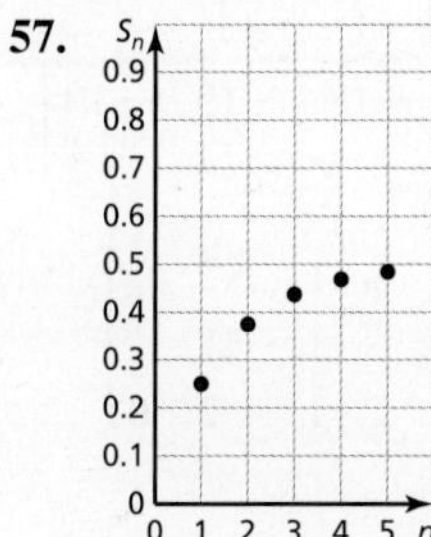

As n increases, S_n approaches $\frac{1}{2}$.

58. $\begin{bmatrix} 6 & -16 \\ 2 & 0 \\ -2 & 8 \end{bmatrix}$

59. not possible; The matrices have different dimensions.

60. $\begin{bmatrix} -10 & 11 \\ 31 & -12 \end{bmatrix}$

61. not possible; The product is not defined.

62. $\begin{bmatrix} -9 & -21 \\ 20 & 2 \end{bmatrix}$

63. $\begin{bmatrix} 10 & -8 & 0 \\ -6 & 4 & 5 \end{bmatrix}$

64. The experimental probability, 17.5%, is greater than the theoretical probability, 12.5%.

65. 3 **66.** −1

12.3 Practice

1. 10 **3.** −12

5. −2 **7.** 12

9. 228 **11.** 26

13. −68 **15.** −61

17. The products were subtracted in the wrong order;

$\begin{vmatrix} 5 & 7 \\ 2 & 4 \end{vmatrix} = 5(4) - 2(7) = 6$

19. D, B, C, A **21.** 11 square units

23. 20 square units **25.** 260 mi^2

27. $y = 3$ **29.** $(2, -1)$

31. $(2, -2)$ **33.** $(2, -1, 1)$

35. $(-3, 4, 3)$

37. $x + y = 6700$

$40x + 25y = 185{,}500$

1200 floor seats, 5500 balcony seats

39. sulfur: 32; chlorine: 35.5; calcium: 40

41. 32 oz

43. $t_1 = 96$ lb, $t_2 = 48$ lb, $a = -16$ ft/s^2

45. no

47. *Sample answer:* Because the blue triangle is a reflection in the origin of the red triangle, the areas are the same; Using the determinant formula for area of a triangle, the areas are both 2.5 square units; Explanations will vary.

49. (40, 120) or (440, 120)

51. *Sample answer:* $\begin{vmatrix} 0 & 1 & 2 \\ 3 & 4 & 5 \\ 6 & 7 & 8 \end{vmatrix} = 0, \begin{vmatrix} 1 & 2 & 3 \\ 4 & 5 & 6 \\ 7 & 8 & 9 \end{vmatrix} = 0,$

$\begin{vmatrix} 2 & 3 & 4 \\ 5 & 6 & 7 \\ 8 & 9 & 10 \end{vmatrix} = 0, \begin{vmatrix} 3 & 4 & 5 \\ 6 & 7 & 8 \\ 9 & 10 & 11 \end{vmatrix} = 0$; The determinant of a 3×3 matrix in which the elements are consecutive integers equals 0.

53. **a.** $x = \dfrac{ed - bf}{ad - bc}, y = \dfrac{af - ce}{ad - bc}$

b. The expressions for x and y are equivalent to those given by Cramer's rule for a 2×2 system.

12.3 Review & Refresh

54. 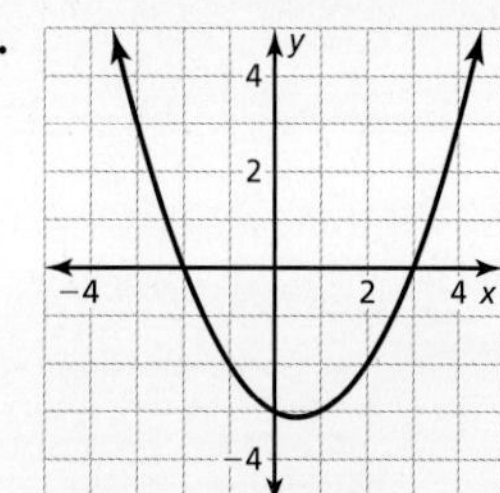

x-intercepts: $(-2, 0)$, $(3, 0)$; local min: $(0.5, -3.125)$; decreasing when $x < 0.5$ and increasing when $x > 0.5$.

55. 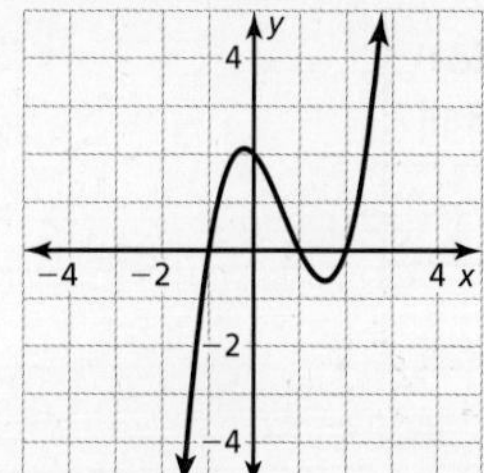

x-intercepts: $(-1, 0)$, $(1, 0)$, $(2, 0)$;
local min: about $(1.55, -0.63)$,
local max: about $(-0.22, 2.11)$;
decreasing when $-0.22 < x < 1.55$ and increasing when $x < -0.22$ and $x > 1.55$.

56. $a = 4, b = 4, c = 22, d = -7$

57. $\begin{bmatrix} 14 & 2 \\ 21 & 12 \end{bmatrix}$

58. $a_1 = 5, a_n = na_{n-1}$ **59.** $x = \frac{11}{2}$

60. (2, 5)

61. quadratic; $a_5 = 24.5$; $a_n = 0.5n^2 + 2.5n - 0.5$

62. $x = -1, x = \frac{1}{2}$, and $x = 3$

63. $\sin\left(\frac{3\pi}{2} - x\right)\tan x = \left(\sin\frac{3\pi}{2}\cos x - \cos\frac{3\pi}{2}\sin x\right)\tan x$

$= [(-1)\cos x - 0 \cdot \sin x]\tan x$

$= -\cos x \tan x$

$= -\cos x \dfrac{\sin x}{\cos x}$

$= -\sin x$

64. not independent

65. $x = -3, x = -1$, and $x = 3$

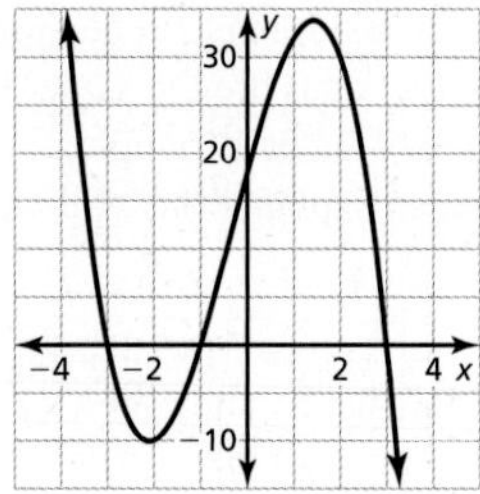

66. $f^{-1}(x) = -\sqrt{\dfrac{x}{9}}$

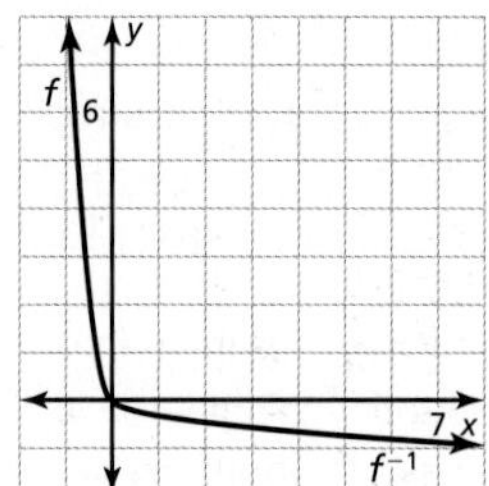

67. $c = 9$; $(x + 3)^2 = x^2 + 6x + 9$

68.

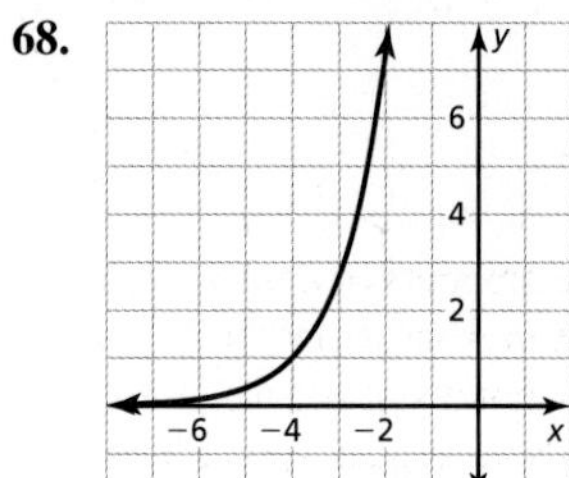

domain: all real numbers, range: $y > 0$

69.

Probability Distribution for Choosing a Table Tennis Ball			
x	1	2	3
P(x)	$\frac{1}{2}$	$\frac{1}{3}$	$\frac{1}{6}$

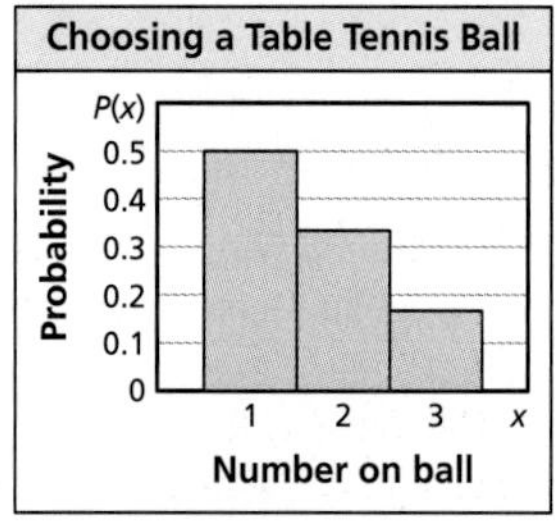

70. $\dfrac{2x^2 + 5x + 6}{(x + 1)(x + 2)}$

71.

12.4 Practice

1. $\begin{bmatrix} 7 & -3 \\ -9 & 4 \end{bmatrix}$

3. $\begin{bmatrix} -7 & 8 \\ 8 & -9 \end{bmatrix}$

5. The inverse does not exist.

7. $\begin{bmatrix} \frac{7}{2} & \frac{3}{2} \\ \frac{11}{2} & \frac{5}{2} \end{bmatrix}$

9. $\begin{bmatrix} -\frac{5}{2} & 1 \\ -7 & 3 \end{bmatrix}$

11. The second matrix is multiplied by the determinant (2) instead of the reciprocal of the determinant $\left(\frac{1}{2}\right)$;

$$\begin{bmatrix} 4 & 1 \\ 6 & 2 \end{bmatrix}^{-1} = \frac{1}{2}\begin{bmatrix} 2 & -1 \\ -6 & 4 \end{bmatrix} = \begin{bmatrix} 1 & -\frac{1}{2} \\ -3 & 2 \end{bmatrix}$$

13. $X = \begin{bmatrix} 1 & 2 \\ 2 & 1 \end{bmatrix}$

15. $X = \begin{bmatrix} 4 & -5 \\ -1 & 3 \end{bmatrix}$

17. $X = \begin{bmatrix} 7 & -7 \\ -3 & -8 \end{bmatrix}$

19. $X = \begin{bmatrix} -18 & -19 & -10 \\ -3 & -4 & -2 \end{bmatrix}$

21. $A^{-1} = \begin{bmatrix} 1 & 1 & 0 \\ 6 & 7 & -2 \\ -3 & -3 & 1 \end{bmatrix}$

23. $A^{-1} = \begin{bmatrix} -1 & -2 & \frac{1}{2} \\ -1 & -1 & \frac{1}{2} \\ 1 & 2 & 0 \end{bmatrix}$

25. $A^{-1} = \begin{bmatrix} 9 & -7 & -6 \\ -\frac{1}{2} & \frac{1}{2} & \frac{1}{2} \\ \frac{11}{4} & -\frac{9}{4} & -\frac{7}{4} \end{bmatrix}$

27. $(3, -1)$

29. $(7, 8)$

31. $(-1, 2)$

33. $(-3, 4)$

35. $(-9, 19, -10)$

37. $(-1, -2, 3)$

39. rose: \$5.00, carnation: \$1.50, tulip: \$2.00

41. C

43. always; The product is always the identity matrix.

45. no; The inverse is only defined for an $n \times n$, or square matrix.

47. *Sample answer:* The product of a real number and 1 is the original number, and the product of an $n \times n$ matrix and the identity matrix is the original matrix.

49. **a.** $p = 2q$

b. $p \neq 2q$

51. **a.** $[3 \quad 1 \quad 20]$

b. $[31 \quad -42 \quad 22]$

c. RUN

d. Answers will vary. *Sample answer:* "SKY" coded is $[7 \quad -58 \quad 33]$.

53. $\begin{bmatrix} a & b \\ c & d \end{bmatrix} \times \dfrac{1}{ad - bc}\begin{bmatrix} d & -b \\ -c & a \end{bmatrix}$

$= \begin{bmatrix} a & b \\ c & d \end{bmatrix} \times \begin{bmatrix} \dfrac{d}{ad - bc} & \dfrac{-b}{ad - bc} \\ \dfrac{-c}{ad - bc} & \dfrac{a}{ad - bc} \end{bmatrix}$

$= \begin{bmatrix} a\dfrac{d}{ad - bc} + b\dfrac{-c}{ad - bc} & a\dfrac{-b}{ad - bc} + b\dfrac{a}{ad - bc} \\ c\dfrac{d}{ad - bc} + d\dfrac{-c}{ad - bc} & c\dfrac{-b}{ad - bc} + d\dfrac{a}{ad - bc} \end{bmatrix}$

$= \begin{bmatrix} \dfrac{ad - bc}{ad - bc} & \dfrac{-ab + ab}{ad - bc} \\ \dfrac{cd - cd}{ad - bc} & \dfrac{-bc + ad}{ad - bc} \end{bmatrix}$

$= \begin{bmatrix} 1 & 0 \\ 0 & 1 \end{bmatrix} = I$

Because $A \bullet A^{-1} = I$ and $A^{-1} \bullet A = I$ (not shown), $A^{-1} = \dfrac{1}{ad - bc}\begin{bmatrix} d & -b \\ -c & a \end{bmatrix}$.

12.4 Review & Refresh

54. $x^3(2x + 1)(x + 5)$

55. $(3t^2 + 10)(3t^2 - 10)$

56. $(y + 6)(y^2 - 6y + 36)$

57. $(n + 3)(n + 4)(n - 4)$

58. domain: $x \geq 5$, range: $y \geq -1$

59.

	2010 Male	2010 Female	2020 Male	2020 Female	Change Male	Change Female
0–19	13	12	15	14	2	2
20–59	26	27	27	29	1	2
60+	7	9	8	10	1	1

From 2010 to 2020, the populations of males ages 0–19 increased by 2000 and females ages 0–19 increased by 2000, the populations of males ages 20–59 increased by 1000 and females ages 20–59 increased by 2000, and the populations of males ages 60+ increased by 1000 and females ages 60+ increased by 1000.

60. $(f + g)(x) = 2x^{1/2}$, domain: $x \geq 0$; $(f - g)(x) = 8x^{1/2}$, domain: $x \geq 0$; $(f + g)(16) = 8$; $(f - g)(16) = 32$

61. -52

62. 2

63. $-\dfrac{\sqrt{3}}{3}$

64. exponential

65. $\begin{bmatrix} 6 & 49 \\ -14 & -46 \\ -7 & 18 \end{bmatrix}$

66. $g(x) = \dfrac{10}{x - 2} + 3$

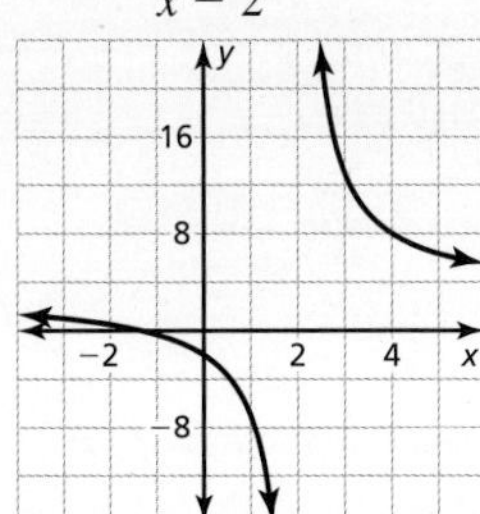

The graph of g is a horizontal translation 2 units right and a vertical translation 3 units up of the graph of $f(x) = \dfrac{10}{x}$.

67. $(-4, 2)$

68. 32; 6

69. $x = -2$ and $x = 10$

Chapter 12 Review

1. $\begin{bmatrix} 3 & -2 \\ -5 & 7 \end{bmatrix}$

2. $\begin{bmatrix} 2 & -4 & 0 \\ 7 & 6 & 7 \end{bmatrix}$

3. $\begin{bmatrix} -15 & 6 \\ -9 & -18 \end{bmatrix}$

4. $\begin{bmatrix} 64 & 32 & 40 \\ -8 & 48 & -16 \end{bmatrix}$

5. $\begin{bmatrix} 7 & 6 \\ 8 & -1 \\ 3 & 1 \end{bmatrix}$

6. $\begin{bmatrix} 3 & 10 \\ 10 & -3 \\ -1 & 6 \end{bmatrix}$

7. $a = -6, b = 3, c = 8, d = -3$

8. $a = 10, b = -3, c = -1, d = 3$

9. $a = -1, b = 2, c = -5, d = -2$

10.

	Year 1 Apples	Year 1 Peaches	Year 2 Apples	Year 2 Peaches
July	450	960	510	930
August	530	1130	650	1260
September	1050	720	990	580

	Average Apples	Average Peaches
July	480	945
August	590	1195
September	1020	650

Over the two years, the average amounts of apples were 480 pounds in July, 590 pounds in August, and 1020 pounds in September, and the average amounts of peaches were 945 pounds in July, 1195 pounds in August, and 650 pounds in September.

11. $[-2 \quad 7]$

12. $\begin{bmatrix} 28 & -76 \\ -20 & 10 \end{bmatrix}$

13. $\begin{bmatrix} 17 & -20 & 10 \\ 26 & 82 & 46 \end{bmatrix}$

14. $\begin{bmatrix} -2 & 6 & -15 \\ 6 & 0 & -3 \end{bmatrix}$

15. not possible; The product is not defined.

16. $\begin{bmatrix} -1 & -31 \\ -17 & 11 \end{bmatrix}$

17. $\begin{bmatrix} -31 & 4 \\ -22 & 8 \end{bmatrix}$

18. $\begin{bmatrix} 10 & -2 \\ -50 & 20 \end{bmatrix}$

19. $\begin{bmatrix} 40 & -20 \\ -6 & -6 \\ 16 & -14 \end{bmatrix}$

20. $\begin{bmatrix} 7{,}381{,}000 \\ 7{,}281{,}000 \end{bmatrix}$

21. -42

22. 28

23. 14

24. *Sample answer:* 0, 2; -4, 0; The value of the determinant is $\det A = 5 + a - 2b$, where a and b are the missing values.

25. about 12.15 ft^2

26. $\begin{bmatrix} -\frac{5}{3} & \frac{2}{3} \\ \frac{4}{3} & -\frac{1}{3} \end{bmatrix}$

27. $\begin{bmatrix} -\frac{1}{8} & \frac{1}{8} \\ -\frac{5}{16} & -\frac{3}{16} \end{bmatrix}$

28. $\begin{bmatrix} \frac{1}{8} & -\frac{1}{6} \\ -\frac{1}{16} & -\frac{1}{12} \end{bmatrix}$

29. $X = \begin{bmatrix} -38 & -13 \\ -54 & -18 \end{bmatrix}$

30. $X = \begin{bmatrix} -\frac{5}{2} & -\frac{9}{2} \\ 4 & 7 \end{bmatrix}$

31. $X = \begin{bmatrix} -2 & -6 \\ -6 & -28 \end{bmatrix}$

32. $(7, 1)$

33. $(-2, 5)$

34. $(-1, -4)$

35. $\begin{bmatrix} \frac{1}{n} & 0 & 0 \\ 0 & \frac{1}{n} & 0 \\ 0 & 0 & \frac{1}{n} \end{bmatrix}$; $\begin{bmatrix} \frac{1}{n} & 0 & 0 \\ 0 & \frac{1}{n} & 0 \\ 0 & 0 & \frac{1}{n} \end{bmatrix}\begin{bmatrix} n & 0 & 0 \\ 0 & n & 0 \\ 0 & 0 & n \end{bmatrix} = \begin{bmatrix} 1 & 0 & 0 \\ 0 & 1 & 0 \\ 0 & 0 & 1 \end{bmatrix}$ and

$\begin{bmatrix} n & 0 & 0 \\ 0 & n & 0 \\ 0 & 0 & n \end{bmatrix}\begin{bmatrix} \frac{1}{n} & 0 & 0 \\ 0 & \frac{1}{n} & 0 \\ 0 & 0 & \frac{1}{n} \end{bmatrix} = \begin{bmatrix} 1 & 0 & 0 \\ 0 & 1 & 0 \\ 0 & 0 & 1 \end{bmatrix}$

36. pancake: $2.25, egg: $0.75, sausage link: $1.25

Chapter 12 Mathematical Practices (Chapter Review)

1. Answers will vary.
2. D^{-1} does not exist; The linear system would have no solution or infinitely many solutions because one row of the matrix is a multiple of the other.

Chapter 12 Practice Test

1. $\begin{bmatrix} -9 & 3 \\ 11 & 14 \end{bmatrix}$
2. not possible
3. $\begin{bmatrix} 0 & 9 \\ 4 & 7 \end{bmatrix}$
4. $\begin{bmatrix} -5 & 3 & 0 \\ -10 & 12 & -5 \end{bmatrix}$
5. 11
6. -54
7. 42 square units
8. $(2, -5, -1)$
9. $(-2, 3)$
10. $X = \begin{bmatrix} 11 & 9 \\ -9 & -6 \end{bmatrix}$
11. **2014** **Norway Germany Canada** $\begin{bmatrix} 11 & 8 & 10 \\ 5 & 6 & 10 \\ 10 & 5 & 5 \end{bmatrix}$ **2018** **Norway Germany Canada** $\begin{bmatrix} 14 & 14 & 11 \\ 14 & 10 & 8 \\ 11 & 7 & 10 \end{bmatrix}$ **Gold** **Silver** **Bronze**

    Average
    Norway Germany Canada
    $\begin{bmatrix} 12.5 & 11 & 10.5 \\ 9.5 & 8 & 9 \\ 10.5 & 6 & 7.5 \end{bmatrix}$ **Gold** **Silver** **Bronze**

    Over the two years, Norway won an average of 12.5 gold medals, 9.5 silver medals, and 10.5 bronze medals. Over the two years, Germany won an average of 11 gold medals, 8 silver medals, and 6 bronze medals. Over the two years, Canada won an average of 10.5 gold medals, 9 silver medals, and 7.5 bronze medals.

12. $y = 3x^2 + 2x + 1$; The system is
    $4a - 2b + c = 9$
    $a - b + c = 2$,
    $a + b + c = 6$
    so solve using matrices to yield $(a, b, c) = (3, 2, 1)$.
13. 450 children, 225 adult, 125 senior citizen

Chapter 12 College and Career Readiness

1. B
2. $\pm\frac{1}{2}\begin{vmatrix} 0 & 0 & 1 \\ 20 & 0 & 1 \\ x & y & 1 \end{vmatrix} = 100$; $y = 10, 0 < x < 20$
3. B
4. B
5. A
6. D
7. C
8. 8

English-Spanish Glossary

English	Spanish

A

amplitude *(p. 546)* One-half the difference of the maximum value and the minimum value of the graph of a trigonometric function

amplitud *(p. 546)* La mitad de la diferencia del valor máximo y el valor mínimo del gráfico de una función trigonométrica

arithmetic sequence *(p. 604)* A sequence in which the difference of consecutive terms is constant

secuencia aritmética *(p. 604)* Una secuencia en la que la diferencia de términos consecutivos es constante

arithmetic series *(p. 606)* An expression formed by adding the terms of an arithmetic sequence

serie aritmética *(p. 606)* Una expresión formada al sumar los términos de una secuencia aritmética

asymptote *(p. 294)* A line that a graph approaches more and more closely

asíntota *(p. 294)* Una recta a la que una gráfica se acerca cada vez más

axis of symmetry *(p. 54)* A line that divides a parabola into mirror images and passes through the vertex

eje de simetría *(p. 54)* Una recta que divide una parábola en imágenes reflejo y que pasa a través del vértice

B

bias *(p. 483)* An error that results in a misrepresentation of a population

sesgo *(p. 483)* Un error que da como resultado una representación errónea de una población

biased question *(p. 485)* A question that is flawed in a way that leads to inaccurate results

pregunta sesgada *(p. 485)* Una pregunta imperfecta que lleva a obtener resultados inexactos

biased sample *(p. 483)* A sample that overrepresents or underrepresents part of a population

muestra sesgada *(p. 483)* Una muestra que representa excesiva o insuficientemente parte de una población

binomial distribution *(p. 451)* A type of probability distribution that shows the probabilities of the outcomes of a binomial experiment

distribución del binomio *(p. 451)* Un tipo de distribución de probabilidades que muestra las probabilidades de los resultados posibles de un experimento del binomio

binomial experiment *(p. 451)* An experiment in which there are a fixed number of independent trials, exactly two possible outcomes for each trial, and the probability of success is the same for each trial

experimento del binomio *(p. 451)* Un experimento en el que hay un número fijo de pruebas independientes, exactamente dos resultados posibles para cada prueba, y la probabilidad de éxito es la misma para cada prueba

Binomial Theorem *(p. 444)* For any positive integer n, the binomial expansion of $(a + b)^n$ is

$$(a + b)^n = {}_nC_0a^nb^0 + {}_nC_1a^{n-1}b^1 + {}_nC_2a^{n-2}b^2 + \cdots + {}_nC_na^0b^n.$$

teorema del binomio *(p. 444)* Por cada número entero positivo n, la expansión del binomio de $(a + b)^n$ es

$$(a + b)^n = {}_nC_0a^nb^0 + {}_nC_1a^{n-1}b^1 + {}_nC_2a^{n-2}b^2 + \cdots + {}_nC_na^0b^n.$$

central angle *(p. 532)* The angle measure of a sector of a circle formed by two radii

ángulo central *(p. 532)* La medida del ángulo de un sector de un círculo formado por dos radios

cluster sample *(p. 482)* A sample in which a population is divided into groups, called clusters, and all of the members in one or more of the clusters are randomly selected

muestra de cluster *(p. 482)* Una muestra en la que una población se divide en grupos, llamados cluster en inglés, y todos los miembros de uno o más de los cluster son seleccionados en forma aleatoria

coefficient matrix *(p. 664)* A matrix consisting of the coefficients of a linear system

matriz de coeficiente *(p. 664)* Una matriz que consiste en los coeficientes de un sistema lineal

combination *(p. 442)* A selection of objects in which order is not important

combinación *(p. 442)* Una selección de objetos en la que el orden no es importante

common difference *(p. 604)* The constant difference d between consecutive terms of an arithmetic sequence

diferencia común *(p. 604)* La diferencia constante d entre términos consecutivos de una secuencia aritmética

common logarithm *(p. 309)* A logarithm with base 10, denoted as $\log_{10}$ or simply by log

logaritmo común *(p. 309)* Un logaritmo de base 10, denotado como $\log_{10}$ o simplemente como log

common ratio *(p. 612)* The constant ratio r between consecutive terms of a geometric sequence

razón común *(p. 612)* La razón constante r entre términos consecutivos de una secuencia geométrica

completing the square *(p. 110)* To add a term c to an expression of the form $x^2 + bx$ such that $x^2 + bx + c$ is a perfect square trinomial

completando el cuadrado *(p. 110)* Agregar un término c a una expresión de la forma $x^2 + bx$ para que $x^2 + bx + c$ sea un trinomio de cuadrado perfecto

complex conjugates *(p. 102)* Pairs of complex numbers of the forms $a + bi$ and $a - bi$, where $b \neq 0$

conjugados complejos *(p. 102)* Pares de números complejos de las formas $a + bi$ y $a - bi$, donde $b \neq 0$

complex fraction *(p. 381)* A fraction that contains a fraction in its numerator or denominator

fracción compleja *(p. 381)* Una fracción que contiene una fracción en su numerador o denominador

complex number *(p. 100)* A number written in the form $a + bi$, where a and b are real numbers

número complejo *(p. 100)* Un número escrito en la forma $a + bi$, donde a y b son números reales

composition *(p. 268)* A combination of functions where the output of one function is used as the input of another function

composición *(p. 268)* Una combinación de funciones en las que el resultado de una función se usa como la entra de otra función

compound event *(p. 434)* The union or intersection of two events

evento compuesto *(p. 434)* La unión o intersección de dos eventos

conditional probability *(p. 418)* The probability that event B occurs given that event A has occurred, written as $P(B|A)$

probabilidad condicional *(p. 418)* La probabilidad de que el evento B ocurra dado que el evento A ha ocurrido, escrito como $P(B|A)$

conditional relative frequency *(p. 414)* The ratio of a joint relative frequency to the marginal relative frequency in a two-way table

frecuencia relativa condicional *(p. 414)* La razón de una frecuencia relativa conjunta a la frecuencia relativa marginal en una tabla de doble entrada

constant of variation *(p. 356)* A constant that describes the relationship between a pair of variables that show direct variation or inverse variation

constante de variación *(p. 356)* Una constante que describe la relación entre un par de variables que muestran una variación directa o una variación inversa

control group *(p. 490)* The group that is not subjected to the treatment during an experiment

grupo de control *(p. 490)* El grupo que no se ve sometido a tratamiento durante un experimento

controlled experiment *(p. 490)* An experiment in which groups are studied under the same conditions with the exception of one or more variables of interest

experimento controlado *(p. 490)* Un experimento en el que grupos son estudiados bajo las mismas condiciones con la excepción de una o más variables de interés

convenience sample *(p. 482)* A sample in which only members of a population who are easy to reach are selected

muestra de conveniencia *(p. 482)* Una muestra en la que únicamente se seleccionan los miembros de una población a los que es fácil de llegar

correlation coefficient *(p. 23)* A number r from -1 to 1 that measures how well a line fits a set of data pairs (x, y)

coeficiente de correlación *(p. 23)* Un número r de -1 a 1 que mide cuán bien ajusta una recta a un conjunto de pares de datos (x, y)

cosecant *(p. 522)* A trigonometric function for an acute angle θ of a right triangle, denoted by $\csc\theta = \dfrac{\text{hypotenuse}}{\text{opposite}}$

cosecante *(p. 522)* Una ecuación trigonométrica de un ángulo agudo θ de un triángulo recto, denotado por $\csc\theta = \dfrac{\text{hipotenusa}}{\text{opuesto}}$

cosine *(p. 522)* A trigonometric function for an acute angle θ of a right triangle, denoted by $\cos\theta = \dfrac{\text{adjacent}}{\text{hypotenuse}}$

coseno *(p. 522)* Una ecuación trigonométrica de un ángulo agudo θ de un triángulo recto, denotado por $\cos\theta = \dfrac{\text{adyacente}}{\text{hipotenusa}}$

cotangent *(p. 522)* A trigonometric function for an acute angle θ of a right triangle, denoted by $\cot\theta = \dfrac{\text{adjacent}}{\text{opposite}}$

cotangente *(p. 522)* Una ecuación trigonométrica de un ángulo agudo θ de un triángulo recto, denotado por $\cot\theta = \dfrac{\text{adyacente}}{\text{opuesto}}$

coterminal *(p. 531)* Two angles whose terminal sides coincide

coterminal *(p. 531)* Dos ángulos cuyos lados terminales coinciden

Cramer's Rule *(p. 664)* A method of using determinants to solve a system of linear equations

Regla de Cramer *(p. 664)* Un método de uso de determinantes para resolver un sistema de ecuaciones lineales

cycle *(p. 546)* The shortest repeating portion of the graph of a periodic function

ciclo *(p. 546)* La porción más corta que se repite en el gráfico de una función periódica

D

decay factor *(p. 294)* The value of b in an exponential decay function of the form $y = ab^x$, where $a > 0$ and $0 < b < 1$

factor de decaimiento *(p. 294)* El valor de b en una función de decaimiento exponencial de la forma $y = ab^x$, donde $a > 0$ y $0 < b < 1$

dependent events *(p. 428)* Two events in which the occurrence of one event does affect the occurrence of the other event

eventos dependientes *(p. 428)* Dos eventos en los que la ocurrencia de un evento afecta la ocurrencia del otro evento

descriptive statistics *(p. 496)* The branch of statistics that involves the organization, summarization, and display of data

estadística descriptiva *(p. 496)* La rama de la estadística que implica la organización, resumen y presentación de datos

determinant *(p. 662)* A real number associated with each square $(n \times n)$ matrix

determinante *(p. 662)* Un número real asociado con cada matriz cuadrada $(n \times n)$

dimensions of a matrix *(p. 646)* The number of rows and columns in a matrix

dimensiones de una matriz *(p. 646)* El número de filas y columnas de una matriz

direct variation *(p. 356)* Two variables x and y show direct variation when $y = ax$, where $a \neq 0$.

variación directa *(p. 356)* Dos variables x e y muestra una variación directa cuando $y = ax$, donde $a \neq 0$.

GLOSSARY

directrix *(p. 64)* A fixed line perpendicular to the axis of symmetry, such that the set of all points (x, y) of the parabola are equidistant from the focus and the directrix

directriz *(p. 64)* Una recta fija perpendicular al eje de simetría de modo tal, que el conjunto de todos los puntos (x, y) de la parábola sean equidistantes del foco y la directriz

discriminant *(p. 120)* The expression $b^2 - 4ac$ in the Quadratic Formula

discriminante *(p. 120)* La expresión $b^2 - 4ac$ en la Fórmula Cuadrática

disjoint events *(p. 434)* Two events that have no outcomes in common

eventos disjunto *(p. 434)* Dos eventos que no tienen resultados en común

elements of a matrix *(p. 646)* The numbers in a matrix

elementos de una matriz *(p. 646)* Los números en una matriz

end behavior *(p. 155)* The behavior of the graph of a function as x approaches positive infinity or negative infinity

comportamiento final *(p. 155)* El comportamiento del gráfico de una función a medida que x se aproxima al infinito positivo o negativo

equal matrices *(p. 646)* Matrices with the same dimensions and with equal elements in corresponding positions

matrices iguales *(p. 646)* Matrices con las mismas dimensiones y con elementos iguales en posiciones correspondientes

even function *(p. 209)* For a function f, $f(-x) = f(x)$ for all x in its domain

función par *(p. 209)* Para una función f, $f(-x) = f(x)$ para toda x en su dominio

event *(p. 404)* A collection of one or more outcomes in a probability experiment

evento *(p. 404)* Una colección de uno o más resultados en un experimento de probabilidades

experiment *(p. 484)* A method that imposes a treatment on individuals in order to collect data on their response to the treatment

experimento *(p. 484)* Un método que impone un tratamiento a individuos para recoger datos con respecto a su respuesta al tratamiento

experimental probability *(p. 407)* The ratio of the number of successes, or favorable outcomes, to the number of trials in a probability experiment

probabilidad experimental *(p. 407)* La razón del número de éxitos, o resultados favorables, con respecto al número de pruebas en un experimento de probabilidades

explicit rule *(p. 626)* A rule that gives a_n as a function of the term's position number n in the sequence

regla explícita *(p. 626)* Una regla que da a_n como una función del número de posición n del término en la secuencia

exponential decay function *(p. 294)* A function of the form $y = ab^x$, where $a > 0$ and $0 < b < 1$

función de decaimiento exponencial *(p. 294)* Una función de la forma $y = ab^x$, donde $a > 0$ y $0 < b < 1$

exponential equations *(p. 330)* Equations in which variable expressions occur as exponents

ecuaciones exponenciales *(p. 330)* Ecuaciones en donde las expresiones de una variable ocurren como exponentes

exponential function *(p. 294)* A function of the form $y = ab^x$, where $a \neq 0$ and the base b is a positive real number other than 1

función exponencial *(p. 294)* Una función de la forma $y = ab^x$, donde $a \neq 0$ y la base b es un número real positivo distinto de 1

exponential growth function *(p. 294)* A function of the form $y = ab^x$, where $a > 0$ and $b > 1$

función de crecimiento exponencial *(p. 294)* Una función de la forma $y = ab^x$, dónde $a > 0$ y $b > 1$

extraneous solutions *(p. 255)* Solutions that are not solutions of the original equation

soluciones externas *(p. 255)* Soluciones que no son soluciones de la ecuación original

factor by grouping *(p. 177)* A method of factoring a polynomial by grouping pairs of terms that have a common monomial factor

factorización por agrupación *(p. 177)* Un método de factorización de un polinomio al agrupar pares de términos que tienen un factor monomio común

factored completely *(p. 176)* A polynomial written as a product of unfactorable polynomials with integer coefficients

factorizado completamente *(p. 176)* Un polinomio escrito como un producto de polinomios no factorizables con coeficientes de números enteros

finite differences *(p. 214)* The differences of consecutive y-values in a data set when the x-values are equally spaced

diferencias finitas *(p. 214)* Las diferencias de valores consecutivos y en un conjunto de datos cuando los valores x están igualmente espaciados

focus *(p. 64)* A fixed point in the interior of a parabola, such that the set of all points (x, y) of the parabola are equidistant from the focus and the directrix

foco *(p. 64)* Un punto fijo en el interior de una parábola, de tal forma que el conjunto de todos los puntos (x, y) de la parábola sean equidistantes del foco y la directriz

frequency *(p. 564)* The number of cycles per unit of time, which is the reciprocal of the period

frecuencia *(p. 564)* El número de ciclos por unidad de tiempo, que es el recíproco del período

geometric probability *(p. 406)* A probability found by calculating a ratio of two lengths, areas, or volumes

probabilidad geométrica *(p. 406)* Una probabilidad hallada al calcular la razón de dos longitudes, áreas o volúmenes

geometric sequence *(p. 612)* A sequence in which the ratio of any term to the previous term is constant

secuencia geométrica *(p. 612)* Una secuencia en donde la razón de cualquier término con respecto al término anterior es constante

geometric series *(p. 614)* The expression formed by adding the terms of a geometric sequence

serie geométrica *(p. 614)* La expresión formada al sumar los términos de una secuencia geométrica

growth factor *(p. 294)* The value of b in an exponential growth function of the form $y = ab^x$, where $a > 0$ and $b > 1$

factor de crecimiento *(p. 294)* El valor de b en una función de crecimiento exponencial de la forma $y = ab^x$, donde $a > 0$ y $b > 1$

hypothesis *(p. 476)* A claim about a characteristic of a population

hipótesis *(p. 476)* Una declaración acerca de una característica de una población

identity matrix *(p. 672)* An $n \times n$ matrix that consists of 1's on its main diagonal (from top left to bottom right) and 0's for all other elements

marcas de identidad *(p. 672)* Una matriz de $n \times n$ que consiste en 1 en su diagonal principal (desde el extremo superior izquierdo al extremo inferior derecho) y 0 en todos los demás elementos

imaginary number *(p. 100)* A number written in the form $a + bi$, where a and b are real numbers and $b \neq 0$

número imaginario *(p. 100)* Un número escrito de la forma $a + bi$, donde a y b son números reales y $b \neq 0$

GLOSSARY

imaginary unit *i* *(p. 100)* The square root of -1, denoted $i = \sqrt{-1}$

unidad imaginaria *i* *(p. 100)* La raíz cuadrada de -1, denotado $i = \sqrt{-1}$

independent events *(p. 426)* Two events in which the occurrence of one event does not affect the occurrence of another event

eventos independientes *(p. 426)* Dos eventos en los que la ocurrencia de un evento no afecta la ocurrencia de otro evento

index of a radical *(p. 232)* The value of n in the radical $\sqrt[n]{a}$

índice de un radical *(p. 232)* El valor de n en el radical $\sqrt[n]{a}$

inferential statistics *(p. 496)* The branch of statistics that involves using a sample to draw conclusions about a population

estadística inferencial *(p. 496)* La rama de la estadística que implica el uso de una muestra para sacar conclusiones acerca de una población

initial side *(p. 530)* The fixed ray of an angle in standard position in a coordinate plane

lado inicial *(p. 530)* El rayo fijo de un ángulo en posición normal en un plano coordenado

intercept form *(p. 57)* A quadratic function written in the form $f(x) = a(x - p)(x - q)$, where $a \neq 0$

forma de intersección *(p. 57)* Una ecuación cuadrática escrita en la forma $f(x) = a(x - p)(x - q)$, donde $a \neq 0$

inverse functions *(p. 274)* Functions that undo each other

funciones inversas *(p. 274)* Funciones que se anulan entre sí

inverse matrices *(p. 672)* Two $n \times n$ matrices whose product is the $n \times n$ identity matrix

matrices inversas *(p. 672)* Dos matrices $n \times n$ cuyo producto es la matriz de identidad $n \times n$

inverse variation *(p. 356)* Two variables x and y show inverse variation when $y = \frac{a}{x}$, where $a \neq 0$.

variación inversa *(p. 356)* Dos variables x e y muestran variación inversa cuando $y = \frac{a}{x}$, donde $a \neq 0$.

J

joint frequency *(p. 412)* Each entry in a two-way table

frecuencia conjunta *(p. 412)* Cada valor en una tabla de doble entrada

joint relative frequency *(p. 413)* The ratio of a joint frequency to the total number of values or observations in a two-way table

frecuencia relative conjunta *(p. 413)* La razón de una frecuencia conjunta con el número total de valores u observaciones en una tabla de doble entrada

L

like radicals *(p. 240)* Radical expressions with the same index and radicand

radicales semejantes *(p. 240)* Expresiones radicales con el mismo índice y radicando

line of best fit *(p. 23)* A line that best models a set of data and lies as close as possible to all of the data points in a scatter plot

recta de mejor ajuste *(p. 23)* Una recta que modela mejor un conjunto de datos y que se acerca lo más posible a todos los puntos de datos en un diagrama de disperión

line of fit *(p. 22)* A line that models data in a scatter plot

recta de ajuste *(p. 22)* Una recta que modela datos en un diagrama de dispersión

linear equation in three variables *(p. 28)* An equation of the form $ax + by + cz = d$, where x, y, and z are variables and a, b, and c are not all zero

ecuación lineal en tres variables *(p. 28)* Una ecuación de la forma $ax + by + cz = d$, donde x, y, y z son variables y a, b, y c no son todas cero

local maximum *(p. 208)* The y-coordinate of a turning point of a function when the point is higher than all nearby points

máximo local *(p. 208)* La coordenada y de un punto de inflexión de una función cuando el punto es mayor que todos los puntos cercanos

local minimum *(p. 208)* The y-coordinate of a turning point of a function when the point is lower than all nearby points

mínimo local *(p. 208)* La coordenada y de un punto de inflexión de una función cuando el punto es menor que todos los puntos cercanos

logarithm of *y* with base *b* *(p. 308)* The function $\log_b y = x$ if and only if $b^x = y$, where $b > 0$, $y > 0$, and $b \neq 1$

logaritmo de *y* con base *b* *(p. 308)* La función $\log_b y = x$ si y solo si $b^x = y$, donde $b > 0$, $y > 0$, y $b \neq 1$

logarithmic equations *(p. 331)* Equations that involve one or more logarithms of variable expressions

ecuaciones logarítmicas *(p. 331)* Ecuaciones que implican uno o más logaritmos de expresiones variables

M

margin of error *(p. 499)* The maximum expected difference between a sample result and the population parameter it is estimating

margen de error *(p. 499)* La máxima diferencia que se espera entre el resultado de una muestra y el parámetro de población que está estimando

marginal frequency *(p. 412)* The sums of the rows and columns in a two-way table

frecuencia marginal *(p.412)* Las sumas de las hileras y columnas en una tabla de doble entrada

marginal relative frequency *(p. 413)* The sum of the joint relative frequencies in a row or a column in a two-way table

frecuencia relativa marginal *(p. 413)* La suma de las frecuencias relativas conjuntas en una hilera o columna en una tabla de doble entrada

matrix *(p. 646)* A rectangular array of numbers

matriz *(p. 646)* Una disposición rectangular de números

matrix of constants *(p. 674)* A matrix consisting of the constants of a linear system

matriz de constantes *(p. 674)* Una matriz que consiste en las constantes de un sistema lineal

matrix of variables *(p. 674)* A matrix consisting of the variables of a linear system

matriz de variables *(p. 674)* Una matriz que consiste en las variables de un sistema lineal

maximum value *(p. 56)* The y-coordinate of the vertex of the quadratic function $f(x) = ax^2 + bx + c$, where $a < 0$

valor máximo *(p. 56)* La coordenada y del vértice de la función cuadrática $f(x) = ax^2 + bx + c$, cuando $a < 0$

midline *(p. 548)* The horizontal line $y = k$ in which the graph of a periodic function oscillates

línea media *(p. 548)* La línea horizontal $y = k$ en la que oscila el gráfico de una función periódica

minimum value *(p. 56)* The y-coordinate of the vertex of the quadratic function $f(x) = ax^2 + bx + c$, when $a > 0$

valor mínimo *(p. 56)* La coordenada y del vértice de la función cuadrática $f(x) = ax^2 + bx + c$, cuando $a > 0$

N

***n* factorial** *(p. 440)* The product of the integers from 1 to n, for any positive integer n

factorial de *n* *(p. 440)* El producto de los números enteros de 1 a n, para cualquier número entero positivo n

natural base *e* *(p. 302)* An irrational number approximately equal to 2.71828…

base natural *e* *(p. 302)* Un número irracional aproximadamente equivalente a 2.71828…

natural logarithm *(p. 309)* A logarithm with base e, denoted by $\log_e$ or ln

logaritmo natural *(p. 309)* Un logaritmo con base e, denotado como $\log_e$ o ln

normal curve *(p. 466)* The graph of a normal distribution that is bell-shaped and is symmetric about the mean

curva normal *(p. 466)* El gráfico de una distribución normal con forma acampanada y es simétrica con respecto a la media

normal distribution *(p. 466)* A type of probability distribution in which the graph is a bell-shaped curve that is symmetric about the mean

distribución normal *(p. 466)* Un tipo de distribución de probabilidades en la que el gráfico es una curva acampanada que es simétrica con respecto a la media

n*th root of *a *(p. 232)* For an integer n greater than 1, if $b^n = a$, then b is an nth root of a.

raíz de orden *n* de *a* *(p. 232)* Para un número entero n mayor que 1, si $b^n = a$, entonces b es una raíz de orden n de a.

O

observational study *(p. 484)* Individuals are observed and variables are measured without controlling the individuals or their environment.

estudio de observación *(p. 484)* Se observan individuos y se miden variables sin controlar a los individuos o a su entorno.

odd function *(p. 209)* For a function f, $f(-x) = -f(x)$ for all x in its domain

función impar *(p. 209)* Para una función f, $f(-x) = -f(x)$ para toda x en su dominio

ordered triple *(p. 28)* A solution of a system of three linear equations represented by (x, y, z)

triple ordenado *(p. 28)* Un solución de un sistema de tres ecuaciones lineales representadas por (x, y, z)

outcome *(p. 404)* The possible result of a probability experiment

resultado *(p. 404)* El resultado posible de un experimento de probabilidad

overlapping events *(p. 434)* Two events that have one or more outcomes in common

eventos superpuestos *(p. 434)* Dos eventos que tienen uno o más resultados en común

P

parabola *(p. 46)* The U-shaped graph of a quadratic function

parábola *(p. 46)* El gráfico en forma de “U” de una función cuadrática

parameter *(p. 475)* A numerical description of a population characteristic

parámetro *(p. 475)* Una descripción numérica de una característica de la población

parent function *(p. 4)* The most basic function in a family of functions

función principal *(p. 4)* La función más básica en una familia de funciones

partial sum *(p. 620)* The sum S_n of the first n terms of an infinite series

sumatoria parcial *(p. 620)* La sumatoria parcial S_n de los primeros términos n de una serie infinita

Pascal's Triangle *(p. 165)* A triangular array of numbers such that the numbers in the nth row are the coefficients of the terms in the expansion of $(a + b)^n$ for whole number values of n

triángulo de Pascal *(p. 165)* Una disposición triangular de números, de tal manera que los números en la fila n son los coeficientes de los términos en la expansión de $(a + b)^n$ para los valores de números enteros de n

period *(p. 546)* The horizontal length of each cycle of a periodic function

período *(p. 546)* La longitud horizontal de cada ciclo de una función periódica

periodic function *(p. 546)* A function whose graph has a repeating pattern

función periódica *(p. 546)* Una función cuyo gráfico tiene un patrón de repetición

permutation *(p. 440)* An arrangement of objects in which order is important

permutación *(p. 440)* Una disposición de objetos en la que el orden es importante

phase shift *(p. 548)* A horizontal translation of a periodic function

desplazamiento de fase *(p. 548)* Una traslación horizontal de una función periódica

placebo *(p. 490)* A harmless, fake treatment that is similar to the actual treatment

placebo *(p. 490)* Un tratamiento falso que es similar al tratamiento real

polynomial *(p. 154)* A monomial or a sum of monomials

polinomio *(p. 154)* Un monomio o una suma de monomios

polynomial function *(p. 154)* A function of the form $f(x) = a_n x^n + a_{n-1}x^{n-1} + \cdots + a_1 x + a_0$, where $a_n \neq 0$, the exponents are all whole numbers, and the coefficients are all real numbers

función polinómica *(p. 154)* Una función de la forma $f(x) = a_n x^n + a_{n-1}x^{n-1} + \cdots + a_1 x + a_0$, donde $a_n \neq 0$, todos los exponentes son números enteros y todos los coeficientes son números reales

polynomial long division *(p. 170)* A method to divide a polynomial $f(x)$ by a nonzero divisor $d(x)$ to yield a quotient polynomial $q(x)$ and a remainder polynomial $r(x)$

división larga de polinomios *(p. 170)* Un método para dividir un polinomio $f(x)$ por un divisor distinto de cero $d(x)$ para obtener un polinomio de cociente $q(x)$ y un polinomio de resto $r(x)$

population *(p. 474)* The collection of all data, such as responses, measurements, or counts, that are of interest

población *(p. 474)* La recolección de datos, tales como respuestas, medidas o conteos que son de interés

probability distribution *(p. 450)* A function that gives the probability of each possible value of a random variable

distribución de probabilidad *(p. 450)* Una función que da la probabilidad de cada valor posible de una variable aleatoria

probability of an event *(p. 404)* A measure of the likelihood, or chance, that an event will occur

probabilidad de un evento *(p. 404)* Una medida de la probabilidad o posibilidad de que ocurrirá un evento

probability experiment *(p. 404)* An action, or trial, that has varying results

experimento de probabilidad *(p. 404)* Una acción o prueba que tiene resultados variables

pure imaginary number *(p. 100)* A number written in the form $a + bi$, where $a = 0$ and $b \neq 0$

número imaginario puro *(p. 100)* Un número escrito en la forma $a + bi$, donde $a = 0$ y $b \neq 0$

Q

quadrantal angle *(p. 539)* An angle in standard position whose terminal side lies on an axis

ángulo cuadrantal *(p. 539)* Un ángulo en posición estándar cuyo lado terminal descansa en un eje

quadratic equation in one variable *(p. 90)* An equation that can be written in the standard form $ax^2 + bx + c = 0$, where a, b, and c are real numbers and $a \neq 0$

ecuación cuadrática en una variable *(p. 90)* Una ecuación que puede escribirse en la forma estándar $ax^2 + bx + c = 0$, donde a, b, y c son números reales y $a \neq 0$

quadratic form *(p. 177)* An expression of the form $au^2 + bu + c$, where u is an algebraic expression

forma cuadrática *(p. 177)* Una expresión de la forma $au^2 + bu + c$, donde u es una expresión algebraica

Quadratic Formula *(p. 118)* The solutions of the quadratic equation $ax^2 + bx + c = 0$ are

$x = \dfrac{-b \pm \sqrt{b^2 - 4ac}}{2a}$, where a, b, and c are real numbers and $a \neq 0$.

Formula Cuadrática *(p. 118)* Las soluciones reales de la expresión cuadrática $ax^2 + bx + c = 0$ son

$x = \dfrac{-b \pm \sqrt{b^2 - 4ac}}{2a}$, donde a, b, y c son números reales y $a \neq 0$.

quadratic function *(p. 46)* A function that can be written in the form $f(x) = a(x - h)^2 + k$, where $a \neq 0$

función cuadrática *(p. 46)* Una función que puede escribirse en la forma $f(x) = a(x - h)^2 + k$, donde $a \neq 0$

quadratic inequality in one variable *(p. 138)* An inequality of the form $ax^2 + bx + c < 0$, $ax^2 + bx + c > 0$, $ax^2 + bx + c \leq 0$, or $ax^2 + bx + c \geq 0$, where a, b, and c are real numbers and $a \neq 0$

desigualdad cuadrática en una variable *(p. 138)* Una desigualdad de la forma $ax^2 + bx + c < 0$, $ax^2 + bx + c > 0$, $ax^2 + bx + c \leq 0$, o $ax^2 + bx + c \geq 0$, donde a, b, y c son números reales y $a \neq 0$

quadratic inequality in two variables *(p. 136)* An inequality of the form $y < ax^2 + bx + c$, $y > ax^2 + bx + c$, $y \leq ax^2 + bx + c$, or $y \geq ax^2 + bx + c$, where a, b, and c are real numbers and $a \neq 0$

desigualdad cuadrática en dos variables *(p. 136)* Una desigualdad de la forma $y < ax^2 + bx + c$, $y > ax^2 + bx + c$, $y \leq ax^2 + bx + c$, o $y \geq ax^2 + bx + c$, donde a, b, y c son números reales y $a \neq 0$

R

radian *(p. 531)* For a circle with radius r, the measure of an angle in standard position whose terminal side intercepts an arc of length r is one radian.

radián *(p. 531)* Para un círculo con radio r, la medida de un ángulo en posición estándar cuyo lado terminal intercepta un arco de longitud r es un radián

radical equation *(p. 254)* An equation with a radical that has a variable in the radicand

ecuación radical *(p. 254)* Una ecuación con un radical que tiene una variable en el radicando

radical function *(p. 246)* A function that contains a radical expression with the independent variable in the radicand

función radical *(p. 246)* Una función que contiene una expresión radical con la variable independiente en el radicando

random sample *(p. 482)* A sample in which each member of a population has an equal chance of being selected

muestra aleatoria *(p. 482)* Una muestra en la que cada miembro de una población tiene igual posibilidad de ser seleccionado

random variable *(p. 450)* A variable whose value is determined by the outcomes of a probability experiment

variable aleatoria *(p. 450)* Una variable cuyo valor está determinado por los resultados de un experimento de probabilidad

randomization *(p. 490)* A process of randomly assigning subjects to different treatment groups

aleatorización *(p. 490)* Un proceso de asignación aleatoria de sujetos a distintos grupos de tratamiento

randomized comparative experiment *(p. 490)* An experiment in which subjects are randomly assigned to the control group or the treatment group

experimento comparativo aleatorizado *(p. 490)* Un experimento en el que los sujetos son asignados aleatoriamente al grupo de control o al grupo de tratamiento

rational expression *(p. 370)* A fraction whose numerator and denominator are nonzero polynomials

expresión racional *(p. 370)* Una fracción cuyo numerador y denominador son polinomios distintos a cero

rational function *(p. 362)* A function that has the form $f(x) = \frac{p(x)}{q(x)}$, where $p(x)$ and $q(x)$ are polynomials and $q(x) \neq 0$

función racional *(p. 362)* Una función que tiene la forma $f(x) = \frac{p(x)}{q(x)}$, donde $p(x)$ y $q(x)$ son polinomios y $q(x) \neq 0$

recursive rule *(p. 626)* A rule that gives the beginning term(s) of a sequence and a recursive equation that tells how a_n is related to one or more preceding terms

regla recursiva *(p. 626)* Una regla para definir el(los) primer(os) término(s) de una secuencia y una ecuación recursiva que indica cómo se relaciona a_n a uno o más términos precedentes

reference angle *(p. 540)* The acute angle formed by the terminal side of an angle in standard position and the x-axis

ángulo de referencia *(p. 540)* El ángulo agudo formado por el lado terminal de un ángulo en posición normal y el eje x

reflection *(p. 5)* A transformation that flips a graph over the line of reflection

reflexión *(p. 5)* Una transformación que voltea un gráfico sobre una recta de reflexión

repeated solution *(p. 184)* A solution of an equation that appears more than once

solución repetida *(p. 184)* Una solución de una ecuación que aparece más de una vez

root of an equation *(p. 90)* A solution of an equation

raíz de una ecuación *(p. 90)* Una solución de una ecuación

S

sample *(p. 474)* A subset of a population

muestra *(p. 474)* Un subconjunto de una población

sample space *(p. 404)* The set of all possible outcomes for an experiment

espacio de muestra *(p. 404)* El conjunto de todos los resultados posibles de un experimento

scalar *(p. 647)* A number used in operations with matrices

escalar *(p. 647)* Un número que se usa en operaciones con matrices

scalar multiplication *(p. 647)* The process of multiplying each element in a matrix by a scalar

multiplicaión escalar *(p. 647)* El proceso de multiplicar cada elemento en la matriz por un escalar

secant *(p. 522)* A trigonometric function for an acute angle θ of a right triangle, denoted by $\sec\theta = \frac{\text{hypotenuse}}{\text{adjacent}}$

secante *(p. 522)* Una ecuación trigonométrica de un ángulo agudo θ de un triángulo recto, denatado por $\sec\theta = \frac{\text{hipotenusa}}{\text{adyacente}}$

sector *(p. 532)* A region of a circle that is bounded by two radii and an arc of the circle

sector *(p. 532)* Una región de un círculo conformada por dos radios y un arco del círculo

self-selected sample *(p. 482)* A sample in which members of a population can volunteer to be in the sample

muestra autoseleccionada *(p. 482)* Una muestra en la que los miembros de una población pueden ofrecerse voluntariamente para formar parte de la misma

sequence *(p. 596)* An ordered list of numbers

secuencia *(p. 596)* Una lista ordenada de números

series *(p. 598)* The sum of the terms of a sequence

serie *(p. 598)* La suma de los términos de una secuencia

sigma notation *(p. 598)* For any sequence $a_1, a_2, a_3, \ldots$, the sum of the first k terms may be written as $\sum_{n=1}^{k} a_n = a_1 + a_2 + a_3 + \cdots + a_k$, where k is an integer.

notación sigma *(p. 598)* Para cualquier secuencia $a_1, a_2, a_3, \ldots$, la suma de los primeros términos k puede escribirse como $\sum_{n=1}^{k} a_n = a_1 + a_2 + a_3 + \cdots + a_k$, donde k es un número entero.

simplest form of a radical *(p. 239)* An expression involving a radical with index n that has no radicands with perfect nth powers as factors other than 1, no radicands that contain fractions, and no radicals that appear in the denominator of a fraction

mínima expresión de un radical *(p. 239)* Una expresión que conlleva un radical con índice n que no tiene radicandos con potencias perfectas de orden n como factores distintos a 1, que no tiene radicandos que contengan fracciones y que no tiene radicales que aparezcan en el denominador de una fracción

simplified form of a rational expression *(p. 370)* A rational expression whose numerator and denominator have no common factors (other than ± 1)

forma simplificada de una expresión racional *(p. 370)* Una expresión racional cuyo numerador y denominador no tienen factores comunes (distintos a ± 1)

simulation *(p. 484)* The use of a model to reproduce the conditions of a situation or process so that the simulated outcomes closely match the real-world outcome

simulación *(p. 484)* El uso de un modelo para reproducir las condiciones de una situación o proceso, de tal manera que los resultados posibles simulados coincidan en gran medida con los resultados del mundo real

sine *(p. 522)* A trigonometric function for an acute angle θ of a right triangle, denoted by

$$\sin \theta = \frac{\text{opposite}}{\text{hypotenuse}}$$

seno *(p. 522)* Una ecuación trigonométrica de un ángulo agudo θ de un triángulo recto, denotado por

$$\sin \theta = \frac{\text{opuesto}}{\text{hipotenusa}}$$

sinusoid *(p. 565)* The graph of a sine or cosine function

sinusoide *(p. 565)* El gráfico de una función seno o coseno

solution of a system of three linear equations *(p. 28)* An ordered triple (x, y, z) whose coordinates make each equation true

solución de un sistema de tres ecuaciones lineales *(p. 28)* Un triple ordenado (x, y, z) cuyas coordenadas hacen verdadera cada ecuación

standard form *(p. 54)* A quadratic function written in the form $f(x) = ax^2 + bx + c$, where $a \neq 0$

forma estándar *(p. 54)* Una función cuadrática escrita en la forma $f(x) = ax^2 + bx + c$, donde $a \neq 0$

standard normal distribution *(p. 467)* The normal distribution with mean 0 and standard deviation 1

distribución normal estándar *(p. 467)* La distribución normal con una media de 0 y desviación estándar 1

standard position *(p. 530)* An angle in a coordinate plane such that its vertex is at the origin and its initial side lies on the positive x-axis

posición estándar *(p. 530)* Un ángulo en un plano coordenado de tal manera que su vértice esté en el origen y que su lado inicial descanse en el eje x positivo

statistic *(p. 475)* A numerical description of a sample characteristic

estadística *(p. 475)* Una descripción numérica de una característica de la muestra

stratified sample *(p. 482)* A sample in which a population is divided into smaller groups that share a similar characteristic and a sample is then randomly selected from each group

muestra estratificada *(p. 482)* Una muestra en la que una población se divide en grupos más pequeños que comparten una característica similar, y una muestra se selecciona en forma aleatoria de cada grupo

summation notation *(p. 598)* For any sequence $a_1, a_2, a_3, \ldots$, the sum of the first k terms may be written as

$\sum_{n=1}^{k} a_n = a_1 + a_2 + a_3 + \cdots + a_k$, where k is an integer.

notación de sumatoria *(p. 598)* Para cualquier secuencia $a_1, a_2, a_3, \ldots$, la sumatoria de los primeros términos k puede escribirse como $\sum_{n=1}^{k} a_n = a_1 + a_2 + a_3 + \cdots + a_k$, donde k es un número entero.

survey *(p. 484)* An investigation of one or more characteristics of a population

encuesta *(p. 484)* Una investigación de una o más características de una población

synthetic division *(p. 171)* A shortcut method to divide a polynomial by a binomial of the form $x - k$

división sintética *(p. 171)* Un método abreviado para dividir un polinomio por un binomio de la forma $x - k$

system of nonlinear equations *(p. 128)* A system of equations where at least one of the equations is nonlinear

sistema de ecuaciones no lineales *(p. 128)* Un sistema de ecuaciones en donde al menos una de las ecuaciones no es lineal

system of quadratic inequalities *(p. 137)* A set of two or more quadratic inequalities in the same variables

sistema de desigualdades cuadráticas *(p. 137)* Un conjunto de dos o más desigualdades cuadráticas en las mismas variables

system of three linear equations *(p. 28)* A set of three equations of the form $ax + by + cz = d$, where x, y, and z are variables and a, b, and c are not all zero

sistema de tres ecuaciones lineales *(p. 28)* Un conjunto de tres ecuaciones de la forma $ax + by + cz = d$, donde x, y, y z son variables y a, b, y c no son todos cero

systematic sample *(p. 482)* A sample in which a rule is used to select members of a population

muestra sistemática *(p. 482)* Una muestra en la que se usa una regla para seleccionar miembros de una población

tangent *(p. 522)* A trigonometric function for an acute angle θ of a right triangle, denoted by $\tan \theta = \dfrac{\text{opposite}}{\text{adjacent}}$

tangente *(p. 522)* Una ecuación trigonométrica de un ángulo agudo θ de un triángulo recto, denotado por $\tan \theta = \dfrac{\text{opuesto}}{\text{adyacente}}$

terminal side *(p. 530)* A ray of an angle in standard position that has been rotated about the vertex in a coordinate plane

lado terminal *(p. 530)* Un rayo de un ángulo en posición normal que ha sido rotado con respecto al vértice en un plano coordenado

terms of a sequence *(p. 596)* The values in the range of a sequence

términos de una secuencia *(p. 596)* Los valores en el rango de una secuencia

theoretical probability *(p. 405)* The ratio of the number of favorable outcomes to the total number of outcomes when all outcomes are equally likely

probabilidad teórica *(p. 405)* La razón del número de resultados favorables con respecto al número total de resultados cuando todos los resultados son igualmente probables

transformation *(p. 5)* A change in the size, shape, position, or orientation of a graph

transformación *(p. 5)* Un cambio en el tamaño, forma, posición u orientación de un gráfico

translation *(p. 5)* A transformation that shifts a graph horizontally and/or vertically but does not change its size, shape, or orientation

traslación *(p. 5)* Una transformación que desplaza un gráfico horizontal y/o verticalmente, pero no cambia su tamaño, forma u orientación

treatment group *(p. 490)* The group that is subjected to the treatment in an experiment

grupo de tratamiento *(p. 490)* El grupo que está sometido al tratamiento en un experimento

trigonometric identity *(p. 572)* A trigonometric equation that is true for all values of the variable for which both sides of the equation are defined

identidad trigonométrica *(p. 572)* Una ecuación trigonométrica verdadera para todos los valores de la variable por la cual se definen ambos lados de la ecuación

two-way table *(p. 412)* A frequency table that displays data collected from one source that belong to two different categories

tabla de doble entrada *(p. 412)* Una tabla de frecuencia que muestra los datos recogidos de una fuente que pertenece a dos categorías distintas

unbiased sample *(p. 483)* A sample that is representative of a population

muestra no sesgada *(p. 483)* Una muestra que es representativa de la población

unit circle *(p. 539)* The circle $x^2 + y^2 = 1$, which has center (0, 0) and radius 1

círculo unitario *(p. 539)* El círculo $x^2 + y^2 = 1$, que tiene como centro (0, 0) y radio 1

V

vertex form *(p. 48)* A quadratic function written in the form $f(x) = a(x - h)^2 + k$, where $a \neq 0$

fórmula de vértice *(p. 48)* Una función cuadrática escrita en la forma $f(x) = a(x - h)^2 + k$, donde $a \neq 0$

vertex of a parabola *(p. 48)* The lowest point on a parabola that opens up or the highest point on a parabola that opens down

vértice de una parábola *(p. 48)* El punto más bajo de una parábola que se abre hacia arriba o el punto más alto de una parábola que se abre hacia abajo

vertical shrink *(p. 6)* A transformation that causes the graph of a function to shrink toward the x-axis when all the y-coordinates are multiplied by a factor a, where $0 < a < 1$

reducción vertical *(p. 6)* Una transformación que hace que el gráfico de una función se reduzca hacia el eje x cuando todas las coordenadas y se multiplican por un factor a, donde $0 < a < 1$

vertical stretch *(p. 6)* A transformation that causes the graph of a function to stretch away from the x-axis when all the y-coordinates are multiplied by a factor a, where $a > 1$

ampliación vertical *(p. 6)* Una transformación que hace que el gráfico de una función se amplíe desde el eje x cuando todas las coordenadas y se multiplican por un factor a, donde $a > 1$

Z

***z*-score** *(p. 467)* The z-value for a particular x-value which is the number of standard deviations the x-value lies above or below the mean

puntaje *z* *(p. 467)* El valor z para un valor particular x que es el número de desviaciones estándar que el valor x tiene por encima o por debajo de la media

zero of a function *(p. 92)* An x-value of a function f for which $f(x) = 0$

cero de una función *(p. 92)* Un valor x de una funcíon f para el cual $f(x) = 0$

Index

D

E

INDEX

F

N

O

P

INDEX

R

Reference

Properties

Properties of Exponents

Let a and b be real numbers and let m and n be rational numbers.

Zero Exponent
$a^0 = 1$, where $a \neq 0$

Negative Exponent
$a^{-n} = \frac{1}{a^n}$, where $a \neq 0$

Product of Powers Property
$a^m \cdot a^n = a^{m+n}$

Quotient of Powers Property
$\frac{a^m}{a^n} = a^{m-n}$, where $a \neq 0$

Power of a Power Property
$(a^m)^n = a^{mn}$

Power of a Product Property
$(ab)^m = a^m b^m$

Power of a Quotient Property
$\left(\frac{a}{b}\right)^m = \frac{a^m}{b^m}$, where $b \neq 0$

Rational Exponents
$a^{m/n} = (a^{1/n})^m = (\sqrt[n]{a})^m$
or $a^{m/n} = (a^m)^{1/n} = \sqrt[n]{a^m}$

Rational Exponents
$a^{-m/n} = \frac{1}{a^{m/n}} = \frac{1}{(a^{1/n})^m} = \frac{1}{(\sqrt[n]{a})^m}$,
where $a \neq 0$

or $a^{-m/n} = \frac{1}{(a^m)^{1/n}} = \frac{1}{\sqrt[n]{a^m}}$, where $a \neq 0$

Properties of Radicals

Let a and b be real numbers and let n be an integer greater than 1.

Product Property of Radicals
$\sqrt[n]{ab} = \sqrt[n]{a} \cdot \sqrt[n]{b}$

Quotient Property of Radicals
$\sqrt[n]{\frac{a}{b}} = \frac{\sqrt[n]{a}}{\sqrt[n]{b}}$, where $b \neq 0$

Square Root of a Negative Number
1. If r is a positive real number, then $\sqrt{-r} = \sqrt{-1}\sqrt{r} = i\sqrt{r}$.
2. By the first property, it follows that $(i\sqrt{r})^2 = i^2 \cdot r = -r$.

Properties of Logarithms

Let b, m, and n be positive real numbers with $b \neq 1$.

Product Property
$\log_b mn = \log_b m + \log_b n$

Quotient Property
$\log_b \frac{m}{n} = \log_b m - \log_b n$

Power Property
$\log_b m^n = n \log_b m$

Other Properties

Zero-Product Property
If A and B are expressions and $AB = 0$, then $A = 0$ or $B = 0$.

Property of Equality for Exponential Equations
If $b > 0$ and $b \neq 1$, then $b^x = b^y$ if and only if $x = y$.

Property of Equality for Logarithmic Equations
If b, x, and y are positive real numbers with $b \neq 1$, then $\log_b x = \log_b y$ if and only if $x = y$.

Patterns

Square of a Binomial Pattern
$(a + b)^2 = a^2 + 2ab + b^2$
$(a - b)^2 = a^2 - 2ab + b^2$

Cube of a Binomial Pattern
$(a + b)^3 = a^3 + 3a^2b + 3ab^2 + b^3$
$(a - b)^3 = a^3 - 3a^2b + 3ab^2 - b^3$

Difference of Two Squares Pattern
$a^2 - b^2 = (a + b)(a - b)$

Sum of Two Cubes Pattern
$a^3 + b^3 = (a + b)(a^2 - ab + b^2)$

Sum and Difference Pattern
$(a + b)(a - b) = a^2 - b^2$

Completing the Square Pattern
$x^2 + bx + \left(\frac{b}{2}\right)^2 = \left(x + \frac{b}{2}\right)^2$

Perfect Square Trinomial Pattern
$a^2 + 2ab + b^2 = (a + b)^2$
$a^2 - 2ab + b^2 = (a - b)^2$

Difference of Two Cubes Pattern
$a^3 - b^3 = (a - b)(a^2 + ab + b^2)$

Theorems

The Remainder Theorem
If a polynomial $f(x)$ is divided by $x - k$, then the remainder is $r = f(k)$.

The Factor Theorem
A polynomial $f(x)$ has a factor $x - k$ if and only if $f(k) = 0$.

The Rational Root Theorem
If $f(x) = a_nx^n + \cdots + a_1x + a_0$ has *integer* coefficients, then every rational solution of $f(x) = 0$ has the form
$\frac{p}{q} = \frac{\text{factor of constant term } a_0}{\text{factor of leading coefficient } a_n}$.

The Irrational Conjugates Theorem
Let f be a polynomial function with rational coefficients, and let a and b be rational numbers such that $\sqrt{b}$ is irrational. If $a + \sqrt{b}$ is a zero of f, then $a - \sqrt{b}$ is also a zero of f.

The Fundamental Theorem of Algebra

Theorem If $f(x)$ is a polynomial of degree n where $n > 0$, then the equation $f(x) = 0$ has at least one solution in the set of complex numbers.

Corollary If $f(x)$ is a polynomial of degree n where $n > 0$, then the equation $f(x) = 0$ has exactly n solutions provided each solution repeated twice is counted as 2 solutions, each solution repeated three times is counted as 3 solutions, and so on.

The Complex Conjugates Theorem
If f is a polynomial function with real coefficients, and $a + bi$ is an imaginary zero of f, then $a - bi$ is also a zero of f.

Descartes's Rule of Signs
Let $f(x) = a_nx^n + a_{n-1}x^{n-1} + \cdots + a_2x^2 + a_1x + a_0$ be a polynomial function with real coefficients.

- The number of positive real zeros of f is equal to the number of changes in sign of the coefficients of $f(x)$ or is less than this by an even number.
- The number of negative real zeros of f is equal to the number of changes in the sign of the coefficients of $f(-x)$ or is less than this by an even number.

Formulas

Algebra

Slope

$m = \frac{y_2 - y_1}{x_2 - x_1}$

Slope-intercept form

$y = mx + b$

Point-slope form

$y - y_1 = m(x - x_1)$

Standard form of a quadratic function

$f(x) = ax^2 + bx + c$, where $a \neq 0$

Vertex form of a quadratic function

$f(x) = a(x - h)^2 + k$, where $a \neq 0$

Intercept form of a quadratic function

$f(x) = a(x - p)(x - q)$, where $a \neq 0$

Quadratic Formula

$x = \frac{-b \pm \sqrt{b^2 - 4ac}}{2a}$, where $a \neq 0$

Standard equation of a circle

$x^2 + y^2 = r^2$

Standard form of a polynomial function

$f(x) = a_n x^n + a_{n-1} x^{n-1} + \cdots + a_1 x + a_0$

Exponential growth function

$y = ab^x$, where $a > 0$ and $b > 1$

Exponential decay function

$y = ab^x$, where $a > 0$ and $0 < b < 1$

Logarithm of y with base b

$\log_b y = x$ if and only if $b^x = y$

Change-of-base formula

$\log_c a = \frac{\log_b a}{\log_b c}$, where a, b, and c are positive real numbers with $b \neq 1$ and $c \neq 1$.

Sum of n terms of 1

$\sum_{i=1}^{n} 1 = n$

Sum of first n positive integers

$\sum_{i=1}^{n} i = \frac{n(n+1)}{2}$

Sum of squares of first n positive integers

$\sum_{i=1}^{n} i^2 = \frac{n(n+1)(2n+1)}{6}$

Explicit rule for an arithmetic sequence

$a_n = a_1 + (n - 1)d$

Sum of first n terms of an arithmetic series

$S_n = n\left(\frac{a_1 + a_n}{2}\right)$

Explicit rule for a geometric sequence

$a_n = a_1 r^{n-1}$

Sum of first n terms of a geometric series

$S_n = a_1\left(\frac{1 - r^n}{1 - r}\right)$, where $r \neq 1$

Sum of an infinite geometric series

$S = \frac{a_1}{1 - r}$ provided $|r| < 1$

Recursive equation for an arithmetic sequence

$a_n = a_{n-1} + d$, where d is the common difference

Recursive equation for a geometric sequence

$a_n = r \cdot a_{n-1}$, where r is the common ratio

Statistics

Sample mean

$\bar{x} = \frac{\Sigma x}{n}$

Standard deviation

$\sigma = \sqrt{\frac{(x_1 - \mu)^2 + (x_2 - \mu)^2 + \cdots + (x_n - \mu)^2}{n}}$

z-Score

$z = \frac{x - \mu}{\sigma}$

Margin of error for sample proportions

$\pm\frac{1}{\sqrt{n}}$

Trigonometry

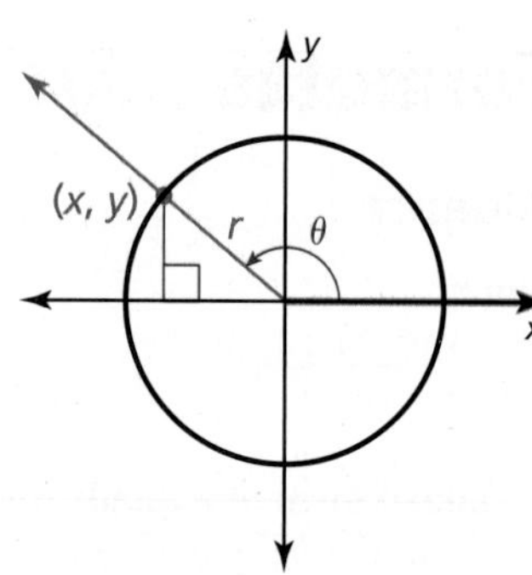

General definitions of trigonometric functions

Let θ be an angle in standard position, and let (x, y) be the point where the terminal side of θ intersects the circle $x^2 + y^2 = r^2$. The six trigonometric functions of θ are defined as shown.

$\sin\theta = \frac{y}{r}$ $\quad\cos\theta = \frac{x}{r}$ $\quad\tan\theta = \frac{y}{x}, x \neq 0$

$\csc\theta = \frac{r}{y}, y \neq 0$ $\quad\sec\theta = \frac{r}{x}, x \neq 0$ $\quad\cot\theta = \frac{x}{y}, y \neq 0$

Conversion between degrees and radians

$180° = \pi$ radians

Arc length of a sector

$s = r\theta$

Area of a sector

$A = \frac{1}{2}r^2\theta$

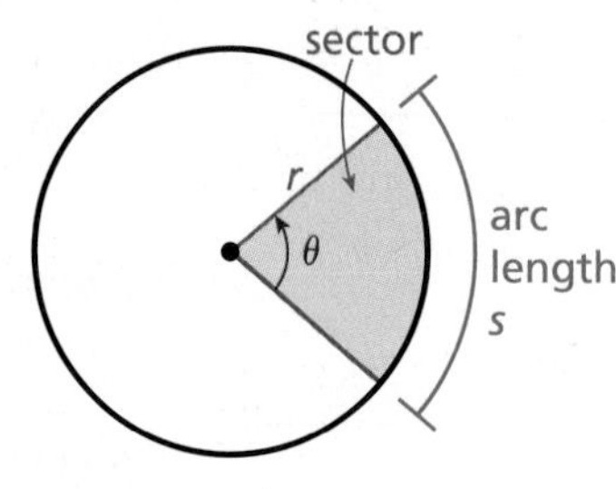

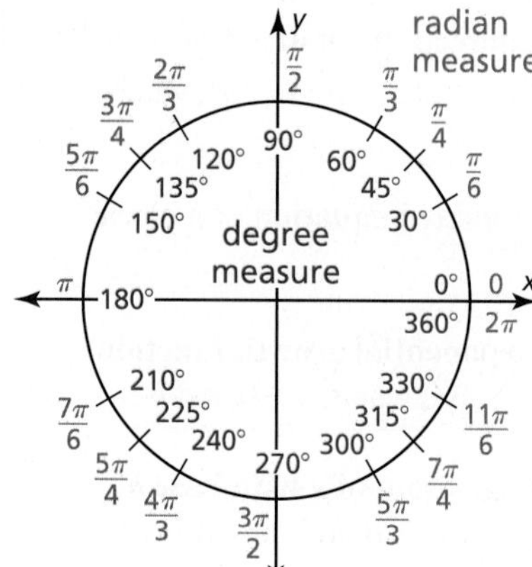

Reciprocal Identities

$\sin\theta = \frac{1}{\csc\theta}$ $\quad\cos\theta = \frac{1}{\sec\theta}$ $\quad\tan\theta = \frac{1}{\cot\theta}$

$\csc\theta = \frac{1}{\sin\theta}$ $\quad\sec\theta = \frac{1}{\cos\theta}$ $\quad\cot\theta = \frac{1}{\tan\theta}$

Tangent and Cotangent Identities

$\tan\theta = \frac{\sin\theta}{\cos\theta}$ $\quad\cot\theta = \frac{\cos\theta}{\sin\theta}$

Pythagorean Identities

$\sin^2\theta + \cos^2\theta = 1$

$1 + \tan^2\theta = \sec^2\theta$

$1 + \cot^2\theta = \csc^2\theta$

Negative Angle Identities

$\sin(-\theta) = -\sin\theta$

$\cos(-\theta) = \cos\theta$

$\tan(-\theta) = -\tan\theta$

Cofunction Identites

$\sin\left(\frac{\pi}{2} - \theta\right) = \cos\theta$

$\cos\left(\frac{\pi}{2} - \theta\right) = \sin\theta$

$\tan\left(\frac{\pi}{2} - \theta\right) = \cot\theta$

Sum Formulas

$\sin(a + b) = \sin a \cos b + \cos a \sin b$

$\cos(a + b) = \cos a \cos b - \sin a \sin b$

$\tan(a + b) = \frac{\tan a + \tan b}{1 - \tan a \tan b}$

Difference Formulas

$\sin(a - b) = \sin a \cos b - \cos a \sin b$

$\cos(a - b) = \cos a \cos b + \sin a \sin b$

$\tan(a - b) = \frac{\tan a - \tan b}{1 + \tan a \tan b}$

Probability and Combinatorics

Theoretical Probability $= \frac{\text{Number of favorable outcomes}}{\text{Total number of outcomes}}$

Experimental Probability $= \frac{\text{Number of successes}}{\text{Number of trials}}$

Probability of the complement of an event

$P(\overline{A}) = 1 - P(A)$

Probability of independent events

$P(A \text{ and } B) = P(A) \cdot P(B)$

Probability of dependent events

$P(A \text{ and } B) = P(A) \cdot P(B \mid A)$

Probability of compound events

$P(A \text{ or } B) = P(A) + P(B) - P(A \text{ and } B)$

Permutations

${}_nP_r = \frac{n!}{(n-r)!}$

Combinations

${}_nC_r = \frac{n!}{(n-r)! \cdot r!}$

Binomial experiments

$P(k \text{ successes}) = {}_nC_k p^k (1-p)^{n-k}$

The Binomial Theorem

$(a + b)^n = {}_nC_0 a^n b^0 + {}_nC_1 a^{n-1} b^1 + {}_nC_2 a^{n-2} b^2 + \cdots + {}_nC_n a^0 b^n$, where n is a positive integer.

Perimeter, Area, and Volume Formulas

Square

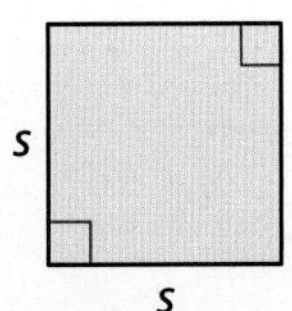

$P = 4s$
$A = s^2$

Rectangle

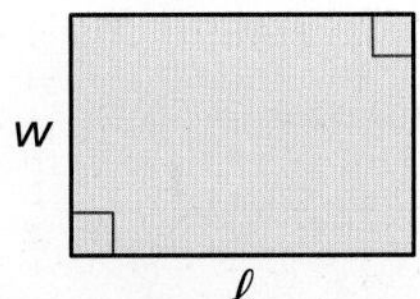

$P = 2\ell + 2w$
$A = \ell w$

Triangle

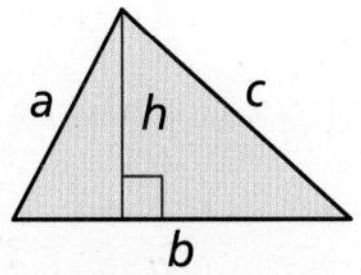

$P = a + b + c$
$A = \frac{1}{2}bh$

Circle

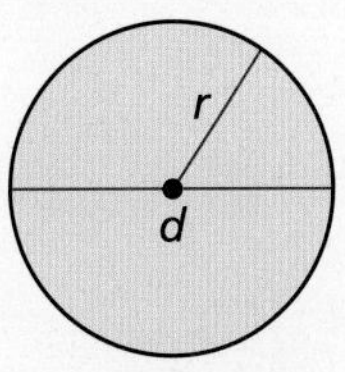

$C = \pi d$ or $C = 2\pi r$
$A = \pi r^2$

Parallelogram

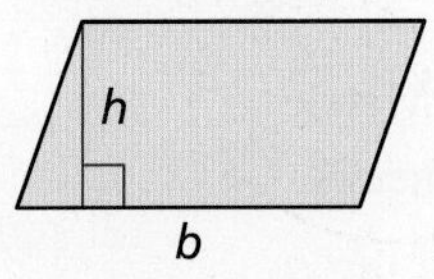

$A = bh$

Trapezoid

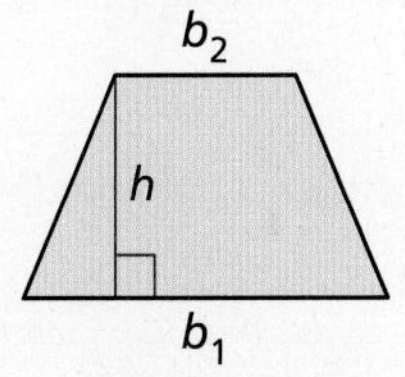

$A = \frac{1}{2}h(b_1 + b_2)$

Rhombus/Kite

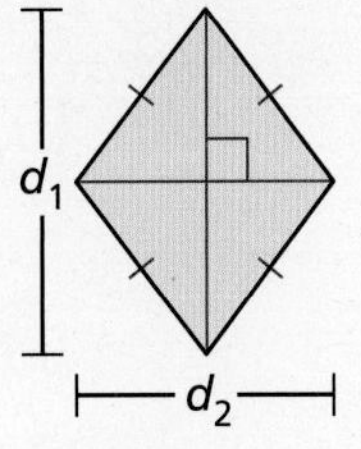

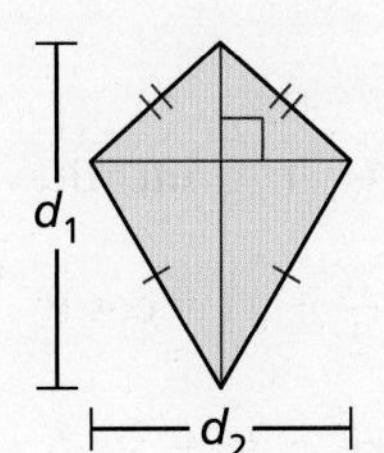

$A = \frac{1}{2}d_1 d_2$

Regular *n*-gon

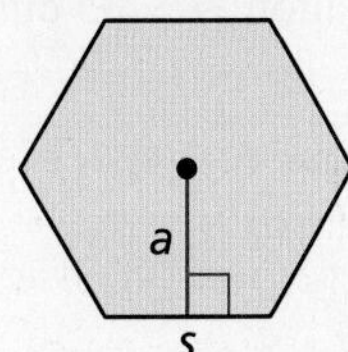

$A = \frac{1}{2}aP$ or $A = \frac{1}{2}a \cdot ns$

Prism

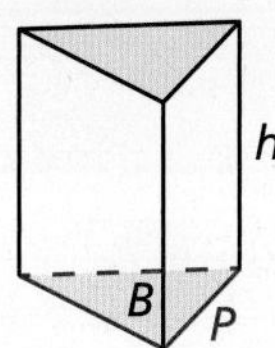

$L = Ph$
$S = 2B + Ph$
$V = Bh$

Cylinder

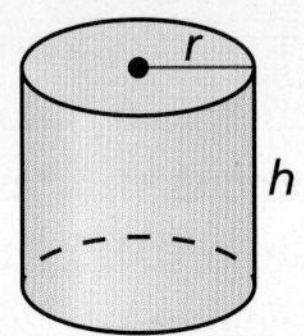

$L = 2\pi rh$
$S = 2\pi r^2 + 2\pi rh$
$V = \pi r^2 h$

Pyramid

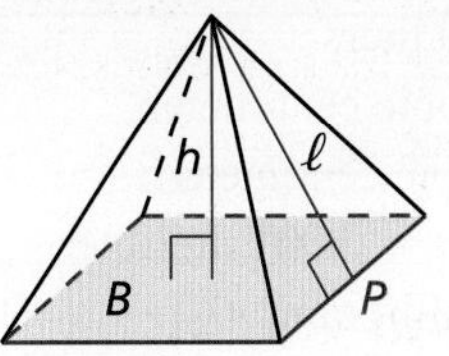

$L = \frac{1}{2}P\ell$
$S = B + \frac{1}{2}P\ell$
$V = \frac{1}{3}Bh$

Cone

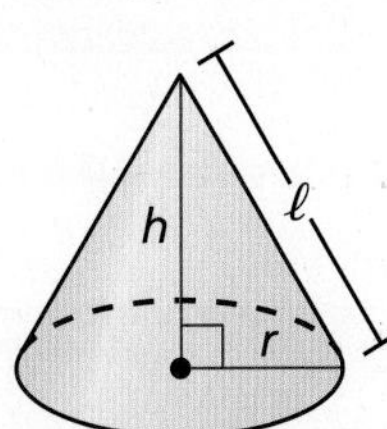

$L = \pi r\ell$

$S = \pi r^2 + \pi r\ell$

$V = \frac{1}{3}\pi r^2 h$

Sphere

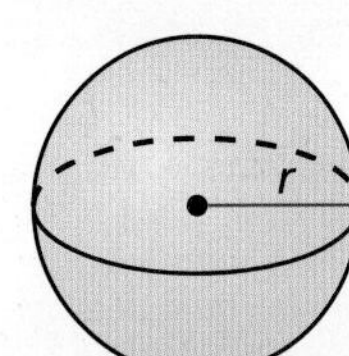

$S = 4\pi r^2$

$V = \frac{4}{3}\pi r^3$

REFERENCE

Other Formulas

Pythagorean Theorem
$a^2 + b^2 = c^2$

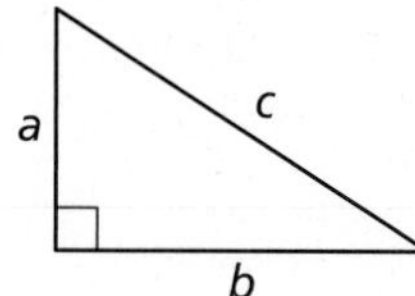

Simple Interest
$I = Prt$

Compound Interest
$A = P\left(1 + \frac{r}{n}\right)^{nt}$

Continuously Compounded Interest
$A = Pe^{rt}$

Distance
$d = rt$

Conversions

U.S. Customary
1 foot = 12 inches
1 yard = 3 feet
1 mile = 5280 feet
1 mile = 1760 yards
1 acre = 43,560 square feet
1 cup = 8 fluid ounces
1 pint = 2 cups
1 quart = 2 pints
1 gallon = 4 quarts
1 gallon = 231 cubic inches
1 pound = 16 ounces
1 ton = 2000 pounds
1 cubic foot = 7.5 gallons

U.S. Customary to Metric
1 inch = 2.54 centimeters
1 foot ≈ 0.3 meter
1 mile ≈ 1.61 kilometers
1 quart ≈ 0.95 liter
1 gallon ≈ 3.79 liters
1 cup ≈ 237 milliliters
1 pound ≈ 0.45 kilogram
1 ounce ≈ 28.3 grams
1 gallon ≈ 3785 cubic centimeters

Time
1 minute = 60 seconds
1 hour = 60 minutes
1 hour = 3600 seconds
1 year = 52 weeks

Temperature
$C = \frac{5}{9}(F - 32)$
$F = \frac{9}{5}C + 32$

Metric
1 centimeter = 10 millimeters
1 meter = 100 centimeters
1 kilometer = 1000 meters
1 liter = 1000 milliliters
1 kiloliter = 1000 liters
1 milliliter = 1 cubic centimeter
1 liter = 1000 cubic centimeters
1 cubic millimeter = 0.001 milliliter
1 gram = 1000 milligrams
1 kilogram = 1000 grams

Metric to U.S. Customary
1 centimeter ≈ 0.39 inch
1 meter ≈ 3.28 feet
1 meter ≈ 39.37 inches
1 kilometer ≈ 0.62 mile
1 liter ≈ 1.06 quarts
1 liter ≈ 0.26 gallon
1 kilogram ≈ 2.2 pounds
1 gram ≈ 0.035 ounce
1 cubic meter ≈ 264 gallons

Credits

Front Matter

xviii Pixel-Shot/Shutterstock.com; **xx** Andrii Vodolazhskyi/Shutterstock.com; **xxi** Dotted Yeti/Shutterstock.com; **xxii** hornyak/Shutterstock.com; **xxiii** Juniors Bildarchiv GmbH / Alamy Stock Photo; **xiv** Steve Byland/Shutterstock.com; **xxv** marktucan/Shutterstock.com; **xxvi** Zyabich/iStock/Getty Images Plus; **xxvii** Trevor Mayes/Shutterstock.com; **xxviii** Lucie Petrikova/Shutterstock.com; **xxix** maloff/Shutterstock.com; **xxx** Rich Carey/Shutterstoc.com; **xxxi** ©Ronan Donovan

Chapter 1

0 *top* ©Rebecca Drobis/National Geographic Image Collection; *bottom* Andrii Vodolazhskyi/Shutterstock.com; **1** Nerthuz/iStock/Getty Images Plus; **3** AaronAmat/iStock/Getty Images Plus; **7** MarcelC/iStock / Getty Images Plus; **9** AlexLMX/Shutterstock.com; **11** Ebtikar/Shutterstock; **15** bennyb/iStock/Getty Images Plus; **16** Mit Kapevski/Shutterstock.com; **17** Rob Wilson/Shutterstock.com; **19** Ekkasit A Siam/Shutterstock.com; **20** forplayday/iStock/Getty Images Plus; **23** angelhell/iStock/Getty Images Plus; **24** Wavebreakmedia/iStock/Getty Images Plus; **27** OvsiankaStudio/iStock/Getty Images Plus; **28** londoneye/E+/Getty Image; **31** Ljupco/iStock/Getty Images Plus; **34** sh22/iStock/Getty Images Plus; **37** pepifoto/E+/Getty Images; **38** Juanmonino/iStock/Getty Images Plus; **39** *center* Wyss Institute at Harvard University.; *background* Nobi_Prizue/iStock/Getty Images Plus

Chapter 2

42 *top* ©Jennifer W. Lopez; *bottom* Dotted Yeti/Shutterstock.com; **45** Flashon Studio/Shuterstock.com;**49** Rob Wilson/Shutterstock.com; **51** Freder/E+/Getty Images; **52** *left* Valery Evlakhov/Shutterstock.com; *right* Tarzhanova/shutterstock.com; **53** Wavebreakmedia Ltd/Wavebreak Media/Getty Images; **54** michaeljung/iStock/Getty Images Plus; **58** Nastco/iStock/Getty Images Plus; **59** nickp37/iStock/Getty Images Plus; **60** *left* Christian Bertrand/Shutterstock.com; *right* Steve Mann/Shutterstock.com; **61** Alphotographic/iStock/Getty Images Plus; **62** gorodenkoff/iStock/Getty Images Plus; **63** Flashon Studio/Shutterstock.com; **68** a_v_d/Shutterstock.com; **71** SpaceKris/Shutterstock.com; **72** meunierd/Shutterstock.com; **74** alex_skp/iStock/Getty Images Plus, Nerthuz/iStock/Getty Images Plus; **80** AlexLMX/Shutterstock.com; **81** NicolasMcComber/E+/Getty Images, Adam Fahey Designs/Shutterstock.com; **82** ivanoel28/iStock/Getty Images Plus; **83** solarseven/iStock/Getty Images Plus

Chapter 3

86 *top* ©Sora Devore/National Geographic Image Collection; *bottom* hornyak/Shutterstock.com; **87** Pixelci/iStock/Getty Images Plus; **89** 1573037932/Shutterstock.com; **93** Krivosheev Vitaly/Shutterstock.com; **95** Asni Maryani/iStock/Getty Images; **96** *top* frentusha/iStock/Getty Images; *bottom* starets/iStock/Getty Images Plus; **97** dottedhippo/iStock/Getty Images Plus; **99** Sinisa92/iStock/Getty Images Plus; **103** Poravute/iStock/Getty Images Plus; **106** chengyuzheng/iStock/Getty Images Plus; **109** Samuel Borges Photography/Shutterstock.com; **113** Eugene Onischenko/Shutterstock.com; **115** makkayak/iStock/Getty Images Plus; **116** *bottom* urfinguss/iStock/Getty Images Plus; **117** arekmalang/iStock/Getty Images Plus; **122** *left* PhotoTalk/E+/Getty Images; *center* South_agency/E+/Getty Images; *right* vgajic/E+/Getty Images; **124** *left* Ben Haslam/iStock/Getty Images Plus; *right* Russell Watkins/Shutterstock.com; **125** chara_stagram/Shutterstock.com; **127** Foremniakowski/iStock/Getty Images Plus; **133** Kphrom/Shutterstock.com; **135** Hugo Felix/Shutterstock.com; **137** viach80/iStock/Getty Images Plus; **139** maradon 333/Shutterstock.com; **140** Drablenkov/iStock/Getty Images Plus; **141** ai_yoshi/iStock Editorial/Getty Images Plus; **144** Antagain/iStock/ Getty Images Plus; **146** Sitade/E+/Getty Images; **147** ClaireMcAdams/iStock/Getty Images Plus

Chapter 4

150 *top* ©Robert Lonsinger/National Geographic Image Collection; *bottom* Juniors Bildarchiv GmbH / Alamy Stock Photo; **151** Freder/iStock/Getty Images Plus; **153** John Sommer//iStock/Getty Images Plus; **157** *left* Susan Schmitz/Shutterstock.com; *right* GlobalP/iStock/Getty Images Plus; **158** tawan/Shutterstock.com; **159** GlobalP/iStock/Getty Images Plus; **161** michaeljung/Shutterstock.com; **165** roseed abbas/Shutterstock.com; **167** Michael Burrell/iStock/Getty Images Plus; **169** *left* laflor/E+/Getty Images; *right* oatintro/iStock/Getty Images Plus; **173** Tuja/Shutterstock.com; **175** drbimages/iStock/Getty Images Plus; **181** junyanjiang/Shutterstock.com; **183** Layland Masuda/Shutterstock.com; **189** Svitlana Unuchko/iStock/Getty Images Plus; **190** Lunatictm/Shutterstock.com; **191** *left* Julia Nikitina/Shutterstock.com; *right* pikselstock/Shutterstock.com; **197** 1082492116/Shutterstock.com; **199** aldomurillo/iStock/Getty Images Plus; **209** Hemera Technologies/PhotoObjects.net / Getty Images Plus; **211** Darryl Brooks/Shutterstock.com; **213** *left* aldomurillo/E+/Getty Images; *right* oatintro/iStock/Getty Images Plus; **216** Benny Marty/Shutterstock.com; **220** pabradyphoto/iStock Editorial/Getty Images Plus; **221** tupungato/iStock Editorial/Getty Images Plus; **223** drakuliren/iStock/Getty Images Plus; **224** Rawpixel/iStock/Getty Images Plus; **225** *background* CaptureLight/iStock/Getty Images Plus; *bottom* photomaster/Shutterstock.com

Chapter 5

228 *top* ©Benjamin Mirin/National Geographic Image Collection; *bottom* Steve Byland/Shutterstock.com; **229** Phant/Sghutterstock.com; **231** Innershadows/iStock/Getty Images Plus; **234** Vereshchagin Dmitry/Shutterstock.com, dimarik/iStock/Getty Images Plus; **237** pathdoc/Shutterstock.com; **239** Djomas/Shutterstock.com; **245** andresr/E+/Getty Images; **248** FABIO BISPO/iStock/Getty Images Plus; **251** PhotographyByMK/Shutterstock.com; **253** rui vale sousa/Shutterstock.com; **255** DNY59/iStock/Getty Images Plus; **258** Byelikova_Oksana/iStock/Getty Images Plus; **259** *left* GlobalP/iStock/Getty Images Plus; *right* OSTILL/iStock/Getty Images Plus; **261** iodrakon/Shutterstock.com; **264** *top* AaronAmat/iStock/Getty Images Plus; *bottom* syabrin/iStock/Getty Images Plus; **267** Rido/Shutterstock.com; *right* Freedom Life/Shutterstock.com; **270** *top* tomazl/E+/Getty Images, amriphoto/E+/Getty Images; *bottom* DanielPrudek/iStock/Getty Images Plus; **273** williv/iStock/Getty Images Plus; **278** hudiemm/iStock/Getty Images Plus; **280** herreid/iStock/Getty Images Plus; **281** Maestrovideo/iStock/Getty Images Plus; **286** bennymarty/iStock/Getty Images Plus; **287** *background* pialhovik/iStock/Getty Images Plus; *bottom* tassel78/iStock/Getty Images Plus

Chapter 6

290 *top* ©Cengage Learning/ National Geographic Learning; *bottom* marktucan/Shutterstock.com; **291** alice-photo/iStock/Getty Images Plus; **293** Dean Drobot/Shutterstock.com; **297** someone25/iStock/Getty Images Plus; **298** *bottom* Gena73/Shutterstock.com; *top* scanrail/iStock/Getty Images Plus; **301** ferlistockphoto/iStock/Getty Images Plus; **307** ferlistockphoto/iStock/Getty Images Plus; **312** dzphotovideo/iStock/Getty Images Plus, German-skydiver/iStock/Getty Images Plus, Mauricio Graiki/iStock/Getty Images Plus, Serg_Velusceac/iStock/Getty Images Plus, **313** Rasica/iStock/Getty Images Plus, mama_mia/Shutterstock.com; **314** Oliver Susemihl/iStock/Getty Images Plus; **318** digitalgenetics/iStock/Getty Images Plus; **321** ozanuysal/iStock/Getty Images Plus; **323** Jeka/Shutterstock.com; **326** Yuri Shevtsov/Shutterstock.com; **327** Maria Spb/Shutterstock.com; **329** michaeljung/iStock/Getty Images Plus; **331** AS Food studio/Shutterstock.com; **334** abadonian/iStock/Getty Images Plus; **337** amenic181/iStock/Getty Images Plus; **339** Eric Isselee/Shutterstock.com; **341** Mette Fairgrieve/Shutterstock.com; **342** Dean Drobot/Shutterstock.com; **343** *top left* AaronAmat/iStock/Getty Images Plus, VladimirFLoyd/iStock/Getty Images Plus, Ranta Images/iStock/Getty Images Plus, Ranta Images/iStock/Getty Images Plus, Ranta Images/iStock/Getty Images Plus, kemalbas/iStock/Getty Images Plus; *top right* design56/iStock/Getty Images Plus; *bottom right* junce/iStock/Getty Images Plus;

346 mrgao/iStock/Getty Images Plus; **348** cosmin4000/iStock/Getty Images Plus, richcarey/iStock/Getty Images Plus, George W. Bailey/Shutterstock.com; **349** Gam1983/iStock/Getty Images Plus; **351** MariuszBlach/iStock/Getty Images Plus

Chapter 7

352 *top* ©Lynn Johnson/National Geographic Image Collection; *bottom* Zyabich/iStock/Getty Images Plus; **355** Wavebreakmedia Ltd/Wavebreak Media/Getty Images Plus; **358** Wavebreakmedia Ltd/Wavebreak Media/Getty Images Plus; **359** *left* gaspr13/iStock/Getty Images Plus, *right* chictype/iStock/Getty Images Plus; **361** opolja/iStock/Getty Images Plus; **365** *left* aerogondo2/Shutterstock.com; *right* PhonlamaiPhoto/iStock/Getty Images Plus; **367** beright/iStock/Getty Images Plus; mishooo/iStock/Getty Images Plus; **369** Hugo Felix/Shutterstock.com; **373** Minerva Studio/Shutterstock.com; **375** Africa Studio/Shutterstock.com; **376** *left* nikolay100/iStock/Getty Images Plus; *right* photomaru/iStock/Getty Images Plus; **377** Ollyy/Shutterstock.com; **381** anon-tae/iStock/Getty Images Plus; **383** nicoolay/E+/Getty Images; **385** VladislavStarozhilov/iStock/Getty Images Plus; **390** Shuttertum/Shutterstock.com; **391** Ljupco Smokovski/Shutterstock.com; **393** Vudhikul Ocharoen/iStock/Getty Images Plus; **395** Ljupco Smokovski/Shutterstock.com; **397** *background* carloscastilla/iStock/Getty Images Plus; *bottom* AlexLMX/iStock/Getty Images Plus; *top* wir0man/iStock/Getty Images Plus; **399** rbv/iStock/Getty Images Plus

Chapter 8

401 *top* ©Scott Degraw/National Geographic Image Collection; *bottom* Trevor Mayes/Shutterstock.com; **403** *In order from left to right* Viktor Fedorenko/Shutterstock.com; fotohunter/Shutterstock.com; VIKTOR FEDORENKO/iStock/Getty Images Plus; *bottom* Pixel-Shot/Shutterstockcom; **404** VIKTOR FEDORENKO/iStock/Getty Images Plus; **407** Tiger Images/Shutterstock.com; **408** hobbit/Shutterstock.com; **411** V.S.Anandhakrishna/Shutterstock.com; **413** Orange Line Media/Shutterstock.com; **415** Andrey Bayda/Shutterstock.com; **417** stockyimages/Shutterstock.com; **420** Africa Studio/Shutterstock.com; **421** 4x6/iStock/Getty Images Plus; **422** Harvepino/iStock/Getty Images Plus; **425** *right* VIKTOR FEDORENKO/iStock/Getty Images Plus; *left* vadimguzhva/iStock/Getty Images Plus; **429** 1550539/iStock/Getty Images Plus, NoDerog/iStock/Getty Images Plus, Pongasn68/iStock/Getty Images Plus; **430** *left* dossyl//iStock/Getty Images Plus; *right* AlexLMX/iStock/Getty Images Plus; **432** EHStock/iStock/Getty Images Plus; **433** *right* empire331/iStock/Getty Images Plus; *left* Ridofranz/iStock/Getty Images Plus; **435** marekuliasz/iStock/Getty Images Plus; **436** Dmitry Lobanov/Shutterstock.com; **437** Koy_Hipster/Shutterstock.com; **438** Vahe 3D/Shutterstock.com; **439** *right* Silense/iStock/Getty Images Plus, Africa Studio/Shutterstock.com, purple_queue/iStock/Getty Images Plus, GlobalP/iStock/Getty Images Plus; *bottom left* ESB Professional/Shutterstock.com; **441** dikkenss/Shutterstock.com; **443** *left* nojustice/iStock/Getty Images Plus, *right* IPGGutenbergUKLtd/iStock/Getty Images Plus; **445** Yganko/Shutterstock.com; **446** Mirko_Rosenau/iStock/Getty Images Plus; **449** Viktor Fedorenko/Shutterstock.com; **451** Undorik/Shutterstock.com; **453** AndreyPopov/iStock/Getty Images Plus; **454** Boarding1Now/iStock/Getty Images Plus; **456** sturti/iStock/Getty Images Plus; **457** Alexander Kondratenko/Shutterstock.com; **459** *background* krystiannawrocki/iStock/Getty Images Plus, momnoi/iStock/Getty Images Plus; *in order from left to right* mofles/iStock/Getty Images Plus; alice-photo/iStock/Getty Images Plus; arogant/iStock/Getty Images Plus; yannp/iStock/Getty Images Plus; Lefteris_/iStock/Getty Images Plus; kovalvs/iStock/Getty Images Plus; Comstock/Stockbyte/Getty Images; Orchidpoet/E+/Getty Images; **461** Slatan/Shutterstock.com

Chapter 9

462 *top* ©Arianna Soldati; *bottom* Lucie Petrikova/Shutterstock.com; **465** Studio-Annika/iStock/Getty Images Plus; **467** Sean Locke Photography/Shutterstock.com; **468** New Africa/Shutterstock.com; **470** tanuha2001/iStock/Getty Images Plus; **471** *left* NosUA/iStock/Getty Images Plus, *right* Dimitris Leonidas/Shutterstock.com, SergeyIT/iStock/Getty Images Plus; **473** chairoij/Shutterstock.com; **475** ImagePixel/iStock/Getty Images Plus; **478** Samuel Borges Photography/Shutterstock.com; **479** UroshPetrovic/iStock/Getty Images Plus; **480** Katrin_Timoff/iStock/Getty Images Plus; **481** Wavebreakmedia Ltd/Wavebreak Media/Getty Images Plus; **482** Rawpixel/iStock/Getty Images Plus, Boarding1Now/iStock/Getty Images Plus, SDI Productions/E+/Getty Images; **483** skodonnell/iStock/Getty Images Plus; **486** *top left* procurator/DigitalVision Vectors/Getty Images; *bottom left* Eriklam/iStock/Getty Images Plus; *right* Warchi/iStock/Getty Images Plus; **487** Nicolas Primola/Shutterstock.com; **488** izusek/E+/Getty Images; **489** *right* ahmetemre/iStock/Getty Images Plus; *left* shipfactory/Shutterstock.com; **491** Lammeyer/Shutterstock.com; **492** inkit/E+/Getty Images; **493** STILLFX/Shutterstock.com; **495** sparklingmoments/iStock/Getty Images Plus; **500** merve zengin/iStock/Getty Images Plus; **501** Mikadun/Shutterstock.com; **502** *top left* g-stockstudio/iStock/Getty Images Plus; *bottom left* FatCamera/E+/Getty Images; *right* scanrail/iStock/Getty Images Plus; *bottom left* FatCamera/E+/Getty Images; *right* scanrail/iStock/Getty Images Plus; **505** wavebreakmedia/Shutterstock.com; **506** chengyuzheng/iStock/Getty Images Plus; **509** *right* AlexeyBorodin/iStock/Getty Images Plus; *left* RapidEye/iStock/Getty Images Plus; **511** *top* Ralf Juergen Kraft/Shutterstock.com; *bottom* GlobalP/iStock/Getty Images Plus; **512** *top* smartstock/iStock/Getty Images Plus; *bottom* Marta Martínez Photo/iStock/Getty Images Plus; **515** *background* Eachat/iStock/Getty Images Plus; *top* switchpipipi/iStock/Getty Images Plus; **517** sweetym/E+/Getty Images

Chapter 10

518 *top* ©Elizabeth Lindsey; *bottom* maloff/Shutterstock.com; **519** abriendomundo/iStock/Getty Images Plus; **521** Ustyujanin/Shutterstock.com; **525** *top* Glenn Young/Shutterstock.com; *bottom* Sergey Ginak/Shutterstock.com; **527** *left* f11photo/Shutterstock.com; *top right* BlueRingMedia/Shutterstock.com; *bottom right* ©iStockphoto.com/Kubrak78; **529** Sean Locke Photography/Shutterstock.com; **533** antpkr/Shutterstock.com; **535** *top left* TimAbramowitz/E+/Getty Images; *bottom left* pathdoc/Shutterstock.com; *right* ©iStockphoto.com/alexsl; **541** George Doyle & Ciaran Griffin/Stockbyte/Getty Images; **542** labsas/iStock/Getty Images Plus, Brian Hook, https://www.flickr.com/photos/brianhook/; **543** antpkr/iStock/Getty Images Plus; **544** Npeter/Shutterstock.com; **545** ASDF_MEDIA/Shutterstock.com; **551** Paul Koomen/Shutterstock.com; **553** *left* Matthew Cole/Shutterstock.com; *right* Delpixart/iStock/Getty Images Plus; **554** Henrik Dolle/Shutterstock.com; **555** 4x6/E+/Getty Images; **561** *Exercise 41* MyCreative/Shutterstock.com, Maxiphoto/iStock/Getty Images Plus; *bottom* klazing/iStock/Getty Images Plus; **563** Beautiful landscape/Shutterstock.com; **564** Courtesy of Grason-Stadler; **566** *left* davidf/E+/Getty Images; *right* Xinhua / Alamy Stock Photo; **567** railway fx/Shutterstock.com; **568** 2stockista/Shutterstock.com; **569** BBP76000/Shutterstock.com; **571** rnl/Shutterstock.com; **576** DanBrandenburg/E+/Getty Images; **577** Antonio_Diaz/iStock/Getty Images Plus; **583** ChrisAt/iStock/Getty Images Plus, ©iStockphoto.com/4x6, ©iStockphoto.com/knape; **585** mama_mia/Shutterstock.com; **586** zimmytws/Shutterstock.com; **588** Gearstd/Shutterstock.com; **589** *background* shaunl/E+/Getty Images; *top* Lebazele/iStock/Getty Images Plus

Chapter 11

592 *top* ©Mark Thiessen/National Geographic Image Collection; *bottom* Rich Carey/Shutterstoc.com; **593** witoldkr1/iStock/Getty Images, krystiannawrocki/E+/Getty Images; **595** *left* B-D-S Piotr Marcinski/ Shutterstock.com; *Explore It! part (a) in order from top to bottom;* by_nicholas/iStock/Getty Images Plus; wwing/E+/Getty Images; DNY59/ E+/Getty Images; **597** Halina Yakushevich/Shutterstock.com; **600** kpalimski/ iStock/Getty Images Plus; **601** Evan-Amos, Vanamo Media; **603** talevr/ iStock/Getty Images Plus; **607** sunlow/iStock / Getty Images Plus; **609** the palms/Shutterstock.com; **611** pomarinus/iStock/Getty Images Plus; **615** Brian Mueller/Shutterstock.com; **617** *left* Bestgreenscreen/iStock/Getty Images Plus; *right* Sky Antonio/Shutterstock.com; **619** Kritchanut/iStock/ Getty Images Plus; **622** FotoHelin/Shutterstock.com; **624** GlobalP/iStock/ Getty Images Plus; **625** *right* MPFphotography/Shutterstock.com, BardoczPeter/iStock/Getty Images Plus; *left* robert cicchetti/ Shutterstock.com; **629** irin717/iStock/Getty Images Plus; **631** luismmolina/ E+/Getty Images; **632** Diego Barbieri/Shutterstock.com; **639** *background* piranka/E+/Getty Images; Isabella/iStock/Getty Images Plus; *top right* Jean-Michel Girard/Shutterstock.com; *bottom right* annalisa e marina durante/Shutterstock.com; Evlakhov Valeriy/Shutterstock.com; Isabella/ iStock/Getty Images Plus

Chapter 12

642 *top* ©Randall Scott/National Geographic Image Collection; *bottom* ©Ronan Donovan; **643** Fly_and_Dive/Shutterstock.com; **645** HomePixel/ iStock/Getty Images Plus; **649** boonchoke/Shutterstock.com; **651** GOLFXShutterstock.com; **653** HomePixel/iStock/Getty Images Plus; **657** nitrub/iStock/Getty Images Plus; **659** Eric Isselee/Shutterstock.com; **661** Ebtikar/Shutterstock.com; **666** Shawn Hempel/Shutterstock.com; **667** Sergey Gordienko/iStock Getty Images Plus; **668** *top right* Rtimages/ iStock/Getty Images Plus; *bottom right* paikong/Shutterstock.com; **669** *top* Albert Russ/Shutterstock.com; **671** pikselstock/Shutterstock.com; **675** Pektoral/iStock/Getty Images Plus, anna1311/iStock/Getty Images Plus, anna1311/iStock/Getty Images Plus; **676** *in order from left to right* dtv2/ iStock/Getty Images Plus; WolfeLarry/iStock/Getty Images Plus; scisettialfio/iStock/Getty Images Plus; **679** *top* Bronwyn Photo/ Shutterstock.com; *bottom* Twister40/iStock/ Getty Images Plus; **680** *top* alexey_boldin/iStock/Getty Images Plus; *bottom* Mega Pixel/ Shutterstock.com; **681** *left* Fudio/iStock/Getty Images Plus; *right* Hurst Photo/Shutterstock.com; **683** *background* ESB Professional/ Shutterstock.com; *in clockwise order* Agami Photo Agency/ Shutterstock.com; cynoclub/iStock/Getty Images Plus; Nick Biemans/ Shutterstock.com; samuelnielsen/iStock/Getty Images Plus; GlobalP/iStock/ Getty Images Plus; Iuliia Morozova/iStock/Getty Images Plus; **684** starush/ iStock/Getty Images Plus

Design Elements

mikimad/iStock/Getty Images Plus; saicle/Shutterstock.com